香港中樂團
HONG KONG CHINESE ORCHESTRA
藝術總監：閻惠昌
ARTISTIC DIRECTOR : YAN HUICHANG

Hong Kong Chinese Orchestra
Anytime! Anywhere!

HKCO
NET CONCERT HALL

www.hkconetconcerthall.com

performing arts YEARBOOK

REST OF THE WORLD

artsDB + performing arts YEARBOOK

The Performing Arts Yearbook is available as an online database:
artsdb.net - the worlds most comprehensive database for the performing arts.

Everyone can have a free listing, plus our featured listings allow companies to add everything from photos, PR and media clippings to event details and biographies.

To add or update your free listing/s visit **www.artsdb.net**

To subscribe to the database visit **wwwperformingartsyearbook.com**

To speak to someone about upgrading to an advanced listing, **call +44 (0)161 638 5615**

The Media Centre
7 Northumberland Street
Huddersfield, HD1 1RL
info@musocommunications.com
www. musocommunications.com

ARD ●

Piano Trio
Voice
Wind Quintet
Oboe
Trumpet
Piano
Percussion
Viola
Clarinet
Flute
Violoncello
Bassoon
Trombone
Harp
French Horn
Piano Duo
String Quartet
Violin
Double Bass
Organ
Guitar

1st ARD International
Music Competition Munich

August 29 to September 16, 2022

Piano Trombone Flute String Quartet

Michael Buchanan
1st prize 2015

Sébastian Jacot
1st prize 2015

JeungBeum Sohn
1st prize 2017

Application
deadline:
March 31, 2022

Quatuor Arod
1st prize 2016

www.ard-musikwettbewerb.de

performing arts
database
online

artsDB.net

artsDB + performing arts
YEARBOOK

Published in 2022 in Great Britain by Muso Communications Ltd
The Media Centre, 7 Northumberland Street,Huddersfield, HD1 1RL.
Tel: +44 (0)161 638 5615
Email: info@musocommunications.com
Website: www. musocommunications.com

ISBN: 978-1-3999-2383-5

Performing Arts Yearbook - Rest of The World 2022
Printed in Great Britain by CPI William Clowes Ltd

orchestre
dechambre
deParis

© JEAN-BAPTISTE PELLERIN

Music brings us together!

orchestredechambredeparis.com

ACKNOWLEDGEMENTS

It's fair to say a lot has changed since we last published the Performing Arts Yearbook. We experienced unprecedented closures in the arts thanks to Covid. Meanwhile, the geopolitical situation become volatile in a way not seen for decades.

What hasn't changed is the inspiration, motivation and invention that the arts can provide – and you'll find plenty of all that in these pages. We have stories on how tech is making the arts more fiscally feasible than ever before. We also speak with artists who are reinventing their practice, creating fusions and, in some cases, entirely new genres. Yes, it's a challenging time, but it's also an exciting one.

But most important of all are our listings, which we've completely revamped for 2022. During lockdown the arts were temporarily put on hold, but that meant more time to hone, refine and reappraise our database. In it you'll find 20,000-plus listings that have been edited and crosschecked by our dedicated team. And of course, if you want see your company listed in next year's edition, please head to **artsdb.net** and create yours now.

In fact, we recently re-launched our website, with additional content and features only available online. For example, you can now present videos, host photos and advertise your events through our site. To create your free listing and benefit from additional exposure, without waiting until the 2023 edition, just go to **artsdb.net**.

This year's book was edited by Andrew Anderson, with support from Katja Rackin. It was designed and produced by Peter Davin. As always, my thank goes to them – and the rest of the PAY/artsdb team – for their dedication to this mammoth task.

Marcus Netherwood, publisher

CONTENTS

INTRODUCTION

Looking beyond our features section, the majority of PAY is given over to a directory of performing arts companies, venues and services across Europe.

To get the most from the book, you should read the guidance entitled How to Use Your Yearbook. The focus is on major and medium-scale professional companies (whether subsidised at national, regional or local level). We also include smaller companies where suitable, giving a full range of options for tour booking, service provision and music ensembles.

We recently relaunched our online database, which is fully searchable at **artsdb.net**. The website includes new functionality and additional content, making it the perfect place to present your company. Head to **artsdb.net** now to create your free listing.

Finally, we are extremely grateful for the support of contributors keeping us up-to- date with changes and new developments in their countries. PAY depends on their support and we would like to encourage comments and information from individuals and organisations as to how we can make it an even more useful publication for the performing arts business.

Please write to us or let us know via our email address at: **info@musocommunications.com**

HOW TO USE YOUR YEARBOOK

Languages
Wherever possible, we have retained the title of companies in the language in which it was presented to us (their original language). English translations of company names are generally provided for the more uncommon or lesser-used languages in the international arena (eg. Finnish, Hungarian, Polish, Serbian, Croatian, Swedish, Russian etc.).

As PAY is intended for an international readership, cities are generally shown in their original language (eg. Firenze for Florence, Köln for Cologne, Torino for Turin, and Wien for Vienna). However, anglicised versions are mostly used for the Russian or Slav countries etc., and for countries that are bilingual. Thus the capital of Belgium is usually referred to as Brussels rather than Brussel (Dutch) or Bruxelles (French), and Antwerpen is referred to as Antwerp.

Index
The index of editorial entries at the back of PAY will enable you to identify on which page an entry for an organisation appears (eg. Festival d'Ile de France, Paris, pgX).

Telephoning
The direct dialling code prefix for each country is listed at the beginning of the entries relating to that country within each section. The area/city code is included within the entries. Please remember, when dialling a number from within a country you are often required to add a digit before the area/city code. In many instances this is a zero: eg. when dialling Glasgow from London or Birmingham you would dial 0141, followed by the number listed.

Each country has its own international access code prefix to enable you to dial directly. The requirement to add this code is indicated in the listings by the + sign before the country code. If you wanted to dial Hungary (country code 36), you would use the international access code before dialling the country code and the direct number. For most countries this code is (00), but for example, if you are phoning from the United States, you would need to dial (011) before the country code. Please contact your local operator if in doubt.

TABLE DE MATIÈRES

INTRODUCTION

Au-delà de notre section de fonctionnalités, la majorité de PAY est consacrée à un répertoire de compagnies, de lieux et de services d'arts de la scène à travers l'Europe.

Pour tirer le meilleur parti du livre, vous devriez lire les conseils intitulés Comment utiliser votre annuaire. L'accent est mis sur les grandes et moyennes entreprises professionnelles (qu'elles soient subventionnées au niveau national, régional ou local). Nous incluons également les petites entreprises, le cas échéant, offrant une gamme complète d'options pour la réservation de tournées, la prestation de services et les ensembles musicaux.

Nous avons récemment relancé notre base de données en ligne, qui est entièrement consultable sur artsdb.net. Le site Web comprend de nouvelles fonctionnalités et du contenu supplémentaire, ce qui en fait l'endroit idéal pour présenter votre entreprise. Rendez-vous dès maintenant sur artsdb.net pour créer votre fiche gratuite.

Enfin, nous sommes extrêmement reconnaissants du soutien des contributeurs qui nous tiennent au courant des changements et des nouveaux développements dans leurs pays. PAY dépend de leur soutien et nous aimerions encourager les commentaires et les informations des individus et des organisations sur la façon dont nous pouvons en faire une publication encore plus utile pour le secteur des arts de la scène.

Veuillez nous écrire ou nous le faire savoir via notre adresse e-mail à: **info@musocommunications.com**

COMMENT UTILISER LE PAY

Langues

Autant que possible, nous avons gardé le nom original des organismes, c'est à dire dans leur langue initiale. En général, dans le cas des langues plus ou moin rares ou peu utilisées comme le russe, le finnois, le serbe, le croate ou encore le suèdois une traduction anglaise est fournie. Comme le *PAY* est destiné aux lecteurs internationaux, nous avons essayé de garder le nom d'origine des villes (ex: Firenze pour Florence ou Wien pour Vienne). En ce qui concerne les villes situées en pays bilingues, une version anglaise est donnée. Par exemple Bruxelles (en français) qui est aussi connue sous le nom de Brussel (en Flamand) sera écrit Brussels, tout comme Antwerp sera écrit sous le nom de Antwerpen.

L'index

L'index des parutions à la fin du *PAY* vous permettra de localiser les pages ou se trouvent les renseignements concernant chaque organisme.

Téléphone

L'indicatif pour chaque pays est situé en tête de chaque rubrique. L'indicatif local est inclus dans le numéro de chaque organisme, aussi, lorsque vous composez un numéro à partir du pays en question veuillez vérifier s'il est nécessaire d'ajouter un numéro (indiquant la ville ou la région). Le numéro ou chiffre en question est pour la plupart des cas un zéro. Chaque pays a son propre indicatif d'accès qui vous permet de téléphoner directement à l'étranger. Le signe + avant l'indicatif du pays signifie qu'il est nécessaire de composer cet indicatif. Par exemple si vous vouliez appeler la Hongrie (indic 36) il vous faudrait utiliser l'accès international (qui est pour la majorité des cas le 00) avant de composer l'indicatif de la Hongrie. En appelant des Etats Unis l'accès serait le 011. En cas de doute veuillez consulter votre opérateur local.

54th INTERNATIONAL GUITAR COMPETITION
michele pittaluga

member of /// WFIMC/WFCIM

CITY OF ALESSANDRIA PRIZE | President Gold medal from 1997

FROM 26 SEPTEMBER TO 1ST OCTOBER 2022

INTERNATIONAL GUITAR COMPETITION FOR YOUNG ARTISTS

6th pittaluga Junior

1st October 2022

registration deadline
21st August 2022

rules updated on the website www.pittaluga.org

SPONSORSHIP

 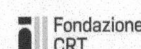       

MONTREAL, CANADA — SINCE 2002

RBDG.CA

Artistic director Victor Quijada combines spontaneous, risky and fearless hip-hop culture with the choreographic sophistication of contemporary dance.

TRENZADO

Exploring the themes of roots, migration and loss – Quijada's return to the stage

Photo: Bill Hebert

AGENTS

QUEBEC — CANADA
Agence Station Bleue
Élisabeth Comtois
e.comtois@stationbleue.com

USA
Pentacle
Sandy Garcia
sandyg@pentacle.org

EUROPE (CH, AT, DE, NL, BE, LUX)
Norddeutsche Konzertdirektion
Franziska Grevesmühl-v. Marcard
info@grevesmuehl.de

INHALT

76ᵉ CONCOURS DE GENÈVE
INTERNATIONAL
MUSIC COMPETITION
22 OCT–3 NOV 2022
Piano & Composition

COMPOSITION FINAL
26 OCT. CONSERVATOIRE, GENEVA
With the Neue Vocalsolisten Stuttgart

PIANO FINAL
3 NOV. VICTORIA HALL, GENEVA
With the Orchestre de la Suisse Romande

JURY CHAIR
PIANO – JANINA FIALKOWSKA
COMPOSITION – BEAT FURRER

CONCOURSGENEVE.CH

HINAKO TAKAGI
1ᵉʳ PRIX EX AEQUO COMPOSITION 2019
© MISA SHINSHI

MEMBER OF THE WORLD
FEDERATION OF INTERNATIONAL
MUSIC COMPETITIONS

EINLEITUNG

Abgesehen von unserem Feature-Bereich wird der Großteil von PAY an ein Verzeichnis von Unternehmen, Veranstaltungsorten und Dienstleistungen für darstellende Künste in ganz Europa übergeben.

Um das Beste aus dem Buch herauszuholen, sollten Sie die Anleitung mit dem Titel How to Use Your Yearbook lesen. Der Fokus liegt auf großen und mittelständischen professionellen Unternehmen (unabhängig davon, ob sie auf nationaler, regionaler oder lokaler Ebene gefördert werden). Wir schließen auch kleinere Unternehmen ein, wo es geeignet ist, und bieten eine vollständige Palette von Optionen für die Tourbuchung, die Bereitstellung von Dienstleistungen und Musikensembles.

Wir haben kürzlich unsere Online-Datenbank neu gestartet, die unter artsdb.net vollständig durchsuchbar ist. Die Website enthält neue Funktionen und zusätzliche Inhalte und ist somit der perfekte Ort, um Ihr Unternehmen zu präsentieren. Gehen Sie jetzt zu artsdb.net, um Ihren kostenlosen Eintrag zu erstellen.

Schließlich sind wir äußerst dankbar für die Unterstützung der Mitwirkenden, die uns über Änderungen und neue Entwicklungen in ihren Ländern auf dem Laufenden halten. PAY ist auf ihre Unterstützung angewiesen, und wir würden gerne Kommentare und Informationen von Einzelpersonen und Organisationen dazu einholen, wie wir es zu einer noch nützlicheren Veröffentlichung für die Branche der darstellenden Künste machen können.

Bitte schreiben Sie uns oder teilen Sie uns dies über unsere E-Mail-Adresse mit:
info@musocommunications.com

HINWEISE ZUR BENUTZUNG DES PAY

Sprache

Wo es möglich war, haben wir die Namen der Organisationen in der Landessprache gehalten. Es gibt allerdings englische Übersetzungen slawischer Namen. In der Regel finden Sie englische Übersetzungen aller im internationalen Raum wenig verbreiteten Sprachen (z.B. Finnisch, Schwedisch, Ungarisch, Polnisch, Serbisch, Kroatisch, Russisch usw.)

Da das PAY sich an eine internationale Leserschaft wendet, erscheinen fast alle Städtenamen in der Landessprache (z.B Firenze anstatt Florenz, Torino anstatt Turin, Köln anstatt Cologne, Wien anstatt Vienna). Allerdings benutzen wir die englische Variante für russische und andere slawische Städtenamen sowie Städtenamen zweisprachiger Länder, d.h die Hauptstadt Belgiens heißt im PAY Brussels und nicht Brussel (Flämisch) oder Bruxelles (Französisch). Antwerpen heißt Antwerp.

Index

Der Index am Ende des PAY ermöglicht ein schnelles Auffinden von Informationen über eine bestimmte Organisation. Alle kostenfreien redakionellen Einträge sind dort aufgeführt. Es gibt natürlich auch einen Index für alle in den Anzeigen aufgeführten Künstler und Organisationen.

Telefonieren

Die internationale Vorwahl für jedes Land steht am Anfang der für das Land aufgeführten Einträge.

Es ist möglich, die meisten aufgeführten Organisationen direkt anzuwählen. Die Vowahlnummer für die jeweilige Stadt finden Sie bei jedem Eintrag. Bitte achten Sie bei Telefonaten innerhalb eines Landes darauf, daß Sie eine Ziffer vor der Stadtvorwahlnummer wählen. In vielen Fällen wählt man die Ziffer –0-, z.B. bei Telefonanrufen aus London oder Birmingham nach Glasgow wählt man –0141 vor der Rufnummer. In manchen Fällen wählt man eine andere Ziffer, z.B. in Spanien wählt man –9. Also, um eine Rufnummer in Barcelona aus Madrid zu wählen, wählt man –93 vor der Rufnummer. Einige der größeren Kulturorganisationen, vor allem in Deutschland und Österreich, haben eine zentrale Rufnummer.

Jedes Land hat seine eigine Landesvorwahl, die am Anfang der jeweiligen Sektion angegeben ist. Das Kennzeichen "+" besagt, daß man die internationale Vorwahlnummer wählen muß. Wenn man zum Beispiel Ungarn (Landesvorwahl 36) anrufen will, würde man vor der 36 und der eigentlichen Nummer die internationle Vorwahl wählen. Für die meisten Länder ist diese Vorwahl (00), aber wenn man zum Beispiel von den Vereinigten Staaten anruft, ist die Vorwahl (011).

INDICE

2022 MAY 9-11

DANISH+

**DANISH
PERFORMING
ARTS
SHOWCASE
FOR CHILDREN
& YOUTH
AARHUS,
DENMARK**

READ MORE: DANISHPLUS.DK

INTRODUZIONE

Guardando oltre la nostra sezione dedicata alle caratteristiche, la maggior parte di PAY è dedicata a un elenco di aziende, luoghi e servizi di arti dello spettacolo in tutta Europa.

Per ottenere il massimo dal libro, dovresti leggere la guida intitolata Come utilizzare il tuo annuario. Il focus è sulle grandi e medie imprese professionali (siano esse sovvenzionate a livello nazionale, regionale o locale). Includiamo anche società più piccole, ove opportuno, offrendo una gamma completa di opzioni per la prenotazione di tour, la fornitura di servizi e gli ensemble musicali.

Di recente abbiamo rilanciato il nostro database online, che è completamente ricercabile su artsdb.net. Il sito Web include nuove funzionalità e contenuti aggiuntivi, che lo rendono il luogo perfetto per presentare la tua azienda. Vai ora su artsdb.net per creare la tua scheda gratuita.

Infine, siamo estremamente grati per il supporto dei contributori che ci tengono aggiornati sui cambiamenti e sui nuovi sviluppi nei loro paesi. PAY dipende dal loro supporto e vorremmo incoraggiare commenti e informazioni da individui e organizzazioni su come renderlo una pubblicazione ancora più utile per il business delle arti dello spettacolo.

Scriveteci o fatecelo sapere tramite il nostro indirizzo email a:
info@musocommunications.com

GUIDA ALL'USO DEL PAY

Lingue

Dove è stato possibile abbiamo mantenuto i nomi delle organizzazion nella lingua originale. Per quanto riguarda la Russia, i Paesi dell'Europa dell'Est ecc. I nomi sono stati traslitterati in inglese. Sono stati inoltre tradotti - in inglese – anche i nomi di tutte quelle organizzazioni di paesi le cui lingue sono meno comuni o meno usate nel panorama internazionale (finlandese, ungherese, polacco, serbo, croato, svedese, russo ecc).

Dal momento che *PAY* è stato pensato per un pubblico internazionale, le città sono generalmente indicate nella loro lingua madre (ad es. London per Londra, Köln per Colonia, Paris per Parigi e Wien per Vienna). Per quanto riguarda la Russia, i Paesi dell'Est ecc. e per quelle nazioni che sono bilingue i nomi sono stati inglesizzati.

Per esempio la capitale del Belgio è indicata come Brussels anzichè Brussel (fiammingo) o Bruxelles (francese), ed Antwerpen (Anversa) è indicata come Antwerp.

Indice

L'indice delle entrate editoriali situato alla fine del *Performing Arts Yearbook*: Europe vi permetterà di trovare su quale pagina appaiono i dati di un'organizzazione.

Telefono

All'inizio di ogni nazione ed in ogni sezione è indicato il prefisso diretto nazionale.
Il prefisso della città è incluso nelle varie entrate. Ricordatevi ogni volta che digitate un numero dalla stessa nazione di aggiungere lo zero o il prefisso corretto della zona o della città. Ad esempio chiamando Glasgow da Londra o da Birmingham dovrete comporre il prefisso 1041 seguito dal numero di telefono.

Ogni paese ha un suo propio codice che vi permette di accedere direttamente alle altre nazioni ed è indicato da un + che dovrà essere preceduto dai numeri qui elencati. Se ad esempio volete chiamare in Ungheria (prefisso nazionale +36) da una delle seguenti nazioni, dovrete usare questi prefissi internazionali prima di quello nazionale e del numero diretto. Per la maggior parte delle nazioni il numero è (00), ma dagli Stati Uniti per esempio, dovete comporre lo (011) prima del prefisso nazionale. Nel dubbio contattate la vostra compagnia telefonica.

CONTENDIDO

INTRODUCCION

Mirando más allá de nuestra sección de funciones, la mayor parte de PAY se dedica a un directorio de empresas, lugares y servicios de artes escénicas en toda Europa.

Para aprovechar al máximo el libro, debe leer la guía titulada Cómo usar su anuario. La atención se centra en empresas profesionales de gran y mediana escala (ya sean subvencionadas a nivel nacional, regional o local). También incluimos compañías más pequeñas donde sea adecuado, brindando una gama completa de opciones para la reserva de giras, la prestación de servicios y conjuntos musicales.

Recientemente relanzamos nuestra base de datos en línea, que se puede buscar por completo en artsdb.net. El sitio web incluye nuevas funciones y contenido adicional, lo que lo convierte en el lugar perfecto para presentar su empresa. Dirígete a artsdb.net ahora para crear tu lista gratuita.

Finalmente, estamos extremadamente agradecidos por el apoyo de los colaboradores que nos mantienen actualizados con los cambios y nuevos desarrollos en sus países. PAY depende de su apoyo y nos gustaría alentar comentarios e información de individuos y organizaciones sobre cómo podemos hacer que sea una publicación aún más útil para el negocio de las artes escénicas.

Por favor escríbanos o háganoslo saber a través de nuestra dirección de correo electrónico a:
info@musocomunicaciones.com

COMO UTILIZAR EL PAY

Idiomas
Donde nos ha sido posible hemos mantenido los nombres de las compañías en la lengua en que nos han sido proporcionados.
En el caso de las lenguas nórdicas, eslavas, etc. se proporciona una traducción del nombre original. Generalmente se da una traducción al ingles de los nombres en idiomas poco conocidos o utilizados en el foro internacional (finlandés, sueco, húngaro, polaco, serbio, croata, ruso, etc.). Dada la naturaleza internacional de los lectores a los que vadirigido el PAY, los nombres de las ciudades aparecen normalmente en su idioma original (p.ej.Firenze para Florencia, Köln para Colonia o Wien para Viena). Sin embargo se utiliza la version inglesa para los países nórdicos, eslavos, etc. y para países bilingües.De este modo, se nombra a la capital de Bélgica como Brussels (ingles) en vez de Brussel (holandés) o Bruxelles (francés), y Antwerpen aparece como Antwerp.

Indice
El Índice de Entradas Editoriales, al final del libro, le indicará dónde encontrar todas las compañías listadas

Teléfonos
Los prefijos telefónicos internacionales figuran en la cabecera del país dentro de cada sección. El prefijo de la region ó ciudad está incluído en la información de cada entrada editorial. Recuerde que al marcar un número dentro de un país a menudo hace falta añadir una cifra antes del prefijo. En muchos casos es un cero (p.ej. para marcar Glasgow desde Londres o Birmingham el número es precedido por 0141).

Cada país tiene su propio prefijo internacional, que le permitirá marcar directamente. La necesidad de añadir este prefijo está señalada en la información de cada país con el símbolo = antes del prefijo nacional. De este modo, para llamar a Hungría (prefijo nacional 36) desde la mayor parte de los países es necesario macar [00],pero esto puede variar según el país desde el que se llama. Si quisiera llamar a Hungría desde los Estados Unidos, tendría que marcar el prefijo internacional [011], seguido del prefijo nacional [36] y finalmente del número deseado. (En caso de duda consulte con la oeradora local.)

Dancing on the ceiling

No Gravity makes dance works like no other company on earth. PAY spoke to founder Emiliano Pellisari about his unique approach to movement, his artistic and romantic partnership, and his constant need for new challenges.

It's hard to think of a company with a more perfect name than No Gravity Dance Company. Using clever mirror techniques, their dancers seem to fly through space, unbound from the Newtonian rules that apply to the rest of us. It's part magic trick, part performance, but entirely beautiful. There really is no dance company quite like No Gravity.

But then again, there really is no one quite like company founder Emiliano Pellisari. Eccentric and energetic, he's always telling wonderful stories and making strange jokes – a rare example of an artist who is as interesting off stage as his works are on it.

"Life is boring if you don't do new things," he says at the start of the interview. "I always want to be moving, to be creating. I don't want to ever be stuck in a rut."

It's an understandable attitude given Pellisari's background. He started out studying philosophy, but ended up working in the theatre, first as a stagehand and then later as a producer and dramaturg. It wasn't the most exciting work, he says, but it paid the bills.

Then disaster struck: in 2005 Pellisari was diagnosed with cancer. He beat the disease, but vowed never again to work on anything he didn't truly believe in.

"I decided to change my life – to make my own company and create my own art" he recalls. "So I started rehearsing and experimenting in a small garage. Eventually, I created my own technique, and I have been exploring and developing it ever since."

Pellisari's technique traces its origins back to old theatre tricks developed in the 17th century. Using mirrors, he creates the illusion

> "I wanted to be more minimalist, more raw, with the bodies of the dancers exposed so that the audience can feel their energy"

that his dancers are floating or flying. As a result, No Gravity performances are very different from every other contemporary dance company, with the performers able to move in any direction.

But this unusual technique had a drawback, because when he was first starting out it was impossible to find the right creative partners.

"I called a choreographer, and it was a disaster," he laughs. "The problem is that with my technique the dancers are lying on the ground, reflected towards the audience using a big mirror, and choreographers are not used to this. They're used to working on the floor, with the dancers' steps as the starting point. But you can't use the feet with this technique. So it took me a long time to find the right person to work with."

That person came along in 2008: Mariana Porceddu. A graduate of the National Academy of Dance in Rome, she has performed with acclaimed companies like Compagnia Danza Prospettiva on stages across Europe and in the US.

"We worked so well together because she is passionate, and she has so many ideas for how to make the dancers move," he enthuses. "As the years went by, we started to become closer as an artistic couple; each new work was more refined, more interesting, more sophisticated. Eventually we fell in love and started a family...so now of course we have a very complicated life!"

It might be complicated, but for Pellisari it's the perfect situation: "Working so closely with the person you love is a really wonderful experience," he says. "Now I can paint the idea for the show in broad strokes and Mariana fills in the detail. When I create worlds they can sometimes feel quite cold, but Mariana breathes life and soul into them. I am the architect, but she is the choreographer, and she creates truly beautiful movements."

You can certainly see the power of their partnership in their two current shows, *inferno* and *Fellini Dream*. The first takes its inspiration from Dante, while the second of course comes from ideas of the great Italian film director.

For *inferno*, Pellisari decided to completely reinvent a show that he originally presented more than 10 years ago.

"Until now you could only watch our shows as a reflection in a mirror, which meant they didn't have any depth," he explains. "But now Mariana and I have developed a new technique so that you can see both the dancer moving on stage and their reflection. It's very difficult to do, but the result is amazing.

"That's why I wanted to revisit this show again, so I could present these ideas inspired by Dante in greater depth. I wanted to be more minimalist, more raw, with the bodies of the dancers exposed so that the audience can feel their energy."

Thematically, the show takes the audience into the world of Dante's *Inferno*, a hot and heavy trip through hell.

"Dante is the most important artist in Italy, and I think *Inferno* is one of the most important books ever written," says Pellisari. "After my experience with cancer, and other tragedies in my life, I have always been interested in journeys to the world of death. This theme comes up again and again, and I am always inspired by art that deals with these ideas."

Death was also a start point for *Fellini Dream*, the other major show that No Gravity has on offer right now: "The director of an international festival in Palermo asked me to make a show about Fellini, and I liked the idea," he remembers. "Fellini was born in Rimini, which is also where I grew up, so that's an interesting connection. As I did more research I found out about a script that he never produced, which was all about a journey into the afterlife. I took inspiration from this and made a new and original drama based on it. It's actually not a dance piece, but a theatre work with dialogue and actors rather than dancers. So this is a new challenge for us, but as I already said – I like challenges."

Both shows will be on tour in 2022 and 2023. *inferno* debuted at the Oxford Festival in 2021 and will head to the US for a tour in 2023. *Fellini Dream*, meanwhile, had its world premiere at the Palermo Festival in December, and the company is planning both Russian and European tours for 2023.

Unsurprisingly, Pellisari is already full of ideas for the company's next show – although that too will be a new challenge: "Our next show deals with immigration," notes Pellisari. "It's actually the first time that we will do a show based on Mariana's idea rather than mine, which I'm very happy about. It will be a new experience for me to help realise her idea and it's a chance to work together in a new way. I can't wait to get started."

To book *Fellini Dream* or *inferno* 2021 contact: produzione@ nogravitytheatre.it

nogravitytheatre.com

> "I always want to be moving, to be creating. I don't want to ever be stuck in a rut."

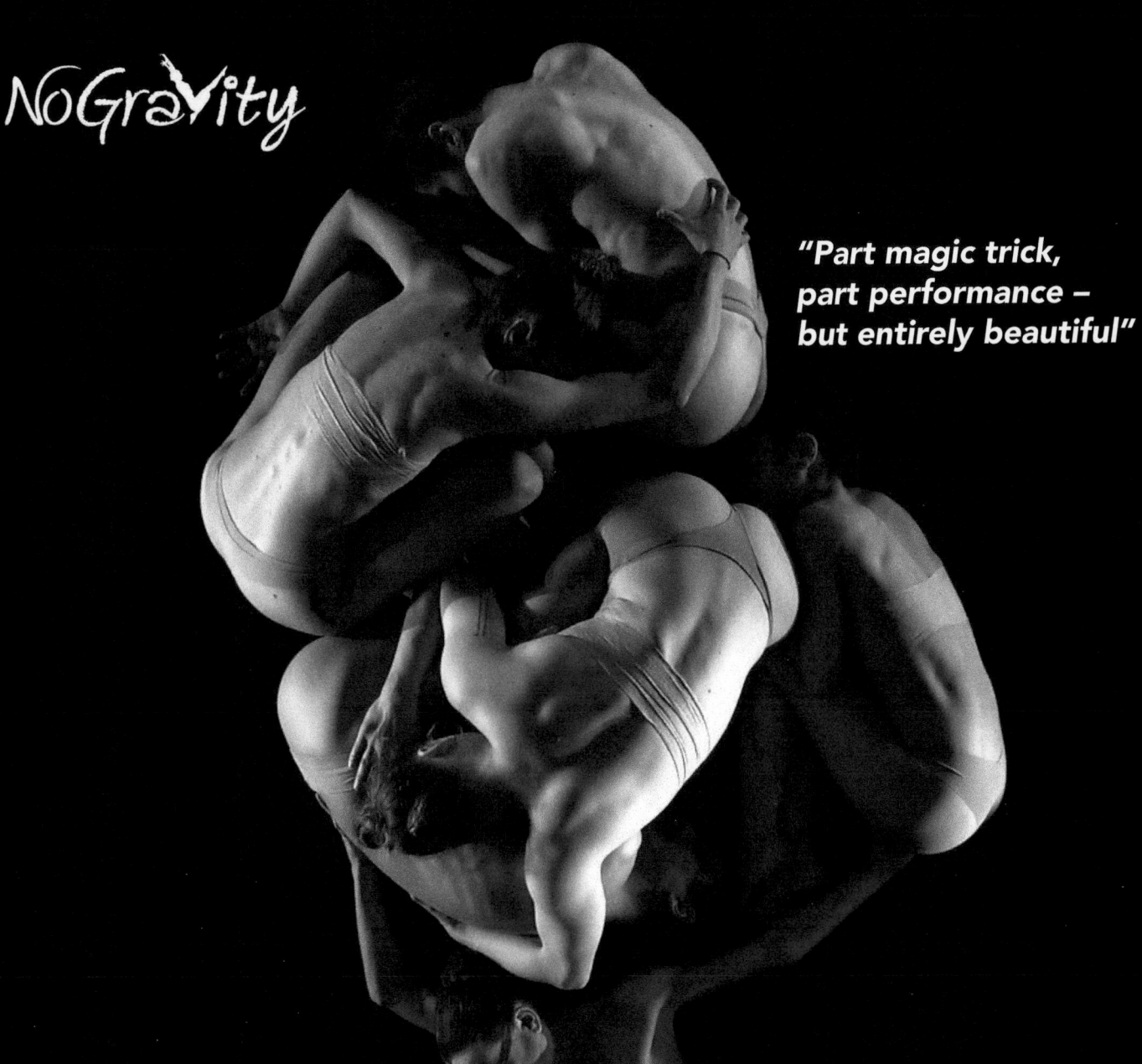

Digital vistas

Hong Kong Chinese Orchestra has fully embraced digital technology in order to reach new audiences. PAY speaks to executive director Celina Chin.

Celina Chin

For the usually busy, built up streets of Hong Kong, the closures and cancellations of the last two years were particularly strange. In a city that never sleeps, which is crammed full of commerce and culture, the idea of stopping and locking down just didn't feel right.

But while the streets might not have been so bustling, behind the scenes there was a lot going on. People were finding new ways to keep the arts going. They were rediscovering themselves and reinventing their practice. And perhaps no other arts organisation better represents this spirit than Hong Kong Chinese Orchestra. Because, over the last 24 months, the orchestra has come up with a string of new ideas for bringing classical Chinese music to the masses.

"The pandemic has changed how we do things in many ways," explains HKCO executive director Celina Chin. "Like so many orchestras, we increased our activities on social media platforms last year. While online concerts and music videos were initially developed as ad hoc measures in response to venue closer, they have proven to be effective in opening up new performance formats and broadening HKCO's audience reach.

"But our work went far beyond just online content," she continues. "We've really embraced all the possibilities that digital can offer – probably faster than we would have done if it was not for the pandemic. And now these new ideas are having an impact on our audience not only here in Hong Kong but also internationally.

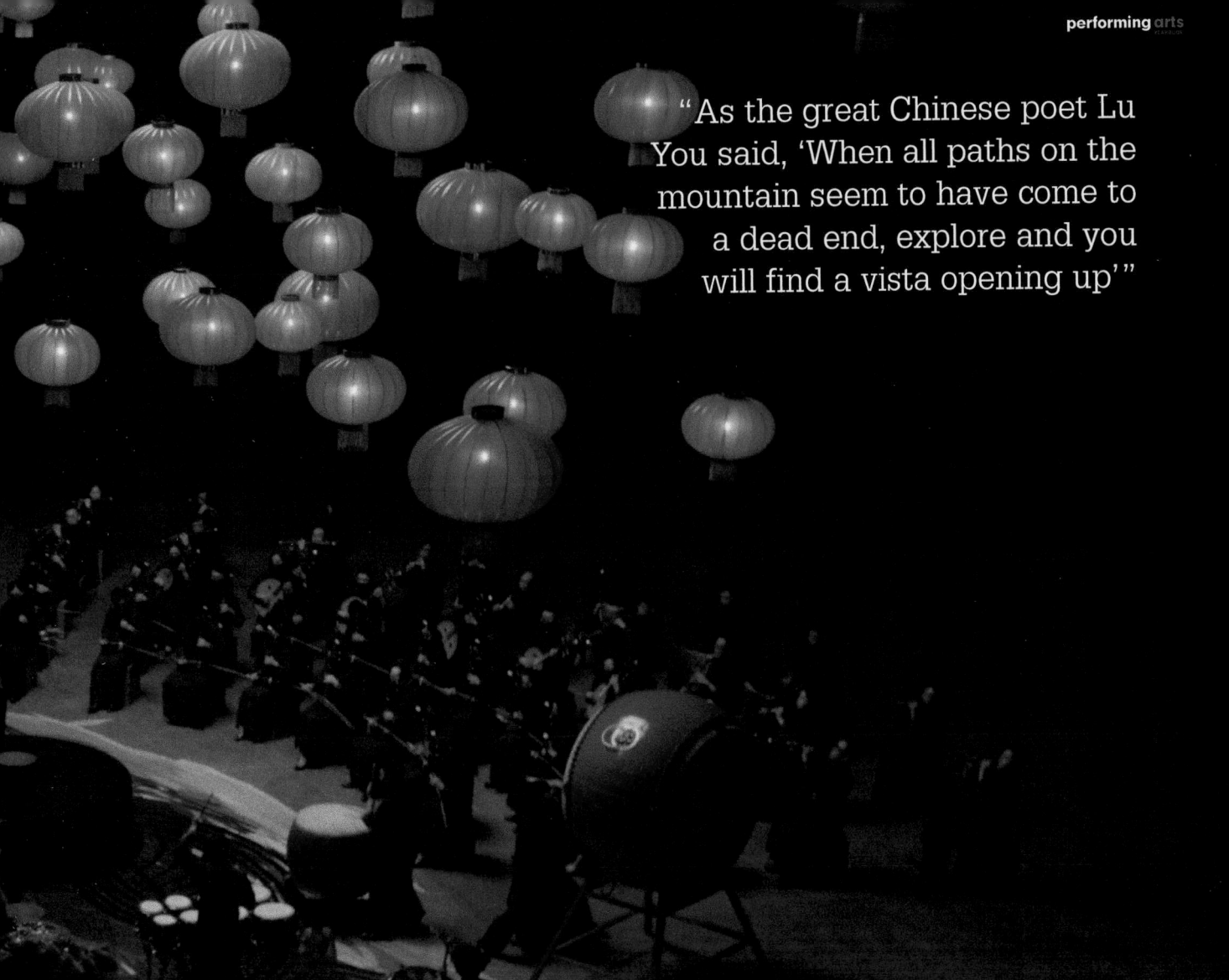

> "As the great Chinese poet Lu You said, 'When all paths on the mountain seem to have come to a dead end, explore and you will find a vista opening up'"

"As the great Chinese poet Lu You said, 'When all paths on the mountain seem to have come to a dead end, explore and you will find a vista opening up'. We have really embraced these wise words and this spirit. We want to create impactful programmes that last beyond the pandemic and become part of our musical culture."

Let's start then with the first major development, which was the creation of a 5G concert series. The first, titled '5G. Syncs with the Power of Drums', saw the HKCO broadcasting an outdoor concert directly to 5G-ready mobile phones.

"The event – which we created with the mobile phone network 3 Hong Kong – reached a much larger audience than would have been possible in a bricks and mortar concert hall," enthuses Chin. "Riding on this successful experience, HKCO will continue its partnership with 3 Hong Kong to deliver more live streamed concerts in the future."

Taking content direct to phones is clearly the future for content of all kinds, particularly in markets like Hong Kong where many people have 5G phones capable of livestreaming high-quality content. But, of course, many classical music fans still don't have 5G phones. So for those consumers, HKCO created a digital concert hall that launched in late 2021.

"The HKCO Net Concert Hall is another effort to boost our online presence," says Chin. "It's a model that has already been tried elsewhere – for example, by the Berlin Philharmonic – but we're the first

Chinese orchestra to do this. Available on YouTube and Facebook, the HKCO Net Concert Hall features a broad selection of complete concerts and individual performances. We have since made this playlist on YouTube a regular fixture, and will continue to upload performances there so that Chinese music lovers can easily find and enjoy them.

"We believe that more people from around the world will access our music thanks to this platform…and we're already seeing statistics that back this up. It's also a useful research resource for academics and composers who are studying the Chinese classics."

As Chin notes, virtual concert halls have been tried elsewhere with great success. However, HKCO's next adventure is breaking entirely new ground: an augmented reality season brochure.

"We have incorporated AR in our season brochure, which will encourage younger generations to learn more about HKCO and Chinese music," says the executive director. "When you view the brochure through an app called SnapPop, enhanced content appears on many of the pages. For example, if you're reading one of the pages about a particular Chinese instrument, a 3D music instrument will pop up and play music so you know what the instrument sounds like. Or when you scan the page with a message from our artistic director, Maestro Yan, and he actually appears as a 3D image and reads his message directly to you.

"We held a launch event for this AR technology at the Hong

Kong Cultural Centre where people could experience these AR effects. The feedback we got was extremely positive, and we're actually one of the first arts organisations in the world to incorporate this technology into a season brochure."

Speaking of the current season – the orchestra's 45th – HKCO will present 30 concerts in a diverse range of formats.

"We have three new programmes as part of the 'One Hundred Chinese Music Classics Select' series," says Chin. "We are also working on a new series to salute giants of Chinese music. We're calling it 'Timeless Classics – A Tribute to Maestro Peng Xiuwen', and we'll debut with a retrospective concert for this highly revered composer and conductor, who played a pivotal role in the early development of orchestral music in China.

"We've also planned a series of 15-minute music programmes tor the coming season, with '24 Solar Terms' that will be featured as videos during our regular concerts."

Listed as one of UNESCO's Intangible Cultural Heritage practices, 24 Solar Terms is a knowledge system developed in ancient China that categorises different times of a year according to the sun's motion. The mini video concerts will take this system as their start point.

"24 Solar Terms has a lot to say about living a nourishing lifestyle by eating foods and engaging in physical activities that are suitable for each season, and in the many festivities celebrated at

> "When you view the brochure through an app called SnapPop, enhanced content appears on many of the pages"

different times of the year," says Chin. "We're really looking forward to creating a musical rendition of this fascinating ancient system on the harmonious integration of time, nature and man."

Continues Chin: "And of course, the Hong Kong Drum Festival is entering its 19th year. We featured two young local drum groups: the Refiner Drums and Gekko. And we premiered a piece featuring jazz drumming and an oue eco-gehu – which is a bass instrument like a cello – alongside the orchestra. It was a really amazing experience for everyone involved."

As for touring, Chin is hopeful that audiences all over the world will soon be able to see HKCO again – and not just on digital stages: "With vaccination becoming prevalent and international travel restrictions easing, HKCO targets to resume regular tours for Fall 2022. Performances have already been confirmed for Singapore, Japan and Mainland China, and we are working on resuming of our European tour that was originally planned for 2022. We really hope to see all our loyal fans soon, along with the many new friends we have made during this difficult time."

hkco.org

Elastic inventor

Victor Quijada has done more than just create his own company: he's invented an entirely new dance style. PAY speaks to the dance pioneer, and his RUBBERBANDance Group executive Fannie Bellefeuille, about what it takes to create and disseminate his unique process and practice.

Fannie Bellefeuille

Victor Quijada

When most people think of a career in the performing arts, they think of themselves in a particular role – an ambition they'd like achieve. Some want to be principal dancers; some would like to lead a company as an artistic or executive; others might want work behind the scenes.

But creating a new genre from scratch? That's not something most people could even imagine, let alone aspire to. However, that's exactly the goal Victor Quijada set himself some 20 years ago. What's more, he managed to achieve it.

"I'd spent my childhood in the hip hop and street dance world as a b-boy," remembers Quijada, when reached at at his home in Montréal. "Then I spent my young adult life with professional dance groups like Les Grands Ballets Canadiens. So I had this dual identity, which was rare at the time.

The result of this dual identity was that Quijada found himself stifled. In ballet, he couldn't tap into the kind of self-expression that he found through cyphering (a kind of hip hop free style dancing). Then again, street dance lacked the coherence and organisation he thought was necessary to express the big ideas he had in his head.

"I thought if I stayed with a company like Le Grands Ballets I'd just be boxed in to what a choreographer was supposed to be," he affirms. "I needed to create a kitchen where I could cook up a new recipe – something with ingredients from both, but that would be its own original dish.

And that is when RUBBERBAND was born. Starting in New York, but really taking root once he moved to Montréal in 2000, RUBBERBANDance Group would become the tree from which Quijada's ideas would grow. Others had tried mixing hip hop and ballet before, but never to this extent – and never with this dedication.

But before he could do all that Quijada first had to find that right dancers. And that, he says, wasn't easy:

RUBBERBANDance Group
performing *Vic's Mix*
© Bill Hebert

"Now it's different, but back then I had no idea where I could recruit from," he says. "Bringing street dancers and classically trained dancers together lead to conflict. The b-boys felt the classical dancers were not real dancers; they couldn't improvise, didn't know anything about cyphering. As for the classical dancers, they felt the same – the b-boys couldn't learn steps, so they didn't see them as real dancers either.

"I was kind of in-between saying 'you're both real'. I saw the validity in each of them, and I saw part of myself in each of them.

"In the end, the best answer was finding ballet dancers who were also club kids – they understood the world of company dancing, but also knew about going out and expressing yourself."

It took, Quijada says, "a lot of trial and error" before RUBBERBAND was ready for its first show. That came in 2002 with *Tender Loving Care*. It was raw, but even then it had the RUBBERBAND aesthetic, – it didn't look like anything else.

"What I needed to do was unlearn what break dancing looks like, unlearn what ballet looks like, and just connect with the inner

"What I needed to do was unlearn what break dancing looks like, unlearn what ballet looks like, and just connect with the inner feelings of both"

feelings of both," he reflects. "It was expressing the different facets of myself."

Quijada's new company and original style were an immediate success, and further shows followed: *Hasta La Próxima* (2002), *Metabolism* (2003), *Elastic Perspective* (2004), *Punto Ciego* (2008) and more.

"The different pieces I've made over the years look very different as I've bounced between a thrashy style, a symmetrical style… working with classical music, jazz music and more. But it's all still within the RUBBERBAND spectrum."

At the same time as choreographing these pieces, Quijada was

RUBBERBANDance Group
performing *Vic's Mix*
© Bill Hebert

"Now I travel all over the world, from ISPA in New York to Tanzmesse in Germany, making sure I spread the word"

starting to think about turning his style into something reproducible – something shareable. This idea, he admits, quickly became an obsession.

"I was teaching some moves to Anne Plamondon – who would later be co-artistic director with me – and she said, 'Victor, these steps are great, but although I'm making the same shapes as you, it's not coming from the same place – you need to tell me where it comes from so I can do exactly the same'.

"So that was the challenge – to find where these shapes initiate from. From around 2006 that was my obsessive focus, and I spent five years just working on that.

"Then in 2013 we premiered *Empirical Quotient*. It was the first piece I wasn't dancing in and I thought, 'okay, this is cooked'. This piece was the proof that this method exists, it is valid – I can create with it, I can transmit it, I can share it.

"Even though I wasn't on stage dancing, my knowledge was. These dancers – already very talented – could grow as artists by using it: they'd be able to go beyond what they'd done before."

Now, sharing the RUBBERBAND Method is a big part of Quijada's life, with summer intensives, workshops and other programmes

He's even working on a new iteration of the method that will make it accessible for younger people and non-dancers.

Then Quijada's life came a quite literal breaking point in 2017, when a leg injury put him out of action for several months.

"I think perhaps I'd plateaued," he says, as he looks back on that time. "I'd finished the RUBBERBAND Method, and made *Empirical Quotient*, which was a huge success. I'd become a dad for the first time, and I'd always wanted to be a parent.

"I'd achieved so much…and it felt like this was the point where I could lay down and get stuck in all that, or step outside of it and explore in another direction. I decided, no, I'm not done yet – it's time for something new. That's where *Ever So Slightly* came from."

Inspired by ideas of change – as something both incremental and sudden, something to be embraced or feared – *Ever So Slightly* premiered in 2018 and has been on tour continually since.

"That show was also part of our new business model," notes RUBBERBAND executive Fannie Bellefeuille, who has led the company alongside Quijada since Plamondon departed in 2015. "We used to do just one major show at a time, but we realised we needed to have different shows to be able to accommodate all the presenters that want us: a small show, a medium show and a large show. We even have an outdoor show now."

An administrator with a background as a playwright and performer, she's been with the company for 10 years, and while Quijada's been changing the world of dance, Bellefeuille's been

RUBBERBANDance Group
performing *Vic's Mix*
© Bill Hebert

making sure people know about it:

"I didn't used to like dance," she confesses, laughing. "But from when I first saw Victor's work I realised that what he does is accessible, but at a high artistic level. That was something I could get behind. So now I travel all over the world, from ISPA in New York to Tanzmesse in Germany, making sure I spread the word."

At least, that was the case until COVID-19 hit. Quijada and Bellefeuille quickly found the company grounded, with tours of *Ever So Slightly* and repertory show *Vic's Mix* cancelled.

"The was very difficult not knowing when we would be back to normal," says Bellefeuille. "So I just focussed my energies on taking care of the people we have. And now we are back on tour again, so that hard work has paid off.

As for Quijada, he is now working on new show *Trenzado* – an autobiographical piece that will put him back on stage as a dancer for the first time in nearly 10 years. But he's also been spending lots of time with his daughter, with plenty of visits to the local park to push her on the swings.

Was the company tempted to go down the online route, putting on digital performances? "I've felt a resistance to putting things online – I really don't think it has the quality that I feel is important," answers Quijada.

Bellefeuille agrees: "It's fine if some companies want to do things that are technology based, but some companies just want to be in the studio and doing shows on stage. Tech can't be the salvation; some people want an in-person experience."

Instead, Quijada has turned to lecturing. "I don't think the RUBBERBAND Method works over video – it's too intense – but I've led seminars around my approach to dance on screen – I've worked on a number of films – and I've given some lectures on my career

> "It's fine if some companies want to do things that are technology based, but some companies just want to be in the studio and doing shows on stage."

and influences. It is really interesting sharing that with other people, and it is something I plan to keep doing post-pandemic."

I have one last question for Quijada: where did the name RUBBERBAND come from?

"When I was a kid every rapper had his dancers," he answers. "My big dream was to be a backup dancer for a rapper, and when I was about 15 I met some rappers and I started touring with them. And they said I looked like a rubber band when I moved, so they gave me that name. For a period of five years in LA nobody knew me as Victor – everyone called me Rubberband.

"I was also studying at an arts high school in the day – learning about postmodernism, the cubists, the fluxus artists, and taking part in cyphers at night. So these ideas of postmodernism and cyphering first came together then.

"When I came to name the group years later, just calling it Victor Quijada company didn't seem right. I wanted to channel that feeling I had when I was cyphering and being exposed to all this great art.

"So the name RUBBERBAND made sense – I wanted to inspire other people, in the same was I was inspired when I was Rubberband. It's that energy and that time that I'm honouring to this day."

rbdg.ca

RUBBERBANDance Group
performing *Vic's Mix*
© Bill Hebert

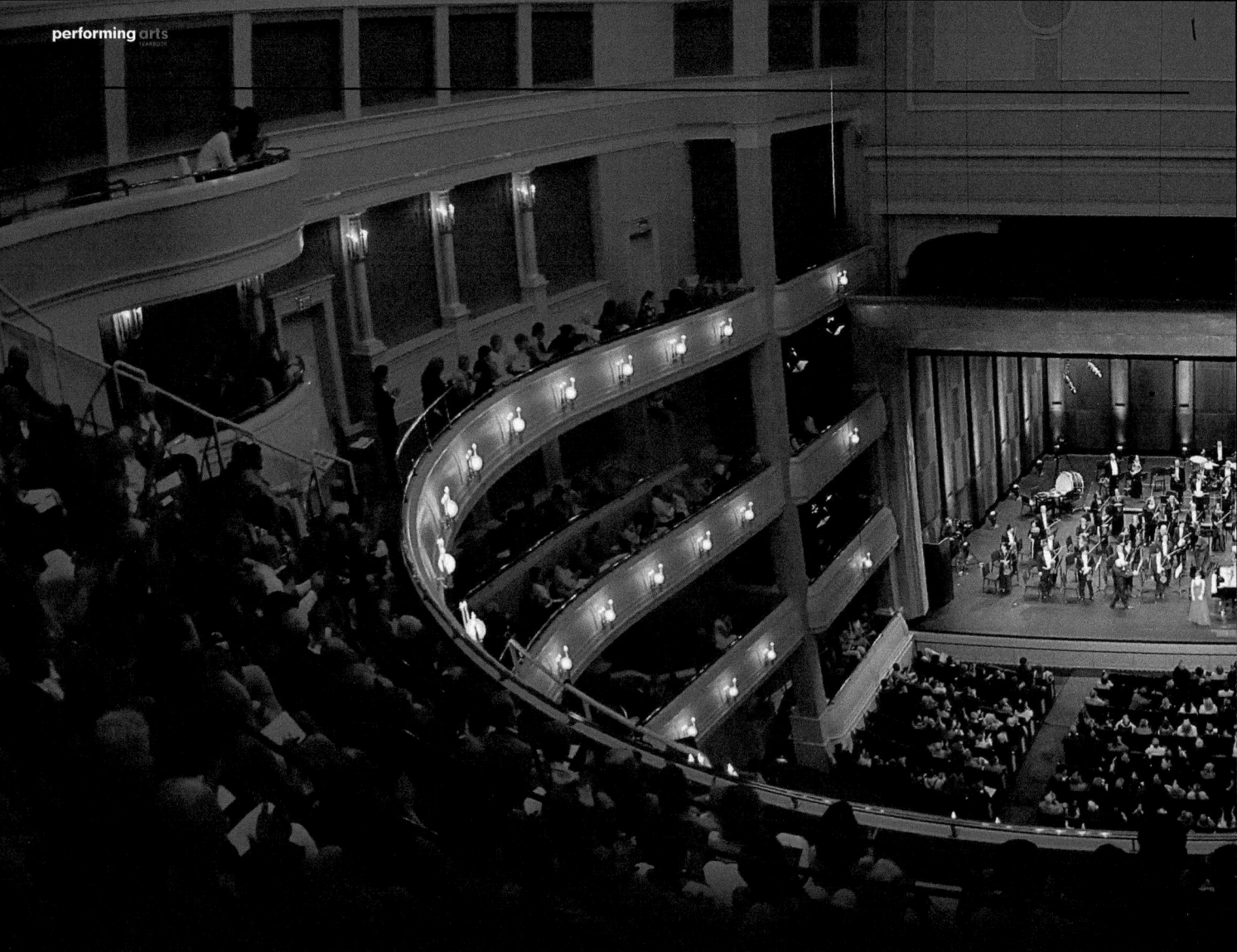

Playing the game

The Cliburn returns this year for its sixteenth instalment. President and CEO Jaques Marquis tells PAY what it takes to build a great career, the secrets of a good jury, and how he's taking inspiration from sports broadcasts.

I have to admit, when we sat down to interview Cliburn International Piano Competition president and CEO Jacques Marquis, we were not expecting to talk about sports. But that's exactly how our conversation began.

"Look at American football," enthuses Marquis. "The game lasts an hour. But the broadcast lasts for three hours; they entertain, they engage the audience, and they explain every play. You might never have watched American football before, but by the end you have some understanding of the game, and you enjoyed watching it. That's what we want to do with the Cliburn competition."

It's probably the first time I've heard an elite piano competition taking lessons from American football, but it is this kind of unexpected inspiration – and a willingness to evolve – that has kept the Cliburn on top for so long.

Continues Marquis: "We need to take lessons from the best examples, whether that's another music competition or the Monday Night Football broadcast. We have to have hosts that explain what's going on so that anyone can understand it. We've got to stop waiting for people to come to us."

Another thing that professional sports does well is tell stories. And Marquis says that, here too, the Cliburn can learn lessons.

"People can be impressed by the playing, but if they don't know anything about the players then there not going to become lifelong fans," says the president and CEO. "And a lot of our competitors have amazing stories, from all over the world. So, we're going to bring in documentary features and tell the stories of the competitors' journeys during the pandemic and then heading into the competition itself. We need to tell these stories and build a direct connection with the fans."

Although Marquis' allusion to the most brash of American sports might be surprising, it's actually entirely keeping with tradition. And that's because the Cliburn, which holds its sixteenth edition from 2-18 June, has always been about both promoting the best young pianists *and* entertaining.

"It's a tradition that goes back to our founder," affirms Marquis. "Van Cliburn himself wanted to share music with the largest audience possible. He would appear on chat shows, he would work with young kids, he'd perform for presidents. He used his talent and charisma to bring people to classical music. With the Cliburn, reaching out and being accessible should always be at the front of our thinking. And if we do that we will have success, because I believe great music will always talk to people."

And on that note, Marquis could not have made a more on-point pick for head of the jury: Marin Alsop. Known as much for her efforts in engaging audiences and supporting young artists as for her incredible skills on the podium, Alsop is the ideal person to push this message of music for the masses.

"A conductor like Marin can make a huge difference helping a young artist get started in their career," observes Marquis. "And not only is Marin a fantastic conductor, but she has this desire to help and support young people.

"She's also an amazing exponent for the music itself, and is great at sharing music with a large audience," he adds. "Every time I talk with her I just get inspired. If we have an idea her first response is

"You might never have watched American football before, but by the end you have some understanding of the game"

always 'yes, we can do it'. There's no limitation on what she thinks we can achieve together, and that makes her really fun to work with.

"For example, this year we've rerplaced the chamber music in the semifinal with a Mozart concerto, along with the two concertos in the final itself. When I told this to Marin and asked if she'd be okay to conduct that many major pieces she said 'no problem'. It's great having someone who is always so positive."

As for the rest of the jury, they are all (with one exception) taking part in the Cliburn for the first time – part of a longstanding policy of keeping things fresh.

"I don't want to have the same people over and over, because if you do that it becomes a club, not a jury," asserts Marquis. "Then there are the different schools: I like to have someone from the Russian school, the French school and the Italian school, as well as someone who works regularly in Asia. It's good to have all these different styles and ideas represented in the jury. We've had a record 388 applications this year from over 50 countries, so our jury needs to reflect that diversity."

"Really though, the most important thing is that they come to the music with an open mind. I want people who think 'I would not play the piece this way, but I can accept this proposal'. They need to be open to different interpretations."

For the lucky competitors that meet with the jurors' approval and finish with a prize, the engagement with the Cliburn will continue for at least several more years, thanks to its career building programme. In the past this mainly focussed on booking concerts, but these days it's far more comprehensive than that.

"Booking concerts is usually the easy part, because everyone wants to have the Cliburn winners on their stages," says the president and CEO. "In fact, we now have new agents in Europe and Asia, so we'll have a wider network to offer our winners.

"Van Cliburn himself wanted to share music with the largest audience possible."

"But actually managing their careers is more important than just booking concerts. We have to teach them about finance, about social media, about contracts. Of course, the playing is the most important thing, but you need to have all these other skills in place so that your artistic vision can come across. That might mean helping them design a website, or teaching them about etiquette so they make a good impression on the artists, donors and supporters that they're going meet along the way."

"This is also why I like to have jury members who are still performing regularly," he continues. "They know the challenges of touring, practicing and building a career. We build relationships between the jury members and the contestants so that when they are on tour they can call them and get their insights and perspectives. It can be a lonely life at first before you adjust to it and know what to expect."

He continues: "We also have to help them on the artistic side. So, if they have an artistic vision of playing, for example, all the *Goldberg Variations*, our job is to help them realise this, while also creating a unique selling point to differentiate them from all the other pianists playing a similar programme.

"But ultimately, this energy has to come from our artists," he concludes. "We can open doors, but it's up to them to walk through those doors. We can't tell them what to do, but we can help them reach their potential. If we do that, then I think that's a big success."

The sixteenth instalment of the Cliburn runs from 2-18 June. The competition will be broadcast across multiple platforms including YouTube, with full details to be announced prior to the event. For more information head to cliburn.org.

cliburn.org

THE CLIBURN

THE WORLD IS LISTENING

SIXTEENTH
VAN CLIBURN
INTERNATIONAL
PIANO
COMPETITION

2–18 JUNE, 2022

FORT WORTH, TEXAS USA

JURY

Marin Alsop, JURY CHAIRMAN
Alessio Bax
Jean-Efflam Bavouzet
Rico Gulda
Wu Han

Andreas Haefliger
Stephen Hough
Anne-Marie McDermott
Orli Shaham
Lilya Zilberstein

**WATCH THE ENTIRE
COMPETITION ONLINE
AT CLIBURN.ORG**

NOW BOOKING 2022 WINNERS

A breath of fresh air

Le Vent du Nord has blown in with a brilliant new album of fresh tunes. PAY speaks to the band about making music after lockdown, new ways of creating and the joy of being back on the road.

L e Vent du Nord certainly live up to their name. This wind from the north creates music that is both a breath of fresh air and can make your spine tingle. Together for more than two decades, they are one of the few folk groups that can truly transcend genres. Yes, they play Francophone folk tunes, but they can also get on stage with an orchestra, a DJ or a troupe of actors and win fans that way.

For a band known for its hard working ways – in those 20 years they've played over 2,100 shows – Covid and lockdown presented a particular set of problems. They had to work out how the band could exist off stage, while still keeping the energy and inspiration alive ready for when they got back on it. But now, thankfully, they are out the other side, and their 11th album *20 Printemps* has just dropped.

"The positive side for the band during Covid was that we had much more time at home to write, find repertoire and have rehearsals for the new album," notes guitarist and bouzouki player Simon Beaudry, as we speak about the past two years. "Luckily, because this band is our job, the rules in Quebec allowed us to meet in a socially-distanced rehearsal space. Personally, spending time together like this also helped us get through this difficult period."

"It also gave us time to broaden our spectrum of creation," adds hurdy-gurdy player Nicolas Boulerice. "I got to write every day, and to spend time on other projects. For example, I finished a collection of poetry that I've been working on for a long time."

He continues: "And as a group it gave us more time to rehearse. We could take songs apart, put them back together, and generally experiment with new approaches and more innovative arrangements."

The result of that is *20 Printemps* (20 springs), a reference to the band's 20th anniversary and the new growth they're still finding after all this time.

"In Québec, we count the passage of time in springs, so it's very appropriate for our anniversary," explains fiddler Olivier Demers. "At the the same time, spring evokes life coming back after the winter, sunlight, love, and a positive vibe after the last two years, which were pretty hard for musicians and for the population in general."

And, he continues, that feeling of joy and rebirth permeates the album: "We really felt a spirit of celebration as we were recording the album: the joy of making music, the celebration of returning to the

stage, the wonder of making contact with other humans…and also of the fact that we're still pushing boundries even after 20 years on the music scene."

As for the recording itself, that took place at Studios Piccolo in Montréal. The band spent just six days in the space, adding to that feeling of freshness, with producer Charles-Émile Beaudin behind the mixing desk.

"It's the third time we've worked with him, and he's just so smooth," says Demers. "He also brought us deeper into the world of analogue sound, which of course really suits folk music like ours. The setup itself helped, too: we recorded in a big room altogether, with hardly any isolation between us. That's why the sound is so thick and everything feels like it's really glued together. The album definitely does capture how it feels to hear us playing live, which I love."

Released on 28 January, *20 Printemps* feels like a natural continuation of their critically acclaimed 2019 album *Territoires*. That, says Boulerice, was intentional.

"I see a direct line between the two albums," he affirms. "We continued on the same path, but at the same time we wanted to handle the material in a lighter way. And with the extra time we had together, that allowed us to create a more meaningful and unified feel to the entire album."

Accordionist Réjean Brunet agrees: "On some albums we've featured other instruments, but for 20 Printemps we decided to record without any guests. We love directly presenting our music to people, and this approach allows that."

Adds Beaudry: "Our music happens naturally from the start – we don't ask too many questions. We just organically renew ourselves, and

"What I really love is that people of all ages come to our shows and find them inspiring"

I think you can really hear that in the music."

Concludes Boulerice: "It's a record that may be more mature, but it's also more positive – and we all need that right now, don't we?"

As always Le Vent du Nord has a diary completely filled with ink, with plenty of both US and European dates. In May, the group heads to both the UK and California, before more UK dates in July and a trip to France in August. When not on the road, they intend to continue work on latest project Les Voix du Vent.

"It means 'voices of the wind', and it will see us working with a string quartet and a pianist," says fiddler André Brunet. "We were supposed to record this back in 2020, but the pandemic prevented us. We are very pleased to see this project become a reality, thus adding another string to our bow. We really like to create projects in parallel to keep the group active and always moving in the wonderful world of traditional music in Québec."

Finally before we finish, there's one important question we have to ask: what's the best thing about being in Le Vent du Nord? Boulerice laughs as he responds: "Even after 20 years I've never been asked this! What I really love is that people of all ages come to our shows and find them inspiring – I'm very proud of that. Of course, it's a nice ego boost, but the main thing is that we're leaving a musical legacy that other people can carry on. This music will survive us, and that's best thing that being a member of this band can give us."

leventdunord.com

The gift
of the app

Giveo is a new fundraising platform that could be a game changer for the non-profit sector. Development expert Doug Evans shares the details.

Let's face it – most of us have too much stuff. The obsolete cell phone sitting in its box. The sweater that stubbornly refuses to fit. The exercise gear that seemed like a good idea at the time, but is now just gathering dust (which goes some way to explaining why that sweater doesn't fit). You could list it for sale online, but that seems like a lot of effort when you don't really need the money. Ideally, you'd donate it to a good cause, but if you simply hand it all to your favourite arts organisation you know that's really just creating more work for them.

into cash and then donate it your favourite orchestra, theatre company or dance troupe, without any hassle, admin or hard work?

Well, now you can, thanks to Giveo, a new app that allows people to sell their unwanted items online and give the cash directly to their favourite charity. Launched in August 2021 and led by experienced software developer Greg Okon, the app is already having a positive impact for thousands of small arts organisations; because, while we might have too much stuff, arts organisations never have enough money.

"Giveo is transformational fundraising," says Doug Evans, chief development officer at Giveo. "It's a very simple way to raise $100 or $100,000, and for small arts organisations that are struggling right now that money could make a huge difference."

Doug should know; he's worked in arts management and fundraising for the last 35 years, leading groups like Nederlander Worldwide Entertainment and the Bushnell Center for the Performing Arts. He's also a long time member of the Broadway League and a founder of the Independent Presenters Network. Along the way, he's raised hundreds of millions of dollars.

"When I started out there was no way to reach out to potential donors except to send them a piece of mail," he reflects. "So to have this app, where users can just point, click and almost instantly raise money for the arts, it's incredible to see that progress."

As for how the app works, it's very simple. Charities can sign up and then let their followers and fans know that they're accepting donations through Giveo. Anyone who has something to sell can download the app and take a photo of the item. The AI in the app will recognise the item and provide a description. Then, when another user buys it, 100% of the money goes directly to the seller's chosen charity.

As a result of this simple and streamlined process, Giveo is very efficient for arts organisations looking to raise funds. "Traditionally you might organise a bake sale, a yard sale or another special event," notes Evans. "But they take a lot of volunteer hours in order to make them happen. With this it's just point and tap and that's it.

"It's also great for smaller groups. Let's say you're a four-piece chamber ensemble: you send out a message about donating via Giveo to your mailing list, and then use the money you raise to record an album, produce a video or anything else."

> "It's a very simple way to raise $100 or $100,000, and for small arts organisations...that money could make a huge difference."

Right now Giveo is fully launched in the US, and the team are currently working on rolling it out across the rest of the globe. "Once we add additional languages and make a few other tweaks it will work anywhere," says Evans. "So, if someone in Poland wants to raise money for the Fryderyk Chopin Institute, or someone in Brazil wants to give money to their favourite samba group, they can."

As well as being easy to use, Giveo is also tied in with Google's NPO Ad Grants scheme. That means that any NPO signing up will get USD120,000 worth of online advertising from Google. "It's basically free marketing dollars, which are normally impossible to find," says Evans. "These grants are a great way of letting people know that you want them to sell things and donate the money to you."

Giveo is actually Evans first foray into the tech sector, and something that he says has truly energised him since he came on board: "When I think about the money that small arts organisations could raise I get very excited…it's going to have a huge impact in communities all over the world."

But while Evans is new to tech, he's an old hand when it comes fundraising and arts leadership. As a result, he's got plenty of advice to share for arts organisations looking to boost their fundraising. "The biggest mistake that they make is not understanding their audience," he asserts. "You have to know what inspires them, what they like, and what turns them off. Once you know that you'll programme the right shows, and the ticket money will follow."

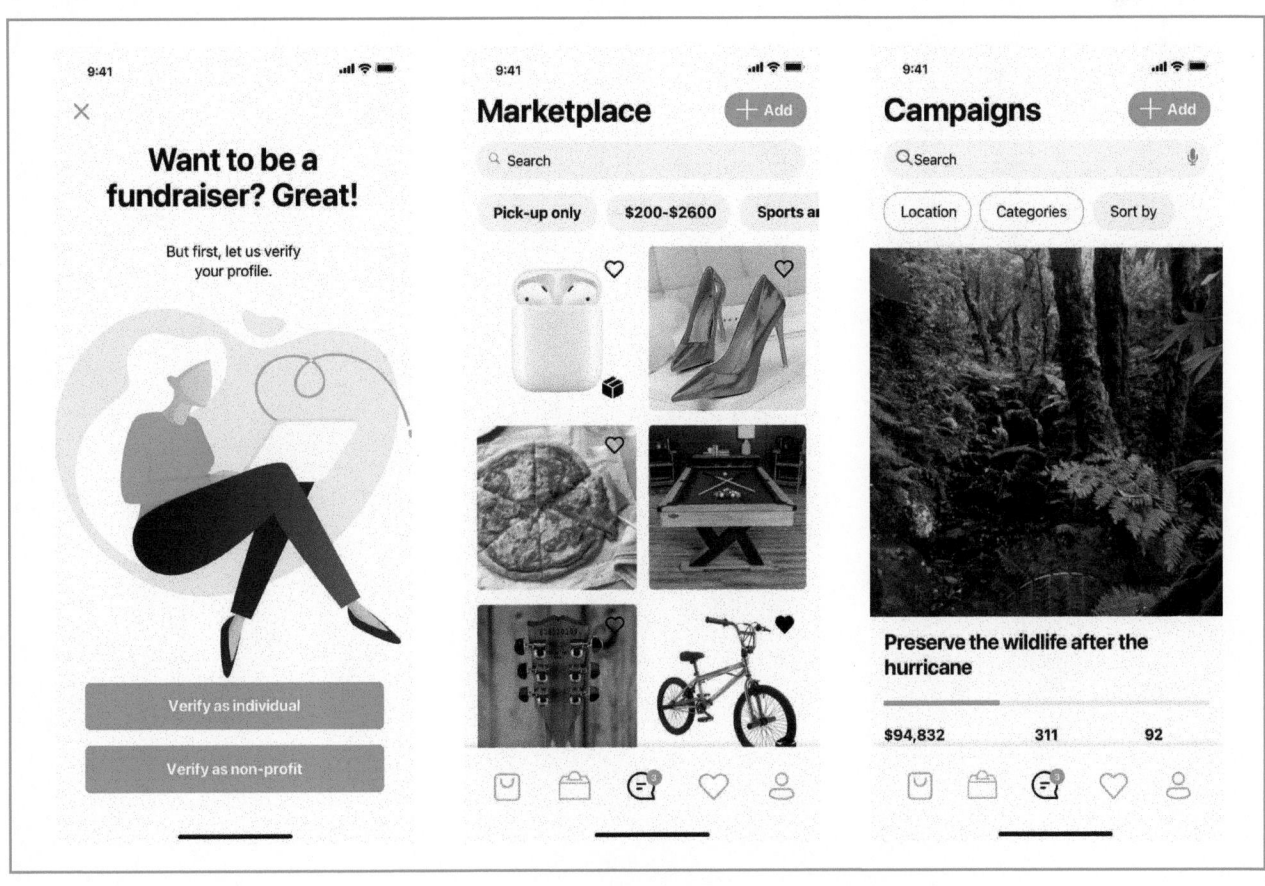

"For example, if your theatre company has always done old fashioned musicals like *Oklahoma*, and then you throw Stephen Sondheim's *Sweeney Todd* in there, your audience will say 'what the heck was that? Give me what I want.'"

That emphasis on understanding also applies to donors, he adds: "If you don't know the motivations of that donor, then you can't possibly to talk to them about increasing their level of support. You have to be brutally honest: fundraising is transactional. A corporation is not supporting you because they care about your art. They're supporting you because they want to get the word out about their product and look good in the community.

He continues: "I had a donor that I asked for a million-dollar gift. I told them 'I know that you love classical and you want to support this.' And they said 'yes, I do, but here's what I really want: I want you to support and promote my other charity'. I said 'great, let's get it done'. It's the same for smaller gifts: if someone is donating to their local classical station, yes, they're doing it to support the music, but they also expect a coffee mug or a tote bag."

As well as listening, it's also about something that people in the arts are usually good at: telling stories. "Everyone has a story to tell," explains Evans. "If it's the million-dollar donor, they want to tell the story of their charity. The person supporting local radio proudly carries that tote bag as part of their identity – that's their story. We have to help our donors and potential donors tell their stories."

> "When I think about the money that small arts organisations could raise I get very excited"

As for the metrics of donations, that's probably too technical of a subject to get into here, but Evans does have some basic pointers. Firstly, whenever possible, keep it personal.

"Working in donations is more like data science nowadays, and it's easy to lose that personal touch," he says. "Whether that's writing a great subject line for your mailer, or sharing a video from your first chair violinist, find whatever opportunities you can to create a personal moment for your donors."

And the best place to do that, he adds, is when you've got them in the building. "When you have the audience in the venue, that's your biggest opportunity to make a connection. When you walk on stage tell them 'we're so happy to have you here tonight, you have no idea what this means to us. Without you being here we can't be here'. It's easy to say because it's true! So just stick with that truth and you'll find it takes you a long way."

You can download Giveo from the App Store and from Google Play. For more information on Giveo head to giveo.app. To learn more about Douglas Evans consultancy work, go to premiereglobalpartners.com.

**Faster, easier, with Giveo.
It's all in the app.**

Give. Buy. Help. Waste Less. Save Planet.

Cashless donation fundraising and marketplace app

GIVEO is the new app that is revolutionising fundraising.

Download it for free right now for Apple and Android and start raising money right away.

"It's a very simple way to raise $100 or $100,000. It's just point and click and that's it."

Fundraising expert and arts leader Douglas Evans

Playing with fire

Maria Radutu's album *Phoenix* explores the emotional and intellectual balance between fiery revolution and cool reflection. Here, the pianist speaks to PAY about her approach to programming, collaborating across artforms, and keeping her playing fresh.

W e tend to think of artists as emotionally driven characters, people who put feelings before thought. And of course, sometimes that's true. But the really great artists are the ones that combine feeling and thought, creating passionate works that also pack an intellectual punch.

Maria Radutu is just such an artist. The Austria-based, Romanian-born pianist has been making a name for herself in recent years with a series of projects that both entertain and engage.

Now, with her new album *Phoenix*, Radutu has reached a new pinnacle. A rollercoaster work that deals with the tensions between extremes and moderation, revolution and consolidation, *Phoenix* is an album that offers multiple perspectives and rewards repeat listens.

"*Phoenix* comes from the tension between revolution and security," affirms Radutu. "Sometimes we want to create change, to revolutionise things. Then at other times we become more stable and find a balance. This isn't just something that happens when we're young – it's a cycle that keeps returning throughout life, and is a very important part of our existence."

The album takes listeners on a journey, with dramatic changes of mood that on the one hand can be surprising but on the other make perfect musical sense. A great example comes right at the start of the album, as the energetic burst of Chopin's *Prelude Op.28* switches seamlessly into the calm of Erik Satie's *Gnossienne No 1*.

"*Gnossienne* is a well-known piece that I would never play just on its own, but by placing it between Chopin and Bartók's *Allegro Barbaro* it gives it an original context – you hear the piece in a completely new way."

As a result of this dense thematic thinking it takes Radutu a long time to create her albums, working on each of them for 18 months

"Phoenix comes from the tension between revolution and security"

or sometimes even longer. And the recording process itself can be quite lengthy.

"I don't just go into the studio and record the album over three days," she says. "I record over a longer time, which means I can just focus on playing and be in the moment without unnecessary time pressure. It also helps that I have an engineer – Georg Burdicek – who I really trust."

Trust was also important for the two original commissions on the album, as she explains: "The people I commissioned – Marco Annau and Mikael Karlsson – are my friends. Because these albums are very emotional and very personal it would feel strange for me if I wasn't friends with the composers.

"Marco really fit in because he writes a lot of what you might call world music, while Mikael writes very modern music that doesn't neglect the past. That made him ideal for the final piece, which had to be a balance of all the elements on the album."

Radutu's attention to detail carries over into the artwork, which she directs herself with the help of collaborators Kristina Bigler (design) and Andreas Staudinger (photography).

"For my last album *Insomnia* I was on the cover, but with a black space where my head should be," she recalls. "The concept was that anyone can be in that head space, so we left it blank."

"For *Phoenix* I wanted a contrast with that album, and I also wanted this feeling of the first breath. So on the cover my eyes look directly into the camera as I emerge from cloudy water."

"I am so involved with the selection of the pieces that I also have to care about how the album looks," she adds. "If I didn't it would be like painting a beautiful picture and then putting it in an ugly frame."

Speaking of painting, for the live show Radutu again works with a close collaborator, this time artist Felicia Gulda. Radutu commissioned Gulda to make paintings for each track on the album which, along with the stories inside the album's booklet, help create the correct atmosphere for each piece. During the concert the paintings are projected onto the back wall of the stage as she plays.

"On the one hand it is quite minimalist, because you have just the pictures and the pianist," she says of the concert experience. "On the other hand, the paintings lead the audience into the story and make it much more immersive."

She continues: "For me working with other artforms is amazing, because you can send the same message but in different languages. Some people come to art from the audio side, some from the visual, and so it helps to combine both. That way, more people can connect with the emotions I am trying to express."

This idea of immersive performance is something Radutu has spent a lot of time thinking about, going right back to her student days.

"A lot of my friends are composers, and I used to think 'I'm not really an artist because I'm not creating something new'," she remembers. "But then after my studies I started researching how to put together programmes, and thinking about how I could create something new using dramaturgy. Now, every time I put a programme together, I ask myself 'what can I bring to this that is new?' I want to be creative and make a musical environment that is totally unique."

As Radutu stated at the start of the interview, *Phoenix* is about the

"Working with other artforms is amazing, because you can send the same message but in different languages"

balance between revolution and security. So how does she achieve that balance in her own playing?

"I think this is the biggest challenge for a musician," she muses. "You have to know a piece very well. That doesn't mean knowing what you're going to do with each note, but instead knowing exactly what you want to express. This gives you the opportunity to change details and stay fresh.

"For example, with the Liszt piece on *Phoenix* [*Mephisto Waltz No 1*] if you play it technically perfectly then you've not tried hard enough. You have to constantly push yourself and take risks."

She continues: "This risk taking and being in the moment is what makes live music so important. If you just listen to music in the background at home then you can always hide from what you feel, you can start doing something else. But at a concert you can't hide – you have to engage with your emotions in that moment.

"That's why the performing arts are different from the visual arts. You can go to the next painting in a gallery, or even to a different gallery. But in a concert hall you can't make it faster or slower – you have to be there and live through it. Bringing the audience with us on this journey is a big challenge, but when it works it is a very beautiful moment of connection.

"This moment is also very important for me personally," she concludes. "Being an artist forces you to always be in touch with yourself – I cannot practice or think about these projects if I am emotionally cold or bored. So it keeps me connected to my emotions, and I think that is a wonderful thing."

MARIA RADUTU + ENO PECI © ASHLEY TAYLOR

Life changing

Flautist Elisabeth Möst overcame a health crisis to become one of the most original players of her generation. She tells PAY about her recovery, her latest projects and her love of mixing music with other art forms.

Elisabeth Möst had everything she wanted. The flautist was a sought-after soloist, a popular teacher, and had albums released on labels like Naxos. But then she woke up one morning and couldn't remember anything.

"I'd just come back from a concert in the US," she recalls. "When I woke up the next morning I had an absolute black out – nothing was there. My whole body was foreign to me. I couldn't remember how to play the flute, how to read the notes – anything. It was a terrible experience."

Möst went to see a specialist in Berlin, who gave her some bad news: she had a rare condition, and would have to learn how to play her instrument all over again. "Although it was bad news, he also gave me hope," says Möst. "He told me 'Don't give up, everything is still inside you, you just have to find it again.'"

That was four years ago, and amazingly Möst has managed a complete recovery. In fact, she says that her playing is better than ever.

"Now my playing is deeper, it has a stronger foundation," she explains. "The interpretations are richer, and I really think my

playing is at another level. So on the one hand, it was a horrible experience, but on the other hand, some good has come from it."

As well as adding a new dimension to her playing, Möst's traumatic experience has also inspired other creative projects. Right now she's working on a whole host of ideas, including her new touring show *TAU: A Sign of Change*. Inspired by the paintings of Valentin Oman, and using the 14 stations of the cross as its structure, *TAU* examines the duality of war and peace.

"Valentin painted these wonderful images that are hanging in a church in the Carinthia region of Austria," says the flautist. "He's originally from Slovenia and he lived through the conflicts that happened in his country, but he never got stuck in powerlessness or hopelessness. So his paintings and his story inspired me. After all, what is a better symbol of change than the transition from war to peace?"

For the project, Möst commissioned works from four composers, covering the 14 stations of the cross: "The music follows that journey, first getting denser and darker, and then becoming lighter," she says. "We had the premiere in the church, with Valentin's paintings as our backdrop. The reaction from the audience was wonderful, and we were immediately asked to perform the programme again."

In fact, Möst and the five other musicians will take *TAU* on tour in 2022 and 2023. The first concert is in the famous Kollegienkirche church in Salzburg on 3 April, with further dates throughout Germany to be confirmed.

Another of Möst's projects also takes inspiration from the visual arts, and again it has a link to a church; this time though, it's a stained glass window that triggered the idea.

"During lockdown I was watching YouTube and I saw an oboist performing in front of a stained glass window," she remembers. "I thought that was a strong image, and I decided to find my own window to perform in front of."

After months of searching, Möst eventually found one in her own backyard.

"I searched in Germany, Switzerland and France, but I couldn't find the right window," says Möst. "And then finally I found this window in Salzburg, which is wonderful. It was created by the artist Margret Bilger inside the St Erntrudis Church, and it's one of the largest stained glass windows in Europe.

"The message of this window is also about change. But this time, it's about the change from frustration to happiness. At the end there is joy, and a 'saved' human life."

Titled *The Glass Window*, this time Möst commissioned the composers Anne de Boysson, Jakob Gruchmann and Nils Östlund to create pieces dealing with these themes. The project will have its debut at the church in the first half of 2022 (with dates to be confirmed).

"I think mixing music with other arts makes the performance richer," says Möst, as she discusses both *The Glass Window* and *TAU*. "When you bring in another art form it makes the music easier to understand…and for myself as a performer, it keeps things fresh."

This kind of cross-genre combination can also be found in Möst's partnership with actress Rita Dummer, as she explains:

"We both love *The Little Prince*, and we decided to perform it together, combining the book with music. The composer Carlo Domeniconi created 12 works inspired by the characters in the book, and you can really visualise them when you hear the music. It's a great mixture between music and theatre, and something I really enjoy performing."

Although her three main projects at the moment all involve contemporary compositions, in her solo shows Möst is actually known for her mixed programmes that create connections between new works and historical pieces.

"For me personally it's really important to have a balance between new works and the classics," she says. "I feel that all epochs spring out from one trunk of a tree and split into different branches. So, you can find links between old the old masters and new composers.

"For example, if you listen to the works of someone like Violeta Dinescu – a very wonderful Romanian composer – you can hear the

"When I woke up the next morning I had an absolute black out – nothing was there"

ideas of Mozart and Schubert. You can't really separate her music from theirs. When I put a programme together, I love to find these connections and share them with the audience – for me it is just a real thrill.

"Sometimes people come up to me after a concert and tell me that I have helped them get a better understanding of the music by showing these links, and I'm very thankful for that."

As well as showing audiences the connections between the old and the new, Möst also wants to shine a light on composers that many people might not have heard before.

"Right now I'm trying to find all the solo concertos for flute and orchestra written by women," she enthuses. "So far I've found about 20, and I want to make sure all of these get the recognition they deserve.

"I also want to record music by Austrian composers that are not so known outside of the country," she adds. "For example, composers like Wolfram Wagner, Cäsar Bresgen, Paul Badura Skoda and Carl Frühlin. It's a real joy for me to introduce audiences to these Austrian composers who created such wonderful music."

The Glass Window and TAU: A Sign of Change *are both available for booking now. For booking requests, please email emoest@web.de. Elisabeth Möst will tour China later this year with 12 piano and flute concerts. She will also perform a concert at the ichard Straus-Institute in autumn 2022.*

www.elisabeth-moest.de

> "A lot of orchestras are not streaming their concerts because it's just too expensive"

The livestream dream

A new automated system could finally make live streaming classic concerts affordable. PAY speaks to developer Jakub Fiebig about his potentially revolutionary new system.

If you're anything like us you've watched a lot of livestreaming performances over the last 24 months. We've enjoyed amazing concerts, ballets and operas that we would have never had a chance to attend, from Asia, Europe and the Americas. But we have to admit it: we've rarely paid for any of it. And that's a problem, because streaming is expensive. And we mean, *really* expensive.

A professional livestream of a concert can cost anywhere from €3,000 to €20,000. Why? Well, there are a lot of people involved: camera operators (as many as 10), the art director (the person in charge of cutting between camera shots) and then someone to read the score and make sure the video follows the music. Then you have to add in someone to actually handle the stream, plus the setup time for your technicians – and don't forget your time for actually coordinating all of this. If you want to stream 10 concerts across your season, it quickly becomes one of the biggest lines in your budget.

But there is a potential solution on the horizon, with a team of developers working together on a system that could solve streaming's fiscal and logistical problems.

"I realised that a lot of orchestras are not streaming their concerts because it's just too expensive," says Jakub Fiebig, CEO of ONSTAGE mobile app. "That might have been okay in the past, but these days a digital presence is really important. If you want classical music to reach a wider global audience and remain relevant, you have to put content online."

In the summer of 2021, Fiebig had an idea. What if the whole process of livestreaming a classical concert could be automated using AI (artificial intelligence)? It would save companies tens of thousands in costs, free up administrators to work on other projects, and increase the reach of classical music. He took the idea to two of his colleagues working in the software and AI fields, and they were intrigued.

"As a classical music lover myself, I truly believe that technology can provide support for the industry," notes Adam Lejman, CEO at Altkom Software and Consulting. "That's why I'm so passionate about developing this software solution that will allow concert promoters worldwide to make classical music more accessible."

"AI is no longer reserved for science fiction movies, Tesla or NASA," adds Dominik Ślęzak, president at QED Software. "AI is for everyone, everywhere, including in classical music."

In June 2021 the three companies started working together on the project. As Fiebig explains, the idea is actually quite straightforward:

"What we have is a piece of AI software that follows the music in real time. We connect our system with a cable to the sound desk, and it is able to match the sound it hears to the score. It then uses that information to decide which shots to show, and it edits it altogether in real time."

For example, if the orchestra is playing Beethoven's *Symphony No. 3*, the software listens along and then cuts to a shot of the flautist for their solo, or to a shot of the conductor during the piece's energetic coda. The AI software is the camera operator, score reader and art director all in one.

"The algorithm can align the sound it hears with the position in the score because it has already heard thousands of compositions," explains Jan Ludziejewski from the ONSTAGE mobile app R&D team. "Each performance of the same composition should have the same score – therefore our system can easily locate where it is at any given moment."

Adds Ludziejewski: "Only a few teams trying to solve this problem have had the opportunity to test it in a real-life philharmonic scenario, and no one else has tried it with classical music – we're the first."

As well as cutting down on expense, another advantage of the system is that it gives you complete control over the broadcast. First, the software reads the score and suggests which shots it thinks will work best. But then it gives the users the chance to change that before the concert starts, picking out moments that they consider important.

"Today, if you're working with a professional company handling the livestream, you really don't have much control," notes Fiebig. "You trust them to show the important moments and create a beautiful stream, but you don't know for sure that in bar five they will show the flute and in bar 10 they will show the clarinet.

"With our system it's different: you can arrange the direction of the livestream in advance, and change whatever you want. You are in control of the artistic statement, which is very important as this livestream could be representing your orchestra to an audience of tens of thousands of people all over the world."

Last year Fiebig and his team put the system through its first tests – including a tricky programme at the Lucerne Summer Festival.

"The repertoire was realty difficult: Stravinsky, Anton Webern and two works by Rebecca Saunders," says Fiebig. "We had no problems, and we think if the system can follow that programme without getting lost, it can work on anything."

The first automated livestream with the software was at the inaugural Lucerne Festival Forward, inNovember last year. Since then, they've been in discussions with as many classical music programmers as possible.

"I've already spoken to orchestras in the US and Europe and the response is the same – 'when can I get this in my hall?,'" enthuses Fiebig. "We're confident there is a market for it."

If the rollout for goes well, the system will be followed by a second-generation model that is already in progress. Instead of using

> "AI is for everyone, everywhere. We believe our idea can really have a practical impact in the music world"

remote control cameras already installed in halls – which the first-generation system needs in order to operate – the second-generation model will work using regular mobile phones.

"If you're a promoter, you can set up multiple mobile phones on stage and they will automatically calibrate according to which phone is covering which area of the stage," asserts Fiebig. "Again, the system will follow the score and handle all of the video direction automatically in real time, streaming it directly to the internet. And will all take place on an app that you download to your phone."

Right now Fiebig has just secured seed funding for the development of this second-generation system, although he insists it will actually be a lot simpler than creating the original software.

"We've already done the hard part in creating the algorithm," he says. "The next steps should be simple, because there are existing solutions already out there – we don't have to invent anything new."

"I'm really excited about what the future will be for this system," he concludes. "It could make high-quality multi-camera concert streams accessible for everyone, and make classical music more accessible than ever before. I cannot even begin to imagine yet what an impact it may have."

MUSO
COMMUNICATIONS

Digital & Print Publishing | Graphic Design
Web Development | Brand design | Marketing

info@musocommunications.com | www.musocommunications.com

BYOM.academy

Make your music a business!

BYOM Academy- Be Your Own Manager
A Career Program for Classical Musicians

Dance to the music

Detmar Leertouwer is bringing together solo cello and dance in an exciting series of dialogues. He shares the details with PAY.

Dutch cellist Detmar Leertouwer had two loves as a child: music and dance. But unlike most of us, he is living out those childhood dreams, thanks to his programme 'Dialogue between a Dancer and a 'Cellist'.

However, it all might have been very different. Because, while Leertouwer is now an established figure in the music world, he almost called it quits on more than one occasion. First, there was ballet itself, which as a child was his primary ambition "I used to love ballet, and trained to become a professional dancer" recalls the cellist, "But when I was about 12 I started to think about my future, and the idea of a dance career ending in my thirties scared me. So I focussed more and more on the cello, and really only rediscovered dancing much later."

That focus on the cello saw him spend many years with a Russian master in Amsterdam and Utrecht. Later, he travelled to Scotland and the US to follow Jane Cowan of the International Cello Centre and her former students.

"Working with a Soviet-style teacher was an intense experience," says Leertouwer. "But it really wasn't until I learned from Jane Cowan and a former student of hers that I began to find the freedom I wanted in music. It wasn't about using all the tools of expression all at once – gladiator style – as I was taught before; instead, it was about letting the music lead you to the right form of expression at the right moment."

Still, Leertouwer wasn't sure that the cello was the correct path for him. So, while studying in the States, he took a soul searching hike through the Grand Canyon. "I did some hiking for about a fortnight, all on my own with a backpack," he remembers. "That gave me a 'green' brain wash and a new kind of perspective on my life and what I wanted to do. At first I was thinking I wanted to do something more useful, like psychology or medical studies of some kind. But then at some point I realised that it was music that I truly loved. And if I want to do music, I have to do it now. Other things could come later, but I couldn't start music at an older age. So that's how I found my way back to music."

After that pivotal year in the US, Leertouwer returned to Europe. He then spent 11 years in Switzerland, first studying and later performing from his Basel base, focussing in particular on early music. He performed in ensembles like Musica Antiqua Köln, Concierto Köln, l'Orfeo Barockorchester and Wiener Akademie. It was during that time that he finally reconnected with dance, thanks to a one-off concert in North Germany.

"I was asked to perform on the island of Föhr, which is right by Denmark," he says. "For the programme, they wanted me to perform solo repertoire with a dancer from Hamburg. She moved so beautifully that a spark lit up inside me, and I wanted to make more performances like this. Unfortunately, she had a phobia of sleeping in any bed that wasn't her own, which meant there was no chance of going on tour with her. So instead, I started looking for other dancers to work with."

Since then Leertouwer has performed all over Europe with his series 'Dialogue between a Dancer and a 'Cellist'. For each performance, he picks a programme of solo cello pieces, with half of them being accompanied by the dancer. Collaborators so far include Introdans from the Netherlands (Bach cello suites and Schubert's *Death and the Maiden*) and Nacho Duato's Compañía Nacional de Danza, Philippe Olza (Basel). The result is an evening of emotional peaks and valleys that has made a seriously big impression on audiences.

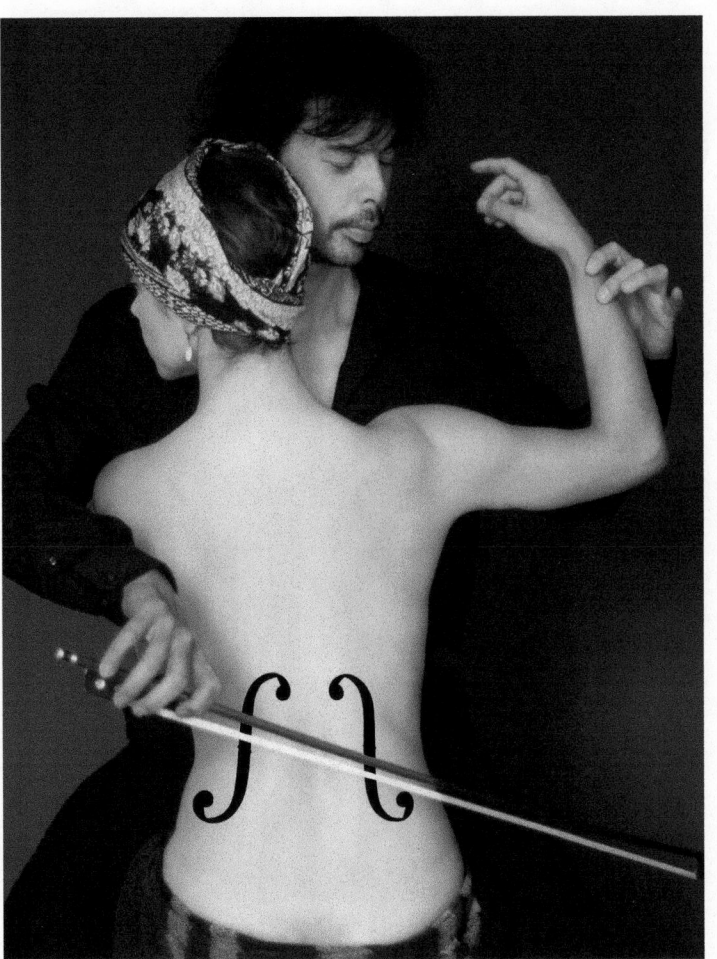

"It flows without interruption from one piece into another, with the dancer joining me for about half of the works I perform," notes Leertouwer. "I start with a Mongolian melody, which is like the sound of the wind, and then pick up the melody of the first piece. We then go through works from the likes of Bach, Britten and Ligeti and Peter Sculthorpe before finally returning to that Mongolian melody – only this time with dance."

The power of the performance is heightened by the setting: they usually take place in a church, with the audience sat in the round. "When the dancer stretches out her hands she can almost touch the audience," explains Leertouwer. "It's not like the theatre with a 10 metre distance between the stage and the audience – it's very intimate. And it's also a very spiritual programme. The fact that we usually perform it in a church only adds to that sense of awe and wonder."

The final surprise comes when Leertouwer himself suddenly takes over the role of the dancer, thanks to his former ballet training,

while the real dancer holds his instrument.

As well as touring his Dialogue series, Leertouwer is working on a video project that takes his cello into some resplendent locations. 'Bach in Castles' will eventually see him film performances of all of Bach's solo cello suites in different castles throughout Europe, putting the great composer's music in an appropriate setting.

"These works were not actually written to be performed in a church," observes Leertouwer. "Performers come up with stories about how the architecture of Bach's music coincides with the architecture of churches and cathedrals, or how a church amplifies the spiritual content of the cello suites. I sense it differently. When he wrote them, he was actually living in Köthen and working for Prince Leopold von Anhalt-Köthen. Because of strict religious reasons music was not allowed in the church at his court. Instead, I perceive the suites as a pleasant pastime. Clearly a very important part of Bach's output is religious and meant for liturgical use, but in my opinion that is not the purpose of the 'cello suites.

"Of course you can play the cello suites in a church, but the more historically accurate venues that create the right mindset are dining halls, bedrooms, dance halls or even cafés. So I thought a castle could actually be an interesting place to film my Bach suites."

For the first suite, Leertouwer took his cello to Doornenburg Castle, as he recalls: "Being embedded in art helps me play, especially when the style matches the piece you're playing. In the music videos, which just came out, you see me playing of course, but half of the footage depicts the castles or the house, the gardens, the paintings. It makes for a visually-rich experience for the viewers."

Leertouwer released the first instalment of the series on Christmas Day, with the music and video coming together as a complete package. "The 'audio-only' component, through streaming platforms like Qobuz, Apple Music and Spotify, is only one part of the project," he notes. "The most important part is the music video, which you can rent or purchase through Vimeo. It also comes with some behind the scenes footage, which I think people will really enjoy. It's an amazing project, and I'm really only at the start of it – there's so much more to come over the next few years."

Detmar Leertouwer's Dance Dialogues and Bach series are available to book right now for dates in 2022-23. For more information, contact info@dm-MusicProductions.com.

RUBBERBAND

MONTREAL, CANADA — SINCE 2002

Artistic Director Victor Quijada combines the spontaneous, risky and fearless hip-hop culture with the choreographic sophistication of contemporary dance.

RBDG.CA

TRENZADO

Exploring the themes of roots, migration and loss – Quijada's return to the stage

VIC'S MIX

Best picks from the repertory – adaptable to any stage

EVER SO SLIGHTLY

Ten dancers and two live musicians – for a large stage

CITY THREAD

Outdoor live dance and music performance – geolocated with exclusive smartphone app

Photo: Marie-Noële Pilon

AGENTS

QUEBEC — CANADA
Agence Station Bleue
Élisabeth Comtois
e.comtois@stationbleue.com

USA
Pentacle
Sandy Garcia
sandyg@pentacle.org

EUROPE (CH, AT, DE, NL, BE, LUX)
Norddeutsche Konzertdirektion
Franziska Grevesmühl-v. Marcard
info@grevesmuehl.de

Laying the foundation

The One Foundation has spent the last 20 years bringing the best European arts and culture to Bulgaria. The team behind One Dance Week share their success – and the challenges ahead – with PAY.

On the face of it, Bulgaria is much like many other countries in Europe. In tech, it has a thriving start-up scene. It's one of Europe's most diverse nations, thanks to large Turkish and Roma populations. And millions of tourists visit each year to experience its beautiful countryside and historic culture (it was founded in the 7th century and is in fact the oldest nation in Europe). It's been a member of the European Union since 2007, and Plovdiv, its second largest city, was European Capital of Culture just a couple of years ago.

But in some ways Bulgaria is quite different, and faces its own set of challenges. It was a communist state until 1990 and, unlike their Balkan neighbours in the former Yugoslavia, Bulgarians weren't allowed to travel outside of the country. That, combined with the fact that it's also one of the EU's poorest nations, and its position right on the edge of the continent, has meant Bulgaria has been slow to integrate with the rest of Europe.

However, there are people and projects out there that are starting to overcome these difficulties, and none is more impressive than the One Foundation. Promoting design, architecture and the arts in general – although primarily focussed on contemporary dance – the One Foundation is building a base from which Bulgarian artists and audiences can grow.

"For us, the most important thing is to give Bulgarians access to high quality contemporary art," explains One Foundation director Assen Assenov. "For example, there's no theatre that presents contemporary dance, and this kind of culture isn't taught in schools. For many people our festival One Dance Week is the only chance to see the kind of productions you get every day in places like Sadler's Wells and the Internationaal Theater Amsterdam."

Founded in 2003, the One Foundation has run all kinds of projects over the years, from arts magazines to electronic music symposiums.

PART 1
WITHOUT
A STORY
WE WOULD
GO MAD

At one point the organisation – which was originally based in Sofia, but is now fixed in Plovdiv – ran as many as five festivals concurrently.

"Back then we were young, and we believed that we could change the whole world," laughs Assenov as he recalls the organisation's early history. "Later we realised that we cannot change everything and that it is better to focus all our energy on the dance festival."

Now One Dance Week is known throughout Europe as an epicentre for great choreographers and performers. Last year's edition, which took place in October, focussed on Greece, and included work by Dimitris Papaioannou, Katerina Andreou and Silvia Gribaudi. Almost the entire programme was sold out – an amazing achievement for a dance festival in a small city.

"When we started there was practically no audience for contemporary dance in Bulgaria," says Assenov. "But we were ambitious, so we acted like we were a big festival and spent a lot of time on marketing and PR. Now, for the first time, we've managed to present the same performance four times, in a hall with 500 seats, and all four evenings were sold out. That proves that the audience is growing, and that our efforts over the last 14 years have been worth it."

"Our success shows that there is a real hunger for these kinds of experiences," states One Dance Week program director Elianna Lilova. "We've built a small family that is getting bigger and bigger each year, and people are really excited when we release the pro-

> "Back then were young, and we believed that we could change the whole world."

gramme. It's a very nice feeling to feel the love and appreciation."

As for the focus on Greece in 2021, that's part of the festival's makeup, with each year bringing in artists from a different country. Past editions have profiled Poland, Lithuania and the Czech Republic.

"Every year we have a different country that presents at least four performances, as well as workshops, talks, movies, discussions and lectures," explains Lilova. "This gives Bulgarian audiences the chance to get familiar with the scenes of different countries. Because this kind of dance is new for audiences here – and because traditionally Bulgarians haven't had the same kind of access to culture from overseas – it is important that we give this context."

The Greek edition was particularly eye-opening, say the organisers, because of that country's recent success in contemporary dance.

"For us a Balkan country, it's a really amazing example," says Assenov. "Artists from Greece are being presented on the biggest stages in Europe, and that's all happened in just the last five years. It shows what is possible when you have the right resources and use them in the right way."

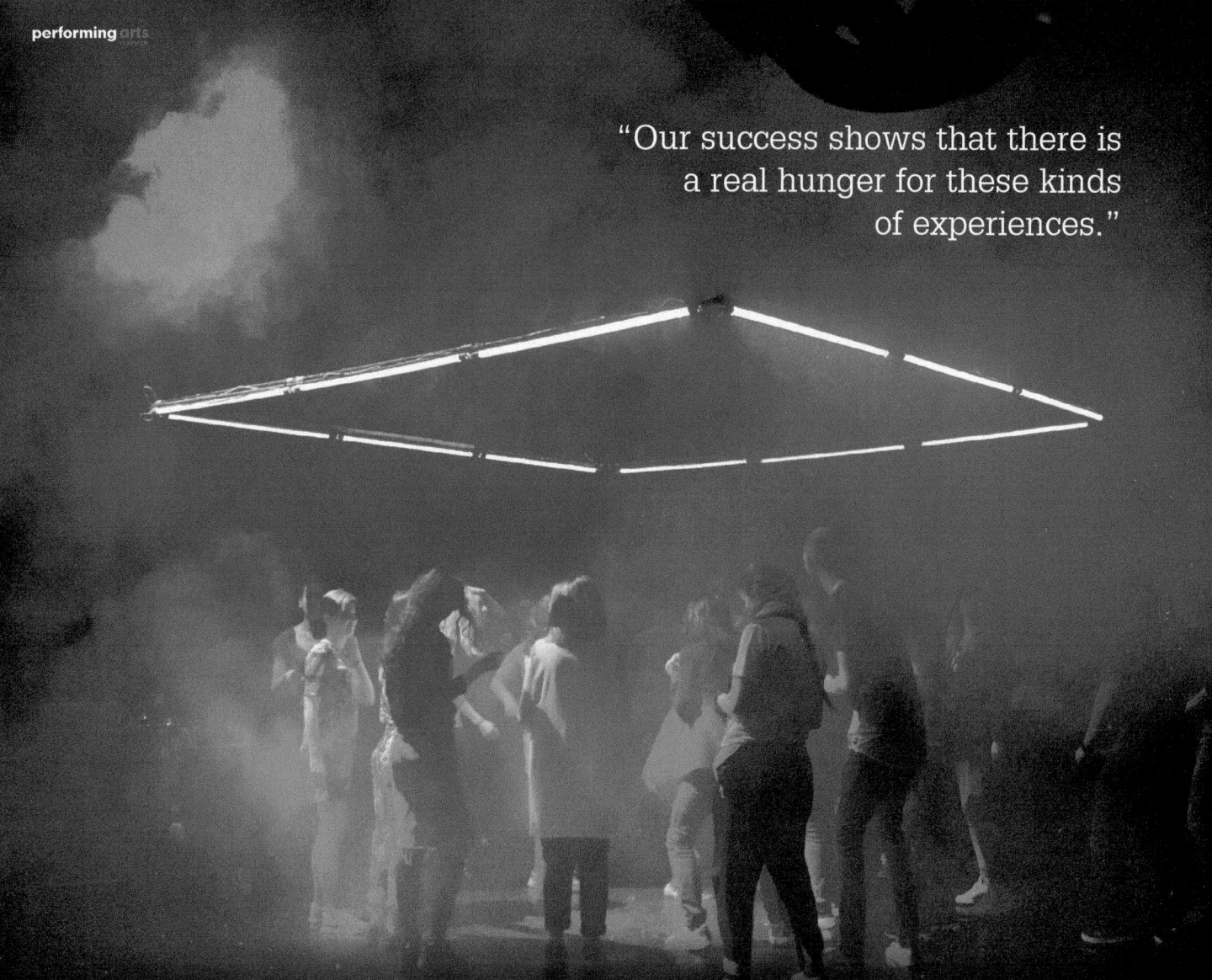

"Our success shows that there is a real hunger for these kinds of experiences."

Agents and Management

The majority of the agents listed are involved with music, opera and dance/ballet. There are a few actor's agents or personal managers. When the organisation's name is that of an individual, the ordering is done by the first name. **The entries are listed in alphabetical order within country.**

Agents et Gestion

La plupart des agents qui apparaissent dans cette section s'occu-pent de musique, d'opéra et de danse/ballet. Il y a aussi quelques agents s'occupant d'acteurs et quelques managers personnels. Dans le cas où le nom de l'organisation est celui d'une personne, le prénom y figure en premie. **Les entrée sont classés par ordre alphabétique dans le pays.**

Agenten und Management

Die meisten der in diesem Kapitel verzeichneten Vermittler befassen sich mit Musik, Oper und Tanz/Ballet. Ebenfalls aufgeführt sind eine kleine Anzahl von Schauspielvermittlern und privaten Künstlermanagern. Organisationen, die nach einer Person benannt sind, werden nach dem Vornamen geordnet. **Die Einträge sind für jedes Land alphabetisch sortiert.**

Agenti e Gestione

La maggior parte degli agenti da noi elencati sono connessi con il mondo della musica, l'opera, il balletto e la danza. In numero minore sono gli agenti di singoli artisti o personal managers. Quelle associ-azioni che hanno lo stesso nome del titolare o il cui nome è un nome di persona, vengono ordinate a seconda del nome di battesi-mo. **Le voci sono pubblicate in ordine alfabetico di paese.**

Agentes y Gestión

La mayoría de los agentes y las organizaciones listados en esta sec-ción trabajan específicamente en el mundo de la música, la ópera y la danza.También aparecen algunos representantes de actores y de compañías de teatro. Cuando la compañía se denomina con un nombre propio (por ejemplo 'Frank Smith'), aparece listada por el nombre de pila (Frank). Cuando no es así (por ejemplo 'Artist Management Frank Smith'), la entrada editorial está clasificada bajo la primera palabra de la frase (Artist). **Las entradas se muestran en orden alfabético dentro de cada país.**

performing arts
database

ARGENTINA

1340 Entertainment
Website: www.1340e.com.ar
Email: info@1340e.com.ar
Phone: 155 147 69684
Address: 3 DZapiola 1989, C1428 CXA, Buenos Aires, Argentina
Description: 1340 Entertainment is a young, innovative and proactive Argentine company, dedicated to the management of artists, the realization of high quality cultural shows, shows and festivals aimed at the wide Argentine, Latin American and world public.
Country: Argentina
Social Media: www.facebook.com/1340Entertainment
www.instagram.com/1340ent

AUSTRALIA

Active Artists Management
Website: www.aam.com.au
Email: jrp@aam.com.au
Phone: 386 690 980
Address: 43 / 38 Manchester Lane, Melbourne 3000 Australia
Description: Active Artists Management (AAM), Melbourne's longest established actors' management agency, has been under the direction of John and Wendy Powell since 2000. AAM's scope now includes writers and Directors. Combined experience in the many facets of the entertainment industry and a personalised management style has seen the careers of AAM's actors profiled internationally.
Country: Australia
Contact: Director Jasper Bagg
Contact: Director Nathalie Antonia

Actors Agency (Vic) Pty Ltd
Website: www.actorsagency.com.au
Email: naomi@actorsagency.com.au
Phone: 393 993 606
Address: 3 Tregutha Way Newport VIC 3015, Australia
Description: The Actors Agency opened it's doors in 1980. Over the years it has guided and supported many performers in finding their niche within the entertainment industry. It has full personal representation for professional performers in theatre, television, film, voice-over, and corporate presentation.
Country: Australia
Contact: Director Naomi West

Ann Peters & Company (South Australian Casting)
Website: www.sacasting.com.au
Email: sacasting@ozemail.com.au
Phone: 088 232 0560
Address: Level 2, 186 Pulteney Street Adelaide, SA 5000, AU
Description: Ann Peters & Co. represent a wide range of actors which includes many of the state's elite. During the 40 years in the industry many known actors and popular television hosts have passed through their doors. It was established in 1975 by Ann Peters and by casting, representation and training it has been part of the fabric and history of the Australian film and television industry.
Country: Australia
Contact: Owner Ann Peters
Social Media: www.facebook.com/southaustralian-casting

Artist Management Australia
Website: www.artistma.com.au
Email: agent@artistma.com.au
Phone: 894 431 311
Address: 2/57 Frobisher St, Osborne Park WA 6017, Australia
Description: Artist Management Australia was established in 1980 by Vivian Poulton. They have represented many prestigious actors including Heath Ledger, Isla Fisher and Adelaide Kane just to name a few. With long standing national and overseas contacts, artists represented by AMA have the opportunity to be widely promoted.
Country: Australia
Social Media: www.facebook.com/artistmanagemen-taustralia/ www.instagram.com/artistmanagemen-taustralia/

Arts Management Pty Ltd.
Website: www.artsmanagement.com.au
Email: enquiries@artsmanagement.com.au
Phone: 292 119 422
Address: Level 1, 405 Elizabeth Street, Surry Hills NSW 2010, Australia
Description: Arts Management is one of the most innovative and respected companies specialising in arts and artist management in Australasia. Established in 1979 by Virginia Braden, the firm is now owned by Graham Pushee. Virginia Braden retired in March 2008. Now in its 37th year, it provides personal management for many distinguished Australasian and international conductors, opera and concert singers, instrumentalists, ensembles, Directors, designers and lighting designers
Country: Australia

Contact: administrator Sonja Patterson
Email: sonja@artsmanagement.com.au
Contact: Owner Graham Pushee
Email: graham@artsmanagement.com.au
Social Media: www.facebook.com/ArtsManagementAU

Australian Jazz Agency
Website: www.australianjazzagency.com.au
Email: leslie@australianjazzagency.com
Phone: 074 045 3035
Address: 4 Lords Rd Leichhardt NSW 2040, Australia
Description: Australian Jazz Agency is a private company offering the very best in acapello groups & choirs, acid jazz, funk, soul & R&B, background music, children's shows, wedding / party bands and many more. Represents over 400 performers across Australia in all styles of music.
Country: Australia
Contact: Owner Leslie Moore

Barbara Gange Management
Website: www.bgmagency.com.au
Email: admin@bgmagency.com.au
Phone: 039 939 7227
Address: 5/400 St Kilda Rd St Kilda VIC 3182, Australia
Description: BGM is a boutique agency representing an imPressive client list ranging from exciting new talent to Australia's best known actors. They provide artists work across film, television, radio, theatre, voice over, corporates and TVC's. BGM prides itself on offering a highly personalised service in career building and management.
Country: Australia
Contact: Director Barbara Gange

Bedford & Pearce Management Pty Ltd
Website: www.bedfordpearce.com.au
Email: bp@bedfordpearce.com.au
Phone: 028 279 6009
Address: PO Box 506, Katoomba, NSW, Australia 2780
Description: Bedford & Pearce Management Pty Ltd. is one of Australia's longest running and trusted talent management agencies in Australia. They have established and managed some of Australia's leading names in film, television and theatre.
Country: Australia
Contact: Director Martin Bedford
Contact: agent and finance Manager Anil Tiwari
Social Media: www.facebook.com/bedfordpearce

Cameron's Management
Website: www.cameronsmanagement.com.au
Email: info@cameronsmanagement.com.au
Phone: 029 319 7199
Address: 75, 61 Marlborough Street, Surry Hills NSW 2010
Description: Cameron's Management is an agency representing writers, Directors, actors, presenters, designers, cinematographers, editors, composers and book authors across the full range of the film, television, live performance and publishing industries.
Country: Australia
Contact: Managing Director Jane Cameron
Contact: Managing Director Anthony Blair
Social Media: twitter.com/CameronsMgt

Carolyn White Management
Website: http://carolynwhitemanagement.com.au
Email: info@carolynwhitemanagement.com.au
Phone: 294 391 182
Address: 204/11 Clarke St, Crows Nest NSW 2065, Australia
Description: Carolyn White Management is a boutique agency representing actors, musical theatre performers and presenters in all areas of performance. Owner/Manager Carolyn White's early background was in film distribution, advertising and the recording industry, but it was later appointments with one of Sydney's top management agencies and then as casting Director for a major advertising agency that set her on the path that would become her lifetime career.
Country: Australia
Contact: Owner Carolyn White
Email: carolyn@carolynwhitemanagement.com.au

Catherine Poulton Management
Website: www.cpmgt.com.au
Email: admin@cpmgt.com.au
Phone: 039 078 0678
Address: 15 Studley Street, Abbotsford VIC 3067, Australia
Description: Catherine Poulton Management was established in 2002 by Company Director Catherine Poulton. Representing a diverse client list, the agency has artists working in some of Australia's leading feature films, television and theatre productions. CPM understands the unique strengths and abilities of each client, ensuring they are represented most effectively to achieve their long term goals.
Country: Australia
Contact: Owner Catherine Poulton
Contact: Director Paul Andersen
Social Media: www.facebook.com/catherinepoulton-management

Cinque Artist Management
Website: www.cinqueartistmanagement.com
Email: info@cinqueartistmanagement.com
Phone: 410 045 582
Address: PO Box 806, Crows Nest NSW 1585 Sydney, Australia
Description: Cinque Artist Management is a specialised classical music agency representing conductors, instrumentalists and ensembles of international and national renown, with a particular focus on Australia, New Zealand and Asia. Based in Sydney, Cinque Artist Management is also committed to supporting the most promising and exciting talents of the next generation of classical music artists.
Country: Australia
Contact: Director Jacqueline Thomas-Piccard
Email: jtp@cinqueartistmanagement.com
Contact: conductor Daniel Smith
Type: Classical, Solo/Chamber, Vocal, Other

City Vibe Entertainment & Management
Website: www.cityvibe.com.au
Email: cityvibe@cityvibe.com.au
Phone: 024 647 8184
Address: PO BOX 3294 Narellan DC NSW 2567 Australia
Description: City Vibe Entertainment and Management was founded by Mark Annesley in 1992. The greatest asset is their friendliness, professionalism & wealth of experience. Business relationships are a priority followed by creativity, organisation, and remaining focused on delivering first class events and experiences for clients and the audience.
Country: Australia
Contact: Managing Director Mark Annesley
Email: mark@cityvibe.com.au
Contact: account administrator Stacie Richardson
Email: stacie@cityvibe.com.au
Social Media: www.facebook.com/CityVibeEntertainment

Dance World Studios
Website: www.danceworldstudios.com
Email: info@danceworldstudios.com
Phone: 039 696 2943
Address: 295 Bank St South Melbourne VIC 3205, Australia
Description: Dance World Studios is celebrating 25 years in the dance industry. Dance World Studios was established in 1987 with a vision: to provide young people with the opportunity to realise their dreams through the creation of a vocational arts training institution offering dance & musical theatre courses. In 25 years, Dance World has earned itself a reputation as a leading Australian performing arts school.
Country: Australia
Contact: Artistic Director Pamela Apostolidis
Contact: Executive Director Chris Apostolidis
Contact: Administration Manager Hayley Russell
Social Media: www.instagram.com/dworldstudios/ www.facebook.com/danceworldstudiosmelbourne

Diva Management
Website: www.divamanagement.com.au
Email: alex@divamanagement.com.au
Phone: 406 674 751
Address: Unit 2/20 Campbell Parade, Manly Vale NSW 2093, Australia
Description: Diva Management takes care of its esteemed artists with an honest and heartfelt approach, offering guidance and advice in collaboration with each individual's needs and requirements. Guidance for young singers on the verge of an operatic or performing career is also offered by Diva Management.
Country: Australia
Contact: Founder Alex Robertson-Jervis
Email: alex@divamanagement.com.au
Contact: conductor Paul Fitzsimon
Social Media: twitter.com/divamanagement1 www.facebook.com/DivaArtistManagement
Type: Classical

Dmand Talent Management
Website: www.dmand.com.au
Email: info@dmand.com.au
Phone: 073 666 0120
Address: PO Box 648 Fortitude Valley QLD Australia 4006
Description: The Dmand team have the experience and the extensive network to deliver concerts, dance and theatrical productions internationally. As tour Producers they deal with logistics, immigration, tax preparation, production requirements, travel and accommodation, Marketing and promotion.
Country: Australia
Social Media: www.facebook.com/DmandMusic

Edgley International P/L
Website: www.edgley.com.au
Email: headoffice@edgley.com.au
Phone: 039 428 7711
Address: 8 Chapel Street, Richmond, Victoria 3121, AU
Description: Edgley International is a theatre and concert promotions company from Australia, first started in the 1930s

Country: Australia
Contact: Director Michael Edgley
Email: headoffice@edgley.com.au
Contact: Director Andrew Guild
Email: guild@edgley.com.au
Contact: Director Phillip Corr
Email: corr@edgley.com.au

Emblem Artists
Website: www.emblemartists.com
Email: elaine@emblemartists.com
Phone: 499 454 240
Address: 21 McCormack St Port Melbourne VIC 3207
Description: Emblem Artists is a classical music agency based in Melbourne and is regarded as one of the leading artist management agencies in Australia. Originally founded in London in 2013 by Elaine Armstrong, Emblem Artists moved its office to Melbourne in 2015 and today enjoys recognition throughout Australia for its select roster of dynamic and exceptional classical musicians. Member of IAMA.
Country: Australia
Contact: Founder and Director Elaine Armstrong
Email: elaine@emblemartists.com
Contact: social media / online Manager & artist assistant
Ella Blackburn
Email: ella@emblemartists.com
Social Media: https://twitter.com/emblemartists www.facebook.com/emblem.artists.au/ www.instagram.com/EmblemArtists/

EPMS Event Management
Website: www.epms.net
Email: events@epms.net
Phone: 418 419 322
Address: 30 Cox Ave Orange NSW 2800, Australia
Description: EPMS: development of events, training in event management, developing events strategies, advice to government and companies on their events portfolio, workshops in project and risk management for events, maximising the return on investment and minimising the risk.
Country: Australia
Contact: Director William O'Toole

Gala Artists Management
Website: http:// www.galaartists.com
Email: info@galaartists.com
Phone: 041 255 7504
Address: PO BOX 340 Terrey Hills NSW 2084
Description: Gala Artists Management is a state-of-the-art management representation for commercials, print, television, theatre and film. Over the last 30 years Gala Artists Management have trained, produced and represented more Logie, AFI and People's Choice Award Winners & Nominees.
Country: Australia
Contact: Owner Brooke Anderson

Harbour Agency, The
Website: www.theharbouragency.com
Email: promotions@theharbouragency.com
Phone: 029 331 5888
Address: 124 Victoria St, Beaconsfield NSW 2015 Australia
Description: The Harbour Agency was established in late 1978 to meet the market needs for a professional music booking agency. Representing world-class established, mid-level and developing talent it has become Australia's largest booking agency. The company provides the very best Australian talent for hotels, clubs, festivals, private functions and major outdoor and industry calendar events throughout metropolitan and regional Australia.
Country: Australia
Contact: senior booking agent Tony Grace Guarrera
Email: tonyg@theharbouragency.com
Contact: agent Colin Baxter
Email: colinb@theharbouragency.com

HLA Management Pty Ltd
Website: www.hlamgt.com.au
Email: hla@hlamgt.com.au
Phone: 029 549 3000
Address: 87 Pitt St Redfern Sydney, NSW Australia 2016
Description: HLA Management Pty Ltd represents many of the best Australian creative artists working in the entertainment industry at home and abroad. They are a passionate and committed team dedicated to providing the highest level of service and support to our clients. HLA has affiliations with Producers and agencies around the world.
Country: Australia
Contact: Director Tim Bullock
Contact: Director Geoff Burton
Social Media: www.facebook.com/HLAManagement

HMMG Pty Ltd
Website:
www.harrymmiller.com.au
Email:
hmm@harrymmiller.com
Phone: 028 088 0792
Address: PO BOX 321 Waverley NSW 2024 Australia

Description: HMMG (formerly Harry M Miller Group) is one of the most recognised brands in the Australian media, arts and entertainment industry. They specialise in the management of high profile and emerging media, literary and Producer talent.
Country: Australia
Contact: chief Executive officer Lauren Miller Cilento
Email: lauren@harrymmiller.com
Contact: Executive Producer Josh Cilento
Email: josh@harrymmiller.com
Social Media: https://twitter.com/hmmg_ www.facebook.com/HMMGPtyLtd/

IMG Talent
Website: www.imgtalent.com.au
Email: imgtalent@img.com
Phone: 029 285 8000
Address: MLC CENTRE Level 25 19 Martin Place Sydney NSW 2000 Australia
Description: For the past 50 years, IMG Clients has been the global leader in talent representation, including over 1000 elite athletes, coaches, industry Executives and prestigious sports organisations across the sports, entertainment, fashion and media industries.
Country: Australia
Social Media: www.instagram.com/imgtalent/ www.facebook.com/IMGWorldwide

Jamari Artist Management
Website: jamari.com.au
Email: james@jamari.com.au
Phone: 073 371 6137
Address: 29/72 Sandford St St Lucia Queensland 4067 Australia
Description: Jamari Artist Management is a member of ACMMA which represent concert, opera and theatre music artists, Directors & designers, based both internationally and in Australia and New Zealand, and performing throughout the world.
Country: Australia
Contact: Director James Christiansen
Contact: Director Christopher Dawes

Joolee Eadie Theatrical Agency
Website: www.thejooleeeadieagency.com.au
Email: jooleeeadie@hotmail.com
Phone: 029 386 0523
Address: 33 Hollywood Avenue, Bondi Junction NSW 2022, Australia
Description: Joolee Eadie Theatrical Agency represents talent in the fields of acting, singing and dancing for film, television, commercials, corporate, videos, and photography industries. The main classification is theatrical Producers and services in Bondi Junction.
Country: Australia
Contact: Director Julia Edwards

Kathryn Morrison Management
Website: www.kathrynmorrisonmanagement.com
Email: kmorrison.work@gmail.com
Phone: 409 878 016
Address: 10/1 Jilmax Court, FOREST HILL, Victoria 3131 Australia
Description: Kathryn Morrison Management was established in 2012 following the retirement of Jenifer Eddy Artists' Management. It is with great pride that they continue to provide the highest level of service, integrity and professionalism. Working closely with Askonas Holt in London, their artists are regularly seen on stages around the world Contact details: kmorrison.work@gmail.com
Country: Australia
Contact: Owner Kathryn Morrison
Social Media: https:// www.facebook.com/kathrynmorrisonmanagement/

Keane Kids Management
Website: http:// www.keanekids.com/
Email: casting@galaproductions.com.au
Phone: 029 450 0022
Address: PO BOX 340, Terrey Hills NSW 2084 Australia
Description: KeaneKids is an innovative management representation agency that casting agents, advertising agencies, Directors and Producers can access to find KeaneKids for commercials, modeling, print, television, film and theatre.
Country: Australia
Contact: Owner Lynda Keane
Contact: chief Executive officer Greg Anderson

Lee Leslie Management
Website: www.leeleslie.com
Email: lee.leslie@bigpond.com
Phone: 966 04777
Address: 72 Glebe Point Road Glebe, NSW, Australia
Description: Lee Leslie has been Managing some of Australia's finest actors for more than 35 years. Part of Lee Leslie Managements aim is to make a difference and create opportunities for actors to work and continue to grow.
Country: Australia
Contact: Managing Director Lee Leslie
Email: lee.leslie@bigpond.com
Social Media: www.facebook.com/Leesliemanagement/

Lisa Mann Creative Management
Website: lmcm.com.au
Email: info@lmcm.com.au
Phone: 293 878 207
Address: 102/13 Bowden St Alexandria NSW 2015 Australia
Description: Established in 1993 by senior agent and company Director Lisa Mann; LMCM agency is home to some of Australia's most high profile and respected performers and boasts an impeccable reputation for services to the arts and entertainment industry.
Country: Australia
Contact: chief Executive officer Lisa Mann
Contact: senior agent Belinda Maxwell
Social Media: twitter.com/LMCM_Australia www.instagram.com/lisamanncreativemanagement/

Lucy Guerin Inc
Website: www.lucyguerininc.com
Email: admin@lucyguerininc.com
Phone: 393 294 213
Address: 130 Dryburgh St North Melbourne, VIC, Australia 3051
Description: Lucy Guerin Inc is an Australian dance company established in Melbourne in 2002 to create and tour new dance works. Renowned for the skill and originality of its small group of performers, it is a flexible organisation dedicated to challenging and extending the art of contemporary dance. The Company is committed to the exploration of everyday events and the redefinition of the formal concerns of dance. New productions are generated through an experimental approach to creative process and may involve voice, video, sound, text and industrial design as well as Guerin's lucid physical structures. Crucially, this is always a choreographic exploration, striving for visual, emotional and physical revelations that could not be generated or communicated in any other artform than dance. Member of ISPA.
Country: Australia
Contact: Artistic Director Lucy Guerin
Email: Lucy@LucyGuerinInc.com
Contact: Executive Producer Annette Vieusseux
Email: Annette@LucyGuerinInc.com
Contact: acting Executive Director Michaela Conventry
Email: michaela@lucyguerininc.com
Social Media: https://twitter.com/lucyguerininc www.facebook.com/LucyGuerinInc/ www.instagram.com/lucyguerininc/

Marguerite Pepper Productions
Website: www.mpproductions.com.au
Email: info@mpproductions.com.au
Phone: 412 231 313
Address: PO Box 7293, AU
Description: Founded by Marguerite Pepper in 1989, MPP is an independent production company based in Sydney, Australia. MPP is dedicated to supporting artists and ensembles in the creation of their work, from inception through to production and touring, in Australia and internationally. As consultants MPP are also frequently engaged as creative and event Producers, offering services to an extensive range of clients, delivering into diverse venues and cultures with budgets ranging from small to significant.
Country: Australia
Contact: Managing Director Marguerite Pepper
Email: marguerite@mpproductions.com.au

Mollison Keightley Management
Website: www.mollisonkeightley.com
Email: mkm@mollison.com
Phone: 028 302 2800
Address: 139 Cathedral Street, Woolloomooloo, NSW 2011 Australia
Description: Mollison Keightley Management enables the creation and development of careers in the performing arts. It has a highly experienced team from diverse backgrounds including law, producing, casting, Marketing/PR and performing. They work in close partnership with clients to help them achieve their Artistic and career goals, whether locally, nationally or globally.
Country: Australia
Contact: General Manager/agent Monica Keightley
Email: mkm@mollison.com
Social Media: https://twitter.com/mkm139 https://www.instagram.com/mollisonkeightleymanagement

Mullinars Casting Consultants
Website: http:// www.mullinars.com.au/
Email: sydney@mullinars.com.au
Phone: 029 331 6613
Address: Level 3, 21 Oxford Street Surry Hills NSW 2010 Australia
Description: Mullinars Casting Consultants are renowned worldwide as Australia's leading casting consultancy. It is Australia's longest established casting consultancy and the depth of expertise and the diversity of casting style is reflected in a long and varied list of credits.
Country: Australia
Contact: chief Executive officer Ann Robinson
Social Media: www.facebook.com/MullinarsCasting/ www.instagram.com/mullinarscasting/

Now Actors
Website: www.nowactors.com.au
Email: perth@nowactors.com.au
Phone: 892 011 822
Address: Level 1, Shop 5, 225 Oxford Street Leederville, WA, Australia 6007
Description: NowActors is an established leading force within the Australian film, television, radio and theatre industry. The style boutique is one of Australia's leading actor's management agencies. They represent not only experienced theatre and film luminaries but also many rising young adult, teen and child stars.
Country: Australia
Contact: Agent Karin Thomson
Email: perth@nowactors.com.au
Contact: Agent Anthony Harden
Contact: Agent Karin Thomson
Email: karin@nowactors.com.au
Social Media: www.facebook.com/nowactors www.instagram.com/nowactors/

ORiGiN Theatrical Pty Ltd
Website: www.origintheatrical.com.au
Email: enquiries@originmusic.com.au
Phone: 028 514 5201
Address: PO Box Q1235, QVB Post Office Sydney NSW 1230 Australia
Description: ORiGiN™ Theatrical is the market leader in Australia and New Zealand for secondary market theatrical exploitation into amateur, community, schools, pro-am, small professional, fringe, regional, stock and repertory productions. Simply this means everything other than first class professional productions.
Country: Australia
Contact: chief Executive officer Philip Walker
Contact: Manager Philip Mortlock
Social Media: twitter.com/origin_theatric www.facebook.com/OriginTheatrical

Patrick Togher Artists' Management
Website: www.patricktogher.com
Email: patrick@patricktogher.com
Phone: 293 196 255
Address: Suite 43, 551 Elizabeth Street Surry Hills NSW 2010 Australia
Description: Patrick Togher Artists' Management was founded in 1998 by Opera Australia Principal and Phantom of the Opera star Patrick Togher and leading operatic and concert soprano Romola Tyrrell. PTAM's principal activity is sourcing, negotiating and servicing contracts for artists with the major opera companies, orchestras, festivals, recording companies and choral organisations in Australia and New Zealand. Member of IAMA
Country: Australia
Contact: Director Patrick Togher
Contact: Director Romola Tyrrell
Social Media: https://twitter.com/patricktogher

Primate Entertainment Services Pty Ltd
Website: www.primate.com.au
Email: salli@primate.com.au
Phone: 396 905 055
Address: Suite 13, 117 Sturt Street, AU
Description: An agency providing clients with performers, musicians and visual artsists to suit a diversity of functions and events.
Country: Australia

Rick Raftos Management
Website: www.rickraftosmanagement.com.au
Email: raftos@raftos.com.au
Phone: 029 281 9622
Address: Suite 202, 59 Great Buckingham Street Redfern, NSW, 2016, Australia
Description: The agency, which has now been going for over 25 years, was initially founded to represent performing arts writers but quickly expanded into representing writers in all media, Directors and, more recently, creative Producers. The agency has also been instrumental in launching the careers of some of Australia's most successful authors, some of which who have turned their books into films.
Country: Australia
Contact: Managing Director/agent Rick Raftos
Contact: agent Wanda Blanch

Skeed Entertainment Agency
Website: www.skeedentertainment.com
Email: skeedent@bigpond.net.au
Phone: 295 807 508
Address: PO Box 166, Bexley South, New South Wales, Australia
Description: Skeed Entertainment have been a trusted name within the entertainment industry for nearly 22 years. During that time, it has successfully operated as Entertainment Booking Agents, Artist Representation and Venue Consultants. Alan and Trish Skeed are committed to providing their clients with professional, easy to use and progressive services each and every time. Skeed Entertainment exclusively represent an extensive range of the highest quality Tribute and Package Shows, Party and Covers Bands, Duo and Solo Artists.
Country: Australia

Sydney Talent Company
Website: www.sydneytalentco.com.au
Email: sydneytalentco@tpg.com.au
Phone: 029 211 6366
Address: 2A The Crescent Beecroft NSW 2119 Australia
Description: Established in 1982, Sydney Talent Company is a full-service theatrical agency representing local, national, and international talent of all ages and cultural types. The roster includes actors, singers, voice artists, dancers, models and even adorable babies.
Country: Australia
Contact: Director Jon-Claire Lee
Email: jonclaire@sydneytalentcompany.com.au
Social Media: www.facebook.com/SydneyTalentCompany

Weaver Artist Management
Website: www.weaverartistmanagement.com.au
Email: jeffweaver@weaverartistmanagement.com.au
Phone: 039 408 1708
Address: PO Box 7670 St. Kilda Road, Melbourne Australia 3004
Description: Weaver Artist Management was founded in Melbourne in 1991 by Jeff Weaver. It is now one of the longest established of the small number of Australian-based artist management agencies and offers representation to Artistic Directors, stage Directors and composers, to solo instrumentalists of all fine-music disciplines, to opera, concert and music-theatre singers and to choral, jazz and chamber music ensembles and orchestras.
Country: Australia
Contact: Director Jeff Weaver
Email: jeffweaver@weaverartistmanagement.com.au
Contact: Artistic Director Paul Grabowsky
Type: Classical, Other

Young Australia Workshop
Website: www.youngaus.com.au
Email: info@youngaus.com.au
Phone: 028 021 5312
Address: 103 Oxford Street, AU
Description: A Sydney based company producing in-school programmes and theatre productions for schools throughout Australia, it is the largest privately owned management company of its kind in Australasia. Established thirty five years ago, the Young Australia Workshop is a Sydney based company producing in-school arts in education programmes and theatre shows for schools throughout Australia.
Country: Australia
Social Media: www.facebook.com/youngaustraliaworks/
Type: Children/Youth, Modern/Contemporary

BRAZIL

ALMA – Academia Livre de Música e Artes
Website: www.almacultura.com.br
Email: fnsanchez@almacultura.com.br
Phone: 112 283 1293
Address: Av. Leôncio de Magalhães, 1027, BR
Description: ALMA offers courses in guitar, electric bass, drums, singing, keyboard, piano, saxophone, transverse flute, flute, clarinet, children's music, violin and cello. In addition to practical classes, the student can take lessons in music theory, harmony and perception. Member of ISPA.
Country: Brazil
Contact: music and arts Director Felipe Cesar Sanchez
Social Media: www.facebook.com/almacultura

Philharmonic Cultural Institute
Website: www.filarmonica.art.br
Email: contato@filarmonica.art.br
Phone: 313 219 9000
Address: Rua Paraíba 330, BR
Description: the Philharmonic Cultural Institute is a non-profit civil association that maintains and manages the Minas Gerais Philharmonic Orchestra
Country: Brazil
Social Media: www.facebook.com/filarmonicamg
Type: Symphonic

Scubidu Music
Website: www.scubidu.com.br
Email: contato@scubidu.com.br
Phone: 212 96699
Address: Rua Cons. Fernandes Torres, 110 / 71, BR
Description: a booking and management agency that boosts young Brazilian talents over the world. The company relies on a Brazilian-centered/World-oriented management that places the artists online and offline. The good music is provided through Scubidu Records and its partner distributor Tratore, placing the tracks on online markets, such as iTunes, e-music, Amazon.com and others. Member of ISPA
Country: Brazil
Contact: Director Flavio de Abreu
Email: flabreu@scubidu.com.br
Social Media: @scubiduprods www.facebook.com/scubidu.prods
Type: All

CANADA

Agence Opéra LM Opera Agency
Website: mopera.com
Email: chalfounleila@gmail.com
Phone: 514 241 7226
Address: 356 St-Eustache Street City of Saint-Eustache (QC) Canada J7R-2M3
Description: L'AGENCE LM OPÉRA is specialized in the representation of opera artists in Quebec, Canada and Europe, since 1998. Our Agency represents many talented artists: opera singers, Directors, chefs orchestra and musicians.
Country: Canada
Contact: President Leila Chalfoun
Email: leila@meti-jori-agency.com
Social Media: https://twitter.com/LeilaChalfoun www.facebook.com/agencelmopera www.instagram.com/leilamariechalfoun/

Agence Station Bleue
Website: www.stationbleue.com
Email: prod@stationbleue.com
Phone: 514 529 5717
Address: 4713, avenue Papineau Montréal (Québec) Canada H2H 1V4
Description: Constantly on the look-out for what is new and innovative, agence Station bleue offers you a wide variety of artists whose musical programmes and diverse activities are sure to transform any show into an unforgettable event. Since 2000, when it started promoting the scenic arts, Station bleue has continued to be an important player, representing artists who distinguish themselves by their quality and professionalism and through the unique services offered by the team. Member of IAMA.
Country: Canada
Contact: agent Claudia Beradi
Email: c.berardi@stationbleue.com
Contact: Executive assistant & tour coordinator Élisabeth Comtois
Email: e.comtois@stationbleue.com
Contact: head agent Annick-Patricia Carrière
Email: ap.carriere@stationbleue.com
Contact: finance Manager Marco Fortier
Email: m.fortier@stationbleue.com
Social Media: www.facebook.com/agencestationbleue/ www.instagram.com/agence.station.bleue

Agence Station Bleue
Website: https://stationbleue.com/
Email: prod@stationbleue.com
Phone: 514 529 0139
Address: 4713 Papineau Avenue, Montreal (Quebec), Canada H2H 1V4
Description: Founded by Annick-Patricia Carrière and Gabriel Paré in 2000, Agence Station Bleue is one of the most recognized Artistic agencies in Canada. Its growing and continuing presence in the national and international performing arts markets, its twenty years of expertise in the promotion and representation of artists , as well as its in-depth understanding of the issues in the field make it a partner. Members of ISPA
Country: Canada
null
Social Media: https:// www.facebook.com/agencestationbleue/ https:// www.instagram.com/agence.station.bleue/?hl=fr-ca
Type: Jazz, Vocal, Classical, Pops/Light Classical, Pop/Rock, Solo/Chamber, Other

Andrew Kwan Artists Management Inc.
Website: www.andrewkwanartists.com
Email: info@andrewkwanartists.com
Phone: 416 445 4441
Address: 14 Davies Crescent East York, ON M4J 2X5, Canada
Description: AKAM is a Canadian artists management agency specialising in career development, promotion and performance arrangements for classical/world musicians
Country: Canada
Contact: Director Andrew Kwan
Email: andrew@andrewkwanartists.com
Contact: artist representative Susan Durnin
Email: susan@andrewkwanartists.com
Social Media: https:// www.facebook.com/andrewkwanartists/
Type: Classical, Other

B C Fiedler Management
Website: www.bcfiedler.com
Email: info@bcfiedler.com
Phone: 416 421 4421
Address: 53 Seton Park Rd, North York, ON M3C 3Z8, Canada
Description: Bernd C. ("B.C") Fiedler is one of Canada's storied names in music. As a Canadian artist Manager, Producer and impresario, he has built an enviable reputation for guiding careers and producing music and musical events. As one of the key figures in the Toronto music explosion of the sixties, Fiedler's legendary Yorkville coffee house, The Riverboat, became a mecca

for first rank talent
Country: Canada
Contact: President Bernie Fiedler
Email: info@bcfiedler.com
Type: Classical, Modern/Contemporary, Pops/Light
Classical, Pop/Rock, Wind/brass band

BAM! Baird Artists Management
Website: www.bairdartists.com
Email: robert@bairdartists.com
Phone: 416 887 2151
Address: P.O. Box 597 Alliston, ON L9R 1V7 Canada
Description: Known internationally for knowledge of
entry requirements, visa requirements and taxation
regulations for Canada and the United States. Available
as a consultant to artists, agents and presenters
Country: Canada
Contact: President Robert Baird
Email: robert@bairdartists.com
Social Media: https://twitter.com/bairdartists www.
facebook.com/bairdartists

Belsher Arts Management
Website: www.belsherartsmanagement.ca
Email: brent@belshers.ca
Phone: 604 209 6337
Address: 202-501 Pacific St, Vancouver, British Columbia,
V6Z 2X6, Canada
Description: Brent Belsher has worked in the arts over
the past 15 years. His roles include that of agent, Pro-
ducer tour Manager, as well as fundraiser. He works with
a variety of companies and artists helping build further
growth and opportunities for them. Member of ISPA
Country: Canada
Contact: Owner Brent Belsher
Social Media: www.facebook.com/belsherarts/
Type: Modern/Contemporary, Other

Boulev'Art Artists' Management
Website: www.boulevart.ca
Email: communications@boulevart.ca
Phone: 514 667 0880
Address: 2684, rue Aylwin Montréal (QC) H1W 3C8
Canada
Description: Since its beginnings in 1995, Boulev'Art
Artists' Management has become known for being
dynamic and professional in the way it manages and
represents artists of international stature. In addition to
concert bookings, Boulev'Art offers artists its manage-
ment expertise, supporting them as needed through
different periods of their career. Boulev'Art represents
top-level artists and musical ensembles, as well as
promising artists whose careers are just beginning, both
nationally and internationally. The team carefully selects
its collaborations in order to maintain a personalized and
professional relationship.
Country: Canada
Contact: General Director Samuel Côté
Email: scote@boulevart.ca
Contact: President Marie-Catherine LaPointe
Email: lapointe@boulevart.ca
Contact: communications Cristine Cimon-Fortier
Email: communications@boulevart.ca
Social Media: twitter.com/boulev_art www.facebook.
com/boulevart1995/

Caline Artists Management
Website: www.caline.com
Email: margot@caline.com
Phone: 800 539 8558
Address: 100 Bing Kee Street, Nanaimo, British Columbia,
Canada V9R 0J4
Description: caline Artists works with Canadian musi-
cians to develop performance opportunities within their
own community and around the world. We consult with
artists and non-profit arts organizations in the areas of
promotion, production and cd projects
Country: Canada
Contact: Managing CEO Margot Holmes
Email: margot@caline.com
Contact: booking agent Bobbi Kurtz
Email: bobbi@caline.com
Social Media: www.facebook.com/CalineArtistsInter-
national

Canada's Royal Winnipeg Ballet
Website: www.rwb.org
Email: customerservice@rwb.org
Phone: 204 956 0183
Address: 380 Graham Ave, Winnipeg, MB R3C 4H2,
Canada
Description: The Royal Winnipeg Ballet enriches the
human experience by teaching, creating and performing
outstanding dance. Versatility, technical excellence and
a captivating style are the trademarks of Canada's Royal
Winnipeg Ballet, qualities that have garnered both criti-
cal and audience acclaim. Founded in 1939 by Gweneth
Lloyd and Betty Farrally, the Royal Winnipeg Ballet holds
the double distinction of being Canada's premiere ballet
company and the longest continuously operating ballet
company in North America. Members of ISPA.
Country: Canada
Contact: Managing Director
David Warburton

Email: dwarburton@rwb.org

Danielle Lefebvre Artist And Concert Agency
Website: www.agencedlefebvre.com/en/home
Email: adl@agencedlefebvre.com
Phone: 819 377 2608
Address: 1035, for Schoolchildren Street Trois-Rivières,
QC G9B 7W1 Canada
Description: Danielle Lefebvre is the Founder and
General Manager of the Danielle Lefebvre Artist &
Concert Agency. She won the 2014 Agent of the Year
award from the British Columbia Touring Council and
was nominated for Capacoa's Agent of the Year award
in 2011. With a background that includes French horn
studies in Quebec's conservatories, piano and teaching
certificates as well as various ear training and dictation
awards, Danielle Lefebvre brings a unique expertise and
synergy to her organization. Boasting an outstanding
roster of artists and a solid team of tour agents, Danielle
Lefebvre's agency enjoys a strong presence in Canada,
Mexico and South America. Member of IAMA.
Country: Canada
Contact: Manager and booking agent Danielle Lefebvre
Email: danielle@agencedlefebvre.com
Contact: development officer Sarah Martineau
Email: sarah@agencedlefebvre.com
Social Media: twitter.com/agencedlefebvre www.
facebook.com/agencedaniellelefebvre/

Dean Artists Management
Website: www.deanartists.com
Email: admin@deanartists.com
Phone: 416 969 7300
Address: 500A Bloor St W, Toronto, ON M5S 1Y3, Canada
Description: specialises in the management of classically
trained singers, conductors of singers, and opera stage
Directors/choreographers
Country: Canada
Contact: senior artist Manager & Artistic advisor
Carrol Anne Curry
Email: carrolanne@deanartists.com
Contact: Managing Director Henry Ingram
Email: henry@deanartists.com
Contact: administrative Director Paul H. Johnson
Email: admin@deanartists.com
Contact: President and CEO Alison Pybus
Email: alison@deanartists.com
Social Media: https://twitter.com/DeanArtists www.
facebook.com/deanartistsmanagement www.insta-
gram.com/deanartistsmanagement/

Envision Management & Production
Website: www.envisionmanagement.com
Email: info@envisionmanagement.com
Phone: 514 274 2099
Address: 6506 Drolet St, Montreal, QC H2S 2S8, Canada
Description: They are a creative artist management and
production company that works with boundary-break-
ing, musical and multi-disciplinary artists. At Envision,
the emphasis is placed on the artist and the art. The
mission is to make artists' visions become realities.
Member of ISPA
Country: Canada
Contact: Founder, President, artist Manager and Pro-
ducer Ryhna Thompson
Email: ryhna@envisionmanagement.com
Social Media: www.facebook.com/envisionman-
agement https://twitter.com/envision_mgmt www.
instagram.com/envisionmanagement/

Eponymous
Website:
www.eponymous.ca
Email: info@eponymous.ca
Phone: 604 683 6552
Address: 104-336 East 1st Avenue Vancouver, BC, Canada
V5T4R6
Description: arts and cultural management agency
supporting and promoting high calibre creative work in
a range of Artistic disciplines and cultural areas. Member
of ISPA
Country: Canada
Contact: accounts Ann Hepper
Email: ann@eponymous.ca
Contact: Marketing & communications Manager
Heather McDermid
Email: heather@eponymous.ca
Contact: administrative assistant Sharon Simpson
Email: sharon@eponymous.ca
Contact: Producer Jim Smith
Email: jim@eponymous.ca
Contact: production Manager Josef Chung
Email: josef@eponymous.ca
Contact: artist and tour Manager Francesca Piscopo
Email: francesca@eponymous.ca
Social Media: twitter.com/eponymousagency www.
facebook.com/eponymousagency www.instagram.
com/eponymousagency/

FAM Group (Fleming Artists Management)
Website:
www.famgroup.ca
Email: info@famgroup.ca
Phone: 514 844 7393

Address: 4102 St Urbain Street, CA
Description: since 1986, FAMgroup (Fleming Artists
Management) has represented jazz, folk, blues and world
music artists, most are from Quebec
Country: Canada
Contact: President Heidi Fleming
Email: heidi@famgroup.ca
Social Media: https://twitter.com/famgroup www.
facebook.com/famgroupmgmt/
Type: Folk/Ethnic/World, Jazz, Other

Fascinator Management
Website: www.fascinatormanagement.com
Email: dani@fascinatormanagement.com
Phone: 604 722 9044
Address: 308-237 Keefer Street, Unceded Coast Salish
Territories V6A 1X6
Description: Fascinator Management is an agency, con-
sultancy and production house based in Vancouver, BC
that connects West Coast artists to the world. Member
of ISPA.
Country: Canada
Contact: President and lead agent Dani Fecko
Email: dani@fascinatormanagement.com
Contact: communications and admin Sophie Barssard
Email: sophie.fascinatormanagement@gmail.com
Social Media: twitter.com/fascinatormgmt www.face-
book.com/fascinatormgmt

Feldman Agency, The
Website: www.feldman-agency.com
Email: info@feldman-agency.com
Phone: 416 598 0067
Address: 8 Elm St, Toronto, ON, M5G 1G7 Canada
Description: The Feldman Agency is one of North
America's premiere entertainment talent agencies and
management groups. With over 40 years in the enter-
tainment business, TFA has a wealth of experience in
artist representation, talent, booking, event services and
corporate consulting. Representing hundreds of artists
from around the world, from hot up-and-coming talent
to critically acclaimed, award-winning artists, TFA's roster
is a diverse spectrum of all genres with a team of 50-plus
passionate people working out of offices in Toronto and
Vancouver.
Country: Canada
Contact: Chief Operating Officer Don Simpson
Social Media: https://twitter.com/FeldmanAgency
www.facebook.com/FeldmanAgency www.instagram.
com/feldmanagency/

Fox Entertainment Agency
Website: www.foxent.ca
Email: tammyfox@thecollectionagency.ca
Phone: 416 553 2516
Address: CA
Description: Established in 2008, Fox Entertainment
Agency (previously The Collection Agency Entertain-
ment) is a full-service interdisciplinary performing arts
booking agency which specializes in professional touring
theatrical productions, while also representing a select
roster of musical artists who are especially suited for
soft seat venues. Worked closely with a wide variety of
arts presenters, both nationally and internationally, from
theatre-producing venues.
Country: Canada
Contact: Owner Tammy Fox
Email: tammyfox@thecollectionagency.ca
Contact: Director Kevin Fox
Email: kevin@foxent.ca

Genovese Vanderhoof & Associates
Website: genovesevanderhoof.com
Email: gvasearch@gmail.com
Phone: 416 340 2762
Address: 77 Carlton Street, Suite 1103 Toronto, Ontario
Canada M5B 2J7
Description: The firm's clients range from the continent's
largest ballet and opera companies, theatres, museums,
art galleries and orchestras, to highly specialised cultural
organisations such as modern dance companies, folk fes-
tivals, theatres for young audiences, science museums,
performing arts facilities, historic theatres, living history
museums, arts service organisations and government
agencies. Member of ISPA. see also Products and Services
Country: Canada
Contact: senior partner Margaret Genovese
Contact: senior partner Dory Vanderhoof
Email: gvadory@aol.com
Contact: partner Rosalind Bell

Imagination – Canada
Website: www.imagination.com
Email: eduardo.braniff@imagination.com
Phone: 416 929 1260
Address: 22 Wellesley St E, Toronto, ON M4Y 1G3, Canada
Description: They offer management for architects,
3D and 2D designers, film makers, journalists, creative
technologists, bloggers and social media experts, art
Directors and copy writers and creative strategists. They
have offices in Sydney, New York, LA, Stockholm, Detroit,
Melbourne, Cologne, Mumbai, Beijing, Shanghai, Hong
Kong, Singapore, Tokyo, London, Doha, Moscow and
Macau

Country: Canada
Contact: business Manager Eduardo Braniff
Email: eduardo.braniff@imagination.com
Social Media: www.facebook.com/ImaginationGLBL
www.instagram.com/imaginationglbl/twitter.com/
ImaginationGLBL

Latitude 45 Arts Promotion, Inc.
Website: www.latitude45arts.com
Email: info@latitude45arts.com
Phone: 514 276 2694
Address: 107, boul. St-Joseph West Montreal (Quebec)
Canada H2T 2P7
Description: Latitude 45 represents a wide array of
artists who work in the field of music. They represent
singers, instrumentalists and composers from across na-
tive Canada, coast to coast and from many corners of the
globe in many styles and techniques. Latitude 45's artists
engage audiences with the power of commitment and
the joys of curiosity. Latitude 45, like the imagination,
embraces the world.
Country: Canada
Contact: President Barbara Scales Scales
Email: scalesb@latitude45arts.com
Contact: Vice President of booking Eoin Ó Catháin
Catháin
Contact: Vice President of artist services Melissa Claisse
Claisse
Email: melissa@latitude45arts.com
Social Media: twitter.com/Latitude45Arts www.
facebook.com/Latitude45Arts/ www.instagram.com/
latitude45artspromotion

Marilyn Gilbert Artists Management
Website: www.mgam.com
Email: marilyn@mgam.com
Phone: 416 534 4993
Address: 1210 – 320 Tweedsmuir Avenue, Suite 1713, CA
Description: Marilyn Gilbert Artists Management has
embraced change with a roster of musicians whose
work challenges the artificial boundaries of genre and
whose sparkling musicianship gives them broad appeal.
Committed to developing the careers of dynamic,
innovative musicians, they represent artists who speak to
a multitude of audiences.
Country: Canada
Contact: Director Marilyn Gilbert
Email: marilyn@mgam.com
Social Media: twitter.com/mgaminc www.facebook.
com/marilyn.gilbert

Menno Plukker Theatre Agent
Website: www.mennoplukker.com
Email: info@mennoplukker.com
Phone: 613 443 6342
Address: 951, chemin du Castor St-Albert (Ontario)
Canada
Description: Menno Plukker Agency is a theatrical agent
and management company for the performing arts and
entertainment in Canada, the United States, and Europe.
Founded in 1997 by Menno Plukker, Menno Plukker Theatre Agent, Inc. has rapidly earned a solid reputation on
the national and international scenes as an agent who
has efficiently broadened touring markets for theatre
and dance companies. The agency's mandate is more
specifically to develop touring opportunities abroad,
and to book performances for theatre, and dance and
music companies, thereby increasing the visibility and
presence of the artists and companies the agency represents. The main goal is to create a stable and sustainable
working environment which will allow these artists to
develop and maintain an international career.
Country: Canada
Contact: Director Menno Plukker
Email: mplukker@hotmail.com
Social Media:
www.facebook.com/mptainc/

NetGain Partners
Website:
netgainpartners.com
Email: info@netgainpartners.com
Phone: 416 367 2392
Address: 53 Berkeley Street, Toronto. M5A 2W5 Canada
Description: NetGain Partners is a team of experienced
management specialists committed to helping not-for-
profit and public sector organizations reach their goals.
Based in Toronto, their teams have provided creative
solutions for cultural, aboriginal and conservation
groups, as well as municipal and provincial departments
and agencies. They are a boutique consulting firm that
supports their clients with highly specialized expertise in
arts management and strategy.
Country: Canada
Contact: senior Managing Director Doug Simpson
Contact: business catalyst Genevieve Tran
Social Media: twitter.com/netgainpartners

Paquin Entertainment Group
Website: www.paquinentertainment.com
Email:
info@paquinentertainment.com
Phone: 416 962 8885
Address: 206B-219 Dufferin Street Toronto, ON M6K 3J1
Canada

Description: They proudly represent world-class artists
on a national and international level. Their roster covers a
wide spectrum of art forms, spanning from music to theatre to dance, and they move seamlessly between these
genres. Whatever the genre, they, as agents, are charged
with developing their artists' careers through innovative
solutions and hard work. They take this responsibility
seriously, working hand-in-hand with their clients, developing and implementing tour strategies proven to create
successful and sustainable careers.
Country: Canada
Contact: President Julien Paquin
Email: contact.julien@paquinartistsagency.com
Contact: Vice President Todd Jordan
Email: contact.todd@paquinartistsagency.com

Philmultic Management & Productions Inc
Website: www.philmultic.com/home
Email: booking@philmultic.com
Phone: 514 482 6750
Address: 8191 Montview, Ville Mont Royal, CA
Description: The Philmultic is an incorporated Manage-
ment and Production Company dedicated to promoting
classical music of all world traditions. Their service
includes: Booking concerts and international tours for
musicians of all world classical traditions. They Produce
concerts of classical music of all world traditions. The
concerts are usually in Montreal (Quebec, Canada), but
may also take place in other cities.
Country: Canada
Contact: President Risheng Wang
Email: booking@philmultic.com
Type: Classical, Baroque, Choral, Early, Solo/Chamber,
Symphonic, Wind/brass band

Pierre Gravel International – PGI
Website: www.pierregravel.com
Email: pgi@pierregravel.com
Phone: 450 372 7764
Address: 89, rue Alexandra Granby (Québec) J2G 2P4
Canada
Description: Pierre Gravel International has emerged
as Canada's premier agency in exclusive corporate
and touring entertainment. Their roster includes both
domestic and international artists whose talents cover
many unique areas of the entertainment industry. PGI
represents the very best singers, bands, imPressionists,
entertainers, comedians, magicians, variety and circus
acts. It is this unique assortment and quality of talent
that makes the PGI family the agency of choice.
Country: Canada
Contact: President Pierre Gravel
Email: pgi@pierregravel.com
Contact: Vice President Marie-Pierre Gravel
Email: marie@pierregravel.com
Contact: agent – public & private international English
market Kimberlea Whitehead
Email: kim@pierregravel.com
Social Media: https://twitter.com/pierre_gravel www.
facebook.com/pierregravelint www.instagram.com/
pierregravelinternational/

Richard Paul Concert Artists
Website: www.greatconcerts.com
Email: richard@greatconcerts.com
Phone: 416 595 9555
Address: 3 Byron Ave, Toronto, ON M4J 3T7, Canada
Description: Representing some of the best performers
on the Classical Music scene currently touring the con-
tinent, they specialise in working with chamber music
presenters, festivals and Orchestras in helping them to
put together a spectacular season.
Country: Canada
Contact: Director Richard Paul
Social Media: www.facebook.com/greatconcerts

Searchlight Partners
Website: www.searchlightpartnersgroup.com
Email:
mark@searchlightcanada.com
Phone: 416 645 3776
Address: 8 Wellington Street East, Toronto, ON M5E 1C5
Description: Searchlight has been building Leadership
teams and finding exceptional global talent for leading
organizations in the Arts & Culture, Technology, Media,
Sports & Entertainment, Consumer and Social Enter-
prise/Not For Profit sectors. They partner with clients to
enhance their leadership across all senior functions. We
synchronize your business strategy with our expertise
in securing game-changing talent, together with innovative leadership coaching, effective Board consultancy
and programmes that enhance workplace culture. They
are specialists in the art and science of Talent – how to
attract, retain and develop leaders to enable organizations to excel.
Country: Canada
Contact: Founder and co-Managing partner Daniel
Weinzweig
Email: Daniel@Searchlightpartnersgroup.com
Contact: co-Managing partner Mark Rubinstein
Contact: Founder and Managing partner Daniel Wein-
zweig Weinzweig
Contact: senior partner John McQuaker

Armstrong Music and Arts Ltd
Website: www.armstrongmusic.cc
Email: info@armstrongmusic.co
Phone: 105 826 3639
Address: No.3-038, North Pingod Arts Community, 32
Baiziwan Road, Chaoyang
Description: The company has been operating in the
fields of artist management, arts touring, consulting and
project management for 6 years, and is pleased to offer a
unique bridge between east and west with our team of
experienced Western and Chinese arts professionals.
Country: China
Contact: CEO Wray Armstrong
Email: wrayarmstrong@gmail.com
Contact: operation Director and Executive assistant
Evita Zhang
Email: evita.zhang@armstrongmusic.co
Type: All

Asian Arts Connection Shanghai (AAC)
Website: www.aacshanghai.com
Email: info@aacshanghai.com
Phone: 215 410 6122
Address: Thames Town 626, Songjiang District
Description: Always maintaining a global view, Asian
Arts Connection© ("AAC") is a Shanghai and Berlin-based
arts management company. It exists to serve the arts
and artists by promoting Western Performing Arts within
China and Chinese Performing Arts abroad.
Country: China
Contact: General Manager Alan Wang
Email: alanwang@aacshanghai.com

Beijing Eurovista Arts Promotion Co. Ltd.
Website: www.eurovista.com.cn
Email: info@eurovista.com.cn
Phone: 106 251 0779
Address: Room 610, Xingfa Plaza, Zhongguancun Road
45 Hao, Haidian District,
Description: null
Country: China
Contact: contact Lin Zhu
Email: lin.zhu@eurovista.com.cn
Type: Classical

Hermark Culture
Website: www.hermarkculture.com
Email: hermark.public@gmail.com
Phone: 105 753 8205
Address: Room 204, Building No.1, 77 Cultural & Creative
Park, , No.77rd Art Museum Backstreet, , Dongcheng
District
Description: Hermark Culture is committed to develop-
ing the careers of dynamic, innovative musicians and art-
ists in China. As a growing creative company established
in 2011, they specialise in orchestral touring and the
development of innovative projects of all kinds.
Country: China
Social Media: www.facebook.com/hermark.culture
Type: All

Donway International Limited
Website: www.donwayinternational.com
Email: enquiries@donwayinternational.com
Phone: 287 03302
Address: 603 Chao's Building, 143 Bonham Strand East,
Sheung Wan, HK
Description:
Country: Hong Kong
Contact: Director John Duffus
Type: All

Imagination – Hong Kong
Website: www.imagination.com
Email: darren.kerr@imagination.com
Phone: 351 31300
Address: 32 F Cambridge House, Taikoo Place, 979 King's
Road, HK
Description: management for architects, 3D and 2D
designers, film makers, journalists, creative technologists,
bloggers and social media experts, art Directors and
copy writers and creative strategists. Also have offices in
Sydney, New York, LA, Stockholm, Detroit, Melbourne,
Cologne, Mumbai, Beijing, Shanghai, London, Singapore,
Tokyo, Toronto, Doha, Moscow, Macau
Country: Hong Kong
Contact: business Manager Darren Kerr
Email: darren.kerr@imagination.com

RhapsoArts Management
Website: www.rhapsoarts.com
Email: info@rhapsoarts.com
Phone: 272 21650
Address: Room 1204, 12/F, Summit Insurance Building
789 Nathan Road Mongkok, Kowloon, HONG KONG
Description: Set up in 1998, RhapsoArts Management
Limited specialises in arts management and provides
professional services in arts Administration for artists and
performing groups.
Country: Hong Kong

INDIA

Inspiration – India
Website: www.imagination.com
Email: Ravishankar.Iyer@imagination.com
Phone: 226 155 4807
Address: Newbridge, 1st Floor, Parinee Crescenzo, C38 & 39 G Block, , Opposite Mumbai Cricket Association, Bandra Kurla Complex, IN
Description: management for architects, 3D and 2D designers, film makers, journalists, creative technologists, bloggers and social media experts, art Directors and copy writers and creative strategists. Also have offices in Sydney, New York, LA, Stockholm, Detroit, Melbourne, Cologne, London, Beijing, Shanghai, Hong Kong, Singapore, Tokyo, Toronto, Doha, Moscow, Macau
Country: India
Contact: business Manager Ravishankar Iyer
Email: Ravishankar.Iyer@imagination.com

Star Beats Entertainment
Website: www.starbeatsentertainment.com
Email: info@starbeatsentertainment.com
Phone: 982 043 2901
Address: 22 Sea-side, Opposite Mount Building, J.P. Road, Versova, IN
Description: Provides a variety of Bollywood celebrities/ non celebrities performers for all types of occasion
Country: India
Contact: CEO Sikandar Khan
Email: starbeatsentertainment@gmail.com
Social Media: StarBeatsEnt www.facebook.com/pages/STAR-BEATS-ENTERTAINMENT-The-World-Of-Stars/128065400540158
Type: Modern/Contemporary, All

The Neemrana Music Foundation
Website: www.tnmf.org
Email: tnmf@fwacziarg.com
Phone: 114 077 5177
Address: A-58, , Nizamuddin East, IN
Description: promotes classical music in India
Country: India
Type: Children/Youth, Classical

ISRAEL

ArtPro Artists Management
Website: www.artpro.co.il
Email: info@artpro.co.il
Phone: 995 05816
Address: 10 Baal Shem Tov Street, Apartment. 96, IL
Description: ArtPro Artists Management represents artists and ensembles internationally, in concert and opera and organises tours of international artists to Israel and concert tours for ensembles and orchestras.
Country: IL
Contact: founding Manager Uri Zur
Email: urizur@artpro.co.il
Social Media: www.facebook.com/pages/ArtPro-Artists-Management/402448456469887
Type: Choral, Classical, Modern/Contemporary, Solo/ Chamber, Symphonic, Vocal, Other

Sarah Meltzer Artists Promoter
Website: www.sarahmeltzer.com
Email: office@sarahmeltzer.com
Phone: 523 682 226
Address: Sarah Meltzer Artists Promoter, 17/7 Shimoni st., IL
Description: promoting musicians worldwide. Member of IAMA
Country: IL
Contact: artist Manager Sarah Meltzer
Email: artistspromoter@gmail.com

JAPAN

Aspen Incorporated
Website: www.aspen.jp
Email: info@aspen.jp
Phone: 354 670 081
Address: 2-20-16 Nishi-Azabu, Minato-ku Minato-ku Tokyo 106-0031
Description: Aspen Inc. manages top classical Japanese artists, produces concerts, and engages world renowned classical artists in classical music activities in Japan as well as other Asian regions. Since 1998, Aspen Inc. has been organising Ishikawa Music Academy inc. Member of IAMA.
Country: Japan
Contact: Chairman and CEO Masami Shigeta
Contact: Director Koji Akiyama
Contact: Director Noriyuki Matsumura
Social Media: @Aspen_Inc www.facebook.com/Aspen-Inc-220737991352503

Concert Agency Soleil Co Ltd
Website:
www.soleilmusic.com
Email:
info@soleilmusic.com
Phone: 426 707 715
Address: 3-2-1-506, Shimo-Yugi, Hachioji, JP

Description: Invites artists mainly from Wien; manages Japanese artists; organises seminars in Austria and Germany.
Country: Japan

Concert Service Co., Ltd.
Website: www.concert.co.jp
Email: concert@concert.co.jp
Phone: 332 357 772
Address: 35 Kaitai-cho, Shinjuku-ku, Tokyo 162-0802 Japan
Description: Concert Service Co., Ltd. promotes both local and overseas artists, hosts and manages concerts, manageres Japanese and overseas artists, provides music classroom development and also operates as a ticket agency business. Member of IAMA.
Country: Japan
Contact: CEO Shuetsu Sato
Social Media: www.facebook.com/concertimagine
Type: Classical

Crystal Arts Inc.
Website: www.crystalarts.jp
Email: mails@crystalarts.jp
Phone: 364 347 997
Address: G-FRONT AOYAMA 6th Floor 2-12-15, Kita-Aoyama Minato-Ku, Tokyo 107-0061, Japan
Description: Crystal Arts Inc. offers commercial services. The Company manages and presents Japanese and international performing artists. Crystal Arts also plans and organises music festivals and educational events.
Country: Japan

Hori-Pro Inc
Website: www.horipro.co.jp
Email: fanclub@horipro.co.jp
Phone:
Address: 1-2-5, Shimo-Meguro, Meguro-ku, Tokyo 153-8660, Japan
Description: Having always produced stars who symbolize the times, HoriPro has a long and successful track record when it comes to discovering and developing talents, as exemplified by the "HoriPro Scout Caravan", started in 1976. Leveraging such experience and achievements, they engage in management activities, aiming to discover hidden raw talents. With talents who can accommodate various needs, including actors and actresses, singers, variety talents, comedians and idols, we engage in strategic promotional activities through media, including TV, radio, movies, stages, magazines and the internet.
Country: Japan
Contact: President Yoshitaka Hori
Contact: Representative Executive Director/ Executive Officer Motoyuki Suzuki
Social Media: www.facebook.com/horiprofanpage https:// www.facebook.com/horipro.stage

Horipiro Inc.
Website: www.horipro.co.jp
Email: web-horipro@horipro.jp
Phone: 334 908 411
Address: 1-2-5 Shimomeguro, Megoru-ku, JP
Description: The HoriPro Group is composed of our business division, subsidiaries and affiliated companies, and is mainly engaged in business development such as management of entertainment talent, video production, music production, and performances such as theater.
Country: Japan
Contact: Producer Iwanaga Satoshi

Imagination – Japan
Website: www.imagination.com
Email: rina.ueshima@imagination.com
Phone: 351 146 147
Address: Roji Akasaka A, 7-6-43 Akasaka, Minato-Ku, Tokyo 107-0052, Japan
Description: Management for architects, 3D and 2D designers, film makers, journalists, creative technologists, bloggers and social media experts, art Directors and copy writers and creative strategists. Also have offices in Sydney, New York, LA, Stockholm, Detroit, Melbourne, Cologne, Mumbai, Beijing, Shanghai, Hong Kong, Singapore, London, Toronto, Doha, Moscow, Macau
Country: Japan
Contact: business Manager Rina Ueshima
Email: rina.ueshima@imagination.com

Japan Arts Corporation Ltd
Website: www.japanarts.co.jp
Email: sekita@japanarts.co.jp
Phone: 357 743 040
Address: Japan Arts Corporation, 2-1-6 Shibuya, Shibuya-ku, JP
Description: Based on this strong conviction, we at Japan Arts have been presenting the world's most outstanding cultural and performing arts to audiences in Japan since our company was founded in 1976. In addition, we believe our company has made a contribution, however modest, to international friendship and peace through cultural exchange with countries around the world. Member of IAMA.
Country: Japan
Contact: CEO Masayuki Sekita

Contact: President Eikazu Ouchi
Contact: Director Eiji Sasajima
Email: sasajima@japanarts.co.jp
Social Media: www.facebook.com/japanarts www.instagram.com/japanarts_corptwitter.com/japan_arts

Kojima Concert Management Co. Ltd.
Website: www.kojimacm.com
Email: kojimacm@ops.dti.ne.jp
Phone: 728 872 560
Address: 1-24-7-408 Shinjuku Shinjuku-ku, Tokyo, 160-0022, Japan
Description: Kojima Concert Management Co. Ltd. (KCM), established in 1997, has offices in Tokyo and Osaka, the two largest music markets in Japan. KCM has the largest audience client base among classical music concert management companies in the Kansai region. In recent years, KCM has achieved significant growth in its artist management business, representing many leading Japanese and international artists.
Country: Japan
Social Media: https:// www.facebook.com/kojimaconcertmanagement

Million Concert Co Ltd
Website: www.millionconcert.co.jp
Email: classic@millionconcert.co.jp
Phone: 335 015 638
Address: Grand Suite 702 1-21-10, Toranomon, Minato-ku, JP
Description: Founded in 1956, the Million Concert Association is one of the oldest music agencies in the Japanese classical music management world, boasting a history and track record of over 60 years. They organize performances, plan concerts, productions and manage artists in Japan.
Country: Japan
Type: Classical

Music Plant Co Ltd
Website: www.mplant.co.jp
Phone: 334 662 258
Address: 1-20-15-102 Kitazawa, Setagaya-ku, Tokyo 155-0031
Description: Music Plant invites foreign musicians and plans and organizes classical concerts.
Country: Japan
Type: Classical

Nichicon Concert Society
Website: www.nichicon.blogspot.com
Email: ncs.music@nifty.com
Phone:
Address: 3-11-8 Kyuden, Setagaya-ku, JP
Description: Nichicon Concert Society manages classical and Japanese music concerts and ballet performances, as well as planning and producing for young people. They support important stages with many years of experience and achievements.
Country: Japan

Nippon Artists, Inc
Website: www.nipponartists.jp
Email: info@nipponartists.jp
Phone: 353 777 766
Address: 4-7-1-4 Koenji Minami, Suginami-ku, Tokyo 166-0003
Description: International representation and management services for classical musicians which includes orchestral touring, concert promotion and the co-ordination of festivals
Country: Japan
Type: Classical, Symphonic, Solo/Chamber

Pacific Concert Management
Website: www.pacific-concert.co.jp
Email: info@pacific-concert.co.jp
Phone: 335 523 831
Address: 5F, 2nd Yamauchi Building, 3-10-11 Minato, Chuo-ku, Tokyo 104-0043
Description: Pacific Concert Management would like to respond to various market requests such as inviting top overseas artists, introducing and Managing domestic artists and Managing concerts. They named it "Pacific Concert Management" with the desire to play a part in Artistic and cultural activities in the Pacific Ocean region, including Japan.
Country: Japan
Contact: Managing Director Tamaki Nakao
Type: Classical, Symphonic, Vocal, Wind/brass band, Solo/Chamber, Early

Set Up Co Ltd
Website: www.setup-co.com
Email:
info@setup-co.com
Phone: 359 548 022
Address: 9F, Sunshine City World Import Mart, 3-1-3 Higashi Ikebukuro, Toshima-ku, JP
Description: Manages artists and produces events & concerts.
Country: Japan
Contact: President Yohzo Koike

AGENTS AND MANAGEMENT

Shin-Ensoka Kyokai Concert Management
Website: www.shin-en.jp
Email: desk@shin-en.jp
Phone: 036 384 2498
Address: Ltd.1F, 1F, Ota Paper Koshinjuku Building, 1-10-3 Shinjuku, Shinjuku-ku, Tokyo 160-0022
Description: Mainly deals with Japanese artists; supports young artists by providing them with performing opportunities.
Country: Japan
Contact: President Hirose Mitsuyasu

Sido Music Planning Co Ltd
Website: www.sido-music.com
Email: info@sido-music.com
Phone: 334 656 115
Address: 17-3 Kamiyama-cho, Shibuya-ku, Tokyo 150-0047 Japan
Description: Established in 1975. Work mainly on planning, production and management. For planning and production, handles concerts such as solo, chamber music, orchestra, and for management, dispatches front-line performers in response to a wide variety of requests such as local performances, music appreciation classes for young people in each region, etc.
Country: Japan
Contact: President Mieko Matsuzaki

Suzuki Art Agency Co Ltd
Website: na
Phone: 354 814 600
Address: Setagaya-ku, 5-30 – 6, Tokyo 157-0062 Japan
Description: Commercial promoter in all the performing arts; presenter of overseas material, mainly ballet and classical music.
Country: Japan
Contact: President Akira Suzuki

Tiny Alice
Website: www.tinyalice.net
Email: tokyo@tinyalice.net
Phone: 333 547 307
Address: Koa Bldg., 2-13-6 Shinjuku, Shinjuku-ku Tokyo, 160-0022 Japan
Description: Established in 1983 with the mottos of "discovering unknown talents" and "cross-border exchanges between cities". From the perspective of being a member of Asia, Japan will devote itself to the development, development and popularization of "small theaters / alternative theater".
Country: Japan
Social Media: twitter.com/tokyo_tinyalice

Tokyo Artists Inc
Website: tokyoartists.jimdo.com
Phone: 334 407 571
Address: 108-0064 4-24-41 Takanawa, Minato-ku, Tokyo Fairness Takanawa 101 Japan
Description: Classical music management.
Country: Japan
Contact: Managing Director Toshishi Nakane Nakane

Tokyo Concerts Inc
Website: www.tokyo-concerts.co.jp
Email: info@tokyo-concerts.co.jp
Phone: 332 269 755
Address: 2-3-18, Nishi-Kanda, Shinjuku City, Tokyo 169-0051, Japan
Description: Musician of management, as well as producing music of planning and recording tape, production of record concert, concert planning, construction as well as the box office foreign musicians invited of music production and the reproduction and maintenance management of copyright on music and publishing of advertising planning and production
Country: Japan
Social Media: twitter.com/tokyoconcerts www.facebook.com/tokyoconcerts

REPUBLIC OF KOREA

BOM Arts Project
Website:
www.bomarts.co.kr
Email:
contact@bomarts.co.kr
Phone: 273 70708
Address: #1124 Seongsu Academy Tower, 118 Seongsui-ro, Seongdong-gu
Description: As the arts management agency specialized in performing arts, BOM has conducted various cultural projects regionally, nationally, and internationally. BOM has promoted classical concerts such as Itzhak Perlman, Kevin Kern, Sunwook Kim & Isang Enders Duo, Evergreen Symphony Orchestra Tour in Korea and organized Great Mountains Music Festival for 4 years as well as ISPA Seoul Conference and more. BOM provides high quality services with accumulated experiences and knowledge of arts management. Member of ISPA
Country: Republic of Korea
Social Media: @ARTSManagerBOM www.facebook.com/BOMARTSPROJECT

Coreamuser
Website: www.coreamuser.com
Email: coreamuser@gmail.com
Phone: 707 893 4433
Address: 38 Dongsung 3gil, #211 Jongnogu
Description: As an accomplished music, theatre and dance booking agency based in Seoul, they've been providing international development services for small and mid scale shows since 2009. Their artists perform at a wide variety of events that fans absolutely love.
Country: Republic of Korea
Contact: Owner Chris Ryu
Social Media: @coreamuser www.facebook.com/niceryu

CultureBiz
Website: www.culturebiz.co.kr
Email: cbiz@culturebiz.co.kr
Phone: 270 14879
Address: #805, Sungji Building, 538 Dowha-dong, Mapo-gu
Description: Founded in 2003 as a sponsor of the Korea Women's Businessmen's Association, Cultural Biz Global Co., Ltd. is a culture and arts management company specializing in culture and arts management, and enhance the quality of human life through the distribution of arts and by creating a positive society through its role as a cultural partner of public institutions and corporations.
Country: Republic of Korea
Contact: Director, artist Manager Sunmi Catherine Park
Type: Classical

Korea Arts Management Service
Website: www.gokams.or.kr
Email: kams@gokams.or.kr
Phone: 270 82244
Address: 12F, Hongik University Daehak-ro Campus, 57, Daehak-ro, Jongno-gu
Description: founded in 2006, the KAMS concentrates on provision of supports and services related to international exchange, and on enhancement of the competitiveness of the Korean performing arts. Offers diverse research, consulting and educational programs for those in the field to boost the industrial competitiveness of the Korean arts. Member of ISPA
Country: Republic of Korea
Contact: President Jae-wal Jung
Type: All

The Bridge
Website: www.thebridgekr.com
Email: thebridge@thebridgekr.com
Phone: 260 941 001
Address: 98, Gangseo-ro 62-gil
Description: The Bridge prides itself on propagating classical music that appeals to a broad cross-section of the listening public.
Country: Republic of Korea
Contact: promoter Dongjin Yoon
Email: djyoon@thebridgekr.com
Social Media: www.facebook.com/thebridgekorea
Type: Classical, Symphonic

MACAO

Imagination – Macau
Website: ww.imagination.com
Email: darren.kerr@imagination.com
Phone: 351 31300
Address: Rua De Zangai, No. 175, 11 Andar, K, MO
Description: management for architects, 3D and 2D designers, film makers, journalists, creative technologists, bloggers and social media experts, art Directors and copy writers and creative strategists. Also have offices in Sydney, New York, LA, Stockholm, Detroit, Melbourne, Cologne, Mumbai, Beijing, Shanghai, Hong Kong, Singapore, Tokyo, Toronto, Doha, Moscow, London
Country: Macao
Contact: business Manager Darren Kerr
Email: darren.kerr@imagination.com

MALAYSIA

Betarecs Sdn Bhd
Website: www.betarecs.com.my
Email: info@betarecs.com.my
Phone: 603 209 25516/17
Address: 71-1 & 71-2, Medan Setia 1, Bukit Damansara, MY
Description: Betarecs is an all-in-one audio visual production house that has been actively involved in music, audio and video productions since the 80's. The headquarters in Plaza Damansara Kuala Lumpur covers three floors of office space in a central and easy to access location. The house two full fledged recording studios, 2 midi suites and 3 video editing and post production suites.
Country: Malaysia

Lee Wushu Arts Theatre
Website: www.wushuart.com
Email:
wushuarts@gmail.com
Phone: 751 13013

Address: 159-02, Jalan Bestari 1/5, Taman Nusa Bestari, MY
Description: Wushu (martial arts) management and promotion, (see also Promoter, Producer, Presenter)
Country: Malaysia
Social Media: www.facebook.com/wushuarts

My Performing Arts Agency
Website: www.mypaa.com.my
Email: info@mypaa.com.my
Phone: 362 079 566
Address: B2-06-13A, Solaris Dutamas (Publika), No.1, Jalan Dutamas 1, MY
Description: A member of the International Federation of Arts Councils and Culture Agencies (IFACCA), MyPAA is one of Malaysia's leading cultural and creative industry's development partners that is set up to cultivate an ecosystem in which creative workers are able to do what they do best: tell stories, heal heartbreaks, explore and challenge their creative realms. Member of ISPA
Country: Malaysia
Contact: Director and co-Founder Brian Johnson Lowe
Contact: General Manager Mudzafar Sanusi
Contact: programme Manager Azirah Azman
Social Media: @MYPAAmsia www.facebook.com/MyPerformingArtsAgency/

MEXICO

Conciertos Guadalajara AC
Website:
Phone:
Address: Av. Ju, Ex Convento del Carmen, MX
Description: own opera productions, season from Sept – Nov; see also Opera
Country: Mexico
Contact: Directora Marta Gonz
Type: Classical

Crepaz Music Management – South America
Website:
Email: southamerica@crepazmusic.com
Phone: 525 519 973 300
Address: c/o 33 Visual, S.A. de C.V., Dickens 17 – 1M, Polanco Chapultepec, MX
Description:
Country: Mexico
Contact: contact Martin Vargas

Mr Cane Live Entertainment
Website: www.mrcane.mx
Email: alejandro@mrcane.mx
Phone: null
Address: Hernán Cortés 131, , Lomas Virreyes, , Miguel Hidalgo, CP 11000, Ciudad de, MX
Description: null
Country: Mexico
Social Media: @mrcane_LE

Muchi Music Management
Website: www.muchimusic.com
Email: josemaria@muchimusic.com
Phone: 554 173 5528
Address: Sevilla No. 415, house 4, Col. Portales Norte, MX
Description:
Country: Mexico
Contact: Director Jose-Maria Alvarez
Email: josemaria@muchimusic.com
Contact: assistant Wolfgang Cottom
Email: wolfgang@muchimusic.com
Contact: Manager Alfredo Valencia
Email: alfredovalencia@muchimusic.com
Social Media: MuchiMusicMuchiMusic
Type: Classical

NEW ZEALAND

Maxima Artist Management Ltd
Website: maximaltd.com
Email: info@maximaltd.com
Phone: 210 743 412
Address: 10 Corinth Street, Remuera, NZ
Description: Maxima Artist Management is a limited-roster agency, representing some of New Zealand's most important musicians, and distinguished international artists throughout the Pacific Rim. In 2007 the company began placing artists in China, and now maintains a large network of relationships for touring groups to China from Europe, the US and Australasia, as well as sending Chinese artists and ensembles throughout the world.
Country: New Zealand
Contact: Director John Ballard
Type: Classical

Music Live Ltd.
Website: www.musiclivenz.com
Email: info@musiclivenz.com
Phone: 212 062 651
Address: 108 A Iles Rd, NZ
Description: Music Live is a New Zealand based arts project management company focussing on the development and export of classical music and musicians. Beth Woollacott heads the small team at Music Live

Playmarket
Website: www.playmarket.org.nz
Email: info@playmarket.org.nz
Phone: 438 28462
Address: F5, 99 Queen Street, NZ
Description: The Playmarket Agency issues and manages performance licences, manages royalty payments, circulates plays to Producers and theatres in NZ and internationally, advises on and negotiates agreements, and maintains an archive of playwrights' work and materials related to it.
Country: New Zealand
Contact: Director Murray Lynch
Contact: client promotion Salesi Le'ota
Type: Modern/Contemporary

PHILIPPINES

Midas Promotions Philippines Inc.
Website: www.midaspromotions.com
Email: mel@midaspromotions.com
Phone: 282 49094
Address: 142 Sherwood Heights, Jerusalem Street, PH
Description: Midas Promotions was founded by Michael Hosking in Bahrain in 1978. Nigel Peters became a Director and shareholder in 1986. The company is the largest independent promoter in the Middle East & Southeast Asia for over 30 years.
Country: Philippines
Contact: Director Mel Tyler
Social Media: https:// www.facebook.com/midaspromotions https://twitter.com/midaspromotions https://www.instagram.com/midaspromotions/
Type: Modern/Contemporary, Pops/Light Classical, Pop/Rock

QATAR

Imagination – Qatar
Website: www.imagination.com
Email: adel.noueihed@imagination.com
Phone: 449 54666
Address: Office Number 7, Ground Floor, Al Mirqab Tower, QA
Description: management for architects, 3D and 2D designers, film makers, journalists, creative technologists, bloggers and social media experts, art Directors and copy writers and creative strategists. Also have offices in Sydney, New York, LA, Stockholm, Detroit, Melbourne, Cologne, Mumbai, Beijing, Shanghai, Hong Kong, Singapore, Tokyo, Toronto, London, Moscow, Macau
Country: Qatar
Contact: business Manager Adel Noueihed
Email: adel.noueihed@imagination.com

SINGAPORE

Arsmedia
Website: www.arsmedia.com.sg
Email: sabrina.zuber@arsmedia.com.sg
Phone: 901 86358
Address: 21 Jalan Kelawar, SG
Description: Arsmedia, founded and directed by Sabrina Zuber in 2004, is an agency which offers arts consultancy and education services. When in December 2009 Arsmedia decided to produce the operetta "Belle Epoque!", all performances drew a full house.
Country: Singapore
Contact: Founder and Director Sabrina Zuber
Social Media: www.facebook.com/ARSMEDIA-81847031185

IMG Artists – Singapore
Website: www.imgartists.com
Email: artistsasia@imgartists.com
Phone: 360 031
Address: 100A Amoy Street, SG
Description: IMG Artists is a global leader of performing arts management. For thirty years, the company has set the standard for excellence across the artist management, touring, dance, attractions, festivals, events and cultural consulting fields. IMGA's specialists in offices across three continents offer unparalleled international reach and depth of experience to the company's artists, clients and partners.
Country: Singapore
Contact: senior projects Manager Sharon Tan
Email: stan@imgartists.com
Contact: General Manager Meera Vijayendra
Email: mvijayendra@imgartists.com
Social Media: www.facebook.com/IMGArtistsOfficial/
Type: All

Music and Movement Singapore Pte Ltd
Website: www.musicmovement.com.sg
Email: accounts@musicmovement.com.sg
Phone: 622 77087
Address: 19 Kim Keat Road, #08 – 01 Fu Tsu Building, SG
Description: Music and Movement (M&M) is an events and entertainment company. M&M started out in 1989 with its main focus on artist management, and later expanded out into events management, music production and publishing as well as television and media production

Country: Singapore
Contact: CEO Lim Sek
Social Media: www.facebook.com/musicmovementpteltd

TAIWAN, PROVINCE OF CHINA

CF Koo Foundation
Website: www.koo.org.tw
Email: koo577@ms49.hinet.net
Phone: 225 682 358
Address: Zhongshan North Road, Sec 113 B1
Description: C.F. Koo Foundation, Taiwan, was founded in 1987 by C. F. Koo, Honorary Chairman of Ho-hsin Group, one of the core business clusters in Taiwan. Today, C. F. Koo Foundation, Taiwan, has grown into an NGO of three main business domains: Production, Theater Management, and Theater Consulting. It is the most active NGO in Taiwan's Cultural Scenery, conducting productions and touring of Peking Opera as well as performances of all other forms, house-Managing two public venues in Taipei, and giving consultation to nearly all venues in Taiwan, old and new. Member of ISPA
Country: Taiwan
Contact: production Manager Thomas Liu
Social Media: www.facebook.com/cfkoofoundation

Concertmaster International Artists Management (CMIAM)
Website: www.cmiam.com
Email: info@cmiam.com
Phone: 722 54100
Address: 10F-1, No. 77, Wu-Fu 1st Road, Kaohsiung City
Description: null
Country: Taiwan
Contact: Administration Director Kuan-Pin Chen
Email: info@cmiam.com
Type: Solo/Chamber

National Theater and Concert Hall (NTCH)
Website: www.ntch.edu.tw
Phone: 233 939 888
Address: 21-1 Chung Shan S Rd
Description: the National Chiang Kai Shek Culture Center is the most international and professional theatre in Taiwan. it has received outstanding achievement in elevating local attention in art and has established an international exchange platform as well as cultivated expertise in management skills
Country: Taiwan

UNITED STATES

Global Talent Associates
Website: www.globaltalentassoc.com
Email: info@globaltalentassoc.com
Phone: 212 921 8500
Address: 350 5th Ave #6719 New York, NY 10118, USA
Description: Global Talent Associates specialises Dancers, Mimes & Dance Groups, Popular & Folk, Special Attractions, Theater Productions & Companies and World Music
Country: United States

1st Mark Artists Management LLC
Website: www.1stmarkartists.com
Phone: 212 865 5123
Address: 315 Riverside Drive Suite 10B New York, NY 10025 USA
Description: Mark Smith, President of 1st Mark Artists Management, graduated from UNC Chapel Hill and earned an MFA in Acting from New York University. Founding actor with the Carolina Repertory Company, he performed in New York City in theater, film and television, receiving the SAG's Joseph C. Riley Award for Service.
Country: United States
Contact: President Mark Smith
Email: msmith@1stmars.com

21C Media Group Inc
Website: www.21cmediagroup.com
Email: info@21cmediagroup.com
Phone: 212 245 2110
Address: 200 West 57th Street, Suite 404 New York, NY 10019 USA
Description: 21C Media Group is an independent public relations, Marketing, and consulting firm specialising in classical music and the performing arts. 21C boasts a top-flight global client roster that encompasses leading performing artists and organizations, prominent Fortune 500 companies, and world-renowned nonprofits
Country: United States
Contact: Owner Albert Imperato
Contact: Managing partner Jessica Lustig
Contact: founding partner and Director of public relations Glenn Petry
Contact: Executive Vice President and chief strategy officer Sean Michael Gross
Social Media: https://twitter.com/21cmediagroup https:// www.facebook.com/21cmediagroup https://www.instagram.com/21cmediagroup/

A+K Management
Website: https://apluskmanagement.com/
Email: apluskmngmnt@gmail.com
Phone: null
Address: Pittsburgh, Pensylvania
Description: A+K is a team of arts Managers with expertise and experience in the Japanese and American performing arts. We support artists and arts organizations to find opportunities abroad. Members of ISPA.
Country: United States
Contact: Arts Manager Anna Okuda
Contact: Arts Manager Kanako Hiyama
Social Media: null

Admission Nation, LLC
Website: admission-nation.com
Email: info@admission-nation.com
Phone: 973 567 0712
Address: 41 Watchung Plaza, Suite #82, US
Description: Admission Nation is the first Flamenco talent management agency in the New York area providing professional level, fully insured and incredibly talented Flamenco artists for shows, performances, demonstrations. They work with a hand-selected pool of Flamenco dancers, choreographers, singers and musicians to fulfill your talent and production needs for corporate, school, film, theater, performance or public events. Their mission is to promote education of the gypsy flamenco culture, preserve its history in a modern world, and to produce high-quality, entertaining events around our passion and expertise of Flamenco dance. Member of ISPA
Country: United States
Social Media: www.facebook.com/admissionnation

AEA Consulting
Website: aeaconsulting.com
Email: info@aeaconsulting.com
Phone: 845 765 8100
Address: 380 Main Street, Suite 300 Beacon, New York 12508 USA
Description: AEA Consulting is one of the world's leading cultural consulting firms. Since 1991, they have helped hundreds of cultural organizations, governments, foundations, businesses, and individuals around the world realize the contribution that culture can make to communities. Member of ISPA
Country: United States
Contact: Director Libby Ellis
Social Media: https://twitter.com/aea_consulting

AEG Themestar LLC
Website: www.aegworldwide.com
Email: info@aegthemestar.com
Phone: 213 763 7700
Address: 800 West Olympic Blvd, Suite 305, US
Description: AEG ThemeSTAR is a world-renowned Producer and presenter of family entertainment, touring multiple productions in over 10 languages across 40 countries since 2008. The company has promoted and produced theatrical and arena productions with Walking with Dinosaurs, Cirque Du Soleil, Warner Bros., Nickelodeon, HIT Entertainment, Mattel, and Universal Studios
Country: United States
Contact: chief Executive officer Craig Hortenstine
Social Media: @AEGworldwide www.facebook.com/AEGWorldwide
Type: All

Aeolian Artists International Management, Inc.
Website: www.aeolianartists.com
Email: aeolianartists@yahoo.com
Phone: 917 379 4384
Address: 2nd Floor Suite J234, 244 Fifth Avenue, US
Description: Aeolian Artists International Management, Inc. was founded by artist Manager Ms. Catherine Sidoti. It was created envisioning to help support classically trained musicians and opera singers with the intention to develop prosperous careers in classical music
Country: United States
Contact: President/artist Manager Catherine Sidoti
Type: Classical, Vocal

Agency for Creative Talent Strategies
Website: www.theactsagency.com
Email: meridith@a-c-t-s-inc.com
Phone: 813 924 0675
Address: 14001 Citrus Crest Circle, US
Description: The ACTS Agency is an independent booking agency devoted not only to the Artistic development and vision of its incredibly talented roster of musicians, but to the coordination of the distinct character of each artist to the performance venue that requests them. The ACTS Agency has grown into one of the most innovative leaders in key aspects of the performing arts industry
Country: United States
Contact: President Meridith Hankenson
Email: meridith@a-c-t-s-inc.com
Contact: promotions/contracts Rhys Butler
Email: contracts@a-c-t-s-inc.com
Social Media: @ACTSAGENCY www.facebook.com/Agency-For-Creative-Talent-Strategies
Type: Classical, Vocal, Other

Faster, easier, with Giveo. It's all in the app.

Give. Buy. Help. Waste Less. Save Planet.

Cashless donation fundraising and marketplace app

GIVEO is the new app that is revolutionising fundraising.

Download it for free right now for Apple and Android and start raising money right away.

"It's a very simple way to raise $100 or $100,000. It's just point and click and that's it."

Fundraising expert and arts leader Douglas Evans

More information at **giveo.app** see how simple it is

Albert Kay Associates, Inc. – Concert Artists Management
Website: na
Email: albkayassc@aol.com
Phone: 212 593 1640
Address: 58 W 58th St #31ENew York, NY 10019, USA
Description: Albert Kay Associates, Inc. – Concert Artists Management a major international organisation dealing with classical music performers, has been in existence for the past thirty-eight years. The principal function of Albert Kay Associates is to find engagements for such musicians in all parts of the world
Country: United States
Contact: President Jay Yoo
Type: Classical

Alison Loerke, L.L.C./Alia Agency
Website: www.aliaprod.com
Email: aliaprod@gmail.com
Phone:
Address: 12258 12th Ave NW, Seattle, Washington, 98177, United States
Description: ALIA Prod is Alison Loerke International Artists, a boutique booking and management company dedicated to promoting world class performing artists. The mission of ALIA Prod is to bring the excitement of emerging and legacy artists to North American audiences. We provide cultural engagement via performances, workshops and residencies.
Country: United States
Contact: Director Alison Loerke
Contact: agent Chloe Powell Powel
Email: chloe@aliaprod.com
Social Media: https://twitter.com/aliaprod https://www.facebook.com/alia.prod.3

Alliance Artist Management
Website: www.allianceartistmanagement.com
Email: info@allianceartistmanagement.com
Phone: 212 304 3538
Address: 5030 Broadway, Suite 812, US
Description: Alliance Artist Management's portfolio boasts some of the most distinguished and sought-after ensembles performing today, from its vocal ensembles, string quartets and chamber music groups, to its touring orchestras and attractions. The ensembles of AAM's roster each embody highest Artistic standards, a unique commercial appeal, and bring a distinctive innovation to their particular art form. Member of ISPA.
Country: United States
Contact: President Rob Robbins
Email: rob@allianceartistmanagement.com
Contact: operations Manager Sarah Johnson
Email: sarah@allianceartistmanagement.com
Contact: Director of media & communications Stuart Wolferman
Email: stuart@unfinishedside.com
Social Media: @AllianceAM www.facebook.com/allianceartistmanagement
Type: Baroque, Choral, Classical, Early, Modern/Contemporary, Vocal, Wind/brass band

Alma Artist Booking
Website: www.almaartistbooking.com
Email: steve@almaartistbooking.com
Phone: 248 905 3966
Address: 4921 Leafdale Blvd Royal Oak, MI 48073, USA
Description: Alma is a booking agency that represents the very best in World Music, including Simon Shaheen, Funkadesi, Los Folkloristas and much much more. Its roster reaches from the Middle East to the Mediterranean, from Punjab Province to Mexico, and Texas to Chicago. Member of ISPA.
Country: United States
Contact: Owner Steve Heath
Email: steve@almaartistbooking.com
Social Media: www.facebook.com/AlmaArtistBooking-Management

American International Artists Inc
Website: www.aiartists.com
Email: cynthia@aiartists.com
Phone: 518 686 0972
Address: 356 Pine Valley Road Hoosick Falls, NY 12090 USA
Description: Begun in 1978, American International Artists is an artist management firm devoted to the building and development of international careers of its world-class composers and jazz and classical performers, and to the development and coordination of special projects
Country: United States
Contact: President Cynthia Herbst
Email: Cynthia@aiArtists.com
Social Media: twitter.com/AIArtistsInc www.instagram.com/aiartists/

American String Teachers Association
Website: www.astastrings.org
Email: asta@astaweb.com
Phone: 703 279 2113
Address: 4155 Chain Bridge Road, Fairfax, US

Description: The American String Teachers Association, founded more than 60 years ago, is a membership organisation for string and orchestra teachers and players, helping them to develop and refine their careers. ASTA's members range from budding student teachers to artist-status performers
Country: United States
Contact: Executive Director & CEO Monika Schulz
Email: monika@astaweb.com
Contact: Chief Operating Officer Beth Danner-Knight
Email: beth@astaweb.com
Contact: communications Manager Susan Simolunas
Email: ssimolunas@astaweb.com
Contact: Director of finance Lynn Murphy
Email: lmurphy@astaweb.com
Social Media: @ASTAweb https://www.facebook.com/American-String-Teachers-Association-104343234646
Type: Children/Youth, Classical, Early, Folk/Ethnic/World, Jazz, Pop/Rock, Solo/Chamber, Symphonic

Amethyst Performing Arts International
Website: www.apa-music.com
Email: info@apa-music.com
Phone: 734 604 2828
Address: 3153 Birchwood DrAnn Arbor, MI 48105, USA
Description: Over the years APA Management has established itself as a boutique company specialized in symphonic, operatic, and theatrical productions. APA Management's rapidly growing roster includes conductors, instrumentalists, vocalists, chamber music ensembles, symphony orchestras, and opera productions
Country: United States
Contact: Executive Director Ellin Chu
Type: Classical, Solo/Chamber, Vocal, Symphonic

Anthony George Artist Management
Website: www.operaag.com
Email: operaag@aol.com
Phone: 212 580 1306
Address: 250 West 77th St, US
Description: Anthony George Artist Management, established in 1989, emerged from Anthony George's experience as a singer, actor, voice teacher and from his knowledge of the operatic repertoire. Anthony George's roster of singers include internationally acclaimed artists who have sung with all of the major companies in the U.S. including the Metropolitan Opera, San Francisco Opera, Lyric Opera of Chicago, Los Angeles Opera; and European houses including Royal Opera Covent Garden, l'Opéra de Bastille, Oper Frankfurt, De Munt/La Monnaie, Rome Opera and Gran Teatre del Liceu
Country: United States
Contact: chief officer Anthony George
Email: anthonygeorge@operaag.com
Type: Classical

Antonia Arts Management
Website: www.antoniaarts.org
Email: antoniaarts2@gmail.com
Phone: 914 393 2382
Address: 925 South St, Nashville, TN 37203, USA
Description: Antonia Arts, Inc. Is a Not-for-Profit creative and performing arts organisation that bridges all communications gaps with the enhancement of life for the individual and the community. Antonia's Arts offers an atmosphere that flourishes in creativity and technical excellence
Country: United States
Contact: Director Scarlett Antonia
Social Media: www.facebook.com/AntoniaTheaterArts

AOR Management Inc
Website: www.aormanagement.com
Email: aormanagement@gmail.com
Phone:
206 729 6160
Address: 6910 Roosevelt Way NE PMB 221. Seattle WA 98115 USA
Description: AOR Management Inc offers international management services for classical soloists, singers and conductors. AOR Management Inc has provided international management services for twenty one years. Emphasis is on a high level of promotion and visibility and provides a close working relationship in partnership with each artist, also collaborating with their recording and publishing companies, chamber ensembles, orchestras and festivals. Member of IAMA, League of American Orchestras Chamber Music America, CMA, Association of British Orchestras, ABO Deutsche Orchestertag. DOT
Country: United States
Contact: Director Jenny Rose
Email: aormanagement@gmail.com
Social Media: https://twitter.com/AORManagement www.facebook.com/AORManagement

APA – Agency for the Performing Arts
Website: www.apa-agency.com
Email: jknobbe@apa-agency.com
Phone: 310 888 4200
Address: 405 S Beverly Dr Ste 500 Beverly Hills, CA 90212 USA

Description: Founded in 1962 by former MCA Executives David Baumgarten, Roger Vorce and Harvey Litwin, APA (Agency for the Performing Arts) is one of the largest diversified talent agencies in Los Angeles with headquarters in Beverly Hills, Nashville and New York. They represent artists, performers, brands, intellectual properties and production across all media platforms, including film, television, music, theater, publishing and digital.
Country: United States
Contact: agent Jackie Knobbe
Email: jknobbe@apa-agency.com
Contact: Executive Vice President/Director of music dept Troy Blakely
Contact: President & CEO James Gosnell
Email: jgosnell@apa-agency.com
Social Media: twitter.com/apaagency www.facebook.com/APA-Agency-288387294653225

Ardani Artists Management, Inc.
Website: www.ardani.com
Email: s.danilian@gmail.com
Phone: 212 399 0002
Address: 130 West 56th Street, Floor 5M New York, New York 10019 USA
Description: Ardani Artists was founded in 1990 by Sergei and Gaiane Danilian, two of the most innovative Producers and impresarios of performing arts in the United States and abroad. In their longtime association with Segerstrom Center for the Arts, Ardani Artists has been integral in staging the Center's 2006 Mariinsky Festival, which featured performances by the renowned Russian opera company
Country: United States
Contact: President Sergei Danilian
Email: s.danilian@gmail.com
Social Media: https://twitter.com/ARDANI www.facebook.com/ArdaniArtists
Type: Vocal, Classical, Other

Art Becofsky Associates
Email: cpruzan@aol.com
Phone: 578 95051
Address: 4709 Paradise D, Tiburon, CA 94920, USA
Description: Art Becofsky Associates is a business management consultants company in Tiburon, California. It provides grant-writing, consulting and advisory services to choreographers, dance companies and their organisations
Country: United States
Contact: Director Art Becofsky
Contact: performance Associate Cathy Pruzan
Contact: development Associate Kit Baker
Social Media: www.facebook.com/pages/Art-Becofsky-Associates/122836154412339

ARTRA Artists Management, Inc.
Website: www.artra.com
Email: artra@aol.com
Phone: 312 648 4100
Address: 130 S. Canal St., #211 Chicago, IL 60606 USA
Description: ARTRA Artists Management, Inc. is well known in the music industry for the personalized service they give to artists and presenters. They talk to soloists and Managers daily and listen to what they have to say. They hear artists exPress the need for more performance opportunities, fair wages, and logical routings
Country: United States
Contact: President Robert Bauchens
Contact: President Robert Bauchens Bauchens
Social Media: www.facebook.com/ArtraArtistsMgmt

Arts Management Associates, LLC
Website: www.ama.bz
Email: eric@ama.bz
Phone: 888 660 4333
Address: 118 Castle Cove Ln, Castle Hayne, NC 28429, USA
Description: AMA's mission is to provide exemplary service to both our presenting clients as well as to the diverse roster of talent that we represent. They highly value these relationships and strive to operate with integrity, superior communication and meticulous attention to detail
Country: United States
Contact: President Eric Amada
Email: eric@ama.bz
Contact: Press and Marketing Joy Amada
Email: joy@ama.bz
Social Media: www.facebook.com/artsmanagementAssociates

Arts Management Group, Inc.
Website: www.artsmg.com
Email: info@artsmg.com
Phone: 212 337 0838
Address: 130 West 57th Street Suite 6A New York NY 10019 USA
Description: Arts Management Group, Inc. offers independent services that include theatrical production management, performing artists, designers, technicians, group/corporate Salespeople and General support staff to cultural and not for profit organizations

Country: United States
Contact: Managing Director William Capone
Email: bill@artsmg.com
Contact: Associate booking agent Felipe Nieto Nieto
Email: felipe@artsmg.com
Contact: Associate Arlene Paskalian
Email: arlene@artsmg.com
Social Media: twitter.com/artsmgmtgroup www.facebook.com/artsmanagementgroup/

Associated Solo Artists Inc
Website: www.asoloartists.org
Email: ideas@creativeleaps.org
Phone: 845 469 7254
Address: 88 Hardscrabble Road, Chester, NY 10918 USA
Description: Associated Solo Artists Inc is a world-class performing artists and educators dedicated to improving the quality of thinking and learning by linking the arts with the processes of creativity, problem-solving and leadership development
Country: United States
Contact: President and chief Executive officer John Cimino

Association for Hispanic Classical Theater
Website: www.wordPress.comedias.org
Email: garcia@denison.edu
Phone:
Address: P.O. Box 206. Cabin John, MD 20818 USA
Description: The Association for Hispanic Classical Theater, Inc. was chartered as a non-profit organization in 1984 to promote and foster greater appreciation for Spain's classical drama in production. An international organization, the Association counts among its members literary scholars, theatrical Directors and Producers, teachers, and other aficionados of Spain's Golden Age of Theater.
Country: United States
Contact: President Susan Paun de García
Contact: Vice President Gwyn Campbell
Social Media: www.facebook.com/Association-for-Hispanic-Classical-Theater-388871281467

Baylin Artists Management
Website: www.baylinartists.com
Email: mbaylin@baylinartists.com
Phone: 215 275 0268
Address: 412 Linden Avenue Doylestown, PA 18901 USA
Description: Baylin Artists Management (est.1993) is a full-service agency Managing the careers, project development, and touring of more than twenty-five professional musicians, ensembles, theater companies, dance companies and family artists. A well-respected name in the industry, our roster consists of several award-winning artists who have performed at the nation's most prominent venues and festivals.
Country: United States
Contact: artist representative Jaymi Gilmour
Email: jgilmour@baylinartists.com
Contact: President Marc Baylin
Email: mbaylin@baylinartists.com
Contact: artist services Manager Jessica Cimini
Email: jcimini@baylinartists.com
Social Media: https://twitter.com/baylin_artists https://www.facebook.com/baylin.artists https:// www.instagram.com/baylinartists/
Type: Classical, Other

Bernstein Artists
Website: www.bernsarts.com
Email: sue@bernsarts.com
Phone: 347 866 6066
Address: 898 Union St. – 3B Brooklyn, NY 11215 USA
Description: Bernstein Artists is on a mission. Dedicated to the development and advancement of artists seeking to extend the boundaries of their given genres, our roster embraces a broad spectrum of arts, from new music to contemporary music theater, early music, theater and jazz
Country: United States
Contact: President Sue Bernstein
Email: sue@bernsarts.com
Contact: Associate Roarke Menzies
Email: roarke@bernsarts.com
Social Media: twitter.com/bernsartsinc www.facebook.com/Bernstein-Artists-60553839735/
Type: Early, Classical, Jazz, Other

Bess Pruitt & Associates, Inc.
Website: www.uniqueartists.com
Email: besspam795@aol.com
Phone: 718 589 0400
Address: 819 E 168th Street, US
Description: Bess Pruitt & Associates, Inc. specialises children, Choreographers, Stage Directors & Producers Dancers, Mimes & Dance GroupsDuos, Classical Jazz & Blues, Narrators & Actors, Popular & Folk, Special Attractions, Vocalist, Classical, Solo, and World Music
Country: United States
Contact: President Bess Pruitt
Contact: Vice President Henry Pruitt
Contact: office Manager Ataahua Papa
Type: Children/Youth, Folk/Ethnic/World, Historic/Authentic, Modern/Contemporary, Vocal

Big League Theatricals, Inc.
Website: www.bigleague.org
Email: Generalinfo@bigleague.org
Phone: 212 575 1601
Address: 630 9th Ave #900New York, NY 10036, USA
Description: Big League is celebrating its 28th season of producing, General Managing and booking Broadway musicals and special attractions for touring throughout North America
Country: United States
Contact: Director of booking John Starr
Email: jstarr@bigleague.org
Contact: President and Executive Producer Daniel Sher
Email: dsher@bigleague.org
Contact: Associate General Manager Ashley Mikel Mikel
Email: amikel@bigleague.org
Contact: coo Tim Hurley Hurley
Email: thurley@bigleague.org

Booking Group, The
Website: www.thebookinggroup.com
Email: rrundle@thebookinggroup.com
Phone: 212 869 9280
Address: 501 Broadway, 24th Floor, New York, NY 10036
Description: The Booking Group, (TBG), is Broadway's premiere booking agency representing more than 18 Tony Award winning best musicals and plays since its inception in 1996. TBG has booked several long running tours such as the "Best Musical of the Century" The Book of Mormon, the most Tony Award winning musical in history Mel Brooks' The Producers, the worldwide hit Mamma Mia!, and the groundbreaking musical Rent. TBG is committed to bringing the best of Broadway to North America and beyond
Country: United States
Contact: business Manager Tamisty Ivory
Email: tivory@thebookinggroup.com
Contact: President Meredith Blair
Email: mblair@thebookinggroup.com
Contact: Vice President, operations Kara Gebhart
Email: kgebhart@thebookinggroup.com
Social Media: www.facebook.com/tbgtours

Brad Simon Organization Inc, The
Website: www.bsoinc.com
Email: brad@bsoinc.com
Phone: 212 730 2132
Address: 2 Klarides Village Dr, #337 Seymour, CT 06483 USA
Description: For three decades, the goal of The Brad Simon Organization has been to provide an array of unique and innovative productions and performing artists to presenters and their audiences. Since 1983, they have provided tour booking services for a diverse roster of artists and productions in a wide variety of performance venues, including performing art centers, commercial theaters, amphitheaters, arenas, festivals, fairs and theme parks
Country: United States
Contact: President Brad Simon
Email: brad@bsoinc.com
Contact: President Barbara Simon
Email: barbara@bsoinc.com
Contact: agent Irene Pazzani
Email: irene@bsoinc.com

Bridge Records Inc.
Website: www.bridgerecords.com
Email: bridgerec@bridgerecords.com
Phone: 914 654 9270
Address: 200 Clinton Avenue, US
Description: Bridge's recordings have had considerable critical success, earning over thirty Grammy and Latin Grammy nominations, three Grammy awards, three MIDEM Awards, five ASCAP 'Deems Taylor Awards', as well as more than 200 awards and citations from publications worldwide, including the New York Times, Gramophone, BBC Music Magazine, Repertoire, International Record Review, the Guardian, the Financial Times, and many others
Country: United States
Contact: Founder and Director David Starobin
Contact: President Becky Starobin
Contact: Vice President Robert Starobin
Social Media: twitter.com/bridgerecords www.facebook.com/BridgeRecordsInc

Bronitsky and Associates
Website: www.bronitskyandAssociates.com
Email: info@bronitskyandAssociates.com
Phone: 505 238 3739
Address: 216 Edith SE, US
Description: Bronitsky and Associates are able to provide to the organization and event with proven quality traditional and contemporary artists, performers and groups from around the world. They also able to facilitate live performances as a part of your program and organize and manage touring opportunities either to your event or taking your act internationally
Country: United States
Contact: Founder/President Gordon Bronitsky

Email: g.bronitsky@att.net

Brumfield & Associates
Website: www.brumfieldAssociates.com
Email: april@brumfieldAssociates.com
Phone: 859 893 0621
Address: 1430 Union City Road, Richmond, Kentucky 40475
Description: Brumfield & Associates is a small boutique agency devoted to a personal, hands-on style of artist management and booking. They represent renowned jazz trombonist Wycliffe Gordon and Pops Organist/Pianist Timothy Brumfield to name a few.
Country: United States
Contact: Managing Director, Founder April Brumfield
Email: april@brumfieldAssociates.com

Burgess Management
Website: www.burgessmgmt.com
Email: robin@burgessmgmt.com
Phone: 504 309 0648
Address: 6 Park Island Drive New Orleans, New Orleans 70122
Description: Burgess Management is an artist management company, structured to provide the full complement of professional services necessary to manage jazz artists
Country: United States
Contact: tour Manager Tondrae Kemp
Email: tondrae@gmail.com
Contact: Marketing Manager Laura Tennyson
Email: lauratennyson_2@msn.com
Contact: President Robin Burgess
Email: robin@burgessmgmt.com
Social Media: https://twitter.com/burgessmgmt
Type: Jazz

Cadence Arts Network, Inc.
Website: www.cadencearts.com
Email: rachel@cadencearts.com
Phone: 310 701 9191
Address: 478 Humboldt Loop Rd, Whitethorn, CA 95589
Description: Celebrating 33 years of service in the performing arts field, Cadence Arts Network, Inc. continues to proudly offer a variety of networking, consulting, coaching, and educational services to artists, agents, Managers, presenters, and students. Cadence includes an international roster of Dance, Cirque, Music and Theater artists, and is best known for mentoring and connecting emerging and established performing artists with North American presenters.
Country: United States
Contact: President Rachel Cohen
Email: rachel@cadencearts.com
Contact:
Social Media: https:// www.facebook.com/CadenceArtsNetwork https:// www.instagram.com/cadenceartsnetwork/ https://twitter.com/cadencearts?lang=en
Type: Jazz, Folk/Ethnic/World, Vocal, Historic/Authentic

Cadenza Artists
Website: www.cadenzaartists.com
Email: info@cadenzaartists.com
Phone: 310 896 8527
Address: 12021 Wilshire Blvd #710 Los Angeles, CA 90049, USA
Description: Cadenza Artists is a powerful collective of authentic, passionate and artist-centered professionals who innovate and curate bold Artistic experiences in partnership with leading arts presenters and institutions, diverse communities, and creative spaces globally.
Country: United States
Contact: CEO and principal Manager Julia Torgovitskaya
Email: julia@cadenzaartists.com
Contact: co-Founder Jennifer Rosenfeld
Email: jennifer@cadenzaartists.com
Contact: Vice President of booking and tour development Benjamin Cohen
Email: ben@cadenzaartists.com
Social Media: twitter.com/cadenzaartist www.facebook.com/CadenzaArtists/

California Artists Management
Website: www.calartists.com
Email: camdon@aol.com
Phone: 415 362 2787
Address: 449 Springs Road Vallejo, CA 94590 USA
Description: California Artists Management has over thirty-five years of experience representing an internationally renowned roster of performing artists to presenters throughout the world. Donald E. Osborne and Susan Endrizzi Morris came together professionally in 1982, and have since been Managing performers, booking concerts, negotiating contracts, and producing national tours for a distinguished international roster of classical chamber ensembles, orchestras and choirs, instrumentalists, singers, new theater artists and world music
Country: United States
Contact: Director Donald Osborne
Email: camdon@aol.com
Contact: Director Susan Endrizzi Morris

Email: sue.endrizzi@gmail.com
Social Media: www.facebook.com/CaliforniaArtists-Management
Center for Black Music Research
Website: www.colum.edu
Phone: 312 369 7559
Address: Columbia College, 600 South Michigan Avenue, US
Description: Center for Black Music Research (CBMR) holds materials highlighting the role of black music in world culture with materials originating or representing black music in the United States, Africa, Europe, Latin America, and the Caribbean in a variety of formats: personal papers, scores, sheet music, audio-visual materials, photographs, books, periodicals, and commercial recordings.
Country: United States
Social Media: @cbmrccc www.facebook.com/centerfor-blackmusicresearch

Centre Stage Artists
Website: www.centerstageartists.com
Email: info@centerstageartists.com
Phone: 562 607 7871
Address: P.O. Box 7023 Ann Arbor, MI 48107 USA
Description: Center Stage Artists is a booking agency representing performing artists and attractions for entertainment in colleges, performing art centers, festivals, corporate events, symphony pops, clubs and schools.
Country: United States
Contact: President and agent Judy Valenti
Email: maryb@centerstageartists.com

Chaplin Entertainment Inc.
Website: www.chaplinentertainment.com
Email: randy@chaplinentertainment.com
Phone: 212 695 8888
Address: 650 Broadway, Suite 303, US
Description: Chaplin Entertainment Inc. is considered one of the premier boutique agencies specializing in booking contemporary music artists to perform individually tailored programs with symphony orchestras throughout North America
Country: United States
Contact: President Randy Chaplin
Email: randy@chaplinentertainment.com
Contact: agent Ross Atamin
Email: ross@chaplinentertainment.com
Type: Jazz, Modern/Contemporary, Pops/Light classical, Pop/Rock, Symphonic

Chesapeake International Artists
Website: www.chesapeakearts.org
Email: info@chesapeakearts.org
Phone: 410 886 2790
Address: 1371 Ferry Landing Road P.O. Box I Tilghman, MD, 21671 USA
Description: Chesapeake International Artists is a management company that represents musical performers, conductors and composers
Country: United States
Contact: Founder Robert Jones
Email: bob@chesapeakeartists.com
Contact: booking Associate Susan Jones
Email: susan@chesapeakeartists.com
Social Media: https://twitter.com/chesapeakeia www.facebook.com/ChesapeakeInternationalArts/
Type: Classical

CHL Artists Inc
Website: www.chlartists.com
Email: chris@chlartists.com
Phone: 818 501 0240
Address: 13547 Ventura Blvd. #192 , 13547 Ventura Blvd, Suite 192, US
Description: CHL Artists Inc is a talent management company located in Sherman Oaks, California. They manages different talents in the field of comedy, music, acting, playing instruments like violin, musician and etc
Country: United States
Contact: President/CEO Christopher H Ling
Contact: advertising Jet Boden
Type: Classical

Christians In Theater Arts (CITA)
Website: www.cita.org
Email: information@cita.org
Phone:
Address: PO Box 26471, US
Description: Christians In Theatre Arts (CITA) has been organized to give Christians a world-wide support network of other believers who are also theatre artists. CITA exists so that working and established artists (in academic, non profit and for profit companies) have a space and time for continuing education, professional encouragement and Artistic and spiritual inspiration
Country: United States
Contact: Executive Director Dale Savidge
Email: exec@cita.org
Contact: administrator Luann Jennings
Email: admin@cita.org
Social Media: www.facebook.com/citheatre

Circuit Network

Website: www.circuitnetwork.com
Email: info@circuitnetwork.com
Phone: 415 863 2441
Address: 499 Alabama Street, Suite 203, San Francisco, CA 94110 US
Description: Circuit Network was founded in 1984 by four contemporary solo choreographers seeking joint management services. By 1987, each of these artists had acquired the infrastructure to produce their home seasons and independently manage their organizations
Country: United States
Contact: Director Nola Mariano
Contact: co-Director Elisabeth Beaird

Class Acts on Tour
Website: www.classactsontour.com
Email: margiecaot@gmail.com
Phone: 252 202 0865
Address: PO Box 653, Hampstead Maryland 21074 USA
Description: This is a full service artist support agency, offering booking, management, Marketing and web design services.They develop CDs, books, teaching materials and other artist driven publications as well as producing unique opportunities to study with master teachers in beautiful settings, from week-long artist-in-residence programs to intimate weekend retreats
Country: United States
Contact: Executive Director Margie T Farmer
Email: margiecaot@gmail.com
Social Media: www.facebook.com/ClassActsOnTour/
Type: Classical, Jazz, Vocal, Other

CM Artists New York
Website: www.cmartists.com
Email: lymarder@aol.com
Phone: 212 864 1005
Address: 127 W 96th Street, Suite 13B, US
Description: CM Artists New York provides artist representation for a select group of American and European based classical musicians. Member of IAMA.
Country: United States
Contact: Manager Linda Marder
Email: lymarder@aol.com
Contact: Manager Charles Cumella
Email: ccumella@aol.com
Type: Classical

Colbert Artists Management, Inc.
Website: www.colbertartists.com
Email: publicity@colbertartists.com
Phone: 212 757 0782
Address: 307 Seventh Avenue, Suite 2006, US
Description: Colbert Artists Management, Inc. represents a list of vocal and instrumental soloists, conductors and chamber music groups. Member of IAMA.
Country: United States
Contact: publicity Emily Motherwell
Email: publicity@colbertartists.com
Contact: vice-President Christina Putnam
Email: putnam@colbertartists.com
Contact: President Charlotte Schroeder
Email: schroeder@colbertartists.com
Contact: senior Manager Lee Prinz
Email: prinz@colbertartists.com
Social Media: @ColbertArtists www.facebook.com/colbertartists
Type: Classical

Concerted Efforts
Website: www.concertedefforts.com
Email: concerted@concertedefforts.com
Phone: 617 969 0810
Address: PO Box 440326 Somerville MA, USA 02144
Description: Concerted Effforts is proud to exclusively represent an outstanding roster of some of the foremost artists in world music, zydeco, blues, folk, country, gospel, jazz, and singer/songwriters
Country: United States

Creative Booking Agency
Website: creativebookingagency.com
Email: info@creativebookingagency.com
Phone: 212 758 8064
Address: 6 East 45th Street, 10th Floor, New York, NY 10017 USA
Description: Christine L. Barkley, a 17-year music industry veteran, has created Creative Booking Agency (CBA), a full-service talent agency based in New York. Before forming her agency, Barkley was VP and head of the New York office of the Agency for the Performing Arts (APA) where for the past seven years she led a successful turnaround of APA's core business into the performing arts market
Country: United States
Contact: President and chief Executive officer Christine Barkley
Email: cbarkley@creativebookingagency.com
Social Media: twitter.com/CreativeBooking www.facebook.com/CreativeBookingAgency

Creative Realization Group
Website: www.creativerealizationgroup.org
Email: ryun@creativerealizationgroup.org

Phone: 347 449 3532
Address: 2246 43rd Street , Astoria, NY 11105
Description: Creative Realization Group was founded in 2015 to serve a national community of artists and arts organisations in the creation of new Artistic work and its dissemination. CRG nourishes and cultivates the appreciation and understanding of artists, their work and its impact on the well-being of society. Member of ISPA,
Country: United States
Contact: Executive Director Ryun Schienbein
Email: ryun@creativerealizationgroup.org
Contact: Managing Director Theresa Perez
Email: theresa@theresaperez.com

Cryptogramophone
Website: www.cryptogramophone.com
Phone: 310 287 1918
Address: 8642 1/2 Venice Blvd, US
Description: Cryptogramophone presents artists like Nels Cline, Bennie Maupin, Alex Cline, Jenny Scheinman, Todd Sickafoose, Myra Melford, Zeena Parkins, Mark Dresser, and other musicians who explore the far reaches of Artistic vision and instrumental technique. Cryptogramophone is all about creativity, emotion and technique coming together in the moment – – the moment when composition and improvisation meet to create art.
Country: United States
Contact: President Jeff Gauther
Social Media: www.facebook.com/cryptogramophone www.twitter.com/cryptogramophon

Dance Films Association, Inc.
Website: www.dancefilms.org
Email: info@dancefilms.org
Phone: 212 727 0764
Address: 75 Broad Street, # 304 New York, NY 10004 USA
Description: Is the catalyst for the production, presentation, and preservation of dance on camera. They are dedicated to furthering the art of dance film by connecting artists and organizations, fostering new works for new audiences, and sharing essential resources.
Country: United States
Contact: Executive Director Beni Matias
Social Media: https:// www.facebook.com/dancefilms https:// www.instagram.com/dancefilms/ https://twitter.com/DanceFilms

David Belenzon Management, Inc.
Website: www.belenzon.com
Email: david@belenzon.com
Phone: 858 832 8380
Address: P.O. Box 5000, PMB 67 Rancho Santa Fe, CA 92067
Description: David Belenzon Management, Inc. Represents world class artists and attractions for theatres, symphony orchestras, casinos, performing arts and more. David's dedication to clients is evidenced by the many long-term relationships. That's why buyers keep coming back
Country: United States
Contact: President David Belenzon
Email: david@belenzon.com
Social Media: https://twitter.com/belenzon www.facebook.com/BelenzonManagement

David Lieberman Artists' Representatives
Website: www.dlartists.com
Email: david@dlartists.com
Phone: 714 979 4700
Address: 2900 Bristol St Suite C-202 Costa Mesa, CA 92626 USA
Description: David Lieberman Artists' Representatives supports a carefully curated roster of fine performing artists from a diverse collection of disciplines. It works to facilitate meaningful DIALOGUE between these artists and the presenters who would engage them to work on their stages and in their communities. Member of ISPA.
Country: United States
Contact: President David Lieberman
Email: david@dlartists.com
Contact: Director of touring and artist management Allen Moon
Email: allen@dlartists.com
Contact: Director of Marketing and new media Amanda Bryant
Email: amanda@dlartists.com
Contact: touring Associate Marcela Giannini
Email: marcela@dlartists.com
Contact: artist Manager, touring & booking Andrew Glick
Email: andrew@dlartists.com
Social Media: www.facebook.com/DLAR.Inc www.instagram.com/david_lieberman_artists

Dietsch Artists International
Website: www.dietschartists.com
Email: dietsch@dietschartists.com
Phone: 973 763 8836
Address: 143 S Centre St South Orange, New Jersey 07079 USA
Description: They represent opera singers internationally, with 6 offices throughout the world. They also work

with young artists to give them direction and guidance for the beginning of their careers

Dispeker Artists, Inc.
Website: www.dispeker.com
Email: office@dispeker.com
Phone: 212 421 7676
Address: 195 Chrystie Street Suite 809J New York, NY 10002
Description: This is a leading classical music artist management firm since 1947. The firm was founded by the late Thea Dispeker who represented some of the most notable names in classical music, including Richard Tucker, Martina Arroyo, Judith Blegen, Roberta Peters, Jan Peerce, Hermann Prey, Pablo Casals and Wieland Wagner among many others. Member of IAMA
Country: United States
Contact: Director Emmy Tu
Email: emmy@dispeker.com
Contact: booking representative Miles Greenberg
Email: miles@dispeker.com
Contact: Director of operations Julian Waddell Waddell
Email: operations@dispeker.com
Contact: consultant Stephen Lugosi
Social Media: twitter.com/dispekerartists www.facebook.com/Dispeker

E, A and G Sharp
Website: www.eagsharp.com
Email: eagsharp@eagsharp.com
Phone:
Address: 711 Amsterdam Avenue, Suite 18 K, New York, N.Y. 10025
Description: Artists Manager – classical music.
Country: United States
Contact: contact Mario Lopez

Elisa Wagner/International Creative Productions
Website: www.elisawagnericp.com
Email: elisa@elisawagnericp.com
Phone: 212 861 6468
Address: 167 East 67th Street, US
Description: Elisa Wagner/International Creative Productions is considered one of the finest production companies for concert and recitals in Mexico, Central and South America. Since 1989, Elisa Wagner has successfully brought the very highest caliber of classical artists to the continents' most prestigious venues, all overseen with her unique blend of professionalism and the personal touch. Member of ISPA.
Country: United States
Contact: Owner Elisa Wagner
Social Media: @ElisaWagnerICP www.facebook.com/ewicp
Type: Choral, Jazz, Modern/Contemporary, Pop/Rock, Vocal, Other

Elsie Management
Website: www.elsieman.org
Email: info@elsieman.org
Phone: 718 797 4577
Address: 132 Prospect Pl. #2R Brooklyn, NY 11217 USA
Description: Promotes the careers of national and international performing arts companies on stages and performance opportunities across the globe. Offering a combination of management and development services, along with artist representation. Member of ISPA.
Country: United States
Contact: Director Laura Colby
Email: laura@elsieman.org
Contact: Vice President Anna Amadei
Email: annaa@elsieman.org
Social Media: https://twitter.com/elsieman https://www.facebook.com/ElsieManagement https:// www.instagram.com/elsiemgmt/

Entourage Talent Associates
Website: www.entouragetalent.com
Email: Administration@entouragetalent.com
Phone: 212 633 2600
Address: 150 West 28th Street, Suite 1503, US
Description: Entourage Talent Associates, Ltd. is a music talent agency and consulting firm which exclusively represents a select number of clients (both domestically and worldwide), services promoters and concert venues throughout the world, and offers fee-based consulting services for the entertainment industry
Country: United States
Contact: President Wayne Forte
Email: wayne@entouragetalent.com
Contact: booking agent Nathaniel Marro
Email: nathaniel@entouragetalent.com
Contact: office administrator and assistant tour coordinator Deborahlee Tirone
Email: deb@entouragetalent.com
Social Media: https://twitter.com/EntourTal https://www.facebook.com/EntourageTalentAssociates

Eye for Talent Inc
Website: www.eyefortalent.com
Email: staff@eyefortalent.com
Phone: 650 595 2274
Address: P.O. Box 280786. San Francisco, CA 94128 USA
Description: Eye for Talent is a world music talent agency

based in the San Francisco Bay Area. They specialize in global music, representing artists from around the world whose music reflects their traditional culture.
Country: United States
Contact: talent Manager Bill Smith
Social Media: https://twitter.com/eyefortalent www.facebook.com/eftworldmusic

Fas Arts Management
Website: www.fasartsmanagement.com
Email: felipe@fasartsmanagement.com
Phone: 718 799 5163
Address: 230 Ashland Pl # 26B, New York, NY, United States, New York
Description: FAS ARTS Management is a New York based arts management company dedicated to bringing world class productions of classical music, dance, avant-garde theater, and world music to the stage. With extensive experience touring and booking in North America, FAS has established solid relationships with local venues, Producers, promoters, arts management companies and sponsors
Country: United States
Social Media: https://twitter.com/FasArtsMgmt https://www.facebook.com/fasartsmanagement/

Firebird Artists Management, Inc
Website:
Email: firebirdart@juno.com
Phone: 410 560 2142
Address: 132 Tregarone Road, US
Description: Firebird Artists Management, Inc represents artist in theater, comedy, classical music, pianist, performing arts. The company is committed to provide quality talent fit for the ocassion
Country: United States
Contact: President Gregory Kuperstein
Type: Classical

Frankel Green Theatrical Management
Website: www.rfpny.com
Email: interncoordinator@frankelgreen.com
Phone: 212 302 5559
Address: 254 W 54th St 10th Floor New York, NY 10019, USA
Description: Richard Frankel Productions Inc. has been an independent theatrical production and General management company since 1985. With partners Marc Routh, Thomas Viertel, and Steven Baruch, RFP produces and General manages plays and musicals, acts as General Manager and/or Executive Producer for other Producers, and provides integrated production, management, and Marketing services through on-site staff, subsidiaries, and affiliated providers.
Country: United States
Contact: Founder Laura Green

Frontera Arts
Website: www.fronteraarts.com
Email: lynn@fronteraarts.com
Phone: 512 261 6979
Address: 3102 Lakeway Blvd Austin, TX 78734, USA
Description: Frontera Arts is an innovative consulting, booking and project management company that explores the performing arts by nurturing and maintaining relationships and creating connections in the field. Having worked with gifted artists over many years Lynn Fisher was inspired to create Frontera Arts as a means to facilitate and deepen an open, ongoing dialogue among audiences and artists in the Americas. Embracing cultural differences and commonalities, Frontera Arts is committed to finding new pathways that lead to opportunities for cross cultural communication, collaboration, exchange and creation. Member of ISPA.
Country: United States
Contact: Director Lynn Fisher
Email: lynn@fronteraarts.com
Social Media: https:// www.facebook.com/fronteraarts/

GAMI/Simonds, Inc.
Website: www.gamisimonds.com
Email: laurelle@att.net
Phone: 860 567 2500
Address: 42 County Rd Morris, CT 06763 USA
Description: GAMI/Simonds, LLC is a full service management and booking agency founded and based in Morris, CT, with a western U.S. office located in Portland, OR. Directors Laurelle Favreau and Don Verdery have each been passionately working in Arts Management for over three decades
Country: United States
Contact: Director Laurelle Favreau
Email: laurelle@att.net
Contact: Director Don Verdery
Social Media: www.facebook.com/GAMISimonds-LLC-Performing-Arts-Management-111512778883877

Gardner Arts Network, Inc.
Website: www.gardnerartsnetwork.com
Email: info@gardnerartsnetwork.com
Phone: 212 496 9121
Address: 155 West 72nd Street, Suite 604, US
Description: GARDNER ARTS NETWORK represents a

wide variety of Dance, Theatre, Music and Family/Young Audiences companies

Country: United States
Contact: President Jeannette Gardner
Email: jgardner@gardnerartsnetwork.com
Type: Children/Youth, All

George M Martynuk Artists Management and Public Relations/Publicity
Website: www.georgemartynuk.com
Email: georgemartynuk@msn.com
Phone: 212 831 9599
Address: 64 East 94th Street, US
Description: For many years, George Martynuk was the Public Relations/Publicity Manager for the Herbert Breslin office, the agency for Luciano Pavarotti and other famous singers. For the past 13 years he has run his own successful Public Relations and Publicity firm, GMM INC. Through a smart Public Relations program, we can increase the name recognition of artists by arranging interviews in such publications as America's Opera News, Musical America, Classical Singer, and Fanfare; England's Opera Now, Opera, Gramophone, and Classical Music; Germany's Das Opernglas, Opernwelt, and Orpheus International; France's Le Monde de la Musique, and Crescendo; and Spain's Opera Actual; and many others
Country: United States
Contact: President George M Martynuk
Social Media: @georgemartynuk www.facebook.com/george.martynuk
Type: Classical, Vocal

Golden Land Concerts & Connections, Inc.
Website: www.goldenland.com
Email: concerts@goldenland.com
Phone: 917 689 0890
Address: 118 East 28th Street – Suite 306 New York, NY 10016 USA
Description: This is a booking agency for Jewish music and performing arts. The agency represent artists who have made enormous contributions to the cultural wealth of Jewish communities worldwide, as well as many who have achieved international acclaim and popularity in the mainstream world
Country: United States
Contact: President Moishe Rosenfeld
Social Media: www.facebook.com/pages/Golden-Land-Concerts-Connections/137610399649122

Great Lakes Performing Artist Associates
Website: www.greatlakespaa.org
Email: glpaaoffice@gmail.com
Phone: 734 665 4029
Address: 415 N. 4th Avenue, US
Description: Great Lakes Performing Artist Associates is a unique non-profit arts organization and was founded in 1978. Its mission is to encourage the cultural and Artistic development of the Great Lakes region by supporting the performance careers of exceptional regional artists
Country: United States
Contact: President Susan Darrow
Email: glpaaDirector@gmail.com
Contact: Executive Director Aileen Rohwer
Social Media: @glpaatweet www.facebook.com/Great-Lakes-Performing-Artist-Associates-209706117756
Type: Classical, Solo/Chamber

GSI Artists
Website: www.gsiartists.com
Email: info@gsiartists.com
Phone: 908 608 1325
Address: 12 Princeton Street Summit, NJ 07901 USA
Description: This is a full service Performing Arts consultancy established to meet the needs of today's concert artists. They offer a unique, diverse range of services and work with each artist to design a personalized program that fulfills distinct strategic goals. Their programmes include a combination of the following disciplines: Publicity, Career Management, Emerging Media Investigation, Creative And Strategic Marketing, Educational And Outreach Consulting, Program Advisory Services, Logistics Coordination, Special Events Planning, Writing Services and Web Design & Promotion.
Country: United States
Contact: Vice President Ann Rosenblum
Contact: President Genevieve Spielberg
Contact: office Manager Toni Rhatican
Social Media: https:// www.facebook.com/gsiartists/

Gurtman & Murtha Associates
Website: www.gmartists.com
Email: jimmurtha87@gmail.com
Phone: 212 967 7350
Address: One Penn Plaza 36th Floor New York, New York 10119 USA
Description: Gurtman and Murtha opened its doors as a public relations organization, representing many of the world's great artists, attractions, and cultural institutions. Through the years, they added the services necessary to foster the growth of artists and the expansion of the business.
Country: United States

Contact: President Jim Murtha Sr.
Email: jimmurtha87@gmail.com
Contact: Associate Director Bill Weir
Email: Weir@GMArtists.com
Contact: Associate Director Jim Murtha Jr.
Email: JMurtha457@aol.com
Contact: Associate Director Katisha Bennett
Email: Katisha@GMArtists.com
Social Media: www.facebook.com/Gurtman-and-Murtha-Artists-125087032795/
Type: Choral, Classical

Guy Barzilay Artists
Website: www.guybarzilayartists.com
Email: guy@guybarzilayartists.com
Phone: 212 741 6118
Address: 269 Townsend Road Bovina Center, NY 13740 USA
Description: Heralded as one of the world's leading independent artist management agencies, Guy Barzilay Artists, Inc. continues to thrive under the dynamic leadership of President Guy Barzilay and Artist Manager Kristin Cowdin as the company enters its 18th season. They remain committed to the intensive development of a select roster and understand the complete and detailed involvement that is imperative to success in building and shaping international careers that encompass the realms of both opera and concert repertoire.
Country: United States
Contact: President Guy Barzilay
Email: guy@guybarzilayartists.com
Contact: Associate artist Manager Michael Denos
Email: michael@guybarzilayartists.com
Social Media: twitter.com/BarzilayArtists www.facebook.com/GuyBarzilayArtists

H-Art Management
Website: www.h-artmanagement.com
Email: info@h-artmanagement.com
Phone: 212 868 2134
Address: The Arts Building, 336 West 37th Street, Suite 1420, US
Description: H-Art Management is a full-service agency for touring theatre, dance & music companies. Harold Norris established H-Art Management in July 2002 as a full-service agency for touring performing arts companies in America and abroad, and for successful artists and collaborations that H-Art has overseen since the company began.
Country: United States
Contact: President Harold Norris
Email: harold@h-artmanagement.com
Contact: Associate Ichun Yeh
Email: ichun@h-artmanagement.com

Harwood Management Group, Inc
Website: harwood-management.com
Email: harwoodmanagement@gmail.com
Phone: 212 864 0773
Address: PO Box 1337 Olivebridge, NY 12461 USA
Description: This innovative Arts Management Organization manages the careers of Classical Singers (sopranos, mezzo-sopranos, tenors, baritones, basses) in: Opera, Orchestra / Choral Works, Recitals, Concerts, Cross-Over / Musical Theater Performers in: Broadway, Off-Broadway, Touring Productions, Pops Concerts, as well as Conductors and Stage Directors for all of the aforementioned venues. In addition this corporation serves as Artistic Consultants, Artistic Administrators and Producers for Performing Arts Festivals, Music Series, Musical Shows, Chamber Music Groups, and Individual Musical Artists.
Country: United States
Contact: President James Harwood
Email: jim@harwood-management.com

Hendrickson Artists Management
Website:
Email: wrhmgt@aol.com
Phone: 352 237 2421
Address: P.O Box 771688, US
Description: Hendrickson Artists Management specialises in Choreographers, Stage Directors & Producers and Vocal & Vocal/Instrumental Groups
Country: United States
Type: Classical, Vocal

Herschel Freeman Agency Inc
Website: www.herschelfreemanagency.com
Email: hfreeman@herschelfreemanagency.com
Phone: 901 757 4567
Address: 7684 Apahon Lane, US
Description: Herschel Freeman Agency, Inc. is known for discovering innovative traditional musicians from around the world. The current roster includes emerging artists like Adonis Puentes and Run Boy Run, who are both showcasing at the 2013 Arts NW conference; established artists like The Wailin' Jennys and Good Lovelies, and an array of international artists from Africa, India, Brazil, Ireland and the British Isles, and throughout North America
Country: United States
Contact: President & CEO

Herschel Freeman
Type: Folk/Ethnic/World

Holden & Arts Associates, Inc.
Website: www.holdenarts.org
Email: sk@holdenarts.org
Phone: 512 477 1859
Address: P.O. Box 49036 Austin, TX 78765 USA
Description: Holden & Arts Associates is a booking and management company serving performing artist and performing arts presenters across all of North America. Founded in 1983 by Michael and Theresa Holden, the Artistic partners are both national and international award winning companies and are among the leaders in their genres. They represent a breadth of cultural experience and aesthetic approach.
Country: United States
Contact: finance and international relations Stacy Meshbane
Email: sm@holdenarts.org
Contact: Sales and Artistic relations Sarah Saltwick
Email: ss@holdenarts.org
Contact: Sales and administrative Associate Dave Buckman
Email: db@holdenarts.org
Type: Classical, Choral, Solo/Chamber

Howard Stokar Management
Website: www.stokar.com
Email: hstokar@stokar.com
Phone: 212 866 5798
Address: 870 West End Avenue, US
Description: Howard Stokar Management was founded in 1989. Today they represent some of the most distinguished composers working in the United States. The approach is personal and hands-on, addressing the unique needs, situations and achievements of each client.
Country: United States
Contact: Director Howard Stokar
Email: hstokar@stokar.com
Social Media: @hstokar
Type: Classical, Modern/Contemporary

Hunstein Artist Services
Website: www.hunsteinartists.com
Email: dah@hunsteinartists.com
Phone: 212 724 2693
Address: 65 West 90th Street Suite 13 F New York, NY 10024 USA
Description: Artist representation specialising in chamber music and orchestral soloists.
Country: United States
Contact: Director DeeAnne Hunstein

Hymn Society in the US and Canada
Website: www.thehymnsociety.org
Email: office@thehymnsociety.org
Phone: 844 639 515
Address: 5 Thomas Circle, NW, 4th Floor, US
Description: The Hymn Society in the United States and Canada is a non-profit organization committed to promoting, enlivening, and encouraging congregational singing.
Country: United States
Contact: President Marilyn Haskel
Email: President@thehymnsociety.org
Contact: Executive Director Mike McMahon
Email: mike@thehymnsociety.org
Contact: operations Manager Courtney Murtaugh
Email: courtney@thehymnsociety.org

ICM Partners (Los Angeles)
Website: www.icmtalent.com
Email: careersla@icmtalent.com
Phone: 310 550 4000
Address: 10250 Constellation Blvd. Los Angeles, CA 90067 USA
Description: talent and literary agencies with offices in New York, Los Angeles, and London, represents creative and technical talent in the fields of motion picture, television, books, music, live performance, branded entertainment, and new media. Formerly ICM Artists
Country: United States
Social Media:
www.facebook.com/ICMPartners
www.instagram.com/icmpartners

ICM Partners (New York)
Website: www.icmtalent.com
Email: careersla@icmtalent.com
Phone: 212 556 5600
Address: 65 E. 55th St. New York, NY 10022 USA
Description: talent and literary agencies with offices in New York, Los Angeles, and London, represents creative and technical talent in the fields of motion picture, television, books, music, live performance, branded entertainment, and new media. Formerly ICM Artists
Country: United States
Social Media: https:// www.facebook.com/ICMPartners/

Imagination – America
Website: www.imagination.com

Email: eduardo.braniff@imagination.com
Phone: 212 813 6400
Address: 155 Franklin St, New York, NY 10013, USA
Description: management for architects, 3D and 2D designers, film makers, journalists, creative technologists, bloggers and social media experts, art Directors and copy writers and creative strategists. Also have offices in Sydney, New York, LA, Stockholm, Detroit, Melbourne, Cologne, Mumbai, Beijing, Shanghai, Hong Kong, Singapore, Tokyo, Toronto, Doha, Moscow, Macau
Country: United States
Social Media: www.facebook.com/ImaginationGLBLtwitter.com/ImaginationGLBL www.instagram.com/imaginationglbl

IMG Artists – America
Website: www.imgartists.com
Email: artistsny@imgartists.com
Phone: 212 994 3500
Address: 7 W 54th St, New York, NY 10019, United States
Description: IMG Artists provides management and touring of musicians, orchestras and attractions; development and operation of music and arts festivals; consulting, advisory and event management work for governments and arts institutions. Member of ISPA.
Country: United States
Contact: artist management Adam Cavagnaro
Contact: artist management Alissa Ordabayeva
Social Media: www.facebook.com/IMGArtistsOfficial
Type: Classical, Jazz, Vocal, Other

Institute of Outdoor Theatre
Website: www.outdoor-theatre.org
Email: outdoor@ecu.edu
Phone: 252 328 5363
Address: East Carolina University, College of Fine Arts and Communication, 201 Erwin Building, US
Description: provide services to organisations who produce theatre in outdoor settings including historical dramas, Shakespeare festivals, religious dramas, and a rich variety of musicals and plays; see also International and National organisations
Country: United States
Contact: Director Michael C. Hardy
Email: hardym@ecu.edu
Contact: business Manager Susan D. Phillips
Social Media: www.facebook.com/instituteoutdoortheatre

International Music Network
Website: www.imnworld.com
Email: info@imnworld.com
Phone: 978 283 2883
Address: 278 Main Street Gloucester, MA 01930
Description: International Music Network is an international Marketing company specialising in the booking and management of tours for artists who represent the highest level of musical and Artistic exPression in their respective genres. IMN's foundation is based upon respect and compassion for the world's music and arts, with a desire to contribute to the cultural growth and awareness of the global audience
Country: United States
Contact: west coast/canadian agent Alycia Mack
Email: alycia@imnworld.com
Contact: european agent Katherine McVicker
Email: katherine@imnworld.com
Contact: Director Scott Southard
Email: scott@imnworld.com
Contact: east coast agent Jeanna Disney
Email: jeanna@imnworld.com
Contact: european agent Eric Small
Email: eric@imnworld.com
Contact: midwest agent Michael Fox
Email: m.fox@imnworld.com
Social Media: https://twitter.com/imnworld www.facebook.com/imnworld
Type: Choral, Classical, Other

J. Chriss & Company
Website: jchriss.squarespace.com
Email: jchriss@aol.com
Phone: 212 353 0855
Address: 60 East 8th Street, Suite 32N, 3440 Broadway 6C, US
Description: J. Chriss & Co. is an artist and promoter friendly agency specializing in jazz, blues and world music booking, management and consulting.
Country: United States
Contact: chief officer Joel Chriss
Email: jchriss@aol.com
Contact: Director Chris Mees Mees
Email: chris@jchriss.com
Type: Classical, Choral, Early, Other

Jeffrey James Arts Consulting
Website: www.jamesarts.com
Email: jamesarts@att.net
Phone: 516 586 3433
Address: 45 Grant Avenue, US
Description: A full service arts agency dedicated to management and public relations for today. Representing composers, ensembles, instrumentalists, and special

attractions since 1992, with a very special interest in the music of the 20th and 21st Centuries we employ many new techniques in career development in conjunction with our own 4Tay Records

Jeffrey James Arts Consulting
Website: www.jamesarts.com
Email: jamesarts@att.net
Phone: 516 586 3433
Address: 45 Grant Avenue Farmingdale, NY 11735 USA
Description: Jeffrey James Arts Consulting specializes in recording projects, promotion, public relations, music publishing, referrals, special projects and most everything else (except bookings) that people in the arts need.
Country: United States
Contact: President Jeffrey James
Email: jamesarts@att.net
Social Media: https:// www.facebook.com/Jamesarts45/ https://twitter.com/Jamesarts45 https://www.instagram.com/jamesarts2018/

Jeffrey Loseff Management
Website: jloseff.com
Email: jclmgmt@aol.com
Phone: 818 505 9468
Address: 4521 Colfax Avenue Suite 205 North Hollywood, California 91602 USA
Description: Serving performers around the world for over 25 years, Jeffrey Loseff Management excels in guiding careers in film, television and stage, whilst keeping the concept of management, personal.
Country: United States
Contact: President Jeffrey Loseff
Social Media: https:// www.facebook.com/jloseffmgmt/

Jensen Artists
Website: www.jensenartists.com
Email:
christina@jensenartists.com
Phone: 646 536 7864
Address: 394 Broadway 5th fl, New York, NY 10013, USA
Description: Founded in 2007 as public relations firm Christina Jensen PR, Jensen Artists expanded in 2015 to include artist management services. Jensen Artists is dedicated to developing the careers and telling the stories of today's most vibrant classical musicians. We are motivated by a desire to illustrate the abundance and appeal of today's classical music world by sharing our clients' personalities, creativity, and art with the public. Member of ISPA
Country: United States
Contact: President Christina Jensen
Email: christina@christinajensenpr.com
Contact: publicity Manager Maggie Stapleton
Email: maggie@jensenartists.com
Contact: booking agent Gina Meola
Email: gina@jensenartists.com
Contact: digital media Manager Aled Roberts
Email: aled@jensenartists.com
Social Media: https://twitter.com/jensenartists www.facebook.com/jensenartists/ https:// www.instagram.com/jensenartists/

Joanne Rile Artists Management, Inc.
Website: www.rilearts.com
Email: artists@rilearts.com
Phone: 215 885 6400
Address: 93 Old York Road, Suite 222, Box 518, Jenkintown Commons, US
Description: They are a full service artists' management company with over 40 years of experience in promoting music, dance, and theatre presentations performed by world class artists. Their artists hail from the U.S. and abroad, performing works from the Renaissance and Baroque as well as new music, including cross-over artists that offer imaginative and creative shows. Member of IAMA.
Country: United States
Contact: President Joanne Rile
Email: joanner@rilearts.com
Type: Classical, Jazz, All

Jodi Kaplan & Associates
Website: www.bookingdance.com
Email: jka@bookingdance.com
Phone:
212 352 0400
Address: 318 West 101 St. Suite 8 New York, NY 10025
Description: Jodi Kaplan & Associates (JK&A) is a personal "boutique agency" that books dance companies on extensive tours throughout the USA and internationally. Director Jodi Kaplan also consults with both established and newly formed dance companies in developing stronger Artistic programming and performance engagement.
Country: United States
Contact: President Jodi Kaplan
Email: JodiKaplan@bookingdance.com
Social Media: https://twitter.com/BookingDance https://www.facebook.com/BookingDanceFestival/ https:// www.instagram.com/bookingdancefestival/

John Gingrich Management Inc.

Website: www.gingarts.com
Email: john@gingarts.com
Phone: 212 799 5080
Address:
PO Box 1515, US
Description: John Gingrich Management applies 30+ years of experience in artist representation & organizational management to offer services to arts organizations & music festivals to facilitate and improve organizational operations. In this role, the company strives to be nearly invisible to the outside eye, working diligently in the background to facilitate and execute requisite logistics.
Country: United States
Contact: President John Gingrich
Type: Classical, Solo/Chamber, Vocal

John Such Artists' Management Ltd.
Website: www.johnsuchartists.com
Email: jsuchmgt@aol.com
Phone: 212 926 4833
Address: 780 Riverside Drive, Suite 7A New York, NY 10032
Description: John Such Artists' Management, Ltd. is a leading source for Broadway and Pops programs throughout the world. Their shows feature leading performers from the Broadway stage with the orchestra.
Country: United States
Contact: Executive Director John Such
Contact: operations Manager Jesse Langston Langston
Email: jesse@bravobroadway.com
Type: Classical, Other

Jonathan Wentworth Associates Ltd.
Website: www.Jwentworth.com
Email: email@Jwentworth.com
Phone: 301 277 8205
Address: 6118 40th Avenue Hyattsville, MD 20782 USA
Description: Jonathan Wentworth Associates Ltd. is a leader in the performing artist management field, serving an elite roster of musicians as agent and Manager in the many aspects of career development and booking. They represent world-class concert artists, ensembles, and special projects with musicians, spoken word and projected images. Member of IAMA
Country: United States
Contact: Vice President Kenneth Wentworth
Email: kenneth@Jwentworth.com
Contact: President Martha Woods
Email: martha@Jwentworth.com
Contact: Associate Alexander Gurevich
Email: office@Jwentworth.com
Contact: artist liason Kathryn Cardy
Email: kcardy@verizon.net
Social Media: www.facebook.com/Jonathan-Wentworth-Associates-Ltd-133007303390235

Joseph H Conlin Concert Management
Website: null
Email: info@jhcbh.com
Phone: 212 333 7844
Address: 853 Seventh Avenue, US
Description:
Country: United States
Contact: President Brian Hunter
Email: bh@jhcbh.com
Type: Baroque, Choral, Classical, Early, Jazz, Modern/Contemporary, Romantic, Solo/Chamber, Symphonic, Vocal, Wind/brass band

Joyce Agency Entertainment Services Inc
Website: www.joyce-agency.com
Email: joyceagen@aol.com
Phone: 914 835 1123
Address: 370 Harrison Ave, Harrison, NY 10528 USA
Description: The Joyce Agency was founded in 1930 by the current President's father and is one of the oldest agencies in the world. The Joyce family has been involved with music for ten generations, starting in the 1600's in Europe and then moving to the United States in 1890. The Joyce Agency has been involved in almost every form of entertainment in the United States and around the world with various offices and worldwide Associates. The Joyce Agency is very proud of its tradition and reputation for initiating and fostering the popularity of many forms of entertainment from vaudeville to country and western, rock and roll, disco, national tours of musicals, dance attractions, and family attractions.
Country: United States
Contact: President Van Joyce

Judson Management Group, Inc.
Website: www.jmginy.com
Email: info@jmginy.com
Phone: United States
Address: 145 East 57th Street, 5th Floor, 145 East 57th Street, US
Description: Judson Management Group, Inc. provides comprehensive management services to a number of the world's leading international artists and attractions.
Country: United States
Contact: Managerial Associate Laura Duni
Email: ld@jmginy.com
Contact: President Stephen Judson
Email: shj@jmginy.com

Contact: Booking Agent Alana Klonoski
Email: ak@jmginy.com
Contact: Senior Vice President Mark Alpert
Email: ma@jmginy.com
Contact: Senior Vice President Desiree Halac
Email: dh@jmginy.com
Social Media: Laura Duni www.facebook.com/jmginy
Type: Classical, Solo/Chamber, Wind/brass band

Kanzen Arts
Website: www.kanzenarts.com
Email: eblackburn@kanzenarts.com
Phone: 917 702 8403
Address: 67-26 Exeter Street, US
Description: Kanzen Arts was established in 2017 by Earl Blackburn, a 30-year veteran in arts management. Dedicated to the successful intersection of performing arts and commerce. Kanzen Arts is a contemporary performing arts management representing artists and touring projects in collaboration with arts presenters throughout the world. Member of ISPA
Country: United States
Contact: President Earl Blackburn
Email: eblackburn@kanzenarts.com
Contact: Associate Łucja Kwasniak
Email: lkwasniak@kanzenarts.com

Karen McFarlane Artists Inc.
Website: www.concertorganists.com
Email: john@concertorganists.com
Phone: 440 542 1882
Address: 33563 Seneca Drive, US
Description: originally founded in 1921 by Bernard LaBerge, Karen McFarlane Artists represents (in North America only) the world's premiere concert organists as well as select choirs in the English choral tradition.
Country: United States
Contact: President John McElliott
Email: john@concertorganists.com
Contact: office Manager Alan Higbee
Email: alan@concertorganists.com
Type: Choral, Classical

Kaylor Management Inc
Website: www.kaylormanagement.com
Email: hughkaylor@msn.com
Phone: 212 977 6779
Address: 130 West 57th Street, Suite 6A New York NY 10019 USA
Description: Kaylor Management, Inc. (KMI) began its seventeenth season in June 2011. Offering management primarily to conductors. KMI now manages a small number of prestigious instrumentalists as well. Member of IAMA.
Country: United States
Contact: President Hugh Kaylor
Email: hugh@kaylormanagement.com
Contact: Associate and business Manager Brent Heath
Email: brent@kaylormanagement.com
Social Media: https://twitter.com/kaylormgmt www.facebook.com/KaylorManagement
Type: , Classical, Other

Kirshbaum Demler and Associates Inc.
Website: www.kirshdem.com
Email: info@kirshdem.com
Phone: 212 222 4843
Address: 711 West End Ave, Suite 5KN, US
Description: specialises in Press campaigns and programmes for the arts, particularly those supporting classical musicians, ensembles and institutions
Country: United States
Contact: Director Susan Demler
Email: sdemler@kirshdem.com
Contact: Director Shirley Kirshbaum
Email: skirshbaum@kirshdem.com
Contact: Associate Ashley Baier
Email: abaier@kirshdem.com
Contact: administrative assistant Katharine Boone
Email: kboone@kirshdem.com
Contact: artist services Associate Peri Stedman
Email: pstedman@kirshdem.com
Contact: Director of booking Jason Belz
Email: jbelz@kirshdem.com
Contact: public relations Associate Ashlyn Damm
Email: adamm@kirshdem.com
Contact: null Luisa Lopez
Email: llopez@kirshdem.com
Social Media: www.facebook.com/KirshbaumDemler
Type: Classical

KMP Artists
Website: www.kmpartists.com
Email: info@kmpartists.com
Phone: 512 888 9895
Address: 1001 Texas Street, #1400, US
Description: Artist Management, Tour Logistics, International Producer, Arts Consultant. An International roster featuring top Dance, Music & Family programs of the World.
Country: United States
Contact: founding partner Kristopher McDowell
Email: kristopher@kmpartists.com
Contact: President Andrew Delicata

Social Media: @KMPartists www.facebook.com/KM-PArtists
Type: Folk/Ethnic/World, Jazz, All

KMP Artists
Website: kmpartists.com
Email: info@kmpartists.com
Phone: 512 888 9895
Address: 700 Milam Street, Suite 1300 Houston, TX 77002 USA
Description: KMP is a tour management firm and production company for live cultural arts since 2004. KMP endeavors to provide programming for broad audiences in genres that include dance, theatre, family and music programs. KMP also offers visual arts exhibits and residency programs. KMP is committed to international exchange by touring exceptional projects from around the globe that stimulate conversation and encourage mutual understanding, with a particular focus on work found around the Pacific Rim. Member of ISPA.
Country: United States
Contact: CEO Kristopher McDowell
Contact: President Andrew Delicata
Contact: Executive Associate Dominador Balao-as
Social Media: https://twitter.com/kmpartists https://www.facebook.com/KMPArtists/ https://www.instagram.com/kmpartists/

Knudsen Productions – Artist Management
Website: www.knudsenproductions.com/
Email: craig@knudsenproductions.com
Phone: 510 549 1777
Address: 1737 Blake St., Berkeley, CA 94703 USA
Description: In 1999, Craig Knudsen founded the talent agency, Knudsen Productions, LLC. With a focus on exceptional vocal talent, Craig quickly established Knudsen Productions as one of the most highly regarded US agencies representing vocal ensembles (both national and international). For 11 years Craig also served as the music Director of the Kaiser Permanente Educational Theatre Project, and, additionally, spent 18 years touring as a singer / Composer / arranger with the EDLOS a cappella quartet (the 1989 Harmony Sweepstakes National Champions). In 2014, by a vote of his peers, Craig was honored with the Coyote Award from Arts Northwest commemorating his leadership and contributions to the continued change and growth in the arena of live performance
Country: United States
Contact: CEO Craig Knudsen
Email: craig@knudsenproductions.com
Social Media: https://twitter.com/knudsenpro
Type: Vocal

Liegner Management
Website: www.liegnermanagement.com
Email: liegnermgt@aol.com
Phone: 202 545 1997
Address: 2846 N Goldcliff Cir, Mesa, AZ 85207, USA
Description: At The Entertainment Management Group they always want people to have fun, whether it is by watching a movie, listening to music or partying.
Country: United States
Contact: Director Mark Painter

LKI Artists International Inc
Website: www.lanaivanovpianostudio.com/lki-artists-international-inc.html
Email: Lanalvanov@me.com
Phone: 908 419 0784
Address: US
Description: Lana Ivanov has distinguished herself as a performer, and a remarkably insightful, technical and Artistic pedagogue; also provides private lessons, competition adjudication and masterclasses.
Country: United States
Contact: President Lana Ivanov
Type: Classical

Lombardo Associates, LLC
Website: www.lombardoAssociates.org
Email: robert@lombardoAssociates.org
Phone: 212 586 4453
Address: 27 West 60th Street P O Box 20145 New York, NY 10023
Description: Music management and promotion company based in New York
Country: United States
Contact: Manager Michael Rosen
Email: Michael@lombardoAssociates.org
Contact: Manager Lewis Ehlers
Email: Lewis@lombardoAssociates.org
Contact: consultant Robert Lombardo
Email: robert@lombardoAssociates.org
Contact: office Manager Joe Povelaitis
Email: Joe@lombardoAssociates.org

LTM Artists Inc
Website: null
Email: info@ltmartists.com
Phone: 323 965 9922
Address: 1834 St. Gramercy Place, US
Description: LTM Artists was founded in Los Angeles in 2002 by Michael Moore when he landed his first client

on "The Late Show with David Letterman." Since then, LTM has expanded significantly (a New York office was opened in April 2006) and evolved into two main areas: artists management and theatrical production
Country: United States

Lucas LaFrance
Website: null
Email: lucaslafrance@aol.com
Phone: 310 836 2722
Address: 11693 San Vincente Boulevard, Suite 135, US
Description:
Country: United States

Marianne Schmoker Artists Ltd
Website: www.marianneschmokerartists.com/
Email: mschmokerartists@gmail.com
Phone: 631 470 0393
Address: 25 Madison St, New York, NY 10038, USA
Description: Providing guidance and representation to international chamber ensembles and piano soloists of the highest echelons.
Country: United States
Contact: Director Marianne Schmoker
Email: marianneschmokerartists@gmail.com
Social Media: www.facebook.com/marianneschmokerartists.1

Mary Ella Collins and Associates
Website: www.mec-sing.com
Email: friends@mec-sing.com
Phone: 972 661 9074
Address: 5025 Briar Tree Drive, US
Description: the agency endeavors to support and inspire all people, particularly those involved in the arts, to create new and universal ways to expand their existing storehouse of knowledge and experience so as to join others in raising human consciousness
Country: United States
Contact: President, Director Mary Ella Collins
Type: Classical

Matthew Laifer Artists Management
Website: www.matthewlaifer.com
Email: laiferart@aol.com
Phone: 212 580 9426
Address: 75 West End Ave New York, NY 10023
Description: Their goal is to bring the finest artists to the finest theaters world wide, with careful attention given to establishing and maintaining professional careers. The Laifer roster is divided among Americans, Europeans and Asians, stars and emerging talents
Country: United States
Social Media: www.facebook.com/MatthewLaiferArtistsManagement/ www.instagram.com/matthew-laiferartistsmanagement/
Type: Classical, Other

Matthew Sprizzo
Website: www.matthewsprizzo.com
Email: matthewsprizzo@gmail.com
Phone: 347 596 3365
Address: 18 Allison Ave Staten Island, NY 10306, USA
Description: Mr. Sprizzo is the exclusive representative for all of his artists in North America but is also the worldwide Manager for many of them. Inquiries for engagements in geographical territories for which the artist-in-question is represented by another agent will be directed accordingly
Country: United States
Type: Baroque, Classical, Vocal, Other

Maurice Montoya Music Agency
Website: www.mmmusicagency.com
Email: info@mmmusicagency.com
Phone: 305 763 8961
Address: 11 Island Avenue – Suite 1711 Miami, FL 33139
Description: The M M Music Agency is dedicated to representing the finest artists in the genres of Jazz, Afro-Caribbean, Brazilian, and Contemporary Music.
Country: United States
Contact: President Maurice Montoya
Social Media: twitter.com/MMMusicagency www.facebook.com/mmmusicagency

Melody Bunting International
Website: www.melodybunting.com/
Email: melbunting@aol.com
Phone: 212 799 4949
Address: PO Box 237140, US
Description: Since 1981, Melody Bunting International has represented classical musicians and specialized in Managing their performance schedules.
Country: United States
Contact: Owner Melody Bunting
Email: melbunting@aol.com
Social Media: www.facebook.com/Melody-Bunting-International-416232028460928
Type: Classical

MIA Management
Website: www.miaartists.com
Email: Info@MIAArtists.com
Phone: 646 620 1313
Address: 205 West 88th Street, Suite 13A, US

Description: MIA Management are committed to bring forth a group of accomplished artists to fulfill today's modern operatic vision with the classic and traditional roots of yesteryear's golden age of opera.
Country: United States
Contact: artist management Maritza Sori Pita
Email: Maritza@MiaArtists.com
Contact: artist management Marlise Sori
Email: Marlise@MiaArtists.com
Social Media: https://www.facebook.com/miaartists-management/
Type: Classical, Vocal, Other

Mirshak Artists Management
Website: www.mirshakartists.com
Email: robert@mirshakartists.com
Phone: 917 282 0687
Address: 1173 Second Avenue, #313 New York, NY 10065 USA
Description: Mirshak Artists Management represents many of the world's finest classical singers, conductors and stage Directors. Their roster is comprised of musicians who strive to make a positive difference in the art of music and to affect people with his or her gifts.
Country: United States
Contact: Director Robert Mirshak
Email: robert@mirshakartists.com
Social Media: twitter.com/dr_mirshak www.facebook.com/Mirshak-Artists-Management-187464204608481/

Monica Robinson Ltd
Website: www.monicarobinson.com
Email: monicarobinsonltd@gmail.com
Phone: 917 309 6283
Address: 293 Central Park West, Suite 1-B New York, NY 10024 USA
Description: Based upon her own training and performance experience in classical singing, Monica Robinson believes in developing a healthy vocal technique, with emphasis on breath management and correct placement of the voice. These basic principles can be applied to all styles of music, including Broadway, classical and pop. Member of the National Association of Teachers of Singing (NATS) and the New York Singing Teachers' Association (NYSTA)
Country: United States
Contact: President Monica Robinson
Email: monicarobinsonltd@gmail.com

Ms. Susan Dearborn
Website: www.conductorscooperative.com
Email: info@conductorscooperative.com
Phone: 617 642 2461
Address: 108 Fayerweather Street, US
Description: null
Country: United States
Contact: Director Susan Dearborn
Social Media: www.facebook.com/Conductors-Cooperative-Management-182031358599568
Type: Classical

Music Theatre Associates
Website: www.columbiaartiststheatricals.com
Email: simpson@broadwaycat.com
Phone: 917 206 4600
Address: 250 West 57th Street, , Suite 901, US
Description: specialises in the booking and tour management of live performances on a worldwide basis
Country: United States
Contact: booking agent Jann Simpson
Email: simpson@broadwaycat.com
Contact: contact Gary McAvay
Email: mcavay@broadwaycat.com
Contact: contact Evelyn Zilberman
Email: zilberman@broadwaycat.com
Contact: contact Rada Angelova
Email: angelova@broadwaycat.com

Music Works International
Website: w www.musicworksinternational.com
Email: booking@musicworksinternational.com
Phone: 781 300 7580
Address: Reading, MA USA
Description: Music Works International collaborates with the world's finest musicians, promoters and venues to develop tours that expand audiences, artists and markets. We use our deep insights, experience, and knowledge to creatively power the Artistic development and vision of an exceptional roster of musicians and bands that spans jazz, blues, world music, and R & B.
Country: United States
Social Media: null
Type: Jazz, Folk/Ethnic/World, Other

ND Artists Management
Website: www.dotoratos-hammond.com
Email: NDartsmgt@msn.com
Phone: 914 723 0960
Address: 7 Ferncliff Rd, Scarsdale, NY 10583, USA
Description: international artists for solo orchestral appearances and recitals; artists also available for master classes; performances include Carnegie Hall, Lincoln Center, The White House, Washington D.C. as well as performances on National Public Radio and WQXR

classical radio
Country: United States
Contact: President Jean Acheson

Nederlander Worldwide Entertainment
Website: www.nederlanderworld.com
Email: info@NederlanderWorld.com
Phone: 212 822 4200
Address: 1450 Broadway, 20th Floor New York, NY 10018
Description: manages theatres and presents Broadway productions in emerging international markets, produces international productions for Broadway and elsewhere around the world, and undertakes cultural educational initiatives. The company's expertise covers theatre management and operations, along with all facets of live entertainment, including ticketing, management, promotion, Marketing, and advertising. see also Promoter, Producer, Presenter. Member of IAMA
Country: United States
Contact: President Robert Nederlander
Contact: General Manager Geoff Cohen Cohen

Neil Funkhouser Artists Management
Website: www.funkhouserartists.com
Email: neil@funkhouserartists.com
Phone: 212 304 4311
Address: 105 Arden Street, Suite 5G, US
Description: With 25 years of experience in the artist management business, Neil Funkhouser has established himself as one of the most respected and knowledgeable individuals in the field. Mr. Funkhouser has held positions with Columbia Artists Management, Inc. and Herbert Breslin, Inc.
Country: United States
Contact: CEO Neil Funkhouser
Email: Neil@funkhouserartists.com
Social Media: @FunkhouserMgmt www.facebook.com/FunkhouserArtists
Type: Classical, Vocal

New Century Artists Inc.
Website: www.newcentury.nu
Email: sgeorge@newcentury.nu
Phone: 941 914 2041
Address: 13901 Shaker Blvd.Suite 1-B Cleveland, Ohio 44120 USA
Description: Serving the unique and diverse needs of classical artists in a rapidly changing world.
Country: United States
Contact: President Scott George
Type: Classical

New World Classics
Website: www.newworldclassics.com
Email: kl@newworldclassics.com
Phone: 802 442 9005
Address: 245 Union Street, US
Description: New World Classics enters its 27th year of activity in 2019. That's just a speck of dust in time compared to the great histories of the artists represented – all seasoned performers, long recognized for their contributions to the world's stages. New World Classics was the first classical artist management agency to create a combination Artist Roster with a compact disc sampler.
Country: United States
Contact: Director Kerby Lovallo
Type: Classical

Nolan Kerr Artists Consultants, Ltd.
Website: www.nolankerr.com
Email: nolanarts@gmail.com
Phone: 513 304 4078
Address: 1325 Lance Ct Lebanon, OH 45036, USA
Description: Nolan Kerr Consulting began in 1996 as Nolan Kerr Artist Consultants, LTD. Their primary mission then was to provide classical and jazz musicians with professional guidance in image development and Marketing in order to build their performance careers.
Country: United States
Contact: Director Nancy Nolan
Social Media: www.facebook.com/nolankerrconsulting

Omicron Artist Management Inc
Website: www.omicronarts.com
Email: donsipe@omicronarts.com
Phone: 414 332 7600
Address: PO Box 11912, US
Description: Career management for musicians, performers and creative professionals. They provide career services for professional musicians and creative professionals.
Country: United States
Contact: President Donald Sipe
Email: donsipe@omicronarts.com
Type: Classical

Opus 3 Artists
Website: www.opus3artists.com
Email: info@opus3artists.com
Phone: 212 584 7500
Address: 348 West 57th Street Suite 282 New York, NY 10019
Description: Opus 3 Artists LLC is a leading company

Managing the careers and touring activities of many of the world's most distinguished performing artists and ensembles. Opus 3 Artists traces its roots to the pioneering role of the legendary Sol Hurok

Country: United States
Contact: President and CEO David Foster
Contact: Executive Vice President Jonathan Brill
Social Media: https://twitter.com/Opus3Artists https://www.facebook.com/opus3artists https://www.instagram.com/opus3artists/
Type: Classical

Ovation! Management
Website: www.ovationmanagement.org
Email: info@OvationManagement.org
Phone: 773 338 4182
Address: 6161 N. Hamilton Chicago, IL 60659 USA
Description: Ovation! Management is an international concert agency representing classical artists.
Country: United States
Type: Classical, Other

Parker Artists
Website: www.parkerartists.com
Email: tom@parkerartists.com
Phone: 212 864 7928
Address: 382 Central Park West, Suite 9G, US
Description: Born in 1949 in Springfield, Massachusetts, THOMAS F. PARKER is a graduate of the University of Massachusetts Amherst. From 1972 to 1974, he was Special Producer and music Director of WTIC-FM in Hartford, Connecticut, winning the prestigious Major Edwin H. Armstrong Award, administered by the Armstrong Memorial Research Foundation at Columbia University. In 1974, he moved to New York City to begin a career in artist management, and during the following sixteen years, was Associated with Colbert Artists Management, Sheldon Soffer Management, and Shaw Concerts, serving the last firm as Vice President. In the fall of 1990, he established his own firm, Parker Artists.
Country: United States
Contact: Owner Thomas F Parker
Type: Classical, Pops/Light classical, Other

Parsons Artists Management, Inc.
Website: www.parsonsartists.com
Email: pamgtinc@aol.com
Phone: 847 433 7374
Address: 1134 Wade St. Highland Park, IL, 60035 USA
Description: Parsons Artists Management, Inc. represent soloists, ensembles and composers.
Country: United States
Contact: President Pamela Parsons
Email: pamgtinc@aol.com
Type: Classical, Early, Other

Pasifika Artists Network
Website: www.pasifika-artists.com
Email: karen@pasifika-artists.com
Phone: 808 283 7007
Address: 661 Kilihau St. Wailuku, Maui, HI 96793 USA
Description: An extensive network of contacts with presenters across the country, as well as throughout the performing arts field, gives Pasifika Artists Network a distinct advantage as the artist's representative in negotiating performance bookings and national/international performance tours. With nearly 30 years of arts management experience, Karen Fischer offers consulting services in the performing arts with a focus on the not-for-profit sector, including programme development and management, organizational management, fundraising, budgeting and finance, Marketing, touring logistics, and other aspects in the business of the arts.
Country: United States
Contact: President Karen A. Fischer

Patricia Alberti Performing Artists Management
Website: www.palbertiartists.com
Email: palbertiarts@msn.com
Phone: 480 504 4581
Address: 13607 North Hamilton Drive, US
Description: Patricia Alberti Performing Artists Management was founded by Patricia Alberti. Patricia has been working as an agent/representative for professional musicians throughout the United States for over 20 years. Her experience has helped her earn a reputation for honesty and integrity among her colleagues and artists.
Country: United States
Contact: President Patricia Alberti
Type: All

Paul Taylor Dance Company
Website: ptamd.org
Email: information@ptamd.org
Phone: 212 431 5562
Address: 551 Grand Street, Top Floor New York, NY 10002 USA
Description: The Paul Taylor Dance Company, established in 1954, has long been one of the world's most highly regarded performing arts companies. The 16-member Company performs Mr. Taylor's works around the world, and has appeared in more than 520 cities in 62 countries to date. Taylor 2, established

in 1993, brings Mr. Taylor's dances to smaller venues around the world as well as giving master classes and teaching people of all ages the Taylor style. Member of ISPA.
Country: United States
Contact: Artistic Director Michael Novak
Social Media: https://twitter.com/paultaylordance https://www.facebook.com/PaulTaylorDance https://www.instagram.com/paultaylordance/

Performing Artists International
Website: www.paiartists.com
Email: info@paiartists.com
Phone: 817 924 2225
Address: 4417 Dunwick, Suite 300 Fort Worth, Texas 76109-2508 USA
Description: Exclusive representation for North America and some are represented internationally.
Country: United States
Contact: Director Angela Fabry
Email: AFabry@PAIArtists.com
Contact: assistant Susan Wilson
Email: Info@PAIArtists.com
Type: Classical, Other

Performing Arts Consultants
Website: www.usafest.org
Email: info@usafest.org
Phone: 732 475 6200
Address: 807 Mantoloking Rd STE 101, Brick Township, NJ 08723, United States
Description: For over 32 years, Performing Arts Consultants have orchestrated premier school music tours for junior high, senior high, and college-level students, providing the opportunity to perform in excellent concert facilities with America's most dedicated adjudicators and music clinicians.
Country: United States
Contact: President Michael Mazzarisi
Email: mike@usafest.org
Contact: Vice President Sherry Mazzarisi
Email: sherry@usafest.org
Contact: General Manager David Mazzarisi
Email: dave@usafest.org
Social Media: https://twitter.com/pacfestivals https://www.facebook.com/usafest

Phillip Truckenbrod Concert Artists
Website: www.concertartists.com
Email: email@concertartists.com
Phone: 860 560 7800
Address: PO Box 6507, US
Description: Phillip Truckenbrod Concert Artists was founded in 1967 and in 2017 celebrates its 50th year of service to the fine art of the pipe organ, its performers, and the presenters of pipe organ recitals throughout the United States and Canada. From its inception, the agency has focused its efforts in the representation of the most celebrated and revered American and European concert organists with an emphasis on the best young talent of the day.
Country: United States
Contact: President Charles Miller
Email: charlesmiller@concertartists.com
Social Media: www.facebook.com/truckenbrodconcertartists
Type: Classical

Pinnacle Arts Management
Website: www.pinnaclearts.com
Email: jmiller@pinnaclearts.com
Phone:
212 795 4473
Address: 801 West 181st Street, Apartment 20 New York, New York 10033
Description: Pinnacle Arts Management, Inc. is a leading firm in the business of providing artists' management, production, and consulting services for performing artists and arts organizations worldwide. Its primary scope of activities is in the world of opera, where one hundred and twenty five of its clients have appeared with seventy five opera companies during the past season.
Country: United States

PMG Arts Management
Website: pmgartsmgt.com
Email: pam@pmgartsmgt.com
Phone:
919 813 6092
Address: PO Box 52346 Durham, NC 27717
Description: PMG Arts Management, LLC provides booking, management and consulting services to performing artists, companies and organizations throughout the country.
Country: United States
Contact: President Pamela Green
Email: pam@pmgartsmgt.com
Social Media: https://twitter.com/PMGArtsMgt https://www.facebook.com/PMGArtsMgt/

Pomegranate Arts, Inc.
Website: www.pomegranatearts.com
Email: info@pomarts.com
Phone: 212 228 2221

Address: 1140 Broadway, Suite 305, US
Description: Founded by Linda Brumbach in 1998, Pomegranate Arts is an independent production company based in New York City dedicated to the development of international performing arts projects that are bold, provocative and emotionally charged
Contact: Founder and Director Linda Brumbach
Email: linda@pomarts.com
Contact: Managing Director Alisa Regas
Email: alisa@pomarts.com
Contact: business Manager Adam Thorburn
Email: adam@pomarts.com
Social Media: @PomegranateArts www.facebook.com/pomegranatearts
Type: Classical, Folk/Ethnic/World, Modern/Contemporary, Pop/Rock, Solo/Chamber, Symphonic, Vocal

POW – Performers of the World, Inc.
Website:
Email: info@powagency.com
Phone: 323 938 0400
Address: 5657 Wilshire Blvd, , #280, US
Description:
Country: United States
Type: All

Primavera Consulting LLC
Website: www.artsprimavera.com
Email: ab@artsprimavera.com
Phone: 646 709 6910
Address: 736 W 186th St #6J New York, NY 10033, USA
Description: Founded in 2015 by Anastasia Boudanoque, Primavera Consulting focuses on producing high-end classical entertainment events and consulting performing arts organisations all over the world. Additionally, Primavera represents a small roster of artists, reinforcing traditional talent management with digital and social media, endorsement opportunities, as well as educational, charitable, and cultural diplomacy initiatives. Member IAMA.
Country: United States
Contact: Founder & Managing Director Anastasia Boudanoque
Email: ab@artsprimavera.com
Contact: Associate artist Manager Elena Yakovleva
Email: eyakovleva@artsprimavera.com
Social Media: www.facebook.com/artsprimavera www.instagram.com/primavera_consulting/

Pro Musicis Foundation, Inc
Website: www.promusicis.org
Email: promusicis@aol.com
Phone: 212 787 0993
Address: 2067 Broadway, Suite 41 New York, NY 10023
Description: Pro Musicis has enjoyed a dynamic and often stormy history since its founding in France in 1965 and introduction to the USA in 1969. The legacy of its charismatic Founder, Father Eugène Merlet, is most visible in the prestigious roster of Pro Musicis artists. His vision launched international ventures and attracted committed fellow travellers. Today Pro Musicis is firmly rooted on both sides of the Atlantic in Paris and New York City thanks to the generosity and passion of those who believe in the precious mission of Pro Musicis to nurture and share the Artistic inspiration of the world's finest concert artists.
Country: United States
Contact: board Chair Bonnie Barrett
Contact: Executive Director John Haag
Social Media: https://twitter.com/promusicis www.facebook.com/promusicis

R2C2 Robert Rund Creative Consulting
Website: robertrund.com
Email: robert@r2c2.us
Phone: 917 588 0777
Address: 1480 Landings Run Mt Pleasant, SC 29464, USA
Description: R2C2 was founded in 1998 by Robert Rund, and has provided consulting services to a variety of individuals and organizations, and specializes in serving the business development needs of performing artists, arts and educational institutions and other nonprofit organizations.
Country: United States
Social Media: https://twitter.com/r2c2consults

Randsman Artists' Management
Website: www.randsman.com
Email: randsman@aol.com
Phone: 212 244 5874
Address: 400 West 43rd Street, Apt. 18E, US
Description: An elite roster of distinguished musical artists to help realize operatic visions
Country: United States
Contact: Manager Peter Randsman
Type: Classical

Rena Shagan Associates, Inc.
Website: www.shaganarts.com
Email:
rena@shaganarts.com
Phone: 212 873 9700
Address: 180 Riverside Drive, New York, NY 10024 USA
Description: Created in 1979 to provide management for

a small group of companies touring in the United States and abroad, RENA SHAGAN ASSOCIATES, INC. (RSA) has grown to become one of the leading arts management firms in the world. RSA specializes in developing and Managing touring activity for major dance and theatre companies.
Country: United States
Contact: President Rena Shagan
Email: rena@shaganarts.com
Social Media: www.facebook.com/RenaShaganAssociatesInc/

Richard Realmuto Artists' Management
Website: null
Email: richard@realmutoartists.com
Phone: 212 923 6131
Address: 824 West 176th Street, US
Description: Richard Realmuto Artists' Management represents artists in the field of opera, classical music, theatre, film and television.
Country: United States
Contact: contact Richard Realmuto
Email: richard@realmutoartists.com
Type: Classical, Vocal, Other

Riot Artists
Website: www.riotartists.com
Email: staff@riotartists.com
Phone: 650 595 2274
Address: PO Box 280786, US
Description: Riot Artists (formerly known as Eye For Talent) is a global talent agency, devoted to the worldwide development and promotion of our artists. It specialises in booking, career enhancement, and production of tours for artists and speakers who exemplify the pinnacle of skill and accomplishment within their respective genres and fields. Member of ISPA.
Country: United States
Contact: Owner William Smith
Social Media: @EyeForTalent www.facebook.com/RiotArtists
Type: Classical, Jazz, Modern/Contemporary, Vocal, Other

Road Company, The
Website: www.theroadcompany.com
Email: tours@trc.nyc
Phone: 212 302 5200
Address: 630 Ninth Avenue, Suite 1212 New York, NY 10036 USA
Description: An independent theatrical booking agency, distributing award-winning musicals, plays and special attractions across North America. The Road Company remains independently owned and operated, discovering and selecting shows and bringing them to a wider audience.
Country: United States
Contact: co-Founder and partner Stephen Lindsay
Email: sl@trc.nyc
Contact: Vice President and Sales Magaly Barone
Email: mb@trc.nyc
Contact: Vice President of operations Shawn Willett
Email: sw@trc.nyc
Social Media: www.facebook.com/theroadco https://www.instagram.com/theroadcompanynyc/

Roots Agency, The
Website: www.therootsagency.com
Email: info@therootsagency.com
Phone: 201 263 9200
Address: 177 Woodland Avenue, Westwood, NJ 07675 USA
Description: The Roots Agency IS a talent booking agency dedicated to developing the touring careers of exceptional touring artists who connect, inspire, and transform audiences .
Country: United States
Contact: agent/President Tim Drake
Email: tim@therootsagency.com
Contact: agent/President Larry Kosson
Email: larry@therootsagency.com
Social Media: https://twitter.com/rootsagency www.facebook.com/TheRootsAgency https:// www.facebook.com/TheRootsAgency
Type: Folk/Ethnic/World, Pop/Rock, Other, Jazz

Roth Arts
Website: www.rotharts.com
Email: info@rotharts.com
Phone: null
Address: US
Description: a production and management company overseeing the touring activities of preeminent performing artists, with a particular interest in the traditional music of Ireland
Country: United States
Contact: Director Elizabeth Roth
Email: liz@rotharts.com

SC Entertainment
Website: www.scentertainmentonline.com
Email: sceusa@gmail.com
Phone: 212 929 0630
Address: 360 West 22nd Street, Ste. 9A New York, NY

10011 USA
Description: Music, comedy, theatre, lecture and variety programmes for performing arts centres, festivals, colleges and corporations.
Country: United States

Schmidt Artists International, Inc.
Website: www.schmidtart.com
Email: info@schmidtart.com
Phone: 212 421 8500
Address: 21 West 74th Street, Suite 1C New York, NY 10023
Description: International classical artist management agency, with world class artists bringing memorable performances to audiences throughout the world. Member of IAMA.
Country: United States
Contact: President and Managing Director Patricia Handy
Email: mph@schmidtart.com
Contact: Vice President Drew Hemenger
Email: drew@schmidtart.com
Contact: senior administrator Katherine Lawhead
Email: katherine@schmidtart.com
Contact: administrator Carrie Davids
Email: carrie@schmidtart.com
Social Media: twitter.com/SchmidtArtists www.facebook.com/SchmidtArtistsIntl www.instagram.com/schmidtartistsinc/
Type: Classical, Other

Sciolino Artist Management LLC
Website: www.samnyc.us
Email: marianne@samnyc.us
Phone: 212 721 9975
Address: 230 Central Park W, Ste 14J New York, NY 10024 USA
Description: SAM is a Manhattan-based artist management firm dedicated to working closely with presenters, orchestras, and festivals to deliver excellent musicianship while meeting their programming and budgetary needs. Established in December 2004 by Founder and Executive Director Marianne Sciolino, SAM represents a select group of instrumental and vocal soloists, ensembles, and conductors. Member of IAMA.
Country: United States
Contact: artist Manager Isaac Bunch
Email: isaac@samnyc.us
Contact: Director of communications Chester Lane
Email: chester@samnyc.us
Contact: database Manager Robyn DeGuzman
Email: robyn@samnyc.us
Social Media: twitter.com/sciolinoartists www.facebook.com/sciolinoartistmanagement

Seidel Artists Management
Website: www.seidelartistsmgmt.com
Email: seidelam@aol.com
Phone: 239 353 2047
Address: 865 New Waterford Dr # S-203 Naples, FL 34104, USA
Description: Seidel Artists Management was created in 1993 in Chicago by Executive Director Jean Seidel, a former singer and artists Manager with a total of more then 30 years working in the professional music industry in the United States and Europe.
Country: United States
Contact: Director Jean Seidel

Seldy Cramer Artists Inc
Website: www.seldycramerartists.com
Email: seldoncramer@gmail.com
Phone: 415 757 0235
Address: 601 Van Ness Avenue, No. 15 San Francisco, CA 94102
Description: Seldy Cramer Artists Inc represents conductors, ensembles and groups, also classical instrumentalists.
Country: United States
Contact: music Director Ray Capiral Capiral
Email: rcapiral@me.com

Shuman Associates Inc
Website: www.shumanAssociates.net
Email: shumanpr@shumanAssociates.net
Phone: 212 315 1300
Address: 229 East 85th Street, PO Box 1309 New York, NY 10028 USA
Description: Shuman Associates is a boutique public relations firm with more than 25 years experience specialising in comprehensive and strategic publicity campaigns and counsel for classical musicians, orchestras, opera companies, and chamber ensembles. They also provide publicity support for special projects including national tours, residencies, recordings, DVDs, radio and television broadcasts, and Artistic and administrative personnel appointments.
Country: United States
Contact: President Constance Shuman
Email: cshuman@shumanAssociates.net
Contact: senior publicist Lisa Jaehnig
Email: ljaehnig@shumanAssociates.net
Social Media: https://twitter.com/shumanpr www.facebook.com/shumanAssociates

Shupp Artists Management
Website: www.shuppartists.com
Email: concerts@shuppartists.com
Phone: 631 928 1531
Address: 202 Michigan Avenue, US

Siegel Artist Management
Website: www.siegelartist.com
Email: jennifer@siegelartist.com
Phone: 570 258 5700
Address: 18 Amherst Avenue Wilkes-Barre, PA 18702 USA
Description: Established in 1970 by the late Ethel Siegel, Siegel Artist Management is an award-winning, boutique agency known for its Artistic excellence, integrity and superior service. They represent an eclectic roster of exceptional artists ranging from special attractions, dance, and music to family entertainment and arts in education.
Country: United States
Contact: artist Manager Laurel Canan
Email: laurel@siegelartist.com
Contact: artist representative Sue Birch
Email: sue@siegelartist.com
Contact: artist representative Julie Eppich
Email: julie@siegelartist.com
Social Media: www.facebook.com/SiegelArtistManagement www.instagram.com/siegelartistmanagement

Sozo Artists
Website: www.sozoartists.com
Email: info@sozomedia.com
Phone: 212 203 0389
Address: 244 Fifth Avenue, R265, US
Description: Sozo Artists, Inc. is an international creative arts agency delivering fresh, accessible and unforgettable experiences to engage and enlighten audiences. Sozo (Japanese for imagine and create) empowers groundbreaking, risk-taking artists of the highest caliber and develops creative content relevant in today's dynamic and diverse world.
Country: United States
Contact: Founder Riko Iino
Contact: business development and Producer Joanna Bowzer
Contact: Director of Marketing and operations, Producer Melissa Higgins
Social Media: @sozoartists www.facebook.com/sozoartists

Sozo Artists
Website: www.sozoartists.com
Email: info@sozomedia.com
Phone: 917 791 3680
Address: 244 Fifth Avenue, R265 New York NY, 10001 USA
Description: Sozo Artists, Inc. is an international arts agency delivering fresh, accessible and unforgettable experiences that engage and enlighten audiences. "Sozo" (Japanese for imagine and create) empowers groundbreaking, risk-taking artists and develops creative content relevant in today's dynamic, diverse world. By building Artistic and cultural bridges through bold, perspective-changing works, Sozo aims to catalyze the possibility of a trusting and understanding society into a reality. Member of ISPA.
Country: United States
Contact: operations coordinator Dana Greenfield
Contact: Director of Marketing, Producer Melissa Higgins
Contact: Founder, Producer Rika Iino
Contact: business Manager, Producer Annie March
Contact: Manager, Producer Chisa Yamaguchi
Social Media: https://www.facebook.com/sozoartists https://twitter.com/sozoartists https://www.instagram.com/sozoartists/

SRO Artists Inc.
Website: www.sroartists.com
Email: gigs@sroartists.com
Phone: 608 664 8160
Address: 6629 University Avenue Suite 206 Middleton, WI 53562
Description: full service booking agency since 1980, SRO exclusively represents North American touring for its roster of established artists and attractions from the US and abroad
Country: United States
Contact: office Manager/contact administrator Toni Ziemer
Contact: President, artist representative international Jeff Laramie
Contact: artist representative John Schimmelman
Contact: artist representative AnneMarie Martins
Contact: assistant artist representative Nina Reynolds
Social Media: www.facebook.com/sroartists

Stanton Management
Website: dev.stantonmgt.com
Email: tdstanton@stantonmgt.com
Phone: 620 563 7312
Address: 25 Cimarron Road Putnam Valley, NY, 10579 USA
Description: For three decades Stanton Consulting has provided services to both for and non-profit organizations as well as management services to select artists.

Their clients have ranged from resident artists at Lincoln Center, to the CEO (a composer at heart) of one of the ten largest US banks, to other organizations and individuals both established and emerging, working from Amsterdam to Singapore.
Country: United States
Contact: chief officer Todd Stanton

Steinway and Sons
Website: www.steinway.com
Email: info@steinway.com
Phone: 718 721 2600
Address: One Steinway Place Astoria, New York 11105 USA
Description: Steinway & Sons was founded in 1853 by Henry E. Steinway and his sons in New York. Together they established a new benchmark in the construction of grand and upright pianos of the highest quality. Having developed more than 125 patents, the company is considered to be the Founder of modern piano construction
Country: United States
Social Media: https://twitter.com/SteinwayAndSons https://www.facebook.com/steinway https://www.instagram.com/steinwayandsons/

The Actors Fund
Website: actorsfund.org
Email: info@actorsfund.org
Phone: 212 221 7300
Address: 729 Seventh Avenue, 10th floor New York, NY 10019 USA
Description: A national human services organization that helps everyone (performers and those behind the scenes) who works in performing arts and entertainment, helping more than 13, 500 people directly each year, and hundreds of thousands online. It serves professionals in film, theatre, television, music, opera, radio and dance.
Country: United States
Social Media: twitter.com/theactorsfund www.facebook.com/theactorsfund www.instagram.com/theactorsfund/

The Agency Group New York
Website: www.theagencygroup.com
Email: ny@theagencygroup.com
Phone: 212 581 3100
Address: 142 West 57th St, 6th Floor, US
Description: The Agency Group is one of the world's leading booking agencies, home to 69 agents with a combined roster of over 1, 500 artists.
Country: United States
Contact: contact Phil Battiato
Email: PhilBattiato@theagencygroup.com
Contact: hr Manager Kate Hanley
Email: KateHanley@theagencygroup.com
Contact: Senior Vice President & Chief Marketing Officer
Eddie Clemens
Email: EddieClemens@theagencygroup.com
Social Media: https://twitter.com/theagencygroup
Type: Classical, Pop/Rock, Folk/Ethnic/World, Other

The Drama League
Website: www.dramaleague.org
Email: info@dramaleague.org
Phone: 212 244 9494
Address: 32 Avenue of the Americas, First Floor, US
Description: Now, more than ever, the theater demands articulate proponents for its urgency, resonance, and universality. As arts participation continues to decline nationwide, Drama League Directors are fully prepared to lead the industry in renewed responsibility to its audiences, delivering heightened relevance, vibrancy, and accessibility to the field. Only to the extent that the field embraces its dedication to audiences –and the role it can play in uplifting and connecting those audiences through their work – will the industry remain a vital element of civilization.
Country: United States
Contact: Executive Artistic Director Gabriel Stelian-Shanks
Email: gabriel@dramaleague.org
Contact: Artistic administrator Julie Solomon
Email: jsolomon@dramaleague.org
Contact: Associate Producer Travis LeMont Ballenger
Email: tballenger@dramaleague.org
Social Media: @dramaleague www.facebook.com/dramaleague
Type: Classical, Vocal

The Kurland Agency
Website: www.thekurlandagency.com
Email: agents@thekurlandagency.com
Phone: 617 254 0007
Address: 173 Brighton Ave, Boston, MA 02134, USA
Description: The Kurland Agency was founded by Ted Kurland in 1975 in Boston. At the time, he was a recent graduate from Brandeis University with a major in Economics. After Kurland graduated, he first worked for a small Boston talent agency, an invaluable experience that launched his career into the talent booking business.
Country: United States
Contact: CEO Ted Kurland

Email: ted@thekurlandagency.com
Contact: President Jack Randall
Email: jack@thekurlandagency.com
Contact: senior vp and Director of management division David Sholemson
Email: davids@thekurlandagency.com
Social Media: https://twitter.com/KurlandAgency https://www.facebook.com/TedKurlandAssociates

The League of Historic American Theatres
Website: www.lhat.org
Email: info@lhat.org
Phone: 443 640 1058
Address: 9 Newport Drive, Suite 200 Forest Hill MD 21050
Description: a non-profit membership association, is a professional network dedicated to sustaining America's historic theatres for the benefit of their communities and future generations
Country: United States
Social Media: https://www.facebook.com/LeagueofHistoricAmericanTheatres/

The Rosebud Agency
Website: www.rosebudus.com
Email: info@rosebudus.com
Phone: 415 386 3456
Address: 650 Delancey Street Suite 309 San Francisco, CA 94107 USA
Description: the Rosebud Agency has wound down its role as an active booking agency as of December 31, 2013. Agency Founder Mike Kappus will continue to work on special projects in addition to select artist management as he has for the past 43 years. The company will continue to service dates already contracted with ongoing staff in addition to Kappus including Lizzie Hill, Connor Martinez and Saori Kappus. New booking representatives for former Rosebud artists are all noted here rosebudus.com/new_agency
Country: United States
Contact: Founder / President Mike Kappus
Email: mikek@rosebudus.com

Tractor Beam
Website: www.tractor-beam.com
Email: dan@tractor-beam.com
Phone: null
Address: 342 East 15th Street, Suite 1A, US
Description: artist management/live event production/televised event production/curatorial programming
Country: United States
Contact: President Daniel Efram
Social Media: www.facebook.com/tractorbeamnyc

Universal Attractions
Website: www.universalattractions.com
Email: info@universalattractions.com
Phone: 212 582 7575
Address: 15 W 36th St #8, New York, NY 10018, USA
Description: In business since 1945, Universal Attractions Agency (UAA) is located in the heart of New York City. The agency's celebrated history includes launching the career of the legendary soul singer James Brown and representing him for more than 40 years. UAA has proven itself as an industry leader among talent agencies, continuing to help direct the careers of some of the most prominent artists, comedians, and entertainers of today.
Country: United States
Social Media: https://twitter.com/uaatalent www.facebook.com/pages/Universal-Attractions-Agency/287887115407
Type: Pop/Rock, Jazz, Other

Unlimited Myles Inc.
Website: www.unlimitedmyles.com
Email: myles@unlimitedmyles.com
Phone: 732 566 2881
Address: 6 Imaginary Pl, Matawan, NJ 07747 USA
Description: Their artists boast an incredible list of awards, including multiple Grammy-winners and multiple nominees; MacArthur Genius Award winners, NEA Jazz Masters, Guggenheim Fellows, Doris Duke Artists and countless "Best" awards in their instrument or vocal categories from the Jazz Journalist Association, JazzTimes Readers and Critics' Polls and Downbeat Critic Readers and Critics' Polls.
Country: United States
Contact: President Myles Weinstein
Email: myles@unlimitedmyles.com
Contact: operations Director Lorraine Kelley Weinstein
Email: lorraine@unlimitedmyles.com
Social Media: www.facebook.com/Unlimited-Myles-169327766416017/ https://twitter.com/UnlimitedMyles

Uzan International Artist Management
Website: www.uzanartists.com
Phone: 212 969 1797
Address: 250 West 57th Street, Suite 1932, US
Description: UIA is a leader in international artist management, with a diverse roster including actors for stage and screen, classical singers for opera and concert, Directors, designers, and conductors; with over 100 years

combined experience in the industry, UIA guarantees the highest level of professionalism available in the entertainment business
Country: United States
Social Media: @UzanArtists www.facebook.com/UzanArtists
Type: Classical, Other

VNI Entertainment
Website: www.vnientertainment.com
Email: info@vnientertainment.com
Phone: 303 814 1500
Address: 200 S. Wilcox, #436, Castle Rock, CO 80104 USA
Description: After more than 21 years in the Music and Entertainment Industry, VNI continues to represent and book many of the brightest acts in Music, Theatre and Family Entertainment. Since its inception in 1981, Vivien Niwes, a graduate of Hofstra University with a bachelor's degree in theatre production, has presented some of the best acts in Jazz, Folk, and Children's Theatre.
Country: United States
Contact: President Vivien Niwes
Email: viv@vnientertainment.com
Contact: Sales Manager Gregg Shively
Email: gregg@vnientertainment.com
Contact: travel and itinerary coordinator Tammy Reardon
Email: itineraries@vnientertainment.com
Contact: public relations and bookkeeper Joelyn Abeyta
Email: pr@vnientertainment.com

William Morris Agency, Inc.
Website: www.wma.com
Email: musicinfo@wma.com
Phone: 212 586 5100
Address: 11 Madison Avenue, US
Description: Formed in 1898, William Morris Agency is the longest-running talent agency. In 2009, WMA merged with Endeavor to become one of the leading entertainment and media companies with an unparalleled list of artists and content creators. In 2014, WME acquired IMG, the global leader in sports, events, media and fashion, forming Endeavor.
Country: United States
Contact: CEO Ari Emanuel
Contact: Executive Vice President Jennifer Walsh
Social Media: @WME www.facebook.com/wmeentertainment
Type: All

William Reinert Associates Inc
Website: www.williamreinert.com
Email: info@williamreinert.com
Phone: 646 236 9702
Address: Post Office Box 1049 Millerton, NY 12546 USA
Description: William Reinert Associates is an independent management company established in 2001 specializing in conductors. The roster features a group of distinguished artists selected for their excellence and diversity. Their continuing commitment to them, as well as to the arts organizations with which we work, is to provide honest and effective representation, and to operate with the highest personal and professional integrity.
Country: United States
Contact: President William Reinert
Email: bill@williamreinert.com
Contact: Manager Alfred Daiboch
Email: alfred@williamreinert.com
Contact: finance and Administration Jennifer Scheuermann
Email: jen@williamreinert.com

Windwood Theatricals
Website: www.windwoodtheatricals.com
Email: paul@windwoodtheatricals.com
Phone: 212 398 3170
Address: 240 W 44th St, New York City, New York, 10036
Description: Established in 2000 by veteran agent Paul Bartz, represents an eclectic blend of mainstream theatrical properties that have been produced on Broadway, Off-Broadway and in regional theaters around the United States.
Country: United States
Contact: President and CEO Paul Bartz
Email: paul@windwoodtheatricals.com
Contact: administrative Manager Diane Bartz
Email: diane@windwoodtheatricals.com

Wolverton Artists Management
Website: www.wolvertonartists.com
Email: dwolverton@wolvertonartists.com
Phone: 703 757 9477
Address: 9704 Beach Mill Road Great Falls, VA 22066 USA
Description: representing a small and select group of gifted artists on the opera, concert and recital stages, WAM's focus is the ongoing development of its roster artists' careers
Country: United States
Contact: Director Donna Wolverton

World Artists
Website: www.lynnmcconnell.com
Email: LynnMc@mindspring.com

Phone: 678 575 0379
Address: 32456 Crown Valley Pkwy, 308, US
Description: work with presenters and artists to create tours throughout the country. This includes organising the tours for the artists, contract negotiations, taking care of promotional material, and attending the conferences
Country: United States
Contact: Director Lynn McConnell
Email: LynnMc@mindspring.com
Type: Children/Youth, Classical, Folk/Ethnic/World, Jazz, Solo/Chamber

Young Concert Artists Inc
Website: www.yca.org
Email: info@yca.org
Phone: 212 307 6655
Address: 1776 Broadway, Suite 1500 New York, New York 10019 USA
Description: Young Concert Artists is a non-profit organisation founded by Susan Wadsworth in 1961, dedicated to discovering and launching the careers of exceptional, but unknown, young musicians from all over the world. YCA artists receive all management services, which bring recitals, educational activities, and concerto appearances with orchestras throughout the United States and abroad, as well as publicity materials, promotion, career guidance and development. Member of IAMA.
Country: United States
Contact: Founder Susan Wadsworth
Email: susan@yca.org
Contact: Director of artist management Monica Felkel
Email: monica@yca.org
Contact: artist Manager Vicki Margulies
Email: vicki@yca.org
Social Media: www.instagram.com/youngconcertartists www.facebook.com/youngconcertartists

Zemsky Green Artists Management
Website: www.zemskygreen.com
Email: info@zemskygreen.com
Phone: 212 579 6700
Address: 104 West 73rd Street, Suite 1, US
Description: Zemsky Green Artists Management manages some of the most important opera artists in the world, at some of the vaunted opera houses internationally.
Country: United States
Contact: co-Founder Bruce Zemsky
Email: bzemsky@zemskygreen.com
Contact: co-Founder Alan Green
Email: agreen@zemskygreen.com
Contact: artists liason Penelope Bussolino
Email: pbussolino@zemskygreen.com
Social Media: https://twitter.com/ZemskyGreen www.facebook.com/Zemsky-Green-Artists-Management-522172261154966/

Zia Artists
Website: www.zia-artists.com
Email: Zia-Artists@nyc.rr.com
Phone: 212 928 6517
Address: 506 Fort Washington Ave #1HNew York, NY 10033, USA
Description: management and representation home for some of the finest talents in contemporary dance
Country: United States
Contact: Director Ken Maldonado
Email: kenmaldonado@me.com

VIRGIN ISLANDS, U.S.

Double M Arts & Events
Website: www.double-m-arts.com
Email: mushalla@mac.com
Phone: 917 864 4137
Address: P.O. Box 793, Cruz Bay Station, VI
Description: Double M Arts & Events, LLC was founded by Michael Mushalla in 1999. The company relocated from New York City to Saint John in the U.S. Virgin Islands in 2014. Michael Mushalla started his career in performing arts management at Columbia Artists Management Inc., in 1981. He served at CAMI as a Vice President and Member of the Board of Directors until 1998.Double M provides comprehensive Creative Producer services to performing artists in the disciplines of music, theater, and dance. Professional consultation services involving strategic planning, programming, and professional development are also available on a limited basis for select clients. Member of ISPA.
Country: Virgin Islands
Contact: Owner Michael Mushalla
Email: mushalla@gmail.com
Social Media: www.facebook.com/DoubleMArts

香 港 中 樂 團
HONG KONG CHINESE ORCHESTRA
藝術總監：閻惠昌
ARTISTIC DIRECTOR : YAN HUICHANG

Hong Kong Chinese Orchestra
Anytime! Anywhere!

H K C O
NET CONCERT HALL

www.hkconetconcerthall.com

BROADCASTING

This section comprises broadcasting stations and television channels that initiate productions of interest to arts organisations. For that reason, many commercial stations and channels, including classical music radio stations, are not included. **The entries are listed in alphabetical order within country.**

Diffusion

Cette section comprend des stations de radiodiffusion et de télévision qui initient des productions d'intérêt aux organismes artistiques. Pour cette raison,de nombreuses stations commerciales et les canaux classiques, y compris les stations de radio de musique, ne sont pas inclus. **Les entrée sont classés par ordre alphabétique dans le pays.**

Rundfunk

Dieser Abschnitt umfasst Rundfunk-und Fernsehsender, die Produktionen von Interesse arts Organisationen initiieren.Aus diesem Grund sind viele kommerzielle Stationen und Kanäle, einschließlich klassischer Musik Radiostationen, nicht im Lieferumfang enthalten. **Die Einträge sind für jedes Land alphabetisch sortiert.**

Emittente

Questa sezione comprende le stazioni di radiodiffusione e canali televisivi che consentono di avviare le produzioni di interesse per le organizzazioni artistiche. Per questo motivo, molte stazioni commerciali e canali, comprese le stazioni radio di musica classica, non sono inclusi. **Le voci sono pubblicate in ordine alfabetico di paese.**

Radiodifusión

Esta sección comprende las emisoras y canales de televisión que inician producciones de interés para las organizaciones artísticas.
Por esa razón, muchas estaciones comerciales y canales, incluyendo estaciones de música clásica de radio, no están incluidos. **Las entradas se muestran en orden alfabético dentro de cada país.**

performing arts
database

AUSTRALIA

2MBS-FM Stereo FM Radio 102.5
Website: www.finemusicfm.com
Email: info@finemusicfm.com
Phone: 294 394 777
Address: 72-76 Chandos Street, AU
Information: A community broadcaster, Fine Music 102.5 is run by more than 320 volunteers – aided by a handful of employees. The first Sydney radio station on the FM band, 2MBS-FM changed to Fine Music 102.5 in July 2012. Fine Mus on Digital and streaming from finemusicfm.com See also Recorded Media. Some 456,000 Sydneysiders and a world-wide audience tune in every month for a vibrant mix of classical, jazz and contemporary music. In Conversation gives an insight into the famous and not-so-famous musicians, composers, conductors and those who influence the local and global musical landscape.
Country: Australia

ABC – Radio Australia
Website: www.abc.net.au/radio-australia/
Address: ABC Ultimo Centre, 700 Harris Street, AU
Information: ABC Radio Australia is the trusted voice in the Pacific, connecting its neighbours with news, music, sport and conversations for all ages.With a focus on the Pacific, ABC Radio Australia offers an Australian perspective on Australian and International issues. Their content on radio, web, mobile and through social media encourages conversation and the sharing of ideas between Australians and the diverse people and cultures of the Pacific.
Country: Australia
Social Media: https:// www.facebook.com/ABCRadioAustralia/ https://twitter.com/radioaustralia
Radio: Yes
Online: Yes

ABC Australia
Website: www.abc.net.au
Phone: 139 994
Address: Sydney, NSW, AU
Information: ABC provides audiences with access to extraordinary Australian stories. It delivers commercial-free, nationally available, free-to-air screen content via a multiplatform multi-channel network. ABC is the destination of choice for audiences seeking high quality, diverse and distinctly Australian content across a wide variety of genres.
Country: Australia
Social Media: https:// www.facebook.com/abc https://twitter.com/abcaustralia/ https:// www.instagram.com/abcaustralia/
Television: Yes
Radio: Yes
Online: Yes

ABC Classic FM
Website: www.abc.net.au/classic
Phone: 437 236 777
Address: PO Box 9994 Melbourne 3001 Victoria, AU
Information: ABC Classic broadcasts the best classical music 24/7 on FM, DAB+, TV and online. Around half of the music they broadcast is performed by Australian artists, and they're committed to developing the next generation of artists – including through the ABC Young Performers Awards.
Country: Australia
Social Media: https:// www.facebook.com/abc.classic/ https://twitter.com/ABCclassic https:// www.instagram.com/abcclassic/
Radio: Yes
Online: Yes

ABC Radio (Perth)
Website: www.abc.net.au
Email: abcradioperth@abc.net.au
Phone: 437 922 720
Address: 30 Fielder Street, AU
Information: ABC Radio Perth is a radio station located in Perth, Western Australia which broadcasts relevant and entertaining programs, reflecting from issues, opinions, and concerns of the local community.
Country: Australia
Social Media: https:// www.facebook.com/abcperth https://twitter.com/abcperth https:// www.instagram.com/abcperth/
Television: Yes
Radio: Yes
Online: Yes

ABC Radio National
Website: www.abc.net.au/radionational/
Phone: 283 332 821
Address: GPO Box 9994, AU
Information: RN shares Australia's best conversations across a diverse range of topics, including arts and culture, business and current affairs, health, science and technology, Indigenous culture and issues, and religion and ethics.
Country: Australia

Board of the Australian Broadcasting Corporation
Website: www.abc.net.au
Email: board@your.abc.net.au
Phone: 139 994
Address: ABC Ultimo Centre, 700 Harris Street, Ultimo, AU
Information: The ABC Board is responsible for the ABC's operations. The duty of the Board is to ensure that the functions of the Corporation are performed efficiently with maximum benefit to the people of Australia, and to maintain the independence and integrity of the Corporation. The Board is also responsible for ensuring that the gathering and presentation of news and information is accurate and impartial, according to recognised standards of journalism.
Country: Australia
Social Media: https:// www.facebook.com/abc https://twitter.com/abcaustralia/ https:// www.instagram.com/abcaustralia/
Television: Yes
Radio: Yes
Online: Yes

Special Broadcasting Service (SBS)
Website: www.sbs.com.au
Phone: 180 050 0727
Address: 14 Herbert Street, Artarmon NSW, AU
Information: SBS is a modern, multiplatform media organisation with a free-to-air TV portfolio spanning five distinctive channels in SBS, NITV, SBS VICELAND, SBS Food and SBS World Movies; an extensive radio network providing 68 communities with services in their own language; and an innovative digital offering, including SBS On Demand, available to audiences anytime and anywhere.
Country: Australia
Social Media: https:// www.facebook.com/SBSAustralia/ https://twitter.com/SBS
Television: Yes
Radio: Yes
Online: Yes

AZERBAIJAN

Azerbaijan Television and Radio Broadcasting Closed Joint-stock Company
Website: www.aztv.az
Email: umumi.shobe@aztv.az
Phone: 559 004 425
Address: AZ1006, Baku city, 1 M. Huseyn Street. AZ
Information: Azerbaijan Radio was established on November 6, 1926, and Azerbaijan Television – on February 14, 1956. Azerbaijan Television has played the most significant role in the formation of television network of the country. Currently, Azerbaijan Television presents talk shows on various themes, autobiographical and travel programmes, music and entertainment programmes, television plays, documentaries and feature films.
Country: Azerbaijan
Social Media: https:// www.facebook.com/aztvresmi/ https://mobile.twitter.com/aztvresmi https:// www.instagram.com/aztv_official/
Television: Yes
Radio: Yes

Baku Independent Television and Broadcasting Company
Website: www.space-az.com
Email: afatbabayeva@space-az.com
Address: 33 Jafar Jabbarly Str, AZ
Country: Azerbaijan

Baku Independent Television and Broadcasting Company
Email: afatbabayeva@space-az.com
Address: 33 Jafar Jabbarly Str, AZ
Country: Azerbaijan

Independent TV and Radio Company 'ANS'
Website: www.ans-dx.com
Email: ans@ans-dx.com
Phone: 124 977 270/4977
Address: 11/28 Kechid, block 504, 1073, AZ
Country: Azerbaijan

Independent TV and Radio Company 'Lider'
Website: www.lidertv.com
Email: mail@media-az.com
Phone: 124 978 899
Address: 83/82, Sh. Mehdieyev str., 1141, AZ
Country: Azerbaijan

Independent TV and Radio Company 'Space'
Website: www.space-az.com
Email: radio@space-az.com
Phone: 124 927 640/4927
Address: 8, H. Javid prosp., 1002, AZ
Country: Azerbaijan

Radio 'Europa Plus' Azerbaijn-Moscow
Website: www.europa.az
Email: radio@europa.az
Phone: 129 77777

Radio 'Space' 104FM
Website: www.space-az.com
Email: radio@space-az.com
Phone: 129 27640
Address: 33 Jafar Jabbarly Str, AZ
Country: Azerbaijan

Radio Antenn 101FM
Website: www.antenn.az
Email: info@antenn.az
Phone: 055 355 4101
Address: Azadlig 189, Binagadi, Baku, AZ
Information: Antenna MTK radio – radio "Antenna" 101 FM has been operating since 1998. The co-founders of the company are Rustam Gadim oglu Aliyev (President) and Rovshan Novruz oglu Javadov (Vice President).In February 2000, the radio channel "Radio Antenna 101 Fm" began broadcasting. During this time, the radio has formed a stable audience, and its coverage has expanded. The company broadcasts news, political, thematic, music programs and produces audio-video advertisements.
Country: Azerbaijan
Social Media: https://fb.com/RadioAntenn/ www.instagram.com/radioantenn101fm/
Radio: Yes
Online: Yes

TV and Radio Station 'Azad Azerbaijan'
Website: www.azadazerbaijan.com
Email: atv@azadazerbvaijan.com
Phone: 124 970 106/4974
Address: 8, A. Abbaszadeh str., 1073, AZ
Country: Azerbaijan

CANADA

Bravo!
Website: www.bravofact.com
Email: bravomail@bravo.ca
Phone: 416 384 2738
Address: 299 Queen St West, CA
Information: bravo delivers compelling stories through clever and immersive programming to viewers across Canada. From high-profile dramas to blockbuster feature films
Country: Canada
Social Media: www.facebook.com/bravoCanada

Canadian Broadcasting Corporation Montreal
Website: www.cbc.ca
Email: io@radio-canada.ca
Phone: 514 597 6000
Address: P.O. Box 6000, B96-1, CA
Information: Canada's national public broadcaster. Le radiodiffuseur public national du Canada
Country: Canada
Social Media: www.facebook.com/CBCMontreal

CBC (Canadian Broadcasting Corporation)
Website: www.cbc.ca
Email: george_anthony@cbc.ca
Phone: 866 306 4636
Address: PO Box 500, Station A, CA
Information: the home of Canadian content. In the 2010-2011 broadcast year, CBC Television showed 85% Canadian programming over the full broadcast day
Country: Canada

CFMX-FM
Website: www.classical963fm.com
Email: classical963fm@cfmx.com
Phone: 416 367 5353
Address: 70 Jefferson Avenue, CA
Information: classical radio station that is one of the largest in Canada
Country: Canada
Social Media: @classical963fm www.facebook.com/thenewclassical

CHINA

China Beijing TV Station (BTV)
Website: www.btv.org
Email: news2144@sohu.com
Phone: 106 841 9824
Address: Jia No. 98, , Jian Guo Road, , Chao Yang District,
Information: 24 hours broadcasting, alternative website: www.webmaster@btv.org
Country: China

China Network Television (CNTV)
Website: www.cctv.com.cn
Email: CCTV-9@mail.cctv.com
Phone: 861 068 506 915
Address: China Network Television, Wang Hai Building D, , No. 10, San Huan Zhong Road, , Hai Dian Western District,
Information: 24-hour broadcasting, founded in 1996 (the earliest information TV in China). Their main focus is on information and entertainment
Country: China

China Radio International
Website: chinaplus.cri.cn
Email: crieng@cri.com.cn
Phone: 106 889 2571
Address: 16A Shijingshan Road, Beijing, 100040, CN
Information: China Radio International (CRI) was founded on December 3, 1941. CRI aims to introduce China to the rest of the world, introduce the world to China, report global affairs to the world, and promote understanding and friendship between the Chinese and peoples from other countries. CRI is China's only state-level radio and television media organization specializing in international communications. CRI is headquartered in Beijing, China.
Country: China
Social Media: twitter.com/chinaplusnewsfacebook.com/chinaplusnews

HONG KONG

Radio Television Hong Kong (RTHK) (1)
Website: www.rthk.org.hk/channel/radio4/
Email: radio4@rthk.org.hk
Phone: 233 96425
Address: Radio 4, Radio Television Hong Kong, 30 Broadcast Drive, Kowloon, HK
Information: mainly for classical music, also jazz, world and chinese music
Country: Hong Kong

Radio Television Hong Kong (RTHK) (2)
Website: www.rthk.org.hk
Email: webmaster@rthk.org.hk
Phone: 233 97600
Address: Television House, 1A Broadcast Drive, HK
Information: direct line to assistant Director: Tel: 2339-7601
Country: Hong Kong

INDONESIA

Indosiar TV
Website: www.indosiar.com
Email: market@indosiar.com
Phone: 215 672 222
Address: Jl. Damai No.11 Daan Mogot, ID
Information: private
Country: Indonesia

Radio Klasik FM
Website: www.klasik.co.id
Email: klasik@dnet.net.id
Phone: 213 521 020
Address: Rukan Tempo Dulu Blok A no.1, Segitiga Senen, Jl. Senen Raya no.135, ID
Country: Indonesia

Rajawali Citra Televisi Indonesia (RCTI)
Website: www.rcti.co.id/channel/
Email: palembang-tx@rcti.tv
Phone: 711 364 724
Address: Lr Pakjo I 88, ID
Information: private
Country: Indonesia

Televisi Republik Indonesia (TVRI)
Website: www.tvri.co.id
Email: tvritivnat@cbn.net.id
Phone: 622 157 31973
Address: Kompl Gelora Senayan, ID
Information: state-owned
Country: Indonesia

JAPAN

AIR-G' – FM Hokkaido
Website: www.air-g.co.jp
Phone: 112 410 804
Address: 14F Sapporo Tokeidai Bldg., Chuo-ku, , JP
Country: Japan
Social Media: @AIRG_FM@airgfm

Alpha-Station FM Kyoto
Website: www.fm-kyoto.jp
Address: 620, Suiginya-cho, Shimogyo-ku, Kyoto 600-8566 COCON Karasuma 8F α-STATION
Information: With the development of IP radio, α-STATION has now become a "national media".α-STATION aims to be the "only one" that cultivates excellent culture and develops its own market by sticking to the city of "Kyoto" that constantly creates new culture and revitalizing it. As a "portal media from Kyoto", α-STATION isacting with the aim of further contributing to regional revitalization as a nationwide unrivaled existence that can support and share "the power of Kyoto".
Country: Japan
Social Media: facebook.com/α-STATION-FM-KYOTO-131174726976156/twitter.com/fmkyoto/ www.instagram.com/fmkyoto89.4/
Radio: Yes

Asahi Broadcasting Corporation (ABC)
Website: www.asahi.co.jp
Phone: 816 458 5321
Address: 2-2-48 Ohyodo-Minami, Kita-ku, JP
Information: Tokyo branch: ABC Kaikan (q.v.), 2-6-3 Shiba Koen, Minato-ku, Tokyo 105-0011 Tel: 3-3436 5771
Country: Japan

Chubu-Nippon Broadcasting Co Ltd. (CBC)
Website: www.hicbc.com
Phone: 522 418 111
Address: Nagoya, Aichi, JP
Information: CBC covers the Chubu region (Aichi, Gifu, Mie) and is located in the center of the island of Japan where leading manufacturers in automotive, aerospace, machinery etc. set-up base. Since its first airing as Japan's first commercial broadcaster in 1951, CBC has consistently adopted contribution to society as a corporate principle through high quality television shows and cultural creation as a corporate principle and continues to strive forward together with the people of the Chubu region.
Country: Japan
Social Media: twitter.com/CBC_GLOBAL
Television: Yes
Radio: Yes

CLASSICA-JAPAN Corp.
Website: www.classica-jp.com
Email: classica@gol.com
Phone: 354 148 848
Address: 4-8-10 Akasaka, Minato-ku, JP
Country: Japan

FM Fukuoka
Website: www.fmfukuoka.co.jp
Phone: 927 816 181
Address: 2-1-82 Watanabe-dori, Chuo-ku, JP
Information: Tokyo Office: 8F, JFN Centre, 1-8 Kohjimachi, Chiyoda-ku 102-0083 Tel: 3-3221 0282
Country: Japan

fm osaka
Website: fmosaka.net
Phone: 643 960 857
Address: 7F, 1-3-1 Minato-machi, Naniwa-ku, JP
Information: Tokyo Office: 8F Millennium Tsukiji, 2-15-19 Tsukiji, Chuo-ku, Tokyo 104-0045; Tel: 3 3543 0191
Country: Japan

FMA
Website: www.fma.co.jp
Phone: 522 635 141
Address: Nagoya Tsushin Bldg., 2-15-18 Chiyoda, Naka-ku, Nagoya, JP
Information: Tokyo Office: 6F JFN Centre, 1-8 Kohjimachi, Chiyoda-ku 102-0083 Tel: 3-3221 0263
Country: Japan

NHK (Japan Broadcasting Corporation)
Website: www.nhk.or.jp
Phone: 334 651 111
Address: NHK Broadcasting Centre, 2-2-1 Jinnan, Shibuya-ku, JP
Information: alternative website: www.nhk.or.jp/englishtop
Country: Japan

NHK Radio 1 (Dai-1)
Website: www.nhk.or.jp
Phone: 334 651 111
Address: NHK Broadcasting Centre, 2-2-1 Jin'nan, Shibuya-ku, JP
Country: Japan

NHK Radio 2 (Dai-2)
Website: www.nhk.or.jp
Phone: 334 651 111
Address: NHK Broadcasting Centre, 2-2-1 Jin'nan, Shibuya-ku, JP
Country: Japan

NHK-FM
Website: www.nhk.or.jp
Phone: 334 651 111
Address: NHK Broadcasting Centre, 2-2-1 Jin'nan, Shibuya-ku, JP
Country: Japan

Nippon Television Network (NTV)
Website: www.ntv.co.jp
Address: Minato-ku, Tokyo, Japan
Information: Nippon Television Network Corporation, doing business as Nippon TV, is a television network based in the Shiodome area of Minato, Tokyo, Japan and is controlled by the Yomiuri Shimbun publishing company. Broadcasting terrestrially across Japan, the network is commonly known as, contracted to, and abbreviated as "NTV" or "AX". One of the founders of Yomiuri Nippon Symphony Orchestra (q.v.)
Country: Japan
Social Media: facebook.com/NipponTVNews24Japan/
Television: Yes

Plankton Co Ltd
Website: www.plankton.co.jp
Email: info@plankton.co.jp
Phone: 362 739 307
Address: Jingumae 5-28-10-1F, Shibuya-ku, JP
Information: Since its establishment in 1984, Plankton Co., Ltd. has been striving to provide high-quality music and consistent music production that is reliable as a professional for many years. Plankton Co Ltd. promotes, produces concerts, manages music publishing and produces music for TV and radio commercials.
Country: Japan
Social Media: facebook.com/%E3%83%97%E3%83%A9%E3%83%B3%E3%82%AF%E3%83%88%E3%83%B3-Plankton-163011970469123/twitter.com/plankton_co_jp

RKB Mainichi Hohsoh
Website: www.rkb.ne.jp/
Phone: 819 285 26666
Address: 2-3-8 Momochihama, Sawara-ku, JP
Country: Japan

Theater Television Co., Ltd.
Website: www.theatertv.co.jp
Email: info@theatertv.co.jp
Phone: 335 686 201
Address: 3F Mitokoh-Bldg., 6-2-4 Akasaka, Minato-ku, JP
Information: a new 24-hour Digital Communication Satellite TV station established exclusively for performing arts both in Japan and abroad; plans/promotes arts-related events
Country: Japan

Tokyo Broadcasting System (TBS)
Website: www.tbs.co.jp
Email: english@best.tbs.co.jp
Phone: 355 712 429
Address: 5-3-6 Akasaka, Minato-ku, JP
Country: Japan

TV Tokyo (2)
Website: www.tv-tokyo.co.jp
Email: ir@tv-tokyo.co.jp
Phone: 334 321 212
Address: 4-3-12 Toranomon, Minato-ku, JP
Country: Japan

Yomiuri Telecasting Corporation
Website: www.ytv.co.jp
Phone: 669 472 275 (pr)
Address: 2-2-33 Shiromi, Chuo-ku, JP
Information: one of the founders of Yomiuri Nippon Symphony Orchestra (q.v.)
Country: Japan

REPUBLIC OF KOREA

Buddhist Broadcasting System (BBS)
Website: www.bbsfm.co.kr
Email: bbsmaster@bbsfm.co.kr
Phone: 270 55114
Address: Dabo Bldg, 140, Mapo-dong, Mapo-gu
Information: local network: Busan, Gwangju, Daegu, Cheongju
Country: Republic of Korea

Christian Broadcasting System (CBS)
Website: www.cbs.co.kr
Phone: 226 505 000
Address: 917-1, Mok 1-dong, Yangcheon-gu
Information: has two channels: General FM and music FM; air time 20 hours
Country: Republic of Korea

EBS Radio-Programming Department
Website: www.ebs.co.kr/contents/radio/
Phone: 215 440 349
Address: 463 Dogok2-dong, Gangnam-gu
Country: Republic of Korea

Korea Educational Broadcasting System (EBS)
Website: www.ebs.co.kr
Email: helpdesk@ebs.co.kr
Phone: 215 440 349
Address: 463, Dogok2-dong, Gangnam-gu
Country: Republic of Korea

Korean Broadcasting System (KBS)
Website: www.kbs.co.kr/radio
Email: webmaster@kbs.co.kr
Phone: 278 11000
Address: 18-Ga, Yeouido-dong, Yeongdeungpo-gu
Information: has two channels – KBS1 and KBS2; local network: Pusan, Taegu, Taejon, Kwangju, Ch'angwon, Chonju, Ch'unch'on, Ch'ongju, Mokp'o, Yosu, Namwon, P'ohang, Kongju, Kangnung, Sokch'o, Wonju, Cheju, Chinju, Yongwol, Andong, Sunch'on, Kunsan, Ch'ungju, Taebaek
Country: Republic of Korea

Korean Broadcasting System (KBS) (2)
Website: www.kbs.co.kr/radio
Email: webmaster@kbs.co.kr
Phone: 278 11000

Address: 18-Ga, Yeouido-dong, Yeongdeungpo-gu
Information: has six channels: AM 1Radio/ 3 Radio/ social education, FM 1FM/ 2FM/ 2 Radio
Country: Republic of Korea

Munwha Broadcasting Corporation (MBC)
Website: www.imbc.com/broad/radio
Phone: 278 00011
Address: 31 Yeoido-dong, Yongdeungpo-ku
Information: local network: Busan, Daegu, Gwangju, Jeonju, Masan, Chuncheon
Country: Republic of Korea

Munwha Broadcasting Corporation (MBC)
Website: www.imbc.com/broad/radio
Email: ichigo51@imbc.co.kr
Phone: 278 00011
Address: 31 Yeoido-dong, Yongdeungpo-ku
Information: has two channels: FM4U, General FM
Country: Republic of Korea
Social Media: @withMBC www.facebook.com/MBC

Pyunghwa Brodcasting Company (PBC)
Website: www.pbc.co.kr
Email: pbc@pbc.co.kr
Phone: 222 702 114
Address: 2-3, 1-ga, Jeo-dong, Joong-gu
Information: local network: Gwangju, Daegu, Busan, Daejeon, Pohang, Andong, Yeosu
Country: Republic of Korea

Seoul Broadcasting System (SBS)
Website: www.sbs.co.kr
Email: webmaster@sbs.co.kr
Phone: 220 610 006
Address: 920 Mok1-dong, Yangcheon-gu
Information: local network: Taeku, Pusan, Kwangju, Taejon, Ulsan, Jeonju, Cheongjju, Gongwon, Jeju
Country: Republic of Korea

Seoul Broadcasting System (SBS)
Website: www.sbs.co.kr
Email: webmaster@sbs.co.kr
Phone: 220 610 006
Address: 920 Mok1-dong, Yangcheon-gu
Information: local network: Daegu, Busan, Gwangju, Daejon, Ulsan, Jeonju, Cheongju, Gangwon, Jeju
Country: Republic of Korea

Tae Jeon Broadcasting (TJB)
Website: www.tjb.co.kr
Phone: 422 811 101
Address: Advertisement Business Team, TJB, 122-1 Hyo-dong, Dong-gu
Country: Republic of Korea

Taeku Brodcasting Corporation (TBC)
Website: www.tbc.co.kr
Phone: 537 601 900
Address: Dept. of Business, TBC, 201-9 Doosan-dong, Soosong-gu
Country: Republic of Korea

TBC Radio-Programming Department
Website: www.tbc.co.kr
Phone: 276 01900
Address: 201-9 Doosan-dong, Soosung-gu
Country: Republic of Korea

MEXICO

Bocero Huasteco
Email: bocerohuasteco@hotmail.com
Address: Sistema Hidalguense de Radio y Televisión, Blvd. López Mateos s/n, colonia aviacion civil, MX
Country: Mexico

Canal 22-XEIMT T.V. Televisión Metropolitana
Website: www.canal22.org.mx
Email: correo@canal22.org.mx
Address: MX
Country: Mexico
Social Media: @Canal22
Country: Mexico

Radio Educacion
Website: www.radioeducacion.mx/
Email: xeepro@conaculta.gob.mx
Phone: 554 155 1050
Address: Radio Educación, Angel Urraza No. 622, MX
Country: Mexico

Radio Formula
Website: www.radioformula.com.mx
Email: orf@radioformula.com.mx
Phone: 555 279 2172
Address: Organizaci, Privada de Horacio 10, Col. Los Morales Potanco, MX
Country: Mexico

Radio Jacala
Phone: 441 673 3431
Address: Sistema Hidalguense de Radio y Televisi, Cuartel Guerrero s/n, MX

Radio Lagarto
Website: radiolagarto.imer.gob.mx/index.php
Email: radiolagarto@imer.com.mx
Phone: 961 616 033
Address: IMER – Instituto Mexicano de la Radio, Mayorazgo 83, Col. Xoco, MX
Country: Mexico

Radio Mexiquense
Email: contacto@tvmexiquense.mx
Phone: 722 275 5624
Address: Sistema de Radio y Televisión Mexiquense, Av. Estado de México Oriente # 1701, Col. Llano Grande, MX
Country: Mexico
Social Media: http:// www.facebook.com/radioytv.mexiquense

Radio UNAM
Website: www.radiounam.unam.mx/index.php
Email: contacto@radiounam.unam.mx
Phone: 553 68989
Address: Radio Universidad Nacional Autónoma de México, Adolfo Prieto No. 133 Colonia del Valle, MX
Country: Mexico
Social Media: www.facebook.com/radiounam

Radio Universidad
Phone: 981 62164
Address: Universidad Aut, Calla Orqu, entre Margaritas y Narciso, MX
Country: Mexico

Radio Universidad Autónoma de Aguascalientes
Website: www.uaa.mx
Email: cvargas@correo.uaa.mx
Address: Av. Universidad 940, MX
Country: Mexico

Radio Universidad Autónoma de Baja California
Website: www.sur.uabc.mx
Email: radio@uabc.edu.mx
Phone: 686 553 6460
Address: Universidad Autónoma, Av. Alvaro Obregón, MX
Country: Mexico

T.V. UNAM
Website: www.tvunam.unam.mx
Address: Circuito Maestro Mario de la Cueva s/n, Frente a la Facultad de Ciencias Pol, CD. Universitaria, MX
Country: Mexico
Social Media: @tvunam www.facebook.com/pages/TVUNAM/111276004723

Television Azteca
Email: contacto@tvazteca.com
Phone: 180 072 71919
Address: Periférico Sur 4121, Fuentes del Pedregal, MX
Country: Mexico
Social Media: @tvaztecaoficial http:// www.facebook.com/tvazteca

Voz del Valle
Phone: 646 165 2023
Address: Instituto Nacional Indigenista, 8va. #139, MX
Country: Mexico

NEW ZEALAND

Radio New Zealand Concert
Website: www.radionz.co.nz/concert
Email: concert@radionz.co.nz
Phone: 447 41999
Address: Level 2 Radio New Zealand House, 155 The Terrace, PO Box 123, NZ
Information: covers a large percentage of New Zealand as well as live streaming via the internet; monthly podcast available for download; part of Radio New Zealand; can also be received throughout the country via satellite on Freeview and Sky Digital
Country: New Zealand
Social Media: @RNZConcert http:// www.facebook.com/RadioNewZealandConcert

Radio New Zealand International
Website: www.rnzi.com
Email: info@rnzi.com
Phone: 447 41437
Address: PO Box 123, NZ
Information: broadcasts mainly to the South Pacific Islands, though it can be heard worldwide
Country: New Zealand

Radio New Zealand Ltd
Website: www.radionz.co.nz
Email: rnz@radionz.co.nz
Phone: 447 41999
Address: 155 The Terrace, L2 Radio New Zealand House, PO Box 123, NZ
Information: New Zealand's publicly funded radio broadcaster, operating domestic networks: National Radio, Concert FM, AM Network; and shortwave: Radio New Zealand International
Country: New Zealand

Television New Zealand
Website: tvnz.co.nz
Phone: 991 67000
Address: Television Centre, 100 Victoria Street West, PO Box 3819, NZ
Information: occasional performing arts programmes
Country: New Zealand

TV3 /TV4 Network Services Limited
Website: www.tv3.co.nz
Phone: 992 89000
Address: 3 Flower Street, Eden Terrace, Private Bag 92624, Symonds Street, NZ
Information: occasional performing arts programmes
Country: New Zealand

TVNZ Channel 2
Website: tvnz.co.nz
Phone: 991 67000
Address: TVNZ Television Centre, 100 Victoria St West, PO Box 3819, NZ
Information: light entertainment
Country: New Zealand

PHILIPPINES

GMA Network Inc.
Website: www.igma.tv
Email: gmaf@gmanetwork.com
Phone: 298 27777
Address: GMA Network Drive cor. Samar Street, Diliman, PH
Information: see also Radio
Country: Philippines
Social Media: @gmakf

GMA Network Inc.
Website: www.igma.tv
Email: gmaf@gmanetwork.com
Phone: 298 27777
Address: GMA Network Drive cor. Samar Street, Diliman, PH
Information: see also TV
Country: Philippines
Social Media: @gmakf

SINGAPORE

Media Development Authority (MDA)
Website: www.mda.gov.sg
Email: mda_input@mda.gov.sg
Phone: 637 73800
Address: 3 Fusionopolis Way, #16-22 Symbiosis, SG
Country: Singapore
Social Media: @MDASingapore www.facebook.com/MDASingapore

MediaCorp Radio Singapore Pte Ltd.
Website: www.mediacorpradio.sg
Address: Caldecott Broadcast Centre, Andrew Road, SG
Country: Singapore

MediaCorp TV Singapore Pte Ltd
Website: www.mediacorptv.com
Email: editor@mediacorp.com.sg
Address: Caldecott Broadcast Centre, Andrew Road, SG
Country: Singapore

Symphony FM 92.4 Mediacorp Radio Singapore Pte Ltd
Website: www.mediacorpradio.sg
Email: symphony@mediacororadio.com
Address: Caldecott Broadcasting Centre, Andrew Road, SG
Information: one of many FM stations organized by Mediacorp Radio Singapore PTE LTD
Country: Singapore

PROVINCE OF CHINA TAIWAN

Broadcasting Corporation of China (BCC)
Website: www.bcc.com.tw
Email: pr@mail.bcc.com.tw
Phone: 225 019 688
Address: No. 375, Sung Chiang Road, Zhung Shan District
Information: 7 different networks including pop, and classical music
Country: Taiwan

China Television Company (CTV)
Website: www.chinatv.com.tw
Email: jiang@mail.chinatv.com.tw
Phone: 227 838 308
Address: No.120, Chung-Yang Road, Nankang district
Country: TW

Philharmonic Radio Taipei
Website: www.e-classical.com.tw
Email: prtweb@e-classical.com.tw
Phone: 287 683 399
Address: 7F, 47 Dong Xing Rd, Xin Yi District
Country: Taiwan

Radio Taiwan International
Website: www.rti.org.tw
Email: prog@rti.org.tw
Phone: 228 856 168
Address: CBS RTI, 55, Pei An Road
Information: broadcasts in Mandarin, Hokkien, Cantonese, Hakka, Tibetan, Mongolian, English, French, German, Russian, Spanish, Arabic, Japanese, Korean, Vietnamese, Thai, Indonesian and Myanmar language; alternative website: www.cbs.org.tw
Country: Taiwan

Taiwan Television Enterprise
Website: www.ttv.com.tw
Email: jeffrey@ttv.com.tw
Phone: 225 781 515
Address: No.10, Sec. 3, Ba De Road, Chong Shan District
Information: established 51 years ago. Taiwan's first television station
Country: Taiwan

UNITED STATES

Classic Arts Showcase (TV)
Website: www.classicartsshowcase.org
Email: casmail@sbcglobal.net
Phone: 238 780 283
Address: 7250 Franklin Avenue, Suite 1401 Los Angeles, CA 90046, US
Information: Classic Arts Showcase is a not-for-profit 24-hour satellite programming service offered free of charge through local public service channels, and both cable and broadcast stations. It is available in more than 50 million homes. The foundation's goal in creating CAS was to inspire viewers to go out and see live performances in their own communities, and to help to build a growing audience for the arts.
Country: United States

CLASSIC99
Website: www.classic99.com
Email: classic99@classic99.com
Phone: 314 725 0099
Address: 85 Founders Lane, US
Country: United States
Social Media: www.facebook.com/pages/CLASSIC-99com/148167235228213

Classical 99.5 WCRB
Website: www.classicalwcrb.org
Phone: 173 003 300
Address: WCRB, One Guest Street, Boston, MA 02135, US
Information: In 2009, WCRB became a listener-supported station, as part of the WGBH Educational Foundation. Previously, WCRB was a commercially-operated station, founded in 1948, with a history of classical music broadcasting dating back to the 1950s. WCRB's mission is to bring the joy and beauty of classical music to as many people as possible and to bring as many people as possible into the world of classical music. WCRB aims to make classical music accessible to all.
Country: United States
Contact: Associate Producer Colin Brumley
Email:
Digital Associate Producer Kendall Todd
Email:
Program Director Rani Schloss
Email:
Station Manager Anthony Rudel
Email:
Social Media: facebook.com/995wcrbtwitter.com/995wcrbinstagram.com/995wcrb
Radio: Yes
Online: Yes

Classical KING FM 98.1
Website: www.KING.org
Email: web@king.org
Phone: 206 691 2981
Address: 10 Harrison Street, Suite 100, US
Country: United States

Classical KUSC
Website: www.kusc.org
Email: info@kdb.com
Phone: 132 257 400
Address: 1149 S. Hill Street Suite H100 Los Angeles, CA 90015, US
Information: KUSC nurtures a love of classical music, inspiring people to make it an enduring part of their lives. The station curates beautiful music, creates compelling experiences and welcomes all on the journey. Listener-supported, the station is the largest classical music station in the US and is a broadcast service of the University of Southern California.
Country: United States
Contact: President, USC Radio Group Judy McAlpine
Email: jmcalpine@kusc.org
Administrative Assistant Jennifer Tuffy
Email:
Vice President, Content, USC Radio Mark Steinmetz
Email: msteinmetz@kusc.org
Social Media: facebook.com/classicalkusc/twitter.com/classicalkuscinstagram.com/classicalkusc/

KCME Classical Music Radio
Website: www.kcme.org
Email: shorton@kcme.org
Phone: 195 785 263
Address: 1921 N Weber St Colorado Springs, CO 80907, US
Information: 88.7 KCME-FM is an independent public radio station that broadcasts classical music twenty-four hours a day. Founded in 1977, KCME's studios were located in a small house near a babbling brook in Manitou Springs, Colorado. In March of 1993 KCME moved its studios and offices to the present location. Over the years, KCME has grown to the point where it now broadcasts its signal over a much wider area from its transmitter high atop Cheyenne Mountain in Colorado Springs.
Country: United States
Contact: KCME Programming Director, Music Director, Librarian, and Weekend Afternoon Host ROBERT BRUCE
Email:
KCME Operations Director and Weekday Late Afternoon host KEITH SIMON
Email:
General Manager / KCME and Jazz 93.5 ROBYN SEDGWICK
Email:
Social Media: www.facebook.com/KCMEClassical887/
Radio: Yes

Ovation
Website: www.ovationtv.com
Email: info@ovationtv.com
Phone: 131 043 07575
Address: 2850 Ocean Park Blvd, #225, US
Information: 20 hours broadcasting
Country: United States

The World from PRX
Website: www.pri.org
Email: facebook@theworld.org
Address: 1 Guest St Boston, US
Information: The World is public radio's longest-running daily global news program. It's goal is to engage domestic US audiences with international affairs through human-centered journalism that consistently connects the global to the local and builds empathy for people around the world. The World is a co-production of PRX and WGBH that broadcasts from the Nan and Bill Harris Studios at WGBH in Boston, Massachusetts.
Country: United States
Social Media: www.facebook.com/pritheworld/twitter.com/TheWorld www.instagram.com/pritheworld/
Radio: Yes
Online: Yes

WAUS-FM
Website: www.waus.org
Email: waus@andrews.edu
Phone: 694 713 400
Address: WAUS-FM Berrien Springs, MI 49104, US
Information: WAUS-FM is located on the beautiful campus of Andrews University in the cozy village of Berrien Springs, MI.nestled on the banks of the St. Joseph river. WAUS-FM's format is Classical Music with inspirational programming and news updates from National Public Radio (NPR). WAUS is one of Andrews University's services to the community, and because of its dedication to education, they hire and train university students in various aspects of the radio business.
Country: United States
Social Media: www.facebook.com/WAUS-FM-18232076982/twitter.com/wausfm
Radio: Yes

WGBH Radio Boston
Website: www.wgbh.org
Phone: 173 005 400
Address: 1 Guest St Boston, MA 02135, US
Information: GBH is the leading multiplatform creator for public media in America. As the largest Producer of content for PBS and partner to NPR and PRX, GBH delivers compelling experiences, stories and information to audiences wherever they are. GBH produces digital and broadcast programming that engages, illuminates and inspires, through drama and science, history, arts, culture and journalism.
Country: United States
Social Media: www.facebook.com/GBH/twitter.com/gbh www.instagram.com/wgbh/
Television: Yes
Radio: Yes

WNYC Radio New York
Website: www.wnyc.org
Email: publicfile@nypublicradio.org
Phone: 468 294 400
Address: 160 Varick Street, 8th floor New York, NY
Information: WNYC 93.9 FM and AM 820 are New York's flagship public radio stations, broadcasting the finest programs from NPR, American Public Media, Public Radio Exchange and the BBC World Service, as well as a wide range of award-winning local programming.
Country: United States
Social Media: www.facebook.com/WNYC/twitter.com/wnyc www.instagram.com/wnyc/

WRR Classical 101.1 FM
Website: www.wrr101.com
Email: info@wrr101.com
Phone: 214 670 8888
Address: 1516 First Ave, US
Information: is the first commercially licensed radio station in Texas; broadcasting since 1921
Country: United States
Social Media: @wrr101 www.facebook.com/wrr101

Major international music competitions are included along with the substantially fewer international dance and drama competitions that exist. **The entries are listed in alphabetical order within country.**

Concours

Ici sont répertoriés les concours internationaux de musique, de danse et de théâtre les plus importants. **Les entrée sont classés par ordre alphabétique dans le pays.**

Wettbewerbe

Eingeschlossen sind die wichtigsten internationlen Musikwettbewerbe, sowie die weniger häufig stattfindenen internationlen Tanz- und Schauspielwettbewerbe. **Die Einträge sind für jedes Land alphabetisch sortiert.**

Concorsi

Sono inclusi tutti i maggiori concorsi internazionali di musica e canto ed alcuni concorsi internazionali di danza e teatro. **Le voci sono pubblicate in ordine alfabetico di paese.**

Concursos

En esta sección aparecen los principales concursos interna-cionales de música y algunos concursos de danza y teatro de cobertura internacional. **Las entradas se muestran en orden alfabético dentro de cada país.**

performing arts
database

AUSTRALIA

Adelaide International Classical Guitar Competition
Website: https://www.adelaideguitarfestival.com.au/about/adelaide-international-classical-guitar-competition/
Email: feedback@adelaidefestivalcentre.com.au
Phone: 882 168 600
Address: GPO Box 1269, Adelaide 5001
Information: The Adelaide International Classical Guitar Competition is the most prestigious guitar competition in the Southern Hemisphere, providing career-launching opportunities for the winners. After two rigorous rounds up to eight finalists under 32 will perform in the culminating, career-defining round.
Country: Australia
Contact: Artistic Director Slava Grigoryan
Social Media: www.twitter.com/guitar_festival www.facebook.com/adelaideguitarfestival www.instagram.com/adlguitarfest/
Frequency: Annual

Australian Singing Competition
Website: aussing.org
Email: info@mostlyopera.org
Phone: 292 314 293
Address: Level 4, Culwulla Chambers 67 Castlereagh Street Sydney NSW 2000
Information: This Australian Singing Competition is recognised as one of the longest-running events of its kind, offering a range of scholarships, prizes, career and network opportunities, which also make the competition one of the richest in terms of financial and career opportunities available to opera and classical singers in Australasia.
Country: Australia
Social Media: facebook.com/AusSingCompt twitter.com/AusSingComp instagram.com/aussingcomp
Awards: A range of prizes for each competition hosted by Australian Singing Competition

Melbourne International Chamber Music Competition
Website: musicaviva.com.au/comp/
Email: contact@musicaviva.com.au
Phone: 283 946 666
Address: c/ – Musica Viva Australia, 757 Elizabeth Street, 2017 Zetland, AU
Information: The Melbourne International Chamber Music Competition is one of the world's great chamber music launching pads. Discovering and nurturing the next generation of ensembles, the competition seeks musicians who personify chamber music's ability to engage the mind and the heart with performances that thrill, delight and inspire. MICMC ensembles ensure a vibrant future for the chamber music, redefining the intimate relationships between players, audiences, and composers for the 21st century.
Country: Australia
Contact: Artistic Director Wilma Smith
Social Media: facebook.com/MusicaVivaAustralia twitter.com/MusicaVivaAU instagram.com/musicavivaau/

Sydney International Piano Competition
Website: thesydney.com.au
Email: info@thesydney.com.au
Phone: 292 413 291
Address: PO Box R104, Royal Exchange NSW 1225, Australia
Information: The Sydney International Piano Competition has, from its inception, held events at the highest international level inspiring pianists and audiences alike and stimulating interest in the piano and music in General. It has provided a showcase platform for outstanding pianists from all over the world and assisted with the development of their careers as concert Artists.
It is one of the major international events of its kind in the world. Founded by the late Miss Claire Dan AM, OBE, Rex Hobcroft AM and Robert Tobias, it was inaugurated in July 1977 and has since been held every four years, except in 1988 when it was brought forward to coincide with the Bicentenary of Australia celebrations. The Sydney was admitted as a member of the Geneva based World Federation of International Music Competitions in 1978, the first Australian competition to be accepted as a member.
Country: Australia
Contact: Artistic Director Piers Lane AO
Email: info@thesydney.com.au
Chief Executive Marcus Barker
Email: marcus@thesydney.com.au
Social Media: facebook.com/sydneypianocomp twitter.com/SydneyPianoComp instagram.com/sydneypianocomp
Awards: A total cash prize pool of over AU$164, 000 is offered
Frequency: Annual
Start: 2021-07-02
End: 2021-07-18

BRAZIL

BNDES International Piano Competition of Rio de Janeiro
Website: http://concursopianorio.com/?lang=en
Phone: 212 225 7492
Address: Rua Marquesa de Santos 42 / 1702, BR
Information: BNDES believes that access to classical music, with its colors, complexity and historic background (music is as ancient as civilization itself), is the approach to one of the noblest forms of enlightenment. BNDES is also convinced that all the manifestations of culture are closely linked to social development. Each concert is a new opportunity to get acquainted with the infinite meanings of music.
Country: Brazil
Contact: Artistic Director Lilian Barretto
Social Media: twitter.com/concpianorio www.facebook.com/concursoBNDESpiano
Eligibility: ages 17-30

CANADA

AIMAC Cultural Manager's Award
Website: https://gestiondesarts.hec.ca/activites/prix-du-gestionnaire-culturel/
Email: gestiondesarts@hec.ca
Phone: 514 340 5629
Address: 3000 chemin de la Côte-Sainte-Catherine, Suite 4.363, Montréal, Quebec, Canada H3T 2A7
Information: THE AIMAC is an international network of researchers in arts and cultural management, whose main activity is a biennial research conference held in various cities around the world.
AIMAC also hosts the biennial AIMAC Cultural Manager's Award. The Cultural Manager Award aims to promote the role of Managers in the cultural community and to showcase their achievements in society by highlighting the excellence of a career in Marketing and management of the arts.
Country: Canada
Contact: Chairholder François Colbert
Email: francois.colbert@hec.ca
Director of business development André Courchesne
Email: andre.courchesne@hec.ca
officer – activities organisation Anne-Marie Panneton
Email: anne-marie.panneton@hec.ca
Administrative Assistant Chantal Downing
Email: chantal.downing@hec.ca
Frequency: Biennial

Banff International String Quartet Competition
Website: https://www.banffcentre.ca/bisqc
Email: bisqc@banffcentre.ca
Phone: 403 762 6231
Address: 107 Tunnel Mountain Drive, PO Box 1020 Banff, Alberta, Canada, T1L 1H5
Information: For over 30 years, Banff International String Quartet Competition has celebrated the art of chamber music while providing career support for emerging string quartets. Intended as a one-time special event, the first competition was held in 1983 to mark the 50th anniversary of Banff Centre for Arts and Creativity. The outstanding success of the first competition inspired organizers to make this a triennial event.
Country: Canada
Contact: Manager Mhiran Faraday
Social Media: www.facebook.com/bisqc
Eligibility: open to quartets of all nationalities whose members are all under the age of 35 at the time of the competition.
Awards: over $300, 000 in cash and prizes
Frequency: Triennial
Start: 2022-08-29
End: 2022-09-04

Canadian International Organ Competition
Website: https://ciocm.org/en/
Email: info@ciocm.org
Phone: 514 510 5678
Address: 1200, rue de Bleury Montreal, Quebec H3B 3J3
Information: The Canadian International Organ Competition (CIOC) promotes organ music, namely by increasing public awareness and interest for this type of music. The CIOC presents, every year in October, a festival with some of the world's finest organists. Every third year, the CIOC organizes an international competition in which a prestigious jury representing various countries, awards important prizes to a selection of the best young organists in the world.
Seeking to actively participate in the cultural life, the CIOC annually develops a programme of activities in collaboration with various organisations of the organ world. These musical and educational activities are designed to emphasize the cultural importance of pipe organs – treasures of our heritage – for a wide and diverse audience. Member of WFIMC.
Country: Canada
Contact: President of the Jury Jean-Willy Kunz
Executive Director Thomas Leslie
Email: thomas.leslie@ciocm.org
communications and Marketing Manager Alexia Jensen
Email: alexia.jensen@ciocm.org

Concours musical international de Montréal (CMIM)
Website: www.concoursmontreal.ca
Email: info@concoursmontreal.ca
Phone: 514 845 4108
Address: 305, Mount-Royal Avenue East, Montreal, QC H2T 1P8, CA
Information: Founded in 2001 by internationally renowned bass Joseph Rouleau and current Chairman of the Board of the Competition and its Foundation André Bourbeau, the Concours musical international de Montréal (CMIM) is an annual event that draws over 6, 000 spectators to concert halls and reaches even more listeners via radio and webcasts. The CMIM is the only international competition in North America to be held annually and to present three disciplines (voice, violin, piano) in a three-year rotation. Since its first edition dedicated to voice in 2002, more than 3, 000 hopefuls have entered the Competition and some 450 have performed in Montreal, much to the delight of music lovers.
Country: Canada
Contact: Executive and Artistic Director Christiane LeBlanc
Email: cleblanc@concoursmontreal.ca
Director of Artistic operations and strategy Scott Tresham
Email: stresham@concoursmontreal.ca
head of logistics & operations/interim Director of communications

Chantal Poulin
Email: cpoulin@concoursmontreal.ca
Social Media: www.facebook.com/CMIMontreal twitter.com/CMIMontreal www.instagram.com/cmimontreal
Frequency: Annual
Start: 2021-11-03
End: 2021-12-15

Honens Piano Competition
Website: https://www.honens.com/
Email: info@honens.com
Phone: 403 299 0130
Address: 1170 – 105 12 Avenue SE Calgary, AB, Canada T2P 2X1
Information: Honens Piano Competition discovers, nurtures and presents Artists and musicians for 21st century audiences. Honens Laureates offer the 'Search for the Complete Artist' awards, the largest prize of its kind, and an Artist development programme valued at half a million dollars. Honens also presents concerts and Canada's International Festival of Piano each year in Calgary in addition to nationwide learning and outreach programmes. Member of WFIMC.
Country: Canada
Contact: Artistic Director Jon Kimura Parker
Email: jkparker@honens.com
President & CEO
Neil Edwards
Email: nedwards@honens.com
Marketing & communications
Amanda Smith
Email: asmith@honens.com
finance & Administration
Mark Mosher
Email: mmosher@honens.com
Social Media: twitter.com/honens www.facebook.com/Honens
Eligibility: Pianists of all nationalities, aged 20 to 30 on September 2, 2021, with the exception of past Honens Laureates and professionally managed Artists, may apply.
Awards: Honens Prize Laureate (one) $100, 000 CAN Finalists (two) $10, 000 CAN each Semifinalists (seven) $2, 500 CAN each
Start: 2022-10-20
End: 2022-10-28

Orchestre Symphonique de Montreal – Standard Life Competition
Website: https://www.osm.ca/en/home-osm/
Email: servicealaclientele@osm.ca
Phone: 514 842 9951
Address: Orchestre Symphonique de Montréal, 1600 Saint-Urbain Street, Montréal, Québec H2X 0S1
Information: The mandate of the OSM Foundation is to guarantee the long-term success of the Orchestre symphonique de Montréal by providing it with the means of fulfilling a vision that will ensure its full development. The Foundation focuses on three main areas: the long-term success of the Orchestra, its international recognition, as well as the maintenance and development of activities in the community.
Country: Canada
Contact: head public relations and media relations Pascale Ouimet
Email: pouimet@osm.ca
public relations officer Michele-Andrée Lanoue
Email: malanoue@osm.ca
music Director Kent Nagano
Social Media: twitter.com/OSMconcerts www.facebook.com/OSMconcerts www.instagram.com/osmconcerts/

The Azrieli Music Prizes
Website: https://azrielifoundation.org/
Email: music@azrielifoundation.org
Phone: 416 322 5928

Address: 22 Street Clair Avenue West, Suite 202, CA
Information: The biennial Azrieli Music Prizes (AMP) offer opportunities for the discovery, creation, performance, and celebration of excellence in new concert music through the awarding of three $50, 000 cash prizes: The Azrieli Commission for Canadian Music, the Azrieli Prize for Jewish Music, and the Azrieli Commission for Jewish Music.
Country: Canada
Contact: Chair Naomi Azrieli
Social Media: twitter.com/azrielifdn www.facebook.com/azrielifoundation/
Awards: First prize $10, 000 to $50, 000 Additional prizes Performances Recording

CHILE

International Musical Competition Dr Luis Sigall
Website: https://www.culturaviva.cl/
Email: info@culturaviva.cl
Phone: 322 680 633
Address: Arlegui 683, CL
Information: Created in 1974 by the Cultural Corporation of Viña del Mar, the competition is organized to honour Dr. Luis Sigall, a dedicated music lover who has contributed by offering quality music activities in the community. Being one of the most prestigious international music events in Viña del Mar, a tourist and beach resort known as "The Garden City" in central Chile, it is held annually in a five-year cycle, each year focusing on a different discipline: violin, cello, guitar, vocal or piano. Prominent musicians and scholars are invited as jurors. Top prize winner will be guaranteed with a series of concert engagements in Chile. Previous prize winners include Sean Kennard and Andras Csaki.
Country: Chile
Contact: Artistic Director Alvaro Gomez administrator Jorge Salomo Flores
Eligibility: age limit: 32 years
Awards: 1st prize: $10000; 2nd prize: $4000; 3rd prize $2000

CHINA

China International Violin Competition
Website: http://www.cimcompetition.com/en/
Email: admin@cimcompetition.com
Phone: 010 648 87659
Address: Room 302, Admin Bldg of China Conservatory of Music, No.1 AnXiang Road, Chaoyang District, Beijing, China, 100101
Information: China International Violin Competition held every three years in Qingdao since 2005, is one of the three international music competitions organised by Ministry of Culture of PRC; the competition plays an important role in discovering talented young violinists and promoting international culture exchanging
Country: China
Contact: President of the China International Music Competition Liguang Wang
Social Media: www.instagram.com/CIMC_Officialtwitter.com/ChinaInternati4?lang=en
Eligibility: Violinists must be between sixteen and twenty-eight years of age on the opening date of the competition
Awards: First Prize: US $150, 000, a Gold Medal, and three years of concert tours. Second Prize: US $ 75, 000 and a Silver Medal. Third Prize: US $ 30, 000 and a Jade Medal. Three Finalists (Non-Medalists): US $ 5, 000 each and a Diploma
Frequency: Triennial

China Shenzhen International Piano Concerto Competition
Website: https://www.csipcc.com.cn/
Email: info@csipcc.com.cn
Phone: 755 825 35441
Address: Shenzhen Arts School, No. 3930, Nanshan Avenue Shenzhen, P.R.CHINA, 518052
Information: The "China Shenzhen International Piano Concerto Competition"(CSIPCC) organized by the Shenzhen Municipal People's Government, and hosted by the Shenzhen Municipal Bureau of Culture, Sports and Tourism and the Shenzhen Association for Cultural Exchanges with Foreign Countries. CSIPCC is held once every three years with the guidance of the Ministry of Culture of the People's Republic of China and the Guangdong Provincial Department of Culture. The first three competitions' great success made a wide social impact and became a great event in the cultural life of Shenzhen citizens. More than 50 high-level contestants from 13 countries and regions such as the United States, Russia and Canada entered for the first CSIPCC, over 70 contestants from 15 countries and regions for the second CSIPCC, and over 63 contestants from 11 countries and regions for the third CSIPCC. More than 80, 000 people were attracted to the three sessions and master classes. Lately the competition is broadcasting live reaching the number of 500, 000 clicks.
Country: China
Contact: Artistic Director Dan Zhaoyi Zhaoyi
Awards: 1stPrize $30, 000; 2ndPrize $20, 000; 3rdPrize $15, 000; 4thPrize $12, 000; 5thPrize $10, 000; 6thPrize $8, 000

International Mozart Competition for Young Musicians
Website: http://en.zhmozart.org/index.html
Email: info@zhmozart.org
Phone: 756 881 6577
Address: Zhuhai International Mozart Competition for Young Musicians Office Huafa & CPAA Grand Theatre, Shizimen CBD, Nanwan Avenue 519000 Zhuhai Guangdong China
Information: The Zhuhai International Mozart Competition for Young Musicians is an international and comprehensive music competition for youngsters. The participants, aged under 23, are divided into three groups. The Competition not only focuses on young musicians' virtuosity, but also attaches great importance to their understanding and interpretation of classical music style. The Salzburg Chamber Soloists, globally renowned for their specialization in Mozart's works, is designated as the orchestra of the Competition.
Country: China
Eligibility: Group A: 12 or younger (born in 2009 or after) Group B: 13 16 (born in 2005 2008) Group C: 17 23 (born in 1998 2004)
Awards: Group A 1st Prize $7500, Group B 1st Prize $15000, Group C 1st Prize $30000
Frequency: Annual
Start: 2022-09-13
End: 2022-09-25

Schoenfeld International String Competition
Website: https://schoenfeldcompetition.com/
Email: info@schoenfeldcompetition.com
Phone: 213 294 9810
Address: Harbin Conservatory Of Music, No.3179 XueZi Street, SongBei District
Information: The Alice and Eleonore Schoenfeld International String Competition for Violin and Cello aims to enrich the culture of music by recognizing and promoting highly gifted young musicians. Schoenfeld International String Competition was established to pay tribute to the legendary sisters, performers, and educators in the string world – Alice and Eleanore Schoenfeld.
Country: China
Social Media: twitter.com/SchoenfeldComp www.facebook.com/schoenfeldsociety www.instagram.com/schoenfeldstringcompetition/
Start: 2022-07-15
End: 2022-07-30

HONG KONG

Hong Kong Int. Piano Competition / The Joy of Music Festival
Website: http://chopin-ipoc.com/?lang=en
Email: info@chopinsocietyhk.org
Phone: 852 286 83325
Address: Room 1909, 19/F., St. George's Building, No.2 Ice House Street, Central, , HK
Information: In every three years since 2005, that is, in 2005, 2008 and 2011 the Society ran its biggest event, the Hong Kong International Piano Competition with a truly exceptional, if not unique jury. The Competition aimed at not only presenting an exceptional group of candidates but also an exceptional musical event. Other innovations included the members of jury performing as well as judging. As part of the Society's plan to offer integrated and continuous series of activities, the triennial Competitions have been linked by annual Joy of Music Festivals taking place in-between Competitions and since 2011 also during the Competitions.The Festivals bring together in performance and master classes members of the jury of the Competition, all the previous first prize winners of the Competition, first prize winners from other important piano competitions as well as invited world-class Artists from all over the world.
The Competition has now established itself as one of the top international piano competitions attracting scores of exceptionally talented candidates from several countries around the world.
Country: Hong Kong
Social Media: www.facebook.com/HKIntPianoComp-JofMFest/
Frequency: Triennial
Start: 2022-10-10
End: 2022-10-27

Hong Kong International Conducting Competition
Website: www.hkconducting.com/
Email: hkconducting@hksinfonietta.org
Phone: 283 63336
Address: c/o Hong Kong Sinfonietta, 3/F Winsan Tower, 98 Thomson Road, HK
Information: The Hong Kong International Conducting Competition, organized by Hong Kong Sinfonietta, is for conductors under the age of 35 to establish a network in Asia.
Country: Hong Kong
Social Media: www.facebook.com/hkconducting

ISRAEL

The Arthur Rubinstein International Piano Master Competition
Website: https://arims.org.il/
Email: competition@arims.org.il
Phone: 368 56684
Address: 12 Huberman Street, IL
Information: The Arthur Rubinstein International Piano Master Competition came into being in 1974 at the initiative of Jan Jacob Bistritzky, whose aim was to unite the name and the Artistic legacy of Arthur Rubinstein with the cultural life of Israel. Rubinstein was honored to give his name to the competition. Conceived in the spirit of this legendary pianist, the competition is committed to attaining standards of the highest order and is a valid international forum for presenting talented, aspiring young pianists and fostering their Artistic careers. Member of WFIMC.
Country: Israel
Contact: Artistic Director Idith Zvi Executive Producer Shuly Haberman office Manager Hila Mizrahi
Social Media: www.facebook.com/PianoArims
Eligibility: 18 – 32 years old
Awards: $40, 000, $20, 000, $10, 000 and more

JAPAN

Asian International Pacific Ballet Competition
Website: http://www.j-b-a.or.jp/
Email: info@j-b-a.or.jp
Phone: 036 304 5681
Address: 6-12-30 Nishi-Shinjuku, Shinjuku-ku , Tokyo 160-0023 Japan
Information: the only ballet competition in and for the Asian Pacific region; corporation has about 2, 600 members all over Japan and aims to contribute to the improvement and development of Japan's arts and culture by establishing and promoting Japanese ballet based on the tradition of dance classics; through various projects, we improve overall quality of Japan's ballet and develop human resources, as well as add new value to this performing art of Western Europe in the cultural tradition unique to Japan.
Country: Japan
Contact: President Momoko Tano Tano
Eligibility: open to all ballet dancers
Frequency: Biennial

International Oboe Competition of Japan
Website: https://oboec.jp/index_e/
Email: smf@sonymusic.co.jp
Phone: 335 155 261
Address: c/o Sony Music Foundation, SME⊠Rokubancho Bldg. 4⊠5, Rokubancho, Chiyoda⊠ku, Tokyo 102⊠8353 JAPAN
Information: THE INTERNATIONAL OBOE COMPETITION OF JAPAN" was founded under the idea originated by our former Chairman, Norio Ohga (1930-2011), who had been intrigued with the innocent and comforting sound of the oboe and had advocated its importance as the instrument that could determine the quality of an entire orchestra and we, Sony Music Foundation, had been presenting it every three years since 1985. It is aimed to promote the true Artistic value of oboe, as well as to contribute to the development of the culture of music with an international perspective by discovering and fostering talented musicians and help them expand their scope of activities in both Japan and abroad.
Country: Japan
Contact: Chairman Masaru Kato chief and secretary General Shigenobu Karube
Eligibility: open to all oboist age 18-30 except for past first-prize winners of this competition
Awards: First Prize: Ohga Award Certificate / cash prize of JPY1, 300, 000 / trophy; Second Prize Certificate / cash prize of JPY700, 000; Third Prize Certificate / cash prize of JPY300, 000; Honorable Mention Certificate / cash prize of JPY100, 000
Frequency: Triennial

International Organ Competition Musashino
Website: http://www.musashino-culture.or.jp/iocm/eng/index.html
Email: musashino.organ@gmail.com
Phone: 422 548 822
Address: 3-9-11 Naka-cho, Musashino-City Tokyo 180-0006 Japan
Information: The purpose of the International Organ Competition Musashino-Tokyo is to discover talented organists, not only in Japan but also from abroad, to contribute to their development, and to promote international exchange.
Country: Japan
Eligibility: open to all organists with no age Limit
Awards: JPY 1, 200, 000; Concerts Japan CD release on NAXOS with worldwide distribution
Frequency: Triennial

ARD🄵

71st ARD International
Music Competition Munich

August 29 to September 16, 2022

Piano Trio
Voice
Wind Quintet
Oboe
Trumpet
Piano
Percussion
Viola
Clarinet
Flute
Violoncello
Bassoon
Trombone
Harp
French Horn
Piano Duo
String Quartet
Violin
Double Bass
Organ
Guitar

Piano Trombone Flute String Quartet

Michael Buchanan
1st prize 2015

Sébastian Jacot
1st prize 2015

JeungBeum Sohn
1st prize 2017

Application
deadline:
March 31, 2022

Quatuor Arod
1st prize 2016

www.ard-musikwettbewerb.de

International Piano Duo Competition for Piano Performance
Website: http://www.ipda-pianoduo.com/ipda-english.html
Email: ipda.2pianos4hands@gmail.com
Phone: 364 341 003
Address: 5-41-3 Jingu-mae, Shibuya-ku Tokyo, 1500001 Japan
Information: The aim of this contest is to raise the Artistic standards of piano duo playing & increase the popularity of this medium by introducing more people to the charms of piano duo performance. International competitions for piano duo compositions and piano duo performance are held on alternate years. In this way we hope to enhance & develop the field of piano duo music by promoting promising composers and performers.
Country: Japan
Contact: President Mariko Horie
Frequency: Biennial

Irino Prize for Chamber Music
Website: http://www.irinoprize.jp/
Email: info@IrinoPrize.jp
Phone: 333 230 646
Address: c/o NPO JML Yoshiro Irino Music Institute 5-22-2 Matsubara, Setagaya-ku, Tokyo, 156-0043 Japan
Information: The Irino Prize was founded in 1980 in honour of the late Yoshiko Irino, one of the most respected Japanese composers of his generation. The Irino Prize is awarded to young composers who explore new directions and demonstrate innovative creativity.
Country: Japan
Contact: President Reiko Takahashi Irino
Chairperson Satoshi Tanaka
Social Media: www.facebook.com/IrinoPrize
Eligibility: open to any nationality; composers must be less than 40 years old
Awards: 200, 000 Japanese yen
Frequency: Annual
Start: 2022-06-23

Kobe International Flute Competition
Website: https://kobe-flute.jp/en/
Address: 4-2-2 Kusunoki-cho, Chuo-ku 650-0017, Kobe
Information: Established in 1985 and held every four years, the Kobe International Flute Competition (KIFC) is committed to providing young promising flutists from around the world the opportunity to launch their professional career on the international stage while enhancing international cultural exchanges and friendships through music. In addition, the Competition aims to promote cultural enrichment of our community in Kobe through music.
Country: Japan
Contact: Chairman Hiroaki Kanda
President Kizo Hisamoto
Social Media: www.facebook.com/KIFC2021/
Frequency: Quadrennial
Start: 2022-03-22
End: 2022-03-28

Mt. Fuji International Opera Competition of Shizuoka
Website: https://www.suac.ac.jp/opera/
Phone: 534 576 446
Address: 2-1-1 Chuo, Naka-ku, Hamamatsu City, Shizuoka Prefecture 430-8533, Japan
Information: Commencing in 1996, the 50 year after the death of MIURA Tamaki, Shizuoka Prefectural Government has held the Mt. Fuji International Opera Competition of Shizuoka once every three years to commemorate the world-famous prima donna, known for her ties to Shizuoka Prefecture. This Competition aims not only to discover more talented Artists in the musical world but also to promote the development of musical culture, strengthen international relations thorough global cultural exchange, and create Shizuoka's unique culture to show throughout the world.
Country: Japan
Social Media: www.facebook.com/shizuoka.opera/twitter.com/shizuokaopera/
Start: 2023-10-28
End: 2023-10-30

Nippon Harp Competition
Website: https://www.harp-japan.com/
Email: info@harp-japan.com
Phone: 364 268 876
Address: Nippon Harp Association, Studio D, 3-6-8 Nishi-shinagawa, Shinagawa-ku, Tokyo 141-0033 JAPAN
Information: The Nippon Harp Competition is organised by the Nippon Harp Association and the Soka City Cultural Association for the purpose of promoting harp music in Japan and fostering young harpists. Since the first competition help in 1989, it has been held annually in cooperation with Soka City.
Country: Japan
Contact: Chairman Fumiko Shinozaki
Eligibility: open to harpists of all nationalities who met the age requirements; 35 years old as of October 20, 2021. The previous winner of the professional division is not qualified to compete
Awards: 1st prize: 300, 000; 2nd prize: 200, 000; 3rd prize: 100, 000

Sendai International Music Competition
Website: www.simc.jp
Email: info@simc.jp
Phone: 227 271 872
Address: 3-27-5, Asahigaoka, Aoba-ku, Sendai City, Miyagi Pref. 981-0904, Japan
Information: Sendai International Music Competition was created by the City of Sendai in 2001 to commemorate the 400th anniversary of the city. The Competition is held every three years, aiming to contribute to the global culture of music and to international cultural exchange, through the nurturing of young, talented musicians.
Country: Japan
Contact: Chairman of the board Tsuyoshi Tsutsumi
Social Media: twitter.com/sendai_simc
Eligibility: Eligibility shall be given to any persons born on or after a separately specified date, irrespective of nationality. The Competition shall consist of Preliminary, Semifinal and Final Rounds. The Competition shall be held in two sections: violin and piano. A Pre-Selection shall be held prior to the Competition.
Awards: 1) First prize: Cash prize of JPY 3, 000, 000, Diploma and Gold Medal 2) Second prize: Cash prize of JPY 2, 000, 000, Diploma and Silver Medal 3) Third prize: Cash prize of JPY 1, 000, 000, Diploma and Bronze Medal 4) Fourth prize: Cash prize of JPY 800, 000 and Diploma 5) Fifth prize: Cash prize of JPY 700, 000 and Diploma 6) Sixth prize: Cash prize of JPY 600, 000 and Diploma
Frequency: Annual
Start: 2022-05-19

Suntory Music Award
Website: https://www.suntory.co.jp/sfa/music/prize/
Phone: 335 821 355
Address: Suntory Foundation for Arts, P.O.Box 509, Ark Mori Bldg 22F, 1-12-32 Akasaka, Minato-ku, Tokyo, 107-6022 Japan
Information: Since it was inaugurated in 1969 with the aim of promoting Western-style music in Japan, the Suntory Music Award (previously known as the Torii Music Award) has been presented every year to an individual or ensemble who made outstanding contributions to the development of musical culture in Japan during the previous year.
Country: Japan
Contact: Director General Tsuyoshi Tsutsumi
Social Media: www.facebook.com/suntoryglobaltwitter.com/SuntoryGlobal www.instagram.com/suntoryglobal/
Frequency: Annual

Takamatsu International Piano Competition
Website: www.tipc.jp
Email: info@tipc.jp
Phone: 878 125 583
Address: Central Tamachi Building 6F 11-5 Tamachi, Takamatsu Kagawa 760-0053 Japan
Country: Japan
Contact: Chairman Katsuhiko Takesaki
adviser Keizo Hamada
adviser Hideto Onishi
Social Media: www.facebook.com/TIPCofficial
Eligibility: open to all pianists age between 15 and 35 who are born during the period specified in the application guidelines
Frequency: Quadrennial
Start: 2022-03-15
End: 2022-03-28

Takarazuka International Chamber Chorus Contest
Website: https://takarazuka-c.jp/ticc_en/
Email: info@takarazuka-c.jp
Phone: 797 858 844
Address: Takarazuka Vega Hall 1-2-18 Kiyoshikojin, Takarazuka City, Hyogo 665-0836 JAPAN
Information: Takarazuka International Chamber Chorus Contest(TICC) was first held in 1984. Since then the contest has been held every year till today, with the purpose of spreading the'Chamber Chorus' widely to the local people, also with the hope of growing international friendship among choirs through the music.The participants compete for gold, silver and bronze medals in each section.
Country: Japan
Social Media: www.facebook.com/takarazukabunkatwitter.com/takaran_c
Awards: gold, silver and bronze prizes will be awarded in each category
Frequency: Annual
Start: 2022-07-22
End: 2021-11-24

The Hamamatsu International Piano Competition
Website: https://www.hipic.jp/
Email: info@hipic.jp
Phone: 534 511 148
Address: 111-1 Itaya-machi, Naka-ku, Hamamatsu-shi, Shizuoka-ken 430-7790 JAPAN
Information: The Hamamatsu International Piano Competition began in 1991 to commemorate Hamamatsu's 80th year anniversary of the city's establishment. It was started as an international project which could fittingly exPress the pride held in Hamamatsu's tradition and history as a city of music and instruments

Country: Japan
Contact: President Yasutomo Suzuki
Chairperson Shuji Ito
Social Media: www.facebook.com/HIPICofficial www.instagram.com/hipicofficialtwitter.com/hipicofficial
Eligibility: open to pianists born on or after January 1, 1991
Awards: First Prize 3, 000, 000, Gold Medal, Certificate of Merit; Second Prize 1, 800, 000, Silver Medal, Certificate of Merit; Third Prize, 1, 200, 000 Bronze Medal, Certificate of Merit; Fourth Prize 750, 000, Certificate of Merit; Fifth Prize 600, 000, Certificate of Merit; Sixth Prize 450, 000, Certificate of Merit; Best Performer of the Japanese Work 300, 000, Certificate of Merit; Diploma of Outstanding Merit 150, 000 Certificate of Merit; Chamber Music Award 150, 00
Frequency: Triennial

Tokyo International Music Competition for Conducting
Website: https://www.conductingtokyo.org/eng/
Email: conductingtokyo@min-on.or.jp
Phone: 353 623 460
Address: c/o Min-On Concert Association, 8 Shina-no-machi, Shinjuku-ku, JP
Information: Established in 1966 with the aim of discovering and supporting outstanding musical talents, the Tokyo International Music Competition vigorously promotes the growth of young musicians who display a broad range of promise in an international forum. It also serves to promote cultural exchanges between representatives of different countries and to contribute to the further development of musical culture. Competitions have been held in the three areas of conducting, singing, and chamber music, and competitions in conducting are currently being held on a triennial basis.
Now preparing for its 18th gathering of contestants, the conducting competition is not only the sole such concours in Asia, but enjoys a remarkable record of introducing conductors who have gone on to achieve world-scale success. Each of these competitions has received applications from more than thirty different countries and regions, and many of the young competitors selected as participants gone on to positions on the world stage.
Through this Competition, the organizers hope to continue contributing to the discovery of new talents from around the world, talents whose endeavors will define the coming era of music.
Country: Japan
Contact: Executive Director Takakazu Watanabe
President Hiroyasu Kobayashi
Social Media: twitter.com/conductingtokyo www.facebook.com/ConductingCompetition
applicants must be under 38 years of age at the time of the competition's final round. Former 1st Prize winners of this competition are not eligible to compete again.
Awards: 1st Prize: Certificate, medal, and cash award of 2, 000, 000 yen 2nd Prize: Certificate, medal, and cash award of 1, 000, 000 yen 3rd Prize: Certificate, medal, and cash award of 500, 000 yen
Frequency: Triennial

Toru Takemitsu Composition Award
Website: https://www.operacity.jp/
Email: award@toccf.com
Phone: 353 530 770
Address: Tokyo Opera City Cultural Foundation, 3-20-2 Nishi-shinjuku, Shinjuku-ku, Tokyo 163-1403 JAPAN
Information: Tokyo Opera City Cultural Foundation aspires to promote and foster the possibility of a more creative music culture for the future. Within the sphere of our activities, carry out the intention of the Foundation's first Artistic Director, the late Toru Takemitsu, under the themes of, "Prayer, Hope and Peace" and "Window to the Future". The Foundation established the "Toru Takemitsu Composition Award" in order to inspire younger generations all over the world to contribute to the creation of new musical compositions.
Country: Japan
Frequency: Annual

Yokohama Dance Collection
Website: https://yokohama-dance-collection.jp/en/
Email: ydc@yaf.or.jp
Phone: 452 111 515
Address: Yokohama Arts Foundation, Yokohama Red Brick Warehouse No.1, 1 Chome-1 Shinko, Naka Ward, Yokohama, Kanagawa 231-0001, Japan
Information: Yokohama Dance Collection (previously the Yokohama Solo x Duo Competition) is a place for choreographers, dancers, and other Artists to pursue composition, direction, and technique in dance, and to challenge themselves to new possibilities of Artistic exPression. It also serves as a platform for Artistic dialogue and exchange.
YDC was launched as a choreography competition in 1996, providing an international platform for dance in Japan. To date, it has featured over 400 finalists.
Country: Japan
Social Media: twitter.com/ydc_ex www.facebook.com/YokohamaDanceCollection www.instagram.com/ydc_yokohama/

REPUBLIC OF KOREA

International ISANGYUN Competition
Website: http://www.isangyuncompetition.org/landing/
Address: Tongyeong International Music Festival Foundation 38, Keunbalgae 1-Gil, Tongyeong-si, Gyeongsang-nam-do (53079)
Information: The International ISANGYUN Competition (previously the Gyeongnam International Music Competition until 2008) has been presented by the Tongyeong International Music Foundation since 2003. Is held in remembrance of Isang Yun, the renowned Korean composer, by promoting cultural exchanges among nations through music, and by supporting talented young musicians from all over the world. The Competition is held annually in early November and offers three different disciplines: violin, cello and piano.
Country: Republic of Korea
Frequency: Annual

Korea International Ballet Competition
Website: https://www.koreaballet.com/
Email: kibc@koreaballet.com
Phone: 023 965 188
Address: Korea international ballet competition, M-512, 7 Hongji-dong, Jongno-gu, Seoul
Information: we have organised an international ballet competition in order to provide young talents from worldwide with a chance to show their abilities, to understand different cultures, and to seek a road to a new horizon. We hope that this competition will promote the development of the world ballet circles and provide a chance for the mutual understanding and cooperation. All the judges with world famous reputations.
Country: Republic of Korea
Contact: President of Korea IBC Jae Keun Park
Eligibility: three age categories: 11-14 years old; 15-18 years old; 19-27 years old
Awards: $19000 in prizes
Frequency: Annual

Seoul International Dance Competition
Website: http://sicf.or.kr/view/sicf/index.php
Email: sicf@sicf.or.kr
Phone: 258 87570
Address: Seoul International Dance Competition Office, 2F, Myeongdal-ro 3, Seocho-gu, Seoul, South Korea, 06714
Information: The Seoul International Dance Competition (SIDC) aims to discover promising young dancers, provide them the opportunity to gain international experience, support cooperation between dancers participating in each category (Ballet, Contemporary and Ethnic dance), and contribute in their improved understanding of the international world.
Country: Republic of Korea
Frequency: Annual

Seoul International Music Competition
Website: www.seoulcompetition.com
Email: seoulcompetition@donga.com
Phone: 236 11415
Address: 3FL, The Dong-A Ilbo Bldg., 29, Chungjeong-ro, Seodaemun-Gu, Seoul 120-715
Information: Seoul International Music Competition was established by the Seoul Metropolitan Government and the Dong-A Ilbo, the most prestigious national newspaper in Korea. The competition is held annually for the categories of piano, violin, and voice, in a rotating sequence, with the aim of promoting cultural exchanges among nations through music, and supporting talented young musicians from all over the world.
Country: Republic of Korea
Eligibility: open to pianists of all nationalities were born on or after March 18, 1989 and on or before March 17, 2003
Awards: cash awards totalling US $127, 000
Frequency: Annual

MEXICO

International Piano Competition Parnassós
Website: https://www.parnassos.com.mx/
Email: parnassos@interclable.net
Phone: 818 356 9633
Address: Amazonas 300 pte, Col. Del Valle, MX
Information: International Piano Competition
Country: Mexico
Contact: President Myrtha Salazar
Email: myrthalasalazar@gmail.com
Eligibility: age limit: 17-33
Awards: 1st prize: $20000; 2nd prize: $6000; 3rd prize: $3000

National Piano Competition for Young Pianists Parnassós
Website:
https://www.parnassos.com.mx/
Email: parnassos@interclable.net
Phone:
818 356 9633
Address: Amazonas 300 pte, Col. Del Valle, MX

Information: organised by Parnassós (see also Promoters, Producers, Presenters, this competition is made for young pianists in Mexico to showcase their outstanding talents and to excel their careers through creating connections and confidence.
Country: Mexico
Contact: President Myrtha Salazar
Email: myrthalasalazar@gmail.com
Eligibility: age limit: 5-25 years

Premio Nacional de Danza INBA-Sinaloa Jos
Website: http://www.culturasinaloa.gob.mx/
Phone: 555 280 5974
Address: Coordinacion, Reforma y Campo Marte s/n, M, Col. Chapultepec Polanco, MX
Information: Since its creation, this cultural body has established and operated cultural programs that have formed a state system for the promotion, dissemination and practice of various Artistic exPressions, which take root in Sinaloans, national and local values, which sustain and invigorate the national unity and identity.
Country: Mexico
Contact: coordinator Horacio Lecona
Social Media: twitter.com/CulturaSinaloa www.facebook.com/InstitutoSinaloenseDeCulturalSIC
Eligibility: open for applications in the first quarter of each year
Awards: prize of $40000

NEW ZEALAND

Auckland "Michael Hill" International Violin Competition
Website: https://michaelhillviolincompetition.co.nz/
Email: annerodda@violincompetition.co.nz
Phone: 963 92010
Address: P.O Box 24657, Royal Oak, NZ
Information: The Michael Hill International Violin Competition aims to recognise and celebrate excellence, distinctiveness and musical Artistry. We encourage talented young violinists from all over the world who are on the verge of launching themselves on the world stage and empower them with the necessary skills to broaden their career opportunities.
We take pride in New Zealand Aotearoa's cultural offerings and showcase our finest Artistic talents. Hosting a major event and inviting the world's celebrated violinists, we are raising the awareness of fine music and the standards of musical performance that richly impacts the next layer of talent in New Zealand.
Founded in 2000, the biennial "Michael Hill" is recognised as one of the world's most compelling violin competitions. The fusion of spine-tingling performances, warm and enthusiastic audiences, breathtaking scenery and Kiwi hospitality create an unparalleled platform for competitor and audience member alike. We take great pride in the knowledge that our laureates hold prestigious positions in a variety of career options and carry on the glorious tradition of violin playing in its highest form.
Country: New Zealand
Contact: Executive Director Anne Rodda
Social Media: www.facebook.com/MHIVC
Start: 2022-02-10
End: 2022-02-12

PHILIPPINES

National Music Competitions for Young Artists
Website: https://www.namcya.com/
Email: info@namcya.com
Phone: 836 4928
Address: NAMCYA Secretariat, Folk Arts Theater, Bukaneg Street CCP Complex, Pasay City 1307
Information: The NAMCYA has been a principal instrument in discovering major music talents from all over the country. The project involves around 1 million musicians, trainers and Administrations, in a long process of selecting the best among them from all seventeen regions, annually.
Country: Philippines
Contact: President Renato B. Lucas
administrative and finance officer Robert Jayson Javellana
project and Artistic Director Ronan Ferrer
Frequency: Annual

SERBIA AND MONTENEGRO

International Competition for Young Musicians 'Petar Konjovic'
Website: https://www.konjovic-competition.rs/
Email: umbps@mts.rs
Phone: 117 193 582
Address: Association of Music and Ballet Pedagogues of Serbia, Džona Kenedija 7, 11080 Zemun, Serbia
Information: the Competition is open for young musicians of all nationalities and the categories change each year; the categories are: violin, viola, cello, double bass, piano, flute, harmonica, harp, voice, ensembles. Konjovic's creative opus is very extensive and is compromised of stage music (operas), symphony and chamber pieces, choirs and solo songs, miniatures for the piano, violin and cello. He had a remarkable contribution to almost all fields of Serbian music development.

SOUTH AFRICA

Unisa International Music Competitions
Website: https://www.unisa.ac.za/sites/corporate/default/About/What-we-do/Arts-%26-culture/Unisa-Music-Foundation
Phone: 124 293 336
Address: PO Box 392, ZA
Information: The first international piano competition was presented in 1982. Since then the Unisa Music Foundation has built a reputation for hosting competitions comparable with the best in the world. In 2015 a jazz category was added running parallel to the classical category during the Unisa National Piano Competition. The two categories were again presented during the 13th Unisa International Piano Competition in 2016 and was a resounding success.
Country: South Africa
Contact: Director Karendra Devroop
Email: kdevroop@unisa.ac.za
music events administrator Alet Venter
Email: joubeae@unisa.ac.za
office administrator Kgomotso Boshielo
Email: boshimk@unisa.ac.za
Social Media: twitter.com/unisa www.facebook.com/UniversityOfSouthAfrica
Eligibility: 32 years (born on or before 4 February 1985).
Awards: First Prize R200 000 Second Prize R130 000 Third Prize R80 000

TAIWAN

Oistat – Theatre Architecture Competition
Website: www.oistat.org
Email: headquarters@oistat.org
Phone: 225 962 294
Address: OISTAT Headquarters, Suite L, Center for Innovation Taipei (CIT), No.1, Yumen St., Taipei 10452, Taiwan
Information: OISTAT stands for "International Organisation of Scenographers, Theatre Architects and Technicians". It is a worldwide organization for scenographers, theatre architects, theatre educators and theatre technicians.
OISTAT enables the ongoing exchange of knowledge: sharing innovations, encouraging experimentation and promoting international collaborations in the development of live performance as well as its technologies and the space that hosts it.
Country: Taiwan, Province of China
Contact: Executive Director Wan-Jung Wei
secretary Szu-Yun Yu
arts administrator Chen-shin Wang
Frequency: Quadrennial
Start: 2022-08-06
End: 2022-08-16

Taishin Arts Award
Website: www.taishinart.org.tw/index_en.php
Email: info@taishinart.org.tw
Phone: 237 076 955
Address: Taishin Bank Foundation for Arts and Culture, 15F, No. 118, Sec 4, Ren-ai Rd. , Taipei 106, Taiwan
Information: The Taishin Arts Award acknowledges creative achievements in works of visual, performing and inter-disciplinary arts, a pioneering idea among arts awards at home and abroad. In addition to its importance in recognizing the professional creative achievements in Taiwan, it is also dedicated to establishing a platform enabling international networking for contemporary Taiwanese Artists.
Country: Taiwan, Province of China
Awards: 1. Taishin Annual Grand Prize, to receive a NT$1.5 million monetary award and trophy. 2. Taishin Performing Arts Award, to receive a NT$1million monetary award and trophy. 3. Taishin Visual Arts Award, to receive a NT$1million monetary award and trophy.

UNITED STATES

AGO/ECS Publishing Award in Choral Composition
Website: https://www.agohq.org/
Email: info@agohq.org
Phone: 212 870 2310
Address: American Guild of Organists, 475 Riverside Drive, Suite 1260, New York, NY 10115
Information: The AGO's choral competition can be traced back to Walter Clemson, a Guild founder. Mr. Clemson sponsored a prize for the choral composition in 1896 where the first prize was a gold medal worth $50. An AGO competition in choral composition continued in several different formats for much of the past century. You can listen to past awarded compositions.
Country: United States
Contact: Executive Director James Thomashower
Email: james.thomashower@agohq.org
Manager of competitions Harold Calhoun
Email: hc@agohq.org
Director Louise Mundinger
Email: louise.mundinger@gmail.com
Social Media: twitter.com/agohq www.facebook.com/agohq/
Frequency: Biennial

Alea III International Composition Prize
Website: https://www.aleaiii.com/
Email: aleaiii@bu.edu
Phone: 781 793 8902
Address: Alea III, 10 Country Lane, Sharon, MA 02067, USA
Information: The ALEA III International Composition Prize was established at Boston University to promote and encourage the creation of new music by young professional composers of all nationalities under 40 years old.
Country: United States
Contact: President Margaret McAllister
vice President Panos Liaropoulos Liaropoulos
Social Media: www.facebook.com/AleaIIItwitter.com/aleaiii
Eligibility: open to young professional composers of all nationalities under 40 years old

American Guild of Organists National Competition in Organ Improvisation
Website: https://www.agohq.org/
Email: info@agohq.org
Phone: 212 870 2310
Address: American Guild of Organists, 475 Riverside Drive, Suite 1260, New York, NY 10115
Information: The National Competition in Organ Improvisation seeks to further the art of improvisation by recognizing and rewarding superior performance in the field. A flourishing tradition of improvisation is fundamental to a truly vital musical culture.
Country: United States
Contact: Executive Director James E. Thomashower
Email: james.thomashower@agohq.org
Director of development and communication F. Anthony Thurman
Email: fathurman@agohq.org
Manager of competiitions and educational resources Harold Calhoun
Email: hc@agohq.org
Social Media: twitter.com/agohq www.facebook.com/agohq
Frequency: Biennial
Start: 2021-12-12

American Guild of Organists National Young Artists Competition in Organ Performance
Website: https://www.agohq.org/
Email: info@agohq.org
Phone: 212 870 2310
Address: 475 Riverside Dr, Ste 1260 New York, NY 10115 USA
Information: the competition is intended to serve as a springboard for emerging organists to develop their performance ability by participating in the various demanding stages of this competition. The final round is held at the Guild's biennial convention held in even-numbered years
Country: United States
Contact: Executive Director James Thomashower
Email: james.thomashower@agohq.org
Director of development and communications Anthony Thurman
Email: fathurman@agohq.org
Manager of competitions and educational resources Harold Calhoun
Email: hc@agohq.org
Social Media: twitter.com/agohq www.facebook.com/agohq/
Frequency: Biennial

American Jazz Piano Competition
Website: www.americanjazzpianistcompetition.org
Email: info@americanjazzpianistcompetition.org
Phone: 321 725 5690
Address: American Jazz Pianist Competition, 150 East Drive Suite C, Melbourne, FL 32904, US
Information: American Jazz Piano Competition delivers opportunities for advancements for young individuals seeking a professional career in Jazz. They pair youth with professional musicians and clinicians who will inspire them and help to create an accessible environment for young musicians to observe and collaborate with legendary jazz performers and clinicians.
Country: United States
Contact: Artistic Director Per Danielsson
President Brian Gatchell
vice President Jamie Younkin
Open to North American Citizens (US & Canada) age 18-25
Awards: GRAND BOHEMIAN PRIZE: ($6, 000 Check, $1, 200 Check for 3 Performances at Kessler Hotels, 3 Nights at Kessler Collection Hotels ($800 value), $300 Travel Allowance); YAMAHA PRIZE (Album Recording & Master at Yamaha NYC ($5000 Value) and $500 Travel Allowance); BSENDERFER PRIZE ($4, 000 Check $1, 500 for 2 Performances in Savannah, 2 Nights hotel stay); BRIAN GATCHELL PRIZE (4 Yamaha Digital Pianos)
Frequency: Annual

American Pianists Awards
Website: https://www.americanpianists.org/
Email: apainfo@americanpianists.org
Phone: 317 940 9945
Address: c/o The American Pianists Association, 4603 Clarendon Road, Suite 030, Indianapolis, Indiana 46208
Information: The American Pianists Association nurtures the Artistic growth of America's top young pianists by focusing on creative exPression and career development. Its largest and most prestigious support is given through a biennial competition known as the American Pianists Awards. Since its founding in 1979, the American Pianists Association has supported 46 winners.
Country: United States
Artistic Director & President/CEO
Joel Harrison
Email: joel@americanpianists.org
Phone: 317 940 9947 General Manager Joanne Bennett
Email: joanne@americanpianists.org
Phone: 317 940 9943 Director of development Lee Ann Smith
Email: leeann@americanpianists.org
Phone: 317 940 9371 Development Associate Greg Porter
Social Media: www.facebook.com/APApianiststwitter.com/APApianists www.instagram.com/apapianists/
Awards: Winners receive cash and two-years of career advancement and support valued at over $100, 000
Frequency: Biennial

American Traditions Competition for Singers
Website: https://www.atcsavannah.org/
Email: msodergren@americantraditionscompetition.com
Phone: 803 702 0305
Address: American Traditions Vocal Competition, P.O. Box 15972, Savannah, Georgia 31416
Information: The American Traditions Vocal Competition was born of the desire to foster and preserve traditions of musical exPression, which have been significant in the culture of the United States, both in past eras and at the present time. In contrast to many music competitions that focus on European repertoire, the American Traditions Competition celebrates the repertoire that represents both the art and the popular cultures of our country.
Country: United States
Contact: Artistic Director Mikki Sodergren
Email: msodergren@americantraditionscompetition.com
President Kellee Love Haselton
secretary Starr Holland
vice President Nathan Godley Godley
Social Media: twitter.com/ATC_Savannah www.facebook.com/ATCSavannah/ www.instagram.com/atc_savannah/
Eligibility: Any singer born before February 9, 2003 is eligible to apply to the American Traditions Vocal Competition. We pride ourselves on being one of the only singing competitions with NO upper age limit. All ATC Gold Medalists are ineligible to compete, as they have previously won the competition. Singers may only compete in Savannah, GA three times in every five years.
Frequency: Biennial
Start: 2022-02-21
End: 2022-02-25

ASCAP Foundation Morton Gould Young Composer Awards
Website: https://www.ascap.com/
Email: concertmusic@ascap.com
Phone: 212 621 6000
Address: The ASCAP Foundation, 250 West 57th Street, New York, NY 10107, US
Information: ASCAP is a membership association of more than 750, 000 songwriters, composers and music publishers. They uphold the value of their members' music, and help them thrive alongside the businesses that use their music every day.
Country: United States
Contact: vice President Cia Toscanini Toscanini
Social Media: twitter.com/ascap www.facebook.com/ascap www.instagram.com/ascap/
Eligibility: To be eligible for participation in the Awards, an entrant must be, at the time of entry, (a) at least 13 years of age; and (b) a U.S. citizen, permanent resident or enrolled student with a valid and current U.S. student visa (each, an Entrant). Entrants must also be under the age of 30 as of February 1, 2021.
Awards: In accordance with these Award Requirements, eligible Entrants will be selected as the Award Recipients and will receive a monetary prize (each, a Prize). The number of Award Recipients and the monetary distribution of the Prize resides within the sole discretion of the judges. The total value of the Prize to be shared among the Award Recipients shall be determined in the Foundations sole discretion. At the sole discretion of the Foundation, an award ceremony may be held to recognize the Award Recipient, the place and time of such celebration determined in the Foundations sole discretion (the Award Ceremony).
Frequency: Annual

Barlow Endowment for Music Composition
Website: https://barlow.byu.edu/
Email:
barlowendowment@byu.edu
Phone: 801 422 8611
Address: Barlow Endowment, 701 East University Parkway, Brigham Young University, Provo, UT 84602, US
Information: In 1983 Milton A. and Gloria Barlow established the Barlow Endowment for Music Composition at Brigham Young University in Provo, Utah. . The Endowment has subsequently been dedicated to promoting excellence in music composition with over 403 total commissions awarded. The Barlow Endowment for Music Composition at Brigham Young University encourages and financially supports composers who demonstrate technical skills and natural gifts for the composition of great music.
Country: United States
Contact: Executive Director Ethan Wickman
Social Media: www.facebook.com/BarlowEndowment
Eligibility: We encourage applicants from a variety of musical aesthetics and backgrounds to apply. There are no restrictions or preferences with regard to musical style, nationality, age, gender, race, religion, locale, or political persuasion. Composers may apply for the Prize and either a General OR a Latter-day Saints commission. Composers should not submit the same pieces to be reviewed for multiple Barlow competitions.
Awards: The winning composer will receive a $12, 000 commission for a major new work for Sinfonietta
Frequency: Annual

BMI Student Composer Awards
Website: https://bmifoundation.org/programs/info/bmi_student_composer_awards
Email: dchadwick@bmifoundation.org
Phone: 212 220 3000
Address: BMI Foundation Inc, 7 World Trade Center, 250 Greenwich Street, New York, NY 10007-0030
Information: The BMI Student Composer Awards is an annual competition open to young composers engaged in the study of classical music. It has a prestigious history of discovering and encouraging many of today's most prominent and talented young composers.
Since its inception, the competition has awarded nearly 600 scholarships to musicians, including fifteen Pulitzer Prize winners, and is widely regarded as the premier recognition for young composers of classical music in the Western Hemisphere.
Country: United States
Contact: President Deirdre Chadwick
Social Media: twitter.com/bmifoundation www.facebook.com/BMIFoundation www.instagram.com/bmifoundation/
Awards: awards totaling $20, 000 are determined annually for vocal, instrumental, and/or electronic compositions submitted by students of classical music.
Frequency: Annual

Carmine Caruso International Jazz Trumpet Solo Competition
Website: https://liberalarts.du.edu/lamont/caruso-competition
Email: cmccull5@depaul.edu
Phone: 206 300 8100
Address: College-Conservatory of Music, University of Cincinnati, P.O. Box 210003, US
Information: Sponsored by International Trumpet Guild, in cooperation with the Herb Alpert Foundation, the Carmine Caruso International Jazz Trumpet Solo Competition honors one of the world's greatest brass teachers. It is to this man and his work that the competition is dedicated.
Country: United States
Eligibility: open to all trumpeters (except previous first-prize winners) born after Sept. 14, 1989, provided that they are not currently under major Artist management.
Awards: First Prize $10, 000 US, Second Prize $5, 000 US
Frequency: Annual

Chamber Music America – Commissioning Program
Website: https://www.chamber-music.org/programs
Email: sdadian@chamber-music.org
Phone: 212 242 2022
Address: Chamber Music America, 12 West 32nd Street, 7th Floor, New York, NY 10001-3813
Information: Chamber Music America's Classical Commissioning Program provides grants to professional U.S. based presenters and ensembles whose programming includes Western European and/or non-Western classical and contemporary music. Grants are provided for the commissioning and performance of new works by American composers. The program supports works scored for 2–10 musicians performing one per part, composed in any of the musical styles Associated with contemporary classical music.
Country: United States
Contact: programme Director Susan Dadian
Email: sdadian@chamber-music.org
Social Media: www.twitter.com/CMA_tweets www.facebook.com/ChamberMusicAmerica
Eligibility: professional U.S.-based presenters and ensembles whose programming includes Western European and/or non-Western classical and contemporary music. Grants are provided for the commissioning and performance of new works by American composers
Awards: Grants Available
Frequency: Triennial

Chamber Music America – Jazz Works: Commissioning and Ensemble Development
Website: https://www.chamber-music.org/programs
Phone: 212 242 2022
Address: Chamber Music America, 12 West 32nd Street, 7th Floor, New York, NY 10001-3813
Information: Chamber Music America is the national service organization for ensemble music professionals. Our members are thousands of individual musicians, ensembles, presenters, Artist Managers, composers, educators and others in the national chamber music community.
Country: United States
Contact: program Director, CMA Jazz Gargi Shindé
Email: gshinde@chamber-music.org
Social Media: twitter.com/CMA_tweets www.facebook.com/ChamberMusicAmerica
Awards: CMA offers its grantees 3 years, July 2020-June 2023, to complete a New Jazz Works grant.

Chamber Music America – Residency Partnership Program
Website: https://www.chamber-music.org/programs
Email: sdadian@chamber-music.org
Phone: 212 242 2022
Address: Chamber Music America, 12 West 32nd Street, 7th Floor, New York, NY 10001-3813
Information: The Residency Partnership Program supports ensembles and presenters in building audiences for classical/contemporary, jazz, and world chamber music through residency projects. Funding is specifically aimed at activities that take place in community settings and that are not part of a regular concert series. Projects must take place in the U.S. or its territories
Country: United States
Contact: program Director Susan Dadian
Email: sdadian@chamber-music.org
chief Executive officer Margaret Lioi
Email: mlioi@chamber-music.org
Social Media: www.twitter.com/CMA_tweets www.facebook.com/ChamberMusicAmerica
Eligibility: To apply, an ensemble must: 1.) consist of 2-10 professional musicians, one musician per part 2.) perform with fixed instrumentation and personnel for the duration of the residency 3.) if a duoperform as equal partners rather than soloist and accompanist and consistently publicize itself as a duo 4.)be able to submit an audio recording that features the musicians who will perform the residency 5.) have 501(c)(3) status, or 6.) if the ensemble does not have 501(c)(3) status, the leader/primary member of the ensemble must be a U.S. citizen or have residency status
Awards: Up to $7, 500 (no matching funds required)
Frequency: Annual

Cleveland International Piano Competition
Website: https://www.pianocleveland.org/
Phone: 216 707 5397
Address: 20600 Chagrin Boulevard, Suite 1110, Shaker Heights, Ohio 44122
Information: The roots of the CIPC were established in 1974 with a biennial competition to honor the great French pianist Robert Casadesus and the warm relationship he had with legendary Cleveland Orchestra conductor George Szell. In the mid-1990s a re-organization reframed the governance and structure of the organization, and created the name under which it operates today.
Country: United States
Marketing & communications coordinator Nicole Mieske Knab
Email: nicole.mieske@pianocleveland.org
Director of development Marissa Glynias Moore
Email: marissa.moore@pianocleveland.org
Director of operations Crystal E. Carlson
Email: crystal.carlson@clevelandpiano.org
President Yaron Kohlberg
Email: yaron.kohlberg@pianocleveland.org
Social Media: twitter.com/pianocleveland www.facebook.com/pianocleveland www.instagram.com/piano_cleveland/
Eligibility: Participants between the ages of 24 and 30
Awards: First Prize: $75, 000 USD, Second Prize: $25, 000 USD, Third Prize: $15, 000 USD, Fourth Prize: $10, 000 USD, Semi Finalist Prizes: $2, 000, Contestant Prizes: $1, 000, and a selection of special prizes in other categories
Frequency: Biennial

Cliburn International Junior Piano Competition and Festival
Website: https://cliburn.org/
Email: Generalinformation@cliburn.org
Phone: 817 738 6536
Address: 201 Main Street, Suite 100 Fort Worth, TX
Information: The Cliburn advances classical piano music throughout the world. Its international competitions, education programs, and concert series embody an enduring commitment to Artistic excellence and the discovery of new Artists.
Country: United States
Contact: Executive Office Jacques Marquis
Email: jmarquis@cliburn.org
Phone: Director of Artistic planning Sandra Doan
Email: sdoan@cliburn.org

Phone: Artistic operations Manager Melinda Willmann Willmann
Email: mwillmann@cliburn.org
Phone: Director of communications and digital content Maggie Estes
Email: mestes@cliburn.org
Phone: Director of development Marianne Pohle
Email: mpohle@cliburn.org
Social Media: twitter.com/TheCliburn www.facebook.com/thecliburn
Eligibility: Applicants must have been born between June 8, 2001, and May 31, 2006.
Awards: First prize $10, 000 to $50, 000 Smallest prize Less than $5, 000
Start: 2022-06-02
End: 2022-06-18

Coleman Chamber Ensemble Competition
Website: http://www.colemanchambermusic.org/
Email: info@colemanchambermusic.org
Phone: 626 793 4191
Address: Coleman Chamber Music Association, 225 South Lake Avenue, Suite 300, Pasadena, CA 91101, US
Information: The oldest independent chamber music series in the country, the Coleman Chamber Concerts were founded in 1904 by Alice Coleman, a gifted musician with a remarkable vision for the future of chamber music.
Country: United States
Social Media: www.facebook.com/ColemanChamberMusic/

Concert Artists Guild Victor Elmaleh Competition
Website: https://www.concertArtists.org/
Email: info@concertArtists.org
Phone: 212 333 5200
Address: 135 East 57th St, 7th Fl New York, NY 10022
Information: CAG seeks to partner with young musicians who exemplify Artistic excellence and engagement with their audience, have an entrepreneurial spirit, and who will go on to create an impact in the world. Prizes include a $5, 000 first prize, management contracts with CAG, and a New York debut.
Country: United States
Contact: President Tanya Bannister
Email: tbannister@concertArtists.org
Manager of Artistic programs Jessica Lightfoot
Email: jlightfoot@concertArtists.org
Director of development Becky Lipkind
Email: blipkind@concertArtists.org
Social Media: twitter.com/concertArtists www.facebook.com/ConcertArtistsGuild www.instagram.com/concert_Artists_guild
Eligibility: open to all instruments, voice, and chamber ensembles
Awards: Grand Prize winners receive: 1.) International management (Americas and Europe) jointly with CAG andYoung Classical Artists Trust (YCAT) 2.)Performances at both Merkin Concert Hall in New York and Wigmore Hall in London 3.)Participation in CAGs new Leadership Development Program Ambassador Award winners receive: 1.) North American management with CAG2.) New York debut performance 3.)Participation in CAGs newLeadership Development ProgramAdditional prizes may include: 1.) Chamber Music America Showcase Performance2.) More than 40 Performance Prizes with leading orchestras, concert series, and festivals
Frequency: Annual

Donald Aird Memorial Composers Competition
Website: http://www.earplay.org/ www/competition.php
Email: aird@earplay.org
Address: Earplay, 2021 Earplay Donald Aird Composers Competition, 560 29th Street, San Francisco, CA 94131-2239
Information: Earplay sponsors the annual Earplay Donald Aird Composers Competition, open to composers of any nationality and any age. Earplay performs the prizewinning piece and presents a cash prize of $1, 000 to the winning composer. The competition honors the late composer and Earplay board member Donald Aird, an ardent supporter of the creation and performance of new music.
Country: United States
Awards: Cash prize: $1, 000.
Frequency: Annual
Start: 2022-03-31

Ellsworth Smith International Trumpet Solo Competition
Website: https://www.2020ellsworthsmith.com/
Email: ellsworthcontest@trumpetguild.org
Address: Brigham Young University School of Music, C-550 Harris Fine Arts Center, Provo, UT 84602-6410 (USA)
Information: The Ellsworth Smith International Trumpet Solo Competition is jointly sponsored by the International Trumpet Guild and the Columbus Foundation, which manages the Helen Smith Trust and the Ellsworth Smith Memorial Endowment. The endowment was started in 1982 by the daughter of amateur cornetist Ellsworth Smith in memory of her father, with the goal of supporting the training of virtuoso cornet and trumpet students.

Country: United States
Contact: competition host Jason Bergman
Email: ellsworthcontest@trumpetguild.org
Eligibility: Any trumpet player born after January 1, 1990, is invited to apply.
Awards: $15, 000 total prizes

Emerging Artist Competition
Website: https://www.cedillerecords.org/emerging-Artist-competition/
Email: competition@cedillerecords.org
Phone: 773 989 2515
Address: 1205 West Balmoral, US
Information: Acclaimed nonprofit Chicago-based classical music label Cedille Records hosts the Emerging Artist Competition. The Competition is open to individual musicians and ensembles of up to six people who reside in or hail from the Chicago metro area. The winner will record and release an album on Cedille Records.
Country: United States
Contact: President James Ginsburg
Email: jim@cedillerecords.org
Director of development Julie Polanski
Email: julie@cedillerecords.org
Social Media: www.twitter.com/CedilleRecords www.facebook.com/CedilleRecords
Eligibility: Individual performers and ensembles (sextet or smaller) who have not appeared as the featured performer on another commercially released CD are eligible to apply; the competition is not open to composers or conductors. The maximum age limit for individual performers is 35 years old as of the application open date. For ensembles, the average age of ensemble members should not exceed 35 and no individual player may exceed 40 years of age. There is no minimum age limit.
Awards: Awards: One winner and one honorable mention will be selected. The winner will record a Cedille Records album. The winners prize will be offered to the honorable mention if the winner is not able to record or release the album as planned.
Frequency: Quadrennial

Fischoff National Chamber Music Competition
Website: https://www.fischoff.org/
Email: miki@fischoff.org
Phone: 574 631 0984
Address: 303 Brownson Hall, US
Information: The Fischoff National Chamber Music Association sponsors the nation's largest chamber music competition. Committed to music education, the Fischoff also partners with competition alumni to bring free, innovative Arts-in-Education programs directly to children in their own schools and community centers.
Country: United States
Contact: Executive Director Carmen Creel
Email: ccreel@fischoff.org
media Director Carrie Lehman
Email: carrie@mail.fischoff.org
Social Media: www.facebook.com/TheFischoff
Eligibility: The competition is open to instrumental ensembles only; U.S. and non-U.S. residents are eligible. Ensembles will consist of three to six musicians. The Competition is unable to accommodate ensembles that have more than one piano, are vocal in nature, or require more than three minutes set-up and tear-down time. All members of the ensemble must perform on separate instruments throughout the competition but can use various instruments. No individual may enter or compete in more than one ensemble.
Awards: First prize $10, 000 to $50, 000 Smallest prize Less than $5, 000
Start: 2022-03-02

Forte International Music Competition
Website: https://fortemusicart.org/
Email: connect@fortemusicart.org
Phone: 718 755 2110
Address: 2733 Cropsey Avenue, Brooklyn, NY
Information: Forte International Music Competition is open to instrumentalists and vocalists ages four to 35. It consists of several rounds culminating with the final round at Carnegie Hall. Participants receive valuable feedback from judges, certificates, medals, cash prizes, and other special awards.
Country: United States
Contact: President Viktoryia Kourbatskaia
vice President Eugene Plotkin
Social Media: @ForteCompete www.facebook.com/Forte-International-Music-Competition-and-Festivals-155537901127751
Frequency: Annual

Gina Bachauer International Artists Piano Competition
Website: https://www.bachauer.com/
Email: info@bachauer.com
Phone: 801 297 4250
Address: 138 W Broadway, Ste 220 Salt Lake City, UT 84101 USA
Information: The mission of the Gina Bachauer International Piano Foundation is to further the pianistic art, foster excellence in performance and teaching, develop opportunities for pianists beyond the scope of the organization and offer leadership in developing a

THE CLIBURN

THE WORLD IS LISTENING

SIXTEENTH
VAN CLIBURN
INTERNATIONAL
PIANO
COMPETITION

2–18 JUNE, 2022
FORT WORTH, TEXAS USA

musically-educated citizenry
Country: United States
Social Media: twitter.com/bachauerpiano www.facebook.com/ginabachauer
Frequency: Quadrennial

Gina Bachauer International Young Artists Competition
Website: https://www.bachauer.com/
Email: info@bachauer.com
Phone: 801 297 4250
Address: 138 West 300 South, Salt Lake City, UT 84101 USA
Information: The Bachauer Foundation is a Salt Lake City-based non-profit organization with a well-established reputation as one of the most significant international piano organizations, which promotes excellence in piano performance and engages the next generation of classical piano enthusiasts. The Bachauer Foundation has provided opportunities for the world's most outstanding pianists to perform for prestige, prizes, and Artistic acclaim over 43 years.
Country: United States
Contact: Artistic Director Douglas Humphreys
Executive Director Kary Billings
Email: kary@bachauer.com
Marketing coordinator Scott Pollei
Email: scott@bachauer.com
Social Media: www.facebook.com/ginabachauertwitter.com/bachauerpiano
Eligibility: pianists ages 11-14 and 27 pianists ages 15-18
Awards: medals and their share of $62, 000 in cash prizes

Global Music Awards
Website: http://www.globalmusicawards.com/
Email: entries@globalmusicawards.com
Phone: 858 255 8309
Address: Global Music Awards, 7752 Fay Avenue, Suite B, La Jolla, California, 92037, USA
Information: The Global Music Awards is a highly rated, well known international music competition that celebrates independent musicians. Global Music Awards is recognized by industry insiders as giving legitimacy to highly talented Artists. It is a competition based strictly on merit.
Country: United States
Social Media: www.twitter.com/GMAMusicAwards www.facebook.com/globalmusicawards
Eligibility: Open to all Artists and composers. Submissions may be of any genre, any length. We look for Artists and composers with outstanding emotional communication, the ability to transcend, to make the listener experience something that is new and compelling. We want to be surprised and moved by what we hear. We want to be convinced that those we honor can really move an audience. The musical joy of Artists we select must be infectious. We want the Artist to remind us why we care about music so much in
Awards: Gold Medal – Best of Show Gold Medal – Award of Excellence – Silver Medal – Outstanding Achievement In Music – Bronze Medal – Finalist Annual Humanitarian Award – Odyssey Award – Lifetime Achievement Award – Heretic Award categories
Frequency: Annual
Start: 2022-01-03

Guild of Temple Musicians Young Composers Award
Website: https://templemusicians.org/young-composers-award/
Email: info@thegtm.org
Phone: 847 781 7800
Address: 1375 Remington Rd, Suite M. Schaumburg, IL 60173 USA
Information: This competition, founded and Chaired by Ben Steinberg, is held annually to promote young Jewish composers' works. The award is one of the few composition awards of any kind which provides the winner with a cash award, a first performance, transportation to the performance, and the possibility of the winning selection being published by Transcontinental Music Publications (TMP).
Country: United States
Contact: founder and President Ben Steinberg
vice President David Shukiar
Email: david.shukiar@thegtm.org
Frequency: Annual

Heida Hermanns International Competition
Website: https://theheida.mocawestport.org/
Email: thenewheida@mocawestport.org
Phone: 203 222 7070
Address: Heida Hermanns International Music Competition, MoCA Westport, 19 Newtown Turnpike, Westport, CT 06880
Information: Founded in 1972, the Heida Hermanns International Music Competition is held annually in Connecticut and showcases exceptional musicians from around the world. Competitions are held each year on a rotating basis in piano, voice and strings. Winners take home cash prizes, are given performance opportunities and achieve professional recognition. The 2022 Competition will focus on the Piano.
Country: United States

Eligibility: musicians between the ages of 18-30
Awards: The winner receives a $10, 000 cash prize and each finalist receives a $2, 500 honorarium and lodging with host families for the week. In addition to the cash prize, the winner receives an invitation to return to Westport for a solo performance at a later date.
Start: 2022-01-13
End: 2022-01-15

Herbie Hancock Institute of Jazz International Competition (Thelonious Monk International Jazz Competition)
Website: https://hancockinstitute.org/
Email: info@hancockinstitute.org
Phone: 202 364 7272
Address: 5225 Wisconsin Avenue NW, Suite 605, Washington, DC 20015
Information: Established in 1987, this is the world's most prestigious jazz competition, recognised for discovering the next generation of jazz masters. Representatives from major jazz labels attend the competition each year because it is one of the most highly respected events in the worldwide music community and the place to discover the rising stars of tomorrow.
Country: United States
Contact: President Thomas R. Carter
Director of special projects Leonard E. Brown
vice President of operations Michelle M. Day
administrative Director Holly Wallace
Social Media: twitter.com/HancockInst www.facebook.com/hancockinstitute/ www.instagram.com/hancockinstitute/
Frequency: Annual

Hilton Head International Piano Competition
Website: https://www.hhipc.org/
Email: pianocomp@hhipc.org
Phone: 843 842 5880
Address: 7 Lagoon Road, Suite 100, 29928 Hilton Head Island, South Carolina
Information: The mission of the Hilton Head International Piano Competition is to encourage and support excellence in the performance of classical piano music by showcasing the talents of young pianists on the threshold of their careers in competitions adjudicated by internationally acclaimed judges, and to offer additional performance opportunities.
Country: United States
Contact: competition Director Mona Huff
Marketing Director/public relations Sarah Bergin
President and CEO Mary Briggs
Social Media: www.facebook.com/HHIPC/
Awards: FIRST PRIZE: $10, 000 and Return engagement with Hilton Head Symphony Orchestra, SECOND PRIZE: $5000, THIRD PRIZE: $3, 000, MEDALISTS: $1000
Frequency: Annual
Start: 2022-03-07
End: 2022-03-14

Houston Symphony Ima Hogg Young Artist Competition
Website: https://houstonsymphony.org/community/young/ima-hogg-competition/
Email: education.community@houstonsymphony.org
Phone: 713 238 1447
Address: Houston Symphony, 615 Louisiana Street, Suite 102, Houston, Texas 77002
Information: The Houston Symphony Ima Hogg Competition is a multi-instrument competition designed to identify outstanding young instrumentalists and support their pursuit of careers in music. Ten contestants are selected to perform in the semi-finals. Four finalists will perform with the Houston Symphony to determine the winner of the $25, 000 award.
Country: United States
Contact: music Director Andrés Orozco-Estrada
senior Director, communications Eric Skelly
Email: eric.skelly@houstonsymphony.org
Social Media: twitter.com/HouSymphony www.facebook.com/houstonsymphony www.instagram.com/housymphony/
Frequency: Annual

IBLA International Music Foundation Award
Website: http://www.ibla.org/
Email: iblanewyork@gmail.com
Phone: 212 387 0111
Address: 568 Grand Street, Suite 2001, New York, NY 10002, USA
Information: The IBLA Grand Prize International Music Competition is an annual music competition that is open to merely all instruments, vocalists and composers with a focus on classical music. The vision of the competition is that the competition could be helpful in the future carrier of competitors by giving experience in performing.
Country: United States
Contact: President Salvatore Moltisanti
Social Media: www.facebook.com/IblaGrandPrize
Eligibility: open to all instruments, vocalists and composers with a focus on classical music. There is no age limit, nor are there repertoire demands except from time limits
Awards: The best performers will be invited for concerts abroad in such venues as Carnegie Hall, which is to be

considered as the Top Prize

International Double Reed Society Norma Hooks Young Artist Competition
Website: https://www.idrs.org/competitions/
Email: jeremias@idrs.org
Phone: 410 871 0658
Address: PO Box 490 Riderwood, MD 21139-0490 USA
Information: The Norma Hooks Young Artist Competition (dedicated to the memory of Norma Hooks, IDRS honorary member and lifeblood of the organization with her tireless dedication to our membership, annual conferences, and Executive Committee meetings) is for those who have not reached their 22nd birthday by the date of the final round of the competition.
Country: United States
Contact: President Eric Stomberg
Email: stomberg@idrs.org
Secretary Benjamin Coelho
Email: coelho@idrs.org
2021 NHYAC Bassoon Competition Contact Jennifer Auerbach
Email: auerbach@idrs.org
Social Media: twitter.com/IDRS https://www.facebook.com/idrsofficial/ www.instagram.com/idrsofficial/
Awards: First prize is $6000; second prize $4, 000; third prize is $2, 000.
Frequency: Annual

International Horn Competition of America
Website: https://www.ihcamerica.org/
Email: gross@music.ucsb.edu
Phone: 805 291 9641
Address: University of Alabama School of Music, Tuscaloosa, Alabama
Information: The International Horn Competition of America (formerly the American Horn Competition) came into being because two people wanted to promote a higher standard for US horn soloists. Its goals are to showcase American horn soloists and encourage horn professors to teach the solo literature in addition to standard etudes and orchestral excerpts.
Country: United States
Contact: Executive Director Steven Gross
Associate Director David Thompson
Artistic coordinator Lowell Greer
media coordinator Natalie Brooke Higgins
Social Media: www.facebook.com/IHCAmerica/
Eligibility: Open to hornists of all nationalities.Previous winners of the International Horn Competition of America are ineligible to compete in the division that they won.
Frequency: Biennial
Start: 2022-08-25
End: 2022-08-28

International Piano Competition for Outstanding Amateurs
Website: https://cliburn.org/
Phone: 817 738 6536
Address: 201 Main Street, Suite 100 Fort Worth, TX 76102
Information: Inaugurated in 1999, the Cliburn International Amateur Piano Competition was the first event of its kind in the United States. Hailed by the Boston Globe as "a celebration of music, and the people who have to make music no matter what;" the contest highlights the importance of music-making in everyday life and provides a forum for musicians age 35 and older who do not perform, teach, or compose piano music for their primary professional pursuit or financial benefit.
Country: United States
Contact: President and CEO Jacques Marquis
Email: jmarquis@cliburn.org
Director of Artistic planning Sandra Doan
Email: sdoan@cliburn.org
Social Media: twitter.com/TheCliburn www.facebook.com/thecliburn/ www.instagram.com/THECLIBURN/
Frequency: Quadrennial
Start: 2022-06-02
End: 2022-06-18

International Piano-e-Competition
Website: https://www.piano-e-competition.com/
Email: piano@ecompetition.org
Phone: 612 460 5640
Address: Stella Sick/e-Piano Junior Competition, P.O. Box 1386, Maple Grove, MN 55311, USA
Information: The Minnesota International Piano-e-Competition was founded in 2002 by Alexander Braginsky in collaboration with the Yamaha Corporation. It took place every two years in Minneapolis–Saint Paul before the 2008 edition was delayed to 2009 due to the arrangement of a junior edition of the competition. The – e – refers to the competition's focus on Internet and Disklavier technologies. The e-competition is one of the biggest, most major competitions available for young Artists. Many of its past competitors have gone onto achievesignificant success on the global competition/concert stage
Country: United States
Contact: artititic Director Alexander Braginsky
Managing Director Stella Sick Sick
Email: piano@ecompetition.org
Frequency: Annual

International Songwriting Competition
Website: https://songwritingcompetition.com/
Email: info@songwritingcompetition.com
Phone: 615 251 4441
Address: 3940 Gallatin Pike, Nashville, TN 37216
Information: their mission is to provide the opportunity for both aspiring and established songwriters to have their songs heard in a professional, international arena. ISC is designed to nurture the musical talent of songwriters on all levels and promote excellence in the art of songwriting
Country: United States
Contact: Director of Marketing Shane Whalen
Email: swhalen@songwritingcompetition.com
Social Media: https://twitter.com/intlsongcomp www.facebook.com/InternationalSongwritingCompetition
Eligibility: ISC is open to all amateur and professional songwriters and anyone regardless of nationality or origin. Employees of ISC, its families, subsidiaries and affiliates are not eligible.
Awards: overall prize package to $225, 000 in cash and prizes to be shared by a total of 71 winners in 23 genre categories

International Violin Competition of Indianapolis
Website: www.violin.org
Email: ivci@violin.org
Phone: 317 637 4574
Address: 32 E. Washington Street, Suite 1320, Indianapolis, IN 46204
Information: The mission of the International Violin Competition of Indianapolis (IVCI) is to recognise, reward and promote the world's finest young classical violinists, and encourage understanding, appreciation and support of the violin repertoire by a large and diverse audience. The IVCI utilises its world prominence to bring international attention to Indianapolis, and maintains its efforts to be a visible and collaborative member of the arts communities in Indianapolis and Indiana. Member of IAMA and WFIMC.
Country: United States
Contact: Executive Director Glen Kwok
Email: kwok@violin.org
Director of communications and Artist advancement Zack French
Email: french@violin.org
Director of operations Mindy Miller
Email: mindy@violin.org
Director of development Mary Jane Sorbera
Email: maryjane@violin.org
Social Media: www.facebook.com/ViolinCompIndy/twitter.com/ViolinCompIndy www.instagram.com/violincompindy/
Eligibility: see website for details
Frequency: Quadrennial
Start: 09/09/2022
End: 25/09/2022

Irving M Klein International String Competition
Website: https://www.californiamusiccenter.org/
Email: info@californiamusiccenter.org
Phone: 415 252 1122
Address: 150 Sutter St #262, San Francisco, CA 94104
Information: the Irving M. Klein International String Competition has attracted some of the world's finest young string players to San Francisco each June.
Country: United States
Contact: Executive Director Marcy Straw
Email: marcy@californiamusiccenter.org
Artistic and board Director Mitchell Sardou Klein
Email: msardou@sbcglobal.net
Social Media: twitter.com/KleinComp www.facebook.com/camusiccenter/
Eligibility: The Irving M. Klein International String Competition is open to violinists, violists, cellists and bassists between the ages of 15-23 at the time of the competition on June 5, 2021.
Awards: cash and performance prizes totaling over $30, 000
Frequency: Annual
Start: 2022-06-04
End: 2022-06-05

Jensen Foundation Vocal Competition
Website: https://www.jensenfoundation.org/
Email: lisa@jensenfoundation.org
Phone: 704 641 4691
Address: c/o Foundation for the Carolinas, 220 N. Tryon Street, Charlotte, NC 28202
Information: The Fritz and Lavinia Jensen Foundation, a Donor-Advised Fund of Foundation For The Carolinas, was established by Lavinia Jensen in honor of her late husband Fritz. The annual Jensen Foundation Vocal Competition supports young Artists pursuing a career in opera. The first competition took place in May 2000 and saw a field of 91 competitors. Since the competition was established, 388 singers have received more than $747, 000 in support.
Country: United States
Contact: President Oliver Worthington
Social Media: www.facebook.com/jensenfoundationtwitter.com/JensenAuditions

Eligibility: To be eligible to compete, singers: must not be a previous first-, second-, or third-place award winner of the Jensen Foundation Vocal Competition; must be a permanent legal resident of the United States for at least one year prior to March 15, 2021; must be between the ages of 25 and 35 as of March 15, 2021; must not be a past or current recipient of a contract for a principal role with an OPERA America Budget Level I company or its international equivalent. Cover, chorus, and comprimario roles with Level 1 companies are acceptable. must submit a completed application online by the deadline of Sunday, March 14, 2021.
Awards: First place – $15, 000 Second place – $10, 000 Third place – $7, 500 Munday Encouragement Award – $3, 000 and automatic entry into the 2022 Jensen Foundation Vocal Competition Peoples Choice – $500 Remaining finalists – $750
Frequency: Annual

Johansen International Competition for Young String Players (JIC)
Website: https://fmmcfoundation.org/johansen-international-competition/
Email: johansencomp@fmmc.org
Phone: 301 825 5515
Address: c/o Calvary Baptist Church, 755 8th St., NW 20001 Washington D.C.
Information: The Johansen International Competition for Young String Players Ages 13–17 (JIC), established in 1997, is sponsored by the Friday Morning Music Club Foundation. The JIC is made possible through the generosity of a charitable trust, established by the late Anna Storch Johansen of Falls Church, Virginia. Mrs. Johansen was a violinist and a Life Member of the Friday Morning Music Club (FMMC). She wanted to encourage young musicians with significant prize awards at a time when they need it most and when they must make decisions about whether to continue with their dedication to music.
Country: United States
Contact: administrative Director Harriet Kaplan
Email: johansencomp@fmmc.org
Social Media: www.facebook.com/johansencompetition/
Eligibility: Students of violin, viola, or cello, no younger than 13 or older than 17 years on the final day of the Competition.
Awards: The JIC offers $67, 000 in prize awards, with separate cash awards for violin, viola, and cello, as well as performance opportunities for winners and scholarships to the prestigious Brevard Summer Institute and Festival and Morningside Music Bridge. Winners receive five years of complimentary FMMC student membership.
Frequency: Triennial
Start: 2022-03-21
End: 2022-03-23

John Simon Guggenheim Memorial Foundation
Website: https://www.gf.org/
Phone: 212 687 4470
Address: John Simon Guggenheim Memorial Foundation, 90 Park Avenue, New York, NY 10016, USA
Information: Guggenheim Fellowships are intended for individuals who have already demonstrated exceptional capacity for productive scholarship or exceptional creative ability in the arts.
Country: United States
Contact: Chairman of the Board Dwight E. Lee
President Edward Hirsch
Social Media: www.twitter.com/GuggFellows www.facebook.com/GuggFellows/
Eligibility: Fellowships are awarded through two annual competitions: one open to citizens and permanent residents of the United States and Canada, and the other open to citizens and permanent residents of Latin America and the Caribbean. Candidates must apply to the Guggenheim Foundation in order to be considered in either of these competitions.
Frequency: Annual

Longwood Gardens International Organ Competition
Website: https://longwoodgardens.org/
Email: questions@longwoodgardens.org
Phone: 610 388 1000
Address: 1001 Longwood Road, US
Information: The Longwood Gardens International Organ Competition is open to organists from around the world who are between the ages of 18 and 30. It begins with a qualification round juried by esteemed members of the organ community, who anonymously evaluate audition recordings and select 10 of the brightest young talents to compete live before a panel of renowned judges in a quest for the top prize. Member of WFIMC.
Country: United States
President & chief Executive officer
Paul Redman
Email: President@longwoodgardens.org
vice President, Marketing & communications
Marnie Conley
Email: Marketingoffice@longwoodgardens.org
Social Media: twitter.com/longwoodgardens www.facebook.com/LongwoodGardens
Eligibility: age 18-30 years old

Marguerite McCammon Competition
Website: https://www.mvcompetition.org/
Email: joann.patton719@gmail.com
Address: 505 Pecan Street, Suite 100, Fort Worth, Texas 76102, US
Information: Since its debut in 1985, the McCammon Voice Competition has grown into one of the world's most important operatic events. Every two years the contest showcases the most compelling young singers of our time.
McCammon winners are immediately catapulted into the operatic "big time, " and now enjoy stellar careers with major opera companies around the world, including New York's Metropolitan Opera and Opera National de Paris.
Country: United States
Social Media: www.facebook.com/mccammonvoicecompetition/

Metropolitan Opera National Council Auditions
Website: https://www.metopera.org/nationalcouncil
Email: MetropolitanOpera@metopera.org
Phone: 212 362 6000
Address: Metropolitan Opera, 30 Lincoln Center, New York, NY 10023
Information: The Metropolitan Opera National Council Auditions is a program designed to discover promising young opera singers and assist in the development of their careers. The Auditions take place in 39 Districts and 12 Regions throughout the US, Canada, and Mexico all run locally by volunteers.
Country: United States
Contact: General Manager Peter Gelb
Music Director Yannick Nézet-Séguin
Music Director Jeanette Lerman-Neubauer
Social Media: twitter.com/metopera www.facebook.com/MetOpera www.instagram.com/metopera/
Eligibility: applicants must be 20 30 years old. Past auditioners may re-enter qualifying auditions as new applicants. Auditions are open to citizens and lawful residents of the United States, Canada, and Mexico.

Michael Ludwig Nemmers Prize in Musical Composition
Website: https://music.northwestern.edu/about/international-prizes/nemmers
Email: nemmersmusic@northwestern.edu
Phone: 847 491 7575
Address: Secretary to the Selection Committee, Michael Ludwig Nemmers Prize in Music Composition, Office of the Dean, Bienen School of Music, Northwestern University, Patrick G. and Shirley W. Ryan Center for the Musical Arts, 70 Arts Circle Drive, Evanston, IL 60208
Information: In Fall 2003, the Henry and Leigh Bienen School of Music established the Michael Ludwig Nemmers Prize in Music Composition, a biennial award honoring classical music composers of outstanding achievement. Nominations are solicited worldwide and the winner is determined by a three-member selection committee, comprising individuals of widely recognized stature in the music community.
Country: United States
Social Media: twitter.com/bienenschoolnu www.facebook.com/BienenSchoolNU
Awards: The prize includes a cash award of $100, 000 and a performance by the Chicago Symphony Orchestra. The recipient is expected to participate in two nonconsecutive weeks of residency at the Bienen School of Music interacting with students and faculty.
Frequency: Biennial

MTNA National Student Competitions
Website: https://www.mtna.org/
Email: mtnanet@mtna.org
Phone: 513 421 1420
Address: 600 Vine St., Ste. 1710 Cincinnati, OH 45202 USA
Information: Music Teachers National Association was founded in 1876 by Theodore Presser and 62 of his colleagues. With the mission to advance the value of musical study and music making within society, and to support the professionalism of music teachers, MTNA offers continuing education, small business resources, peer-to-peer networking, student performance opportunities and much more.
Country: United States
Contact: President Scott McBride Smith
Email: scottsmith@iiym.com
vice President Peter Mack
Email: mackpeter@earthlink.net
Social Media: twitter.com/MTNA1 www.facebook.com/mtnapage www.instagram.com/mtnaorg
Eligibility: All entrants must be a U.S. citizen or must hold a U.S. visa or permanent residence (green card), which is valid throughout the competition year. All entrants must study with a teacher who is (1) a member of MTNA or (2) has paid the Nonmember Teacher Fee of $150. MTNA active membership dues must be paid before submission of the application to avoid the $150 nonmember fee. Elementary Division (ages 5-10); Junior Division (ages 11-14); Senior Division (ages 15-18); Young Artists Division (ages 19-25)
Awards: various prizes, smallest prize less than $5, 000
Frequency: Annual

Murray Dranoff International Two Piano Competition
Website: https://www.dranoff2piano.org/
Email: mail@dranoff2piano.org
Phone: 305 572 9900
Address: 3550 Biscayne Blvd., Suite 702, Miami, FL 33137
Information: Since 1987, the Dranoff International 2-Piano Foundation has been the world's leading organization to champion exclusively two piano repertoire and Artistry. It is the only international foundation recognized by the World Federation of International Music Competitions, to discover, promote, and award honors to top professional duo piano Artists through its competition, commissions, and presentations of duo piano concerts.
Country: United States
Contact: Artistic Director Aglika Genova
Artistic Director Liuben Dimitrov
Social Media: twitter.com/Dranoff2Piano www.facebook.com/Dranoff2Piano www.instagram.com/dranoff2piano/
Awards: First Prize: $25, 000, Second Prize: $15, 000 , Third Prize: $10, 000

National Association of Teachers of Singing – Competitions
Website: https://www.nats.org/
Email: info@nats.org
Phone: 904 992 9101
Address: 9957 Moorings Drive, Suite 401, Jacksonville FL 32257
Information: The National Association of Teachers of Singing, celebrates the art of singing through a series of competitions and programs that are designed to showcase the talented singers and performers who are soon to be rising stars in the profession. Events are held annually or biennially, some in conjunction with the NATS National Conference and others in conjunction with the NATS Summer or Winter Workshops.
Country: United States
Contact: President Carole Blankenship
Email: President@nats.org
international coordinator Marvin Keenze
Email: international@nats.org
Social Media: twitter.com/OfficialNATS www.facebook.com/OfficialNATS
Eligibility: Applicant must be at least 21 but not more than 35 years of age as of competition date; either the applicant or his/her teacher for the last year must be a full or Associate member of NATS for at least one year prior to competition date.
Awards: variety of cash prizes. Prizes for 1st, 2nd and 3rd place will total at least $35, 000.

National Chopin Piano Competition of the U.S.
Website: https://www.chopin.org/
Email: info@chopin.org
Phone: 305 865 5150
Address: 1440 79th Street Causeway, Suite 117, Miami, Florida 33141
Information: The National Chopin Piano Competition of the United States ("National Competition") is designed to offer performance opportunities & financial support to young American pianists, & to enable the Prize Winners to take part in the 18th International Fryderyk Chopin Piano Competition in Warsaw. Initiated in 1975, & held in Miami every five years, the National Competition rules reflect closely the regulations and requirements of the International Fryderyk Chopin Piano Competition in Warsaw, Poland.
Country: United States
Contact: Executive Director Barbara E. Muze
President and founder Blanka A. Rosenstiel
Social Media: https://twitter.com/ChopinMiami www.facebook.com/chopinus www.instagram.com/Chopin-Miami/
Awards: First Prize $100, 000, Second Prize $30, 000, Third Prize $20, 000
Frequency: Quinquennial

Naumburg International Competition
Website: https://www.naumburg.org/home
Email: debra.kinzler@naumburg.org
Phone: 917 493 4040
Address: 130 Claremont Avenue NY, NY 10027
Information: The Walter W. Naumburg Foundation sponsors competitions and provides awards for young classical musicians in North America. It was founded in 1925 by Walter Wehle Naumburg, a wealthy amateur cellist and son of noted New York City music patron and philanthropist Elkan Naumburg.
Country: United States
Contact: President Nicholas Mann
vice President David Geber
Executive Director Lucy Rowan Mann
Social Media: www.facebook.com/naumburgfoundation www.facebook.com/naumburgfoundation
Eligibility: In residence in North America; Ensemble members ages must not exceed 34 as of September, 2021
Awards: $15, 000; A fully subsidized New York Recital; A Commissioned Work, Composer TBA
Frequency: Annual

New Jersey Sinfonietta International Vocal Competition
Website: https://www.njsinfonietta.com/competition.php
Email: info@njsinfonietta.com
Phone: 201 702 8190
Address: New Jersey Sinfonietta, 200 Sylvan Ave Suite 21, Englewood Cliffs, NJ 07632
Information: The competition aims to identify promising new talent and provide them with an opportunity to perform with NJS (a young and rising orchestra) at the Merkin Concert Hall in New York City.
Country: United States
Contact: music Director Taeyoung Lee
President Jihyun Park
Executive Director Bo Yeon Han
Director of public relations Sue Yun
Director of Administration Angela Jung
Social Media: www.facebook.com/njsinfonietta www.instagram.com/njsinfonietta/
Eligibility: Age Limit: 30. Applicants must have the date of birth after May 3, 1989. Performers of all nationalities are welcome to apply.
Awards: 1st prize: $3000; 2nd prize: $2000; 3rd prize: $1000; five honourable mentions at $200 each
Frequency: Triennial

New Orleans International Piano Competition
Website: http://www.masno.org/
Email: Director@masno.org
Phone: 504 899 4826
Address: Musical Arts Society of New Orleans (MASNO), P.O. Box 750698, New Orleans, LA 70175-0698
Information: MASNO's vision is to be a primary source in establishing New Orleans as a vital and vibrant center for the musical arts, recognized regionally, nationally, and internationally.
Since its beginning, MASNO has provided both Artists and students an opportunity to perform for appreciative audiences and has assisted students in developing skills necessary to build Artistic discipline within a comfortable and supportive environment.
Country: United States
Contact: Executive and Artistic Director Cara McCool Woolf
Email: Director@masno.org
Phone: 504 899 4826
Social Media: www.facebook.com/MASNO1980/twitter.com/CaraMasno www.instagram.com/masno1980/
Eligibility: Previous First Prize winners are not eligible to compete again.
Awards: Cash, Performance, and Recording Prizes Totaling Over $75, 000
Frequency: Annual
Start: 2022-07-24
End: 2022-07-31

Olga Kern International Piano Competition
Website: https://olgakerncompetition.org/
Email: info@olgakerncompetition.org
Phone: 505 814 5355
Address: PO Box 14314, Albuquerque, NM 87191, US
Information: The mission of the Competition is to provide a venue for young pianists to develop international careers through a competition that is recognized globally for its value and excellence.
Country: United States
Contact: Artistic Director Olga Kern
Executive Director Marian Tanau
board President Maureen Baca
Social Media: www.twitter.com/OlgaKernComp www.facebook.com/olgakerncompetition www.instagram.com/olgakerncomp/
Eligibility: The Competition is open to pianists of all nationalities between the ages of 18 and 32 .
Awards: Awards include $30, 000 in cash prizes. The first-prize winner will be awarded international concert engagements throughout the US and Europe and a professional recording.

Operalia – Placido Domingo The World Opera Competition
Website: https://www.operaliacompetition.org/
Email: Info@OperaliaCompetition.com
Phone: 212 580 3011
Address: 155 West 70th Street #5F New York, NY 10023 USA
Information: Operalia was founded in 1993 by Plácido Domingo to discover and help launch the careers of the most promising young opera singers of today. Operalia's goal is to attract singers between the ages of eighteen and thirty-two, of all voice types from and all over the world, to have them audition and be heard by a panel of distinguished international personalities, in the most prestigious and competitive showcase in the world.
Country: United States
Social Media: www.facebook.com/Operaliatwitter.com/operaliacomp www.instagram.com/operaliacomp/
Frequency: Annual

PianoArts
Website: https://pianoarts.org/
Email: info@pianoarts.org
Phone: 414 962 3055

Address: 2642 North Summit Avenue, Milwaukee, WI 53211
Information: Finalists have four rehearsals: with a second pianist, a conductor, chamber ensemble, and a full orchestra, prior to performing a full concerto with the Milwaukee Symphony Orchestra. Through the Artist Training Institute, contestants have classes on engaging audiences with concert conversations. During the concurrent festival, all participants perform community concerts.
Country: United States
Contact: founder and Artistic Director Sue Medford
Social Media: twitter.com/pianoartsmke www.facebook.com/PianoArts
Eligibility: pianists ages 16-21, living or studying full time in North America
Awards: Over $30, 000 in cash prizes shared among ten semifinalists, numerous performance engagements, competition solo and duo recitals with MSO musicians, and final concerto round with the Milwaukee Symphony Orchestra
Frequency: Annual
Start: 2022-06-01

Plowman Chamber Music Competition
Website: https://www.plowmancompetition.org/
Email: info@OdysseyMissouri.org
Phone: 573 825 0079
Address: Plowman Chamber Music Competition c/o Odyssey, First Baptist Church, 112 E. Broadway, Columbia, Missouri
Information: The purpose of the Plowman Chamber Music Competition is to assist emerging chamber ensembles in their Artistic development, to encourage them to pursue careers in chamber music, and to provide a forum for their talents. Plowman intends to raise Columbia's cultural status nationally through promotion of quality music. Plowman will support ensembles in achieving the highest level of accomplishment and foster a collegial environment among the participating musicians.
Country: United States
Contact: Executive Director Peter Miyamoto
Artistic Director Ayako Tsuruta
Social Media: www.facebook.com/groups/207614089397/
Awards: various cash awards including a grand prize of $5, 000.
Frequency: Biennial
Start: 2023-03-25
End: 2023-03-26

Primrose International Viola Competition
Website: https://www.primrosecompetition.org/
Email: info@primrosecompetition.org
Phone: 213 621 4747
Address: 200 S Grand Ave Los Angeles, CA 90012 USA
Information: Founded in 1979 by the American Viola Society as the first international competition solely for violists, the Primrose International Viola Competition is proud of the rich history and legacy it promotes. Over 40 years, the Competition has continued to attract distinguished jurors and talented participants worldwide, serving as an inspiration to young Artists across the globe.
Country: United States
Social Media: www.facebook.com/primrosecompetition
Frequency: Annual

Rosalyn Tureck International Bach Competition
Website: https://www.tureckbachcompetition.com/
Email: TureckBach@gmail.com
Phone: 212 873 6087
Address: P.O. Box 230851 New York, NY 10023 US
Information: The Competition welcomes pianists aged 8-28 from all over the world, who pursue the musical ideals espoused by the late Rosalyn Tureck. The Competition consists of eight categories divided by repertoire difficulty. A competitor may compete in up to three categories and is required to perform one contemporary piece of work.
Country: United States
Contact: Artistic Director Golda Vainberg-Tatz
Assistant Director Kati Gleiser
Social Media: www.facebook.com/TureckBachCompetition
Awards: Category 1 $300 Category 2 $350 Category 3 $600 Category 4/A $700 4/B $1, 000 Category 5 $1, 000 Category 6 $1, 000 Category 7 $1, 500 Category 8 $2, 500
Frequency: Biennial
Start: 2022-07-22
End: 2022-07-25

Salvatore Martirano Memorial Composition Award
Website: https://music.illinois.edu/martirano-award
Email: zbrownin@illinois.edu
Phone: 217 333 2620
Address: University of Illinois School of Music, 1114 W. Nevada St., Urbana, IL 61801
Information: The Salvatore Martirano Memorial Composition Award is an international composers' competition held annually in memory of Mr. Martirano who was a faculty member at the University of Illinois from 1963 to 1995.

Country: United States
Contact: Associate professor Zach Browning
Email: zbrownin@illinois.edu
Eligibility: Any composer, regardless of age or nationality is eligible. Previous winners, faculty, and currently-enrolled students at the University of Illinois are ineligible for the competition.
Awards: First Prize cash award of $1000, second prize cash award of $500 plus performances by the Illinois Modern Ensemble,
Start: 2022-04-11

Schmidt Vocal Competition
Website: https://schmidtvocalarts.org/
Email: info@schmidtvocalarts.org
Phone: 513 783 2583
Address: 6 East 5th Street, Suite 406, Covington, KY 41011
Information: The Schmidt Vocal Competitions have touched the lives of thousands of young students like you over the past two decades. We invite high school sophomores, juniors, and seniors to participate in these one-day events, hosted at 17 locations throughout the United States. Some students will win cash awards. But everyone comes away with valuable performance experience and a new group of music-loving friends!
Country: United States
Contact: Executive Director Linda Mcalister
program Assistant Brie Williams
Social Media: www.facebook.com/SchmidtVocal www.instagram.com/schmidtvoca
Eligibility: 1.) singers must be high school sophomores, juniors, or seniors who are recommended by their choral Directors or vocal teachers. 2.) Singers are allowed to enter only one Schmidt Vocal Competition per competition season, whether live or virtual. 3.) To be eligible for cash awards, contestants must have a United States Social Security Number and must be United States citizens, Green Card holders, or have DACA approved status. 4.) Participants are required to pay a non-refundable registration fee after submitting an application. 5.) Applications will be considered complete when the fee, both parts of the application form, and teacher recommendation have been received.
Awards: Cash Awards First Place, $2, 500 Second Place, $2, 000 Third Place, $1, 500 Finalists, $250 Encouragement, $100 Most Promising Sophomore, $100 Matching Scholarships with Host Organizations Should you place among the top three winners at the competition, whether live or virtual, you may also qualify for a $4, 000 matching scholarship to the host institution where you compete. Applicants must apply and meet university requirements, and a matching scholarship must be provided by the host institution. Scholarships will be dispersed over four years of study ($1, 000 per year).
Frequency: Annual

Sphinx Competition
Website: https://www.sphinxmusic.org/
Email: competition@sphinxmusic.org
Phone: 888 404 7073
Address: 2200 Hunt Street, Suite 461 Detroit MI 48207, US
Information: The Sphinx Organization is social justice organization dedicated to transforming lives through the power of diversity in the arts. Sphinx's four program areas – Education & Access, Artist Development, Performing Artists, and Arts Leadership – form a pipeline that develops and supports diversity and inclusion in classical music at every level: music education, Artists performing on stage, the repertoire and programming being performed, the communities represented in audiences, and the Artistic and administrative leadership within the field.
Country: United States
Contact: President and Artistic Director Afa Dworkin
Email: Afa@SphinxMusic.org
senior Director for education and Artist engagement Andre Dowell
Email: Andre@SphinxMusic.org
Director of Artist engagement Dana McGarr
Email: Dana@SphinxMusic.org
Social Media: twitter.com/SphinxOrg www.facebook.com/sphinxorganization
Eligibility: The Competition is open to all junior high, high school, and college-age Black and Latinx string players residing in the U.S.
Awards: SENIOR DIVISION (Ages 18 30) 1st Place $50, 000 Robert Frederick Smith Prize, solo appearances with major orchestras, and a performance with the Sphinx Symphony Orchestra at the Finals Concert 2nd Place $20, 000 cash prize, performance with the Sphinx Symphony Orchestra at the Finals Concert 3rd Place $10, 000 cash prize, performance with the Sphinx Symphony Orchestra at the Finals Concert Audience Choice $5, 000 cash prize, sponsored by Mercedes-Benz Financial Services
Frequency: Annual
Start: 2022-01-26
End: 2022-01-29

Stulberg International String Competition
Website:
https://www.stulberg.org/
Email:
stulbergcomp@yahoo.com
Phone: 269 343 2776
Address: Stulberg International String Competition, Epic Center, 359 South Kalamazoo Mall, Suite 14, Kalamazoo, MI 49007
Information: Established in 1975, the Stulberg is one of the longest standing string competitions in the U.S. Its uniqueness stems from its focus on young string musicians, its high caliber of judges, its reputation for excellence, and its longevity.
Country: United States
Contact: President Alisa Carrel
secretary Naomi Siegel Morse
Executive Director Megan Yankee
Social Media: https://twitter.com/stulbergcomp www.facebook.com/StulbergComp
Frequency: Annual

The AGO/Marilyn Mason Award in Organ Composition (previously The Holtkamp-AGO Award)
Website: https://www.agohq.org/
Email: competitions@agohq.org
Phone: 212 870 2310
Address: 475 Riverside Drive, Suite 1260, New York, NY 10115
Information: The AGO/Marilyn Mason Award in Organ Composition is held every two years. Originally known as the AGO/Holtkamp Award, the competition began in partnership with the Holtkamp Organ Company in 1984. In 2012, Marilyn Mason became the new sponsor. The winner of this competition receives a $2, 000 prize, publication of the piece by Hinshaw Music Inc., A Fred Bock Music Company, and a world premiere performance at the AGO National Convention.
Country: United States
Contact: Director Louise Mundinger
Email: louise.mundinger@gmail.com
Social Media: twitter.com/agohq www.facebook.com/agohq
Eligibility: Composers of all ages are welcome to enter, and the applicant need not be a member of the American Guild of Organists. Previous winners of the AGO/Holtkamp, AGO, or AGO/Marilyn Mason Award in Organ Composition may not enter.
Frequency: Biennial
Start: 2022-06-01
End: 2022-06-30

The American Prize. National Nonprofit Competitions in the Performing Arts
Website: https://www.theamericanprize.org/
Email: theamericanprz@aol.com
Phone: 203 746 2694
Address: 25 Hamilton Drive, Suite 100 Danbury, CT 06811, US
Information: Providing evaluation, recognition, and reward to America's finest performing Artists, ensembles, and composers, based on recorded performances. Professional, college/university, community, high school—no age limits. The American Prize is proud to have awarded over $60, 000 in cash prizes in all categories since 2010.
Country: United States
Contact: Cheif Judge David Katz
Email: theamericanprz@aol.com
Social Media: twitter.com/americanprize www.facebook.com/The-American-Prize-celebrating-American-excellence-in-the-arts-214320622728/
Eligibility: The competitions of The American Prize are open to all U.S. citizens, whether living in this country or abroad, and to others currently living, working, and/or studying in the U.S., its protectorates and territories. There are separate categories for professional, college/university, community, and high-school age solo musicians and ensembles.
Frequency: Annual

The Gerda Lissner Foundation in Association with the Liederkranz Foundation
Website:
https://www.gerdalissner.org/
Email:
mail@gerdalissner.org
Phone: 212 826 6100
Address: 15 East 65th Street, 4th Floor New York, NY 10065 USA
Information: The Gerda Lissner Foundation was created by Mrs. Lissner, a Metropolitan Opera subscriber for 77 years, to provide young opera singers with the financial support they need to pursue their craft and excel in the world of Opera. We believe that the encouragement and assistance to young Artists toward achieving their goals are imperative for the continuation of this demanding art form.
Country: United States
Contact: President Michael A. Fornabaio Fornabaio
vice President and secretary Cornelia A. Beigel Beigel
Eligibility: Applicants must be between 20 and 30 years of age. Lieder/songs written for voice and piano must be submitted in the original language. At least two Lieder must be in German, with one by Schubert. No ensemble items are permitted. Eligible participants only will be advised of the date and time for the audition by email.
Start: 2022-03-28
End: 2022-03-30

The Gurwitz International Piano Competition
Website: https://musicalbridges.org/the-gurwitz/
Email: elena@musicalbridges.org
Phone: 210 630 9711
Address: 23705 Frontage Road, Suite 101, US
Information: The Gurwitz International Piano Competition is a member of the WFIMC. Twelve competitors, selected by a preliminary jury, will compete live in San Antonio, TX. The Gurwitz consists of four rounds, including commissioned piece, chamber music round, and the final round with the San Antonio Symphony.
Country: United States
Eligibility: The Gurwitz is open to professional pianists from around the world 18 to 32 years old. First prize winners of The San Antonio International Piano Competition, as well as students and family members of jury members, are not eligible to enter.
Awards: In addition to Gold, Silver, and Bronze Medals awarded for first, second and third place, additional cash prizes are awarded for best performance of the Commissioned New Work, plus a Baroque work; a Classical work; a Romantic work; a 20th-21st Century work; a work by a Russian composer and a work by a Spanish or Latin American composer.

The Kuleshov International Piano Festival and Competition
Website: https://www.uco.edu/cfad/academics/music/the-kuleshov/
Email: spollack@uco.edu
Phone: 405 974 5948
Address: The University of Central Oklahoma School of Music, 100 North University Drive, US
Information: The Kuleshov Festival and Competition is a biennial piano competition for high school and college students aged 15-24 and is held on the campus of the University of Central Oklahoma in Edmond, OK. Participants and audiences enjoy a weekend of guest Artist recitals, interest sessions, master classes, and competition performances
Country: United States
Social Media: twitter.com/UCOCFAD www.facebook.com/uco.cfad
Eligibility: Ages 15-24
Awards: First prize Less than $10, 000 Smallest prize Less than $5, 000
Start: 2022-03-24
End: 2022-03-27

The Lotte Lenya Competition
Website: https://www.kwf.org/lotte-lenya-competition/
Email: kwfinfo@kwf.org
Phone: 212 505 5240
Address: The Kurt Weill Foundation for Music, 7 East 20th Street, 3rd Floor, New York, US
Information: A unique international theatre singing contest that emphasizes a wide-ranging repertoire and the acting of songs and arias within a dramatic context. The Competition recognizes talented young singer/actors who are dramatically and musically convincing, in repertoire ranging from opera/operetta to contemporary Broadway scores, including the works of Kurt Weill.
Country: United States
Contact: Director of programs and business affairs Brady Sansone
Email: bsansone@kwf.org
Phone: 212 505 5240 x204Manager of programs and business affairs Veronica Chaffin
Email: vchaffin@kwf.org
Phone: 212 505 5240 x201
Social Media: www.twitter.com/KurtWeillFndn www.facebook.com/LenyaCompetition https://www.instagram.com/lottelenyacompetition/
Frequency: Annual

The New York International Piano Competition
Website: https://thenyipc.org/
Email: info@stecherandhorowitz.org
Phone: 212 581 8380
Address: The Stecher and Horowitz Foundation, 119 West 57th Street, Suite 1401, New York, NY 10019
Information: The Stecher and Horowitz Foundation is committed to furthering the education, recognition, and fostering of gifted young musicians, helping sustain and preserve the essence of our cultural life through audience development and community involvement. Serving pianists aged 16-25, the foundation seeks and develops emerging talent through its flagship programs: the New York International Piano Competition and the Young Artists Series. The foundation mentors aspirants, helping them to achieve their personal and professional goals through career guidance, Artistic development, and performance opportunities. Individuality and excellence are mainstays of the foundation's core objectives, focusing the young Artists' horizons toward the pursuit of a realistic and attainable career in music.
Country: United States
Contact: founding and Executive Director Melvin Stetcher
founding and Executive Director Norman Horowitz
Chairman of the board William S. Hearst
Social Media:
https://www.facebook.com/NYIPC/
Awards: First Prize $20, 000; Second Prize $15, 000; Third

Prize $5, 000; Fourth Prize $2, 500; Ensemble Prizes $6, 000; Best Performance of Commissioned Work $2, 000; Finalist Award to each of the remaining contestants $1, 000.
Start: 2022-06-19
End: 2022-06-24

The Parkening International Guitar Competition
Website:
https://arts.pepperdine.edu/events/parkening/
Email: arts.pepperdine.edu/parkening
Phone: 310 506 4522
Address: 24255 Pacific Coast Highway, Malibu, CA 90263
Information: The Parkening International Guitar Competition is the most prestigious classical guitar competition in the world, honoring Christopher Parkening's lifetime commitment to fostering musical excellence in young Artists as demonstrated by his mentor, the great Spanish guitarist Andrés Segovia.
Country: United States
Contact: Theatre Operations Manager Paul Vacchiano
Email: paul.vacchiano@pepperdine.edu
Managing Director Rebbeca Carson
Email: rebecca.carson@pepperdine.edu
Box Office and Patron Communications Manager Tyler Gabbard
Email: tyler.gabbard@pepperdine.edu
Director of Production Dani Lobello
Email: danielle.lobello@pepperdine.edu
Marketing and publicity Manager Tyler Flynn
Email: tyler.flynn@pepperdine.edu
Social Media: www.facebook.com/PepperdineCFA www.instagram.com/Pepperdinecfa/

Thomas & Evon Cooper International Competition
Website: https://www.oberlin.edu/conservatory
Email: ahoffman@oberlin.edu
Phone: 440 775 8044
Address: Oberlin Conservatory of Music Office of Summer Programs, 77 West College Street, US
Information: Cooper International Competition at Oberlin Conservatory is open to musicians ages 13-18. It alternates annually between piano and violin. Its final round is showcased with The Cleveland Orchestra at Severance Hal, and will include the top three competitors in performances of full concertos.
Country: United States
Contact: Director of conservatory communications Cathleen Partlow Strauss
Email: cstrauss@oberlin.edu
Director of public relations Justin Holden
Email: JHolden@clevelandorchestra.com
Social Media: www.facebook.com/coopercompetition
Eligibility: competition is for young musicians 1318 years of age
Awards: Cash prizes total $40, 000, and includes a $20, 000 first prize. Three finalists from the field advance to perform full concertos with The Cleveland Orchestra at its renowned home, Severance Hall.
Frequency: Annual

University of Louisville Grawemeyer Award for Music Composition
Website: http://grawemeyer.org/music-composition/
Email: charlie.leonard@louisville.edu
Phone: 502 852 7034
Address: The University of Louisville Grawemeyer Awards, 209 Grawemeyer Hall, University of Louisville, Louisville, KY 40292
Information: The University of Louisville offers an international prize in recognition of outstanding achievement by a living composer in a large musical genre: choral, orchestral, chamber, electronic, song-cycle, dance, opera, musical theater, extended solo work and more
Country: United States
Contact: Executive Director Charles Leonard
Email: charlie.leonard@louisville.edu
coordinator Billye Potts
Email: billye.potts@louisville.edu
Social Media: www.facebook.com/grawemeyerworldorder
Frequency: Biennial

USA International Ballet Competition
Website: www.usaibc.com
Email: contact@usaibc.com
Phone: 601 355 9853
Address: P.O. Box 3696, Jackson, MS 39207-3696
Information: The USA International Ballet Competition's mission is to provide an opportunity for dancers to test themselves against recognized international standards of dance excellence and showcase their technical skill and Artistic talent and to provide a forum for communication and intercultural exchange, as well as to educate, enlighten and develop future Artists and audience support for the art of dance.
Country: United States
Contact: Executive Director and development Mona Nicholas
Email: mnicholas@usaibc.com
Artistic administrator Elizabeth VanDeburgh

Email: evan@usaibc.com

finance and operations Sara Berry Lee
Email: sberrylee@usaibc.com
founder Thalia Mara
Social Media: twitter.com/usaibc www.facebook.com/usaibc
Eligibility: see website for rules and regulations of next competition
Awards: cash prizes and awards; see website
Frequency: Quadrennial
Start: 11/06/2022
End: 15/06/2022

USA International Harp Competition
Website: https://usaihc.org/
Email: harpcomp@indiana.edu
Phone: 812 856 5715
Address: USA International Harp Competition Inc., P.O. Box 5008, Bloomington, IN 47407
Information: The USAIHC performance competition is paired with a globally recognized triennial Composition Contest producing myriad new works for the harp. The USAIHC also recognizes the need to engage its local community by presenting a biannual Concert Series of distinguished harpists and introducing hundreds of students to the harp through its educational program, Harp Start.
Country: United States
Contact: Artistic Director Susann McDonald
President David Rollo
vice President Linda Rollo
Artistic Director Susann McDonald
secretary Beatrice Carlyss
Social Media: www.facebook.com/usaihc www.instagram.com/usaihc/twitter.com/usaihc
Awards: FIRST PRIZE: Lyon & Healy Concert Grand Harp, up to a value of $55, 000, Debut Recital at Lyon & Healy Hall in Chicago, CD Recording sponsored, Hong Kong Harp Centre Winners Recital in Hong Kong, Hantang Culture Award, Hantang Culture Trophy (Chinese Bronze Trophy), China five city concert tour over two weeks with $1, 500 USD Artist fee per concert performance, $5, 000; SECOND PRIZE: $5000; THIRD PRIZE:$4000; FOURTH PRIZE: $3000
Frequency: Triennial
Start: 2022-06-29
End: 2022-07-09

Van Cliburn International Piano Competition
Website: www.cliburn.org
Email: Generalinformation@cliburn.org
Phone: 817 738 6536
Address: 201 Main Street, Suite 100, Fort Worth, TX 76102
Information: First held in 1962, the quadrennial Van Cliburn International Piano Competition quickly established itself as an event that inspires and engages the local community, while gracing the international stage. The Cliburn Competition is one of the few musical events in the world to arrange for competitors to stay with host families, often resulting in close, long-term relationships: this has resulted in southern hospitality becoming a singular trademark of the Cliburn Competition.
Country: United States
Director of communications & digital content Maggie Estes
Email: mestes@cliburn.org
chief financial officer Alissa Ford
Email: aford@cliburn.org
Director of Artistic planning Sandra Doan
Email: sdoan@cliburn.org
President & CEO Jacques Marquis
Email: jmarquis@cliburn.org
Director of Marketing Kim Blouin
Email: kblouin@cliburn.org
Artistic operations Manager Melinda Willmann
Email: mwillmann@cliburn.org
Director of development Mariann Pohle
Email: mpohle@cliburn.org
Social Media: twitter.com/TheCliburn www.facebook.com/thecliburn/ www.instagram.com/THECLIBURN/
Eligibility: The Sixteenth Van Cliburn International Piano Competition is open to pianists of all nationalities. First-prize winners of previous editions of the Van Cliburn International Piano Competition are not eligible to compete. Applicants must have been born after June 12, 1990, and on or before June 2, 2004.
Awards: various cash prizes and awards; see website cliburn.org/2022prizes
Frequency: Annual
Start: 2022-06-02
End: 2022-06-18

Vendome Prize
Website: https://vendomeprize.com/
Email: info@vendomeprize.com
Phone: 646 352 1007
Address: 907 Fifth Avenue, NY 10021, USA
Information: the Vendome Prize extends help to those who do not win prizes that it considers particularly talented through living allowances, scholarships, travel grants, concert appearances, career advice and recommendations to leading teaching institutions.
Country: United States

Contact: Chairman Alexis Gregory
project Manager Matei Varga
Email: info@vendomeprize.com
Social Media: www.facebook.com/2021VendomePiano
Awards: total of $50, 000 in prizes includes: First prize $25, 000; Second prize $15, 000; Third prize $10, 000. The first prize winner will play a recital at the Verbier Festival.

Virginia Waring International Piano Competition
Website: https://www.vwipc.org/
Email: info@vwipc.org
Phone: 760 773 2575
Address: 73-710 Fred Waring Drive # 201, Palm Desert, CA 92260
Information: The Waring brings classical piano music to the California Desert through outreach concerts to schools, the community and by hosting eight days of an international piano competition every other year with participants coming from around the world. Alternates every two years between Junior and Intermediate Competitions (17 & under), and the Senior Competition (18-30).
Country: United States
Contact: Artistic Director John Bayless
Chairman of the board of Directors Peggy Cravens
Social Media: twitter.com/VWIPC www.facebook.com/vwipc
Eligibility: open to pianists of any nationality between the ages of 18 and 30 at the beginning of the Competition. not open to previous first prize winners of the Senior Divisions of the Waring International Piano Competition.
Awards: performance prizes, cash prizes, scholarships and other awards.
Frequency: Biennial
Start: 2022-04-10
End: 2022-04-18

VSA International Young Soloists
Website: https://www.kennedy-center.org/education/opportunities-for-Artists/competitions-and-commissions/vsa-international-young-soloists
Email: vsainfo@kennedy-center.org
Phone: 202 416 8898
Address: 2700 F Street NW, US
Information: Each year, outstanding young musicians with disabilities from around the world are selected to receive the VSA International Young Soloists Award of $2000, and the opportunity to perform at the John F. Kennedy Centre for the Performing Arts in Washington, DC.
Country: United States
Social Media: twitter.com/VSAIntl www.facebook.com/VSAInternational
Eligibility: Musicians with disabilities between the ages of 14 and 25. This program is open to U.S. and international soloists and ensembles of any genre or instrument, including voice.
Frequency: Annual

Washington International Competition
Website: https://fmmc.org/
Email: wicpiano2020@gmail.com
Phone: 202 333 2075
Address: 755 8th Street NW, Washington DC 20001
Information: The Washington International Competition (WIC) was established in 1950 to support outstanding young classical musicians in their pursuit of professional careers. The WIC occurs in a three-year rotation for piano, strings and voice. As of 1976, a competition for composition of a string quartet is also held concurrently with the strings competition.
Country: United States
Contact: co-Chair Grace McFarlane
co-Chair Junko Takahashi
Social Media: www.facebook.com/WashIntlComp/
Eligibility: Applicants must be between the ages of 18 and 30 (as of the date of the competition). Proof of age will be required. Applicants must not be under professional management. Previous first-prize winners of the competition and current students of the judges may not apply.
Awards: First Prize: $10, 000 Second Prize: $5, 000 Third Prize: $3, 000 Three Finalist Awards: $1, 000 each Audience Prize: $1, 000
Frequency: Annual

William C. Byrd Young Artist Competition
Website: http://www.byrdArtists.com/
Email: Chairman@byrdArtists.com
Phone: 810 793 0538
Address: W. C. Byrd Competition, Flint Institute of Music, 1025 E. Kearsley Street, Flint, MI 48503
Information: The William C. Byrd Young Artist String Competition was started by William C. Byrd, conductor of the Flint Symphony Orchestra, for the purpose of helping launch careers for young musicians. The international music competition held annually on the first Saturday of March. It rotates annually among the four disciplines listed below. It is sponsored by the St. Cecilia Society of Flint, Michigan in collaboration with the Flint Institute of Music and the Flint Symphony Orchestra.
Country: United States
Contact: Director Carol Hinterman

Social Media: www.facebook.com/ByrdArtists
Eligibility: open to all Artists who will be no more than
32 years old on the date of the competition, with the
exception of voice contestants, who can be up to 35
on the date of the competition. Contestants cannot be
represented by a Manager or an agent.
Frequency: Annual
Start: 2022-03-05

William Knabe International Piano Competition
Website: https://www.knabeinstitute.org/competitions.html
Email: info@knabeinstitute.org
Phone: 888 978 5332 Ext. 4
Address: University of Maryland, Baltimore County Performing Arts & Humanities Building 1000 Hilltop Circle
Baltimore, MD 21250
Information: Piano Competition featuring Solo and
Concerto competitions. Promoted by the William Knabe
Institute, a nonprofit organization dedicated to drawing
awareness to the cultural legacy of the piano in America,
and enriching lives through piano-related activities and
educational programs.
Country: United States
Contact: President Dr. Jarl Hulbert
Secretary Peter Becker
Social Media: https://www.facebook.com/knabeinstitute/ https://twitter.com/knabeinstitute
Eligibility: pianists; age limit: 6-26 years
Awards: First place awards range from $50 to $500

Wilson Center Guitar Festival
Website: www.wilson-center.com/guitar-competition-festival
Email: jgrokowsky@wilson-center.com
Phone: 262 781 9520
Address: Sharon Lynne Wilson Center for the Arts, 3270
Mitchell Park Drive Brookfield, WI 53045
Information: It is the goal of the Wilson Center Guitar
Festival to celebrate the greatest guitarists of today and
tomorrow. Featuring four competitions: Classical, Fingerstyle, Jazz, and Rock/Blues, the Wilson Center Guitar
Festival is open to competitors of all ages.
Country: United States
Contact: Executive Director Anna Thompson
Email: amthompson@wilson-center.com
Director of operations Susan Hornung
Email: shornung@wilson-center.com
Social Media: twitter.com/wcguitarfest www.facebook.
com/wcguitarfest www.instagram.com/wcguitarfest
Eligibility: open to individuals of all ages; candidates
under the age of 18 at the time of their video submission
must provide the name and contact information for
a legal guardian who is granting permission for their
participation in this event.
Awards: First-place winners in each category will be
awarded a $1, 000 cash prize. Additional awards include
a $250 second prize and a $100 third prize in each category. Supplementary non-cash prizes may be announced
at a later date.
Frequency: Annual
Start: 2021-08-12
End: 2021-08-14

Young Concert Artists International Auditions
Website: https://yca.org/
Email: info@yca.org
Phone: 212 307 6655
Address: Young Concert Artists, Inc. 1776 Broadway,
Suite 1500, New York, New York 10019
Information: The Young Concert Artists International
Auditions are held annually to discover and launch the
careers of extraordinary musicians from all over the
world. Winners are selected by a jury of distinguished
musicians. The criteria includes exceptional musicianship, virtuosity, individuality, projection as a performer,
and promise. Musicians compete against a standard of
excellence – not each other, and there can be any number of winners each year.
Country: United States
Contact: Director of Artist management Monica Felkel
Email: monica@yca.org
Artist Manager Vicki Margulies
Email: vicki@yca.org
pr and media Beth Stewart
President Danie Kellogg
Email: dan@yca.org
program Manager Ero Gurol
Email: erol@yca.org
operations Manager Alana Klonoski
Email: alana@yca.org
Social Media: www.facebook.com/youngconcertArtists
www.instagram.com/youngconcertArtists/
Awards: will join the roster of Young Concert Artists,
which provides management services for a minimum
of three years, concert engagements including debuts
in New York and Washington, D.C., publicity, and career
guidance.
Frequency: Annual

76ᵉ CONCOURS DE GENÈVE
INTERNATIONAL
MUSIC COMPETITION
22 OCT–3 NOV 2022
Piano & Composition

COMPOSITION FINAL
26 OCT. CONSERVATOIRE, GENEVA
With the Neue Vocalsolisten Stuttgart

PIANO FINAL
3 NOV. VICTORIA HALL, GENEVA
With the Orchestre de la Suisse Romande

JURY CHAIR
PIANO – JANINA FIALKOWSKA
COMPOSITION – BEAT FURRER

CONCOURSGENEVE.CH

HINAKO TAKAGI
1ᵉʳ PRIX EX AEQUO COMPOSITION 2019
© MISA SHINSHI

MEMBER OF THE WORLD
FEDERATION OF INTERNATIONAL
MUSIC COMPETITIONS

member of /// WFIMC/WFCIM

54th INTERNATIONAL GUITAR COMPETITION

michele pittaluga

CITY OF ALESSANDRIA PRIZE | President Gold medal from 1997

FROM 26 SEPTEMBER TO 1ST OCTOBER 2022

INTERNATIONAL GUITAR COMPETITION FOR YOUNG ARTISTS

6th *pittaluga Junior*

1st October 2022

registration deadline
21st August 2022

rules updated on the website www.pittaluga.org

SPONSORSHIP

 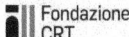     

---

11. INTERNATIONALER WETTBEWERB

FRANZ SCHUBERT UND DIE MUSIK DER MODERNE

https://schubert.kug.ac.at

kunst uni graz

CHAMBER MUSIC
COMPETITION
20. – 24.07.2022
GRAZ / AUSTRIA

LIVE STREAMING

FINALS ON JULY 23

Member of the Alink-Argerich Foundation

WORLD FEDERATION OF INTERNATIONAL MUSIC COMPETITIONS

DUO FOR VOICE AND PIANO (LIED)

TRIO FOR PIANO, VIOLIN AND VIOLONCELLO

Universität für Musik und darstellende Kunst Graz
Leonhardstraße 15, A-8010 Graz
franz.schubert@kug.ac.at | T +43 316 389 1900

We have included a wide range of conferences and trade shows that we think will be of the interest to those working in the performing arts industry. **The entries are listed in alphabetical order within country.**

Conférences et Foires Commerciales
Nous avons inclus une large gamme de conférences et foires com-merciales que nous estimons intéressants pour ceux qui travaillent dans les arts de la scène. **Les entrée sont classés par ordre alphabétique dans le pays.**

Konferenzen und Messen
Wir haben in diesem Kapitel eine Reihe von Konferenzen und Messen vorgestellt, die unserer Meinung nach von Interesse für Berufstätige im Bereich der Musik und darstellenden Kunst sind. **Die Einträge sind für jedes Land alphabetisch sortiert.**

Convegni e Fiere
Sono stati incluse numerose conferenze e mostre/fiere che pensiamo possano interessare a chi opera nel settore artistico. **Le voci sono pubblicate in ordine alfabetico di paese.**

Conferencias y Ferias Comerciales
Se ha incluido una amplia gama de conferencias y ferias comerciales que creemos serán de interés para aquellas personas u organismos relacionados con las artes escénicas. **Las entradas se muestran en orden alfabético dentro de cada país.**

performing arts database

AUSTRALIA

Australasian Music Week Conference
Website: australianmusicweek.com
Email: info@australianmusicweek.com
Phone: 295 443 844
Address: Cronulla, Sydney, NSW 2230, Australia
Information: Australian Music Week is Australia's most accessible, grassroots music industry conference, taking over Sydney's beachside town of Cronulla for 5 days each November. Australian Music Week is all about real music discovery, relevant industry advice and good times with people. Showcasing more than 150 artists, Australian Music Week boasts genuine music discovery across an incredibly diverse cross-section of Australian and international music.
Country: Australia
Contact: media contact Jo
Email: jocorbettpublicity@gmail.com
Social Media: www.facebook.com/AustMusicWeek/ www.instagram.com/australianmusicweektwitter.com/AustMusicWeek
Other Venues: Cronulla Beach
Start: 2021-11-06
End: 2021-11-10

Australian Performing Arts Market
Website: apam.org.au
Email: hello@apam.org.au
Phone: 039 947 1020
Address: G5, 152 Sturt St Soutbank Melbourne, VIC, Australia 3006
Information: APAM champions contemporary Australian performance nationally and internationally by deepening relationships and stimulating new markets and pathways through exchange, reciprocity, and hospitality. APAM is a strategic initiative of the Australia Council for the Arts. It is designed to showcase Australian and New Zealand contemporary dance, theatre, emerging and experimental arts nationally and internationally. For 2020-2024, APAM is delivered by Creative Victoria.
Country: Australia
Contact: Director Catherine
program Producer Naomi
Social Media: www.facebook.com/AustralianPerformingArtsMarket www.instagram.com/apam_office/
Frequency: Biennial

CANADA

Canadian Arts Presenting Association (CAPACOA) Conference
Website: www.capacoa.ca
Email: mail@capacoa.ca
Phone: 613 562 3515
Address: 17 York street, suite 200, Ottawa, ON, K1N 5S7 Canada
Information: CAPACOA began hosting an annual conference for the sector in 1988, bringing together cultural entrepreneurs and key industry stakeholders working across national and international performing arts sectors. In 2016, CAPACOA innovated its annual conference model by holding it in conjunction with the CINARS Biennale. As the national leader of Canada's touring and presenting communities, CAPACOA cultivates a vibrant, healthy and equitable performing arts ecosystem, from artists to audiences.
Country: Canada
Contact: operations Manager Mélanie
Email: melanie.bureau@capacoa.ca
Executive Director Sue
Email: sue.urquhart@capacoa.ca
operations coordinator Andrew
Email: andrew.giguere@capacoa.ca
program coordinator Brit
Email: brittany.johnston@capacoa.ca
Social Media: twitter.com/capacoa www.facebook.com/CAPACOA/ www.instagram.com/capacoa_arts/

CINARS – International Exchange for the Performing Arts
Website: www.cinars.org
Email: arts@cinars.org
Phone: 514 842 5866
Address: 69 rue Sherbrooke Ouest, Montréal, Québec, H2X 1X2 Canada
Information: the CINARS Biennale has made a name for itself as an indispensible multidisciplinary event, in which one can develop real international touring opportunities, build solid relationships with professionals from all over the world, as well as sharpen one's professional skill-set and knowledge base. The event gathers around 1, 300 participants from 40 countries and presents over 150 shows throughout the week. Member of ISPA
Country: Canada
Contact: President, Executive Director and founder Alain
communications Director Valérien
Email: communications@cinars.org
international development Director Gilles
Email: gdore@cinars.org
coordinator Élodie
Email: coordination@cinars.org
Social Media: twitter.com/cinars www.facebook.com/cinars.org/ www.instagram.com/cinars_org/

ISCM World Music Days
Website: www.iscm2017.ca/home/
Email: info@iscm2017.ca
Phone: 604 879 9888
Address: ISCM World New Music Days 2017 c/o Music on Main, 110-750 Hamilton Street Vancouver, BC V6B 2R5 Canada
Information: Since its founding in 1922, the International Society for Contemporary Music has been the world's premier network for new music. Each year, its festival is hosted in a different city around the globe. The 2018 event shall be held in Beijing, China.
Country: Canada
Contact: Artistic Director David
Email: david@iscm2017.ca
administrative Director Morna
Email: morna@iscm2017.ca
President, ISCM canadian section Jim
Email: jim@iscm2017.ca
Social Media: www.facebook.com/international.society.for.contemporary.musictwitter.com/ISCM_WMD

CHINA

China Shanghai International Performing Arts Fair (SPAF)
Website: www.artsbird.com/en
Email: info@spafchina.com
Phone: 216 272 0440
Address: 24th Floor, Yihai Building, No 211, Kangding Road, Shanghai
Information: China Shanghai International Arts Festival (CSIAF), which is hosted by the Ministry of Culture of the People's Republic of China and organized by Shanghai Municipal People's Government, is the only state-level International Arts Festival in China. Since 1999, CSIAF, driven by the concept of "innovation and development" with the emphasis on brand-effect development, has grown into a flagship project for cultural exchange of the country as well as one of the most influential festivals in the international art circles.
Country: China
Contact: performance and exhibitio Jie
Email: jruan@artsbird.com
exhibition Jing
Email: jbao@artsbird.com
public relations and media Shengrong
Email: srmao@artsbird.com
secretary Yang
President Li
Start: 15/10/2020
End: 19/10/2020

China Shenzhen International Cultural Industry Fair
Website: en.cnci.net.cn
Email: icif@cnicif.com
Phone: 755 835 21157
Address: 10/F., Olympic Building, Economic Daily Road, Futian District, Shenzhen, P. R. China
Information: Shenzhen International Cultural Industry Fair Co., Ltd.(ICIF Company) is the only perennial organizer of the China (Shenzhen) International Cultural Industries Fair (ICIF).
Officially founded in April 2005, it holds nearly 100 professional talents in cultural and exhibition industry. It has since scaled up its business and become a renowned enterprise in cultural and exhibition industry, gradually forming the core value of 'Culture based, Diversity grows'.
Country: China
Social Media: www.facebook.com/chinaicif/
Frequency: Annual
Start: TBA
End: TBA

HONG KONG

2021 Hong Kong Youth Music Camp – Music Office
Website: www.lcsd.gov.hk/musicoffice
Email: tcamp@lcsd.gov.hk
Phone: 384 27761
Address: 5/F, South Tower, West Kowloon Government Offices, 11 Hoi Ting Road, Yau Ma Tei, Kowloon
Information: Established in October 1977 by the Government, the Music Office promotes knowledge and appreciation of music in the community, especially among young people, through the provision of instrumental and ensemble training and the organisation of various music activities with a view to building a new generation of concert audiences.
Country: Hong Kong
Social Media: www.facebook.com/musicoffice.concerts www.instagram.com/musicoffice.concerts
Frequency: Annual
Other Venues: Music Office Mongkok Music Centre, Music Office Kwun Tong Music Centre, Music Office Tsuen Wan Music Centre
Start: 2021-07-24
End: 2021-07-31

prolight + sound Shanghai
Website: prolight-sound-shanghai.hk.messefrankfurt.com/shanghai/en.html

Email: info@hongkong.messefrankfurt.com
Phone: 280 27728
Address: 35/F China Resources Building, 26 Harbour Road, Wanchai, HK
Information: Prolight + Sound Shanghai is one of Asia's best known professional audio and lighting, event and entertainment technology show. The show is organised by INTEX Shanghai Co Ltd and Messe Frankfurt (HK) Ltd, attracting 500+ leading brands and companies to showcase their latest products and technologies at the Shanghai New International Expo Centre. A massive area for outdoor demonstrations and series of seminars and forums provide you an all-in-one platform for sourcing, networking and education.
Country: Hong Kong
Social Media: www.instagram.com/prolightandsoundchina/ www.facebook.com/prolightandsoundchina
Start: TBA (check website for updates)
End: TBA

JAPAN

Performing Arts Meeting in Yokohama
Website: www.tpam.or.jp
Phone: 452 646 514
Address: Performing Arts Meeting in Yokohama Secretariat, BankART Temporary 2F, 6-50-1 Honcho, Naka-ku, Yokohama, Kanagawa 231-8315
Information: TPAM–Performing Arts Meeting in Yokohama (originally the Tokyo Performing Arts Market) is a space where people from various places in the world who are professionally involved in performing arts get together to exchange through diverse performance & meeting programs & gain information, inspiration creativity, dissemination and vitalization of performing arts. Having celebrated the 20th anniversary, it is internationally recognized as one of the most influential performing arts platforms in Asia.
Country: Japan
Frequency: Annual
Start: February 2021
End: February 2021

REPUBLIC OF KOREA

Performing Arts Market in Seoul (PAMS)
Website: www.pams.or.kr
Email: pams@gokams.or.kr
Phone: 270 82280
Address: 3F, Education Building, Daehak-ro Campus, Hongik University, 57, Daehak-ro, Jongno-gu, Seoul
Information: PAMS is a promotion and exchange platform for Korean and international performance arts organizations.
Country: Republic of Korea
Social Media: www.facebook.com/pams.or.kr/ www.instagram.com/pams_seoul/
Frequency: Annual
Start: 12/10/2020
End: 15/12/2020

NEW ZEALAND

World Symposium on Choral Music (WSCM)
Website: www.wscm2020.com
Email: info@wscm2020.com
Address: New Zealand Choral Federation National Office, PO Box 188, Wellington 6140, New Zealand
Information: The first World Symposium on Choral Music was held in Vienna in 1987. Following a three-city experiment three years later, the IFCM resolved that the event's location would thereafter alternate triennially between the five continents.
It is a one-week event organised every 3 years, and is a meeting of the world's most prestigious choral conductors and choirs. Organised by International Federation for Choral Music (IFCM) – see International and National Organisations
Country: New Zealand
Contact: Artistic Director Joh
relationships Manager Juliet
festival Manager Kylie
Email: kylie.sealy@wscm2020.com
Social Media: www.facebook.com/wscm2020 www.instagram.com/wscm2020/twitter.com/wscm2020
Frequency: Triennial
Venue: Next event: Quatar: 2023
Start: 2023
End: 2023

SINGAPORE

Federation for Asian Cultural Promotion (FACP)
Website: www.facp.asia
Email: info@facp.asia
Address: International
Information: A group of professionals, impresarios and performing arts Managers from Manila, Taipei, Seoul and Tokyo founded the FACP in Manila in 1981. It now draws participants and observers from almost every city in the region and from every corner of the world which share an interest in the development of cultural exchange in the Asia-Pacific.
Country: Singapore

Live Singapore – Global Performing Arts Exchange
Website: www.koelnmesse.com.sg
Email: live-singapore@koelnmesse.com
Phone: 650 06700
Address: SG
Country: Singapore
Contact: project Manager Frédéric
Email: live-singapore@koelnmesse.com
project Manager Grace
Email: g.tan@koelnmesse.com.sg
project Manager Lim
Email: sy.lim@koelnmesse.com.sg
Social Media: @Koelnmesse www.facebook.com/koelnmesse?ref=hl

UNITED STATES

Arts Reach National Arts Marketing, Development & Ticketing Conference
Website: www.artsreach.com
Email: arts@ruddle.com
Phone: 888 881 5861
Address: Arts Reach Unlimited, P.O. Box 91446, Long Beach, CA 90809-1446
Information: Arts Reach is the association that supports leading arts professionals who are committed to "Advancing Arts Revenue Growth Together." They are advancing the field with cutting-edge breakthrough ideas they share with each other regarding leadership, Marketing, fundraising and ticketing.
Country: United States
Contact: President John
Social Media: www.facebook.com/artsreachassn/twitter.com/artsreachassn

Association of Arts Administration Educators Conference
Website: www.artsAdministration.org
Email: hello@artsAdministration.org
Phone: 401 787 5995
Address: Association of Arts Administration Educators, P.O. Box 25094 Providence, Rhode Island 02905
Information: Association of Arts Administration Educators is a membership organization representing the world's leading arts Administration programs, leadership, management, cultural policy, and more. AAAE serves as a convener, a resource, & an advocate for formal arts Administration education.
Conferences offer programs in research, pedagogy, and practice. Hosted by AAAE members in a different location every year, they afford members & attendees an opportunity to explore the arts & culture of new places.
Country: United States
Contact: Executive Director Lee Ann
Email: ladams@artsAdministration.org
Phone: 401 787 5995programs and operations Manager Haley
Email: hcarlson@artsAdministration.org
Phone: 618 713 0144
Social Media: www.facebook.com/artsadmineducators/www.twitter.com/AAAEducators
Frequency: Annual

Association of Performing Arts Presenters (APAP) – Annual Members Conference
Website: www.apap365.org
Email: nnmadison@apap365.org
Phone: 202 207 3845
Address: APAP, Association of Performing Arts Professionals, 919 18th St. NW, Suite 650, Washington, DC 20006
Information: APAP is the national service, advocacy and membership organization for the performing arts presenting industry and the convener of APAP|NYC, the world's leading gathering of performing arts professionals, held every January in New York City
Country: United States
Contact: Director, conference and meetings Niiyo
Email: nnmadison@apap365.org
Phone: 202 207 3845President and CEO Lisa
Email: lrtoney@apap365.org
Director, Marketing and communications Jenny
Email: jthomas@apap365.org
Phone: 202 207 3857Director, finance and operations Theresa
Email: tbennett@apap365.org
Phone: 202 207 3840
Social Media: www.twitter.com/apap365 www.facebook.com/APAPNYC/ www.instagram.com/apap365/
Frequency: Annual
Other Venues: New York Hilton Midtown and Sheraton New York Times Square

Chamber Music America – National Conference
Website: www.chamber-music.org
Email: conference@chamber-music.org
Phone: 212 242 2022
Address: Chamber Music America, 12 West 32nd Street, 7th Floor, 10001 New York, US
Information: At CMA's annual conference, ensemble music professionals hear inspiring speakers, engage with industry leaders, network with peers, and discuss important issues that affect the field.

Country: United States
Contact: Executive Director Lecolion
Artistic and Executive Director Ashleigh
Social Media: www.twitter.com/CMA_Tweets www.facebook.com/chambermusicamerica www.instagram.com/chambermusicamerica/
Frequency: Annual

Creative Placemaking Leadership Summit
Website: www.southarts.org
Email: gcombs@southarts.org
Phone: 404 874 7244
Address: c/o Southern Arts Federation, 1800 Peachtree Street NW, Suite 808, US
Information: An annual gathering of artists, community leaders, educators, and other professionals exploring how arts and cultural activities help make communities more inclusive, connected and resilient.
Country: United States
President & CEO
Suzette
Vice President of Programs Joy
Director of Special Projects & Accessibility Coordinator Leland
Social Media: https:// www.facebook.com/southarts/ www.twitter.com/southarts www.instagram.com/southartsorg

Cutting Edge Music Business Conference and Roots Music Gathering
Website: www.cuttingedgenola.com
Email: eric@cuttingedgenola.com
Phone: 504 322 3540
Address: 1524 N Claiborne Ave, 70116 New Orleans, Louisiana, US
Information: New Orleans is the home of the Cutting Edge C.E. In New Orleans, music is more than business; it's also cultural exPression. Every artist that performs during the Cutting Edge C.E. becomes a part of New Orleans cultural history.
Country: United States
Social Media: www.facebook.com/CuttingEdgeNOLA/
Frequency: Annual

Early Music America
Website: www.earlymusicamerica.org
Phone: 412 642 2778
Address: 801 Vinial Street, Suite 300, Pittsburgh, PA 15212
Information: Early Music America is a North American community of people who find joy, meaning, and purpose in studying and experiencing historically informed performance. For more than 30 years, EMA has enriched the field of early music in North America by developing and supporting interest in the music of the past, so that it informs and shapes our lives today.
See website for more upcoming events.
Country: United States
Contact: Executive Director K Annarin
assistant Director Dina
secretary Derek
Social Media: twitter.com/EMA_Tweets www.facebook.com/earlymusicamerica www.instagram.com/earlymusicamerica/
Venue: World Fellowship Center, 368 Drake Hill Rd, Albany, MA 03818 United States
Start: 25/06/2021
End: 02/07/2021

Early Music America – Biennial Conference
Website: www.earlymusicamerica.org/
Email: info@earlymusic.org
Phone: 412 642 2778
Address: 801 Vinial Street Suite 300 Pittsburgh, PA 15212, US
Information: EMA's mission is to develop, strengthen, and celebrate early music in North America by supporting the people and organizations that perform, study, and find joy in it, and by championing the contributions they make to the health and vibrancy of their communities.
Country: United States
Contact: Executive Director Karin
Email: karin@earlymusic.org
Assistant Director Dina
Email: dina@earlymusic.org
Programs Dire tor David
Email: david@earlymusic.org
Social Media: https:// www.facebook.com/earlymusicamerica
https:// www.instagram.com/earlymusicamerica

International Folk Alliance Conference
Website: www.folk.org
Email: fai@folk.org
Phone: 816 221 3655
Address: 601 Avenida Cesar E. Chavez Suite #100, Kansas City, MO 64108
Information: Folk Alliance International (FAI) is an arts nonprofit founded in 1989 to connect folk music leaders aiming to sustain the community and genre worldwide. Our annual conference brings together 3, 000 members of the folk community and features showcases, educational panels and workshops, networking, and more.

Country: United States
Contact: Executive Director Aengus
Director of operations Jennifer
Email: operations@folk.org
communications Manager Marisa
Email: marisa@folk.org
program Manager Michelle
Email: programming@folk.org
Social Media: www.facebook.com/folkalliancetwitter.com/folkalliance www.instagram.com/folk_alliance/
Frequency: Annual
Start: February 2021
End: February 2021

International Ticketing Association (INTIX)
Website: https:// www.intix.org/
Email: info@intix.org
Phone: 212 629 4036
Address: International Ticketing Association, 5868 East 71st Street, Suite E 367, Indianapolis, IN 46220
Information: INTIX, the International Ticketing Association, is the leading forum for ticketing professionals, representing the most comprehensive view of the industry and its practices, products and services.
INTIX is a nonprofit membership organization that represents over a thousand ticketing, Sales, technology, finance and Marketing professionals from over 25 countries. They work in the world of arts, sports and entertainment, as well as a full range of public venues and institutions.
Country: United States
Contact: Chair Anthony
Marketing Manager Christine
Email: media@intix.org
meeting Manager Stacey
Social Media: twitter.com/intixassoc www.facebook.com/intixassoc/ www.instagram.com/intixassoc/
Frequency: Annual
Start: 2022-01-18
End: 2022-01-21

International Ticketing Association (INTIX)
Website: www.intix.org
Email: info@intix.org
Phone: 212 629 4036
Address: One College Park, 8910 Purdue Road, Suite 480, US
Information: A three-day event that includes a comprehensive educational program highlighting industry trends and innovations, an exhibition featuring companies that offer a wide range of ticketing products and services and opportunities to network with peers and business partners.
Country: United States
Social Media: https:// www.facebook.com/intixassoc/ https://twitter.com/intixassoc https:// www.instagram.com/intixassoc/

League of American Orchestras – National Conference
Website: www.americanorchestras.org
Email: member@americanorchestras.org
Phone: 212 262 5161
Address: 520 8th Avenue, Suite 2005, 20th Floor, New York, NY 10018
Information: The League brings together the best minds from in and outside the field to provide practical knowledge, develop effective leadership, relay best practices, provoke debate, and identify emerging trends.
Its conferences and events, award-winning Symphony magazine, website, and other publications inform people around the world about orchestral activity and developments.
Country: United States
Contact: President and CEO Simon
Email: swoods@americanorchestras.org
senior Director, finance and Administration Marc
Email: mmartin@americanorchestras.org
Manager, Administration Alex
Email: amajor@americanorchestras.org
senior Director, development Audrey
Email: arisbud@americanorchestras.org
Director, conferences and business engagement Stephen
Email: salter@americanorchestras.org
vice President, Marketing and communications Celeste
Email: cwroblewski@americanorchestras.org
Social Media: https:// www.facebook.com/orchleague https:// www.instagram.com/orchleague/ https://twitter.com/orchleague
Frequency: Annual
Other Venues: Online Conference in 2021

National Arts Marketing, Development & Ticketing Conference
Website: www.artsreach.com
Email: admin@artsreach.com
Phone: 888 881 5861
Address: Arts Reach Unlimited, P.O. Box 91446, Long Beach, CA 90809-1446, US US
Information: Arts Reach is the association that supports leading arts professionals who are committed to "Advancing Arts Revenue Growth Together." Joined together through the Arts Reach website, conferences, magazine, webinars and e-letters

Country: United States
Contact: President, arts reach John
Social Media: https:// www.facebook.com/artsreachas-sn/ https://twitter.com/artsreachassn
Frequency: Annual

National Performing Arts Convention
Website: www.performingartsconvention.org
Email: info@performingartsconvention.org
Address: US
Information: The National Performing Arts Convention (NPAC) is a collaboration among national service organisations for all of the performing arts. Founded in a realisation that there are many issues that are common to all of the performing arts and that can be more effectively addressed together, the NPAC partners work to take action to build a better future for and with the performing arts.
Country: United States
Contact: exhibitor committee Chair Stephen
Frequency: every 4 Years

Opera America Annual Conference
Website: www.operaamerica.org
Email: Conference@operaamerica.org
Phone: 212 796 8620
Address: National Opera Center America, 330 Seventh Avenue, New York, NY 10001
Information: OPERA America's annual Opera Conference is the largest assembly of opera administrators, artists, trustees, and Associates in the world.
Hosted by one of our Professional Company Members, hundreds of stakeholders convene in a different location each spring for discussions, networking, and performances that move opera forward.
Country: United States
Contact: President/CEO Marc
Chief Programs Officer Laura
Email: LEverett@operaamerica.org
Phone: 212 796 8625
Social Media: https:// www.facebook.com/operaamerica https://twitter.com/operaamerica https:// www.insta-gram.com/operaamerica/
Other Venues: 2021-Online
Start: 2021-05-10
End: 2021-05-17

Opera Volunteers International Conference
Website: www.operavolunteers.org
Email: info@operavolunteers.org
Address: Opera Volunteers International, PO Box 7032, Evanston, IL 60201-2284
Information: OVI is a non-profit volunteer organisation that celebrates the hard work of volunteers and offers ways to help make more volunteer involvement possible by recognizing achievement and creativity, supporting volunteer projects, and advocating for continuing involvement of volunteers in opera.
Country: United States
Contact: President Susan
vice President Administration Sandra
vice President communications and Marketing Mary
secretary Vikie
treasurer Sheila
Social Media: www.facebook.com/OperaVolunteers/ www.twitter.com/OperaVolunteer
Frequency: Annual

USITT Conference & Stage Expo
Website: www.usitt.org
Phone: 800 938 7488
Address: United States Institute for Theatre Technology, USITT National Office, 290 Elwood Davis Road, Suite 100, Liverpool, NY, 13088
Information: USITT connects performing arts design and technology communities to ensure a vibrant dialogue among practitioners, educators, and students. USITT was founded in 1960 as an organization to promote dialogue, research, and learning among practitioners of theatre design and technology.
Today, the Institute boasts thousands of members at all levels of their careers and has embraced the new technologies being used in entertainment.
Country: United States
Contact: Stage Expo Manager Cody
Director of finance and human resources Carol
Executive Director David
Social Media: ww.wtwitter.com/usitt www.facebook.com/usitt/ www.instagram.com/usitt/
Frequency: Annual
Other Venues: 2021-Online

Education and Training Institutions
This section lists schools, universities and conservatoires for music, dance and theatre. **The entries are listed in alphabetical order within country.**

Éstablissements d'Enseignement et de Formation
Cette rubrique contient les écoles, universités et conservatoires de musique, dance et théâtre. **Les entrée sont classés par ordre alphabétique dans le pays.**

Bildungs-und Ausbildungseinrichtungen
Hier werden weiterbildende Schulen aufgeführt. **Die Einträge sind für jedes Land alphabetisch sortiert.**

Istruzione e Formazione Istituzioni
In questa sezione vengono elencati i scuole, università e conservatori. **Le voci sono pubblicate in ordine alfabetico di paese.**

Educación y Formación Instituciones
En esta sección se listan las escuelas, universidades y conservatorios. **Las entradas se muestran en orden alfabético dentro de cada país.**

performing arts
database

AUSTRALIA

Australian Institute of Music
Website: www.aim.edu.au
Email: enquiries@aim.edu.au
Phone: 292 195 444
Address: 1 Foveaux St, Surry Hills NSW, 2010 Australia
Information: AIM students can individually tailor their studies to integrate performance skills, business management, Marketing, individual instrument or voice lessons, audio & sound engineering, music production and other specialised units
Country: Australia
Social Media: twitter.com/AIMnational www.facebook.com/AustralianInstituteofMusic www.instagram.com/australianinstituteofmusic/
Courses: aim.edu.au/courses

Barker College
Website: www.barker.nsw.edu.au
Email: reception@barker.nsw.edu.au
Phone: 284 387 999
Address: 91 Pacific Highway Hornsby NSW 2077 Australia
Information: Barker is an Anglican day and boarding school situated 25 kms to the north of Sydney at the junction of the North Shore and Central Coast railway lines, and just at the start of the Sydney-Newcastle Freeway. Established in 1890 it now has just over 1900 students
Country: Australia
Contact: Director of studies Jeremy Von Einem
Email: jeremy_von_einem@barker.nsw.edu.au
Phone: Director of alumni relations Mandy Loomes
Email: mandy_loomes@barker.nsw.edu.au
Social Media: www.facebook.com/barkercollegetwitter.com/BarkerCollege www.instagram.com/barkercollege/

Edith Cowan University
Website: www.ecu.edu.au/
Email: enquiries@ecu.edu.au
Phone: 863 040 000
Address: 270 Joondalup Drive, Joondalup WA 6027 Australia
Information: Edith Cowan University is an Australian public university located in Perth, Western Australia. It was named after the first woman to be elected to an Australian Parliament, Edith Cowan, and is the only Australian university named after a woman.Country: Australia
Contact: vice-chancellor Kerry Cox
Social Media: https:// www.facebook.com/ECUjourney/ https://twitter.com/EdithCowanUni

Elder Conservatorium of Music
Website: music.adelaide.edu.au/
Email: music@adelaide.edu.au
Phone: 883 135 995
Address: The University of Adelaide, AU
Information: With a long and distinguished history dating back to 1883, the Elder Conservatorium is the oldest tertiary music school in Australia and widely respected as one of the country's leading music institutions.
Country: Australia
Social Media: www.facebook.com/ElderConservatorium
Entry Requirements: audition and aural theory test
Scholarships Available: Yes

Le Piano Academy
Website: www.lepianoacademy.com.au
Email: info@lepianoacademy.com.au
Phone: 029 559 8638
Address: Unit 12, 6-10 Myra Road, Dulwich Hill NSW, 2203, Australia
Information: The Le Piano Academy is a Sydney-based piano studio that provides personalised piano and music theory tuition for adults, teens, and children as young as five.
Country: Australia
Social Media: https:// www.facebook.com/lepianoacademy

Queensland Conservatorium
Website: www.griffith.edu.au/music/queensland-conservatorium
Email: domesticenquiries@griffith.edu.au
Phone: 737 356 111
Address: Griffith University, 140 Grey Street, AU
Information: Queensland Conservatorium is one of Australia's leading music schools, offering a wide variety of specialist degrees, from classical music, jazz, opera, and popular music to musical theatre, music technology and music education. Queensland Conservatorium helps aspiring musicians to find their places on the world stage.
Country: Australia
Social Media: @QldCon_Griffith www.facebook.com/pages/Queensland-Conservatorium-Griffith-University/135355203154368

QUT Creative Industries Academy of the Arts
Website: www.qut.edu.au
Email: askqut@qut.edu.au
Phone: 731 388 114
Address: 2 George St, Brisbane, QLD 4000, Australia

Information: The Queensland Academies – Creative Industries Campus is a selective entry senior state high school in Queensland, Australia which offers the International Baccalaureate Diploma Programme. The Creative Industries Faculty generates ideas and talent for the creative arts, entertainment, media and design.
Country: Australia
Email: r.wissler@qut.edu.au
Social Media: www.facebook.com/QUTBrisbane https://www.instagram.com/qutrealworld/ https://twitter.com/qut

Sydney College of the Arts
Website: sydney.edu.au/sca/
Email: sca.enquiries@sydney.edu.au
Phone: 293 512 222
Address: Balmain Road, Lilyfield, AU
Information: the University of Sydney's school of contemporary art is a premier provider of art and media education and research. The college has been the major training ground for Sydney's leading contemporary artists for nearly forty years
Country: Australia
Social Media: www.facebook.com/pages/Sydney-College-of-the-Arts-The-University-of-Sydney/173358039483373
Full Time: Yes

AZERBAIJAN

Azerbaijan State Institute of Arts and Culture
Website: admiu.edu.az/english/index.php
Email: info@admiu.edu.az
Phone: 124 384 310
Address: Inshaatchilar Street 9, AZ
Country: Azerbaijan
Contact: Director Timuchin Afendiyev
54 study bachelor's degree, 3 study master's degree
Course Length: 6 months

Azerbaijan State Musical College
Phone: 124 936 585
Address: 28 May St, 1005, AZ
Country: Azerbaijan

Baku College of Dance
Phone: 991 249 57343
Address: 54, BulBul Ave 1014, AZ
Country: Azerbaijan
Contact: Director Kerimova Niylyufar Iban kizi

BRAZIL

Santa Marcelina Cultura
Website: www.gurisantamarcelina.org.br
Email: sau@santamarcelinacultura.org.br
Phone: 322 17326
Address: Largo General Osório, 147, Luz, BR
Information: Department of culture – Through quality music education, supported by a social care service, it offers students 6-18 years of education and a real opportunity for cultural growth and social inclusion. Member of ISPA
Country: Brazil
Social Media: @gurism www.facebook.com/gurisantamarcelina

CANADA

Canada's National Ballet School
Website: www.nbs-enb.ca
Email: info@nbs-enb.ca
Phone: 416 964 3780
Address: 400 Jarvis Street Toronto, ON, Canada M4Y 2G6
Information: established in 1959, Canada's National Ballet School is one of the world's foremost training institutions for aspiring young dancers and teachers. Attracting students from across the country and around the world, NBS is the only ballet academy in North America to provide elite dance training, academic instruction and residential care on the same campus
Country: Canada
Artistic Director & co-CEO
Mavis Staines
Executive Director & co-CEO
Grant Troop
Social Media: www.facebook.com/NBSENBtwitter.com/nbs_enb www.instagram.com/nbs_enb/

Canadian Society for Traditional Music
Website: www.yorku.ca/cstm/
Email: cstmsctm@ualberta.ca
Address: CSTM/SCTM c/o folkwaysAlive!, 3-47 Old Arts Bldg., University of Alberta, CA
Information: CSTM is dedicated to the study and promotion of musical traditions. The Canadian Society for Traditional Music is dedicated to the study and promotion of musical traditions of all communities and cultures, in all their aspects. The scope of the Society's activities is intended to reflect the interests of all its members, including ethnomusicologists, folklorists, performers, music enthusiasts, and the music community at large.
Country: Canada

Contact: President Sherry Johnson
Email: sherryj@yorku.ca
Social Media: www.facebook.com/CSTM.SCTM

École supérieure de ballet du Québec
Website: www.esbq.ca
Email: info@esbq.ca
Phone: 514 849 4929
Address: 4816 Rivard Street Montréal (Québec) H2J 2N6 Canada
Information: Unique French-speaking institution in North America offering world-class ballet training The École supérieure de ballet du Québec offers comprehensive professional ballet education.
Country: Canada
Contact: Director of studies Beverley Aitchison Aitchison
Email: beverley.aitchison@esbq.ca
Social Media: www.instagram.com/ecole_superieure_de_balle www.facebook.com/ecolesuperieuredeballetduquebec

Schulich School of Music
Website: www.mcgill.ca/music/
Email: reception.music@mcgill.ca
Phone: 514 398 4535
Address: 555 Sherbrooke St W, Montreal, Quebec H3A 1E3, Canada
Information: The Schulich School of Music of McGill University embodies the highest international standards of excellence in professional training and research.
Country: Canada
Contact: Director Joel Wapnick

The Royal Conservatory
Website: www.rcmusic.ca
Email: jeff.embleton@rcmusic.ca
Phone: 416 408 2824 x46
Address: 273 Bloor St W Toronto, ON, Canada M5S 1W2
Information: Since its inception in 1886, The Royal Conservatory has united generations of Canadians in shared creative and musical experiences.
Country: Canada
Social Media: twitter.com/the_rcm www.facebook.com/theroyalconservatory www.instagram.com/theroyalconservatory
Courses: RCM Certificate Program

Work In Culture
Website: www.workinculture.ca
Email: info@workinculture.ca
Phone: 416 340 0086
Address: 27 Carlton Street Suite 304 Toronto, Ontario M5B 1L2 Canada
Information: to support the people who work in the cultural sector through life-long career development and business skills training. Also known as 'Cultural Careers Council Ontario' (legal name). Member of ISPA
Country: Canada
Contact: Executive Director Karen Ennis
Phone: Diane Davy
Email: diane@workinculture.ca
Social Media: twitter.com/workinculture www.facebook.com/WorkInCulture

CHINA

Beijing Midi School of Music
Website: www.midischool.com.cn
Email: midi@midischool.com.cn
Phone: 106 259 0101/625
Country: China
Contact: Director Fan Zhang

Centre for Electroacoustic Music of China
Website: cemc.ccom.edu.cn
Email: cemcyxg@sina.com
Country: China
Contact: Director Xiaofu Zhang

INDIA

KM Music Conservatory
Website: www.kmmc.in
Email: info@kmmc.in
Phone: 444 344 4786
Address: No. 5, Dr. Suburaya Nagar 5th Street, Kodambakkam, IN
Information: provides students with a strong Artistic, intellectual, and technical foundation for pursuing professional careers in music
Country: IN
Contact: Executive Director Fathima Rafiq
Phone: Administration Manager Syed Irshad Ahmed
Social Media: @KMMC_Chennai
Part Time: Yes
Full Time: Yes
Courses: Music, Electronic Music Production,

EDUCATION AND TRAINING INSTITUTIONS

JAPAN

Kunitachi College of Music
Website: www.kunitachi.ac.jp
Email: peri@lib.kunitachi.ac.jp
Phone: 425 360 321
Address: 5-5-1 Kashiwa-cho, Tachikawa-shi, Tokyo 190-8520 Japan
Information: Kunitachi aims to develop students as well-rounded music professionals by providing a balanced educational environment with facilities and programs comprehensively crafted to support their dreams and passion for music excellence
Country: Japan
Social Media: www.instagram.com/kunitachi_college_of_musictwitter.com/Kunitachi_C_Mus/ www.facebook.com/KunitachiCollegeOfMusic

LEBANON

Ecole des Arts Ghassan Yammine
Website: www.edagy.com
Email: info@edagy.com
Phone: 120 2820
Address: Sodeco, Abu El Ula Bldg, Hamra, Hamra Street, Broadway Bldg, Jal El Dib, Highway, Mazda Bldg, LB
Country: LB
Social Media: EcoleDesArtsGYEcole des Arts Ghassan Yammine

MEXICO

Strum Guitar Center
Website: www.strumgc.com/
Phone: 216 54678
Address: MX
Information: member of ISPA
Country: Mexico
Social Media: @StrumGC www.facebook.com/StrumGC/timeline/

Strumgc
Website: www.strumgc.com
Email: info@strumgc.com
Phone: +5215515837012
Address: Paseo Vallescondido 13, , Club de Golf Vallescondido, , Atizapán de Zarago, MX
Country: Mexico
Social Media: @StrumGC www.facebook.com/StrumGC

NEW ZEALAND

Victoria University of Wellington
Website: www.vuw.ac.nz
Email: info@victoria.ac.nz
Phone: 447 21000
Address: PO Box 600, NZ
Information: Victoria University is a research-led university with high standards of teaching, which attracts exceptional students and staff from around the world.
Country: New Zealand
Social Media: www.facebook.com/victoriauniversityofwellington

SINGAPORE

Nanyang Academy of Fine Arts
Website: www.nafa.edu.sg
Phone: 651 24000
Address: 80 Bencoolen Street, SG
Country: Singapore
Contact: President President's Office
Email: President@nafa.edu.sg

National University of Singapore
Website: www.nus.edu.sg
Email: fasbox4@nus.edu.sg
Phone: 651 66666
Address: 21 Lower Kent Ridge Road, SG
Country: Singapore
Social Media: @NUSingapore www.facebook.com/nus.singapore
Full Time: Yes

UNITED STATES

Academy of Vocal Arts (AVA)
Website: www.avaopera.org
Email: info@avaopera.org
Phone: 215 735 1685
Address: 1920 Spruce Street · Philadelphia, PA 19103 USA
Information: Academy of the Vocal Arts is devoted to the training of young opera singers, tuition-free. Only those with tremendous potential are accepted to the Academy, where they receive the equivalent of $100,000 in training each year, free of charge
Country: United States
President & Artistic Director
 K. James McDowell
Phone: music Director Christofer Macatsoris
Phone: public relations and Marketing Manager Camille Mola
Social Media: twitter.com/avaopera www.facebook.com/avaopera/ www.instagram.com/avaopera

Albright College
Website: www.albright.edu
Phone: 610 921 2381
Address: 1621 North 13th Street, US
Information: connecting fields of learning, collaborative teaching and learning, and a flexible curriculum that allows students to create an individualized education. Albright College enrolls more than 1,660 undergraduates in traditional programs, another 800 adult students in accelerated degree programs, and 100 students in the master's program in education
Country: United States
Social Media: @AlbrightCollege@AlbrightCollege
Part Time: Yes
Full Time: Yes
Courses: art, digital media, fashion, film/video, music, theatre
Course Length: 29 weeks
Fees: $1,616 per course

Baldwin Wallace University
Website: www.bw.edu
Email: info@bw.edu
Phone: 440 826 2900
Address: 275 Eastland Rd. Berea, Ohio 44017 USA
Information: an academic community committed to the liberal arts and sciences as the foundation for lifelong learning. Classes are small—averaging 19 students—and are taught by experienced faculty providing individual attention and mentoringCountry: United States
Contact: Administration Caroline Arendec
Email: carendec@bw.edu
Social Media: twitter.com/BaldwinWallace www.facebook.com/baldwinwallaceuniversity www.instagram.com/baldwinwallace
Courses: Bachelor of Music (B.M.) Music Theatre Programs

Belmont College
Website: www.belmontcollege.edu
Email: belmontinfo@belmontcollege.edu
Phone: 740 695 9500
Address: 120 Fox Shannon Pl, St Clairsville, OH 43950, USA
Information: For more than 40 years, Belmont College has been assisting the residents of the Ohio Valley in achieving their educational and career goals. They offer students access to on-site and online classes for a variety of credit and non-credit programs.
Country: United States
Social Media: www.facebook.com/belmontcollegetwitter.com/belmontcollege
Courses: Bachelor of Fine Arts (B.F.A.) in Theatre Emphasis Areas, Bachelor of Arts Degree

Bowling Green State University
Website: www.bgsu.edu
Email: musicadmissions@bgsu.edu
Phone: 419 372 2531
Address: College of Musical Arts, Bowling Green State University Bowling Green, Ohio 43403-0001
Information: Widely known as one of the country's outstanding collegiate music programs in music education and contemporary music, the College of Musical Arts prepares students to be educators, performers, and scholars on an international level. Celebrated faculty members position students to live and achieve their passion, and our unique contemporary music program has inspired alumni to Pulitzer and Grammy level achievements.
Country: United States
Contact: Administration and Associate Dean Per F. Broman
Email: pbroman@bgsu.edu
Phone: Administration and Laura Charland
Email: lechar@bgsu.edu
Social Media: www.facebook.com/BGSU.CMA https://twitter.com/BGSUCMA https:// www.instagram.com/bgsucma/
 Brass & Percussion, Composition, Keyboard, Music Education, Musicology/Ethnomusicology, String, Theory, Vocal Arts, Woodwinds
 Scholarships Available: Yes

Carnegie Mellon School of Music
Website: www.music.cmu.edu
Email: dcasto@cmu.edu
Phone: 412 268 4921
Address: 5000 Forbes Avenue Pittsburgh, PA 15213 USA
Information: offers a wide variety of Music Degree programmes at the Undergraduate and Graduate level, as well as Certificate and Artist Diploma programmes. The School of Music educates outstanding, intellectually gifted musicians through excellence in performance, creativity, scholarship and pedagogy. We inspire imagination and creativity in music and in the construction of musical knowledge in all its diverse forms; through an understanding of both tradition and innovation, we enrich the community within and beyond Carnegie Mellon. See also Venues
Country: United States
Contact: Marketing and communication Director Dana Casto
Email: dcasto@cmu.edu
Phone: Director of graduate studies Natalie Ozeas
Email: nlozeas@andrew.cmu.edu
Phone: Director of recruitment and enrollment Katherine Drago
Email: kdrago@cmu.edu
Phone: coordinator of special music programs Daniel Barrett
Email: dbarrett@andrew.cmu.edu
Social Media: twitter.com/cmumusic www.instagram.com/cmumusic/ www.facebook.com/CarnegieMellonMusic/

Castleman Quartet Program
Website: www.quartetprogram.com
Email: ccastleman@aol.com
Phone: 305 284 6812
Address: 520 Brickell Key Drive, Unit A1913 Miami, FL 33131
Information: The Quartet Program is the best program of its kind. Every young person not only learns many of the great works written for this genre, but they must also learn how to work with each other and to communicate the most personal thoughts to their colleagues. No one emerges from the program without great love of music and better knowledge of interpersonal relationships.
Country: United States
Contact: Executive Director Charles Castleman
Email: ccastleman@aol.com
Social Media: www.facebook.com/followquartet-program
Courses: develops both individual and ensemble skills and explores group dynamics, with at least 3 hours quartet rehearsal and 3 hours solo practice scheduled daily

Center for Black Music Research
Website: www.colum.edu
Email: sflandreau@colum.edu
Phone: 312 369 7346
Address: Columbia College Chicago, 618 South Michigan Avenue, 6th Floor, Chicago, IL 60605 USA
Information: Center for Black Music Research (CBMR) holds materials highlighting the role of black music in world culture with materials originating or representing black music in the United States, Africa, Europe, Latin America, and the Caribbean in a variety of formats: personal papers, scores, sheet music, audio-visual materials, photographs, books, periodicals, and commercial recordings.
Country: United States
 head librarian & archivist
 Suzanne Flandreau
Email: sflandreau@colum.edu

Cleveland State University
Website: class.csuohio.edu/music/
Email: Call.Center@csuohio.edu
Phone: 216 687 2033
Address: Department of Music, 2121 Euclid Ave Cleveland, OH 44115
Information: offers the Bachelor of Music degree with concentrations in performance, composition, music education and music therapy and the Bachelor of Arts degree for those students seeking broader liberal arts study
Country: United States
Contact: Chair, music department John M. Perrine
Email: j.m.perrine@csuohio.edu
Social Media: twitter.com/CLE_State www.facebook.com/clevelandstateuniversityinstagram.com/cle_state

College Band Directors National Association – CBDNA
Website: www.cbdna.org
Email: mspede@clemson.edu
Phone: 615 322 7651
Address: 2400 Blakemore Ave. Nashville, TN 37212 USA
Information: The College Band Directors National Association is a grassroots organization that serves a wide variety of constituents, from the conservatory wind ensemble, to the athletic band, to the small college band, and everything in between.
Country: United States
Contact: senior band conductor Thomas Verrier Verrier
Email: thomas.verrier@vanderbilt.edu
Phone: 615 322 7651
Social Media: www.facebook.com/CBDNANational/ https://twitter.com/cbdna_national www.instagram.com/CBDNA_National/

College of Arts and Sciences : American University
Website: www.american.edu/cas/
Email: admissions@american.edu
Phone: 202 885 1000
Address: 4400 Massachusetts Avenue, US
Country: United States
Social Media: @AmericanU www.facebook.com/AmericanUniversity

College of Charleston
Website: www.cofc.edu/
Email: urbanskia@cofc.edu
Phone: 843 805 5507
Address: 66 George Street, US

Information: over 10, 000 undergraduates and approximately 1, 500 graduate students at the College enjoy a small-college feel blended with the advantages and diversity of a mid-sized, urban university
Country: United States
Contact: President George Benson
Part Time: Yes
Full Time: Yes

Columbia University
Email: ahofc@tc.colombia.edu
Phone: 212 854 1754
Address: 116th Street and Broadway, US
Information: founded in 1754 as King's College by Royal Charter of King George II of England. It is the oldest institution of higher learning in the state of New York and the fifth oldest in the United States
Country: United States
Contact: President Lee C. Bollinger
Part Time: Yes
Full Time: Yes

Cornish College of the Arts
Website: www.cornish.edu
Email: admission@cornish.edu
Phone: 800 726 2787
Address: 1000 Lenora Street, US
Information: Cornish College of the Arts is an exhilarating place to study. One of only three private, nonprofit performing and visual arts colleges in the nation, Cornish offers a distinctive blend of visual and performing arts grounded in a core curriculum of humanities. Member of ISPA
Country: United States
Contact: President Nancy Uscher
Email: President@cornish.edu
Phone: professor, composition, department Chair Kent Devereaux
Email: kdevereaux@cornish.edu
Social Media: @CornishCollege www.facebook.com/CornishCollegeOfTheArts
Courses: Cornish is a four-year college offering a Bachelor of Music degree and Bachelor of Fine Arts degrees in art, dance, design, music, performance production and theatre. We encourage students to exchange ideas, experiment and find their unique Artistic voice

Curtis Institute Of Music
Website: http:// www.curtis.edu
Email: infotech@curtis.edu
Phone: 215 893 5252
Address: 1726 Locust Street Philadelphia, PA 19103
Information: The Curtis Institute of Music educates and trains exceptionally gifted young musicians for careers as performing artists on the highest professional level. It provides full-tuition scholarships to all of its students, ensuring that admissions are based so
Country: United States
Contact: President Roberto Díaz
Email: roberto.diaz@curtis.edu
Social Media: www.facebook.com/CurtisInstitute/ www.instagram.com/curtisinstitute/twitter.com/CurtisInstitute

Daemen College
Website: daemen.edu
Email: admissions@daemen.edu
Phone: 800 462 7652
Address: 4380 Main Street, Amherst, NY 14226 USA
Information: Daemen College is a private, nonsectarian, co-educational, comprehensive college, chartered to award both undergraduate and graduate level degrees
Country: United States
Social Media: twitter.com/daemencollege www.facebook.com/DaemenCollege www.instagram.com/daemencollege

Dean College
Website: www.dean.edu
Email: alumni@dean.edu
Phone: 877 879 3326
Address: 99 Main St, Franklin, MA 02038 USA
Information: Dean College is a private residential college offering a variety of Associate degree programmes, four year institution transfer preparation, and various baccalaureate degrees
Country: United States
Contact: President Paula Rooney
Phone: vice President Gregg Chalk
Social Media: twitter.com/DeanCollege www.facebook.com/DeanDifference www.instagram.com/deancollege

DeBartolo Performing Arts Center
Website: performingarts.nd.edu
Email: perform@nd.edu
Phone: 574 631 2800
Address: 100 Performing Arts Center, US
Information: an inclusive, second-city destination for its Presenting Series—art with a point of view—informed by reflection on our Catholic character and inspired by the academy's pursuit of knowledge. Member of ISPA
Country: United States
Contact: Executive Director Anna M. Thompson
Email: amthompson@nd.edu
Phone: senior Associate Director Ted Barron

Email: ebarron2@nd.edu
Phone: special events program Manager Denise Sullivan
Email: sullivan.183@nd.edu
Social Media: @DeBartoloArtsND www.facebook.com/DeBartoloPerformingArtsCenter

Debartolo Performing Arts Center – Notre Dame University
Website: performingarts.nd.edu/
Email: amthompson@nd.edu
Phone: 574 631 2800
Address: 100 Performing Arts Center, US
Country: United States
Social Media: @DeBartoloArtsND www.facebook.com/DeBartoloPerformingArtsCenter

Drexel University
Website: www.drexel.edu
Email: ucomm@drexel.edu
Phone: 215 895 2000
Address: 3141 Chestnut St, Philadelphia, PA 19104, USA
Information: Drexel is an academically comprehensive and globally engaged urban research university, known for the nation's premier co-operative education programme. The university offers a variety of educational and employment opportunities to students through study and internship programmes in Europe, Asia and Latin America, and the co-operative education programme
Country: United States
Social Media: twitter.com/drexeluniv www.facebook.com/drexeluniv www.instagram.com/drexeluniv/

Drury University
Website: www.drury.edu
Email: drury@drury.edu
Phone: 417 873 7879
Address: 900 North Benton Avenue Springfield, MO 65802 USA
Information: Drury offers bright, achieving students a commitment to personalized education and diversity. A Drury education combines professional training with the liberal arts
Country: United States
Social Media: www.facebook.com/DruryUniversitytwitter.com/DruryUniversity www.instagram.com/DruryUniversity/

Florida International University School of Music
Website: www.music.fiu.edu
Email: music@fiu.edu
Phone: 305 348 2896
Address: Herbert and Nicole Wertheim Performing Arts Center, Modesto A. Maidique Campus, 10910 SW 17 ST, US
Country: United States
Contact: Director Orlando Garcia
Email: garciao@fiu.edu
Phone: assistant events Manager Christopher Delgado
Email: cdelg022@fiu.edu
Phone: Marketing coordinator Michelle Vires
Email: mvires@fiu.edu
Social Media: @FIUMusic https:// www.facebook.com/FIUMusic
Full Time: Yes
Courses: Choral, Composition, Jazz, Keyboard, Music Business, Music Education, Music Technology, Strings, Vocal, Wind
Entry Requirements: audition and interview
Scholarships Available: Yes
Qualifications: Yes

Goucher College
Website: www.goucher.edu
Email: admissions@goucher.edu
Phone: 410 337 6000
Address: 1021 Dulaney Valley Road, Baltimore, MD 21204 USA
Information: a selective, private, co-ed, liberal arts college dedicated to providing a multidisciplinary, international education, and it is the first college in the nation to make study abroad an undergraduate degree requirement
Country: United States
Contact: President assistant William Lederer
Email: william.lederer@goucher.edu
Social Media: www.facebook.com/gouchercollegetwitter.com/gouchercollege www.instagram.com/gouchercollege
Courses: theatre production, applied performance study

Heinz College : Carnegie Mellon University
Website: www.heinz.cmu.edu/index.aspx
Email: hnzadmit@andrew.cmu.edu
Phone: 412 268 2159
Address: 5000 Forbes Ave, US
Country: United States
Contact: dean Ramayya Krishnan
Email: rk2x@andrew.cmu.edu
Social Media: @HeinzCollege www.facebook.com/heinzcollege

Hopkins Center for the Arts
Website: hop.dartmouth.edu
Email: hopkins.center@dartmouth.edu
Phone: 603 646 2424
Address: Hopkins Center for the Arts, 4 East Wheelock Street, Dartmouth College, US
Information: The Hopkins Center's mission is to ignite and sustain a passion for the arts within Dartmouth and its greater community and to provide the core educational environment for the study, creation, and presentation of the arts. Member of ISPA
Country: United States
Social Media: @HopkinsCenter www.facebook.com/hopkinscenter

LA Dance Project
Website: ladanceproject.com
Email: info@ladanceproject.com
Address: US
Information: an artist collective founded in 2012 by renowned choreographer and dancer Benjamin Millepied, along with composer Nico Muhly, art consultant Matthieu Humery, Founding Producer Charles Fabius and Nicholas Britell
Country: United States

Manchester Community College
Website: www.mcc.commnet.edu
Email: jmcdowell@manchestercc.edu
Phone: 860 512 3000
Address: Great Path, US
Country: United States
Contact: dean – administrative affairs James McDowell
Email: jmcdowell@manchestercc.edu
Phone: chief academic officer Sandra Palmer
Email: spalmer@manchestercc.edu
Social Media: @MCC_CT www.facebook.com/myMCC

Manhattan School of Music
Website: www.msmnyc.edu
Email: jgandre@msmnyc.edu
Phone: 212 749 2802
Address: 120 Claremont Avenue, US
Information: Manhattan School of Music is a major national and international institution in professional music education and was founded 90 years ago; today it is the largest private conservatory in the nation offering both classical and jazz training; the School fulfils a major role in society by preparing talented men and women for careers as performing musicians, teachers, administrators, and involved audience members
Country: United States
Contact: President James Gandre
Email: jgandre@msmnyc.edu
Phone: Director of Administration Carol Matos
Email: cmatos@msmnyc.edu
Social Media: www.facebook.com/msmnyc
Full Time: Yes
Courses: offers classical and jazz training
Fees: $36000 a year

Massachusetts College of Liberal Arts (MCLA)
Website: www.mcla.edu
Email: webmaster@mcla.edu
Phone: 800 969 6252
Address: 375 Church Street, US
Information: MCLA is the Commonwealth's public liberal arts college and is part of the Massachusetts State University system offering small undergraduate classes for more interactive and personal teaching
Country: United States
Contact: President Mary K. Grant
Social Media: @MCLA_EDU www.facebook.com/pages/Massachusetts-College-of-Liberal-Arts/82654875561
Full Time: Yes
Courses: offers undergraduate degrees in art, arts management and other academic faculties

Millersville University
Website: www.millersville.edu
Email: mu@millersville.edu
Phone: 717 871 4636
Address: 1 S George St Millersville, PA 17551 USA
Information: Millersville University of Pennsylvania is a public university in Millersville, Pennsylvania. It is one of the fourteen schools that comprise the Pennsylvania State.
Country: United States
Social Media: twitter.com/millersvilleu www.facebook.com/millersvilleu www.instagram.com/millersvilleu

Missouri State University
Website: www.missouristate.edu
Email: info@missouristate.edu
Phone: 417 836 5000
Address: 901 S. National Ave. Springfield, MO 65897 USA
Information: Missouri State University was founded in 1905 as the Fourth District Normal School. During its early years, the institution's primary purpose was preparing teachers for the public school systems in the southwest region of Missouri.
Country: United States

National Youth Orchestra of the United States of America
Website: www.carnegiehall.org/Education/National-Youth-Orchestra-of-the-United-States-of-America/
Email: nyo-usa@carnegiehall.org
Phone: 212 903 9600
Address: 881 Seventh Avenue New York, NY 10019 USA
Information: each summer, Carnegie Hall's Weill Music Institute brings together 120 of the brightest young players from across the country to form the National Youth Orchestra of the United States of America. Following a two-week training residency with leading professional orchestra musicians, these remarkable teenagers embark on a tour to some of the great music capitals of the world and serve as dynamic musical ambassadors
Country: United States
Contact: Chairman Ronald O Perelman
Phone: orchestra Director James Ross
Social Media: https:// www.facebook.com/nyousa

Northwest Missouri State University Performing Arts Series
Website: www.nwmissouri.edu
Email: admissions@nwmissouri.edu
Phone: 660 562 1212
Address: 800 University Drive Maryville, MO 64468 USA
Information: The Department of Fine and Performing Arts provides an exciting combination of performance, classroom and internship opportunities for emerging professionals in the areas of art, music and theatre. All experiences are directed and/or mentored by highly respected and experienced faculty and guest artists.
Country: United States
Social Media: www.facebook.com/nwmissouritwitter.com/nwmostate www.instagram.com/nwmostate/
Courses: B.M.E. (Bachelor of Music Education), and the B.A. (Bachelor of Arts) in Music

NY Public Library for Perf. Arts
Website: www.nypl.org/about/locations/lpa
Email: esol@nypl.org
Phone: 917 275 6975
Address: 40 Lincoln Center Plaza, US
Information: The New York Public Library for the Performing Arts houses one of the world's most extensive combinations of circulating, reference, and rare archival collections in its field. These materials are available free of charge, along with a wide range of special programs, including exhibitions, seminars, and performances.
An essential resource for everyone with an interest in the arts—whether professional or amateur—the Library is known particularly for its prodigious collections of non-book materials such as historic recordings, videotapes, autograph manuscripts, correspondence, sheet music, stage designs, Press clippings, programs, posters and photographs
Country: United States
Social Media: @nypl_lpa www.facebook.com/nypl.lpa

Penn State University Behrend
Website: www.behrend.psu.edu
Email: behrend.admissions@psu.edu
Phone: 814 898 6000
Address: 4701 College Dr, Erie, PA 16510, USA
Information: Penn State Behrend is a four-year, residential college offering thirty-four bachelor's degrees, two master's degrees, and five Associate degree programmes
Country: United States
Social Media: twitter.com/psbehrend www.facebook.com/pennstatebehrend www.instagram.com/ps-behrend

Purchase College
Website: www.purchase.edu
Email: admissions@purchase.edu
Phone: 914 251 6200
Address: 735 Anderson Hill Road, PO Box 140, Purchase College, US
Information: Purchase College offers a unique education that combines programs in the liberal arts with conservatory programs in the arts in ways that emphasize inquiry, mastery of skills, and creativity. The college's graduates contribute to the arts, humanities, sciences, and society
Country: United States
Contact: President Thomas J.Schwarz
Social Media: @SUNY_Purchase www.facebook.com/SUNYPurchaseCollege
Full Time: Yes
Courses: offers courses in sciences, humanity subjects and courses in the arts

Rider University
Website: www.rider.edu
Phone: 609 896 5000
Address: 2083 Lawrenceville Road, US
Information: Rider is a private, co-educational university featuring two campuses in New Jersey with one in Lawrenceville and one in Princeton
Country: United States
Contact: President Mordechai Rozanski
Email: mrozanski@rider.edu
Social Media: @RiderUnivComm www.facebook.com/RiderUniversity

---

Full Time: Yes

Salem International University
Website: www.salemu.edu/index
Email: darlene.rodriguez@salem.edu
Phone: 888 235 5024
Address: 223 West Main Street, US
Information: established in 1888 as Salem College, Salem International University has a tradition of academic excellence and innovation. Salem International University offers Associate, Bachelor and Graduate degrees in high demand fields including: Business, Education, Information Technology and Criminal Justice
Country: United States
Part Time: Yes
Full Time: Yes
Courses: offers Associate, Bachelor and Graduate degrees in high demand fields including: Business, Education, Information Technology and Criminal Justice

San Diego State University
Website: music.sdsu.edu
Email: musicdance@mail.sdsu.edu
Phone: 619 594 6031
Address: 5500 Campanile Drive, US
Country: United States

Santa Barbara Dance Arts
Website: www.sbdancearts.com
Email: julie@sbdancearts.com
Phone: 805 966 5299
Address: 1 N. Calle Cesar Chavez, Suite 100, US
Information: offers classes in Jazz, Hip Hop, Contemporary, Ballet, Aerial, Broadway, Acro/Tricks, Conditioning, Combo classes for tots, and a full spectrum of adult friendly classes
Country: United States
Contact: Director Alana Tillim
Email: alana@sbdancearts.com
Phone: assistant Director Laurie Greene
Email: laurie@sbdancearts.com
Social Media: @SBDanceArts https:// www.facebook.com/SantaBarbaraDanceArts
Part Time: Yes

School of the Art Institute of Chicago (SAIC)
Website: www.saic.edu/index.html
Email: admiss@saic.edu
Phone: 800 232 7242
Address: 36 South Wabash, US
Information: the institution has been a leader in educating artists, designers, and scholars since 1866. The School of the Art Institute of Chicago offers numerous exceptional special collections and programming venues to its students and the public
Country: United States
Social Media: @saic_news www.facebook.com/saic.events
Full Time: Yes
Courses: offers courses in art history, visual and critical studies, fine arts in studio, interior architecture and many others

Seattle University
Website: www.seattleu.edu
Email: gilmerl@seattleu.edu
Phone: 206 296 6000
Address: 901 12th Avenue, PO Box 222000, US
Information: Seattle University is a Jesuit Catholic university located in Seattle's Capitol Hill neighborhood. The University has more than 7500 students and is ranked in the top 10 universities in the West
Country: United States
Contact: President Stephen V. Sundborg
Social Media: www.facebook.com/seattleu
Full Time: Yes
Courses: offers courses in all academic areas of education
Fees: $52, 605 a year
Scholarships Available: Yes
Qualifications: Yes

Skidmore College
Website: www.skidmore.edu
Email: fgs@dfgd.com
Phone: 518 580 5000
Address: 815 N. Broadway, Saratoga Springs, US
Information: Skidmore is a highly selective liberal arts college with a reputation for creative approaches to just about everything
Country: United States
Social Media: @SkidmoreCollege www.facebook.com/SkidmoreCollege
Full Time: Yes
Courses: offers courses in all academic areas of education

SMU Meadows School of the Arts
Website: www.smu.edu/meadows
Email: meadows@smu.edu
Phone: 214 768 2787
Address: Meadows School of the Arts, Bishop, US
Information: the Meadows School of the Arts is one of

---

the foremost arts education institutions in the United States
Country: United States
Contact: dean José Antonio Bowen
Phone: Associate dean for academic affairs Kevin Paul Hofeditz
Email: hofeditz@smu.edu
Social Media: @smumeadows www.facebook.com/SMUMeadows
Full Time: Yes
Courses: courses for dance, art, film, journalism, music, theatre and others

Society for American Music
Website: www.american-music.org
Email: sam@american-music.org
Phone: 412 624 3031
Address: Post Office Box 75073 Seattle, WA 98175 USA
Information: The Society was founded in 1975 and was first named in honor of Oscar G.T. Sonneck, early Chief of the Music Division in the Library of Congress and pioneer scholar of American music. The Society for American Music is a non-profit scholarly and educational organization incorporated in the District of Columbia as a 501 (c) (3) and is a constituent member of the American Council of Learned Societies.
Country: United States
Contact: officer Tammy Kernodle Kernodle
Phone: officer Christina Baade Baade
Social Media: www.facebook.com/SocietyforAmericanMusic/ https://twitter.com/socammusic www.instagram.com/socammus/

Society for Music Theory – University of Chicago
Website: www.societymusictheory.org
Email: smt@societymusictheory.org
Phone: 812 855 8846
Address: Indiana University 1201 E Third Street Bloomington, IN 47405
Information: The Society for Music Theory promotes the development of and engagement with music theory as a scholarly and pedagogical discipline. We construe this discipline broadly as embracing all approaches, from conceptual to practical, and all perspectives, including those of the scholar, listener, composer, performer, teacher, and student. The Society is committed to fostering diversity, inclusivity, and gender equity in the field.
Country: United States
Contact: President Patricia Hall Hall
Email: President@societymusictheory.org
Phone: Executive Director Jennifer Diaz Diaz
Email: smt@societymusictheory.org
Social Media: www.facebook.com/societymusictheory/ https://twitter.com/smt_musictheory

Southern Utah University
Website: www.suu.edu
Email: suutbirds@suu.edu
Phone: 435 586 7700
Address: 351 W University Blvd, Cedar City, UT 84720, USA
Information: Southern Utah University, is a dynamic teaching and learning community inspired by its natural surroundings. As Utah's designated public liberal arts and sciences university, SUU engages students in a personalised and experiential education, helping them to be productive citizens, socially responsible leaders, high achievers and lifelong learners
Country: United States
Contact: President Richard Kendell
Email: richkendell@suu.edu
Social Media: twitter.com/suutbirds www.facebook.com/SUUTBirds www.instagram.com/suutbirds/

State University of New York College at Fredonia (SUNY)
Website: www.fredonia.edu
Email:
webteam@fredonia.edu
Phone: 716 673 3111
Address: 280 Central Ave. Fredonia, NY 14063 USA
Information: SUNY Fredonia is an accredited, four-year university in Fredonia, that educates, challenges, and inspires students to become skilled, connected, creative, and responsible global citizens and professionals. The university enriches the world through scholarship, Artistic exPression, community engagement, and entrepreneurship
Country: United States
Contact: President Virginia Schaefer Horvath
Social Media: https://twitter.com/fredoniau www.facebook.com/fredoniau www.instagram.com/fredoniau/

Taos School of Music
Website:
www.taosschoolofmusic.com
Email: tsofm@newmex.com
Phone: 575 776 2388
Address: PO Box 2630 Taos, NM 87571 USA
Information: dedicated to immersing young musicians in chamber music study with the finest faculty in a world class setting and providing Taos audiences with exceptional chamber music performances
Country: United States

Social Media: www.facebook.com/Taos-School-of-Mu-sic-264280346933665/

The Juilliard School
Website: www.juilliard.edu
Email: news@juilliard.edu
Phone: 212 799 5000
Address: 60 Lincoln Center Plaza New York, NY 10023
Information: Founded in 1905, The Juilliard School is a world leader in performing arts education. The school's mission is to provide the highest caliber of Artistic education for gifted musicians, dancers, and actors from around the world so that they may achieve their fullest potential as artists, leaders, and global citizens.
Country: United States
Contact: admissions Lee Cioppa
Email: admissions@juilliard.edu
Phone: communication Alexandra Day
Email: news@juilliard.edu
Social Media: www.facebook.com/TheJuilliardSchool www.instagram.com/juilliardschool/twitter.com/juilliardschool

The Peabody Institute
Website: www.peabody.jhu.edu
Email: admissions@peabody.jhu.edu
Phone: 410 234 4800
Address: 1 E Mt Vernon Pl, Baltimore, MD 21202 USA
Information: The Peabody Conservatory strives to provide aspiring artists with the skills to pursue professional careers in music as well as with the education to become leaders in the cultural life of their communities.
Country: United States
Contact: Director Jeffrey Sharkey
Phone: dean of the conservatory/deputy Director Mellasenah Morris
Phone: contact Bozena Brown
Email: bozenajb@att.net
Social Media: www.facebook.com/PeabodyConservatory/twitter.com/george_peabody www.instagram.com/peabodyinstitute/

Tisch School of the Arts
Website: www.tisch.nyu.edu
Email: tisch.student.affairs@nyu.edu
Phone: 212 998 1900
Address: 721 BROADWAY, US
Information: When the School of the Arts was founded at NYU in 1965, it was heralded as a daring adventure — to be a school unlike any other. We met that challenge, and what has emerged over the last 50 years is the country's preeminent center for the study of the performing, cinematic and emerging media arts. member of ISPA
Country: United States
Social Media: @NYUTischSchool www.facebook.com/nyutischschool/

University of Buffalo Arts Management Program
Website: www.artsmanagement.buffalo.edu
Email: ub-artsmanagement@buffalo.edu
Phone: 716 645 2437
Address: 1023 Clemens Hall, US
Information: offers a dynamic two year course of study comprising core courses in the subject as well as additional courses tailored to students' individual interests
Country: United States
Full Time: Yes
Course Length: 2 years

University of Cincinnati
Website: www.uc.edu
Email: board.trustees@uc.edu
Phone: 513 556 6000
Address: 2600 Clifton Avenue, US
Information: the University of Cincinnati is one of America's top public research institutions with a student population of more than 40, 000
Country: United States
Social Media: @uofcincy www.facebook.com/uofcincinnati
Part Time: Yes
Full Time: Yes
Courses: features courses from all faculties of education

University of Kentucky
Website: www.uky.edu
Email: dgfh@sdfg.com
Phone: 859 257 9000
Address: 410 Administration Dr, Lexington, KY 40508, USA
Information: the University of Kentucky is a public, land grant university dedicated to improving people's lives through education, research and creative work, service, and health care
Country: United States
Contact: President Eli Capilouto
Social Media: twitter.com/universityofky www.facebook.com/universityofky www.instagram.com/universityofky/

University of North Carolina Wilmington
Website:
www.uncw.edu/music
Email:
seymoura@uncw.edu

Phone: 910 962 3390
Address: 601 S. College Road, US

Information: dedicated to fostering excellence in performance, teaching and scholarship by guiding and preparing students through a comprehensive curriculum that provides a strong foundation for an array of opportunities in the music profession, as well as for graduate study in a range of music specialties; offering Bachelor of Arts in music (three options: Performance; Jazz and Commercial Music; Music Entrepreneurship), Bachelor of Music (music education), and minors in music, choral music, and jazz studies; National Association of Schools of Music accredited member
Country: United States
Contact: music department Chairman Frank Bongiorno
Email: bongiornof@uncw.edu
Social Media: UNCW Department of Music
Full Time: Yes
Courses: undergraduate
Entry Requirements: audition
Fees: UNCW tuition and fees
Scholarships Available: Yes
Qualifications: Yes

Festivals

The emphasis of this list is on major festivals or those distinguished for other reasons, e.g. new work. Folk festivals have gen-erally been excluded, as have festivals that are primarily amateur. Preference has been given to events that are arranged for a short period, rather than a season of concerts spread over several months; however, some exceptions have been made, especially where such events have a long established or significant reputation. **The entries are listed in alphabetical order within country.**

Festivals

Nous avons mis l'accent sur les festivals les plus importants ou sur ceux qui se distinguent par leur originalité, par exemple ceux qui pro-mulguent des œuvres contemporaines ou nouvelles. Nous avons accordé une préférence à des festivals de courte durée plutot qu'à des series de concerts qui durent quelques mois. Pourtant nous avons fait des exceptions, notemment pour les festivals établis depuis longtemps qui jouissent d'une certaine réputation. **Les entrée sont classés par ordre alphabétique dans le pays.**

Festspiele

Im Mittelpunkt dieses Kapitels stehen die größeren und remommierteren Festspiele (z.B. Festspiele die sich mit Weltaufführungen, neuer Musik usw. befassen). Folkloreveranstaltungen sowie Laienfestspiele werden kaum genannt. Festspiele, die für einen Zeitraum stattfinden werden gegenüber Konzertreihen, die im Laufe einiger Monate stattfinden und dennoch als Festival bezeichnet wer-den, bevorzugt. Es gibt aber Ausnahmen, besonders wenn solche Festspiele jahrelang stattgefunden haben und einen besonderen Ruf haben. **Die Einträge sind für jedes Land alphabetisch sortiert.**

Festivals

Per quanto riguarda i festivals abbiamo selezionato i festivals più importanti o quelli che si sono distinti per una ragione particolare (es. festivals di sperimentazione teatrale). Sono stati privile-giati eventi di breve durata al posto di quelli che si protraggono nei mesi come le stagioni concertistiche. Sono state fatte delle eccezioni per quei festivals di lunga tradizione e grande notorietà. **Le voci sono pubblicate in ordine alfabetico di paese.**

Festivales

Esta sección se centra en los festivales más importantes y en aquellos que destacan por otras razones, por ejemplo los referentes a nuevas producciones o los de arte vanguardista. Como norma general, los fes-tivales folklóricos han sido omitidos, ya que generalmente son de nivel amateur. Se ha dado preferencia a aquellos acontecimientos organiza-dos por un período corto de tiempo en vez de a temporadas de espec-tacúlos con una duración de varios meses. **Las entradas se muestran en orden alfabético dentro de cada país.**

performing arts
database
online

ARGENTINA

Ciudad Cultural Konex
Website: https://www.cckonex.org/
Email: comunidad@cckonex.org
Phone: 114 864 3200
Address: 3131 Sarmiento, Buenos Aires, AR
Information: Konex Cultural City's programming consists of theatre, music, festivals, dance, cinema, circus, exhibitions, events and workshops. Its goal is to bring art in its various forms closer to the community.
Country: Argentina
Social Media: twitter.com/CCKonex www.facebook.com/CIUDADCULTURALKONEX
Frequency: Annual

AUSTRALIA

Adelaide Bank Festival of Arts
Website: www.adelaidefestival.com.au
Email: info@adelaidefestival.com.au
Phone: 882 164 444
Address: Level 9, 33 King William Street, Adelaide SA
Information: Adelaide Festival is one of the world's great arts events. For 60 years now the festival's audiences have delighted in an outstanding mix of internationally acclaimed theatre productions, an eclectic array of world-class musicians, breathtaking dance pieces, renowned writers and striking visual arts displays. Enjoyed amid warm March days and starry nights, Adelaide Festival's celebration of creative excellence makes for an event of truly epic proportions.
Country: Australia
Contact: Media Publicisit Anthea Hagar
Email: ahagar@adelaidefestival.com.au
Contact: Chair Judy Potter
Social Media: twitter.com/adelaidefest www.facebook.com/adelaidefestival/ www.instagram.com/adelaidefestival/
Type: Concert, Dance/Ballet, Theatre, Performance art

Adelaide Fringe Inc
Website: www.adelaidefringe.com.au
Email: buzz@adelaidefringe.com.au
Phone: 881 002 000
Address: 136 Frome St, Adelaide, SA 5000, Australia
Information: The open-access nature of Adelaide Fringe means that anyone with a show, exhibition or cultural event is able to register and be part of Australia's largest arts event. It's Carnivale meets Mardi Gras, with the entire city of Adelaide transformed for one mind-blowing month, in the summer sun and across balmy, star-filled nights. At the Adelaide Fringe you'll be awash with choices, with artists of all genres, in venues of all sizes and styles. We foster new talent, independence and risk-taking. We aim to surprise and forever present the unexpected. We have open access for all, and this is the place to see ground breaking work, new talent, original voices, new ideas and innovative thinking, day and night.
Country: Australia
Contact: Director/CEO Heather Croall
Contact: head of people and culture Aggy
Contact: Marketing and communication Manager Danielle
Contact: office Manager Gemma
Social Media: twitter.com/ADLfringe www.facebook.com/ADLfringe www.instagram.com/adlfringe/
End: 2022-03-20
Other Venues: various venues including Tandanya National Aboriginal Cultural Institute, Thebarton Theatre(2000 capacity), and RSASA Gallery
Type: Concert, Multi-media, Performance art, Other

Antipodes Festival
Website: https://www.greekcentre.com.au/
Email: info@greekcommunity.com.au
Phone: 396 622 722
Address: 168 Lonsdale St, Melbourne VIC 3000
Information: The Lonsdale St. Greek Festival, sees Melbourne's biggest Greek street party bring a weekend of Greek culture, food and entertainment to the city's historic Greek Precinct. It features three stages of free entertainment, children's rides and activities, and over 60 food, drink and craft stalls.
Country: Australia
Contact: Administration Director Antonia Tsamis
Email: antonia@greekcommunity.com.au
Social Media: https://www.facebook.com/thegreekcentre/ www.twitter.com/greekcentre www.instagram.com/greekcentre/

Australian Festival of Chamber Music
Website: https://www.afcm.com.au/
Email: info@afcm.com.au
Phone: 477 14144
Address: Level 1, Breakwater Terminal, Sir Leslie Thiess Drive, Townsville Qld 4810
Information: The Australian Festival of Chamber Music is a friendly, unique and internationally acclaimed event presenting a 9 day programme of over 30 concerts and special events. Experience the world's finest chamber musicians performing in various combinations exclusively in the tropical winter warmth of Townsville, North Queensland

Country: Australia
Contact: Marketing Manager Sheridan Helft
Email: sheridan.helft@afcm.com.au
Contact: Executive Director Gavin Findlay
Email: gavin.findlay@afcm.com.au
Contact: Marketing and development Executive Jacqui Ferry
Email: jacqui.ferry@afcm.com.au
Contact: office Manager Denise Kaitira
Email: denise.kaitira@afcm.com.au
Social Media: twitter.com/afcmtownsville?lang=en www.facebook.com/australianfestivalofchambermusic
Start: 2022-07-29
End: 2022-08-07
Type: Concert

Barossa Vintage Festival
Website: https://www.barossavintagefestival.com.au/
Email: info@tourismbarossa.com.au
Phone: 428 031 444
Address: Barossa, South Australia
Information: The Barossa Vintage Festival has a long-standing history as a celebration of vintage, dating back to 1947 when the Barossa community got together to celebrate the end of grape harvest and vintage. The festival is acknowledged as the largest and longest running wine tourism event in Australia. The Barossa Vintage Festival has always been a celebration 'by Barossans for Barossans' to which we have now invited the rest of the world to come and celebrate, as we engage visitors in an immersive food and wine experience, against the back drop of Barossan history and heritage.
Country: Australia
Contact: Festival Director Jenny O'Brien
Email: jenny@tourismbarossa.com.au
Contact: PR/Marketing Taryn Wills
Email: taryn@tourismbarossa.com.au
Social Media: www.facebook.com/BarossaVintageFestival/ www.instagram.com/MyBarossa/
Frequency: Biennial
Type: Multi-media

Blues at Bridgetown Festival
Website: http://www.bluesatbridgetown.com/
Email: media@bluesatbridgetown.com
Phone: 897 612 921
Address: 154 Hampton Street, Bridgetown, WA, 6255, Australia
Information: An international celebration of blues & roots music, held over three days in the beautiful and idyllic setting of the Bridgetown, 272kms south-east of Perth. The programme, in excess of 135 hours, showcases a diverse range of blues and roots music at various venues in and around the town.
Mix in the uniqueness of the local region and the result is an event and organisation that hasn't been consigned to history like so many others.
Country: Australia
Social Media: twitter.com/BluesBridgetown www.facebook.com/bluesatbridgetownfestival
Frequency: Annual
Type: Concert

Bluesfest Byron Bay
Website: www.bluesfest.com.au
Email: admin@bluesfest.com.au
Phone: 266 858 310
Address: 2/142 Bangalow Road, Byron Bay, AU
Information: Bluesfest Byron Bay is Australia's biggest contemporary blues and roots music festival, showcasing over 200 artists across its long weekend each April. Now welcoming over 100000 people to Tyagarah Tea Tree Farm, just north of Byron Bay, Bluesfest is a weekend filled with music, fun and games for all the family.
Country: Australia
Contact: Festival Director Peter Noble
Social Media: www.twitter.com/BluesfestByron www.facebook.com/bluesfestbyronbay
Frequency: Annual
End: 2021-04-05
Other Venues: Campground near Byron Bay
Type: Concert

Brisbane Festival
Website: www.brisbanefestival.com.au
Email: brisbanefestival@brisbanefestival.com.au
Phone: 738 335 400
Address: Level 2, 381 Brunswick Street, Fortitude Valley, QLD 4006, AU
Information: This is a world class arts festival held every September with a programme of music, theatre, dance, comedy, opera, circus and much more. Brisbane Festival is Brisbane's most anticipated event of the year, and has been embraced by the city and admired by the world-
Country: Australia
Contact: media enquiries Natalie Ogbourne
Email: nat@aruga.com.au
Contact: Artistic Director Louise Bezzina
Contact: chief Executive officer Charlie Cush
Contact: Marketing and communications Director Karen Soennichsen
Contact: Administration coordinator Marcia Ferreira
Contact: Media Natalie Ogbourne
Email: nat@aruga.com.au

Contact: Artistic Director Louise Bezzina
Contact: Chief Executive Officer Charlie Cush
Social Media: twitter.com/brisfestival www.facebook.com/BrisbaneFestival www.instagram.com/brisbanefestival/
Start: 2022-09-02
End: 2022-09-24
Type: Concert, Dance/Ballet, Musical theatre, Performance art, Opera, Theatre

Canberra International Music Festival
Website: https://cimf.org.au/
Email: info@cimf.org.au
Phone: 262 305 880
Address: Ainslie Arts Centre, Canberra International Music Festival Ainslie Arts Centre
Information: The Canberra International Music Festival is an annual musical extravaganza in the nation's capital. With a focus on premiering new works and featuring diverse voices the festival is an unmissable and quintessential Canberra experience.
Over ten beautiful autumn days let music become your guide to Canberra's cultural treasures and hidden gems as artists celebrate musical works new and old.
Country: Australia
Contact: Artistic Director Roland Peelman
Email: ArtisticDirector@cimf.org.au
Contact: General Manager Angela Hannan
Email: General.Manager@cimf.org.au
Contact: Marketing coordinator Claire Holland
Email: claire.holland@cimf.org.au
Contact: Artist Coordinator Olivia Swift
Email: olivia.swift@cimf.org.au
Contact: Production Manager David Howe
Email: David.Howe@cimf.org.au
Social Media: twitter.com/TheCIMF www.facebook.com/canberrafest/ www.instagram.com/the_cimf/
Frequency: Annual
Start: 2022-04-29
End: 2022-05-08
Type: Concert

Carnevale in Adelaide
Website: https://carnevale-adelaide.com/
Email: carnevaleys@gmail.com
Phone: 883 620 233
Address: 84 Payneham Road Adelaide, SA, Australia 5009
Information: Carnevale is the only festival of its type in Australia. It is an opportunity for South Australia's Italian community to share its vibrant culture and traditions with the rest of the community.
Country: Australia
Social Media: twitter.com/carnevale_adel www.facebook.com/carnevale.adelaide
Other Venues: Rymill Park
Type: Concert, Dance/Ballet

Castlemaine State Festival
Website: https://castlemainefestival.com.au/
Email: information@castlemainefestival.com.au
Phone: 354 723 733
Address: 19 Kennedy St Castlemaine, VIC, Australia 3450
Information: The Castlemaine State Festival is a biennial ten-day multi-arts celebration that draws on the distinctive culture of the central Victorian goldfields region – of old and new, of the Artistic and the agricultural, and its dynamic community strengths. The Festival showcases works from the region's finest artists and performing arts companies, alongside those by national and international artists.
Country: Australia
Contact: festival Director/CEO Glyn Roberts
Contact: General Manager Krista Horbatuik
Social Media: https://twitter.com/statefestival www.facebook.com/CastlemaineFestival/ www.instagram.com/castlemainefestival/
Type: Concert, Dance/Ballet, Performance art

Chapel Jazz Festival
Website: http://www.chapeljazz.com/
Email: info@chapeljazz.com
Phone: 414 254 230
Address: Morpeth, New South Wales 2321, Australia
Information: In 2009 Jazz returned to Morpeth when the three churches got together to revive the Morpeth Jazz Festival as ChapelJazz. The aim of ChapelJazz is to present traditional jazz in a welcoming environment to jazz lovers and their families and provide an enjoyable community experience.
Country: Australia
Social Media: www.facebook.com/ChapelJazz-Morpeth-2296710833940822/ https://twitter.com/ChapelJazz
Frequency: Annual
Type: Concert

Darling Harbour Jazz Festival
Website: https://www.darlingharbour.com/
Email: darlingharbour@shfa.nsw.gov.au
Phone: 292 408 500
Address: PO Box N408, Grosvenor Place, AU
Information: Darling Harbour's legendary Jazz & Blues Festival celebrates the true greats of international and Australian jazz with a large line up.

Country: Australia
Social Media: twitter.com/darlingharbour www.facebook.com/DarlingHarbourSydney
Frequency: Annual
Type: Concert

Darling Harbour's Christmas Program
Website: https://www.darlingharbour.com/whats-on/campaigns/christmas
Email: darlingharbour@shfa.nsw.gov.au
Phone: 292 408 500
Address: PO Box N408, Grosvenor Place, AU
Information: Darling Harbour hosts a variety of events to celebrate Christmas, with art displays, face painting and decorations in Sydney's favourite venue, which hosts a huge range of restaurants and experiences. Fun for people of all ages.
Country: Australia
Contact: Media
Email: media@dpie.nsw.gov.au.
Contact: Venue Hire and Commercial Opportunities
Email: venuehire@property.nsw.gov.au
Social Media: www.facebook.com/darlingharbourtwitter.com/darlingharbour
Frequency: Annual

Darling Harbour's Fiesta
Website: https://www.darlingharbour.com/whats-on
Email: darlingharbour@shfa.nsw.gov.au
Phone: 292 408 500
Address: PO Box N408, Grosvenor Place, AU
Information: Darling Harbour Fiesta is one of Australia's largest and hottest Latin American dance and music festivals. This highly popular festival has been running for many years and it attracts thousands of visitors each year.
Country: Australia
Social Media: https://www.facebook.com/darlingharbour https://twitter.com/darlingharbour https://www.instagram.com/darlingharbour/
Frequency: Annual
Type: Dance/Ballet, Concert

Darwin Festival
Website: https://www.darwinfestival.org.au/
Email: hello@darwinfestival.org.au
Phone: 889 434 200
Address: Level 2, Harbour View Plaza, 8 McMinn St, Darwin NT 0801
Information: Darwin Festival is held over 18 days and nights every August, with local and touring performances and events including outdoor concerts, workshops, theatre, dance, cabaret, music and comedy, film and visual arts. During the Festival, Darwin buzzes with performers, artists, locals and visitors enjoying the vibrant and colourful atmosphere and festivities of Darwin Festival.
Country: Australia
Contact: Media Matt Fraser
Email: matt@originalspin.com.au
Contact: Media Amber Forrest-Bisley
Email: amber@originalspin.com.au
Social Media: twitter.com/darwinfestival?lang=en www.facebook.com/darwinfestival/ www.instagram.com/darwinfestival/
Start: 2022-08-04
End: 2022-08-21
Type: Concert, Dance/Ballet, Film, Theatre

Desert Harmony Arts & Cultural Festival
Website: https://www.desertharmonyfestival.com/
Email: events@barklyarts.com.au
Phone: 889 622 799
Address: 65 Staunton Street, Tennant Ck, NT, Australia
Information: The Desert Harmony Festival is hosted by Barkly Regional Arts in Tennant Creek, Northern Territory, and is our region's platform for the culturally diverse population to present, engage with, and participate in the arts. The Festival program presents world-class music talent, along with a healthy combination of professional locally produced work that showcases the talents in the Barkly region, community performances and Australian productions that travel in.
Country: Australia
Social Media: www.facebook.com/desertharmonyfestival/ www.instagram.com/desert_harmony_festival/
Frequency: Annual
Type: Concert, Film, Multi-media, Theatre

DreamBIG Children's Festival
Website: https://www.dreambigfestival.com.au/
Email: feedback@adelaidefestivalcentre.com.au
Phone: 882 168 600
Address: Adelaide Festival Centre, GPO Box 1269, Adelaide 5001
Information: The DreamBIG Children's Festival (previously Come Out Children's Festival) is renowned internationally as the largest and longest standing regional festival for young people in the Southern Hemisphere. This biennial children's festival emerged from the Adelaide Festival of Arts in 1974 and is now Australia's premier for young people and the arts event. Each festival reaches more than 100, 000 young people aged 0-14 years and engages them in high quality, professional, interactive arts experiences
Country: Australia
Contact: Executive Producer Kate Donnelly
Contact: Assistant Producer Sam Prior
Social Media: www.facebook.com/DreamBigChildrensFestival/ www.instagram.com/adelaidefescent/
Type: Multi-media, Musical theatre, Puppetry, Theatre, Film

Fairbridge Festival
Website: https://fairbridgefestival.com.au/
Email: hello@fairbridgefestival.com.au
Phone: 892 463 311
Address: Fairbridge Village, South Western Highway 6208 Pinjarra, WA, Australia
Information: A weekend-long family-orientated celebration of folk, roots and world music, both contemporary and traditional brings around 100 acts from within WA, across Australia and from overseas to perform at the festival each year. The continually growing audience is at approximately 17500 over the course of the weekend. FF is three festivals in one, with events for lovers of the arts and music as well as a youth festival and a festival for children.
Country: Australia
Social Media: twitter.com/FairbridgeFesti www.facebook.com/FairbridgeFestival www.instagram.com/fairbridge_festival/
Start: 2022-04-22
End: 2022-04-24
Type: Concert

Festivale
Website: https://festivale.com.au/
Email: info@festivale.com.au
Phone: 363 349 990
Address: City Park, Launceston Tasmania
Information: Festivale is an annual event, attracting around 35 thousand patrons, and is held on the second weekend of February. Originally established in 1988 as a multi-cultural street party, it has transformed itself into an iconic Tasmanian event, drawing people together to celebrate what Tasmania has to offer the world.
Country: Australia
Contact: Chairman David Dunn
Contact: secretary Andrew Hirst
Contact: event coordinator Hayle Chugg
Social Media: www.facebook.com/festivaletas/ www.instagram.com/festivaletas/
Frequency: Annual
Start: 2023-02-03
End: 2023-02-05

Fremantle Festival: 10 Nights in Port
Website: https://www.10nightsinport.com.au/
Email: festivals@fremantle.wa.gov.au
Phone: 894 329 999
Address: 6959 Fremantle, WA, Australia
Information: Fremantle Festival celebrates the city's culture with 10 days of music, art and performances in a variety of venues in and around the city. Originating in 1905, the event is Australia's oldest community festival.
Country: Australia
Social Media: www.facebook.com/fremantlefestival/ www.instagram.com/10nightsinport/
Other Venues: classic live venues like Mojos, Clancys and the Norfolk to audiences of stalwart locals
Type: Performance art, Multi-media, Concert

Glebe Music Festival
Website: https://www.glebemusicfestival.com/
Email: edgmci@aol.com
Phone: 294 166 136
Address: 3/8 Russell Avenue, Lindfield, NSW 2070
Information: The Glebe Music Festival in Sydney, Australia, grew out of the many informal musical soirées held at the early 19th century building, Margaretta Cottage, since the late 1960s. The late Dr Vincent Sheppard built up a unique collection of keyboard instruments including an 18th century Dutch chamber organ, a 19th century Kapps grand piano, a Sperrhake harpsichord, a pedal piano and a clavichord.
Country: Australia
Contact: Artistic Director E. David G. McIntosh
Frequency: Annual
Margaretta Cottage, Gleebooks, The Glebe Town Hall, St Scholastica's Chapel, Record Reign Hall, The Great Hall
Type: Concert

Grampians Jazz Festival – Halls Gap
Website: https://www.grampiansjazz.com/
Email: festival@hallsgapjazzblues.com
Phone: 042 822 7261
Address: 126 Grampians Road Halls Gap, VIC, Australia 3381
Information: The amazing Grampians Jazz festival is an event not to be missed. With over 5000 musicians and thousands of spectators, this annual event is considered a major tourist drawcard in the region. The event's high popularity is what makes it a major hit amongst jazz fans each year.
Country: Australia
Contact: festival coordinator Don Calvert

Email: festival@hallsgapjazzblues.com
Huntington Estate Music Festival in association with Musica Viva
Website: https://www.huntingtonestate.com.au/
Email: musicfestival@huntingtonestate.com.au
Phone: 180 099 5931
Address: 641 Ulan Road Buckaroo (Mudgee) NSW 2850 Australia
Information: The 27th Huntington Estate Music Festival celebrates everything audiences have come to love about this event: an exclusive and exciting mix of artists from around the world and across Australia, performing favourite pieces and delicious new discoveries, all paired with glorious food and wine and a beautiful country estate.
Country: Australia
Contact: owner and General Manager Nicky Stevens
Email: nicky@huntingtonestate.com.au
Social Media: www.facebook.com/huntingtonestatemusic
Other Venues: Barrel Room of the winery in Mudgee
Type: Concert

Kiama Jazz & Blues Festival
Website: https://www.kiamajazzandbluesfestival.com.au/
Email: jazzbeckyblue@gmail.com
Phone: 415 062 466
Address: Kiama, Sydney, NSW 2533, AU
Information: Kiama Jazz & Blues Festival is a free three-day south coast signature event. It is set on the stages, streets, parks, cafes, bars and clubs across the breathtaking Kiama region.
This unique, jam-packed weekend celebrates two music genres that refuse to sit still, set against one of the country's most picturesque backdrops. The exciting music content tips its hat to the original genres and celebrates all forms of contemporary interpretation, there is something for everyone.
Country: Australia
Social Media: www.facebook.com/kiamajazzandblues/ www.instagram.com/kiamajazzandblues/
Frequency: Annual
Type: Concert

Mackay Festival of Arts
Website: https://www.themecc.com.au/mackayfestivals/mackay_festival_of_arts
Email: festival@mackay.qld.gov.au
Phone: 749 619 777
Address: Mackay, QLD, Australia 4740
Information: Mackay's flagship festival, spans over 10 days and includes live music, cabaret, circus, comedy, wine and food, family events and more.
Country: Australia
Social Media: https://twitter.com/mackayfestivals www.facebook.com/mackayfestivals/
Frequency: Annual
Type: Concert, Dance/Ballet, Performance art, Puppetry, Theatre

Manly International Jazz Festival
Website: https://www.sydneypoint.com.au/events/manly-jazz-festival/
Address: Manly Beach, Northern Beaches of Sydney, NSW
Information: The internationally acclaimed Manly Jazz is known worldwide for its beautiful location and the diversity of music it presents, from traditional New Orleans jazz to funk, Latin, fusion, blues, gospel, swing and roots – with performances in multiple indoor and outdoor venues including major stages alongside the world famous Manly Beach.
Country: Australia
Social Media: www.facebook.com/manlyjazz/
Frequency: Annual
Type: Concert

Melbourne Fringe Festival
Website: https://www.melbournefringe.com.au/
Email: info@melbournefringe.com.au
Phone: 396 609 600
Address: G2, 152 Sturt Street, Southbank, Melbourne 3006 Australia
Information: The Melbourne Fringe Awards are an opportunity for Melbourne's arts community to celebrate and acknowledge the diversity, professionalism and exceptional quality of work in each year's festival.
Country: Australia
Contact: head of programs and projects Danny Delahunty
Email: artists@melbournefringe.com.au
Contact: creative Director and CEO Simon Abrahams
Email: info@melbournefringe.com.au
Contact: head of Marketing and development Miranda Borman
Email: development@melbournefringe.com.au
Contact: communications and partnerships Manager Caitlin McNaughton
Email: Marketing@melbournefringe.com.au
Contact: General Manager and deputy CEO Will Dawson
Email: info@melbournefringe.com.au
Social Media: twitter.com/melbournefringe www.facebook.com/melbfringe www.instagram.com/melbfringe

Frequency: Annual
Type: Concert, Dance/Ballet, Theatre

Melbourne International Comedy Festival
Website: https://www.comedyfestival.com.au/2022
Email: info@comedyfestival.com.au
Phone: 392 453 700
Address: 240 Exhibition Street (above Comedy Theatre), Melbourne, Victoria 3000, Australia
Information: An annual event, the Melbourne International Comedy Festival literally takes over Australia's comedy capital, Melbourne, each autumn with an enormous programme of stand-up comedy, cabaret, theatre, street performance, film, television, radio and visual arts.
Country: Australia
Contact: festival Director/CEO Susan Provan
Contact: Executive Director Damien Hodgkinson
Contact: Marketing and partnership Director Denise Damianos
Social Media: twitter.com/micomfestival www.facebook.com/melbournecomedy www.instagram.com/melbcomedyfestival/
Start: 2022-03-30
End: 2022-04-24
Type: Other

Melbourne International Singers Festival
Website: https://www.playitforward.org.au/events/misf
Email: misf@playitforward.org.au
Phone: 419 337 283
Address: Melbourne, VIC, 3004 Australia
Information: Play It Forward presents Australia's most exciting Singers Festival for all school & community choirs and individual singers. Melbourne International Singers Festival has an even bigger and more diverse program over the Queen's Birthday long weekend
Country: Australia
Contact: operations and projects Manager Jan Hamilton
Email: jan@playitforward.org.au
Social Media: www.facebook.com/MelbSingersFest/twitter.com/melbsingersfest
Type: Concert

Multicultural Festivals
Website: https://www.multiculturalfestival.com.au/
Email: inbox@Multiculturalfestival.act.gov.au
Phone: 262 078 698
Address: no address provided
Information: The National Multicultural Festival began in 1996 and has since evolved into the biggest occasion on Canberra's event landscape. In the very beginnings of the Festival, it was a one-day event, eventually moving to a 2-week Festival. Over the course of the last 21 years it has developed into the 3-day Festival it is now, which allows Canberrans, national and international visitors alike to congregate in Canberra over one weekend for what is one of the biggest celebrations of cultural diversity across Australia.
Country: Australia
Contact: festival Director Azra Khan
Email: inbox@Multiculturalfestival.act.gov.au
Contact: Media Enquiries
Email: CSD.Media@act.gov.au
Social Media: twitter.com/NatMultiFest www.facebook.com/national.multicultural.festival/ www.instagram.com/Multicultural.Festival/
Type: Concert, Dance/Ballet, Multi-media, Performance art, Other

National Folk Festival (NFF)
Website: https://www.folkfestival.org.au/
Email: info@folkfestival.org.au
Phone: 262 624 792
Address: PO BOX 179, Mitchell ACT, Australia 2911
Information: The National Folk Festival is a limited-liability, not-for-profit company, formed for the purpose of presenting the event. From high-end entertainment to the exPression of folk-life through grassroots and community activities our multifaceted National Folk Festival is the ultimate celebration of all things folk. It's designed to inspire, enliven and entertain. From traditional and contemporary grooves to the quirky and the endearing it features all the key elements that make people want to come!
Country: Australia
Contact: President Stephen Gallacher
Contact: Vice President David Gilks
Contact: Managing Director Helen Roben
Social Media: twitter.com/natfolkfest www.facebook.com/folkfestival www.instagram.com/nationalfolkfestival/
Frequency: Annual
Start: 2022-04-14
End: 2022-04-18
Type: Concert

Newcastle Jazz Festival
Website: https://newcastlejazz.com.au/
Email: enquirieshjc@gmail.com
Phone: 249 296 315
Address: Newcastle & Hunter Jazz Club, PO Box 2262, Dagnar, NSW 2309
Information: Newcastle Jazz Festival regarded as one of the best jazz festivals in Australia, has top local and interstate bands performing 50 superb hours of jazz over three days
Country: Australia
Contact: President Judy Preston
Contact: secretary Val Jones
Contact: treasurer An Gibson
Social Media: www.facebook.com/NewcastleJazz-ClubandFestival
Frequency: Annual
Start: 2022-08-19
End: 2022-08-22
Type: Concert

Next Wave
Website: https://nextwave.org.au/
Email: nextwave@nextwave.org.au
Phone: 393 299 422
Address: Office 4, 5 Blackwood Street, North Melbourne, VIC 3051
Information: Next Wave Festival is a biennial festival held in Melbourne. For three decades, the Festival has shaped the Australian arts landscape through imagination, bold ideas and passion for the new. Established in 1984 to foster creativity and experimentation, Next Wave's focus has always been on the next generation of artists in a changing world. Career development, presentation opportunity and multi-disciplinary representation have been integral since our inception.
Country: Australia
Contact: Director/CEO Roslyn Helper
Contact: General Manager Jacqueline Hanlin
Contact: Marketing and communications Manager Brigitte Trobbiani
Contact: Administration and operations coordinator Magenta Sheridan
Social Media: twitter.com/next_wave www.facebook.com/NextWaveFestival/ www.instagram.com/next_wave/
Frequency: Biennial
Type: Multi-media

Noosa Jazz Party
Website: http:// www.noosajazzclub.com/
Email: richard@noosajazzclub.com
Phone: 754 472 229
Address: 34 Weyba Street Sunshine Beach Queensland 4567 Australia
Information: The Noosa Heads Jazz Club Inc holds the annual Noosa Jazz Party and regular Classic Jazz events at Noosa Heads, Sunshine Coast Queensland. The Club is an Incorporated Association and is a volunteer run, not for profit group.
Country: Australia
Social Media: www.facebook.com/noosajazzclub/
Frequency: Annual
Other Venues: Noosa Tewantin Bowls Club Hilton Terrace

Perth International Arts Festival
Website: www.perthfestival.com.au
Email: festival@perthfestival.com.au
Phone: 864 882 000
Address: M418, 3 Crawley Avenue, Crawley Perth, WA, Australia 6009
Information: The Festival was born as a 'festival for the people' on 3 January 1953. Since then, Perth Festival has seeded and cultivated decades of cultural growth as the oldest arts festival in the Southern Hemisphere. It is Australia's premier curated multi-arts festival and one of the greatest in the world, known for commissioning major new works, celebrating the unique qualities of Perth and engaging diverse audiences. Held every summer.
Country: Australia
Contact: Artistic Director Iain Grandage
Contact: Executive Director Natha Bennett
Contact: head of Marketing Tony Millar
Contact: communications Manager Stephen Bevis
Contact: head of development and strategy Sara Tompkin
Contact: program Manager Jessica Darlow
Social Media: twitter.com/perthfest www.facebook.com/perthfest www.instagram.com/perthfest/
Start: 2022-02-11
End: 2022-03-06

Perth International Jazz Festival
Website: https://perthjazzfest.com/
Email: festival@perthfestival.com.au
Phone: 408 949 275
Address: Perth Cultural Centre, Francis Street and William St, Northbridge WA 6003, Australia
Information: Presenting an array of incredible jazz performances in numerous venues across the city, the three day festival will feature a blend of ticketed and free community events. Showcasing a host of celebrated local, national and international artists, this year's Jazz program offers something for everyone. Come and be seduced by the language of Jazz; sometimes intimate, often boisterous, layered with experience and life profoundly lived, it's found in the act of creating the form itself.
Country: Australia
Contact: Artistic Director Mace Francis
Contact: Chairperson Mar Knox
Contact: secretary Georgie Holst
Contact: Director and founder Graham Wood
Social Media: twitter.com/PerthJazzFest www.instagram.com/PerthJazzFestival www.facebook.com/PerthJazzFest

Port Fairy Folk Festival (PFFF)
Website: www.portfairyfolkfestival.com
Email: admin@portfairyfolkfestival.org
Phone: 355 682 227
Address: Port Fairy Folk Festival, PO Box 176, Port Fairy, VIC 3284 Australia
Information: The festival's story started in December 1977 when the festival came to town. It was literally on the back of a truck, as a freewheeling cultural freedom ride of sorts. In 2017 we celebrated the 41st event as the achievement of our community, volunteers, music industry, artists and staff along with our passionate audience, inspired by folk & roots music and powered by volunteers.
Country: Australia
Contact: founding Director Jami McKew
Contact: office Manager Natasha Mills
Email: admin@portfairyfolkfestival.org
Contact: program Director Justin Rudge
Email: program@portfairyfolkfestival.com
Contact: publicity Ali Web
Email: hello@houseofwebb.com.au
Social Media: twitter.com/PortFairyFF www.facebook.com/portfairyfolkfestival www.instagram.com/portfairyfolkfestival/
End: 2022-03-14
several venues around the Village including churches, halls, the Reardon Theatre and and free entertainment on Fiddlers' Green. There are three market areas; Sackville Street, Railway Place and Fisherman's Walk, as well as food and craft stalls in the Arena
Type: Concert

Port Fairy Spring Music Festival
Website: https://portfairyspringfest.com.au/
Email: contact@portfairyspringfest.com.au
Phone: 355 683 030
Address: PO Box 53, Port Fairy, Victoria, Australia 3284
Information: The Port Fairy Spring Music Festival was created in 1990 by the late British/ Australian composer, Michael Easton ARAM and the pianist Len Vorster and has been staged as an annual regional music festival since then. The current Festival Director is Iain Grandage, the distinguished Australian composer and performer. The festival presents classical and contemporary ensemble music in fresh and collaborative programming. It combines the talents of highly regarded established artists with the very best of Australia's new and emerging young performers and composers.
Country: Australia
Contact: Artistic Director Monica Curro
Contact: Artistic Director Stefan Cassomenos
Contact: secretary Alison Lansley
Contact: administrator Emma Moloney
Social Media: www.facebook.com/PortFairySpringMusic/ www.instagram.com/portfairyspringmusic/
Start: 2022-10-14
End: 2022-10-16
Type: Concert

QMF – Queensland Music Festival
Website: https://www.qmf.org.au/
Email: info@qmf.org.au
Phone: 730 106 600
Address: Level 1, 381 Brunswick St, Fortitude Valley, QLD 4006
Information: QMF has redefined the traditional festival model to engage deeply with communities over time, igniting Artistic potential and leaving a lasting legacy. In collaboration with councils and communities, QMF inspires participation in music-making and performances that reflect local culture and tell local stories.
Country: Australia
Contact: Manager Jess Cuddihy
Email: info@qmf.org.au
Contact: Marketing coordinator Alex Komarowski
Email: Marketing@qmf.org.au
Contact: Managing Producer Jane Jennison
Email: info@qmf.org.au
Contact: programming and technical Director Katrina Torenbeek
Email: info@qmf.org.au
Social Media: twitter.com/qldmusicfest www.facebook.com/qldmusicfest/ www.instagram.com/qldmusicfest/
Frequency: Annual
Other Venues: various locations across Queensland
Type: Concert

Sydney Festival
Website: www.sydneyfestival.org.au
Email: mail@sydneyfestival.org.au
Phone: 282 486 500
Address: Level 5 10 Hickson Road The Rocks, NSW 2000 Sydney, Australia
Information: Every January, Sydney Festival livens and transforms Sydney with a bold cultural celebration based on the highest quality of art and big ideas. The programme is kaleidoscopic in its diversity, from burlesque, cheeky cabaret and Canadian circus, to high energy jazz, indie rock and Russian theatre; from contemporary dance to family programmes to traditional indigenous arts practice.

Country: Australia
Contact: festival Director Wesley Enoch
Email: execoffice@sydneyfestival.org.au
Contact: Executive Producer Vivia Hickman
Email: vivia.hickman@sydneyfestival.org.au
Contact: Producer Kate Williams
Email: kate.williams@sydneyfestival.org.au
Program Administrator & Associate Producer
Rebecca Gribble
Email: rebecca.gribble@sydneyfestival.org.au
Contact: Marketing Manager Aimee Ocampo
Email: aimee.ocampo@sydneyfestival.org.au
Contact: Ticketing Manager Tara Harding
Email: tara.harding@sydneyfestival.org.au
Contact: Head of Production John Bayley
Email: john.bayley@sydneyfestival.org.au
Contact: Project Manager Alycia Bangma
Email: alycia.bangma [at] sydneyfestival.org.au
Social Media: twitter.com/sydney_festival www.
facebook.com/SydneyFestival www.instagram.com/
sydney_festival
Frequency: Annual
Other Venues: 22 Various locations
Type: Concert, Dance/Ballet, Theatre, Multi-media,
Performance art, Other

Sydney Gay and Lesbian Mardi Gras
Website: https://www.mardigras.org.au/
Email: reception@mardigrasarts.org.au
Phone: 293 830 900
Address: Suite 6, 94 Oxford Street, Darlinghurst NSW
2010
Information: Sydney Gay and Lesbian Mardi Gras is
one of Australia's most famous and well-loved events,
bringing thousands of visitors to Sydney to join in the
celebrations. It captures the imagination of Australia's
LGBTQI and mainstream communities, taking over the
city for weeks on end and culminating in the world-fa-
mous Parade a colourful and dazzling night of pride,
celebration and self-exPression.
Country: Australia
Contact: CEO Albert Kruger
Contact: Executive Producer Grant Lowe
Contact: office Manager Callu McLean
Contact: festival Producer Broc Taffe
Contact: Marketing Manager Anne-Marie Mina
Social Media: twitter.com/sydneymardigras www.
facebook.com/sydneymardigras www.instagram.com/
sydneymardigras/
Frequency: Annual
Start: 2022-02-18
End: 2022-03-06
Type: Concert, Dance/Ballet, Film, Performance art, Other

Tamworth Country Music Festival
Website: https://www.tcmf.com.au/
Email: trc@tamworth.nsw.gov.au
Phone: 267 675 300
Address: 2 The Ringers Road, Tamworth NSW 2340
Information: Tamworth Country Music Festival is the
largest music festival in the southern hemisphere and
one of the top 10 in the world. The variety of country
music is endless during the festival with over 700 per-
formers and 2800 shows across 120 different venues.
Country: Australia
Contact: festival Director Barry Harley
Email: trc@tamworth.nsw.gov.au
Contact: official guide enquiries Cheryl Byrnes
Email: trc@tamworth.nsw.gov.au
Contact: Marketing Karlee Cole
Email: trc@tamworth.nsw.gov.au
Social Media: https://twitter.com/tcmf_official www.
facebook.com/tamworthcountrymusicfestival www.
instagram.com/tcmf_official/
Frequency: Biennial
Start: 2022-01-14
End: 2022-01-23
Type: Concert

Ten Days on the Island
Website:
https://www.tendays.org.au/
Email:
hello@tendays.org.au
Phone: 364 060 200
Address: PO Box 157 Burnie TAS 7320, AUS
Information: Tasmania's statewide international arts
festival is unique in Australia. It presents a multi-art form
programme of free and ticketed events across Tasmania
every two years.
Country: Australia
Contact: Artistic Director Lindy Hume
Contact: CEO Jane Haley
Contact: Executive Producer Vernon Guest
Contact: head of Marketing and partnerships Georgia
Malone
Contact: Administration Manager Stephanie Finn
Contact: Head of Production Christian Storen
Contact: head of programming Laura Sheedy
Social Media: www.twitter.com/tendaystas www.face-
book.com/tendaystas www.instagram.com/tendaystas/
Frequency: Biennial
Start: 2023-03-03
End: 2023-03-19

Type: Multi-media

Thredbo Blues Festival
Website: thredboblues.com.au
Email: admin@thredbochamber.com.au
Phone: 264 576 882
Address: Thredbo Alpine Hotel, 8 Friday Dr, Thredbo
NSW 2625, Australia
Information: The Thredbo Blues Festival is a three day
boutique festival held in various venues around Thredbo
Village. From cosy restaurants, booming alfresco gigs
and indoor music hall settings, the layout and variety
makes this festival a standout.
It has carved a niche as one of the countries longest run-
ning festivals, adored by blues fans and musicians alike
for its friendly feel with small intimate venues and plenty
of opportunity to get up close personal with some of
Australia's best blues performers
Country: Australia
Social Media: www.facebook.com/ThredboBluesFestival
Frequency: Annual
End: 2022-01-16
Other Venues: spectacular outdoor venues
Type: Concert

Wangaratta Festival of Jazz & Blues
Website: https://wangarattajazz.com/
Email: businessManager@wangarattajazz.com
Phone: 404 248 765
Address: Wangaratta Festival of Jazz & Blues, PO Box 860,
Wangaratta VIC 3676 Australia
Information: The Wangaratta Jazz Festival is an annual
festival of jazz and blues held in the town of Wangaratta,
2.5 hours from Melbourne in the north-east of Victoria,
Australia. It has become the premier jazz event in Aus-
tralia and is renowned internationally. Since its inception
in 1990, the Wangaratta Jazz Festival has grown to
include 90 events and over 350 national and internation-
al artists performing each year.
Country: Australia
Contact: Artistic Director Zoe Hauptmann
Contact: Artistic team Zoe Hauptmann
Contact: Artistic team Eugene Ball
Contact: Artistic team Scott Solimo
Contact: Chair Dave Fuller
Social Media: www.facebook.com/WangarattaJazzFesti-
val/ www.instagram.com/wangarattajazzandblues/twit-
ter.com/WangarattaJazz
End: 2022-10-30
Other Venues: held at various venues in the town of
Wangaratta

Winter Concert Series, Music for Pleasure
Website: https://www.cottesloe.wa.gov.au/
events-bookings/whats-on/music-for-pleasure-nomi-
nation.aspx
Email: town@cottesloe.wa.gov.au
Phone: 928 55000
Address: PO Box 606, Cottesloe WA 6911 Australia
Information: The popular winter concert series Music
for Pleasure is held in the beautiful War Memorial Hall at
Cottesloe Civic Centre every Sunday afternoon through-
out July and August.
Country: Australia
Type: Concert

WOMADelaide
Website: www.womadelaide.com.au
Email: info@womadelaide.com.au
Phone: 882 711 488
Address: Arts Projects Australia, 12 King William Road,
Unley, SOUTH AUSTRALIA 5061
Information: Since its first presentation in 1992, WOM-
ADelaide has grown to be a four-day outdoor festival
of music, arts and dance held in Adelaide's inner city
Botanic Park. It features multi-staged music performanc-
es, street theatre, performance installations, workshops
and discussion sessions, a Taste The World food program,
children's activities, and 100 food, retail and charity stalls.
The programme of more than 60 traditional and contem-
porary groups from 20+ countries on 7 stages attracts
over 20, 000 people per day and is staged as a part of the
Adelaide Festival.
Country: Australia
Social Media: twitter.com/WOMADelaide www.
facebook.com/WOMADelaide www.instagram.com/
WOMADelaide/
Start: 2022-03-11
End: 2022-03-14
Type: Concert, Dance/Ballet, Theatre, Multi-media,
Performance art

Woodford Folk Festival
Website: https://woodfordfolkfestival.com/
Email: info@woodfordfolkfestival.com
Phone: 754 961 066
Address: 87 Woodrow Road, Woodford, Queensland
4514, Australia
Information: The Woodford Folk Festival, an event of
international standing, is held annually over six days and
six nights from Dec 27th through to January 1st. More
than 2000 performers and 438 events are programmed
featuring local, national and international guests. The
Woodford festival experience is deep, rich and colourful

Country: Australia
Social Media: twitter.com/Woodfordia www.facebook.
com/woodfordfolkfestival www.instagram.com/wood-
fordfolkfestival/
Frequency: Annual
End: 2022-01-01
Other Venues: housed in over 35 venues around
Woodford

AZERBAIJAN

Baku Jazz Festival
Website: https://www.bakujazzfestival.com/
Email: bakujazzfestival@gmail.com
Phone: 412 597 1375
Address: 100 Mardanov Qardashlari Street, 10 AZ 1022,
Baku, Azerbaijan
Information: Even though jazz music traces its origins
to the beginning of the twentieth century, it made its
way to Azerbaijan rather quickly, and already in the
1930s it was well-received by the elite circles in Baku
and appreciated as one of the most interesting music
genres. It is widely known that the period of jazz history
referred to as the Jazz Age featured New Orleanais jazz,
or jazz traditionally played in New Orleans between 1900
and 1917, as well as by musicians from New Orleans who
performed in Chicago and produced vinyl records from
1917 and throughout the '20s. At this time, Baku had
approximately ten concert venues, including the Nikitin
Brothers' Circus of Baku, Taghiyev's Theatre, the Palais
de Cristal variety theatre, the hall of the Grand Hotel and
others where touring musicians and theatre troupes
from Russia and Europe would give performances.
Country: Azerbaijan
Social Media: www.facebook.com/bakujazzfest https://
mobile.twitter.com/baku_jazz
Start: 2022-09-09
End: 2022-09-17
Type: Concert

Gabala International Music Festival
Website: https://www.gabalamusicfestival.com/
Email: mct@mct.gov.az
Phone: 124 934 398
Address: AZ
Information: A wonderful music festival in Azerbaijan
full of breath-taking concerts, orchestras and pianists.
Country: Azerbaijan
Frequency: Annual
Type: Concert

BERMUDA

Bermuda Festival of the Performing Arts
Website: www.bermudafestival.org
Email:
adminoffice@bermudafestival.org
Phone: 295 1291
Address: P.O. Box HM 297 Hamilton HMBX
Information: For two months at the beginning of each
year Bermuda becomes an international hub for cultural
exchange and Artistic growth. Performing artists from
a range of disciplines come from around the globe to
present a schedule of events designed to appeal to a
wide and diverse audience.
It owes its conception to world renowned violinist, the
late Lord Menuhin, who worked with the then Governor
of Bermuda the late Sir Edwin Leather, and the late John
Ellison who became its first Chairman, to launch the
Festival in January 1976.
Country: Bermuda
Contact: Executive Director Cindy Campbell
Contact: Project Manager Mariya Tsitron
Contact: Chairman of the Board David Skinner
Social Media: www.facebook.com/BermudaFestival
Frequency: Annual
Type: Concert, Theatre, Musical theatre, Dance/Ballet

CANADA

Algoma Fall Festival
Website: www.algomafallfestival.com
Email:
admin@algomafallfestival.com
Phone: 705 949 0822
Address: 680 Albert St. E., Sault Ste. Marie, ON P6A 2K6
Information: The Algoma Arts Festival Association is the
presenter of the Algoma Fall Festival, a multi-disciplinary
arts celebration held each year in Sault Ste. Marie, Ontario, Canada in October. The Festival maintains a range
of programming that includes music, theatre, dance and
the visual arts. The Association also delivers the Festival
of Learning; an extensive arts outreach and education
program. The Association was incorporated in 1972 and
celebrated its 40th anniversary in 2012. The Algoma Fall
Festival wishes to engage the community on a variety
of levels.
Country: Canada
Social Media: https://twitter.com/AlgomaFallFest www.
facebook.com/AlgomaFestival/
Frequency: Annual
Type: Theatre, Concert, Multi-media

Brott Music Festivals
Website: https://brottmusic.com/
Email: info@brottmusic.com
Phone: 905 525 7664
Address: 301 Bay St. South Hamilton, ON L8P 3J7 Canada
Information: The Brott Music Festival is renowned for its extremely high Artistic standard, world class soloists, its exuberant young orchestra and its eclectic mix of orchestral, chamber, jazz, pops and education concerts at various venues in the Greater Hamilton and Burlington area
Country: Canada
Social Media: twitter.com/BrottMusicFesti www.facebook.com/pages/Brott-Music-Festival
Other Venues: various throughout the city
Type: Concert

Canada Dance Festival
Website: https://www.candance.ca/
Email: office@candance.ca
Phone: 613 947 7000
Address: PO Box 1376, Station B, CA
Information: The Canada Dance Festival will take you to places you've never been before. Held annually each June in partnership with Canada's National Arts Centre in Ottawa, they showcase dance artists from across the country. CDF balances expanding Artistic boundaries with popular dance programming and experiences – for dance artists and dance enthusiasts alike.
Country: Canada
Contact: Artistic Producer Jeanne Holmes
Email: jholmes@nac-cna.ca
Social Media: twitter.com/canadadancefest www.facebook.com/Canadadancefest
Frequency: Annual
Other Venues: National Arts Centre, National Gallery, Arts Court
Type: Dance/Ballet

CanAsian Dance Festival
Website: https://www.canasiandance.com/
Email: info@canasiandance.com
Phone: 416 593 8455
Address: 509 Parliament Street, 2nd Floor Toronto, Ontario, M4X 1P3 Canada
Information: CanAsian Dance Festival includes performances of traditional and contemporary dance work and also contemplative photography workshops, calligraphy classes, noodle night, and a labyrinth walk to the sounds of Japanese shakuhachi flute. CanAsian Dance supports choreographers in the creation of dance through the commissioning, presentation and promotion of live performance inspired by Asian ideas, and the cultivation of intercultural and intergenerational knowledge exchange.
Country: Canada
Contact: Artistic Director Denise Fujiwara
Contact: General Manager Adina Herling
Email: adina@canasiandance.com
Social Media: twitter.com/canasiandance www.facebook.com/CanAsianDance
Other Venues: Harbourfront Centre Theatre
Type: Dance/Ballet

Carrefour International de Théâtre de Québec
Website: https://www.carrefourtheatre.qc.ca/
Email: adm@carrefourtheatre.qc.ca
Phone: 418 692 3131
Address: 369 Crown Street, 4th Floor Quebec (QC) G1K 6E9, CA
Information: The Carrefour international de théâtre in Quebec City produces an exhilarating festival each spring. Festival and Producer, the Carrefour international de théâtre is a place of convergence for artists, arts professionals and audiences.
Country: Canada
Contact: chief Executive officer Dominique Violette
Email: d.violette@carrefourtheatre.qc.ca
Contact: Artistic Director Marie Gignac
Email: m.gignac@carrefourtheatre.qc.ca
Social Media: twitter.com/festivaltheatre www.facebook.com/pages/Carrefour-international-de-th%C3%A9%C3%A2tre-de-Qu%C3%A9bec/111154888904694?fref=ts
Frequency: Annual
Other Venues: various venues in Qubec with up to (1800 capacity)
Type: Theatre

Comox Valley Youth Music Centre (CYMC) Summer School & Festival
Website: https://www.cymc.ca/
Email: info@cymc.ca
Phone: 250 338 7463
Address: 204 580 Duncan Ave., Courtenay BC., V9N 2M7
Information: Founded as a summer retreat for the Vancouver Junior Symphony, the Comox Valley Youth Music Centre (CYMC) is now in its 50th year. Our mandate, to provide musical improvement and advancement to music students, is achieved primarily with the operation of the CYMC International Summer Youth Music School and Festival, a school for aspiring instrumentalists, singers and actors.
Country: Canada
Contact: President Marcia Haley
Contact: Vice President Myrna Wallace
Contact: Secretary Shari Jakubiec
Social Media: www.facebook.com/CYMCcamps
Other Venues: Sid Williams Theatre; North Island College; Filberg Lodge; Park Estate.
Type: Concert

Dawson City Music Festival
Website: http:// www.dcmf.com/
Email: info@dcmf.com
Phone: 867 993 5584
Address: P.O. BOX 456, Dawson City, CA
Information: Famously named Canada's "tiny, perfect music festival" by Vancouver's Georgia Straight, the Dawson City Music Festival presents three days of wildly diverse music in six venues around the tiny town of Dawson City, Yukon, in Canada's far North. Small but mighty, the Festival has developed a reputation for unparalleled intimacy, uniqueness, production quality, and hospitality.
Country: Canada
Social Media: twitter.com/DawsonCityMusic www.facebook.com/dawsoncitymusicfestival/ https://www.instagram.com/dawsoncitymusicfest/
Frequency: Annual
Type: Concert

Domaine Forget International Music Festival
Website: https://www.domaineforget.com/
Email: info@domainforget.com
Phone: 418 452 8111
Address: 5, rang Saint-Antoine, CP 672 Saint-Irénée, Quebec G0T 1V0 Canada
Information: Domaine Forget is first and foremost the Academy of Music and Dance for young talent, recognized internationally for the high quality of its teaching. The unmissable summer musical festival in Quebec is an international festival with over 80 events (conferences, brunches, masterclasses, Festival concerts and students). From the large orchestra to the aperitif concert through jazz evenings, music comes to the air.
Country: Canada
Contact: General Manager Ginette Gauthier
Email: ggauthier@domaineforget.com
Contact: assistant Artistic Director Edith Allaire
Email: eallaire@domaineforget.com
Contact: Artistic Director Paul Fortin
Email: dir.artistique@domaineforget.com
Contact: Artistic coordinator Solange Callejon
Email: adminart@domaineforget.com
Social Media: twitter.com/DomaineForget www.facebook.com/pages/Le-Domaine-Forget/400033360549
Frequency: Annual
Type: Concert, Dance/Ballet

Elora Festival
Website: https://elorafestival.ca/
Email: info@elorasingers.com
Phone: 519 846 0331
Address: Elora Centre For The Arts 75A Melville Street Elora, ON • N0B 1S0
Information: The Elora Festival Singers (EFS), an all-professional Grammy, and Juno-nominated chamber choir, were founded in 1980 by Noel Edison as the principal choral ensemble of the Elora Festival. The Festival has been recognized as one of North America's signature music festivals for vocal/choral and chamber music, performed by Canadian and international artists.
Country: Canada
Contact: Artistic Director Mark Vuorinen
Contact: Executive Director Laura Adlers
Social Media: twitter.com/elorafestival www.facebook.com/elorafestival www.instagram.com/elorafestival/
Frequency: Annual
Other Venues: Local churches, the Gambrel Barn, outdoor Elora Quarry
Type: Concert

Festival Antigonish Summer Theatre
Website: https://www.festivalantigonish.ca/
Email: boxoffice@festivalantigonish.com
Phone: 902 867 3333
Address: PO Box 5000 Antigonish NS B2G 2W5, CA
Information: Festival Antigonish Summer Theatre is committed to developing an understanding and appreciation for theatre within the community through the production of high quality professional work
Country: Canada
Contact: Artistic Director Andrea Boyd
Email: aboyd@stfx.ca
Contact: Managing Director Reema Fuller
Email: rfuller@stfx.ca
Contact: Production Manager Ingrid Risk
Email: irisk@stfx.ca
Social Media: www.facebook.com/FestivalAntigonish
Frequency: Annual
Other Venues: Bauer Theatre (200 capacity), Immaculata Auditorium (125 capacity)
Type: Theatre

Festival d'été de Québec
Website: https://www.feq.ca/
Email: infofestival@feq.ca
Phone: 418 523 4540
Address: 683, rue Saint-Joseph Est, bureau 150 Quebec, QC, Canada G1K 3C1
Information: This is Québec city's great music festival and Canada's largest outdoor musical event. 1000 artists, 300 shows, 10 venues come together to presetnt world-renowned stars as well as up-and-coming bands in all styles: rock, hip-hop, electro, pop, reggae, world beat, and more. Québec city's historical centre is taken over by tens of thousands of festival-goers
Country: Canada
Contact: Chairman Alain-Jacques Simard
Social Media: twitter.com/FestivalEteQc www.facebook.com/FestivaldetedeQuebec www.instagram.com/festivaleteqc
Start: 2022-07-07
End: 2022-07-17
Type: Concert

Festival International de Jazz de Montréal
Website: https://www.montrealjazzfest.com/
Email: commentaires_jazz@equipespectra.ca
Phone: 514 871 1881
Address: 400 Blvd de Maisonneuve O 9 étages Montreal, QC, Canada H3A 1L4
Information: The Festival International de Jazz de Montréal is an annual jazz festival held in Montreal, Quebec, Canada. The Montreal Jazz Fest holds the 2004 Guinness World Record as the world's largest jazz festival
Country: Canada
Contact: Chairman and CEO Jacques K. Primeau Primeau
Contact: Chairman of the board and co-founder Alain simard Simard
Social Media: twitter.com/FestivalJazzMtl www.facebook.com/montrealjazzfest www.instagram.com/festivaljazzmtl
Type: Concert

Festival International de Lanaudi
Website: https://www.lanaudiere.org/fr/
Email: festival@lanaudiere.org
Phone: 450 759 7636
Address: 1500 boul. Base-de-Roc Joliette, QC, Canada J6E 0L2
Information: The Festival de Lanaudière, founded in 1978, is the most important classical music festival in Canada. It is also a member of the Grouping of major international events. Year after year, it welcomes more than 50, 000 participants for all of its activities. Its programming is accessible and made up of great artists of international reputation.
Country: Canada
Contact: General Manager François Bédard
Email: fbedard@lanaudiere.org
Contact: Administration Director Sylvie Gagné
Email: sgagne@lanaudiere.org
Social Media: www.instagram.com/festivaldelanaudiere www.facebook.com/festivaldelanaudiere
Other Venues: Joliettes Amphithtre Fernand-Lindsay (2000 capacity) Salle Rolland-Brunelle(8000 capacity) Rolland-Brunelle hall

Festival International de Musique Baroque de Lameque
Website: https://www.festivalbaroque.com/
Email: baroque@lameque.ca
Phone: 506 344 3261
Address: 2-28 Rue de l'Hôpital, NB E8T 1C3 CA
Information: The Lamèque International Baroque Music Festival is an annual festival dedicated to music from the period of 1600 to 1760, performed on period instruments. Founded in 1975 by harpsichordist Mathieu Duguay, the Festival has earned an enviable reputation on the New Brunswick and Canadian musical scenes.
Country: Canada
Contact: Chairman Jean-René Noël
Contact: vice Chairman Marcel Lanteigne
Contact: Artistic Director Vincent Lauzer
Contact: Executive Director Nathalie Stewart
Social Media: www.twitter.com/LamequeBaroque www.facebook.com/pages/Festival-International-de-Musique-Baroque-de-Lamèque https://www.instagram.com/lamequebaroque/
Frequency: Annual
End: 2022-07-23
Other Venues: Churches on Lamque Island, CA
Type: Concert

Festival International du Film sur l'Art
Website: https://lefifa.com/
Email: festival@artfifa.com
Phone: 438 509 7556
Address: 5333 Casgrain, bureau 403 Montreal, QC, Canada H2T1X3
Information: The International Festival of Films on Art (FIFA) is dedicated to the promotion and dissemination of films, videos and interactive and/or immersive works on art and media arts. Each year, its selection reflects the quality and diversity of world film production. FIFA aims to increase the public's knowledge and appreciation of art. It also seeks to highlight the work of artists and the contributions of professionals working in the fields of film, video and television.

Country: Canada
Contact: founder and Director René Rozon
Contact: Director of production André Vaillancourt
Email: admin@artfifa.com
Social Media: twitter.com/ARTFIFA www.facebook.com/festivalinternationaldufilmsurlart www.instagram.com/festival_filmsurlart
Other Venues: Canadian Centre for Architecture, Cinematheque Quebecoise, Montreal Contemporary Art Museum, Montreal Museum of Fine Arts, Place des Arts, Concordia University
Type: Film

Festival Montréal Baroque
Website: www.montrealbaroque.com
Email: info@montrealbaroque.com
Phone: 514 845 7171
Address: 1097, rue Saint-Alexandre, bureau 408, Montreal (Quebec) H2Z 1P8 Canada
Information: he Montreal Baroque Festival is a big annual celebration of early music. The festival welcomes both famous musicians and young artists, all of whom charm listeners with performances of Baroque music from all around the world
Country: Canada
Contact: production Manager Maurice-Gaston Du Berger
Email: mtlbaroqueproduction@gmail.com
Contact: Artistic Director Susie napper Napper
Contact: Artistic Director Matthias maute Maute
Contact: General Manager Ève Gendreau
Email: info@montrealbaroque.com
Contact: Ticket coordinator Kyran Assing
Email: billetterie@montrealbaroque.com
Social Media: https://twitter.com/MtlBaroque www.facebook.com/montrealbaroque www.instagram.com/montrealbaroque
Type: Dance/Ballet, Concert, Multi-media, Opera

Festival of the Sound
Website: https://festivalofthesound.ca/
Email: info@festivalofthesound.ca
Phone: 866 364 0061
Address: Festival of the Sound P.O. Box 750 Parry Sound, ON P2A 2Z1, CA
Information: It was renamed, "The Festival Station Gallery", to maintain its heritage and honour. The Festival of the Sound intends to continue to make this building a community space. The Festival of the Sound hopes to create a space where visual art, music, culture, and community meet
Country: Canada
Contact: Executive Director Alison Scarrow
Contact: Artistic Director James Campbell
Social Media: twitter.com/FestoftheSound www.facebook.com/FestivaloftheSoundinstagram.com/festivalofthesound/
Frequency: Annual
Other Venues: Charles W. Stockey Centre for the Performing Arts (470 capacity), St James United Church (200 capacity), Island Queen V tour boat (400 capacity), performance hall on the Parry Sound waterfront
Type: Concert

Festival TransAmeriques
Website: https://fta.ca/en/
Email: info@fta.qc.ca
Phone: 514 842 0704
Address: 460 Rue Sainte-Catherine Ouest, CP 1206, succursale Desjardins, CA
Information: This is an international event celebrating new works in contemporary dance and theatre. The Festival TransAmériques combines disciplines and Artistic trends under cohesive programming. The Festival presents exciting forms of the art of our era, featuring works by choreographers, writers and Directors. The only criterion is to present strong work, regardless of theme or place of origin
Country: Canada
Contact: co-Executive Director and Artistic Director Martin Faucher
Email: artistique@fta.ca
Contact: co-Executive Director and administrative Director David Lavoie
Email: david.lavoie@fta.ca
Contact: Administration coordinator Christine Meslin
Email: christine.meslin@fta.ca
Social Media: twitter.com/FTAMontreal www.facebook.com/Festival.TransAmeriques
Frequency: Annual
Type: Dance/Ballet, Theatre

Guelph Contemporary Dance Festival
Website: http:// www.guelphdance.ca/
Email: info@guelphdance.ca
Phone: 519 780 2220
Address: 42 Carden St, Suite 2L, CA
Information: Guelph Dance, formerly the Guelph Contemporary Dance Festival, aims to engage and enthral as they strive to be a nationally recognized leader in contemporary dance, by offering a platform for professional, new-generation, and youth dance artists to share their vision, push creative boundaries, and engage community audiences
Country: Canada

Contact: otreach and development Manager Leslie Fisher
Email: leslie@guelphdance.ca
Contact: Artistic Director Catrina von Radecki
Email: catrina@guelphdance.ca
Contact: General Manager Adriana Rosselli Londoño
Email: info@guelphdance.ca
Social Media: twitter.com/guelphdance www.facebook.com/guelphdance www.instagram.com/guelphdance
Frequency: Annual
End: 2022-06-05
Type: Dance/Ballet

Guelph Musicfest
Website: http:// www.guelphmusicfest.ca/
Email: musicfest@artset.net
Phone: 519 993 7591
Address: Recital Hall, Guelph Youth Music Centre, 75 Cardigan St. Guelph, ON, Canada N1H 3Z7
Information: Guelph Musicfest celebrates classical music and invites artists and audience members to come together to appreciate the magic of live performances.
Country: Canada
Contact: Artistic Director Ken Gee
Social Media: twitter.com/guelphmusicfest www.facebook.com/guelphmusicfest
Frequency: Annual
Type: Concert

Hornby Festival
Website: https://www.facebook.com/HornbyFestival
Email: GeneralManager@hornbyfestival.bc.ca
Phone: 250 335 2734
Address: 2125 Sollans Road Hornby Island, BC V0R 1Z0, Canada
Information: Since its inception in 1982, the Hornby Festival Society has earned a national reputation for Artistic excellence and adventurous programming. In its early years, the Festival focused primarily on the classical genre, and has evolved to include jazz, world and traditional music, modern dance, and spoken word
Country: Canada
Contact: administrative Director Charmaine Logan
Email: hornbyfestival@uniserve.com
Contact: Artistic Director Dierdre Atkinson
Email: festivaldir@uniserve.com
Social Media: www.facebook.com/HornbyFestival www.instagram.com/hornbyfestival
Other Venues: Venues include: Hornby Island Community Hall (200 capacity) and 3 outdoor venues
Type: Concert, Dance/Ballet, Performance art

Huntsville Festival of the Arts
Website: www.huntsvillefestival.on.ca
Email: info@huntsvillefestival.on.ca
Phone: 705 788 2787
Address: PO Box 5465, Hunstsville, Ontario, P1H 2K8, CA
Information: The Festival employs local musicians and reinvests money back into the community. A number of educational initiatives link the festival with the community's youth and specifically its aspiring young musicians
Country: Canada
Contact: founder and Artistic Director Attila Glatz
Contact: President Carol Gibson
Social Media: www.twitter.com/HuntsFestArts www.facebook.com/HuntsvilleFestivaloftheArts https://www.instagram.com/huntsvillefestival/
Frequency: Annual
End: 2022-03-06
Other Venues: Algonquin Theatre, Hunstville, CA

Luminato – Toronto Festival of Arts and Creativity
Website: https://luminatofestival.com/
Email: info@luminato.ca
Phone: 416 368 3100
Address: 180 Shaw Street, Suite 301, Toronto, M6J 2W5, CA
Information: Luminato Festival Toronto is an international arts festival dedicated to performance, media and visual arts, and programming that cuts across traditional artform boundaries.
Country: Canada
Contact: Artistic Director Naomi Campbell
Contact: chief Executive officer Celia Smith
Social Media: twitter.com/Luminato www.facebook.com/luminatofestival
Frequency: Annual
Type: Concert, Dance/Ballet, Performance art, Theatre, Multi-media

Manifesto Festival of Community and Culture
Website: https://www.mnfsto.com/
Email: info@mnfsto.com
Phone: 647 436 8404
Address: 130 Queens Quay East Toronto, ON, Canada M5A 0P6
Information: The festival is organised by the Manifesto Community Projects organisation, and helps the company to achieve its aim to provide a platform and the resources needed for talented individuals to advance. Manifesto predominantly works within Artistic practices that have evolved from hip hop and R&B culture. The topics, themes and messages communicated in these art

forms strongly resonate with historically underserved, marginalized and racialized communities.
Country: Canada

Montreal Chamber Music Festival
Website: www.festivalmontreal.org/
Email: info@festivalmontreal.org
Phone: 514 489 7444
Address: 34-5235, Côte-Saint-Luc Road, Montréal, Qc, H3W 2H8, CA
Information: Founded in 1995 by cellist Denis Brott, the Festival promotes chamber music in all its forms and is sometimes combined with other Artistic disciplines. It aims to involve artists of international reputation and upcoming new talent.
Country: Canada
Contact: project Manager Julie Brott
Contact: Artistic Director Denis Brott
Social Media: www.twitter.com/FMCMMCMF www.facebook.com/festivalmtl https://www.instagram.com/fmcmontreal/
Frequency: Annual
Other Venues: Montreal Arts Venues
Type: Concert

Montréal en Lumière
Website: https://www.montrealenlumiere.com/
Email: montrealhighlights@equipespectra.ca
Phone: 514 288 9955
Address: 400 De Maisonneuve Blvd. West, 9th floor, CA
Information: One of the largest winter festivals in the world, this annual celebration draws 900, 000 fans to experience the joy of Montréal wintertime through a unique programme that combines performing arts, gastronomy, free outdoor family activities, and a full night of exquisitely original discoveries – the Nuit blanche à Montréal!
Country: Canada
Contact: President Alain Simard
Contact: vice-President program Laurent Saulnier
Contact: vice-President Marketing Jacques-André Dupont
Social Media: twitter.com/MTLenLumiere www.facebook.com/Montrealenlumiere www.instagram.com/MTLenLumiere
Frequency: Annual
Start: 2022-02-07
End: 2022-02-27
Type: Performance art

Montreal New Music Festival – Montreal Nouvelles Musiques (MNM)
Website: http://smcq.qc.ca/mnm/en/2021
Email: smcq@smcq.ca
Phone: 514 843 9305
Address: 300, boulevard de Maisonneuve Est, Montréal, QC H2X 3X4, Canada
Information: The Montreal / New Musics festival (MNM) is reinventing itself to offer an unprecedented sound odyssey with the theme "Beyond Borders." MNM 2021 will stand out for the global aspect that webcast now offers, and through its programming, tinged with openness and discovery.
Country: Canada
Contact: Artistic Director Walter Boudreau
Contact: Director General Aïda Aoun
Contact: Director of communications Claire Cavanagh
Contact: production and technical Manager Benoît Bilodeau
Social Media: twitter.com/smcq_qc_ca www.facebook.com/smcq.qc.ca
Other Venues: held at different Montral venues including Chapelle historique du Bon-Pasteur
Type: Concert

Orford Festival
Website: https://www.orford.mu/
Email: info@orford.mu
Phone: 819 843 3981
Address: 3165 Chemin du Parc, ORFORD (QUÉBEC) J1X 7A2, CA
Information: The Orford Music Festival is a prestigious international event that attracts nearly 25, 000 festival-goers annually during the summer season. Its rich Artistic programming consists mainly of twenty professional concerts, forty free concerts offered by students of the Orford Music Academy and visual arts exhibitions.
Country: Canada
Contact: Executive Director Wonny Song
Email: wsong@orford.mu
Contact: Director of Concerts Sophie Cusson
Email: scusson@orford.mu
Social Media: www.twitter.com/OrfordMusique www.facebook.com/orfordmusique
Frequency: Annual
Other Venues: Orford Musique
Type: Concert

Ottawa Chamber Music Festival
Website: https://www.chamberfest.com/
Email: info@chamberfest.com
Phone: 613 234 8008
Address: 4 Florence Street, Suite 201, Ottawa, K2P 0W7
Information: Since 1994, Ottawa Chamberfest has

presented from among the most distinguished names in solo and ensemble performance. Today, Chamberfest is a culturally significant institution and the largest international festival of its kind.
Country: Canada
Contact: Artistic Director Carissa Klopoushak
Email: www.carissaklopoushak.com
Contact: Marketing and communications coordinator Chloe Squance
Email: csquance@chamberfest.com
Social Media: twitter.com/Chamberfest www.facebook.com/ottawachamberfest www.instagram.com/Chamberfest/
Frequency: Annual
Other Venues: Churches, museums, theatres and galleries across Ottawa
Type: Concert

Ottawa International Children's Festival
Website: www.ottawachildrensfestival.ca
Email: contact@ottawachildrensfestival.ca
Phone: 613 241 0999
Address: 294 Albert Street Ottawa, ON, Canada K1A 0M8 Canada
Information: Since 1985, the Ottawa Children's Festival (OCF) has hosted an annual celebration of the best in live performing arts for children. Creating programs for children, the Festival focuses on enriching school curriculum and promoting the arts as an integral part of children's education. From dance and music to theater and the visual arts, the arts give children a unique means of exPression, capturing their passions and emotions, and allowing them to explore new ideas, subject matter, and cultures.
Country: Canada
Contact: President Nick Masciantonio Masciantonio
Social Media: https://twitter.com/ottchildfest www.facebook.com/OttawaChildrensFestival www.instagram.com/ottawachildrensfest
Other Venues: Lebreton Flats and War Museum
Type: Concert, Dance/Ballet, Film, Multi-media, Theatre, Other

Pacific Rim Summer Festival
Website: https://pacificrimarts.ca/
Email: pacificrimarts@gmail.com
Phone: 250 726 2443
Address: PO Box 468, Ucluelet, BC V0R 3A0, CA
Information: Pacific Rim Summer Festival offers world class concerts of distinguished musicians held in the spectacular region of the west coast of Vancouver Island. At the time of going to the Press, the future of this festival was still in doubt
Country: Canada
Type: Concert

PuSh International Performing Arts Festival
Website: https://pushfestival.ca/
Email: info@pushfestival.ca
Phone: 604 605 8284
Address: 110–750 Hamilton Street, Vancouver, British Columbia V6B 2R5 Canada
Information: PuSh International Performing Arts Festival showcases acclaimed international, Canadian and local artists and mixes them together with an alchemy that inspires audiences, rejuvenates artists, stimulates the industry and forges productive relationships around the globe
Country: Canada
Contact: interim Artistic Director Joyce Rosario
Email: joyce@pushfestival.ca
Contact: interim Executive Director Minna Schendlinger
Email: minna@pushfestival.ca
Contact: communication Director Jackie Hoffart
Email: jackie@pushfestival.ca
Contact: operation coordinator Leila Toledo
Email: leila@pushfestival.ca
Contact: operations Manager Lindsay McMahon
Email: lindsay@pushfestival.ca
Social Media: twitter.com/PuShFestival www.facebook.com/pushfestival www.instagram.com/pushfestival
End: 2022-02-06
Other Venues: various venues across the Lower Mainland.
Type: Performance art

Schulich School of Music
Website: https://www.mcgill.ca/music/events
Email: reception.music@mcgill.ca |
Phone: 514 398 4535
Address: SMCQ Centre Pierre-P, boulevard de Maisonneuve Est, Montreal, CA
Information: The Schulich School of Music hosts concerts and events throughout the year
Country: Canada
Contact: co-Artistic Director Walter Boudreau
Contact: co-Artistic Director Denys Bouliane
Contact: CEO Aida Aoun
Social Media: www.facebook.com/smcq.qc.ca
Type: Concert

Scotia Festival of Music
Website: https://www.scotiafestival.com/
Email: admin@scotiafestival.ns.ca
Phone: 902 429 9467
Address: 6181 Lady Hammond Road, Halifax, NS B3K 2R9, CA
Information: An annual two-week chamber music festival held in Halifax, NS, Canada, during the first two weeks of June. Boasting over fifty public events and featuring international talent of the highest calibre, the festival offers Highlight Concerts, Recitals, open rehearsals, masterclasses, coaching sessions, lectures, and more.
Country: Canada
Contact: General Manager Cindy Haines
Email: admin@scotiafestival.ns.ca
Contact: Managing and Artistic Director Simon Docking
Email: admin@scotiafestival.ns.ca
Contact: Festival Manager Andrew Coll
Social Media: twitter.com/scotiafestival www.facebook.com/scotiafestivalofmusic www.instagram.com/scotiafestival/
Frequency: Annual
Other Venues: The Music Room, Halifax, Nova Scotia
Type: Concert

Shakespeare on the Saskatchewan Festival
Website: https://www.shakespearesask.com/
Email: om@shakespearesask.com
Phone: 306 653 2300
Address: 948 Spadina Cr. East Saskatoon, SK, Canada S7K 3R8 Canada
Information: A not-for-profit, registered charity incorporated in 1985, Shakespeare on the Saskatchewan Festival Inc. continues to provide exciting contemporary and traditional productions of plays by Shakespeare and his contemporaries. Each summer, two full-length plays are performed in repertory by professional artists, in large tents on the banks of the beautiful South Saskatchewan River in the heart of Saskatoon.
Country: Canada
Contact: Artistic Producer Will Brooks
Email: ap@shakespearesask.com
Contact: Operations Manager Melanie Rogowski
Email: om@shakespearesask.com
Contact: Director of Marketing and Development Alan Long
Email: pr@shakespearesask.com
Festival & Administrative Coordinator Brandi Roy
Email: festival@shakespearesask.com
Publicity & Admin Intern Katie Blackburn-Dust
Email: publicity@shakespearesask.com
Social Media: twitter.com/shakespearesask www.facebook.com/ShakespeareSask www.instagram.com/shakespearesask
Frequency: Annual
The Shakespeare on the Saskatchewan Festival site is nestled along the river's edge next to the Mendel Art Gallery at the foot of the University Bridge in the heart of Saskatoon
Type: Theatre

St-Ambroise Montréal Fringe Festival
Website: https://montrealfringe.ca/
Email: fringe@montrealfringe.ca
Phone: 514 849 3378
Address: 3997 St-Laurent Montreal, QC, Canada H2W 1Y4
Information: The St-Ambroise Montreal FRINGE Festival is an international multidisciplinary arts festival celebrating creativity without limits that includes theatre, music, comedy, dance, spoken word and more from over 500 performers.
Country: Canada
Contact: Executive and Artistic Director Amy Blackmore
Contact: General Manager Geoffrey Agombar
Contact: assistant Director Kenny Streule
Contact: operation Manager Deirdre Grégoire
Social Media: twitter.com/fringemtl www.facebook.com/FRINGEmtl
Type: Concert, Dance/Ballet, Theatre, Performance art, Multi-media

Stephenville Theatre Festival
Website: https://stephenvilletheatrefestival.com/
Email: stfManager@outlook.com
Phone: 709 643 4982
Address: 35 Carolina Avenue, Stephenville, NL, A2N 3P8 Canada
Information: Since its very beginning, Stephenville Theatre Festival has enriched the economic and cultural sectors of the Town of Stephenville and has become a major draw for the tourism of the Bay St. George area. The Festival has provided training and hands on experience for numerous artists, many of whom are now counted among Canada's top professionals
Country: Canada
Contact: Artistic Director Heather Braaten
Contact: Chair Don Dunphy
Social Media: www.facebook.com/StephenvilleTheatreFestival
Other Venues: Stephenville Arts and Culture Centre (houses a 435 seat proscenium theatre, a 142 seat black box theatre, an art exhibition area, conference room and lounge)
Type: Theatre

Stratford Shakespeare Festival of Canada
Website: www.stratfordfestival.ca
Email: orders@stratfordfestival.ca
Phone: 519 273 1600
Address: PO Box 520 Stratford, ON N5A 6V2, CA
Information: The Festival's primary mandate is to present productions of William Shakespeare's plays, but it also produces a wide variety of theatre from Greek tragedy to contemporary works. Shakespeare's work typically represents about a third of the Festival's offerings
Country: Canada
Contact: Artistic Director Antoni Cimolino
Social Media: twitter.com/stratfest www.facebook.com/StratfordFestival
Frequency: Annual
Other Venues: the Festival Theatre, the Avon Theatre, the Tom Patterson Theatre, and the Studio Theatre
Type: Theatre

TD Ottawa Jazz Festival
Website: https://ottawajazzfestival.com/
Email: contact@ottawajazzfestival.com
Phone: 613 241 2633
Address: 294 Albert Street, Suite 602 Ottawa, ON K1P 6E6
Information: Nestled in the heart of beautiful downtown Ottawa, the TD Ottawa Jazz Festival attracts hundreds and thousands of people who gather to hear some of the jazz world's most renowned and celebrated musicians. There is something for everyone throughout the 11-day event with performances day and night in the most idyllic indoor and outdoor settings.
Starts: 6:00 pm | June 22
Ends: 10:30 pm | July 2
Featured artists: Feist, Serena Ryder, Joss Stone, Caravan Palace, Mavis Staples, Jacob Collier, Robert Glasper Experiment, St Paul & The Broken Bones, Pierre Kwenders, Bill Frisell & Thomas Morgan, Charles Bradley & His Extraordinaires, MaCEO Parker & The Ray Charles Orchestra, Hannah Georgas, Kandace Springs, The Bad Plus, Charlie Haden's Liberation Music Orchestra featuring Carla Bley
Country: Canada
Contact: Executive Producer Catherine O'Grady
Email: Director@ottawajazzfestival.com
Contact: programming Manager Petr Cancura
Email: petr@ottawajazzfestival.com
Contact: Artistic Associate and programming coordinator Jacqie MacKay
Email: jacqie@ottawajazzfestival.com
Contact: operations Manager Adi Cajo
Email: adi@ottawajazzfestival.com
Social Media: www.facebook.com/Ottawajazz
Start: 2022-01-28
End: 2022-01-29
Type: Concert

The Charlottetown Festival, Prince Edward Island
Website: https://confederationcentre.com/
Email: info@confederationcentre.com
Phone: 902 628 1864
Address: 145 Richmond Street, CA
Information: From June to September, The Charlottetown Festival unites Canada's finest performers, designers, playwrights, composers, and Directors in a professional showcase of musical theatre and comedy.
Country: Canada
Contact: Artistic Director Adam Brazier
Contact: Chair Robert Sear
Social Media: twitter.com/ConfedCentre www.facebook.com/charlottetownfestival
Type: Musical theatre, Theatre, Performance art

Toronto Jazz Festival
Website: http://torontojazz.com/photos
Email: tdjs@tojazz.com
Phone: 416 928 203
Address: Toronto Downtown Jazz, 40 Holly Street, Suite #403, CA
Information: The Toronto Jazz Festival is a jazz event in Toronto and takes place for 10 days in late June. Unlike the Toronto Beaches Jazz Festival, most of the events are indoors and located throughout the downtown core. The TD Toronto Jazz Festival has become known as one of North America's premier jazz festivals produced annually by Toronto Downtown Jazz
Country: Canada
Contact: Executive Producer and CEO Patrick Taylor
Contact: Director of operations Patti Marshall
Social Media: twitter.com/TorontoJazzFest www.facebook.com/torontojazzfest
Type: Concert

Toronto Summer Music Festival
Website: www.torontosummermusic.com
Email: info@torontosummermusic.com
Phone: 647 430 5699
Address: PO Box 40008 Liberty Village Post Office Toronto, ON M5V 0K7 Canada
Information: An international classical music festival and

academy that is entering its eleventh season, Toronto Summer Music Festival (TSMF) brings world-renowned performing artists to Toronto for an unparalleled combination of concerts, guest lectures and Masterclasses
Country: Canada
Contact: Artistic Director Jonathan Crow
Email: jcrow@torontosummermusic.com
Contact: Executive Director Vanessa Goymour
Email: vgoymour@torontosummermusic.com
Contact: development Manager Elisha Denburg
Email: edenburg@torontosummermusic.com
Contact: Artistic operations Manager Jennifer Mak
Email: jennifer@torontosummermusic.com
Contact: publicist Karen Lorenowicz
Email: karen.lorenowicz@gmail.com
Social Media: twitter.com/tsmfestival www.facebook.com/TorontoSummerMusic
Other Venues: Koerner Hall (1, 135 capacity), Walter Hall (490 capacity), Heliconian Hall (124 capacity)
Type: Concert

Vancouver Early Music Festival
Website: https://www.earlymusic.bc.ca/
Email: staff@earlymusic.bc.ca
Phone: 604 732 1610
Address: 1254 W 7th Avenue, VancouverCA
Information: Early Music Vancouver (EMV) is an organization that reaches back into history and casts beautifully preserved antiquities in fresh light. By preserving and presenting this music with the instruments and traditions intended, Early Music Vancouver fosters an understanding and appreciation of these unique moments in time. Early Music Vancouver brings light and life to Artistic treasures that could otherwise be all too easily lost. It has a Main Season that runs through the Fall, Winter and Spring, and an annual, three-week-long summer festival and educational programme
Country: Canada
Contact: business Manager Nathan Lorch
Email: nathan@earlymusic.bc.ca
Contact: Executive and Artistic Director Suzie LeBlanc
Email: suzie@earlymusic.bc.ca
Social Media: twitter.com/EarlyMusicVan www.facebook.com/earlymusicvancouver www.instagram.com/earlymusicvancouver/
Frequency: Annual
Type: Concert

Vancouver Folk Music Festival
Website: https://thefestival.bc.ca/
Email: info@thefestival.bc.ca
Phone: 604 602 9798
Address: 1945 McLean Drive Vancouver, British Columbia, V5N 3J7, CA
Information: Vancouver Folk Music Festival has attracted artists from all over the world and from all walks of life, including Adam Cohen, Ani Difranco, Utah Phillips, Tuvan Throat singers, Sarah Harmer, Veda Hille, Feist, K'naan, and Ferron, among many others. In addition to folk music, the festival features bluegrass, world, blues, celtic, americana, soul, rock and pop music. The Vancouver Folk Music Festival, founded in 1978, is an outdoor multistage music festival, located at Jericho Beach Park on the west side of Vancouver, British Columbia. It takes place annually, on the third weekend of July
Country: Canada
Contact: Executive Director Laurie-Ann Goodwin
Email: laurie-ann@thefestival.bc.ca
Contact: Artistic Director Debbi Salmonsen
Email: debbi@thefestival.bc.ca
Contact: Marketing and publicity Manager Jennifer Racco
Email: jennifer@thefestival.bc.ca
Contact: production Manager Ken Daskewech
Email: ken@thefestival.bc.ca
Social Media: twitter.com/VanFolkFest www.facebook.com/VanFolkFest www.instagram.com/vanfolkfest/
Type: Concert

Vancouver International Children's Festival
Website: https://www.childrensfestival.ca/
Email: info@childrensfestival.ca
Phone: 604 708 5655
Address: 1360 E 3rd Ave. Vancouver, BC V5N 5R8 Canada
Information: The Vancouver International Children's Festival Society presents contemporary, inter-disciplinary arts including performance and interactive arts activities that speak to the various ages of our audience. Our inclusive programming is culturally diverse and representative of regional, national and international artists. A world-renowned festival of performing arts for young audiences, the Vancouver International Children's Festival has been educating, entertaining and inspiring young audiences since 1978
Country: Canada
Contact: Artistic and Executive Director Katharine Carol
Email: info@childrensfestival.ca
Contact: operations Manager Leanne Zacharias Zacharias
Email: operations@childrensfestival.ca
Social Media: twitter.com/VICF www.facebook.com/KidsFest www.instagram.com/vankidsfest
End: 2022-06-05
Other Venues: Granville Island

Type: Multi-media

Vancouver International Dance Festival
Website: https://www.vidf.ca/
Email: contact@vidf.ca
Phone: 604 662 7441
Address: 236 – 111 West Hastings St. Vancouver, BC,
Information: The Vancouver International Dance Festival is produced by Kokoro Dance in partnership with other Vancouver dance presenters. The Vancouver International Dance Festival has featured artists from China, Spain, the United States of America, France, Germany, Japan, Poland, Lithuania, Mexico, and Canada, performing techniques and styles as diverse as butoh, hip hop, flamenco, ballet, as well as cutting edge contemporary dance
Country: Canada
Contact: co-Producer Jay Hirabayashi
Contact: co-Producer Barbara Bourget
Contact: production Manager Terry Podealuk
Social Media: twitter.com/vidf www.facebook.com/vidf.ca www.instagram.com/vidfestival
Type: Dance/Ballet

Vancouver International Jazz Festival
Website: https://www.coastaljazz.ca/
Email: cjbs@coastaljazz.ca
Phone: 604 872 5200
Address: Coastal Jazz and Blues Society, , 295 West 7th Ave. – 2nd floor, CA
Information: The story of Coastal Jazz and Blues Society is the story of determination, passion, idealism, community, and of course, music. Founded in 1985 and incorporated in 1986, as a community based, not-for-profit, charitable arts organization located in Vancouver, British Columbia, the society from the very beginning, has worked diligently to establish Vancouver as a centre for the creation and exchange of sounds and ideas between the local, national and international music communities
Country: Canada
Contact: Managing Director and Artistic programming Rainbow Robert
Contact: Managing Director, Marketing and development Emma Lancaster
Contact: Managing Director, finance and Administration Isaac Wolfe
Contact: operation Director Eduardo Ottoni
Social Media: twitter.com/coastaljazz www.facebook.com/coastaljazz
Frequency: Annual
Type: Concert

Victoria Fringe Theatre Festival / UNO Festival of Solo Performance
Website: https://intrepidtheatre.com/festivals/fringe-festival/
Email: info@intrepidtheatre.com
Phone: 250 383 2663
Address: #2 – 1609 Blanshard Street, CA
Information: A Vancouver Island festival tradition for nearly thirty years, Victoria Fringe Theatre Festival takes over downtown Victoria BC each summer for a 12-day celebration of live performance from around the world, featuring an eclectic mixture of spoken word, drama, musicals, dance, comedy, magic, theatre for young audiences and more
Country: Canada
Contact: Producer Sammie Gough
Email: sammie@intrepidtheatre.com
Contact: Executive Director Heather Lindsay
Email: heather@intrepidtheatre.com
Contact: Marketing and development Manager Sean Guist
Email: sean@intrepidtheatre.com
Contact: production Manager Owen Schellenberger
Email: owen@intrepidtheatre.com
Social Media: twitter.com/IntrepidTheatre www.facebook.com/IntrepidTheatre
Type: Theatre, Dance/Ballet, Performance art

Victoria Jazz Society Jazz Fest International
Website: https://jazzvictoria.ca/
Email: info@jazzvictoria.ca
Phone: 250 388 4423
Address: 977 Alston St Victoria, BC V9A 3S5 Canada
Information: The TD Victoria International JazzFest (formerly known as JazzFest International), is a 10 day music festival featuring jazz, blues, world and roots music of local, Canadian, and internationally acclaimed musicians. This "grandfather" of music festivals serves the communities in the Vancouver Island and Gulf Islands region
Country: Canada
Contact: operations Manager / assistant Producer Lora McIntosh
Email: lora@jazzvictoria.ca
Contact: volunteer coordinator and programming assistant Ashley Wey
Email: volunteer@jazzvictoria.ca
Social Media: twitter.com/vicjazzsociety www.facebook.com/VicJazzSociety
Includes "The Jazz Room" at Harbour Towers Hotel; Centennial Square
Type: Concert

Winnipeg Folk Festival

Website: https://www.winnipegfolkfestival.ca/
Email: info@winnipegfolkfestival.ca
Phone: 204 231 0096
Address: 203-211 Bannatyne Ave., CA
Information: This is a hand-made craft village with over 40 artisans and a food village with over 20 booths
Country: Canada
Contact: Chairman Noreen Mian
Contact: Director Carolyn Abbott
Social Media: twitter.com/Winnipegfolk www.facebook.com/winnipegfolkfestival www.instagram.com/winnipegfolkfestival
Other Venues: Birds Hill Provincial Park
Type: Concert, Other

Winnipeg Fringe Theatre Festival
Website: https://www.winnipegfringe.com/
Email: info@winnipegfringe.com
Phone: 204 943 7464
Address: 174 Market Avenue, Winnipeg, CA
Information: Every summer, the Winnipeg Fringe Festival presents 12 days of innovative, engaging & affordable theatre in Winnipeg.
Presenting live theatre in an informal, accessible and inexpensive environment, the Fringe strives to break down traditional boundaries between audiences and artists, encouraging open dialogue between theatre-goers and theatre-creators.
Country: Canada
Contact: assistant festival Manager Tori Popp
Email: festivalassistant@winnipegfringe.com
Social Media: twitter.com/WinnipegFringe www.facebook.com/WinnipegFringe
Frequency: Annual
Other Venues: Street and venues around Winnipeg
Type: Theatre

World Stage
Website: https://harbourfrontcentre.com/
Email: info@harbourfrontcentre.com
Phone: 416 973 4859
Address: Harbourfront Centre, 235 Queens Quay West Toronto, ON, Canada M5J 2G8
Information: This has evolved into Canada's most diverse season-length international performance series. With a bold curatorial vision and highly subsidized ticketing structure, World Stage brings today's most innovative and groundbreaking performance leaders here to share and develop Toronto's understanding of the contemporary
Country: Canada
Contact: Artistic Director Tina Rasmussen
Email: trasmussen@harbourfrontcentre.com
Contact: Artistic Associate Chris Reynolds
Email: creynolds@harbourfrontcentre.com
Social Media: twitter.com/worldstageto www.facebook.com/WorldStageTO
Frequency: Annual
Type: Theatre, Performance art

WSO New Music Festival
Website: https://www.wnmf.ca/
Email: wso@wso.mb.ca
Phone: 204 949 3999
Address: 555 Main Street, CA
Information: The WSO's New Music Festival showcases 50 pieces being performed in just 7 days. Since 1992, the Festival has presented 680 works by 266 composers, half of which are Canadian and local composers. Over the past 20 years the attendance has totalled 155000, averaging 10300 per year, making the New Music Festival one of the highest attended of its kind
Country: Canada
Contact: Director of Sales Ryan Diduck
Email: rdiduck@wso.mb.ca
Social Media: www.facebook.com/winnipegnewmusicfestival
Frequency: Annual
Other Venues: Centennial Concert Hall
Type: Concert

CHINA

Beijing International Music Festival
Website: http:// www.bimfa.org/
Email:
info@bimfa.org
Phone: 917 385 9554
Address: Renmin University of China – School of Arts, 100872 Beijing, China
Information: Established in 2004, Beijing International Music Festival & Academy (BIMFA) is the first and only annual international summer music festival of its kind today's China. Open to Pianists, String Players and Selected Woodwind Instrumentalists of all nationalities, BIMFA brings together established performing artists, pedagogues and serious music students from around the world in a unique collaboration to promote high-level teaching, performance and cultural harmony through music.
Country: China
Social Media: www.facebook.com/Beijing-International-Music-Festival-Academy-BIMFA-279943332369/

MONTREAL, CANADA — SINCE 2002

Artistic Director Victor Quijada combines
the spontaneous, risky and fearless
hip-hop culture with the choreographic
sophistication of contemporary dance.

RBDG.CA

TRENZADO

Exploring the themes of roots, migration and loss – Quijada's return to the stage

VIC'S MIX

Best picks from the repertory – adaptable to any stage

EVER SO SLIGHTLY

Ten dancers and two live musicians – for a large stage

CITY THREAD

Outdoor live dance and music performance – geolocated with exclusive smartphone app

Photo: Marie-Noële Pilon

AGENTS

QUEBEC — CANADA
Agence Station Bleue
Élisabeth Comtois
e.comtois@stationbleue.com

USA
Pentacle
Sandy Garcia
sandyg@pentacle.org

EUROPE (CH, AT, DE, NL, BE, LUX)
Norddeutsche Konzertdirektion
Franziska Grevesmühl-v. Marcard
info@grevesmuehl.de

Frequency: Annual
Type: Concert

China Shanghai International Arts Festival
Website: https://www.artsbird.com/
Email: info@artsbird.com
Phone: 216 272 0346
Address: 24th Floor, Yihai Building, No.211, Kangding Road, Shanghai
Information: Since 1999, CSIAF, driven by the concept of "innovation and development" with the emphasis on brand-effect development, has grown into a flagship project for cultural exchange of the country as well as one of the most influential festivals in the international art circles. Integrating stage performances and exhibitions into its programme, it displays excellent performing arts, promotes cultural trade, promotes cultural exchanges and incubates Artistic talents.
Country: China
Contact: music and dance projects Joe Feifei
Email: ffqiao@artsbird.com
Performance & Exhibition
Jie Ruan
Email: jruan@artsbird.com
Contact: Drama Juan Du
Email: jdu@artsbird.com
Contact: Exhibition Jing Bao
Email: jbao@artsbird.com
Type: Concert, Dance/Ballet, Performance art

Meet in Beijing Arts Festival
Website: http://meetinbeijing.org.cn/
Email: meetinbeijing@caeg.cn
Phone: 106 403 2703
Address: F16-17, Juran Plaza, A3, Dongzhimen South Street, Dongcheng District, Beijing
Information: An international arts festival held yearly in Beijing. The festival aims at promoting cultural exchanges by presenting Chinese culture while introducing international arts. Usually takes place from late April to the end of May annually.
Country: China
Social Media: www.facebook.com/meetinbeijing
Frequency: Annual

Midi Music Festival (Beijing)
Website: https://www.facebook.com/beijingmidi/
Email: master@midischool.com.cn
Phone: 106 285 8616
Address: Beijing, CH
Information: The Midi Music Festival, sometimes also called Midi Modern Music Festival or simply Midi Festival is among China's largest rock music festivals and is hosted by the Beijing Midi School of Music
Country: China
Contact: Director Fan Zhang
Social Media: www.facebook.com/beijingmidi/
Frequency: Annual
Other Venues: Kuangbiao Paradise
Type: Concert

MusicAcoustica (Beijing)
Website: http://musicacoustica.ccom.edu.cn/en2019/
Address: Central Conservatory of Music, 43 Baojia Street, Xicheng District, Beijing, China, 100031
Information: Established in 1994, MUSICACOUSTICA – BEIJING has become one of the most important music festivals, throughout China as well as the world. It annually presents a series of electroacoustic/computer music concerts by prestigious musicians within different schools and styles from all over the world in Beijing every October.
Country: China
Social Media: www.facebook.com/MaggieQMJ/
Frequency: Annual

Sub Jam
Website: https://www.subjam.org/
Email: subjam@gmail.com
Address: Hangzhou
Information: Sub Jam is a label and organization based in Beijing. Since 2000, it's been working on underground music, film and literature. It's main focus now is improvised music and experimental sound practice. It also publishes and curates events, involving music, poetry, visual art and other forms.
Country: China
Type: Multi-media, Other

HONG KONG

Chinese Opera Festival
Website: www.cof.gov.hk/2014/tc
Email: cp2@lcsd.gov.hk
Phone: 226 87325
Address: Cultural Presentations Section, The Leisure and Cultural Services Department Podium, Administration Building, Hong Kong Cultural Centre, 10 Salisbury Road, Tsim Sha Tsui, Kowloon
Information: When it comes to evoking the mystery and charm of ancient China, few art forms can compare to Chinese opera and this festival, which is presented every summer by the Leisure and Cultural Services Department, is a tremendous showcase of the its cultural

richness. Traditional yet innovative, the Chinese Opera Festival sees celebrated artists from all over China captivate audiences in Hong Kong through a compelling mix of opera genres
Country: Hong Kong
Social Media: https://www.facebook.com/chineseoperafestival

Hong Kong Arts Festival
Website: https://www.hk.artsfestival.org/en/
Email: afgen@hkaf.org
Phone: 282 43555
Address: Hong Kong Arts Festival Society Ltd., Room 1205, 12/F, 2 Harbour Road, Wanchai, Hong Kong
Information: HKAF launched in 1973, is a major international arts festival committed to enriching the cultural life of the city by presenting leading local and international artists in all genres of the performing arts as well as a diverse range of "PLUS" and educational events. HKAF actively promotes Hong Kong's own creative talents and emerging artists, and has commissioned and produced over 100 new local productions in the past decade, including theatre, chamber opera, music and contemporary dance.
Country: Hong Kong
Contact: Executive Director Tisa Ho
Contact: Marketing Director Katy Cheng
Contact: development Director Flora Yu
Contact: programme Director Grace Lang
Social Media: twitter.com/HKArtsFestival www.facebook.com/HKArtsFestival www.instagram.com/hkartsfestival
Frequency: Annual
Other Venues: Tai Kwun, Yuen Long Theatre (923 capacity)
Type: Opera, Dance/Ballet, Theatre

Hong Kong International Chamber Music Festival
Website: www.pphk.org/index.php/festivals/
Email: info@pphk.org
Phone: 954 56851
Address: Unit C, 10/F Queen's Centre, 58-64 Queen's Road East, HK
Country: Hong Kong
Contact: Artistic Director Cho-Liang Lin
Frequency: annual
Venue: Hong Kong City Hall, he Hong Kong past venues include Academy for Performing Arts
Type: Concert

Hong Kong Youth Music Interflow
Website: https://www.lcsd.gov.hk/en/mo/activities/youthmusicinterflows.html
Phone: 384 27761
Address: Music Office Head Office, 5/F, South Tower, West Kowloon Government Offices, 11 Hoi Ting Road, Yau Ma Tei, Kowloon
Information: The Hong Kong Youth Music Interflows is an annual major event held in November/December. Featuring contests of Chinese orchestras, string orchestras, symphonic bands, and symphony orchestras, it provides a platform for student musicians to share their musical experience and to learn from each other. Professional musicians are invited to serve as adjudicators and their comments on the performances help enhance participants' standards.
Country: Hong Kong
Social Media: https://www.facebook.com/musicoffice.concerts https://www.instagram.com/musicoffice.concerts/
Frequency: Annual
Type: Concert

International Arts Carnival
Website: https://www.hkiac.gov.hk/2021/tc/index.html
Email: fo@lcsd.gov.hk
Phone: 237 01044
Address: Festivals Office, Level 5, Administration Building, Hong Kong Cultural Centre, 10 Salisbury Road, Tsimshatsui, Kowloon, Hong Kong
Information: The International Arts Carnival is held during the summer months to provide children, young people and their families with cultural diversions during the summer holiday. The performances include music, dance, drama, puppetry, film, magic, acrobatics, musicals, multimedia theatre, comedy, electroluminescent puppetry and more. All are suitable for family audiences and are intended to nurture the interest of children and young people in the performing arts. Source: www.discoverhongkong.com
Country: Hong Kong
Social Media: www.facebook.com/WeWebCarnival
Frequency: Annual
Type: Film, Multi-media, Performance art, Other

New Vision Arts Festival
Website: https://www.newvisionfestival.gov.hk/
Email: fo@lcsd.gov.hk
Phone: 237 01044
Address: 10 Salisbury Road, Tsimshatsui, Kowloon, HK
Information: First launched in 2002, the festival has developed its own identity with innovative, cross-cultural programming featuring an Asian focus over the years. It has brought local arts lovers leading-edge, highly original programmes from all over the world, with the purpose of enriching the performing arts in the region

Country: Hong Kong
Contact: senior Manager Esmond Chan
Social Media: en-gb.facebook.com/NewVisionArtsFestival
Frequency: biennial
Venue: past venues include Hong Kong Repertory Theatre

Thematic Arts Festival
Website: https://www.lcsd.gov.hk/en/artist/arts/arts.html
Email: fo@lcsd.gov.hk
Phone: 237 01044
Address: Level 5, Administration Building, Hong Kong Cultural Centre, 10 Salisbury Road, Tsim Sha Tsui, Kowloon, Hong Kong
Information: The thematic arts festival is organized every autumn with a different theme set for each year. It aims to enhance the public's awareness, understanding and appreciation of the arts and culture of Hong Kong, Asia and other parts of the world and promote Hong Kong's image as a cultural metropolis of Asia.
Country: Hong Kong
Frequency: Annual
Type: Dance/Ballet, Multi-media, Performance art, Musical theatre

INDIA

Song of Soul and Kolkata International Music Festival
Website: www.songsofsoulindia.com
Email: songsofsoulindia@gmail.com / singtoliveindia@gmail.com / contactus@songofsoulindia.com
Phone: 913 364 444 507 /
Address: 4A Nasiruddin Road, Kolkata-700017, West Bengal, IN
Information:
Country: India

INDONESIA

Indonesian Dance Festival (IDF)
Website: http://indonesiandancefestival.id/en/
Email: office@indonesiandancefestival.id
Phone: 213 905 051
Address: Lantai II Gedung Fakultas Seni Pertunjukan – Institut Kesenian Jakarta Jl. Cikini Raya No. 73 Jakarta 10330
Information: Indonesian Dance Festival (IDF) started in 1992 was trying to fll the absence of a dance festival, which helped the regeneration of the dance workforce in Indonesia. Up to now, Indonesian Dance Festival is the only prominent dance festival in Indonesia that consistently runs its programs.
Country: Indonesia
Social Media: https://twitter.com/idfjakarta www.facebook.com/IndonesianDanceFestival www.instagram.com/idfjakarta/
Type: Dance/Ballet

Jakarta International Java Jazz Festival
Website: https://www.javajazzfestival.com/
Email: info@javafestivalproduction.com
Phone: 217 278 3601
Address: Simprug Gallery Blok A1, Jl. Teuku Nyak Arief No.10, Jakarta Selatan 12220, Indonesia
Information: Jakarta International BNI Java Jazz Festival (JJF) is one of the largest jazz festival in the world and arguably the biggest in Southern Hemisphere, held in Jakarta, Indonesia. The annual Jazz Festival is held every early March.
Country: Indonesia
Social Media: twitter.com/javajazzfest www.facebook.com/JavaJazzFestival www.instagram.com/javajazzfest/
Frequency: Annual
Type: Concert

Yogyakarta Arts Festival
Website: www.tourismindonesia.com
Email: info@tourismindonesia.com
Phone: 622 163 25960
Address: c/o Tourism Indonesia, PT Internet Nusa Bhakti, Komplek Sangaji Megah 11 G, ID
Information:
Country: Indonesia
Frequency: annual
Venue: Vredenburg Fort: The centre of Yogyakarta
Type: All

Yogyakarta Gamelan Festival
Website: www.gayam16.net/YGF/
Email: gamelan@gayam16.net
Phone: 274 511 058
Address: Geronimo FM, Gayam 24, ID
Information:
Country: Indonesia
Frequency: annual

ISRAEL

Red Sea Jazz Festival
Website: www.redseajazzeilat.com/en
Email: jazz@redseajazzeilat.com
Phone: 863 40253

Address: PO Box 4298, IL
Information: the Red Sea Jazz Festival was launched in 1987, initiated by the Eilat municipality and supported by the Israel Ministry of Education and Culture, the Israel Ministry of Tourism, Eilat Port, Eilat Hotels Association and other business sponsors

JAPAN

Affinis Music Festival
Website: https://www.affinis.or.jp/
Phone: 357 977 135
Address: 4th floor, Akasaka Kaikan Building, 2-13-5 Akasaka, Minato-ku, Tokyo 107-0052
Information: The Affinis Music Festival (AMF) is a seminar-based music festival organised by the Affinis Arts Foundation for musicians who belong to professional orchestras in Japan. Members of professional orchestras nationwide and invited musicians who perform music at first-rate orchestras around the world gather to participate in various activities, which are divided into three main programs: seminars, concerts, and cultural program for citizens.
Country: Japan
Contact: President/Chairman Yoji Wakui
Contact: Executive Director Hisato Segawa
Type: Concert

Beppu Argerich Music Festival
Website: https://www.argerich-mf.jp/en/
Email: info@argerich-mf.jp
Phone: 977 272 299
Address: Argerich Arts Foundation, Noguchibaru 3030-1, Beppu-shi, Oita-ken 874-0903 Japan
Information: The Argerich Arts Foundation was established in March 2007 looking 100 years ahead considering Artistic activities as an infrastructure of human education.
The first music festival to bear Argerich's name (Argerich Festival) began in Beppu and Oita. This Music Festival (Argerich Festival) has spread from Japan worldwide to Buenos Aires, Lugano, and Hamburg.
Country: Japan
Contact: President/General Director Martha Argerich
Contact: General Producer Kyoto Ito
Social Media: www.facebook.com/Argerichs-Meeting-Point-114461033575142/
Frequency: Annual
Type: Concert

Earth Celebration
Website: http://earthcelebration.jp/en/
Phone: 259 814 100
Address: c/ – Kodo Cultural Foundation, 148-1 Ogi Kanetashinden, Sado, Niigata 952-0611, Japan
Information: Since 1988, the rich natural splendour of Sado has set the stage for arts and culture festival Earth Celebration. Each year the festival features different guest artists who perform in collaboration with Kodo. The three day event is held in mid to late August in and around Ogi Town. Thousands of people come from all over Japan and the world to enjoy the festival's many events. In addition to the various concerts, workshops, performances to date, an array of new offerings were added in 2018.
Country: Japan
Social Media: www.facebook.com/EarthCelebration/twitter.com/earthsado www.instagram.com/earthcelebration_sadoisland/
Frequency: Annual
Start: 2022-08-19
End: 2022-08-23
Type: Concert, Multi-media, Performance art, Other

Festival Tokyo
Website: https://www.festival-tokyo.jp/
Email: toaiwase@festival-tokyo.jp
Phone: 359 615 202
Address: Festival/Tokyo Executive Committee Secretariat, 4th floor, 5-24-12 Mejiro, Toshima-ku, 171-0031 Tokyo
Information: Festival/Tokyo (F/T) is a festival that explores the new possibilities of art in society by diversifying the appeal of the performing arts of the same period. Since the beginning in 2009, cutting-edge artists from Japan and overseas have gathered every autumn to perform and perform programs such as drama, dance, music, art, and video in the Ikebukuro area of Tokyo.
Country: Japan
Contact: Director Satoshi Nagashima
Contact: co-Director Chika Kawai
Social Media: www.instagram.com/festivaltokyo/twitter.com/festivaltokyo www.facebook.com/FestivalTokyo
Frequency: Annual
Type: Theatre, Performance art, Concert, Dance/Ballet, Film

Fuji Rock Festival
Website: https://en.fujirockfestival.com/
Address: Naeba Ski Resort, 949-6292 Yuzawa-machi, Minamiuonuma-gun, Niigata, Japan
Information: The Fuji Rock Festival is one of those magical events. Fantastic food at a great price, no queues to buy beer, all night hot spring baths, a stunning mountain setting, an incredibly friendly crowd and, of course, some of the best in British, American & Japanese indie, dance and world music
Country: Japan
Social Media: www.facebook.com/fujirockfestivaltwitter.com/fujirock_jp www.instagram.com/fujirock_jp/
Frequency: Annual
Type: Concert

Iida Puppet Festa
Website: https://www.iida-puppet.com/
Email: festa@iida-puppet.com
Phone: 265 233 552
Address: Iida Puppet Festa Executive Committee, 5-5-1, Takaha-cho, Iida, Nagano, 395-0051 Japan
Information: Iida Puppet Festa is the largest festival of puppet shows in Japan, which anyone can participate in. Citizens and Performers create the festa together every August.
Various styles of puppet shows gather in Iida, and the city is full of puppet shows. Every year about 1, 700 performers of 300 groups get together in Iida to perform their own puppet shows.
Country: Japan
Social Media: www.facebook.com/iidapuppet.xcom/twitter.com/iidapuppet
Frequency: Annual
Other Venues: about 120 venues in Iida city, including: Iida Cultural Hall, Iida City Hall, Festa Central Park,
Type: Puppetry

International Arts Festival in Kanagawa
Website: https://www.kanagawa-arts.or.jp/
Phone: 456 333 711
Address: 3-1 Yamashita-cho, Naka-ku, Yokohama, JP
Information: International Arts Festival in Kanagawa is a performance art festival in the city of Kanagawa. It provides many Kanagawa residents with opportunities to appreciate art in a familiar and high-quality manner by creating and disseminating art and culture in an integrated manner with the operation of prefectural cultural facilities.
Country: Japan
Social Media: www.facebook.com/kaatkanagawa/
Other Venues: KAAT Kanagawa Arts Theatre; Kanagawa Kenmin Hall; Kanagawa Kenritsu Ongakudo; Kanagawa Art Hall
Type: Performance art

International Music Festival Mino Shirakawa
Website: http:// www.town.shirakawa.lg.jp/
Phone: 574 721 311
Address: 715 Kawamata, Shirakawa-cho, Kamo-gun, JP
Information: Annual Music festival in the city of Shirakawa showcasing a diverse talent and bringing a cultural feast to Japan's Kamo-gun.**Country: Japan**
Contact: Chairman of the festival committee Teruo Hosoe
Contact: secretary General Kazuyuki Yashue
Frequency: Annual
Other Venues: Shirakawa Town Hall
Type: Concert

International Organ Festival in Japan
Website: http://iofj.net/
Email: cecilian-k@nifty.com
Phone: 333 750 164
Address: IOFJ Organizing Committee Secretariat Office, Cecilia Hall, 3-12-3 Honmachi, Nakano-ku, Tokyo
Information: The International Organ Festival in Japan (IOFJ) is Japan's first and only "International Organ Festival" to promote cultural exchange and international friendship through organ music through concerts by organists invited from all over the world. Founded in 1991.
Country: Japan
Start: 2022-06-02
End: 2022-06-08
Type: Concert

Kirishima International Music Festival
Website: https://kirishima-imf.jp/en/home
Email: kirishima@jesc-music.org
Phone: 334 994 530
Address: c/o Japan Music Foundation JESC, 2-1-6 Shibuya, Shibuya-ku, Tokyo, 150-0002 Japan
Information: Kirishima International Music Festival was founded in 1980. The outset of the festival was an approach made in 1975 by an educator of Kagoshima to Mr. Gerhard Bosse, first concertmaster of Gewandhaus Orchestra of that time, who was staying in Japan, to hold a master course. The purpose was "to provide students who wish but cannot study abroad with an opportunity to study with and listen to first classed musicians"
Country: Japan
Contact: music Director Tsuyoshi Tsutsumi
Frequency: Annual
Type: Concert

KISO Music Festival
Website:
https://www.town-kiso.com/manabu/event/100210/
Email:
music@town-kiso.net
Phone: 264 211 222
Address: Kiso Music Festival Secretariat, 5129 Fukushima, Kiso Town, Kiso District, Nagano Prefecture 397-0001 (Kiso Town Cultural Exchange Center)
Information: The Kiso Music Festival began as a regularly held concert produced voluntarily by local classical music lovers in 1975, and has grown to be an annual event held in the mountain town of Kiso, with the support of volunteers

Country: Japan
Contact: music Director Masaharu Yamamoto
Contact: Chairman Kunio Hara
Frequency: Annual
Type: Concert

Kitakyushu International Music Festival
Website: http:// www.kimfes.com/
Phone: 936 636 567
Address: Kitakyushu International Music Festival Secretariat, Inside the Hibiki Hall, 1-1-1 Hirano, Hachiman-to-ku, Kitakyushu Inside the Hibiki Hall, 1-1-1 Hirano, Hachimanto-ku, Kitakyushu Inside the Hibiki Hall, 1-1-1 Hirano, Hachimanto-ku, Kitakyushu 805-0062
Information: Kitakyusyu International Music Festival, featuring classical music, has originally staged as part of Kitakyusyu-city 25th anniversary celebrations in 1988. The program is not only "classical" chamber music, but also, various arranged classical music like jazzy version and audience-friendliness program. There are 20 programs in total.
Country: Japan
Social Media: twitter.com/music_kimfes
Other Venues: Kitakyushu Soleil Hall (2000+ capacity), Hibiki Hall, The Industrial Club of West Japan
Type: Concert

Kusatsu International Summer Music Academy & Festival
Website: https://kusa2.jp/
Phone: 357 905 561
Address: Kusatsu Academy Office, Wako Bldg.2F, 14-3 Motoyoyogi, Shibuyaku, Tokyo 151-0062, Japan
Information: Kusatsu International Summer Music Academy & Festival started in 1980 as the first summer music academy and festival in Japan. It is an opportunity for young Japanese musicians to learn directly from world-renowned musicians, has been running continuously for the past 40 years.
Country: Japan
Social Media: twitter.com/kusa2ac/ www.facebook.com/kusa2ac/ www.instagram.com/kusatsuacademy_official/?hl=ja
Frequency: Annual
Type: Concert

La For Djurne TOKYO
Website: https://www.lfj.jp/lfj_2021/
Phone: 357 46833
Address: c/o Tokyo International Forum, 3 Chome-5-1 Marunouchi, Chiyoda City, Tokyo 100-0005, Japan
Information: La Folle Journe is a classical music festival that was born in 1995 in the port city of Nantes in western France. "La Folle Journe (Day of Enthusiasm)" is the most exciting of all the music festivals in Europe. A theme composer and genre are set every year. At the 9 venues of the convention center, "Cite de Congress", a concert of about 45 minutes will be held from morning till night. The performers include both new and established names, in 300 performances over 5 days of the festival!
Country: Japan
Contact: Artistic Director René Martin
Social Media: twitter.com/lfjtokyoblog www.facebook.com/lafollejourneeaujapon/ www.instagram.com/lafollejournee/
Frequency: Annual
Other Venues: fhfhygfhjfv
Type: , Concert

Miyazaki International Music Festival
Website: https://miyazaki-ac.jp/
Phone:
985 283 208
Address: c/o Medikit Cultural Center (Miyazaki Prefectural Arts Theater), 3-210, Funatsuka, Miyazaki City, Miyazaki Prefecture 880-8557
Information: The Music Festival was established in 1996, and is held every May. It takes place for about three weeks.The Miyazaki Music Festival offers a broad-ranging programme including traditional chamber music and full orchestras.
Country: Japan
Contact: General Director Toshimi Sato
Contact: music Director Fumio Tokunaga
Social Media: www.facebook.com/miyazaki.ac
Other Venues: Medkit Arts Center (1112 capacity)
Type: Concert

Niigata Festival
Website:
http://niigata-matsuri.com/
Phone: 252 904 411
Address: Niigata Chamber of Commerce, 5-1 Bandaijima, Chuo Ward, Niigata, 950-0078, Japan
Information: The Niigata Festival has four historical festivals, the Sumiyoshi Festival, the Commerce and Industry

Festival, the Kawadagi Festival, and the Opening Port Memorial Festival, which began in 1955.
Held every Friday, Saturday and Sunday in early August.
Country: Japan
Contact: Chairman Katsuyuki Fukuda
Type: Performance art, Other

Nissay Theatre Family Festival
Website: https://www.nissaytheatre.or.jp/
Phone: 335 033 111
Address: 1-1-1, Yurakucho, Chiyoda-ku, Tokyo, Japan
Information: The Nissay Theater Family Festival started in 1993 to commemorate the 30th anniversary of the opening of the Nissay Theater in the hope that the family can experience authentic performing arts.
The performances for children from elementary school and junior high school students are performed, and it is a content that even adults can fully enjoy.
Country: Japan
Social Media: www.facebook.com/nissaytheatre1963/twitter.com/nissaytheatre
Frequency: Annual
Type: Puppetry, Object theatre, Musical theatre, Theatre

Ogaki Music Festival
Website: http:// www.ogakikanko.jp/event/ogakimaturi/english/
Phone: 584 771 535
Address: The End of the Narrow Road to the Interior Memorial Hall, 2-26-1 Funamachi, Ogaki-shi, Gifu-ken 503-0923
Information: The Ogaki festival is a product of the interaction and exchange of festival culture between the eastern and western regions of Japan. The dashi (festival car) events of the Chukyo area have influenced the karakuri dolls in Ogaki, just as the dashi events in the Kinki region have influenced the performances on the yama. This interaction is considered to be very important in understanding the dissemination and changes in Japan's yama, hoko, and yatai events.
Country: Japan
Type: Concert, Multi-media, Performance art, Other

Osaka International Festival
Website: www.festivalhall.jp
Email: jimukyoku@asahizaidan.or.jp
Phone: 362 699 441
Address: 6th. Fl. Meiji Seimei Kan, 2-1-1 Marunouchi, Chiyoda-ku, JP
Information: The program also includes dance, drama, and opera, with performances given in the 2, 709-seat Osaka Festival Hall, one of the largest and most modern in the Far East. The Comedie Française, Vienna Burgtheater, and ThÉâtre de France Renaud-Barrault have performed there, as have the New York City Ballet, the Alwin Nikolais Dance Theatre, and the Ballet Aztlan de Mexico. Every Osaka Festival features classical Japanese Noh dance-dramas and Kabuki theatrical performances. The Bunraku Puppet Theatre also presents traditional Japanese dramas using dolls that are two-thirds human size. The two-week festival is scheduled to take place in April, which is cherry-blossom time in Osaka.
Country: Japan
Frequency: annual
Venue: Osaka Festival Hall
Type: Concert, Theatre

Pacific Music Festival PMF
Website: https://www.pmf.or.jp/en/
Phone: 112 422 211
Address: Sumitomo Seimei Sapporo Chuo Bldg. 1F 1-14, Minami 2 jo, Higashi 1 chome, Chuo-ku Sapporo 060-0052
Information: Founded in 1990 by Leonard Bernstein, the festival is an international educational music festival held annually in Sapporo, Japan. Principals and performers from major orchestras in Europe and America, as well as soloists, serve as faculty, providing 4 weeks of instruction to young musicians from around the world who are selected through auditions.
Country: Japan
Contact: Artistic Director Valery Gergiev
Social Media: twitter.com/PMF_Sapporo www.facebook.com/PacificMusicFestival www.instagram.com/pacific_music_festival/
Frequency: Annual
Type: Concert

Saito Ozawa Matsumoto Festival
Website: https://www.ozawa-festival.com/en/
Email: omf@city.matsumoto.lg.jp
Phone: 263 390 001
Address: Seiji Ozawa Matsumoto Festival Executive Committee, 3F 3-18-13 Ote Matsumoto-shi Nagano 390-0874 JAPAN
Information: In 1984, a decade after the passing of the magnificent educator Hideo Saito, Seiji Ozawa assembled globally acclaimed fellow students to perform a concert in his memory. The Saito Kinen Orchestra was thus born, and formed the basis of the Saito Kinen Festival Matsumoto (SKF), a musical festival launched in 1992 with the two pillars of orchestral concerts and opera.
In 2015, the festival has been renamed into Seiji Ozawa Matsumoto Festival (OMF), to mark a new stage.
Country: Japan
Contact: Director Seiji Ozawa
Contact: Executive officer Akio Tsubota
Contact: President Tadashi Hori
Social Media: www.facebook.com/SeijiOzawa.MatsumotoFestivaltwitter.com/Ozawa_Festival www.instagram.com/ozawa_festival/

Soka International Harp Festival
Website: https://soka-bunka.jp/
Phone: 489 319 325
Address: 1-1-5 Matsue, Soka City, Saitama Prefecture 340-0013
Information: Organised by Soka City Cultural Association, Japan Harp Association and Ueno Gakuen University and Junior College; Japan Harp Competition is held during the Festival.
At the climax of the two-day main concert,
You can enjoy the harp ensemble that can only be heard here.
We also invite top artists active in Japan and overseas as special guests.
Country: Japan
Type: Concert

Spring Arts Festival Shizuoka
Website: https://spac.or.jp/
Email: mail@spac.or.jp
Phone: 542 035 730
Address: 2-3-1 Higashishizuoka Suruga-ku Shizuoka-shi 422-8019
Information: Shizuoka Performing Arts Center (SPAC) was founded in 1995 by Shizuoka Prefecture, Japan.
As a creative base of the performing arts, it generates programs of creation, presentation, education plus programs of exchange/collaboration with artists.
SPAC has been introducing Shizuoka international and domestic masterpieces of theatre play, dance, puppet play, film, etc. This festival combines artists, audiences and people from local community to directly exchange and communicate with each other.
Country: Japan
Contact: Chairman Sumiko Suzuki
Contact: General Artistic Director Satoshi Miyagi
Social Media: twitter.com/_SPAC_ www.facebook.com/SPACshizuoka www.instagram.com/spacshizuoka/
Frequency: Annual
Type: Theatre

Takasaki Music Festival
Website: http:// www.takasakiongakusai.jp/
Phone: 273 229 195
Address: Takasaki Music Festival Committee, Takasaki City
Information: As an event that colors autumn in Takasaki, the "Takasaki Music Festival", which has been firmly established not only by Takasaki citizens but also by people who love music both inside and outside the prefecture.
The Takasaki Music Festival is a music event that begins with the "1st Argentinian Wind" held as a commemorative project for the 90th anniversary of the city system in 1990, and sends the breath of the creation of new urban culture in Takasaki.
Country: Japan
Contact: Chairman Shozo Kodama
Social Media: twitter.com/TakasakiMusicF
Frequency: Annual
Type: Concert

Takefu International Music Festival
Website: http://takefu-imf.com/en/
Email: info@takefu-imf.com
Phone: 778 235 057
Address: Takefu International Music Festival Board, 2-3-3, Takase, Echizen, Fukui, 915-0832 Japan
Information: Takefu International Music Festival (TIMF) is held every year in a local town Takefu (Echizen city in Fukui prefecture). Takefu has a rich history and culture, while its citizens also look ahead for the hometown.This festival is one of projects for Takefu's future. To make the festival innovative and unique, Toshio Hosokawa, a worldwide famous Japanese composer of contemporary music, is appointed as music Director.
Country: Japan
Contact: music Director Toshio Hosokawa
Contact: concert Producer Kei Itoh
Social Media: www.facebook.com/Takefu-International-Music-Festival-103568433036648/
Frequency: Annual
Other Venues: Echizen City Cultural Center, Fukui Prefecture
Type: Concert

Tateshina Music Festival
Website: http://megamikomc.com/
Email: mail@megamikomc.com
Address: Tateshina Music Festival, Megami Lake Music Camp Secretariat, 3-4-2 Roppongi, Minato-ku, Tokyo 106-0032
Information: The Tateshina Music Festival is a part of the Megami Lake Music Camp, an international music seminar for those who want to become a high-level musician from the basic class.
The performance and the sense of accomplishment that can attract the audience as the original form of music activities will surely add brilliance to the performance technique, in order to exert their usual ability in competitions and practical tests.
Country: Japan
Contact: music Director Asako Yoshikawa
Social Media: www.facebook.com/megamikomc
Frequency: Annual

The Tochigi Autumn Festival
Website: http:// www.tochigi-kankou.or.jp/event/akimatsuri
Address: Tochigi City, Japan
Information: The Tochigi Autumn Festival is the largest festival in Tochigi City, where gorgeous floats run through the streets of Kura.
Country: Japan
Frequency: Biennial
Type: Multi-media, Performance art, Other

Theater Green Festival
Website: https://theater-green.com/
Email: theater-green@coffee.ocn.ne.jp
Phone: 339 830 644
Address: c/o Theater Green, 2-20-4 Minami-Ikebukuro, Toshima-ku, JP
Information: In 1968, Senryoji temple started a handmade theater called "Ikebukuro Art Theater" with the aim of fostering a new theater company, presenting new works by Japanese playwrights, and experimental theater, with the aim of providing a place for theater activities as part of the social work of temples in the city center. In 1972, the name of the theater was restarted as "Theater Green".
Country: Japan
President & contact
Anjoh Asahina
Frequency: Annual
Other Venues: Theater Green
Type: Theatre

Theater X International Performing Arts Festival
Website: http:// www.theaterx.jp/
Email: info@theaterx.jp
Phone: 356 241 181
Address: 2nd floor, 2-10-14 Ryogoku, Sumida-ku, Tokyo Theater 1st and 2nd floor, Ryogoku City Core
Information: A wonderful theatre and performing arts festival which has a different theme biennialy; co-produces pieces on the theme with artists from abroad
Country: Japan
Frequency: Biennial
Type: Theatre

Theatre Olympics
Website: https://www.theatre-oly.org/en/
Phone: 334 458 013
Address: 2-15-24-201, Takanawa, Minato-ku, Tokyo 108-0074
Information: The main idea behind the Theatre Olympics is to bring together various schools of theatre under one banner. During this event the most irreconcilable of opponents, adherents of often directly opposite views on theatre, come together to present the most comprehensive view on the contemporary theatre.
Country: Japan
Contact: Artistic Director Suzuki Tadashi
Type: Theatre

Tokyo Jazz Festival
Website: www.tokyo-jazz.com
Phone: 357 778 600
Address: 3 Chome-5-1 Marunouch, Chiyoda, JP
Information: Tokyo Jazz Festival also delivers jazz throughout Japan by touring artists who appear at the festival in different cities in Japan. The festival also presents concerts and events throughout the year to enhance the jazz music scene in Japan and also brings Japanese artists overseas to introduce Japanese jazz abroad.
Country: Japan
Frequency: annual
Venue: Tokyo International Forum Hall A, Tokyo International Forum Plaza, Cotton Club
Type: Other

Tokyo Jazz Festival
Website:
www.tokyo-jazz.com
Email: info@tokyo-jazz.com
Phone: 357 778 600
Address: 2-2-1 Jinnan Shibuya, Tokyo 150-8001 Japan
Information: Tokyo Jazz Festival, launched in 2002 has grown to be Japan's largest international jazz festival. The festival is held early September at Tokyo International Forum and its surrounding area in the very heart of Tokyo. Every year, nearly 80, 000 fans gather together to enjoy a weekend full of jazz music. More than 200 artists from all over the globe join the festival and perform in various styles. The festival theme is to celebrate jazz "beyond borders, beyond generations" and dispatch new culture from Tokyo through music.
Country: Japan
Social Media: www.facebook.com/tokyojazzfestival www.instagram.com/tokyojazzfestival_officialtwitter.

com/Tokyo_Jazz_Fes
Frequency: Annual
Type: Concert

Tokyo Tokyo Festival
Website: https://tokyotokyofestival.jp/en/
Phone: 353 204 232
Address: c/o Planning and Coordination Section, Culture
Information: Tokyo Tokyo FESTIVAL is a festival staged in various locations in Tokyo that allows a multitude of people to encounter programs covering diverse genres including art, music, the performing arts, traditional arts, dance, and performances from Japan and countries around the world.
Country: Japan
Social Media: twitter.com/TTF_official_PR
Frequency: Annual
Other Venues: Venues around Tokyo
Type: Dance/Ballet, Performance art, Theatre, Concert

Tsukuba International Music Festival
Website: http:// www.tsukubainfo.jp/event/
Phone: 298 831 111
Address: 1-1-1 Kenkyu-Gakuen, Tsukuba-shi, Ibaraki 305-8555 Japan
Information: Tsukuba Festival – an iternational exchange event which apeals the charm of the international city Tsukuba. Featuring the theme "Interaction and International Exchange", it provides an opportunity for citizens living in and out of Tsukuba to interact with various cultures of the world. Held Mid May at the Tsukuba Center Area.
Country: Japan
Frequency: Annual
Type: Concert, Performance art, Other

Tsuyama International All-Round Music Festival
Website: http:// www.t-arts.or.jp/
Phone: 086 824 0201
Address: c/o Tsuyama Foundation for the Arts, 5F, Alne Tsuyama, 17, Shin-Uo-machi, Tsuyama, JP
Information: Tsuyama International All-Round Music Festival is an event of outstanding talent, showcasing classical music performances, including chamber music, every three years.
Country: Japan
Contact: Chairman (mayor of tsuyama city) Yoshinobu Nakao
Contact: administrator Takashi Kanemichi
Frequency: Triennial
Other Venues: Tsuyama National College of Technology
Type: , Concert

JORDAN

Amman Jazz Festival
Website: www.ammanjazz.com
Email: info@ammanjazzfestival.com
Address: JO
Information: Amman Jazz Festival (AJF) is the only major event dedicated to Jazz in Jordan, which has succeeded in gathering local and international professionals, attracting a wide audience over the years and expanding globally, while creating opportunities for sustainable cultural exchanges. The Festival is known to celebrate diversity, cultural fusion, creativity, unity, and dialogue, by featuring international, regional and local Jazz musicians.
Country: Jordan
Social Media: https://twitter.com/AmmanJazzFest www.facebook.com/AmmanJazzFest https://www.instagram.com/ammanjazzfestival/
Frequency: Annual
Type: Concert

REPUBLIC OF KOREA

Andong Mask Dance Festival
Website: http:// www.maskdance.com/2019/main.asp
Email: webmaster@maskdance.com
Phone: 548 416 397
Address: Andong Festival Tourism Foundation, 239, Yuksa-ro, Andong-si, Gyeongsangbuk-do 36709
Information: The Andong area has a variety of socio-historical and religious heritages from different periods, from ancient times to the present. Andong holds the largest number of cultural properties in Korea. Andong has been preserving the largest cultural properties in Korea and it reveals a very vivid picture of the aesthetics and traditions of the Orient. These socio-cultural, historical and religious heritages are the basis of the Maskdance Festival.
Country: Republic of Korea
Social Media: www.facebook.com/andongmaskdance/
Type: Dance/Ballet, Theatre

Changmu International Arts Festival
Website: https://changmufestival.com/
Email: changmuart@naver.com
Phone: 704 264 8252
Address: ChangMu Arts Center, South Korea, Seoul Jung-gu, Heungin-dong, Toegye-ro
Information: ChangMu International Arts Festival is organized by ChangMu Arts Center to promote international cultural exchange since 1993 with a view to

"Globalization of Asian arts through succession traditions in modern style". It has introduced the trend of world performing arts, it has been acknowledged one of the leading international performing dance festival in Korea intended to the globalization of Korean arts.
Country: Republic of Korea
Social Media: www.facebook.com/Changmuart/ www.instagram.com/changmu_festival/

Chuncheon International Mime Festival
Website: http:// www.mimefestival.com/
Email: mime@mimefestival.com
Phone: 332 420 585
Address: 112, Chuncheon-ro, Chuncheon-si, Gangwon-do, Korea
Information: CIMF is the first festival in Korea to realize the importance of international exchange for the mime arts. With its vast international network that has been growing since 1993, the festival will keep developing its status as one of the three biggest mime festivals in the world, not to mention it will also develop the nation's performing arts scene itself
Chuncheon International Mime Festival (CIMF) is the only people-led festival supported by the Korean Ministry of Culture, Sports and Tourism
Country: Republic of Korea
Contact: Chair Kim Joongsoo
Contact: Chairman Kang Young-gyu
Social Media: www.facebook.com/festivalmime/ www.instagram.com/mimefestival/
Frequency: Annual
Type: Mime

Council of International Organisation of Folklore Festivals CIOFF, Korea
Email: info@cioff.org
Phone: 246 62174
Address: 13-442 Idong, Sungsu 1-ka, Sungdong-gu
Information: CIOFF promotes, safeguards and spreads traditional culture and folklore in 111 countries. Official Partner of UNESCO, accredited to the ICH Committee. It includes many forms of exPression such as dance, music, games, rituals, customs and other arts.
Country: Republic of Korea
Contact: President Philippe Beaussant
Email: President@cioff.org
Contact: Vice President for Administrative Affairs Norbert Mueller
Email: vicePresident-admin@cioff.org
Contact: Vice President for Cultural Affairs Alejandro Camacho González
Email: info@cioff.org
Contact: Secretary General Olga Maloney
Email: info@cioff.org
Contact: Chairman of the Culture Commission Monika Tomingas
Email: Chair-cultural-commission@cioff.org
Social Media: https://www.facebook.com/CIOFF.NGO
Frequency: Annual
Type: Multi-media

Daegu International Musical Festival
Website: https://dimf.or.kr/main.do
Email: dimf@dimf.or.kr
Phone: 536 221 945
Address: DIMF Office, 2F, Daegu Samsung Creation Campus, 51 Hoam-ro, Buk-gu, Daegu
Information: Daegu City is an international event held by the Ministry of Culture, Sports and Tourism every year since 2006. It is an international performance festival attracting attention from musicals all over the world. DIMF is Asia's first international musical festival that encompasses production, performances, and the public around the world, and is a cultural industry brand representing Daegu, Korea.
Country: Republic of Korea
Contact: Overseas business
Email: intl@dimf.or.kr
Contact: Musical academy
Email: academy@dimf.or.kr
Contact: Musical star
Email: dimfstar@dimf.or.kr
Contact: Dimple Keeper
Email: dimfzigi@dimf.or.kr
Social Media: https://www.facebook.com/DIMFEST/ https://twitter.com/dimfmusical https://www.instagram.com/dimf_official/
Type: Musical theatre, Theatre

Daegu International Opera Festival
Website: http:// www.daeguoperahouse.org/eng/
Email: doh2013@hanmail.net
Phone: 536 666 000
Address: 15, Hoam-ro, Buk-gu, Daegu, Republic of Korea, 41585
Information: Daegu International Opera Festival (DIOF) is a festival that is held in Daegu, South Korea. The festival takes place in mid October. It is the representative music festival in South Korea and is the largest International Opera Festival in Asia. The festival has accomplished an enormous growth since its commencement. DIOF continuously endeavors to culturally enlighten people.
Country: Republic of Korea
Social Media: www.facebook.com/DaeguOpera www.

instagram.com/daeguoperahouse/
Frequency: Annual
Type: Opera

Gwacheon Hanmadang Festival
Website: www.gcfest.or.kr
Email: gcfest_official@naver.com
Phone: 250 40938
Address: 13807 Gwacheon Citizen Hall 2F, 5 Tongyeong-ro, Gwacheon-si, Gyeonggi-do
Information: Gwacheon Hanmadang Festival is an annual festival held every autumn. It is a non-profit organisation.
Country: Republic of Korea
Social Media: www.instagram.com/gcfest_official/ www.facebook.com/gcfestofficial/
Frequency: Annual
Type: Concert

Gwangju Biennale
Website: https://www.gwangjubiennale.org/en/index.do#
Email: biennale@gwangjubiennale.org
Phone: 626 084 114
Address: Gwangju Biennale Foundation, 111 Biennale-ro, Buk-gu, Gwangju, 61104 Republic of Korea
Information: The vision of Gwangju Biennale is to pursue value of facilitating and deepeningn key issues and discourses of the time through theme-based exhibition and academic seminars based on the identity it has been building and fulfilling its role as a medium of visual culture, to unleash the energy of creative innovation throughout the humane societies.
Country: Republic of Korea
Contact: General secretary Hyeondae Shin
Contact: head of pr and Marketing Kwangmee Jun
Contact: President Sunjung Kim
Frequency: Biennial
Type: Multi-media, Other

Jarasum International Jazz Festival
Website: http:// www.jarasumjazz.com/the18th/home
Email: info@jarasumjazz.com
Phone: 315 812 813
Address: 2F #31 Bonap-ro Gapyeong-eup Gapyeong-gun Gyeonggi-do Korea 12412
Information: The Jarasum Jazz Festival, held on the beautiful island in the Bukhan River every October, is one of the largest jazz festivals in Asia. This festival has more than 15 different venues throughout the picturesque surroundings.
Country: Republic of Korea
Social Media: www.facebook.com/jarasumjazz
Frequency: Annual
Type: Concert

Jeonju International Sori Festival
Website: http:// www.sorifestival.com/
Email: sorifestival@sorifestival.com
Phone: 632 328 398
Address: 1F Conference Hall, Sori Arts Center of Jeollabuk-do, Sori-ro 31, Deockjin-gu, Jeonju-si, Jeollabuk-do, South Korea (54901)
Information: The Jeonju Int'l Sori Festival is an international music festival that showcases various traditional music from the world and present Korean traditional music including Pansori which has been registered as a Masterpiece of Oral and Intangible Heritage of Humanity by UNESCO and promotes exchange among them.
Country: Republic of Korea
Contact: Executive Director Jechun Park
Email: Director@sorifestival.com
Contact: program Director Jiyoun Han
Email: soriprogram1@sorifestival.com
Social Media: www.facebook.com/sorifestivaltwitter.com/sorifestival www.instagram.com/sori_festival/
Frequency: Annual
Type: Concert

Keochang International Festival of Theatre
Website: http:// www.kift.or.kr/
Email: kift-1989@hanmail.net
Phone: 559 434 152
Address: 750-3 Hwagnsan-ri, Wecheon-myon
Information: claimed to be Korea's best arts festival and is held in Suseungdae, a famous tourist attraction which helps to bring culture to the festival
Country: Republic of Korea
Social Media: www.facebook.com/pages/Keochang-International-Festival-of-Theatre/174048609320231?bookmark_t=page
Frequency: Annual
Type: Concert, Dance/Ballet, Film, Multi-media, Other

Music in PyeongChang (International Great Mountains Music Festival & School)
Website: https://mpyc.kr/en/?ckattempt=1
Email: op@mpyc.kr
Phone: 332 401 363
Address: 2nd Floor, 11, Kumkang-ro, Chuncheon-si, Gangwon Province, South Korea (24272)
Information: Music in PyeongChang, formerly Great

Mountains Music Festival & School, is one of South Korea's largest classical music festival held annually in PyeongChang, Korea. It was launched by Professor Hyo Kang of the Juilliard School in 2004 and is currently led by the pianist Yeol Eum Son.
Country: Republic of Korea
Contact: Artistic Director Yeol Eum Son
Contact: administrator/management Kyungsook Oh
Contact: production Manager Jaemin Seo

Music Isle Festival in Jeju
Website: www.euroasianphil.com
Email: kate@euroasianphil.com
Phone: 234 738 758
Address: Chungmu Art Hall, 387, Toegyero, Jung-gu
Country: Republic of Korea
Contact: Artistic Director Nanse Gum
Type: Concert

Puppet Festival Chuncheon
Website: http:// www.cocobau.com/
Phone: 332 428 452
Address: Chuncheon Puppet Theater and Chuncheon Puppet Theater, 277-3 Sanong-dong, Chuncheon-si, Gangwon-do, 24235 3017 Yeongseo-ro
Information: Chuncheon Puppet Festival, the largest puppet show in Korea, started in 1989 and celebrated its 32nd year this year.
It presents international & national puppet theatre companies mainly for children
Country: Republic of Korea
Social Media: www.facebook.com/cocobau89 www.instagram.com/puppet_festival_chuncheon/
Start: 2022-05-28
End: 2022-05-30
Type: Theatre, Puppetry, Performance art, Film

Seoul Drum Festival
Website: http:// www.seouldrum.go.kr/
Phone: 707 462 1109
Address: Seoul Drum Festival Secretariat, Department of Culture and Arts, 4F, Deoksugung-gil, Jung-gu, Seoul
Information: The Seoul Drum Festival is an exciting performing arts festival that anyone can easily enjoy through non-verbal contents called 'drums'.
Country: Republic of Korea
Social Media: www.facebook.com/drumfestival/ www.instagram.com/drumfestival/
Frequency: Annual
Type: Performance art

Seoul Fringe Festival
Website: https://www.seoulfringe.net:5633/
Email: seoulfringe@hanmail.net
Phone: 232 58150
Address: 201-2 2nd floor, 83, Yeonnam-ro, Mapo-gu, Seoul
Information: Seoul Fringe Festival originated from 'Indie Arts Festival' held at Daehak-ro in 1998. Seoul Fringe Festival believes that arts connect people. Support us in our effort to connect artists and citizens, so that more artists can create and more people can enjoy art.
Country: Republic of Korea
Frequency: Annual
Type: Multi-media, Performance art

Seoul Marginal Theater Festival
Website: https://en.smtfestival.org/
Email: info@smtfestival.org
Address: 2nd Floor/40 Sungkyunkwan-ro, Hyehwa-dong, Jongno-gu, Seoul
Information: Seoul Marginal Theatre Festival (SMTF) began in 1999 as a platform for young Directors with Choi Chi Rim as the first Artistic Director. Its aim was to be a contemporary performing arts festival that captured the aesthetics and social contexts from the perspectives of 'the marginalized.' SMTF is a platform where the concept of contemporary is challenged and re-illuminated.
Country: Republic of Korea
Contact: Artistic Director Lee Kyung-Sung
Contact: Artistic Director Adriano Cortese
Contact: Festival Executive/Programming Director Jeon Kang-Hee
Contact: communications Han Min Zoo
Social Media: www.facebook.com/smtfestival/ www.instagram.com/smtfestival/twitter.com/smt_festival?lang=en
Frequency: Annual
Type: Theatre

Seoul Performing Arts Festival
Website: http://spaf.or.kr/2021/
Email: spaf@gokams.or.kr
Phone: 220 982 986
Address: Seoul Performing Arts Festival (SPAF), 3F, Hongik University Daehak-ro Campus 57, Daehak-ro, Jongno-gu, Seoul, Korea 03082
Information: the Seoul Performing Arts Festival is one of the most prestigious culture and arts festivals in Korea; every autumn, SPAF attracts large public audiences and media attention by introducing major international and domestic companies, whose performances cover everything from theatre to dance to experiments in multidisciplinary genres
Country: Republic of Korea

Social Media: www.facebook.com/SPAFinSeoul/
Other Venues: Arko Arts Theater, Daehakro Arts Theater
Type: Concert, Dance/Ballet

SIDance (Seoul International Dance Festival)
Website: https://artsdb.net/listings/edit/3b0e67ef-9e27-4c2f-b517-d3fd2b916798
Email: inquiry@sidance.org
Phone: 232 161 185
Address: 2F, 56, World Cup buk-ro 5-gil, Mapo-gu, Seoul, 04002, Korea
Information: SIDance(Seoul International Dance Festival) is a regular international festival, hosted by Seoul Section of CID-UNESCO(President: LEE Jong-Ho). It is made through close tie and collaboration with government organizations such as Ministry of Culture, Sports and Tourism, and Seoul Foundation for Arts and Culture, as well as foreign governments and embassy of each country stationed in Korea.
Country: Republic of Korea
Contact: Artistic Director Jong-Ho Lee
Contact: Marketing and communication Ki Yoona
Email: yoona@sidance.org
Frequency: Annual
Type: Dance/Ballet

SIDance Festival (Seoul International Dance Festival)
Phone: 232 161 185
Address: Room No. 401, Buam Buillding, 208-42 Buam-dong, Jongno-gu Seoul 110-817
Information:
Country: Republic of Korea

Tongyeong International Music Festival
Website: https://www.timf.org/kr/
Phone: 556 500 400
Address: Tongyeong International Music Foundation, 38, Keunbalgae 1-Gil, Tongyeong-si, Gyeongsangnam-do (53079)
Information: recently changed from being an annual 10-day festival to season of events throughout the year; see also Competitions (Gyeongnam International Music Competition)
Tongyeong International Music Festival is currently one of the most promising international music festivals in Asia. With the efforts of young intellectuals made up of composers and scholars and the city of Tongyeong, the 1st Tongyeong International Music Festival was held in 2002 and developed into a large-scale music festival.
Country: Republic of Korea
Contact: head of art planning Le Yong-Min
Email: ymlee@timf.org
Social Media: twitter.com/timf_pr www.facebook.com/TIMF2014 www.instagram.com/timf_tongyeong/
Type: Concert

LEBANON

Al Bustan Festival for Music and the Arts
Website: https://albustanfestival.com/
Email: info@albustanfestival.com
Phone: 375 2000
Address: Al Bustan Festival Office P. O. Box 11-3764 Riad El Solh-Beirut 1107 2150 Lebanon
Information: An international festival of mainly classical music which takes place in Lebanon in February and March every year. Member of IAMA and ISPA
Country: Lebanon
Contact: President Myrna Bustani
Contact: Vice President Sheikh Fouad El Khazen
Contact: London Office
Email: festival@albustan.co.uk
Social Media: twitter.com/albustanfest www.facebook.com/AlBustanFestival www.instagram.com/albustanfestival/
Frequency: Annual
Other Venues: Emile Bustani Auditorium
Type: Concert

Baalbeck International Festival
Website: www.baalbeck.org.lb
Email: baalbeck@baalbeck.org.lb
Phone: 137 3150
Address: Karakone El Druze, Osman Ben Affan Street, Doursoumian Buikding, 11-4215 Riad El Solh, Beirut, Lebanon
Information: The festival hosts world-renowned artists with Lebanese roots such as Ibrahim Maalouf and Matthieu Chedid along with other international stars such as Angelique Kidjo and Ben Harper.
Today, the Baalbeck International Festival continues to project a positive image of Lebanon to the world and aims for a better country by promoting culture, tourism, and peace.
Country: Lebanon
Contact: President Nayla de Freige
Contact: General secretary Elga Trad
Contact: General Manager Guy Yazbeck
Social Media: https://twitter.com/BaalbeckFest www.facebook.com/BaalbeckInternationalFestival
Type: Concert

Beirut Chants Festival

Website: www.beirutchants.com
Email: ✉info@beirutchants.com
Address: LB
Information: The festival of sacred music in downtown Beirut is a unique experience in Lebanon, combining spirituality, culture and history.
Music speaks louder than violence,
Beirut will chant for peace and tolerance.
Country: Lebanon
Contact: Director Toufic Maatou
Email: contact@touficmaatouk.com
Social Media: https://twitter.com/beirutchants www.facebook.com/BeirutChants/
Frequency: Annual
Type: Concert

Beirut Spring Festival
Website: www.beirutspringfestival.org
Email: info@beirutspringfestival.org
Phone: 139 7331
Address: Samir Kassir Foundation, riverside Bloc C, 6th floor Charles Helou Street, Sin el-Fil Metn – Lebanon
Information: The Beirut Spring Festival, created and launched in 2009 by the Samir Kassir Foundation, is inspired by the title of one of the last articles written by Samir Kassir, shortly before his assassination in 2005. The Festival features multidisciplinary international performances (theater, music, dance, conferences...) revolving around the themes of tolerance and cultural diversity, especially in societies facing violence and injustice.The Festival supports contemporary art creation and energizes Lebanon's cultural and Artistic life, built on the belief that art is the ultimate way to tolerance.
Country: Lebanon
Social Media: https://twitter.com/SK_Eyes www.facebook.com/BeirutSpringFestival
Type: Theatre, Dance/Ballet, Concert

Beiteddine Art Festival
Website: www.beiteddine.org
Email: info@beiteddine.org
Phone: 134 9060
Address: Jaroudi Bldg, 4th floor, Kantari street, Beirut
Information: The Beiteddine Festival is one of the leading festivals in the Middle East. It takes place in a large and magnificent 200-year old Palace in the Chouf Mountains, in Lebanon. The Palace is a jewel of Lebanese architecture with its many courtyards, monumental gates, elegant arcades and leveled galleries.
Each year, in the months of July and August, the Festival presents outstanding performances by world famous stars and Lebanese artists.
Country: Lebanon
Contact: President Nora Joumblatt
Email: nora@beiteddine.org
Contact: Director Hala Chahine
Email: hala@beiteddine.org
Contact: project Manager Hollie Ghandour
Email: info@beiteddine.org
Contact: logistics Manager Emily-Jane Aouad
Email: info@beiteddine.org
Social Media: https://twitter.com/Beiteddinef www.facebook.com/BeiteddineFestival https://www.instagram.com/Beiteddinefestival/
Frequency: Annual
Venue: Palace in the Chouf Mountains, in Lebanon
Type: Concert, Musical theatre

MALAYSIA

Kuala Lumpur International Arts Festival
Website: https://www.diversecity.my/
Email: info@diversecity.my
Phone: 216 60788
Address: Suite 14-9, Level 14, Wisma UOA II, 21 Jalan Pinang 50450 Kuala Lumpur, Malaysia
Information: Launched in 2015, the KLIAF is an annual celebration of arts and culture that is produced by DiverseCity, a non-profit organization that advocates, develops and invests in Artistic and cultural experiences that enrich people's lives. As much as the Festival acts as a springboard for up and coming art practitioners, it also seeks to showcase the power of the arts to heal the mind, body and soul.
Country: Malaysia
Social Media: www.facebook.com/DiverseCityKL www.instagram.com/kldiversecity/ www.twitter.com/DiverseCityKL
Frequency: Annual
Type: Performance art

Malaysia Fest
Website: www.malaysiafest.com
Email: sunny_sab23@yahoo.com
Phone: 326 158 188
Address: Malaysia Tourism Promotion Board, 17th Floor, Menara Dato' Onn, Putra World Trade Centre, 45, Jalan Tun Ismail, MY
Information:
Country: Malaysia
Contact: Marketing Executive Producer Mohd Sunny Tan
Contact: chief Executive Producer Alan Lau
Frequency: annual

Melaka Art and Performace Festival
Website: www.melakafestival.com
Email: info@melakafestival.com
Phone: 374 919 233
Address: Jln SS7/26, Kelana Square, Kelana Jaya, MY
Information: Melaka Arts and Performance Festival is an innovative contemporary festival, featuring dance, performance art, visual art, film and music

Rainforest World Music Festival
Website: www.rainforestmusic-borneo.com
Email: pauline@sarawaktourism.com
Phone: 824 23600
Address: Sarawak Tourism Board, 6th & 7th Floor, Yayasan Sarawak Building, Jalan Masjid, MY
Information: organises workshops, ethno-musical lectures, jam sessions and mesmerising evening performances
Country: Malaysia
Frequency: annual

MEXICO

Danza Extrema / Encuentro Internacional
Website: http://talulahcid.com.mx/
Email: talulahescuela@gmail.com
Phone: 998 884 1884
Address: Durazano 43, 2A, 77500, Cancun, MX
Information: The International Dance Encounter began in 2003. Since that year important figures and national and international Ballet companies have participated including: School of the American Ballet Theatre, Pro Ver en Pro of Veracruz Talent, Ballet of the Teatro de la Scala in Milan, Ballet de Camaguey and Kiev National Theatre Company.
Country: Mexico
Contact: Director General Elizabeth Duarte
Contact: Artistic Director Vanessa Villanueva
Social Media: www.facebook.com/escueladedanzatalulah/
Frequency: Biennial
Other Venues: Talulah Cancun Integral Dance Center
Type: Film, Dance/Ballet

Encuentro Internacional de Mujeres en el Arte
Website: https://comuarte.org/
Email:
murmullodesirenas@hotmail.com
Phone: 559 116 6925
Address: El Colectivo Mujeres en la Música A.C. Coordinadora Internacional de, Miguel Negrete 34-402 Col Niños Héroes de Chaputepec, B, MX
Information: part of the commemoration of the international women's day; the main objective is to promote and popularise the Artistic work of women
Country: Mexico
Contact: contact Leticia Armijo
Social Media: twitter.com/NotifemAgencia
Other Venues: Palace of Fine Arts, Palacio de Bellas Artes, Centro Nacional de las Artes, Teatro de la danza, National Arts Centre, University Cultural Centre

Encuentro Nacional e Internacional de Jovenes Guitarristas
Website: www.encuentroguitarraqueretaro.com
Address: MX
Country: Mexico
Social Media: www.facebook.com/GuitarraQueretaro
Frequency: annual
Type: Other

Festival Cultural de Mayo
Website: https://www.festivaldemayo.org/
Email: contacto@festivaldemayo.org
Phone: 333 030 9780
Address: 4to Piso Teatro Degollado, MX
Information: Festival of culture and arts, an exploration of creativity and passion; a shared experience between performer and viewer
Country: Mexico
Contact: General Director Sergio Alejandro Matos
Social Media: www.facebook.com/festivaldemayo
Other Venues: Teatro Degollado (1400 capacity)

Festival Cultural Mazatl
Website: http://culturamazatlan.com/es/festivales/festival-cultural-mazatlan/
Email: contacto@culturamazatlan.com
Phone: 669 982 4444
Address: Ayuntamiento de Mazatl, Carnaval s/n, Col. Centro, MX
Information: It emerged in 1993 with a careful and attractive billboard that places it among the most important forums for the manifestation of Artistic exPressions. The quality of its programming gives it a predominant place at the national level and distinguishes Mazatlan among the main cultural destinations of northwestern Mexico.
Local, national and guest artists appear, in the realms of music, theatre, dance, ballet, singing and literature.
Country: Mexico
Social Media: www.facebook.com/culturamazatlan/
Frequency: Annual
Other Venues: Angela Peralta Theater, churches, plazas

and outside spaces of the urban and rural area of the municipality of Mazatln, Sinaloa.
Type: Concert, Dance/Ballet, Theatre, Performance art, Multi-media

Festival de Cultura del Caribe La Mar de las Artes
Website: fecuca.com
Email: info@fecuca.com
Phone: 984 803 0010
Address: Av. 10 norte no. 6 entre calle 12 y 14, Plaza 10, Local 7 – Planta Alta, Col. Centro, MX
Country: Mexico
Contact: Producer Cecilia Vicente
Contact: communications Maximiliano Torres
Type: All

Festival de la Frontera
Website: fronterafestival.com
Email: info@fronterafestival.com
Phone: 686 554 1276
Address: Instituto Cultural de Baja California, Av., Col. Nueva, MX
Country: Mexico
Social Media: @tuiterfrontera www.facebook.com/fronterafestival
Frequency: annual
Type: Concert

Festival Internacional Cervantino
Website: www.festivalcervantino.gob.mx
Email: 40cervantinoprensa@gmail.com
Phone: 554 155 0331
Address: Mercaderes 52,
Colonia San José Insurgentes, MX
Information: during its four decades of existence, the festival has enjoyed the participation of performers from 92 different countries
Country: Mexico
Social Media: @cervantino www.facebook.com/cervantino.festival

Festival Internacional de Danza Zacatecas
Website:
Email: jesteban-izc@yahoo.com
Phone: 492 922 3370
Address: Instituto Zacatecano de Cultura, Lomas del Calvario s/n, Col. D, MX
Information:
Country: Mexico
Frequency: annual

Festival Internacional de Folklore
Website: https://folkmexico.org/
Email: festival@folkmexico.org
Phone: 686 566 4276
Address: UABC/ Direcci, Av. Alvaro Obreg, Col. Nueva, MX
Information: ⬜The "International Folklore Festival, Mexico" (FIFMX), brings together in our city groups and couples of dance and folk music from various countries.⬜
Country: Mexico
Social Media: www.facebook.com/FIFMX
Frequency: Annual
Other Venues: Ciudad de Mexico CDMX
Type: Concert, Dance/Ballet

Festival Internacional de Órgano de Morelia "Alfonso Vega Núñez"
Website: www.festivaldeorganodemorelia.org
Email: contacto@festivaldeorganodemorelia.org
Phone: 443 314 1515
Address: Blvd. García de León #1775 Col. 5 de Diciembre. C.P:58280 Morelia, Michoacán, México
Information: With more than half a century since its first edition in 1966, the International Organ Festival of Morelia Alfonso Vega Núñez, was consolidated as the First Cultural Festival of America, thus being a precursor to the great cultural events of the continent and contributing through international cooperation to the creation of organ festivals in Buenos Aires (Argentina), San Juan (Puerto Rico) , Guatemala (Guatemala), Medellin (Colombia) and Sao Paulo (Brazil).
Country: Mexico
Social Media: https://www.facebook.com/FIOMorelia/ https://www.instagram.com/fiom_morelia/ https://twitter.com/FIOMorelia
Frequency: Annual
Other Venues: Alfonso Vega Nez Hall, Catedral de Morelia
Type: Concert

Festival International Cervantino
Website:
https://festivalcervantino.gob.mx/
Email: difusionfic@conaculta.gob.mx
Phone:
554 155 0331
Address: Comit, Paseo de la Reforma 175, Piso 10, Esq. Rio T, MX
Information: Festival International Cervantino has been running since 1953, taking theater to the streets, to a public stage where the community, artists and visitors can converge in the same space to celebrate universal cultural wealth.
Country: Mexico

Contact: contact Angelica Valenzuela
Email: angelicamariavalenzuela@gmail.com
Contact: General Director Gerardo Kleinburg
Email: gkleinburg@conaculta.gob.mx
Social Media: www.facebook.com/pages/Festival-Internacional-Cervantino-México/41183706608
Other Venues: 10 venues in the city of Guanajuato
Type: Concert, Multi-media

Un Desierto para la Danza
Website: plazasol.uson.mx/isc
Email: iscson@rtn.uson.mx
Phone: 662 213 4411
Address: Instituto Sonorense de Cultura, Obreg, Col. Centro, MX
Information:
Country: Mexico
Contact: coordinadores Ra
Frequency: annual
Venue: Teatro de la Ciudad Hermosillo 500, venues in Nogales, Guaymas, Ciudad Obreg

NEW ZEALAND

Adam Chamber Music Festival
Website: https://www.music.org.nz/
Email: info@music.org.nz
Phone: 274 384 048
Address: 92 Collingwood Street, NZ
Information: Every two years we host a 10 day international festival of wonderful chamber music in Nelson – a small resort town at the top of New Zealand's South Island – famous for its boutique vineyards, seafood, wild places and relaxed lifestyle.
The Adam Chamber Music Festival attracts audiences from around the world who enjoy rarely performed chamber music made possible through exciting collaborations between renowned international artists and leading New Zealand chamber musicians.
Country: New Zealand
Contact: Manager Bob Bickerton
Email: Manager@music.org.nz
Contact: Communications Sarah Wilson
Email: Manager@music.org.nz
Social Media: https://www.facebook.com/adamchambermusicfestival https://www.instagram.com/adamchambermusicfestival/
Frequency: Biennial
Start: 2022-02-03
End: 2022-02-06
Type: Concert

Auckland Arts Festival
Website: www.aucklandfestival.co.nz
Email: info@aaf.co.nz
Phone: 930 90101
Address: Level 5, Wellesley Centre, 44-52 Wellesley Street, NZ
Information: The Auckland Arts Festival is Auckland's premier festival of New Zealand and international arts every March, presenting music, theatre, cabaret, dance, circus, visual arts, free and family events.
Country: New Zealand
Contact: Artistic Director Carla Van Zon
Email: ArtisticDirector@aaf.co.nz
Contact: chief Executive David Inns
Email: CEO@aaf.co.nz
Contact: Artistic Director Shona McCullagh
Email: ArtisticDirector@aaf.co.nz
Business & Finance Manager
Vanessa Zigliani
Email: vanessa.zigliani@aaf.co.nz
Social Media: https://twitter.com/Aklfestival https://www.facebook.com/Aklfestival https://www.instagram.com/aklfestival/
Frequency: Annual
End: 2021-03-21
Venue: 130 venues and locations across Auckland
Type: Concert, Musical theatre, Theatre, Dance/Ballet, Performance art

Auckland Festival Trust
Website: www.aucklandfestival.co.nz
Email: info@aaf.co.nz
Phone: 930 90101
Address: Level 5, Wellesley Centre,
44-52 Wellesley Stree, NZ
Information: All roads at the Auckland Arts Festival lead back to the iHeartRadio FESTIVAL CLUB at the Aotea Centre, a hangout space and music stage for audiences, artists and the creative community to meet, mix and celebrate. In the centre of the Aotea Arts Precinct, this comfortable and upbeat pop-up club is your place to gather before and after a show, grab a delicious meal from a bespoke menu, enjoy live music from instrumentalists and DJs, or unwind over the long summer nights with a special Festival cocktail. Member of ISPA
Country: New Zealand
Contact: Chair John Judge
Social Media: @Aklfestival www.facebook.com/Aklfestival
Frequency: annual
Venue: Bruce Mason Centre

Christchurch Arts Festival
Website: www.artsfestival.co.nz
Email: admin@artsfestival.co.nz
Phone: 336 52223
Address: PO Box 705 Christchurch, New Zealand 8140
Information: Christchurch Arts Festival is a major feature on the South Island event calendar, showcasing a programme of arts and entertainment by leading international and New Zealand performers and artists
Country: New Zealand
Contact: Artistic Director George Parker
Email: george@artsfestival.co.nz
Social Media: https://twitter.com/ChchFest www.facebook.com/ChristchurchArtsFestival https://www.instagram.com/chchartsfest/
Frequency: Annual
Venue: past venues include Market Square , The Arts Centre, Worcester Blvd Christchurch
Type: Concert, Dance/Ballet

Festival of Colour
Website: www.festivalofcolour.co.nz
Email: info@festivalofcolour.co.nz
Phone: 344 34172
Address: Unit 10, Helard House, 4 Helwick Street, NZ
Information: The Festival of Colour is six exciting days and nights of astounding performances and inspiring exhibitions set against the spectacular autumnal backdrop of the Southern Lakes.
Country: New Zealand
Contact: festival Director Philip Tremewan
Contact: General Manager Lindsey Schofield
Email: info@festivalofcolour.co.nz
Social Media: @festivalcolour www.facebook.com/Festivalofcolour
Frequency: biennial (odd years)
Venue: Wanaka, Queenstown, Luggate, Hawea and Cromwell

New Zealand Festival
Website: https://www.festival.nz/
Email: nzfestival@festival.co.nz
Phone: 447 30149
Address: St James Theatre, 77-87 Courtenay Place, NZ
Information: At the New Zealand Festival, they've been creating extraordinary encounters between artists and audiences since 1986. The New Zealanders who established the Festival were pioneers, achieving their highly ambitious goal of bringing the best live arts experiences from across the world to audiences in New Zealand.
Country: New Zealand
Contact: creative Director Marnie Karmelita
Contact: Executive Director Meg Williams
Email: megan.williams@festival.co.nz
Contact: Executive coordinator Suzy Cain
Email: suzy.cain@festival.co.nz
Contact: head of programming Angela Green
Email: angela.green@festival.co.nz
Contact: senior Producer Eva Prowse
Email: eva.prowse@festival.co.nz
Social Media: @NZFestival/ www.facebook.com/nzfestival
Start: 2022-02-21
End: 2022-03-20
Type: Concert, Dance/Ballet, Film, Performance art, Theatre

NZ Fringe Festival
Website: www.fringe.co.nz
Email: welcome@fringe.co.nz
Phone: 421 24725
Address: Level 1, 40 Taranaki Street, Te Aro, NZ
Information: The New Zealand Fringe Festival in Wellington, New Zealand, is an arts festival which showcases grass-roots art and entertainment. The festival includes contemporary work in art forms including audio (podcast), busking, cabaret, comedy, circus, dance, improvisation, music, online, physical theatre, poetry, puppetry, spoken word/story telling, theatre and visual & digital art.
Country: New Zealand
Social Media: @NZFringe www.facebook.com/NZFringe
Start: 2022-02-18
End: 2022-03-12
Type: Dance/Ballet, Theatre, Performance art, Puppetry

Taranaki Festival of the Arts, The
Website: https://www.taft.co.nz/
Email: events@taft.co.nz
Phone: 675 98412
Address: 50 Brougham St, PO Box 4251, NZ
Information: Every second year, in the depths of winter, the Taranaki International Festival of the Arts heats up the region, literally and figuratively, with a programme of wonderfully inspiring shows and activities.Taranaki's arts festival is the longest running regional festival in the country, and in fact it is second only to the New Zealand Festival (Wellington) in continuous duration
Country: New Zealand
Contact: chief Executive Suzanne Porter
Email: suzanne@taft.co.nz
Contact: Artistic Director Craig Cooper
Contact: artist festival Director Lisa Haskell
Email: lisa@taft.co.nz

Contact: business Manager Tracey Bell
Email: tracey@taft.co.nz
Social Media: @TIAFnz www.facebook.com/TaranakiInternationalArtsFestival
Type: Concert, Dance/Ballet, Film, Multi-media, Theatre

Tauranga Arts Festival
Website: https://www.taurangafestival.co.nz/
Email: info@taurangafestival.co.nz
Phone: 792 86213
Address: PO Box 13011, Tauranga 3143
Information: Tauranga Arts Festival was Established in 1999. The festival delivers a world-class programme directly from leading artists and performers at the peak of their practice. It's a live experience that you don't have to travel to Auckland for or be living in London – it happens in Tauranga.
Country: New Zealand
Contact: General Manager Nikki Hansen
Social Media: twitter.com/tgafestival www.facebook.com/taurangafestival www.instagram.com/taurangafestival/?hl=en
Frequency: Biennial
Type: Concert, Dance/Ballet, Performance art, Theatre

UPSURGE Bay of Islands Arts Festival
Website: http://upsurgefestival.co.nz
Email: ops@centakeri.com
Phone: 940 70260
Address: PO Box 995, NZ
Information: UPSURGE Bay of Islands Arts Festival is delivered by the Bay of Islands Arts Festival Trust, a registered charitable trust. Our mission as an organisation is to be a unique must-do arts experience, inspiring and connecting our communities.
We partner with artists, our communities and supporters to develop distinctive arts experiences to the region, designed to inspire people to come together, to participate and to enjoy.
Country: New Zealand
Social Media: https://www.facebook.com/UPSURGEFestival/
Frequency: Biennial
Type: Concert, Dance/Ballet, Theatre

PHILIPPINES

Bamboo Organ Foundation, Inc.
Website: https://www.bambooorgan.org/
Email: bambooorganoffice@gmail.com
Phone: 632 825 7190
Address: Diego Cera Ave. Poblacion, Las Piñas City, Phillipines
Information: the annual Bamboo Organ Festival is organized by the Bamboo Organ Foundation, Inc. The instrument is housed at the St. Joseph's Parish Church of Las Piñas. Mailing Address: DiegoCera Ave. Poblacion, Las Piñas City, Phillipines
Country: Philippines
Contact: Artistic Director Armando Salarza
Contact: Marketing/adminstration Bernard Lopez
Frequency: Annual
Type: Concert

Dance Xchange: The Philippine International Dance Workshop and Festival
Website: https://www.facebook.com/dancexchange-philippines/
Email: philippinesdancex2020@gmail.com
Phone: 285 272 214
Address: NCCA, 633 Gen. Luna St., Intramuros, 1002 Manila, Philippines
Information: Dance Xchange: The Philippine International Dance Workshop and Festival is a project organized by the National Committee on Dance of the National Commission for Culture and the Arts. It was conceptualized as a Philippine celebration of the International Dance Day and in accordance with Presidential Proclamation No. 154, declaring the last week of April as the "National Dance Week".
Country: Philippines
Social Media: www.facebook.com/dancexchangephilippines/ www.instagram.com/dancexchangephilippines
Frequency: Annual
Type: Dance/Ballet

Manila Chamber Orchestra Festival
Website:
Address: c/o Manila Chamber Orchestra, Francisco Santiago Hall, PCI Bank Building, Horacio dela Costa St, PH
Information: music: chamber
Country: Philippines
Frequency: every 4 years

National Theatre Festival
Website:
www.admu.edu.ph/ccpap/ccp
Email: denmar@ccpap.admu.edu.ph
Phone: 283 21125
Address: Dramatic Arts Division, Cult Cen of the Philippines, CCP Complex, Roxas Blvd, PH
Information: alternative E-mail address: ccp@portaline.com
Country: Philippines

Contact: officer-in-charge Clotilde Gealogo-Lucero
Frequency: every 4 years

SERBIA AND MONTENEGRO

BELEF – Belgrade Summer Festival
Website: https://www.belef.rs/index.php?lang=sr-cir
Email: info@cebef.rs
Phone: 114 039 182
Address: Svetogorska bb 11000, Belgrade, Serbia
Information: Belgrade's soul during the summer is defined by the Belgrade Summer Festival, BELEF; this festival combines three large Artistic fields: stage performing arts, visual art, and music.
Country: Serbia and Montenegro
Contact: Artistic Director Aleksandar Ilić
Contact: President Jasmina Trumbetaš Petrović
Social Media: www.facebook.com/belef.festival/
Other Venues: Courtyard of the Fifth Belgrade Gymnasium
Type: Concert, Multi-media

Belgrade Music Festival – Bemus
Website: www.bemus.rs
Email: info@cebef.rs
Phone: 114 039 182
Address: Svetogorska w / n 11000 Beograd Srbija
Information: Belgrade Music Festival – BEMUS, founded in 1969, it is the oldest and most important music festival in Serbia and one of the most recognizable art music festivals in Southeast Europe, enjoying the status of a cultural event of special importance for the city of Belgrade. It has hosted some of the most famous ensembles and soloists of our time, as well as world class soloists and conductors. It also opens doors for young musicians at the start of their careers.
Country: Serbia and Montenegro
Contact: President Milan Lazović
Contact: Artistic Director Bojan Sudjic
Social Media: www.facebook.com/bemus.festival
Frequency: Annual
Type: Concert

SINGAPORE

Da:ns Festival
Website: www.esplanade.com/festivals-and-series/dans-festival
Email: dansfestival@esplanade.com
Phone: 682 88377
Address: The Esplanade Co Ltd, 1 Esplanade Drive Singapore, 038981
Information: This festival includes 10 days of dance with some of the most exciting companies from around the world, as well as workshops and the availability to dance. Da:ns Festival includes a wide range of opportunities to learn different kinds of dance, this 11-day festival will open your mind, lift your spirit and get your body moving.
Country: Singapore
Social Media: www.facebook.com/dansfestival
Venue: past venues include: Esplanade Theatre, Concert Hall, Theatre Studio, Recital Studio, Rehearsal Studio
Type: Concert, Dance/Ballet, Theatre, Performance art

Huayi – Chinese Festival of Arts
Website: www.huayifestival.com
Email: huayi@esplanade.com
Phone: 682 88377
Address: 1 Esplanade Dr, SG
Information: Huayi showcases the works of outstanding Chinese artists of all genres – whether they're traditional or contemporary, mainstream or cutting-edge – by providing them with a platform on which they can present their works to international audiences in Singapore. With this goal, we sow the seeds for what we hope will become an internationally recognised arts festival that represents the Chinese diaspora
Country: Singapore
Social Media: www.facebook.com/huayifestival/
Frequency: annual
Venue: The Esplanade
Type: Concert

Singapore International Festival of Arts
Website: https://www.sifa.sg/
Address: 28 Aliwal Street #03-07, Aliwal Arts Centre, Singapore 199918
Information: As Singapore's annual pinnacle performing arts festival, the Singapore International Festival of Arts (SIFA) presents captivating and diverse works across theatre, music, dance, film and visual arts. First launched as the Singapore Festival of Arts in 1977, the festival has gone through several evolutions and inspired generations of arts lovers and practitioners. Today, the highly anticipated festival is a high point on Singapore's arts and cultural calendar.
Country: Singapore
Contact: festival Director Gaurav Kripalani
Social Media: twitter.com/sifa_sg www.facebook.com/sifa.sg www.instagram.com/sifa_sg/
Frequency: Annual
Type: Theatre, Concert, Dance/Ballet, Film, Multi-media

Singapore International Piano Festival
Website: https://www.sso.org.sg/sipf
Email: corporate@sso.org.sg
Phone: 660 24200
Address: 11 EmPress Place #01-02, Victoria Concert Hall, Singapore 179558
Information: The Singapore International Piano Festival was established in 1994, when solo piano recitals were a rare event in the country

Country: Singapore
Contact: festival Director Lim Yan
Contact: Ticketing Enquiries
Email: ticketing@sso.org.sg
Contact: Audition Enquiries
Email: Auditions@sso.org.sg
Social Media: twitter.com/SingaporeSymph www.facebook.com/singaporesymphony www.instagram.com/singaporesymphony/
Frequency: Annual
Type: Concert

Xpostion 'O' Contemporary Dance Fiesta
Website: http:// www.xposition-o.com/2017/index.html
Email: odtinternational@gmail.com
Phone: 622 15229
Address: 28 Aliwal Street, Aliwal Arts Centre #03-08, SG
Information: ODT has astounded global audiences on a number of accounts while the vision and ambition of its works exhibit utmost commitment to professionalism and innovation. ODT has earned wide respect for its consistency and extensive profile in delivering imPressive numerous initiatives and productions that have impacted many people's lives.
Country: Singapore
Contact: Artistic Director Danny Tan
Social Media: www.facebook.com/odyssey.dancesg
Type: Concert, Dance/Ballet, Theatre, Performance art

SOUTH AFRICA

ASSITEJ World Congress and Performing Arts Festival
Website: https://www.assitej2017.org.za/
Email: comms@assitej.org.za
Phone: 218 220 070
Address: Postnet Suite X22, Private Bag X7, Muizenberg, 7950 Cape Town
Information: The World Congress is the most important meeting of all members of ASSITEJ (International Association of Theatre for Children and Young People), which takes place once every three years. It is the culmination of the working life of the association for that three-year period, reflecting on the last three years of activity and creating a vision collectively with its members for the future.
Country: South Africa
Contact: Director Jaqueline Dommisse
Email: jaqueline@theatre4youth.co.za
Contact: Co-ordinator Faye Kabali-Kagwa
Email: theatre4youthwc@assitej.org.za
Contact: education project Manager Tsholofelo Shounyane
Email: jhb@theatre4youth.co.za
Frequency: Triennial
Type: Theatre

Clover Aardklop National Arts Festival
Website: aardklop.co.za
Email:
navrae@aardklop.co.za
Phone: 182 947 509
Address: Posbus 20313, ZA
Information: This is one of the largest arts festivals in South Africa. The Festival attracts an imPressive line-up of South African artists and performers from around the country. Although the festival's focus is on the Afrikaans language and culture, it is accessible to non-Afrikaans speakers too
Country: South Africa
Contact: Director AlexaStrachan
Email: alexa@aardklop.co.za
Contact: Programming Jacinda Doinet
Email: jacinda@aardklop.co.za
Contact: Operations Manager Bosman Purén
Email: bosman@aardklop.co.za
Contact: Manager: Sponsors, media and Marketing Delmari van Zyl
Email: delmari@aardklop.co.za
Contact: Coordinator Deon van Niekerk
Email: deon@aardklop.co.za
Contact: General Inquiries
Email: navrae@aardklop.co.za
Social Media: https://twitter.com/AardklopFees www.facebook.com/Aardklop
Venue: Potchefstroom

Klein Karoo Arts Festival (KKNK)
Website:
www.absakknk.co.za
Email: info@kknk.co.za
Phone: 442 038 600
Address: Voortrekker Road, ZA

Information: Klein Karoo Arts Festival (KKNK) is an Afrikaans arts and culture festival in the Karoo town of Oudtshoorn. The festival always offers a first class programme to classical music enthusiasts
Country: South Africa
Frequency: annual
Venue: town of Oudtshoorn
Type: Concert, Musical theatre

National Arts Festival Grahamstown
Website: www.nationalartsfestival.co.za
Email: info@nationalartsfestival.co.za
Phone: 086 000 2004
Address: 1820 Settlers Monument, Fort Selwyn Drive, ZA
Information: The National Arts Festival, now in its 39th year, has proved its sustainability and has grown to be one of the leading arts festivals in southern Africa. Its objectives are to deliver excellence, encourage innovation and development in the arts by providing a platform for both established and emerging South African artists, create opportunities for collaboration with international artists, and to build new audiences
Country: South Africa
Social Media: @artsfestival www.facebook.com/nationalartsfestival
Frequency: annual
Venue: Grahamstown
Type: Concert, Performance art

THAILAND

Bangkok International Festival of Dance and Music
Website: https://www.bangkokfestivals.com/
Phone: 662 247 0028
Address: Thailand Cultural Centre, Ratchadapisek Rd, Huay Kwang, Bangkok 10320 THAILAND
Information: The Festival was established in the year 1999, commemorating His Majesty the late King Bhumibol Adulyadej's 6th cycle birthday. From just having 6 performances and 200 artists, the Festival has now grown in scale where over 20 performances with more than a thousand artists are taken to the stage over a 5-6 week period. Through the years, the Festival has attracted an audience of millions of people.
Country: Thailand
Social Media: www.facebook.com/BangkoksInternationalFestivalOfDanceMusic
Frequency: Annual
Type: Dance/Ballet, Concert

UNITED ARAB EMIRATES

Abu Dhabi Festival
Website: https://abudhabifestival.ae/
Email: info@admaf.org
Phone: 233 36400
Address: Makneen Tower (floor 3), , PO Box 47488, AE
Information: Abu Dhabi Festival is organised by the Abu Dhabi Music & Arts Foundation (ADMAF). Founded in 2004 and organised by Abu Dhabi Music & Arts Foundation, the annual multidisciplinary Festival is the largest cultural celebration in the entire region and reaches across the world through co-commissions and the international presentation of innovative Arab creativity. In essence, Abu Dhabi Festival strives to deepen global cross-cultural dialogue whilst inspiring a deeper interest in the Arab world.
Country: United Arab Emirates
Founder & Artistic Director
 Huda Alkhamis Kanoo
Email: admfauh@emirates.net.ae
Social Media: twitter.com/abudhabi_fest www.facebook.com/abudhabifestival/ www.instagram.com/abudhabifestival
Frequency: Annual
Type: Multi-media

Al Ain Classics Festival
Website: https://www.alainmusicfest.com/
Email: aamf@ladolcevita.ae
Phone: 373 31121
Address: AE
Information: The Al Ain Music Festival is a community-based event located across the oasis city of Al Ain in the U.A.E. It aims to provide an entertaining programme – featuring a variety of genres – for lovers of live musical performance across the region.
Country: United Arab Emirates
Social Media: www.facebook.com/alainmusicfest www.instagram.com/alainmusicfest/
Frequency: Annual
Type: Multi-media

UNITED STATES

African American Atelier
Website: www.africanamericanatelier.org
Email: arts@africanamericanatelier.org
Phone: 336 333 6885
Address: 200 N Davie St # 14, US
Information: this non-profit art organisation, seeks to promote an awareness, appreciation and sensitivity to

the visual arts and culture of African Americans and to work in harmony with other ethnic groups

Country: United States
Social Media: @aaatelier@AfricanAmericanAtelier
Frequency: annual
Venue: Downtown Greensboro
Type: Other

Alma Music and Arts Festival
Website: www.almamusicandartsfest.org
Email: almabeachfest@gmail.com
Phone: 608 685 3303
Address: 125 Beach Harbor Road Alma, WI, US 54610
Information: For 19 years, the Alma Music and Arts Festival has been bringing great music, arts and food to the banks of the the the Mississippi in Alma.
Country: United States
Social Media: https://www.facebook.com/AlmaMusicAndArtsFestival/
Frequency: Annual

American Dance Festival
Website: www.americandancefestival.org
Email: adf@americandancefestival.org
Phone: 919 684 6402
Address: 721 Broad Street Durham, NC 27705
Information: American Dance Festival aims to encourage and support the creation and presentation of new modern dance work by both established and emerging choreographers. It also offers professional education and training, a forum for integrating and disseminating information on dance education.
Country: United States
Contact: President Jodee Nimericher
Email: adf@americandancefestival.org
Contact: ADF School Dean Leah Cox
Email: leahcox@americandancefestival.org
Contact: Director of Finance and Administration Cynthia Wyse
Email: cwyse@americandancefestival.org
Social Media: https://twitter.com/AmerDanceFest https://www.facebook.com/AmerDanceFest https://www.instagram.com/amerdancefest/

An Appalachian Summer Festival
Website: appsummer.org
Email: theschaefercenter@appstate.edu
Phone: 828 262 4046
Address: An Appalachian Summer Festival, Schaefer Center for the Performing Arts, 733 Rivers St. Boone, NC 28608
Information: this annual celebration of the performing and visual arts is held every July in venues across the university campus, and features an eclectic, diverse mix of music, dance, theatre, visual arts and film programming. An Appalachian Summer Festival began in 1984 as a chamber music series, and retains strong roots in classical music, combined with a variety of other programming geared to almost every Artistic taste and preference. Celebrating its 32nd season in 2016, the festival has risen in stature to become one of the nation's most highly respected summer festivals, acclaimed for the breadth and quality of its Artistic programming. With an audience of 27, 000, the festival has been named one of the "Top Twenty Events in the Southeast" by the Southeast Tourism Society.
Country: United States
Contact: Director of arts Denise Ringler
Email: weissbergdr@appstate.edu
Contact: Director of Artist Relations, Arts and Cultural Programs Laura Kaufman
Email: kaufmanlc@appstate.edu
Director of Arts Education & Outreach, Office of Arts Engagement
 Christy Chenausky
Email: chenauskyc@appstate.edu
Social Media: https://twitter.com/AppalachianArts https://www.facebook.com/anappalachiansummerfestival/ https://www.instagram.com/appsummerfestival/
Frequency: Annual
Venue: Schaefer Center for the Performing Arts
Type: Concert, Dance/Ballet, Theatre

Ann Arbor Summer Festival
Website: www.a2sf.org
Email: info@a2sf.org
Phone: 734 994 5999
Address: 210 Huronview Blvd, Suite 1, US
Information: The Ann Arbor Summer Festival is a celebration of performing arts, outdoor entertainment, and community spirit. A boutique music and arts festival, the three-week gathering offers dozens of performances, activities, exhibitions, and screenings representative of the best in music, dance, comedy, film, street arts and family entertainment. Today, the Ann Arbor Summer Festival produces two concurrent programmes, one indoor and one outdoor, at various venues and spaces across the University of Michigan campus and in downtown Ann Arbor. The indoor Mainstage series includes ticketed performances of world-class music, dance, theater and comedy. The outdoor program, Top of the Park, is held along a beautiful campus green and offers admission-free

concerts, movies under the stars, open-air spectacles and unique family attractions.
Country: United States
Contact: General Manager Mike Michelon
Email: michelon@a2sf.org
Contact: development Director Heather Steenrod
Email: steenrod@a2sf.org
Contact: Marketing and programs Manager James Carter
Contact: Marketing and Communications Natalie Robbins
Email: robbins@a2sf.org
Social Media: https://twitter.com/AASummerFest https://www.facebook.com/AASummerFest/ https://www.instagram.com/aasummerfest/
Venue: various venues and spaces across the University of Michigan campus
Type: Dance/Ballet, Concert, Theatre, Multi-media

Apple Hill Center for Chamber Music
Website: https://applehill.org/
Email: music@applehill.org
Phone: 603 847 3371
Address: 410 Apple Hill Rd, US
Information: Apple Hill exists to create, perform, and teach chamber music at the highest standard, broaden the appreciation of chamber music through the development of educational programs, and cultivate a connection and understanding amongst people of diverse backgrounds and cultures through the Playing for Peace programme.
Country: United States
Contact: Director Leonard Matczynski
Email: lenny@applehill.org
Contact: facilities Manager Richard Anderson
Email: richard@applehill.org
Contact: summer coordinator Amelia Perron
Email: amelia@applehill.org
Social Media: www.facebook.com/applehill
Other Venues: Concert Barn up to (300 capacity)
Type: Concert

Arizona Musicfest
Website: https://azmusicfest.org/
Email: azmusicfestoffice@azmusicfest.org
Phone: 480 488 0806
Address: 7518 Elbow Bend, US
Information: Presenting top artists of classical, chamber, jazz, Broadway, country, blues, opera, bluegrass, and pop music in Scottsdale and Phoenix.
Country: United States
Contact: Executive Director Allan Naplan
Email: allan@azmusicfest.org
Contact: Director of operations Jay Good
Email: jay@azmusicfest.org
Social Media: @arizona.musicfest
Other Venues: Highlands Church (2, 000 capacity); Desert Hills Presbyterian Church (350 capacity); Pinnacle Presbyterian Church (750 capacity); Temple Chai (400 capacity)
Type: Concert

Art Song Festival
Website: https://www.artsongfest.com/
Email: info@artsongfest.com
Phone: 216 373 9353
Address: Art Song Festival, Cleveland Institute of Music, 11021 East Boulevard Cleveland, Ohio 44106
Information: Cleveland's Art Song Festival was founded in 1985 at the Cleveland Institute of Music by George Vassos, who taught at CIM for fifty years and was Head of the Voice Department for twenty-seven years.
The Festival's mission is to promote the rich and enticing art song repertoire and to cultivate its performance through recitals by major guest artists and master classes. Many of the world's foremost performers and scholars have participated in the Festival since its inception.
Country: United States
Contact: Founder and Artistic Director George Vassos
Contact: Executive Director Dean Southern
Contact: Artistic Administrator Lenore Rosenberg
Social Media: www.facebook.com/artsongfestival
Other Venues: Cleveland Institute of Music
Type: Concert

Artscape – Baltimore's Festival of the Arts Inc.
Website: http:// www.artscape.org/
Email: artscape@promotionandarts.org
Phone: 410 752 8632
Address: 7 E Redwood Street, Suite 500, US
Information: America's largest free arts festival, attracting over 350, 000 attendees over three days. Artscape features over 150 fine artists, fashion designers and craftspeople. It offers visual art exhibits on and off-site, including outdoor sculpture, art cars, photography and the Janet & Walter Sondheim Prize, as well as incredible live concerts on outdoor stages, a full schedule of performing arts including dance, opera, theatre, film, experimental music and the Baltimore Symphony Orchestra, family events such as hands-on projects, demonstrations, competitions, children's entertainers and street theater, and a delicious international menu of food and beverages.
Country: United States
Contact: Corporate Sponsorship Director Bob Sicard
Email: bsicard@promotionandarts.org
Social Media: twitter.com/ArtscapeBmore www.facebook.com/Artscape.Baltimore
Type: Multi-media

ArtsQuest
Website: www.musikfest.org
Email: info@artsquest.org
Phone: 610 332 1300
Address: 101 Founders Way, US
Information: during its 10-day run, Musikfest features more than 300 performers on 13 indoor and outdoor stages throughout the city of Bethlehem
Country: United States
President & CEO
Kassie Hilgert
Contact: Director Joann Lee
Email: jlee@artsquest.org
Social Media: @Musikfest@musikfest
Frequency: annual
Venue: Sands Steel Stage at PNC Plaza; Aetna Americaplatz; Mutual of Omaha Banana Island; Wells Fargo Festplatz; Handwerkplatz; National Penn Bank Jazz Cabaret Stage; Downtown Bethlehem Assoc Liederplatz and others

Asian-American Lunar New Year Festival
Website: https://www.lunarnewyearhouston.com/
Email: jimmynguyen@innovasiamedia.com
Phone: 713 861 8270
Address: Viet Hoa Center, Beltway 8 Plaza, 8388 W. Sam Houston Parkway, South, Houston, Texas 77072
Information: Our mission is to preserve, present and promote authentic pan-Asian cultural arts through annual special events for Greater Houston. All our professional productions are free-admission events for Houston audiences and visitors to the Region. It includes, music, dance, food and cultural activities and showcases.
Country: United States
Contact: festival Director Glenda Joe
Email: GlendaJoe@gkjoe.com
Social Media: www.facebook.com/LunarNewYearHouston www.instagram.com/explore/tags/LunarNewYear-Houston/
End: 2022-02-06
Other Venues: Viet Hoa Center @ Beltway 8 Plaza
Type: Concert, Dance/Ballet, Multi-media

Aspen Music Festival and School
Website: https://www.aspenmusicfestival.com/
Email: info@aspenmusic.org
Phone: 970 925 3254
Address: 225 Music School Road Aspen, CO 81611, USA 970 925 3254
Information: This is a classical music festival, presenting more than 300 musical events during its eight-week summer season. The institution draws top classical musicians from around the world for performances and music education. Many events are free, and seating on the David Karetsky Music Lawn and in the Music Garden is always free
Country: United States
Contact: music Director Robert Spano
Contact: President and CEO Alan Fletcher
Email: afletcher@aspenmusic.org
Social Media: twitter.com/aspenmusic www.facebook.com/aspenmusic/photos
Start: 2022-06-30
End: 2022-08-21
Type: Concert

Aston Magna Festival
Website: http://astonmagna.org/
Email: astonmagna@optonline.net
Phone: 413 528 3595
Address: Aston Magna Foundation for Music and the Humanities, Inc. P.O. Box 28 Great Barrington, MA 01230
Information: The mission of the Aston Magna Foundation is to enrich the appreciation of music of the past and the understanding of the cultural, political, and social contexts in which it was composed and experienced. The goal is to reach a larger public through the use of historical instruments and practices in performances, recordings, and workshops, and through innovative interdisciplinary educational programs, publications, and electronic media.
Country: United States
Social Media: twitter.com/astonmagnafesti?lang=en www.facebook.com/AstonMagnaMusic
Other Venues: The Mahaiwe Performing Arts Centre; Slosberg Auditorium; The Daniel Arts Centre; Olin Hall.
Type: Concert

Atlanta Jazz Festival
Website: https://atlantafestivals.com/
Email: atlantajazz@atlantaga.gov
Phone: 404 546 6826
Address: 55 Trinity Ave. SW Atlanta, GA, US 30303
Information: Established in 2012, Atlanta Jazz Festival, Inc. is a registered 501(c)(3) non-profit corporation. The mission and purpose of Atlanta Jazz Festival, Inc. is to raise awareness, provide support, solicit corporate sponsorships, and conduct fundraising activities in support of the three-day Atlanta Jazz Festival event in Piedmont Park. It also aims to present educational programs to teach and preserve the rich history of jazz, raise visibility of the Atlanta Jazz Festival and the Associated 31 Days of Jazz during the month of May as a cultural institution in Atlanta and beyond.
Country: United States
Contact: Board Chair Hillary Dunson
Contact: Volunteer Opportunities
Email: jazzteers@atlantaga.gov
Contact: Vending Inquiries
Email: rob@premiereventslive.com
Social Media: twitter.com/AtlantaJazzFest www.facebook.com/atlantajazzfestival
Frequency: Annual
Type: Concert

Bach Festival of Philadelphia
Website: https://www.choralarts.com/bach-festival-of-philadelphia.html
Email: info@choralarts.com
Phone: 267 240 2586
Address: Bach Festival of Philadelphia P.O. Box 22445 Philadelphia, PA 19110
Information: Making music since 1982, Choral Arts Philadelphia celebrates local, professional and amateur musicians. As Philadelphia's premier chamber chorus, Choral Arts Philadelphia presents concert experiences that delight and engage the community as well as contribute to their appreciation of the repertoire. Choral Arts Philadelphia is committed to musical excellence, historically informed performance practices, and furthering the great tradition of choral music.
Country: United States
Contact: Artistic Director Matthew Glandorf
Email: auditions@choralarts.com
Social Media: twitter.com/ChoralArtsPhila www.facebook.com/ChoralArtsPhiladelphia
Other Venues: churches, museums and schools
Type: Concert

Bach Festival Society of Winter Park
Website: https://www.bachfestivalflorida.org/
Email: info@BachFestivalFlorida.org
Phone: 407 646 2182
Address: 1000 Holt Avenue, Box #2763, US
Information: The Bach Festival Society is well known internationally and has enjoyed a long tradition of bringing world-class talent to Central Florida. Since its inception, the society has expanded its offerings beyond the annual Bach Festival to include choral masterworks and visiting artists performances, as well as a variety of educational and community outreach programs to encourage participation in music at all levels. The Bach Festival Society of Winter Park has the distinction of being the third-oldest continuously operating Bach Festival in the United States, as well as being Central Florida's oldest operating performing arts organization.
Country: United States
Artistic Director & conductor
John V. Sinclair
Email: jsinclair@bachfestivalflorida.org
Social Media: twitter.com/BachFestivalWP www.facebook.com/BachFestivalWP
Other Venues: Knowles Memorial Chapel
Type: Concert

Bach Week Festival
Website: https://bachweek.org/
Email: info@bachweek.org
Phone: 269 9050
Address: Bach Week Festival 1555 Sherman Avenue, Suite 312 Evanston, IL 60201
Information: Bach Week Festival also explores the music of other Baroque composers, with a few 20th-century icons (Stravinsky, among them).
Country: United States
Contact: music Director Richard Webster
Social Media: https://twitter.com/BachWeek https://www.facebook.com/BachWeek
Other Venues: Nichols Hall in the Music Institute of Chicago
Type: Concert

Baltimore Symphony Orchestra Summerfest
Website: https://www.bsomusic.org/
Email: education@BSOmusic.org
Phone: 410 783 8118
Address: 1212 Cathedral Street, US
Information: The Baltimore Symphony Orchestra (BSO) is internationally recognized as having achieved a preeminent place among the world's most important orchestras. Acclaimed for its enduring pursuit of Artistic excellence, the BSO has attracted a devoted national and international following while maintaining deep bonds throughout Maryland through innovative education and community outreach initiatives.**Country: United States**
Contact: music Director Marin Alsop
Contact: President and CEO Paul Meecham
Contact: Chairman of the board Barbara Bozzuto
Social Media: www.facebook.com/BSOmusic
Other Venues: Joseph Meyerhof Symphony Hall (2440 capacity)
Type: Concert

Bay Chamber Concerts Summer Festival
Website: https://www.baychamber.org/
Email: info@baychamberconcerts.org
Phone: 236 2823
Address: 18 Central St., 5th floor, Rockport, ME 04856, US
Information: Founded in 1961 by brothers, Andrew and Thomas Wolf, Bay Chamber Concerts features world-renowned artists year-round. Our Summer Concert Series and Screen Door Summer Music Festival take place in July and August
Country: United States
Contact: Artistic Director Manuel Bagorro
Email: manuel@baychamberconcerts.org
Contact: Executive Director Monica Kelly
Email: monica@baychamberconcerts.org
Contact: Advancement Officer Josie Davis
Email: josie@baychamberconcerts.org
Social Media: twitter.com/BayChamber www.facebook.com/BayChamberME
Other Venues: Rockport Opera House (400 capacity) The Strand Theatre (350 capacity) Strom Auditorium (810 capacity)Camden Opera House (500 capacity), and other venues located in Midcoast maine.
Type: Concert

Bear Valley Music Festival
Website: https://www.bearvalleymusicfestival.org/
Email: info@bearvalleymusicfestival.org
Phone: 209 813 0554
Address: Bear Valley Music Festival, P. O. Box 5068, Bear Valley, CA 95223
Information: The Bear Valley Music Festival is a yearly summer event in Bear Valley, California. The festival currently begins on the second-to-last Friday in July and ends three Sundays later, drawing a total audience of roughly four thousand attendees. Under the direction of internationally recognized conductor Michael Morgan since 2012, the festival strives to appeal to a wide demographic by presenting a variety of artists and styles of music including classical, rock, country and jazz.
Country: United States
Music Director & Conductor
 Michael Morgan
Contact: Executive Director Eman Isadiar
Social Media: twitter.com/BVMusicFestival www.facebook.com/BearValleyMusicFestival/ www.instagram.com/bearvalleymusicfestival/
Frequency: Annual
Start: 2022-07-22
Type: Concert

Berkeley Festival & Exhibition
Website: https://berkeleyfestival.org/
Email: exhibition@sfems.org
Phone: 510 528 1725
Address: P.O. Box 10151, Berkeley, US
Information: The Berkeley Festival & Exhibition is produced by The San Francisco Early Music Society and was conceived of and founded by Robert Cole, the then Director of Cal Performances, and the late Joseph Spencer, proprietor of the Musical Offering and then, the SFEMS President. Over the years, the Festival has presented unique and amazing events: Mark Morris Dance Group's interpretation of Rameau's Platée, Le Carousel du Roi, featuring dressage horses and riders executing elaborate ballets from seventeenth-century France accompanied by shawms and sackbuts in their natural setting (outdoors), and the North American premiere of a long-lost Mass by Alessandro Striggio for 40 and 60 voices.
Country: United States
Contact: box office and patrons services Manager Craig Hanson
Email: chanson@sfems.org
Contact: Head of Exhibitions Greta Haug-Hryciw
Email: exhibition@sfems.org
Contact: Fringe Paulina Francisco
Email: bfx.fringe@sfems.org
Social Media: www.facebook.com/berkeleyfx/
Other Venues: Hertz Hall (711 capacity), First Congregational Church (750 capacity)
Type: Concert

Berkshire Choral Festival
Website:
https://berkshirechoral.org/
Email: info@berkshirechoral.org
Phone: 413 229 8526
Address: 406 Main Street, Suite 1 Great Barrington, MA 01230
Information: Berkshire Choral International creates one-of-a-kind experiences for amateur singers, inspires participation in life-long singing, and builds appreciation for choral music. Over the past 39 years, BCI has enriched the lives of almost 9000 singers through our week-long choral music programs under the batons of dozens of the world's great conductors in prestigious venues throughout the US.
Country: United States
Contact: Chorister Services Director Stephen Hager
Email: shager@berkshirechoral.org
Contact: Operations Director Christopher Tucci
Email: ctucci@berkshirechoral.org
Contact: Music Director Frank Nemhauser
Email: fnemhauser@berkshirechoral.org
Social Media: www.facebook.com/berkshirechoralinternational/twitter.com/BerkshireChoral www.instagram.com/berkshirechoral_international/
Type: Concert

Big Muddy Folk Music Festival
Website:
http://www.bigmuddy.org/2021pix/index.html
Email: fohboonville@gmail.com
Phone: 882 7977
Address: 614 E Morgan Street (Old Cooper County Jail & Hanging Barn)
Information: The Friends of Historic Boonville is proud to sponsor the Big Muddy Folk Festival, held in April each year. This two day, nationally-recognized folk festival focuses on traditional, ethnic and folk music with concerts, workshops, jam sessions, demonstrations, master classes, exhibits, a dance and barbeque.
Country: United States
Social Media: www.facebook.com/FOHBoonville/twitter.com/FOHBoonville
Frequency: Annual
Type: Concert

Blossom Festival
Website: https://www.clevelandorchestra.com/
Email: info@clevelandorchestra.com
Phone: 216 231 7300
Address: 11001 Euclid Ave Cleveland, Ohio 44106 216-231-7300
Information: The Cleveland Orchestra presents the Blossom Festival of weekend concerts featuring the Orchestra in symphonic repertoire, along with performances by the Blossom Festival Band, Blossom Festival Orchestra, and visiting artists and performers. in addition, Live Nation presents a summer-long season of concerts devoted to rock, jazz, country, and other musical presentations.
Country: United States
Contact: Chair Richard K. Smucker
President & CEO
André Gremillet
Social Media: twitter.com/CleveOrchestra www.facebook.com/clevelandorchestra
Frequency: Annual
Other Venues: Blossom Music Centre 5281 pavilion seating, 13500 outdoors
Type: Concert

Booking Dance Festival
Website: www.bookingdance.com
Email: artists@bookingdance.com
Phone: 352 0400
Address: 318 West 101 Street, Suite 8 New York, NY, US 10025
Information: The BOOKING DANCE FESTIVAL is the brainchild of Producer Jodi Kaplan, born with the intention of creating a cultural exchange between performing artists and international communities. The Festival occurs at different locations around the globe, continually bridging dance artists and audiences worldwide. Through both performances and educational outreach, the festival offers underserved dance companies the opportunity to expand their visibility to a global scale.
Country: United States
Contact: Director Jodie Kaplan
Email: jka@bookingdance.com
Social Media: https://twitter.com/BookingDanceww.facebook.com/BookingDanceFestival/ https://www.instagram.com/bookingdancefestival/?hl=en
Type: Dance/Ballet

Boston Early Music Festival & Exhibition
Website: https://bemf.org/
Email: bemf@bemf.org
Phone: 617 661 1812
Address: Boston Early Music Festival 43 Thorndike Street, Suite 302 Cambridge, MA 02141, USA
Information: The Boston Early Music Festival (BEMF) is universally recognized as a leader in the field of early music. Since its founding in 1980 by leading practitioners of historical performance in the United States and abroad, BEMF has promoted early music through a variety of diverse programs and activities, including an annual concert series that brings early music's brightest stars to the Boston and New York concert stages, and the biennial weeklong Festival and Exhibition.
Country: United States
Contact: Executive Director Kathleen Fay
Email: kathy@bemf.org
Contact: General Manager Carla Chrisfield
Email: carla@bemf.org
Contact: Director of Marketing Brian Stuart
Email: brian@bemf.org
Social Media: twitter.com/bostonearly www.facebook.com/bostonearly
Frequency: Biennial
Other Venues: Cutler Emerson Majestic Theatre; Emmanuel Church; First Church in Cambridge, Congregational; New England Conservatorys Jordan Hall and others
Type: Concert

Boulder Bach Festival
Website: https://www.boulderbachfestival.org/
Email: info@boulderbachfest.org
Phone: 720 507 5052
Address: Boulder Bach Festival 3300 Arapahoe Avenue, Suite 206 Boulder, Colorado 80303
Information: The Boulder Bach Festival presents a multitude of thought-provoking concerts and education events, exploring performance practice from diverse perspectives and programming in meaningful ways
Country: United States
Contact: Executive Director Zachary Carrettin
Social Media: www.facebook.com/boulderbachfestival
Other Venues: Theater in Obstinate Pearl
Type: Concert

Bowdoin International Music Festival
Website: https://www.bowdoinfestival.org/
Email: info@bowdoinfestival.org
Phone: 207 373 1400
Address: 6300 College Station, Brunswick, ME 04011-8463
Information: The Bowdoin International Music Festival is one of the world's premiere music institutes. Founded in 1964, the Festival engages exceptional students and enthusiastic audiences through world-class education and performances. Each summer, 250 students from more than 20 countries and nearly every state attend the Festival to study with distinguished faculty and guest artists.
Country: United States
Contact: Artistic Director David Ying
Email: davidying@esm.rochester.edu
Contact: Artistic Director Phillip Ying
Email: pying@esm.rochester.edu
Contact: Admissions Grace Bell
Email: grace@bowdoinfestival.org
Contact: Executive Director Daniel Nitsch
Email: dan@bowdoinfestival.org
Social Media: www.facebook.com/Bowdoin.International.Music.Festival/
Frequency: Annual
Other Venues: Stuzinski Recital Hall (350 capacity), Crooker Theatre (600 capacity)
Type: Concert

Bravo! Vail Valley Music Festival
Website: https://www.bravovail.org/
Email: info@bravovail.org
Phone: 970 827 5700
Address: 2271 N Frontage Rd W, Suite C Vail, Colorado 81657
Information: In 1987, founding Executive Director John Giovando and founding Artistic Director Ida Kavafian established Bravo! Vail as public 501 (c) 3 Colorado non-profit corporation. Since then, Bravo! Vail has evolved from a small chamber music series to an international music festival with dozens of performances throughout the Vail Valley, and summer home to the world's greatest musicians and orchestras.
Country: United States
Contact: Executive Director Caitlin Murray
Contact: Artistic Director Anne-Marie McDermott
Social Media: twitter.com/BravoVail www.facebook.com/bravovail www.instagram.com/bravovail/
Other Venues: Ford Amphitheater (3000 capacity), Vilar Center (500 capacity)
Type: Concert

Brevard Music Centre
Website: https://www.brevardmusic.org/
Email: bmc@brevardmusic.org
Phone: 828 862 2130
Address: 349 Andante Lane, Brevard, NC 28712, USA
Information: The Brevard Music Center is an international summer institute and festival located in Brevard, North Carolina. It enrolls about four hundred students, age fourteen and older, who participate in orchestra and other large ensembles, an opera program, play chamber music, study composition, and take private lessons. A faculty of sixty is drawn from orchestras, conservatories, and universities.
Country: United States
Contact: President and chief Executive officer Mark Weinstein
Contact: Artistic Director Keith Lockhart
Social Media: twitter.com/brevardmusic www.facebook.com/brevardmusiccenter www.instagram.com/brevardmusic
Frequency: Annual
Other Venues: Primary BMC performance venues include the 2200-seat, open-air Whittington-Pfohl Auditorium and the new Parker Concert Hall(400 capacity)
Type: Concert

BRIC Celebrate Brooklyn! Festival
Website: https://www.bricartsmedia.org/events-performances/bric-celebrate-brooklyn-festival-live-everywhere
Email: bric@bricartsmedia.org
Phone: 718 683 5600
Address: 647 Fulton Street, US
Information: There's only one free summer-long outdoor concert and performance series in New York City that

has been presenting talent from around the world and around the block for more than 40 years: the BRIC Celebrate Brooklyn! Festival
Country: United States
Contact: President Kristina Newman-Scott
Email: knewmanscott@bricartsmedia.org
Contact: Director of Performing Arts Lia Camille Crockett
Email: lcrockett@BRICartsmedia.org
Social Media: https://www.facebook.com/BRICcelebrateBK/
Frequency: Annual
Venue: Prospect Park, Bandshell (8000 capacity) and various other Brooklyn venues
Type: Concert, Dance/Ballet, Other

Bridgehampton Chamber Music Festival
Website: www.bcmf.org
Email: info@bcmf.org
Phone: 212 741 9073
Address: 135 E. 57th Street, 14th FL, New York, NY 10022
Information: Since 1984, the Bridgehampton Chamber Music Festival has brought the very best of chamber music to Long Island's East End. From a pair of concerts over a single weekend, to a series of concerts over 5 weeks in the summer as well as a series of concerts each spring, BCMF has become one of the country's most highly regarded chamber music organizations in the country. Each year, some of the world's finest chamber musicians gather in Bridgehampton to create unique musical experiences.
Country: United States
Contact: Executive Director Michael Lawrence
Email: michaellawrence@bcmf.org
Social Media: https://www.facebook.com/bridgehampton.chamber https://twitter.com/bcmftweets https://www.instagram.com/bcmfphoto/
Frequency: Annual
Venue: Presbyterian Church of Bridgehampton 400
Type: Concert

Britt Festivals
Website: www.brittfest.org
Email: info@brittfest.org
Phone: 180 088 27488
Address: 350 S 1st St Jacksonville, OR, US 97530
Information: Britt Music & Arts Festival, a non-profit organization, is the Pacific Northwest's premier outdoor summer performing arts festival. Located in the historic 1850s gold rush town of Jacksonville, Oregon (USA), Britt presents dozens of summer concerts, featuring world-class artists in classical music, jazz, blues, folk, bluegrass, world, pop and country music. Britt's performance venue is a naturally formed amphitheater set among majestic ponderosa pines and native madrones.**Country: United States**
Contact: Chair Dominic Campanella
Contact: Vice-Chair Mark Damon
Social Media: https://twitter.com/brittfestivals https://www.facebook.com/BrittFestivals/ https://www.instagram.com/brittfestival/
Frequency: Annual
Venue: Britt pavilion, Britt Gardens in Jacksonville
Type: Concert

Cabrillo Music Festival
Website: https://cabrillomusic.org/
Email: info@cabrillomusic.org
Phone: 831 426 6966
Address: Cabrillo Festival of Contemporary Music 147 South River Street, Suite 232 Santa Cruz, CA 95060
Information: During the first two weeks of August each year, audiences are joined by both preeminent and emerging composers, an orchestra of dedicated professional musicians, and renowned guest artists from across the globe to give voice to works which are rarely more than a year or two old, and sometimes still wet on the page.
Country: United States
Contact: Artistic Director Cristian Macelaru
Social Media: twitter.com/CabrilloFest www.facebook.com/CabrilloFest www.instagram.com/cabrillofestival/
Other Venues: Santa Cruz Civic Auditorium (900 cap); Mission San Juan Bautista (400 cap)
Type: Concert

Cape Cod Chamber Music Festival
Website: https://capecodchambermusic.org/
Email: info@capecodchambermusic.org
Phone: 508 247 9400
Address: PO Box 1934, North Eastham, MA 02651
Information: The Cape Cod Chamber Music Festival has grown to become an established year-round presenter of chamber music and a major contributor to the cultural life of Cape Cod since 1979.CCCMF presents four weeks of intensive chamber music programming in various Cape locations during July and August. Throughout the balance of the year, CCCMF presents an Autumn and Spring series, a community outreach program, and benefit concerts in N
Country: United States
Contact: President David B. Farer
Contact: Artistic Director Jon Nakamatsu
Contact: Artistic Director Jon Manasse
Social Media: www.facebook.com/capecodchambermusicfestival
Frequency: Annual
Other Venues: First Congregational Church, Chatham; Provincetown Art Association Museum; Cotuit Center for the Arts; Cape Cod Museum of Art, Dennis; First Congregational Church, Wellfleet; Dennis Union Church; Cultural Center of Cape Cod, South Yarmouth.
Type: Concert

Cape May Music Festival
Website: https://capemaymac.org/experience/special-events/cape-may-music-festival/
Email: info@capemaymac.org
Phone: 609 884 5404
Address: 1048 WASHINGTON ST. CAPE MAY, NJ 08204
Information: The Cape May Music Festival presents classical, chamber, jazz and more each year at the grounds of the Physick Estate. Featuring live music as well as family entertainment.
Country: United States
Contact: President Tom Carroll
Contact: Vice President Brian Groetsch
Social Media: twitter.com/capemaymac www.facebook.com/capemaymac www.instagram.com/capemaymac
Frequency: Annual
Other Venues: Cape May Convention Hall
Type: Concert

Carmel Bach Festival
Website: https://bachfestival.org/about-us/
Email: info@bachfestival.org
Phone: 831 624 1521
Address: 10th Ave at Mission St Carmel, CA, US 93921
Information: The Carmel Bach Festival celebrates the works, inspiration, and ongoing influence of J.S.Bach worldwide by immersing audiences in a festival experience integrating music, education and ideas. CBF began in 1935 as a four-day series of concerts at the Sunset School Auditorium and the Carmel Mission Basilica. Over the years, it grew to a three-week celebration of concerts, recitals, master classes, lectures, and open rehearsals, and in 2009 the festival was shortened to two weeks.
Country: United States
Contact: Executive Director Steve Friedlander
Email: steve@bachfestival.org
Contact: Development Manager Olivia Colombo
Email: olivia@bachfestival.org
Social Media: twitter.com/CarmelBach www.facebook.com/bachfestival/ www.instagram.com/carmelbachfestival/?hl=en
Type: Concert

Central City Opera Festival
Website: https://centralcityopera.org/
Email: info@centralcityopera.org
Phone: 303 292 6700
Address: 124 Eureka St Central City, CO, US 80427
Information: Founded in 1932, Central City Opera is the nation's fifth-oldest opera company, located just 35 miles west of Denver in one of Colorado's official National Landmark Historic Districts. The company continues to present Artistically excellent professional opera in its annual summer festival; to offer career-entry training to young singers; to produce education and community service programs; and to preserve and maintain the Opera House and 28 other Victorian-era properties
Country: United States
Contact: General and Artistic Director Pelham G. Pearce
Email: ppearce@centralcityopera.org
Contact: music Director John Baril
Email: jbaril@centralcityopera.org
Contact: Chief Operating Officer/Chief Financial Officer Scott A. Dessens
Email: sdessens@centralcityopera.org
Social Media: twitter.com/ccityopera www.facebook.com/CentralCityOpera https://www.instagram.com/ccityopera/
Other Venues: Central City Opera House
Type: , Opera

Central Park SummerStage
Website: www.summerstage.org
Email: info@cityparksfoundation.org
Phone: 212 360 2756
Address: 830 5th Avenue, US
Country: United States
Contact: Executive Director Heather Lubov
Contact: chief financial officer Simon Chu
Email: schu@cityparksfoundation.org
Contact: Director, Marketing and partnerships Rosemary Jorda
Email: rjorda@cityparksfoundation.org
Social Media: @SummerStage www.facebook.com/SummerStageNYC
Frequency: annual
Venue: Rumsey Playfield, Central Park 5000
Type: Concert, Dance/Ballet, Film, Musical theatre, Opera, Performance art, Theatre

Central Pennsylvania Festival of the Arts
Website: www.arts-festival.com
Phone: 814 237 3682
Address: Central Pennsylvania Festival of the Arts 403 S. Allen Street, Suite 205A P.O. Box 1023 State College, PA 16804
Information: This festival takes place every summer and in the years since the first festival, it has evolved to encompass the Sidewalk Sale and Exhibition, performances on outdoor and indoor stages, a banner competition, Children & Youth Day, a juried gallery exhibition, and the Italian Street Painting Festival

Country: United States
Contact: operations Manager Carol Baney
Contact: Executive Director Rick Bryant
Contact: Director of development Jennifer Shuey
Social Media: https://twitter.com/CPArtsFestival https://www.facebook.com/CentralPAFestivaloftheArts/

Centrum – Ukulele Festival
Website: https://centrum.org/
Email: info@centrum.org
Phone: 360 385 3102
Address: Centrum 223 Battery Way Port Townsend, WA 98368
Information: Centrum Ukulele Festival includes instruction and community building with some of the finest ukulele instructors and players working today. The workshop offerings feature a wide variety of styles – jazz, blues, swing, Hawaiian, pop, novelty, and jugband ukulele. The Port Townsend Ukulele Festival is a gathering appropriate for advanced-beginner, intermediate, and advanced players.
Country: United States
Contact: Executive Director Robert Birman
Email: rbirman@centrum.org
Contact: Program Manager Peter McCracken
Email: peter@centrum.org
Social Media: twitter.com/ptcentrum www.facebook.com/ptcentrum
Other Venues: Fort Worden State Park, McCurdy Pavilion (1400 capacity)
Type: Concert

Chamber Music Albuquerque
Website: www.chambermusicabq.com
Email: chambermusicABQ@gmail.com
Phone: 505 268 1990
Address: 407 Menaul Blvd NE, US
Country: United States
Contact: board President Jonathon Gerson
Contact: stage Manager Curtis Mark
Contact: financial consultant Amy Bauer
Social Media: @chambermusicalbuquerque
Frequency: annual
Venue: Albuquerque Academy 550
Type: Concert

Chamber Music Northwest
Website: www.cmnw.org
Email: info@cmnw.org
Phone: 503 223 3202
Address: 2300 SW 1st Ave, Suite 103, US
Country: United States
Contact: Artistic Director David Shifrin
Contact: Executive Director Peter Bilotta
Email: bilotta@cmnw.org
Contact: development Director Leslie Tuomi
Email: tuomi@cmnw.org
Contact: finance and Administration Director Barbara Bailey
Email: bailey@cmnw.org
Social Media: @chambermusicn w www.facebook.com/chambermusicnorthwest
Frequency: annual
Venue: Reed College 550, Catlin Gabel School 500
Type: Concert

Chamber Music Port Townsend
Website: https://centrum.org/
Email: info@centrum.org
Phone: 360 385 3102
Address: 223 Battery Way Port Townsend, WA 98368 USA
Information: Centrum's vital chamber music series exists to showcase the brilliant talent of many of the world's finest classical artists along with the top echelon of the most promising young talents in the field today.
Country: United States
Contact: Artistic Director Lucinda Carver
Social Media: twitter.com/ptcentrum www.facebook.com/ptcentrum
Frequency: Annual
Type: Concert

Chamber Music Society of the Carolinas
Website: https://www.cmscarolina.com/
Email: chamber@warren-wilson.edu
Phone: 828 771 3050
Address: Chamber Music Society of the Carolinas, Warren Wilson College CPO 6062, P.O. Box 9000, US
Information: The Chamber Music Society of the Carolinas is unique amongst classical music festivals for its approach to performance – which values the audience experience, and favors close, intimate interaction between listener and performer. All performance venues,

artists, and ensembles that take part in CMSC share this common value.
Country: United States
Contact: festival Director Inessa Zaretsky
Email: chamber@warren-wilson.edu
Social Media: www.facebook.com/ChamberMusicFestival
Other Venues: Kittredge Theater, Warren Wilson College (323 capacity), Waynesville Performing Arts Centre, Shelton House (250 capacity), Blue Ridge Community College Auditorium (150 capacity)

Charlottesville Opera
Website: https://www.charlottesvilleopera.org
Email: info@charlottesvilleopera.org
Phone: 434 293 4500
Address: PO Box 2498 / 226 E High Street, Charlottesville, VA
Information: Our Mission is to produce high quality opera and musicals at affordable prices, to provide training opportunities and experience for oung Artists, Apprentice Singers, and Interns, to provide educational nourishment for all sectors of the community, and to enrich the cultural vitality and quality of life in Virginia. Charlotesville Opera also hosts Ash Lawn Opera Festival, which has been incorporated under its new name of Charlottesville Opera.
Country: United States
Contact: General Director Christina DeMarea
Email: General.Director@charlottesvilleopera.org
Contact: Operations Manager Nicole Thompson
Email: nicole.thompson@charlottesvilleopera.org
Social Media: https://twitter.com/CvilleOpera https://www.facebook.com/CharlottesvilleOpera/ https://www.instagram.com/charlottesvilleopera/
Venue: The Paramount Theatre
Type: Opera

Chautauqua Music School Festival
Website: https://chq.org/schools
Email: music@ciweb.org
Phone: 800 836 2787
Address: P.O. Box 28 One Ames Ave. Chautauqua, N.Y. 14722
Information: Every summer, Chautauqua Institution brings some of the world's most talented musicians, vocalists, dancers and visual artists to the grounds for educational and performance opportunities amid our world-class culture and arts environment.
Country: United States
Contact: Chair Candace L. Maxwell
Email: trustees@chq.org
Contact: President Michael E. Hill
Email: mhill@chq.org
Contact: Vice President Sebastian Baggiano
Email: sbaggiano@chq.org
Contact: Director of Production Joseph Futral
Email: jfutral@chq.org
Contact: Schools Assistant Jennifer Barczak
Email: jbarczak@chq.org
Contact: Director of Arts Education Suzanne Fassett Wright
Email: sfassett@chq.org
Social Media: https://twitter.com/chq https://www.facebook.com/chq1874
Venue: Chautauqua Institution
Type: Concert, Dance/Ballet

Chicago Blues Festival
Website: https://www.chicago.gov/city/en/depts/dca/supp_info/chicago_blues_festival.html
Email: dcase@cityofchicago.org
Phone: 312 744 5000
Address: City Hall 121 N. LaSalle Street Chicago, Illinois 60602
Information: As the "Blues Capital of the World, " Chicago produces the largest free blues celebration in the world, featuring a month of programming throughout the city. The Chicago Blues Festival has hosted Blues royalty including Buddy Guy, B.B. King, Koko Taylor, Mavis Staples, Buckwheat Zydeco and Jonny Winter with James Cotton. The event draws an international audience and continues to be a hometown favorite**Country: United States**
Social Media: twitter.com/ChicagoDCASE www.facebook.com/ChicagoBluesFestival
Frequency: Annual
Other Venues: Millennium Park
Type: Concert

Chicago Jazz Festival
Website: https://www.chicago.gov/city/en/depts/dca/supp_info/chicago_jazz_festival.html
Email: dcase@cityofchicago.org
Phone: 312 744 3315
Address: Millennium Park, 201 E Randolph St Chicago, IL, US 60601
Information: Known for its Artistic creativity, the Chicago Jazz Festival is a favorite Labor Day Weekend tradition. It promotes awareness and appreciation for all forms of jazz through free, quality live musical performance. Since 1979, the festival's mission is to showcase Chicago's vast jazz talent alongside national and international artists to encourage and educate a jazz audience of all ages. FREE Admission.
Country: United States
Social Media: www.facebook.com/ChicagoJazzFestival
Other Venues: Chicago Cultural Center, Millennium Park and Venues Across Chicago
Type: Concert

Cincinnati May Festival
Website: www.mayfestival.com
Email: contact@mayfestival.com
Phone: 513 621 1919
Address: Music Hall 1241 Elm Street Cincinnati, OH 45202
Information: Cincinnati May Festival features the 147-member May Festival Chorus and the Cincinnati Symphony Orchestra. Its repertoire ranges from choral masterworks with orchestra and soloists to standard classical choral a-cappella works**Country: United States**
Contact: Executive Director Steven Sunderman
Email: ssunderman@mayfestival.com
Contact: Box Office
Director of Advancement & Engagement
Cat Dixon
Email: cdixon@mayfestival.com
Contact: Associate Director of Choruses Matthew Swanson
Email: MSwanson@mayfestival.com
Contact: Chorus Manager Kathryn Zajac Albertson
Email: kalbertson@mayfestival.com
Contact: Chorus Librarian Joe Basel
Email: jbasel@mayfestival.com
Social Media: https://twitter.com/CincyMayFest https://www.facebook.com/MayFestival
Venue: Music Hall; Cathedral Basilica of the Assumption; Covington.
Type: Concert

Cincinnati Opera Summer Festival
Website: www.cincinnatiopera.com
Email: info@cincinnatiopera.com
Phone: 513 768 5500
Address: 1243 Elm Street Cincinnati, OH 45202
Information: One of the world's leading Opera festivals, Cincinnati Opera is one of the oldest and most highly regarded opera companies in the United States. It's known for its longstanding partnership with the Cincinnati Symphony Orchestra, a roster of world-class singers, and its spectacular performance venue, Cincinnati Music Hall. Cincinnati Opera has received numerous accolades and awards, including a recent nomination for the prestigious International Opera Award.
Country: United States
Contact: Executive Assistant and Office Manager Kelly Holterhoff
Email: kholterhoff@cincinnatiopera.org
Contact: Artistic Director Evans Mirageas
Email: evans@evansmirageas.com
General Director & CEO
Christopher Milligan
Email: cmilligan@cincinnatiopera.org
Contact: Artistic Administrator Jane Hulburt
Email: jhulburt@cincinnatiopera.org
Contact: Artistic Coordinator Hannah Hoffman
Email: hhoffman@cincinnatiopera.org
Contact: Education Manager: Jemannie Severson Luong
Email: jluong@cincinnatiopera.org
Social Media: https://twitter.com/cincinnatiopera https://www.facebook.com/cincinnatiopera
Frequency: Annual
Venue: Music Hall; SCPAs Corbett Theatre.
Type: Opera

Colorado Music Festival
Website: https://centerformusicalarts.org/comusic-landing-page/
Email: Marketing@comusic.org
Phone: 303 440 7666
Address: Colorado Music Festival 200 E. Baseline Road, Lafayette, CO 80026
Information: Six weeks every summer experience 100+ all-star orchestral musicians from around the globe united on one Boulder stage: Chautauqua Auditorium.
Country: United States
Contact: Executive Director Elizabeth McGuire
Email: mcguire@comusic.org
Contact: General Manager Alberto Gutierrez
Social Media: twitter.com/comusicfestival www.facebook.com/COmusicfestival
Frequency: Annual
Other Venues: Chautauqua Auditorium
Type: Concert

Columbia Festival of the Arts
Website: https://columbiafestival.org/
Email: info@columbiafestival.com
Phone: 410 715 3044
Address: 10475 Little Patuxent Parkway Columbia, MD 21044
Information: The Columbia Festival of the Arts is a two-week summer festival that provides unique arts and entertainment experiences for the region surrounding Columbia, Maryland. From the fun-filled Lakefest Free Weekend to legendary performances by artists such as Judy Collins, Aretha Franklin, and Pilobolus, the Festival creates a world class celebration of the arts and entertainment that attracts, engages and inspires the broad and diverse community it serves.**Country: United States**
Contact: Treasurer Bram Berlin
Contact: Vice President Senior Manager Alison Hickman
Contact: office and event services coordinator Heather Huling
Contact: Secretary Laura Wetherald
Social Media: twitter.com/ColumbiaFestArt www.facebook.com/ColumbiaFestival
Frequency: Annual
Other Venues: Howard Community College Horowitz Centre

Columbus Arts Festival
Website: www.columbusartsfestival.org
Email: festival@gcac.org
Phone: 614 224 2606
Address: 233 Civic Center Dr Columbus, OH, US 43215
Information: The Columbus Arts Festival is produced by the Greater Columbus Arts Council and takes place in early June along the downtown riverfront of Columbus, Ohio. Exhibiting artists are chosen via a blind jury process. The event also include performing arts.
Country: United States
Contact: festival coordinator Kez Hall
Email: khall@gcac.org
Contact: Columbus Arts Festival Coordinator Inal Elbeyli
Email: ielbeyli@gcac.org
Contact: President Tom Katzenmeyer
Email: tkatzenmeyer@gcac.org
Contact: Executive Assistant Sue Jones
Email: sjones@gcac.org
Grants & Services Director
Ruby Harper
Email: rharper@gcac.org
Programs & Services Coordinator
Deanna Poelsma
Email: dpoelsma@gcac.org
Contact: Columbus Arts Festival Director Scott Huntley
Email: shuntley@gcac.org
Social Media: https://twitter.com/cbusartsfest https://www.facebook.com/ColumbusArtsFestival/
Frequency: Annual
Venue: Columbus Riverfront
Type: Theatre, Concert, Dance/Ballet, Performance art, Other

Contemporary American Theatre Festival
Website: www.catf.org
Email: info@catf.org
Phone: 304 876 3304
Address: PO Box 429, US
Information: The Contemporary American Theater Festival produces the newest plays in America, in the oldest town in West Virginia. Discover the ultimate theater experience in historic Shepherdstown.
Named as one of the top theater festivals in the world, by publications such as The New York Times, American Theatre, and World Guide, the Contemporary American Theater Festival shapes the future of American theater. Each summer, the Festival produces six new plays in rotating repertory.
Country: United States
Contact: producing Director Ed Herendeen
Email: eherendeen@catf.org
Contact: Associate producing Director Peggy McKowen
Email: pmckowen@catf.org
Contact: Director of development Vicki Willman
Email: vwillman@catf.org
PRESS, ADVERTISING & PROMOTIONS
Gabrielle Tokach
Email: gtokach@catf, org
Social Media: https://twitter.com/thinktheater https://www.facebook.com/CATFatSU
Frequency: Annual
Venue: Marinoff Theatre; Frank Centre Stage; Centre for Contemporary Arts and others
Type: Musical theatre, Theatre

CSU Summer Arts
Website: https://www.calstate.edu/summerarts/Pages/default.aspx
Email: summerarts@calstate.edu
Phone: 562 951 4060
Address: 401 Golden Shore, Long Beach, US
Information: in residence during the months of June and July, CSU offers intensive two-week workshops in visual art, photography, dance, animation, film editing, sound design, music, creative writing, and theatre. In addition to this, over 30 public performances/lectures are presented by world-renown guest artists
Country: United States
Contact: Director Rachel Lee Nardo
Email: rnardo@calstate.edu
Contact: logistics and hospitality Manager Kelley Lansing-Moreno
Email: klansing@calstate.edu
Contact: business Manager Laura Schultz
Email: lschultz@calstate.edu
Contact: assistant Director Joanne Sharp
Email: jsharp@calstate.edu
Social Media: www.facebook.com/CSUSummerArts
Other Venues: Fresno State Campus
Type: Concert, Dance/Ballet, Film, Performance art, Theatre, Multi-media

Dance Now NYC
Website: https://www.dancenownyc.org/
Email: info@dancenownyc.org
Phone: 917 664 8065
Address: 93 4th Avenue PO Box 1480 New York City, NY 10003 – 9998, US
Information:
DANCE NOW (DN) offers an interdependent network of performance, creative development, and educational opportunities, serving a diverse roster of multi-generational artists
Country: United States
Contact: Executive Artistic Director and Producer Robin Staff
Email: robin@dancenownyc.org
Contact: General Manager and Lighting Designer Lauren Parrish
Email: lauren@laurenaparrish.com
Contact: Press contact and information Janet Stapleton
Email: stapleton.janet@gmail.com
Social Media: twitter.com/DanceNOWNYC www.facebook.com/DANCENOWNYC/about
Frequency: Annual
Other Venues: Various venues across New York
Type: Dance/Ballet, Concert, Multi-media

Dance on Camera Festival
Website: https://www.dancefilms.org/
Email: info@dancefilms.org
Phone: 347 505 8649
Address: Dance Films Association, 75 Broad Street, Suite 304, US
Information: Dance on Camera Festival accepts dance films of all genres and lengths. Screen adaptations of stage choreographies, narratives, documentaries, abstract and experimental shorts, and music videos are all welcome. Films that uniquely interpret the relationship between dance and film and exceptionally convey the pervasive affinity between the two mediums are encouraged
Country: United States
Social Media: twitter.com/DanceFilms www.facebook.com/dancefilms/
Other Venues: Walter Reade Theatre; Lincoln Center Plaza.
Type: Dance/Ballet

Dance Salad
Website: https://www.dancesalad.org/
Email: info@dancesalad.org
Phone: 713 355 9011
Address: Houston International Dance Coalition, PO Box 130511, US
Information: Dance Salad Festival is an international contemporary ballet and dance festival. The world's top dance companies and choreographers converge in Houston every spring with unique performances on three separate nights.
Country: United States
Contact: Director Nancy Henderek
Social Media: www.facebook.com/DanceSaladFestival/
Frequency: Annual
Other Venues: Wortham Centre; Cullen Theater
Type: Dance/Ballet

Decibel Festival
Website: dbfestival.com
Email: info@dbfestival.com
Address: US
Information: Founded in 2003, Decibel Festival has become a unique platform for exposing attendees to leading-edge multimedia art from around the globe. With a focus on live performance, interactive multimedia art, state-of-the-art sound and technology based education; Decibel has solidified itself as one of the premier electronic music festivals and promotional organizations in the world. The five-day festival program averages over 25, 000 attendees a year.
Country: United States
Social Media: https://twitter.com/dBFestival https://www.facebook.com/DecibelFestival
Frequency: Annual
Venue: Showbox Soda and at the Market, A Nightclub
Type: Concert, Multi-media, Other

Des Moines Metro Opera
Website: https://desmoinesmetroopera.org/
Email: dmmo@dmmo.org
Phone: 515 961 6221
Address: 106 West Boston Avenue, US
Information: Des Moines Metro Opera is a major American Summer Opera Festival and is one of the state's largest performing arts organizations, annually producing over 100 performances in the metro area and around the region. The company's Summer Festival Season runs from May through July of each year during which three operas are performed in repertory for 15 mainstage performances. The Summer Festival Season takes place at the 467-seat Pote Theater at the Blank Performing Arts Center in Indianola, Iowa.
Country: United States
Contact: Artistic and General Director Michael Egel
Contact: Artistic Director emeritus Robert L Larsen
Social Media: twitter.com/DesMoinesOpera www.facebook.com/DesMoinesMetroOpera
Other Venues: Blank Performing Arts Center (488 capacity), Civic Center of Greater Des Moines (2750 capacity)
Type: Opera

Detroit International Jazz Festival
Website: https://www.detroitjazzfest.org/
Email:
info@detroitjazzfest.org
Phone:
313 469 6564
Address: 19908 Harper Avenue, Harper Woods, MI 48225
Information: For nearly 40 years, the Detroit Jazz Festival Foundation has celebrated Detroit's rich history of jazz music by providing year-round concerts and educational programming, and of course, organizing the world's largest free jazz festival, featuring world-class talent, over Labor Day weekend.
Country: United States
Social Media: twitter.com/detroitjazzfest www.facebook.com/detroitjazzfestival
Frequency: Annual
Other Venues: city streets in Detroit from Hart Plaza to Campus Martius.
Type: Concert

Eastern Music Festival and School
Website: www.easternmusicfestival.org
Email: info@easternmusicfestival.org
Phone: 336 333 7450
Address: EASTERN MUSIC FESTIVAL P.O. Box 22026 Greensboro, NC 27420
Information: For six decades, Eastern Music Festival (EMF), a nationally recognized classical music festival and summer educational program, has been produced each summer on the campus of Guilford College, UNCG, and other venues in the Greensboro area. EMF is distinguished by its accomplished faculty, exhilarating repertoire, and world-renowned visiting artists under the Artistic direction of Gerard Schwarz.
Country: United States
Contact: Executive Director Chris Williams
Email: cwilliams@easternmusicfestival.org
Contact: Director of Operations Beverly Naiditch
Email: beverly@easternmusicfestival.org
Contact: Director of Development Deborah Kintzing
Email: dkintzing@easternmusicfestival.org
Contact: Media and Communications Director Kelly Swindel
Email: kswindell@easternmusicfestival.org
Social Media: https://twitter.com/EMFSummerStudy https://www.facebook.com/easternmusicfestival https://www.instagram.com/emfsummerstudy/
Frequency: Annual
Venue: Guilford College: Dana Auditorium (1005 capacity), Carnegie Room (200 capacity), Sternberger Hall (200 capacity), Triad Stage (300 capacity), Flying Anvil (600 capacity), Memorial Auditorium (2400 capacity), Reynolds House (180 capacity) and others
Type: Concert

Essentially Ellington Jazz Festival
Website: http://academy.jazz.org/ee/
Email: ee@jazz.org
Phone: 212 258 9861
Address: 3 Columbus Cir New York, NY, US 10019
Information: For more than fifteen years, the Essentially Ellington High School Jazz Band Program has brought the music of Duke Ellington and other legendary big band composers to jazz bands throughout the United States. A unique resource, Essentially Ellington provides recordings, teaching guides, original arrangements, and expert feedback for teachers and students alike, and encourages collaboration through non-competitive regional festivals as well as an annual competition and festival.
Country: United States
Social Media: www.twitter.com/jalcnyc https://www.facebook.com/EssentiallyEllington/
Venue: 59cecab2-d1c5-4c8f-bf06-6f3dcf267527
Other Venues: New York Venues: Alice Tully Hall at Lincoln Centre (1096 capacity), Avery Fisher Hall at Lincoln Center (2738 capacity), Stanley Kaplan Penthouse (250)
Type: Concert

Exito International Jazz Festival
Website: https://www.exitzerojazzfestival.com/
Email: michael@exit0jazzfest.com
Phone: 609 849 9202
Address: Beach Drive, US
Information: Spring and Autumn Festivals held in the nation's most beautiful seaside resort of Cape May, NJ., featuring world class musicians on main stages and clubs.
Country: United States
Social Media: @exit0jazzfest@Exit0jazzfestival
End: 2022-05-15
Cape May Convention Hall; First Presbyterian Church; Harry's Ocean Bar and Grille and others.
Type: Concert

Fairbanks Summer Arts Festival
Website: https://www.fsaf.org/
Email: festival@alaska.net
Phone: 907 474 8869
Address: PO Box 82510, US
Information: Nearly 10, 000 people come together at the Festival every July to study, perform and engage their spirit in an empowering way. Offering 200 workshops and over 100 events every season, our multidisciplinary, study-performance Festival offers opportunities for both personal growth and arts appreciation in a variety of genres including music, dance, visual arts, healing arts, culinary arts, creative writing, and theatre.
Country: United States
Contact: Executive Director James Menaker
Email: Director@fsaf.org
Contact: production Manager Adam Gillette
Contact: personnel Manager Dan Wiley
Social Media: www.facebook.com/FairbksArtsFest/
End: 2022-07-31
Other Venues: UAF campus and various venues around Fairbanks
Type: Concert, Dance/Ballet, Theatre, Multi-media, Opera

Festival at Sandpoint
Website: https://www.festivalatsandpoint.com/
Email: info@festivalatsandpoint.com
Phone: 888 265 4554
Address: 525 Pine St. Sandpoint, ID 83864 USA
Information: The Festival at Sandpoint strives to provide a rich music experience presenting a wide range of concerts in an intimate outdoor setting accessible to local and regional audiences, cultivate culture and ethnic diversity, foster a love of music through ongoing youth education programs, and stimulate economic growth for our community.
Country: United States
Contact: Executive Director Diana Wahl
Email: festival@sandpoint.net
Contact: Executive Director Ali Baranski Baranski
Email: info@festivalatsandpoint.com
Contact: office Manager Carol Winget
Email: cwingnut@yahoo.com
Contact: production Manager Dave Nygren
Email: d_nygren@hotmail.com
Contact: President Bob Witte Witte
Email: President@festivalatsandpoint.com
Social Media: twitter.com/FestivalatSndpt www.facebook.com/festivalatsandpoint
End: 2022-08-07
Other Venues: Outdoor venues including Memorial Field (2500 capacity)
Type: Concert

Festival Miami
Website: https://frost-music-live.miami.edu/
Email: festivalmiami.music@miami.edu
Phone: 305 284 4940
Address: UM Maurice Gusman Concert Hall, 1314 Miller Drive, US
Information: The mission of the Frost School of Music is to foster musical leadership by providing an innovative, relevant, and inspiring education; advance performance, creativity and scholarship; and enrich the world community with meaningful outreach and brilliant cultural offerings.
Country: United States
Social Media: www.facebook.com/FrostSchoolUM/
Other Venues: UM Maurice Gusman Concert Hall
Type: Concert

Festival Mozaic
Website: https://www.festivalmozaic.org/
Email: info@festivalmozaic.org
Phone: 805 781 3009
Address: 265 South Street, Suite G, San Luis Obispo, CA 93401
Information: Festival Mozaic is presented by the Mozart Festival Association, a nonprofit organization with headquarters in San Luis Obispo. Governed by a dedicated board of Directors, the Festival is a vital community organization and treasured asset in San Luis Obispo County.
Country: United States
Contact: Executive Director Lloyd Tanner Tanner
Contact: General Manager David George George
Contact: music Director Scott Yoo Yoo
Social Media: twitter.com/festivalmozaic www.facebook.com/festivalmozaic www.instagram.com/festivalmozaic
Frequency: Annual
Other Venues: Indoor and outdoor venues that will ensure your health and safety
Type: Concert

Fiddle Tunes
Website: https://centrum.org/
Email: info@centrum.org
Phone: 360 385 3102
Address: PO Box 1158 Port Townsend, WA 98368, US
Information: Living, learning, and playing music with masters of a wide variety of fiddling styles. Fiddle Tunes provides an opportunity to be in community with the bearers of fiddle traditions. Discover culture through music, learn about music in a cultural context, and build lifelong relationships in the fiddle music community.
Country: United States
Contact: Artistic Director Joel Savoy

Social Media: twitter.com/ptcentrum www.facebook.com/ptfiddle/
Frequency: Annual
Other Venues: Ford Warden, WA, US
Type: Concert

First Night Celebration
Website: https://www.firstnightboston.org/
Email:
info@firstnightboston.org
Phone: 617 439 7700
Address: c/o Conventures, Inc., 88 Black Falcon Avenue, Suite 202, US
Information: First Night Boston is a highly anticipated city-wide celebration that is free and open to the public. The long running festival features family-friendly activities such as a parade down Boylston Street, a spectacular pyrotechnics show, ice sculptures, performances from local artists/musicians, and of course, the "Copley Countdown", a highly anticipated annual countdown to the New Year.
Country: United States
Social Media: twitter.com/FirstNight www.facebook.com/FirstNightBoston/
Frequency: Annual
Other Venues: Copley Square Boston
Type: Concert, Dance/Ballet, Performance art

Fontana Chamber Arts
Website: https://www.rockportmusic.org/
Email: info@fontanachamberarts.org
Phone: 269 382 7774
Address: 359 S. Kalamazoo Mall, Suite 200, US
Information: Rockport Music presents world-class musicians year-round in the stunning, seaside Shalin Liu Performance Center.
Country: United States
Contact: Executive and Artistic Director David Baldwin
Email: dbaldwin@fontanachamberarts.org
Contact: accounting assistant Terri Hunter
Email: thunter@fontanachamberarts.org
Contact: General Manager Jill Perney
Email: jperney@fontanachamberarts.org
Contact: operations co-ordinator Charlie Tomlinson
Email: ctomlinson@fontanachamberarts.org
Contact: Artistic administrator Betsy Wong
Email: bwong@fontanachamberarts.org
Social Media: www.facebook.com/RockportMusic
Other Venues: Dalton Center Recital Hall
Type: Concert

Fort Worth Opera Festival
Website: https://www.fwopera.org/
Email: boxoffice@fwopera.org
Phone: 817 731 0726
Address: 505 Pecan Street, Suite 100, Fort Worth, TX 76102, USA
Information: Fort Worth Opera is committed to producing opera of the highest possible Artistic quality and integrity; to identifying and training talented young American singers; to serving as a crucible for creating new American operas; to joining forces with other arts organizations in significant collaborations; and to stimulating curiosity and creativity in people of all ages through its Education Program.
Country: United States
Contact: General Director Afton Battle
Email: afton@fwopera.org
Contact: Artistic Director Joe Illick
Email: jillick@aol.com
Contact: Director of production Marie Barrett
Email: marie@fwopera.org
Social Media: twitter.com/FortWorthOpera www.facebook.com/FortWorthOpera
Frequency: Annual
Other Venues: Bass Performance Hall Fort Worth (2056 capacity)
Type: Opera

Fredericksburg Festival of the Arts
Website: http://artsliveva.org/
Email: thearts@fredfest.org
Phone: 540 374 5040
Address: P.O. Box 7816, US
Information: Did you know that ArtsLIVE! is the longest and continuously active performing arts nonprofit organization in the Fredericksburg region?
Country: United States
Contact: founder and Artistic Director Heidi Lehwalder
Social Media: www.facebook.com/ArtsLIVE.fxbg/
Type: Concert

Fringe Festival
Website:
https://www.bu.edu/cfa/opera/news/fringe/
Email:
ogregorian@bu.edu
Phone: 617 353 5201
Address: Boston University Opera Institute, 855 Commonwealth Avenue, US
Information: For over two decades, the Boston University School of Music: Opera Institute and School of Theatre have brought unique theatrical performances to the University's stages. The Schools have worked together to

create over two dozen diverse and extraordinary productions that combine a masterful blending of drama and music compiled into three main events every October.
Country: United States
Contact: Director of opera programs Sharon Daniels
Contact: Director of public relations Ellen Carr
Contact: Manager of the opera institute Oshin Gregorian
Social Media: www.facebook.com/BU.Opera
Frequency: Annual
Other Venues: College of Fine Arts School of Music: Opera Institute and School of Theatre

Glimmerglass Opera
Website: www.glimmerglass.org
Email: info@glimmerglass.org
Phone: 607 547 0700
Address: 7300 State Highway 80, PO Box 191, US
Information: 2015 is the 40th anniversary of the festival
Country: United States
Contact: Artistic Director Francesca Zambello
Email: fzambello@glimmerglass.org
Contact: Managing Director Linda Jackson
Email: ljackson@glimmerglass.org
Frequency: annual
Venue: Alice Busch Opera Theater 920
Type: Opera

Grand Canyon Music Festival
Website: https://grandcanyonmusicfest.org/
Email: gcmf@infomagic.net
Phone: 928 638 9215
Address: PO Box 1332 Grand Canyon, AZ 86023
Information: Each year the Grand Canyon Music Festival presents three weekends of music at the Grand Canyon with some additional concerts in Flagstaff and Phoenix. The music festival also operates two educational programs, the Native American Composer Apprentice Project and the School of Rock. These programs bring music education to schools serving Native American communities and rural populations.
Country: United States
Contact: President Claire West
Social Media: www.facebook.com/grandcanyonmusicfest
Frequency: Annual
Other Venues: Shrine of the Ages on the south rim of the Grand Canyon
Type: Concert

Grand Rapids Arts Festival
Website: https://festivalgr.org/
Phone: 616 459 1300
Address: P.O. Box 68440, Grand Rapids, MI 49516-8440, US
Information: Large scale inclusive festival of all art forms, based in Grand Rapids in Michigan.
The Festival provides many different arts experiences and cultural opportunities that promote excellence, cross-cultural understanding and strong community.
Country: United States
Contact: Executive Director David Abbott
Contact: Chairperson Baird Hawkins
Social Media: twitter.com/FestivalGR https://www.facebook.com/FestivalGR/
Frequency: Annual
End: 2022-06-05
Other Venues: Grand Rapids, Michigan, US
Type: Multi-media

Grand Teton Music Festival
Website: https://gtmf.org/
Email: gtmf@gtmf.org
Phone: 307 733 3050
Address: 175 S. King Street, PO Box 9117, Jackson, WY 83002, US
Information: The festival was founded in 1962 by the Jackson Hole Fine Arts Festival to foster classical music experiences for performers and audiences and to improve and enrich the cultural awareness and opportunities for people in Wyoming and the adjacent area. Sixty years since its humble beginnings performing in a tent at the base of the Tetons, the Festival is now sought after for both listeners and performers alike as a destination to experience the finest in classical music throughout the summer.
Country: United States
President & CEO
Andrew Palmer Todd
Contact: Artistic Director Richard Brown
Email: richard@gtmf.org
Contact: General Manager Jeff Counts
Email: jeff@gtmf.org
Social Media: www.facebook.com/GrandTetonMusicFestivaltwitter.com/gtmf www.instagram.com/grandtetonmusic/
Frequency: Annual
End: 2022-08-27
Other Venues: Walk Festival Hall
Type: Concert

Grant Park Music Festival
Website: https://www.grantparkmusicfestival.com/
Email: info@gpmf.org
Phone: 312 742 7638
Address: 205 East Randolph Street, Chicago, 60601, US

Information: The Grant Park Summer Music Festival began in the 1930s and is one of the longest running Classical Music Festivals in Illinois. It is situated in Chicago, and since 2004 has been centred on the Jay Pritzker Pavilion. The Festival is a ten week long season of concerts, workshops, radio broadcasts and outreach programmes.
Country: United States
Contact: President and CEO Paul Winberg
Email: paul.winberg@gpmf.org
Contact: Artistic Director Carlos Kalmer
Email: carlos.kalmer@gpmf.org
Contact: Chief Development Officer Emily Canham
Email: emily.canham@gpmf.org
Social Media: twitter.com/gpmf www.facebook.com/grantparkmusicfestival www.instagram.com/grantparkmusicfestival/
Frequency: Annual
Type: Concert

Great River Folk Festival
Website: https://www.greatriverfolkfest.org/
Email: grff@GreatRiverFolkFest.org
Phone: 608 784 3033
Address: PO Box 1434, US
Information: Held the weekend before Labor Day is moving to the Riverside Park downtown La Crosse, the Great River Folk Festival is an interactive community event for all ages that preserves and promotes traditional and contemporary folk culture through music, crafts, dance and food.
Country: United States
Social Media: twitter.com/GRFolkFest www.facebook.com/greatriverfolkfest www.instagram.com/greatriverfolk
Frequency: Annual
Other Venues: Riverside Park
Type: Concert, Dance/Ballet, Other

Gretna Music
Website: gretnamusic.org
Email: music@mtgretna.com
Phone: 717 361 1508
Address: Gretna Music, PO Box 366, Mt. Gretna, PA 17064
Information: In 1975 the Pennsylvania Chautauqua's Summer Program Director asked new Mt. Gretna resident, physician/flutist Carl Ellenberger, to organize two concerts in the Mt. Gretna "Hall of Philosophy." Ellenberger invited old friends from Interlochen and Eastman to visit and play chamber music. They had so much fun that the next summer he organized 4 concerts in the Playhouse. The Festival developed from there.
Country: United States
Contact: Executive Director Suzanne Stewart
Email: suzannestewart@gretnamusic.org
Contact: Artistic Director Carl Kane
Email: carlkane@gretnamusic.org
Social Media: https://www.facebook.com/GretnaMusic
Frequency: Annual
Other Venues: Mt. Gretna Playhouse (708 seats)
Type: Concert

Historic Brass Society – Early Brass Festival
Website: www.historicbrass.org
Email: President@historicbrass.org
Phone: 917 359 3430
Address: 148 West 23rd Street, #5F New York, NY 10011 USA
Information: The Historic Brass Society is an international music organization concerned with the entire range of early brass music, from Ancient Antiquity and the Biblical period through the present including the development of jazz and its influence on brass instruments, literature and playing techniques. The history, music, literature and performance practice of early brass instruments such as natural trumpet, natural horn, early trombone, cornetto, serpent, keyed bugle, keyed trumpet, early valve horn, 1
Country: United States
Contact: President Jeffrey Nussbaum
Contact: Executive editor Stewart Carter
Contact: advertising Manager Bodie Pfost
Social Media: www.facebook.com/historicbrass/
Frequency: Annual
End: 2021-05-26
Other Venues: held in conjunction with Vintage Band Festival in Northfield, Minnesota
Type: Concert

Hollywood Bowl Summer Festival
Website: https://www.hollywoodbowl.com/
Email: information@hollywoodbowl.com
Phone: 213 972 7300
Address: 2301 Highland Avenue Los Angeles, CA 90068
Information: Since its opening in 1922, the Hollywood Bowl has been the premier destination for live music in Southern California, hosting everyone from Billie Holiday to The Beatles to Yo-Yo Ma under the iconic silhouette of its concentric-arched band shell. The festival held annually and attendees can expect an eclectic musical spirit.
Country: United States
Contact: chief Executive officer Simon Woods
Contact: Executive Director Gail Samuel
Contact: chief financial officer Alison Sowden
Social Media: twitter.com/HollywoodBowl www.facebook.com/HollywoodBowl www.instagram.com/

HollywoodBowl/
Frequency: Annual
End: 2022-06-26
Other Venues: Hollywood Bowl (capacity 17, 500)
Type: Concert

Honest Brook Music Festival
Website: www.hbmf.org
Email: hbmf@aol.com
Phone: 607 746 3770
Address: PO Box 309 Delhi, NY 13753 USA
Information: Honest Brook Music Festival presents a stunning line-up of world-class chamber music performers during July and August and January, February and March.
Country: United States
Contact: President Michael Cannon
Email: hbmf@aol.com
Contact: vice President Doree Hubar
Social Media: www.facebook.com/Honest-Brook-Music-Festival-115728758479086
Frequency: Annual
Other Venues: beautifully restored barn

Huntington Summer Arts Festivals
Website: www.huntingtonarts.org
Email: info@huntingtonarts.org
Phone: 631 271 8423
Address: 213 Main Street Huntington NY 11743
Information: Not for profit organization, promotes arts and culture generated by Long Island artists to our children and to the General population. We work to enrich the cultural, social and economic life of the community by nurturing the professional development of artists, and by providing timely news and events
Country: United States
Contact: Executive Director Marc Courtade
Email: Director@huntingtonarts.org
Contact: business Manager Kieran Johnson
Email: development@huntingtonarts.org
Contact: performing arts Director John Chicherio
Email: jchicherio@huntingtonarts.org
Social Media: twitter.com/HuntingtonArts www.facebook.com/HuntingtonArts www.instagram.com/huntingtonarts
Frequency: Annual
Other Venues: CHAPIN Rainbow Stage, Heckscher Park, Huntington
Type: Other

Icicle Creek Chamber Music Festival
Website: www.icicle.org
Email: info@icicle.org
Phone: 509 548 6347
Address: 7409 Icicle Road, US
Information: dedicated to celebrating excellence in the lively arts and inspiring generations of artists and audiences through exceptional experiences, live performances, and special events – all in the breathtaking, natural setting of the mountain meadows. Alternative phone number: 50 9548 6347
Country: United States
Contact: Executive Director Rebecca Ryker
Email: rebecca@icicle.org
Contact: Director of programming Mike Caemmerer
Email: michael@icicle.org
Contact: development Director Jamie Howell
Email: jamie@icicle.org
Social Media: @ICMCmusic/IcicleCreek
Frequency: annual
Venue: Icicle Creek Center for the Arts; The Snowy Owl Theatre
Type: Theatre

Interlochen Shakespeare Festival
Website: https://www.interlochen.org/
Email: boxoffice@interlochen.org
Phone: 231 276 7200
Address: 4000 Highway M-137 Interlochen, MI 49643
Information: The Interlochen Shakespeare Festival draws on the unique resources of Interlochen Center for the Arts to present bold and innovative interpretations of the classics. Founded in 2008 and led by Artistic Director William Church, a core ensemble of Interlochen faculty, staff and alumni commits itself to engaging northwest Michigan audiences through professional theatre that celebrates the Shakespearean imagination.
Country: United States
Social Media: twitter.com/InterlochenArts www.facebook.com/interlochencenterforthearts www.instagram.com/interlochenarts
Other Venues: Upton-Morley Pavilion (467 capacity), Kresge Auditorium (4000 capacity), Corson Auditorium (1000 capacity), The Bowl (1200 capacity), Harvey Theatre (200 capacity), Phoenix Theatre (200 capacity)
Type: Theatre

International Ballet Festival of Miami
Website: https://www.internationalballetfestival.org/
Email: contact@internationalballetfestival.org
Phone: 786 747 1877
Address: 111 SW 5th Ave, Miami, FL 33130, US
Information: This Festival represents the most ambitious ballet project ever conceived in South Florida, the magnitude of its program, along with the prestige of the participating companies and the renowned principal ballet stars, have captured the attention of the most demanding audiences.
The International Ballet Festival is held every year in Miami from the last week of August through mid-September.
Country: United States
Contact: Artistic Director Eriberto Jimenez
Social Media: twitter.com/intballetfest www.facebook.com/miamihispanicballet/

International Festival of Arts and Ideas
Website: artidea.org
Email: festivalinfo@artida.org
Phone: 888 278 4332
Address: 195 Church Street, 12th Floor, US
Information: This is a 15-day festival of performing arts, lectures, and conversations that celebrates the greatest artists and thinkers from around the world. Each June, the Festival takes over the theaters, open spaces, and courtyards of New Haven, Connecticut with performances and dialogues that tickle the senses, engage the mind, and inspire the soul. Member of ISPA
Country: United States
Contact: co-Director, Director of programming Chad Herzog
Email: cherzog@artidea.org
Contact: co-Director, Managing Director Elizabeth Fisher
Email: lfisher@artidea.org
Contact: Director of production and operations Doug Harry
Email: dharry@artidea.org
Contact: Associate Director of Marketing Alexis Kellogg
Email: akellogg@artidea.org
Social Media: @ArtIdea@artidea
Frequency: annual
Venue: Theaters and open spaces in New Haven
Type: All

Irving S Gilmore International Keyboard Festival
Website: https://www.thegilmore.org/
Email: info@thegilmore.org
Phone: 269 342 1166
Address: 359 S. Kalamazoo Mall Suite 101 Kalamazoo, MI 49007 USA
Information: the Gilmore is a non-profit organisation that fosters and supports achievement in keyboard music and performance. The aim of the festival is to promote and develop world-class keyboard musical experiences that inspire present and future artists and audiences by identifying exceptional pianists through a noncompetitive process and providing significant support to enhance their careers
Country: United States
Contact: education and operations coordinator Leslie Boughton
Email: lboughton@thegilmore.org
Contact: Director of development Alisa Carrel
Email: acarrel@thegilmore.org
Contact: Director of Marketing and public relations Curtis Cunningham
Email: ccunningham@thegilmore.org
Social Media: twitter.com/gilmorefestival www.facebook.com/GilmoreFestival
Frequency: Annual
Type: Concert

Jacksonville Jazz Festival
Website: https://jacksonvillejazzfest.com/
Email: events@coj.net
Phone: 904 360 3690
Address: 117 West Duval Street, Suite 280, Jacksonville Florida, US
Information: The Jacksonville Jazz Festival began as the Mayport and All That Jazz Festival in 1980. Now there is a vibrant street festival atmosphere as different performers enthral the crowds.
Country: United States
Social Media: twitter.com/JaxJazzFest www.facebook.com/JacksonvilleJazzFestival www.instagram.com/JaxJazzFest/
Frequency: Annual
End: 2022-05-29
Other Venues: Duval County Courthouse at Pearl and Adams streets
Type: Concert

Jacob's Pillow Dance Festival and School
Website: https://www.jacobspillow.org/
Email: info@jacobspillow.org
Phone: 413 243 9919
Address: 358 George Carter Road, US
Information: Supports dance creation, presentation, education, and preservation, and engages and deepens public appreciation and support for dance. The school at Jacob's Pillow provides training by eminent faculty that not only produces great dancers, but also great artists. The Intern Program, Public School Programs, and Community Classes educate people of all ages about the art of dance. Member of ISPA
Country: United States
Contact: President Christopher Jones
Contact: Executive Director Ella Baff
Social Media: www.facebook.com/jacobspillowdance

Other Venues: Ted Shawn Theatre (628 capacity), Doris Duke Studio Theatre (220 capacity), Inside/Out – unlimited
Type: Dance/Ballet

Jazz Greats at Glenora Winery
Website: www.glenora.com
Email: info@glenora.com
Phone: 800 243 5513
Address: 5435 Route 14, US
Information: jazz festival overlooking the vineyards and Seneca Lake
Country: United States
Frequency: annual
Venue: outdoor pavilion 1600 on lawn
Type: Concert

June in Buffalo
Website: usic21c.buffalo.edu/june-in-buffalo
Email: jtrinker@buffalo.edu
Phone: 716 645 0624
Address: University at Buffalo, 220 Baird Hall, Department of Music, US
Information:
Country: United States
Contact: Artistic Director David Felder
Social Media: June in Buffalo Festival
Frequency: annual
Venue: University at Buffalo: halls 150 to 1300
Type: Concert, Multi-media

Kent/Blossom Music Festival
Website: https://www.kent.edu/blossom
Email: kbm@kent.edu
Phone: 330 672 2613
Address: 1325 Theatre Drive, Kent, Ohio 44242 USA
Information: the Kent/Blossom Music Festival emphasises the intensive study of chamber music under professional Artistic standards and time frames. Each student performs an average of five major works during the five weeks.The Kent Blossom Music Festival is an advanced training institute for professional music training operated by Kent State University in cooperation with The Cleveland Orchestra and Blossom Music Center
Country: United States
Social Media: www.facebook.com/KentBlossomMusic
Frequency: Annual
End: 2022-08-08
Other Venues: The Center for the Performing Arts (640 capacity)
Type: Concert

Killington Music Festival
Website: https://www.killingtonmusicfestival.org/
Email: kmfest@kmfest.org
Phone: 802 773 4003
Address: PO Box 386 Rutland, VT 05702 USA
Information: the music festival is a non-profit organisation and is the only resident professional classical music organisation in central Vermont. Each summer about 100 students gather at Killington from different educational institutions to learn and perform
Country: United States
Contact: Executive Director Maria Napolitano Fish
Contact: Artistic Director Daniel Andai
Social Media: www.facebook.com/KillingtonMusicFestivaltwitter.com/killingtonmusic www.instagram.com/killingtonmusicfestival
Frequency: Annual
Other Venues: Juilliard School of Music, Boston Conservatory, The New England Conservatory, The Manhattan School of Music, Peabody Conservatory, Eastman School of Music and the University of Arizona
Type: Concert

Kingston Chamber Music Festival at the University of Rhode Island
Website: www.kingstonchambermusic.org
Email: info@kingstonchambermusic.org
Phone: 401 308 3614
Address: PO Box 1733, US
Information: presents quality chamber music to a wide audience and world-class musicians appear annually during a two-week summer festival of six reasonably priced, evening concerts
Country: United States
Contact: Artistic Director Natalie Zhu
Contact: Managing Director Charlotte Toolan
Contact: contract Manager Jonathan Garber
Social Media: @kingstonchambermusic
Frequency: annual
Venue: URI Fine Arts Center Concert Hall
Type: Concert

Kneisel Hall Chamber Music Festival
Website: https://kneisel.org/
Email: festival@kneisel.org
Phone: 207 374 2811
Address: PO Box 648, US
Information: takes place in the coastal village of Blue Hill. A chamber music school, a concert series and chamber music advocate. Features performances from internationally acclaimed chamber musicians and over

50 talented young artists
Country: United States
Contact: Executive Director Ellen Werner
Email: ellen@kneisel.org
Contact: business Manager Danielle Sargent
Email: danielle@kneisel.org
Social Media: www.facebook.com/kneiselhall/
Other Venues: Kneisel Hall Concert Hall
Type: Concert

La Jolla Music Society – SummerFest
Website: https://ljms.org/
Email: boxoffice@ljms.org
Phone: 858 459 3728
Address: 7600 Fay Avenue La Jolla, CA 92037, US
Information: A nationally-recognised chamber music festival featuring over 70 world-class artists and ensembles.
Country: United States
President & CEO
Todd Schultz
Contact: music Director Inon Barnatan
Social Media: www.facebook.com/LaJollaMusicSociety/twitter.com/ljmusicsociety www.instagram.com/ljmusicsociety/
Frequency: Annual
Other Venues: The Conrad Prebys Performing Arts Center, San Diego
Type: Concert

Lancaster Festival
Website: www.lancasterfestival.org
Email: lanfest@lanfest.org
Phone: 740 687 4808
Address: 117 West Wheeling Street , Lancaster, OH 43130
Information: The Lancaster Festival celebrates the Artistic creativity of all cultures, serving as the foundation of year-round community efforts to nurture participation in the arts.
Country: United States
Contact: Artistic Director Gary Sheldon
Email: gsheldon@lancasterfestival.org
Contact: Executive Director Deb Connell
Contact: President Jack Janoso
Contact: vice President Amie Cohen
Social Media: www.facebook.com/lancasterfestival
Other Venues: various locations around town including Ohio University, Lancaster Amphitheater (9000 capacity), Zane Square (2500 capacity)
Type: Concert

Lincoln Center Out-of-Doors Festival
Website: lcoutofdoors.org
Email: webmaster@lincolncenter.org
Phone: 212 875 5000
Address: 70 Lincoln Center Plaza, US
Information: Enjoy longstanding favorites and discover something new when Out of Doors brings three jam-packed weeks of world-class music, dance, and spoken word to the plazas of Lincoln Center. Free entry
Country: United States
Social Media: @LincolnCenter@LincolnCenterNYC
Frequency: annual
Venue: Damrosch Park 3500, various plazas totalling 3500

Lionel Hampton Jazz Festival
Website: https://www.uidaho.edu/class/jazzfest
Email: jazzinfo@uidaho.edu
Phone: 208 885 5900
Address: 875 Perimeter Dr., MS 4257, University of Idaho, US
Information: Since the 1960s, the University of Idaho Lionel Hampton Jazz Festival has been honoring the music, dance and history of jazz music and one of its most cherished artists Lionel Hampton.
Music enthusiasts have the opportunity to attend artist and educational workshops, perform and receive feedback from world-class artist educators, and view phenomenal concerts featuring live performances of present jazz stars and archival footage of past greats including Hamp himself.
Country: United States
Contact: Festival Director Josh Skinner
Email: jwskinner@uidaho.edu
Contact: Director Vanessa Sielert
Email: vanessas@uidaho.edu
Contact: Artistic Director Vern Sielert
Email: verns@uidaho.edu
Social Media: www.twitter.com/hampjazz www.facebook.com/hampjazz
Frequency: Annual
End: 2022-02-26
Other Venues: University of Idaho
Type: Concert

Litchfield Performing Arts Inc Jazz Festival
Website: https://litchfieldperformingarts.org/
Email: info@litchfieldperformingarts.org
Phone: 860 361 6285
Address: P.O. Box 69, Litchfield, Connecticut 06759 USA
Information: Since 1981, Litchfield Performing arts has been promoting arts throughout Connecticut starting

with living room concerts and eventually producing both the Litchfield Jazz Camp and the Litchfield Jazz Festival.
Country: United States
Contact: Executive and Artistic Director Vita West Muir
Email: vmuir@litchfieldjazzfest.com
Contact: Managing Director Tegan Ryan
Email: Tegan@LitchfieldJazzFest.com
Social Media: twitter.com/litchfieldjazz www.instagram.com/litchfieldjazz
Frequency: Annual
streamed live from TELEFUNKEN Studios & Soundstage

Luzerne Chamber Music Festival
Website: www.luzernemusic.org
Email: info@luzernemusic.org
Phone: 518 696 2771
Address: P.O. Box 39 203 Lake Tour Road Lake Luzerne, NY 12846, US
Information: Founded in 1980, this chamber music festival offers everything from the Baroque Era to New American works, including jazz. Regularly presents Resident Faculty Artists, members of the Philadelphia Orchestra and NYC Ballet Orchestra, and others of world renown
Country: United States
Contact: President/CEO/Artistic Director Elizabeth Pitcairn
Email: epitcairn@luzernemusic.org
Contact: Program Director Emily Dobmeier
Email: edobmeier@luzernemusic.org
Contact: Camp Manager Emily Brown
Email: ebrown@luzernemusic.org
Social Media: https://www.facebook.com/luzernemusiccenter/ www.twitter.com/luzernemusic www.instagram.com/luzernemusic
End: 2021-08-09
Venue: 4a84035b-0622-4459-98ca-653c88f37077

Mainly Mozart Festival
Website: https://www.mainlymozart.org/
Email: boxoffice@mainlymozart.org
Phone: 619 239 0100
Address: 404 Euclid Ave, Suite 221 San Diego, CA 92114 USA
Information: For over 30 years, the Mainly Mozart Festival Orchestra has been home to the largest gathering of Concertmasters and Principal Players in the United States. The famed Mainly Mozart Festival boasts top level players from the world's greatest orchestras.
Country: United States
Contact: festival music Director Michael Francis
Contact: Executive Director Nancy Laturno
Email: nlaturno@mainlymozart.org
Contact: Marketing Director Gregory Miles Parry
Social Media: twitter.com/mainlymozart www.facebook.com/MainlyMozart www.instagram.com/mainlymozart
Frequency: Annual
Other Venues: Del Mar Fairgrounds West Lot
Type: Concert

Manchester Music Festival, Inc.
Website: www.mmfvt.org
Email: office@mmfvt.org
Phone: 802 362 1956
Address: 42 Dillingham Ave. Manchester, VT 05254 USA
Information: Manchester Music Festival is a world-class chamber music festival providing classical music performance, music education, and music outreach to the Southern Vermont community.
Country: United States
Contact: business Manager Kathleen O'Connor
Contact: President Peggie Telscher
Contact: vice President Walter Miller
Social Media: twitter.com/mmfvt www.facebook.com/mmfvt www.instagram.com/mmfvt_1974
Other Venues: Southern Vermont Art Center (399 capacity), Riley Center for the Performing Arts (250 capacity), First Congregational Church (350 capacity)
Type: Concert

Marlboro Music School & Festival
Website: www.marlboromusic.org
Email: info@marlboromusic.org
Phone: 215 569 4690
Address: 1616 Walmut St, Suite 1600, US
Information: exceptional professional musicians aged 18-25 from all over the world & 10-20 senior musicians; address during the festival: Box K, Marlboro VT 05344
Country: United States
Contact: Manager Philip Maneval
Contact: Artistic administrator Miles Cohen
Contact: admissions Director Jennifer Loux
Contact: communications Director Brian Potter
Email: bpotter@marlboromusic.org
Frequency: annual
Venue: Marlboro College 642, Persons Auditorium

Marrowstone Summer Music
Website: https://www.marrowstone.org/
Email: marrowstone@syso.org
Phone: 206 362 2300
Address: 11065 Fifth Ave NE, Suite A Seattle, WA 98125 USA

Information: An institution since 1943, Marrowstone Music Festival is the Pacific Northwest's premier orchestral training program. Marrowstone is presented by Seattle Youth Symphony Orchestra and is hosted by Western Washington University. Located in picturesque Bellingham, overlooking the Puget Sound and the Cascade Mountains, the WWU campus offers a uniquely intimate environment for Marrowstone's Pre-College, University, and Fellowship divisions.
Country: United States
Contact: music Director Christian Knapp
Contact: Executive Director Daniel Petersen
Contact: marrowstone admissions/operations Scott Teske

Massachusetts International Festival of the Arts (MIFA) Victory Theatre
Website: https://www.mifafestival.org/
Email: info@mifafestival.org
Phone: 413 540 0200
Address: 56 Suffolk Street, Suite 300 Holyoke, MA 01040 USA
Information: MIFA's mission is to present the finest examples of contemporary practice in the performing, visual and literary arts for the purposes of educating, entertaining and enriching lives. MIFA serves the economic revitalization of Holyoke through the preservation and reopening of the historic landmark Victory Theatre. The Massachusetts Int'l Festival of the Arts (MIFA) has presented great art since 1994.
Country: United States
Contact: Executive Artistic Director Donald Sanders
Contact: Managing Director Kathy McKean
Contact: communications officer Emily Mann
Social Media: twitter.com/MIFAHolyoke www.facebook.com/MIFAVictoryTheatre www.instagram.com/mifa_victory_theatre
Frequency: Annual
Other Venues: Victory Theatre (1600 capacity)
Type: Concert, Theatre, Other

Matrix: Midland Festival
Website: https://www.midlandcenter.org/
Email: sabin@mcfta.org
Phone: 989 631 5930
Address: 1801 W St Andrews Road, US
Information: Shift your perspective! Imagine a place where art, science, history, music, theatre, dance, films, camps, classes and professional world-class entertainers all live under one roof! This is Midland Center for the Arts, a beautiful landmark facility where people of all ages are invited to create as well as appreciate and explore these many areas of interest.
Country: United States
Contact: General Manager Phyllis Sabin
Contact: President William Henninger
Social Media: www.facebook.com/midlandcenter/
Other Venues: Midland Center for the Arts Auditorium (1538 capacity)
Type: Concert, Dance/Ballet, Theatre

Mayfair Festival of the Arts, Mayfair, Inc
Website: www.mayfairfestival.org
Email: info@mayfairfestival.org
Phone: 610 437 6900
Address: 2141 Downyflake Lane, 2nd Floor, US
Information: a visual and performing arts festival, located in the West End of Allentown, PA
Country: United States
Contact: Executive Director Arlene Daily
Social Media: @mayfairfestival
Frequency: annual
Venue: Cedar Crest College
Type: Concert, Dance/Ballet, Mime, Multi-media, Musical theatre, Object theatre, Opera, Performance art, Puppetry, Theatre, Other, All

Memphis in May International Festival – Beale Street Music Festival
Website: www.memphisinmay.org
Email: mim@memphisinmay.org
Phone: 901 525 4611
Address: 56 S Front St, Memphis, TN 38103, USA
Information: The mission of Memphis in May International Festival is to promote and celebrate Memphis culture, foster economic growth, and enhance international awareness through education.**Country: United States**
Contact: President and CEO James Holt
Email: jholt@memphisinmay.org
Contact: Executive vice President and cfo Mack Weaver
Email: mweaver@memphisinmay.org
Contact: vice President of sponsorship Kevin Grothe
Email: kgrothe@memphisinmay.org
Social Media: twitter.com/memphisinmay www.facebook.com/memphisinmay www.instagram.com/memphisinmay
Frequency: Annual
End: 2021-05-29
Other Venues: Tom Lee Park, a 30-acre stretch on the Mississippi, where most Memphis in May events will be held
Type: Concert, Other

Midsummer Mozart Festival
Website:

https://www.midsummermozart.org/
Email: mozartinjuly@gmail.com
Phone: 415 627 9141
Address: PO Box 882754, San Francisco, CA 94188, US
Information: The Midsummer Mozart Festival is a San Francisco Bay Area music festival that exclusively performs the music of Mozart. Since 1974 the Midsummer Mozart Festival has offered audiences a variety of solo, chamber, orchestral, and operatic performances.
Country: United States
Contact: musical and Executive Director Robin Hansen
Contact: conductor and Artistic Director Paul Schrage
Social Media: www.facebook.com/Midsummer-Mozart-Festival-69201312813/
Other Venues: Various venues such as: Herbst Theatre (1000 capacity); California Theatre, San Jose (1000 capacity); Villa Montalvo, Saratoga (1000 capacity); 1st Congregational Church of Berkeley (800 capacity); Gundlach Bundschi Winery (500 capacity).
Type: Concert

Moab Music Festival
Website: https://moabmusicfest.org/
Email: info@moabmusicfest.org
Phone: 435 259 7003
Address: 58 East 300 South Moab, UT 84532 USA
Information: The Moab Music Festival was founded in 1992 by New York based musicians Michael Barrett, pianist/conductor and violist Leslie Tomkins. Captivated by the red rocks of Moab, they were inspired to combine the magical landscape with the joys of music-making. "Starting a music festival seemed like the perfect way to make sure we would return again and again, " says Tomkins.
Country: United States
Contact: Executive Director Laura Brown
Email: laura@moabmusicfest.org
Contact: music Director Michael Barrett Barrett
Email: michael@moabmusicfest.org
Contact: Artistic Director Leslie Tomkins Tomkins
Email: leslie@moabmusicfest.org
Social Media: twitter.com/moabmusicfest www.facebook.com/MoabMusicFest www.instagram.com/moabmusicfest
Frequency: Annual
End: 2022-09-16
Other Venues: stunning red rock venues around Moab, Utah
Type: Concert

Montana International Choral Festival
Website: https://www.choralfestival.org/
Email: info@choralfestival.org
Phone: 406 721 7985
Address: P.O. Box 8203, Missoula, MT 59807 USA
Information: The International Choral Festival was founded in 1987 by Donald Carey, a Missoula choral conductor and music professor, . Carey had been inspired by a similar Festival in Nancy, France four years earlier. The first Festival was a huge success.
Country: United States
Contact: Executive Director Jennifer Cooper
Contact: Artistic Director David Heidel
Contact: vice President Lance Collister, Collister
Social Media: www.facebook.com/InternationalChoralFestivalofMissoula
Frequency: Triennial
End: 2022-07-16
Other Venues: Northern Rocky Mountains
Type: Concert

Monterey Jazz Festival
Website: https://montereyjazzfestival.org/
Email: jazzinfo@montereyjazzfestival.org
Phone: 831 373 3366
Address: 9699 Blue Larkspur Lane, Suite 204 Monterey, CA 93940 USA
Information: Held every September on the Monterey Fairgrounds site where the Festival was first presented in 1958 the Monterey Jazz Festival began as a dream for founder Jimmy Lyons and his co-founder and colleague, Ralph Gleason. It was a dream of a "sylvan setting with the best jazz people in the whole world playing on the same stage, having a whole weekend of jazz."
Country: United States
Contact: Executive Director Colleen Finegan Bailey
Email: colleen@montereyjazzfestival.org
Contact: Artistic Director Tim Jackson
Contact: development and administrative coordinator Lidia Wilding
Email: lidia@montereyjazzfestival.org
Contact: production Manager Bill Wagner
Email: bill@montereyjazzfestival.org
Social Media: www.facebook.com/MontereyJazzFestival www.instagram.com/montereyjazzfestivaltwitter.com/MontereyJazz
End: 2022-09-25
Other Venues: Monterey County Fairgrounds (main arena is 6500 capacity but total no. of people over 3 days: 40-45k)
Type: Concert

Mostly Mozart Festival
Website: www.lincolncenter.org/mostly-mozart-fes-

tival/
Email: webmaster@lincolncenter.org
Phone: 212 875 5456
Address: 70 Lincoln Center Plaza, New York, NY 10023, USA
Information: Reimagined as a radio event, Mostly Mozart Festival on WQXR was a seven-day multimedia festival that reflected on the meaning of Mozart's work and sought to remind audiences of the power of music to bring communities together. Presented by Lincoln Center and WQXR, the festival featured specially curated musical broadcasts, live events, digital content, and a range of programming that illuminates how racism and inequality have shaped classical music, past and present.
Country: United States
Contact: Director, music programming Hanako Yamaguchi
Contact: vice President of programming Jane Moss
Contact: conductor Louis Langr
Social Media: twitter.com/lincolncenter www.facebook.com/LincolnCenterNYC https://www.instagram.com/lincolncenter/
Other Venues: Lincoln Center for the Performing Arts (2700 capacity), Avery Fisher Hall (2775 capacity), Alice Tully Hall (1098 capacity)
Type: Concert

Music Academy of the West Summer Festival
Website: https://www.musicacademy.org/
Email: festival@musicacademy.org
Phone: 805 969 4726
Address: 1070 Fairway Road Santa Barbara, CA 93108 USA
Information: The Music Academy of the West is among the nation's preeminent summer schools and festivals for gifted young classically-trained musicians. At its oceanside, ten-acre campus in Santa Barbara, California, the Academy provides these musicians with the opportunity for advanced study and performance under the guidance of internationally renowned faculty artists, guest conductors, and soloists during its eight-week Summer School and Festival
Country: United States
Contact: Chair Warren Staley
Contact: vice Chair Eileen Sheridan
Contact: President and CEO Scott Reed
Contact: chief advancement officer Jonathan Bishop
Social Media: www.facebook.com/MusicAcademyoftheWest www.instagram.com/musicacademywtwitter.com/musicacademyw
Other Venues: Music Academy, Hahn Hall (350 capacity), Lobero Theatre (680 capacity), Lehmann Hall (200 capacity), Granada Theatre (1500 capacity), Santa Barbara Bowlcampus and in downtown Santa Barbara
Type: Concert

Music from Angel Fire
Website: www.musicfromangelfire.org
Email: info@musicfromangelfire.org
Phone: 575 377 3233
Address: PO Box 502, US
Information: Featuring international, world-class soloists in varying ensembles performing the great chamber music literature of Europe, South America and the United States. Additionally, a Young Artist Program includes students from Curtis Institute of Music in PA
Country: United States
Contact: Artistic Director Ida Kavafian
Contact: board of Director Judie Hass
Contact: board of Director Robyn Atkinson
Social Media: @MusicAngelFire@musicfromangelfire
Frequency: annual
Venue: Angel Fire Community Center 400, Taos Community Auditorium 300, Ilfeld Auditorium 400, United Church of Angel Fire 200, Shuler Theater 400
Type: Concert, Performance art

Music From Japan Festival
Website: www.musicfromjapan.org
Email: mfjrc@aol.com
Phone: 212 529 1888
Address: 7 E 20th St #6FNew York, NY 10003, USA
Information: Music From Japan continues to preside as the leading presenter of Japanese contemporary and traditional music in the United States and the world. Music From Japan Festival 2021 will introduce a radical new format for MFJ. Interdisciplinary artists Tomoko Hojo and Kazuya Ishigami will bring a weekend of performances coupled with sound installations and multi-channel electronic compositions.
Country: United States
Contact: Artistic Director Naoyuki Miura
Contact: Executive Director Robyn Ono
Social Media: www.facebook.com/musicfromjapan
Other Venues: various venues including, Scandinavia House, New York City
Type: Concert

Music in the Mountains
Website: https://musicinthemountains.com/
Email: info@musicinthemountains.com
Phone: 970 385 6820
Address: 515 East College Drive Durango, CO 81301
Information: This three-week classical music festival oc-

curs every July in Durango, Colorado. Experience world-class music featuring musicians of the highest caliber.
Country: United States
Contact: festival Artistic Director Gregory Hustis Hustis
Social Media: www.facebook.com/musicinthemountainsCO www.instagram.com/musicinthemountainsfestival/
Other Venues: Community Concert Hall at Fort Lewis College (600 capacity),
Type: Concert

Music in the Vineyards
Website: https://www.musicinthevineyards.org/
Email: info@musicinthevineyards.org
Phone: 707 258 5559
Address: PO Box 6297 Napa, CA. 94581
Information: Brings together internationally recognized musicians in unique, intimate winery settings where both performers and audiences experience chamber music as it was meant to be heard. Every August, Music in the Vineyards' festival features over 40 renowned musicians from the U.S., Europe and Canada in a dozen of the Napa Valley's most stunning spaces. 2019 celebrates the 25th season.
Country: United States
Contact: co-Artistic Director Daria Adams
Contact: Executive Director Evie Ayers
Email: evie@musicinthevineyards.org
Contact: co-Artistic Director Michael Adams
Contact: Public Relations Natasha Biasell
Email: natasha@musicinthevineyards.org
Social Media: twitter.com/MITV_Info www.facebook.com/MusicIntheVineyards www.instagram.com/musicinthevineyards/
Frequency: Annual
Other Venues: Wine Valleys in the Napa Valley
Type: Concert

Music@Menlo
Website: https://musicatmenlo.org/
Email: info@musicatmenlo.org
Phone: 650 330 2030
Address: Music@Menlo, 50 Valparaiso Avenue, US
Information: Music@Menlo is an internationally acclaimed chamber music festival and institute in the San Francisco Bay Area. Founded by David Finckel and Wu Han as a program of Menlo School, Music@Menlo features unique immersive programming, a roster of world-class artists, and a Chamber Music Institute for emerging and pre-professional musicians.
Country: United States
Contact: Executive Director Edward Sweeney
Email: edward@musicatmenlo.org
Contact: General Manager and Education programs Director Marianne LaCrosse
Email: marianne@musicatmenlo.org
Contact: communications Director Claire Graham
Email: claire@musicatmenlo.org
Contact: development Director Lee Ramsey
Email: lee@musicatmenlo.org
Social Media:
www.facebook.com/musicatmenlo/?ref=sgm
Menlo School: Stent Family Hall (140 capacity), Martin Family Hall (180 capacity) St Mark's Episcopal Church (320 capacity)
Type: Concert

Natchez Opera Festival
Website: https://www.natchezfestivalofmusic.com/
Email: natchezfestival@gmail.com
Phone: 601 446 1104
Address: 64 Homochitto Street. Natchez, MS, 39120 USA
Information: The mission is to enlighten and enrich the lives of the citizens of the greater Mississippi/Louisiana region and neighbouring areas by producing a variety of musical events including popular music, broadway musicals, recitals and musical theater.
Country: United States
Contact: Artistic Director Jay Dean
Contact: Chairman Charlotte Franklin Franklin
Social Media: www.facebook.com/NatchezFestivalOfMusic www.instagram.com/natchezfestivalofmusic
Type: Musical theatre, Theatre, Concert

National Black Arts Festival
Website:
https://nbaf.org/
Email: pr@nbaf.org
Phone: 470 284 7300
Address: 429 Fairmont Ave. NW, Suite J Atlanta, GA 30318, US
Information: The NBAF (National Black Arts) is a nonprofit organization with a legacy of providing stellar Artistic and educational programs in music, dance, film, visual arts, theater and the literary arts. Celebrated within and outside of Atlanta, NBAF is recognized as the oldest multidisciplinary arts organization in the United States focused exclusively on the arts and on artists of African descent.
Country: United States
Contact: Managing Director Stephanie Owens
Email: sowens@nbaf.org
Contact: Artistic Director Tiffany Latrice
Email: tlatrice@nbaf.org
Contact: special events and fundraising Judy Hanenkrat

Email: jhanenkrat@nbaf.org
Social Media: twitter.com/NBAF www.facebook.com/nbafreimagined www.instagram.com/nbaf
Other Venues: Over 20 venues in Atlanta
Type: Dance/Ballet, Theatre, Performance art, Concert, Film, Multi-media

National Orchestral Institute
Website:
https://theclarice.umd.edu/noi
Email:
noi@umd.edu
Phone: 301 405 2317
Address: 2110 Clarice Smith Performing Arts Center, University of Maryland, US
Information: The National Orchestral Institute is a four-week program of intensive study covering chamber music, unconducted chamber orchestras, orchestral performance.
Country: United States
Contact: Director, national orchestral institute and festival Richard Scerbo
Email: rscerbo@umd.edu
Contact: Artistic administrator Yarina Conners
Email: yconners@umd.edu
Contact: artist services coordinator Andrew Giza
Email: giza@umd.edu
Social Media: www.facebook.com/noifestival
Other Venues: Dekelboum Concert Hall
Type: Concert

New Hampshire Music Festival
Website: https://www.nhmf.org/
Email: info@nhmf.org
Phone: 603 238 9007
Address: 42 Main Street, Plymouth, NH, United States, New Hampshire
Information: The New Hampshire Music Festival is a summer festival that honors the tradition of classical music while exploring new Artistic paths. The organization offers patrons an engaging, immersive festival experience by presenting world-class performances of symphonic, choral and chamber music. Strong collaborations with community partners are a hallmark of this important cultural institution, enabling transformative music experiences and educational programs to students of all ages.**Country:** United States
Contact: vice Chairman Tom Reicher
Email: info@nhmf.org
Contact: Chairman Phil Boulter
Email: info@nhmf.org
Contact: Executive Director Lucinda Williams
Email: info@nhmf.org
Social Media: twitter.com/NHMusicFest www.facebook.com/NHMusicFestival www.instagram.com/nhmusicfest
Frequency: Annual
Other Venues: Silver Center for the Arts at Plymouth State University (674 capacity)
Type: Concert

New Orleans Keyboard Festival
Website: http:// www.masno.org/
Email: Director@masno.org
Phone: 504 899 4826
Address: Musical Arts Society of New Orleans, PO Box 750698, US
Information: As part of the New Orleans Keyboard Festival, NOPI is an intensive solo performance program for advanced and intermediate college, high school, and junior high school pianists. Participants receive private lessons, perform in master classes, attend lectures and discussions, have competition opportunities, and perform in the Showcase Recital.
Country: United States
Contact: Executive Director Cara McCool Woolf
Contact: Artistic Director Daniel Weilbaecher
Contact: President Andrea Brown
Social Media: twitter.com/CaraMasno www.facebook.com/MASNO-Musical-Arts-Society-of-New-Orleans-129624680451934 www.instagram.com/masno1980
Frequency: Annual
Other Venues: Musical Arts Society of New Orleans
Type: Concert

New Orleans Jazz & Heritage Festival
Website: https://www.nojazzfest.com/
Email: info@nojazzfest.com
Phone: 504 558 6100
Address: 1205 North Rampart Street, US
Information: Presenting the best of the genre in the US jazz capital!
Country: United States
Social Media: @JazzFest
End: 2022-05-08
Other Venues: Fairground (100000 capacity) , and 12 stages
Type: Concert

Newport Jazz Festival
Website: https://www.newportjazz.org/
Email: info@fpiny.com
Phone: 212 501 1390
Address: 90 Fort Adams Dr Newport, RI 02840 USA
Information: From 1984 to 2008, the festival was known

as the JVC Jazz Festival. However, during the economic downturn of 2009, JVC ceased its support of the festival and was replaced by CareFusion.As of 2012, the festival is sponsored by Natixis Global Asset Management.
Country: United States
Contact: Producer George Wein
Social Media: twitter.com/newportjazzfest www.instagram.com/newportjazzfest/ www.facebook.com/NewportJazzFest
Frequency: Annual
End: 2022-07-31
Other Venues: Ft Adams State Park
Type: Concert

Newport Music Festival
Website: www.newportmusic.org
Email: staff@newportmusic.org
Phone: 401 846 1133
Address: P.O. Box 3303, Newport, RI 02840 USA
Information: in all, 60+ concerts are scheduled with music ranging from Bach to Bernstein—three to five per day—in multiple locations, including the famous Newport Mansions. There will be concerts of chamber music favorites and programs of lesser-known works. Some 70 musicians from 18 countries will participate, creating an international group of resident artists. Many will be familiar, but a record 30 musicians will make their Newport debuts, joining what the Festival terms its "family of artists"
Country: United States
Contact: Executive Director Pamela Pantos
Contact: Director of development David Burnham
Contact: Director of business and operations Erin Metcalf
Contact: development consultant Ellen Kulik
Social Media: twitter.com/newportmusic www.facebook.com/NewportMusicFestival www.instagram.com/newportmusicfestival
Frequency: Annual
End: 2021-07-20
Other Venues: various venues including Bellevue House, The Breakers Lawn, Castle Hill Inn and The Chanler
Type: Concert, Other

North Country Chamber Players Summer Festival – Music in the White Mountains
Website: https://northcountrychamberplayers.org/
Email: nccp@ncia.net
Phone: 603 444 0309
Address: PO Box 865, US
Information: an ensemble of world class musicians presents their WHITE MOUNTAINS MUSIC FESTIVAL weekends from July 12th through August 17th, 2014 with performances in historic venues – Sugar Hill Meetinghouse in Sugar Hill, NH., Mountain View Grand Hotel in Whitefield, NH., Alumni Hall in Haverhill, NH., Papermill Theater in Lincoln, NH
Country: United States
Social Media: www.facebook.com/northcountrychamberplayers/
Other Venues: Sugar Hill Meetinghouse, Mountain View Grand, Alumni Hall
Type: Concert

Northwest Folklife Festival
Website: www.nwfolklife.org
Email: folklife@nwfolklife.org
Phone: 206 684 7300
Address: 305 Harrison St, Seattle, WA 98109 USA
Information: Celebrating its 50th anniversary in 2021, the annual Northwest Folklife Festival is a community-powered celebration of the arts, culture, and heritage that make up the brilliant cultural tapestry of the greater Pacific Northwest. Prior to 2020, over 6, 000 artists and culture-bearers brought cultural exPressions to audiences across 25 stages alongside 200 food and craft vendors and 500 volunteers annually.
Country: United States
Contact: Executive Artistic Director Kelli Faryar
Email: kelli@nwfolklife.org
Contact: Managing Director Reese Tanimura
Email: reese@nwfolklife.org
Contact: festival and production Director Michael Chandler
Email: mike@nwfolklife.org
Contact: operations Manager, production Manager and technical Director Annie O'Dowd
Email: anne@nwfolklife.org
Social Media: twitter.com/NWFolklife www.facebook.com/nwfolklife www.instagram.com/nwfolklife
Frequency: Annual
End: 2021-05-31
Other Venues: Seattle Center (2900 capacity)
Type: Concert, Performance art, Dance/Ballet, Other

Northwest New Works Festival
Website: https://www.ontheboards.org/staff-and-board
Email:
info@ontheboards.org
Phone:
206 217 9886
Address: On the Boards, PO Box 19515, US
Information: On the Boards invests in leading contem-

porary performing artists near and far, and connects them to a diverse range of communities interested in forward-thinking art and ideas.
Country: United States
Contact: Executive Director Betsey Brock
Email: betsey@ontheboards.org
Contact: Artistic Director Rachel Cook
Email: rachel@ontheboards.org
Contact: technical Director Rich Bresnahan
Email: rich@ontheboards.org
Other Venues: On the Boards: mainstage (360 capacity), studio (99 capacity)
Type: Concert, Theatre, Performance art

Ojai Music Festival
Website: https://www.ojaifestival.org/
Email: info@ojaifestival.org
Phone: 805 646 2094
Address: PO Box 185, US
Information: maintains music education program to expose public school children to classical music
Country: United States
Contact: President Jamie Bennett
Email: jbennett@ojaifestival.org
Contact: Chief Operating Officer Gina Gutierrez
Email: ggutierrez@ojaifestival.org
Contact: festival operations and events Manager Amber Young
Email: ayoung@ojaifestival.org
End: 2022-06-12
Other Venues: Libbey Bowl, Libbey Park (1500 capacity)
Type: Concert

OK Mozart International Festival
Website: okmmusic.org
Email: hello@okmmusic.org
Phone: 918 336 9900
Address: 415 S.E. Dewey Ave., Bartlesville, Oklahoma 74003 USA
Information: This annual summer celebration features nine days of music, from classical instrumentalists to crossover artists that fuse country, jazz, world music and more.
Country: United States
Contact: Chairman of the board and event Chair Mary Lynn Mihm-Howk
Contact: Marketing and social media Director Ryan Martin
Email: rmartin@okmozart.com
Contact: production Manager Cassie Mihm
Email: mihm@okmozart.com
Social Media: twitter.com/okmmusic www.facebook.com/okmfestival
Frequency: Annual
End: 2021-06-17
Other Venues: gorgeous location overlooking tranquil Clyde Lake, and the ravine makes a natural amphitheater
Type: Concert

Oklahoma Arts Institute at Quartz Mountain
Website: https://oaiquartz.org/
Email: oai@oaiquartz.org
Phone: 405 605 7500
Address: The Oklahoma Arts Institute, 111 NW 9th Street, US
Information: The Oklahoma Arts Institute at Quartz Mountain is a private, non-profit organization with a mission to provide exceptional multidisciplinary arts experiences that develop individual talent and inspire a lifelong passion for the arts. Since 1977, the Oklahoma Arts Institute has recruited nationally renowned artists to teach a fine arts program for talented Oklahoma youth and a series of continuing education workshops for adults.
Country: United States
Contact: vice President and Director of programs Emily Claudé
Email: eclaude@oaiquartz.org
Contact: President and CEO Julie Cohen
Email: jcohen@oaiquartz.org
Contact: Director of development Shana Gibelyou
Email: sgibelyou@oaiquartz.org
Social Media: www.facebook.com/oaiquartz/twitter.com/OAIQuartz www.instagram.com/oaiquartz/
Quartz Mountain Arts & Conference Center, Lone Wolf OK – Amphitheater (500 capacity), 5 Pavillions each at (100 capacity), Performing Arts Hall (700 capacity), Lodge 120 rooms

Olympic Music Festival
Website: https://www.olympicmusicfestival.org/
Email: info@olympicmusicfestival.org
Phone: 360 385 9699
Address: PO Box 897, Port Townsend, WA 98368 USA
Information: The Olympic Music Festival's mission is to present world-class chamber musicians in performances of diverse repertoire for the enjoyment, enrichment, and education for the community.
Country: United States
Contact: Artistic Director Julio Elizalde
Contact: Artistic Director Julio Elizalde Elizalde
Contact: President Carol Thornburgh Thornburgh
Contact: Managing Director Emilie Baker Baker

Social Media: www.instagram.com/omfconcerts www.facebook.com/theolympicmusicfestival
Frequency: Annual
Other Venues: Northwest Maritime Center (350 capacity)
Type: Concert

Opera in the Ozarks
Website: https://opera.org/
Email: info@opera.org
Phone: 479 253 8595
Address: Inspiration Point Fine Arts Colony, 16311 Hwy 62 West, US
Information: The nationally acclaimed summer music festival and training program for up-and-coming opera professionals
Country: United States
Contact: Artistic Director Thomas Cockrell
Email: ArtisticDirector@opera.org
Contact: General Director Nancy Preis
Email: GeneralDirector@opera.org
Contact: Operations Director Chris Langley
Email: opsDirector@opera.org
Phone:
Social Media: www.facebook.com/operaozarkstwitter.com/operaozarks
End: 2022-07-22
Other Venues: Inspiration Point in Eureka Springs
Type: Opera, Concert

Opera Theatre of Saint Louis, a Festival Season
Website: https://opera-stl.org/
Email: info@opera-stl.org
Phone: 314 961 0171
Address: Sally S. Levy Opera Center, 210 Hazel Avenue, US
Information: Opera Theatre of Saint Louis is one of the leading American opera companies, known for a spring festival of inventive new productions, sung in English, featuring the finest American singers and accompanied by members of the St. Louis Symphony Orchestra. As of 2021, Opera Theatre has presented 31 world premieres and 27 American premieres – which may be the highest percentage of new work in the repertory of any U.S. company.
Country: United States
Contact: Artistic Director James Robinson
Contact: music Director Stephen Lord
Contact: General Director Andrew Jorgensen
Social Media: www.facebook.com/OperaTheatre/
Other Venues: Loretto-Hilton Theatre (978 capacity)
Type: Opera

Orcas Island Chamber Music Festival
Website: https://oicmf.org/
Email: info@oicmf.org
Phone: 360 376 6636
Address: PO Box 646 Eastsound, WA 98245, US
Information: The annual Chamber Music Festival is dedicated to the highest standards of performance – to bring Chamber Music to a wide audience, all amidst the beautiful setting of Orcas island. Alongside the wonderful concerts, there are daytime lectures given by music professors, conductors, and specialist music Producers.
Country: United States
Contact: Executive Director Anita Orne
Email: anita@oicmf.org
Contact: Artistic Director Aloysia Friedman
Email: aloysia@oicmf.org
Contact: festival Director Linda Slone
Email: linda@oicmf.org
Contact: festival production Manager Sarah Ogmundson
Email: sarah@oicmf.org
Social Media: twitter.com/OICMF www.facebook.com/OICMF
Frequency: Annual
Type: Concert

Oregon Bach Festival
Website: www.oregonbachfestival.com
Email: bachfest@uoregon.edu
Phone: 541 346 5666
Address: 1257 University of Oregon, US
Information: children's concerts, pre-concert lectures, ""Let's Talk' with festival artists, conducting masterclasses
Country: United States
Contact: education and outreach coordinator Erica Abbe
Email: abbee@uoregon.edu
Contact: Director of Artistic Administration Michael Anderson
Email: mander@uoregon.edu
Contact: Executive Director Janelle McCoy
Email: janellem@uoregon.edu
Social Media: @oregonbachfest@oregonbachfestival
Frequency: annual
Venue: Beall Hall, School of Music 545, Silva Hall, Hult Center for the Performing Arts 2444

Oswego Harbor Festival
Website: www.oswegoharborfest.com
Email: info@oswegoharborfest.com
Phone: 315 343 6858
Address: 41 Lake Street, US
Information:
Country: United States

Contact: vice President Colleen Carmella
Contact: treasurer Robert Baldwin
Social Media: @oswegoharborfest
Frequency: annual
Venue: various venues
Type: All

Other Minds Festival
Website: www.otherminds.org
Email: otherminds@otherminds.org
Phone: 415 934 8134
Address: 55 Taylor Street San Francisco, CA 94102, US
Information: The first Other Minds Festival took place during the grand opening of the Center for the Arts at Yerba Buena Gardens in San Francisco in November 1993
Country: United States
Contact: Executive and Artistic Director Charles Amirkhanian
Email: charles@otherminds.org
Contact: Associate Director Blaine Todd
Email: blaine@otherminds.org
Contact: Administrative Director Randall Wong
Email: randall@otherminds.org
Contact: Production Director Mark Abramson
Email: mark@otherminds.org
Social Media: https://www.facebook.com/Other.Minds/about/ https://twitter.com/OtherMindsSF
Frequency: Annual
Other Venues: Taube Atrium Theater, San Francisco
Type: Concert

Parade Company
Website: https://theparade.org/
Email: clownie@theparade.org
Phone: 313 923 7400
Address: 9500 Mt Elliott, Studio A, Detroit, MI 48211, US
Information: Spectacular Thanksgiving Parade for Detroit. Floats and festivities for Thanksgiving and other Festivals.
Country: United States
Contact: President and CEO Tony Michaels
Email: tmichaels@theparade.org
Contact: Chief Operating Officer Jessica Kaminskas
Email: jkaminskas@theparade.org
Contact: Director of events CarolAnn Barbb
Email: cbarbb@theparade.org
Contact: assistant art Director Alex Fedirko
Email: afedirko@theparade.org
Social Media: twitter.com/ParadeCo www.facebook.com/TheParadeCo www.instagram.com/paradecompany
Other Venues: Woodward Avenue, Detroit
Type: Multi-media

Peninsula Music Festival
Website: www.musicfestival.com
Email: musicfestival@musicfestival.com
Phone: 920 854 4060
Address: 10347 N. Water Street, Suite B, P.O. Box 340, Ephraim, WI 54234, USA
Information: The Peninsula Music Festival is located in Door County, Wisconsin, an area that is on a peninsula and attracts a large tourist population in the summer. Many of the people who attend the concerts are on vacation and may have spent the day at the beach, hiking, or on a boat. Concertgoers attend in everything from jeans to dresses, shorts to suits.
Country: United States
Contact: music Director Victor Yampolsky
Contact: Executive Director Christoph Ptack
Email: christoph@musicfestival.com
Contact: operations administrator Chris Risch
Email: chris@musicfestival.com
Contact: social media Manager Jill Quigley
Social Media: twitter.com/penmusicfest www.facebook.com/PeninsulaMusicFestival
Other Venues: various venues around Door County Wisconsin including Door Community Auditorium, Fish Creek (750 capacity) plus assorted churches and schools
Type: Concert

Philadelphia Folk Festival
Website: pfs.org
Email: pfs@pfs.org
Phone: 215 242 0150
Address: 6156 Ridge Avenue, US
Information: alternative Internet: www.pfs.org
Country: United States
Contact: exective Director Justin Nordell
Email: jnordell@pfs.org
Contact: Director of business development Jennifer Rajotte
Email: jrajotte@pfs.org
Contact: operations Manager Desireé Haney
Email: dhaney@pfs.org
Contact: office and membership Manager Katie Kresz
Email: kkresz@pfs.org
Social Media: @folksongsociety@PFSOfficialPage
Frequency: annual
Venue: Old Pool Farm

Piccolo Spoleto Festival
Website: www.piccolospoleto.com
Email: culturalaffairs@charleston-sc.gov
Phone: 843 724 7305

Address: City of Charleston Office of Cultural Affairs , 75 Calhoun Street, Suite 3800 Charleston, SC 29401. USA
Information: The Piccolo Spoleto Festival annually presents a varied program that includes visual arts exhibitions, performances of classical music, jazz, dance, theater, and choral music, as well as cultural events and community celebrations, poetry readings, children's activities, craft shows, and film screenings.
Country: United States
Contact: Associate Producer Mindy Manziano
Contact: development Manager Gordon Rooney
Contact: production Manager Ray Swagerty
Contact: finance Manager Rachel Workman
Social Media: twitter.com/Piccolo_Spoleto www.facebook.com/PiccoloSpoletoFestival
Frequency: Annual
End: 2021-06-13
Other Venues: Charleston Gaillard Center (2750 capacity)
Type: Concert, Other

Pine Mountain Music Festival
Website: https://www.pmmf.org/
Email: info@pmmf.org
Phone: 906 482 1542
Address: PO Box 406 Hancock, MI 49930, US
Information: The PMMF is one of only a few summer festivals nationwide producing a season of professional opera, chamber music, and other genres of music, including folk and jazz – it is the only one to tour all its acts in multiple cities hundreds of miles apart.
The Pine Mountain Music Festival (PMMF) was founded in Iron Mountain, Michigan, in 1991 by Laura Jean Deming, a cellist and member of the orchestra of Lyric Opera of Chicago.
Country: United States
Contact: Executive Director Douglas Day
Contact: President Diane Eshbach
Contact: Secretary/Treasurer GLORIA MELTON
Social Media: twitter.com/PineMtnMusic www.facebook.com/pinemountainmusicfestival/
Frequency: Annual
Other Venues: Venues around Michigan: HOUGHTON COUNTY, MARQUETTE COUNTY, DICKINSON COUNTY
Type: Concert

Pittsburgh International Children's Theater and Festival
Website: pghkids.trustarts.org
Email: boxoffice@pghkids.org
Phone: 412 321 5520
Address: 803 Liberty Avenue, US
Information:
Country: United States
Social Media: @CulturalTrust@CulturalTrust
Frequency: annual
Downtown Pittsburgh's vibrant Cultural District
Type: All

Prescott Arts Festival
Website: https://www.prescottpark.org/
Email: info@prescottarts.org
Phone: 603 436 2848
Address: PO Box 4370, US
Information: Prescott Park Arts Festival celebrates its 45th season of presenting music, art, theater and dance on the banks of the Piscataqua River.
Country: United States
Contact: President Ben Anderson
Email: ben@prescottpark.org
Contact: Director of operations Angela Greene
Email: angela@prescottpark.org
Contact: operations Associate Stephen Goodrow
Email: stephen@prescottpark.org
Contact: production Manager Sara Martin
Email: sara@prescottpark.org
Contact: development Director Lee Frank
Email: lee@prescottpark.org
Social Media: www.facebook.com/PrescottParkArtsFestival/
Other Venues: Prescott Park (10000 capacity)

Raritan River Music Festival
Website: https://www.raritanrivermusic.org/
Email: info@raritanrivermusic.org
Phone: 908 213 1100
Address: PO Box 454, US
Information: Raritan River Music works year round to fulfill our commitment to make music an important part of people's everyday lives.
Raritan River Music serves the community through music presentation, creation, and programs of educational, therapeutic, and cultural enrichment.
Country: United States
Contact: Artistic Director Michael Newman
Social Media: www.facebook.com/RaritanRiverMusic/
Other Venues: various venues
Type: Concert

Ravinia Festival
Website: https://www.ravinia.org/
Email: tickets@ravinia.org
Phone: 847 266 5000
Address: 418 Sheridan Road, US
Information: Ravinia is a not-for-profit & outdoor music

festival just north of Chicago. Hear your favorite stars, under the stars!
Box office: PO Box 896, Highland Park IL 60035, Tel: 847-266 5100, Fax: 847-433 4582
Country: United States
Contact: President and chief Executive officer Welz Kauffman
Contact: Director, ticket operations Jennifer Butler
Contact: Director, information technology Jamie Laing
Contact: Director, human resources Leslie Muir
Social Media: www.facebook.com/RaviniaFestival
Other Venues: Pavilion (3200 capacity); MartinTheatre (850 capacity), Bennett-Gordon Hall (450 capacity)
Type: Concert

Red River Revel Arts Festival
Website: https://redriverrevel.com/
Email: rrr@redriverrevel.com
Phone: 318 424 4000
Address: 101 Crocket Street, US
Information: festival admission fee – -$5
Country: United States
Social Media: www.facebook.com/RedRiverRevel
Other Venues: 5 open-air stages on the riverfront
Type: Concert

Redlands Bowl Summer Music Festival
Website: https://redlandsbowl.org/
Email: info@redlandsbowl.org
Phone: 909 793 7316
Address: Mission Gables Bowl House 168 South Eureka Street, Redlands, CA 92373 USA
Information: The Redlands Bowl holds the distinction of being America's longest continuously running summer music festival where no admission is charged.
Country: United States
Contact: Executive Director Beverley Noerr
Contact: operations Director Kristi Marnell
Contact: program Director Valerie Peister
Contact: Marketing and communications coordinator Courtney Camp
Social Media: twitter.com/redlandsbowl www.facebook.com/redlandsbowl
Other Venues: Redlands Bowl (6000 capacity – bench and lawn seating)
Type: Concert

Riverbend Festival
Website: www.riverbendfestival.com
Email: info@riverbendfestival.com
Phone: 423 756 2211
Address: 200 Riverfront Parkway, US
Information:
Country: United States
Contact: Executive Director Chip Baker
Email: chip@riverbendfestival.com
Contact: Executive assistant/office coordinator Barbara Agee
Email: barbara@riverbendfestival.com
Contact: entertainment Director Joe Fuller
Email: dixie@riverbendfestival.com
Contact: Director of Sales Karen Shostak
Email: karen@riverbendfestival.com
Contact: Director of operations Mitchell Hall
Email: mitchell@riverbendfestival.com
Contact: Director of Marketing Amy Morrow
Email: amy@riverbendfestival.com
Social Media: @rbfestival/@rbfestival
Frequency: annual
Ross's Landing Park on the banks of the Tennessee River 100000

Rochester International Jazz festival
Website: www.rochesterjazz.com
Email: john@rochesterjazz.com
Phone: 585 454 2060
Address: 250 East Avenue Rochester, NY 14604 USA
Information: One of the world's leading jazz festivals. From legendary performers and familiar favorites, to rising stars and new discoveries, RIJF navigates all genres of creative improvised music from all corners of the world.
Country: United States
Contact: Producer and Executive Director sponsor and vendor opportunities Marc Iacona
Email: marc@rochesterjazz.com
Contact: public relations, advertising, Marketing Jean Dalmath
Email: jdalmath@dalmath.com
Contact: Producer and Artistic Director John Nugent
Social Media: twitter.com/rocjazzfest www.facebook.com/rochesterintjazzfest
Frequency: Annual
End: 2021-08-07
20+ diverse venues throughout downtown Rochester New York's East End cultural and entertainment district, including Kodak Hall at Eastman Theatre (2400 capacity)
Type: Concert

Rockport Chamber Music Festival
Website: https://www.rockportmusic.org/
Email: info@rockportmusic.org
Phone: 978 546 7391
Address: 16 Main StRockport, MA 01966, USA

Information: The Rockport Chamber Music Festival celebrated its 25th Anniversary Season in 2006 with a gala concert season and special events; Educational Outreach Committee works closely with local schools to present special, instructional music programs to students
Country: United States
Contact: Artistic Director Barry Shiffman
Contact: President Tony Beadle
Contact: Executive assistant Shannon Mason
Contact: Director of Marketing Karen Herlitz
Social Media: twitter.com/RockportMusic www.facebook.com/RockportMusic
Frequency: Annual
Type: Concert

San Francisco Ethnic Dance Festival and People Like Me children's festival
Website: https://www.worldartswest.org/
Email: info@worldartswest.org
Phone: 415 474 3914
Address: Fort Mason Center, 2 Marina Blvd., Bldg. D, #230, US
Information: People Like Me festival of dance for children combined with an educational program; San Francisco Ethnic Dance Festival is 3 weekends of ethnic dance with northern Californian companies selected on audition basis; see also Presenters and Venues (World Art
Country: United States
Contact: Executive Director Julie Mushet
Email: julie@worldartswest.org
Contact: festival Artistic Director Patrick Makuakāne
Email: patrick@worldartswest.org
Contact: production Manager Sonia Pina
Email: sonia@worldartswest.org
Contact: festival Managing Director Arlene Kato
Email: arlene@worldartswest.org
Social Media: / www.facebook.com/SanFranciscoEthnicDanceFestival
Other Venues: Palace of Fine Arts (1000 capacity)
Type: Dance/Ballet

San Francisco International Arts Festival
Website: www.sfiaf.org
Email: info@sfiaf.org
Phone: 415 399 9554
Address: The Flood Building, 870 Market Street, Suite 1256, US
Information: celebrates the arts through an annual gathering that brings together a global community of artists and audiences. The organisation presents and produces innovative projects that are focused on increasing human awareness and understanding
Country: United States
Contact: Executive Director Andrew Wood
Email: info@sfiaf.org
Social Media: @SFIAF/@SfInternationalArtsFestival
Frequency: annual
Venue: Fort Mason Center
Type: Concert, Dance/Ballet, Mime, Multi-media, Musical theatre, Object theatre, Opera, Performance art, Puppetry, Theatre

San Francisco Symphony, Summer Festival
Website: https://www.sfsymphony.org/
Email: patronservices@sfsymphony.org
Phone: 415 864 6000
Address: Davies Symphony Hall, 201 Van Ness Ave. San Francisco, CA 94102
Information: Esa-Pekka Salonen assumes his post as the San Francisco Symphony's twelfth Music Director in the 2020–21 season, embarking on a new vision for the present and future of the orchestral landscape. In their inaugural season together, Esa-Pekka Salonen and the San Francisco Symphony introduce a groundbreaking Artistic leadership model anchored by eight Collaborative Partners from a variety of cultural disciplines
Country: United States
Contact: chief Executive officer Mark Hanson
Contact: Director Matthew Spivey
Contact: Artistic administrator James Utz
Contact: music Director Esa-Pekka Salonen Salonen
Social Media: twitter.com/sfsymphony www.facebook.com/sfsymphony www.instagram.com/sfsymphony
Frequency: Annual
Other Venues: Davies Symphony Hall (2743 capacity)
Type: Concert

San José Comcast Jazz Festival
Website: https://sanjosejazz.org/
Email: info@sanjosejazz.org
Phone: 408 288 7557
Address: 38 West Santa Clara Street, US
Information: Founded in 1986, San Jose Jazz is a public benefit corporation celebrating jazz as a dynamic, evolving art form and is Producer of the Live From Home online concert series and the annual San Jose Jazz Summer Fest, which celebrated 30 years in 2019. It is a free festival and encourages all jazz enthusiasts to come along and enjoy their spectacular performances.
Country: United States
Contact: Executive Director Brendan Rawson
Email: brendanr@sanjosejazz.org
Contact: Artistic and festival Director Bruce Labadie
Email: brucel@sanjosejazz.org

Contact: Director of Marketing Massimo Chisessi
Email: massimoc@sanjosejazz.org
Contact: Artistic and festival Director Bruce Labadie
Email: brucel@sanjosejazz.org
Social Media: www.facebook.com/sanjosejazz
9 stages set in city venues & in parks
Type: Concert

Santa Fe Chamber Music Festival
Website: www.santafechambermusic.com
Email: info@sfcmf.org
Phone: 505 983 2075
Address: PO Box 2227, US
Information:
Country: United States
Contact: Executive Director Steven Ovitsky
Contact: Artistic Director Marc Neikrug
Contact: operations and production Manager Angelica Bernaert
Contact: Director of development Cece Derringer
Social Media: @SFChamberMusic@SFChamberMusic
Frequency: annual
Venue: St Francis Auditorium 430, Lensic Performing Arts Centre 830

Sarasota Music Festival (Florida West Coast Symphony)
Website: https://www.sarasotaorchestra.org/
Email: web@sarasotaorchestra.org
Phone: 941 953 3434
Address: 709 N Tamiami Trail, Sarasota, FL 34236, USA
Information: The Sarasota Music Festival brings the best up-and-coming young musicians from around the world to Sarasota for three weeks each June. This, coupled with the world-renowned faculty artists who travel here to mentor and perform, makes it a magical experience of exceptional concerts.
Country: United States
Contact: festival founder Paul Wolfe
Contact: music Director Jeffrey Kahane
Contact: vp of festival Administration RoseAnne McCabe
Social Media: www.facebook.com/SarasotaMusicFestivaltwitter.com/srqorchestra
Frequency: Annual
Other Venues: Holley Hall, Sarasota Opera House
Type: Concert

Savannah Music Festival
Website: https://www.savannahmusicfestival.org/
Email: info@savannahmusicfestival.org
Phone: 912 234 3378
Address: 200 E St Julian St, Ste 601 Savannah, GA 31401 USA
Information: The Savannah Music Festival (SMF) is dedicated to presenting world-class celebrations of the musical arts by creating timeless and adventurous productions that stimulate arts education, foster economic growth and unite artists and audiences in Savannah. Member of ISPA
Country: United States
Contact: Executive Director David Pratt
Email: info@savannahmusicfestival.org
Contact: Artistic Director Ryan McMaken, McMaken
Email: info@savannahmusicfestival.org
Social Media: twitter.com/savmusicfest www.facebook.com/SavannahMusicFestival www.instagram.com/savannahmusicfestival
End: 2022-04-29
Other Venues: Usually takes place in historic churches, synagogues, museums and theatres, but this year rather than the large-scale outdoor presentations originally planned, performances will take place at two indoor venues with limited-capacity crowds with social distancing in place.
Type: Concert

Seattle Chamber Music Society
Website: https://www.seattlechambermusic.org/
Email: info@seattlechambermusic.org
Phone: 206 283 8710
Address: 10 Harrison Street, Suite 306, US
Information: A wonderful programme of classical music, with more than 40 renowned musicians and 12 outstanding concerts.
box-office tel: 206-283-8808; 45 performances
Country: United States
Contact: Executive Director Connie Cooper
Email: connie@seattlechambermusic.org
Contact: Director of education and operations Rachel Ciprotti
Email: rachelc@seattlechambermusic.org
Contact: Director of development Kimberly Fulghum
Email: kimberly@seattlechambermusic.org
Contact: Director of Marketing and communications Seneca Garber
Email: seneca@seattlechambermusic.org
Contact: administrative assistant Amanda Sharp
Email: amanda@seattlechambermusic.org
Social Media: www.facebook.com/SeattleChamberMusic/
End: 2022-01-30
Other Venues: Illsley Ball Nordstrom Recital Hall at Benaroya Hall
Type: Concert

Sewanee Summer Music Festival
Website: https://ssmf.sewanee.edu/
Email: ssmfDirector@gmail.com
Phone: 931 598 1225
Address: 735 University Ave Sewanee, TN 37375 USA
Information: The Festival was established in 1957 to provide a comprehensive training program emphasizing performance experience. Sewanee not only prepares students for the challenges professional musicians must meet, but also makes them lifetime lovers of music.
Country: United States
Contact: Artistic Director John Kilkenny
Contact: Managing Director Hilary Dow Ward
Contact: office Manager Anna Burklin
Social Media: www.facebook.com/sewaneemusicfestival www.instagram.com/sewaneesmf
End: 2022-07-17
Other Venues: The University of the South – Guerry Hall (1000 capacity)
Type: Concert

Shenandoah Valley Music Festival
Website: http://musicfest.org/
Email: info@musicfest.org
Phone: 540 459 3396
Address: PO Box 528, US
Information: summer concert series on the grounds of a restored 1890s resort hotel in the Shenandoah Valley of Virginia, about 2 hours west of Washington DC. Symphonic, country, bluegrass and other types of music offered each summer
Country: United States
Contact: President and Executive Director Dennis Lynch
Contact: Chair Leigh Devier
Contact: administrative and Marketing specialist Lorraine Halsted
Social Media: www.facebook.com/svmusicfest
Shrine Mont Camp & Conference Center, Orkney Springs: Covered Pavilion 600, Facility Pavillion & Lawn up to 1800
Type: Concert

Sitka Summer Music Festival
Website: https://www.sitkamusicfestival.org/
Email: info@sitkamusicfestival.org
Phone: 907 747 6774
Address: PO Box 3333, US
Information: The Sitka Music Festival has been bringing world-class musicians to perform chamber music in Sitka and across Alaska since 1972.**Country:** United States
Contact: President Don Lehmann
Email: info@sitkamusicfestival.org
Contact: vice President Mary Hames
Email: info@sitkamusicfestival.org
Contact: Associate Director Amy Kramer Johnson
Email: info@sitkamusicfestival.org
Social Media: www.facebook.com/SitkaMusicFestival
End: 2022-03-06
Other Venues: various locations across town including Harrigan Centennial Hall (500 capacity)
Type: Concert

Skaneateles Festival
Website: www.skanfest.org
Email: music@skanfest.org
Phone: 315 685 7418
Address: 97 E Genesee Street, US
Information:
Country: United States
Contact: Artistic Director Aaron Wunsch
Contact: Executive Director Susan Mark
Contact: Director of operations Steve Frackenpohl
Social Media: @skaneatelesfestival
Frequency: annual
Venue: Brook Farm outdoor 700, 1st Presbytarian Church 400

Spoleto Festival USA
Website: www.spoletousa.org
Email: info@spoletousa.org
Phone: 843 722 2764
Address: 14 George Street Charleston, SC 29401 USA
Information: For 17 days and nights each spring, Spoleto Festival USA fills Charleston, South Carolina's historic theaters, churches, and outdoor spaces with performances by renowned artists as well as emerging performers in opera; theater; dance; and chamber, symphonic, choral, and jazz music. Now approaching its 45th season, Spoleto Festival USA is internationally recognized as America's premier performing arts festival.
Country: United States
Contact: General Director Nigel Redden
Email: nredden@spoletousa.org
Contact: Director of Artistic planning and operations Nicole Taney
Email: ntaney@spoletousa.org
Contact: Director of development Julia Forster
Email: jforster@spoletousa.org
Contact: company Manager Allison Ross-Spang
Email: arspang@spoletousa.org
Contact: Director of production Rhys Williams
Email: rhys.tts@gmail.com
Social Media: twitter.com/spoletofestival www.facebook.com/SpoletoFestivalUSA www.instagram.com/spoletofestivalusa
Frequency: Annual
End: 2021-06-13
Other Venues: various venues including Charleston Gaillard Center (2750 capacity), Charleston Library Society, City Hall, Dock Street Theatre (500 capacity)
Type: Concert, Performance art, Other

Springfield Summer Arts Festival
Website: www.springfieldartscouncil.org
Email: saconline@springfieldartscouncil.org
Phone: 937 324 2712
Address: 117 South Fountain Avenue, PO Box 745 Springfield, OH 45501 USA
Information: In May 1967, a group of Springfield, Ohio community members, interested in the arts, met with representatives from existing arts organizations to organize a "Summer Arts Festival" under the leadership of Jackson Wiley, then-conductor of the Springfield Symphony Orchestra. The Summer Arts Festival was created to provide summer activities for the community and arts activity for local arts organizations during their down season.
Country: United States
Contact: development Director Sarah McPherson
Email: sarah@springfieldartscouncil.org
Contact: Executive Director Tim Rowe
Email: tim@springfieldartscouncil.org
Contact: arts education Director Krissy Hartman
Email: krissy@springfieldartscouncil.org
Contact: festival and event Manager Jordan Keating
Email: jordan@springfieldartscouncil.org
Contact: office Manager Melanie Ellis
Email: melanie@springfieldartscouncil.org
Social Media: twitter.com/artsspringfield www.facebook.com/SpringfieldArtsCouncil
Frequency: Annual
Other Venues: Veterans Park Amphitheater (2500 capacity)
Type: Concert

Stern Grove Festival
Website: https://www.sterngrove.org/
Email: info@sterngrove.org
Phone: 415 252 6252
Address: 832 Folsom Street, Suite 1000 San Francisco, CA 94107
Information: Stern Grove Festival Association is a non-profit organization whose mission is to make live musical experiences accessible to all.
Every year since 1938, the organization presents Stern Grove Festival, a free concert series spanning 10 consecutive weeks
Country: United States
Contact: Executive Director Bob Fiedler
Email: bfiedler@sterngrove.org
Contact: Director of Marketing Audrey Faine
Email: afaine@sterngrove.org
Contact: development Manager Esther Flaharty
Email: eflaharty@sterngrove.org
Contact: Director of development Ilana Vasconcelos
Email: ivasconcelos@sterngrove.org
Social Media: twitter.com/sterngrovefest www.facebook.com/sterngrovefestival www.instagram.com/sterngrovefestival
Frequency: Annual
Other Venues: a beautiful outdoor amphitheater located at 19th Avenue and Sloat Boulevard in San Francisco.
Type: Concert

Strings in the Mountains Festival of Music
Website: https://stringsmusicfestival.com/
Email: strings@stringsmusicfestival.com
Phone: 970 879 5056
Address: PO Box 774627 Steamboat Springs, CO 80477 USA
Information: Strings Music Festival offers world-class music experiences and education at our Pavilion and throughout the Yampa Valley. The festival features orchestra, chamber, soloists, world, blues, jazz, and rock music along with a youth and family series, plus free programs at the Yampa River Botanic Park and other locations.
Country: United States
Contact: Music Director Michael Sachs
Contact: CEO Elissa Greene
Email: elissa@stringsmusicfestival.com
Social Media: twitter.com/StringsFestival www.facebook.com/stringsmusicfestival/
Frequency: Annual
Other Venues: Strings Music Pavilion (569-seats)
Type: Concert

Summer Festival of the Arts
Website: www.fpa.ysu.edu
Email: lafactor@ysu.edu
Phone: 330 941 2307
Address: Youngstown State University, 1 University Plaza, US
Information: see also Presenters & Venues
Country: United States
Contact: festival coordinator Lori A. Factor
Frequency: annual

Venue: Bliss Recital Hall 350, Butler Art Museum Hall 350, McDonough Museum of Art 40

SunFest of Palm Beach County, Inc
Website: https://www.sunfest.com/
Email: info@sunfest.com
Phone: 561 659 5980
Address: 525 Clematis Street, US
Information: Florida's largest music, art and waterfront festival. Held annually in downtown West Palm Beach the first weekend of May, SunFest attracts more than 300,000 people over five days
Country: United States
Contact: event Director Dan Goode
Email: dgoode@sunfest.com
Contact: Executive Director Paul Jamieson
Email: pjamieson@sunfest.com
Contact: Sales Director Dianna Dawson Craven
Email: dcraven@sunfest.com
Contact: Marketing Manager Melissa Sullivan
Email: msullivan@sunfest.com
Social Media: @SunFestFL www.facebook.com/SunFest
End: 2022-05-01
Other Venues: downtown West Palm Beach
Type: Concert, Other

Sunflower Music Festival
Website: https://sunflowermusicfestival.org/
Email: music@washburn.edu
Phone: 785 670 1396
Address: Music Dept, Washburn University, 1700 SW College, US
Information: Sunflower Music Festival presents 8 free orchestra, chamber ensemble, and jazz concerts performed by world-renowned musicians every year in June on the campus of Washburn University in Topeka.
Country: United States
Contact: festival coordinator Kelly Clevenger
Contact: Artistic Director Charles Stegeman
End: 2022-06-25
Other Venues: White Concert Hall, Garvey Fine Arts Center, Washburn University
Type: Concert

Sunriver Music Festival
Website: https://www.sunrivermusic.org/
Email: information@sunrivermusic.org
Phone: 541 593 1084
Address: PO Box 4308, US
Information: vocal and instrumental masterclasses and workshops, scholarships, winter concert series with 4 concerts throughout the winter months. See also Orchestras
Country: United States
Contact: board member Peter Gustavson
Social Media: www.facebook.com/SunriverMusicFestival/
End: 2022-08-21
Other Venues: The Great Hall (400 capacity)
Type: Concert

Tanglewood Music Festival
Website: https://www.bso.org/tanglewood/
Email: customerservice@bso.org
Phone: 617 266 1492
Address: c/o Tanglewood Festival Office, 301 Massachusetts Ave, US
Information: The Tanglewood Popular Artists Series offers music concerts all summer long. It is also the home of the Boston Symphony Orchestra. The festival is a mixture of classical music and pop/rock/jazz performers.
Country: United States
Contact: Director Ellen Highstein
Contact: CEO Mark Volpe
Social Media: www.facebook.com/TanglewoodMusicFestival/twitter.com/tanglewoodma www.instagram.com/tanglewoodmusicfestival/
Frequency: Annual
Other Venues: Tanglewood Campus
Type: Concert

Taos School of Music Chamber Music Festival (1)
Website: https://taosschoolofmusic.com/
Email: tsofm@newmex.com
Phone: 575 776 2388
Address: PO Box 2630, US
Information: emphasis on young international artists; 8 week chamber music school for conservatory level students (for violin, viola, cello and piano only)
Country: United States
Contact: chief Executive officer David Norden
Social Media: www.facebook.com/Taos-School-of-Music-264280346933665/
Other Venues: Taos Community Auditorium, Hotel St Bernard (150 capacity)
Type: Concert

The International Festival of Arts & Ideas
Website: artidea.org
Email: festivalinfo@artidea.org
Phone: 203 498 1212
Address: 195 Church St New Haven, CT 06510 USA
Information: The International Festival of Arts & Ideas celebrates its 25th anniversary with a variety of online

Artistic experiences, virtual food experiences, cell phone-guided walking tours, and various NEA Big Read activities
Country: United States
Contact: co-Director and Managing Director Elizabeth Fisher
Email: lfisher@artidea.org
Contact: Executive Director Shelley Quiala Quiala
Email: squiala@artidea.org
Contact: Director of programming and community impact Malakhi Eason Eason
Email: meason@artidea.org
Social Media: twitter.com/pmf2019 www.facebook.com/artidea www.instagram.com/artsideasct
Frequency: Annual

Three Rivers Arts Festival
Website: https://traf.trustarts.org/
Phone: 412 456 6666
Address: 803 Liberty Avenue Pittsburgh, PA 15222, US
Information: Mulit-Art Festival in the Pittsburgh area, run by the Pittsburgh Cultural Trust.
Country: United States
Contact: performing arts coordinator Gary Hinston
Contact: festival coordinator Jane Shilling
Contact: Executive Director Elizabeth Reiss
Social Media: www.facebook.com/3riversartsfest/ www.instagram.com/culturaltrust www.twitter.com/CulturalTrust
Frequency: Annual
End: 2022-06-12
Other Venues: Pittsburgh Cultural District, Point State Park
Type: Multi-media

Tri-C JazzFest
Website: www.tri-c.edu/jazzfest
Email: terri.pontremoli@tri-c.edu
Phone: 216 987 0241
Address: Cuyahoga Community College, 2900 Community College Ave Cleveland, OH 44115 USA
Information: Tri-C JazzFest Cleveland, presented by KeyBank, is a 3-day summer music and educational festival that takes place in the theaters of Playhouse Square and outdoors on the streets. This year's festival will be virtual.
Country: United States
Contact: Director Terri Pontremoli
Email: terri.pontremoli@tri-c.edu
Contact: community and education outreach program assistant Kyra Price
Email: Kyra.Price@tr-c.edu
Contact: Marketing and publicity Madeline Shepherd
Email: madeline.shepherd@tri-c.edu
Social Media: twitter.com/tricjazzfest www.facebook.com/tricJazzFest
Frequency: Annual
Other Venues: various Cleveland venues, including Playhouse Square, the Tri-C Metropolitan Campus, the Cleveland Museum of Art, BOP STOP at The Music Settlement, BLU Jazz+ and Nighttown
Type: Concert

Utah Arts Festival
Website: www.uaf.org
Email: artsfest@uaf.org
Phone: 801 322 2428
Address: 230 South 500 West, Suite 120 Salt Lake City, Utah 84101 USA
Information: The Utah Arts Festival is the largest outdoor multi-disciplinary arts event in Utah with attendance hovering over 70, 000 each summer. Having garnered numerous awards internationally, nationally and locally, the event remains one of the premiere events that kicks off the summer in Utah each June.
Country: United States
Contact: Executive Director Lisa Sewell
Email: lisa@uaf.org
Contact: Executive Director Aimée Dunsmore Dunsmore
Email: aimee@uaf.org
Contact: program Director Amanda Neff Neff
Email: amanda@uaf.org
Contact: development Director Meagan Mod Mod
Social Media: twitter.com/utahartsfest www.facebook.com/utahartsfestival www.instagram.com/utahartsfest
Frequency: Annual
End: 2021-06-27
Other Venues: Library Square in downtown Salt Lake City
Type: Concert, Other

Utah Festival Opera Company (1)
Website: www.utahfestival.org
Email: opera@ufomt.org
Phone: 435 750 0300
Address: 59 South 100 West, US
Information: see also Presenters
Country: United States
Contact: founding General Director Michael Ballam
Contact: development Director Annette Macfarlane
Contact: Managing Director Gary Griffin
Contact: Marketing Director Kendal Bates
Frequency: annual
Venue: Ellen Eccles Theatre, Logan 1100
Type: Opera

Utah Shakespearean Festival
Website: www.bard.org
Email: usfinfo@bard.org
Phone: 435 586 7880
Address: 351 West Center Street, US
Information: 9 productions: 6 summer, 3 autumn
Country: United States
Contact: Executive Producer Frank Mack
Email: mack@bard.org
Contact: Artistic Director Brian Vaughn
Email: vaughn@bard.org
Contact: General Manager Kami Terry Paul
Email: kpaul@bard.org
Social Media: @UtahShakespeare www.facebook.com/utahshakespeare

Vail International Dance Festival
Website: https://vaildance.org/
Email: info@vvf.org
Phone: 970 777 2015
Address: 90 Benchmark Rd, PO Box 6550, US
Information: The outdoor splendor of the Colorado Rocky Mountains is the perfect backdrop to Artistic brilliance, and each year Vail plays host to the world's finest dancers.
Now in its 31st year, the Vail Dance Festival has developed into a treasured celebration of dance, renowned for its Artistic excellence and unparalleled programming. More than twenty-thousand people visit Vail each summer for the Festival's two-week residency.
Country: United States
Contact: festival Manager Martha Brassel
Contact: Artistic Director Damian Woetzel
Contact: development officer Shawn Kirschner
Contact: Director of Marketing and pr Shelley Woodworth
Social Media: www.facebook.com/VailDance/
Other Venues: Gerald R. Ford Amphitheater, adjacent to the Betty Ford Alpine Gardens at Ford Park
Type: Dance/Ballet

Vermont Mozart Festival
Website: www.vermontmozartfestival.org
Email: info@vermontmozartfestival.org
Phone: 802 598 9520
Address: Vermont Mozart Festival, Inc., P.O. Box 5489, US
Information:
Country: United States
Contact: founder and leader Michael Dabroski
Contact: Marketing Director Kevin O'Leary
Contact: public relations Director Stephen Mease
Contact: volunteer Director Bill Frasier-Harris
Social Media: @MozartVt www.facebook.com/VTMozart/
Frequency: annual
Venue: 13 various sites around NW Vermont 300-2300
Type: All

Water Music Festival
Website: www.watermusicfestival.com
Email: info@watermusicfestival.com
Phone: 360 642 3254
Address: PO Box 524, Seaview, WA 98644 USA
Information: The Water Music Festival Society, a non-profit organization, provides high-quality, affordable music programs for residents and visitors in southwest Washington State. WMF expands cultural opportunities, increases awareness of diverse types of music, and promotes educational outreach.
Country: United States
Contact: President Diane Marshall
Social Media: www.facebook.com/watermusicfest
Frequency: Annual
Other Venues: Wilson Field in Ocean Park
Type: Concert

Windham Chamber Music Festival
Website: www.windhammusic.com
Email: info@windhammusic.com
Phone: 518 734 3868
Address: 740 County Route 32C, Windham, NY 12496 USA
Information: Robert Manno and Magdalena Golczewski founded the Windham Chamber Music Festival fifteen seasons ago and in those years have brought classical music to the Catskills as splendidly as any venue in the region, from Tanglewood to the Bard Summer Festival.
Country: United States
Contact: Director Robert Manno
Contact: Director Magdalena Golczewski Golczewski
Social Media: www.facebook.com/Windham-Chamber-Music-Festival-144951585517895
Frequency: Annual
Other Venues: Windham Civic Centre Concert Hall (250 capacity)
Type: Concert

Yellow Barn Music Festival
Website: www.yellowbarn.org
Email: info@yellowbarn.org
Phone: 802 387 6637
Address: Yellow Barn, PO Box 507, Putney VT 05346 USA
Information: Yellow Barn, an international center for chamber music, encourages discovery in the studio, classroom, and concert hall; explores the craft of musical interpretation; and illuminates our world through the unique experience of music.
Country: United States
Contact: Artistic Director Seth Knopp
Email: seth@yellowbarn.org
Contact: Executive Director Catherine Stephan
Email: catherine@yellowbarn.org
Contact: General administrator Joohyun Lee
Email: joohyun@yellowbarn.org
Contact: festival Manager Hannah Rushing
Email: hannah@yellowbarn.org
Social Media: twitter.com/yellowbarnmusic www.facebook.com/YellowBarn
Other Venues: Various outdoor venues
Type: Concert

Journals and directories selected for inclusion are those that it was considered would be of particular interest to Performing Arts Yearbook readers.They cover management issues, financing, products, perform-ances or contain contact addresses. In general, periodicals concerned primarily with the theory or study of art forms have been excluded, as have those aimed principally at the amateur enthusiast or layman. **The entries are listed in alphabetical order within country**

Revues

Les périodiques et guides/annuaires qui figurent ici sont ceux que nous estimons être intéressants pour les lecteurs du Performing Arts Yearbook. Ils englobent les problèmes de direction, finance, produit, présentation, et autres, ou contiennent des adresses de contacts utiles. En général, les journaux qui s'occupent principalement de l'é-tude ou de la théorie des arts sont exclus ainsi que ceux s'adressant aux amateurs. **Les entrée sont classés par ordre alphabétique dans le pays.**

Zeitschriften

Aufgeführten sind die Veröffentlichungen und Jahrbücher, die unsere Meinung nach für den Benutzer des Performing Arts Yearbook am nüt-zlichsten sind. Sie befassen sich mit Managementfragen, Finanzierung, Produktion, Aufführungen oder nennen

Kontaktadressen. Nicht eingeschlossen sind Veröffentlichungen, die sich vor allem mit der Theorie oder dem Studium von Kunstformen befassen, sowie solche, die sich an Amateure richten. **Die Einträge sind für jedes Land alphabetisch sortiert.**

Reviste

Le pubblicazioni (giornali, riviste ed annuari) selezionate per essere inserite in questa sezione sono quelle che abbiamo ritenuto possano essere più utili ai lettori del Performing Arts Yearbook. Includono pub-blicazioni di vario genere: management, finanza, produzioni, recen-sioni oppure contengono indirizzi utili a chi opera in questo settore. In generale i periodici riguardanti semplicemente la teoria o gli studi sulle varie forme artistiche sono stati esclusi essendo pubblicazioni per lo più rivolte ad un pubblico amatoriale e/o profano. **Le voci sono pubblicate in ordine alfabetico di paese.**

Revistas

Esta sección incluye aquellos periódicos y directorios que consider-amos de mayor interés para los lectores del Performing Arts Yearbook. Dichas publicaciones cubren temas de dirección, financiación, pro-ductos y espectáculos y contienen direcciones de contacto. En gener-al, periódicos y revistas sobre la teoría y el estudio de las artes han sido excluidos, así como los de carácter aficionado. **Las entradas se muestran en orden alfabético dentro de cada país.**

performing arts
database

AUSTRALIA

Art & Australia
Website: www.artaustralia.com
Email: art-australia@unimelb.edu.au
Address: 234 St Kilda Road, AU
Information: Art + Australia has established A+A Online as an exciting online platform designed to allow for current and quick responses to contemporary art issues. A+A Online provides opportunities for emerging and established writers to develop reactive, creative, critical and reflective considerations of Artistic content.
Country: Australia
Online: Yes

Art Monthly Australia
Website: www.artmonthly.org.au
Email: artmonthly.admin@anu.edu.au
Phone: 261 253 988
Address: Art Monthly Australia, LPO Box 8321, ANU ACT, AU
Information: A non-profit charitable institution whose income is derived from Sales of the magazine, advertising, sponsorship and government funding, Art Monthly Australasia prints and distributes 5000 issues quarterly. As Australia's magazine of record since 1987, it is distributed to most leading schools, universities and libraries, with a strong subscription base, and sold through most leading news agencies and bookstores. In addition, they have a digital version that is also available internationally.
Country: Australia
Social Media: facebook.com/ArtMonthlyAustralia/ https://twitter.com/ArtMonthlyAU https:// www.instagram.com/artmonthly/
Online: Yes

Australian Artist
Website: www.australianartist.com.au
Email: Sales@internationalartist.com
Phone: 294 196 333
Address: International Artist, PO Box 1084, AU
Information: Australian Artist Magazine, a guide for artists, by artists. In every issue of the magazine, there is a new Art Competition for readers to enter using the Official Entry Form inside the magazine. In one year there are 6 subject categories. Launched in 1984.
Country: Australia
Social Media: https:// www.instagram.com/australian_artist_magazine/

Limelight Arts Media Pty Ltd
Website: www.limelightmagazine.com.au
Email: support@limelight-arts.com.au
Phone: 285 994 204
Address: Unit 11, Level 1, 183 Macquarie Street, AU
Information: Limelight is Australia's premier arts platform. It has a unique place in Australia's performing arts scene, and is recognised as the journal of record in classical music, as well as providing extensive coverage of related art forms.
Limelight publishes reviews, news, interviews, artist profiles, event and listening guides through its website and via 11 print magazines each year.
Country: Australia
Social Media: https:// www.facebook.com/limelightclassical https://twitter.com/LimelightEd https://instagram.com/limelightmagazine

RealTime
Website: www.realtime.org.au
Email: realtime@realtimearts.net
Phone: 293 324 549
Address: 84 Womerah Avenue Rushcutters Bay, Australia AU
Information: RealTime is Australia's critical guide to national and international contemporary arts. RealTime's E-ditions and website offer a comprehensive view of Australian contemporary art with an international perspective, featuring weekly-updated reviews, previews, interviews, opinion pieces, festival reports and video and sound content.
Country: Australia
Social Media: https:// www.facebook.com/realtimearts/ https://twitter.com/RealTime_Arts https:// www.instagram.com/realtime_arts/
Frequency: Weekly
Online: Yes

AZERBAIJAN

Azerbaijan International
Website: www.azer.com
Email: ai@azdata.net
Phone: 129 89353
Address: 7 Alizade Str 1005, AZ
Information:
Country: Azerbaijan
Print: Yes
Online: No

Jazz Dunyasi Jazz World
Website: www.jazzdunyasi.jazz.az
Email: leyla@jazz.az
Phone: 124 936 196/9003

Address: 19 Rashid Behbudov Str.1001, AZ
Information:
Country: Azerbaijan
Print: Yes
Online: No

Musigi Dunyasi World of Music
Website: www.musigi-dunya.az
Email: musiqidunyasi@gmail.com
Phone: 598 4370
Address: 98 Shamsi Badalbeyli str., AZ
Information: The magazine, which combines scientific-pedagogical, critical-publicist and cultural-educational, cultural aspects, is an influential media outlet that covers innovations, intercultural dialogue in the global virtual space created by globalization, bringing Azerbaijani music to the third millennium, preserving national musical heritage.
Country: Azerbaijan

CANADA

Canada Arts Connect
Website: www.canadaartsconnect.com/magazine
Email: info@CanadaArtsConnect.com
Address: CA
Information: Canada Arts Connect Magazine is a website offering a look into the world of Canadian visual art, literature, dance, theatre, film, television, music, craft, fashion, and anything else creative
Country: Canada
Social Media: @CANArtsConnect
Print: Yes
Online: No

Canadian Musician Magazine
Website: www.canadianmusician.com
Email: mail@nor.com
Phone: 905 374 8878
Address: 4056 Dorchester Rd., #202, CA
Information: Canadian Musician is distributed across Canada through newsstands, music stores and record stores and by subscription across Canada and internationally
Country: Canada
Social Media: @cdnmusician www.facebook.com/cdnmusician
Print: Yes
Online: Yes

Music Vice
Website: www.musicvice.com
Email: info@musicvice.com
Address: Music Vice Magazine, 1117 Queen St W, PO Box 445, CA
Information: Now based in Canada, we have a strong focus on music in Toronto but cover music internationally, with writers in three continents
Country: Canada
Social Media: @MusicVice www.facebook.com/MusicVice
Print: Yes
Online: No

NOW Magazine
Website: www.nowtoronto.com
Email: web@nowtoronto.com
Phone: 416 364 1300
Address: NOW Magazine, 189 Church Street, CA
Information: NOW is Toronto's weekly news and entertainment voice, published every Thursday
Country: Canada
Social Media: @nowtoronto www.facebook.com/now-magazine
Frequency: Weekly
Print: Yes
Online: No

Playwrights Canada Press
Website: www.playwrightscanada.com
Email: info@playwrightscanada.com
Phone: 416 703 0013
Address: 269 Richmond Street West, Suite 202, CA
Information: Playwrights Canada Press distributes its own titles and those of two non-Canadian drama publishers, Nick Hern Books and Theatre Communications Group
Country: Canada
Social Media: @PlayCanPress www.facebook.com/PLCNP
Print: Yes
Online: No

Straight
Website: www.straight.com
Email: gs.info@straight.com
Phone: 604 730 7000
Address: Vancouver Free Press Publishing Corp., 1701 West Broadway, CA
Information: Canada's largest urban weekly
Country: Canada
Social Media: @georgiastraight www.facebook.com/georgiastraight
Frequency: Weekly
Print: Yes
Online: No

The Porcupine's Quill
Website: www.porcupinesquill.ca
Email: pql@sentex.net
Phone: 519 833 9158
Address: The Porcupine's Quill, 68 Main St., Box 160, CA
Information: The Porcupine's Quill is an artisanal publisher that values the art and craft of the book, both in content and in form
Country: Canada
Social Media: @porcupinesquill www.facebook.com/theporcupinesquill
Print: Yes
Online: No

REPUBLIC OF KOREA

Kult
Website: www.kultura-fb.sk
Email: redakcia@kultura-fb.sk
Phone: 265 412 388
Address: Solosnick
Information: bi-weekly
Country: Republic of Korea
Print: Yes
Online: No

UNITED STATES

Acoustic Guitar
Website: www.acousticguitar.com
Email: acousticguitarservice@stringletter.com
Address: Stringletter 941 Marina Way S, Suite E Richmond, CA 94804, US
Information: Acousticguitar.com is the online home of Acoustic Guitar, a family of print magazines, e-newsletters, digital services, and books for every player in any style, and the Acoustic Guitar Club, the national membership organization for guitar enthusiasts.
Country: United States
Social Media: https:// www.facebook.com/AcousticGuitarMagazine https://twitter.com/AcousticGuitar_ https://www.instagram.com/acousticguitarmag/

ART TIMES Journal
Website: www.arttimesjournal.com
Email: info@arttimesjournal.com
Phone: 845 246 6944
Address: PO Box 730, Mt. Marion, US
Information: Our ART TIMES Journal is one of those arts magazines that has two distinct personalities. Available to you both online and in print formats, it is a vibrant literary journal with art essays about painting, sculpting, drawing, film, theater, dance, music, book reviews, poetry, short fiction
Country: United States
Social Media: @arttimesjournal www.facebook.com/ArtTimesJournal
Frequency: Monthly
Print: Yes
Online: No

Dance Spirit
Website: www.dancespirit.com
Email: info@dancespiritmagazine.com
Phone: 212 979 4800
Address: DanceMedia, LLC, 333 7th Avenue, 11th Fl, US
Information: Dance Spirit keeps you up to date on everything new in dance
Country: United States
Social Media: @Dance_SpiritMa www.facebook.com/DanceSpiritMagazine
Print: Yes
Online: No

Dance Teacher Magazine
Website: www.dance-teacher.com
Email: jharp@dancemedia.com
Phone: 179 700 017
Address: 535 Fifth Avenue, 4th Floor New York, NY 10017, US
Information: A magazine for those self-sacrificing lovers of dance who work diligently and creatively to pass on their art to the younger generations.
Country: United States
Social Media: facebook.com/DanceTeacherMagazine/twitter.com/dance_teacher/instagram.com/danceteachermagazine/

Musical America
Website: www.musicalamerica.com
Email: info@musicalamerica.com
Phone: 094 483 346
Address: Musical America PO Box 1330 Hightstown, NJ 08520, US
Information: For over 100 years, Musical America Worldwide has been the voice of the performing arts industry. Musical America provides digital and print touchpoints for performing arts professionals to reach out to each other to further their art and their businesses.
Country: United States
Social Media: facebook.com/MusicalAmerica/twitter.com/MusicalAmerica

Pointe
Website: www.pointemagazine.com
Email: acogan@dancemedia.com
Phone: 212 979 4800
Address: DanceMedia, LLC, 333 7th Avenue, 11th Fl, US
Information: magazine for ballet and classical dance
Country: United States
Social Media: @pointe_magazine www.facebook.com/
pages/Pointe/208452120187
Frequency: Monthly
Print: Yes
Online: No

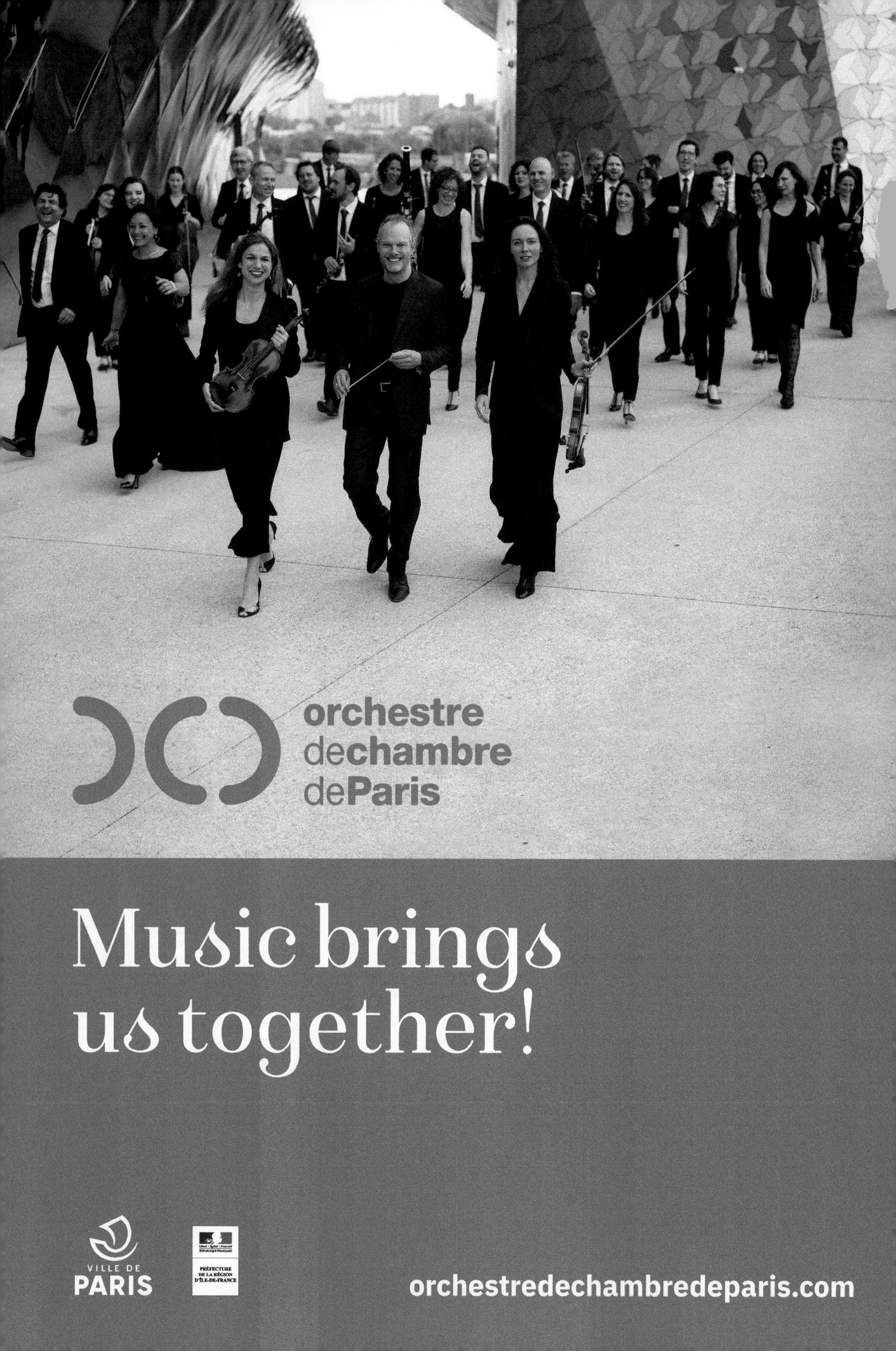

orchestre
dechambre
deParis

Music brings us together!

VILLE DE PARIS

PRÉFECTURE DE LA RÉGION D'ÎLE-DE-FRANCE

orchestredechambredeparis.com

We have included a wide range of international organisations and networks that we think will be of interest to those working in the performing arts. **The entries are listed in alphabetical order within country.**

Organisations Internationales

Une large gamme de réseaux que nous estimons intéressants pour ceux qui travaillent dans le monde des arts vivants est inclue. **Les entrée sont classés par ordre alphabétique dans le pays.**

Internationale Organisationen

Wir haben in diesem Kapitel Angaben einer Reihe von Organisationen und Netzwerken zusammengestellt, die unserer Meinung nach interessant für die Bereiche Musik und darstellende Kunst sind. **Die Einträge sind für jedes Land alphabetisch sortiert.**

Organizzazioni Internazionali

Sono stati inclusi numerosi networks che pensiamo possano interessare a chi opera nel settore artistico. **Le voci sono pubblicate in ordine alfabetico di paese.**

Organizaciones Internacionales

Se ha incluido una amplia gama de organizaciones internacionales que prometen ser de interés para todo tipo de empresarios relacionados con las artes escénicas. **Las entradas se muestran en orden alfabético dentro de cada país.**

performing arts
database

AUSTRALIA

Aboriginal and Torres Strait Islander Arts (ATA-SIA) – Australia Council
Website: www.australiacouncil.gov.au/artforms/aboriginal-and-torres-strait-islander-arts
Email: enquiries@australiacouncil.gov.au
Phone: 292 159 000
Address: Level 5, 60 Union St Pyrmont NSW 2009, AU
Information: Aboriginal and Torres Strait Islander arts include classical, traditional and contemporary practice, including all new forms of cultural exPression.
The Australia Council for the Arts regards Aboriginal and Torres Strait Islander cultures as living forces with their own strengths and influences, not as remnants of the past. They aim to make these cultural exPressions of Aboriginal and Torres Strait Islander people a source of pride for all Australians.
Country: Australia
Social Media: www.facebook.com/auscouncilartstwitter.com/auscouncilartsinstagram.com/auscouncilarts

Alliance Française Sydney
Website: www.afsydney.com.au
Email: enquiries@afsydney.com.au
Phone: 292 925 700
Address: 257 Clarence Street, AU
Information: The Alliance Française de Sydney (AFS) is an independent, not-for-profit language and cultural organisation promoting Franco-Australian exchange. With 120 years' experience in teaching French, the AFS offers a wide range of French courses and services for all levels and ages at its CBD and Chatswood locations, a Media Centre, cultural events and much more...
Country: Australia
Social Media: www.facebook.com/AllianceFrancaiseDeSydney/twitter.com/afdesydney www.instagram.com/afsydney

Arts Law Centre of Australia
Website: www.artslaw.com.au
Email: artslaw@artslaw.com.au
Phone: 293 562 566
Address: New South Wales, AU
Information: Arts Law is Australia's independent national community legal centre for the arts, a not-for-profit company limited by guarantee. They provide free or low cost specialised legal advice, education and resources to Australian artists and arts organisations across all art forms, on a wide range of arts related legal and business matters. Arts Law's Artists in the Black program delivers targeted services to Aboriginal and Torres Strait Islander artists nationally.
Country: Australia
Social Media: www.facebook.com/ArtsLawtwitter.com/ArtsLawAu www.instagram.com/artslawaustralia

Arts NSW
Website: www.create.nsw.gov.au
Email: mail@create.nsw.gov.au
Phone: 299 950 533
Address: PO Box A226, AU
Information: Create NSW is the NSW Government's new arts and cultural driver, which brings together arts, screen and culture functions in a new integrated entity. Create NSW was established on 1 April 2017, and has responsibility for many of the functions previously undertaken by Arts NSW and Screen NSW. The new entity forms part of the Arts & Culture Division within the Department of Planning and Environment, and is responsible for furthering Government's vision for NSW to be known for its bold and exciting arts and culture that engages the community and reflects the state's rich diversity.
Country: Australia
Social Media: @Create_NSW www.facebook.com/CreateNSWOfficial

Arts NT, Department of Community Development, Sport and Cultural Affairs
Website: www.arts.nt.gov.au
Email: arts.office@nt.gov.au
Phone: 889 998 981
Address: GPO Box 37037, AU
Information: Arts NT supports, develops and promotes the growth of the creative arts sector. Arts NT gives advice, develops partnerships and provides financial and infrastructure support for the arts. Arts NT programs include the NT Arts Grants Program and the Australian Government Regional Arts Fund.
Funded programs help the development of artists and organisations in the Northern Territory (NT). These programs aim to explore, exPress and showcase NT identity through arts and culture.
Country: Australia
Social Media: www.facebook.com/ntgovernment/ www.instagram.com/ntgovernment

Arts on Tour
Website: www.artsontour.com.au
Email:
admin@artsontour.com.au
Phone: 280 381 880
Address: Level 1, 4 Pitt Street, Redfern NSW 2016, AU

Information: Arts on Tour (AoT) is the peak servicing organisation for Performing Arts touring in NSW.
Arts on Tour's overarching purpose is to bring culturally distinctive and resonant arts experiences to regional and remote towns across Australia, and maximise the lasting impact of this activity for communities and audiences, artists and the sector.
Country: Australia
Social Media: www.facebook.com/artsontour/twitter.com/ArtsonTour www.instagram.com/artsontour/

Arts Queensland
Website: www.arts.qld.gov.au
Email: reception@arts.qld.gov.au
Phone: 730 344 016
Address: Level 16, 111 George Street, AU
Information: At Arts Queensland, their objective is to enhance cultural and economic outcomes for Queensland through an innovative arts and cultural sector. They use their social media accounts to post about funding information, industry news, career opportunities, and updates on events and programs relating to Queensland's arts and culture sector, as well as national and international resources.
Country: Australia
Contact: Arts Acumen
Email: artsacumen@arts.qld.gov.au
Phone: Funding
Email: investment@arts.qld.gov.au
Phone: RAF Queensland
Email: raf@arts.qld.gov.au
Phone: Communications
Email: communications@arts.qld.gov.au
Phone: Leasing
Email: leasing@arts.qld.gov.au
Phone: Policy
Email: aqpolicy@arts.qld.gov.au
Phone: Judith Wright Centre of Contemporary Art
Email: jwac@arts.qld.gov.au
Social Media: www.facebook.com/artsqueenslandAQtwitter.com/artsqueenslandinstagram.com/artsqueensland
Offers/Grants: true

Arts South Australia
Website: www.dpc.sa.gov.au
Email: artssa@sa.gov.au
Phone: 884 635 444
Address: 200 Victoria Square Adelaide, AU
Information: Arts South Australia is the arts and cultural agency of the South Australia Government. They support and advise the Minister for the Arts and manage the South Australian Government's funding to artists and arts organisations. They also support the development and maintenance of the State's cultural heritage collection and recognise and promote the strengths and needs of the State's makers, presenters and collectors of art and cultural heritage.
Country: Australia
Social Media: facebook.com/arts.southaustralia/ www.instagram.com/artssouthaus/

Arts Tasmania
Website: www.arts.tas.gov.au
Email: arts.tasmania@arts.tas.gov.au
Phone: 361 656 666
Address: Arts Tasmania, Level 4, 4 Salamanca Place, AU
Information: Arts Tasmania is part of the Cultural and Tourism Development division of the Department of State Growth. At Arts Tasmania, they manage a range of opportunities for the support and development of the cultural and creative industries in Tasmania and are guided by the Cultural and Creative Industries Strategy.
Country: Australia
Social Media: www.facebook.com/ArtsTasmaniatwitter.com/arts_tasmania

artsACT
Website: www.arts.act.gov.au
Email:
artsACT@act.gov.au
Phone: 262 072 384
Address: Level 4/1 Constitution Ave, Canberra ACT 2601, AU
Information: artsACT is the ACT Government's arts agency, they provide policy and funding advice to the government, manage the ACT Arts Fund and design and deliver a range of arts development initiatives, manage the ACT Government's public art collection of over 100 artworks, oversee the development and management of key ACT arts facilities and maintain links with other arts and cultural organisations in Australia and internationally.
Country: Australia
Social Media: www.facebook.com/ACTGovtwitter.com/artsACT1

Asialink Arts
Website: www.asialink.unimelb.edu.au/arts
Email:
Enquiries-asialink@unimelb.edu.au
Phone: 383 444 800
Address: Level 4, Sidney Myer Asia Centre, The University of Melbourne, Parkville, AU

Information: Asialink was founded in 1990 with the support of The Myer Foundation and The University of Melbourne.
Asialink works to build an Asia-capable, deeply Asia-engaged Australia through thought leadership and innovative programs that build knowledge, skills and partnerships.
Asialink delivers high-level forums, international collaborations, leadership training, education and cultural exchange programs in Australia and Asia.
Country: Australia
Social Media: www.facebook.com/Asialink.Autwitter.com/Asialink_au

AUSDANCE ACT
Website: www.ausdanceact.org.au
Email: act@ausdance.org.au
Phone: 261 884 250
Address: Gorman House Arts Centre, Ainslie Avenue, AU
Information: Ausdance ACT provides high quality, accessible and inclusive dance programs, from across all genres, which engage and inspire dance makers, performers, audiences, and other participants in the ACT and surrounds. Their services, 'normally', include: – support for independent professional dancers; help with career pathways for emerging artists; professional development and performance opportunities; and promotion of dance and dance education.
Country: Australia
Contact: Director CATHY ADAMEK
Phone: Marketing and Communications Manager EMMA DYKES
Email: act@ausdance.org.au
Phone: Administration Officer NATSUKO YONEZAWA
Email: act@ausdance.org.au
Phone: Projects Officer DEBORA DI CENTA
Email: act@ausdance.org.au
Yuin Business Services Pty Ltd Bookkeeping & Accounting services
CHRIS DRAGISIC
Email: act@ausdance.org.au
Social Media: www.facebook.com/ausdanceacttwitter.com/ausdance www.instagram.com/ausdanceact

AUSDANCE QLD
Website: www.ausdanceqld.org.au
Email: admin@ausdanceqld.org.au
Phone: 731 227 628
Address: Judith Wright Centre of Contemporary Arts, Level 3, 420 Brunswick Street, AU
Information: Ausdance Queensland was established in 1978 and provides professional advocacy and industry development for Queensland dance through strong local, regional, national and international networks. Ausdance QLD works to bring recognition to the many roles that dance plays in the cultural life of Queensland and to maximise opportunities for practitioners.
Country: Australia
Social Media: www.facebook.com/AusdanceQldinstagram.com/ausdanceqld

Ausdance SA
Website: www.ausdance.org.au
Email: sa@ausdance.org.au
Phone: 412 183 533
Address: 68 North Terrace Adelaide, SA, AU
Information: Ausdance SA is the peak body for dance in South Australia. It represents dance, in all its varied forms. Ausdance SA is part of the Ausdance National network, the national peak body. Also recognised as a leader in the field of dance through the provision of dance services, advocacy, activity, education, and professional development for dance artists, practitioners and enthusiasts throughout South Australia.
Country: Australia
Social Media: facebook.com/AusdanceSA/ https://twitter.com/ausdancesa/ https:// www.instagram.com/ausdancesa/

AUSDANCE WA
Website: www.ausdancewa.org.au
Email:
wa@ausdance.org.au
Phone:
400 618 293
Address: 16 Lochee Street Mosman Park, WA, AU
Information: Ausdance WA is the leading dance service organisation in Western Australia. With a membership base across the entire dance sector we provide supporting advocacy for all forms of dance.
Country: Australia
Social Media: https:// www.facebook.com/ausdancewa/ https://twitter.com/ausdancewa/ https:// www.instagram.com/ausdancewa/

Australasian Classical Music Managers' Association (ACMMA)
Website: www.acmma.org
Address: AU
Information: ACMMA is an association of Managers of classical concert, opera and theatre-music artists, who also represent Directors, designers and lighting designers
Country: Australia

Contact: Director of Emblem Artists Elaine Armstrong
Email: elaine@emblemartists.com
Phone: 049 945 4240Director of Jamari James Christiansen
Email: james@jamari.com.au
Phone: Director of MAXIMA ARTIST MANAGEMENT LIMITED John Ballard
Email: info@maximaltd.com
Phone: Director of PAMELA WRIGHT ARTIST MANAGEMENT Pamela Wright
Email: pampwam@ihug.co.nz
Phone: Director of PATRICK TOGHER ARTISTS' MANAGEMENT Patrick Togher
Email: patrick@patricktogher.com
Phone: 041 112 9690

Australia Council for the Arts
Website: www.australiacouncil.gov.au
Email: enquiries@australiacouncil.gov.au
Phone: 292 159 000
Address: Level 5, 60 Union St, AU
Information: The Australia Council for the Arts is the Australian Government's arts funding and advisory body. They support Australia's arts through funding, strengthening and developing the arts sector. Member of ISPA
Country: Australia
Contact: Media Manager Brianna Roberts
Email: b.roberts@australiacouncil.gov.au
Phone: 292 159 030
Social Media: www.facebook.com/auscouncilartstwitter.com/auscouncilartsinstagram.com/auscouncilarts

Australia Council for the Arts, Community Partnerships
Website: www.australiacouncil.gov.au/artforms/community-arts-and-cultural-development
Email: enquiries@australiacouncil.gov.au
Phone: 292 159 000
Address: Level 5/60 Union St, AU
Information: Community arts and cultural development encompasses collaborations between professional artists and communities based on a community's desire to achieve Artistic and social outcomes. The Australia Council supports community arts and cultural development artists, practitioners, organisations, projects and programs through a range of grants and initiatives. Member of ISPA
Country: Australia
Social Media: www.facebook.com/auscouncilartstwitter.com/auscouncilartsinstagram.com/auscouncilarts

Australia Council for the Arts, Major Performing Arts Board
Website: www.australiacouncil.gov.au/programs-and-resources/major-performing-arts-overview/
Email: enquiries@australiacouncil.gov.au
Phone: 292 159 000
Address: Level 5/60 Union St, AU
Information: Australia's MPA sector comprises 30 leading performing arts companies in the fields of dance, theatre, circus, opera, and orchestral and chamber music. The companies play a vital role in supporting the careers of Australian performing artists and creatives, bring works of scale to Australian and international audiences, and are critical to some of Australia's most iconic venues, festivals and other arts infrastructures. Member of ISPA.
Country: Australia
Social Media: www.facebook.com/auscouncilartstwitter.com/auscouncilartsinstagram.com/auscouncilarts

Australian Directors' Guild (ADG)
Website: www.adg.org.au
Email: admin@adg.org.au
Phone: 295 557 045
Address: 28/330 Wattle StUltimo NSW 2007, AU
Information: The Australian Directors' Guild (ADG) is a registered union and industry association representing the interests of film, television and digital media Directors, documentary makers and animators throughout Australia.
The ADG works to promote excellence in screen direction, encourage communication and collaboration between Directors and others in the industry, and provide professional support for its members.
Country: Australia
Social Media: facebook.com/AustralianDirectorsGuild/ www.instagram.com/australianDirectorsguild/

Australian Multicultural Foundation
Website: www.amf.net.au
Email: info@amf.net.au
Phone: 393 476 622
Address: Level 1, 185 Faraday Street, AU
Information: The aims and objectives of the foundation are to cultivate in all Australians a strong commitment to Australia as one people drawn from many cultures and by so doing to advance its social and economic well-being; the promotion of awareness among the people of Australia of the diversity of cultures within Australia and the contribution of people from all cultures to the development of Australia; and the spread of respect and understanding between all cultural groups

Australian National Commission for UNESCO
Website: www.unescoinaustralia.com/
Email: natcom.unesco@dfat.gov.au
Address: International Organisations and Legal Division, Department of Foreign Affairs and Trade, R G Casey Building, John McEwen Crescent, AU
Information: The Australian National Commission for UNESCO is the Australian Government focal point for the United Nations Educational, Scientific and Cultural Organization (UNESCO). The National Commission provides expert analysis and policy advice to the Australian Government on UNESCO matters and is a point of liaison between government, the community and UNESCO in Australia. UNESCO's mandate includes education, the natural sciences, the social and human sciences, culture and communications/information technology.
Country: Australia
Social Media: twitter.com/AusAmbUNESCO

Australian Record Industry Association (ARIA)
Website: www.aria.com.au
Email: aria.mail@aria.com.au
Phone: 285 691 144
Address: PO Box Q20, QVB Post Office, AU
Information: ARIA is a national industry association representing major and independent record Producers, manufacturers and distributors. It acts as an advocate for the Australian music industry, administers the labeling code of practice, provides a 'blanket' non-exclusive licensing function for copyright users and compiles industry information and research.
Country: Australia
Contact: Media
Email: media@aria.com.au
Email: charts.mail@aria.com.au
Phone: 028 569 1155Awards
Email: awards@aria.com.au
Phone: 028 569 1144Licensing
Email: business.affairs@aria.com.au
Phone: 028 569 1144
Social Media: https://www.facebook.com/ARIA.Official/ https://twitter.com/ARIA_Official https://www.instagram.com/aria_official/

Community Arts Network (CAN), Western Australia
Website: www.canwa.com.au
Email: admin@canwa.com.au
Phone: 892 262 422
Address: Ground Floor 357-365 Murray St, AU
Information: Community Arts Network is a not-for-profit community arts and cultural development organisation. CAN creates positive social change through the arts, building inclusion and understanding between people.
Country: Australia
Contact: CHIEF EXECUTIVE OFFICER Monica Kane
Email: monica@canwa.com.au
Phone: CHIEF EXECUTIVE OFFICER June Moorhouse
Email: june@canwa.com.au
Phone: PARTNERSHIPS AND MEDIA MANAGER Michelle White
Email: michelle@canwa.com.au
Phone: SENIOR FINANCIAL COORDINATOR Pauline Sikweti
Email: accounts@canwa.com.au
Phone: ARTIST DEVELOPMENT MANAGER Jill Brown
Email: jill@canwa.com.au
Social Media: https://www.facebook.com/canwa https://twitter.com/CANWA_Perth https://www.instagram.com/communityartsnetwork/

Creative Victoria
Website: creative.vic.gov.au
Email: creativevic@creative.vic.gov.au
Phone: 386 833 100
Address: Level 31, 121 Exhibition Street, AU
Information: Creative Victoria supports and develops Victoria's artists and creative industries. They provide policy advice to the government on all things related to the creative industries; offer funding and opportunities for Victorian creatives to further their careers; work to safeguard the state's cultural facilities and collections; and strive to ensure that all Victorians have opportunities to get creative and enjoy Victoria's vibrant cultural life.
Country: Australia
Social Media: https://www.facebook.com/CreativeVictoria https://twitter.com/Creative_Vic https://www.instagram.com/creative_vic

Dancehouse
Website: www.dancehouse.com.au
Email: info@dancehouse.com.au
Phone: 393 472 860
Address: 150 Princes Street, AU
Information: Dancehouse offers accessible and affordable spaces to an array of movement practitioners, teachers, audiences and communities. As a producing and presenting house, Dancehouse hosts large-scale events and festivals that support both local artists and international guests and offer programs that are incubators, catalysts and connectors; spanning presentations, commissions, training, residencies, research, capacity building, public programs, digital content and publications. See also Venues.
Country: Australia

Social Media: https://www.facebook.com/Dancehouse-Melbourne/ https://twitter.com/dancehouse_melb?lang=en https://www.instagram.com/dancehouse.melb/

Department of Communications and the Arts – Australian Government
Website: www.communications.gov.au
Phone: 262 747 111
Address: Nishi Building 2 Phillip Law Street CANBERRA ACT 2601, AU
Information: The Department of Communications and the Arts provides an environment in which all Australians can access and benefit from communications services, creative experiences and culture. This is through delivering strategic advice and policy development, effective program and grants management, regulatory management and collaborative stakeholder engagement.
Country: Australia
Social Media: twitter.com/AusGovArts

Department of Culture and Arts – Government of West Australia
Website: www.dca.wa.gov.au
Email: info@dca.wa.gov.au
Phone: 865 527 300
Address: Gordon Stephenson House, 140 William Street, Gordon Stephenson House 140 William Street Perth 6000, AU
Information: Department of Culture and Arts – Government of West Australia, works with partners across government and within its diverse sectors to enliven the Western Australian community and economy through support for and provision of sporting, recreational, cultural and Artistic policy, programs and activities for locals and visitors to the state.
Country: Australia
Social Media: @ARTalkWA www.facebook.com/cultureandtheartswa/

Department of Foreign Affairs & Trade – Australian Government
Website: www.dfat.gov.au
Phone: 262 611 111
Address: R.G. Casey Building John McEwen Crescent, AU
Information: The department works to make Australia stronger, safer and more prosperous, to provide timely and responsive consular and passport services, and to ensure a secure Australian Government presence overseas.
The department provides foreign, trade and development policy advice to the government. They work with other government agencies to ensure that Australia's pursuit of its global, regional and bilateral interests is coordinated effectively.
Country: Australia
Social Media: facebook.com/dfat.gov.autwitter.com/dfat www.instagram.com/dfat/

Goethe-Institut Australien
Website: www.goethe.de
Email: info-sydney@goethe.de
Phone: 283 568 333
Address: 90 Ocean Street Woollahra, NSW 2025, AU
Information: The Goethe-Institut is the cultural institute of the Federal Republic of Germany with a global reach. They promote knowledge of the German language abroad and foster international cultural cooperation. They convey a comprehensive picture of Germany by providing information on Germany's cultural, social and political life.
Country: Australia
Social Media: https://www.facebook.com/goetheinstitut.australien https://twitter.com/GI_Australien https://www.instagram.com/goetheinstitut_australien/

International Federation of Arts Councils and Culture Agencies (IFACCA)
Website: www.ifacca.org
Email: info@ifacca.org
Phone: 292 159 018
Address: 372 Elizabeth St, Surry Hills, AU
Information: The International Federation of Arts Councils and Culture Agencies (IFACCA) is the global network of arts councils and ministries of culture, with member organisations in over 70 countries. The IFACCA Secretariat provides services, information and resources to member organisations and their staff – from senior Executives and policy makers, to researchers, grant makers and administrators – as well as the wider community.
Country: Australia
Social Media: @ifacca www.facebook.com/IFACCA

International Society for Music Education (ISME)
Website: www.isme.org
Email: isme@isme.org
Address: SME, Suite 148, , 45, Glenferrie Road, AU
Information: ISME is the International Society for Music Education. Supporting and promoting music education and music making for all.
ISME is affiliated to the International Music Council and UNESCO
Country: Australia

Japan Cultural Centre, Sydney The Japan

Foundation
Website: www.jpf.org.au
Email: reception@jpf.org.au
Phone: 282 390 055
Address: Level 4, Central Park 28 Broadway, 2 Chifley Square, AU
Information: The Japan Foundation, Sydney is the Australian arm of the Japan Foundation, which was established by the Japanese government to promote cultural and intellectual exchange between Japan and other nations. It runs a diverse range of programs and events, including exhibitions, talk events, grant programs and Japanese language courses for all levels. The Japan Foundation was established in 1972 with a global network of 24 offices in 23 countries. The Australian office was founded in 1978.
Country: Australia
Social Media: @JPFSydney www.facebook.com/japan-foundationsydney

Media Entertainment & Arts Alliance (MEAA), Federal Office
Website: www.meaa.org
Email: members@meaa.org
Phone: 130 065 6513
Address: 245 Chalmers St, AU
Information: For decades MEAA has been the union for people who work in the industries that inform or entertain Australians. As the largest and most established union and industry advocate for creative professionals, they successfully campaign on major issues, fight for their members' rights at work, workplace health and safety, and protecting wages and conditions.
Country: Australia
Social Media: www.facebook.com/withMEAAtwitter.com/withMEAA www.instagram.com/withmeaa

Multicultural Arts Alliance
Phone: 295 600 005
Address: Building 41, Addison Road, Marckville, AU
Country: Australia

Multicultural Arts Victoria (MAV)
Website: www.mav.org.au
Email: office@multiculturalarts.com.au
Phone: 391 883 681
Address: Northcote Town Hall Arts Centre, Level 1/189 High St, Northcote VIC 3070, AU
Information: Multicultural Arts Victoria (MAV) is Victoria's peak arts organisation promoting cultural diversity in the arts. MAV is a not for profit organisation and proudly represents artists and communities from culturally and linguistically diverse backgrounds.
Country: Australia
Social Media: www.facebook.com/MAVArtsAU/twitter.com/MAVArtsAU www.instagram.com/mavartsau/

Musica Viva Australia
Website: www.musicaviva.com.au
Email: contact@musicaviva.com.au
Phone: 283 946 666
Address: 757 Elizabeth Street Zetland NSW 2017, AU
Information: Musica Viva seeks to be the leading organisation in the world for connecting audiences with chamber music, inspiring personal fulfillment and cultural vibrancy.
Founded in 1945, Musica Viva is Australia's oldest independent professional performing arts organisation. As an independent non-profit arts organisation, Musica Viva relies on the essential support of donors, funding partners, government support, corporate partners, and the many volunteers who freely give their time.
Country: Australia
Contact: Box Office
Email: boxoffice@musicaviva.com.au
Phone: 180 068 8482MUSICA VIVA IN SCHOOLS
Email: contact@musicaviva.com.au
Phone: 130 066 3608STRIKE A CHORD
Email: championship@musicaviva.com.au
Phone: Brisbane Office
Email: queensland@musicaviva.com.au
Phone: CANBERRA OFFICE
Email: ccook@musicaviva.com.au
Social Media: www.facebook.com/MusicaVivaAustraliatwitter.com/MusicaVivaAU www.instagram.com/musicavivaau/

Queensland Cultural Events
Website: www.queenslandculturalevents.org
Email: info@queenslandculturalevents.org
Phone: 755 005 888
Address: PO Box 356, AU
Information: Queensland Cultural Events Association (QCEA) was formally registered in 2012 to provide support to talented Artists from the many varied Cultural Communities in Queensland. Its Directors have a proud history of Managing Major Cultural Events & Festivals in Queensland, including the annual Gold Coast Multicultural Festival (first established in 2006).
Country: Australia
Social Media: facebook.com/QueenslandCulturalEventsAssociation/

Regional Arts NSW
Website: www.regionalartsnsw.com.au
Email: admin@regionalartsnsw.com.au
Phone: 292 702 500
Address: Level 1, 10 Hickson Road, AU
Information: Regional Arts NSW is committed to increasing access to cultural opportunities and resources for communities in rural and regional NSW. They value the importance of working together and partnering with stakeholders to deliver outcomes for Regional Arts Organisations and their communities while supporting sustainable cultural development. They recognise and support diversity in communities, and respect the right to self-determination for Aboriginal people in their cultural affairs and creative practices.
Country: Australia
Contact: CHIEF EXECUTIVE OFFICER Elizabeth Rogers
Email: elizabeth@regionalartsnsw.com.au
Phone: 412 099 935MANAGER, PROGRAMS Prudence Tan
Email: pru@regionalartsnsw.com.au
Phone: 438 077 593MANAGER, GRANTS AND PROJECTS Lexie Reeves
Email: funding@regionalartsnsw.com.au
Phone: 478 676 403PROJECTS COORDINATOR David Bleach
Email: david@regionalartsnsw.com.au
Phone: FINANCE COORDINATOR Jessie Yin
Email: finance@regionalartsnsw.com.au
Phone: 300 755 577
Social Media: facebook.com/RegionalArtsNSWLtdtwitter.com/RegionalArtsNSWinstagram.com/regional-artsnsw

Union Internationale de la Marionnette (UNIMA), Australia
Website: www.unima.org.au/
Email: secretary@unima.org.au
Phone: 396 960 652
Address: c / o Kay Yasugi – 40 Greenway Drive NSW 2073 PYMBLE, AU
Information: UNIMA Australia was founded in 1970 and incorporated in 2004. In 2008, UNIMA Australia hosted the 20th UNIMA Congress and World Puppetry Festival. It was the first time the congress and festival was held in the southern hemisphere.
UNIMA Australia supports and connects puppeteers, companies and all enthusiasts through the website, projects, events, festivals and the biannual Australian Puppeteer magazine. It offers courses, scholarships and publications.
Country: Australia
Social Media: facebook.com/UnimaOz/twitter.com/UNIMAOz

Willoughby City Council – Community, Culture & Leisure
Website: www.willoughby.nsw.gov.au
Email: email@willoughby.nsw.gov.au
Phone: 297 771 000
Address: 31 Victor Street Chatswood, NSW, AU
Information: Community, Culture & Leisure is responsible for enhancing community life through aged and disability services. The Directorate is also responsible for community development through delivery of Multicultural services, seven Libraries, Willoughby Leisure Centre, visual arts programs including management of Art Space on The Concourse and Incinerator Art Space and development of open space for sport and recreation.
Country: Australia
Social Media: https:// www.facebook.com/WilloughbyCityCouncil/ http://twitter.com/willoughbycity https://www.instagram.com/willoughbycity/

AZERBAIJAN

Ministry of Culture and Tourism of Nakhchivan Autonomous Republic
Website: imp.nakhchivan.az
Email: turizm@nakhchivan.az
Phone: 365 457 755
Address: Nakhchivan city, Heydar Aliyev Avenue 17, AZ
Information: Nakhchivan Tourism Information Center has several duties: to participate in the preparation of the electronic version of unified data collection of tourism resources of Nakhchivan Autonomous Republic – tourism data bank (TIBK); to form the tourism database of Nakhchivan Autonomous Republic and submit it to the Department; to construct the tourism databank server technically; to provide its operating and updating constantly and efficiently, and maintaining it to meet the current requirements.
Country: Azerbaijan
Social Media: facebook.com/Naxcivanturizminformasiyamerkezi/

Ministry of Culture and Tourism of the Republic of Azerbaijan
Website: www.culture.az
Email: mugam@culture.az
Phone: 124 934 398
Address: 40, Government House, Uzeyir Hajibeyov str., 1046, AZ
Country: Azerbaijan

Ministry of Culture of the Republic of Azerbaijan
Website: mct.gov.az
Email: mct@mct.gov.az
Phone: 124 933 002
Address: 40 Uzeyir Hajibeyov St, Baku, AZ
Information: The Ministry of Culture of the Republic of Azerbaijan is the MIHO, which implements state policy and regulation in the field of protection of culture, art, history and cultural monuments, publishing and cinematography.
Country: Azerbaijan
Social Media: facebook.com/culture.gov.az/

BRAZIL

British Council Brazil
Website: www.britishcouncil.org/brazil
Email: centro.info@britishcouncil.org.br
Phone: 112 126 7500
Address: Rua Ferreira de Araújo, 741 – Térreo – Pinheiros, BR
Information: the United Kingdom's international organisation for cultural relations and educational opportunities. Member of ISPA.
Country: Brazil
Social Media: @brBritish www.facebook.com/British-CouncilBrasil/

CAMBODIA

Amrita Performing Arts
Website: www.amritaperformingarts.org
Email: info@amritaperformingarts.org
Phone: 232 20424
Address: 128-G9 Sothearos Boulevard, PO Box 1140, KH
Information: International NGO based in Phnom Penh, with US nonprofit status, founded in 2003 with a mission to help revive and preserve the wide spectrum of Cambodia's traditional performing arts, produces fully staged productions of contemporary Cambodian dance and theatre featuring professional Cambodian performers. Member of ISPA.
Country: Cambodia
Social Media: @amritacambodia www.facebook.com/amritaperformingarts

CANADA

Alberta Community Development
Website: www.alberta.ca/community-development-unit.aspx
Email: communitydevelopment@gov.ab.ca
Phone: 780 963 2281
Address: 905 Standard Life Centre, 10405 Jasper Avenue, CA
Information: To promote, develop and preserve Alberta's culture and heritage in support of vibrant and inclusive communities.
Country: Canada

Association franco-yukonnaise
Website: www.afy.yk.ca
Email: relations@afy.yk.ca
Phone: 867 668 2663
Address: 302 Strickland St, CA
Information: the agency creates and develops services, activities and institutions necessary to the full development and sustainability of the Yukon Francophone community
Country: Canada
Social Media: www.facebook.com/AFY.Yukon

Association Internationale du Théâtre pour l'enfance et la Jeunesse (ASSITEJ), Canada
Website: www.assitej.ca
Email: boomers24@mac.com
Phone: 613 241 0999
Address: ASSITEJ CANADA, 602-294 Albert St., CA
Information: ASSITEJ Canada is a bilingual organization that operates in both French and English. The organization is dedicated to the celebration of excellence in the performing arts for young audiences and to the sharing of information between its members across the country
Country: Canada

Association of Cultural Executives
Website: ccm.uwaterloo.ca/ace/
Email: info@acecontact.org
Phone:
519 579 8564
Address: Westmount PO Box 22044, 50 Westmount, CA
Information: membership organisation; national professional association for cultural Managers; encompasses Managers from all disciplines of culture, all levels of government, and private and non-profit organizations
Country: Canada

British Columbia – Ministry of Tourism, Sport and the Arts
Website: www.bcartscouncil.ca
Email: BCArtsCouncil@gov.bc.ca
Phone: 250 356 1718
Address: 2nd Floor, 800 Johnson Street, CA

Information: the British Columbia Arts Council is an independent agency that supports arts and cultural activity in communities across British Columbia. From professional dance companies, to art galleries, local museums and music festivals – the Council works to enrich the lives of British Columbians in virtually every community in the province
Country: Canada
Social Media: @TourismBC www.facebook.com/HelloBC

Canada Council for the Arts
Website: www.canadacouncil.ca
Email: info@canadacouncil.ca
Phone: 613 566 4414
Address: 150 Elgin St, PO Box 1047, CA
Information: the Canada Council for the Arts is a national arm's-length agency whose role is to foster and promote the study and enjoyment of, and the production of works in the arts. Member of ISPA
Country: Canada
Social Media: @CanadaCouncil www.facebook.com/canadacouncil

Canadian League of Composers
Website: www.composition.org
Email: info@clc-lcc.ca
Phone: 416 964 1364
Address: Chalmers House, 20 St. Joseph St., CA
Information: membership organisation; the CLC Council is an elected board comprised of 12 CLC members that represent the various regions of Canada. Elections for Council positions are held every two years; the next elections will take place in June 2015. Council members belong to one or more CLC Committee(s), to dedicate their work to specific issues and projects relevant to composers
Country: Canada
Social Media: @CLC_LCC www.facebook.com/pages/Canadian-League-of-ComposersLa-Ligue-Canadienne-des-Compositeurs

Canadian Musical Reproduction Rights Agency Ltd (CMRRA)
Website: www.cmrra.ca
Email: inquiries@cmrra.ca
Phone: 416 926 1966
Address: Canadian Musical Reproduction Rights Agency Ltd., 56 Wellesley St. W. #320, CA
Information: membership organisation; (CMRRA) is a non-profit music licensing agency, which represents the vast majority of music copyright owners (usually called music publishers) doing business in Canada
Country: Canada

CanDance Network
Website: www.candance.ca
Email: info@candance.ca
Phone: 416 204 1082
Address: The Historic Distillery District, 15 Case Goods Lane, Studio 304, CA
Information: membership organisation; Canada's national network supporting the creation and distribution of contemporary dance; Its 40 members across the country are professional dance presenters
Country: Canada

City of Toronto, Economic Development, Culture and Tourism, Culture Division
Website: www.toronto.ca/culture
Email: culture@toronto.ca
Phone: 416 392 8674
Address: 9th Floor, East Tower, 100 Queen Street West, CA
Information: council arts and culture department
Country: Canada

City of Vancouver – Office of Cultural Affairs
Website: www.vancouver.ca/culture
Email: oca@vancouver.ca
Phone: 604 873 7000
Address: 453 West 12th Avenue, CA
Information: Vancouver has four main arts and cultural centres. Britannia Community Services Centre, Jericho Arts Centre, Moberly Arts and Cultural Centre and Roundhouse
Country: Canada
Social Media: @CityofVancouver www.facebook.com/CityofVancouver

Commission des Loisirs de la Sarre
Website: www.ville.lasarre.qc.ca/culture
Email: slafleur@ville.lasarre.qc.ca
Phone: 819 333 2294
Address: 195 rue Principale, CA
Information: the Recreation Commission Saarland manages municipal infrastructure in connection with the leisures of Quebec
Country: Canada
Social Media: www.facebook.com/pages/Bibliothèque-municipale-Richelieu-de-La-Sarre/333704643348589

Conseil des Arts de Montreal – CAM
Website: www.artsmontreal.org
Email: artsmontreal@ville.montreal.qc.ca
Phone: 514 280 3580
Address: 1210, rue Sherbrooke Est, CA
Information: The Conseil identifies, supports and recognizes Artistic excellence. Through its subsidy programmes, operating grants, residencies, mobilization activities and awards—including the Grand Prix du Conseil des arts de Montréal, the Conseil is the proud partner of over 400 Montreal cultural organizations and collectives. Member of ISPA
Country: Canada
Social Media: @ConseilArtsMtl www.facebook.com/ArtsMontreal

Conseil provincial des sociétés culturelles
Website: www.cpscnb.com
Email: cpsc.projets@nb.aidn.com
Phone: 506 858 8000
Address: 27 rue John, CA
Information: the Conseil provincial des sociétés culturelles supports 16 regional organisations dedicated to cultural activities through its support
Country: Canada

Department of Community Services – Arts & Heritage Division
Website: www.ottawa.ca/
Email: info@ottawa.ca
Phone: 613 580 2400
Address: 110 Laurier Avenue West, CA
Information: agency for the city of Ottawa
Country: Canada
Social Media: @ottowacity

Department of Foreign Affairs and International Trade, Canada/ Affaires
Website: www.international.gc.ca/arts
Email: culture.pcr@international.gc.ca
Address: Arts & Cultural Industries Promotion Division:, 125 Sussex Drive, CA
Information: canadian companies must apply to International Cultural Relations programme of Dept. of Foreign Affairs and International Trade; apply through the website: www.dfait-maeca.gc.ca/arts
Country: Canada
Social Media: @DFATDCanadah www.facebook.com/cida.gc.ca

Government of Newfoundland and Labrador
Website: www.tcr.gov.nl.ca/tcr
Email: bmeade@gov.nl.ca
Phone: 709 729 0862
Address: Dept of Tourism, Culture and Recreation, PO Box 8700, CA
Information: the department operates historic sites, visitor information centres and arts and culture centres
Country: Canada
Social Media: @NLtweets www.facebook.com/pages/Government-of-Newfoundland-and-Labrador/126836060693124

International Association of Arts and Cultural Management (AIMAC)
Website: www.gestiondesarts.com
Email: gestiondesarts@hec.ca
Phone: 514 340 5629
Address: 3000, chemin de la Côte-Sainte-Catherine, CA
Information: see also Conferences and Trade Shows
Country: Canada

International Resource Centre for Performing Artists
Website: www.ircpa.net
Email: info@ircpa.net
Phone: 416 362 1422
Address: 43 Bright St., Ontario, CA
Information: projects include a Career Development Centre in Toronto, a retail outlet and Reference Library with donated libraries from retired artists
Country: Canada
Social Media: www.facebook.com/pages/International-Resource-Centre-for-Performing-Artists-IRCPA

Jeunesses Musicales Canada – Montreal International
Website: www.jmcanada.ca
Email: info@jmcanada.ca
Phone: 514 845 4108
Address: Maison des Jeunesses Musicales du Canada, 305, Avenue du Mont-Royal Est, CA
Information: a non-profit organisation founded in 1949 by the late Gilles Lefebvre, Jeunesses Musicales of Canada (JMC) has a dual mission: to promote the performance of classical music, especially for young audiences, and to help young professional instrumentalists, singers and composers to develop their careers at the national and international levels
Country: Canada

Manitoba Arts Council
Website: www.artscouncil.mb.ca
Email: info@artscouncil.mb.ca
Phone: 204 945 5925
Address: 525 – 93 Lombard Avenue, CA
Information: the Manitoba Arts Council is an arm's-length agency of the Province of Manitoba, established in 1965 "to promote the study, enjoyment, production and performance of works in the arts."
Country: Canada

Music Canada
Website: www.musiccanada.com
Email: info@musiccanada.com
Phone: 416 967 7272
Address: 85, Mowat Avenue, CA
Information: represents Canada's major labels
Country: Canada
Social Media: @Music_Canada www.facebook.com/MusicCanada

Nova Scotia Department of Tourism and Culture (Heritage & Cultural Division)
Website: www.gov.ns.ca/dtc
Email: cultaffs@gov.ns.ca
Address: World Trade Centre, 6th Floor, PO Box 456, CA
Information: Government and council heritage sector.
Country: Canada
Social Media: www.facebook.com/CreativeNovaScotia

Ontario Arts Council
Website: www.arts.on.ca
Email: info@arts.on.ca
Address: 151 Bloor Street West, 5th Floor, CA
Country: Canada

Organization of Saskatchewan Arts Councils (OSAC)
Website: www.osac.sk.ca
Email: info@osac.sk.ca
Phone: 306 586 1550
Address: 1102 8th Avenue, CA
Country: Canada

Prince Edward Island Department of Communities, Cultural Affairs and Labour
Website: www.gov.pe.ca/commcul/chal-info
Email: island@gov.pe.ca
Phone: 902 368 4663
Address: 16 Fitzroy Street, PO Box 2000, 2nd Floor, Sullivan Building, CA
Information: Government information website.
Country: Canada

Saskatchewan Arts Board
Website: www.artsboard.sk.ca
Email: info@artsboard.sk.ca
Phone: 306 787 4056
Address: 1355 Broad Street, CA
Information: The Saskatchewan Arts Board serves the people of Saskatchewan through programs, services and partnerships designed to build a strong and vibrant arts sector.
Country: Canada
Social Media: @saskartsboard www.facebook.com/saskartsboard

Swift Current Allied Arts Council
Website: www.swiftcurrent.ca
Email: swiftcurrentartscouncil@sasktel.net
Phone: 306 773 1338
Address: PO Box 1387, CA
Information: Runs it's own events: Stars for Saskatchewan, Literary Cafes, Windfall
Country: Canada
Social Media: www.facebook.com/pages/Swift-Current-Allied-Arts-Council

The Glenn Gould Foundation
Website: glenngould.ca/
Email: info@glenngould.ca
Phone: 416 962 6200
Address: 69 Yonge Street, Suite 1401, CA
Information: their mission is to honour Glenn Gould's spirit and legacy by celebrating brilliance, promoting creativity and transforming lives through the power of music and the arts with the Foundation's signature activities, including The Glenn Gould Prize. Member of ISPA
Country: Canada
Social Media: @GlennGouldFndn www.facebook.com/pages/The-Glenn-Gould-Foundation/33015846435

Toronto Arts Council
Website: www.torontoartscouncil.org
Email: mail@torontoartscouncil.org
Phone: 416 392 6800
Address: 26 Grand Trunk Cres., Suite 200, CA
Country: Canada
Social Media: @TorontoArts www.facebook.com/TorontoArts

Ville de Quebec
Website: www.ville.quebec.qc.ca
Email: mylene.verreaunt@palaismontcalm.ca
Phone: 418 691 5171
Address: 995 Place d'Youville, CA
Country: Canada
Social Media: @villequebec

Winnipeg Arts Council
Website: www.winnipegarts.ca
Email: info@winnipegarts.ca
Phone: 204 943 7668
Address: 103-110 Princess Street, CA
Information: The Winnipeg Arts Advisory Council (WAAC) was established in 1984 by Winnipeg City Council to assist the City in determining funding to arts and cultural organizations, and to provide advice on cultural policy development
Country: Canada
Social Media: @WinnipegArts www.facebook.com/winnipegartscentral

CHINA

An Hui Provincial Department of Culture
Website: www.ahwh.gov.cn
Phone: 551 636 55564
Address: No. 435, Tunxi Road
Information: to promote Anhui culture and interests
Country: China

Beijing Municipal Bureau of Culture
Website: www.ebeijing.gov.cn/Government/Departments/t929924.htm
Email: information@bjfao.gov.cn
Address: 7 Xichang'an Street, Xicheng district
Country: China

Centre of International Cultural Exchange
Website: www.cicec.org.cn
Email: office@cicec.org.cn
Phone: 106 448 9600
Address: No. 9, , Dong Tu Cheng Road, , Chao Yang District
Information: division of China's Ministry of Culture
Country: China

Chang Chun Municipal Bureau of Culture
Website: www.ccwh.gov.cn
Email: ccwhjxxgk@changchun.gov.cn
Phone: 431 887 77600
Address: No. 10111, , Ren Min Main Street,
Country: China

Cheng Du Municipal Bureau of Culture
Website: www.chengdu.gov.cn
Email: whj@chengdu.gov.cn
Phone: 286 188 3775
Address: 4F, No. 966, , Tian Fu Da Dao Northern sector, , Gao Xin District,
Country: China

Chinese Cultural Centre
Website: www.chinaculturecenter.org/
Email: info@chineseculturalcentre.org.uk
Phone: 106 432 9341
Address: Room 101, Kent Center No. 29, Anijalou, Liangmaqiao Road
Information: venue base for London Chinese Orchestra, Chinese Dance and Mime Theatre Companies
Country: China

Chinese Culture Promotion Society (CCPS)
Website: www.ccps.com.cn
Email: wencuhui1992@163.com
Phone: 108 498 8118
Address: Block E, No. 506, , Hui Yuan Gong Yu, , Ya Yun Cun
Country: China

Chinese People's Association for Friendship with Foreign Countries CPAFFC
Website: www.cpaffc.org.cn
Phone: 861 065 128 354/
Address: No 1, Tai Ji Chang Da Jie, Dong Cheng District,
Information: has different office for different countries; founded in 1954
Country: China

Chong Qing Municipal Bureau of Culture
Email: cq_whg@sina.com.cn
Phone: 862 363 708 049
Address: 69 Cang Bai Road, Yu Zhong District
Country: China

Da Lian Municipal Bureau of Culture
Website: www.whj.dl.gov.cn
Email: whj_lcl@dl.gov.cn
Phone: 411 836 00793 /
Address: No. 87 Xin K Road, Xi Gang District
Country: China

Department of Culture, Radio, Television, Publication and Sports of Hai Nan Province
Website: wtt.hainan.gov.cn
Email: wtt@hainan.gov.cn
Phone: 898 653 38119
Address: NO.59, Haifu Road,
Country: China

Dong Guan Bureau of Culture
Email: dgwhjbgs@dg.gov.cn
Phone: 769 222 2530
Address: 5/F 2 Xiang Yang Road, Cheng District
Country: China

Gan Su Province Culture Authority
Phone: 931 887 2317
Address: No 323 Jing Ning Road
Country: China

Guang Dong Province Dramatists' Association
Phone: 203 848 6920
Address: No. 79, , Wen De Bei Road,
Country: China

Guang Xi Province Culture Authority
Website: www.ccnt.gov.cn
Email: gx_wenhuating@163.com
Phone: 771 562 3675
Address: No. 13 – 1 Min Zhu Road, Guang Xi Zhuang Zu Autonomous
Country: China

Guangzhou Municipal Bureau of Culture
Website: www.gzwh.gov.cn
Phone: 208 739 8780 (ar
Address: No. 58-64, , Ji Xiang Road, , Guang Dong Province,
Country: China

Gui Zhou Province Culture Authority
Phone: 851 557 8613
Address: 54 Zun Yi Road
Country: China

Ha Er Bin Municipal Bureau of Culture
Website: cb.harbin.gov.cn
Email: whj@hrb.com.cn
Address: Shi Zheng Fu Main Building 7F, No. 1, , Shi Ji Da Dao, , Song Northern District,
Country: China

He Bei Province Culture Authority
Website: www.hebwh.gov.cn
Phone: 311 859 18010 /
Address: No. 275, , He Ping Xi Road,
Country: China

Hu Bei Province Culture Authority
Address: No. 167 Dong Hu Road
Country: China

Hu Nan Province Culture Authority
Address: No. 66 Xing Tao Nan Road
Country: China

International Theatre Institute (ITI), China
Website: www.iti-worldwide.org/china.php
Email: china_iti@bbn.cn
Phone: 105 975 9516
Address: B508, Bldg.32, No.1, Bei Shatan, Chaoyang District
Country: China

Ji Lin Province Culture Authority
Website: wht.jl.gov.cn/
Email: zjp2000cn@jl.gov.cn
Phone: 431 856 14100
Address: No. 2779, , Jian She Street, , Ji Lin Province
Country: China

Jiang Xi Province Culture Authority
Website: www.jxwh.gov.cn
Email: hdb@jxwh.gov.cn
Phone: 867 916 213 953/
Address: Government Building, Beijing West Road
Country: China

Jiangsu Provincial Department of Culture
Website: www.jscnt.gov.cn
Email: jswhxx@yahoo.cn
Phone: 258 779 8779
Address: No. 9, , Longpan Village,
Information: website: www.ccnt.gov.cn will give some brief information of this culture authority
Country: China

Ministry of Culture
Website: www.mcprc.gov.cn
Email: webmaster@ccic.gov.cn
Phone: 105 988 1193 / 1
Address: No. 10, , Chao Yang Men Southern Street, , Chao Yang District
Country: China

Music Council (IMC), China / China Musicians Association
Website: www.musician.org.cn
Phone: 106 500 5451
Address: No. 10, Nong Zhan Guan Nan Li, , Chaoyang District,
Country: China

Nan Jing Bureau of Culture
Email: s-wh-j@nj.gov.cn
Phone: 862 557 716 149
Address: No.43 Cheng Xian Street
Country: China

Ning Bo Bureau of Culture
Website: www.nbwh.gov.cn
Email: webmaster@nbwh.gov.cn
Phone: 057 487 189 109
Address: No.148, , Jie Fang Bei Road,
Country: China

Ning Xia Hui Zu Autonomous Region Culture Authority
Phone: 951 602 5080
Address: 8 Wen Hua Dong Street
Country: China

Qing Dao Municipal Bureau of Culture
Website: www.qdwhw.com
Phone: 532 828 65999 /
Address: No. 7, Da Xue (University) Road, , North Gate
Country: China

Qing Hai Province Culture Authority
Website: www.qhwh.gov.cn
Email: qhswht@163.com
Phone: 971 823 9036 / 9
Address: 12 Xi Da Street
Country: China

Shan Dong Province Culture Authority
Website: www.sdwht.gov.cn
Phone: 865 318 656 8899
Address: No. 59, , He Ping Road, , Li Xia District
Information: division of China Ministry of Culture
Country: China

Shan Xi Province Culture Authority
Address: No. 19 Ti Yu Road, Shan Xi
Information: division of China Ministry of Culture
Country: China

Shanghai International Culture Association (2)
Email: sicax_sh@yahoo.com.cn
Phone: 216 294 9931
Address: 20/F, Block 2, , 543 Xin Hua Road
Information: founded in 1986; a non-governmental and non-profit organisation that specialises in culture exchanges between Shanghai and other countries and regions of the world
Country: China

Shanghai Municipal Administration of Culture Radio, Film and TV
Website: wgj.sh.gov.cn
Email: culture@online.sh.cn
Phone: 8621 – 63, 290, 08
Address: No. 276, , Si Chuan Zhong Road,
Country: China

Shen Zhen Municipal Bureau of Culture
Website: www.szwen.gov.cn
Phone: 755 820 02357
Address: No. 1043, Shen Nan Zhong Road, , Fu Tian District, Guang Dong Province,
Information: division of China Ministry of Culture
Country: China

Tian Jin Municipal Bureau of Culture
Website: www.tjwh.gov.cn
Phone: 222 331 2783 / 6
Address: No.12, Cheng De Dao, He Ping District
Information: division of China Ministry of Culture
Country: China

Tibet Autonomous Region Culture Authority
Website: www.ccnt.gov.cn
Email: religion@qov.tibet.net
Address: Department of Religion & Culture, Gangchen Kyishong
Information: division of China Ministry of Culture
Country: China

World Ethnic Music Institute
Website: iom.ccom.edu.cn/index.asp
Email: djiafang@ccom.edu.cn
Phone: 106 641 7455
Country: China

Wu Han Municipal Bureau of Culture
Website: www.whwhj.gov.cn
Phone: 278 283 2030
Address: No.16, You Yi Street, , Han Kou,
Country: China

Xia Men Municipal Bureau of Culture
Website: www.xmculture.gov.cn
Email: whj@xm.gov.cn
Phone: 592 213 2182
Address: No. 11, Gong Yuan Southern Road, , Si Ming District,
Country: China

Xin Jiang Autonomous Region Culture Authority
Phone: 991 286 3854/240
Address: No. 193 Sheng Li Road
Information: some breif infomation in the website: www.ccnt.gov.cn
Country: China

Yun Nan Province Culture Authority
Phone: 871 361 1529
Address: 107 Dong Feng Xi Road
Country: China

Zhejiang Province Culture Authority
Website: www.zjwh.gov.cn
Email: swht@zjwh.gov.cn
Phone: 571 851 13157 /
Address: No. 53, , Shuguang Road, , Zhejiang Province,
Country: China

COLOMBIA

Asia-Iberoamerica Cultural Foundation
Website: asiaiberoamerica.org
Email: asiaibero@gmail.com
Phone: 163 61906
Address: 46 No. 93-59, La Castellana, CO
Information: Asia-Iberoamerica Cultural Foundation dedicates cultural exchange between Asia and Latin-America through the collaboration with important festivals, arts centres and prominent artists. Member of ISPA.
Country: Colombia
Social Media: www.facebook.com/pages/HO-LA-ASIA-Festival-de-Artes-de-Asia-en-Colombia/276735309006961

GUAM

Guam Council on the Arts and Humanities Agency
Website: www.guamcaha.org
Email: kaha1@guam.net
Phone: 671 475 2781/2
Address: P.O. Box 2950, 238 Archbishop Flores Street DNA Building, Suite 405, GU
Country: Guam

HONG KONG

Asian Composers League
Website: www.asiancomposersleague.com
Email: info@asiancomposersleague.com
Phone: 285 97045
Address: c/ – Dr. Joshua Chan, Department of Music, University of Hong Kong, Pokfulam Road Hong Kong, Hong Kong
Information: The Asian Composers League (ACL) is the most vibrant and active contemporary music organization in the Asia-Pacific region today. It was established in 1973 by leading composers from Taiwan, Japan, Hong Kong and Korea. Its primary objectives are: To promote, preserve, and develop the musical cultures of the Asia-Pacific region, particularly in the field of music composition; and To further interests of composers in the Asia-Pacific region through representation and negotiation.
Country: Hong Kong
Social Media: facebook.com/asiancomposersleague/

Asian Cultural Council Hong Kong
Website: www.asianculturalcouncil.org.hk
Email: acc@acc.org.hk
Phone: 212 843 0403
Address: Room 702, Hong Kong Arts Centre, 2 Harbour Road, HK
Information: an organisation devoted to supporting cultural exchange in the visual and performing arts between Asia, the United States and among the countries of Asia
Country: Hong Kong
Social Media: www.facebook.com/asianculturalcouncil

Home Affairs Bureau
Website: www.hab.gov.hk
Email: hab1@hab.gov.hk
Phone: 283 52056
Address: 31/F, Southorn Centre, , 130 Hennessy Road, , Wanchai, HK
Country: Hong Kong

Hong Kong Arts Development Council
Website: www.hkadc.org.hk
Email:
hkadc@hkadc.org.hk
Phone: 282 78786
Address: 14/F, East Warwick House, , Taikoo Place, 979

King's Road, HK
Information: established in 1995 under the Hong Kong Arts Development Council Ordinance, Chapter 472, the Hong Kong Arts Development Council (ADC) is a statutory body set up by the Government to support the broad development of the arts in Hong Kong. Its major roles include grant allocation, policy and planning, advocacy, promotion and development, and programme planning
Country: Hong Kong
Social Media: @hkadc www.facebook.com/HKADCpage

Hong Kong Culture and Art Foundation
Phone: 288 09737
Address: 18F Java Commercial Centre, 128 Java Road, North Point, HK
Information: non-profit making
Country: Hong Kong

Hong Kong Recording Industry Alliance (HKRIA)
Website: www.hkria.com
Email: enquiries@hkria.com
Phone: 252 07000
Address: Units 907-909, 9/F., FTLife Tower, 18 Sheung Yuet Road, Kowloon Bay, Kowloon, HK
Information: Established in Oct 2008, HKRIA is a not-for-profit copyright management organization to handle the copyrights of members who are record companies from Hong Kong and overseas regarding the broadcast, public performance and relevant usage of sound recordings (recorded music) and music videos. They license the use of sound recordings (recorded music) and music videos in broadcast, public performance and new media in Hong Kong, Macau and other territories. Member of IFPI.
Country: Hong Kong

International Federation of the Phonographic Industry (Hong Kong Group) Limited
Website: www.ifpihk.org
Email: enquiry@ifpihk.org
Phone: 286 14318
Address: Unit A, 18/F, Tower A, Billion Centre, No.1 Wang Kwong Road, HK
Information: IFPI is the voice of the recording industry worldwide. IFPI and its National Group network, representing the recording industry worldwide, has some 8, 000 record company members in 70 countries and affiliated industry associations in 57 countries. IFPI (Hong Kong Group) Ltd is a part of IFPI International.
Country: Hong Kong

International Federation of the Phonographic Industry (IFPI) – Asian Regional Office
Website: www.ifpi.org
Email: asia@ifpi.org
Phone: 270 29270
Address: 2 Wing Yip St, Kwun Tong, HK
Information: IFPI is the voice of the recording industry worldwide. IFPI and its National Group network, representing the recording industry worldwide, has some 8, 000 record company members in 70 countries and affiliated industry associations in 57 countries. IFPI is a not-for-profit international organisation registered in Switzerland, with a head office in London. We have regional offices in Brussels, Hong Kong Miami and Nairobi plus a representative office in Beijing.
Country: Hong Kong
Social Media: www.facebook.com/IFPIOrg/twitter.com/IFPI_org www.instagram.com/ifpi_org/

Leisure and Cultural Services – Cultural Presentation office, Cultural Centre
Website: www.leisurecentre.gov.hk
Email: hkcc@lcsd.org.hk
Phone: 273 42009
Address: Podium, Administration Building, HK Culture Centre, 10 Salisbury Rd, Tsim Sha Tsui, HK
Information: Our mission is to cultivate an ecology that will allow cultural endeavours to flourish
Country: Hong Kong

Leisure and Cultural Services – Cultural Presentation office, Performing Arts Division
Website: www.lcsd.gov.hk/cp
Phone: 260 18699
Address: 14/F LCSD Headquarters, 1-3 Pai Tau Street, HK
Country: Hong Kong

Leisure and Cultural Services – Cultural Services Branch, Culture Division
Website: www.lcsd.gov.hk
Email: enquiries@lcsd.gov.hk
Phone: 260 18700
Address: 14F LCSD Headquarters, 1-3 Pai Tau St, Sha Tin , New Territories, HK
Country: Hong Kong

Leisure and Cultural Services – Entertainment Office
Website: www.lcsd.gov.hk/eo
Email: akwma@lcsd.gov.hk
Phone: 259 11390
Address: 8F Queen Elizabeth Stadium, 18 Oi Kwan Road, Wanchai, HK
Country: Hong Kong

INDIA

India Foundation for the Arts
Website: www.indiaifa.org
Email: contactus@indiaifa.org
Phone: 802 341 4681
Address: 'Apurva' Ground Floor, No 259, 4th Cross, Raj Mahal Vilas IInd Stage, IInd Block, IN
Information: IFA enriches the practice and knowledge of, widens public access to, and strengthens capacities and infrastructure in the arts in India, by supporting innovative projects, commissioning research and creating public platforms.
Country: India

The Neemara Music Foundation
Website: www.tnmf.org/
Email: tnmf@fwacziarg.com
Phone: 114 077 5177
Address: A-58, Nizamuddin East, IN
Country: India

INDONESIA

ASEAN Secretariat
Website: www.aseansec.org
Email: public@aseansec.org
Phone: 217 262 991
Address: 70A Jl. Sisingamangaraja, ID
Information: established in 1967, the Association of South East Nations sets out to accelerate economic growth, social progress and cultural development in the region
Country: Indonesia
Social Media: @ASEAN www.facebook.com/aseansecretariat

Jakarta Capital City Government
Website: www.jakarta.go.id
Email: dkiweb@dki.go.id
Address: City Jakarta Administration, Jl. Medan Merdeka Selatan 8-9, Blok G Lantai 3, ID
Country: Indonesia

Ministry of Culture and Tourism
Website: www.budpar.go.id
Email: info@budpar.go.id
Phone: 213 838 167
Address: Sapta Pesona Building, Jl. Medan Merdeka Barat No. 17, ID
Country: Indonesia

ISRAEL

Arthur Rubinstein International Music Society
Website: www.arims.org.il
Email: competition@arims.org.il
Phone: 368 56684
Address: Huberman 12, IL
Country: Israel
Social Media: www.facebook.com/pages/Arthur-Rubinstein-Piano-Competition/182848245082202

JAPAN

Aichi Prefectural Government
Website: www.pref.aichi.jp
Email: web@pref.aichi.lg.jp
Phone: 052 971 5511
Address: Dept. of General Affairs, Culture Promotion Office, 3-1-2 Sannomaru, Naka-ku, Nagoya, JP
Information: the Aichi Arts Center is composed of the following four facilities:
The Aichi Prefectural Museum of Art, the Aichi Prefectural Art Theater, Aichi Prefectural Arts Promotion Service, the Aichi Prefectural Library
Country: Japan

Akita Prefectural Office
Website: www.city.akita.lg.jp
Email: info@mail2.pref.akita.jp
Phone: 188 601 111
Address: 4-1-1 Sanno, Akita City, Akita Prefecture 010-8570
Information: Akita City is located in the central part of Akita Prefecture, and is a green park city with the Dewa Mountains with Mt. Taihei in the east and the Sea of Japan with beautiful sunsets in the west. They are promoting the creation of a people-friendly town where citizens can live in a lively and relaxed manner while taking advantage of the abundant nature.
Country: Japan
Social Media: www.facebook.com/pref.akita/twitter.com/pref_akita

Aomori Municipal Government
Website: www.city.aomori.aomori.jp
Email: shiminkyoudou@city.aomori.aomori.jp
Phone: 017 734 1111
Address: Aomori City Hall, Aomori Chuo-chome, JP
Information: represents the arts and cultural interests of the city of Aomori
Country: Japan

Aomori Prefectural Government (cultural promotion)
Website: www.city.aomori.aomori.jp
Phone: 177 341 111
Address: Aomori City Hall, Aomori Chuo-chome, JP
Information: represents the arts and cultural interests of the city of Aomori
Country: Japan

Arts Council, Japan (National Theatre Library) Resources Division
Website: www.ntj.jac.go.jp
Phone: 332 657 411
Address: 4-1 Hayabusa-cho, Chiyoda-ku, JP
Information: the national theatre consists of a large theatre with 1610 seats and a small theatre with 590 seats
Country: Japan

Asia/Pacific Cultural Centre for UNESCO (ACCU)
Website: www.accu.or.jp
Email: General@accu.or.jp
Phone: 332 694 435
Address: Japan Publishers Building, 6 Fukuromachi, Shinjuku-ku, JP
Information: a not-for-profit organisation that helps local councils with arts programmes
Country: Japan

Asian Cultural Council (Japan)
Website: www.asianculturalcouncil.org/japan
Email: acc@accjpn.org
Phone: 335 350 287
Address: 8F, Toka Bldg., 1-16-1 Ginza, Chuo-ku, JP
Information: Japan office of the American foundation
Country: Japan
Social Media: @ACCNY www.facebook.com/asianculturalcouncil

Association for Corporate Support of the Arts (Kigyo Mecenat Kyogikai)
Website: www.mecenat.or.jp
Email: mecenat@mecenat.or.jp
Address: Daiichi Tekko Bldg. 1F, 1-8-2, Marunouchi, Chiyoda-ku, JP
Country: Japan

Association for Promoting Music Choruses
Email: kobayashi@tokyo-concerts.co.jp
Phone: 332 269 755
Address: 6F Bellux Shinjuku Bldg part II, 23 Aizumi-cho, Shinjuku-ku, JP
Country: Japan

Chiba Municipal Government
Website: www.city.chiba.jp
Phone: 432 455 111
Address: 1-1 Chibaminato, Chuo-ku, JP
Country: Japan

Chiba Prefectural Cultural Promotion Foundation
Website: www.cbs.or.jp
Phone: 432 220 077
Address: 11-2 Ichiba-cho, Chuo-ku, JP
Country: Japan

Chiba Prefectural Government
Website: www.pref.chiba.jp
Phone: 814 322 32110
Address: 1-1 Ichiba-cho, Chuo-ku, JP
Country: Japan

Delegation of the European Commission
Website: jpn.cec.eu.int
Phone: 332 390 441
Address: Europa House, 9-15 Sanban-cho, Chiyoda-ku, JP
Country: Japan

Ehime Prefectural Government
Website: www.pref.ehime.jp
Phone: 899 412 111
Address: 4-4-2 Ichiban-cho, Matsuyama, JP
Country: Japan

Fukui Municipal Government
Website: www.city.fukui.lg.jp/
Phone: 817 762 05670(c
Address: 3-10-1 Ohte, JP
Country: Japan

Fukui Prefectural Government
Website: www.pref.fukui.jp
Email: bunka@pref.fukui.lg.jp
Phone: 776 211 111
Address: 3-17-1 Ohte, JP
Country: Japan

Fukuoka Municipal Government
Website: www.city.fukuoka.jp
Email: bunka.CAB@city.fukuoka.jp
Phone: 927 114 111
Address: Cultural Affairs Promotion Section, 1-8-1 Tenjin, Chuo-ku, JP
Country: Japan

Fukuoka Prefectural Government – Cultural Affairs Division
Website: www.pref.fukuoka.lg.jp/
Phone: 819 264 33224 (
Address: 7-7 Higashi Koen, Hakata-ku, JP
Information: the Division is part of Second Department of Supervision, Fukuoka Regional Board of Education
Country: Japan

Fukushima Municipal Government
Website: www.city.fukushima.fukushima.jp
Email: info@fukushima.fukushima.jp
Phone: 245 351 111
Address: 3-1 Gorouchi-machi, JP
Country: Japan

Fukushima Prefectural Government
Website: www.pref.fukushima.jp
Email: jyohou@pref.fukushima.jp
Phone: 245 211 111
Address: 2-16 Sugizuma-cho, JP
Country: Japan

Gifu Municipal Government (Cultural Education Div.)
Website: www.city.gifu.gifu.jp
Email: bunka@city.gifu.gifu.jp
Phone: 582 654 141
Address: 1-11 Kanda-machi, JP
Country: Japan

Gifu Prefectural Government
Website: www.pref.gifu.lg.jp/
Email: webmaster@pref.gifu.lg.jp
Phone: 582 721 111
Address: 2-1-1 Yabuta Minami, JP
Country: Japan

Gunma Prefectural Government
Website: www.pref.gunma.jp
Email: k-kyoi@pref.gunma.jp
Phone: 812 725 27762/
Address: 1-1-1 Ohte-machi, Maebashi, JP
Country: Japan

Hiroshima Municipal Government
Website: www.city.hiroshima.jp
Phone: 822 452 111
Address: 1-6-34 Kokutaiji-machi, Naka-ku, JP
Country: Japan

Hiroshima Prefectural Government
Website: www.pref.hiroshima.jp
Phone: 818 222 82111
Address: 10-52 Moto-machi, Naka-ku, JP
Country: Japan

Hokkaido International Music Exchange Society (HIMES)
Phone: 112 327 592
Address: c/o SIS, 6F MN Bldg., KITA-1 NISHI-3, Chuo-ku, Sapporo, JP
Country: Japan

Hokkaido Prefectural Government
Website: www.pref.hokkaido.jp
Phone: 112 314 111
Address: Nishi 6-chome, Kita San-jo, Chuo-ku, Sapporo, JP
Country: Japan

Hyogo Prefectural Government
Website: web.pref.hyogo.jp
Email: geijutsubunkaka@pref.hyogo.jp
Phone: 783 417 711
Address: 5-10-1 Shimo-Yamate-dori, Chuo-ku, Kobe, JP
Information: see Hyogo Arts & Culture Association
Country: Japan

Ibaraki Prefectural Government
Website: www.pref.ibaraki.jp
Phone: 293 011 111
Address: 978-6 Kasahara-cho, Mito, JP
Country: Japan

International Association of Music Libraries, Archives and Documentation Centre (IAML) – Japan Branch
Website: www.lib.kunitachi.ac.jp
Email: yumiko@lib.kunitachi.ac.jp
Phone: 425 360 799
Address: c/o Nippon Kindai Ongakukan, 1-8-14 Azabu-dai, Minato-ku, JP
Country: Japan

International House of Japan, Inc.
Website:
www.i-house.or.jp
Email: info@i-house.or.jp
Phone: 334 703 212
Address: 5-11-16 Roppongi, Minato-ku, JP
Country: Japan

International Piano Duo Association
Email: international-piano-duo@h5.dion.ne.jp
Phone: 424 616 160
Address: 2-23-35 Hanakoganei, Kodaira, JP
Country: Japan

International Theatre Conference Nagoya
Website: www.2m.biglobe.ne.jp/
Email: itcn@msc.biglobe.ne.jp
Phone: 529 341 452
Address: 225, 2nd Sho-unji Bildg., 2-22-26 Higashisakura, Naka-ku, Nagoya, JP
Country: Japan

International Theatre Institute (ITI), Japan
Website: www.iti-worldwide.org/japan.php
Email: iti@topaz.dti.ne.jp
Phone: 334 782 189
Address: c/o National Noh Theatre, 4-18-1 Sendagaya, Shibuya-ku, JP
Country: Japan

Ishikawa Prefectural Government
Website: www.pref.ishikawa.jp
Email: e130700@pref.ishikawa.jp
Phone: 762 251 371
Address: 1-1 Kuratsuki, , Kanazawa, JP
Information: organizes Ishikawa Music Academy (q.v.)
Country: Japan

Iwate Prefectural Government
Website: www.pref.iwate.jp
Phone: 196 513 111
Address: 10-1 Uchimaru, Morioka, JP
Country: Japan
Social Media: @ Pref_iwate

Japan Arts Council
Website: www.ntj.jac.go.jp
Phone: 332 657 411
Address: 4-1 Hayabusa-cho, Chiyoda-ku, JP
Country: Japan

Japan Arts Fund
Website: www.ntj.jac.go.jp
Phone: 332 657 411
Address: 4-1 Hayabusa-cho, Chiyoda-ku, JP
Country: Japan

Japan Ballet Association
Phone: 334 995 524
Address: 6F Dai-san Namiki Bldg, 3-16-5 Shibuya, Shibuya-ku, JP
Information: membership organisation
Country: Japan

Japan Council of Performers' Organisations
Website: www.geidankyo.or.jp
Email: pr@geidankyo.or.jp
Phone: 353 536 600
Address: 11F Tokyo Opera City Tower, 3-20-2 Nishi-Shinjuku, Shinjuku-ku, JP
Information: consists of 61 member organisations 60,000 performers of theatre, music, dance, variety, folk, etc.; its purposes are to promote performing activities of artists through the mutual co-operation of all associations formed by the artists and by providing th
Country: Japan

Japan Folklore Association (C.I.O.F.F. JAPAN)
Email: cwf2000@db3.so-net.ne.jp
Phone: 334 771 055
Address: 2-28-10-307 Meguro-honcho, Meguro-ku, JP
Information: Japanese office of C.I.O.F.F. (Conseil International des Organisations de Festivals de Folklore et d'Arts Traditionnels), which is a world-wide organisation of UNESCO
Country: Japan

Japan Foundation
Website: www.jpf.go.jp
Email: butai2006@jpf.go.jp
Phone: 813 556 23500 (
Address: 20F/21F Ark Mori Bldg., 1-12-32 Akasaka, Minato-ku, JP
Information: check website, Performing Arts Network Japan at www.performingarts.jp ; have launched a grant program for performing arts organizations in Europe
Country: Japan

Japan Foundation for Regional Art-Activities
Website: www.jafra.nippon.net.ne.jp
Phone: 355 734 050
Address: 8F Kokusai Shin-Akasaka Bldg. Nishi-kan, 6-1-20 Akasaka, Minato-ku, JP
Country: Japan

Japan Foundation Library
Website: www.jpf.go.jp
Email: Lib@jpf.go.jp
Phone: 353 696 084
Address: 4-4-1 Yotsuya, Shinjuku-ku, JP
Information: open to the General public
Country: Japan

Make your music a business!

BYOM Academy - Be Your Own Manager

A Career Program for Classical Musicians

Kagawa Prefectural Government
Website:
www.pref.kagawa.jp
Phone: 878 311 111
Address: 4-1-10 Ban-cho, Takamatsu, JP
Country: Japan

Kagoshima Municipal Government
Website:
www.city.kagoshima.lg.jp
Email: bunka4@city.kagoshima.kagoshima.jp
Phone: 819 921 61134 (
Address: 11-1 Yamashita-cho, JP
Country: Japan

Kagoshima Prefectural Government
Website:
www.pref.kagoshima.jp
Phone: 992 862 111
Address: 10-1 Kamoikeshinmachi, JP
Country: Japan

Kanagawa Arts Foundation
Website:
www.kanagawa-arts.or.jp/
Phone: 456 625 901(gene
Address: Kikaku-ka, 3-1 Yamashita-cho, Naka-ku, Yokohama, JP
Country: Japan

Kanagawa Prefectural Government
Website: www.pref.kanagawa.jp
Phone: 452 101 111
Address: 1 Nihon Oh-dori, Naka-ku, Yokohama, JP
Information: see Kanagawa Arts Foundation
Country: Japan

Kanazawa Municipal Government
Website: www.city.kanazawa.ishikawa.jp
Phone: 817 622 02061(g
Address: 1-1-1 Hirosaka, Kanazawa, JP
Country: Japan

Kobe Municipal Government
Website: www.city.kobe.jp
Phone: 783 318 181
Address: 6-5-1 Kano-cho, Chuo-ku, JP
Country: Japan

Kochi Municipal Government
Website: www.city.kochi.kochi.jp
Phone: 888 228 111
Address: 5-1-45 Hon-machi, JP
Country: Japan

Kochi Prefectural Government
Website: www.pref.kochi.jp
Email: 140201@ken.pref.kochi.lg.jp
Phone: 818 882 39296 (
Address: 1-2-20 Marunouchi, JP
Country: Japan

Kofu Municipal Government Department of Culture and Arts
Website: www.city.kofu.yamanashi.jp
Phone: 552 237 324
Address: 10-1 Otamachi, Kofu, JP
Country: Japan

Kumamoto Municipal Government
Website: www.city.kumamoto.kumamoto.jp
Phone: 963 282 111/2039
Address: 1-1 Tetori Hon-cho, JP
Country: Japan

Kumamoto Prefectural Government
Website: www.pref.kumamoto.jp
Email: bunka@pref.kumamoto.lg.jp
Phone: 819 638 19829(g
Address: 6-18-1 Suizenji, JP
Country: Japan

Kyoto Municipal Government
Website: www.city.kyoto.jp
Email: bunka@city.kyoto.jp
Phone: 817 522 24109(d
Address: 488 Kamihonnojimae-cho, Oike-agaru, Teramachi-dori, Nakagyo-ku, JP
Country: Japan

Kyoto Prefectural Government
Website: www.pref.kyoto.jp
Email: kokusai@pref.kyoto.lg.jp
Phone: 754 144 313
Address: Yabunouchi-cho, Shinmachi Nishiiru, Shimotachiuri-dori, Kamigyo-ku, JP
Country: Japan

Maebashi Municipal Government
Website: www.city.maebashi.gunma.jp
Phone: 272 241 111
Address: 2-12-1 Ohte-machi, Maebashi, JP
Country: Japan

Matsue Municipal Government
Website: www.city.matsue.shimane.jp
Email: koe@city.matsue.lg.jp
Phone: 852 555 555
Address: 86 Suetsugu-cho, Matsue, JP
Country: Japan

Matsuyama Municipal Government
Website: www.city.matsuyama.ehime.jp
Phone: 818 994 86688
Address: 4-7-2 Niban-cho, Matsuyama, JP
Country: Japan

Mayuzumi Folk Dance Culture Foundation
Website: www.mayuzumi.or.jp
Email: info@mayuzumi.or.jp
Phone: 335 833 633
Address: 4th floor, Mayu Building, 3-10-3 Akasaka, Minato-ku, Tokyo 107-0052
Information: The Mayuzumi Folk Dance Culture Foundation was approved by the Minister of Education, Culture, Sports, Science and Technology in March 1986 for the purpose of establishing Japanese traditional folk dance as a performing art and promoting its spread and international cultural exchange. Includes performances, study groups, workshops and folk performance art research.
Country: Japan
Contact: Chairman Moriyuki Kato

Medium Theatre Council
Phone: 333 540 141
Address: c/o Kinokuniya Hall, 3-17-7 Shinjuku, Shinjuku-ku, JP
Country: Japan

Mie Prefectural Government
Website: www.pref.mie.jp
Phone: 592 242 176 (cul
Address: 13 Kohmei-cho, Tsu, JP
Country: Japan

Mito Municipal Government
Website: www.city.mito.ibaraki.jp
Phone: 812 922 41111
Address: 1-4-1 Chuo, Mito, JP
Country: Japan

Miyagi Prefectural Government
Website: www.pref.miyagi.jp
Phone: 812 221 12111
Address: 3-8-1 Hon-cho, Aoba-ku, 3-8-1 Hon-cho, Aoba-ku, Sendai, JP
Country: Japan

Miyazaki Municipal Government
Website: www.city.miyazaki.miyazaki.jp
Phone: 985 252 111
Address: 1-1-1 Tachibana-dori Nishi, JP
Country: Japan

Miyazaki Prefectural Government
Website: www.pref.miyazaki.lg.jp
Phone: 985 267 111/ 26
Address: 2-10-1 Tachibana-dori Higashi, JP
Country: Japan

Morioka Municipal Government
Website: www.city.morioka.iwate.jp
Phone: 196 514 111/ext
Address: 12-2 Uchimaru, Morioka, JP
Country: Japan

Music Council (IMC), Japan
Email: imcjapan@nifty.com
Phone: 424 681 413
Address: c/o Japan Mozart Research Institute, 4-2-17 Minami-cho, Nishi-Tokyo, JP
Country: Japan

Nagano Municipal Government
Website: www.city.nagano.nagano.jp
Phone: 262 264 911
Address: 1613 Midori-cho, Oaza Tsuruga, JP
Country: Japan

Nagano Prefectural Government
Website: www.pref.nagano.jp
Phone: 262 320 111
Address: 692-2 Aza Habashita, Oaza Minami Nagano, JP
Country: Japan

Nagasaki Municipal Government
Website: www1.city.nagasaki.nagasaki.jp
Email: info@city.nagasaki.nagasaki.lg.jp
Phone: 958 255 151
Address: 2-22 Sakura-machi, JP
Country: Japan

Nagasaki Prefectural Government
Website: www.pref.nagasaki.jp
Phone: 958 241 111
Address: 2-13 Edo-machi, JP
Country: Japan

Nagoya Municipal Government
Website: www.city.nagoya.jp
Phone: 529 611 111
Address: 3-1-1 Sannomaru, Naka-ku, Nagoya, JP
Country: Japan

Naha Municipal Government
Website: www.city.naha.okinawa.jp
Phone: 819 885 55089 (
Address: 1-1-1 Izumizaki, Naha, JP
Country: Japan

Nara National Research Institute for Cultural Properties
Website: www.nabunken.go.jp
Email: webinfo_nabunken@nich.go.jp
Phone: 742 306 752
Address: 2-9-1, Nijo-cho, Nara City 630-8577 Japan
Information: Nara National Research Institute for Cultural Properties, is an organization committed to comprehensive research on ancient cultural heritage. The ancient city of Nara is known for its wealth of ancient architecture and historical works of art, and the Institute was established to conduct research on these materials.
Country: Japan
Social Media: facebook.com/nabunken/

Nara Prefectural Government (cultural promotion)
Website: www.pref.nara.jp
Email: bumka-naraken@mahoroba.ne.jp
Phone: 742 278 478
Address: 30 Noboriohji-cho, JP
Country: Japan

National Council of Theatres for Children and Youth
Website: www.clarte-net.co.jp
Email: office@clarte-net.co.jp
Phone: 666 855 601
Address: c/o La Clart, 3-1-7 Minami-Kagaya, Suminoe-ku, JP
Country: Japan

Nihon Buyo Foundation
Website: www.nihonbuyo.or.jp/
Email: office@nihonbuyo.or.jp
Phone: 333 545 496
Address: 301 Katagiri Bldg., 10-8 Sumiyoshi-cho, Shinjuku-ku, JP
Information: participate in an Arts Festival sponsored by the Colrural Agency
Country: Japan

Niigata Municipal Government
Website: www.city.niigata.niigata.jp
Email: joho@city.niigata.lg.jp
Phone: 252 281 000
Address: 602-1 Ichiban-cho, Gakkocho-dori, JP
Country: Japan

Niigata Prefectural Government
Website: www.pref.niigata.jp
Email: bunkashinko@mail.pref.niigata.jp
Phone: 252 855 511
Address: 4-1 Shinko-cho, JP
Country: Japan

Niigata Prefecture Cultural Foundation
Website: www.niigata-bunka.jp/ncf
Email: ncf@msg.biglobe.ne.jp
Phone: 252 283 577
Address: 3-13 Ichibanbori-dori-machi, JP
Country: Japan

Oita Municipal Government
Website: www.city.oita.oita.jp/
Phone: 819 753 46111
Address: 2-31 Niage-machi, JP
Country: Japan

Oita Prefectural Government
Website: www.pref.oita.jp/
Phone: 975 361 111
Address: 3-1-1 Ohte-machi, JP
Country: Japan

Okayama Municipal Government
Website: www.city.okayama.okayama.jp
Phone: 868 031 000
Address: 1-1-1 Daiku, JP
Country: Japan

Okayama Prefectural Government
Website: www.pref.okayama.jp
Phone: 862 242 111
Address: 2-4-6 Uchisange, JP
Country: Japan

Okinawa Prefectural Government
Website: www.pref.okinawa.jp
Email: okinawa@pref.okinawa.jp
Phone: 988 662 333 (inf
Address: 1-2-2 Izumizaki, Naha, JP

Osaka Foundation of Culture
Phone: 647 908 525
Address: Osaka-fu Shinbettkan Kita-kan, 03/01/1943, Ohtemae, Chuo-ku, JP
Country: Japan

Osaka International Festival Society
Phone: 362 699 441
Address: 3F Shin-Asahi Bldg., 2-3-18 Nakanoshima, Kita-ku, JP
Country: Japan

Osaka Municipal Government
Website: www.city.osaka.jp
Phone: 816 620 88181
Address: 1-3-20 Nakanoshima, Kita-ku, JP
Country: Japan

Otsu Municipal Government
Website: www.city.otsu.shiga.jp
Phone: 817 752 31234
Address: 3-1 Goryo-cho, JP
Country: Japan

Saga Bank Cultural Foundation
Website: www.sagabank.co.jp
Phone: 952 251 620
Address: 2-7-20 Tojin, JP
Country: Japan

Saga Municipal Government
Website: www.city.saga.saga.jp
Phone: 952 243 151
Address: 1-1 Sakae-machi, JP
Country: Japan

Saga Prefectural Government
Website: www.pref.saga.lg.jp
Phone: 952 242 111
Address: 1-1-59 Jonai, JP
Country: Japan

Saitama Municipal Government
Website: www.city.saitama.jp
Phone: 814 882 91969 (
Address: 6-4-4 Tokiwa, Urawa-ku Saitama, JP
Country: Japan

Saitama Prefectural Government – Cultural Affairs Division
Website: www.pref.saitama.lg.jp
Email: a2875@pref.saitama.lg.jp
Phone: 488 302 875
Address: 3-15-1 Takasago, Urawa-ku, JP
Country: Japan

Sapporo Municipal Government
Website: www.city.sapporo.jp/city
Phone: 112 18515
Address: Nishi 2-chome, Kita Ichi-jo, Chuo-ku, Sapporo, JP
Country: Japan

Sendai Municipal Government
Website: www.city.sendai.jp
Phone: 222 611 111
Address: 3-7-1 Kokubun-cho, Aoba-ku, Sendai, JP
Country: Japan

Shiga Prefectural Government
Website: www.pref.shiga.jp
Email: ck00@pref.shiga.lg.jp
Phone: 775 241 121
Address: 4-1-1 Kyo-machi, Ohtsu, JP
Information: the prefecture's Biwako Hall Foundation manages Biwako Hall (q.v.)
Country: Japan

Shimane Prefectural Government-Cultural Promotion Division
Website: www.pref.shimane.jp
Email: bunkashinko@pref.shimane.lg.jp
Phone: 852 225 878
Address: 1 Tono-machi, Matsue, JP
Country: Japan

Shizuoka Municipal Government
Website: www.city.shizuoka.jp
Email: info@city.shizuoka.jp
Phone: 815 425 42111
Address: 5-1 Ohte-machi, JP
Country: Japan

Shizuoka Performing Arts Centre (SPAC)
Website: www.spac.or.jp
Email: info@spac.or.jp
Phone: 542 035 730
Address: 100-1 Hirasawa, JP
Information: Shizuoka prefectural foundation for performing arts established in 1995; aiming to provide creative base for the artists of national and international basis; generates programmes of creation, presentation and education as well as programmes of exchange
Country: Japan

Shizuoka Prefectural Government – Living/cultural department (Seikatsu Bunka)
Website: www.pref.shizuoka.jp/seibun
Email: seibun@pref.shizuoka.jp
Phone: 542 212 252
Address: 9-6 Ohte-machi, Aoi-ku, JP
Information: see Shizuoka Performing Arts Centre
Country: Japan

Sony Music Foundation
Website: www.smf.or.jp
Email: smf@sonymusic.co.jp
Phone: 332 619 831
Address: 7F JS Ichigaya Bldg., 5-1 Goban-cho, Chiyoda-ku, JP
Country: Japan

Takamatsu Municipal Government
Website: www.city.takamatsu.kagawa.jp
Phone: 878 392 011
Address: 1-8-15 Ban-cho, Takamatsu, JP
Country: Japan

Tochigi Prefectural Government
Website: www.pref.tochigi.jp
Email: kokusai@pref.tochigi.lg.jp
Phone: 286 233 165
Address: 1-1-20 Hanawada, Utsunomiya-SHI, JP
Country: Japan

Tokushima Municipal Government
Website: www.city.tokushima.tokushima.jp
Phone: 886 215 111(gene
Address: 2-5 Saiwai-cho, JP
Country: Japan

Tokushima Prefectural Government
Website: www.pref.tokushima.jp
Phone: 886 212 500
Address: 1-1 Bandai-cho, JP
Country: Japan

Tokyo Metropolitan Government
Website: www.chijihonbu.metro.tokyo.jp
Phone: 353 882 115
Address: 2-8-1 Nishi Shinjuku, Shinjuku-ku, JP
Country: Japan

Tottori Municipal Government
Website: www.city.tottori.tottori.jp
Phone: 857 228 111
Address: 116 Shohtoku-machi, JP
Country: Japan

Tottori Prefectural Government
Website: www.pref.tottori.jp
Email: bunkageijutsu@pref.tottori.jp
Phone: 857 268 111
Address: 1-220 Higashi-machi, JP
Country: Japan

Toyama Municipal Government
Website: www.city.toyama.toyama.jp
Phone: 817 643 16111
Address: 7-38 Shinsakura-machi, JP
Country: Japan

Toyama Prefectural Government
Website: www.pref.toyama.jp
Phone: 764 314 111
Address: 1-7 Shinsohgawa, JP
Country: Japan

Tsu Municipal Government Division of Culture
Website: www.info.city.tsu.mie.jp
Phone: 592 293 256
Address: 23-1 Nishi Marunouchi, Tsu, JP
Country: Japan

UK-Japan Music Society (Tokyo Office)
Phone: 359 504 552
Address: c/o Mr Jiko Nishiyama, 1-7-15 Ikebukuro, Toshima-ku, JP
Information: headquarters: 27 Heron Close, Great Glen, Leicester LE8 9DZ, UK, Tel/Fax: +44 0 116 259 3891; UK-Japan Music Society: founder & music Director: Jonathan Gregory; administrator: Yoshimi Gregory
Country: Japan

Union Internationale de la Marionnette (UNIMA), Japan – Nihon (UNIMA)
Website: member.nifty.ne.jp/unima
Email: unima-jp@mbg.nifty.com
Phone: 333 793 370
Address: 503, 2-26-4 Yoyogi, Shibuya-ku, JP
Country: Japan

Utsunomiya Municipal Government
Website: www.city.utsunomiya.tochigi.jp
Phone: 286 322 222
Address: 1-1-5 Asahi, Utsunomiya, JP
Country: Japan

Wakayama Municipal Government
Website: www.city.wakayama.wakayama.jp
Phone: 817 343 20001(g
Address: 23 Shichiban-cho, Wakayama, JP
Country: Japan

Wakayama Prefectural Government
Website: www.pref.wakayama.lg.jp
Phone: 734 324 111
Address: 1-1 Komatsubara-dori, JP
Country: Japan

Yamagata Municipal Government
Website: www.city.yamagata.yamagata.jp
Email: bunka@city.yamagata.yamagata.jp
Phone: 812 362 49618 (
Address: 2-3-25 Hatago-machi, JP
Country: Japan

Yamagata Prefectural Government
Website: www.pref.yamagata.jp
Phone: 236 302 211
Address: 2-8-1 Matsunami, JP
Country: Japan

Yamaguchi Municipal Government
Website: www.city.yamaguchi.yamaguchi.jp
Phone: 818 392 24111
Address: 2-1 Kameyama-cho, JP
Country: Japan

Yamaguchi Prefectural Government – Department of Cultural Promotion
Website: www.pref.yamaguchi.jp
Email: a19300@pref.yamaguchi.lg.jp
Phone: 839 223 111(gene
Address: 1-1 Taki-machi, JP
Country: Japan

Yamanashi Prefectural Government
Website: www.pref.yamanashi.jp
Email: shougai-gk@pref.yamanashi.lg.jp
Phone: 552 371 111
Address: 1-6-1 Marunouchi, Kofu, JP
Country: Japan

Yokohama Municipal Government
Website: www.city.yokohama.jp
Phone: 456 712 121
Address: 1-1 Minato-cho, Naka-ku, JP
Country: Japan

REPUBLIC OF KOREA

Arts Council Korea
Website: www.arko.or.kr
Phone: 276 04500
Address: 1-26 Guro-dong Guro-gu
Information: a state funded, non-profit organisation. The aim of the Council is to make the arts more central to the lives of the Korean citizens by supporting arts organisations and artists in and abroad through grant-giving services and programs
Country: Republic of Korea

ASSITEJ Korea
Website: www.assitejkorea.org
Email: assitej@assitejkorea.org
Phone: 274 55863
Address: 1F 50-34 Dongsung-Dung, Jongro-Gu
Information: ASSITEJ stands for International Association of Theatre for Children and Young People. It was established in 1965 to help the lives of children and young people. It involves individuals, professional theatres and theatre organisations in order to raise the Artistic standards of theatre for children and young people
Country: Republic of Korea
Social Media: www.facebook.com/assitejkorea

Australia-Korea Foundation
Email: inform@australia.or.kr
Phone: 220 030 105
Address: 11F Kyo-Bo Bldg, 1 Jong-ro 1-ka, Jongro-gu
Country: Republic of Korea

Business Council for the Arts, Korean
Website: www.mecenat.or.kr
Email: mecenat@mecenat.or.kr
Phone: 276 13101
Address: 18th Floor, FKI Building 18-1, Yoido-dong, Youngdung-po-gu
Country: Republic of Korea

Conseil International de la Danse-CID-UNESCO, Korean Chapter
Address: Kyungdong Apt #105-502, Gangseo-gu, Gayang-dong 1474
Country: Republic of Korea

International Theatre Institute (ITI), South Korea
Website: www.iti-worldwide.org/korea.php
Email: isooshin@hanmail.net
Phone: 222 200 789

Address: ITI Korea office, 86-8 Ihwajang-gil, Jongno-Gu
Information: established in 1958 by UNESCO
Country: Republic of Korea

Korea Arts & Culture Education Service
Website: www.arte.or.kr
Email: contact@arte.or.kr
Phone: 237 045 911
Address: 4F 108-5, Samsung 1-dong, , Kangnam-gu
Country: Republic of Korea

Korea Cultural & Tourism Policy Institute
Email: presi@kctpi.co.kr
Phone: 266 99800
Address: 827 3-dong, Bang Hwa, Ganseo-gu
Country: Republic of Korea

Korean Council for the Arts
Website: www.mecenat.or.kr
Email: mecenat@mecenat.or.kr
Phone: 276 13101
Address: 18 Fl, FKI B/D 28-1 Yoido-dong, Youngdung-po-ku
Country: Republic of Korea

Kumho Asiana Cultural Foundation
Website: www.kumhoarthall.com
Email: musiana@kumho.net
Phone: 263 031 919
Address: 3F Kumho Building, 57, Sinmunro1-ga, Jongro-gu
Country: Republic of Korea

Ministry of Culture and Tourism
Website: www.mct.go.kr
Email: webmaster@mct.go.kr
Phone: 237 049 114
Address: 215 Changgyeonggung-ro, Jongno-gu
Information: responsible for affairs in the areas of culture, the arts, religion, tourism, sports and youth. The ministry has one assistant minister, two main offices, six bureaus, four officers, 27 divisions
Country: Republic of Korea

Ministry of Culture and Tourism – Arts Bureau – Arts and Culture Education Division
Phone: 237 049 590
Address: 82-1 Sejong-ro, Jongno-gu
Country: Republic of Korea

Ministry of Culture and Tourism – Arts Bureau – Arts Policy Division
Website: www.mct.go.kr
Email: webmaster@mct.go.kr
Phone: 237 049 510
Address: 82-1 Sejong-ro, Jongno-gu
Country: Republic of Korea

Ministry of Culture and Tourism – Arts Bureau – Performing Arts Division
Website: www.mct.go.kr
Phone: 237 049 530
Address: 82-1 Sejong-ro, Jongno-gu
Country: Republic of Korea

Ministry of Culture and Tourism – Arts Bureau – Traditional Arts Division
Phone: 237 049 565
Address: 82-1 Sejong-ro, Jongno-gu
Country: Republic of Korea

Ministry of Culture and Tourism – Cultural Industry Bureau
Phone: 237 049 610
Address: Cultural Industry Policy Division, 82-1 Sejong-ro, Jongro-gu
Country: Republic of Korea

Ministry of Culture and Tourism – Cultural Industry Bureau – Content Promotion Division
Phone: 237 049 380
Address: 82-1 Sejong-ro, Jongno-gu
Information: deals with affairs related to distribution structure improvement, active investments and global advancement of the Korean character, comics and animation industries; develops and cultivates the advanced culture contents
Country: Republic of Korea

Ministry of Culture and Tourism – Cultural Industry Bureau – Copyright Division
Phone: 237 049 470
Address: 82-1 Sejong-ro, Jongno-gu
Country: Republic of Korea

Ministry of Culture and Tourism – Cultural Policy Bureau – Cultural Policy Division
Phone: 237 049 410
Address: 82-1 Sejong-ro, Jongno-gu
Information: conducts survey on cultural consciousness and cultivates the national cultural consciousness; collects, analyses and maintains the culture-related statistics; establishes, arbitrates and executes the leisure policies; revitalises cultural activities

Ministry of Culture and Tourism – Cultural Policy Bureau – Intl. Cultural Cooperation Division
Phone: 237 049 570
Address: 82-1 Sejong-ro, Jongno-gu
Information: establishes and promotes an exchange plan among global artists as well as a supporting plan for overseas Korean artists; affairs related to cultural pacts and international agreements on culture and arts; cooperates with international cultural and artisti
Country: Republic of Korea

Ministry of Culture and Tourism – Cultural Policy Bureau – Regional Culture Division
Phone: 237 049 569
Address: 82-1 Sejong-ro, Jongno-gu
Information: coordinates and manages regional culture supporting networks; affairs related to the Regional Culture Arts Promotion Commission and other regional cultural foundations; cultivates, nurtures and supports regional cultural resources excluding cultural asset
Country: Republic of Korea

Ministry of Culture and Tourism – Culture Industry Bureau – Cultural Technology and H.R. Division
Phone: 237 049 690
Address: 82-1 Sejong-ro, Jongno-gu
Country: Republic of Korea

Music Council (IMC), Korea / Korean Music Association
Website: www.mak.or.kr
Phone: 274 48060
Address: 403 Yechong Building, 1-117 Dongsoong-Dong, Jongro-Gu
Information: holds the Seoul Music Festival annually since 1969
Country: Republic of Korea

Union Internationale de la Marionnette (UNIMA), Korea Republic of
Email: yusa22@kornet.net
Phone: 277 80261
Address: Theatre Department, Seoul Institute of the Arts, 8-19 Yejang-dong, Jung-gu
Country: Republic of Korea

LEBANON

Samir Kassir Foundation
Website: www.samirkassirfoundation.org
Email: info@samirkassirfoundation.org
Phone: 139 7331
Address: 63 Zahrani Street, Sioufi, Ashrafieh, LB
Information: a non-profit organisation, working within the civil society and cultural circles to spread the democratic culture in Lebanon and the Arab world, encourage the new talents of free Press, and build the movement for a cultural, democratic, and secular renewal in honor of Samir Kassir. Member of ISPA
Country: Lebanon

MALAYSIA

Japan Foundation – Cultural Affairs Department
Website: www.jfkl.org.my
Email: jpcc@jfkl.org.my
Phone: 322 846 228
Address: 18th Floor, North Point, Block B, Mid-Valley City, Medan Syed Putra, MY
Country: Malaysia

Kedah State Theatre Council
Phone: 473 15930
Address: Taman Kebudayaan Negeri, Lot BTD 400, Pumpong, Alor Setar, MY
Country: Malaysia

Ministry of Culture, Arts and Heritage
Website: www.heritage.gov.my
Email: info@heritage.gov.my
Phone: 326 127 600
Address: Floor 16, Menara TH Perdana, Maju Junction, 1001 Jalan Sultan Ismail, MY
Country: Malaysia

Sarawak State Cultural Council
Phone: 824 15894
Address: c/o Kementerian Pembangunan Social, Rumah Sarawak, Jalan Taman Budaya, Kuching, MY
Country: Malaysia

World Dance Alliance Asia-Pacific (WDA-Asia Pacific)
Website: www.mydancealliance.org
Email: contact@mydancealliance.org
Phone: 173 103 769
Address: c/o MyDance Alliance, PO Box 12409, MY
Country: Malaysia

World Dance Alliance Asia-Pacific (WDA-Asia Pacific)
Website: www.wda-ap.org
Email: yunyuw@hotmail.com

MEXICO

Consejo Estatal para la Cultura y las Artes de Chiapas
Website: www.conecultachiapas.gob.mx
Email: informacion@conecultachiapas.gob.mx
Address: Blvd., Fracc. San Roque, MX
Country: Mexico

Consejo Estatal para la Cultura y las Artes de Hidalgo
Website: www.hidalgo.gob.mx
Email: cecultah@e-hidalgo.gob.mx
Phone: 771 715 0497
Address: Palacio de Gobierno, Plaze Juárez, Col. Centro, MX
Information: see also Venues, alternative Email address: cecultah@hotmail.com
Country: Mexico
Social Media: @gobiernohidalgoes-la.facebook.com/gobhidalgo

Consejo Estatal para la Cultura y las Artes de Nayarit
Email: corinaramirez@nayarit.gob.mx
Phone: 311 217 9326
Address: Av. Allende 329 Pte., Col. Ce, MX
Information: alternative Email addresses: cecan@tepic.megared.net.mx, sarche@culturaspopulares.gob.mx
Country: Mexico

Consejo Mexicano de la Música/Consejo Internacional de la Música
Phone: 525 556 665 143
Address: Paseo del Cantil 6, Cantil del Pedral, MX
Country: Mexico

Consejo Nacional para la Cultura y las Artes (CONACULTA)
Website: www.conaculta.gob.mx
Email: redes_sociales@cultura.gob.mx
Phone: 554 155 0200
Address: Paseo de la Reforma 175 06500 Mexico City, Distrito Federal, MX
Information: The National Council for Culture and the Arts (Conaculta) was created in order to coordinate policies, organizations and agencies of both a cultural and Artistic nature. Likewise, it has tasks of promotion, support and sponsorship of events that promote art and culture. The immediate antecedent of Conaculta was the Undersecretariat of Culture of the Ministry of Public Education.
Country: Mexico
Social Media: www.facebook.com/CulturaGobPue/twitter.com/cultura_mx https:// www.instagram.com/culturamx/

Consejo para la Cultura y las Artes de Nuevo León
Website: www.conarte.org.mx
Email: contacto@conarte.org.mx
Phone: 812 020 6705
Address: Antiguo Palacio Postal, Washington 648 Ote. piso 8, Col. Centro, MX
Country: Mexico

Cultural Institute of the State of Durango
Website: iced.durango.gob.mx
Email: webmaster@durango.gob.mx
Phone: 618 137 5807
Address: Nte 143 Constitution Street, MX
Country: Mexico
Social Media: @iceddgo www.facebook.com/cultura.durango

Fundacion Jazzfest
Website: www.fundacionjazzfestac.org/
Email: info@fundacionjazzfestac.org
Address: MX
Information: support and promote jazz education, as well as contributing to the attraction of new audiences to preserve the growth and perpetuation of America's original music. Members of ISPA
Country: Mexico

Instituto Veracruzano de la Cultura
Website: www.ivec.gob.mx
Email: ehpm@ivec.gob.mx
Address: Francisco Canal esq Zaragoza, Colonia Centro, MX
Country: Mexico

International Theatre Institute (ITI), México
Website: www.cemexitiunesco.org
Email: teatro@cemexitiunesco.org
Phone: 555 336 2471
Address: Calle Pestalozzi 315, Col. Narvarte Poniente, MX
Information: alternate website: www.iti-worldwide.org/mexico.php
Country: Mexico

Mexican Centre for Music and Sonic Arts
Website: www.cmmas.org
Email: info@cmmas.org
Phone: 443 317 5679
Address: Av. Morelos Norte 485, MX
Information: Created in September 2006 at the initiative of the National Council for Culture and Arts (CONAC-ULTA), today the Federal Ministry of Culture, through the National Arts Centre (CENART) and the Ministry of Culture of the State of Michoacan (SECUM), the Mexican Centre for Music and Sonic Arts (CMMAS) is a unique technology-musical space in Latin America. It consists of internationally recognised experts, and has the support of an academic committee that brings together various personalities most prestigious in the field of musical composition with new technologies. Member of ISPA.
Country: Mexico

Promotora de Cultura para Niños
Website: www.promotoradecultura.com
Email: mhinojosa@att.net.mx
Phone: 555 554 766
Address: Apartado postal, Coyoacán, MX
Information: member of the Mexican Centre of the Asia-Pacific Producers, Presenters and Promotors Network (APPN)
Country: Mexico

Secretaría de Cultura de Puebla
Website: www.sc.pue.gob.mx
Email: scultura@pue.gob.mx
Phone: 222 246 4885
Address: 3 Oriente 209, Centro Histórico, MX
Country: Mexico

Secretaría de Cultura del Estado de Michoacán
Website: www.michoacan.gob.mx/cultura
Email: scsecretario@michoacan.gob.mx
Phone: 443 313 8026
Address: Isidro Huarte 545, Colonia Cuauhtémoc, MX
Country: Mexico

Secretaría de Cultura del Estado de Oaxaca
Website: www.oaxaca.gob.mx
Email: secretariadecultura@oaxaca.gob.mx
Phone: 951 132 5683
Address: MX
Country: Mexico

Secretaría de Cultura del Gobierno de San Luis Potosí
Website: www.culturaslp.gob.mx
Email: cultura@culturaslp.gob.mx
Phone: 444 812 8512
Address: Jardín Guerrero 6, Zona Centro, MX
Country: Mexico

Secretaría de Cultura del Gobierno del estado de Jalisco
Website: www.cultura.jalisco.gob.mx
Email: ccomunic@jalisco.gob.mx
Phone: 333 942 1200
Address: Av. La Paz No. 875, Zona Centro, MX
Country: Mexico

Secretaría de Cultura DF
Website: www.cultura.df.gob.mx
Email: n_serratos@df.gob.mx
Phone: 551 719 3000
Address: Av. de la Paz 26, Colonia Chimalistac, MX
Country: Mexico

Secretaría de Cultura DF
Website: www.cultura.df.gob.mx
Email: n_serratos@df.gob.mx
Phone: 551 719 3000
Address: Av. de la Paz 26, Colonia Chimalistac, MX
Country: Mexico

Secretaría de Cultura, Recreación y Deporte del Estado de Tabasco
Email: sriadecultura@prodigy.net.mx
Phone: 993 312 7497
Address: Calle Andr, Colonia Centro, MX
Information: alternative Email address: maximo_evia@hotmail.com
Country: Mexico

Sociedad Internacional de Valores de Artes Mexicanos (SIVAM)
Website: www.sivam.org.mx/
Email: sivam@infosel.net.mx
Phone: 555 202 9810
Address: Av. De Cuspide No. 4755 2do piso, col Parques del Pedregal, MX
Country: Mexico
Social Media: @FundacionSIVAM https:// www.facebook.com/pages/Fundación-SIVAM-AC/183692635021959

Tlaxcala Institute of Culture
Website: www.culturatlaxcala.com.mx
Email: culturatlaxcala@prodigy.net.mx
Phone: 124 646 23623
Address: Av. Juárez No. 62, Col. Centro Tlaxcala, Tlax, MX
Country: Mexico

Union Internationale de la Marionnette (UNIMA)
Website: www.unima.org
Email: sgi@unima.org
Phone: 228 812 2487
Address: 13 de Septiembre, Col. Marco, MX
Information: alternative email: President@unima.org
Country: Mexico

NEW ZEALAND

Archives New Zealand
Website: www.archives.govt.nz
Email: General.enquiries@dia.govt.nz
Phone: 449 95595
Address: 10 Mulgrave Street, NZ
Information: Archives New Zealand, Te Rua Mahara o te Kāwanatanga is the official guardian of New Zealand's public archives
Country: New Zealand

Asia New Zealand Foundation
Website: www.asianz.org.nz
Email: asianz@asianz.org.nz
Phone: 447 12320
Address: Level 16, Fujitsu Tower, 141 The Terrace, NZ
Information: visiting address: Level 16, 141 The Terrace, Wellington, New Zealand
Country: New Zealand
Social Media: asianewzealandAsia New Zealand Foundation

Creative New Zealand – Arts Council of New Zealand – Northern Office
Website: www.creativenz.govt.nz
Email: northern@creativenz.govt.nz
Phone: 937 33066
Address: Third Floor, Southern Cross Building, 57-61 High Street, NZ
Country: New Zealand

Creative New Zealand – Arts Council of New Zealand – Southern Office
Website: www.creativenz.govt.nz
Email: southern@creativenz.govt.nz
Phone: 336 62072
Address: PO Box 3806, NZ
Country: New Zealand

Creative New Zealand – Arts Council of New Zealand, Wellington, National Office
Website: www.creativenz.govt.nz
Email: info@creativenz.govt.nz
Phone: 447 30880
Address: Old Public Trust Building, Level 2, 131-135 Lambton Quay, NZ
Information: Creative New Zealand is the national arts development agency developing, investing in and advocating for the arts.
Country: New Zealand

Dance Aotearoa New Zealand (DANZ)
Website: www.danz.org.nz
Email: danz@danz.org.nz
Phone: 480 19885
Address: Ground Floor, 69 Abel Smith Street, NZ
Information: DANZ has been a registered charitable organisation since 1997. DANZ is a membership organisation for those involved in the professional, education and recreation sectors of New Zealand dance. We work with the industry towards the success and health of New Zealand dance.
Country: New Zealand
Social Media: https:// www.facebook.com/DANZdance

Ministry for Culture and Heritage (Te Manatu Taonga)
Website: www.mch.govt.nz
Email: info@mch.govt.nz
Phone: 449 94490
Address: Level 4, ASB House, , 101 The Terrace, PO Box 5364, NZ
Country: New Zealand

PHILIPPINES

Arts Council of Aklan Foundation, Inc (ACAFI)
Email: eqfnvc@hptmail.com
Phone: 362 623 937
Address: NVC RSO Building, Capitol Subdivision, Kalibo, PH
Information: aims to promote various arts for their community by sponsoring and implementing performances and arts activities including training activities
Country: Philippines

Arts Council of Cebu Foundation, Inc (ACCFI)
Website: www.artscouncilcebu.org
Email: garcia@cl-cebu.com.ph
Phone: 233 0452
Address: Room 221, 2nd floor, Krizia Building, F. Gonzales Compound, Gorordo Avenue, PH
Information: founded in 1960 the council holds the annual Festival of the Arts in Cebu City
Country: Philippines

Arts Council of Iloilo Foundation, Inc.
Phone: 353 200 870
Address: College of Arts and Sciences, Central Philippine University, PH
Information: contributes to the cultural growth of not only the city of Iloilo but the entire province; provides the community with an annual programme of performances, festivals, workshops and grants
Country: Philippines

Cagayan de Oro Arts Council
Phone: 882 272 5453
Address: Nr. 83 cor. 15th & 13th St. Nazareth, PH
Country: Philippines

Capiz Arts Council (CAC)
Phone: 366 212 070
Address: ang Panublion, PH
Information: Alternative E-mail address: Cgortiz@i.rox.net.ph
Country: Philippines

Ibabao Arts Council of Calbayog, Inc.
Phone: 552 091 597
Address: 2F Jimenez Bldg., Magasaysay Blvd., Calbayog City, PH
Information: sponsors national and international productions, exposition of various art productions; has launched a training programme that provides development opportunities for the professional and artists in the community; also supports competitions and festivals i
Country: Philippines

Iligan Arts Council
Email: ribo@ccl.suit.edu.ph
Phone: – 221 6183
Address: No.2 Oxford Street, Celdran Village, PH
Information: supports the development of its members, whether they be individual artists or groups; contributes to cultural development of the entire province through participation in local government planning programmes and regular arts programmes for the community
Country: Philippines

Kandaya Arts Council (Tacloban)
Phone: 635 332 32836 (
Address: Riverside Village, Burayan, San Jose, PH
Country: Philippines

Kutawato Arts Council (KAC)
Phone: 644 212 221
Address: 11Bonifacto St., PH
Country: Philippines

Lucena Council for Culture and Arts (LCCA)
Phone: 423 730 830
Address: c/o Sangguniang Panlunsod Office, City Hall Annex, PH
Information: creates public interest on culture and the arts through various projects that they implements in collaboration with other organisations; with well-recognized artists as members, the council constantly supports some community festivals and celebrations; al
Country: Philippines

Marawi Arts Council
Phone: – 524 094
Address: Mindanao State University, PH
Information: largely based in the campus of Mindanao State University; provides arts programmes strongly reflects the creative tradition of Maranaw culture
Country: Philippines

Nueva Ecija Historical, Cultural and Arts Council (NEHCAC)
Phone: 444 630 952
Address: Provincial Capitol Compound, PH
Information: provides technical and financial support to local arts and cultural groups in the province; carrys out research and documentary activities regarding some indigenous cultural practices of the local community; a major undertaking of the NEHCAC is the ""Isan
Country: Philippines

Obando Arts Council
Phone: 252 42131
Address: c/o DOT International Marketing & Planning Office, 4F DOT Bldg, Rizal Park, PH
Country: Philippines

Pagadian City Culture and Arts Council (PCCAC)
Phone: 622 141 541
Address: St. Cecilia Music Studio, Rizal Ave., PH

Information: sponsors and produces arts activities to the community; also involved with the revitalization of the traditional arts and culture of indigenous communities in the province through research and promotion
Country: Philippines

Pamanang Bulakan Foundation Inc.
Phone: 447 912 490
Address: Provincial, Capitol Compound, Malolos, PH
Information: supports many local festivals; encourages and supports the development of performing arts groups in the community
Country: Philippines

Provincial Culture and Arts Council
Phone: 352 250 988
Address: c/o Pinpi Beach or Office of the Governor, Dumaguete City, PH
Country: Philippines

Sorsogon Arts Council
Email: info@sorsogonarts.com
Phone: 562 111 408
Address: 190 T. Dino Highway, Balogo, PH
Information: in coordination with local government and community institutions, the council provides programmes of training, sponsorship of performances and arts events; also tries to revitalise its heritage through research, creative production and popularisation
Country: Philippines
Social Media: www.facebook.com/pages/Sorsogon-Arts-Council/261276600613553

Tuguegarao Arts Council
Phone: 637 844 61862
Address: DECS Region II Craig, Tuguegarao, PH
Country: Philippines

SINGAPORE

Asia-Europe Foundation (ASEF)
Website: www.asef.org
Email: info@asef.org
Phone: 687 49700
Address: 31 Heng Mui Keng Terrace, SG
Information: not-for-profit foundation that helps both communities and organisations
Country: Singapore
Social Media: @aseforg www.facebook.com/AsiaEurope-Foundation

Asia-Pacific Performing Arts Network (APPAN)
Website: www.aappac.net/aappac/index1.jsp
Email: aappac@esplanade.com
Phone: 682 88341
Address: 1 Esplanade Drive, Gulmohar Park, SG
Information: AAPPAC was established in 1996 with the assistance of a number of prominent performing arts centres in the Asia Pacific region
Country: Singapore
Social Media: www.facebook.com/AssociationofAsia-PacificPerformingArtsCentres

Association of Asia Pacific Performing Arts Centres (AAPPAC)
Website: www.aappac.net
Email: aappac@esplanade.com
Phone: 682 88341
Address: 1 Esplanade Drive, SG
Information: a network of 75 members from over 20 countries, comprising prominent performing arts centres in the Asia-Pacific region as its full members, as well as internationally reputable arts venues, organisations and associations as our Peak Business Circle and Business Circle Representatives. AAPPAC was established in 1996 to establish the Asia Pacific region as a leader in the performing arts industry; promote the exchange of Artistic programmes in arts centres; foster closer ties and better understanding amongst the people of the region; establish and provide an information network for arts centres and fostering development and growth of technical, administrative and management skills and expertise available within the region
Country: Singapore
Social Media: www.facebook.com/AssociationofAsia-PacificPerformingArtsCentres

Federation for Asian Cultural Promotion (FACP)
Website: www.facp.asia
Email: info@facp.asia
Address: International
Information: The Federation for Asian Cultural Promotion (FACP) is an association for individuals or corporations who are involved or interested in the performing arts. FACP is a non-profit, non-political organization which works to promote networks for performing arts Managers in the region and to foster understanding of the rich cultural heritage of Asia around the world.
Country: Singapore
Contact: CHAIRMAN – Kuala Lumpur JOE ROSLI SIDEK
Social Media: www.facebook.com/FACP.ORG/twitter.com/FacpAsia www.instagram.com/facpasia/

International Confederation of Societies of Authors & Composers (CISAC)
Website: www.cisac.org
Email: ang_kt@cisacap.com.sg
Phone: 622 55025
Address: Regional Office Asia-Pacific, 77A Duxton Road, SG
Country: Singapore
Social Media: @CISACNews

Istituto Italiano di Cultura
Website: www.iicsingapore.esteri.it
Email: iicsingapore@esteri.it
Phone: 633 63705
Address: 43A Beach Road, Level 2, Evershine & Century Complex, SG
Information: The Italian Cultural Institute in Singapore, i.e. Istituto Italiano di Cultura (IIC Singapore) is the official organisation of the Italian government dedicated to the promotion of Italian language and culture. It is a part of a network including more than 80 centres in the world. It has particularly active role in presenting cultural events either on its own either with other cultural institutions in Singapore in various fields like music, visual and performing arts.
Country: Singapore
Social Media: @IICSingapore

Ministry of Information, Communication and Arts (MICA)
Website: www.mica.gov.sg
Email: mica@mica.gov.sg
Phone: 627 07988
Address: 140 Hill Street, #02-02, Mita Bldg., SG
Country: Singapore

National Arts Council
Website: www.nac.gov.sg
Phone: 634 69400
Address: Goodman Arts Centre, 90 Goodman Road, SG
Country: Singapore

SOUTH AFRICA

Department of Arts and Culture of South Africa
Website: www.dac.gov.za
Email: minister@dac.gov.za
Phone: 124 413 000
Address: 10th Floor, Kingsley Centre 481, Stanza Bopape, Cnr Steve Biko & Pretorius Streets Arcadia, ZA
Country: South Africa

eThekwini Municipality
Website: www.durban.gov.za
Email: sizakala@durban.gov.za
Phone: 313 111 111
Address: ZA
Country: South Africa
Social Media: @eThekwiniM www.facebook.com/eThek-winiM

UNISA International Music Competitions
Website: www.unisa.ac.za/musicfoundation
Email: musicomp@unisa.ac.za
Phone: 124 293 344
Address: P.O. Box 392 UNISA, Pretoria 0003, South Africa, ZA
Country: South Africa
Social Media: www.facebook.com/unisamusicfoundation

PROVINCE OF CHINA TAIWAN

Asian Cultural Council Taipei
Website: www.asianculturalcouncil.org
Email: acctw@acctf.com
Phone: 287 718 836
Address: 10F-2, No. 303, , Zhong Xiao East Road, Section 4,
Information: Asian Cultural Council Taiwan Foundation (ACCTF) is a non-profit organisation designed to work with the Asian Cultural Council (ACC) cooperation, the Asian Cultural Council Grants Program in Taiwan
Country: Province of China Taiwan

Council for Cultural Affairs, R.O.C
Website: www.cca.gov.tw
Email: adm@cca.gov.tw
Phone: 223 434 000
Address: No. 30-1, Bei Ping East Road, , Zhong Zheng District,
Information: to promote, co-ordinate and evaluate programs in the R.O.C.
Country: Province of China Taiwan

Ministry of Education – Bureau of International Cultural and Educational Relations
Website: www.edu.tw
Email: moemail@mail.moe.gov.tw
Phone: 277 366 666
Address: 10051 South Zhongshan Road

Information: aims: to develop and imporove global career including to extend to study abroad and the concerns of the whole society in the area of economy, education etc
Country: Province of China Taiwan

Organisation Internationale des Scénographes, Techniciens et Architects de Théâtre
Website: www.oistat.org
Email: headquarters@oistat.org
Phone: 277 260 088
Address: Suite A, 2F, No.7, Sec. 2, Renai Rd
Information: in any one country only one organisation can be a member of OISTAT; the members of each national organisation are automatically members of OISTAT, hence total membership 20, 000 from 36 countries; generates, promotes and maintains a global network of specialist practitioners, educators and researchers who shape, challenge and imagine elements, events and environments for the live performing arts
Country: Province of China Taiwan
Social Media: www.facebook.com/oistat

Pacific Cultural Foundation (PCF)
Website: www.pcf.org.tw
Email: arts@pcf.org.tw
Phone: 223 377 167
Address: No. 38, Chong Ching South Road, , Section 3, , Zhong Zheng District,
Information: mainly for visual arts and performing arts; see also Presenters
Country: Province of China Taiwan

Recording Industry Foundation – RIT (Taiwan IFPI)
Website: www.rit.org.tw
Email: info@ifpi.org.tw
Phone: 271 88818
Address: 3F, 83 BaDe Rd., Sec. 4, Songshan District, Taipei City, Taiwan
Information: The Recording Industry Foundation in Taiwan, or RIT for short, is the representative organization of Taiwan's recording industry and a member of IFPI. The purpose of this association is to assist the national recording industry to export music creations and introduce international music creations to achieve international music and cultural exchanges, and to improve the recording level of domestic music, and to protect the recording and distribution of works.
Country: Province of China Taiwan

Taipei Arts International Association
Website: www.taf.org.tw
Email: office@taia.tw
Phone: 227 728 528
Address: 12F (C), No. 25, , Jen Ai Road Section 4, , Da An District,
Information: With the aim of broadening the landscape of the arts industry, TAIA was founded by Serina Chen, who has received recognition from the European Festivals Association as the head of festivals for her outstanding work in festival curation.
Country: Province of China Taiwan
Contact: founder/Director Serina Chen

THAILAND

UNESCO Asia and Pacific Bureau for Education (1)
Website: www.unescobkk.org
Email: bangkok@unescobkk.org
Phone: 239 10577
Address: PO Box 967, Prahanong Post Office, TH
Country: Thailand

UNESCO Asia and Pacific Bureau for Education (2)
Website: www.unescobkk.org
Email: bangkok@unescobkk.org
Phone: 239 10577
Address: PO Box 967, Prahanong Post Office, TH
Country: Thailand

UNITED ARAB EMIRATES

Department of Culture and Tourism – Abu Dhabi
Website: www.tcaabudhabi.ae
Email: info@dctabudhabi.ae
Phone: 124 440 444
Address: PO Box 94000, Abu Dhabi
Information: The Department of Culture and Tourism conserves and promotes the heritage and culture of Abu Dhabi emirate and leverages them in the development of a world-class, sustainable destination of distinction, which enriches the lives of visitors and residents alike.
Country: United Arab Emirates
Social Media: facebook.com/DCTAbuDhabi/twitter.com/dctabudhabiinstagram.com/dctabudhabi/

UNITED STATES

West Virginia Department of Arts, Culture and History
Website: www.wvculture.org
Phone:
045 580 220

Address: 1900 Kanawha Blvd E Charleston, WV 25305, US
Information: The mission of the West Virginia Department of Arts, Culture and History is to identify, preserve, protect, promote and present the ideas, arts and artifacts of West Virginia's heritage.
Country: United States
Social Media: facebook.com/wvdach

Arts & Science Council – Culture For All
Website: www.artsandscience.org
Email: asc@artsandscience.org
Phone: 043 332 272
Address: 222 S. Church St., Suite 300, Charlotte, NC 28202, US
Information: ASC serves as the designated "Office of Cultural Resources" for the City of Charlotte, Mecklenburg County, and six suburban towns by providing advocacy, cultural education programs, cultural planning, fundraising, grant making, public art and workshops and trainings for the cultural community.
Country: United States
Contact: Acting President Krista Terrell
Email: krista.terrell@artsandscience.org
Phone: 043 353 034Special Assistant to the President Ann Parker
Email: ann.parker@artsandscience.org
Phone: 043 353 059Chief Financial Officer Nina Schultz
Email: nina.schultz@artsandscience.org
Phone: 043 353 031Director of Operations Bonnie Carter
Email: bonnie.carter@artsandscience.org
Phone: 043 353 046Director of Database Management Shameeka Henderson
Email: shameeka.henderson@artsandscience.org
Phone: 043 353 049Staff Accountant Melissa Huskins
Email: melissa.huskins@artsandscience.org
Phone: 043 353 268Finance Assistant Antwane Folk
Email: antwane.folk@artsandscience.org
Phone: 043 353 045
Social Media: facebook.com/asccharlottetwitter.com/asccharlotteinstagram.com/asccharlotte

City of Detroit Parks & Recreation Department
Website: www.detroitmi.gov/recreation
Email: detroitrecreation@detroitmi.gov
Phone: 132 241 100
Address: 18100 Meyers Rd Detroit, MI, US
Information: Detroit Parks & Recreation (DPRD) provides recreation and leisure activities for all who live, work and play in Metro Detroit. With 309 parks and 11 recreation centers, DPRD connects communities with parks, programs and facilities to positively impact their health and wellness.
Country: United States
Social Media: facebook.com/DetroitParksRec/twitter.com/detroitparksrecinstagram.com/detroitparksrec/
Offers/Grants: true

Division of Cultural Affairs – Florida Department of State
Website: www.dos.myflorida.com/cultural/
Email: dcainfo@dos.myflorida.com
Phone: 502 456 470
Address: 500 S Bronough St Tallahassee, FL 32399, US
Information: The Mission of the Florida Department of State, Division of Cultural Affairs is to advance, support, and promote arts and culture to strengthen the economy and quality of life for all Floridians.
Country: United States
Contact: Division Director Sandy Shaughnessy
Phone: 502 456 480Operations Management Consultant II Curtis Young
Phone: 502 456 337Chief of Grants Administration Teri Abstein
Phone: 502 456 299Arts Consultant Rachelle Ashmore
Phone: 502 456 490Grants Specialist IV Summer Callahan
Phone: 502 456 482Arts Consultant Danila Coppola
Phone: 502 456 431Arts Consultant Hillary Crawford
Phone: 502 456 462Arts Consultant Michelle Smith Grindberg
Phone: 502 456 475Administrative Assistant III Suzanne Lucas
Phone: 502 454 298Grant Specialist V Christopher Orr
Phone: 502 456 483Arts Consultant Sarah Stage
Phone: 502 456 459Grant Specialist II Stephanie Walton
Phone: 502 456 494
Social Media: facebook.com/FLCulturalAffairs/twitter.com/CultureBuildsFL
Offers/Grants: true

PA Council on the Arts
Website: www.arts.pa.gov
Email: RA-arts@pa.gov
Phone: 177 876 883
Address: 216 Finance Building Harrisburg, PA 17120, US
Information: PCA, a PA state agency, established in 1966, accomplishes its mission through a combination of grants to the arts; partnerships and initiatives; technical assistance to partners and applicants; and serving as a resource for arts-related information for state, federal, and local government, the public, other funding entities, the arts field, and other interested organizations and individuals.
Country: United States
Contact: Executive Director Karl Blischke

Email: kablischke@pa.gov
Phone: 177 871 530Deputy Executive Director Heather Doughty
Email: hdoughty@pa.gov
Phone: 177 871 517
Chief of Creative Catalysts & Lifelong Learning Jamie Dunlap
Email: jadunlap@pa.gov
Phone: 175 255 542
Chief of Finance & Administration Amy Gabriele
Email: agabriele@pa.gov
Phone: 175 255 547
Director of External Affairs & Public Awareness Norah Johnson
Email: norajohnso@pa.gov
Phone: 175 255 549Executive Secretary Laura Kline
Email: laurakline@pa.gov
Phone: 174 257 600Director of Creative Communities Sarah Merritt
Email: skmerritt@pa.gov
Phone: 177 871 521
Director of DEI Initiatives, Diverse Cultures & Heritage Dana Payne
Email: danpayne@pa.gov
Phone: 175 255 544
Director of Data Systems & Creative Services Seth Poppy
Email: spoppy@pa.gov
Phone: 177 871 520Grants Liaison Ian Rosario
Email: irosario@pa.gov
Phone: 175 255 548
Social Media: facebook.com/Pennsylvaniacouncilonthearts/
Offers/Grants: true

Actors' Equity Association
Website: www.actorsequity.org
Email: info@actorsequity.org
Phone: 128 698 530
Address: 165 West 46th Street New York, NY 10036, US
Information: Actors' Equity Association, founded in 1913, represents more than 51, 000 professional Actors and Stage Managers nationwide. Equity seeks to foster the art of live theatre as an essential component of society and advances the careers of its members by negotiating wages, improving working conditions and providing a wide range of benefits including health and pension plans. Actors' Equity is a member of the AFL-CIO and is affiliated with FIA, an international organization of performing arts unions.
Country: United States
Social Media: facebook.com/ActorsEquity/twitter.com/ActorsEquity/media

American Composers Forum
Website: www.composersforum.org
Email: mail@composersforum.org
Phone: 651 228 1407
Address: 332 Minnesota Street, Suite East 145, US
Information: the Forum's 2, 000 members include composers and performers, presenters, organisations, individuals and institutions
Country: United States
Social Media: @ComposersForum www.facebook.com/pages/American-Composers-Forum/52335075016

American Dance Abroad
Website: americandanceabroad.org
Email: americandanceabroad@gmail.com
Phone: 412 422 1864
Address: 156-08 Riverside Drive West #3B, US
Information: the primary focus is to provide services and resources to U.S. – based artists engaged in international exchange by facilitating relationship building with international colleagues. Objectives: Promote American dance abroad at global marketplaces, festivals and international convenings; provide support and resources that better enable choreographers and Artistic Directors to expand their relationships with foreign colleagues; provide support and resources that will enable foreign colleague to see American dance. Member of ISPA

Country: United States
Social Media: www.facebook.com/AmericanDanceAbroad

American Friends of the Israel Philharmonic Orchestra
Website: www.afipo.org
Email: info@afipo.org
Phone: 126 972 949
Address: 122 East 42nd Street, Suite 4507, New York, NY, United States, New York
Information: The Israel Philharmonic Orchestra (IPO) is the leading orchestra in Israel and globally recognized as a world class symphonic ensemble. Founded in 1936 by famed Polish violinist Bronislaw Huberman, the IPO performs regularly in its home, the Charles Bronfman Auditorium in Tel Aviv, as well as across Israel, including Jerusalem and Haifa. Additionally, it tours internationally, from Europe to Asia to North and South America.

Country: United States
Executive Vice President & CEO DANIELLE AMES SPIVAK
Email: CEO@AFIPO.ORG
Phone: Chief Financial Officer CATHERINE LOU
Email: FINANCE@AFIPO.ORG
Phone: Executive Director, West Coast JUSTIN PRESSMAN
Email: WCDIRECTOR@AFIPO.ORG
Phone: Executive Director, Eastern Region MAAYAN DAUBER
Email: ECDIRECTOR@AFIPO.ORG
Phone: Development and Executive Assistant BETH ANN BARLOW
Email: INFO@AFIPO.ORG
Phone: Development and Event Associate LILACH CARMI
Email: EVENTASSOC@AFIPO.ORG
Social Media: facebook.com/afipotwitter.com/amfriendsipoinstagram.com/amfriendsipo/

American Guild of Musical Artists
Website: www.musicalartists.org
Email: AGMA@MusicalArtists.org
Phone: 212 265 3687
Address: 1430 Broadway, 14th floor, US
Information: an organisation formed to protect the interests of American opera, choral and dance artists
Country: United States
Social Media: @AGMusicalArtist www.facebook.com/AmericanGuildofMusicalArtists

American Pianists Association
Website: www.americanpianists.org
Email: apainfo@americanpianists.org
Phone: 317 940 9945
Address: 4603 Clarendon Rd Ste 30 Indianapolis, IN 46208 USA
Information: The APA is a national, not-for-profit organization which has flourished because of its Artistic reputation for selecting uniquely talented fellows and producing high-calibre performances across the globe. The mission of the American Pianists Association is to discover, promote and advance the careers of young, American, world-class jazz and classical pianists. We celebrate the beauty of music through America's premier jazz and classical awards.
Country: United States
Artistic Director & President/CEO Joel Harrison
Email: joel@americanpianists.org
Phone: 317 940 9947General Manager Joanne Bennett
Email: joanne@americanpianists.org
Phone: 317 940 9943Director of development Lee Ann Smith
Email: leeann@americanpianists.org
Phone: 317 940 9371Director of Marketing Lee Clifford
Email: lee@americanpianists.org
Phone: 317 940 9334Development Associate Greg Porter
Email: greg@americanpianists.org
Phone: 317 940 8198Artistic Administrator Milner Fuller
Email: milner@americanpianists.org
Phone: 317 940 8445Media Specialist Daniel McCullough
Email: daniel@americanpianists.org
Phone: 317 940 9944
Social Media: www.facebook.com/APApianists www.twitter.com/APApianists www.instagram.com/apapianists/

American Society of Composers, Authors and Publishers (ASCAP)
Website: www.ascap.com
Email: info@ascap.com
Address: 1 Lincoln Plaza, US
Information: a membership association of more than 470, 000 US composers, songwriters, lyricists and music publishers of every kind of music
Country: United States
Social Media: @Ascap www.facebook.com/ascap

American String Teachers Association
Website: www.astaweb.com
Email: asta@astaweb.com
Phone: 703 279 2113
Address: American String Teachers Association, 4155 Chain Bridge Road, US
Information: membership organisation; founded more than 60 years ago, The American String Teachers Association is a membership organisation for string and orchestra teachers and players
Country: United States
Social Media: @ASTAweb www.facebook.com/AstaAmerica?fref=ts

ArKtype
Website: www.arktype.org
Email: info@arktype.org
Phone: 173 865 468
Address: P.O. Box 180241, Brooklyn, NY 11215, US
Information: ArKtype is recognized as among the industry's leading supporters of new, experimental work. Established in 2005 by Producer Thomas O. Kriegsmann to support the finest in emerging and established artists based in NYC and worldwide, they support risk in live performance, creating an ever-shifting mechanism for the fulfillment of artists' visions for new work

Country: United States
Contact: President Thomas Kriegsmann
Email: tommy@arktype.org
Social Media: facebook.com/ArKtypeBK/twitter.com/ArKtype

Arts Council New Orleans
Website: www.artsneworleans.org
Email: joycelyn@artsneworleans.org
Phone: 504 523 1465
Address: 1307 Oretha Castle Haley Blvd, US
Information: The Arts Council New Orleans is a private, nonprofit organization dedicated to supporting arts and culture in the city and demonstrating how art transforms communities.
Working in partnership with the City of New Orleans, community groups, and other nonprofit organizations, they work to elevate their arts ecosystem, expand and create opportunities for diverse Artistic exPression, and bring the community together through programming and events that celebrate their rich multicultural heritage.
Country: United States
Social Media: https://twitter.com/ArtsNewOrleans www.instagram.com/artsneworleans/

Arts Council of Indianapolis
Website: www.indyarts.org
Email: indyarts@indyarts.org
Phone: 317 631 3301
Address: 924 N Pennsylvania St Indianapolis, IN
Information: The Arts Council is an organization that advocates for the need and importance of broad community funding and support for a thriving arts scene; innovates by constantly pursuing and promoting innovative ideas and programs that better serve the area, its artists, and arts organizations; and connects artists, audiences, businesses, foundations, and arts and cultural organizations with opportunities to explore and expand central Indiana's creative vitality.
Country: United States
President & CEO
 Julie Goodman
Email: jgoodman@indyarts.org
Phone: 317 631 3301
Vice President, Artist Engagement & Director of Gallery 924
 Shannon Linker
Email: slinker@indyarts.org
Phone: 317 631 3301
Vice President, Community Impact & Investment
 Ernest Disney-Britton
Email: ebritton@indyarts.org
Phone: 317 631 3301
Social Media: facebook.com/artscouncilindy/twitter.com/artscouncilindyinstagram.com/artscouncilindy/

Arts Council of Oklahoma City
Website: www.artscouncilokc.com
Email: info@artscouncilokc.com
Phone: 405 270 4848
Address: 400 West California, US
Information: Founded in 1967 with the Festival of the Arts, the Arts Council of Oklahoma City has grown to present year-round performances and events to connect the community with the arts. In addition, the organization provides arts education and outreach activities to underserved populations in Oklahoma City.
Country: United States
Contact: EXECUTIVE DIRECTOR Peter Dolese
Phone: ALL ACCESS ARTS COORDINATOR Nick Caudle
Phone: ALL ACCESS ARTS DIRECTOR Jillian Coker
Phone: COMMUNICATIONS DIRECTOR Alonna Dray
Phone: OFFICE MANAGER /DEVELOPMENT ASSISTANT Lindsay Fritts-Koskie
Phone: DEVELOPMENT COORDINATOR / EXECUTIVE ASSISTANT Kristin Frosco
Phone: ART MOVES DIRECTOR / OUT OF THE BOX COORDINATOR Chase Kerby
Phone: FESTIVAL OF THE ARTS DIRECTOR Seth Lewis
Phone: FINANCE ASSISTANT Constance Lindley
Phone: FESTIVAL OF THE ARTS ASSISTANT Laurena Sherrill
Phone: FINANCE DIRECTOR Marie Smith
Social Media: https:// www.facebook.com/ArtsCouncilOKC https://twitter.com/artscouncilokc?lang=en https:// www.instagram.com/artscouncilokc/

ArtsMemphis
Website: www.artsmemphis.org
Email: info@artsmemphis.org
Phone: 015 782 787
Address: 575 S Mendenhall Rd Memphis, TN 38117, US
Information: ArtsMemphis sustains Memphis' world-renowned cultural vitality and strengthens local communities through the arts. Founded by volunteer community leaders in 1963.
Country: United States
Contact: Director of Marketing and Donor Engagement Josie Ballin
Email: jballin@artsmemphis.org
Phone: 013 410 401
Grants & Initiatives Manager
Colleen Chandler

Email: cchandler@artsmemphis.org
Phone: 013 410 403Chief Operating Officer Tracy Lauritzen Wright
Email: tlauritzenwright@artsmemphis.org
Phone: 013 410 407Chief Financial Officer Ellen Lester
Email: elester@artsmemphis.org
Phone: 013 410 404
Development & Operation Coordinator
 Kelsea Lewis
Email: klewis@artsmemphis.org
Phone: 015 782 787
President & Chief Executive Officer
 Elizabeth Rouse
Email: erouse@artsmemphis.org
Phone: 013 410 410
Social Media: facebook.com/artsmemphistwitter.com/artsmemphisinstagram.com/artsmemphis

Asia Society
Website: www.asiasociety.org
Email: info@asiasociety.org
Phone: 212 288 6400
Address: Asia Society and Museum, 725 Park Avenue, 70th Street, US
Information: Asia Society is an organisation dedicated to promoting partnerships among people, leaders and institutions of Asia and the United States. Member of ISPA
Country: United States
Contact: President Kevin Rudd
Social Media: https://twitter.com/AsiaSociety www.facebook.com/asiasociety

Asian Cultural Council
Website: www.asianculturalcouncil.org
Email: acc@accny.org
Phone: 128 430 403
Address: 333 West 39th Street, Suite 1502 New York, NY 10018, US
Information: The Asian Cultural Council is a nonprofit foundation that provides opportunities for international cultural exchange to artists, scholars, and arts professionals in Asia and the United States. Through fellowships, grants, achievement awards, public programs, alumni engagement, and other cultural exchange initiatives, ACC aims to build global arts communities whose individual and collective work serves to advance international understanding and respect.
Country: United States
Social Media: www.facebook.com/asianculturalcouncil/twitter.com/accny www.instagram.com/asianculturalcouncil/
Offers/Grants: true

Association of Fundraising Professionals – International Conference
Website: www.afpglobal.org
Email: afp@afpglobal.org
Phone: 703 684 0410
Address: 4300 Wilson Blvd, Suite 300, Arlington, VA 22203
Information: The Association of Fundraising Professionals empowers individuals and organizations to practice ethical fundraising through professional education, networking, research and advocacy.
Country: United States
Social Media: www.facebook.com/AFPFan/ www.twitter.com/afpihq

Austin Parks and Recreation Department
Website: www.austintexas.gov/department/parks-and-recreation
Phone: 512 974 6700
Address: 200 S. Lamar Blvd. Austin, US
Information: The Austin Parks and Recreation Department has been the steward of the City of Austin's public lands since 1928. As such, it protects and maintains parkland and its urban forest. Preserves trails and offers a variety of sports, recreation, educational enrichment, arts programs, cultural opportunities, nature and aquatic activities.
Country: United States
Social Media: https:// www.facebook.com/AustinCityParks https://twitter.com/austincityparks https://instagram.com/austincityparks

Australian Consulate
Website: www.usa.embassy.gov.au/new-york
Phone:
123 516 500
Address: 150 E 42nd St (34th Floor), New York, NY, 10017, US
Information: The Australian Embassy and Consulates-General advances Australia's foreign policy, security, international development, trade, investment and business interests in the United States and fosters a strong partnership between the governments and people of Australia and the United States. The Embassy promotes Australian culture and offers passport and consular services to Australian citizens living in or visiting the United States.
Country: United States
Social Media: facebook.com/australianconsulateGeneralnyc/twitter.com/ausintheusinstagram.com/ausintheus

Broadcast Music, Inc. (BMI)
Website: www.bmi.com
Email: newyork@bmi.com
Phone: 122 203 000
Address: 7 World Trade Center 250 Greenwich Street New York, NY 10007, US
Information: BMI was founded in 1939 by forward-thinkers who wanted to represent songwriters in emerging genres, like jazz, blues and country, and protect the public performances of their music. Operating on a non-profit-making basis, BMI is now the largest music rights organization in the U.S. and is still nurturing new talent and new music.
Country: United States
Social Media: facebook.com/broadcastmusicinctwitter.com/bmiinstagram.com/bmi

Business Committee for the Arts Inc. (BCA)
Website: www.americansforthearts.org/about-americans-for-the-arts/business-committee-for-the-arts
Email: bca@artsusa.org
Phone: 212 223 2787
Address: 1 East 53rd St New York, US
Information: Founded in 1967 by David Rockefeller, Business Committee for the Arts (BCA) encourages, inspires, and stimulates businesses to support the arts in the workplace, in education, and in the community. The BCA committee provides leadership on key initiatives including messaging, advocacy, and strategic alliances within the private-sector community.
Country: United States

California Arts Council
Website: arts.ca.gov
Email: info@arts.ca.gov
Phone: 916 322 6555
Address: 1300 I Street, Suite 930, US
Information: At the California Arts Council, it's their mission to strengthen arts, culture, and creative exPression as the tools to cultivate a better California for all. They support local arts infrastructure and activities statewide through grants, programs, and services.
Country: United States
Contact: Executive Director Anne Bown-Crawford
Email: anne.bown.crawford@arts.ca.gov
Phone: 916 322 6335Deputy Director Ayanna Kiburi
Email: ayanna.kiburi@arts.ca.gov
Phone: 916 322 6376
Social Media: www.facebook.com/californiaartscouncil/twitter.com/calartscouncil www.instagram.com/calartscouncil/
Offers/Grants: true

City of Seattle Office of Arts & Cultural Affairs
Website: www.seattle.gov/arts
Email: arts.culture@seattle.gov
Phone: 668 47171
Address: 303 S. Jackson Street, Top Floor, Seattle, WA , 98104
Information: The Office of Arts & Culture promotes the value of arts and culture in, and of, communities throughout Seattle. It strives to ensure that a wide range of high-quality Artistic experiences are available to everyone, encourage artist-friendly arts and cultural policy, and promote Seattle as a cultural destination. The Office is a resource for the entire City, focusing on the artist, the creative life of the community, and the next generation.
Country: United States
Contact: Acting Director Calandra Childers
Email: Calandra.Childers@seattle.gov
Phone: 668 47306Executive Assistant Allie Lee
Email: allie.lee@seattle.gov
Phone: 673 39378Communications Manager Erika Lindsay
Email: erika.lindsay@seattle.gov
Phone: 668 44337Digital Media Specialist Ronald Bolisay
Email: otts.bolisay@seattle.gov
Phone: 673 39591Events Coordinator Jenny Ku
Email: jenny.ku@seattle.gov
Phone: 668 44186
Social Media: facebook.com/SeattleArts/instagram.com/seaoffiCEOfarts/twitter.com/SeattleArts/

Cityfest Wilmington
Website: www.cityfestwilm.com
Email: cityfest@wilmingtonde.gov
Phone: 025 762 136
Address: 800 N French St Wilmington, DE 19801, US
Information: Cityfest, Inc., a 501(c)(3) tax-exempt corporation, solicits sponsorships and grants that subsidize the City of Wilmington's financial and staffing contributions. It uses funding to improve the quality of life for citizens of Wilmington, primarily through cultural and arts programming; promoting economic development; promoting City life; and all other charitable purposes.
Country: United States
Social Media: www.facebook.com/CityfestWilm/
Offers/Grants: true

Classical Action: Performing Arts Against AIDS
Website: www.classicalaction.org
Email: classicalaction@broadwaycares.org
Phone: 129 977 717

Address: 165 W 46th St, Ste 1300 New York, NY 10036, US
Information: Founded in 1993, Classical Action: Performing Arts Against AIDS draws upon the talents, resources and generosity of the classical, opera and jazz communities to raise money for those battling HIV/AIDS and other critical illnesses. Classical Action helps provide access to life-saving medications, health care, counseling, nutritious meals and emergency financial assistance to men, women and children across the country.
Country: United States
Social Media: facebook.com/classicalaction/twitter.com/classicalaction/

Conductors Guild
Website: www.conductorsguild.org
Email: guild@conductorsguild.org
Phone: 026 434 791
Address: 15 E. Market Street, #22 Leesburg, VA 20178, US
Information: The International Conductors Guild is the only international nonprofit organization dedicated to the art and profession of music conducting. The Guild's overall goal is to enhance the professionalism of conductors by serving as a clearing house for knowledge and information regarding the art and practice of conducting; further, to support the Artistic growth of orchestras, bands, choruses and other conducted ensembles.
Country: United States
Contact: Executive Director Jan Wilson
Email: guild@conductorsguild.org

Connecticut Department of Economic and Community Development
Website: www.ct.gov
Email: decd@ct.gov
Phone: 860 500 2300
Address: 450 Columbus Blvd #5, US
Information: The state offers grants and programs to enhance the state's art scene, upgrade and promote tourist destinations identify and preserve historic properties, and educate the public about Connecticut's history and tourism sites. Connecticut invests in artists and arts organizations and encourages the public's participation as creators, learners, supporters and audience members. Training and professional development is also provided.
Country: United States
Contact: Director of Arts, Preservation and Museums Elizabeth Shapiro
Email: Elizabeth.Shapiro@ct.gov
Phone: 860 500 2360Program Specialist, Art in Public Spaces Tamara Dimitri
Email: Tamara.Dimitri@ct.gov
Phone: 860 500 2377Program Associate Kolton Harris
Email: Kolton.Harris@ct.gov
Phone: Senior Program Associate, Arts in Education Bonnie Koba
Email: Bonnie.Koba@ct.gov
Phone: 860 500 2379
Program Associate & Special Projects Coordinator Rhonda Olisky
Email: Rhonda.Olisky@ct.gov
Phone: 860 500 2452Grants Administrator Lourdes "Lu" Rivera
Email: Lu.Rivera@ct.gov
Phone: 860 500 2332Administrative Assistant Jane Schneider
Email: Jane.Schneider@ct.gov
Phone: 860 500 2393
Social Media: www.facebook.com/CTDECD/twitter.com/CTDECD
Offers/Grants: true

Cultural Council of Greater Jacksonville
Website: www.culturalcouncil.org
Email: info@culturalcouncil.org
Phone: 904 358 3600
Address: 40 East Adams Street Jacksonville, US
Information: The Cultural Council of Greater Jacksonville champions the appreciation, relevance and exPression of art and culture. The council leads individuals and families, artists and organizations, businesses and government to unique collaborations that establish art and culture as a key driver of Jacksonville's economy, growth, and quality of life.
Country: United States
Contact: EXECUTIVE DIRECTOR Diana Donovan
Email: Diana@CulturalCouncil.org
Phone: DIRECTOR OF GRANTS ADMINISTRATION Amy Palmer
Email: amy@culturalcouncil.org
Phone: 904 358 3614INTERIM DIRECTOR OF PUBLIC ART PROGRAMS Jen Jones Murray
Email: jen@culturalcouncil.org
Phone: 904 358 3612PUBLIC ART PROJECT MANAGER Hilda Ettedgui
Email: hilda@CulturalCouncil.org
Phone: 904 358 3613OPERATIONS COORDINATOR Ashanta Williamson
Email: ashanta@culturalcouncil.org
Phone: 904 358 3621PUBLIC ART PROGRAM COORDINATOR Ashley Wolfe
Email: Ashley@CulturalCouncil.org
Phone: 904 358 3620COMMUNICATION AND PUBLIC ENGAGEMENT COORDINATOR Ellen Cottrill
Email: ellen@culturalcouncil.org

Phone: 904 358 3611
Social Media: https://facebook.com/moreartculture https://twitter.com/moreartculture https://instagram.com/moreartculture

CulturePath
Website: culturepath.com
Email: hello@culturepath.com
Phone: 650 391 7723
Address: 302A West 12th Street, Suite 205, US
Information: CulturePath is a collaborative presenting platform for the arts. Member of ISPA
Country: United States
Social Media: @culturepath www.facebook.com/culturepath

Department of Arts and Cultural Affairs, City of San Antonio
Website: www.sanantonio.gov/art
Email: sarah.wates@sanantonio.gov
Phone: 210 222 2787
Address: Office of Cultural Affairs, PO Box 839966, US
Country: United States

Department of Cultural Affairs and Special Events
Website: www.cityofchicago.org/dcase
Email: dcase@cityofchicago.org
Phone: 127 443 316
Address: 78 E Washington St Chicago, IL 60602, US
Information: The Department of Cultural Affairs and Special Events (DCASE) is dedicated to enriching Chicago's Artistic vitality and cultural vibrancy. This includes fostering the development of Chicago's non-profit arts sector, independent working artists and for-profit arts businesses.
Country: United States
Social Media: facebook.com/ChicagoDCASE/twitter.com/chicagodcaseinstagram.com/chicagodcase/

Department: Arts and Cultural Affairs – City of Newark
Website: www.newarknj.gov/departments/arts-and-cultural-affairs
Email: shakurf@ci.newark.nj.us
Phone: 737 337 451
Address: City Hall 920 Broad Street Newark, NJ 07102, US
Information: The Division of Arts and Cultural Affairs is the catalyst for participation, education, collaboration and development to encourage and support excellence in the arts within the City of Newark.
Country: United States
Contact: Arts and Cultural Affairs Director Fayemi Shakur
Email: shakurf@ci.newark.nj.us
Phone: 737 337 451

Division of Recreation's Bureau of Cultural Arts – City of Cleveland
Website: www.city.cleveland.oh.us
Phone: 216 664 2562
Address: Cleveland City Hall 601 Lakeside Ave, Us
Information: The Division of Recreation's Bureau of Cultural Arts provides active recreational opportunities and cultural experiences in art and performance art for all ages and interest groups. Roving art instructors develop and teach a variety of arts including Arts & Crafts, Airbrush, Dance and Ceramics.
Country: United States
Social Media: https://www.facebook.com/CityofCleveland/ https://twitter.com/cityofcleveland https://www.instagram.com/CityofCleveland/

Georgia Council for the Arts
Website: www.gaarts.org
Email:
gaarts@gaarts.org
Phone: 404 962 4000
Address: 75 Fifth Street, NW, Suite 1200, US
Information: Georgia Council for the Arts is a division of the Georgia Department of Economic Development that provides support for nonprofit arts organizations throughout the state. The mission of Georgia Council for the Arts is to cultivate the growth of vibrant, thriving Georgia communities through the arts.
Country: United States
Contact: Executive Director Tina Lilly
Email: tlilly@gaarts.org
Phone: 404 962 4827Grants Administrative Coordinator Delilah Johnson-Brown
Email: dbrown@gaarts.org
Phone: 404 962 4837Arts Education Manager Allen Bell
Email: abell@gaarts.org
Phone: 404 962 4839Sr. Communications Specialist Emily Murray
Email: emurray@georgia.org
Phone: 404 962 4078
Social Media: facebook.com/GeorgiaCouncilfortheArts/

Grantmakers in the Arts
Website: www.giarts.org
Email: gia@giarts.org
Phone:
929 452 3740
Address: 522 Courtlandt Avenue, 1st Floor, Bronx, US

Information: The mission of Grantmakers in the Arts (GIA) is to provide leadership and service to advance the use of philanthropic resources on behalf of arts and culture. GIA is the only national association of private and public funders making grants to artists and arts organizations in America. GIA's strength is in its diversity of members: private, family, community and corporate foundations, national, state and local governmental agencies, nonprofit national, regional and local service organizations.
Country: United States
Web & Knowledge Manager
Steve Cline
Email: steve@giarts.org
Communications & Publications Manager
Carmen Graciela Díaz
Email: carmen@giarts.org
Vice President & Director of Programs
Nadia Elokdah
Email: nadia@giarts.org
Phone: Senior Development Manager Sylvia Jung
Email: sylvia@giarts.org
Director of Finance & Operations
Champ Knecht
Email: champ@giarts.org
Program & Administrative Assistant
George Marfo II
Email: george@giarts.org
Phone: Program Manager Sherylynn Sealy
Email: sherylynn@giarts.org
President & CEO
Eddie Torres
Email: eddie@giarts.org
Phone: Development Associate Zoë Williams
Email: zoe@giarts.org
Social Media: https://www.facebook.com/GrantmakersArts https://twitter.com/GIArts https://www.instagram.com/grantmakersinthearts/

Greater Columbus Arts Council
Website: www.gcac.org
Phone: 142 242 606
Address: 182 E. Long St. Columbus OH 43215, US
Information: The Greater Columbus Arts Council (Arts Council) funds artists and arts organizations and provides Marketing services that support artists and organizations through the ColumbusMakesArt.com event calendar and Artist Directory.
Country: United States
Contact: President Tom Katzenmeyer
Email: tkatzenmeyer@gcac.org
Phone: 142 218 738Executive Assistant Sue Jones
Email: sjones@gcac.org
Phone: 142 218 667
VP Marketing Communications & Events
Jami Goldstein
Email: jgoldstein@gcac.org
Phone: 142 218 492
Marketing, Communications & Events Strategist
Lacey Luce
Email: lluce@gcac.org
Phone: 142 218 691
Marketing, Communications & Events Administrator
Nick Dekker
Email: nick@ohioeventfinder.com
Phone: 142 218 626
Social Media: facebook.com/GCACCbus/twitter.com/GCAC_cbus

Hawaii State Foundation on Culture and the Arts
Website: www.sfca.hawaii.gov
Email: hawaiisfca@hawaii.gov
Phone: 085 860 300
Address: 250 S Hotel St Fl 2 Honolulu, HI 96813, US
Information: The Hawai'i State Foundation on Culture and the Arts is a government agency, established by the Hawai'i State Legislature in 1965, to promote, perpetuate, preserve and encourage culture and the arts, history and the humanities as central to the quality of life of the people of Hawai'i. HSFCA funding is provided by the State of Hawai'i and the National Endowment for the Arts.
Country: United States
Social Media: facebook.com/hawaiisfca/twitter.com/hawaii_sfcainstagram.com/hawaii_sfca/
Offers/Grants: true

Honolulu Mayor's Office of Culture and the Arts
Website: www.honolulu.gov/moca
Email: moca-info@honolulu.gov
Phone: 808 768 6622
Address: 550 South King Street, 2nd Floor, US
Information: Founded in 1971. The mission of MOCA is to promote the value of arts and culture throughout communities in the City and County of Honolulu. Guided by the belief and affirmation of cultural self-determination, MOCA works as a partner and catalyst for increasing opportunities, awareness and involvement in cultural activities for the benefit of all. In this capacity, MOCA administers the Art in City Buildings Program, culture and Arts Programs, and a Collaborative Arts Program.
Country: United States
Social Media: facebook.com/HonoluluMOCA

Houston Arts Alliance
Website: www.houstonartsalliance.com/
Email: INFO@HAATX.COM
Phone: 135 279 330
Address: 5280 Caroline St, Suite 100 Houston, TX 77004, US
Information: Houston Arts Alliance (HAA) is a local arts and culture organization whose principal work is to implement the City of Houston's vision, values, and goals for its arts grantmaking and civic art investments. HAA's work is conducted through contracts with the City of Houston, overseen by the Mayor's Office of Cultural Affairs.
In short, HAA helps artists and nonprofits be bold, productive, and strong.
Country: United States
Contact: Chief Executive Officer JOHN ABODEELY
Phone: 135 279 114Manager, Executive Office AHRIF SARUMI
Email: ahrif@haatx.com
Phone: 135 279 114
Social Media: facebook.com/houstonartsalliance/twitter.com/haatx/instagram.com/houstonartsalliance/

Illinois Arts Council Agency
Website: arts.illinois.gov
Email: iac.info@illinois.gov
Phone: 312 814 6750
Address: 100 W Randolph St Ste 10-500 Chicago, IL, US
Information: IACA was created as a state agency by the Illinois General Assembly in 1965. IACA is governed by a Council of private citizens appointed by the Governor who are charged with developing the state's public arts policy, fostering quality culturally diverse programs, and approving grants expenditures. Resources to support the Illinois Arts Council Agency are provided by the Governor and General Assembly of Illinois and the National Endowment of the Arts.
Country: United States
Contact: Executive Director Joshua Davis-Ruperto
Email: joshua.davis@illinois.gov
Phone: 312 814 6758Deputy Director Encarnacion Teruel
Email: encarnacion.teruel@illinois.gov
Phone: 312 814 4991Chief Fiscal Officer Yazoo Hall
Email: yazoo.hall@illinois.gov
Phone: 312 814 6772Executive Assistant Pamela Thomas
Email: pam.thomas@illinois.gov
Phone: 312 814 6794Director of Administration Romie Munoz
Email: romie.munoz@illinois.gov
Phone: 312 814 8250Program Director Teresa Davis
Email: Teresa.N.Davis@illinois.gov
Phone: 312 814 6753Program Representative Jackie Banks-Mahlum
Email: Jackie.Banks-Mahlum@Illinois.gov
Phone: 312 814 4990Accountant Supervisor Sandra Velazquez
Email: Sandra.Velazquez@illinois.gov
Phone: 312 814 4993Director of Grants Management Pius Zacharias
Email: pius.zacharias@illinois.gov
Phone: 312 814 3300Office Specialist Willie Lin
Email: willie.lin@illinois.gov
Phone: 312 814 6070
Social Media: facebook.com/illinoisartscouncilagency/
Offers/Grants: true

International Alliance for Women in Music (IAWM)
Website: www.iawm.org
Address: US
Information: The International Alliance for Women in Music builds awareness of women's contributions to musical life through its publications, website, international competitions, conferences, concert promotion, and presentation, and through its support of entrepreneurial and publishing activities, scholarly research and publications, broadcasts, educational initiatives, and advocacy work.
Country: United States
Social Media: facebook.com/IAWMusic/

International Archive of Jewish Music
Website: jmwc.org/international-archive-of-jewish-music/
Email: zipmusic@bignet.net
Phone: 248 552 0025
Address: c/o Oakland Performing Arts, Inc., 17333 W. Ten Mile Road, Suite B, US
Information: Burton A. Zipser, Director. Located in Southfield, Michigan, the mission of the IAJM is to discover, collect, preserve, and disseminate information about music for adult choirs and instrumental groups of varying sizes.
Country: United States

International Association of Venue Managers (IAVM)
Website: www.IAVM.org
Email: Marketing@iavm.org
Phone:
729 067 441
Address: 635 Fritz Dr, Ste 100 Coppell, TX 75019, US

Information: Representing public assembly venues from around the globe, IAVM's 6, 800+ active members include Managers and senior Executives from auditoriums, arenas, convention centers, exhibit halls, stadiums, performing arts centers, university complexes, amphitheaters and fairgrounds. IAVM's mission is to educate, advocate for, and inspire public assembly venue professionals worldwide.
Country: United States
Contact: President and CEO BRAD MAYNE
Email: brad.mayne@iavm.org
Phone: 725 381 021CFO / COO RONALD MELTON
Email: ronald.melton@iavm.org
Phone: 725 381 034Director of Education MARK HERRERA
Email: Mark.Herrera@iavm.org
Phone: 725 381 005Education Manager GREG WOLFE
Email: greg.wolfe@iavm.org
Phone: 693 714 724Director of Governance/Operations ROSANNE DUKE
Email: rosanne.duke@iavm.org
Phone: 725 381 025Director of Web Development ROB PRICE
Email: rob.price@iavm.org
Phone: 725 381 007Database Manager LORI WEHMER
Email: lori.wehmer@iavm.org
Phone: 725 381 018Research Specialist KAYOUNG KIM
Email: kayoung.kim@iavm.org
Phone: 725 381 001Director of Marketing AMY FITZPATRICK
Email: amy.fitzpatrick@IAVM.org
Phone: 725 381 006Senior Editor R.V. BAUGUS
Email: rv.baugus@IAVM.org
Phone: 725 381 014Creative Services Manager CHUCK POPE
Email: chuck.pope@iavm.org
Phone: 725 381 017
Social Media: facebook.com/IAVMWHQ/twitter.com/IAVMWHQinstagram.com/iavmhq/

International Bluegrass Music Association
Website: www.ibma.org
Email: info@ibma.org
Phone: 152 563 222
Address: 4206 Gallatin Pk Nashville, TN 37216, US
Information: The IBMA is the non-profit music association that connects, educates, and empowers bluegrass professionals and enthusiasts, honoring tradition and encouraging innovation in the bluegrass community worldwide.
Country: United States
Contact: Operations Specialist Ethan Charles
Email: info@ibma.org
Phone: Communications Director Casey Campbell
Email: casey@ibma.org
Phone: Member Services Director Amy Beth Hale
Email: amybeth@ibma.org
Social Media: facebook.com/intlbluegrass/twitter.com/Intlbluegrass

International Clarinet Association
Website: www.clarinet.org
Email: edo@clarinet.org
Phone: 889 835 441
Address: 829 Bethel Road, #216 Columbus, OH 43214, US
Information: The association is dedicated to fostering communication and fellowship of clarinetists on a worldwide basis through publishing a quarterly scholarly journal, The Clarinet, producing an annual clarinet festival, ClarinetFest®, supporting a research library with materials available to all members, and promoting a variety of other endeavors related to the clarinet and clarinet playing.
Country: United States
Contact: EXECUTIVE DIRECTOR OF OPERATIONS JESSICA HARRIE
Email: EDO@clarinet.org
Phone: EDITOR, THE CLARINET RACHEL YODER
Email: editor@clarinet.org
Phone: SOCIAL MEDIA COORDINATOR JENNY MACLAY
Email: assistant@clarinet.org
Phone: ASSOCIATE EDITOR, THE CLARINET EMILY KERSKI
Email: Associateeditor@clarinet.org
Social Media: facebook.com/icaclarinet/twitter.com/icaclarinet/instagram.com/icaclarinet/

International Conference of Symphony & Opera Musicians
Website: www.icsom.org
Address: 505 West Aycock Street, US
Information: ICSOM represents over 4, 000 musicians from 52 major symphony orchestras throughout the United States, and is a Player Conference of the American Federation of Musicians.
One of the missions of ICSOM is to facilitate communication among its member orchestras and among all members of the greater musical community, offering support and assistance wherever needed.
Country: United States
Contact: Chairperson Meredith Snow
Email: meredsnow@gmail.com
Phone: President Paul Austin
Email: AustinLPaul@gmail.com

Phone: Secretary Laura Ross
Email: lar2vln@comcast.net
Social Media: http:// www.facebook.com/ICSOM https://twitter.com/ICSOM

International Double Reed Society
Website: www.idrs.org
Email: support@idrs.org
Phone: 108 710 658
Address: Maryland, US
Information: The International Double Reed Society is a member-based organization made up of professional double reed players, amateurs, hobbyists, university/college instructors, music teachers, institutions, instrument manufacturers, double reed product retailers, reed makers, and enthusiasts.
Country: United States
Contact: President Eric Stomberg
Email: stomberg@idrs.org
Phone: First Vice President Sarah Roper
Email: roper@idrs.org
Phone: Second Vice President Mingjia Liu
Email: Liu@idrs.org
Phone: Secretary Benjamin Coelho
Email: coelho@idrs.org
Phone: At Large Member: Oboe Lora Schaefer
Email: schaefer@idrs.org
Phone: Bassoon Member-At-Large Billy Short
Email: short@idrs.org
Phone: At Large Business Trevor Cramer
Email: cramer@idrs.org
Social Media: facebook.com/idrsofficial/twitter.com/idrsofficialinstagram.com/idrsofficial/

International Federation for Choral Music (IFCM)
Website: www.ifcm.net
Email: office@ifcm.net
Address: 545 Couch Drive, US
Information: The International Federation for Choral Music (IFCM) was founded in 1982 for the purpose of facilitating communication and exchange between choral musicians throughout the world. Through its diverse range of projects and programs since that time, the IFCM is fulfilling its purpose. Also organises World Symposium on Choral Music (see Conferences and Trade Shows).
Country: United States
Contact: OPERATIONS MANAGER Iva Radulovic
Phone: OFFICE MANAGER Nadine Robin
Phone: ICB MANAGING EDITOR Isabelle Métrope
Phone: COMMUNICATION OFFICER João Siva
Social Media: www.facebook.com/IFCMoptwitter.com/IfcmOfficial

International Festivals & Events Association (IFEA)
Website: www.ifea.com
Email: ifea@ifea.com
Phone: 208 433 0950
Address: 2603 W. Eastover Terrace, US
Information: IFEA is The Premier Association Supporting and Enabling Festival & Event Professionals Worldwide. With a target audience that includes all those who produce and support quality celebrations for the benefit of their respective "communities, " the IFEA's primary focus is identifying and providing access to the professional resources and networks that will inspire and enable those in our industry to realize their dreams, build community and sustain success through celebration.
Country: United States
President & CEO, CFEE
Steven Wood Schmader
Phone: 208 433 8180
Vice President Director of Marketing & Communications, CFEE
Nia Forster Hovde
Phone: 208 433 8140
Director of Partnerships, Programs & Finance, CFEE
Kaye Campbell
Phone: 208 433 8150Director of Member Services Beth Petersen
Phone: 208 433 8160
Creative & Publications Director
Craig Sarton
Phone: 208 433 8190CFEE Program Coordinator, CFEE
Cindy Lerick
Phone: 314 614 7152Associate Director of Business Development, CFEE Ira Rosen
Phone: 732 701 9323Associate Director of Business Development, CFEE Penny McBride
Phone: 830 997 5000IFEA Regional Director TFEA Executive Director, CFEE Kay Wolf
Phone: 830 997 0741
Social Media: https:// www.facebook.com/IFEAWorld https://twitter.com/IFEAWorld https:// www.instagram.com/ifeaworld/

International Society for Improvised Music (ISIM)
Website: www.improvisedmusic.org
Email: info@improvisedmusic.org
Phone: 734 926 9403
Address: P.O. Box 1603, Ann Arbor, US
Information: ISIM promotes performance, education, and research in improvised music, illuminating the transformative impact of improvisatory creativity in education

and society at large.
Country: United States
Contact: PRESIDENT ED SARATH
Phone: VICE PRESIDENT JIN HI KIM
Social Media: www.facebook.com/ISIMprov/ www.twitter.com/ISIMprov

International Society for the Performing Arts (ISPA)
Website: www.ispa.org
Email: contact@ispa.org
Phone: 122 068 490
Address: 630 9th Ave New York, NY 10036, US
Information: ISPA is a global network of more than 500 leaders in the performing arts with representation from more than 185 cities and all regions of the globe. ISPA members include facilities, performing arts organizations, artist Managers, festivals, funders, consultants and other professionals working in the performing arts.
Country: United States
Contact: Chief Executive Officer David Baile
Email: dbaile@ispa.org
Phone: 122 068 206
Manager of Membership & Events
 Marissa Oliver
Email: moliver@ispa.org
Phone: 122 068 202Program and Advancement Senior Lead Nora Fleury
Email: nfleury@ispa.org
Phone: 122 068 201Administrator Allegra Levy
Email: alevy@ispa.org
Phone: 122 068 204Communication and Events Lead Kally Zhao
Email: kzhao@ispa.org
Phone: 122 068 205
Social Media: facebook.com/InternationalSocietyforthePerformingArts/twitter.com/ISPA_global

International Tap Association (ITA)
Website: www.tapdance.org
Email: ita@tapdance.org
Phone: 303 443 7989
Address: PO Box 356, US
Country: United States

International Theatre Institute (ITI), United States
Website: www.tcg.org
Email: iti@tcg.org
Phone: 212 609 5900
Address: Theatre Communications Group, , 520 Eighth Avenue, 24th Floor, US
Information: ITI-U.S. assists international theatre professionals and scholars by providing information about American theatre practice, introductions to American theatre professionals, and help in planning productive and appropriate visits to the U.S. Advice, information, and contacts are similarly offered to American theatre professionals traveling and working abroad. ITI-U.S.
Country: United States
Contact: Executive Director, TCG Teresa EYRING
Email: teyring@tcg.org
Phone: Director of Institutional Advancement and Partnerships, TCG Kevin BITTERMAN
Email: kbitterman@tcg.org
Phone: Director of Artistic and International Programs, TCG Emilya CACHAPERO
Email: ecachapero@tcg.org
Social Media: http://facebook.com/tcg.org https://twitter.com/TCG

International Ticketing Association (INTIX) (2)
Website: www.intix.org
Email: info@intix.org
Phone: 212 629 4036
Address: 8910 Purdue Road, Suite 480, US
Information: members include box office Managers, MIS and financial Directors, pr, Marketing and General Managers
Country: United States

International Trombone Association
Website: www.trombone.net
Email: info@trombone.net
Phone: 888 236 6241
Address: PO Box 3214, US
Country: United States

International Trumpet Guild
Website: www.trumpetguild.org
Email: website@trumpetguild.org
Address: United States
Information: The International Trumpet Guild is a non-profit organization founded in 1975 to promote communications among trumpet players around the world and to improve the Artistic level of performance, teaching, and literature Associated with the trumpet.
Country: United States
Contact: Affiliate Chapters Coordinator
Email: chapters@trumpetguild.org
Membership & Journal Delivery
Email: membership@trumpetguild.org
Phone: ITG Web Site Director
Email: website@trumpetguild.org
Phone: ITG Legacy Endowment

Email: legacy@trumpetguild.org

Italian Cultural Centre in New York
Website: www.iicnewyork.esteri.it
Email: iicnewyork@esteri.it
Phone: 212 879 4242
Address: 686 Park Avenue, US
Country: United States
Social Media: @IIC_NewYork www.facebook.com/IICNewYork

Kentucky Arts Council
Website: artscouncil.ky.gov
Email: christopher.cathers@ky.gov
Phone: 256 43757
Address: 500 Mero St. Fifth Floor Frankfort, KY 40601, US
Information: The Kentucky Arts Council is the state arts agency and is responsible for developing and promoting support for the arts in Kentucky. Strategically placed in the Tourism, Arts and Heritage Cabinet, the Kentucky Arts Council is publicly funded by the Kentucky General Assembly and the National Endowment for the Arts, an independent agency of the federal government.
Country: United States
Contact: Executive Director Chris Cathers
Email: Christopher.Cathers@ky.gov
Phone: 289 23126Arts Marketing Director Dave Blevins
Email: David.Blevins@ky.gov
Phone: 289 23120Executive Staff Advisor Emily Moses
Email: EmilyB.Moses@ky.gov
Phone: 289 23109Folk and Traditional Arts Director Mark Brown
Email: Mark.Brown@ky.gov
Phone: 289 23115Communications Director Tom Musgrave
Email: TomR.Musgrave@ky.gov
Phone: 289 23122Organization Support and Individual Tamara Coffey
Email: Tamara.Coffey@ky.gov
Phone: 289 23121Information Technology Manager Eric Shelton
Email: Eric.Sheltons@ky.gov
Phone: 289 25807Fiscal Analyst Holly Likes
Email: Holly.Likes@ky.gov
Phone: 289 23180Grants Manager Jessica Taylor
Email: Jessicat@ky.gov
Phone: 278 24982Arts Education Director Samuel Lockridge
Email: Samuel.Lockridge@ky.gov
Phone: 289 23124
Social Media: facebook.com/kentuckyartscouncil/twitter.com/KYArtsCouncilinstagram.com/kyartscouncil/
Offers/Grants: true

Los Angeles Department of Cultural Affairs
Website: www.culturela.org
Email: performingartsdir@earthlink.net
Phone: 213 202 5500
Address: 201 North Figueroa Street, Suite 1400, US
Information: Formed in 1925, DCA promotes arts and culture as a way to ignite a powerful dialogue, engage LA's residents and visitors, and ensure LA's varied cultures are recognized, acknowledged, and experienced. DCA's mission is to strengthen the quality of life in Los Angeles by stimulating and supporting arts and cultural activities, ensuring public access to the arts for residents and visitors alike.
Country: United States
Contact: General Manager Danielle Brazell
Email: danielle.brazell@lacity.org
Phone: 213 202 5522Assistant General Manager Daniel Tarica
Email: daniel.tarica@lacity.org
Phone: 213 202 5533
Social Media: https:// www.facebook.com/culturela/ https://twitter.com/culture_la https://instagram.com/culture_la/

Maryland State Arts Council
Website: www.msac.org
Email: msac.commerce@maryland.gov
Phone: 410 767 6555
Address: 175 West Ostend Street, Suite E, US
Information: Founded in 1967, The Maryland State Arts Council (MSAC) is an agency of the State of Maryland's Department of Commerce that plays an essential role, ensuring every person has access to the transformative power of the arts. MSAC advances the arts by providing leadership that champions creative exPression, diverse programming, equitable access, lifelong learning, and the arts as a celebrated contributor to the quality of life for all the people of Maryland.
Country: United States
Contact: Program Director, Arts in Education Precious Blake
Email: precious.blake@maryland.gov
Phone: 410 767 6476State Folklorist Chad Buterbaugh
Email: chad.buterbaugh@maryland.gov
Phone: 410 767 6450Special Projects and Grants Associate Rosa Chang
Email: rosa.chang@maryland.gov
Phone: 410 767 8879Marketing and Communications Manager Amelia Evans
Email: amelia.evans@maryland.gov
Phone: 410 767 6542Program Director, Public Art Liesel Fenner
Phone: 410 767 6484Program Director, Arts Services; Disciplines: Dance, Literary Arts, Music, Public Art, Theatre Laura Weiss
Email: laura.weiss@maryland.gov
Phone: 410 767 6545
Social Media: www.facebook.com/mdartscouncil/twitter.com/mdartscouncil www.instagram.com/mdartscouncil/
Offers/Grants: true

Mayor's Office of Art, Culture & Film
Website: www.artsandvenuesdenver.com
Email: socialmedia@artsandvenues.com
Phone: 208 654 220
Address: 1345 Champa St. Denver, CO 80204, US
Information: The Denver Commission on Cultural Affairs acts as an advisory board to Denver Arts & Venues' cultural programs department. The Commission is comprised of dynamic and accomplished Denver leaders in the areas of the arts, business and education, all of whom are appointed by the Mayor. The Commissioners are strong advocates for arts and culture, and are committed to the mission and goals of Cultural Programs and Denver Arts & Venues.
Country: United States
Contact: Executive Director Ginger White Brunetti
Email: Ginger.White@denvergov.org
Phone: 208 654 314Deputy Director Molly Wink
Email: Molly.Wink@denvergov.org
Phone: 208 654 202Executive Assistant to Ginger White Brunetti Nicole Medina
Email: Nicole.Medina2@denvergov.org
Phone: 208 654 306Office Manager Pamela Lintern
Email: Pamela.Lintern@denvergov.org
Phone: 208 654 305Director of Strategic Projects Mark Najarian
Email: Mark.Najarian@denvergov.org
Phone: 208 654 236
Social Media: facebook.com/denverarts/twitter.com/denverartsinstagram.com/DenverArts/

Mayor's Office of Arts & Culture Boston
Website: www.boston.gov/departments/arts-and-culture
Email: arts@boston.gov
Phone: 617 635 3911
Address: 1 CITY HALL SQUARE ROOM 802 BOSTON, MA
Information: The Mayor's Office of Arts & Culture Boston enhances the quality of life, the economy, and the design of the City through the arts. The role of the arts in all aspects of life in Boston is reinforced via equitable access to arts and culture in every community, its public institutions, and public places.
Key areas of work include support to the cultural sector through grants and programs, as well as the production and permitting of art in public places.
Country: United States
Contact: Chief of Arts and Culture KARA ELLIOTT-ORTEGA
Email: KARA.ELLIOTT-ORTEGA@BOSTON.GOV
Phone: 617 635 4445Program Manager, Boston AIR SHARON AMUGUNI
Email: SHARON.AMUGUNI@BOSTON.GOV
Phone: Technical Director, Strand Theatre MATTHEW BRETON
Email: MATTHEW.BRETON@BOSTON.GOV
Phone: 617 504 8967Assistant to General Manager, Strand Theatre ALENE BURROUGHS
Email: ALENE.BURROUGHS@BOSTON.GOV
Phone: Communications Director KRISTINA CARROLL
Email: KRISTINA.CARROLL@BOSTON.GOV
Phone: 617 635 0081
Social Media: facebook.com/ArtsinBoston/twitter.com/artsinboston/instagram.com/artsinboston/

Miami-Dade County Department of Cultural Affairs
Website: www.miamidadearts.org
Email: culture@miamidade.gov
Phone: 053 754 634
Address: 111 NW 1st St, Ste 625 Miami, FL 33128, US
Information: The Miami-Dade County Department of Cultural Affairs and the Cultural Affairs Council develop cultural excellence, diversity and participation throughout Miami-Dade County by strategically creating and promoting opportunities for artists and cultural organizations.
Country: United States
Contact: Department Director MICHAEL SPRING
Email: ms4@miamidade.gov
Phone: 053 754 634Deputy Director MARIALAURA LESLIE
Email: ml8@miamidade.gov
Phone: 053 755 042Construction Projects Manager CAROLINA ALFONSO
Email: carana@miamidade.gov
Phone: 053 753 671Cultural Projects Administrator KELLY ALLOCCO
Email: kellya@miamidade.gov
Phone: 053 754 636Chief of Education, Outreach and Access FRANCINE ANDERSEN
Email: fran@miamidade.gov
Phone: 053 755 024Cultural Projects Administrator ROXANA BARBA

Email: rbarba@miamidade.gov
Phone: 053 754 209

Michigan Council for Arts and Cultural Affairs
Website: facebook.com/mcacaarts/
Email: badgeroc@michigan.org
Phone: 517 241 4011
Address: 300 N Washington Sq Lansing, US
Information: As the state government's lead agency charged with developing arts and culture policy and grant-making, MCACA is made up of up to 15 members who are appointed by the Governor, and also has an internal staff at MEDC. MCACA serves to encourage, initiate and facilitate an enriched environment of Artistic, cultural and creative environment in Michigan.
Country: United States
Social Media: facebook.com/mcacaarts/
Offers/Grants: true

Missouri Arts Council
Website: www.missouriartscouncil.org
Email: moarts@ltgov.mo.gov
Phone: 664 074 752
Address: 815 Olive St, St. Louis, MO 63101, US
Information: The Missouri Arts Council is the state agency dedicated—as public leader, partner, and catalyst—to broadening the growth, availability, and appreciation of the arts in Missouri and fostering the diversity, vitality, and excellence of Missouri's communities, economy, and cultural heritage.
Country: United States
Contact: Executive Director Michael Donovan
Email: michael.donovan@ltgov.mo.gov
Phone: 143 404 740Program Specialist Julie Hale
Email: julie.hale@ltgov.mo.gov
Phone: 143 406 853Program Specialist Keiko Ishida
Email: keiko.ishida@ltgov.mo.gov
Phone: 143 406 859Public Information Coordinator Barbara MacRobie
Email: barbara.macrobie@ltgov.mo.gov
Phone: 143 406 852Program Specialist Donald Rice
Email: donald.rice@ltgov.mo.gov
Phone: 143 406 854Accountant Jim Riordan
Email: jim.riordan@ltgov.mo.gov
Phone: 143 406 856Special Initiatives Coordinator Virginia Sanders
Email: virginia.sanders@ltgov.mo.gov
Phone: 143 406 851Program Coordinator Sarah Skaggs
Email: sarah.skaggs@ltgov.mo.gov
Phone: 143 406 857Program Specialist Jason Vasser-Elong
Email: jason.vasser-elong@ltgov.mo.gov
Phone: 143 406 858Grants Manager Joan White
Email: joan.white@ltgov.mo.gov
Phone: 143 406 855
Social Media: facebook.com/missouriartscouncil/twitter.com/moartscouncil
Offers/Grants: true

Montana Arts Council
Website: www.art.mt.gov
Email: mac@mt.gov
Phone: 406 444 6548
Address: 830 N Warren St, Helena, MT 59601, US
Information: The Montana Arts Council is the agency of state government established to develop the creative potential of all Montanans, advance education, spur economic vibrancy and revitalize communities through involvement in the arts.
Country: United States
Contact: Chief Financial Officer Jenifer Alger
Email: jeniferalger@mt.gov
Phone: 406 444 6489Executive Director Tatiana Gant
Email: tatiana.gant@mt.gov
Phone: 406 444 6546Deputy Director, Grants Director and 504/ADA Accessibility Coordinator Kristin Han Burgoyne
Email: kburgoyne@mt.gov
Phone: 406 444 6449Communication Specialist Eric Heidle
Email: Eric.Heidle@mt.gov
Phone: 406 444 6133Business Specialist Ginny Newman
Email: virginia.newman@mt.gov
Phone: 406 444 6354
Social Media: facebook.com/MontanaArtsCouncil/twitter.com/montanaarts www.instagram.com/montanaartscouncil/
Offers/Grants: true

Mu Phi Epsilon Professional Music Fraternity
Website: www.muphiepsilon.org/
Email: President@muphiepsilon.org
Phone: 559 277 1898
Address: 4705 N. Sonora Avenue, Suite 114, US
Information: a coeducational membership organization. Its mission is to advance music in the community, nation, and world through promotion of musicianship, scholarship, and music education, with emphasis on service through music
Country: United States
Social Media: @MuPhiFrat www.facebook.com/pages/Mu-Phi-Epsilon-Professional-Music-Fraternity

Music Teachers National Association (MTNA)
Website: www.mtna.org

Email: mtnanet@mtna.org
Phone: 885 125 278
Address: 600 Vine St., Ste. 1710 Cincinnati, OH
Information: Founded in 1876, MTNA is a nonprofit organization of independent and collegiate music teachers committed to furthering the art of music through teaching, performance, composition and scholarly research.
Country: United States
Social Media: www.facebook.com/mtnapage/ www.twitter.com/MTNA1/ www.instagram.com/mtnaorg/

NAMM, the International Music Products Association
Website: www.namm.org
Email: info@namm.org
Phone: 760 438 8001
Address: 5790 Armada Drive Carlsbad, US
Information: Founded in 1901, NAMM (National Association of Music Merchants) has a mission to strengthen the music products industry and promote the pleasures and benefits of making music. Its programs promote and support music education and music making for all, advancing active participation across the lifespan by supporting scientific research, philanthropic giving and public service programs.
Country: United States
Contact: Director of Marketing and Communications Andy Tompkins
Email: andyt@namm.org
Social Media: https://www.facebook.com/nammorg https://twitter.com/namm https://www.instagram.com/thenammshow/

Nebraska Arts Council
Website: www.artscouncil.nebraska.gov
Email: nac.info@nebraska.gov
Phone: 259 52122
Address: 1004 Farnam Street, Plaza Level, Omaha, NE
Information: The Nebraska Arts Council is an agency of the state of Nebraska. The mission of the Nebraska Arts Council is to promote, cultivate and sustain the arts for the people of Nebraska. In doing so, the Nebraska Arts Council provides grants and services to artists, organizations and communities.
Country: United States
Contact: Program Specialist Anne Alston
Email: anne.alston@nebraska.gov
Phone: 259 52196Public Art and Artist Programs Specialist Meagan Dion
Email: meagan.dion@nebraska.gov
Phone: 259 53935Communications Manager Chad Dolezal
Email: Chad.Dolezal@nebraska.gov
Phone: 259 53938Grants and Database Administrator Jennifer Dreibelbis
Email: jennifer.dreibelbis@nebraska.gov
Phone: 259 52124Program Coordinator Linda Hilliar
Email: linda.hilliar@nebraska.gov
Phone: 259 53940Deputy Director Mike Markey
Email: mike.markey@nebraska.gov
Phone: 259 52195Program Specialist Rachel Morgan
Email: rachel.morgan@nebraska.go
Phone: 259 52142Program Coordinator Stephanie Plummer
Email: Stephanie.Plummer@nebraska.gov
Phone: 259 53937Business Manager Robin Richards
Email: robin.richards@nebraska.gov
Phone: 259 53934Executive Director Suzanne Wise
Email: suzanne.wise@nebraska.gov
Phone: 259 5941
Social Media: facebook.com/NebraskaArtsCouncil/instagram.com/neartscouncil/
Offers/Grants: true

Nevada Arts Council
Website: www.nvartscouncil.org
Email: infonvartscouncil@nevadaculture.org
Phone: 756 876 680
Address: 716 N Carson St Carson City, NV 89701, US
Information: The Nevada Arts Council, a division of the Nevada Department of Tourism and Cultural Affairs, supports the work of Nevada artists, arts organizations and institutions and is funded by the Nevada State Legislature, the National Endowment for the Arts.
Country: United States
Contact: Executive Director TONY MANFREDI
Email: tmanfredi@nevadaculture.org
Phone: 756 877 111Administrative Services Officer KARI WARD
Email: krward@nevadaculture.org
Phone: 756 877 118Accountant Technician CATHLEEN WYATT
Email: cjwyatt@nevadaculture.org
Phone: 756 877 112Arts Learning Specialist MARYJANE DOROFACHUK
Email: mdorofachuk@nevadaculture.org
Phone: 024 863 738Folklife Specialist REBECCA SNETSELAAR
Email: rsnetselaar@nevadaculture.org
Phone: 024 863 739Artist Services Specialist/ Art Installer STEPHEN REID
Email: sreid@nevadaculture.org
Phone: 756 877 108
Grants & Projects Analyst II

SIERRA SCOTT
Email: s.scott@nevadaculture.org
Phone: 756 87104Grants Program Assistant KRISTA FICKEN
Email: k.ficken@nevadaculture.org
Phone: 756 877 102
Social Media: facebook.com/nvartscouncil/twitter.com/nv_artscouncilinstagram.com/nvartscouncil/

New Hampshire State Council on the Arts
Website: www.nh.gov/nharts
Email: Virginia.A.Lupi@dncr.nh.gov
Phone: 603 271 2789
Address: 19 Pillsbury St 1st Floor, USA
Information: The State Arts Council was established in 1965 as the official state arts agency with legislation (RSA 19-A) designed "to insure that the role of the arts in the life of our communities will continue to grow and play an ever more significant part in the welfare and educational experience of our citizens." The NHSCA is advised by a 15-member council that meets at least four times a year. Councilors are appointed by the Governor and confirmed by the Executive Council.
Country: United States
Contact: Director Ginnie Lupi
Email: Virginia.A.Lupi@dncr.nh.gov
Phone: 603 271 8418Chief Grants Officer Cassandra Erickson Mason
Email: Cassandra.A.Mason@dncr.nh.gov
Phone: 603 271 7926
Grants Coordinator – Creative Communities & Arts in Health
Lisa Burk-McCoy
Email: Lisa.M.Burk-McCoy@dncr.nh.gov
Phone: 603 271 0794
Grants Coordinator – Heritage & Traditional Arts
Kayla Schweitzer
Email: Kayla.M.Schweitzer@dncr.nh.gov
Phone: 603 271 0795Visual Arts Associate Emily Killinger
Email: Emily.R.Killinger@dncr.nh.gov
Phone: 603 271 0790Curatorial Specialist Carey Johnson
Email: Carey.A.Johnson@dncr.nh.gov
Phone: 603 271 0792
Social Media: facebook.com/NHArtsCouncil/

New Jersey State Council on the Arts – NJ.gov
Website: www.nj.gov/state/njsca/
Email: michelle.baxter-schaffer@sos.nj.gov
Phone: 092 926 130
Address: 33 W State St Trenton, NJ 08608, US
Information: Created as an agency of state government, the State Arts Council operates as a division within the New Jersey Department of State. Its purpose is to encourage and give financial support to artists, nonprofit arts organizations, and projects throughout New Jersey.
Country: United States
Contact: Executive Director Allison Tratner
Email: allison.tratner@sos.nj.gov
Phone: 096 331 218Assistant to the Executive Director Irene Wells
Email: irene.wells@sos.nj.gov
Phone: 099 847 127
Communications & Engagement Specialist
Michelle Baxter-Schaffer
Email: michelle.baxter-schaffer@sos.nj.gov
Phone: 099 847 023Communications Associate Christopher Benincasa
Email: christopher.benincasa@sos.nj.gov
Phone: 092 925 263
Director of Artist Services & Public Art
Danielle Bursk
Email: danielle.bursk@sos.nj.gov
Phone: 096 331 184Grants Manager, Operational Support (interim) Dance, Media Arts, Music Lindsay Dandeo
Email: lindsay.dandeo@sos.nj.gov
Phone: 099 847 020Program Officer Crafts, Multidisciplinary, Visual Arts Diane Felcyn
Email: diane.felcyn@sos.nj.gov
Phone: 096 331 244
Social Media: facebook.com/NJStateCouncilontheArts/twitter.com/NJArtsCouncil

New York City Department of Cultural Affairs
Website: www1.nyc.gov/site/dcla/index.page
Phone: 125 139 300
Address: 31 Chambers Street New York, New York 10007, US
Information: The New York City Department of Cultural Affairs (DCLA) is dedicated to supporting and strengthening New York City's vibrant cultural life. Among their primary missions is to ensure adequate public funding for non-profit cultural organizations, both large and small, throughout the five boroughs.
Country: United States
Contact: Commissioner, Department of Cultural Affairs Gonzalo Casals
Social Media: twitter.com/NYCulture/instagram.com/nyculture/
Offers/Grants: true

New York Foundation for the Arts
Website: www.nyfa.org
Email: help@nyfa.org
Phone:

123 666 900
Address: 20 Jay Street, Suite 740 Brooklyn, NY
Information: NYFA was established in 1971 to serve individual artists throughout New York State. Since then, they have extended their programs and services throughout the United States and internationally and expanded our scope to serve additional members of the arts community.
Country: United States
Contact: Executive Director Michael Royce
Phone: Director of Development Katherine Delaney
Senior Officer Individual Giving & Special Events
Kimberly Goodis
Phone: Development Officer, Individual Giving and Foundations Ryan Hudak
Phone: REDC Fellow Sarah Overton
Social Media: facebook.com/nyfacurrent/twitter.com/nyfacurrentinstagram.com/nyfacurrent/
Offers/Grants: true

New York State Council on the Arts
Website: www.nysca.org
Email: info@arts.ny.gov
Phone: 212 459 8800
Address: 300 Park Avenue South, 10th Floor, US
Information: the council believes in supporting: Artistic excellence and the creative freedom of artists without censure; the rights of all New Yorkers to access and experience the power of the arts and culture
Country: United States

North Carolina Arts Council
Website: www.ncarts.org
Email: ncarts@ncdcr.gov
Phone: 198 076 500
Address: 109 E Jones St Raleigh, NC 27601, US
Information: Founded in 1967 with the democratic vision of "arts for all citizens," the North Carolina Arts Council sustains and grows the arts for the benefit of North Carolinians and their communities. The Arts Council strives to deliver resources for arts development to all 100 counties of the state through programs that are fair, transparent, and accountable.
Country: United States
Contact: Executive Director Wayne Martin
Email: wayne.martin@ncdcr.gov
Phone: 198 146 505Deputy Director Tamara Brothers
Email: tamara.brothers@ncdcr.gov
Phone: 198 146 526
Director of Operations & Arts Learning
Vicki Vitiello
Email: vicki.vitiello@ncdcr.gov
Phone: 198 146 504Senior Program Director Carly Jones
Email: carly.jones@ncdcr.gov
Phone: 198 146 531
Visual Arts Director & Accessibility Coordinator
Kathleen Collier
Email: kathleen.collier@ncdcr.gov
Phone: 198 146 515
Social Media: facebook.com/ncarts/twitter.com/NCArtsCouncilinstagram.com/ncartscouncil/

North Dakota Council on the Arts
Website: www.nd.gov/arts
Email: comserv@nd.gov
Phone: 701 328 7590
Address: 1600 East Century Avenue, Suite 6, US
Country: United States

Office of Arts, Culture and the Creative Economy
Website: www.phila.gov
Email: arts@phila.gov
Phone: 215 686 8446
Address: City Hall Room 116 Philadelphia, US
Information: The Office of Arts, Culture and the Creative Economy (OACCE) closes the gap in access to the arts for all Philadelphians and is committed to equitable support of culture and creativity throughout the city's neighborhoods. OACCE supports free cultural programming; creates opportunities for local artists and creative organizations; connects Philadelphians to quality arts experiences; and preserves the City's public art assets.
Country: United States
Social Media: https://www.facebook.com/creativephl/ https://www.twitter.com/creativephl https://www.instagram.com/creativephl

Ohio Arts Council
Website: www.oac.ohio.gov
Email: oac.publicinformation@oac.ohio.gov
Phone: 144 662 613
Address: 30 E Broad St, Fl 33rd Columbus, OH 43215, US
Information: The Ohio Arts Council was created in 1965 to foster and encourage the development of the arts and assist the preservation of Ohio's cultural heritage. With funds from the Ohio Legislature and the National Endowment for the Arts, the OAC provides financial assistance to artists and arts organizations.
Country: United States
Social Media: facebook.com/OhioArtsCouncilPage/

Oklahoma Arts Council
Website: www.arts.ok.gov
Email: OKarts@arts.ok.gov

Phone: 405 521 2931
Address: PO Box 52001-2001, US
Opera Volunteers International
Website: www.operavolunteers.org
Email: info@operavolunteers.org
Address: PO Box 7032 Evanston, IL 60201-2284, US
Information: Opera Volunteers International is a non-profit volunteer organization that advocates for and supports volunteerism in opera throughout North America and beyond. OVI works to connect individuals and local opera support organizations so that successful ideas and projects are championed, publicized and shared among members.
Country: United States
Contact: President Susan Malott
Phone: Vice President Administration Sandra Pelfrey Amarillo
Vice President Communications & Marketing
Mary Svela Gladstone
Vice President Membership & Outreach
Anne Pennington Brentwood
Phone: Secretary Vikie Hariton Tucson
Email: memberservices@operavolunteers.org
Phone: Treasurer Sheila McNeill Omaha
Phone: Nominating Julie Todaro Pembroke Pines
Phone: Immediate Past President Rhonda Sweeney
Social Media: facebook.com/OperaVolunteers/twitter.com/OperaVolunteer

PAMAR (Pan American Musical Art Research, Inc.)
Website: www.pamar.org
Email: pamar@pamar.org
Phone: 646 701 0010
Address: 644 West 185th Street Suite – 6B, US
Information: PAMAR is a non-profit organization seeking to promote better understanding between the various cultures and countries of the Americas, primarily through an ongoing and vital exchange of their music, musicians and dancers. Founded in 1984 in New York City by Uruguayan born pianist Polly Ferman, PAMAR has taken significant steps toward establishing itself as an Artistic resource center.
Country: United States
Contact: Founder/Artistic Director Polle Ferman
Email: pollyferman@pamar.org
Phone: Executive Director Raul Orlando Edwards
Email: rauloedwards@gmail.com
Phone: Project Coordinator Graphic Designer Andrea Nalerio
Email: andrea@pamar.org
Social Media: facebook.com/PanAmericanMusicalArtResearch/ https://twitter.com/PAMAR_LACW https://www.instagram.com/latinamericanculturalweek/

Percussive Arts Society
Website: www.pas.org
Email: percarts@pas.org
Phone: 317 974 4488
Address: 110 W. Washington Street Suite A, US
Country: United States
Social Media: @PercussiveArtsPercussive.Arts.Society

PRX
Website: www.prx.org
Email: jason.saldanha@prx.org
Phone: 617 576 5455
Address: P.O. Box 382234 Cambridge, US
Information: Public Radio International (PRI) merged with PRX in 2018 to form a combined nonprofit media company doing business as "PRX." Today PRX works in partnership with hundreds of public radio stations and thousands of independent Producers. Since 2016, their work has also included a substantial training program, which is helping journalists and storytellers from across the country and around the world adapt to and succeed in the highly competitive podcast market.
Country: United States
Contact: Chief Executive Officer Kerri Hoffman
Phone: Chief Technology Officer Andrew Kuklewicz
Phone: Chief Marketing Officer Donna Hardwick
Phone: Chief Finance Officer Cory Zanin
Phone: Chief Development Officer Janetta Stringfellow
Chief of Business Development & Content
Jason Saldanha
Phone: Executive Producer, Radiotopia Julie Shapiro
Phone: Marketing Manager, Audience Growth Shaquille Anderson
Director, Financial Operations & Reporting
Beth Aldridge
Phone: Director, Individual Giving Lisa Baumert
Phone: Senior Manager, PRX Podcast Garage Alex Birch
Phone: Manager, Administrative Support Mary Brennan
Social Media: http://www.facebook.com/prxofficial https://twitter.com/prx http://instagram.com/prxofficial

Regional Arts & Culture Council (RACC)
Website: www.racc.org
Email: info@racc.org
Phone: 038 235 111
Address: 411 NW Park Ave, Ste 101 Portland, OR 97209, US
Information: A non-profit organization, the Regional Arts & Culture Council supports the creative economy in greater Portland by equitably providing funding and

services to artists and art organizations

Country: United States
Contact: Communications and Advocacy Design Andrea Blanco
Email: ablanco@racc.org
Phone: 038 235 100Director of Public Art Kristin Calhoun
Email: kcalhoun@racc.org
Phone: 038 235 401Executive Director Madison Cario
Email: mcario@racc.org
Phone: 038 235 400Grants Officer Ingrid Carlson
Email: icarlson@racc.org
Phone: 038 235 417Director of Grants Helen Daltoso
Email: hdaltoso@racc.org
Phone: 038 235 402Public Art Collections Registrar Danielle Davis
Email: ddavis@racc.org
Phone: 038 235 405Arts Education Access Fund (AEAF) Specialist Chanda Evans
Email: cevans@racc.org
Phone: 038 235 849Digital Communications Specialist Eugenie Jolivett Fontana
Email: ejfontana@racc.org
Phone: 038 235 053Grants Specialist Molly Gray
Email: mgray@racc.org
Phone: 038 232 969Communications Manager Heather Nelson Kent
Email: hnkent@racc.org
Phone: 038 235 426
Social Media: facebook.com/RegionalArts/twitter.com/R_A_C_Cinstagram.com/regionalarts/

Regional Arts Commission of St. Louis
Website: www.racstl.org
Email: info@racstl.org
Phone: 148 635 811
Address: 6128 Delmar Blvd St. Louis, MO 63112, US
Information: The Regional Arts Commission was founded in 1985 to promote, encourage and foster the arts and cultural institutions in St. Louis City and County, and to contribute to the economic development of the area through a strong presence of the arts.
Country: United States
President & CEO
VANESSA COOKSEY
Offers/Grants: true

Rhode Island State Council on the Arts
Website: www.arts.ri.gov
Email: info@arts.ri.gov
Phone: 401 222 3880
Address: 1 Capital Hill 3rd Floor, US
Country: United States

Rodgers and Hammerstein Organization
Website: www.rnh.com
Address: 229 W. 28th St., 11th Floor, US
Information: Founded by the legendary team of Richard Rodgers and Oscar Hammerstein II and headquartered in New York City, The Rodgers & Hammerstein Organization owns the rights to the world's most popular stage and film musicals, including OKLAHOMA!, CINDERELLA, CAROUSEL, SOUTH PACIFIC, THE KING AND I and THE SOUND OF MUSIC.
Country: United States
Social Media: www.facebook.com/RodgersandHammersteintwitter.com/RNH_org www.instagram.com/rodgersandhammerstein/

Screen Actors Guild – American Federation of Television and Radio Artists
Website:
www.sagaftra.org
Email:
info@sagaftra.org
Phone: 557 242 387
Address: 5757 Wilshire Boulevard, 7th Floor Los Angeles, California 90036, US
Information: SAG-AFTRA represents approximately 160, 000 actors, announcers, broadcast journalists, dancers, DJs, news writers, news editors, program hosts, puppeteers, recording artists, singers, stunt performers, voiCEOver artists and other media professionals.
Country: United States
Contact: SAG-AFTRA National Executive Director David White
Phone: Chief Broadcast Officer Mary Cavallaro
Executive Producer, SAG Awards & National Programming
Kathy Connell
Phone: Chief Operating Officer and General Counsel Duncan Crabtree-Ireland
Phone: Associate National Executive Director Mathis Dunn
Chief Communications & Marketing Officer
Pamela Greenwalt
Phone: Chief People Officer Tashia Mallette
Phone: Senior Advisor John McGuire
Phone: Chief Financial Officer Arianna Ozzanto
Phone: Chief Contracts Officer Ray Rodriguez
Phone: Chief Economist David Viviano
Social Media: facebook.com/SAGAFTRA/twitter.com/sagaftra/instagram.com/sagaftra/

SnowHill Strategies
Website: snowhillstrategies.com
Email: inquiries@snowhillstrategies.com
Phone: 617 797 7301
Address: 111 Beach Street, Suite 4A, US
Information: helps cultural organisations and funders align their missions and business models with the reality of today, particularly the reality of changing demographics
Country: United States

Society for Research in Music Education (SRME)
Website: nafme.org
Email: nafme@nafme.org
Phone: 800 336 3768
Address: 1806 Robert Fulton Dr Reston, VA
Information: The Association has supported music educators at all teaching levels for more than a century. With more than 60, 000 members teaching millions of students nationwide, the organization is the national voice of music education in the United States.
Country: United States
Contact: Interim Executive Director Christopher Woodside
Social Media: www.facebook.com/nafme/ www.twitter.com/NAfME/ www.instagram.com/nafme/

South Carolina Arts Commission
Website: www.southcarolinaarts.com
Email: info@arts.sc.gov
Phone: 037 348 696
Address: 1026 Sumter St, Ste 200 Columbia, SC 29201, US
Information: On June 7, 1967, Governor Robert E. McNair signed legislation that established the South Carolina Arts Commission, an autonomous state agency charged with guiding the development of the arts. For more than 50 years, the agency has worked to build a thriving arts environment that benefits all South Carolinians, regardless of their circumstances or where they live.
Country: United States
Contact: Coordinator for Accessibility | Executive Director of Arts Access South Carolina Julia Brown-DuBose
Email: jbrown@arts.sc.gov
Phone: 037 340 445
Coordinator for Executive, Program & Department Support | Procurement Officer
Kevin Flarisee
Email: kflarisee@arts.sc.gov
Phone: 037 348 687Executive Coordinator | Arts Directory Coordinator Ann H.N. McBride
Email: amcbride@arts.sc.gov
Phone: 037 348 766
Social Media: facebook.com/scartscomm/twitter.com/scartscomminstagram.com/scartscomm/

South Dakota Arts Council-SDAC
Website: www.artscouncil.sd.gov
Email: sdac@state.sd.us
Phone: 605 773 3301
Address: 711 East Wells Avenue, US
Information: Established in 1966 and funded by the State Legislature and the National Endowment for the Arts, the South Dakota Arts Council (SDAC) is a state agency serving South Dakotans and their communities through the arts. Recognizing the importance of creativity in the lives of all South Dakotans, the Council makes quality arts accessible throughout the state by providing grants, services and information to artists, arts organizations, schools and the public.
Country: United States
Contact: Director Patrick Baker
Email: patrick.baker@state.sd.us
Phone: Deputy Director Rebecca Cruse
Email: rebecca.cruse@state.sd.us
Arts Grant Specialist & Accessibility Coordinator Kate Vandel
Email: Kathryn.Vandel@state.sd.us
Phone: Arts Program Specialist Sarah Carlson
Email: Sarah.Carlson@state.sd.us
Phone: South Dakota Traditional Arts Program Manager Anne Hatch
Email: SDTraditionalArts@outlook.com
Social Media: facebook.com/SouthDakotaArts/

The Actors' Fund
Website: www.actorsfund.org/
Email: info@actorsfund.org
Phone: 212 221 7300
Address: 729 Seventh Avenue, 10th floor, US
Country: United States

The Arts Foundation for Tucson and Southern Arizona
Website: www.artsfoundtucson.org
Email: info@artsfoundtucson.org
Phone: 206 240 595
Address: 236 S. Scott, Ste 150 Tucson, AZ 85701, US
Information: The Arts Foundation for Tucson and Southern Arizona is a 501(c)3 nonprofit and funding agency. We consist of staff, a board of Directors, and community members who serve on grant panels and committees and are passionate about the arts
Country: United States
Contact: Executive Director Adriana Gallego
Email: agallego@artsfoundtucson.org
Phone: Senior Public Art Manager Jeff DaCosta
Email: jdacosta@artsfoundtucson.org
Phone: Public Art Assistant Manager Woods Fairchild
Email: woods@artsfoundtucson.org
Phone: Grants and Services Manager Yurika Isoe
Email: yurika@artsfoundtucson.org
Social Media: facebook.com/ArtsFoundTucson/twitter.com/artsfoundtucson/instagram.com/artsfoundtucson/

The College Music Society
Website: www.music.org
Email: cms@music.org
Phone: 067 219 616
Address: 312 East Pine Street | Missoula MT 59802, US
Information: The College Music Society promotes music teaching and learning, musical creativity and exPression, research and dialogue, and diversity and interdisciplinary interaction. A consortium of college, conservatory, university, and independent musicians and scholars interested in all disciplines of music, the Society provides leadership and serves as an agent of change by addressing concerns facing music in higher education.
Country: United States
Contact: Executive Director William Pelto
Email: ExecutiveDirector@music.org
Phone: Membership Specialist Shannon Devlin
Email: membership@music.org
Phone: Information Services Specialist Julie Johnson
Email: information@music.org
Phone: Director of Information Delivery/Webmaster Beth Mast
Email: webmaster@music.org
Phone: Director of Professional Activities Peter Park
Email: profact@music.org
Phone: Director of Information Technology David Schafer
Email: itDirector@music.org
Phone: Bookkeeper Candice Davis
Email: cms@music.org
Social Media: facebook.com/CollegeMusicSoc/twitter.com/CollegeMusicSoc/

The League of Chicago Theatres
Website: www.chicagoplays.com
Email: info@chicagoplays.com
Phone: 312 554 9800
Address: 17 N. Wabash, Suite #520, US
Information: The League of Chicago Theatres is proud to serve a membership of more than 200 theaters, a rich and varied theater community ranging from storefront, non-union theaters with budgets under $10, 000 to major cultural centers with multi-million dollar shows. No other theater service organisation in the country has such a diverse theater membership. Whether you call yourself a Chicagoan or are just visiting for the weekend, the League of Chicago Theatres is your source for Chicago theater. Member of ISPA.
Country: United States
Social Media: @chicagoplays www.facebook.com/ChicagoPlays

The Massachusetts Cultural Council
Website: www.massculturalcouncil.org
Email: carmen.plazas@art.state.ma.us
Phone: 178 582 700
Address: 10 St. James Avenue, 3rd Floor Boston, MA, US
Information: The Mass Cultural Council is a state agency that promotes excellence, inclusion, education, and diversity in the arts, humanities, and sciences to foster a rich cultural life for all Massachusetts residents.
Country: United States
Contact: Contracts Officer Cyndy Gaviglio
Email: cyndy.gaviglio@art.state.ma.us
Phone: 178 582 711Information Systems Coordinator D. Scott Hufford
Email: scott.hufford@art.state.ma.us
Phone: 178 582 715Fiscal Officer Elsie Sanon
Email: elsie.sanon@art.state.ma.us
Phone: 178 582 702Grant Operations Officer Evelyn Nellum
Email: 17 858 2716
Phone: Fiscal Operations Officer Carina Ruiz-Esparza
Email: carina.ruiz.esparza@art.state.ma.us
Phone: 178 582 726
Social Media: facebook.com/masscultural/twitter.com/massculturalinstagram.com/masscultural/

Union Internationale de la Marionnette (UNIMA), United States of America
Website: www.unima-usa.org
Email: unimausa@gmail.com
Phone: 048 815 110
Address: 1404 Spring Street NW Atlanta, Georgia 30309, US
Information: UNIMA-USA is the North American Center of Union Internationale de la Marionnette, the oldest international theatre organization in the world, founded in 1929. The organization's mission is to promote international understanding and friendship through the art of puppetry.
Country: United States
Contact: President Kathy Foley
Phone: Vice President Stephen Kaplin
Phone: Secretary Trudi Cohen
Phone: Treasurer Brad Clark
Phone: Academic Liaison/Puppet Training Claudia Orenstein
Phone: Archives Laurie Swygert
Phone: Bylaws/Procedures Kristin Haverty
Phone: Haverty Steve Widerman
Phone: Conferences/Symposia/Festival Liaison Paulette Richards
Phone: Development Steven Widerman
Phone: Electronic Information (social media and website) Geoffrey Comier
Phone: Hands across the Sea Kristin Haverty
Phone: Liaison to Puppeteers of America Geoffrey Comier
Phone: Long Range Planning Steven Widerman
Phone: Membership Karen Smith
Phone: Publications Paulette Richards
Phone: Scholarships Stephen Kaplin
Social Media: facebook.com/UNIMA.USA/twitter.com/UNIMAUSA

Utah Arts Council
Website: www.arts.utah.gov
Email: aboulton@utah.gov
Phone: 801 236 7555
Address: 617 East South Temple, US
Country: United States

Vermont Arts Council
Website: www.vermontartscouncil.org
Email: info@vermontartscouncil.org
Phone: 802 828 3291
Address: 136 State Street, Montpelier, US
Information: Since 1965, the Vermont Arts Council has been the state's primary provider of funding, advocacy, and information for the arts in Vermont. The Vermont Arts Council is unique. It is the only designated state arts agency in the U.S. that is also an independent nonprofit organization.
Country: United States
Contact: Senior Program Manager, ADA Coordinator Michele Bailey
Email: mbailey@vermontartscouncil.org
Phone: 802 402 4614Grants and Database Administrator Meredith Bell
Email: mbell@vermontartscouncil.org
Phone: 802 402 4478Executive Assistant and Office Manage Deirdre Connelly
Email: dconnelly@vermontartscouncil.org
Phone: 802 828 3291Communications Director Catherine Crawley
Email: ccrawley@vermontartscouncil.org
Phone: 802 402 4601Deputy Director Amy Cunningham
Email: acunningham@vermontartscouncil.org
Phone: 802 828 5423Finance Director Anne Gould
Email: agould@vermontartscouncil.org
Phone: 802 828 5426Artist Services Manager, Curator for the Spotlight Gallery and Sculpture Garden Dominique Gustin
Email: dgustin@vermontartscouncil.org
Phone: 802 402 4602Education Program Manager Troy Hickman
Email: thickman@vermontartscouncil.org
Phone: 802 402 4496Executive Director Karen Mittelman
Email: kmittelman@vermontartscouncil.org
Phone: 802 828 5420Content Manager Desmond Peeples
Email: dpeeples@vermontartscouncil.org
Phone: 802 402 4592Finance Administrator Tom Pilon
Email: tpilon@vermontartscouncil.org
Phone: 802 402 4632
Social Media: https:// www.facebook.com/vermontartscouncil https://twitter.com/VTArtsCouncil https://www.instagram.com/vtartscouncil

World Dance Alliance Americas (WDAA)
Website: www.wda-americas.com
Phone: 144 606 844
Address: US
Information: World Dance Alliance Americas (WDA-Americas) is an independent, non-profit, non-political, and non-religious member-driven organization. It is part of the larger World Dance Alliance including the Asia-Pacific Network and other global regions. WDA provides information, advocacy, and communication for dance organizations and individuals; a forum for the exchange of ideas; and information expertise and resources in all areas of dance.
Country: United States
Social Media: facebook.com/groups/391530240932466

Wyoming Arts Council
Website: wyomingartscouncil.org
Email: brittany.perez@wyo.gov
Phone: 307 777 7742
Address: 2301 Central Ave Cheyenne, US
Information: Through grants, partnerships, programs and unique opportunities, the Wyoming Arts Council provides funding and support statewide for projects big and small. The WAC plays an important role in the

economic and social development of every community by investing in the arts

Country: United States
Contact: Executive Director Michael Lange
Email: michael.lange@wyo.gov
Phone: 307 275 4476Assistant Director Rachel Clifton
Email: rachel.clifton@wyo.gov
Phone: 307 256 0500Grants Manager Karen Merklin
Email: karen.merklin@wyo.gov
Phone: 307 214 7819Public Outreach and Events Coordinator Brittany Perez
Email: brittany.perez@wyo.gov
Phone: 307 214 2701Arts Education Specialist Mary Billiter
Email: mary.billiter1@wyo.gov
Phone: 307 757 8806Creative Arts Specialist Taylor Craig
Email: taylor.craig@wyo.gov
Phone: 307 274 6673
Folklorist and Health & Wellness Specialist
 Josh Chrysler
Email: joshua.chrysler@wyo.gov
Phone: 307 256 2010
Social Media: http:// www.facebook.com/wyomingartscouncil/ https://twitter.com/wyomingarts

VIRGIN ISLANDS U.S.

Virgin Islands Council on the Arts
Website: www.vicouncilonarts.org
Email: vlmahony@vica.gocomtek.com
Phone: 340 774 5984
Address: 5070 Norre Gade, VI
Information: member of the mid-Atlantic State Arts Foundation
Country: Virgin Islands U.S

This section seeks to provide details of some of the key organisa-tions involved with the performing arts in each country, who operate on a national level. Some of these are better resourced than others and the level of advice and help they provide often reflects this fact. **The entries are listed in alphabetical order within country.**

Organisations Nationales

Cette section vise à fournir des détails sur quelques-unes des principales organisations impliquées dans les arts de la scène dans chaque pays, qui opèrent à l'échelle nationale. Certains d'entre eux sont mieux que d'autres ressources et le niveau de conseils et l'aide qu'ils fournissent est souvent le reflet de ce fait. **Les entrée sont classés par ordre alphabétique dans le pays.**

Nationale Organisationen

Dieser Abschnitt soll Details einiger der wichtigsten Organisationen der darstellenden Künste in jedem Land, die auf nationaler Ebene tätig beteiligt sind. Einige von ihnen sind bess-er als andere, und das Niveau der Beratung Ressourcen und helfen sie meist spiegelt diese Tatsache. **Die Einträge sind für jedes Land alphabetisch sortiert.**

Organizzazioni Nazionali

Questa sezione si propone di fornire i dettagli di alcune delle principali organizzazioni coinvolte con le arti dello spettacolo in ogni paese, che operano a livello nazionale. Alcuni di questi sono più risorse di altri e il livello di consulenza e assistenza che forniscono spesso riflette questo fatto. **Le voci sono pubblicate in ordine alfabetico di paese.**

Organizaciones Nacionales

Esta sección busca proporcionar detalles de algunas de las organizaciones clave involucradas con las artes escénicas en cada país, que operan a nivel nacional. Algunos de estos son más recursos que otros y el nivel de asesoramiento y la ayuda que proporcionan a menudo refleja este hecho. **Las entradas se muestran en orden alfabético dentro de cada país.**

performing arts
database

ARGENTINA

Mozarteum Argentino
Website: www.mozarteumargentino.org
Email: info@mozarteumargentino.org
Phone: 114 814 0903
Address: Rodriguez Peña 1882 PB "A", Capital Federal, AR
Information: An institution dedicated to the promotion and dissemination of classical music in Argentina.
Country: Argentina
Social Media: facebook.com/mozarteumargentino.orgtwitter.com/MozarteumAinstagram.com/mozarteumargentino_/

AUSTRALIA

Accessible Arts
Website: www.aarts.net.au
Email: info@aarts.net.au
Phone: 292 516 499
Address: Level 3, The Arts Exchange, 10 Hickson Road, AU
Information: The peak arts and disability organisation across NSW. Established in 1986, they work with and for their community to accelerate and celebrate the diverse professional, cultural and social impacts of arts and disability in NSW. Their mission is to advance the rights of, and opportunities for, people with disability and/or who are Deaf to develop and sustain professional careers in the arts and have equitable access to arts and culture across NSW.
Country: Australia
Social Media: https:// www.facebook.com/AccessibleArts/ https://twitter.com/accessiblearts https:// www.instagram.com/aartsnsw/

AMPCOM (Australian Music Performance Committee)
Website: www.aria.com.au/pages/ampcom.htm
Email: aria.mail@aria.com.au
Phone: 285 691 144
Address: Australian Recording Industry Association, PO Box Q20, Queen Victoria Building, AU
Information: For many years the Australian Music Performance Committee (AMPCOM), a voluntary association comprised of representatives of Commercial Radio Australia (CRA), the Australian Recording Industry Association (ARIA), and the Australian Music Publishers' Association Ltd (AMPAL), the Musicians' Union of Australia and the Media Entertainment and Arts Alliance (MEAA) co-ordinated annual reports on the compliance of the commercial radio industry with the Commercial Radio Codes of Practice related to the playing of Australian music on radio.
Country: Australia
Social Media: https:// www.facebook.com/ARIA.Official/ https://twitter.com/ARIA_Official https:// www.instagram.com/aria_official/

APRA/ AMCOS
Website: apraamcos.com.au
Email: apra@apra.com.au
Phone: 299 357 900
Address: 16 Mountain Street, AU
Information: APRA AMCOS grants licences for the live performance, broadcast, communication, public playing or reproduction of its members' musical works. APRA AMCOS then distributes the licence fees to its 108, 000+ songwriter, composer and music publisher members and affiliated societies worldwide.
APRA AMCOS is the trading name of Australasian Performing Right Association Limited (APRA) and Australasian Mechanical Copyright Owners Society (AMCOS).
Country: Australia
Social Media: https:// www.facebook.com/apraamcos https://twitter.com/apraamcos https:// www.instagram.com/apraamcos/

Arts Industry Council of Victoria (AICV)
Website: aicv.org.au
Email: jtoohey@rav.net.au
Phone: 407 511 438
Address: AU
Information: AICV was established in November 1989 to enable all sectors of arts activity in Victoria to work together and to speak with a united voice. Convened by industry peak bodies, AICV represents individual practitioners and arts organisations ranging from small independent companies to large state cultural institutions. AICV advocates on behalf of its constituency and contributes to public debate by providing leadership and forums for discussion within the sector.
Country: Australia

Association of Community Theatre Inc.
Website: www.communitytheatre.com.au
Email: david@communitytheatre.com.au
Phone: 153 56035
Address: PO Box Q544 QVB Post Office, AU
Information: The Association of Community Theatre Inc was formed in the early 1990's after a visit to Sydney from members of the Executive of the Federation of New Zealand Operatic Societies – now called Musical Theatre New Zealand

Ausdance National
Website: www.ausdance.org.au
Email: national@ausdance.org.au
Phone: 262 488 992
Address:
PO Box 45, Braddon ACT 2612, AU
Information: Ausdance National provides advocacy and representation services and creates programs and resources to support and sustain professional dance practice in Australia. Ausdance grew out of a 1977 conference convened by leading artists and educators who determined that the future of dance in Australia should be guided by understanding the art form at all levels: political, economic, Artistic, in communities and in education systems.
Country: Australia

Ausdance NSW
Website: www.ausdancensw.com.au
Email: admin@dance.net.au
Phone: 292 564 800
Address: 10 Hickson Road, Level 3, Arts Exchange Buliding, The Rocks, AU
Information: Ausdance NSW is the peak body for dance, for NSW they have a 40-year history of educating, inspiring and supporting the dance community. They are a membership organisation. NSW provides advice, advocacy and dance programs in different contexts and environments, both directly and indirectly and in partnership with other State and Federal government departments, Local Government Authorities, dance companies, organisations, educational institutions, businesses, and dance studios.
Country: Australia
Social Media: https:// www.facebook.com/AusdanceNSW https:// www.twitter.com/AusdanceNSW https:// instagram.com/ausdance_nsw

Ausdance Victoria
Website: www.ausdancevic.org.au
Email: victoria@ausdance.org.au
Phone: 123 63803
Address: 59 Francis Street, AU
Information: Ausdance VIC exists to support, enrich, advance and advocate dance in all its forms. They provide services, advice, classes, workshops and professional development to the dance sector as a whole. They also present forums, events, projects and other exciting activities to the wider Victorian community.
Ausdance VIC supports the ongoing growth and expansion of the dynamic and vibrant dance sector that exists across Victoria today.
Country: Australia
Contact: Executive Director Michelle Silby
Email: sonja.leipold@gmx.atGeneral Manager Robbie Carmellotti
Email: sonja.leipold@gmx.atDirector of Education and Life Long Learning Katrina Rank
Email: sonja.leipold@gmx.atRTO Operations Manager Cathy Smith
Email: sonja.leipold@gmx.at
Associate Producer, Programs & Events
Jess Zintschenko
Email: sonja.leipold@gmx.atManager Marketing, Digital Media and Memberships Alison McIntosh-Deszcz
Email: sonja.leipold@gmx.at
Social Media: https://facebook.com/AusdanceVic https://twitter.com/AusdanceVic https://instagram.com/ausdance_victoria

Australasian Association for Theatre, Drama and Performance Studies (ADSA)
Website: www.adsa.edu.au
Email: glen.mcgillivray@sydney.edu.au
Phone: 171 7870
Address: Communication And Creative Arts Deakin University Burwood VIC 3125, AU
Information: ADSA is the peak academic association promoting the study of drama in any performing medium throughout the region. ADSA represents members of staff and postgraduate students of Australasian institutions of tertiary education who are engaged in teaching, research and practice in theatre, drama and performance studies. Directors of Associated theatres and members of the theatrical profession are also active members. ADSA's annual conference is usually held in late June.
Country: Australia
Social Media: facebook.com/Australasian-Association-for-Theatre-Drama-and-Performance-Studies-ADSA-236293563101080/

Australia Council for the Arts, Dance Board
Website: www.australiacouncil.gov.au/artforms/dance/
Email: enquiries@australiacouncil.gov.au
Phone: 292 159 000
Address: Level 5/60 Union St, AU
Information: A host of outstanding dancers and choreographers has earned Australia a global reputation for taking the art form to new heights. The Australia Council fosters the development and growth of Australian dance. It supports excellence, encourages participation, increases distribution and builds Artistic sustainability. Its vision is to see dance thrive.
Country: Australia

Australia Council for the Arts, Music Board
Website: www.australiacouncil.gov.au/artforms/music
Email: enquiries@australiacouncil.gov.au
Phone: 292 159 000
Address: Level 5/60 Union St, AU
Information: Australia Council for the Arts supports composers, musicians and organisations to create new music and present it to audiences. Its goal is to reflect and promote the diversity, excellence and energy of contemporary Australian musical culture.
Country: Australia
Social Media: https:// www.facebook.com/auscouncilarts https://twitter.com/auscouncilarts http://instagram.com/auscouncilarts

Australia Council for the Arts, Theatre Board
Website: www.australiacouncil.gov.au/artforms/theatre/
Email: enquiries@australiacouncil.gov.au
Phone: 292 159 000
Address: Level 5/60 Union St, AU
Information: The theatre sector in Australia is a 'broad church' which encompasses several spheres of activity. This includes commercial, professional subsidised, unsubsidised independent, participatory, community, and amateur theatre. Within these spheres there is a diversity of genres, including: plays and scripted work, music theatre and cabaret, circus and physical theatre, installation theatre performance, puppetry, media-based theatre work, live art, and contemporary inter-disciplinary performance. Member of ISPA
Country: Australia
Social Media: https:// www.facebook.com/auscouncilarts https://twitter.com/auscouncilarts http://instagram.com/auscouncilarts

Australia Council for the Arts, Visual Arts
Website: www.australiacouncil.gov.au/artforms/visual-arts/
Email: enquiries@australiacouncil.gov.au
Phone: 292 159 000
Address: Level 5/60 Union St, AU
Information: The Australia Council for the Arts supports the contemporary exPression of visual art through the broadest range of visual media, including craft, design, media arts and visual arts. This support includes grants to living artists and funding for contemporary arts organisations as well as national and international exhibitions and events.
Country: Australia
Social Media: https:// www.facebook.com/auscouncilarts https://twitter.com/auscouncilarts http://instagram.com/auscouncilarts

Australian Music Centre
Website: www.australianmusiccentre.com.au
Email: info@australianmusiccentre.com.au
Phone: 299 357 805
Address: PO Box N690, Grosvenor Place, AU
Information: The Australian Music Centre (AMC) is the national service organisation dedicated to the promotion and support of art music in Australia. Their important work covers contemporary classical, contemporary jazz and improvised music, experimental music and sound art. They provide career support, manage professional development programs, presents annual and biennial awards and maintain an extensive online catalogue and library, and an online shop.
Country: Australia
Social Media: facebook.com/australianmusiccentre/ https://twitter.com/ausmusiccentre https:// www.instagram.com/australianmusiccentre/

Australian Music Examinations Board
Website: www.ameb.edu.au
Email: online@ameb.edu.au
Phone: 130 072 5709
Address: Level 8, 21 Victoria Street, AU
Information: In 1887 a programme of music examinations was initiated in Australia by the Universities of Adelaide and Melbourne. Subsequently the Australian Music Examinations Board (AMEB) emerged in 1918 as a national body with the purpose of providing graded assessments of the achievements of music students. Later, examinations were also provided for students of speech and drama.
Country: Australia
Social Media: https:// www.facebook.com/AustralianMusicExaminationsBoard/ https://twitter.com/amebexams/

Australian Music Therapy Association (AMTA™)
Website: www.austmta.org.au
Email: info@austmta.org.au
Phone: 398 954 430
Address: Suite 5, 250 Gore Street, AU
Information: AMTA is Australia's industry peak body for music therapy. AMTA started in 1975 and now has over 700 members. The AMTA represents Registered Music Therapists (RMTs), music therapy students and the community. Its mission is to enable, advance and advocate for excellence in music therapy. AMTA also publishes the peer reviewed Australian Journal of Music Therapy.
Country: Australia

Australian National Choral Association
Website: www.anca.org.au
Email: admin@anca.org.au
Phone: 392 541 041
Address: 1 Smith St Melbourne, VIC, AU
Information: ANCA publishes Sing Out magazine 3 times annually and holds Choralfest every two years (Melbourne 2015, Brisbane 2017). Membership with ANCA offers discounted insurance to choral groups and conductors, Sing Out subscription, discounted registration to workshops and choral events throughout Australia, subscription to the Choral Enewsletter, free event and job listings on the ANCA website and much more! Visit anca.org.au for more details
Country: Australia

Australian National Playwrights' Centre
Website: www.pwa.org.au
Email: info@pwa.org.au
Phone: 282 740 900
Address: Level 3, 10 Hickson Road, AU
Information: Playwriting Australia is the national peak body for playwriting with a mission to support the development and promotion of great new Australian writing for performance. They also offer playwrights investment in the creative development of their new work, as well as the opportunity to participate in one of our professional development programs.
Country: Australia

Australian Publishers Association Ltd.
Website: www.publishers.asn.au
Email: office@publishers.asn.au
Phone: 292 819 788
Address: 60/89 Jones Street, AU
Information: The Australian Publishers Association (APA) is the peak national body responsible for representing the Australian publishing industry and for promoting the importance of the published word to the educational, social, cultural and intellectual life of Australia.
An advocate, collaborator, advisor and educator, the APA represents the diversity of publishing businesses: big and small, commercial and non-profit, popular and academic, large multinational and local independent.
Country: Australia

Australian Script Centre Inc
Website: www.ozscript.org
Email: admin@australianplays.org
Phone: 362 234 675
Address: Level 1, 77 Salamanca Place Hobart, TAS, AU
Information: Australian Plays is a national organisation based in Hobart, a not-for-profit incorporated association providing services to playwrights by – publishing and licensing plays and by promoting and supporting their work with Producers and educators nationally and internationally. Australian Plays is the trading name of the Australian Script Centre and their stakeholders represent a diverse community of theatre makers, including playwrights, drama educators, students, theatre companies and Producers.
Country: Australia

Australian Society for Music Education (ASME)
Website: www.asme.edu.au
Email: asme@asme.edu.au
Phone: 881 255 749
Address: P.O. Box 7184, AU
Information: The Australian Society for Music Education exists to encourage and advance music education at all levels as an integral part of General education and community life, and as a profession within the broad field of music.
Country: Australia

Australian Voice Association
Website: www.australianvoiceassociation.com.au
Email: ava@australianvoiceassociation.com.au
Phone: 300 406 191
Address: PO Box 5290 Mordialloc VIC 3195, AU
Information: The Australian Voice Association is a multi-disciplinary organization which exemplifies high quality practice and research into all aspects of voice.
The membership is comprised of performers and teachers in the arts and entertainment industries, clinicians, researchers, medical specialists and paramedical practitioners.
Country: Australia

Australian Youth Orchestra
Website: www.ayo.com.au
Email: info@ayo.com.au
Phone: 293 561 400
Address: 19/285a Crown St, Surry Hills, AU
Information: The Australian Youth Orchestra (AYO) has a reputation for being one of the world's most prestigious and innovative training organisations for young pre-professional musicians. Its training pathway has been created to nurture the musical development of Australia's finest young instrumentalists across metropolitan and regional Australia. AYO presents tailored training and performance programs each year for aspiring musicians, composers, arts administrators and music journalists aged 12 to 30.

Carclew
Website: carclew.com.au
Email: info@carclew.org.au
Phone: 882 675 111
Address: 11 Jeffcott St., AU
Information: Carclew is South Australia's only multi-art form and cultural organisation dedicated to Artistic outcomes by and for people aged 26 and under. It provides young people with opportunities to try different art forms, supports emerging artists to develop their craft and advocates for youth arts practice.
Country: Australia

Centre for Aboriginal Studies in Music (CASM)
Website: www.arts.adelaide.edu.au/ncalms/casm/
Email: ncalms@adelaide.edu.au
Phone: 883 133 652
Address: c/o Wilto Yerlo, The University of Adelaide, AU
Information: The Centre for Aboriginal Studies in Music (CASM) is the only devoted university-based centre for studies in Australian Indigenous music. Located in the Elder Conservatorium of Music and is a node of NCALMS, CASM offers an innovative program that responds to the learning needs and aspirations of Aboriginal and Torres Strait Islander students and offers state-of-the-art learning and sound recording facilities.
Country: Australia

Community Arts Network (CAN), Queensland
Website: www.culture.com.au/exhibition/qcan/welcome.html
Email: mail@qldcan.org.au
Phone: 732 544 922
Address: PO Box 3460, AU
Information: The Queensland Community Arts Network provides professional support to communities and artists involved in community cultural development activities including visual arts, theatre, music and performance and also has an Aboriginal and Torres Strait Islander arts and cultural development programme.
Country: Australia

Community Arts Network (CAN), South Australia
Website: www.cansa.net.au
Email: admin@cansa.net.au
Phone: 882 310 900
Address: 234a Sturt Street, AU
Information: The Community Arts Network is a peak organisation for community cultural development.It provides advice on planning projects, sources of funding or any specialist information on local arts development and activity. It publishes monthly bulletins on events, activities and new resources. A brochure outlining all services will be sent on request.
Country: Australia

Confederation of Australian International Arts Festivals
Website: caiaf.org.au
Email: secretariat@caiaf.org.au
Phone: 738 335 400
Address: C/O Brisbane Festival Level 2, 381 Brunswick Street Fortitude Valley, QLD 4006
Information: The Confederation of Australian International Arts Festivals (CAIAF) is a not-for-profit incorporated association of the nation's major state-based festivals.
Country: Australia

Country Arts SA
Website:
www.countryarts.org.au
Email: email@countryarts.org.au
Phone: 884 440 400
Address: 2 McLaren Parade, AU
Information: Country Arts provides arts and services across regional South Australia through a range of arts programs and initiatives, the management of performing and visual arts venues, and the provision of grant funding which supports the creative endeavours of communities and individuals. Each year it tours world class productions that entertain, challenge and stimulate a wide variety of audiences in their five performing arts centres in Mount Gambier, Port Pirie, Renmark, Noarlunga and Whyalla.
Country: Australia
Social Media: https://facebook.com/CountryArtsSA
https://twitter.com/CountryArts_SA https:// www.instagram.com/CountryArts_SA/

Country Music Association of Australia
Website:
www.country.com.au
Email: information@cocof.isisnet.be
Phone: 267 661 577
Address: PO Box 298, AU
Information: The CMAA is the peak organisation for country music artists and related industries in Australia. Key activities include Administration of the Golden Guitar Awards and the CMAA Snr Academy of Country Music and CMAA Jnr Academy of Country Music.
Country: Australia

Drama Australia – National Association for Drama Education
Website: www.dramaaustralia.org.au
Email: admin@dramaaustralia.org.au
Phone: 730 090 664
Address: PO Box 1510, AU
Information: Drama Australia is the peak national body that represents and advocates on behalf of all state and territory drama education associations in Australia. All members of state and territory Drama associations are automatically members of Drama Australia. Drama Australia represents drama teachers, academics, applied theatre workers and drama in education practitioners at national arts and curriculum forums and in national and international peak associations such as NAAE (National Advocates for Arts Education) and IDEA (International Drama Education Association).
Country: Australia

Glen Eira Arts and Culture
Website: www.gleneira.vic.gov.au
Email: mail@gleneira.vic.gov.au
Phone: 395 243 333
Address: Glen Eira Road (Corner of Hawthorn Road), AU
Information: Glen Eira City Council provides a diverse program of activities including exhibitions, events, concerts and festivals to entertain, engage and culturally enrich the lives of those who live, work, study and visit in the City of Glen Eira.
Country: Australia

Jazz Queensland
Website: www.jazzqueensland.com
Email: jazzqld@yahoo.com.au
Phone: 410 391 379
Address: PO Box 3135, AU
Information: They are a site dedicated to talking about the history of jazz music! From Coltrane to Dizzy to Louis, anything and everything about the music they love. They are going to share their favorite songs with you and they hope that you share your favorite songs with them.
Country: Australia

JazzSA Superbands
Website: jazzsa.org.au
Email: superbands@jazzsa.org.au
Phone: 403 417 256
Address: AU
Information: Formed in 2009 by Adelaide Jazz legend Mike Stewart, the JazzSA Superband program was designed to bring together South Australia's leading jazz professionals and its keenest students in one highly dynamic and inclusive educational platform. Experienced conductors work weekly with students to rehearse and prepare for an end of term showcase playing repertoire that pays homage to the greats but also exposes them to the music of the future.
Country: Australia
Social Media: www.facebook.com/SouthAustraliaJazz

JazzWA
Website: www.jazzwa.com
Email: Manager@jazzwa.com
Address: PO Box 8170, AU
Information: JAZZWA (The Jazz Co-ordination Association of WA inc) is a not-for-profit organisation which was established in 1983 for the purposes of promoting and developing Western Australian jazz music and musicians statewide, nationally and internationally. It is managed by a committee of jazz enthusiasts, musicians, educators, arts Managers and promoters.
Country: Australia

Live Performance Australia
Website: www.liveperformance.com.au
Email: info@liveperformance.com.au
Phone: 386 142 000
Address: 15-17 Queen Street, Level 1, AU
Information: Live Performance Australia (LPA) is the peak body for Australia's live performance industry. Their role is to protect and promote the interests of their Members. They are a registered employer organisation under the Fair Work (Registered Organisation) Act 2009, which allows them to negotiate industrial agreements on behalf of their Members.
Country: Australia

Music Australia
Website: www.musicaustralia.org.au
Email: office@musicaustralia.org.au
Phone: 295 199 778
Address: 104 Erskineville Rd, AU
Information: Music Australia is a not for profit national umbrella body and champion for all music. They work independently and with members and partners to stimulate and promote the value of music, school music education, sector professional development and public engagement. They provide advocacy and information services to strengthen music in Australia, and run projects including Australia's largest school music program Music: Count Us In; and a contemporary music industry conference.
Country: Australia

Musicians' Union of Australia, Federal Office
Website: www.musicians.asn.au
Email: industrial.officer@musicians.asn.au
Phone: 882 725 013
Address: Unit 4, 23A King William Road, AU
Information: The Musicians' Union of Australia is a membership based, not for profit association, formed by working musicians to represent and advance the interests of working musicians. The Union is run entirely on the funds paid by its members and receives no funding from Governments, or any other entity. Office bearers of the Musicians' Union must be members of the Union and are elected by the membership. Hence, members can be assured that the Union will only ever act in the interests of its members.
Country: Australia

National Aboriginal Islander Skills Development Association (NAISDA) Dance College
Website: www.naisda.com.au
Email: reception@naisda.com.au
Phone: 243 403 100
Address: 31 The Avenue KARIONG NSW 2250, AU
Information: NAISDA Dance College offers professional expertise and word class training facilities to deliver accredited training programs that are rich in cultural learning and practice. They provide a creative learning space designed to inspire and equip Aboriginal & Torres Strait Islander young people for the future.
Country: Australia
Social Media: facebook.com/naisdadancecollege/ https://twitter.com/naisda https://www.instagram.com/naisda_dance_college/

National Film and Sound Archive of Australia (NFSA)
Website: www.nfsa.gov.au
Email: enquiries@nfsa.gov.au
Phone: 262 482 000
Address: McCoy Cct, Acton ACT 2601, AU
Information: The National Film and Sound Archive is Australia's 'living' archive – the custodian of over 3 million items that they not only collect, but preserve for future generations and share in many diverse ways.
Country: Australia

National Institute of Dramatic Art (NIDA)
Website: www.nida.edu.au
Email: info@nida.edu.au
Phone: 296 977 600
Address: 215 Anzac Parade, AU
Information: NIDA is Australia's National Institute of Dramatic Art, a centre of excellence in training for theatre, film and television. NIDA selects and trains talented young people in a range of disciplines, including acting, directing, writing for performance, design, music theatre, production, costume, properties and staging. Students gain an unrivalled educational foundation in their chosen fields. Since 1959, NIDA has grown to become one of the world's leading dramatic and performing arts institutes.
Country: Australia
Social Media: www.facebook.com/NIDACommunitytwitter.com/NIDACommunityinstagram.com/nidacommunity

Nexus Multicultural Arts Centre Inc
Website: www.nexusarts.org.au
Email: info@nexusarts.org.au
Phone: 882 124 276
Address: Lion Arts Centre, Corner North Terrace & Morphett St., AU
Information: Nexus Arts has worked consistently to create performance and presentation opportunities, develop programs, and to advocate for inclusion of CALD artists and communities within mainstream arts. Nexus is committed to fostering contemporary culturally diverse Artistic excellence and innovation through its diverse programs and presentation opportunities. Nexus strives to be a national leader in culturally diverse arts presentation.
Country: Australia
Social Media: https://www.facebook.com/NexusArts https://twitter.com/nexusarts https://www.instagram.com/nexusarts/

Performance Space
Website: www.performancespace.com.au
Email: admin@performancespace.com.au
Phone: 285 719 111
Address: 245 Wilson St Sydney, NSW, AU
Information: Performance Space is the crucible for risk-taking artists. Emerging over 30 years ago in response to artists' articulated desire to explore and investigate new forms of art, they have consistently identified, nurtured and presented new directions in contemporary practice. Performance Space continues to evolve and renew to meet the needs of the independent sector and explore new models for developing and presenting the most critical and important new work.
Country: Australia
Social Media: https://www.facebook.com/performancespaceau https://twitter.com/pspace https://www.instagram.com/performancespace/

Performing Arts Collection
Website: www.artscentremelbourne.com.au/discover/collections-and-research.aspx
Email: researchservice@theartscentre.net.au
Phone: 392 818 000
Address: 100 St Kilda Rd, AU
Information: Arts Centre Melbourne is both a defining Melbourne landmark and Australia's largest and busiest performing arts centre. Last year they staged more than 4, 000 performances and events to more than 2.7 million people. For nearly 30 years, we have played a leading role in showcasing the best local and international performing arts. We are host and partner to the national and state music, opera, theatre and dance companies, together with local companies, festivals and a multitude of commercial partners.
Country: Australia
Social Media: @artscentremelb www.facebook.com/artscentremelbourne

Performing Arts Connections Australia – PAC Australia
Website: www.paca.org.au
Email: admin@paca.org.au
Phone: 892 218 992
Address: Level 2, 533 Hay Street PERTH WA 6000, AU
Information: Performing Arts Connections Australia is the national peak body representing and supporting performing arts presenters and creators in Australia by providing leadership, building capacity and facilitating relationships that strengthen the connection between the art and the audience.
Country: Australia

Perth Theatre Trust
Website: www.ptt.wa.gov.au
Email: Marketing@ptt.wa.gov.au
Phone: 892 650 900
Address: His Majesty's Theatre, 825 Hay St, AU
Information: The Perth Theatre Trust is a statutory authority established and constituted under the Perth Theatre Trust Act 1979, to manage and operate theatres vested in or leased to it. The Trust's venues are used by local, national and international performing arts companies, performers and artists, both professional and amateur. School and children's performances and activities are also presented at these venues. The Trust supports the presentation or co-production of some events in its theatres.
Country: Australia
Social Media: https://www.facebook.com/perththeatretrust/ https://www.instagram.com/perththeatretrust/

Phonographic Performance Company of Australia Ltd (PPCA)
Website: www.ppca.com.au
Email: ppca.mail@ppca.com.au
Phone: 285 691 100
Address: Level 4, 11 – 17 Buckingham Street, AU
Information: Established in 1969, the PPCA is a national, non government, non-profit organisation that represents the interest of record companies and Australian recording artists. They work together with their licensors, being thousands of Australian recording artists and hundreds of labels both major and independent. They also safeguard the rights of thousands of Australian recording artists and labels, ensuring that they receive a fair return for their music.
Country: Australia

Playing Australia
Website: www.australiacouncil.gov.au
Email: enquiries@australiacouncil.gov.au
Phone: 292 159 000
Address: Level 5, 60 Union St Pyrmont NSW 2009, AU
Information: The Regional Performing Arts Touring program supports performing arts to reach regional and remote communities across Australia. Grants are available to support the net touring costs Associated with a national tour. There is no limit on the amount that can be requested.
Country: Australia

QL2 Dance
Website: www.ql2.org.au
Email: admin@Ql2.Org.Au
Phone: 262 473 103
Address: Gorman Arts Centre, 55 Ainslie Avenue Braddon, ACT, AU
Information: QL2 Dance is dedicated to diverse, challenging and rigorous youth dance which develops the next generation of dance-makers and contributes to a dynamic, caring and diverse society. They run programs for ages 8–26 that focus on igniting and developing young people's creative energy and dance skills. QL2 Dance provides a continuous support path right through to professional development after tertiary dance training.
Country: Australia

Regional Arts Victoria
Website: www.rav.net.au
Email: enquiry@rav.net.au
Phone: 396 441 800
Address: Level 3, 370 Lt Bourke St Melbourne
Information: Regional Arts Victoria inspires art across the state. Through creative facilitation, touring, education, specialised resources, Artistic projects and advocacy, they develop and sustain creative communities and Artistic practice all over Victoria. Regional Arts Victoria is an independent, not-for-profit, membership-based organisation working in long-term partnerships with every level of government, fostering contemporary and innovative regional cultural practice across five decades.
Country: Australia

Regional Arts WA
Website: www.egionalartswa.org.au
Email: info@regionalartswa.org.au
Phone: 892 006 200
Address: 357/365 Murray St, Perth WA 6000, AU
Information: Established in 1994, Regional Arts WA is the state's only multi-arts organisation with a purely regional focus. Their service delivery is diverse with a suite of programs including funding for arts projects large and small, development support for key regional arts organisations and artists, opportunities for the state peak organisations to develop regional programs, youth and First Nations' specific projects, and an extensive professional performing arts touring program.
Country: Australia

Screen Producers Australia
Website: www.screenProducers.org.au
Email: info@screenProducers.org.au
Phone: 293 608 988
Address: Suite 2, Level 1, 34 Fitzroy St, AU
Information: Screen Producers Australia unites screen businesses to campaign for a healthy commercial environment. They support the interests of screen businesses, both large and small, in their production of feature films, television programs, interactive content and games across all genres and formats.
Country: Australia

Songlines Aboriginal Music Corporation
Website: www.songlines.net.au
Email: info@songlines.net.au
Phone: 428 833 218
Address: 45 Moreland St, Footscray VIC 3011, AU
Information: Songlines aim is to provide a platform to advocate as a collective voice for greater recognition of contemporary Aboriginal Music as an important cultural art form.
Songlines Artistic aim is to promote, support and present contemporary Indigenous music, arts and culture and to stimulate dialog around the role of Indigenous arts in Australian culture. This provides a platform for artists to be a voice of the Indigenous community, which in turn will contribute to the overall voice of Australia.
Country: Australia

Stage Queensland
Website: www.stagequeensland.com.au
Email: suzan@stagequeensland.com.au
Phone: 413 929 417
Address: PO Box 3076, AU
Information: Stage Queensland is the peak body for performing arts centres in Queensland supporting a vibrant network of members to provide quality arts and cultural experiences to their communities. Individually Stage Queensland members are primarily the main presenters and advocates of cultural product within their region. Collectively Stage Queensland members provide access to the largest presenter group of performing arts product in Northern Australia.
Stage Queensland was known as NARPACA until 2017.
Country: Australia

Support Act Ltd (SAL)
Website: www.supportact.com.au
Email: admin@supportact.org.au
Phone: 300 731 303
Address: PO Box 805, AU
Information: Support Act is a registered charity and non-profit organisation raising funds to provide relief from hardship and/or illness amongst workers in the Australian music industry. Support Act Limited was formed in 1997 when it became all too evident that there was no longer any final safety net whatsoever available for professional musicians both classical and contemporary, as well as those working around them in the Australian music business.
Country: Australia

Tandanya National Aboriginal Cultural Institute
Website: www.tandanya.com.au
Email: web@tandanya.com.au
Phone: 882 243 200
Address: 253 Grenfell Street, AU
Information: The National Aboriginal Cultural Institute Inc., Australia's oldest Aboriginal-owned and managed multi-arts centre, trades as Tandanya.
Tandanya is a visionary and vibrant place for all to experience contemporary and traditional Aboriginal and Torres Strait Islander cultural exPressions through the visual and performing arts

Tasmanian Music Industry Association
Website: www.tasmusic.com.au
Email: info@tasmusic.com.au
Phone: 610 363 314 470
Address: GPO Box 435, AU
Information: Southern Branch: 27 Tasma St North Hobart Tas. 7000
Country: Australia

Victorian Association of Performing Arts Centres (VAPAC)
Website: www.vapac.org.au
Email: exec@vapac.org.au
Phone: 354 270 180
Address: 79 Bryces Lane, AU
Information: VAPAC is an active network of professionally managed venues, volunteer presenters and industry experts. VAPAC will be the peak body representing performing arts centres across Victoria, playing a key role in developing and maintaining a vibrant and sustainable performing arts sector.
Country: Australia

AZERBAIJAN

Azerbaijan Union of Film-Makers
Website: aki.az
Email: info@aki.az
Phone: 124 371 667
Address: 18 Hasan Seyidbayli Street, Baku, AZ
Information: The Azerbaijan Union of Film-makers (AUF) is a creative public organization uniting which brings together, on a voluntary basis, cinema workers – Azerbaijan's professional cinema workers. The main objective of the Union is to develop national cinema as an integral part of national culture and world cinema.
Country: Azerbaijan

Azərbaycan Rəssamlar İttifaqı / Union of Azerbaijan Artists
Website: facebook.com/ressam.az/
Email: ari@ressam.az
Phone: 124 936 230
Address: Xaqani küçəsi, 43 AZ 1000 Baku, AZ
Information: The Union of Artists of Azerbaijan is a creative voluntary public organization uniting professional artists and art critics operating in the territory of Azerbaijan. The Union of Artists of Azerbaijan actively participates in the organization of national and international symposiums, competitions, does serious work, does its best in the aesthetic education of children and youth, helps orphanages, the sick and disabled, and supervises military units.
Country: Azerbaijan

Foundation of Friends of Azerbaijan Culture
Website: www.hddu.hr
Email: ibragim@azmd.baku.az
Phone: 129 82259
Address: 9A Aliev str., AZ
Country: Azerbaijan

Union of Artists of Azerbaijan
Email: hdgu@zg.hinet.hr
Phone: 124 936 230/4934
Address: 19, Khagani Str., 1000, AZ
Country: Azerbaijan

Union of Composers of Azerbaijan
Website: facebook.com/Azerbaycan-Bestekarlar-Ittifaqi-Composers-Union-of-Azerbaijan-157554924274795/
Email: info@composersunion.az
Phone: 598 0886
Address: 27 Khagani Street, Baku, AZ
Information: The Union of Composers of Azerbaijan is the biggest creative organization of professional composer and musicians of Azerbaijan and in it activity it focuses on preservation of creative multi profile of Azerbaijani music art creativity, best traditions of the national music classics and world music culture and its renewal principles. The establishment of the Union of Composers of Azerbaijan dates back to 1934.
Country: Azerbaijan

Union of Theatre Figures of Azerbaijan
Website: azteatr.musigi-dunya.az
Email: teatral-az@mail.ru
Phone: 124 931 703
Address: 10, Khagani Str., 1000, AZ
Information: The Union of Theatre Figures of Azerbaijan uniting actors, Directors, playwrights and theater professionals on a voluntary basis is the public organization. The main duty of the Union is to revive the theater process, to stimulate all new beginnings; try to integrate our national theater art with the modern art and to use all potentials for getting it.
Country: Azerbaijan

Writers' Union of Azerbaijan
Website: www.azyb.az
Email: azerbwu@mail.ru

Phone: 124 937 481
Address: 53 Khagani Street, Baku, AZ
Information: The Azerbaijan Writers' Union is the largest public organization of Azerbaijani writers, poets and translators. The main task of the union is to provide practical support to the literary and Artistic activities of young writers, to unite creative Azerbaijanis living in different countries around the national literature, to expand artist-reader relations, to promote Azerbaijani literature abroad.
Country: Azerbaijan

Yarat Contemporary Art Space
Website: www.yarat.az
Email: info@yarat.az
Phone: 125 051 414
Address: Baku, AZ
Information: YARAT is a not-for-profit organisation dedicated to nurturing an understanding of contemporary art and creating a hub for Artistic practice, research and thinking in the Caucasus, Central Asia and the surrounding region. Based in Baku, Azerbaijan, YARAT was founded by Aida Mahmudova in 2011. YARAT realises its mission through an on-going program of exhibitions, education events and festivals.
Country: Azerbaijan

BRAZIL

Instituto Cultural Filarmonica
Website: www.filarmonica.art.br
Email: contato@filarmonica.art.br
Phone: 313 219 9000
Address: Rue Paraíba ST. 330, 12th Floor, Brazil, BR
Information: a non-government society whose members are Croatian and foreign professional ballet dancers, choreographers, ballet pedagogues and masters, freelance ballet artists and professional folk dancers who work and live in Croatia and abroad. The Society organises the International Ballet Competition Mia Corak Slavenska and other such events that contribute to the promotion of classical ballet in Croatia and abroad
Country: Brazil

CAMBODIA

Cambodian Living Arts
Email: info@cambodianlivingarts.org
Phone: 239 86032
Address: #128 G9, Sothearos Blvd, KH
Information: They were founded in 1998 by genocide survivor and musician Arn CHORN-POND. For a decade, they are focused on endangered performing art forms and rituals. As 90% of Cambodia's artists did not survive the Khmer Rouge regime, Cambodia's Artistic heritage was in danger of being lost forever.
Country: Cambodia

CANADA

Alberta Foundation for the Arts
Website: www.affta.ab.ca
Email: afacontact@gov.ab.ca
Phone: 780 427 9968
Address: 10708 – 105 Avenue, CA
Information: The Alberta Foundation for the Arts is a public agency and a provincial corporation of the Government of Alberta with a mandate to support and contribute to the development of the arts in Alberta. We provide grant funding to artists and art organizations to encourage the growth and development of the arts sector. We also promote the arts and manage an extensive provincial art collection featuring work from artists all over the province.
Country: Canada

Alliance for Canadian New Music Projects
Website: www.acnmp.ca
Email: info@acnmp.ca
Phone: 416 963 5937
Address: 20 St Joseph Street, CA
Information: membership organisation; held annually in November during Canada Music Week, Contemporary Showcase celebrates Canadian Contemporary Music.
Country: Canada

Association of Canadian Women Composers
Website: www.acwc.ca
Email: acwcafcc@gmail.com
Address: ACWC / AFCC, C/O Canadian Music Centre, 20 St. Joseph Street, CA
Information: build on the achievements of the past, encourage women composers of the present and develop a body of well researched, catalogued and preserved archival material accessible to students, researchers and performers in the future
Country: Canada
Social Media: www.facebook.com/pages/Association-of-Canadian-Women-Composers-ACWCAFCC-C/215231155239835?ref=t

Banff Centre for Arts and Creativity
Website: www.banffcentre.ca

Email: arts_info@banffcentre.ca
Phone: 403 762 6100
Address: 107 Tunnel Mountain Drive Banff, AB, Canada T1L 1H5
Information: Founded in 1933, Banff Centre for Arts and Creativity is a learning organization built upon an extraordinary legacy of excellence in Artistic and creative development. What started as a single course in drama has grown to become the global organization leading in arts, culture, and creativity across dozens of disciplines. From our home in the stunning Canadian Rocky Mountains, Banff Centre for Arts and Creativity aims to inspire everyone who attends our campus – artists, leaders, and thinkers – to unleash their creative potential.
Country: Canada
Social Media: twitter.com/banffcentre www.facebook.com/BanffCentre

Canadian Arts Presenting Association
Website: www.capacoa.ca
Email: sue.urquhart@capacoa.ca
Phone: 613 562 3515
Address: 17 York Street, suite 200, CA
Information: The Canadian Arts Presenting Association/l'Association canadienne des organismes artistiques (CAPACOA) serves the performing arts touring and presenting community through its commitment to integrate the performing arts into the lives of all Canadians. CAPACOA takes initiative in providing leadership, knowledge, communications, skills development and advocacy on behalf of its members and within the arts presenting community. Member of ISPA.
Country: Canada

Canadian Conference of the Arts
Website: www.ccarts.ca
Email: info@ccarts.ca
Phone: 613 238 3561
Address: 406 – 130 Slater Street, CA
Information: membership organisation; the Canadian Conference of the Arts is a not-for-profit, non-partisan member-based organisation that represents over 400,000 artists, cultural professionals from all disciplines of the nation's arts, culture and heritage community
Country: Canada

Canadian Dance Assembly
Website: www.dancecanada.net
Email: info@dancecanada.net
Phone: 416 515 8444
Address: Canadian Dance Assembly, 2nd Floor, 476 Parliament St., CA
Information: membership organisation; strives to cultivate a strong national voice for Canadian professional dance and to support the development of resources for this field of Artistic exPression
Country: Canada

Canadian Federation of Musicians
Website: www.cfmusicians.org
Email: afmcan@afm.org
Phone: 416 391 5161
Address: 150 Ferrand Drive, Suite 202, CA
Information: membership organisation; (CFM) (formerly known as AFM Canada) is the leading professional organisation of its kind available to Canadian musicians; CFM is recognised under the Federal Status of the Artist Act as the sole bargaining agent on behalf of musicians performances within Canada
Country: Canada
Social Media: @cfmusicians www.facebook.com/cfmusicians

Canadian Music Centre (CMC), British Columbia Region
Website: www.musiccentre.ca
Email: bcregion@musiccentre.ca
Phone: 604 734 4622
Address: 837 Davie Street, CA
Information: Since 1959, the Canadian Music Centre has been proudly supporting, preserving and promoting the works of Canadian composers. Not only does it maintain an extensive archive of scores and works of Canadian composers, it strives to make it easily accessible through its lending library, publishing house and repertoire consultation service. It offers quality commercial recordings through their award-winning Centrediscs label and archival recordings via CentreStreams, its online streaming service. Member of ISPA.
Country: Canada

Canadian Music Centre (CMC), national office
Website: www.musiccentre.ca
Email: info@musiccentre.ca
Phone: 416 961 6601
Address: Chalmers House, 20 St Joseph Street, CA
Information: Founded in 1983, CMC Ontario Region works province-wide to advance the CMC's mandate: to promote the music of our Associate composers, to encourage the performance and appreciation of Canadian music, and to make this music widely available and accessible around the world.
CMC Ontario delivers a balanced portfolio of pro-

grammes, projects, and services to help promote and distribute Canadian music for performance, recording, broadcast, research, and General appreciation

Canadian Music Centre (CMC), Prairie Region
Website: www.musiccentre.ca
Email: prairie@musiccentre.ca
Phone: 403 220 7403
Address: Violet Archer Library, University of Calgary, 2500 University Drive NW, CA
Information: The Prairie Region of the Canadian Music Centre is located on the University of Calgary campus in the state-of-the-art Taylor Family Digital Library. It is home to the Violet Archer Library which contains over 20, 000 scores available for free circulation. The Prairie Region office also offers a wide collection of books, music periodicals, composer information, and CDs for sale or free listening. Many of these items are unavailable elsewhere. Services available at the Centre include photocopying, printing, and binding of scores. Member of ISPA.
Country: Canada

Canadian Music Centre (CMC), Quebec
Website: www.musiccentre.ca
Email: quebec@centremusique.ca
Phone: 514 866 3477
Address: 1085, Côte du Beaver Hall, Suite 200, CA
Information: Since 1959, the Canadian Music Centre (CMC) has been proudly supporting, preserving and promoting the works of Canadian composers. Not only does it maintain an extensive archive of scores and works of Canadian composers, it also strives to make it easily accessible through their lending library, publishing house and repertoire consultation service. It offers quality commercial recordings through their award-winning Centrediscs label and archival recordings via Centre-Streams, its online streaming service. Member of ISPA.
Country: Canada

Canadian Music Education Association
Website: cmea.ca/
Email: markreid@cmea.ca
Phone: 261 215 309
Address: c/o Mark Reid, President, F8 – 1100 W 6th Avenue, CA
Information: the CMEA/ACME fosters the advancement of teaching and the lifelong learning of music
Country: Canada

Canadian Music Publishers Association
Website: www.musicpublishercanada.ca/
Phone: 416 926 7952
Address: Canadian Music Publishers Association, 320 – 56 Wellesley Street West, CA
Information: as the oldest music industry association in Canada, CMPA is committed to educating and acting as a mentor body for the next generation of music publishers and young songwriters
Country: Canada

CCI – Ontario Presenting Network
Website: www.ccio.on.ca
Email: info@ccio.on.ca
Phone: 416 703 6709
Address: Centre for Social Innovation, 125-215 Spadina Avenue, CA
Information: membership organisation; CCI is a member-based, not-for-profit arts service organisation that serves the arts presenting industry in Ontario. Our network comprises of performing arts centres, municipal venue presenters, academic venue presenters, festivals, Artistic companies, performing artists, artist Managers, arts consultants and individuals who work collaboratively to improve arts presentation practice in the Province of Ontario
Country: Canada

Choral Federation, Nova Scotia
Website: www.nscf.ns.ca
Email: office@nscf.ns.ca
Phone: 902 423 4688
Address: 1113 Marginal Road, CA
Information: NSCF is governed by a board of Directors elected by and drawn from its membership; funding comes from membership fees, program fees, fund raising activities and continuing grants from the Nova Soctia Department of Education and Culture
Country: Canada

City of Calgary
Website: www.calgary.ca
Email: ccweb@gov.calgary.ab.ca
Phone: 403 268 2489
Address: PO Box 2100, Station M, Mail Code # 63, , CA
Country: Canada

Conseil Culturel et Artistique Francophone de la Colombie-Britannique
Website: www.ccafcb.com
Email: admin@ccafcb.com
Phone: 160 473 25562
Address: 229-1555 W 7th avenue, CA
Information: the CCAFCB promotes, represents and works on the development of Francophone Arts and Cul-

ture in British Columbia, Canada. The organisation works with a network of 15 local presenters and it collaborates with French-speaking artists

Conseil des Arts et des Lettres du Quebec
Website: www.calq.gouv.qc.ca
Email: info@calq.gouv.qc.ca
Phone: 514 864 3350
Address: 500, place d'Armes, 15e étage, CA
Information: may hold competitions to grant awards for Artistic excellence and administer financial support programs through an endowment fund
Country: Canada

Conseil québécois de la musique
Website: www.cqm.qc.ca
Email: info@cqm.qc.ca
Phone: 514 524 1310
Address: 1908 rue Panet, Bureau 302, CA
Information: membership organisation; council québécois de la musique (CQM) is a non-profit organization. Its mission is to bring together professional organizations and individuals working in the field of concert music
Country: Canada

Historic Theatres' Trust/ Société des salles historiques
Website: www.martinu.cz
Email: theatres@total.net
Phone: 257 320 076
Address: 327 Melville St., Station Victoria, Suite 2, CA
Information: also have a Publications Catalogue through which sell current books and videos on theatre history and architecture
Country: Canada

ICASC
Website: www.icasc.ca
Email: info@icasc.ca
Phone: 604 319 8436
Address: Discovery 2, Room 109, 8900 Nelson Way, CA
Information: The International Centre of Art for Social Change (ICASC) is a global centre for networking, training, professional development, research and community outreach in the burgeoning field of art for social change. ICASC is also a hub where people working for progressive change in fields such as health, social justice and human rights, environmental education and community economic empowerment, can learn about the many ways that art for social change practices can be used as highly-effective tools in their work
Country: Canada

Kapralova Society, The
Website: www.kapralova.org
Email: society@kapralova.org
Phone: 422 241 42512
Address: 34 Beacham Crescent, CA
Information: the Kapralova Society is a non-profit arts organization based in Toronto, Canada. Founded by Karla Hartl in 1998, the Society's mission is to build awareness of women's contributions to musical life and to promote the music of Czech composer Vitezslava Kapralova (1915-1940)
Country: Canada

Manifesto
Website: www.themanifesto.ca
Email: nfo@themanifesto.ca
Phone: 647 436 8404
Address: 37 Bulwer Street, CA
Information: a non-profit organisation working to unite, inspire and empower diverse communities of young people through arts and culture. It aims to provide a platform and the resources needed for talented individuals to advance. Member of ISPA
Country: Canada

New Brunswick Culture and Sports Secretariat, Arts Development Branch
Website: www.gnb.ca/culture/arts
Email: artsnb@gnb.ca
Phone: 241 445 404
Address: PO Box 6000, CA
Information: founded in 1996, the Czech Association of Music Festivals is a member of the European Festival Association. They are organizers of the most important Czech music festivals, especially classical music. They are also the founding members of the Prague Spring, Janáček May, the Brno International Music Festival.
Country: Canada

Newfoundland Department of Tourism, Culture and Recreation – Cultural Affairs Division
Website: www.artsandculturecentre.com
Email: info@haendel.be
Phone: 709 729 5952
Address: PO Box 1854, Prince Philip Drive, CA
Country: Canada

Ontario Presents
Website: ontariopresents.ca
Email: info@ontariopresents.ca
Phone:

416 703 6709
Address: 125-215 Spadina Avenue, CA

Information: Ontario Presents is a province-wide network of performing arts touring and presenting organisations that work collaboratively to facilitate the distribution of live, performing arts shows and their engagement with citizens into communities across Ontario. The organisation was incorporated as a not-for-profit network of performing arts venues in 1988 and has grown over the years to be an effective champion for the practice of performing arts presentation and community engagement. Member of ISPA.
Country: Canada

Orchestras Canada/Orchestres Canada
Website: www.orchestrascanada.org
Email: info@oc.ca
Phone: 416 366 8834
Address: 425 Adelaide Street W, Suite 700, CA
Information: offers services: conference, workshops, seminars, in-field consulting, employment service, publicises orchestra openings/auditions
Country: Canada

Overture with the Arts
Website: owta.org
Email: info@overturewiththearts.org
Phone: 514 889 8678
Address: CA
Information: Overture with the Arts (OWTA) is a non-profit organization based in Montreal, offering education in music, dance, drama and vocal training. The free and low-cost programs enable young people to pursue their passion in the performing arts when they wouldn't otherwise have the finances to afford classes. OWTA helps kids find a creative outlet for self-exPression and builds confidence and poise. Since 2009 approximately 20, 000 youth have benefitted from their after-school programs and school tours. Member of ISPA
Country: Canada

Place des Arts
Website: placedesarts.com
Email: info@placedesarts.com
Phone: 514 285 4200
Address: 260, blvd. de Maisonneuve West, CA
Information: This organisation plays a vital role on the Québec and Montréal stage. Not only is it at the forefront of the development of local performing arts and Québec's openness to the international Artistic world, it is also one of the key players. Its more than four decades of history are marked by superb events and discoveries. Member of ISPA
Country: Canada

Professional Association of Canadian Theatres (PACT)
Website: www.pact.ca
Email: info@pact.ca
Phone: 416 595 6455
Address: 215 Spadina Avenue, , Suite 555, CA
Information: PACT works on behalf of its member theatre companies in four major areas: advocacy, communications, labour relations, and professional development. ISPA member
Country: Canada

Réseau des Organisateurs de Spectacles de l'Est du Québec Inc (ROSEQ)
Website: www.roseq.qc.ca
Email: roseq@globtrotter.net
Phone: 418 722 9310
Address: 84 Rue Saint Germain Est, Bureau 203, CA
Information: ca 200 members in different towns, that act as local organisers of concerts
Country: Canada

Réseau Indépendant des Diffuseurs d'Événements Artistiques Unis (RIDEAU)
Website: www.rideau-inc.qc.ca
Email: admin@rideau-inc.qc.ca
Phone: 514 598 8353
Address: 1550 St. Joseph E. Blvd, CA
Country: Canada

Royal Canadian College of Organists
Website: https:// www.rcco.ca/
Email: info@rcco.ca
Phone: 416 929 6400
Address: 414 – 15 Case Goods Lane Toronto, ON M5A 3C4 Canada
Information: The RCCO provides support to its members in the development and practice of fine organ and choral performance and sound church musicianship, and works to promote these interests to the wider Canadian public
Country: Canada

Service des Communications et des Relations avec les Citoyens
Website: www.ville.montreal.qc.ca/culture
Email: crocher@ville.montreal.qc.ca
Phone: 514 872 0425
Address: 303, rue Notre-Dame Est, bureau 2.710 (2nd

Elisabeth Möst

Flautist

The internationally
acclaimed flautist
has three shows
on tour right now,
including the
critic's favourite
*TAU: A Sign of
Change*

For booking enquiries, email emoest@web.de

floor), CA
Country: Canada

Society of Composers, Authors and Music Publishers of Canada (SOCAN)
Website: www.socan.ca
Email: wilsonb@socan.ca
Phone: 416 445 7108
Address: 41 Valleybrook Dr., CA
Information: the Society licenses public performance of music and distributes performance royalties to composers, lyricists, authors and music publishers; ASCAP, BMI and SESAC license the public performance of SOCAN's repertoire in the USA
Country: Canada

Springboard Performance
Website: www.springboardperformance.com
Email: info@springboardperformance.ca
Phone: 403 265 3230
Address: 2nd Floor, 205 8 Avenue SE, CA
Information: Springboard is a non-profit organization devoted to connecting artists, mediums, audiences, the body and the mind through physical contemporary creation. We facilitate artist and audience development, illuminate process, inspire creation, and encourage g
Country: Canada

Tangente
Website: www.tangente.qc.ca
Email: info@tangente.qc.ca
Phone: 514 525 5584
Address: 460, rue Ste-Catherine Ouest, #505, CA
Information: full season of contemporary, innovative dance presenting in an intimate theatre space
Country: Canada

The Dance Centre
Website: www.thedancecentre.ca
Email: info@thedancecentre.ca
Phone: 604 606 6400
Address: Scotiabank Dance Centre, Level 6, 677 Davie Street, CA
Information: established in 1986 as the resource centre for the dance profession and the public in British Columbia, The Dance Centre offers programmes supporting the professional development of dance artists, presents public performances and events, operates Scotiabank Dance Centre, Canada's flagship dance facility, and promotes BC dance
Country: Canada

Theatre Nova Scotia
Website: www.theatrens.ca
Email: theatrens@theatrens.ca
Phone: 902 425 3876
Address: 1113 Marginal Road, CA
Information: aim is to provide a voice for professional theatre and community theatre in Nova Scotia, and to encourage and support all aspects of live theatre through programs and services
Country: Canada

Toronto Alliance for the Performing Arts – TAPA
Website: www.tapa.ca
Email: info@tapa.ca
Phone: 416 536 6468
Address: 215 Spadina Avenue, Suite 210., CA
Information: TAPA is the voice of theatre, dance and opera in Toronto.
Country: Canada

Urban Music Association of Canada
Website: www.umacunited.com
Email: Marketing@umacunited.com
Phone: 416 504 7343
Address: 675 King Street West, Suite 210, CA
Information: established in 1996, UMAC – – The Urban Music Association of Canada – – serves as the lone music industry service provider for urban music in Canada & the work of Canadian urban cultural entrepreneurs
Country: Canada
Social Media: @UMACUnited www.facebook.com/umacunited

CHINA

China Academy of Arts
Website: eng.caa.edu.cn
Email: yb@caa.edu.cn
Phone: 571 871 64609
Address: No. 218, , Nan Shan Road, , Zhe Jiang Province,
Information: established by the Ministry of Culture of the Czech Republic on the date 1st January 1991
Country: China

China Audio Video Association
Website: www.chinaav.org
Email: cava2008@163.com
Phone: 106 512 2882 / 1
Address: No. A7, , Xi Rong Xian Hu Tong, , Xi Cheng District,
Information: alternative E-Mail: lad.horak@seznam.cz, coorganizer of European Festival of Accordion Orchestras

(April)
Country: China

China Heaven Creation International Performing Arts Co. Ltd
Website: www.heaven-creation.com
Email: china-art@heaven-creation.com
Phone: 105 120 6992
Address: 18F Huasheng International Building, No.12, Yabao Road, Chao Yang District
Country: China

China National Children's Art Theatre, China
Website: www.ccat.name
Email: ccat@ccat.name
Phone: 106 513 4115
Address: No. 64, , Dong An Men Dai Street, , Dong Cheng District,
Country: China

China National Culture & Art Co. Ltd (CNCAC)
Website: www.cncac.com
Email: office@cncac.com
Phone: 106 551 8888, 10 65546520
Address: 2nd Floor, Building C, Meihui Building, No.58, Dongzhong Street, Dong Cheng District
Information: China Culture and Art Co. Ltd. is the only company retained and indirectly controlled by the Ministry of Culture of the People's Republic of China. It is China's first central-level art import and export, central-level performance brokerage agency, and the perennial host and distribution organization of the central-level and national newspaper "Music Life".
Country: China

China Performing Arts Agency (CPAA) – Cultural Exchanges Division
Website: www.cpaa.com.cn
Email: cpaa@cpaa.cn
Phone: 106 403 1315
Address: No.25 A. 10th, East Beijing
Information: see also Presenters and Agents, alternatively contact on: 10-8402 5515; fax 10-8401 7671; email cpaa@cpaa.cn
Country: China

China Performing Arts Agency (CPAA) – Cultural Exchanges Division
Website: www.cpaa.com.cn
Email: cpaa@cpaa.cn
Phone: 108 402 5515
Address: A25 Dong Si Shitiao Street, Dongcheng District
Country: China

China Record Corporation (CRC)
Website: www.china-crc.com.cn
Email: crcjrout@126.com
Phone: 106 525 3768 / 1
Address: Xun Mai Jin Zhuan Building level 22, , Jia No. 52, San Huan (Nan) Southern Road, , Chao Yang Eastern District,
Country: China

Chinese Dancers' Association
Email: rv.oad@omadeg.cz
Phone: 106 500 5779
Address: 16F, Wen Lian Building, , 10 Nong Zhan Guan Nan Li, , Chao Yang District
Information: funded by government; Chinese traditional dance
Country: China

Chinese Dramatists' Association
Website: www.concert-melodrama.com
Email: hfj@chinavista.com
Phone: 106 403 3923
Address: No.52, Alley 8, , Dongsi, , Dong Cheng District
Country: China

Chinese Musicians' Association (CMA)
Website: www.musician.org.cn
Email: info@musician.org.cn
Phone: 106 500 5451
Address: No. 10, , Nan Li, , Nong Zhan Guang, Chang Yang District,
Country: China

Chinese Theatre Association
Website: www.scenograf.dk
Email: ds@scenograf.dk
Phone: 640 33923
Address: No.52, Alley 8, Dongsi
Information: organises Chinese Opera Festival every two years
Country: China

Federation of Literary and Art Circles, China
Website:
www.cflac.org.cn
Email: cflac@126.com
Phone: 336 96500
Address: No. 32, No.1 Bei Sha Tan, , Chao Yang District,
Information: funding of the CFLAC comes from state allocations, membership dues and donations from the

public
Country: China

Foshan Bureau of Culture
Website: www.fswenhua.gov.cn
Email: fswenhua@fswenhua.gov.cn
Phone: 757 830 31825
Address: Level 8, No. 2, Shi Fu Da Yuan, , No. 12, Lin Nan Da Dao, Chan Cheng District
Information: Foshan Bureau of Culture is a small organisation in the educational cooperative organisations industry located in Foshan, China.
Country: China

Fujian Province Culture Authority
Website: www.fjwh.gov.cn
Email: fjwhxx@163.com
Phone: 860 591 876 6663
Address: Bei Fu 5/6F, , Zhong Fu Xi Hu Hua Yuan, No. 66, , Hu Bin Road,
Information: umbrella organisation for Danish Actors Association and Danish Association for Theatre Technicians e-mail: tef@tef.dk
Country: China

Guang Dong Province Culture Authority
Website: www.kunst.dk
Email: post@kulturstyrelsen.dk
Phone: 409 84929
Address: No 32 Shui Yin Si Heng Road
Information: The company promotes Artistic development in Denmark and Danish art abroad. The Council's two principal tasks are to provide support for Artistic endeavours within the fields of literature, the performing arts, the visual arts and music and to advise public authorities regarding matters within the Council's sphere of activity. It may also be referred to as 'Danish Arts Agency'. Member of ISPA
Country: China

He Nan Province Culture Authority
Website: www.dccd.dk
Email: hawh@hawh.cn
Phone: 371 655 06281 /
Address: No.11 Huang He Road
Country: China

Hei Long Jiang Province Culture Authority
Website: www.lwhxxj.cn
Email: dkf@komponistforeningen.dk
Phone: 451 826 40273
Address: No.197 Zhong Shan Road, Room 305, Nan Gang District, Hei Long Jiang
Information: membership organisation; The Danish Composers' Society has been set up for professional creators of art-music and sound-art, regardless of genre. It is the association's mission to support composers and sound artists in their efforts to make full use of their Artistic potentials.
Country: China

Hong Kong Dance Federation
Website: www.hkdf.org.hk/pages/index2.htm
Email: hkdf@netvigator.com
Phone: 331 35448
Address: 26B Grandion Plaza, 932 Cheung Sha Wan Rd
Information: see also Dance
Country: China

Inner Mongolia Autonomous Region Culture Authority
Website: www.dansenshus.dk
Email: nwhdgh@sina.com
Phone: 471 696 6206
Address: Inner Mongolia Cultural Buliding, , Xi Road, Wu Lan Cha Bu, , Inner Mongolia Autonomous Region
Information: Department of Dansens Hus: www.dansenshus.dk
Country: China

Inner Mongolia Autonomous Region Culture Authority
Website: www.dititu.dk
Email: nwhdgh@sina.com
Phone: 471 696 8114
Address: Inner Mongolia Cultural Buliding, Xi Road, Wu Lan Cha Bu, Inner Mongolia Autonomous Region
Country: China

Shanghai International Culture Association
Website: en.sica.sh.cn/
Email: office@sica.sh.cn
Phone: 216 473 0940
Address: 5F, No.1 Building, 543 Xinhua Road, Shanghai, China
Information: Shanghai International Culture Association (SICA) was founded in 1986 as a municipal-level people's organization that conducts non-governmental international cultural exchanges. Its function is to strengthen mutual understanding and friendly cooperation between Shanghai and the rest of the world. It serves to enhance Shanghai's economic growth, scientific progress, and cultural output through people to people engagement in international cultural exchange

Country: China

Shanghai Performing Arts Association
Website: www.dmf.dk
Email: ycjxhs@yahoo.com
Phone: 216 466 5710
Address: No. 597, , Fu Xing Zhong Road,
Country: China

Si Chuan Province Culture Authority
Website: www.sccnt.gov.cn
Email: Zyx@sccnt.gov.cn
Phone: 288 627 2987
Address: No. 19, , Dong Sheng Street,
Country: China

TV Artists Association, China
Website: www.ctaa.org.cn
Email: shixiewz@126.com
Phone: 338 88000
Address: 13/F, Wen Lian Building, 10 Nong Zhan Guan Nan Li, Chaoyang District
Information: Dansehallerne is a national resource for dance and choreography as well as an international forum for contemporary performative art, the only institution of its kind in Denmark. As a national centre, an international hub and an important actor in international networks, Dansehallerne is always engaged in development work to create the best possible conditions for Artistic production and audience out-reach in the whole country.
Country: China

COLUMBIA

Batuta Foundation
Website: www.fundacionbatuta.org
Email: mariaclaudiaparias@fundacionbatuta.org
Phone: 174 49510
Address: Calle 9 No. 8 – 97, Centro Histórico La Candelaria, CO
Information: The National Batuta Foundation was created in 1991 on the initiative of the national government in partnership with private enterprise. The main objective of the founders was to strengthen and enhance the enjoyment, practice and teaching of music in the country and create greater opportunities for the exercise of the cultural rights of Colombian children.
Member of ISPA
Country: Columbia

Colombia Ministry of Culture
Website: www.mincultura.gov.co
Email: prensamincultura@mincultura.gov.co
Phone: 156 19213
Address: Carrera 8, CO
Information: the Ministry of Culture is the governing entity of the Colombian cultural sector and has as its objective the formulation, coordination, execution and control of State policy in culture, sports, recreation and leisure time matters. It is an organisation that acts in good faith, with ethical integrity and observes relevant norms for the benefit of the community, clients and its own officials. Member of ISPA
Country: Columbia

ECUADOR

Fundacion Teatro Nacional Sucre
Website: www.teatrosucre.com/
Email: comunicacion@teatrosucre.com
Phone: 295 1661
Address: Manabí N8-131 entre Guayaquil y Flores, EC
Information: member of ISPA
Country: Ecuador

EGYPT

Haraka Dance Development and Research
Website: www.harakaproject.org
Email: info@harakaproject.org
Address: 1 Ahmed Shokry Street, Tahrir Square, EG
Information: HaRaKa is a project that started in 2006 in Cairo – Egypt, focusing on dance research and methods of supporting, producing, promoting and archiving contemporary dance and body-based practices, which makes it the first program in Egypt with such nature.
Member of ISPA
Country: Egypt

Tamasi Performing Arts Collective
Website: www.tamasicollective.org
Email: info@tamasicollective.org
Phone: 121 113 8330
Address: 2 AbdelHamdi Said St, EG
Information: TAMASI is a collective of 11 performing arts organisations from Egypt, Jordan, Lebanon, and Palestine working locally, regionally and internationally. The organisations have been identified for their experience, diversity & Artistic excellence, in addition to their firm commitment and strong vision for arts and culture as a pivotal contributor to the achievement of social and political justice. They have come together to strengthen,

individually and collectively, our capacity to increase access to resources, withstand marginalisation of the arts, break the isolation of Arab artists in General and Palestinian artists in particular

GUATEMALA

Fundación Paíz para la Educación y la Cultura
Website: www.fundacionpaiz.org.gt
Email: info@fundacionpaiz.org.gt
Phone: 246 44545
Address: 11 Avenida 33-32 Zona 5, GT
Country: Guatemala

HONG KONG

Association of Hong Kong Dance Organisations
Website: zethyrto.com
Email: tslzethyr@yahoo.com.hk
Phone: 241 70792
Address: 6F, Rear Block, 100 Chung On St, Tseun Wan, New Territories, HK
Information: more than 30 dance groups and school members over Hong Kong
Country: Hong Kong

Chamber Music Society, Hong Kong
Website: www.chambermusic.homestead.com
Email: chambermus@yahoo.com
Phone: 852 536 4567
Address: GPO Box 5987, HK
Information: Society concerts are usually held on Tuesdays, Wednesdays and Thursdays. The Society normally does not present concerts in July, August and December
Country: Hong Kong

Chinese Artists Association of Hong Kong
Email: hkbarwo@netvigator.com
Phone: 277 07956
Address: 4/F Block A Prospect Building, 493 Nathan Rd., Kowloon distric, HK
Information: nearly 1100 members; see also Opera
Country: Hong Kong

Composers and Authors Society of Hong Kong Ltd.
Website: www.cash.org.hk
Email: General@cash.org.hk
Phone: 284 63268
Address: 18F, Universal Trade Centre, 3 Arbuthnot Road Central, HK
Information: non-profit making, to promote and sponsor musical activities, encourage local composition and award music scholarships to improve the local standard of music.
Country: Hong Kong

Dance Alliance, Hong Kong
Website: www.hkdanceall.org
Email: hkdalli@netvigator.com
Phone: 858 522 58487
Address: c/o Graduate Education Center, HKAPA, 1 Gloucester Road, , HK
Information: the official Hong Kong organization of the World Dance Alliance
Country: Hong Kong

Folkdance Association of Hong Kong
Website: www.geocities.com/folkdancehk
Email: folkdancehk@yahoo.com.hk
Phone: 810 72026
Address: PO Box 79278, Mongkok Post Office, Kowloon, HK
Country: Hong Kong

Hong Kong Drama/Theatre and Education Forum (TEFO)
Website: www.tefo.hk
Email: info@tefo.hk
Phone: 258 20215
Address: 8/F, Hong Kong Arts Centre, No 2, Harbour Road, Wan Chai, , HK
Information: more than 150 members members, also organizes congresses
Country: Hong Kong

Jingkun Theatre Limited
Website: jingkun.org.hk
Email: jingkun@jingkun.org.hk
Phone: 280 52577
Address: Unit 18, 12/F, Metro Centre ⊠, 21 Lam hing St., Kowloon Bay, HK
Information: non-profit making & charitable organisation; see also Opera (Performing Companies)
Country: Hong Kong

Leisure and Cultural Services – Cultural Presentation office
Website: www.lcsd.gov.hk/CE/CulturalService/Programme/en/aboutus.html
Email: cp2@lcsd.gov.hk
Phone: 699 9150
Address: Cultural Presentations Section, HK
Information: activities of the Cultural Endowment are governed by a Supervisory Board. The Board makes

principle decisions affecting the Endowment's activities and finances projects that embrace multiple areas of cultural activity
Country: Hong Kong

Leisure and Cultural Services – Festivals Office
Website: www.lcsd.gov.hk/en/cs_pa_festival.php
Email: fo@lcsd.gov.hk
Phone: 237 01044
Address: Level 5 Administration Bldg., HK Cultural Centre, 10 Salisbury Rd, Tsim Sha Tsui, Kowloon, Kowloon, HK
Information: alternative website: www.newvisionfestival.gov.hk
Country: Hong Kong

Leisure and Cultural Services Department – Festivals Office
Website: www.lcsd.gov.hk
Email: fo@lcsd.gov.hk
Phone: 274 11453
Address: Level 5, Administration Building, , Hong Kong Cultural Centre, 10 Salisbury Road, Tsim Sha Tsui, Kowloon, HK
Information: member of ISPA
Country: Hong Kong

Music Publishers Association of Hong Kong Ltd.
Website: www.kooriyhing.ee
Email: ampsltd@netvigator.com
Phone: 231 12701
Address: c/o peermusic S.E. Asia Ltd, Suite 627, 6/F., Ocean Centre, Harbour City, 5 Canton Road, Tsimshatshi, Kowloon, HK
Country: Hong Kong

Piano & Music Association, Hong Kong
Website: www.helilooja.ee
Email: heliloojate.liit@gmail.com
Phone: 857 288 8128 pag
Address: PO Box 1591, Shatin, N.T., HK
Information: members are mainly piano teachers, pianists, musicians and conductors
Country: Hong Kong

Piano Teachers Association, Hong Kong
Website: www.tantsuagentuur.ee
Email: hongkongpta@gmail.com
Phone: 271 18341
Address: 4F, Hannover Court, 87 Waterloo Road, Kowloon, HK
Information: non-profit making society; members should have a degree or diploma in piano performance or pedagogy, or substantial teaching experience; Associate membership open to undergraduates and others interested in piano education
Country: Hong Kong
Social Media: www.facebook.com/pages/The-Hong-Kong-Piano-Teachers-Association/213741622123282

INDIA

Artsforward Ideas and Events Pvt Ltd
Website: http:// www.artsforward.in
Email: info@artsforward.in
Phone: 983 009 0527
Address: CF 80 Salt Lake City, Kolkata, West Bengal 700064, India
Information: Artsforward designs strategic encounters between businesses and artists to create opportunities of nurturing the creative industries and their contribution to the community. As an ideation agency we work to create new and exciting stories for our brands that engage their target audiences in compelling and creative ways. We are a 7 year old outfit and work out of Kolkata and Bangalore. Our major areas of interest are the arts, youth, heritage and environmental sustainability. Members of ISPA
Country: India

INDONESIA

Arts Council (DKJ), Jakarta
Website: www.dkj.or.id/en
Email: dkj@centrin.net.id
Phone: 213 193 7639
Address: Taman Ismail Marzuki, Jl. Cikini Raya 73, ID
Information: supporting the arts and culture in Jakarta
Country: Indonesia

Gelar Nusantara PT
Website: www.gelar.co.id
Email: contact@gelar.co.id
Phone: 566 78695
Address: Joglo Rempoa Art House, Jl. Gelatik Ujung 1D, Rempoa, Ciputat, ID
Information: GELAR was established by Bram Kushardjanto and Kumoratih Kushardjanto dedicated to developing Indonesian art and cultural assets. It is acknowledged as a consultant and cultural program Producer. Its program includes stage productions, local and international touring, multi-media conservation and documentary programs, television programs, sustainable festival management, community development pro-

grams, sustainable travel and program consultancies for the government and corporate partners.
Country: Indonesia

Higher Education for the Arts (STSI Surakarta)
Website: www.stsi-ska.ac.id
Email: direct@stsi-ska.ac.id
Phone: 271 47658
Address: J1. Ki Hadjar Dewantara 19, Kentingan, Jebres, ID
Country: Indonesia

Jakarta Foundation for the Arts (YKJ)
Email: pia026@rad.net.id
Phone: 213 147 818
Address: Kompleks Kesenian TIM, Jl. Cikini Raya, ID
Country: Indonesia

Jakarta Institute of the Arts
Email: info@teater.ee
Phone: 622 743 71233
Address: Academic Administration Building, Jl. Parang Tritis Km 6.5, ID
Information: has information on Estonian productions ready for touring abroad and profiles on people connected to them and also annotations of contemporary Estonian plays that are translated and ready for productions abroad
Country: Indonesia

KELOLA Foundation
Website: www.kelolaarts.or.id
Email: kelola@cbn.net.id
Phone: 217 399 311
Address: Jl. Cikatomas II No. 33 Kebayoran Baru, ID
Country: Indonesia

Society for Indonesian Performing Arts (MSPI)
Website: www.mspi.org
Email: mspimail@cbn.net.id
Phone: 646 4517
Address: Gd. PKJ-TIM Taman Ismail Marzuki, Jl. Cikini Raya No. 73, ID
Country: Indonesia

Taman Ismail Marzuki Arts Center
Email: anneli.saro@ut.ee
Phone: 622 131 54087
Address: Kompleks Kesenian TIM, Jalan Cikini Raya, 73, ID
Country: Indonesia

JAPAN

Affinis Arts Foundation
Website: www.affinis.or.jp
Email: emik@emic.ee
Phone: 035 797 7135
Address: Akasaka Kaikan Building 4F, 2-13-5, Akasaka, Minato-ku, JP
Information: With the Affinis Ensemble Selection, we support the pro-competitive chamber music activities of professional orchestra members in Japan in hope of improving the development of Japanese music culture.
Country: Japan

Agency for Cultural Affairs
Website: www.bunka.go.jp
Email: info@sinfoniaorkesterit.fi
Phone: 813 359 52056
Address: 3-2-2 Kasumigaseki, Chiyoda-ku, JP
Information: The Association of Finnish Symphony Orchestras (Suosio) promotes and develops Finland's symphony and chamber orchestras, and safeguards their interests and rights. It was founded in 1965 and has been actively championing orchestral music ever since. It is here primarily to ensure the maximum well-being of Finnish orchestras: to see that they have sufficient funding, that their activities are made known, and that their standards are as high as possible. Member of ISPA.
Country: Japan

Aichi Arts & Culture Network (ANET)
Website: www1.odn.ne.jp/anet
Email: anet@tree.odn.ne.jp
Phone: 522 317 171
Address: Nagoya City Naka Ward Sakae 1-14-14, Misono Palace No. 202, JP
Information: Based in Aichi Prefecture, it is a private cross-cutting organization organized by leading artists and arts and cultural groups. Based on horizontal collaboration and exchange across genres, we are developing various businesses to promote Aichi's art culture.
In order to make Artistic and cultural activities leap further rich, being able to create horizontal connections across genres is a great force. Such an organization is quite unique across the country.
Experts cooperate and speak out to the outside, such as Administration. The existence of the association is now well recognized, and its remarks are received with weight. Being an ANET member gives you pride as well as a sense of art culture.
Country: Japan

Aichi Arts Center
Website: www.aac.pref.aichi.jp
Phone:
052 971 5511
Address: 1-13-2 Higashisakura, Higashiku, JP
Information: The Aichi Arts Center is a consolidated culture facility constructed by Aichi Prefecture. With its sights set on the future, it now acts as a major focus to promote activities in culture and the arts.
The Aichi Arts Center is composed of the following four facilities:
The Aichi Prefectural Museum of Art, the Aichi Prefectural Art Theater, Aichi Prefectural Arts Promotion Service, the Aichi Prefectural Library.
Country: Japan

All Japan Accordion & Harmonica Federation
Website: www.tombo-m.co.jp
Email: info@tombo-m.co.jp
Phone: 033 802 2105
Address: 2-37-22 Nishi Nippori, Arakawa-ku, JP
Information: produces and supports the creation and distribution of accordions
Country: Japan

All Japan Band Association
Website: www.ajba.or.jp
Email: info@ajba.or.jp
Phone: 033 234 6028
Address: 24th Sanbancho, Chiyoda-ku, JP
Information: membership organisation; holds various competitions throughout the year for different styles of Japanese music in schools including marching and brass bands
Country: Japan

All Japan Children's Dance Association
Website: www.jidoubuyou.or.jp
Email: info@skr.fi
Phone: 033 915 2153
Address: 3rd Leiden Building 4F, 1-56-12 Nishigahara, Kita-ku, JP
Information: aims to improve the quality and technique of child dancers and promote the art of childrens dance across Japan
Country: Japan

All Japan Concert Hall Association
Website: www.sunplaza.jp
Email: qa-sogo-ml@sunplaza.jp
Phone: 333 881 151
Address: 4-1-1, Nakano, Nakano-ku, JP
Information: has its own venue for performances called the Sun Plaza Hall
Country: Japan

All Japan Folk Performing Arts Association
Website: www.jfpaa.jp
Email: info@jfpaa.jp
Address: 206, Mikawadai Heights, 4-3-6 Roppongi, Minato-ku, JP
Information: membership organisation; Japan Folk Performing Arts Association was established in 1973, for the purpose of reservation and promotion of folk performing arts of Japan
Country: Japan

All Japan Harmonica Federation
Website: www.tombo-m.co.jp
Email: info@tombo-m.co.jp
Phone: 033 802 2105
Address: 2-37-22 Nishi-Nippori, Arakawa-ku, JP
Information: membership organisation; creates and distributes harmonicas across Japan and the world
Country: Japan

Arion-Edo Foundation
Website: www.performingarts.jp/E/society/0708/1.html
Email: info@arion-edo.org
Phone: 354 650 755
Address: OT Building, @F, 1-46-9, Tomigawa, Shibuya-ku, JP
Information: the Arion-Edo Foundation is promoting the musical arts of Japan by offering prizes and grants for young musicians and organising various types of concerts
Country: Japan

Asahi Beer Arts Foundation
Website: www.asahibeer.co.jp/culture/ab-art/index.html
Email: partisan@nic.fi
Phone: 813 560 85201
Address: 1-23-1 Azumabashi, Sumida-ku, JP
Country: Japan

Asahi Shimbun Foundation
Website: www.esek.fi
Email: asahizaidan@ma.neweb.ne.jp
Phone: 968 03400
Address: 4F Asahi Bldg., 6-6-7 Ginza, Chuo-ku, JP
Country: Japan

Association for Cultural Exchange (ACE), Japan
Website: www.acejapan.or.jp
Email: ace@acejapan.or.jp
Phone:
913 56796
Address: 4F, Akasaka 1-chome Mori Bldg., 1-11-28, Akasaka, Minato-ku, JP
Information: provides Japan Performing Arts Net: www.jpan.org; alternative E-mail address: jpan@acejapan.or.jp
Country: Japan

Association for Japanese Noh Plays
Website: www.nohgaku.or.jp
Email: office@nohgaku.or.jp
Phone: 359 253 871
Address: Sohshu-Bldg., 4-40-13 Takadanobaba, Shinju-ku-ku, JP
Country: Japan

Association for Young Artists
Website: www.seinen-geijutuka.org
Email: info@seinen-geijutuka.org
Phone: 332 601 832
Address: 6-56 Kagurazaka, Shinjuku-ku, JP
Information: Music Finland promotes awareness and the success of Finnish music at home and abroad
Country: Japan

Association of Children's Songwriters in Japan
Website: www.douyou.jp
Email: doyo@sweet.ocn.ne.jp
Phone: 332 635 766
Address: 7F Gobancho Grand Bldg., 3-1 Goban-cho, Chiyoda-ku, JP
Country: Japan

Association of Japanese Symphony Orchestras
Website: www.orchestra.or.jp
Email: tutti@orchestra.or.jp
Phone: 356 107 275
Address: 7F Arca Central, 1-2-1 Kinshi, Sumida-ku, JP
Country: Japan

Association of Japanese Theatre Companies
Website: www1.biz.biglobe.ne.jp/
Email: Gekidankyo@aol.com
Phone: 333 418 151
Address: 4F Sawada 2nd Bldg., 3-35-5 Shinjuku, Shinju-ku-ku, JP
Country: Japan

Association of Kanze
Website: www.kanzekai.com
Email: tnl@tnl.fi
Phone: 813 346 95566
Address: 1-16-4 Shohtoh, Shibuya-ku, JP
Information: Kanze is one of the major schools of Noh play; the Association was founded in 1900
Country: Japan

Association of Public Theatres and Halls in Japan (KOUBUNKYO)
Website: kor.theapro.kr
Email: bunka@zenkoubun.jp
Phone: 353 530 320
Address: PO Box 2572 Tokyo Opera City Tower 11F, 3-20-2 Nishi-Shinjuku, Shinjuku-ku, JP
Information: a public corporation affiliated with the Ministry of Education; has 1396 public theatres and halls as its member; PLAZA, its information centre, opened in 1995 to encourage communication among administrators and artists
Country: Japan

Biwako Hall Foundation
Website: www.biwako-hall.or.jp/
Email: koho@biwako-hall.or.jp
Phone: 775 237 133
Address: 15-1 Uchidehama, Ohtsu, JP
Country: Japan

Bunraku Association
Website: www.bunraku.or.jp
Phone: 662 111 350
Address: c/o National Bunraku Theatre, 1-12-10 Nipponbashi, Chuo-ku, JP
Information: Administration des Droits des Artistes et Musiciens Interprètes manages the intellectual copyrights for artists/performers, singers, musicians, conductors, comedians and dancers. It deals with everyone whose recorded performances have been broadcast, and is therefore an essential collective management tool for every professional category.
Country: Japan

Butai Geijutsu Kankyo Forum
Website: www.arcade-paca.com
Email: arcade@arcade-paca.com
Phone: 334 660 552
Address: 3F Nanheidai Heits, 4-13 Nanheidai, Shibuya-ku, Setagaya-ku, JP
Information: the Arcade supports the development of the performing arts sector of Provence-Alpes-Côte d'Azur

Country: Japan

Chikuzen-Biwa Federation
Website: www.artfactories.net
Email: e-fujimaki@jcom.home.ne.jp
Phone: 467 519 798
Address: c/ o Kyokkou Fujimaki, 6-11-29, Kagawa, JP
Information: Chikuzen-Biwa is a type of Japanese classical flute; alternative address: President: Kyokusoh Tachibana, Chikuzen-Biwa Dantai, 903, Pviyon-Meguro, 1-3-31 Meguro, meguro-ku, Tokyo 153-0063
Country: Japan

Contemporary Dance Association of Japan
Website: www.alpha-net.ne.jp/modance
Email: modance@m13.alpha-net.ne.jp
Phone: 334 004 544
Address: 1-6-2 Shibuya, Shibuya-ku, JP
Information: The ABC is 75 years old and full of stories to tell. Stemming from the post-war popular education movements, the association initiated and supported the development of cultural life in Dijon and the entire region.
Country: Japan

Copyright Research & Information Center
Website: www.cric.or.jp
Email: copyright@cric.or.jp
Phone: 353 536 921
Address: 11F Tokyo Opera City Tower, 3-20-2 Nishi-Shinjuku, Shinjuku-ku, JP
Information: founded in 1959 by the following four bodies: the Japan Broadcasting Corporation NHK, the National Association of Commercial Broadcasters in Japan NAB, the Japanese Society for Rights of Authors, Composers and Publishers JASRAC and the Recording Industry
Country: Japan

Dentsu Institute for Human Studies
Website: www.dihs.dentsu.co.jp
Phone: 335 751 711
Address: Dentsu Ginza Bldg., 7-4-17 Ginza, Chuo-ku, JP
Information: The Cdmc is a link between composers, performers and organisers for innovative projects. It encourages new repertories as well as taking part in promoting works with programmers.
The Cdmc regularly organises encounters, seminars and professional day sessions; these events facilitate an exchange of ideas between specialists and professionals, and allow composers and performers to get together. The Cdmc's catalogue lists numerous documents concerning 16, 000 contemporary works: symphonic music, chamber music, opera, music theatre, electroacoustic music, etc.
Country: Japan

Division of Japan Choral Association, Zen-Nippon Gassho Renmei
Website: www.jcanet.or.jp
Email: jcme@jcanet.or.jp
Phone: 334 401 161
Address: 6F Yaginuma Bldg., 1-5-8 Ebisu, Shibuya-ku, JP
Information: also organizes workshops, the World Symposium on Choral Music in Kyoto, Japan
Country: Japan

Forval Foundation
Website: www.forvalfoundation.org
Email: info@forvalfoundation.org
Phone: 354 743 699
Address: 411 Tokyo Central Omotesando, 4-3-15 Jingumae, Shibuya-ku, JP
Country: Japan

Foundation for Promoting Music Education
Website: www.onkyozaidan.or.jp
Email: contact@cndc.fr
Phone: 353 857 738
Address: 2-7-6 Nakano, Nakano-ku, JP
Country: Japan

Foundation for the Kanze School Library
Website: www.kanze.net
Email: contact@domaine-musiques.com
Phone: 354 371 334
Address: 5-9-3-301 Ozaki, Shinagawa-ku, JP
Information: specialized resource centre, focused on the development of cultural, performing arts and music scene in the region; offers services primarily in terms of information, observation, advice, expertise, support, qualification, coordination and networking
Country: Japan

Foundation Library Centre of Japan
Website: www.eucreafrance.fr
Email: eucrea.france@wanadoo.fr
Phone: 147 978 726
Address: Josei Zaidan Shiryo Centre, JP
Information: see Japan Foundation Centre
Country: Japan

Foundation Modern Puppet Centre
Website: www.deaf-puppet.or.jp

Email: deaf@deaf-puppet.or.jp
Phone: 447 772 228
Address: 3-10-31 Ida, Nakahara-ku, Kawasaki, JP
Information: member of EMU, a non-governmental organisation regrouping 20 National Federations of music schools; groups about 12000 schools in total
Country: Japan

Fukuoka Culture Foundation
Website: www.fcb.co.jp/bunkazaidan
Email: cdesbordes@fevis.com
Phone: 924 721 676
Address: 3-1-1 Hakata Ekimae, Hakata-ku, JP
Information: FEVIS is a collective of French tax-registered professional vocal and instrumental ensembles regardless of musical structure or repertoire with legal independence or operating independently under the auspices of a larger legal structure
Country: Japan

Gendai Hohgaku Sakkyokuka Renmei
Website: www.francefestivals.com
Email: contact@francefestivals.com
Phone: 339 907 813
Address: c/o Mr Hohzan Yamamoto, 2-40-23 Fujimidai, Nerima-ku, JP
Information: the Federation helps member festivals to develop their Artistic identity and to promote the economic, social and cultural contribution they make to France both regionally and nationally
Country: Japan

Gidayu Kyokai
Website: www.gidayu.or.jp/
Email: am-giday@gidayu.or.jp
Phone: 335 415 471
Address: 3F Bunmeido, 4-13-11, Ginza, Chuo-ku, JP
Information: Gidayu is an accompanying narrative chanting to Bunraku doll puppetry
Country: Japan

Gotoh Memorial Foundation
Website: www.la-nouvelleaquitaine.fr
Email: gotoh_mf@01.246.ne.jp
Phone: 334 776 671
Address: 1-21-6 Dohgenzaka, Shibuya-ku, JP
Information: The Regional Committee of Performing Professions, COREPS Nouvelle-Aquitaine, is today the only body where the professional organizations and the representatives of the State, the local authorities and the joint bodies meet.
Country: Japan

Hakuhodo Institute of Life and Living
Website: www.athill.com
Email: info@athill.com
Phone: 332 336 450
Address: 3-22 Kanda Nishiki-machi, Chiyoda-ku, JP
Country: Japan

Hosei University Institute of Nogaku Studies
Website: www.hosei.ac.jp/
Email: info@leslaboratoires.org
Phone: 332 649 815
Address: 2-17-1 Fujimi, Chiyoda-ku, JP
Information: artists in residence, organise 2 shows per year over a period of 6 months
Country: Japan

Hoshikawa Yoshio Art and Education Institute
Website: www.nyudougumo.com
Email: info@nyudougumo.com
Phone: 339 647 857
Address: 1-25-18 Kasuga-cho, Nerima-ku, JP
Information: enquiries from overseas drama, musical, puppet theatre companies are always welcome
Country: Japan

Hyogo Arts & Culture Association
Website: www.hyogo-arts.or.jp
Email: contact@cpdo.fr
Phone: 783 212 001
Address: 6F Hyogo Kenminkaikan, 4-16-3 Shimoyamate-dori, Chuo-ku, Kobe, JP
Information: see also Presenters and Venues (Hyogo Performing Arts Center)
Country: Japan

Inamori Foundation
Website: www.inamori-f.or.jp
Email: sec@inamori-f.or.jp
Phone: 752 552 688
Address: KI shijyo building, 88 Kankoboko-cho, Shimogyo-ku, JP
Country: Japan

Information Centre for Performing Arts & Entertainment
Website: www.geidankyo.or.jp
Email: infope@geidankyo.or.jp
Phone: 353 536 600
Address: c/o Geidankyo, Tokyo Opera City Tower 11F, 3-20-2 Nishi-shinjuku, Shinjuku-ku, JP
Country: Japan

Institute for the Arts (IFA)
Website: netcity.or.jp/ifa/
Email: bunka@ifa.co.jp
Phone: 335 820 011
Address: 2F, Fres Akasaka Bldg., 1-9-29 Akasaka, Minato-ku, JP
Information: formerly known as Pia Institute for the Arts, is now an independent organisation
Country: Japan

Institute of Dramatic Arts (DARTS)
Website: www.bekkoame.ne.jp
Email: darts@bekkoame.ne.jp
Phone: 339 445 451
Address: 2-29-10 Honkomagome, Bunkyo-ku, JP
Information: The company Opéra Éclaté, created in 1986 as an extension of the Saint-Céré Festival, specializes in the production of musical theater and Opera adaptable to national distribution. It is dedicated to meeting all audiences and to discovering and integrating young artists. At the same time, she develops creative projects around the repertoire of French song, world music and jazz.
Country: Japan

Japan Actors Union
Website: www.nippairen.com
Email: postmaster@nippairen.com
Phone: 353 681 687
Address: 2F Sumiyoshi-cho-Ohta Bldg., 2-11, Sumiyoshicho, Shinjuku-ku, JP
Information: Parallèle is production platform for international artists based in Marseille. It works for the development of Artistic projects, within and from Marseille and its surroundings, at an international scale. Festival Parallèle, a highlight of visibility for the Platform, shares such forms with an ever-increasing and dedicated audience. At the heart of the programme lie the projects by the artists supported in terms of production-distribution.
Country: Japan

Japan Art Academy
Website: www.geijutuin.go.jp
Email: jimubu@geijutuin.go.jp
Phone: 338 217 191
Address: 1-30 Ueno Koen, Taitoh-ku, JP
Country: Japan

Japan Arts Culture Federation
Website: www.t-onkyo.jp
Email: 1acte@1acte.fr
Phone: 332 143 591
Address: 2F Fuji-Bldg, 3-2-3 Marunouchi, Chiyoda-ku, JP
Information: benefit from the support of the ministry of culture
Country: Japan

Japan Arts Foundation
Website: www.jpartsfdn.org
Email: proquartet@proquartet.fr
Phone: 352 690 347
Address: 10F, 13-7 Minami Moto-machi, Shinjuku-ku, JP
Information: non-profit association that produces concert series and festivals of chamber music; organizes master classes for young professional ensembles; initiates awareness to a wider public; enriches chamber music repertoire by commissioning new works for today's composers
Country: Japan

Japan Association for Cultural Economics
Website: www.jace.gr.jp/
Email: info@jace.gr.jp
Phone: 359 093 068
Address: c/o Geidankyo, 2F Geinoukadensha, 6-12-30 Nishi-shinjuku, Shinjuku-ku, JP
Information: organises Le Festival Chopin.
Country: Japan

Japan Association of Classical Music Presenters
Website: www.classic.or.jp/
Email: info@classic.or.jp
Phone: 156 695 858
Address: 402 Grand Plaza Uchikawa, , 2-21-16, Kami-osaki, Shinagawa, JP
Information: member of International Artist Managers' Association (IAMA)
Country: Japan

Japan Association of Major Theaters
Website: www.enkokyo.or.jp
Email: enko453m@enkokyo.or.jp
Phone: 335 613 977
Address: 602, 1-27-8 Ginza, Chuo-ku, JP
Country: Japan

Japan Association of Music Enterprises (JAME)
Website: www.jame.or.jp
Email: Jame@jame.or.jp
Phone: 334 044 133
Address: 7F NH Aoyama Bldg., 3-2-5 Kita-Aoyama, Minato-ku, JP
Country: Japan

Japan Association of Theatre Designers and Technicians (JATDT), Nihon Butai Bijutsuka Kyokai
Website: www.jatdt.com
Email:
contact@svbretagne.fr
Phone: 354 083 644
Address: 201 Tsuda Bldg., , 6-18-2, Shinbashi, Minato-ku, JP
Information: supports, funds and develops the dissemination of the professional Artistic companies that are based in Brittany
Country: Japan

Japan Biwa Music Association
Website: www.spedidam.fr
Email: spedidam@wanadoo.fr
Address: 305 Shinjuku Parkside Nagatani, 4-14-7 Nishi-Shinjuku, Shinjuku-ku, JP
Information: Biwa is a Japanese lute
Country: Japan

Japan Cello Society (JCS)
Website: www.jcs.gr.jp
Email: contact@snepmusique.com
Phone: 335 051 001
Address: c/o Suntory Hall, 1-13-1Akasaka, Minato-ku, JP
Country: Japan

Japan Center, Pacific Basin Arts Communications (PARC)
Website: www.parc-jc.org
Email: parc@jah.ne.jp
Phone: 357 244 660
Address: 3-1-2-3F Ebisu-minami, Shibuya, JP
Information: host organisation of the Tokyo Performing Arts Market – together with the Japan Foundation and the Japan Foundation for Regional Arts Activities
Country: Japan
Social Media: @P_A_R_C www.facebook.com/pacificbasinartscommunication

Japan Chamber Music Foundation (JCMF)
Website: www.jcmf.or.jp/competition
Email: osaka-comp@jcmf.or.jp
Phone: 669 472 184
Address: 2-2-33 Shiromi, Chuo-ku, JP
Country: Japan

Japan Choral Association (JCA)
Website: www.jcanet.or.jp/
Phone: 355 407 813
Address: c/o Asahi Shimbun, 5-3-2 Tsukiji, Chuo-ku, JP
Information: has approx. 5000 members
Country: Japan

Japan Choral Directors Association
Website: www.themaa-marionnettes.com
Email: jcda@d3.dion.ne.jp
Phone: 339 527 207
Address: 402, 3-2-18 Shimo-Ochiai, Shinjuku-ku, JP
Information: Founded in 1992, THEMAA – National Association of Puppet Theaters and Associated Arts – unites more than 300 members. THEMMA is the French center of UNIMA – Union Internationale de la Marionnette. Also a member of the UFISC – Union Fédérale d'Intervention des Structures Culturelles – on which it relies to include the issues of the puppet arts sector in the broader field of questions related to performing arts as a whole.
Country: Japan

Japan Committee of Music and Dance
Website: www.5c.biglobe.ne.jp/onbukai
Email: onbukai@mua.biglobe.ne.jp
Phone: 333 697 496
Address: #305, 4-1-6, Takadanobaba, Shinjyuku, JP
Information: also organize Festival 'Mino' more information on www.festivalmino.fr ; see also Promoters
ogodart@lesjmf.org
areveillon@lesjmf.org
sarcelin@lesjmf.org
fbouanani@lesjmf.org
dmaignant@lesjmf.org
Country: Japan

Japan Directors Association Nihon Enshutusha Kyokai
Website: www.uspa.fr
Email: japan-Director-a@mail.goo.ne.jp
Phone: 333 558 287
Address: 507 Shinjuku-Gyoen Daikan Plaza, 1-31-7 Shinjuku, Shinjuku-ku, JP
Information: consists of 510 members
Country: Japan

Japan Federation of Composers (JFC) Inc.
Website: www.composer.or.jp
Email: info@composer.or.jp
Phone: 354 741 853
Address: 311 Dai-5 Sky Bldg., 3-3-8 Sendagaya, Shibuya-ku, JP
Information: Associate member of International Society for Contemporary Music ISCM
Country: Japan

Japan Federation of Musicians
Website: www.jfm.or.jp
Email:
jfm@jfm.or.jp
Phone: 334 376 837
Address: 2F Kaga Bldg, 5-2-8 Toranomon, Minato-ku, JP
Information: a villa that artists and groups can hire out for residencies and small conferences
Country: Japan

Japan Flutists Association
Phone: 334 427 420
Address: 604 Meguro New Heim, 2-13-32 Kami-Osaki, Shinagawa-ku, JP
Country: Japan

Japan Folk Performing Arts Association
Website: www.caucasusfoundation.ge/camn
Email: camn-info@lingua.edu.ge
Phone: 339 820 402
Address: c/o Mr Harumitsu Hosei, 1004 Maison Asahi, 2-24-2 Ikebukuro, Toshima-ku, JP
Information: alternative e-mail: IURI@caucasusfoundation.ge; see also International Organisations
Country: Japan

Japan Harp Association
Email: jphpass@jasmine.ocn.ne.jp
Phone: 354 235 666
Address: 201, 2-13-20 Kami-Osaki, Shinagawa-ku, JP
Country: Japan

Japan Internet Co Ltd.
Website: www.jin.ne.jp
Email: maka@gacgeorgia.org
Phone: 322 93133
Address: c/o Japan Center for Intercultural Communications, 2-7-7 Hirakawa-cho, Chiyoda-ku, JP
Country: Japan

Japan Music Foundation (JESC)
Website: www.jesc-music.org
Phone: 334 994 530
Address: 1F Kohcho Bldg., 2-1-6 Shibuya, Shibuya-ku, JP
Country: Japan

Japan Opera Companies Association
Website: www.jof.or.jp
Email: jof@jof.or.jp
Phone: 354 663 185
Address: c/o Nihon Opera Shinkokai, 8F Nishiazabu 28 Mori Bldg., 4-16-13 Nishi-Azabu, Minato-ku, JP
Information: See CAMN for further information.
Country: Japan

Japan Opera Foundation
Website: www.jof.or.jp
Email: jof@jof.or.jp
Phone: 354 663 185
Address: 8F Nishi-Azabu 28 Mori Bldg., 4-16-13 Nishi-Azabu, Minato-ku, JP
Information: manages Japan opera Companies Association (q.v.)
Country: Japan

Japan Operetta Society
Website: www.operettahouse.com
Email: operetta@fa.mbn.or.jp
Phone: 334 791 535
Address: Les Fleurs Nishiazabu 104, 1-4-35 Nishi-Azabu, Minato-ku, JP
Information: see entry under Opera for details
Country: Japan

Japan Performing Arts Foundacion
Website: www.jpaf.or.jp
Email: engekijin@jpaf.or.jp
Phone: 763 682 356
Address: Kami-Momose, Toga-mura, Nanto-shi, JP
Information: regional programmes coordinated by IBCCP International Bureau for Caucasian Cultural Programmes, educational programmes, management training centre, information centre; office in the Netherlands see also Stichting Caucasus Foundation (Promoter, Producer, Presenter) in Georgia and Netherlands

Japan Piano Technicians Association (JPTA)
Website: www.jpta.org/
Email: info@jpta.org
Phone: 332 553 897
Address: 5F Gakki Kaikan, 2-18-21 Soto-Kanda, Chiyoda-ku, JP
Country: Japan

Japan Playwrights Association
Website: www.jpwa.jp
Email: office@jpwa.jp
Phone: 357 383 150
Address: 1-24-5, 103, Komaba, Meguroku, JP
Country: Japan

Japan Puppeteers Association

Website: www.bp-berlin.com
Email: ningeki@mvf.biglobe.ne.jp
Phone: 333 760 456
Address: c/o Puk Ningyo Gekijo, 2-12-3 Yoyogi, Shibuya-ku, JP
Information: Directors' email: Director@bp-berlin.com
Country: Japan

Japan Sankyoku Association
Website: www.bund-der-theatergemeinden.de
Email: bund_tg@t-online.de
Phone: 335 859 916
Address: 403 Pearl Akasaka, 2-15-12 Akasaka, Minato-ku, JP
Information: Sankyoku is a type of Japanese classical music
Country: Japan

Japan Saxophonist Association
Website: www.homepage2.nifty.com/jsajsa/index.htm
Email: info@bbtk.de
Phone: 449 553 115
Address: 3-3-18 Chiyogaoka, Asao-ku, Kawasaki, JP
Information: association of ballet and dance theatre Directors for the purpose of mutual information and cooperation
Country: Japan

Japan Society for Contemporary Music
Website: www.jscm.net
Email: gen-on@jscm.net
Phone: 334 463 506
Address: 501 Yamaichi Bldg, 2-5-7 Higashi-Gotanda, Shinagawa-ku, JP
Information: organized ISCM World Music Days 2002, which was an international festival and annual event with contemporary music written by world wide composers
Country: Japan

Japan Symphony Foundation
Website: www.symphony.or.jp
Email: post@darstellende-kuenste.de
Phone: 332 532 032
Address: 4F Daini Kameda Bldg., 2-3-2 Awaji-cho, Kanda, Chiyoda-ku, JP
Information: The German Association of Independent Performing Arts is the federal umbrella organisation of all state associations for professional independent performing arts in Germany. Founded in 1990, it is today one of the largest theatre associations in the country. On a federal level, the association represents the interests of around 1.500 members nationwide – individual artists, groups, dance and theatre venues, and production structures.
Country: Japan

Japan Theatre Arts Association
Website: www.jtaa.or.jp
Email: info@jtaa.or.jp
Phone: 334 787 881
Address: c/o Kokuritsu Nohgakudo, 4-18-1 Sendagaya, Shibuya-ku, JP
Information: The Bundesverband Soziokultur e.V. currently represents around 600 self-governing sociocultural centers and initiatives in all parts of Germany. It was founded in 1979 as a registered, non-profit association. The federal association and its members, a total of 14 state working groups or state associations, have the task of supporting the work of the centres and initiatives at the state or federal level as well as representing their interests to the public and political bodies.
Country: Japan

Japan Union of Theatrical Companies for Children and Young People
Website: www.jienkyo.or.jp
Email: info@jienkyo.or.jp
Phone: 359 093 064
Address: Geino-Kadensha2-4, 6-12-30, Nishi-shinjuku, Shinjuku-ku, JP
Country: Japan

Japan Video Software Association
Website: www.jva-net.or.jp
Email: info@jva-net.or.jp
Phone: 335 424 433
Address: 3F, 26-gohkan, Tsukiji MF Bldg., 2-12-10 Tsukiji, Chuo-ku, JP
Information: cultural information and advice; promotion; presenter of all kinds of arts (literature, dance, drama, music
Country: Japan

Japanese Classical Dance Association Inc
Website: www.dresden.de/Culture.php
Email: nichibu@pd5.so-net.ne.jp
Phone:
335 336 455
Address: 210 Reimei Sky Resitel, 2-18-1 Kachidoki, Chuo-ku, JP
Information: The state capital Dresden promotes culture in a variety of ways. In addition to the city's cultural institutions, there are a large number of artists, associations and independent initiatives that are supported

within the framework of municipal cultural funding . Institutional funding serves to finance club activities, while project funding refers to individual projects with a limited duration.
Country: Japan

Japanese Cultural Mission
Website: www.class-germany.de
Email: class@classgermany.de
Phone: 663 446 685
Address: c/o Tanimura Yohsuke Office, 4F Daito Bldg., 2-1-39 Dohjima, Kita-ku, JP
Information: In the association CLASS – Association of Classical Independents in Germany e.V., independent sound Producers and distributors from the fields of classical music, world music and jazz have come together. While respecting the independence of all companies, CLASS undertakes joint activities for its members, such as trade fair and media appearances as well as advertising and Marketing activities.
Country: Japan

Japanese Federation of Dancing Artists
Website: www.buyorengo.com
Email: webmaster@buyorengo.com
Phone: 353 536 620
Address: 2-11-5-1105 Yoyogi, Shinjuku-ku, JP
Information: membership organisation; postaddress:Postfach 02 12 75
10124 Berlin
Country: Japan

Japanese Federation of Pueri Cantores
Email: geschaeftsstelle@dbft.de
Phone: 333 610 381
Address: 1-15-28 Hyakunin-cho, Shinjuku-ku, JP
Information: DBfT was founded in 1975 under the name "Association of Ballet Schools in Germany" and in 1983 initiated the award of the "German Dance Prize". This prize is awarded annually to personalities who have made a special contribution to Artistic dance in Germany.
The purpose of the professional association is to stand up for all professional concerns of its members and to ensure the quality of dance education at private schools for Artistic dance.
Country: Japan

Japanese Society for Rights of Authors, Composers and Publishers (JASRAC)
Website: www.jasrac.or.jp
Email: debue@buehnenverein.de
Phone: 334 812 121
Address: 3-6-12 Uehara, Shibuya-ku, JP
Information: The Deutsche Bühnenverein aims to preserve, promote and cultivate the unique diversity of its theater and orchestra landscape and its cultural offerings. In this sense, the stage association sees itself as an association that places art and culture as an indispensable part of urban life at the center of its endeavors. The Deutsche Bühnenverein is the association of interests and employers for theaters and orchestras. It addresses all Artistic, organizational and cultural-political issues.
Country: Japan

Japanese Society for Theatre Research
Website: www.soc.nii.ac.jp
Email: info@dbt-remscheid.de
Phone: 668 506 111 (swi
Address: 1-5 Kaneyama-, Toyonaka-shi, JP
Information: represents the whole spectrum of dance: modern dance, jazz dance, hip hop and contemporary dance
Country: Japan

Jyu-yonsei Kita Roppeita Kinen Zaidan
Website: www.kita-noh.com/
Email: info@kita-noh.com
Phone: 334 918 813
Address: 4-6-9 Kami-Osaki, Shinagawa-ku, JP
Information: school of Noh play
Country: Japan

Kabuki Hayashi Kyokai
Website: www.miz.org
Email: info@miz.org
Phone: 332 601 780
Address: c/ o Mr Denzaemon Tanaka, 28 Naka-machi, Shinjuku-ku, JP
Information: also manages Kansai Kageki Danq.v.
Country: Japan

Kansai Geijutsu Bunka Kyokai
Website: www.deutsches-tanzarchiv.de
Email: tanzarchiv@sk-kultur.de
Phone: 669 434 567
Address: 3F Uchi-Honmachi Green Bldg, 2-3-11 Uchi-Honmachi, Chuo-Ku, JP
Information: Deutsches Tanzarchiv Köln (German Dance Archive Cologne) is a globally networked information, documentation and research center for dance. With unique items in its inventory and adjacent exhibition space, it is among the most renowned archives for the

art of dance in the world.
In addition to preserving records and items related to the art of dance, the archive, founded in 1948 by Kurt Peters, is dedicated to their scholarly appraisal and presentation in exhibitions and publications.
Country: Japan

Kao Foundation for Arts and Sciences
Website: www.kao-foundation.or.jp
Email: IMS@mendelssohn-stiftung.de
Phone: 336 607 055
Address: 1-14-10 Nihombashi-Kayaba-cho, Chuo-ku, JP
Country: Japan

Katsushika Foundation for Culture and International Exchange
Website: www.kccf.or.jp
Email: portal@fidena.de
Phone: 356 702 222
Address: 6-33-1 Tateishi, Katsushika-ku, JP
Information: The Deutsche Forum für Figurentheatre and Puppenspiel Kunst (or dfp. The German Forum for Puppet Theatre and the Art of Puppetry) is a registered non-profit association based in Bochum. The institution is funded by the City of Bochum, the State of North Rhine-Westphalia, the Landschaftsverband Westfalen-Lippe and the Federal Government. The aim of the statutes is to promote the interests of puppet, figure and object theatre throughout Germany.
Country: Japan

Kokyoku Society
Website: www.gedok.de
Email: gedok@gedok.de
Phone: 335 710 216
Address: c/o Shinbashi Kaikan, 8-6-3 Ginza, Chuo-ku, JP
Information: Kokyoku is a type of Japanese classical music
Country: Japan

Komparu-kai
Website: www.buehnengenossenschaft.de
Email: gdba@buehnengenossenschaft.de
Phone: 333 343 967
Address: c/o Mr Hiroshi Takahashi, 5-3-2 Kugayama, Suginami-ku, JP
Information: GDBA is the union organization of stage members. Founded in Weimar in 1871 by Ludwig Barnay. The GDBA organizes members of the Artistic and Artistic-technical area of the theaters of the Federal Republic of Germany. It is regionally divided into seven state associations and covers the special occupational problems in the four professional groups: solo, dance, opera choir and ATuV (equipment, technology and Administration).
Country: Japan

Kosei Cultural Association (Kosei Bunka Kyokai)
Website: www.initiative-musik.de
Email: mail@initiative-musik.de
Phone: 353 411 148
Address: Fumonkan, 2-6-1 Wada, Suginami-ku, JP
Information: Initiative Musik is the promotion and export office for the German music industry. As the support platform for the German Federal Government and the music industry, they support the presentation and dissemination of music from Germany both at home and abroad. Yet Initiative Musik doesn't live from subsidies alone, it is also creating structures that promote the music industry and individual artists – in the first ten years, they've initiated more than three thousand funding projects.
Country: Japan

Kunitachi College of Music Library
Website: www.lib.kunitachi.ac.jp
Email: peri@lib.kunitachi.ac.jp
Phone: 425 360 799
Address: 5-5-1 Kashiwa-cho, Tachikawa, JP
Information: promotes contemporary music in all areas and their educational placement. The themes range from the tradition of the avant-garde compositional sound art, performance, new media and transnational concepts to improvisation of jazz and the music of youth culture
Country: Japan

Kyoto Umewaka-kai
Website: www.umewaka.com
Email: umewaka_support@umewaka.com
Phone: 757 112 600
Address: 25-8 Nakanosaka-cho, Kamigamo, Kita-ku, JP
Information: The Umewaka branch of the Kanze school is a professional Noh performers and singers
Country: Japan

Lighting Designers & Engineers Association of Japan
Website: www.ldeaj.or.jp
Email: info@kulturkreis.eu
Phone: 333 637 680
Address: Minami Bldg., 1-23-26 Hyakunin-cho, Shinjuku-ku, JP
Information: The association is the longest-standing institution for entrepreneurial support of the arts in Ger-

many. Since 1951, it has promoted emerging artists in the areas of architecture, visual art, literature, and music through the contributions and donations of its members. As a nationwide, independent network focused on corporate arts sponsorship, it connects culturally committed companies, business associations, corporate foundations, and entrepreneurs.
Country: Japan

Min-On Concert Association
Website: www.min-on.or.jp
Email: info@min-on.or.jp
Phone: 353 623 400
Address: 8 Shinano-machi, Shinjuku-ku, JP
Information: The Mime Centrum cooperates in various networks and alliances in the field of archiving and regarding the accessibility of objects on dance and theatre in order to be able to act strongly both locally and nationally in cultural policy for the protection and preservation of the cultural heritage of the performing arts.
The Mime Centrum is a member of the Dachverband Tanz Deutschland, the Verbund Deutscher Tanzarchive as well as part of the working group for an Archiv des Freien Theaters.
Country: Japan

Min-On Music Library
Website: www.min-on.or.jp/
Email: m-lib@min-on.or.jp
Phone: 353 623 555
Address: 8 Shinano-machi, Shinjuku-ku, JP
Information: JOINT ADVENTURES, founded in 1990 by Walter Heun, is an organizer based in Munich that operates on a national and international level in the field of contemporary dance and other contemporary art disciplines. In close cooperation with regional, national and international partners, JOINT ADVENTURES curates and organizes festivals, guest performance series, residency programs, workshops, symposia and a choreographic short film project in public space.
Country: Japan

Minzoku Geijutsu Kenkyujo
Website: www.tanzmesse-nrw.com
Email: nrw@landesbuerotanz.de
Phone: 187 443 903
Address: 430 Aza Waseda, Sotsuda, Tazawako-machi, Senboku-gun, JP
Information: Communicator, initiator, information broker and advice center for the dance scene in North Rhine-Westphalia.
The nrw landesbuero tanz has existed since 1995 and is carried out by the Society for Contemporary Dance NRW e.V. on behalf of the state of North Rhine-Westphalia in order to take into account the diverse dance culture of the state and to foster national and international exchange.
Country: Japan

Misonoza Theatrical Library
Website: www.misonoza.co.jp
Email: post@kulturrat.de
Phone: 522 228 223
Address: 1-6-14 Sakae, Naka-ku, Nagoya, JP
Information: The Council for Performing Arts and Dance forms the section for performing arts and dance with 29 associations. The council deals with the Artistic, political and social concerns of all performing artists, dancers and the professional groups active in public and private theaters as well as in the independent scene.
Country: Japan

Mitsubishi Trust Foundation for the Arts
Website: www.schumann-portal.de
Email: infoschumann-portal@bonn.de
Phone: 332 810 604
Address: Nihombashi Eiraku Bldg., 2-2-4 Nihombashi, Chuo-ku, JP
Information: delivers programmes and activities on the subject of Robert Schumann
Country: Japan

Miyagi – The Culture Foundation of Miyagi
Website: www1.neweb.ne.jp/wb/kenmin
Email: kenmin@mb.neweb.ne.jp
Phone: 222 258 641
Address: c/o Miyagi Kenmin Kaikan, 3-3-7 Kokubun-cho, Aoba-ku, Sendai, JP
Country: Japan

Musashino Women's College Nohgaku Archives
Website: www.tanzplan-deutschland.de
Email: info@diehl-ritter.de
Phone: 424 683 147
Address: 1-1-20 Shin-machi, Nishi-Tokyo, JP
Information: funding for dance companies in Germany
Country: Japan

Muse Company
Website: www.musekk.co.jp
Email: MuseKK@aol.com
Phone: 364 265 182
Address: 4-6-10-101, Minami Aoyama, Minato-ku, JP
Information: Muse Company plans and produces various

workshops and community art projects; promotes and manages foreign artists and arts organisations.
Country: Japan

Museum of Noh Artifacts
Website: www.nohgakushiryoukan.jp
Email: tannaka@hk.sun-ip.or.jp
Phone: 795 523 513
Address: 175 Kawara-machi, Sasayama, JP
Information: the VdO is a professional association and trade union with members of the opera choirs and dance groups from the German stage
Country: Japan

Music Library of The Tokyo Metropolitan Festival Hall
Website: www.kalme.gr
Email: info@kalme.gr
Phone: 338 282 111
Address: 5-45 Ueno Koen, Taitoh-ku, JP
Information: non-profit legal entity, acknowledged by the Greek State. Collaborations: Greek Parliament, Ministries of Culture and Education, Ministry of Aegean, Paedagogic Institute, Bank of Cyprus Cultural Foundation.
Country: Japan

Music Sharing (Specified Non-Profit Corporation), Tokutei Hieri Katsudo
Website: www.gotomidori.com/foundation/
Email: midorif@mint.ocn.ne.jp
Phone: 332 611 855
Address: 9F D Kohjimachi Garden Bldg, 2-3 Kohji-machi, Chiyoda-ku, JP
Information: In 2002, Sep, The Midori Foundation Inc. changed the name to 'Music Sharing'
Country: Japan

Musicians' Union of Japan
Website: www.muj.or.jp
Email: honbu@muj.or.jp
Address: 9F, NK Fuji Bldg., 3-21-1 Shimo-Ochiai, Shinjuku-ku, JP
Information: GAPMET aims to meet the challenge of educational reform and the application of innovative ideas by bridging the gap between research theories and practices
Country: Japan

Nagauta Kyokai
Website: www.nagauta.org.jp
Email: nagauta@nagauta.org.jp
Phone: 335 426 564
Address: 4F Ginza Ichikawa Bldg., 2-11-19 Ginza, Chuo-ku, JP
Information: member of FERA and FISTAV
Country: Japan

Nagoya Nihon Buyoh Kyokai
Phone: 528 317 106
Address: c/o Nishikawa-kai, 1-23 Hatsuhi-cho, Mizuho-ku, Nagoya, JP
Information: organise for the coming season: an exhibition of figures and sets from performers past and new, a series of lectures on the history of karaghiozis and a 26-episode documentary series to be presented on national TV about the origins and development of shad
Country: Japan

Nakajima Kenzo Kinen Gendai Ongaku Shinko Kikin
Website: www.aepi.gr
Phone: 332 709 511
Address: Nihonbashi Eigyou-Dai-Ichi-bu, cyuoh Mitsui Shinta, 2-1-1 Nihombashi Muromachi, Chuo-ku, JP
Information: AEPI is a member of: CISAC Conf
Country: Japan

Nara Independent Research Institute of Cultural Properties, Dokuritsuhohjin Nara Bunkazai Kenkyujo
Website: www.iema.gr/home/?lang=en
Email: protocol@iema.gr
Address: 2-9-1 Nijo-cho, JP
Country: Japan

National Archives
Website: www.archives.co.jp
Email:
info@ifpi.gr
Phone: 332 140 621
Address: 3-2 Kitanomaru Koen, Chiyoda-ku, JP
Information: The IFPI (International Federation of the Phonographic Industry) represents over 8000 record companies in 57 countries and affiliated industry associations in 70 countries, and is the official organ of the music industry worldwide.
IFPI Greece, the collective body of the Greek music industry, has been responsible since the 1980s for the weekly publication of the only official Sales charts in Greece.
Country: Japan

National Diet Library
Website:

www.ndl.go.jp
Email: info@isadoraduncancenter.org
Phone: 335 812 331
Address: 1-10-1 Nagata-cho, Chiyoda-ku, JP
Information: educational activities, site-specific projects, community work, work-in progress performances; supported by the Municipality of Byron-Athens
Country: Japan

National Research Institute for Cultural Properties, Tokyo
Website: www.tobunken.go.jp
Email: info@emse.gr
Phone: 338 234 925
Address: Geino-bu Department of Performing Arts, 13-43 Ueno Koen, Taito-ku, JP
Information: independent administrative institution
Country: Japan

New National Theatre Tokyo
Website: www.nntt.jac.go.jp
Email: sada@otenet.gr
Phone: 353 513 011
Address: c/o New National Theatre Foundation, 1-1-1 Hon-machi, Shibuya-ku, JP
Country: Japan

Nihon Opera
Website: www.jof.or.jp
Email: jof@jof.or.jp
Phone: 354 663 185
Address: 8F Nishiazabu 28 Mori Bldg., 4-16-13 Nishi-Azabu, Minato-ku, JP
Information: member of International Federation of Actors
Country: Japan

Nihon Shingeki Seisakusha Kyokai
Website: www.artpool.hu
Email: artpool@artpool.hu
Phone: 339 371 101
Address: c/o Dora Theatrial Company, 1-4-4 Nagakai, Itabashi-ku, JP
Information: Artpool, founded in 1979, after 10 years in illegality and operating for 25 years as a non-profit institution, in 2015 joined the Museum of Fine Arts in Budapest, thus securing its continuous operation and the accessibility of its archives.
Its main tasks: curating and co-ordinating exhibitions and events to present contemporary trends, media, practices and resources in art. Artpool is an art archive with a multimedia library – a documentation center and place of research concerning the progressive, non official Hungarian art tendencies from the 70s, and of the new international art tendencies and movements from the 60s (Fluxus, Performance, Conceptual Art, etc.)
By the end of 2019 Artpool will be relocated and become part of KEMKI, the Central European Research Institute of Art History.
Country: Japan

Niigata City Art & Culture Foundation
Website: www.mzmsz.hu
Email: info@mzmsz.hu
Phone: 252 344 520
Address: 1-613-69 Hakusanura, JP
Information: representation of the interests of music and art schools; visiting address: Vorosmarty street 65. 1064 Budapest
Country: Japan

Nikikai Opera Foundation (Nikikai Opera Shinkohkai)
Website: www.nikikai-opera.or.jp
Email: nikikai@mx3.alpha-web.ne.jp
Phone: 337 964 711
Address: 1-25-12 Sendagaya, Shibuya-ku, JP
Information: The Budapest Brand Nonprofit Zrt. is Budapest's official organisation for tourism, culture and Marketing activities. Budapest Brand Zrt. can simultaneously develop the city's brand and tourism strategy, and is also responsible for creating content related to the city, along with organising cultural festivals.
Country: Japan

Nippon Cultural Centre
Email: ncc@smile.ocn.ne.jp
Phone: 335 800 031
Address: 31F Kasumigaseki Bldg., 3-2-5 Kasumigaseki, Chiyoda-ku, JP
Country: Japan

Nippon Foundation
Website: www.nippon-foundation.or.jp
Email: webmaster@ps.nippon-foundation.or.jp
Phone: 362 295 181
Address: 1-2-2 Akasaka, Minato-ku, JP
Information: formerly known as The Sasakawa Foundation
Country: Japan

Nippon Kindai Ongakukan
Email: office@zeneszerzo.t-online.hu

Phone: 332 241 584
Address: 1-8-14 Azabudai, Minato-ku, JP
Information: visiting address: Szenth
Country: Japan

Nippon Music Foundation
Website: www.nmf.or.jp
Email: info@nmf.or.jp
Phone: 362 295 566
Address: 1-2-2 Akasaka, Minato-ku, JP
Information: national association for the protection of interests of dance artists, dance associations and institutions
Country: Japan

Nissay Culture Foundation
Website: www.nissaytheatre.or.jp
Email: haydntarsasag@haydn-eszterhaza.hu
Phone: 335 033 111
Address: 1-1-1 Yuraku-cho, Chiyoda-ku, JP
Information: membership organisation
Country: Japan

NLI Research Institute
Website: www.nli-research.co.jp
Email: mitch@nli-research.co.jp
Phone: 335 121 795
Address: 4-1-7 Kudankita, Chiyoda-ku, JP
Information: Hungarian Heritage House is a National Institute of the Ministry of Education and Culture; see also Dance (Hungarian State Folk Ensemble)
Country: Japan

NPO Glovill
Website: www.glovill.jp/
Email: glovill@glovill.jp
Phone: 335 683 260
Address: 1-9-39-422 Roppongi, Minato-ku, JP
Country: Japan

OISTAT Japan Centre
Website: www.oistat.jp
Email: info@oistat.jp
Address: Daiichi Furukawa Building 2F-A, 3-8-6 Kanda Kajicho, Chiyoda-ku, JP
Information: Member organisations: Theatre & Entertainment Technology Association, Japan (q.v.); Lighting Designers & Engineers Association of Japan (q.v.); Japan Stage & Television Designers Association (q.v.), Japan Electrial Sound Specialists Association (q.v.), Ja
Country: Japan

Okinawa Performers' Group
Website: www.oszmi.hu
Email: oszmi@ella.hu
Phone: 988 509 382
Address: 163 Aza Ueda, Tomigusuku-son, JP
Country: Japan

Ongaku Bunka Kyogikai
Website: www.komedias.hu
Email: raksi@mail.tvnet.hu
Phone: 455 827 045
Address: c/o Mr Kohei Fujita, 2-5-14 Yakoh, Tsurumi-ku, Yokohama, JP
Information: member of International Federation of Actors (FIA)
Country: Japan

Organisation for the Preservation of Kabuki, The
Website: www.kabuki.or.jp
Email: titkarsag@iroszovetseg.hu
Phone: 352 121 243
Address: c/o National Theatre, 4-1 Hayabusa-cho, Chiyoda-ku, JP
Country: Japan

Osaka Philharmonic Society
Website: www.osaka-phil.com
Email: info@hungarofest.hu
Phone: 666 567 701
Address: 1-1-44 Kishinosato, Nishinari-ku, JP
Information: coordination of cultural events, abroad and in Hungary, promoting all art forms – classical, modern music, jazz, exhibitions, theatre, film, literature
Country: Japan

Pia Institute for the Arts
Website: www.ica-d.hu
Email: info@ica-d.hu
Address: JP
Information: see Institute for the Arts IFA
Country: Japan

Pola Foundation for the Promotion of Traditional Japanese Culture
Website: www.polaculture.jp
Email: jmh@jmh.hu
Phone: 335 617 408
Address: 5F Pola Ginza Bldg., 1-7-7 Ginza, Chuo-ku, JP
Information: organising live music concerts for children and young people, helping to assist them in entering the musician profession
Country: Japan

Pro Musica Nipponia
Website: www.promusica.or.jp/
Email: office@promusica.or.jp
Phone: 333 784 741
Address: 302 Takizawa Bldg., 3-17-1 Sasazuka, Shibuya-ku, JP
Information: see also Performing Companies
Country: Japan

Puppetry Library
Website: www.puppet-net.jp/
Email: torokko@nifty.com
Phone: 775 785 455
Address: c/o Torokko Puppets, 8-22-15 Sakamoto, JP
Information: Theatre, dance, music and, occasionally, literature and kids' events in the Old Synagogue, a unique performing arts venue in Szeged, which they call ALTER-RA – Contemporary Performing Arts Centre. The events are organised by MASZK Association, a cultural NGO.
Country: Japan

Recording Industry Association of Japan (RIAJ)
Website: www.riaj.or.jp
Email: info@riaj.or.jp
Phone: 355 751 305
Address: 2-2-5 Toranomon, Minato-ku, Tokyo, JP
Information: The Recording Industry Association of Japan (RIAJ) was founded in 1942 as an organization representing Japanese music recording industry. Since that time, RIAJ has been playing a leading role in the development and expansion of Japanese music culture. RIAJ is the Japanese National Group of the IFPI.
Country: Japan

RILM National Committee of Japan
Website: www.szinhaz.hu/maszk
Email: rilm@music.email.ne.jp
Phone: 339 913 018
Address: c/o Musashino Music College, 1-13-1 Hazawa, Nerima-ku, JP
Country: Japan

Rohm Music Foundation
Website: www.rohm.co.jp/rmf
Email: kota@kota.hu
Phone: 753 117 710
Address: 1 Nishinakamizu-cho, Saiin, Ukyo-ku, JP
Information: alternative email: zeneszo@kota.hu
Country: Japan

Saison Foundation, The
Website: www.saison.or.jp
Email: foundation@saison.or.jp
Phone: 335 355 566
Address: 8F Toka Bldg., 1-16-1 Ginza, Chuo-ku, JP
Information: The Federation of Icelandic Artists, BÍL, was founded in 1928 in Reykjavík. The main task of the federation is to encourage the authorities to increase their role in the cultural and Artistic development of the society and emphasize the essential contribution of authors and performers to promoting cultural identity and cultural development of the society.
Country: Japan

Seiha Hohgakukai
Website: www.mic.is
Email: itm@mic.is
Phone: 332 606 806
Address: 3 Ichigaya Sanai-cho, Shinjuku-ku, JP
Information: group of Japanese traditional music performers
Country: Japan

Shochiku Otani Library
Website: www.shochiku.co.jp/shochiku-otani-toshokan
Email: info@artscouncil.ie
Phone: 813 555 01694
Address: ADK Shochiku Tsukuair 3F, 1-13-1 Tsukiji, Chuo-ku, JP
Information: the Arts Council of Ireland is the Irish government agency for developing the arts in Ireland
Country: Japan

Society for the Advancement of Musical Appreciation
Website: www.pioneer.co.jp/onkan
Email: zai_onkan@post.pioneer.co.jp
Phone: 334 956 885
Address: 1-4-1 Meguro, Meguro-ku, JP
Information: supports and promotes excellence in choral music in Ireland by providing information and advice and presenting a range of educational programmes, courses, workshops and activities; more info from aoic@ul.ie
Country: Japan

Society of Japanese Theatre Designers (SJTD), The
Website: www.composers.ie
Email: info@composers.ie
Phone: 337 709 230
Address: Ebisu Mansion, 1-2-1 Ebisunishi, Shibuya-ku, JP

Information: AIC is funded by the Arts Council/An Chomhairle Eala
Country: Japan

Sound Engineers & Artists Society of Japan (SEAS)
Website:
www.seas.or.jp
Email:
info@seas.or.jp
Phone: 903 246 8766
Address: 412, 2-18-1 Sumiyoshi-cho, Fuchu, JP
Information: Business to Arts is a membership-based, charitable organisation that brokers, enables and supports creative partnerships between businesses, individuals and the arts.
Country: Japan

Stage Sound Association of Japan
Website: www.SSAJ.gr.jp
Email: jimukyoku@SSAJ.gr.jp
Phone: 332 056 943
Address: 205 Kotobuki Bldg., 1-29-22 Takadano-baba, Shinjuku-ku, JP
Information: the Centre's website contains extensive information on Irish composers and their works, along with articles, interviews and regular news relating to contemporary Irish music
Country: Japan

Sumida Arts Foundation
Website: www.triphony.com
Email: sumida@triphony.com
Phone: 356 081 290
Address: 1-2-3 Kinshi, Sumida-ku, JP
Country: Japan

Suntory Music Foundation
Website: www.suntory.co.jp/culture/smf
Email: paulaphelan@ireland.com
Phone: 335 893 694
Address: Suntory Bldg., 1-2-3 Moto-Akasaka, Minato-ku, JP
Country: Japan

Talent Education Institute
Website: www.suzukimethod.or.jp
Email: talent@suzukimethod.or.jp
Phone: 263 327 171
Address: Sainoh Kyoiku Kaikan, 3-10-3 Fukashi, Matsumoto, JP
Information: the headquarters of Suzuki method of violin teaching
Country: Japan

Telemann Institute Japan
Website: www.cafe-telemann.com
Email: telemann@mui.biglobe.ne.jp
Phone: 663 451 046
Address: 2-1-17 Sonezaki-Shinchi, Kita-ku, JP
Information: a group of baroque ensembles: Telemann Chamber Orchestra (q.v.) with modern instruments, Telemann Chamber Choir (q.v.), and Collegium Musicum Telemann (q.v.) with period instruments; also a commercial agent/promoter; management of concerts for both Japane
Country: Japan

Theatre and Entertainment Technology Association, Japan (JATET)
Website: www.jatet.or.jp/
Email: jatet@jatet.or.jp
Phone: 352 898 858
Address: 2F-A, Daiichi-Furukawa Bldg.3-8-6, Kandaka-jicho, Chiyoda-ku, JP
Information: members: 34 organisations, 40 individuals; supporting members: 24 organisations, 61 individuals
Country: Japan

Tokyo Ballet Association
Website: www.musicnetwork.ie
Email: tbass@gold.ocn.ne.jp
Phone: 357 257 470
Address: #411 6-7-1 Himonya, Meguro-ku, JP
Information: see also Promoters
Country: Japan

Tokyo Kinrohsha Engeki Kyogikai
Website:
www.theatreforumireland.com
Email: theatreforum@ireland.com
Phone: 332 564 651
Address: 2-12-14 Uchi-Kanda, Chiyoda-ku, JP
Country: Japan

Tokyo Metropolitan Central Library
Website: www.library.metro.tokyo.jp
Email: info@associazioneartu.it
Phone: 334 428 451
Address: 5-7-13 Minami Azabu, Minato-ku, JP
Information: the cultural association ARTU – arts for urban regeneration and transformation – has been founded by young professionals to promote the arts and contribute to the urban development of Genova

Country: Japan

Tokyo Metropolitan Foundation for History and Culture
Website:
www.rekibun.or.jp
Email: info@rekibun.or.jp
Phone: 334 430 020 (pr)
Address: 5-21-9 Shiroganedai, Minato-ku, JP
Country: Japan

Tokyo Ongaku Bunka Kyokai (Tokyo Onkyo)
Website: www.sferisterio.it
Email: info@sferisterio.it
Phone: 332 138 591
Address: 218 Fuji Bidg., 3-2-3 Marunouchi, Chiyoda-ku, JP
Information: The Arena Sferisterio Association, set up by the Municipality of Macerata and the Province of Macerata, promotes and organizes the opera season of the Macerata Opera Festival.
Country: Japan

Tokyo Opera Association
Website: www.tokyo-opera.gr.jp/
Email: afi@afi.mi.it
Phone: 352 697 895
Address: 2-14-6-405 Shinjuku, Shinjiku-ku, JP
Information: see entry under Opera for details
Country: Japan

Tokyo Opera City Cultural Foundation
Website: www.operacity.jp
Email: info@toccf.com
Phone: 353 530 770
Address: 3-20-2 Nishi-Shinjuku, Shinjuku-ku, JP
Country: Japan

Tokyo Workers' Music Councils (RO-ON)
Website: www.ro-on.com
Email: tokyo@ro-on.com
Phone: 352 730 801
Address: 1-9-10 Ohkubo, Shinjyuku-ku, JP
Country: Japan

Tomin Gekijyo Foundation
Website: www.tomin-gekijo.jp
Email: f-tomin@tomin-gekijo.or.jp
Phone: 335 724 311
Address: Sukiyabashi Bldg., 5-1-7 Ginza, Chuo-ku, JP
Country: Japan

Toyota Foundation
Website: www.toyotafound.or.jp
Email: info@cidim.it
Phone: 333 441 701
Address: 37F Shinjuku Mitsui Bldg., 2-1-1 Nishi Shinjuku, Shinjuku-ku, JP
Information: member of the International Music Council
Country: Japan

Tsubouchi Memorial Theatre Museum, Waseda University
Website: www.waseda.ac.jp/enpaku/index-j.html
Email: enpaku-ml@list.waseda.ac.jp
Phone: 352 861 829
Address: 1-6-1 Nishi-Waseda, Shinjuku-ku, JP
Information: the only theatre museum in Japan
Country: Japan

Ueno Gakuen Nihon Ongaku Shiryoshitsu
Website: www.uenogakuen.ac.jp
Email: info@uenogakuen.ac.jp
Phone: 338 421 021 (swi
Address: 4-24-12 Higashi Ueno, Taitoh-ku, JP
Country: Japan

University Art Museum, Tokyo National University of Fine Arts and Music
Website: www.geidai.ac.jp/museum
Email: eti@enteteatrale.it
Phone: 356 857 755
Address: c/o Tokyo Geijutsu Daigaku, 12-8 Ueno Koen, Taito-ku, JP
Information: Press office phone number 06-4401 3239
Country: Japan

Yasuda Life Cultural Foundation
Website:
www.yasuda-qol-bunka.or.jp
Email: ufficiomusicadanza@agisweb.it
Phone: 333 496 194
Address: 10 F Yasudaseimei Dai-2 Bldg., 1-10-1 Nishi-Shinjuku, Shinjuku-ku, JP
Country: Japan

Yokohama Assocation for International Communications & Exchanges
Website:
www.yoke.or.jp
Email: yoke@city.yokohama.jp
Phone: 456 717 128
Address: Yokohama International Organization Center

5F, Pacifico Yokohama 1-1-1 Minato Mirai, , Nishi-ku, Yokohama, JP
Information: see also Festivals
Country: Japan

Yokohama Theatre Institute
Website: www.yokohama-engeki.or.jp
Email: kenkyujyo@yokohama-engeki.or.jp
Phone: 452 614 865
Address: 52 Nishi-dori, Fukutomi-cho, Naka-ku, Yokohama, JP
Country: Japan

Zenshokyo
Website: www.fimi.it
Email: info@fimi.it
Phone: 333 174 375
Address: 101 Maison Tanaka, 2-39-10 Wada, Suginami-ku, JP
Information: FIMI (Italian Music Industry Federation) was founded in 1992, it is a founding member of Confindustria Cultura Italia and a member of IFPI, it represents the major Producers and distributors of the recording sector for a total of over 2, 500 of the most famous brands in the world. FIMI collects and disseminates data and sector research, both national and international, on the development of the market.
Country: Japan

JORDAN

Studio 8
Website: www.studio8jo.com
Email: studio8amman@gmail.com
Phone: 797 727 691
Address: 2 Muath Bin Jabal Street, JO
Information: Studio 8 is an independent art and dance collective that runs a community-based performing arts space in Amman, Jordan. Studio 8 focuses on dance and the performing arts as practices of healing that bring people from diverse backgrounds together. The studio is a hub where community members and performing artists can experiment with and learn diverse art forms. Our artists specialise in various genres of the performing arts including dance, theater, circus arts, puppeteering, installation, costuming, and dance film production. Studio 8 is an open space for the performing arts that gives the local community an alternative to commercialised artistsic exPression. They run a creative space where artists and community members meet, ideas are generated and projects developed. Member of ISPA.
Country: Jordan

REPUBLIC OF KOREA

Arts Council Korea (ARKO)
Website: arko.or.kr
Email: arko@arko.or.kr
Phone: 619 002 100
Address: 640 Bitgaram-ro, Naju-si
Information: state funded, nonprofit organization; supports arts organizations and artists in and abroad through grant-giving services and programs
Country: Republic of Korea

Copyright Deliberation and Conciliation Committee
Website: www.copyright.or.kr
Email: sai-slc@cgil.it
Phone: 226 699 900
Address: 827 Banghwa3-dong, Gangseo-Gu
Information: part of FIA International Federation of Actors
Country: Republic of Korea

Daesan Foundation
Website: www.daesan.or.kr
Email: daesan@daesan.or.kr
Phone: 272 13202/3
Address: #907 Kyobo Bldg, 1, jongno1-ga, Jongno-gu
Country: Republic of Korea

Dance Association of Korea
Website: www.agisweb.it
Email: dance77@chollian.net
Phone: 274 48066
Address: 304 Yechong Bldg, 1-117 Dongsoong-Dong, Jongno-gu
Country: Republic of Korea

Federation of Artistic and Cultural Organisations of Korea
Website: www.yechong.or.kr
Address: 1-117 Dongsoong-dong, Jongro-Gu
Country: Republic of Korea

Gyeonggi Cultural Foundation
Website: www.ggcf.or.kr
Email: webmaster@ggcf.or.kr
Phone: 312 317 200
Address: 1116-1 Ingae-Dong, Paltal-gu, Suwon
Country: Republic of Korea

Hanguk Performing Arts Centre

Website: www.hanpac.or.kr
Email: webmaster@hanpac.or.kr
Phone: 236 680 007
Address: Daehak-ro 10-gil 17, Jongno-gu
Information: Member of ISPA
Country: Republic of Korea

Korea Culture Foundation
Website: www.agisweb.it
Email: UfficioTeatro@agisweb.it
Phone: 222 041 030
Address: 25 Neung-Dong, Kwangjin-Gu
Country: Republic of Korea

Korea Culture Promotion Ltd
Website: www.agisweb.it
Email: UfficioTeatro@agisweb.it
Phone: 256 25300
Address: 7F Bokwang Bldg., 141-32 Samsung-Dong, Kanagnam-Gu
Country: Republic of Korea

Korea Foundation
Website: www.kf.or.kr
Email: webmaster@kf.or.kr
Phone: 234 635 600/1
Address: 10th Fl. Diplomatic Center Bldg, 2558 Nambu sunhwanno, Seocho-gu
Country: Republic of Korea

Korea Music Copyright Association (KOMCA)
Website: komca.or.kr
Email: webmaster@komca.or.kr
Phone: 226 600 400
Address: KOMCA Bldg, 649 Naebalsan-Dong, Kangseo-gu
Information: see also Novurgia Association; www.novurgia.it
Country: Republic of Korea

Korea National University of Arts – School of Music, Drama, Dance of Korean Traditional Arts
Website: www.kuna.ac.kr
Email: feedback@kuna.ac.kr
Phone: 822 520 8114
Address: 1753 Seocho-Dong, Seocho-gu
Country: Republic of Korea

Korea National University of Arts, The
Website: www.knua.ac.kr
Email: feedback@knua.ac.kr
Address: 146-37 Hwarang-ro 32-gil, Sungbuk-gu
Information: alternative address: 1753 Seocho-dong, Seocho-gu, Seoul 137-070
Country: Republic of Korea

Korean Actors Association
Website: www.kactor.or.kr
Email: laipa@laipa.org
Phone: 276 45086/7
Address: 3F Samyong Bldg., 135 Ewha-Dong, Jongno-gu
Information: collecting society
Country: Republic of Korea

Korean People's Artist Federation
Website: www.kpaf.org
Email: webmaster@kpaf.org
Phone: 273 96851
Address: 5F Kungook 1ho Bldg., 280-4, Nakwon Dong, Jongno-gu
Information: also publish information about concerts, records, festivals and competitions for symphonic bands; alternative address: Galdnieku iela 10, Smiltene, LV-4729
Country: Republic of Korea

Korean Theater Association
Website: www.ktheater.or.kr
Phone: 274 48055
Address: 401 Yechong Building, 1-117 Dongsoong-Dong, Jongro-gu
Information: annually holds the 'Seoul Drama Festival' in autumn, in which major theatrical companies take part: 'Korean drama': holds annual actors workshops
Country: Republic of Korea

Korean Theatre Artists Association (OISTAT), Korean Center
Website: www.music.lv/Composers/Union
Email: lks@td.lv
Phone: 276 37301
Address: 2F Samkwang Bldg, 1-79 Dongsoong-dong, Jongno-gu
Information: The LCU is a voluntary and independent organisation of composers working in various genres as well as musicologists and music critics; the board of the LCU is made up of both composers and musicologists. The LCU maintains cooperative ties with the Riga Ci
Country: Republic of Korea

Korean Traditional Music Association
Email: Vox.Humana@inbox.lv
Phone: 274 48051
Address: 301 Yechong Building, 1-117 Dongsoong-Dong, Jongro-gu
Country: Republic of Korea

Korean TV & Radio Writers Association
Website: www.ktrwa.or.kr
Email: ktrwa@ktrwa.or.kr
Phone: 822 782 1696
Address: 4F, Kumsam Bldg, 17-1 Yoido-dong, Yongdeungpo-ku
Country: Republic of Korea

Music Industry Association of Korea
Website: www.miak.or.kr
Email: master@miak.or.kr
Phone: 233 81562/4
Address: 3F Sinseong Bldg, 108-4 Seongsan-Dong, Mapo-Gu
Information: The LMIC is a non-govern mental organisation founded in July 2002 by the Latvian Composers' Union, the Latvian Academy of Music, the National Library of Latvia, the Latvian Concert Agency, the Latvian Association of New Music.
In 2003, music publisher Musica Baltica became a member of the Centre.
Country: Republic of Korea

National Academy of Arts
Website: www.naa.go.kr
Email: webmaster@naa.go.kr
Phone: 259 66213
Address: San 94-1, Banpo4-Dong, Seocho-Gu
Information: the Academy is divided into the following subdivisions: literature, fine arts, music, theatre, and cinema & dance
Country: Republic of Korea

National Association of Cultural and Arts Centers
Website: www.sac.or.kr
Email: webmaster@sac.or.kr
Phone: 258 61997/5
Address: 700 Seocho-Dong, Seocho-gu
Country: Republic of Korea

National Committee for Copyright Deliberation and Conciliation
Email: cdcc@caibs.kcaf.or.kr
Phone: 259 68405
Address: San 60-1, Banpo-dong, Seocho-ku
Country: Republic of Korea

National Gugak Center
Website: www.gugak.go.kr
Email: kukak@kukak.ncktpa.go.kr
Phone: 258 03300
Address: 700 Seocho-dong, Seocho-gu
Information: see also Early Music
Country: Republic of Korea

Performing Arts Management Association of Korea
Website: www.artsmanagement.or.kr
Email: pamak1982@naver.com
Phone: 278 56843
Address: 705 Daesung building, 17-16, Yeoido-dong, Youngdeungpo-gu
Information: Member of ISPA
Country: Republic of Korea

Samil Cultural Foundation
Website: www.samil31.com
Email: kijung31@hanmail.net
Phone: 544 524 949
Address: 5F Samil building, 1032-8 Wonpyung-Dong, Gumi, Gyeongbuk
Information: organise International Festival of Contemporary Theatre 'Homo Novus'; initiates training seminars, lectures, and workshops, promotes the accessibility and circulation about events in the field of performing arts
Country: Republic of Korea

Samsung Foundation of Culture
Website: www.sfoc.org
Email: sabline@samsung.co.kr
Phone: 275 07842
Address: 20F Choongang Daily Newspaper Bldg., 7 Sunhwa-Dong, Joong-Gu
Country: Republic of Korea

Yonkang Foundation
Website: www.yonkang.co.kr
Email: webmaster@yonkang.co.kr
Phone: 277 67706
Address: 270 Yeonji-Dong, Jongno-gu
Information: organises the Latvia Theatre Award
Country: Republic of Korea

Arab Arts Focus
Website: https://arabartsfocus.org
Email: info@arabartsfocus.org
Phone: 633 784 611
Address: 1599 Rwaiss St., Haret Hreik, Beirut, Lebanon
Information: The better part of this decade has seen a number of new chapters added to world history, with armed conflicts and extremist currents taking hold of entire regions. Nowhere is this felt more clearly than in the Arab world, which has become the site of ongoing

struggles over power and ideology.We believe that arts and culture can act as a vehicle for resistance and change. The arts are humanity's way of asserting the right to freedom and enabling individual exPression. Members of ISPA
Country: LB

MEXICO

Asociación Nacional de Actores
Website: www.anda.org.mx
Email: casting@actores-anda.com.mx
Phone: 556 68494
Address: Altamirano 126 y 128, Col. San Rafael, MX
Information: the organisation is legally constituted and recognised in Mexico and brings the guild acting and art throughout the country, ensuring the interests of its members
Country: Mexico

Centro de Investigación Coreográfica
Website: www.cico.bellasartes.gob.mx/
Email: cicodanza@yahoo.com.mx
Phone: 555 542 9022
Address: Xocongo Núm. 138, Col. Tránsito, Delegación Cuauhtémoc, MX
Country: Mexico

Centro Nacional de investigación, Documentation e Informatión Teatral Rodolfo Usigli (CITRU)
Website: www.cnca.gob.mx
Email: cenidim@conaculta.gob.mx
Phone: 415 50000
Address: Río Churubusco 79, Col. Country Club, MX
Country: Mexico

Centro Nacional de las Artes
Website: www.cenart.gob.mx/
Email: contacto@conaculta.gob.mx
Phone: 554 155 0000
Address: Río Churubusco 79, Country Club, MX
Information: Centro Nacional de las Artes is a sprawling art institute near Coyoacán that has many free events across the Artistic spectrum, including contemporary dance and classical concerts. Member of ISPA

Country: Mexico

Chihuahua Institute of Culture
Website: www.ichicult.gob.mx
Phone: 614 214 4800
Address: Ave North Division and University Ave S, N, Col. Altavista, MX
Country: Mexico

Coordinación Nacional de Danza
Website: www.bellasartes.gob.mx
Email: cnd.danza@correo.inba.gob.mx
Phone: 555 280 5974
Address: Instituto Nacional de Bellas Artes, Reforma y Campo Marte s/n, MX
Country: Mexico

Coordinadora del Encuentro Binacional de Danza Contemporáneo
Email: lks1@auste.elnet.lt
Phone: 220 759
Address: Agust, Frace Alamada, MX
Country: Mexico

Culturarte, AC
Website: www.lks.lt/index.php
Email: info@lks.lt
Phone: 521 23611
Address: Durango 20, Col. Roma, MX
Information: creative public organization, which unites professional composers and musicologists of Lithuania. It was founded in Kaunas in 1941, by composer Juozas Gruodis and his colleagues. Nowadays LCU counts 103 composers and 62 musicologists
Country: Mexico

Dirección General de Culturas Populares
Website: www.difocur.gob.mx
Email: rgonzalezv_difocur@hotmail.com
Phone: 527 52777
Address: MX
Information: see also Presenters
Country: Mexico

Guerrero Institute of Culture
Website: www.institutoguerrerensedelacultura.gob.mx
Phone: 174 747 27051
Address: Av. Costera Miguel Alem, Fracc. Costa Azul, MX
Country: Mexico
Social Media: @Secugro www.facebook.com/Secretaria-DeCulturaDeGuerrero

Instituto Anglo-Mexicano de Cultura (AC)
Website: www.tamf.org.mx
Email: anglocultura@compuserve.com
Phone: 306 78800
Address: Antonio Caso 127, Col. San Rafael, MX
Information: member of ISPA

Country: Mexico

Instituto Coahuilense de Cultura
Website: www.icocult.gob.mx
Phone: 844 410 2033
Address: Calle Juárez esquina con Hidalgo, Zona Centro, MX
Information: alternative Email addresses: icocult_publicaciones@hotmail.com , institutocoahuilensedecultura@yahoo.com.mx
Country: Mexico

Instituto Cultural de Aguascalientes
Website: www.aguascalientes.gob.mx/ica/
Email: informacion.ica@gmail.com
Phone: 449 910 2010
Address: Venustiano Carranza 101, Colonia Centro, MX
Information: organises and coordinate live concerts, diverse classical/classical contemporary/jazz music events and tours throughout Lithuania and abroad. See also Venues
Country: Mexico
Social Media: www.facebook.com/InstitutoCultural

Instituto de Cultura de Baja California
Website: www.bajacalifornia.gob.mx/icbc
Email: mjacobo@baja.gob.mx
Phone: 686 553 5044
Address: Av.Alvaro Obregón 1209, Col. Nueva 2da Sección, MX
Country: Mexico

Instituto de Cultura de Campeche
Website: www.institutodecultura.gob.mx
Email: icc@campeche.gob.mx
Phone: 981 816 2957
Address: Calle 12 No. 173, Centro Histórico, San Francisco de Campeche, MX
Information: alternative Email address: iccampeche@prodigy.net.mx; alternative contact number: 981-816 1424
Country: Mexico

Instituto de Cultura del Yucatán
Website: www.culturayucatan.com
Email: icy@yucatan.gob.mx
Phone: 999 942 3800
Address: 25 Ginerés, Col. Garcia, MX
Information: see also Promoters
Country: Mexico

Instituto Sudcaliforniano de Cultura
Website: www.bcs.gob.mx
Email: culturabcs@yahoo.com.mx
Phone: 612 12394
Address: Zona Centro, MX
Country: Mexico

Instituto Tamaulipeco para la Cultura y las Artes
Website: www.tamaulipas.gob.mx
Email: coorproyectos@prodigy.net.mx
Phone: 834 318 8000
Address: 5 y 16 Juárez – Palacio de Gobierno – 3er Piso, Cd. Victoria, MX
Country: Mexico

Instituto Zacatecano de Cultura Ramón López Velarde
Website: www.zacatecas.gob.mx
Email: gustavo.salinas@zacatecas.gob.mx
Phone: 492 922 3370
Address: Domicilio Calle Lomas del Calvario No. 105, , Col. D, MX
Country: Mexico

Los Talleres
Website: www.lostalleres.com.mx/
Email: talleres@prodigy.net.mx
Phone: 555 658 7288
Address: Centro Cultural "Los Talleres", Francisco Sosa #29, Colonia Del Carmen Coyoacán, MX
Information: see also Festivals (Thomas Mann Festival)
Country: Mexico

Mexican Institute of Culture
Website: www.edomexico.gob.mx/imc
Email: gemimcda@edomex.gob.mx
Phone: 172 227 41200
Address: 302 Boulevard Jesus Reyes, Delegacion San Buenaventura, MX
Information: see also Venues
Country: Mexico

Mexico: Gateway to the Americas
Email: rroquet@puertadelasamericas.org
Phone: 125 39049
Address: Hamburgo 115, colonia Juarez, Delegacion Cuauhtemoc 06600, Mexico, D.F., MX
Country: Mexico

National Centre for Dance Investigation, Documentation and Research José Limón
Website: www.conaculta.gob.mx

Address: Río Churubusco No. 79, Tlalpan y Miramontes, Col. Country Club, MX
Information: alternative email address: mramos@correo.cnart.mx; see also Festivals
Country: Mexico

National Institute for the Arts (CENART)
Website: www.cenart.gob.mx
Email: relacionespublicas@correo.cnart.mx
Phone: 555 280 4865
Address: Rio Churubusco 79, esq. calzada de Tlalpan, Colonia Country Club, MX
Country: Mexico

National Institute of Fine Arts (Instituto Nacional de Bellas Artes) Music and Opera Coordination
Website: www.bellasartes.gob.mx
Email: infoinba@inba.gob.mx
Phone: 528 21964
Address: Coordinaci, Calle 5 de mayo, 3, Colonia Centro, Delegaci, MX
Country: Mexico

National Institute of Fine Arts (Instituto Nacional de Bellas Artes) National Dance Coordination
Website: www.danza.bellasartes.gob.mx
Email: gentededanza@inba.gob.mx
Phone: 528 34600
Address: Coordinación Nacional de Danza, Reforma y Campo Marte s/n, Módulo A, segundo piso, Colonia Chapultepec Polanco, Del Miguel Hidalgo, MX
Information: see also International and National organisations, and Venues (Palacio de Bellas Artes)
Country: Mexico

National Institute of Fine Arts (Instituto Nacional de Bellas Artes) National Theatre Coordination
Website: www.bellasartes.gob.mx
Email: infoinba@inba.gob.mx
Phone: 528 34600
Address: Coordinacion Nacional de Teatro, Paseo de la Reforma y Campo Marte S/N, Col. Polanco Chapultepec, MX
Information: see also International Organisations: National Institute of Fine Arts (Instituto Nacional de Bellas Artes) National Dance Coordination, and National Institute of Fine Arts (Instituto Nacional de Bellas Artes) Music and Opera Coordination
Country: Mexico

Organización del Teatros Independientes de México
Phone: 231 66854
Address: Arizona 156, Col. Napoles, MX
Country: Mexico

Queretano Institute of Culture and Arts
Website: www.culturaqueretaro.gob.mx
Email: lpedraza@queretaro.gob.mx
Phone: 442 251 9850
Address: And. Venustiano Carranza n, Centro Hist, MX
Country: Mexico

Quintana Roo Institute of Culture
Website: www.secqr.gob.mx
Email: webmaster_cultura@qroo.gob.mx
Phone: 983 832 1350
Address: Av. Héroes No. 68, Colonia Centro, MX
Information: see also Venues
Country: Mexico

Sociedad de Autores y Compositores de México
Website: www.sacm.org.mx
Email: sacm@sacm.org.mx
Phone: 560 47733
Address: Mayorazgo 129, Col. Xoco, Delegaci, MX
Country: Mexico

Sociedad Mexicana de Core
Email: aulestia@dfl.telmex.net.mx
Phone: 555 619 9020
Address: Dipizahua 74, Pedregal de Santo Domingo, Delegaci, MX
Information: currently has 150 members: works in close contact with Instituto Nacional de Bellas Artes and Consejo Nacional para la Cultura y las Artes
Country: Mexico

Sociedad Mexicana de México
Phone: 555 604 7923
Address: Mayorazgo 129, Col. Xoco., Delegaci, MX
Country: Mexico

Sonoran Institute of Culture
Website: www.isc.gob.mx
Email: info@isc.gob.mx
Phone: 662 213 4411
Address: Instituto Sonorense de Cultura, Obregon #5 entre Yanes y Garmendia, MX
Information: see also Venues
Country: Mexico

State Institute of Culture of Guanajuato
Website: www.guanajuato.gob.mx/cultura
Email: jalcocerf@guanajuato.gob.mx

**Faster, easier, with Giveo.
It's all in the app.**

Give. Buy. Help. Waste Less. Save Planet.

Cashless donation fundraising and marketplace app

GIVEO is the new app that is revolutionising fundraising.

Download it for free right now for Apple and Android and start raising money right away.

"It's a very simple way to raise $100 or $100,000. It's just point and click and that's it."

Fundraising expert and arts leader Douglas Evans

Phone: 147 310 22700
Address: Plazuela de Cata 1 y 2, Ex-Cava Domecq, Col. Mineral de Cata, MX
Country: Mexico

NEW ZEALAND

APRA/AMCOS, New Zealand
Website: www.apra.co.nz
Email: nz@apra.com.au
Phone: 962 32173
Address: Unit 113 – Zone 23, 21-23 Edwin Street, Mt Eden, NZ
Information: Head office in Sydney, Australia (q.v.), see also International Organisations; APRA also administers the rights of AMCOS; visiting address:Unit 113, Zone 23, 21-23 Edwin St, Mt Eden; alternative Email address: ahealey@apra.com.au
Country: New Zealand

Centre for NZ Music (SOUNZ)
Website: www.sounz.org.nz
Email: info@sounz.org.nz
Phone: 480 18602
Address: Level 3, Toi Poneke Arts Centre, 61 Abel Smith Street, Te Aro, NZ
Information: member of International Association of Music Information Centres
Country: New Zealand

Composers Association of NZ (CANZ)
Website: www.canz.net.nz
Email: info@canz.net.nz
Address: PO Box 4065, NZ
Information: Alternative website: www.dancingdutch.nl
Country: New Zealand

Copyright Council of NZ Inc
Website: www.copyright.org.nz
Email: council@copyright.co.nz
Phone: 948 02711
Address: PO Box 36477, Northcote, NZ
Country: New Zealand

EVANZ (Entertainment Venues Association of New Zealand)
Website: www.evanz.co.nz
Email: admin@evanz.co.nz
Phone: 497 71144
Address: PO Box 27501, NZ
Information: The Entertainment Venues Association of New Zealand (EVANZ) is the peak body representing the venue industry in New Zealand with a membership of 88 venues nationally. This includes 40 theatres, 30 event centres, 10 outdoor stadia and 8 convention centres.
Country: New Zealand

New Zealand Choral Federation Inc
Website: www.nzcf.org.nz
Email: grant.hutchinson@nzcf.org.nz
Phone: 211 546 923
Address: PO Box 49105, Mt Roskill South, NZ
Information: present Annual Conference, The Big Sing, Secondary Schools Choral Festivals annually Sing Aotearoa Festival triannual, next in 2010
Country: New Zealand

New Zealand Opera Society
Website: www.opera.net.nz
Email: gowmjv@xtra.co.nz
Phone: 438 72559
Address: PO Box 2014, NZ
Information: offers a variety of scholarships and prizes for opera singers and opera professionals
Country: New Zealand

New Zealand Writers Guild
Website: www.nzwritersguild.org.nz
Email: info@nzwg.org.nz
Phone: 936 01408
Address: 1/243 Ponsonby Rd, Ponsonby, NZ
Information: The New Zealand Writers Guild is a professional association of script writers. We represent the professional interests of writers in the fields of film, television, theatre, radio, comics and new media. The Guild's members include most of the professional script writers working in New Zealand
Country: New Zealand

NZ Musicians Union
Website: www.sfwu.org.nz
Email: peter.shannon@sfwu.org.nz
Phone: 272 046 337
Address: Private Bag 68-914, Newton, NZ
Information: The New Zealand Musicians Union is involved in all aspects of the industrial side of music and assists its members free of charge with contracts, taxation, copyright, royalty and legal advice. The union also provides a comprehensive instrument insurance policy for members
Country: New Zealand

NZ On Air
Website: www.nzonair.govt.nz

Email: info@nzonair.govt.nz
Phone: 438 29524
Address: Level 2, 119 Ghuznee Street, PO Box 9744, NZ
Information: visiting address: Jan Tooropstraat 1, 1062 BK Amsterdam
Country: New Zealand

Phonographic Performances New Zealand Ltd (PPNZ)
Website: www.ppnz.co.nz
Email: info@ppnz.co.nz
Phone: 936 05085
Address: Level 1, 2A Hakanoa Street, Grey Lynn, NZ
Information: PPNZ Music Licensing is a division of Recorded Music NZ Limited, and was established to obtain fair compensation for recording artists and record companies for their public performance rights. Representing many thousands of artists and record companies both locally and internationally, PPNZ licenses recorded music for public performance, broadcast and new media/online (communication)
Country: New Zealand

Radio Broadcasters Association (RBA)
Website: www.rba.co.nz
Email: info@rba.co.nz
Phone: 937 80788
Address: Level 4 Textile Centre, Kenwyn St, Parnell, NZ
Country: New Zealand

Recorded Music NZ Ltd
Website: recordedmusic.co.nz
Email: info@recordedmusic.co.nz
Phone: 936 05085
Address: Level 1, 2a Hakanoa Street, Grey Lynn, NZ
Information: member of the IFPI; visiting address: 2A Hakanoa Street, Grey Lynn, Auckland
Country: New Zealand
Social Media: @recordedmusicnz www.facebook.com/RecordedMusicNZ

Service Workers Union, Musicians Division
Website: www.sfwu.org
Email: membersupport@sfwu.org.nz
Phone: 937 52680
Address: Private Bag 68-914, Newton, NZ
Information: branches in Wellington, Canterbury and Otago
Country: New Zealand

Toi Maori Aotearoa – Maori Arts New Zealand
Website: www.maoriart.org.nz
Email: toimaori@maoriart.org.nz
Phone: 480 17914
Address: Level 1, Korea House, 29 Tory Street, PO Box 9570, NZ
Information: organises national programmes/workshops on Maori art; has a strong interest in other indigenous arts; holds biennial festival of Maori art; visiting address: Level 1, Korea House, 29 Tory Street
Country: New Zealand

PHILIPPINES

Arts Foundation of the Cordilleras (AFC)
Website: www.tin.nl
Email: debbi611@yahoo.com
Phone: 744 439 867
Address: University of Baguio, General Luna St., PH
Information: in full support of the arts community, the AFC initiates livelihood programmes for local performing artists, craftsmen, visual and audio-visual artists, musicians and theatre artists through the use of local resources
Country: Philippines

Baguio Arts Guild
Website: www.nto.no
Email: rdomirez@rocketmail.com
Address: Leonard Wood Road, Botanical Garden, PH
Information: sustains its regular programmes such as exhibitions, performances, workshops and community work; conducts the annual summer arts workshop for community residents as well as summer visitors
Country: Philippines

Concerned Artists of the Philippines (CAP)
Website: www.mrfylke.no
Email: post@mrfylke.no
Phone: 271 15184
Address: c/o PHSA Office Folk Arts Theatre, CCP Complex Roxas Blvd., PH
Country: Philippines

Cultural Centre of the Philippines – Dramatic Arts Division
Website: www.culturalcenter.gov.ph
Email: clotildel@excite.com
Phone: 283 22314
Address: Performing Arts Department, Upper Basement CCP Complex, Roxas Blvd., PH
Information: current CCP President is Nestor O. Jardin; alternative E-mail address: performance@culturalcenter.gov.ph

Country: Philippines

Filipino Society of Composers, Authors & Publishers (Filscap)
Website: www.oppland-f.kommune.no
Email: postmottak@oppland.org
Phone: 272 26981
Address: 1365 E. Rodriguez Sr. Avenue, PH
Information: visiting address: Kirkegaten 76, 2626 Lillehammer
Country: Philippines

Grassroot Development Theatre
Website: www.ostfold-f.kommune.no
Email: sentralpost@ostfold-f.kommune.no
Phone: 691 17000
Address: Social Laboratory-Sual, Pangasinan, 25 Botola cor. Bayani St., Araneta Subd., PH
Country: Philippines

Kalinangan Batangan (KB)
Website: www.st-f.kommune.no
Email: knut.moller@st-f.kommune.no
Phone: 439 804 525
Address: St. Michael Bldg., D. Silang Street, PH
Country: Philippines

Kodally Society of the Philippines
Website: www.danseinfo.no
Email: post@danseinfo.no
Phone: 237 09440
Address: c/o St. Paul College of Music, 680 Pedro Gil St., PH
Information: formerly known as Senter for Dansekunst (The Norwegian Center for the Art of Dance)
Country: Philippines

League of Filipino Composers
Website: www.du-store-verden.no
Email: post@du-store-verden.no
Phone: 283 21120 ext.
Address: NAMCYA-Folk Theatre, CCP Complex, Roxas Blvd., PH
Information: membership organisation
Country: Philippines

Manila Chamber Orchestra Foundation
Website: www.gramo.no
Email: fellesmail@gramo.no
Phone: 281 81403
Address: 8F equipable, PCI Bank Tower2, Makati Ave., PH
Information: formally known as Manila Chamber Orchestra
Country: Philippines

National Commission for Culture and the Arts (NCCA)
Website: www.ncca.gov.ph
Email: info@ncca.gov.ph
Phone: 252 72192
Address: 633 Gen Luna St., Intramuros, PH
Country: Philippines

Organisasyon Ng Pilipinong Mang-Aawit (OPM)
Website: www.mic.no
Email: info@mic.no
Phone: 632 817 7414
Address: 611 FMSG Bldg, 9 Balete Drive Cor., 3rd St., PH
Information: MIC's primary goal is to promote Norwegian music of all genres and styles, domestically as well as internationally. Through a number of promotional initiatives and information projects the institution strives to raise awareness levels on Norwegian music among music industry execs, cultural organisation representatives, media reps and the General public at home and abroad.
Country: Philippines

Philippine Educational Theater Association (PETA)
Website: petatheater.com
Email: petafr@petatheater.com
Phone: 272 56244
Address: No.5 Eymard Drive, New Manila, Quezon City, Metro Manila, PH
Information: see also Performing Companies
Country: Philippines

Philippine Folk Dance Society
Website: www.danseogteatersentrum.no
Email: tove@scenekunst.no
Phone: 252 80563
Address: c/o Dr. Larry A. Gabao, Philippine Normal University, Taft Ave., PH
Information: The Norwegian Association for Performing Arts (NAPA) is a state-subsidized network organisation for the performing arts sector in Norway. It has its national office in Oslo. NAPA's main vision is "to promote the Artistic exPression of dance and theatre, and to stimulate access and increased interest for dance and theatre amongst all audiences"
Country: Philippines

Philippine Musicians Guild
Website: www.ntks.com
Email: ole@olebohn.com
Phone: 632 806 1031
Address: Lot 14, Block 6, Jamin Street, Do, Talon V, PH
Information: Norwegian artist Tone Society (NTKS) is an organization for soloists and chamber musicians in serious music. Da organisasjonen ble dannet i 1912, var det realiseringen av en idé som blant annet komponisten Johan Svendsen hadde fremmet. When the organization was formed in 1912, was the realization of an idea such as composer Johan Svendsen had promoted.
Country: Philippines

Philippine Society for Music Education
Website: www.noda.no
Email: noda@noda.no
Phone: 210 27180
Address: Music & Arts Dept., Philippine Normal College, Taft Ave., PH
Information: the association of dancers, choreographers and educators, is an independent national academic and Artistic association with about 870 members. Formed in 1947 as the Norwegian Ballet Association. Norwegian Dance Artists are lobbyist and target government, parliamentary, cultural council, municipalities and counties with cases that will enhance the art of dance in Norway
Country: Philippines

Philippine Stagers Foundation
Website: www.norwayfestivals.com
Email: norfest@online.no
Phone: 293 14882
Address: G Tuazon, PH
Information: a multi-awarded and fast rising professional theatre company based in the Philippines
Country: Philippines
Social Media: www.facebook.com/pages/Philippine-Stagers-Foundation/390094505995

Philippines Dance Alliance
Website: www.skuespillerforbund.no
Email: nsf@skuespillerforbund.no
Phone: 283 23657
Address: Cultural Centre of the Philippines, Roxas Blvd., PH
Country: Philippines

Piano Teachers Guild of the Philippines
Website: www.kor.no
Email: nk@korforbundet.no
Phone: 524 76868
Address: c/o St. Scholastica's College of Music, Leon Guinto St., PH
Information: The Norwegian Choir Association seeks to increase awareness and quality of choral singing. This is best achieved through creating a strong musical community which is open to all genres, ages and levels of ambition
Country: Philippines

Samahan Ng Mga Manunuri at Manunulat Ng Musika Sa Pilipinas (SAMMPI)
Website: www.nscf.no
Email: nscf@online.no
Phone: 632 801 6286
Address: BF Resort, Pamplona, PH
Information: Organise between 90 and 100% of the Norwegian stageDirectors. NScF is a politically neutral union whose purpose is to secure its members' Artistic and economic interests. Foreign Directors working within theatre, opera and television in Norway may gain a temporary membership.
Country: Philippines

Samahang Pangkultura at Sining ng Koronadal (SPSK)
Website: denif.no
Email: morning7@marbel.weblingo
Phone: 832 282 816
Address: Marbel Institute of Technology, Alunan Ave., PH
Information: provides sponsorships, training programmes and workshops for theatre arts, modern and folk dance, mask and puppet making etc; carrys out research for the indigenous communities found in the region
Country: Philippines

Society of Film Archivists (SOFIA)
Website: www.nmff.no
Email: cathrine@nmff.no
Phone: 292 04395
Address: c/o Mortion Picture Division, Philippine Information Agency, Visayas Ave., PH
Country: Philippines

Tangadan Community Organization (COP)
Website: www.notam02.no
Email: admin@notam02.no
Phone: 223 58060
Address: Barangay Tangadan, San Quintin, PH
Information: Notam works with developing technical solutions and imparting knowledge about potentials and possibilities that technology offers within the cultural domain. The center operates on several levels within the Norwegian music and arts scene, and in the international music technology environment. We provide support musicians and artists, and we develop our own music technology.
Country: Philippines

Theatre Council Philippines
Website:
www.komponist.no
Email:
komponist@komponist.no
Phone: 632 924 0145
Address: 60 Scout de Guia, PH
Information: founded in 1917. The Society's main objectives are to promote its members' music and secure their rights. As of today the Society counts 181 members who meet regularly for discussions and seminars
Country: Philippines

SINGAPORE

Artists Academy
Website: www.artists-academy.com.sg
Email: info@artists-academy.com.sg
Phone: 665 91860
Address: TIDES, 217 East Coast Road, SG
Information: a school for music tuition for children and young adults. Also sells instruments and lessons to individual people
Country: Singapore
Social Media: @ArtistsAcademy www.facebook.com/ArtistsAcademy

Arts House Limited
Website: https://sifa.sg
Email: sifa@artshouse.sg
Address: 28 Aliwal Street, Aliwal Arts Centre 03-07, Singapore
Information: Arts House Limited is a not-for-profit organisation committed to enriching lives through the arts. AHL manages these key landmarks located in the heart of Singapore's Civic District: The Art House, Victoria Theatre & Victoria Concert Hall, Goodman Arts Centre, Aliwal Arts Centre and Drama Centre. AHL also presents the Singapore International Festival of Arts, the annual pinnacle celebration of performance and interdisciplinary arts, commissioned by the National Arts Council. Members of ISPA
Country: Singapore

Chinese Dance Artistes' Association
Website: www.iam.pl
Email: iam@iam.pl
Phone: 627 31524
Address: c/o Geylang P.O. Box 0014, SG
Information: A state cultural institution whose task is to promote Polish culture around the world and actively participate in international cultural exchange. Member of ISPA
Country: Singapore
Social Media: www.facebook.com/pages/Chinese-Dance-Artistes-Asso

Composers and Authors Society of Singapore Ltd – (COMPASS)
Website: www.compass.org.sg
Email: membership@compass.org.sg
Phone: 632 36630
Address: 37 Craig Road, , 03-05, Tulip Garden, SG
Information: alternative Email address: compass-licence@compass.org.sg; part of CISAC; see under International Organisations
Country: Singapore

National Arts Council (NAC)
Website: www.nac.gov.sg
Email: mita_pa@mita.gov.sg
Phone: 674 64622
Address: 140 Hill Street, 03-01 MITA Building, SG
Information: see more detail in Ministries & Funding Agencies
Country: Singapore

National ArtsCouncil
Website: www.nas.org.sg
Email: leonard_cheong@nac.gov.sg
Phone: 634 69695
Address: Goodman Arts Centre, 90 Goodman Road, Blk A #01-01, SG
Information: their mission is to nurture the arts and make it an integral part of the lives of the people of Singapore; member of ISPA
Country: Singapore

Nrityalaya Aesthetics Society
Website: www.nas.org.sg
Email: nas@pacific.net.sg
Phone: 633 66537
Address: Stamford Arts Centre, 155 Waterloo Street, SG
Information: provides the following courses: Dance: Bharata Natyam, Kuchipudi, Odissi, Mohini Attam, Kathak; Karnatic Music: vocal, flute, violin, veena, mridangam; Hindustani Music: vocal, sitar, harmonium, tabela, guitar, keyboard & Indian choir
Country: Singapore

NUS Centre For the Arts
Website: www.nus.edu.sg/cfa
Email: cfaMarketing@nus.edu.sg
Phone: 651 62492
Address: University Cultural Centre, 50 Kent Ridge Crescent, National University of Singapore, SG
Information: established in 1993, NUS Centre For the Arts (CFA) is a multifaceted arts organisation that nurtures triple arts – performing, visual and literary – on campus and beyond. CFA's three main functions are in the areas of management, programmes and education.

Recording Industry Association (Singapore)
Website: www.rias.org.sg
Email: info@rias.org.sg
Phone: 622 04166
Address: 4 Leng Kee Road, #03-07 SiS building, SG
Country: Singapore

Singapore Indian Fine Arts Society
Website: www.sifas.org
Email: admin@sifas.org
Phone: 629 95929
Address: 2A Starlight Rd, SG
Information: also give music and dance performances; non-profit organisation
Country: Singapore

TAIWAN

Chinese Folk Arts Foundation
Website: www.folk.org.tw
Email: info@chopin.edu.pl
Phone: 223 770 794
Address: 6F, No.131-3 Ji Long Road, , Section 2
Information: see also Further Education
Country: Taiwan

Wind Flyers Dance Laboratory
Email: paper@paperwindmill.org
Phone: 022 392 6170
Address: 1F, No. 59 of 2, , Chong Qing South Road Section 2,
Information: consists of three units: Paper Windmill Theatre Group, Green Ray Theatre and Wind Flyers Dance Laboratory; founded in 1992 with the original purpose of coordinating the operation of the three units; aims to take part in promoting arts and culture;
Country: Taiwan

THAILAND

Friends of the Arts Foundation
Website: www.friends-of-the-arts.info
Email: info@friends-of-the-arts.info
Phone: 662 258 9227
Address: 5323 Sukumvit rd 33, Klongton Nua, TH
Information: see also Promoters
Country: Thailand

UGANDA

32° East | Ugandan Arts Trust
Website: ugandanartstrust.org
Email: info@ugandanartstrust.org
Phone: 793 325 372
Address: Ggaba Road, UG
Information: 32° East | Ugandan Arts Trust is an independent non-profit organisation, focused on the creation and exploration of contemporary art in Uganda. 32° East believes in providing a long term, sustainable and open platform for Artistic exPression. Member of ISPA.
Country: Uganda

Bayimba Cultural Foundation
Website: bayimba.org
Email: info@bayimba.org
Phone: 414 591 670
Address: Plot 50, Kiira Road, Kenneth, Dale Drive, UG
Information: a multiple-branched organization that focuses on uplifting arts and culture in Uganda through cultural exchange and creativity. Member of ISPA
Country: Uganda

UNITED ARAB EMIRATES

Abu Dhabi Music & Arts Foundation – ADMAF
Website: www.admaf.org
Email:
info@admaf.org
Phone: 123 336 400
Address: 3rd Floor, Makeen Tower (Ajman Bank Building), Tourist Club Area
Information: Through arts education, community arts and special projects, Abu Dhabi Music & Arts Foundation (ADMAF) has been nurturing creativity across the UAE for more than two decades. Since its establishment by Huda I. Alkhamis-Kanoo in 1996, it has been at the forefront of the UAE's arts sector, inspiring young people, the public and artists, enabling creative exPression through a wide range of programmes and projects.
Country: United Arab Emirates

UNITED STATES

National Chorale
Website: www.nationalchorale.com
Email: music@nationalchorale.org
Phone: 123 335 333
Address: 1650 Broadway Ste 301 New York, NY 10019, US
Information: The Chorale is the only professional choral organization to establish and maintain an annual choral-orchestral series in a major New York City concert hall—for 52 years at Lincoln Center—with additional concerts at Carnegie Hall

ACB Association of Concert Bands
Website: www.acbands.org
Email: secretary@acbands.org
Phone: 007 268 720
Address: 6613 Cheryl Ann Drive Independence, Ohio, US
Information: The ACB was formed to support adult concert, community, and municipal bands. Members include bands, adult musicians, conductors, composers, and corporations who are dedicated and equipped to serve the needs of musicians that perform in and/or lead adult concert bands. The ACB publishes a magazine, the ACB Journal, to exchange information among people involved in adult concert bands and sponsors many projects to fulfill its mission.
Country: United States

City of Dallas Office of Arts and Culture
Website: www.dallasculture.org
Email: polmic@polmic.pl
Phone: 146 703 687
Address: 1925 Elm St, Fl 4th Dallas, TX 75201, US
Information: The Office of Arts and Culture (OAC) is a division of the City Manager's office and fosters support, partnerships, and opportunities for Dallas citizens, visitors, artists, and arts and cultural organizations.
Country: United States

Delaware Division of the Arts – State of Delaware
Website: www.arts.delaware.gov
Email: delarts@delaware.gov
Phone: 025 778 278
Address: 820 N French St 4th floor, Wilmington, DE 19801, US
Information: The Delaware Division of the Arts, a branch of the Delaware Department of State, is dedicated to cultivating and supporting the arts to enhance the quality of life for all Delawareans. Together with its advisory body, the Delaware State Arts Council, the Division administers grants and programs that support arts programming, educate the public, increase awareness of the arts, and integrate the arts into all facets of Delaware life.
Country: United States

New York Live Arts
Website: www.newyorklivearts.org
Email: info@newyorklivearts.org
Phone: 126 916 500
Address: 219 W 19th Street, New York, NY 10011, US
Information: New York Live Arts was founded in 2011 by a merger of the Bill T. Jones/Arnie Zane Dance Company and Dance Theater Workshop. The Institution strives to create a robust framework in support of the nation's dance and movement-based artists through new approaches to producing, presenting, and educating.
Country: United States

Alabama State Council on the Arts
Website: www.arts.alabama.gov
Email: yvette.jones-smedley@arts.alabama.gov
Phone: 334 242 4076
Address: 201 Monroe Street, Suite 110, US
Information: the Alabama State Council on the Arts is set up to promote Alabama's Artistic and cultural resources
Country: United States

Alaska State Council on the Arts
Website: www.arts.alaska.gov
Email: asca.info@alaska.gov
Phone: 072 696 610
Address: 161 Klevin Street, Suite 102 • Anchorage, AK 99508, US
Information: The Alaska State Council on the Arts is a state agency that helps the development of the arts for all Alaskans through education, partnerships, grants and services.
Country: United States

American Arts Alliance
Website: www.theperformingartsalliance.org/site/PageServer?pagename=paa_home_page
Email: robrian@artspresenters.org
Phone: 202 207 3850
Address: 1211 Connecticut Avenue, NW, Suite 200, US
Information: now known as the Performing Arts Alliance. It is a national network of more than 33, 000 organisational and individual members comprising of the professional, nonprofit performing arts and presenting fields
Country: United States

American Association of Community Theatre (AACT)
Website: www.aact.org
Email: info@aact.org
Phone: 177 323 177
Address: 1300 Gendy St, US
Information: Founded in 1986, AACT is a nonprofit corporation that serves both individuals and organizations by providing expertise, assistance and support so that community theatres can provide the best possible theatrical experience for participants and audience alike.
Country: United States

American Bandmasters Association
Website: www.americanbandmasters.org
Email: thomas.fraschillo@usm.edu
Phone: 228 276 061/69,
Address: 11738 Big Canoe, 209 Cherokee Trail Jasper, GA 30143, US
Information: The American Bandmasters Association, founded in 1929, with John Philip Sousa as Honorary Life President, recognizes outstanding achievement on the part of Concert Band conductors and composers. The current membership (invitational) comprises approximately 300 band conductors and composers in the USA and Canada, and 70 Associate Members (music businesses and corporations that provide significant services to bands and to the publication of band music.)
Country: United States

American Berlin Opera Foundation's Annual Scholarship Competition
Website: www.operafoundation.org
Email: gala@operafoundation.org
Phone: 212 664 8843
Address: The Opera Foundation, Inc. c/o Mannheim LLC, 712 Fifth Avenue 32nd Floor, New York, NY 10019
Information: non-profit organisation that supports young American opera singers abroad and build cross-cultural bridges between the United States and other important opera supporting countries; the organisation provides scholarships and study grants; auditions are held annually to award these programmes to qualified applicants
Country: United States

American Choral Directors Association
Website: www.acda.org
Email: membership@acda.org
Phone: 052 328 161
Address: 545 Couch Dr Oklahoma City, OK 73102, US
Information: The mission of the American Choral Directors Association is to inspire excellence in choral music through education, performance, composition, and advocacy.
Country: United States

American Composers Alliance
Website: www.composers.com
Email: info@composers.com
Phone: 212 925 0458
Address: 802 W. 190th Street, First Floor, US
Information: keeps scores of music by American composers in print and available to the public through sheet music publication services, through Managing and licensing the music in the ACA catalogue for various professional uses, and through its ongoing series of live concerts
Country: United States

American Dance Guild
Website: www.americandanceguild.org
Email: adgfest@gmail.com
Phone: 212 874 6947
Address: American Dance Guild, 320 West 83rd Street, Apt. 7D, US
Information: American Dance Guild, Inc. is a dance service organization serving dance artists, educators and professionals since 1956.
Country: United States

American Federation of Musicians
Website: www.afm.org
Email: presoffice@afm.org
Phone: 212 869 1330
Address: 1501 Broadway, Suite 600, US
Information: membership organisation; a large organisation that helps musicians with contract agreements, record ownership, health care amongst other advice
Country: United States

American Guild of English Handbell Ringers
Website: www.handbellmusicians.org
Email: jcauhorn@agehr.org
Phone: 937 438 0085
Address: Handbell Musicians of America, 1055 E. Centerville Station Road, US
Information: Established in 1954, the American Guild of English Handbell Ringers grew out of the previously established New England Guild of English Handbell Ringers. In 2010, AGEHR became Handbell Musicians of America. It's primary objectives are to educate, promote

the exchange of ideas relating to handbell and handchime ringing, and sponsor educational activities.
Country: United States

American Guild of Variety Artists
Website: www.agvausa.com
Email: agva@agvausa.org
Phone: 126 751 003
Address: 363 Seventh Avenue 17th Floor New York, NY 10001, US
Information: The American Guild of Variety Artists (AGVA) is an AFL-CIO affiliated labor union founded in 1939 to represent performing Artists and Stage Managers in live performances in the Variety field

American Harp Society
Website: www.harpsociety.org
Email: socialmediaManager@harpsociety.org
Phone: 054 104 277
Address: Po Box 260 Bellingham, MA, US
Information: With over 3, 000 members from all 50 states and 20 countries, the American Harp Society, Inc. is the largest national organization of harpists in the world. Members include leading soloists, orchestral players, commercial, jazz and popular performers, freelancers, harp therapists, college and university professors, adult amateurs, and students of all ages. Founded in 1962.
Country: United States

American Musicological Society
Website: www.amsmusicology.org
Email: ams@amsmusicology.org
Phone: 129 982 099
Address: 20 Cooper Square, Room 225 New York, NY 10003, US
Information: The AMS exists to expand understanding of music and sound through research, teaching, learning, and advocacy. To realize its mission, the Society fosters new work through a range of grants, fellowships, publication subventions, and awards; encourages exchange through publications, meetings, performances, lectures, and other public programs; and supports the professional lives of its members and constituents through workshops, mentoring, discussion forums, and other resources.
Country: United States

American Opera Projects Inc
Website: www.operaprojects.org
Email: info@operaprojects.org
Phone: 718 398 4024
Address: American Opera Projects, Inc., 138 South Oxford St., Brooklyn, US
Information: produces and develops opera in and around America
Country: United States

American Recorder Society
Website: www.americanrecorder.org
Email: Director@americanrecorder.org
Phone: 704 509 1422
Address: P.O. Box 480054 Charlotte, NC, US
Information: The American Recorder Society is a non-profit membership organization that promotes the pleasures of recorder playing. For 80 years, the ARS has provided a supportive community for all who value the recorder and its music. Its members are more than 2, 000 chapters, consorts, individuals, and businesses, representing a community of players throughout the U.S., Canada, and 30 countries around the world.
Country: United States

American Society of Theatre Consultants (ASTC)
Website: www.theatreconsultants.org
Email: elustig@swbell.net
Phone: 855 800 2782
Address: American Society of Theatre Consultants, PO Box 22, US
Information: an organisation where theatre consultants from around the United States and Canada can contribute new and traditional ideas with to develop entertainment, educational, and business facilities for theatre
Country: United States

Americans for the Arts
Website: www.artsusa.org
Email: marszalek@woj-pomorskie.pl
Phone: 202 371 2830
Address: 1000 Vermont Avenue NW, 6th floor, US
Information: Americans for the Arts serves, advances, and leads the network of organizations and individuals who cultivate, promote, sustain, and support the arts in America. Founded in 1960, Americans for the Arts is the nation's leading nonprofit organization for advancing the arts and arts education.
Country: United States

AMRA (American Mechanical Rights Agency Inc.)
Website: www.amermechrights.com
Email: info@amermechrights.com
Phone: 310 440 8778
Address: American Mechanical Rights Agency Inc., 149 South Berrington Avenue, Suite 810, US
Information: membership organisation; deals with the

protection, distribution and collection of royalties on behalf of artists and their recorded music
Country: United States

Arizona Commission on the Arts
Website:
www.azarts.gov
Email: info@azarts.gov
Phone:
602 771 6501
Address: 417 W Roosevelt St, Phoenix, AZ, USA
Information: The Arizona Commission on the Arts is an agency of the State of Arizona whose mission is to create opportunities for all Arizonans to participate in and experience the arts

Arizona Presenters Alliance
Website: www.azpresenters.org
Email: info@azpresenters.org
Phone: 480 965 0190
Address: Arizona Presenters Alliance, P.O. Box 1312, US
Information: the Arizona Presenters Alliance is a service organisation for the presentation of the arts in Arizona
Country: United States

Arkansas Arts Council
Website: www.arkansasarts.org
Email: info@arkansasarts.com
Phone: 501 324 9766
Address: Arkansas Arts Council, 323 Center Street, Suite 1500, US
Information: the Arkansas Arts Council promotes the arts for the city of Arkansas
Country: United States

Arts & Business Council of New York
Website: www.artsandbusiness.org
Email: info@artsandbusiness.org
Phone: 212 223 2787
Address: 2nd Floor, 1 East 53rd St, , US
Information: founded in 1960, Americans for the Arts is a nonprofit organisation for helping the arts and arts education
Country: United States

Arts & Humanities Council of Tulsa
Website: www.ahct.org
Email: info@ahct.org
Address: 101 East Archer Street, US
Information: council on arts in Tulsa. Focusing on young children gaining access to arts
Country: United States

Arts Commission of Greater Toledo
Website: www.acgt.org
Email: info@theartscommission.org
Phone: 192 542 787
Address: 1838 Parkwood Ave #120, Toledo, OH 43604, US
Information: Since 1959, The Arts Commission has provided quality arts programming and services to the metropolitan Toledo area. The Arts Commission is the longest-standing arts commission in the state of Ohio. The Arts Commission works to build a creative and cultural community in Toledo, inspire vibrancy in neighborhoods, and to celebrate life through art.
Country: United States

Arts Council of the Morris Area
Website: www.morrisarts.org
Email: info@morrisarts.org
Phone: 973 285 5115
Address: 14 Maple Avenue, Suite 301, Morristown, US
Information: art and education program, services to arts organisations, promotion and professional training in administrative skills, community program, artist registry
Country: United States
Social Media: @MorrisArts www.facebook.com/ArtsCounciloftheMorrisArea

Arts for the Schools
Website: www.artsfortheschools.org
Email: admin@artsfortheschools.org
Phone: 305 828 278
Address: 11045 Donner Pass Road, Suite 2A Truckee, CA 96161, US
Information: Arts For The Schools is 501 (c)3 non-profit that fundamentally believes that access and exposure to the arts is essential for all. Arts For The Schools mission is to inspire, teach and build our rural communities through equitable access to the arts and arts education. Arts For The Schools serves as the primary provider of arts education for schools in our service area and builds awareness about the importance of the arts, through advocacy, rich programming and community partnerships.
Country: United States
Social Media: facebook.com/Arts4theSchoolstwitter.com/arts4theschools

Arts International
Email: info@artsinternational.org
Phone: 213 230 092
Address: 526 West 26th Street, Suite 516, US
Country: United States

Arts Midwest

Website: www.artsmidwest.org
Email: emily@artsmidwest.org
Phone: 123 410 755
Address: Arts Midwest, 2908 Hennepin Avenue, Suite 200, US
Information: A non-profit regional arts organization located in Minneapolis, Arts Midwest promotes creativity, nurtures cultural leadership, and engages people in meaningful arts experiences, bringing vitality to Midwest communities and enriching people's lives.
Country: United States
Social Media: facebook.com/artsmidwest/twitter.com/ArtsMidwestinstagram.com/arts_midwest/

Arts Northwest
Website: www.artsnw.org
Email: admin@artsnw.org
Phone: 360 457 9290
Address: 104 N. Laurel Street, Ste. 116, US
Information: serves a membership of 500 organisations and individuals with services ranging from technical support and publications, mentoring and professional development programmes and the annual convening of the Arts Northwest Booking Conference
Country: United States
Social Media: @Artsnw
www.facebook.com/ArtsNorthwest?ref=ts&fref=ts

ArtsEmerson
Website: https://artsemerson.org/Online/default.asp
Email: tickets@artsemerson.org
Phone: 617 824 8400
Address: 120 Boylston Street, Boston, Massachusetts 02116, United States
Information: ArtsEmerson is Boston's leading presenter of contemporary world theatre. We are dedicated to engaging all communities through stories that reveal and deepen our connection to each other.
we are committed to building a cultural institution that reflects the diversity of our city. We program a full season of performances, film and dialogue that invites each of us to engage in a more contemporary narrative of Boston as a truly global city. Members of ISPA
Country: United States

Association for Hispanic Classical Theater
Website: www.comedias.org
Email: lvidler@comedias.org
Address: US
Country: United States

Association for Recorded Sound Collections
Website: www.arsc-audio.org
Email: execdir@arsc-audio.org
Phone: 259 330 770
Address: P.O. Box 543, US
Country: United States

Association of Arts Administration Educators
Website: www.artsAdministration.org
Email: info@artsAdministration.org
Phone: 608 561 2040
Address: N4460 Allan Rd., US
Information: see also Conferences
Country: United States

Association of California Symphony Orchestras
Website: www.acso.org
Email: ksinclair@acso.org
Phone: 916 484 6744
Address: 2755 Cottage Way, Suite 3, US
Information: membership organisation
Country: United States

Association of Hispanic Arts
Website: www.latinoarts.org
Email: events@latinoarts.com
Phone: 414 384 3100
Address: 1028 South 9th Street, US
Information: ArCuB is a public institution under the authority of The General Council of Bucharest
Country: United States

Association of Performing Arts Presenters (APAP)
Website: www.apap365.org
Email: info@apap365.org
Phone: 202 833 2787
Address: 919 18th St. NW, Suite 650, US
Information: APAP is the national service, advocacy and membership organization for presenters of the performing arts. They are dedicated to developing and supporting a robust performing arts industry and the professionals who work within it through our annual conference and year-round professional development, leadership programs, resource sharing, advocacy and networking. Member of ISPA.
Country: United States

Association of Performing Arts Professionals
Website: https:// www.apap365.org/
Email: info@apap365.org
Phone: 202 833 2787
Address: 919 18th St. NW, Suite 650 Washington D.C.,

DC, US 20006
Information: Serving thousands of member organizations and individuals since 1957, APAP works to strengthen the field and advance careers through professional development, grant support, advocacy, networking and the annual APAP|NYC conference. Members of ISPA
Country: United States

Atlanta Bureau of Cultural Affairs, City of
Website: www.ocaatlanta.com
Email:
atlantajazz@atlantaga.gov
Phone: 404 546 6788
Address: 233 Peachtree Street NE, Harris Tower, Suite 1700, US
Information: (OCA) was established in 1974 to encourage and support Atlanta's cultural resources. The initial mission was to solidify the role that arts and other cultural resources play in defining and enhancing the social fabric and quality of life of Atlanta citizens and visitors. Today the OCA understands that the arts play an essential role in defining the cultural vitality of the city and is working to enhance Atlanta's reputation as a cultural destination. The OCA aims to provide programmes that contribute substantially to the city's economy and quality of life
Country: United States

Atlatl Inc.
Website: www.uniter.ro
Email: atlatl@atlatl.org
Phone: 213 113 214
Address: 49 East Thomas, Suite 105, US
Information: UNITER is a professional, apolitical, non-governmental and non-profit organization, resulted from the free association of artists from the theatre industry. The founding principles of this professional organization were the freedom of exPression, of creation and association, the right to autonomy, the right to exPress oneself freely within the national and international cultural medium, an opening free of complexes towards world culture and, without a doubt, the defense of common interests of the many kinds of professionals working in the theatre industry. UNITER was founded in February 1990. As a consequence of its sustained activity, UNITER has obtained the statute of an establishment of public service by the Decision of Government no. 746 / 31 August 2000.
Country: United States

Baltimore Office of Promotion and the Arts
Website: www.promotionandarts.com
Email: bgilmore@promotionandarts.com
Phone: 410 752 8632
Address: 10 E. Baltimore Street, 10th Floor, US
Information: Producing high-quality special events, festivals and arts programming that stimulate communities economically, Artistically and culturally.
Country: United States

Breckenridge Music
Website: www.breckmusic.org
Email: admin@breckmusic.org
Phone: 970 453 9142
Address: 201 S. Ridge Street Breckenridge, CO 80424
Information: Founded in 1981, Breckenridge Music impacts the community by improving the quality of life for Summit County residents and visitors, increasing access to the arts, fostering a deeper understanding of music for all ages and contributing to a robust Breckenridge economy. The non-profit organization serves approximately 15, 000 people each year through its three core programs: Breckenridge Music Festival, Breck Music Education and Breck Music Presents.
Country: United States

California Presenters
Website: www.elcamino.edu/commadv/centerforarts
Email: calpresenters@gmail.com
Phone: 054 711 840
Address: P.O. Box 750182, Petaluma, CA 94975
Information: California Presenters, founded in 1985, is a statewide organization committed to advancing professional touring and presenting of the performing arts.
Country: United States

Candid | GuideStar and Foundation Center
Website: www.candid.org
Email: answers@candid.org
Phone: 126 204 230
Address: 32 Old Slip, 24th Floor, New York, NY, 10005, US
Information: Candid was born February 1, 2019, when Foundation Center and GuideStar joined forces. A nonprofit organization that maintains one of the most comprehensive databases in the U.S., offering a robust, accessible knowledge bank for the social sector.
Country: United States

Caribbean Cultural Center
Website: www.cccadi.org
Email: info@cccadi.org
Phone: 212 307 7420
Address: 1825 Park Avenue, Suite 602, US
Information: a not for profit cultural organisation

based in New York City dedicated to promoting and promulgating the cultures of people of African Descent brought before and after the Transatlantic Slave Trade. Through concerts, gallery tours, workshops, performances, conferences, professional development sessions, spiritual gatherings, and teaching artists residencies, we support teachers, and students across New York to learn and grow through the arts
Country: United States

Center for Contemporary Opera
Website: www.centerforcontemporaryopera.org
Email: info@conopera.org
Phone:
172 074 397
Address: 475 Park Ave. South, 21st Floor New York, NY 10016, US
Information: The Center for Contemporary Opera, founded in 1982 by Richard Marshall and Robert Ward in New York, is devoted to developing, producing, and promoting new opera and music-theater works and to reviving neglected operas written since WW2. CCO has developed a tradition of bringing European opera to the American stage, and of taking American works abroad.
Country: United States

Chamber Music America
Website: www.chamber-music.org
Email: membership@chamber-music.org
Phone: 122 422 022
Address: 12 West 32nd Street, 7th Floor New York, NY 10001, US
Information: CMA defines chamber music as music for small ensembles in which players perform one to a part, Generally without a conductor. Historically, the term chamber music was restricted to Western classical music for small ensembles, such as the string quartet. Today, however, chamber music comprises many different musical styles and genres. At the heart of this art form is a spirit of collaboration. Democratic in essence, chamber music demands that each individual engage in a close musical dialogue with the other performers. Their collective musical instinct, experience, knowledge, and talent guide the process of interpreting, rehearsing, and performing. Member of ISPA.
Country: United States

Children's Creative Project
Website: ccp.sbCEO.org
Email: ccp@sbCEO.org
Phone: 805 964 4710
Address: 1235-B Veronica Springs Road, Santa Barbara, US
Information: At its inception in 1972, a small group of the Children's Creative Project (CCP) volunteer artists served 200 children at Franklin Elementary School in Santa Barbara. In 1975 the CCP acquired non-profit status and became a program of the Santa Barbara County Education Office under then-Superintendent William J. Cirone.
Now the CCP reaches more than 50, 000 children annually, in 100 Santa Barbara and San Luis Obispo County Schools.
Country: United States

Chinese Music Society of North America (CMSNA)
Website: www.ChineseMusic.Net
Email: syshen@megsinet.net
Phone: 630 910 1551
Address: PO Box 5275, US
Information: founded in 1969
Country: United States

Chorus America
Website: www.chorusamerica.org
Email: service@chorusamerica.org
Phone: 023 317 577
Address: 1200 18th Street NW, Suite 1250 Washington, DC 20036, US
Information: Chorus America is the advocacy, research, and leadership development organization that advances the choral field. We support and serve conductors, administrators, board members and singers with tools, training, networking and access so that choruses are better able to contribute to their communities.
Country: United States

Christians in Theater Arts (CITA)
Website: www.cita.org
Email: hello@cita.org
Phone: 044 527 070
Address: US
Information: CITA cultivates environments that empower and sustain all Christians in Theatre Arts.
Country: United States

Cincinnati Recreation Commission
Website: www.cincyrec.org/
Email: info.crc@cincinnati-oh.gov
Phone: 133 524 000
Address: 805 Central Ave #800, Cincinnati, OH 45202, US
Information: The Cincinnati Recreation Commission was created in 1927 to enrich the lives of the community by providing recreational and cultural activities.

Country: United States

City of Minneapolis Art in Public Places
Website: www.minneapolismn.gov/things-to-do/public-art/
Email: publicart@minneapolismn.gov
Phone: 126 733 006
Address: City of Minneapolis, 250 S 4th Street, Room 110 Minneapolis, MN 55107, US
Information: The City of Minneapolis has enriched the lives of citizens and visitors by integrating public art into city planning, service design, and infrastructure. Art in Public Places has been a regular part of the City's Capital Improvement Program since 1992

College Orchestra Directors Association
Website: www.codaweb.org
Email: udus@udus.org.rs
Phone: 112 631 464
Address: US
Information: The College Orchestra Directors Association is dedicated to the promotion and advancement of college and university orchestra programs through the collaborative assistance, insights, knowledge, creativity, resources and shared vision of its members.
Country: United States

Colorado Arts Consortium
Email: balletartstheatre@yahoo.com
Address: P.O. Box 40362, US
Information: CAC is realigning as a consortium for arts education, through dance as fitness, heritage and environment with all the arts.
Country: United States

Columbia Music Festival Association
Website: www.cmfaonline.com
Email: cmfa5678@aol.com
Phone: 803 771 6303
Address: 914 Pulaski Street, Columbia, SC 29201, US
Information: Columbia Music Festival Association – CMFA – founded in 1897, as a joint partnership between local government and the private sector continues today as a vital and vibrant arts incubator for the midlands of South Carolina. Throughout its distinguished history CMFA has undergone many changes in focus; but has never strayed from its original mandate "to Educate, Discover, Develop, Train, Assist, Present, Produce and Promote the performing arts among the area's own citizens for the edification of all and to serve as a council and resource for the community."
Country: United States

Country Music Association
Website: www.cmaworld.com
Email: info@cmaworld.com
Phone: 152 442 840
Address: 35 Music Square East, Suite 201, Nashville, TN, United States
Information: CMA was founded in 1958 in response to the burgeoning popularity of Elvis Presley. The organization's mission is to heighten the awareness of Country Music and support its on-going growth by recognizing excellence in the genre, serving as a repository for critical and timely information and communication, while providing a forum for industry leadership dialogue toward its goals.
Country: United States

Dance Notation Bureau
Website: www.dancenotation.org
Email: dnbinfo@dancenotation.org
Phone: 212 571 7011
Address: 111 John Street, Room 704, US
Information: library and archive of dance scores
Country: United States

Dance/USA
Website: www.danceusa.org
Email: communications@danceusa.org
Phone: 028 331 717
Address: 1029 Vermont Ave NW, Suite 400 Washington, DC 20005, US
Information: Dance/USA champions an inclusive and equitable dance field by leading, convening, advocating, and supporting individuals and organizations. Dance/USA's core programs are focused in the areas of engagement, advocacy, research, and preservation.
Country: United States

DC Commission on the Arts and Humanities
Website:
www.dcarts.dc.gov
Email: cah@dc.gov
Phone:
027 245 613
Address: 200 I Street, SE, Suite 1400, Washington, DC 20003, US
Information: First established in 1968, the DC Commission on the Arts and Humanities (CAH) is an independent agency in the District of Columbia government that evaluates and initiates action on matters relating to the arts and humanities and encourages programs and the development of programs that promote progress in the

arts and humanities.
Country: United States

Early Music America
Website: www.earlymusic.org
Email: info@earlymusicamerica.org
Phone: 126 422 778
Address: 801 Vinial Street Suite 300 Pittsburgh, PA 15212, US
Information: A non-profit organization serving and strengthening the early music community in North America and raising public awareness of early music.
Country: United States

Florida Professional Presenters Consortium
Website: www.flapresenters.com
Email: web.master@flapresenters.com
Phone: 727 712 2704
Address: c/o Ruth Eckerd Hall, 1111 McMullen Booth Road, US
Country: United States

Gospel Music Association
Website: www.gospelmusic.org
Email: service@gospelmusic.org
Phone: 615 277 1376
Address: 741 Cool Springs Blvd., US
Country: United States

Guadalupe Cultural Arts Centre
Website: www.guadalupeculturalarts.org
Email: info@guadalupeculturalarts.org
Phone: 102 713 151
Address: 723 S Brazos St San Antonio, TX 78207, US
Information: The Guadalupe Cultural Arts Center was founded in 1980 as a nonprofit, multidisciplinary organization.
Located in the heart of San Antonio's Westside, the Guadalupe is one of the
largest community-based, multidisciplinary organizations in the U.S. The Guadalupe Cultural Arts Center cultivates, promotes, and preserves traditional and contemporary
Chicano, Latino and Native American arts and culture through multidisciplinary programming.
Country: United States

Historic Brass Society
Website: www.historicbrass.org
Email: President@historicbrass.org
Phone: 212 627 3820
Address: 148 West 23rd Street, Suite 5F, US
Country: United States

Hymn Society in the US and Canada
Website: www.thehymnsociety.org/
Email: deb@thehymnsociety.org
Phone: 804 204 1226
Address: 3400 Brook Road, US
Information: founded in 1922, The Hymn Society was formerly known as The Hymn Society of America, but the name of the organization was changed in 1991 to The Hymn Society in the United States and Canada
Country: United States

Idaho Commission on the Arts
Website: www.arts.idaho.gov
Email: info@arts.idaho.gov
Phone: 083 342 119
Address: 9543 W Emerald Street, Suite 204 Boise, ID 83704 US
Information: The Commission promotes excellence, education in the arts, access to the arts, and community investment in the arts. Its professional staff administers and develops the programs and services of the agency, assists grant applicants, and provides technical assistance. The board of thirteen commissioners, appointed to four-year terms by the Governor, sets policy for the agency and makes the final determination on grants and awards.
Country: United States

Indiana Arts Commission
Website: www.iac.in.org
Email: indianaartscommission@iac.in.gov
Phone: 317 232 1268
Address: 150 West Market St, Suite 618, US
Information: The Music Centre Slovakia is a State-subsidised institution established by the Ministry of Culture of the Slovak Republic. Its mission is to encourage Slovak music culture by organising concerts, bringing pieces of Slovak composers to the stages, publishing sheet music and music books, documenting the music life in Slovakia and promoting Slovak music culture abroad.
Country: United States

Jamaica Center for Arts and Learning
Website: www.jcal.org
Email: info@jcal.org
Phone: 718 658 7400
Address: 161-04 Jamaica Ave, Jamaica, US
Information: The Jamaica Center for Arts & Learning (JCAL), founded in 1972, is a multidisciplinary arts center

based in the diverse community of Southeast Queens. It devoted its mission to offer quality visual, performing, and literary arts, and to provide accessible education programs to encourage participation in the arts. More than 52, 000 people of all ages and backgrounds participate in their wide array of education, performing arts, and visual arts programs annually.
Country: United States

JazzReach Inc.
Website: www.jazzreach.org
Email: info@jazzreach.org
Phone: 189 719 750
Address: 45 Main Street Suite 728 Brooklyn, NY 11201, US
Information: Established in 1994, JazzReach is a nationally recognized New York City-based not-for-profit organization dedicated to the promotion, performance, creation and teaching of jazz music.
Country: United States

Kansas Creative Arts Industries Commission
Website: www.kansascommerce.gov/program/kcaic/
Email: KAC@arts.ks.gov
Phone: 852 963 481
Address: 1000 SW Jackson, Suite 100 Topeka, KS 66612, US
Information: The Kansas Creative Arts Industries Commission (KCAIC) is dedicated to promoting, supporting and expanding Kansas' creative industries and enriching communities through arts and culture.
Country: United States

Kohler Foundation, Inc.
Website: www.kohlerfoundation.org/
Email: kohlerfoundation@kohler.com
Phone: 204 581 972
Address: 725 Woodlake Rd, Ste X Kohler, WI 53044, US
Information: Kohler Foundation, Inc., located in Kohler, Wisconsin and established in 1940, has long supported the arts and education. The work of Kohler Foundation encompasses five major areas of concentration: art preservation, grants, scholarships, a performing arts series (the Distinguished Guest Series), and the management of the Waelderhaus, an historic home.
Country: United States

Latin American Music Center: Indiana University
Website: www.lamc.indiana.edu
Email: lamc@indiana.edu
Phone: 128 552 991
Address: Merrill Hall – MU 117 Jacobs School of Music Indiana University Bloomington, IN 47405, US
Information: The LAMC fosters the research and performance of Latin American art, popular, and traditional music. Founded by Juan Orrego-Salas in 1961, it commemorates in 2011 its 50th anniversary under the direction of Carmen Helena Tellez.
Country: United States

League of American Orchestras
Website: www.americanorchestras.org
Email: member@americanorchestras.org
Phone: 468 224 010
Address: 520 8th Avenue, Suite 2005, 20th Floor New York, NY 10018, US
Information: The League of American Orchestras leads, supports, and champions America's orchestras and the vitality of the music they perform. Founded in 1942 and chartered by Congress in 1962, the League links a national network of thousands of instrumentalists, conductors, Managers and administrators, board members, volunteers, and business partners.
Country: United States

League of American Theatres and Producers
Website: www.broadway.org
Email: league@broadway.org
Phone: 276 41122
Address: 729 Seventh Avenue, 5th Floor New York, NY 10019
Information: The Broadway League is the national trade association for the Broadway industry. Each year, League members bring Broadway to more than 30 million people in New York and more than 240 cities across the U.S. and Canada.
Country: United States

League of Historic American Theatres
Website: www.lhat.org
Email: info@lhat.org
Phone: 443 640 1058
Address: 2105 Laurel Bush Road, Suite 201, US
Information: 38th Annual Conference & Theatre Tour: July 16-19, 2014 in New York, NY
Country: United States

Louisiana Division of the Arts
Website: www.crt.state.la.us/arts
Email: arts@crt.state.la.us
Phone: 225 342 8180
Address: PO Box 44247, US
Information: visiting address – Suite 420, 1051 N.3rd Street, Baton Rouge LA 70802

Country: United States

Maine Arts Commission
Website: www.mainearts.com
Email: mainearts.info@maine.gov
Phone: 072 872 724
Address: 193 State St Augusta, ME 04333, US
Information: The Maine Arts Commission provides funding to support all Artistic endeavors. The agency has many partnerships, nationally and regionally and besides grant funding, supports convening the field, providing professional development and offering advice. The agency is fully engaged in education for all ages.
Country: United States

Major Orchestra Librarians' Association
Website: www.mola-inc.org
Email: admin@mola-inc.org
Address: 14070 Proton Rd. Suite 100 LB9, US
Country: United States

Metro Nashville Arts Commission
Website: www.artsnashville.org
Email: arts@nashville.gov
Phone: 615 862 6720
Address: 800 2nd Avenue S, 4th floor, US
Country: United States

Mid Atlantic Arts Foundation
Website: www.midatlanticarts.org
Email: tom@midatlanticarts.org
Phone: 410 539 6656
Address: 201 North Charles Street, Suite 401, US
Information: Mid Atlantic Arts Foundation was established in 1979 to promote and support multi-state arts programming in a region that includes Delaware, the District of Columbia, Maryland, New Jersey, New York, Pennsylvania, the US Virgin Islands, Virginia, and West Virginia. Over the last 35 years, the Foundation has expanded its reach to include national and international initiatives. The Foundation's work is focused on performing arts touring, jazz, independent film, support for individual artists, and international cultural exchange. Member of ISPA.
Country: United States

Mid-America Arts Alliance
Website: www.maaa.org
Email: communications@maaa.org
Phone: 164 211 388
Address: 2018 Baltimore Ave. Kansas City, MO 64108, US
Information: A nonprofit, regional arts organization—representing Arkansas, Kansas, Missouri, Nebraska, Oklahoma, and Texas—that focuses on strengthening communities and improving lives through extraordinary cultural experiences.
Country: United States

Milwaukee Arts Board
Website: www.milwaukee.gov/MAB
Email: artsboard@milwaukee.gov
Phone: 414 286 5794
Address: 809 N Broadway Milwaukee, WI 53202, US
Information: The Milwaukee Arts Board (MAB) was created to enhance the development, cultural diversity, accessibility and enjoyment of the arts for Milwaukee's citizens. The Arts Board provides a range of support to arts and community organizations that produce innovative projects or programs.
Country: United States

Minnesota State Arts Board
Website: facebook.com/mnartsboard/
Email: msab@arts.state.mn.us
Phone: 008 662 787
Address: 540 Fairview Ave N, St Paul, MN 55104, US
Information: The Minnesota State Arts Board is a state agency that stimulates and encourages the creation, performance, and appreciation of the arts in the state.
Country: United States

Mississippi Arts Commission
Website: www.arts.state.ms.us
Email: info@arts.state.ms.us
Phone: 601 359 6030
Address: 501 North West St, Suite 1101 A, US
Information: ADETCA currently has 45 Associated companies involved in the production, distribution and theatrical exhibition.
THE ASSOCIATION OF CATALONIA THEATER COMPANIES (ADETCA), was created in 1992 with the objective of ensuring the development of the private initiative theater in any of its manifestations; Since then, he has been working on promoting and disseminating sociocultural issues and is committed to offering society a plural, free and independent theater option.
Country: United States

Museums and Cultural Affairs Department – City of El Paso
Website:
www.elpasoartsandculture.org
Email:
mcad@elpasotexas.gov

Phone: 152 120 110
Address: 400 W San Antonio Ave, Ste A El Paso, TX, US
Information: The Museums Division is comprised of the El Paso Museum of Art, the El Paso Museum of Archaeology and the El Paso Museum of History, each dedicated to providing exhibitions and educational activities that recognize the region's mutli-cultural heritage. The Cultural Affairs Division implements funding programs, public art programs, cultural tourism initiatives and performing/visual arts events that provide a variety of opportunities to engage in arts and cultural activities.
Country: United States
Social Media: facebook.com/MCADElPaso/

Music Associates of America
Website: www.musicAssociatesofamerica.com
Email: maasturm@sprynet.com
Phone: 015 692 898
Address: 224 King Street Englewood, New Jersey 07631, US
Information: Music Associates of America (maa) services several leading American and European music publishers and distributors in the administrative and promotional sectors, and maintains a select roster of composers, including a number of Pulitzer Prize winners, whom we serve as representatives. In tending to the individual needs of different creative artists, our function is akin to the literary agent's role in behalf of authors and playwrights.
Country: United States

Music Library Association
Website: www.musiclibraryassoc.org
Email: mla@areditions.com
Phone: 608 836 5825
Address: Business Office, 8551 Research Way, Suite 180, US
Information: in collaboration with Asociación Cultural Por la Danza
Country: United States

Music Publishers' Association of the United States
Website: www.mpa.org
Email: admin@mpa.org
Phone: 212 327 4044
Address: 243 5th Ave., Ste. 236, US
Information: membership organisation; represents artists and promoters; also directs festivals
Country: United States

National Academy of Recording Arts & Sciences, Inc.
Website: www.grammy.com
Email: Musicares@grammy.com
Phone: 310 392 3777
Address: MusiCares West Region and MAP Fund, 3030 Olympic Blvd, US
Information: a cultural association, which aims to promote the development of theatre for children and youth in Spain
Country: United States

National Alliance for Musical Theatre
Website: www.namt.org
Email: info@namt.org
Phone: 127 146 668
Address: 520 Eighth Avenue, Suite 301 New York, NY 10018, US
Information: The National Alliance for Musical Theatre, founded in 1985, is a not-for-profit organization serving the musical theatre community. The organization's mission is to be a catalyst for nurturing musical theatre development, production, innovation and collaboration.
Country: United States
Social Media: facebook.com/NAMTmusicals/twitter.com/NAMT

National Assembly of State Arts Agencies (NA-SAA)
Website: www.nasaa-arts.org
Email: nasaa@nasaa-arts.org
Phone: 202 347 6352
Address: 1029 Vermont Avenue NW, 2nd Floor, US
Information: see also Agents and Producers
Country: United States

National Association for Campus Activities
Website: www.naca.org
Email: aland@naca.org
Phone: 803 732 6222
Address: 13 Harbison Way, US
Information: publishes the magazine 'Musica d'Ara'; see also Publications
Country: United States

National Association for Music Education
Website:
www.nafme.org
Email:
memberservices@nafme2.org
Phone: 703 860 4000/800
Address: 1806 Robert Fulton Drive, US

Information: National Association for Music Education (NAfME), among the world's largest arts education organizations, is the only association that addresses all aspects of music education. NAfME advocates at the local, state, and national levels; provides resources for teachers, parents, and administrators; hosts professional development events; and offers a variety of opportunities for students and teachers. The Association orchestrates success for millions of students nationwide and has supported music educators at all teaching levels for more than a century
Country: United States

National Association of College Wind and Percussion Instructors (NACWPI)
Website: www.nacwpi.org
Email: NACWPI@montevallo.edu
Phone: 932 684 736
Address: NACWPI Station 6670 Montevallo, AL
Information: The National Association of College Wind and Percussion Instructors is a forum for communication within the profession of applied music on the college campus. The Association is composed of university, college, and conservatory teachers.
Country: United States

National Association of Composers, USA (NACUSA)
Website: www.music-usa.org/nacusa
Email: nacusa@music-usa.org
Phone: 541 765 2406
Address: PO Box 49256, Barrington Station, US
Information: (NACUSA) was founded by Henry Hadley in 1933. It is one of the oldest organizations devoted to the promotion and performance of American music. Many of the most distinguished American composers have been among its members; information about coming concerts
Country: United States

National Association of Japan-America Societies (NAJAS)
Website: www.us-japan.org
Email: contact@us-japan.org
Phone: 202 429 5545
Address: 1819 L Street, NW, Suite 200, US
Information: collective negotiation with national organisations, institutions and authorities; publishes 'El Pateo' magazine, organises the 'Feria de Artes Esc
Country: United States

National Association of Latino Arts and Culture
Website: www.nalac.org
Email: info@nalac.org
Phone: 210 432 3982
Address: 1208 Buena Vista Street, US
Country: United States

National Association of Schools of Music
Website: www.arts-accredit.org
Email: info@arts-accredit.org
Phone: 703 437 6312
Address: 11250 Roger Bacon Drive, Suite 21, US
Information: see also Dance
Country: United States

National Association of Teachers of Singing, Inc.
Website: www.nats.org
Email: info@nats.org
Phone: 904 992 9101
Address: 9957 Moorings Dr STE 401, USA
Information: Founded in 1944, National Association of Teachers of Singing, Inc. (NATS) is the largest professional association of teachers of singing in the world with more than 7, 000 members in the United States, Canada, and over 35 other countries. Driven by its mission statement, NATS offers a variety of lifelong learning experiences to its members, with workshops, intern programs, master classes, and conferences, all beginning at the chapter level and progressing to national events.
Country: United States

National Band Association
Website: www.nationalbandassociation.org
Email: info@nationalbandassociation.org
Phone: 349 559 29216
Address: P.O. Box 25136, Baton Rouge, US
Information: member of the European Network of Information Centres for the Performing Arts (ENCIPA) (q.v.); see also Further Education
Country: United States

National Collegiate Choral Organization
Website: www.ncco-usa.org
Email: contact@ncco-usa.org
Phone: 958 563 504
Address: 25800 Carlos Bee Boulevard, US
Information: publishes books and CD on sacred music and Andalucian music & folk
Country: United States

National Council of Acoustical Consultants
Website: www.ncac.com
Email: info@ncac.com
Phone: 317 328 0642

Address: 7150 Winton Drive, Suite 300, US
Country: United States

National Endowment for the Arts
Website: www.arts.endow.gov
Email: webmgr@arts.gov
Phone: 202 682 5400
Address: 1100 Pennsylvania Avenue, NW, 400 7th Street, SW, US
Information: organisers of Festival Dansa Valencia, see also Festivals
Country: United States

National Endowment for the Humanities
Website: www.neh.gov
Email: questions@neh.gov
Phone: 026 068 400
Address: 400 7th Street, SW Washington, DC 20506 US
Information: Founded in 1965, the National Endowment for the Humanities (NEH) is a grant-making institution of the United States government dedicated to supporting research, education, preservation, and public programs in the humanities.
Country: United States

National Foundation for Advancement in the Arts (NFAA)
Website: www.artsawards.org
Email: nfaa@nfaa.org
Phone: 305 377 1140
Address: 777 Brickell Avenue, Suite 370, US
Information: founded in 1981, NFAA is a non-governmental, philanthropic, and service organisation
Country: United States

National Guild for Community Arts Education
Website: www.nationalguild.org
Email: guildinfo@nationalguild.org
Phone: 226 83337
Address: 520 8th Avenue, Suite 302, New York, NY
Information: Founded in 1937, the National Guild for Community Arts Education is the sole national service organization for providers of community arts education. In order to strengthen organizations and further advance community arts educators' practice, the Guild offers learning opportunities and resources, leadership development, and connection with fellow practitioners.
Country: United States

National Music Council of the United States
Website: www.musiccouncil.org
Email: sandersd@montclair.edu
Phone: 736 557 974
Address: 425 Park Street, US
Information: NMC was founded in 1940 to act as a clearinghouse for the joint opinion and decision of its members and to work to strengthen the importance of music in our life and culture. The Council's initial membership of 13 has grown to almost 50 national music organizations, encompassing every important form of professional and commercial musical activity. NMC is an annual national co-sponsor of Arts Advocacy Day and an active member of the Music Education Roundtable and SupportMusic Coalition.
Country: United States

National Music Publishers' Association, Inc. (NMPA)
Website: www.nmpa.org
Email: info@fundacioromea.com
Phone: 023 936 672
Address: 1900 N St NW Suite 500 Washington, DC 20036, US
Information: The National Music Publishers' Association (NMPA) is a trade association for the American music publishing industry. Founded in 1917, NMPA represents American music publishers and their songwriting partners. The NMPA's mandate is to protect and advance the interests of music publishers and songwriters in matters relating to the domestic and global protection of music copyrights.
Country: United States

National Music Theater Network
Website: www.nmtn.org
Email: info@broadwayusa.org
Phone: 212 664 0979
Address: 242 West 38th Street, #1102, US
Information: Co-founded by el Ayuntamiento de Valencia, la Diputación de Valencia and la Generalitat Valenciana through the Conselleria de Cultura. promotes drama arts in Valencia;see also Festivals (Festival Veo)
Country: United States

National Performance Network (NPN)
Website: www.npnweb.org
Email: info@npnweb.org
Phone: 045 958 008
Address: 8121 Fig St New Orleans, LA 70118, US
Information: The National Performance Network (NPN) supports artists in the creation and touring of new work, and advances cultural equity in the arts presenting field. As an artist-centered, field-generated network, the National Performance Network is unique in its structure.

Its active and engaged network of presenters form an interconnected web or relationships through which support and services are strategically designed, effectively distributed, and successfully leveraged.
Country: United States

National Public Radio (NPR)
Website: www.npr.org
Email:
info@gracia-territori.com
Phone:
128 803 500
Address: 11 W 42nd St # 19, New York, NY 10036, US
Information: NPR is an independent, nonprofit media organization that was founded on a mission to create a more informed public. Every day, NPR connects with millions of Americans on the air, online, and in person to explore the news, ideas, and what it means to be human. Through its network of member stations, NPR makes local stories national, national stories local, and global stories personal.
Country: United States
Social Media: facebook.com/NPR/instagram.com/npr/twitter.com/NPR

New England Foundation for the Arts
Website: www.nefa.org
Email: info@nefa.org
Phone: 617 951 0010
Address: 1000 Washington Street, Second Floor, Boston, MA 02118, US
Information: Founded in 1976, NEFA is one of six regional arts organizations established with funding from the National Endowment for the Arts to strengthen the national arts infrastructure by cultivating the arts on a regional level. Today, NEFA's programs are regional, national, and international in scope, and support artists and communities through grants and other opportunities in dance, music, theater, and public art.
Country: United States

New England Presenters
Website: www.nepresenters.org
Email: mdurling@fsc.edu
Phone: 197 866 53709
Address: NEP President, Fitchburg State Univeristy, 160 Pearl Street, US
Information: see also Festivals, Further Education and Venues
Country: United States

New Mexico Arts
Website: www.nmarts.org
Email: anna.blyth@state.nm.us
Phone: 505 827 6490
Address: PO Box 1450, 407 Galisteo, US
Information: Latin-American address: Celcit Venezuela: Edificio Caroata, Nivel OF:1, Oficina 106 – Parque Central, Caracas, Venezuela; tel/fax: +58-212-577 7938, alternative e-mail: celcit@cantv.net; Celcit Argentina: Calle Bol
Country: United States

New Mexico Presenters Alliance
Website: www.nmpresenters.org
Email: uniondeactores@uniondeactores.com
Phone: 052 329 868
Address: 1013 Vassar Dr NE, Albuquerque, New Mexico, 87106, US
Information: The New Mexico Presenters Alliance is a coalition of performing arts presenters who gather two times a year, Fall and Spring, to share information on programming opportunities and resources with the goal of organizing tours.
Country: United States

New Music USA
Website: www.newmusicusa.org
Email: info@newmusicusa.org
Phone: 212 645 6949
Address: New Music USA, 90 John Street, Suite 312, US
Information: New Music USA was formed by the merger of the American Music Center and Meet The Composer. New Music USA supports the sounds of tomorrow by nurturing the creation, performance, and appreciation of new music for adventurous listeners around the world.
Country: United States

NextMove Dance (NMD)
Website: www.danceaffiliates.org
Email: info@nextmovedance.org
Phone: 156 369 000
Address: 4701 Bath Street Bldg. 46B Philadelphia, PA, US
Information: NextMove Dance brings the world's most exciting and awe-inspiring dance to the greater Philadelphia area through an annual series of live performances, interactive outreach and arts education programming, and original productions. NMD's mission is to inspire passion, joy, and appreciation for dance and movement in all its forms in the Philadelphia region.
Country: United States
Social Media: twitter.com/NextMoveDance/instagram.com/nextmovedance/

North American Performing Arts Managers and Agents (NAPAMA)
Website: www.napama.org
Email: info@napama.org
Address: 459 Columbus Avenue, Suite 133, US
Information: member of IAMA
Country: United States

Oakland's Craft and Cultural Arts Department
Website:
www.oaklandculturalarts.org
Email: emflores@oaklandnet.com
Phone: 510 238 2103
Address: 1 Frank H. Ogawa Plaza, 9th Floor, US

OPERA America
Website: www.operaamerica.org
Email: info@operaamerica.org
Phone: 212 796 8620
Address: 330, 7th Avenue, 16th Floor, US
Information: OPERA America is the national service organization for opera and is dedicated to the creation, presentation and enjoyment of the art form. Founded in 1970, OPERA America has an international membership that includes nearly 150 Professional Company Members, 300 Associate and Business Members, 2,000 Individual Members and over 16,000 subscribers to its electronic news service.
Country: United States

Oregon Arts Commission
Website: www.oregonartscommission.org
Email: oregon.artscomm@state.or.us
Phone: 503 986 0082
Address: 775 Summer Street NE, Suite 200, US
Country: United States

Outward Visions, Inc.
Website: www.outwardvisions.com
Email: outwardvisions@gmail.com
Phone: 520 743 3240
Address: P.O. Box 86533 Tucson, AZ 85754-6533
Information: Outward Visions, Inc. is a not-for-profit arts and education service organization founded in 1976 and incorporated in 1980. The common thread that connects the various Artistic endeavors to which Outward Visions is committed is the intensity of the human spirit involved and the Artist's desire and need to expand the potential and awareness of the audience as well as the Artist.
Country: United States

Phoenix Office of Arts and Culture, Division of Phoenix
Website: www.phoenix.gov/arts
Email: mary.muesegades@phoenix.gov
Phone: 602 262 4637
Address: 200 West Washington, 10th Floor, US
Information: has a department of theater scholars and critics, part of the AICE (International Association of Theatre Critics)
Country: United States

Piano Technicians Guild
Website: www.ptg.org
Email: ptg@ptg.org
Phone: 913 432 9975
Address: 4444 Forest Avenue, US
Country: United States

Planet Arts Inc.
Website: www.PlanetArts.org
Email: PlanetArts@gmail.com
Phone: 518 945 2669
Address: PO Box 387, Catskill, US
Information: see also Venues and Festivals
Country: United States

Public Broadcasting Service (PBS)
Website: www.pbs.org
Email: admon@actoresvascos.com
Phone: 943 314 822
Address: Public Broadcasting Service 1225 S. Clark Street Arlington, VA, US
Information: PBS is a membership organization that, in partnership with its member stations, serves the American public with programming and services of the highest quality, using media to educate, inspire, entertain and exPress a diversity of perspectives. PBS empowers individuals to achieve their potential and strengthen the social, democratic, and cultural health of the U.S.
Country: United States
Social Media: www.facebook.com/pbs/twitter.com/PBS/ www.instagram.com/pbs/

Recording Industry Association of America, Inc. (RIAA)
Website: www.riaa.com
Email: webmaster@riaa.com
Phone: 202 775 0101
Address: 1025 F Street, NW, Floor 10th, US
Information: partly funded by Instituto de la Mujer, Ministerio de Asuntos Sociales
Country: United States

Russian Arts Foundation
Website: www.russianarts.org
Email: info@russianarts.org
Phone: 022 234 955
Address: PO Box 567 Montpelier, VT 05602
Information: The Russian Arts Foundation (RAF) is a US 501(c) organization dedicated to promoting international understanding. Its programs bridge borders with the goal to bring people together via the universal language of music. Since its founding in 1992, the RAF has provided management, fundraising, Marketing and financial assistance to Russian performing arts groups. The foundation has actively worked with the Russian National Orchestra, founded in 1990 by a pianist.
Country: United States

Sacramento Office of Arts and Culture
Website: www.arts.cityofsacramento.org
Email: saccityarts@cityofsacramento.org
Phone: 168 083 992
Address: 915 I Street Sacramento, CA 95814, US
Information: The Sacramento Metropolitan Arts Commission was established in 1977 by a City Ordinance and a County Ordinance. Devoted to supporting, promoting, & advancing the arts in the region. Provide funding to local artists & arts groups; promote the arts via Marketing, outreach, & education initiatives; provide resources to support & increase regional art education.
Country: United States

San Diego Commission for Arts and Culture, City of
Website: www.sandiego.gov/arts-culture
Email: christinej@sandiego.gov
Phone: 619 236 6800
Address: 1200 Third Avenue, Suite 924, US
Information: serves in an advisory capacity to the Mayor and City Council on promoting, encouraging and increasing support for the region's Artistic and cultural assets, integrating arts and culture into community life and showcasing San Diego as an international tourist destination
Country: United States

San Francisco Arts Commission
Website: www.sfartscommission.org
Email: ART-Info@sfgov.org
Phone: 152 522 255
Address: 401 Van Ness, Suite 325 San Francisco, CA 94102, US
Information: The San Francisco Arts Commission is the City agency that champions the arts as essential to daily life by investing in a vibrant arts community, enlivening the urban environment and shaping innovative cultural policy. Programs include: Civic Art Collection, Civic Design Review, Community Investments, Public Art, SFAC Galleries and Street Artist Licensing.
Country: United States

Santa Fe Opera
Website: https:// www.santafeopera.org/
Email: boxoffice@santafeopera.org
Phone: 505 986 5955
Address: 301 Opera Drive Santa Fe, NM 87506-2823
Information: The Santa Fe Opera's mission is to advance the operatic art form by presenting ensemble performances of the highest quality in a unique setting with a varied repertoire of new, rarely performed and standard works.
Country: United States
Social Media: twitter.com/santafeopera www.facebook.com/santafeopera www.instagram.com/santafeopera/

Schubert Club
Website: www.schubert.org
Email: schubert@schubert.org
Phone: 651 292 3267
Address: 302 Landmark Center, 75 W 5th Street, US
Information: Founded over 135 years ago, Schubert Club is today one of the nation's most vibrant music organizations, enriching Minnesota with dynamic concerts, music education programs and museum exhibits. Schubert Club remains as relevant, respected, and resilient today as it has throughout its history.
Country: United States
Social Media: https:// www.facebook.com/schubertclub/ https://twitter.com/schubertclub/ https:// www.instagram.com/schubertclub/

SESAC Inc (headquarters)
Website: www.sesac.com
Email: sesac@sesac.com
Phone: 615 320 0055
Address: 55 Music Square East, US
Information: exclusive north American rights agency employing Broadcast Data Systems (BDS) computer technology for positive detection of radio/tv airplay; also with a Latin Repertory subsidiary, SESAC Latina
Country: United States

Society for Ethnomusicology
Website: www.ethnomusicology.org/
Email: sem@indiana.edu
Phone: 128 556 672
Address: Indiana University, 1165 E. 3rd St., Morrison Hall 005, US
Information: Society for Ethnomusicology was founded in 1955 to promote the research, study, and performance of music in all historical periods and cultural contexts.
Country: United States

Songwriters Guild of America
Website: www.songwritersguild.com
Email:
nash@songwritersguild.com
Phone: 615 742 9945
Address:
209 10th Avenue South, Suite 321, US
Country: United States

South Arts
Website: www.southarts.org
Email: communications@southarts.org
Phone: 048 747 244
Address: 1800 Peachtree St NW, Suite 808 Atlanta, GA 30309, US
Information: Headquartered in Atlanta, Georgia, South Arts is a nonprofit regional arts organization empowering artists, organizations, and communities, and increasing access to arts and culture. South Arts supports artists and organizations through a rich and responsive portfolio of grants, fellowships, and programs.
Country: United States
Social Media: facebook.com/southartstwitter.com/ southartsinstagram.com/southartsorg

Southeastern Theatre Conference – SETC
Website: www.setc.org
Email: info@setc.org
Phone: 362 656 148
Address: 5710 W. Gate City Boulevard Suite K, Box # 186 Greensboro, NC 27407, US
Information: SETC is a nationwide organization that helps connect theatre practitioners of all experience levels with training and resources. Services include Auditions, Professional Hiring, Scholarships, Training, Competitions, Conferences, Publications, and Events.
Country: United States

Stage Directors and Choreographers Society (SDC)
Website: www.SDCweb.org
Email: info@sdcweb.org
Phone: 123 911 070
Address: 321 W 44th St, Ste 804 New York, NY 10036, US
Information: SDC is the theatrical union that unites, empowers, and protects professional Stage Directors and Choreographers throughout the United States. SDC's mission is to foster a national community of professional stage Directors and choreographers by protecting the rights, health and livelihoods of all its Members; negotiating and enforcing employment agreements across a range of jurisdictions; facilitating the exchange of ideas, information and opportunities;
Country: United States
Social Media: www.facebook.com/StageDirectorsand-ChoreographersSociety/ www.twitter.com/SDCweb www.instagram.com/sdc_union/

Stecher and Horowitz Foundation
Website: www.stecherandhorowitz.org
Email: info@stecherandhorowitz.org
Phone: 212 581 8380
Address: 119 West 37th St, suite 1401, US
Information: SAMI is a member of AEPO, COPYSWEDE and SCAPR (q.v.)
Country: United States

Talent Managers Association
Website: www.talentManagers.org
Email: info@skl.se
Phone: 845 27000
Address: 4821 Lankershim Boulevard, Suite F 160, North Hollywood, CA
Information: Originally incorporated in 1956 as the Conference of Personal Managers, the Talent Managers Association (TMA) strives to encourage the level of ethical business standards and practices expected of professional talent Managers. The TMA membership reaches across the country, and serves as a trusted resource of information while providing a sense of support and community within the professional of personal management.
Country: United States

Tennessee Arts Commission
Website: www.arts.state.tn.us
Phone: 615 741 1701
Address: 401 Charlotte Avenue, US
Information: coordinator of national activities on the International Dance Day; responsible for the Swedish Dance Biennial; also do seminars
Country: United States

Texas Commission on the Arts
Website: www.arts.state.tx.us
Email: front.desk@arts.state.tx.us
Phone: 512 463 5535
Address: PO Box 13406, suite 501, US

Information: publish a journal of early music quarterly
Country: United States

The Drama League of New York
Website: www.dramaleague.org
Email: info@dramaleague.org
Phone: 212 244 9494
Address: 520 8th Avenue, Suite 320, US
Country: United States

The Hampsong Foundation
Website: www.hampsongfoundation.org
Email: office@hampsongfoundation.org
Phone: 462 330 074
Address: 347 Fifth Ave. Suite 1402-325 New York, NY 10016, US
Information: Founded in 2003 by American baritone Thomas Hampson, the Hampsong Foundation is a non-profit organization which creates platforms to support and proliferate the art of classic song—poetry set to music—from around the world as a means to enhance communication and understanding among cultures.
Country: United States

The Pittsburgh Cultural Trust
Website: www.trustarts.org
Email: pct@pgharts.org
Phone: 124 716 070
Address: 803 Liberty Avenue Pittsburgh, PA 15222, US
Information: The Pittsburgh Cultural Trust is a nonprofit organization created to stimulate the economic and cultural development of Pittsburgh through the development and promotion of a downtown arts and entertainment district.
Country: United States

The Playwrights' Center
Website: www.pwcenter.org
Email: info@pwcenter.org
Phone: 123 327 481
Address: 2301 E Franklin Ave Minneapolis, MN 55406, US
Information: Founded in 1971 by five writers seeking Artistic and professional support, the Playwrights' Center today serves more playwrights in more ways than any other organization in the country.
One of the nation's most generous and well-respected theater organizations, the Playwrights' Center focuses on both supporting playwrights and promoting new plays to production at theaters across the country.
Country: United States

The Sphinx Organization
Website: www.sphinxmusic.org
Email: info@sphinxmusic.org
Phone: 884 047 073
Address: 2200 Hunt Street Detroit, MI 48207, US
Information: The Sphinx Organization is a social justice organization dedicated to transforming lives through the power of diversity in the arts. Founded in 1997 by Aaron P. Dworkin with the goal of addressing the underrepresentation of people of color in classical music.
Country: United States

Theatre Communications Group
Website: www.circle.tcg.org
Email: info@tcg.org
Phone: 126 095 900
Address: 520 8th Ave, Fl 24th New York, NY 10018, US
Information: TCG's is the national organization for theatre, with a membership network of 500+ member theatres & over 250 university, funder, trustee, and business affiliates & over 10, 000 individuals. TCG's mission is to lead for a just and thriving theatre ecology.
Country: United States

Theatre for Young Audiences/USA
Website: www.tyausa.org
Email: info@tyausa.org
Phone: 174 387 010
Address: 340 E 46th St, New York, NY 10017
Information: TYA/USA is the leading national organization for the professional field of theatre for children and families, representing nearly 900 member theatres, organizations, and individual artists across 42 states. Dedicated to ensuring that all young people have access to high-quality theatre experiences, TYA/USA offers a variety of programming and provides a network of exchange that connects professionals working across the industry.
Country: United States

United Scenic Artists Local 829
Website: www.usa829.org
Email: ar@syntjuntan.se
Phone: 258 10300
Address: United Scenic Artists Local USA 829 IATSE, 29 W 38th St #15, New York, NY 10018, US
Information: United Scenic Artists, Local USA 829, IATSE, founded in 1896, is a labor union and professional association of Designers, Artists, Craftspeople, and Department Coordinators, organized to protect craft standards, working conditions and wages for the entertainment and decorative arts industries. The members of Local USA 829 work in film, theatre, opera, ballet, television,

industrial shows, commercials and exhibitions.
Country: United States
Social Media: www.facebook.com/USA829.IATSE/ www.twitter.com/USA829IATSE/ www.instagram.com/explore/tags/usa829/?hl=en

United States Institute for Theatre Technology (USITT) Inc
Website: www.usitt.org
Email: info@usitt.org
Phone: 009 387 488
Address: New York, US
Information: The United States Institute for Theatre Technology (USITT) is a nonprofit association for entertainment design and tech.

US Department of State Fulbright Grants
Website: us.fulbrightonline.org
Email: FBstudent@iie.org
Phone: 180 027 26994
Address: Fulbright U.S. Student Program Division, 809 United Nations Plaza, New York, NY 10017-3580
Information: The Fulbright U.S. Student Program is the largest U.S. exchange program offering opportunities for students and young professionals to undertake international graduate study, advanced research, university teaching, and primary and secondary school teaching worldwide. The program currently awards approximately 2, 000 grants annually in all fields of study and operates in more than 140 countries worldwide.
Country: United States

Viola d'Amore Society of America
Website: www.violadamoresocietyofamerica.org
Email: roseviola20@gmail.com
Phone: 718 729 3138
Address: 39-23 47th Street, Sunnyside, US
Information: Swiss dance artists
Country: United States

Virginia Beach Arts and Humanities Commission
Website: www.vabeach.com/vbahc
Email: artsinfo@vbgov.com
Phone: 757 385 2526
Address: 717 General Booth Boulevard, US
Information: IFPI Switzerland is the industry association for music labels (sound and audio-visual recorder manufacturers) in Switzerland. The association has around 36 national independent labels as well as the Swiss representatives of the three major global companies Universal, Sony and Warner Music. Together, their members represent over 90% of the Swiss music market. Member of the world association IFPI.
Country: United States

Virginia Commission for the Arts
Website: www.arts.virginia.gov
Email: arts@arts.virginia.gov
Phone: 804 225 3132
Address: Lewis House, 223 Governor Street, 2nd Floor, US
Country: United States

Volunteer Lawyers for the Arts (VLA)
Website: www.vlany.org
Email: vlany@vlany.org
Phone: 212 319 2787
Address: 1 East 53rd Street, 6th Fl, US
Information: artists or arts organizations interested in VLA's legal services should initiate contact by calling the VLA Art Law line at 212-319 2787 – 9, 19 or 20
Country: United States

Washington State Arts Commission
Website: www.arts.wa.gov
Email: michellez@arts.wa.gov
Phone: 360 753 3860
Address: PO Box 42675, US
Country: United States

WESTAF
Website: www.westaf.org
Email: staff@westaf.org
Phone: 303 629 1166
Address: Western States Arts Federation, 1743 Wazee Street, Suite 300, US
Information: is supported by the National Endowment for the Arts; the state arts agencies of Alaska, Arizona, California, Colorado, Idaho, Montana, Nevada, New Mexico, Oregon, Utah, Washington, and Wyoming; private and corporate foundations; and individuals
Country: United States

Western Arts Alliance
Website: www.westarts.org
Email: staff@westarts.org
Address: 715 SW Morrison, Suite 600, US
Information: Western Arts Alliance (WAA) is a membership association of touring and performing arts professionals engaged in promoting and presenting performing arts throughout the western states and provinces. Serving members since 1967, WAA's annual booking conference and its year-round programmes are essential for artists, artist Managers, presenters, and

other performing arts professionals in the west. More than 680 artists, Managers, presenters, arts service organisations, and state arts agencies know WAA as a trusted and vital resource. Member of ISPA.
Country: United States

Western States Arts Federation
Website: www.westaf.org
Email: staff@westaf.org
Phone: 036 291 166
Address: 1888 Sherman St. Ste 375 Denver, CO 80203, US
Information: WESTAF (Western States Arts Federation) is a regional nonprofit arts service organization dedicated to strengthening the financial, organizational, and policy infrastructure of the arts in the West. WESTAF assists state arts agencies, arts organizations, and artists in their quest to serve diverse audiences

Wharton Center for Performing Arts
Website: www.whartoncenter.com
Email: wharton@msu.edu
Phone: 517 353 1982
Address: Michigan State University, 750 E Shaw LN, US
Information: to enrich the lives of Michigan residents and strengthen the value of the arts in everyday life by serving as a leading resource for renowned arts entertainment and education programmes
Country: United States

Wisconsin Arts Board
Website: www.arts.state.wi.us
Email: artsboard@arts.state.wi.us
Phone: 608 266 0190
Address: 101 East Wilson Street, 1st Floor, US
Country: United States

Young Audiences, Inc.
Website: www.youngaudiences.org
Email: admin@arts4learning.org
Phone: 212 831 8110
Address: 115 East 92nd Street, Suite 1A, US
Information: Professional association joining together the Swiss professional musicians for the promotion of a new an innovationg music.
Composers, soloists, improvisers, musicologists, conductors of orchestra and choir, musical Managers.
Goals: Promotion of Swiss contemporary music and defens of the Artistic and material inerests of its members.
Country: United States

Entries on choirs/vocal ensembles in this section have been based on information received about engagements. We do not intend to pass judgement on quality. If you wish to be considered for inclusion, please send information regarding perform-ances and touring engagements to the editor. **The entries are listed in alphabetical order within country.**

Chœurs et Ensembles Vocaux

Les chœurs et les ensembles vocaux inclus dans cette rubrique ont été sélectionnés selon les informations reçues quant à leurs engagements. Nous ne faisons ainsi aucun jugement qualitatif. Si vous désirez être inclus, veuillez nous envoyer des informa-tions sur vos représentations et vos tournées. **Les entrée sont classés par ordre alphabétique dans le pays.**

Chöre und Vokalensembles

Die in dieser Rubrik aufgeführten Chöre und Vokalensembles wurden aufgrund ihrer Angaben zu Engagements ausgewählt. Diese Auswahl entspricht keiner qualitativen Beurteilung. Falls Sie Interesse daran haben, ebenfalls in dieser Rubrik zu erscheinen, senden Sie uns bitte Informationen zu ihren Auftritten und Engagements. **Die Einträge sind für jedes Land alphabetisch sortiert.**

Cori e Gruppi Vocali

Per la scelta dei gruppi vocali e dei cori si è considerato il numero di spettacoli a cui il gruppo ha partecipato. L'inclusione in questa sezione non può perciò essere considerata in base alla qualità del gruppo. Se siete interessati ad essere inseriti in ques-ta sezione vi preghiamo di inviare alla nostra redazione le infor-mazioni riguardanti il numero di spettacoli e/o di tournée effet-tuati dal vostro coro o gruppo vocale. **Le voci sono pubblicate in ordine alfabetico di paese.**

Coros y Conjuntos Vocales

La información incluída en esta sección ha sido seleccionada en base al número de actuaciones realizadas. El listado incluye grupos tanto profesionales como aficionados que trabajan a nivel profesional, sin ser nuestra intención juzgar la calidad de los mismos. Si algún grupo quisiera ser incluído, rogamos envíe información sobre sus actuaciones y giras a nuestro editor. **Las entradas se muestran en orden alfabético dentro de cada país.**

performing arts
database
online

artsDB.net

AUSTRALIA

Bel a capella
Website: www.belacappella.org.au
Email: arpasquill@googlemail.com
Address: Glebe, AU
Information: Bel a cappella is a chamber choir of 25-30 experienced singers who are dedicated to the performance of diverse, high quality choral music in fine venues around Sydney. Established in 1995 by a few members of Sydney University Musical Society who were looking for the challenges of singing in a smaller group, Bel a cappella continues to attract able singers who are keen to explore the more demanding repertoire to the highest possible standard.
Country: Australia
Type: Choir and Vocal Ensemble
Contact: music Director Anthony Pasquill
Email: arpasquill@googlemail.com
Social Media: @belacappella https:// www.facebook. com/Belacappella
Touring Countries: Germany, Czech Republic, Slovakia, Hungary and Poland
Touring: Nationally
Annual Performances: 3
Number of Performers: 25

Darwin Chorale Inc
Website: www.darwinchorale.org.au
Email: darwinchorale@gmail.com
Phone: 040 803 6252
Address: PO Box 41523, AU
Information: Darwin Chorale is a community choir which began in 1985. The chorale performs at community events and presents several concerts a year, often in conjunction with local musical groups such as the Darwin Symphony Orchestra, peforming in Darwin, regional NT, and overseas. The aim of the chorale is to present good choral music, to foster young singers and to develop our repertoire and expertise.
Country: Australia
Type: Choir and Vocal Ensemble
Contact: Chairman Kevin Davis
Social Media: @DarwinChorale1 https:// www.facebook. com/DarwinChoraleInc

Mandurah City Choral Society
Website: www.mandurahchoral.org.au
Email: mandurahchoral@gmail.com
Phone: 405 182 741
Address: PO Box 970, AU
Information: The purpose of the Mandurah City Choral Society (MMCS) is to rehearse and perform choral music to a high standard and promote choral singing in the community. Its members come from all walks of life and from all age groups. Members work hard and enjoy their music.
Country: Australia
Type: Choir and Vocal Ensemble
Contact: musical Director Christopher Ryland
Social Media: www.facebook.com/Mandurah-City-Choral-Society-1450802261902739

Perth Harmony Chorus
Website: perthharmonychorus.com.au
Email: teamChair@perthharmonychorus.com.au
Phone: 413 255 844
Address: Nollamara Tennis Club, Kindra Way, Nollamara, AU
Information: Perth Harmony Chorus is a repeat national champion on the Sweet Adelines stage and a regular competitor on the International Sweet Adelines stage. PHC consists of around 100 women who come from all walks of life and range in age from those in their teens to the early 70's. Most have had no formal background in music and simply have a love of singing and performing.
Country: Australia
Type: Choir and Vocal Ensemble
Contact: musical Director Carole Macintyre assistant Director Jen Squires
Social Media: www.facebook.com/perthharmonychorus
Number of Performers: 100

Perth Symphonic Chorus
Website: www.perthsymphonicchorus.com.au
Email: conductor@perthsymphonicchorus.com.au
Phone: 416 120 662
Address: 45 Whitfeld Terrace, Winthrop, AU
Information: Since its inception in 1997 as the Collegium Symphonic Chorus, Perth Symphonic Chorus has imPressed and mesmerised audiences throughout Australia and overseas, including New York, Salzburg and Vienna. Led by internationally-acclaimed conductor, Dr Margaret Pride, the Chorus comprises close to 100 disciplined, enthusiastic and passionate individuals who are skilled in performing the works of some of the best choral composers throughout the ages.
Country: Australia
Type: Choir and Vocal Ensemble
Contact: Director Margaret Pride
Social Media: www.facebook.com/Perth-Symphonic-Chorus-117650591697382/
Touring Countries: USA, Austria

Touring: Nationally and Internationally

Song Company, The
Website: www.songcompany.com.au
Email: mail@songcompany.com.au
Phone: 282 729 500
Address: Pier 4 The Wharf Hickson Road, AU
Information: Vocalisation is all about the sound and the story. The Song Company of Australia comprises the continent's leading vocal ensemble, singing music of all times and places. Since the dawn of history, the human voice and the act of singing have been intrinsically linked with storytelling and the acquisition of culture. The Song Company belongs to a land whose first peoples used songlines and vocal music to pass knowledge and culture from generation to generation, and is proud to continue that tradition, in a unique way, sharing music from across western and non-western art traditions.
Country: Australia
Type: Choir and Vocal Ensemble
Contact: General Manager David Sidebottom
Email: gm@songcompany.com.au
Marketing coordinator Aziza Green operations Manager Alicia Gibbons
Email: alicia@songcompany.com.au
Social Media: @SongCompanyfacebook.com/songcompany
Touring Countries: USA, England, Europe, Asia, New Zealand, South America
Regular Venue: Range from intimate acoustic to larger open air concerts

South West Opera Company Inc
Website: swoc.com.au
Email: Marketing@swoc.com.au
Phone: 972 63206
Address: PO Box 1298, AU
Information: The South West Opera Company (SWOC) is a fun-loving family of all ages, with a shared love of music. We enjoy a happy balance of choral concerts and stage shows. SWOC is blessed with many talented and generous performers, including Musical Director Marguerite Monagle, Artistic Director Rob Hill, both of whom are Life Members of SWOC. Joining them in the Artistic leadership team for The Wizard of Oz is our favourite choreographer Mary-Ellen Sutherland and fantastic designer Deb Prentice.
Country: Australia
Type: Choir and Vocal Ensemble
Contact: musical Director Marguerite Monagle Artistic Director Rob Hill
Artistic Director Deb Prentice
Chair Marianne Lehmann
Social Media: www.facebook.com/swoperacompany

Soweto Gospel Choir
Website: www.sowetogospelchoir.com
Email: margot@akaaustralia.com.au
Phone: 398 205 477
Address: Level 2, 157 Toorak Road, AU
Information:
Country: Australia
Type: Choir and Vocal Ensemble
Contact: Executive Producer/Director Beverly Bryer
Email: eventsco@worldonline.co.za
vice President Dean Shultz
Email: dshultz@imgartists.com
Social Media: @Sowetogospel www.facebook.com/Official-Soweto-Gospel-Choir-102718979800619

The Ten Tenors
Website: thetentenors.com
Email: info@dmand.com.au
Phone: 736 660 120
Address: PO Box 648, AU
Information: The TEN Tenors are undoubtedly one of Australia's greatest entertainment success stories, with more than 90 million people worldwide witnessing their unmistakable charm, camaraderie and vocal power. Following 16 years of sell-out performances across the globe, including more than 2000 of their own headline concerts, The TEN Tenors have cemented their place as Australia's premier classical-crossover group.
Country: Australia
Type: Choir and Vocal Ensemble
Contact: musical Director Benjamin Kiehne
Social Media: @thetentenors www.facebook.com/thetentenors
Touring Countries: Europe, USA

University of Western Australia Choral Society
Website: www.uwacs.com.au
Email: registrar@uwacs.com.au
Phone: 894 870 221
Address: University of Western Australia Choral Society, PO Box 262, AU
Information: On 8th December 1931 at the Assembly Rooms in Pier Street, Mr A.J. Leickie raised his baton to conduct the first appearance of the newly formed UWA Choral Society in a performance of Stanford's "The Revenge" and a selection of part-songs. There was no orchestra and Miss Elsie Watson accompanied the choir on the piano
Country: Australia

Type: Choir and Vocal Ensemble
Contact: conductor Christopher Van Tuinen
Social Media: @UWACS www.facebook.com/pages/UWA-Choral-Society/333331653431462
Regular Venue: University of Western Australia campus and other venues

AZERBAIJAN

Choir of Azerbaijan State Academic Opera and Ballet Theatre
Website: www.tob.az/
Email: info@tob.az
Phone:
Address: No. 95 Nizami str., AZ
Information:
Country: Azerbaijan
Type: Choir and Vocal Ensemble
Contact: Director Melikof Akif Turau chief conductor Milena Hajiyeva

Choir of Azerbaijan State Radio and Television Company
Website:
Phone: 124 396 007
Address: 1 Mehti Huseyn St., AZ
Information:
Country: Azerbaijan
Type: Choir and Vocal Ensemble
Contact: chief conductor Ramiz Mustafayev

Choir of Khazar University
Website:
Email: contact@khazar.org
Phone:
Address: 11 Mashati str., AZ
Information:
Country: Azerbaijan
Type: Choir and Vocal Ensemble

BARBADOS

The Cecilian Singers of Barbados
Website: www.angelfire.com/ms2/ceciliansingers
Email: cwpb419@caribsurf.com
Address: St. Mary's Anglican Church, BB
Information: the Singers have travelled throughout Canada, the U.S.A., the Caribbean and West Germany
Country: Barbados
Type: Choir and Vocal Ensemble

CANADA

Cadence
Website: www.cadence-unplugged.com/
Email: info@cadence-unplugged.com
Phone: 416 738 8128
Address: 145 Clifton Ave, CA
Information: The stage lights fall, the crowd goes quiet, and four harmonious voices rise up and fill the air.
The melodies unfurl into something both familiar and fresh. What comes next may be a classic song by Joni Mitchell or Louis Prima; tt may be an old bebop standard or cheeky arrangement of a 1980s hit, but these are arrangements like you've never heard them before. They contain all the richness of a full band, but performed using just four voices.
Country: Canada
Type: Choir and Vocal Ensemble
Social Media: @cadencetweet www.facebook.com/cadenceunplugged
Touring: Nationally and Internationally

CapriCCio Vocal Ensemble
Website: www.capriccio.ca
Email:
choir@capriccio.ca
Phone: 250 652 3508
Address: Capriccio Vocal Ensemble, PO Box 48089, CA
Information: Now in its 28th season, CapriCCio continues to captivate audiences with outstanding performances of choral music ranging from the 15th century to the present. From Tallis and Gabrieli to Pärt, Whitacre and even younger contemporaries, from simple folk songs to Bach's B Minor Mass and Handel's Messiah, all are performed in CapriCCio's signature style: with virtuosic clarity and a sensitive, compelling spirit.
Country: Canada
Type: Choir and Vocal Ensemble
Contact: Director Michael Gormley
Social Media: @CapriCCioVE www.facebook.com/pages/CapriCCio-Vocal-Ensemble/182366408440305?fref=ts
Annual Performances: 8

HONG KONG

Cantoria Hong Kong
Website:
mus.hkbu.edu.hk/cantoria.html
Email:
jwinzenb@gmail.com
Phone: 341 15153
Address: Rm AST801, Sing Tao Building, Hong Kong

Baptist University, Kowloon Tong, HK

Information: The Cantoria Hong Kong is a mixed chamber choir of select students from the HKBU Department of Music. "Cantoria" is an old Spanish word meaning "choir," but it is especially appropriate for the Baptist University setting, since it highlights the multiple languages and cultures experienced in the Hong Kong landscape. The group was established in September 2009 to develop a wide range of advanced choral repertoire representing various periods and styles both old and new. It sings an eclectic blend of works from the 16th to the 20th centuries, specializing in contemporary repertoire from China and around the world
Country: Hong Kong
Type: Choir and Vocal Ensemble
Social Media: www.facebook.com/hkbumus

Hong Kong Bach Choir
Website: bachchoir.org.hk
Email: info@bachchoir.org.hk
Address: GPO Box 2334, HK
Information: The Hong Kong Bach Choir is Hong Kong's leading classical chorus. Formed in 1970, the original Choir was a group of 15 singers assembled to support the Baroque Ensemble for a single Bach cantata performance. Over the years it has grown significantly and now has a multinational membership of more than 100 singers. The Choir presents two concerts in major venues each year
Country: Hong Kong
Type: Choir and Vocal Ensemble
Contact: Chairperson Astrid Strømnes
Email: Chair@bachchoir.org.hk
Social Media: @HKBachChoir www.facebook.com/HKBachChoir

The Chinese University of Hong Kong Chorus
Website: www.cuchorus.org.hk
Email: cuchorus@cuchorus.org.hk
Phone: 394 37000
Address: CU Chorus Association Limited, Unit 104, 1/F, Block B, Wing Kut Industrial Building, HK
Information: In 40 years of pursuing excellence, The Chinese University of Hong Kong Chorus (CU Chorus) has become one of the best local university choirs in Hong Kong. With a global vision, CU Chorus has performed not only on local stages, but also in various cities in southern China and Southeast Asia. With its high quality performances and innovative programmes, CU Chorus is dedicated to promote the art of choral music to the General public
Country: Hong Kong
Type: Choir and Vocal Ensemble
Contact: musical Director Leon Chu
Social Media: @cuhkchorus www.facebook.com/cuhk-chorus

The Hong Kong Bach Choir
Website: www.bachchoir.org.hk
Email: info@bachchoir.org.hk
Address: GPO Box 2334, Central, HK
Information: The Hong Kong Bach Choir is one of Hong Kong's longest-established and finest choirs. From a small group of 15 music lovers gathered for a single performance in 1969, the Choir has developed into a year-round, multi-national ensemble of more than 80 members. The HKBC presents a wide repertoire, from the Renaissance to World Premieres, whilst concentrating on music of the Baroque, Classical and Romantic periods. They present two concerts at major venues each year, as well as a variety of more specialized performances
Country: Hong Kong
Type: Choir and Vocal Ensemble
Contact: Chairperson Astrid Strømnes
secretary Xiaoli Wang
Social Media: @HKBachChoir www.facebook.com/HKBachChoir
Number of Performers: 80

The Hong Kong Oratorio Society
Website: www.oratorio.org.hk
Email: hkosig@yahoo.com
Address: HK
Information: The Hong Kong Oratorio Society (HKOS) is a non-profit-making organisation founded in 1956 by Mr Wong Ming Tung and a group of music enthusiasts who believed that choral singing and music would bring joy to the singers and the listeners alike, as well as enhancing the personal quality and enriching the spiritual and cultural life of the audience
Country: Hong Kong
Type: Choir and Vocal Ensemble
Contact: President Alvin Chan
Chairman Eric Au Yeung
Social Media: www.facebook.com/HKOratorioSociety
Touring Countries: China, Canada, Israel, the Philippines, Korea, Taiwan, Singapore

JAPAN

Japan Choral Association

Email: international@jcanet.or.jp
Phone: 355 407 813
Address: c/o The Asahi Shimbun, 5-3-2 Tsukiji, Chuo-ku, , JP
Information: a choir based in Tokyo
Country: Japan
Type: Choir and Vocal Ensemble
Contact: President Shinsuke Kishi

Singakademie Tsukuba
Website: koten.sakura.ne.jp/en
Email: tsukuba-koten1988@koten.sakura.ne.jp
Address: Namiki Public Hall, JP
Information: performs choral music ranging from 16th century to 20th century, with special attention to the early music
Country: Japan
Type: Choir and Vocal Ensemble
Contact: Director Masaru Suzuki
Number of Performers: 45

The CoroOrfine
Website: www.ne.jp/asahi/coro/orfine/e-index.htm
Email: orfine@tokyo.email.ne.jp
Address: JP
Information: the CoroOrfine is a choral group in Tokyo, Japan
Country: Japan
Type: Choir and Vocal Ensemble
Contact: conductor Minori Masuda

Tokyo Embassy Choir
Website: bec.ac/index.html
Email: info.tcc2013@gmail.com
Address: JP
Information: TEC sings a wide variety of music from sacred and secular choral repertoire, as well as ballads, light opera, folk and popular songs
Country: Japan
Type: Choir and Vocal Ensemble
Contact: musical Director Steven Morgan
assistant Director Scott Ponzani
accompanist Mariko Sano

MEXICO

Arte Corporal Esc
Website:
Phone: 555 659 8241
Address: Callej, Col. del Carmen Coyoac, MX
Information:
Country: Mexico
Type: Choir and Vocal Ensemble
Contact: Director C. Mtz

Caverna 7
Website:
Phone: 555 564 2418
Address: Coahuila, Col. Roma, MX
Information:
Country: Mexico
Type: Choir and Vocal Ensemble
Contact: Director Ivonne Muñoz

NEW ZEALAND

Auckland Choral Society
Website: www.aucklandchoral.com
Email: admin@aucklandchoral.com
Phone: 935 82892
Address: PO Box 7228, Wellesley Street, NZ
Information: Auckland Choral, Auckland's only symphonic choir, is as vibrant and dynamic as ever! Since 1855, Auckland Choral has been performing timeless classic choral works as well as exciting contemporary compositions, including New Zealand premieres, alongside some of our finest soloists and orchestras. Its members, wide-ranging in age, work intensely at rehearsals and are passionately committed to the music they sing. Bringing a unique blend of Artistic excellence, professional polish and community spirit to their performances, they are proud to be part of a choir that continues to play such a significant role in Auckland's arts scene.
Country: New Zealand
Type: Choir and Vocal Ensemble
Social Media: @AucklandChoral www.facebook.com/AKLChoral
Regular Venue: Auckland Town Hall, Holy Trinity Cathedral

Taki Rua Productions
Website: www.takirua.co.nz
Email: info@takirua.co.nz
Phone: 438 53110
Address: Level 1, Toi Poneke, 274 – 278 Taranaki Street, Mount Cook, NZ
Information: Taki Rua produce, commission and develop theatre with a distinctively Māori voice. It collaborates with the brightest voices in the industry, touring productions both locally and internationally. Since 1983, Taki Rua has been an arts industry leader – a creative rule breaker, continually evolving the definition of Māori theatre. It exists to connect the past and present and

ensure Māori voices are heard worldwide.
Country: New Zealand
Type: Choir and Vocal Ensemble
Social Media: www.facebook.com/takiruaproductions

PHILIPPINES

A Capella Manila
Website: www.acapellamanila.com
Email: info@acapellamanila.com
Phone: 917 528 8062
Address: 4849 Buntal Alley, Cor. Durban Street, PH
Information: the A Cappella Manila (ACM) is one of the Philippines' most respected vocal ensembles today, with a mission to promote peace and goodwill through their brand of music. In its almost twenty years of existence, the group has concertized extensively in the Philippines, Asia, Europe and North America. Available to hire for concerts, weddings, masses as well as corporate / private parties
Country: Philippines
Type: Choir and Vocal Ensemble
Social Media: @ACappellaManila@ACappellaManila

SOUTH AFRICA

City of Tygerberg Choir
Website: www.stadskoortygerberg.co.za/en
Email: stadskoor@gmail.com
Phone: 082 927 7196
Address: Meerlust Street, ZA
Information: the City of Tygerberg Choir was established in 1997. The choir consists of members mainly from the northern suburbs, but also as far as the Helderberg region and Mitchells Plain
Country: South Africa
Type: Choir and Vocal Ensemble
Contact: musical Director Linda Claasen
Social Media: www.facebook.com/stadskoortygerberg

UNITED STATES

Abington Choral Club
Website: www.abingtonchoralclub.org
Email: auditions@abingtonchoralclub.org
Phone: 267 225 7464
Address: US
Information: The mission of Abington Choral Club (ACC) is to provide its members the opportunity to study and perform all types of choral literature and to serve the General public through regularly scheduled concerts that entertain, educate, and enlighten. As a non-profit organisation, ACC also seeks to present musical programs that meet the diverse needs of community organisations in the Philadelphia metropolitan area
Country: United States
Type: Choir and Vocal Ensemble
Contact: President Richard Gustafson
Director Peter Hilliard
Social Media: @abingtonchoralclub

Central Virginia Masterworks Chorale
Website: cvamc.org
Email: cvmc.Director@gmail.com
Phone: 804 798 4907
Address: CVMC, P.O. Box 415, US
Information: aims to create performances of choral music through community participation, education, and inspiration
Country: United States
Type: Choir and Vocal Ensemble
Contact: Artistic Director David Sinden
sponsorship and ads Stephanie Hesse
Social Media: @CentralChorale www.facebook.com/CentralVirginiaMasterworksChorale
Touring: Nationally
Annual Performances: 2
Number of Performers: 40

Choral Arts Ensemble
Website: www.choralartsensemble.org
Email: info@choralartsensemble.org
Phone: 507 252 8427
Address: Choral Arts Ensemble, 1001 14th Street NW, US
Information: Choral Arts Ensemble coordinates the Rosemary and Meredith Willson Harmony for Mayo Program, a free weekly concert series
Country: United States
Type: Choir and Vocal Ensemble
Contact: Artistic Director Rick Kvam
Social Media: @ChoralArtsMN www.facebook.com/ChoralArtsEnsemble

Choral Arts Society of Washington, The
Website: www.choralarts.org
Email: carriehalpert@choralarts.org
Phone: 202 244 3669
Address: 5225 Winconsin Avenue, Suite 603, Washington, D.C. 20015-2016, US
Information:
Country: United States
Type: Choir and Vocal Ensemble
Contact: Artistic Director Scott Tucker

KITKA Women's Vocal Ensemble
Website: www.kitka.org
Email: staff@kitka.org
Phone: 510 444 0323
Address: 1201 Martin Luther King Jr. Way, US
Information:
Country: United States
Type: Choir and Vocal Ensemble
Contact: Executive Director Shira Cion
Annual Performances: 35
Regular Venue: Various

Manchester Choral Society
Website: www.mcsnh.org
Email: info@mcsnh.org
Phone: 603 472 6627
Address: 88 Hanover Street, US
Information: established in 1961, MCS is a non-profit,
auditioned community choir
Country: United States
Type: Choir and Vocal Ensemble
Contact: music Director Dan Perkins
Social Media: www.facebook.com/mcsnh.org

Melodia Women's Choir
Website: www.melodiawomenschoir.org
Email: jenny@melodiawomenschoir.org
Phone: 212 252 4134
Address: 446 West 47th Street, 1B, US
Information: ensemble of 32 singers, Melodia explores
and performs rarely heard music for women's voices in
many different styles, and nurtures emerging women
composers through commissions, residencies and
performances
Country: United States
Type: Choir and Vocal Ensemble
Contact: Executive Director Jenny Clarke
Email: jenny@melodiawomenschoir.org
Artistic Director Cynthia Powell
Social Media: @MelodiaSings www.facebook.com/
melodiawomenschoir
Regular Venue: Holy Apostles Church, NYC

The Philadelphia Singers
Website: www.philadelphiasingers.org
Email: megan@philadelphiasingers.org
Phone: 215 751 9494
Address: 1211 Chestnut St, US
Country: United States
Type: Choir and Vocal Ensemble
Contact: Executive Director Megan M. Machnik
Email: megan@philadelphiasingers.org
music Director David Hayes
Social Media: @ThePhilaSingers https:// www.facebook.
com/ThePhilaSingers
Touring: Nationally

BALLET AND DANCE COMPANIES

The ballet and dance companies listed here represent a broad range of types and sizes, including contemporary and classical dance. Some of the ballet companies listed perform in theatres that pres-ent opera and drama and do not have an existence outside that theatre. **The entries are listed in alphabetical order within country.**

Compagnies de Ballet et de Danse
Les compagnies de ballet et de danse énumérés ici représentent un large éventail de types et de tailles,y compris la danse contemporaine et classique.Certaines des compagnies de ballet énumérés jouer dans des théâtres que l'opéra et le théâtre présente et ne dispose pas d'un ouside existence que le théâtre. **Les entrée sont classés par ordre alphabétique dans le pays.**

Ballett und Tanz
Die Ballett und Tanz hier aufgeführten Unternehmen repräsentieren ein breites Spektrum von Arten und Größen, einschließlich zeit-genössischen und klassischen Tanz. Einige der Ballett-Kompanien aufgeführt im Theater führen, dass derzeit Oper und Schauspiel und haben nicht eine Existenz ouside, dass das Theater. **Die Einträge sind für jedes Land alphabetisch sortiert.**

Compagnie di Danza e Balletto
Le compagnie di balletto e danza elencati qui rappresentano una vasta gamma di tipi e dimensioni, tra cui la danza contemporanea e classica. Alcune delle compagnie di balletto di cui esibirsi in teatri che l'opera presente e dramma e non hanno un ouside esistenza quel teatro. **Le voci sono pubblicate in ordine alfabetico di paese.**

Ballet y Danza Compañías
Las compañías de ballet y danza figuran en esta lista representan una amplia gama de tipos y tamaños, incluyendo la danza contem-poránea y clásica. Algunas de las compañías de ballet realizar enu-merados en los cines que la ópera y el teatro actual y no tiene una existencia ouside ese teatro. **Las entradas se muestran en orden alfabético dentro de cada país.**

performing arts
database
online

artsDB.net

AUSTRALIA

Australian Ballet
Website: www.australianballet.com.au
Email: customerservice@australianballet.com.au
Phone: 130 036 9741
Address: Level 5, 2 Kavanagh Street, Southbank, AU
Information: The Australian Ballet exists to inspire, delight and challenge audiences through the power of its performances. The Australian Ballet is one of the world's premier ballet companies and has delivered extraordinary performances for over 50 years. A commitment to Artistic excellence, a spirited style and a willingness to take risks have defined the company from its earliest days, both onstage and off.
Country: Australia
Type: Ballet and Dance Company
Contact: Artistic Director David McAllister
Executive Director Libby Christie
senior Artistic coordinator Alex Wyatt
Social Media: @TheAusBallet www.facebook.com/theaustralianballet
Touring Countries: USA, China, Japan, UK, France
Annual Performances: 250
Number of Performers: 62
Venues: State Theatre, Victorian Arts Centre, Melbourne; Opera Theatre, Sydney Opera House, Sydney; Lyric Theatre, Queensland Performing Arts Complex, Brisbane; Canberra Theatre Centre, Canberra; Festival Theatre, Adelaide Festival Centre, Adelaide, His Majesty's

BalletLab
Website: www.balletlab.com
Email: admin@balletlab.com
Phone: 396 459 937
Address: Temperance Hall, 199 Napier St, AU
Information: Phillip Adams BalletLab is a vital contributor to Australian dance and performance culture today. It is an arresting company led by Artistic Director Phillip Adams, an interdisciplinary choreographer and artist. Their philosophy acknowledges that everything begins with the body. They think physically and visually to create and curate new and unmediated experiences that contest the boundaries of contemporary arts practice. Adams' process draws on collaboration and is an investigation through mediums of music, design, fashion, architecture, cinema, visual arts, photography and live arts, engaging with the unorthodox, queer and popular culture.
Country: Australia
Type: Ballet and Dance Company
Contact: Executive Producer Kristy Ayre
Email: kristy@balletlab.com
Artistic Director Phillip Adams
Email: phillip@balletlab.com
project officer Briony Galligan
Email: briony@balletlab.com
Social Media: @balletlab www.facebook.com/BalletLab
Touring Countries: USA, China, Denmark, Scotland, Germany, England, Korea, Mongolia, Romania and Bulgaria

Bangarra Dance Theatre
Website: www.bangarra.com.au
Email: bangarra@bangarra.com.au
Phone: 292 515 333
Address: Pier 4, 15 Hickson Road, Walsh Bay, AU
Information: Bangarra is an Aboriginal and Torres Strait Islander organisation and one of Australia's leading performing arts companies, widely acclaimed nationally and around the world for their powerful dancing, distinctive theatrical voice and utterly unique soundscapes, music and design. Bangarra's annual program includes a national tour of a world premiere work, performed in Australia's most iconic venues, a regional tour allowing audiences outside of capital cities the opportunity to experience Bangarra, and an international tour to maintain our global reputation for excellence.
Country: Australia
Type: Ballet and Dance Company
Contact: chief financial officer Ashwin Rathod
Email: ashwin@bangarra.com.au
finance & operations coordinator
Elizabeth Timbery
Email: elizabeth@bangarra.com.au
Director Kitty Walker
Email: kitty@bangarra.com.au
Social Media: @BangarraDance www.facebook.com/Bangarra

Big Steps Little Feet
Website: www.bigstepslittlefeet.com.au
Email: enquiries@bigstepslittlefeet.com.au
Phone: 293 880 118
Address: PO Box 769, AU
Information: Big Steps Little Feet is a vibrant community of busy families who all share one thing in common – a love of dance to create happy and inspired young children. We're proud to say that through the dance experience, we assist hard working parents to develop deeper connections with their children whilst producing skilled, creative and confident young dancers.
Country: Australia

Type: Ballet and Dance Company
Contact: owner Kate Barber
Social Media: www.facebook.com/BigStepsLittleFeet

Buzz Dance Theatre
Website: www.buzzdance.com.au
Email: admin@buzzdance.com.au
Phone: 892 262 322
Address: PO Box 7332, Cloisters Square, AU
Information: Buzz Dance Theatre was Australia's premier dance theatre company for children and young people. Nationally awarded as a leader in its field, it created performances and led workshops that were designed specifically to foster creativity in all its shapes and forms. The company's creative teams used contemporary dance, music, theatre, design and technology to capture the imagination of children and young people, inviting them to explore, create and play, not only as audience members but also as collaborators.
Country: Australia
Type: Ballet and Dance Company
Contact: education and Administration Manager Mary Wolfla
Email: admin@buzzdance.com.au
Social Media: www.facebook.com/pages/BUZZ-DANCE-THEATRE/295617829356
Touring Countries: Europe, South Africa
Venues: theatres, parks, outdoor venues

Chunky Move
Website: www.chunkymove.com
Email: info@chunkymove.com.au
Phone: 396 455 188
Address: 111 Sturt Street, AU
Information: Chunky Move constantly seeks to redefine what is or what can be contemporary dance in an ever-evolving Australian culture. Our work is diverse in form and content, encompassing Productions for the stage, site specific, new-media and installation work.
Country: Australia
Type: Ballet and Dance Company
Contact: Artistic Director Anouk Van Dijk
Email: info@chunkymove.com.au
Social Media: @ChunkyMove www.facebook.com/chunkymove
Venues: theatres 400+, site specific spaces

Circus Oz
Website: www.circusoz.com
Email: admin@circusoz.com.au
Phone: 396 760 300
Address: 50 Perry Street, AU
Information: Circus Oz are Australia's premier contemporary circus. With a history spanning 3 decades of performance around the globe, Circus Oz performances are a mix of breathtaking agility, death-defying stunts, awe-inspiring acrobatic performances, irreverent comedy and a spectacular live band.
Country: Australia
Type: Ballet and Dance Company
Contact: Chairman Nicholas Yates
Social Media: @circusoz https:// www.facebook.com/circusoz
Touring Countries: UK, Europe, America, Australia
Venues: purpose-built Big Top tent 1390

Dance North
Website: www.dancenorth.com.au
Email: admin@dancenorth.com.au
Phone: 747 722 549
Address: Cnr of Stanley Street and Walker Street, AU
Information: Dancenorth is a contemporary dance company based in Townsville, Tropical North Queensland. An epicenter for Artistic exchange and collaboration Dancenorth balances a dynamic regional presence with a commitment to creating bold, adventurous and critically acclaimed contemporary dance. Member of ISPA.
Country: Australia
Type: Ballet and Dance Company
Contact: General Manager Deanna Smart
Email: deanna@dancenorth.com.au
Production Manager Murray Dempsey
Email: murray@dancenorth.com.au
Social Media: @dancenorthtsv www.facebook.com/dancenorthAUS
Touring Countries: USA, Europe
Venues: Townsville Civic Theatre 1050, The School of Arts Studio 200

Dancehouse
Website: www.dancehouse.com.au
Email: info@dancehouse.com.au
Phone: 393 472 860
Address: 150 Princes Street, AU
Information: Dancehouse is Australia's premier centre for independent dance. The role is threefold: to advance independent dance artists, to build dance audiences, and to develop the artform itself. With artists and audiences, they are co-creating a context for independent dance, in its diversity, to be accessed and appreciated. Together, they are nurturing dance making and dance thinking; they are building dance literacy and dance's legacy.
Country: Australia

Type: Ballet and Dance Company
Contact: Artistic Director & CEO
Angela Conquet
chief Executive James Ostroburski
Social Media: @Dancehouse_Melb www.facebook.com/DancehouseMelbourne/

Danza Viva Spanish Dance Company & Academy
Website: www.danzaviva.com
Email: danzavivaperth@gmail.com
Phone: 422 953 817
Address: 70 Roberts St, AU
Information: Synonymous with Spanish Dance, Danza Viva is one of the few outside of Spain to incorporate the full range of Spanish dance from classical to flamenco. Danza Viva has become synonymous with Spanish Dance in Australia and abroad and is one of the few organisations of its kind outside of Spain to incorporate in its programme, the full range of Spanish dance styles from classical through to flamenco.
Country: Australia
Type: Ballet and Dance Company
Contact: Artistic Director Deanna Blacher
Social Media: www.facebook.com/Danza-Viva-Spanish-Dance-Company-302377499795200/

Diana Reyes Flamenco
Website: www.dianareyesflamenco.com.au
Email: diana@dianareyesflamenco.com.au
Phone: 295 571 825
Address: 585B King Street, AU
Information: Study flamenco with Australia's most renowned flamenco dancer/choreographer and teacher, Diana Reyes. The Flamenco Studio is located in Newtown, Sydney. Classes are available from beginners to advanced levels and most classes are accompanied by a flamenco guitarist and singer. Diana Reyes studied flamenco dance in Madrid and performed in Spain and Europe in 'tablaos flamenco' and theatre before establishing her own company in Australia 'Diana Reyes Flamenco' in 1991.
Country: Australia
Type: Ballet and Dance Company
Contact: Artistic Director Diana Reyes
Social Media: www.facebook.com/Diana-Reyes-Flamenco-143477805694208
Touring Countries: Spain, Europe

ExPressions Dance Company
Website: www.exPressionsdancecompany.org.au
Email: admin@exPressionsdancecompany.org.au
Phone: 732 574 222
Address: Level 3/420 Brunswick Street, AU
Information: ExPressions Dance Company (EDC) is Queensland's premier contemporary dance company with an ensemble of 6-8 dancers. For 32 years EDC has created more than 170 works by 75 different choreographers and has enjoyed 22 international tours to 17 countries and 23 major Queensland tours. EDC is defined by its commitment to excellence in performance, sector development and education, all contributing to the evolution and future of contemporary Australian dance.
Country: Australia
Type: Ballet and Dance Company
Contact: Chair Marian Gibney
Artistic Director Natalie Weir
Executive Director Christine Johnstone
Social Media: @_EDC www.facebook.com/exPressionsdancecompany
Touring Countries: United States, Europe, Mexico, New Caledonia and Asia

Force Majeure
Website: www.forcemajeure.com.au
Email: forcemajeure@forcemajeure.com.au
Phone: 285 719 084
Address: 245 Wilson Street, AU
Information: The company is based around a collective of multi-disciplinary artists committed to creating stimulating movement-based theatre. Artists include dancers, actors, writers, visual artists, musicians, composers and filmmakers. Since its inception Force Majeure has created six major works, two collaborative works and a short film series. This highly produced body of work engages with and questions contemporary culture using intelligence, pathos, humour and insight. Member of ISPA
Country: Australia
Type: Ballet and Dance Company
Contact: Artistic Director Danielle Micich
Email: danielle@forcemajeure.com.au
Executive Producer Colm O'Callaghan
Email: colm@forcemajeure.com.au
accounts Manager Rhanda Mansour
Email: accounts@forcemajeure.com.au
Marketing Manager Georgia McKay
Email: georgia@forcemajeure.com.au
Social Media: @majeurenews www.facebook.com/ForceMajeureAustralia

Leigh Warren and Dancers
Website: www.lwd.com.au
Email: lwd@lwd.com.au
Phone: 882 125 660
Address: Lion Arts Centre, Cnr Morphett St & North Terrace, AU
Information: Formed in 1993, Adelaide-based LWDance Hub has established itself as a formidable force in

both the Australian and international contemporary dance scenes. Led by Artistic Director Leigh Warren, the company has produced and toured many original dance works, worked with seminal Australian visual artists and musicians and collaborated with distinguished choreographers.
Country: Australia
Type: Ballet and Dance Company
Contact: Artistic Director Leigh Warren
company Manager Jo Jacobs
open house Producer Callan Fleming
Chairman Nigel Stevenson
Social Media: www.facebook.com/lwdancehub
Touring Countries: Europe
Venues: Adelaide Festival Centre

Lucy Guerin Inc
Website: www.lucyguerininc.com
Email: admin@LucyGuerinInc.com
Phone: 393 294 213
Address: 28 Batman Street, AU
Information: Lucy Guerin Inc is an Australian dance company established in Melbourne in 2002 to create and tour new dance works. Renowned for the skill and originality of its small group of performers, it is a flexible organisation dedicated to challenging and extending the art of contemporary dance. The company is committed to the exploration of everyday events and the redefinition of the formal concerns of dance. New Productions are generated through an experimental approach to creative process and may involve voice, video, sound, text and industrial design as well as Guerin's lucid physical structures.
Country: Australia
Type: Ballet and Dance Company
Contact: Executive Producer Annette Vieusseux
Email: Annette@LucyGuerinInc.com
company Manager Claire Bradley Duke
Email: Claire@LucyGuerinInc.com
Artistic Director Lucy Guerin
Email: Lucy@LucyGuerinInc.com
Social Media: @LucyGuerinInc www.facebook.com/Lucy-Guerin-Inc-162719537080159
Touring Countries: France, Belgium

Mirramu Dance Company
Website: www.mirramu.com
Email: info@mirramu.com
Phone: 262 381 492
Address: 849 Lake Rd, AU
Information: Mirramu believes in sharing and communicating through the creative process and invites artists from different disciplines to guest with the company. Much of its work is done in an inter-disciplinary and cross-cultural context with high levels of community involvement via workshops, forums and events Associated with each professional Production.
Country: Australia
Type: Ballet and Dance Company
Contact: Artistic Director and choreographer Elizabeth Cameron Dalman
Email: mirramucreativeartscentre@gmail.com
Social Media: www.facebook.com/mirramu
Touring Countries: Japan, Taiwan, Malaysia, Singapore the Netherlands and Senegal

Queensland Ballet
Website: www.queenslandballet.com.au
Email: mail@queenslandballet.com.au
Phone: 730 136 666
Address: Thomas Dixon Centre, 406 Montague Rd, West End, AU
Information: Queensland Ballet is a vibrant, creative company which connects people and dance across Queensland. They offer a program of world-class Productions of the best classical ballets and inspired contemporary dance works. The company engages renowned choreographers and designers from around the world and nurtures emerging local talent by presenting exciting new works in an intimate studio series.
Country: Australia
Type: Ballet and Dance Company
Contact: Artistic Director Li Cunxin
music Director Andrew Mogrelia
Chair Brett Clark
Social Media: @qldballet www.facebook.com/QldBallet
Venues: Playhouse 500, Lyric Theatre 1500, Gardens Theatre 400, Conservatorium Concert Hall 600, Thomas Dixon Centre 149

Raw Dance
Website: rawcompany.net
Email: info@rawcompany.net
Phone: 130 072 9326
Address: 46 Evesham Street, AU
Information: RAW is an Australian Company performing and educating globally and locally.RAW is an energetic fusion of popular street youth culture, featuring elements of Funk Tap, Hip Hop, Break Dance, Beat-boxing, Circus, Contemporary and Percussion. RAW follows in the footsteps of some of Australia's greatest entertainment exports
Country: Australia
Type: Ballet and Dance Company

Contact: chief Executive Andrew Fee
Email: andrew@rawdancecompany.com
Artistic Director Jack Chambers
Email: jack@rawcompany.net
Marketing Jon Adams
Email: Marketing@rawcompany.net
Social Media: @rawcompany www.facebook.com/rawcompany

Shaun Parker & Company
Website: www.shaunparkercompany.com
Email: info@shaunparkercompany.com
Phone: 293 511 941
Address: C/O Seymour Centre, PO Box 553, AU
Information: Shaun Parker & Company is an exhilarating and bold new Australian dance company that has exploded onto the international dance scene. The company creates critically acclaimed dance Productions, which are renowned for their integration of stimulating choreographic forms, arresting musical scores and theatrical invention. Part of ISPA.
Country: Australia
Type: Ballet and Dance Company
Contact: Artistic Director Shaun Parker
Executive Producer Katherine Fyffe
Chair Toby Heap
Social Media: @ShaunParkerCo www.facebook.com/Shaun.Parker.Company
Venues: Sydney, Wentworth Park, Ultimo and Sydney, Sydney Park, Alexandria

Sue Healey Company
Website: www.suehealey.com
Email: sue.healey@optusnet.com.au
Address: 115 Barcom Ave, AU
Information: Sue is a multi-award-winning choreographer, educator, filmmaker and installation artist. Originally from New Zealand, Sue graduated from the Victorian College of the Arts, before becoming a founding member of Nanette Hassall's Dance Works in Melbourne. Sue performed and choreographed with the company from 1983-88, and then continued her training in New York with such luminaries as Merce Cunningham and Trisha Brown Companies.
Country: Australia
Type: Ballet and Dance Company
Touring Countries: Japan, New Zealand, USA, UK and Asia

Sydney Dance Company
Website: www.sydneydancecompany.com
Email: sdc@sydneydancecompany.com
Phone: 292 214 811
Address: Pier 4, The Wharf, 15 Hickson Road, Walsh Bay, AU
Information: Sydney Dance Company has a broad community beyond the practice and performance of their lead dancers. They believe in the universality of dance, and with the largest public dance class programme in Australia, they help over 80, 000 people a year connect with the grace, strength and creativity that lives within all of us. Their nation-wide education program offers a strategic curriculum targeting primary and secondary students through to career focused study for pre-professional dancers and university graduates.
Country: Australia
Type: Ballet and Dance Company
Contact: Artistic Director Rafael Bonachela
Executive Director Anne Dunn
Chair Karen Moses
Social Media: @sydneydanceco www.facebook.com/sydneydanceco
Touring Countries: Europe, China
Venues: Sydney Theatre 800

Tango Fire
Website: www.tango-fire.com
Email: toni@akaaustralia.com.au
Phone: 398 205 477
Address: Suite 1311, 9 Yarra Street, AU
Information: The Tango Fire Company of Buenos Aires was conceived in 2005 with its world premiere in Singapore. In that same year, the show was presented at the Edinburgh Fringe Festival where it received critical acclaim, resulting in engagements in the most prestigious venues around the world.
Country: Australia
Type: Ballet and Dance Company
Social Media: @TangoFire1 www.facebook.com/pages/Tango-Fire/536493189704261
Touring Countries: USA, Europe

Tasdance
Website: www.tasdance.com.au
Email: info@tasdance.com.au
Phone: 363 316 644
Address: 197 Wellington Street, AU
Information: Tasdance is a vital force in Tasmania and is a valuable player in the national dance scene, providing an important professional development hub for dancers and choreographers and is a leader in audience development
Country: Australia
Type: Ballet and Dance Company

Contact: Artistic Director Felicity Bott
Production Manager Darren Willmott
adminstrative assistant Shannon Douglas
Chair Peter Matthews
Social Media: www.facebook.com/tasdance
Touring Countries: Korea, India, China
Venues: average capacity 150-300

Te Vaka
Website: www.tevaka.com
Email: management@tevaka.com
Phone: 614 209 84842
Address: PO Box 875, Five Dock, AU
Information: Te Vaka is a group of musicians and dancers from Tokelau, Tuvalu, Samoa, Cook Islands and New Zealand brought together under the inspired leadership of Opetaia Foa'i. Te Vaka has been enchanting the world with their own brand of South Pacific Fusion since 1997. Using the rhythms of the log drum ("pate"), combined with traditional and contemporary instruments, Opetaia Foa'i and the band deliver a kaleidoscopic array of Pacific flavors in a genre all on its own.
Country: Australia
Type: Ballet and Dance Company
Contact: Manager Julie Foa'i
Social Media: @tevaka www.facebook.com/tevaka
Touring Countries: USA, Europe, UK, South Pacific, Asia, Australia and New Zealand

Tracks Inc.
Website: www.tracksdance.com.au
Email: info@tracksdance.com.au
Phone: 889 411 410
Address: Frog Hollow Centre for the Arts, 56 McMinn Street, AU
Information: Tracks is a recognised centre of excellence, producing exceptional performances built on an extended history of trusted community collaboration. Tracks is an innovator, developing an Australian dance idiom that values and utilises a diversity of dance practice while remaining fiercely local, producing dynamic, site-specific dance performances that celebrate an important part of Australian culture – the frontier of the Northern Territory.
Country: Australia
Type: Ballet and Dance Company
Contact: General Manager Agnes Michelet
Email: gm@tracksdance.com.au
co-Artistic Director Tim Newth
Email: tim@tracksdance.com.au
Director Adelaide Wood
Email: adelaide@tracksdance.com.au
administrator Jessica Mellor
Email: admin@tracksdance.com.au
Social Media: @tracksdance www.facebook.com/tracks.dance

West Australian Ballet
Website: www.waballet.com.au
Email: info@waballet.com.au
Phone: 892 140 707
Address: 134 Whatley Crescent, AU
Information: West Australian Ballet stages everything from full length classical ballets, narrative ballets and shorter works, and encompasses a variety of choreographic styles. Based in Perth, it resides at the West Australian Ballet Centre in Maylands, and also tours nationally and internationally.
Country: Australia
Type: Ballet and Dance Company
Contact: Artistic Director Aurelien Scannella
Executive Director Jessica Machin
head of operations Marcus Whelan
Social Media: @WABallet www.facebook.com/waballet
Touring Countries: China, Japan, Indonesia, Taiwan, Philippines
Venues: The Quarry Amphitheatre, City Beach, Perth; His Majesty's Theatre, Perth

AZERBAIJAN

Azerbaijan State Dance Ensemble
Website:
Phone: 124 931 651
Address: Istiglaliyyat St. 2, AZ
Country: Azerbaijan
Type: Ballet and Dance Company

Azerbaijan State Song and Dance Ensemble named after F Amirov
Website:
Phone: 124 931 651
Address: Istiglialiyat St. 2, AZ
Country: Azerbaijan
Type: Ballet and Dance Company
Contact: Director Gorkhmaz Guranov

Baku Choreography School
Website:
Phone: 124 957 807
Address: 54, Bul-Bul Avenue 1014, AZ
Country: Azerbaijan
Type: Ballet and Dance Company
Contact: Director t.b.a. t.b.a

Social Media: www.facebook.com/pages/Baku-Chore-ographic-S

Ballet Company of the Azerbaijan State Academic Opera and Ballet
Website:
Phone: 124 931 651
Address: 8, 28 May str. 1000, AZ
Information: see also Opera
Country: Azerbaijan
Type: Ballet and Dance Company
Contact: ballet master Yulana Alikishi-zade

Dance Ensemble of Khazar University
Website:
Email: contact@khazar.org
Phone: 124 989 379
Address: 11 Mashati str., AZ
Country: Azerbaijan
Type: Ballet and Dance Company

Folk Dance and Vocal group 'Sisters'
Website:
Phone: 506 479 718
Address: Separadi village in Lenkaran area, AZ
Country: Azerbaijan
Type: Ballet and Dance Company
Contact: Director Mammadov Farhad Qulam oglu

BRAZIL

Deborah Colker Dance
Website: www.ciadeborahcolker.com.br/
Email: je@ciadeborahcolker.com.br
Phone: 213 806 0650
Address: Rua Benjamin Constant, 30, Gloria, BR
Information: The embryo of what would be Companhia de Dança Deborah Colker was born in 1993, in the dance halls of Casa do Minho in Rio de Janeiro, Brazil, where Deborah used to teach; a year later the company made its debut at the Globo em Movimento festival at Rio's Municipal Theatre, in a double bill with Momix Dance Group; the company quickly earned an official sponsorship from the Brazilian State Oil Company, Petrobras, which has allowed it to invest in soaring flights of creation and establish a strong reputation in the world of dance
Country: Brazil
Type: Ballet and Dance Company

CANADA

Across Oceans Arts
Website: https:// www.acrossoceans.org
Email: info@acrossoceans.org
Address: Toronto Canada
Information: AcrossOceansArts facilitates platforms for creation & exchange of perspectives investigating the Art & Community of Collaboration, believing all art exPression is inherently collaborative & somatic between individuals & communities, whether formal events or casual get-togethers. Local & international programs include live performance, 2D & 3D exhibits, screenings, public forums, workshops, advanced training & research. For all people, across forms, generations, backgrounds, experiences.

Country: Canada
Type: Ballet and Dance Company
Contact: Artistic Director Maxine Heppner
Email: ia@acrossoceans.org
Social Media: https:// www.facebook.com/AcrossOceansArts https://twitter.com/AcrossOceansArt

Alberta Ballet
Website: www.albertaballet.com
Email: info@albertaballet.com
Phone: 403 245 4222
Address: 141 18 Avenue SW, CA
Information: Alberta Ballet is Canada's second-largest ballet company, renowned around the world for its contemporary and classical repertoire.
Country: Canada
Type: Ballet and Dance Company
Contact: Chair Alfred Sorensen
Director Marco Simonelli
Associate Artistic Director Christopher Anderson
Artistic Director Jean Grand-Maître
Executive Director Chris George
Social Media: @albertaballet
Touring Countries: Italy, USA, UK
Venues: Southern Alberta Jubilee Aud., Calgary 2350; Northern Alberta Jubilee Aud., Edmonton 2350

Atlantic Ballet Atlantique Canada
Website: www.atlanticballet.ca/en/home/
Email: info@atlanticballet.ca
Phone: 506 383 5951
Address: 68 Highfield Street, Suite 200, CA
Information: One of Canada's most exciting ballet companies, and based in Moncton, New Brunswick, Atlantic Ballet Theatre of Canada tours nationally and internationally
Country: Canada

Type: Ballet and Dance Company
Contact: chief Executive officer Susan Chalmers Gauvin
Email: susan@atlanticballet.ca
founding Artistic Director and choreographer Igor Dobrovolski
Email: igor@atlanticballet.ca
operations and community relations Manager Louis Philippe Dionne
Email: louis@atlanticballet.ca
Social Media: @AtlanticBallet www.facebook.com/AtlanticBalletAtlantique/
Touring Countries: Europe

Ballet BC
Website: www.balletbc.com
Email: info@balletbc.com
Phone: 604 732 5003
Address: 6th floor, 677 Davie Street, CA
Information: internationally acclaimed collaborative and interactive contemporary ballet company that is a leader and resource in the research, creation, Production, presentation and education of contemporary ballet. 15 select dancer
Country: Canada
Type: Ballet and Dance Company
Contact: Artistic Director Emily Molnar
office coordinator Pedro Peters
Email: officecoord@balletbc.com
Artistic administrator Francesca Fung
Email: Artisticadmin@balletbc.com
Executive Director John Clark
Email: ExecutiveDirector@balletbc.com
Social Media: @BalletBC www.facebook.com/pages/Ballet-BC
Touring Countries: USA
Venues: Queen Elizabeth Theatre

Canada's Royal Winnipeg Ballet
Website: www.rwb.org
Email: customerservice@rwb.org
Phone: 204 956 0183
Address: 380 Graham Avenue, CA
Information: The Royal Winnipeg Ballet enriches the human experience by teaching, creating and performing outstanding dance. Versatility, technical excellence and a captivating style are the trademarks of Canada's Royal Winnipeg Ballet, qualities that have garnered both critical and audience acclaim. Founded in 1939 by Gweneth Lloyd and Betty Farrally, the Royal Winnipeg Ballet holds the double distinction of being Canada's premiere ballet company and the longest continuously operating ballet company in North America. In 1953, the Company received its royal title, the first granted under the reign of Queen Elizabeth II. Member of ISPA
Country: Canada
Type: Ballet and Dance Company
Contact: Executive Artistic Director André Lewis
Director of company operations Christopher Turyk
Manager Isabelle Ly
administrative coordinator Nicki Kirton
Social Media: @RWBallet www.facebook.com/RWBallet
Touring Countries: USA
Venues: Manitoba Centennial Concert Hall 2100

Canadian Opera Company
Website: www.coc.ca
Email: info@coc.ca
Phone: 416 363 8231
Address: 145 Queen. St. W., CA
Information: Based in Toronto, the Canadian Opera Company is the largest Producer of opera in Canada and one of the largest in North America. The company enjoys an international reputation for Artistic excellence and creative innovation.
Country: Canada
Type: Ballet and Dance Company
Contact: General Director Alexander Neef
Managing Director Robert Lamb
Chair Justin Linden
Director Yael Woodward Amarel
Social Media: @CanadianOpera www.facebook.com/canadianoperacompany
Annual Performances: 65
Venues: Four Seasons Centre for the Performing Arts 2130 (see Venues)

Cirque Eloize
Website: www.cirque-eloize.com
Email: eloize@cirque-eloize.com
Phone: 514 596 3838
Address: DALHOUSIE STATION, 417, rue Berri, CA
Information: A driving force in the circus art reinvention movement, Cirque Éloize has been creating award-winning entertainment content for nearly 25 years and ranks among the world's leading contemporary circuses. Cirque Éloize has taken part in numerous prestigious international festivals and has seduced both New York's Broadway and London's West End. Its Productions are crafted for a wide range of audiences and have been embraced by over fifty cultures. Member of ISPA
Country: Canada
Type: Ballet and Dance Company

Contact: President and chief creative officer Jeannot

Painchaud
Artistic Director Émilie Émiroglou
Social Media: @cirque_eloize www.facebook.com/CirqueEloize
Touring Countries: China, Hong Kong, Japan, Lebanon, Mexico, Angola, Colombia

Co. ERASGA
Website: www.companyerasgadance.ca
Email: info@companyerasgadance.ca
Phone: 604 687 6185
Address: 1408-207 West Hastings Street, CA
Information: This is a group who specialise in creating specific dances based on the city of Toronto as well as international projects
Country: Canada
Type: Ballet and Dance Company
Contact: Artistic Director Alvin Erasga Tolentino
Social Media: @coERASGA www.facebook.com/Co.ERASGA
Touring Countries: Philippines. USA, Belgium, France, Croatia, Dominican Republic, Switzerland and Japan
Venues: medium to large venues capacity of 100-1000 seats

Compagnie Marie Chouinard
Website: www.mariechouinard.com
Email: info@mariechouinard.com
Phone: 514 843 9036
Address: Compagnie Marie Chouinard, Espace Marie Chouinard, 4499 av. de l'esplanade, CA
Information: The international reputation of the Compagnie Marie Chouinard is the result of twenty-eight years of work by Montreal artist Marie Chouinard. Now a fixture on the world's major stages and festivals, the company has its roots in Chouinard's first creation in 1978, the solo Crystallization. This piece, which immediately earned her a reputation for originality, was followed by over fifty choreographic Productions, action-performances, vocal works, installations and films, in which she refined her lifelong interest in formal research and the human body. From 1978 to 1990, Marie Chouinard performed alone throughout the world, developing a personal language with a universal resonance.
Country: Canada
Type: Ballet and Dance Company
Contact: Artistic and Executive Director Marie Chouinard
Managing Director Julie Beaudoin
Email: jbeaudoin@mariechouinard.com
Producer and technical Director Jimmy Lakatos
Email: jlakatos@mariechouinard.com
Social Media: @mariechouinard www.facebook.com/ciemariechouinard/
Touring Countries: Europe, Canada, USA, Latin America, Asia

dance OREMUS danse
Website: danCEOremusdanse.org
Email: pauljamesdwyer@yahoo.ca
Phone: 613 756 3284
Address: 240 Dovercourt Road, CA
Information: Isadora Duncan technique & early music specialises in French repertoire (operatic, keyboard & liturgical) Productions, master Classes, and residency, as well as children's programmes. It also operates a Duncan Integrated Arts Studio & School in Combermere ON (Address: P) Box 322 Combermere ON K0J1L0 Canada)
Country: Canada
Type: Ballet and Dance Company
Contact: Artistic Director/dancer Paul-James Dwyer
Email: pauljamesdwyer@yahoo.ca
General Manager Peter Stadnyk
Europe & Japan, South America

Annual Performances: 6
Venues: Jane Mallett Theatre, Massey Hall, Glenn Gould Studio, George Weston Recital Hall

Dancemakers
Website: www.dancemakers.org
Email: info@dancemakers.org
Phone: 416 367 1800
Address: 15 Case Goods Lane, Studio 301, CA
Information: Dancemakers invites artists and members of the public to engage in dance
Country: Canada
Type: Ballet and Dance Company
Contact: General Manager Frances Shakov
Email: frances@dancemakers.org
finance Chair Chelsea Omel
Social Media: @DancemakersTO www.facebook.com/dancemakersTO
Annual Performances: 12
Venues: The Centre for Creation

Daniel Léveillé nouvelle danse
Website: www.danielleveilledanse.org
Email: info@danielleveilledanse.org
Phone: 514 504 8715
Address: bureau 302, 2025, rue Parthenais, CA
Information: Daniel Léveillé Danse supports the creation, Production and distribution of creative projects that are at the forefront of dance and performing arts.
Country: Canada

Type: Ballet and Dance Company
Contact: General Manager Marie-Andrée Gougeon
Email: dg@danielleveilledanse.org
Artistic Director Daniel Léveillé
communication Marie-Ève Trahan
Email: com@danielleveilledanse.org
Social Media: @DLDanse www.facebook.com/danielleve-eilledanse/
Touring Countries: Europe
Number of Performers: 5

Danny Grossman Dance Company
Website: www.dannygrossman.com
Email: info@dannygrossman.com
Phone: 416 469 0917
Address: PO Box 367, 100 King Street West, CA
Information: The Danny Grossman Dance Company was founded in Toronto in 1977 by American-born dancer and choreographer Danny GROSSMAN as a platform for his own choreography. In total, the company has presented 36 works by Grossman, from solos to large ensemble pieces. Like many choreographers in the first phase of their creative career, Grossman produced a steady stream of successful works.
Country: Canada
Type: Ballet and Dance Company
Contact: Managing Director Helen Chapman
Email: christina@dannygrossman.com
Artistic Director Danny Grossman
Touring Countries: Europe, Israel, South America, USA
Venues: Premiere Dance Theatre 450

Danse Danse
Website: www.dansedanse.net
Email: info@dansedanse.net
Phone: 514 848 0623
Address: 2, Sainte-Catherine St. East, Suite 200, CA
Information: Since its inception in 1998, Danse Danse has been actively involved in presenting and promoting contemporary dance; both new dance pieces and works from the repertoire. Danse Danse is a dynamic showcase for outstanding performances by dance professionals from here and abroad.
Country: Canada
Type: Ballet and Dance Company
Contact: Artistic and Executive Director Pierre Des Marais
Email: pierre@dansedanse.ca
Director of development and programming Caroline Ohrt
Email: caroline@dansedanse.ca
Director of accounting and Administration Kim Hoang
Email: kim@dansedanse.ca
President Louis-François Hogue
Social Media: www.facebook.com/DanseDanseMontreal
Touring Countries: USA, Europe
Annual Performances: 30
Venues: Thtre Maisonneuve

David Pressault Danse
Website: www.davidPressaultdanse.com
Email: davidPressault@gmail.com
Phone: 514 524 4684
Address: 4301, Chapleau, CA
Information: A dance of flesh, is among the characteristic themes that the company explores. It also delves into themes such as myths, the feminine universe, romantic relationships and the desire for evolution and transformation of Man. Dance of alchemy, dance of states, the approach of David Pressault aims to create strong images using a search for metaphors and rich movements. The choreographer pays particular attention to how to reach and reach his audience.
Country: Canada
Type: Ballet and Dance Company
Contact: Artistic Director David Pressault
Social Media: www.facebook.com/david.Pressault
Touring Countries: Belgium, Italy

Decidedly Jazz Danceworks
Website: www.decidedlyjazz.com
Email: djd@decidedlyjazz.com
Phone: 403 245 3533
Address: 111 12 Avenue S.E., CA
Information: Rooted in the history of jazz dance and music, DJD is constantly innovating and evolving this art form. DJD, a registered charity, is a professional dance company that creates original performances; at least one per year with live music. DJD also offers professional training to those wishing to specialize in jazz dance, outreach programs that educate the community about the history and importance of jazz in North American culture, and is Calgary's largest recreational dance school.
Country: Canada
Type: Ballet and Dance Company
Contact: Executive Director Kathi Sundstrom
Email: ksundstrom@decidedlyjazz.com
founder in residence Vicki Adams Willis
Email: vwillis@decidedlyjazz.com
Artistic Director Kimberley Cooper
Email: kcooper@decidedlyjazz.com
technical Director Cameron Clowe
Email: cclowe@decidedlyjazz.com
Social Media: @DecidedlyJazz www.facebook.com/

Destins Croises – Dance
Website: www.destins-croises.com
Email: info@destins-croises.com
Phone: 514 764 3573
Address: 2450, rue Workman – Centre culturel Georges Vanier, bureau 2.120, CA
Information: The whole philosophy of the company resides in its name, "Destins Croisés" – meaning crossed fates in French. It finds its essence both in the meaning of the term and in its choreographer's personal story. Founded in 2003 by French-Moroccan-Canadian dancer and choreographer Ismaël Mouaraki, DC is a Montreal-based dance company that brings together urban and contemporary dances with different mediums of creative languages, such as slam, circus, video or theatre in intense, physical and abstract choreographic pieces where everyone, every art form, every approach has a place.
Country: Canada
Type: Ballet and Dance Company
Contact: General and Artistic Director Ismael Mouaraki administrative Director Lydie Revez
Email: Administration@destins-croises.com
communications Manager Camille Kersébet
Email: communications@destins-croises.com
Social Media: @Destins_Croises www.facebook.com/CompagnieDestinsCroises

Fortier Danse-Création
Website: www.fortier-danse.com
Email: com@fortier-danse.com
Phone: 514 529 8158
Address: 2022, Sherbrooke East, Office 301, CA
Information: Fortier Danse-Création is a contemporary dance company founded in 1981, whose primary mandate is to support the creation and Production of choreographic works by Paul-André Fortier
Country: Canada
Type: Ballet and Dance Company
Contact: Artistic Director Paul-André Fortier
General Manager Gilles Savary
Email: admin@fortier-danse.com
communications coordinator and General Manager's assistant Julie Bariteau
Email: diffusion@fortier-danse.com
Social Media: @FortierDanse www.facebook.com/fortier.dansecreation
Touring Countries: Europe, USA

Free Flow Dance Company
Website: www.freeflowdance.com
Email: freeflowdance@hotmail.com
Phone: 306 665 5998
Address: 224 25th Street West, CA
Information: Free Flow is a leading edge Canadian Dance Company known for its innovative and risk-taking modern choreography. The driving philosophy behind the company's projects is that dance is fun and should be accessible to people of all ages and interests.
Country: Canada
Type: Ballet and Dance Company
Contact: Artistic Director Jackie Latendresse
Email: freeflowdance@hotmail.com
Annual Performances: 20

Go-On Productions / Nadine Thouin
Website: www.go-on.ca
Email: info@go-on.ca
Phone: 418 507 1947
Address: CA
Information: General and Artistic Director of Go-On Productions Inc, internationally acclaimed dancer, choreographer, stage and Production Director, Nadine Thouin is renowned for her boldness and creativity. Her prodigious career spans over 25 years, encompassing 27 Productions performed in more than 20 countries and 40 cities around the globe.
Country: Canada
Type: Ballet and Dance Company
Contact: Artistic Director & choreographer Nadine Thouin
Email: info@go-on.ca
Touring Countries: world

José Navas/Compagnie Flak
Website: www.flak.org
Email: info@flak.org
Phone: 514 876 1313
Address: 460, rue Sainte-Catherine Ouest, Suite 411, CA
Information: José Navas/Compagnie Flak is a contemporary dance company based in Montreal, Canada under the direction of Venezuelan born choreographer José Navas
Country: Canada
Type: Ballet and Dance Company
Contact: General & Artistic Director José Navas
Director of development Adrien Bussy
Email: adrien@flak.org
communications coordinator Loriane Takla
Email: loriane@flak.org
administrative assistant François Richard
Email: correspondance@flak.org
Social Media: @_JoseNavas www.facebook.com/JoseNavas.CompagnieFlak

Kaeja d'Dance
Website: www.kaeja.org
Email: kaeja@kaeja.org
Phone: 416 516 6030
Address: 734 Euclid Avenue, CA
Information: Kaeja d'Dance is an award-winning contemporary dance company known for innovation, choreography, performance, outreach, site-specific work ("Best Site Specific Work" Globe and Mail), and groundbreaking community engagement projects ("I Love Dance Community Award" Canadian Dance Assembly).They thrive on developing professional performance platforms, collaborations with partners, peers and performers of all ages and abilities, while aiming to bridge the gap between professional artists and everyday people.
Country: Canada
Type: Ballet and Dance Company
Contact: Artistic Director Karen Kaeja
Artistic Director Allen Kaeja
Email: allen@kaeja.org
Managing Director Yolanda Ferrato
Email: kaeja@kaeja.org
Social Media: @KaejadDance www.facebook.com/KaejadDance
Touring Countries: USA, UK, Japan, Israel, Singapore, Portugal, Mexico, Sweden, Spain, India, Venezuela, Thailand
Venues: Harbourfront Centre Theatre, Toronto

Kaha:wi Dance Theatre
Website: www.kahawidance.org
Email: info@kahawidance.org
Phone: 416 923 7373
Address: 720 Bathurst St, Suite 307, CA
Information: This dance company explores the intersection of Indigenous and new dance performance, to create and present theatrical Productions, and to educate and engage artists, audiences and diverse communities through Indigenous performing arts encompassing disciplines of music, storytelling, theatre and design.
Country: Canada
Type: Ballet and Dance Company
Contact: General Manager Cynthia Lickers-Sage
Email: cynthia@kahawidance.org
Artistic Director Santee Smith
Email: santee@kahawidance.org
Social Media: @kahawi www.facebook.com/pages/Kaha-wi-Dance-Theatre

Kala Nidhi Fine Arts Ltd
Website: www.kalanidhifinearts.org
Email: kalanidhi@kalanidhifinearts.org
Phone: 416 229 0369
Address: 295 Maple Hurst Avenue, CA
Information: Kala Nidhi Fine Arts is committed to nurturing Indian Dance by supporting the growth and creativity of Indian Dance Artists and to creating a larger awareness of traditional and contemporary Indian dance in Canada
Country: Canada
Type: Ballet and Dance Company
Contact: Artistic Director/curator Sudha Thakkar Khandwani
Social Media: www.facebook.com/Kalanidhi-Fine-Arts-of-Canada-1416904681885013
Venues: Markham Theatre, Fleck Dance Theatre

Kokoro Dance
Website: www.kokoro.ca
Email: jayh@kokoro.ca
Phone: 604 662 7441
Address: 250 – 111 Hastings St W, CA
Information: Kokoro Dance Theatre Society was incorporated as a non-profit society in Vancouver, British Columbia on July 31, 1986. Its mandate is to re-define the meaning of Canadian culture through teaching, producing and performing new dance theatre with an emphasis on multi-disciplinary collaboration and cross-cultural exploration.
Country: Canada
Type: Ballet and Dance Company
Contact: Artistic Director Barbara Bourget
Executive Director Jay Hirabayashi
lighting Director Gerald King
Social Media: @kokorodance www.facebook.com/kokorodance
Touring Countries: Canada, United States, Germany, The Netherlands, Poland
Venues: proscenium stage, site specific, alternate venues, schools

La La La Human Steps
Website: www.lalalahumansteps.com
Email: info@lalalahumansteps.com
Phone: 514 277 0862
Address: 5655 Avenue du parc, Bureau 206, CA
Information: La La La Human Steps was a Québécois contemporary dance group in Canada, active between 1980 and 2015, known for its energetic, acrobatic style involving fast-paced and athletic physical contact. Its signature move was the barrel jump, which resembled a horizontal pirouette in the air.
Country: Canada
Type: Ballet and Dance Company

Contact: communication Director Laura Bayle
Email: communications@lalalahumansteps.com
Executive Director Peter Mc Farlane
Email: pmcfarlane@lalalahumansteps.com
Artistic Director Edouard Lock
Email: elock@lalalahumansteps.com
administrative Director Claudine Ballaux Veillette
Touring Countries: Germany, Serbia, Switzerland
Venues: 1000 to 3000

Le Carré-des-Lombes
Website: www.lecarredeslombes.com
Email: tessagoulet@lecarredeslombes.com
Phone: 514 287 9415
Address: 2022, Sherbrooke Street, local 401, CA
Country: Canada
Type: Ballet and Dance Company
Contact: assistant coordinator Céline Perey
Email: Production@lecarredeslombes.com
Executive Director Tessa Goulet
Email: tessagoulet@lecarredeslombes.com
Artistic Director Daniele Desnoyers
Email: danieledesnoyers@lecarredeslombes.com
Social Media: www.facebook.com/pages/Le-Carré-des-Lombes
Touring Countries: Europe

Les Ballets Jazz de Montréal – BJM Danse Montréal
Website: www.bjmdanse.ca
Email: info@bjmdanse.ca
Phone: 514 982 6771
Address: 1210, Sherbrooke E. Street, CA
Information: an internationally renowned repertory company, BJM has continued to grow with all the energy and spirit of exploration for which it has been known since its birth in 1972. Renowned for its radiant, exPressive style, BJM presents dance that is based on classical technique while promoting exceptional voices of contemporary dance.
Country: Canada
Type: Ballet and Dance Company
Contact: Artistic Director Louis Robitaille
Email: lrobitaille@bjmdanse.ca
Artistic coordinator Céline Cassone
Email: cassone@bjmdanse.ca
administrative Director Alexandre Colpron
Email: Administration@bjmdanse.ca
Production Director Gildas Percevault
Email: dt@bjmdanse.ca
Social Media: @BJMDANSE www.facebook.com/LESBAL-LETSJAZZDEMONTREAL
Touring Countries: USA
Venues: touring company international venues

Les Grands Ballets Canadiens de Montréal
Website: www.grandsballets.com
Email: info@grandsballets.com
Phone: 514 849 8681
Address: 4816 rue Rivard, CA
Information: Les Grands Ballets Canadiens de Montréal has become a world-renowned creation, Production and performance company, dedicated to the development of ballet in all its forms, while remaining faithful to the spirit of classical technique. It connects with audiences at home and abroad, spurring discovery, stirring emotion, stimulating the imagination and conveying the passion for dance.
Country: Canada
Type: Ballet and Dance Company
Contact: Artistic Director Ivan Cavallari
Director of touring and guest companies Corinne Jozsef
Director of Marketing & communications
Anna Bedic
President Constance Pathy
Social Media: @GrandsBallets www.facebook.com/lesgrandsballets
Touring Countries: USA, Europe
Venues: Salle Wilfrid-Pelletier, Place des Arts 2982; Th

Les Sortilèges
Website: www.lessortileges.com
Email: info@lessortileges.com
Phone: 514 522 2257
Address: 5563 rue Fullum, Suite 210, CA
Information: According to its charter, the Charms mission is to preserve, promote, transmit and radiate at home and abroad, our intangible cultural heritage and especially folk dance.
Country: Canada
Type: Ballet and Dance Company
Contact: Artistic and assistant coach Renata Skultetyova
Artistic/General Director Jocelyn Parent
Social Media: @LesSortileges www.facebook.com/lessortileges
Touring Countries: USA

Louise Bédard Danse Inc.
Website: www.lbdanse.org
Email: infos@lbdanse.org
Phone: 514 982 4580
Address: 2011 Sherbrooke Street East, # 300, CA
Information: Louise Bédard Danse was founded in 1990 and has been led by choreographer and dancer Louise

Bédard
Country: Canada
Type: Ballet and Dance Company
Contact: Artistic Director Louise Bedard
Administration Lise Tremblay
Social Media: @lbdanse www.facebook.com/lbdanse/
Venues: Sony Centre for the Performing Arts

Lynda Gaudreau/Compagnie De Brune
Website: www.lyndagaudreau.com
Email: debrune@videotron.ca
Phone: 514 284 9334
Address: PO Box 25, Station Place du Parc, CA
Information: Lynda Gaudreau / Compagnie De Brune is a contemporary dance company whose work incorporates elements from sound, video, light and architecture in its performances
Country: Canada
Type: Ballet and Dance Company
Contact: assistant to the Artistic Director Pierre Tanguay
Artistic Director Lynda Gaudreau
Email: debrune@videotron.ca
Social Media: www.facebook.com/Compagnie-De-Brune-Lynda-Gaudreau-159582764946
Venues: De Studio

Made in BC Dance on Tour
Website: www.madeinbc.org
Email: jane@madeinbc.org
Phone: 604 893 8830
Address: 303 – 268 Keefer Street, CA
Information: Made in BC Dance on Tour is a non-profit industry association dedicated to building a culture for dance throughout the province of British Columbia. The programs create opportunities for people from all over BC to learn about the arts, exPress themselves creatively and celebrate a shared humanity through dance performance and activities. Member of ISPA
Country: Canada
Type: Ballet and Dance Company
Contact: General adminstration Julie Mamias
Email: jm@madeinbc.org
program Manager Julie Lebel
Email: julie@madeinbc.org
Executive Director Jane Gabriels
Email: jane@madeinbc.org

Margie Gillis Dance Foundation
Website: www.margiegillis.org
Email: info@margiegillis.org
Phone: 514 845 3115
Address: 1908 Panet Street, Suite 304, CA
Information: Internationally acclaimed solo modern dancer and choreographer Margie Gillis has been creating original works for over forty years. Her repertoire includes more than one hundred creations, including her signature solos, as well as duets and group pieces. She also gives lectures on dance and the role of art in society and with her unique approach of "Dancing from the Inside Out", she teaches her art form to professionals and aficionados. She also mentors fellow artists and new dancers alike. Margie Gillis' masterful interpretation of the different facets of the human soul has won her loyal audiences over the years. Unwaveringly, she continues to develop her craft through experimenting, teaching and creating
Country: Canada
Type: Ballet and Dance Company
Contact: President Richard Cyr
vice President Margie Gillis
General Manager Linda Foy
Email: linda@margiegillis.org
Social Media: @fdmargiegillis www.facebook.com/fdmargiegillis
Touring Countries: Asia, India, Europe and the Middle East

Mascall Dance International
Website: www.mascalldance.ca
Email: admin@mascalldance.ca
Address: 1130 Jervis Street, CA
Information: experimental company involving many different and diverse artists; educational programs for young audiences available
Country: Canada
Type: Ballet and Dance Company
Contact: Artistic Director Jennifer Mascall
Social Media: www.facebook.com/Mascall.Dance

Menaka Thakkar Dance Company
Website: www.menakathakkardance.org
Email: admin@menakathakkardance.org
Phone: 905 763 6083
Address: 293 Maplehurst Avenue, CA
Information: Touring Indian dance company.
Country: Canada
Type: Ballet and Dance Company
Contact: Artistic Director Menaka Thakkar
Email: admin@menakathakkardance.org
touring Manager Alex Gangurean
Email: touring@menakathakkardance.org
Touring Countries: United Kingdom

Montréal Danse
Website: www.montrealdanse.com
Email: questions@montrealdanse.com
Phone: 514 871 4005
Address: 372 Rue Ste – Catherine Ouest, bureau 109, CA
Country: Canada
Type: Ballet and Dance Company
Contact: Artistic Director Kathy Casey
Email: artistique@montrealdanse.com
administrative Manager Claire Ranger
Email: Administration@montrealdanse.com
tour Manager Denis Bergerand
technical Director Karine Gauthier
Email: technique@montrealdanse.com
Social Media: @MontrealDanse www.facebook.com/pages/Montréal-Danse
Touring Countries: Europe (France), Canada

National Ballet of Canada
Website: www.national.ballet.ca
Email: info@national.ballet.ca
Phone: 416 345 9595
Address: The Walter Carsen Centre for The National Ballet of Canada, 470 Queens Quay West, CA
Information: it is the only Canadian ballet company to present a full range of traditional full-length classics
Country: Canada
Type: Ballet and Dance Company
Contact: Director of communications Julia Drake
Artistic Director Karen Kain
Executive Director Kevin Garland
senior public relations Manager Catherine Chang
Email: cchang@national.ballet.ca
publicity coordinator Christina McGrath
Email: cmcgrath@national.ballet.ca
music Director and principal conductor David Briskin
Social Media: @nationalballet www.facebook.com/nationalballet
Venues: Four Seasons Centre for the Performing Arts

Newton Moraes Dance Theatre
Website: www.newtonmoraes.com
Email: newtonmoraes@hotmail.com
Address: 537 Jones Avenue, CA
Information: Newton Moraes Dance Theatre is a company dedicated to the creation, performance and Production of contemporary dance works to explore, maintain and develop the links between the arts of Canada and Latin America through the Artistic vision and knowledge of its founder and Artistic Director: Newton Moraes
Country: Canada
Type: Ballet and Dance Company
Contact: Artistic Director Newton Moraes
Email: newtonmoraes@hotmail.com
tour Manager Robert Shirley
assistant Director Tatiana Ramos
Social Media: @newtondance www.facebook.com/NewtonMoraesDanceTheatre
Touring Countries: Europe, South America
Number of Performers: 10

Nu! Canada's Royal Winnipeg Ballet
Website: www.rwb.org
Email: customerservice@rwb.org
Phone: 204 956 0183
Address: 380 Graham Avenue, CA
Information: teaching, creating and performing outstanding dance. Member of ISPA.
Country: Canada
Type: Ballet and Dance Company
Contact: music Director & conductor
Tadeusz Biernacki
Email: TBiernacki@rwb.org
Director of Marketing and communications Larah Luna
Email: lluna@rwb.org
Artistic Director André Lewis
Director of company relations Christopher Turyk
Email: cturyk@rwb.org

O Vertigo
Website: www.overtigo.com
Email: info@overtigo.com
Phone: 514 251 9177
Address: 175 Sainte Catherine Street West, CA
Information: O Vertigo has been dedicated to dance creation, research, and training, as well as the development of the discipline in all its aspects. With the opening of the Creation Centre (CCOV), the company has reaffirmed its mission and broadened its activities
Country: Canada
Type: Ballet and Dance Company
Contact: General Director Pascale Correia
Email: pascale.correia@overtigo.com
administrative Director Jacques Vecerina
Email: jacques.vecerina@overtigo.com
communication assistant Melissa Basora
Email: melissa.basora@overtigo.com
Artistic Director Ginette Laurin
Email: info@overtigo.com
Social Media: www.facebook.com/pages/O-Vertigo
Touring Countries: France, Canada, United States, Mexico, Brazil, Argentina, United Kingdom, Germany, Holland, Belgium, Switzerland, Italy, Austria. Japan, China, etc.
Venues: Creation Centre (CCOV)

RUBBERBAND

MONTREAL, CANADA — SINCE 2002

Artistic director Victor Quijada combines
spontaneous, risky and fearless
hip-hop culture with the choreographic
sophistication of contemporary dance.

RBDG.CA

EVER SO SLIGHTLY

Ten dancers and two live musicians – for a large stage

AGENTS

QUEBEC — CANADA

Agence Station Bleue
Élisabeth Comtois
e.comtois@stationbleue.com

USA

Pentacle
Sandy Garcia
sandyg@pentacle.org

EUROPE (CH, AT, DE, NL, BE, LUX)

Norddeutsche Konzertdirektion
Franziska Grevesmühl-v. Marcard
info@grevesmuehl.de

Photo: Marie-Noële Pilon

Ontario Ballet Theatre
Website: www.ontarioballettheatre.com/
Email: tara@ontarioballettheatre.com
Phone: 416 656 9568
Address: 1133 St Clair Avenue West, CA
Information: the primary objectives of the Ontario Ballet Theatre is to take ballet to people everywhere – to attract, introduce and educate audiences
Country: Canada
Type: Ballet and Dance Company
Contact: Director of tour & development Tara Roberts
Email: tara@ontarioballettheatre.com
Touring Countries: Canada, USA
Venues: Premiere Dance Theatre 500

Productions Cas Public
Website: www.caspublic.com
Email: info@caspublic.com
Phone: 514 390 1110
Address: 3505 Durocher, CA
Country: Canada
Type: Ballet and Dance Company
Contact: administrative Director Lydie Revez
Email: Administration@caspublic.com
Artistic Director Hélène Blackburn
Email: artistique@caspublic.com
Touring Countries: Canada, Allemagne, France

Red Sky
Website: www.redskyperformance.com
Email: info@redskyperformance.com
Phone: 416 585 9969
Address: 401 Richmond Street, West Suite 420, CA
Information: internationally renowned for its artistry and innovation, Red Sky is Canada's leading company of world indigenous performance in dance, theatre and music. Member of ISPA
Country: Canada
Type: Ballet and Dance Company
Contact: Artistic Director Sandra Laronde Managing Director Jackie McAlpine
rehearsal Director Carlos Rivera
Social Media: @Redskyconnect www.facebook.com/redskyperformance
Touring Countries: USA, Canada, Iceland, Australia, Switzerland, China, Mongolia

Red Sky Performance
Website: www.redskyperformance.com/
Email: info@redskyperformance.com
Phone: 416 585 9969
Address: 401 Richmond Street West, Suite 420, CA
Information: Internationally renowned for its artistry and innovation, Red Sky is Canada's leading company of world Indigenous performance in dance, theatre and music. Member of ISPA
Country: Canada
Type: Ballet and Dance Company
Contact: Executive & Artistic Director Sandra Laronde
Managing Director Catherine Baldwin
Social Media: @Redskyconnect www.facebook.com/redskyperformance

RUBBERBAND
Website: https://rbdg.ca/en/
Email: info@rbdg.ca
Phone: 514 725 7868
Address: 460, rue Sainte-Catherine Ouest, bureau 726
Information: RUBBERBAND is an organization dedicated to creation and Production with the mission of supporting the research of choreographer Victor Quijada, disseminating his works, and ensuring the transmission and impact of his practice.
RUBBERBAND wishes to be recognized worldwide for its innovation, its significant contribution in dance, and for its role in the development of a new style inspired by break, classical ballet, and dance theatre.
Country: Canada
Type: Ballet and Dance Company
Contact: Artistic Director Victor Quijada
administrative Director Fannie Bellefeuille
Email: fannie@rubberbandance.com
communications officer Erika Malot
Email: communications@rbdg.ca
Social Media: @RUBBERBANDance www.facebook.com/rubberbandance https:// www.instagram.com/rubber-bandance/

RUBBERBANDDance Group
Website: www.rubberbandance.com
Email: info@rubberbandance.com
Phone: 514 725 7868
Address: 940 Rue Sainte-Marguerite Street, CA
Information: RUBBERBANDance Group is a Montreal-based company exploring the fusion of contemporary ballet and urban dance. Member of ISPA
Country: Canada
Type: Ballet and Dance Company
Contact: Artistic Director Victor Quijada
Artistic Director Anne Plamondon
administrative Director Fannie Bellefeuille

Email: fannie@rubberbandance.com
tour Manager Brent Belsher
Email: brent@belshers.ca
Social Media: @RUBBERBANDance www.facebook.com/rubberbandance
Touring Countries: Canada, USA, UK
Number of Performers: 4
Venues: The Cultch; Yukon Art Centre; The Port Theatre; Island Arts Centre Society and others

Ruth Cansfield Dance
Email: info@ruthcansfield.com
Phone: 204 284 5810
Address: 525 Beresford Ave, CA
Country: Canada
Type: Ballet and Dance Company
Contact: Artistic Director Ruth Cansfield
Touring Countries: United States

Sinha Danse
Website: www.sinhadanse.com
Email: info@sinhadanse.com
Address: 4430 Parthenais, CA
Information: His work merges classical Indian dance and contemporary dance, martial arts, new technologies, digital performance, video and Bharata Natyam, a dance from south India.
Country: Canada
Type: Ballet and Dance Company
Contact: Artistic and General Director Roger Sinha
Email: roger@sinhadanse.com
Marketing Director Adrien Bussy
Email: adrien@sinhadanse.com
vice-President Johane Bergeron
administrative agent Géraldine Fricard
Email: geraldine@diagramme.org
Social Media: @SinhaDanse http:// www.facebook.com/pages/Sinha-Danse
Venues: Segal Centre

Skindivers Dance
Email: skindiversdance@gmail.com
Address: CA
Information: skindivers is a contemporary dance company based in Toronto, Ontario, performing choreographies by Hanna Kent
Country: Canada
Type: Ballet and Dance Company
Contact: Artistic Director Hanna Kent
Social Media: @skindiversdance

Sylvain Émard Danse
Website: www.sylvainemard.com
Email: communication@sylvainemard.com
Address: 2022 rue Sherbrooke Est 0400, CA
Country: Canada
Type: Ballet and Dance Company
Contact: Artistic Director & choreographer Sylvain Emard
Director of development Maya Daoud
communications officer Véronique Beaudoin
Email: communications@sylvainemard.com
administrative agent Claire Piétin
Email: claire@diagramme.org
Social Media: @sylvainemard www.facebook.com/pages/Sylvain-%C3%89mard-Danse
Touring Countries: Mexique France Canada
Venues: l'Agora de la danse 250 and Usine C 472Montral, Espace culturel Beaumarchais France, Volcan du Havre France, Centre National des ArtsOttawa, Grand Thtre de Lorient France, Theatre Royal Glasgow Scotland, Theater Brycheiniog in the Wales

The Choreographic Marathon
Website: https:// www.choreographicmarathon.ca
Email: choreomarathon@acrossoceans.org
Address: Toronto/T'karonto
Information: For Movement Artists in All Forms of dance and movement arts> Creation & Development Exchange to advance process within an intentional community of similarly rigorous supportive and challenging movement artists over a 4 month program that includes ultra-intensive group gatherings, independent work and mentoring, led by Across Oceans Arts Maxine Heppner and a circle of world-renowned dance facilitators & mentors. Proposals received ongoing for annual program.
Country: Canada
Type: Ballet and Dance Company
Contact: Administration Christos Giotis
Email: choreomarathon@acrossoceans.org
Social Media: facebook.com/AcrossOceansArts

Toronto Dance Theatre
Website: www.tdt.org
Email: info@tdt.org
Phone: 416 967 1365
Address: 80 Winchester Street, CA
Information: Toronto Dance Theatre is one of Canada's contemporary dance companies. Founded in 1968 by Peter Randazzo, Patricia Beatty and David Earle, and under the Artistic direction of Christopher House since 1994, TDT has produced a lot of original Canadian choreography
Country: Canada

Type: Ballet and Dance Company
Contact: Artistic Director Christopher House Managing Director Andrea Vagianos
Email: andrea@tdt.org
Social Media: @TDTWinch www.facebook.com/torontodancetheatre
Number of Performers: 14
Venues: Fleck Dance Theatre 496, Winchester Street Theatre 115

TRIP dance company
Website: www.tripdance.com
Email: info@tripdance.com
Address: 28 Mortimer Place, CA
Country: Canada
Type: Ballet and Dance Company
Contact: General Manager Randy Joynt
Artistic Director Karen Kuzak

Van Grimde Corps Secrets
Website: www.vangrimdecorpssecrets.com
Email: info@vangrimdecorpssecrets.com
Address: 3680 Jeanne-Mance Street, Suite 420, CA
Country: Canada
Type: Ballet and Dance Company
Contact: General and Artistic Director Isabelle van Grimde
Email: ivangrimbe@gmail.com
administrative Director Louise Dubeau
Email: louise.vgcorpssecrets@gmail.com
communications Catherine Lavoie-Marcus
Email: catherine.vgcorpssecrets@gmail.com
Touring Countries: Canada, , Europe
Venues: Centennial Theatre, Lennoxville

Vinok Worldance
Website: www.vinok.ca
Email: vinok@vinok.ca
Phone: 780 454 3436
Address: Box 4867, CA
Information: Artistic Directors available for workshops, masterclasses; visiting address: 11727 Kingsway, Edmonton, AB T5G 3A1
Country: Canada
Type: Ballet and Dance Company
Contact: Artistic Director Leanne Koziak
Email: leanne@vinok.ca
Executive Director Al Rasko
Social Media: @VinokWorldance www.facebook.com/vinok.worldance
Venues: Arden Theatre, St Albert, Alberta 520; various others capacity more than 1000

Winnipeg's Contemporary Dancers
Website: www.winnipegscontemporarydancers.ca
Email: info@winnipegscontemporarydancers.ca
Phone: 204 452 0229
Address: 204-211 Bannatyne Avenue, CA
Information: WCD Studio Theatre for hire (see Venues)
Country: Canada
Type: Ballet and Dance Company
Contact: General Manager Cheryl Ashton
Email: wcd@mts.net
Artistic Director Brent Lott
Email: brent@winnipegscontemporarydancers.ca
Social Media: @WpgContemps www.facebook.com/WpgContemps
Venues: WCD Studio Theatre 100, Gas Station Theatre 235

CHINA

Beijing Dance Theater
Website: www.beijingdancetheater.org
Email: beijingcdt@gmail.com
Phone: 108 437 6100
Address: National Olympic Sports Center, Room 169-185, 1, Anding Road, Chaoyang District
Information: Founded in 2008, Beijing Dance Theater (BDT) is led by its choreographer Wang Yuanyuan together with visual artists Tan Shaoyuan and Hanjiang. It has collaborated with many internationally renowned dramatists, musicians and designers, enriching the international dance stages with its world-class Productions, each of which represents the highest level of Chinese contemporary dance
Country: China
Type: Ballet and Dance Company
Touring Countries: Serbia, Spain, Germany, France, Israel
Number of Performers: 15
Venues: Theater Im Pfalzbau, Tianqiao Theater, Stadthalle

Beijing Modern Dance Company
Website: www.beijingldtx.com
Email: admin@beijingldtx.com
Phone: 106 405 4842
Address: 16 Xiadianchangpo Village, Xidawang Road, Chaoyang District
Information: The birth of BeijingDance / LDTX (Lei Dong Tian Xia , literally translated as Thunder Rumbles Under Heaven) in September of 2005 not only caught widespread international attention, but also captured the imagination of many artists in China

Cheng Du Music and Dance Theatre
Website:
Address: Du Hu Chao Tang, 15 Zongfu Jie
Information: Is one of the professional performing arts groups, belonging to the national level professional performing arts groups. Including the National Symphony Orchestra, orchestra, chorus. The performance of the entity can be combined, complementary advantages. Company brings together a variety of Arts, expand many related functions; to attract a large number of concentrated ethnic art, inheriting the ancient Shu culture
Country: China
Type: Ballet and Dance Company

China Central Song and Dance Ensemble of Nationalities
Website:
Phone: 106 842 0022
Address: No. 19, Nan Da Jie, Zhong Guan Cun, Haidian District
Country: China
Type: Ballet and Dance Company

China Dancers' Association
Website:
Phone: 106 500 5779
Address: 16F, 10 Wen Lian Building, , Nong Zhan Guan Nan Li, , Chao Yang District
Information: China Dancers' Association is a highly varied art form, consisting of many modern and traditional dance.
Country: China
Type: Ballet and Dance Company

China National Chinese Opera and Dance Drama Company
Email: china_opera@163.com
Phone: 105 975 2010
Address: 1F No. 23, Nan San Huan East Road, Feng Tai District
Information: The China National Chinese Opera and Dance Drama Company was founded in December, 1950, and is affiliated to Ministry of Culture of People's Republic of China. Within the theater there are opera troupe, dance drama troupe, folk music troupe, symphony orchestra, creation studio and stage designing department
Country: China
Type: Ballet and Dance Company
Venues: Four Seasons Theatre 1700, Min Zhu Theatre

Guang Dong Modern Dance Company
Website: www.gdmdc.com
Email: admin@gdmdc.com
Phone: 208 704 9512
Address: Guangzhou Dance Academy, No.13, Shui Yin Heng Road, Sha He Ding
Information: Guangdong Modern Dance Company, founded in 1992, is mainland China's first professional modern dance company. Based in one of the most vigorous regions in China, the company has attracted some of the most talented and daring artists in China. Works created by its dancers, resident choreographers, Artistic Directors and international guest artists have won critical acclaim and overwhelming audience responses around the world
Country: China
Type: Ballet and Dance Company
Contact: General Manager Willy Tsao (Cheng-yuan Cao)
Touring Countries: USA, Europe, Korea, Japan, Hong Kong , Taiwan, Macau, Philippines, Indonesia

National Ballet of China
Website: www.ballet.org.cn
Email: chinaballet@hotmail.com
Phone: 106 353 4962
Address: No 3, Taipingjie Street, Xuan Wu District
Information: The National Ballet of China was founded in December of 1959. All of The National Ballet of China's outstanding artists come from professional academies. During decades of care and support from the government and friends from all social sectors, the company has never ceased enriching its solid Russian foundations with works of different schools and styles

Country: China
Type: Ballet and Dance Company
Contact: vice Director Ying Feng
Touring Countries: Mexico
Venues: The Sky Bridge Theatre 1300

Reckless Moments
Website: www.reckless.on.net
Email: barry.plews@reckless.on.net
Phone: 216 267 0852
Address: 1529 Tong Ji Garden, 1033 Kang Ding Road
Information: specialises in the development of international co-Productions and collaborations; often undertakes acrobatic performance collaborations with dedicated acrobatic companies; see also Agents & Producers and Drama
Country: China
Type: Ballet and Dance Company
Contact: creative Producer & dramaturge Barry Plews

Sanjiang Dance Troupe
Phone: 871 809 7975
Address: 5th Floor, Athletes Dept, Renmixi Road 134, Kunming
Information: does not exist anymore
Country: China
Type: Ballet and Dance Company

Shaanxi Song and Dance Troupe
Website:
Phone: 298 525 2001
Address: 98 Chang An Zhong Road, Xi An
Information: Shaanxi Song and Dance Troupe boasts a powerful staff of artists. The young performers are highly gifted and have also recieved rigorous training in the arts since 1982. It initiated the first show of song and dance in the imperial style of the Tang Dynasty. Shaanxi Song and Dance Troupe has performed in over 40 foreign countries and has received government heads of state and VIPs from over 100 countries. It is reputed to be the oriental art and treasure of distictive songs and music in the Tang Dynasty style
Country: China
Type: Ballet and Dance Company
Touring Countries: France, Thailand
Venues: Xi An Tang Yue Gong, Xi An Ren Min Mansion Theatre

Shanghai Ballet
Website: www.shanghaiballet.com
Email: renshi@shanghaiballet.com
Phone: 216 115 2525
Address: Block 88, No. 2577 Longhua Road, Xuhui District
Information: The Shanghai Ballet was formally renamed in 1979 at the base of The White-haired Girl performing team. Ballet The White-haired Girl won the Gold Medal for the Best Classical Dance Works of the 20th Century in China, which helped establish the Ballet's predominant position in ballet circle in China.
Country: China
Type: Ballet and Dance Company
Venues: Mei Qi Theatre 1000, Shanghai Grand Theatre 1800 ((q.v.))

Shanghai City Dance Company Limited
Website: www.shcitydance.com
Email: zhoulj@shcitydance.com
Phone: 216 232 7111
Address: 4th Floor, West Mansion, NO.767, Chang Shou Road
Information: Shanghai City Dance Company Limited in April 2003 co-founded by the Wenhui-Xinmin United Press Group and Shanghai Peony film and television communications company. Company principally engaged in investment, Production, operators, brokers, agents and choreographic works, activities, events, and derivative products related to operating. Has a vibrant, familiar with the market, knowledge of foreign languages, are familiar with the norms of the professional team of international operators to maintain a good relationship at home and abroad to the world of dance and performance community
Country: China
Type: Ballet and Dance Company

Shanghai Youth Arts Group
Website: www.shqzx.com
Phone: 216 353 5988
Address: No. 188, Han Zhong Road, , Zha Bei District
Information: Shanghai Youth Activity Center (Shanghai Youth Development Center) is directly under the Communist Youth League Shanghai Municipal Committee of-school educational activities and public service positions
Country: China
Type: Ballet and Dance Company
Contact: arts group Director Zhi-Wei Guo
Touring Countries: Japan

CUBA

Ballet Nacional de Cuba
Website: www.balletcuba.cult.cu/
Email: bnc@cubarte.cult.cu
Address: Calzada 509, entre D y E, Vedado, CU
Information: The National Ballet of Cuba is one of the world's most prestigious dance companies. The Artistic-technical rigour of its dancers and the scale and diversity of its aesthetic conception of the choreographers give this group a relevant place among the great institutions of its genre in the international scene.
Country: Cuba
Type: Ballet and Dance Company
Contact: Director Alicia Alonso
Social Media: https:// www.facebook.com/balletnacionaldecubaoficial/
Venues: Gran Teatro de La Habana

HONG KONG

Ark Dance Theatre
Website:
Email: ypmcck@netvigator.com
Phone: 942 35067

Address: Flat F, 12F Block 2, Dawning Views, 23 Yan Ming Road, Fan Ling, N.T., HK
Country: Hong Kong
Type: Ballet and Dance Company
Contact: Administration/Artistic Director Poo Meng Yip Artistic Director Eve Cheng

City Contemporary Dance Company (CCDC)
Website: www.ccdc.com.hk
Email: info@ccdc.com.hk
Phone: 232 68597
Address: 11/F, 26-28 Tai Yau Street, San Po Kong, Kowloon, HK
Information: Founded by modern dance master Willy Tsao in 1979, the City Contemporary Dance Company is a Hong Kong-based professional dance troupe that brings top Chinese talents to modern Productions that reflect the culture and landscape of contemporary China
Country: Hong Kong
Type: Ballet and Dance Company
Contact: Managing Director Raymond Wong founder and Artistic Director Willy Tsao Chairman Hayley Mee-lin Kan
Social Media: www.facebook.com/ccdc.page
Touring Countries: China, Europe
Venues: Hong Kong Cultural Centre Studio Theatre, Kwai Tsing Theatre Auditorium

Dance Art Hong Kong
Website: www.danceart.com.hk
Email: danceart@danceart.com.hk
Phone: 279 39957
Address: L3-07, JCCAC, 30 Pak Tin Street, Shek Kip Mei, Kowloon, HK
Information: DanceArt is a pioneer in self-choreographed solo Productions in Hong Kong. In this dance theatre, the group will be presenting a poignant work featuring themes on Hong Kong. Under the Artistic direction of Francis Leung, and building on fifteen years of collaboration between Leung and Andy Wong since they founded DanceArt in 1995, the group will strive to take the art of dance to wider and higher realms of excellence
Country: Hong Kong
Type: Ballet and Dance Company
Contact: Artistic Director Francis Leung
Touring Countries: USA, Taiwan, Germany, Japan, China

E-Side Modern Dance Company
Website: www.esidehk.com
Email: esidehk.com@gmail.com
Phone: 237 29351
Address: Flat E, 24F Block 12, Nan Fung Sun Chuen, 15 Greig Crescent, Quarry Bay, HK
Information: Established by Jacky Yu in 1988, E-Side Dance Company is one of the reputable modern dance organizations in Hong Kong. in addition to create unconventional works of local dance Production over the years, the company constantly sets up Asian art exchange opportunities
Country: Hong Kong
Type: Ballet and Dance Company
Contact: Artistic Director Jacky Yu

Hong Kong Ballet
Website: www.hkballet.com
Email: Administration@hkballet.com
Phone: 257 37398
Address: G/F, 60 Blue Pool Road, Happy Valley, HK
Information: One of Asia's premier ballet companies, Hong Kong Ballet is internationally recognised as a top institution that represents Hong Kong's unique character. Since its inception in 1979, HKB has evolved into a vibrant performing arts organisation with a dynamic repertoire, forward-thinking community engagement initiatives and an emphasis on excellence. Septime Webre, former Artistic Director of The Washington Ballet, joined HKB as its Artistic Director in July 2017.
With nearly 50 dancers from all over the globe – Company has won recognition both regionally and internationally. The Company's repertoire includes celebrated re-stagings of the classics by Nina Ananiashvili, Cynthia Harvey, Anna-Marie Holmes, John Meehan and many other notable artists, original full-lengths created for the Company and an award-winning series of ballets for young audiences. In addition, HKB performs works by some of today's most sought-after choreographers, including Alexei Ratmansky, Christopher Wheeldon, Jiří Kylian and many others.
Country: Hong Kong
Type: Ballet and Dance Company
Contact: Executive Director Paul Tam Artistic Director Septime Webre financial Director Belinda Lau
Social Media: @HongKongBallet www.facebook.com/hongkongballet
Touring Countries: China, US
Number of Performers: 48
Venues: Grand Theatre, Hong Kong Cultural Centre

Hong Kong Ballet Group
Website: www.hkbg.org
Email: info@hkbg.org
Phone: 254 15587

Address: Unit 507, Youth Square, 238 Chai Wan Road, Chai Wan, HK
Information: The Hong Kong Ballet Group, a non-profit organisation, was formed in July 1964 by a group of local ballet teachers with the support of the then Education Department. The Ballet Group is dedicated to promoting ballet education and nurturing local ballet talents, by staging full length ballet performances, and organizing not only workshops and seminars but also the first open ballet competition in Hong Kong. Promising talents will be encouraged by scholarships, and international artists are invited to dance alongside local students to give them an exposure to international professional standards. The Ballet Group strives to instill its passion for this art form into the younger generation and to the wider public audience of Hong Kong
Country: Hong Kong
Type: Ballet and Dance Company
Social Media: www.facebook.com/HKballetgroup

Hong Kong Dance Company
Website: www.hkdance.com
Email: hkdance@hkdance.com
Phone: 310 31888
Address: 4/F Sheung Wan Municipal Services Building, 345 Queen's Road Central, HK
Information: Established in 1981 with the aim of promoting Chinese dance, the Hong Kong Dance Company was incorporated in 2001 as a charitable and non-profit-making institution, and is financially supported by the Government of the Hong Kong Special Administrative Region. Since its inception, the Hong Kong Dance Company has staged over 100 Productions, many of which were highly popular with critical acclaim
Country: Hong Kong
Type: Ballet and Dance Company
Contact: Executive Director Gerard Tsang
Artistic Director Yang Yuntao
Social Media: www.facebook.com/hkdance1981

Hong Kong Dance Federation
Website: www.hkdf.org.hk
Email: hkdf@netvigator.com
Phone: 296 78253
Address: Room B 26/F, Grandion Plaza, 932 Cheung Sha Wan, Kowloon, HK
Information: founded in 1978, the main work includes dance instructor training, delegated judge, and the contractor Beijing Dance Academy Chinese Dance Graded Examination Course and the Australian Federal Dance Dance Teachers Association Grading courses
Country: Hong Kong
Type: Ballet and Dance Company
Contact: Chairman Yuen Sin
Social Media: www.facebook.com/hongkongdancefederation
Touring Countries: China

Hong Kong Evangelical Dancing Troop Limited
Website: www.edt.org.hk
Email: info@edt.org.hk
Phone: 820 63646
Address: PO Box 11518, General Post Office, Jing Hui Gdn, Aberdeen, HK
Information: Hong Kong Evangelical Dancing Troop Limited performs in churches and for religious retreats and events
Country: Hong Kong
Type: Ballet and Dance Company
Contact: Chairman Constance Tsang-Lam

Miranda Chin Dance Company
Website: www.mcdc.com.hk
Email: info@mcdc.com.hk
Phone: 256 63365
Address: 2/F Bank Tower, 351-353 King's Road, North Point, HK
Information: Dr. Miranda Chin founded the Miranda Chin Dance Company in 1989 which is dedicated to promoting Chinese Culture in Modern dance. Its vitality lies both in creativity and endeavours at opening up new horizons by blending the essence of Eastern and Western dance, aspiring to reflect in modern dance the uniqueness of Hong Kong culture. Recent credits include Innovative Chinese Rhythms & Movements, Calligraphy Fantasia, Four Seasons and Chinese Martial Arts Dance which received high acclaim
Country: Hong Kong
Type: Ballet and Dance Company
Contact: Artistic Director Miranda Chin
Email: miranda@mcdc.com.hk
Social Media: www.facebook.com/mirandachindancecompany

Spring Poetry
Website: www.springpoetry.org
Email: enquiry@springpoetry.org
Phone: 251 15551
Address: 6/F, 180 Hennessy Road, Wanchai, HK
Information: Spring Poetry is committed to promoting artists with mental difficulties, deaf children and the blind
Country: Hong Kong
Type: Ballet and Dance Company

INDONESIA

E-KAY Dance Ensemble
Website: www.ekaydance.com
Address: Wijaya Grand Center, Block G-15, Wijaya II, ID
Information: produce solo dance programs, many include classical mask dances; also interested in Arts in education and Artist-in Residency projects
Country: Indonesia
Type: Ballet and Dance Company
Contact: Artistic Director Elvian Kawulusan

Eksotika Karmawibhangga Indonesia
Website: www.ekidanceco.co.id
Email: info@ekidanceco.co.id
Phone: 218 312 377, 21 8313029
Address: Jl. Padang No.32, Jakarta 12970, Indonesia
Information: Eksotika Karmawibhangga Indonesia respects cultural exchange with individuals and cultural bodies in different countries around the world through various forms of collaborations, festivals, workshops, etc; manages Puppetmasters Network (see Performing Companies). They come with a mission to narrow the gap between the arts and the people by emphasising the importance of the arts in people's lives.
Country: Indonesia
Type: Ballet and Dance Company
Contact: Managing Director Aiko Senosoenoto
Artistic Director Rusdy Rukmarata
Social Media: @EKIdanceco www.facebook.com/ekidanceco

Kreativitat Dance Company
Website:
Email: krea@pacific.net.id
Phone: 622 176 90254
Address: J1. Ciputat Raya, Pondok Pinang, ID
Information: consists of three choreographers: Farida Oetojo, Judy Syuman and Cendra Effendi; the three trained in classical ballet and modern dance in Europe and Australia; the company also invites guest choreographers
Country: Indonesia
Type: Ballet and Dance Company
Contact: Managing Director Chendra E. Panatan

Namarina Dance Academy
Website: www.namarina.com
Email: namarina@indosat.net.id
Phone: 218 294 777
Address: Jl Halimun 43, ID
Information: one of the oldest ballet schools in Indonesia, founded by the late Nani Lubin; teaches classical ballet English style to children as young as 4 years; stage classical and contemporary ballet performances, mainly for children
Country: Indonesia
Type: Ballet and Dance Company
Contact: Artistic Director Maya Tamara Sianturi
Social Media: @_Namarina www.facebook.com/namarinabjf

Sardono Dance Theatre
Website:
Email: senisolo@indo.net.id
Phone: 622 716 6931
Address: J1. Empu Gandring 40, Kemlayan, ID
Information: Sardono is considered the guru of Indonesian modern dance: training as a dancer in Javanese classical dance tradition, he then studied in the United States in the 1960s; innovative, experimental choreography.
Country: Indonesia
Type: Ballet and Dance Company
Contact: contact Amna Kusumo

Sono Seni Solo
Website:
Email: senisolo@indo.net.id
Phone: 271 740 0880
Address: J1 Empu Gandring 40, Kemlayan, ID
Information: located in a historical kampong (enclave) where the gurus of Javanese court music and dance once lived: facilities include a set of old gamelan Slendro Pelon, an open dance studio; workshops, performances, international collaboration
Country: Indonesia
Type: Ballet and Dance Company
Contact: Artistic Director Sardono W Kusumo
contact Amna

Sumber Cipta Dance School
Website:
Phone: 217 659 467
Address: J1. Ciputat Raya, Pondok Pinang, ID
Information: a respected ballet school (Russian-style) gaining its reputation by sending its best dancers to study and dance abroad; among them are to Folkwangschule in Essen, Germany and Alvin Ailey in New York; founded by Farida Oetojo
Country: Indonesia
Type: Ballet and Dance Company

ISRAEL

Kibbutz Contemporary Dance Company
Website: www.kcdc.co.il/en
Email: office@kcdc.co.il
Phone: 498 59730
Address: D.N. Ashrat, IL
Information: Kibbutz Contemporary Dance Company (KCDC), one of the leading dance companies in the world, is widely identified with the work of acclaimed Artistic Director Rami Be'er whose exclusive and unique choreographic character has become the company's trademark both in Israel and abroad. The company performs regularly in some of the most respected theaters and festivals worldwide.
Country: Israel
Type: Ballet and Dance Company
Contact: international Director Yoni Avital
Email: yoni@kcdc.co.il
Social Media: www.facebook.com/modern.dance.israel
Germany, Italy, Spain, France, United States, United Kingdom, Austria, Australia, The Netherlands, China, South Korea, Japan, Canada, Mexico, Argentina, Brazil, Chile, Columbia, Turkey, Poland, Greece, France, Croatia, Romania, Russia, & More

Number of Performers: 17
Venues: Theaters

JAPAN

ALOK Dance Drama Company
Website: alok7513.wixsite.com/mysite
Phone: 035 386 8192
Address: 1-13-9 Hyakunincho, Shinjuku-ku, JP
Information: founded by Director-choreographer Eri Kyo in 1982; 'Dance drama' is her original performance style, which tells a story only through dance and body movements; wishes to expand awareness of its dance drama worldwide
Country: Japan
Type: Ballet and Dance Company
Social Media: @ALOKddc@ALOKddc
Venues: Space Zero 575 (q.v.), Yokohama Akarenga, Theatre Apple, Alok Atelier

Arisaka Company Agua Gala
Website: www.aguagala.com
Email: center@aguagala.com
Address: 203 Sun Miyazaki, 6-4-9 Minami Aoyama, Minatoku, JP
Information: founded in 1987 to establish a new movement that breaks preconceived idea of dance/play
Country: Japan
Type: Ballet and Dance Company
Contact: choreographer & performer Hikako Kagami
Touring Countries: Korea, Swiss, Poland
Venues: Yushima Seido Open Air Space/Landmark Hall, Art Sphere q, v, National theatrer of Korea, Reithalle Gross Halle Swiss. Theatre wybrzeze Malarnia

Art-Dance Theater Function
Website: http// www.art-dancetheaterf.com
Email: info@art-dancetheaterf.com
Phone: 045 580 7595
Address: 1-16-25-301 Kamisueyoshi Tsurumiku Yokohama, JAPAN
Information: Art-Dance Theater Function is a dance&physical theater company. They are seeking out a dreation of mysterious space in the motif of "contour" and "light and shadow"
The company was founded in 1994 headed up by Kimitaka Shibahara and Mami Yokoyama.
Starting by Festival d'Avignon in 2000, which is the first performance in foreign countries, Company has performed in France, Spain, Germany, Scotland, Russia and China.

Country: Japan
Type: Ballet and Dance Company
Contact: Mami Yokoyama
Email: info@art-dancetheaterf.com
Number of Performers: 0-5

Art-Dance Theatre Function
Website: www.art-dancetheaterf.com
Email: info@art-dancetheaterf.com
Address: 1-16-25-301 Kamisueyoshi, Tsurumi-ku, JP
Country: Japan
Type: Ballet and Dance Company
Contact: President /Director Kimitaka Shibahara
Email: info@art-dancetheaterf.com
Touring Countries: St. Petersburg, China, UK
Venues: East Gallery, Die Pratze

Asami Maki Ballet Tokyo
Website: ambt.jp
Email: a.m.ba@triton.ocn.ne.jp
Phone: 362 763 451
Address: 6-27-13 Nakano, Nakano-ku, JP
Information: included in its repertoire are the majority of classical ballet works as well as a significant number of original creations.

Country: Japan
Type: Ballet and Dance Company
Contact: Artistic Director Kyohzo Mitani
Venues: Tokyo Bunka Kaikan

BujinKobo
Website:
Phone: 429 771 658
Address: 508-10, Nakagou, Nakatou, Han'no, JP
Information: Goi is a renowned contemporary solo Butoh dancer; has worked with Min Tanaka (q.v.) and Tatsumi Hijikata who is regarded as one of the founders of Butoh along with Kazuo Ohno (q.v.), Akira Kasai (q.v.)
Country: Japan
Type: Ballet and Dance Company
Contact: leader & dancer
Teru Goi
Venues: Plan-B (q.v.) Terupushi Call (q.v.)

Buto-sha Tenkei
Website: www.kh.rim.or.jp
Email: tenkei@kh.rim.or.jp
Phone: 377 21396
Address: B15-B, Nakameguro Bldg, 1-5-10 Kami-Meguro, Meguro-ku, JP
Country: Japan
Type: Ballet and Dance Company
Venues: Kitazawa Town Hall 300 (q.v.)

China Song and Dance Troupe
Website: www.china-art.co.jp
Email: cac@jg8.so-net.ne.jp
Phone: 356 168 822
Address: 5F, New Nishi-shin Bldg, 1-18-2 Nishi-shinbashi, Minato-ku, JP
Information: members are all leading artists from China; mainly performs with China Youth Opera Troupe (q.v.) and presents comprehensive programmes of Chinese traditional performing arts all over Japan; promotes cultural exchange
Country: Japan
Type: Ballet and Dance Company
Contact: Director Cheng Bo

Condors
Website: www.condors.jp
Email: katsu@condors.jp
Phone: 352 720 991
Address: 2-13-5-201, Nishi-Waseda, Shinjuku-ku, JP
Information: well known for their theatre costume: Gaku-Ran (school uniform) in Japan; has colaborated with Pascal Conrad. also act as choreographer of Kishi-dan Japanese rock band & the film of Takashi Miyake
Country: Japan
Type: Ballet and Dance Company
Contact: representative & choreographer
Ryohei Kondo
Venues: Shinjuku Theatre Apple

Crystal Ballet Studio
Website: homepage3.nifty.com/crystal_ballet
Phone: 292 446 505
Address: 3F Yokoken Bldg., 2-8 Moto-machi, Hitachinaka, JP
Information: the School invited principal dancers from German ballet companies in Berlin, Bonn, Mainz to perform Don Quixote, etc. in July 1999; they have invited dancers from the Deutsche Oper Berlin: Alexej Dublnin, Dmitri Boulgakov, Bart de blook
Country: Japan
Type: Ballet and Dance Company
Contact: Managing Director & Artistic Director
Motoko Tanaka
Venues: Ibaraki Kenritsu Kenmin Bunka Centre (q.v.) Hitachinakashi Bunkakaikan

Dairakudakan
Website: www.dairakudakan.com
Email: temputenshiki@dairakudakan.com
Phone: 422 214 982
Address: 2-1-18, Kichijoji-Kitamachi, Musashinoshi, JP
Information: Dairakudakan represents an early stage in the development of Butoh Japanese contemporary dance performance, from which grew many other companies such as Sankaijuku (q.v.), then Byakkosha Ohsuka Isamu Dance Opera, (q.v.), Zokucho-no-Tabi (q.v.)
Country: Japan
Type: Ballet and Dance Company
Contact: Director Akaji Maro
company Manager Yoko Shinfune
Venues: Setagaya Public Theatre, New York Japan Society,

Dance Company Nomade~s
Website: www.nomade-s.com
Email: nomade-s@t3.rim.or.jp
Phone: 338 284 858
Address: 5-15-7 Sendagi, Bunkyo-ku, JP
Information: incorporated as Dance Company in 1992, Nomade~s has been active in the modern dance field under the tutelage of company leader Noriko Kumagai and Nakao Ikemiya. Nomade~s claims to search for undiscovered methods of exPression that fit our modern society

Country: Japan
Type: Ballet and Dance Company
Contact: joint Manager Shinobu Shimizu
lighting Reiko Fukuda
joint Director & choreographer
Noriko Kumagai
sound Norimasa Ushikawa
joint Manager Yoko Kawasaki
joint Director & choreographer
Nakao Ikemiya
stage Manager Eiji Torakawa
Germany, Austria & Finland, Hungary, France, UK, Holland, Greece, a showcase in New York
Venues: Space Zero (q.v.) Land Mark Hall (q.v.) East Gallery (q.v.) Setagaya Public Theatre (q.v.) Tokyo International Forum (q.v.) Spiral Hall, Yokohama Red Brick Warehouse (q.v.)

Dance Theatre Ludens
Website: ludens.at.infoseek.co.jp
Email: can@contemporary-art-network.com
Phone: 354 573 164
Address: # 601 NOA Shibuya Part-2 36-22, Udagawa-cho Shibuya-ku, JP
Country: Japan
Type: Ballet and Dance Company
Contact: Artistic Director Takiko Iwabuchi
Social Media: @D_T_LUDENS

Fuji Dance Arts of Japan
Email: k.takako@eos.ocn.ne.jp
Phone: 449 543 066
Address: c/o Ms. Kanshichiko Fujima, 2-23-4 Kami-Asao, Asao-ku, Kawasaki, JP
Information: www10.ocn.ne.jp/~nichibu/
Country: Japan
Type: Ballet and Dance Company
Contact: President Kanshichiko Fujima
contact Takako Kato
Venues: National Theatre

Fumie Kanai
Email: dance@big.or.jp
Phone: 333 002 757
Address: 2-34-12-403 Matsubara, Setagaya-ku, JP
Information: www12.big.or.jp/~dance
Country: Japan
Type: Ballet and Dance Company

H.Art Chaos
Website: h-art-chaos.com
Email: kashiwa@h-art-chaos.com
Phone: 354 770 120
Address: 2F Kamiuma Kashiwa Bldg., 5-20-21 Kamiuma, Setagaya-ku, JP
Information: founded in 1989, renowned for its skill in involving audiences in a chaotic, energetic world
Country: Japan
Type: Ballet and Dance Company
Contact: Manager Masahiro Kashiwa
Artistic Director Sakiko Oshima
Touring Countries: Canada, USA, Germany, Korea, France, Singapore, Austria, Russia, Poland, Finland
Venues: Setagawa Public Theatre

Hokkaido Federation of preservation associations for Traditional Ainu Dance
Website: www.ainu-assn.or.jp
Phone: 112 210 462
Address: c/o Hokkaido-ritsu Ainu Sogo Centr, 7F Kaderu 2.7, Nishi 7-chome, Kita 2-jo, Chuo-ku, JP
Information: consists of 17 groups which conserve Ainu traditional dances the dances are divided into various types: work songs and dances, ceremonial dances, imitation dances, entertainment dances and impromptu dances
Country: Japan
Type: Ballet and Dance Company
Contact: Chairman Tadashi Kato
vice Chairman Kenichi Kawamura

Hosenko Dance Art Company
Website: www.hosenko-dance.com
Email: hosenko@so7.itscom.net
Phone: 333 209 834
Address: 2-44-3, Yoyogi, Shibuya-ku, JP
Information: the Hosenko dance based on traditional Chinese dancing combined with western-style ballet and ethnic folk rhythms.using the elements of Chi Ki, radiating inner strength
Country: Japan
Type: Ballet and Dance Company
Contact: General Director Zhenyang Dafeng
Venues: Tokyo Metropolitan Art Space (q.v.) Saitama Arts Theater (q.v.) Art Sphere (q.v.)

Iberia Co Ltd
Website: www.iberia-j.com
Email: andaluza3@iberia-j.com
Phone: 354 481 271
Address: 1-16-28 Ebisu, Shibuya-Ku, Tokyo TK 1F, Japan, 150 – 0013
Information: Importer of flamenco groups and other Spanish artists

Inoue Ballet Foundation
Website: inoue.ballet.ne.jp
Email: inoueballet@k2.dion.ne.jp
Phone: 334 163 656
Address: 8-4-13 Kinuta, Setagaya-ku, JP
Country: Japan
Type: Ballet and Dance Company
Contact: Artistic Director Naoto Seki
secretary General Katsumi Morozumi
Chairman of the board Tadashi Inumaru
Venues: Mielpaque Hall 1500, Bunkyo Civic Hall 1800

Ishii Kaoru and Tokyo Dance Theater
Website:
Phone: 337 815 460
Address: 4-7-2 Hatanodai, Shinagawa-ku, JP
Information: performances, workshops, symposia with choreographers from Japan, China, Korea, Malaysia, Thailand, Australia, Canada; Management: Collecta Co Ltd (q.v.) e-mail: vyw00171@niftyserve.or.jp
Country: Japan
Type: Ballet and Dance Company
Contact: Artistic Director & choreographer
Kaoru Ishii

Japan Folkloric Art Dance Troupe
Email: iactokyo@d1.dion.ne.jp
Phone: 354 262 047
Address: c/o International Arts Center, 206, 3-20-10, Miyasaka, Setagaya-ku, JP
Information: established in 1963 within the framework of the International Artists Centre (q.v.); visited many countries to promote traditional Japanese folk dances; this has been supported by an active programme of research on the nation's traditional folk dances www.d1.dion.ne.jp/~iactokyo/
Country: Japan
Type: Ballet and Dance Company
Contact: Director-General Youichi Yamaguchi
Director Shinichi Fujii
Artistic Director Sanae Ishii

Japan Performing Arts Foundation – NBS
Website: www.nbs.or.jp
Email: info@nbs.or.jp
Phone: 337 918 888
Address: 4-26-4, Meguro, Meguro-ku, JP
Information: The Japan Performing Arts Foundation was founded in 1981 to develop and promote cultural life in Japan by advancing and popularizing the performing arts, particularly music and dance, and by promoting international exchange in the performing arts.
Country: Japan
Type: Ballet and Dance Company
Social Media: www.facebook.com/nbs.or.jptwitter.com/NBS_operatwitter.com/NBS_ballet

K-Ballet Company
Website: www.k-ballet.co.jp
Email: k-ballet@company.email.ne.jp
Phone: 358 058 812
Address: 3-22-6-402, Koishikawa, Bunkyo-ku, JP
Information: London office: assistant Director, Iain Webb. Tel/fax: +44 020 8580 1734
Country: Japan
Type: Ballet and Dance Company
Contact: Artistic Director/principal dancer Tetsuya Kumakawa

Kato Miyako Dance Space
Website: as-factory.jp
Email: asf@mac.com
Phone: 333 097 200
Address: Annex Sengawa Factory, B1, 2-18-21 Sengawa-cho, Chofu, JP
Information: also do workshops & symposiums
Country: Japan
Type: Ballet and Dance Company
Contact: Director Miyako Kato
Venues: Spiral Hall (q.v.), Space Zero, Chofu tazukuri Hall

Katsuko Orita
Website:
Phone: 339 521 213
Address: 4-17-12 Nishi-Ochiai, Shinjuku-ku, JP
Information: Orita is a contemporary dancer/teacher/choreographer
Country: Japan
Type: Ballet and Dance Company
Venues: new national theatre, Mielparque Hall Tokyo

Kei Takei's Moving Earth
Website: www2.gol.com/users/keitakei/index.html
Email: keitakei@gol.com
Phone: 333 237 797
Address: 2-5-9 Akazutsumi, Setagaya-ku, JP
Country: Japan
Type: Ballet and Dance Company
Contact: Artistic Director Kei Takei
Associate Director Laz Brezer
Venues: Theatre X Theatre Kai, Moving Earth Butai

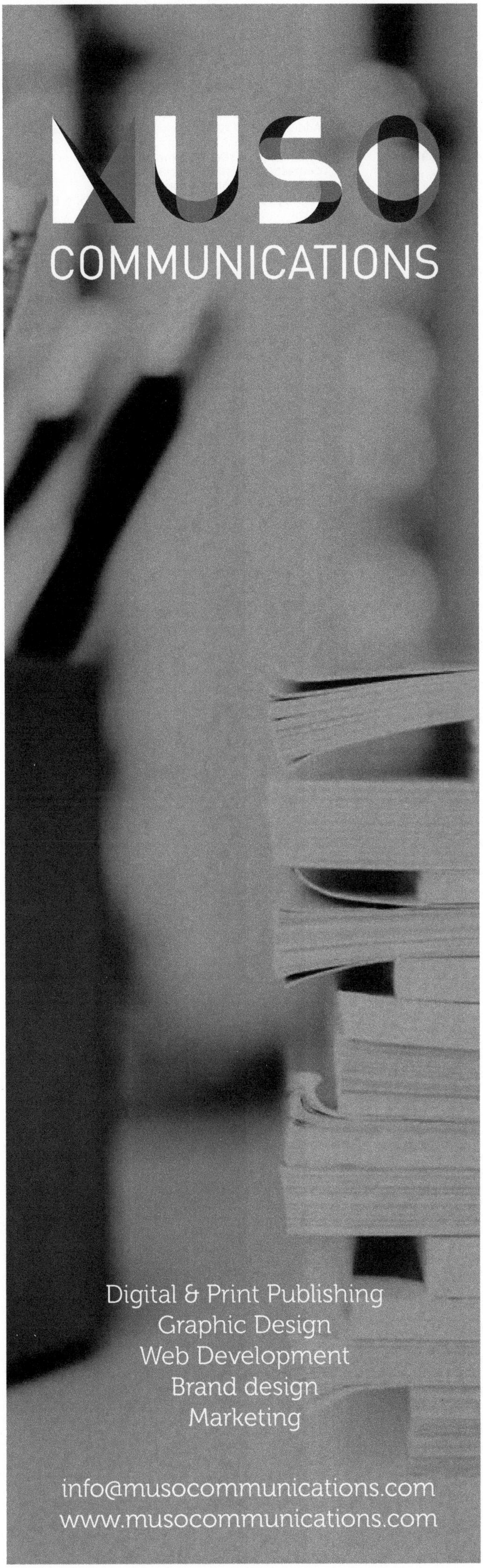

2022 MAY 9-11
DANISH+

DANISH PERFORMING ARTS SHOWCASE FOR CHILDREN & YOUTH
AARHUS, DENMARK

READ MORE: DANISHPLUS.DK

BALLET AND DANCE COMPANIES

Keiko Nakano & Dance Museum Yagi
Website:
Email: kekoyagi@gold.ocn.ne.jp
Phone: 476 803 118
Address: 2-25-7 Wakahagi, Innba Mura, Inba gun, JP
Information: seeks to explore and examine the modern times in which lives the individual, "I", by extracting various questions and curiosities scattered in daily life through the eyes of the "I"
Country: Japan
Type: Ballet and Dance Company
Contact: lighting designer Takeaki Iwashina
costume Kaoru Mitsukura
choreographer, dancer Keiko Nakano
Artistic Director Shoji Takahara
Keiko Nakano
Venues: Saitama Arts Theater chamber hall 266-346 (q.v.); International exchange fund Kokusai Kouryu Kikin Forum, Setagaya public theatre

Kiku no Kai
Website: www.kikunokai.co.jp/
Email: info@kikunokai.co.jp
Phone: 359 836 001
Address: 2-21-23 Nishi-Ochiai, Shinjuku-ku, JP
Country: Japan
Type: Ballet and Dance Company
Contact: kikunokai Director Michiyo Hata
Venues: National Theatre; Nihon Seinenkan Hall (q.v.)
Sun Plaza Hall (q.v.) Shimbashi Embujo (q.v.)

Kisanuki Dance Office
Website: www.kisanuki.jp
Phone: 337 113 930
Address: 202, 2-28-1 Ebisu Minami, Shibuya-ku, JP
Country: Japan
Type: Ballet and Dance Company
Contact: Director Kuniko Kisanuki

Kobayashi Noriko Ballet Theater
Website:
Phone: 339 873 648
Address: 5F Commerce Bldg., 2-39-3 Mejiro, Toshima-ku, JP
Country: Japan
Type: Ballet and Dance Company
Contact: President Noriko Kobayashi
Venues: New National Theatre, Melparque Hall Tokyo

Leni-Basso
Website: www.leni-basso.com
Email: info@leni-basso.com
Phone: 353 472 143
Address: 102, 3-18-17 Ogikubo, Suginami-ku, JP
Information: stylish and highly visual dance works for the senses. Images, light, sound and space intertwine and evolve with fiery and wild movements to create a dance of speed and subtle balance
Country: Japan
Type: Ballet and Dance Company
Contact: Artistic Director & choreographer
Akiko Kitamuraf
General Manager Ryuichi Fuse
Touring Countries: Netherlands, Germany, Belgium, Switzerland, Sweden, Denmark, Norway, Finland, Poland, Canada, USA, Chile, Taiwan, Hong-Kong, Singapore, Australia

Masashi Action Machine
Website: www.dancepro.co.jp/action-machine
Email: dance@dancepro.co.jp
Phone: 529 734 188
Address: 7-13-4F Nishiki 3chome Nakaku, Nagoya, JP
Information: 12 dancers, 5 Productions; booking agent: AP Arte Artists Management and Productions, Kurfürstendamm 30, D-10719 Germany; email: pfeifer@ap-arte.com; website: www.ap-arte.com
Country: Japan
Type: Ballet and Dance Company
Contact: booking agent Andreas Pfeifer
joint Artistic Director Masashi Mishiro
joint Artistic Director Kumiko Sakamoto
General Manager Mihoko Sakamoto
Touring Countries: worldwide

Mieko Fuji Contemporary Dance Company
Website: www.fujimieko.jp
Email: dance@fujimieko.jp
Phone: 339 826 273
Address: 2-12-4 Mejiro, Toshima-ku, JP
Information: Fuji also choreographs opera Productions; Chairperson of Japan Dance Therapy Association; has written a book on Dance Therapy
Country: Japan
Type: Ballet and Dance Company
Contact: Director Mieko Fuji
Venues: Tokyo Metropolitan Art Space (q.v.) Art Sphere 746 (q.v.)

Min Tanaka & Maijuku
Website: min-tanaka.com/
Email: tokason@min-tanaka.com
Phone: 552 770 071

Address: Kamiashizawa 64, Shikishimacho, Manakoma-gun, JP
Information: recently moved his Production base to Dance Resources on Earth (q.v.)
Country: Japan
Type: Ballet and Dance Company

New National Theatre, Tokyo, Ballet & Dance
Website: www.nntt.jac.go.jp
Phone: 353 513 011
Address: 1-1-1 Hon-machi, Shibuya-ku, JP
Country: Japan
Type: Ballet and Dance Company
Contact: Artistic Director dance Asami Maki
Venues: New National Theatre – Opera House 1814, Playhouse 1010-1038, The Pit 340-468 (q.v.)

Nibroll
Website: www.nibroll.com
Email: info@precog-jp.net
Phone: 357 862 503
Address: 3-14-8 Minami-Aoyama, Minato-ku, JP
Country: Japan
Type: Ballet and Dance Company
Contact: representative Mikuni Yanaihara
Touring Countries: USA , France, Germany, The Netherlands, Thailand, India, Switzerland

Okinawa Culture Association
Website: www.okinawa-culture.com
Email: tamaki@okinawa-culture.com
Phone: 337 760 579
Address: c/o Okinawa Culture Association, 4-13-6 Minami-magome, Ohta-ku, JP
Information: non-profit-making group; performs traditional music and dance from the Okinawa islands of southern Japan, including court dances and folk dances; its aim is to improve the profile of Japan as well as cultural exchanges
Country: Japan
Type: Ballet and Dance Company
Contact: Chairman Masayasu Tamaki
secretary General Jun Tamaki

Omayumi Mayumi Hamada
Website:
Email: mayuming@mbd.ocn.ne.jp
Phone: 663 347 175
Address: 1-16-22 Hounan-cho Nishi, Toyonaka, JP
Information: Hamada has been performing solo multimedia dance works which are inspired by her own life since 1983; her 'movement' works appears in various art forms such as dance, performance art, installation art, etc.
Country: Japan
Type: Ballet and Dance Company
Contact: choreographer & performer
Mayumi Hamada

op. eklekt
Website:
Email: opeklekt@yahoo.co.jp
Phone: 755 519 065
Address: 32-2F Yumiya-cho, Nishi-hairu, Yamato-oji, Matsubara Higashi-iru, Higashiyama-ku, JP
Information: hopes to create a new stage art; challenges both tradition and overly westernized arts in Japan; participated in many festivals and competitions both in Japan and abroad
Country: Japan
Type: Ballet and Dance Company
Contact: President Nobuo Kanetani

Pappa Tarahumara
Website: www.pappa-tara.com
Email: info@pappa-tara.com
Phone: 333 852 066
Address: 1F Maruha Bldg., 1-1-5 Arai, Nakano-ku, JP
Information: Pappa TARAHUMARA is a Performing Arts company founded by the Director, Hiroshi Koike in 1982. They use dance, drama, music, and art.
Country: Japan
Type: Ballet and Dance Company
Contact: Artistic Director Hiroshi Koike
Executive Director Yuka Narasaki
Touring Countries: UK, Belgium, Netherland, Germany, France, Italy, Hong-Kong, Korea, Taiwan, Myanmar, Philipine, Malaysia, Singapore, Indonesia, Australia, USA

Performance Troupe Taihen (2)
Website: www.ne.jp/asahi/imaju/taihen
Email: taihen@japan.email.ne.jp
Phone: 663 200 344
Address: 1-15-15 Nishi-Awaji, Higashi-Yodogawa-ku, JP
Country: Japan
Type: Ballet and Dance Company
Contact: leader/Artistic Director Manri Kim

Roussewaltz
Website: www.kalin-net.com/roussewaltz
Email: roussewaltz@aol.com
Phone: 359 740 445
Address: 4-6-1 Raison 202, Nishisugamo, Toshima-ku, JP
Country: Japan

Sol de España Co Ltd, Ballet de Yoko Komatsubara
Website: www.komatubara.com
Email: flamenco@komatubara.com
Phone: 333 142 568
Address: 4-34-13 Koenji Minami, Suginami-ku, JP
Country: Japan
Type: Ballet and Dance Company
Contact: administrator Kumiko Takamatsu
President Yoko Komatsubara
Touring Countries: Spain, Singapore, Thailand, USA, Brazil

Star Dancers Ballet Company
Website: www.sdballet.com
Email: info-sd@sdballet.com
Phone: 334 012 293
Address: 1F, 2-22-4 Minami-Aoyama, Minato-ku, JP
Information: its repertoire includes classics such as Peter Wright edition Giselle, modern masterpieces including works by Tudor, Balanchine, Jooss, Robbins and premiere performances of contemporary Japanese and foreign works
Country: Japan
Type: Ballet and Dance Company
Touring Countries: Germany, China, South Korea

Strange Kinoko Dance Co.
Website: www.strangekinoko.com
Email: mail@strangekinoko.com
Phone: 334 467 996
Address: Pavlov 1-15-1-4B, Hiroo, Shibuya-ku, JP
Country: Japan
Type: Ballet and Dance Company
Contact: Artistic Director Chie Ito

Suzushi Hanayagi
Website:
Phone: 663 453 810
Address: 1-7-16 Sonezaki Shinchi, Kita-ku, JP
Information: post-modern soloist & choreographer; participated in the Production by Robert Wilson as a choreographer in 1999
Country: Japan
Type: Ballet and Dance Company

Tokyo Ballet
Website: www.nbs.or.jp/tokyoballet
Phone: 337 917 000/5721
Address: 4-26-4, Meguro, Meguro-ku, JP
Information: only ballet company in the world which has the stage rights to Bejart's masterpieces
Country: Japan
Type: Ballet and Dance Company
Contact: General Manager Tadatsugu Sasaki
ballet mistress Hiroko Tomoda
technical Director Yoshiharu Tachikawa
company Manager Yutaka Fujimoto
Production Manager Naoko Arita
Artistic Manager Munetaka Iida
Associate Artistic Director Naoki Takagishi
lighting Director Tatsuo Takasawa
administrative Director Noriko Takahashi
Press officer Mayumi Iwamoto
Touring Countries: Europe, Russia, South America, Middle East, Southeast Asia, China, Cuba, etc.
Venues: The Tokyo Festival Hall 2303 (q.v.)

Tokyo City Ballet
Website: www1.odn.ne.jp/tokyocity
Email: tokyocity-ballet@hkg.odn.ne.jp
Phone: 356 382 720
Address: 1-9-8 Sumiyoshi, koto-ku, JP
Information: has performed both classical and modern ballet works; has many writers and choreographers; trains young dancers
Country: Japan
Type: Ballet and Dance Company
Contact: Chairperson and Director Kiyoko Ishii
secretary General Tatsuo Noguchi
stage Director Hiroshi Hashimoto
Director and choreographer Taneo Ishida
prima ballerina and choreographer Etsuko Adachi
Venues: New National Theatre (q.v.) Teara Kohtoh 1102 (q.v.)

Tokyo Contemporary Dance Company
Website:
Phone: 488 852 789
Address: 1-11-13 Motobuto, Urawa-ku, Saitama-shi, JP
Information: founded in 1960
Country: Japan
Type: Ballet and Dance Company
Contact: Artistic Director Koh Fujii
Venues: Haiku-za Theatre, Sainokuni Arts Theatre, Melparqu

Tokyoza Dance Company
Website: www.tokyoza.com
Phone: 339 982 007
Address: 1-29-10 Nukui, Nerima-ku, JP
Information: aimed at a crossover of dance, beyond the realm of jazz, modern, and classical
Country: Japan

Type: Ballet and Dance Company
Contact: chief instructor Yuki Suganuma
Director Emuzaburou
junior ballet teacher Kurumi Iwai
Venues: Nakano ZERO Hall (q.v.) Sogetsu Hall 530 (q.v.),
Nerima Culture Hall, Haiyu Za

Tomoko Ehara Dance Company
Website:
Email: ehara@path.ne.jp
Phone: 332 918 649
Address: 2-21-4 Kanda Tsukasa-cho, Chiyoda-ku, JP
Information: performs mainly solo and group works
Country: Japan
Type: Ballet and Dance Company
Contact: Artistic Director, choreographer, dancer Tomoko Ehara
Venues: Theatre X (Theatre Kai)

Yanagishita Norio Modern Ballet Group
Website:
Phone: 447 775 756
Address: 2-20-5 Ida, Nakahara-ku, Kawasaki, JP
Country: Japan
Type: Ballet and Dance Company
Contact: President Norio Yanagishita

Yukio Waguri & Kohzensha Butoh Company
Website: www.otsukimi.net/koz
Email: koz-waguri@nifty.com
Phone: 425 806 152
Address: 105, 2-22-1 Nishi-machi, Kokubunji, Kokobunji, JP
Information: CD-ROM ""Butoh Kaden"" which complies ""Butoh-fu""notion of Butoh, choreographic ratations instructed to Wagri by Hijikata, is released in Jan, 1998 in Japan by Just System Inc.; available from website English
Country: Japan
Type: Ballet and Dance Company
Contact: lighting designer Masaru Soga
President Yukio Waguri
costume desinger Kaori Taniguchi
General Manager Johanna Mochidome
Venues: Theatre X caiq.v.

Za Ondekoza (1)
Website: www.ondekoza.com
Email: taron@pop12.odn.ne.jp
Phone: 357 701 457
Address: c/o Victor Entertainment Inc., 1-14-5, Senda-gaya, Shibuya-ku, JP
Country: Japan
Type: Ballet and Dance Company
Touring Countries: Taiwan, Europe
Venues: Shinjuku Bunka Centre (q.v.) Tokyo Kohsei Nenkin Kaikan (q.v.)

Zampa Ufujishi Daiko (1)
Website:
Email: zampa@nyc.odn.ne.jp
Phone: 988 959 467
Address: c/o Zampa Ufujishi Daiko Jimkyoku Southern Press, Chimdon Stage, 718 Yagi, Nakagusu-ku, JP
Information: since 1986 the company has performed throughout Japan; in 1991 the company was selected as a promotional image for the third annual International Track and Field Competition in Tokyo and thus received worldwide exposure as a representative of Japan;
Country: Japan
Type: Ballet and Dance Company
Contact: Artistic Director Takejyo Arakaki
Manager Keiko Uehara
Venues: Okinawa Convention Centre (q.v.)

MALAYSIA

A.S.K. Dance Company
Website: www.dancemalaysia.com/Dance/Dance_Companies/Contemporary/ASK_Dance_Co_/ask_dance_co_.htm
Email: gonzales@dancemalaysia.com
Phone: 603 216 49180
Address: National Arts Academy, 33rd Floor, Empire Tower, MY
Information: In 1994, the ASK DANCE Co. was established by the Dance Program of the National Arts Academy, Ministry of Culture, Arts and Tourism. The company was created with the intention to further promote local performances and to encourage the creative development of its lecturers and students. It was in this fertile soil of cross-cultural exchange that the founding members Suhaimi Magi, Aida Redza, Lena Ang and Joseph Gonzales worked, striving to break contemporary boundaries, redefine forms and norms to build the base of a unified dance culture in Malaysia. The company has built its reputation on the strong use of traditional elements, spirit and vocabulary as the starting point of its creative discovery. The ASK Dance Co. has a good reputation in Malaysia and its performances have been very well received thus far.
Country: Malaysia
Type: Ballet and Dance Company
Contact: head of dance Joseph Gonzales

Adikara Dance Theatre
Website:
Email: adidanza@hotmail.com
Phone: 193 97500
Address: 352 Fasa 5, Pantai Hill Park, 59200, MY
Country: Malaysia
Type: Ballet and Dance Company

Ah-Yoke-Kyoka Dance Ensemble
Website:
Email: ahyoke_kyoka@yahoo.com
Address: Pentas Gerak School of Contemporary Performance, 15, Gat Lebuh Cina, MY
Country: Malaysia
Type: Ballet and Dance Company

Batu Dance Theatre
Website: www.batudt.com.my
Email: admin@batudt.com.my
Phone: 333 247 568
Address: No.1, 3rd Floor, Persiaran Pegaga, Taman Bayu Perdana, MY
Country: Malaysia
Type: Ballet and Dance Company
Contact: Artistic Director Tan Lian Ho

Federal Academy of Ballet
Website:
Email: lllan@myjaring.net
Phone: 379 573 413
Address: 1-3 Jalan 14/22, MY
Country: Malaysia
Type: Ballet and Dance Company
Contact: founder & Director
Lee Lee Lan

Khazana Stage Creations
Website:
Email: ragamaliga@hotmail.com
Address: 19 Jalan 8/1, Petaling Jaya, MY
Country: Malaysia
Type: Ballet and Dance Company

Khuan Loke Association Lion Dance Troupe
Website:
Email: khuanloke@hotmail.com
Phone: 012 373 7637
Address: No. 90, Jln 18A, Sg. Way, MY
Country: Malaysia
Type: Ballet and Dance Company
Contact: contact Albert Fong

Kuala Lumpur Dance Theatre
Website:
Email: kldancetheatre@dancemalaysia.com
Phone: 379 573 413
Address: 1-3 Jalan 14/22, MY
Country: Malaysia
Type: Ballet and Dance Company
Contact: Director Lee Lee-Lan
Touring Countries: China, The Phillipines and Germany

Tandak Dance Theatre
Website:
Email: tandak_dance@hotmail.com
Address: 17-01-24 The Palladium, Jalan Gurney 2, MY
Country: Malaysia
Type: Ballet and Dance Company

Yayasan Warisan Johor
Website: www.ywj.gov.my/warisan/
Email: ywj@tm.net.my
Phone: 072 245 488 / 60
Address: JKR 304, Jalan Marimah, MY
Country: Malaysia
Type: Ballet and Dance Company

MEXICO

A-Quo Danza Contemporánea
Website:
Email: A_quodanza@yahoo.com
Phone: 443 327 3099
Address: Colima 69, Col. Molino de parras, MX
Country: Mexico
Type: Ballet and Dance Company

Academia Danzjafora
Website: danzjafora0.wixsite.com/danzjafora/
Phone: 552 52878
Address: Marsella n 60, 3er piso, Colonia Juárez, MX
Country: Mexico
Type: Ballet and Dance Company
Contact: Director Farahilda Sevilla
Social Media: @MundoWix@FarahildaSevilla

Academia de la Danza Mexicana
Website:
Phone: 554 122 8000
Address: Calle Xicoténcatl, San Diego Churubusco, MX

Information: The Mexican Dance Academy works under a line that links tradition with new Artistic and dance trends; scientific knowledge with art; knowledge and exPressions of local cultures, with the parameters of the globalized world. All this in order to enhance and develop the skills, abilities and skills of future dance professionals. The Mexican Dance Academy seeks to be a professional educational institution that promotes the valuation and dissemination of various dance, Artistic and cultural exPressions, both nationally and internationally. Its principles and values are the development of creativity, sensitivity, professional ethics and solidarity; as well as the inclusion and respect of the aesthetic manifestations of other individuals, societies and cultures. That is why the Mexican Dance Academy remains in a permanent work of analysis, reflection, adaptation and renewal of the didactic strategies used to guarantee a quality education that is open to the aesthetic, educational, social and cultural imprints of the world.
Country: Mexico
Type: Ballet and Dance Company

Aksenti Danza Contemporánea
Website: www.aksentidanza.com
Email: aksenti@aksentidanza.com
Phone: 555 414 0579
Address: MX
Information: AKSENTI Contemporary Dance, is an independent group that proposes a continuous renewal of the movement in search of new styles and forms of exPression. Founded in 1991 by its current Director Duane Cochran, the company arises from obtaining the XII National INBA-UAM Dance Award with the choreography "LAZOS". Since its foundation, it has appealed for a constant search for language and new creative tools for the consolidation of its own dance aesthetic. At the time of recognizing in the work of other choreographers a valuable contribution to the group, because it encourages contact with various creative trends.
Country: Mexico
Type: Ballet and Dance Company
Contact: Director Duane Cochran
Social Media: @aksentidanza@aksentidanza

Anajnu Veatem
Website:
Email: yanitshannon@anajnuveatem.com
Phone: 555 515 6749
Address: Camargo 20, Col. Hip, MX
Country: Mexico
Type: Ballet and Dance Company
Contact: General Director Moisés Covalín
Email: moycovalin@anajnuveatem.com
communications and public relations officer Yanit Shannon
Email: yanitshannon@anajnuveatem.com
Number of Performers: 26

Andanza
Website: www.andanzapr.org/Andanza/inicio_andanza.html
Email: andanzapr@gmail.com
Phone: 787 723 1358
Address: 657 Calle Condado Ste. 3, MX
Country: Mexico
Type: Ballet and Dance Company
Contact: Artistic Director Lolita Villanúa
educational program Director María Teresa Robles
Associate Artistic Director Carlos Iván Santos

Andanzas 3030 de la U.P.N.
Website:
Email: comelunas@hotmail.com
Address: Carretera al Ajusco, MX
Country: Mexico
Type: Ballet and Dance Company
Contact: Director Sonia Pabello

Antares Danza Contemporánea
Website: www.antaresdanza.com
Email: imchau@hotmail.com
Address: Duraznos 6, Col. Fuentes del Mezquital, MX
Information: Services: Shows, Permanent Resident Activities, Choreographic set-up, Workshops, Illustrated Conferences, Dancing for Children
Country: Mexico
Type: Ballet and Dance Company
Touring Countries: Canada, USA, Venezuela, Italy, Spain, Colombia, Costa Rica, India

Anzar Compañía de Danza Contemporánea de la Universidad de Guadalajara
Website: www.cge.udg.mx/cpdc/anzar
Email: bavrazo@cencar.udg.mx
Address: Casa de la Danza de la Universidad de G, Lopez Cotilla n, Sector Ju, MX
Country: Mexico
Type: Ballet and Dance Company

Arte M
Website:
Email: naranjoestudio@yahoo.com
Phone: 818 342 0187

Address: Abasolo 1099, Col. Centro, MX
Information: alternative email: artemovildanzaclan@hotmail.com
Country: Mexico
Type: Ballet and Dance Company
Contact: Director Emma Lozano
Touring Countries: Spain, Cuba, USA

Atelier Balleteatro Contemporáneo
Website:
Phone: 523 336 158 065
Address: Hidalgo 2920, MX
Country: Mexico
Type: Ballet and Dance Company
Contact: Director Sergio Vicencio

Ballet de la Ciudad de México
Website:
Email: isabel_avalos@academiadeballet.com
Phone: 555 604 1834
Address: Prolongacion Uxamal 989, Santa Cruz Atoyac, Benito Juárez, MX
Country: Mexico
Type: Ballet and Dance Company

Ballet Folclórico de la Universidad de Guadalajara
Website: www.balletfolcloricoudg.com
Email: josetodofolklore@gmail.com
Phone: 333 826 8119
Address: MX
Country: Mexico
Type: Ballet and Dance Company

Ballet Folclórico Nacional de México Aztlán
Website: www.balletfolclorico.com
Address: MX
Country: Mexico
Type: Ballet and Dance Company

Ballet Folklórico de México
Website: balletamalia.com
Email: infoballetamalia@yahoo.com.mx
Phone: 552 99320
Address: Violeta 31. Esq. Riva Palacio, Col. Guerrero, MX
Country: Mexico
Type: Ballet and Dance Company
Venues: up to 6000

Ballet Folklórico de México de Amalia Hernández
Website: www.balletamalia.com/eng.html
Email: infoballetamalia@yahoo.com.mx
Phone: 552 99320
Address: Violeta 31, Riva Palacio, Col. Guerrero, MX
Information: Official Folkloric Ballet of the Government of Mexico City. alternative email
Country: Mexico
Type: Ballet and Dance Company
Social Media: www.facebook.com/balletdeamalia
Touring Countries: USA, South America, Europe, Australia, Japan, Korea, United Arab Emirates

Ballet Independiente
Website: www.balletindependiente.org
Email: balletindependiente2003@yahoo.com.mx
Phone: 555 512 4332
Address: Vizcaínas Poniente 13, Colonía Centro, MX
Country: Mexico
Type: Ballet and Dance Company

Ballet Mexicano de Baile Fino de Salón
Website:
Phone: 555 764 2129
Address: Iglesias Clader, Col. Jard, MX
Country: Mexico
Type: Ballet and Dance Company

Ballet Moderno Mexicano Japonés
Website:
Phone: 555 271 1999
Address: Camino a Sta. Teresa 1500, Pedregal de San Ángel, MX
Country: Mexico
Type: Ballet and Dance Company

Ballet Nacional de México
Address: Sierra de Tilaco n, Col. Villas del Sol, MX
Country: Mexico
Type: Ballet and Dance Company
Touring Countries: USA, Europe, Asia

Ballet Neoclásico de la América Latina
Website:
Email: balletneoclasico@yahoo.com.mx
Phone: 525 555 810 093
Address: Retorno 202-3, Col. Unidad Modelo, MX
Country: Mexico
Type: Ballet and Dance Company

Ballet Teatro del Espacio
Website: www.balletteatrodelespacio.com
Email: ballet_teatro@yahoo.com.mx
Phone: 555 511 6260

Address: Hamburgo 218, Zona Rosa, MX
Country: Mexico
Type: Ballet and Dance Company
Contact: Director David Attie

Barro Rojo
Website: www.barrorojoartsenico.com
Email: laurarochamx@barrorojo.com
Address: Corregidora n, Col. Miguel Hidalgo Villa Ol, Tlalpan, MX
Information: founded in 1982
Country: Mexico
Type: Ballet and Dance Company
Contact: Directora art Laura Rocha
Social Media: http:// www.facebook.com/pages/Barro-Rojo-Arte-Esc%C3%A9nico/242325142481084
Touring Countries: Latin America, USA and Europe

Belly Dancers del Centro Liban
Website:
Email: centrocultural@centrolibanis.org.mx
Phone: 555 228 9933
Address: Hermes, Col. Credito Constructor, MX
Country: Mexico
Type: Ballet and Dance Company
Contact: Directora Shamira –

Compañía Bajo Luz
Website:
Address: Col. Roma, MX
Country: Mexico
Type: Ballet and Dance Company

Compañia de Danza de Baja California
Website:
Email: bajacaliforniaballet@hotmail.com
Phone: 684 5487
Address: MX
Country: Mexico
Type: Ballet and Dance Company

Compañía de Danza Tradicional Mexicana
Website:
Address: Plaza Juárez 1, San Cristobal Centro, MX
Country: Mexico
Type: Ballet and Dance Company
Contact: General Director Francisco Jaime Díaz Ríos
Email: jaime_diaz@nizarindani.com.mx
official speaker Francisca Martínez
Email: francisca@nizarindani.com.mx
website designer Claudia Chávez
Email: diseno@nizarindani.com.mx

Compañía de Danza Urbana
Website: www.companiadedanzaurbana.jimdo.com
Email: info@companyofdanceurban.com
Phone: 237 42960
Address: MX
Country: Mexico
Type: Ballet and Dance Company
Social Media: @Danza urbana

Compañía de la Danza Narciso Medina
Website: www.cniae.cult.cu/Cia.Narciso_MEdina.htm
Email: medinadanz@cubarte.cult.cu
Address: Centro Habana, MX
Country: Mexico
Type: Ballet and Dance Company

Compañia de Musica y Danza Flamenca Caña y Candela Pura
Website:
Email: canaycandelapura@gmail.com
Phone: 525 556 302 349
Address: MX
Country: Mexico
Type: Ballet and Dance Company
Social Media: www.facebook.com/canaycandelapura

Compañía Nacional de Danza
Website: www.companianacionaldedanza.com
Email: cnddifusion@yahoo.com.mx
Phone: 525 552 817 490
Address: Plaza Angel Salas s/n, Centro Cultural del Bosque, Col. Chapultepec Polanco, MX
Country: Mexico
Type: Ballet and Dance Company
Touring Countries: USA, France

Compañia Tania Pérez-Salas
Website: www.taniaperezsalas.org/principal.html
Email: contacto@taniaperezsalas.com
Address: MX
Country: Mexico
Type: Ballet and Dance Company
Touring Countries: USA, Canada, Spain, France and Italy

Corpus Danza Contemporánea
Website:
Email: corpusdza@hotmail.com
Phone: 555 660 6028
Address: MX
Country: Mexico
Type: Ballet and Dance Company

Danza Contemporánea
Website:
Phone: 528 183 496 663
Address: Col. Las Torres, MX
Country: Mexico
Type: Ballet and Dance Company

Danza Contemporánea
Website:
Email: raquelvazquezv@prodigy.net.mx
Address: Salina Cruz No. 5, Col. Roma Sur, MX
Information: presents programs for adults and children
Country: Mexico
Type: Ballet and Dance Company

Danza Contemporánea XXI
Website:
Phone: 555 611 8795
Address: Col. Nonoalco Mixcoac, MX
Country: Mexico
Type: Ballet and Dance Company

Danza Libre Universitaria
Website:
Phone: 562 27051
Address: Nuevo Edificio de las Direcciones PB, Centro Cultural Universitario, Insurgentes Sur 3000, , MX
Country: Mexico
Type: Ballet and Dance Company
Contact: Director Cristina Gallegos

Danza Teatral Contemporánea
Website:
Phone: 525 558 416 505
Address: Juan de Dios Peza n, Col. Santiago Zapotitl, MX
Country: Mexico
Type: Ballet and Dance Company

Danzaire Ballet Teatro
Website:
Phone: 333 618 5375
Address: Alvaro Obreg, Sector Libertad, MX
Country: Mexico
Type: Ballet and Dance Company

Danzarte
Website: www.danzarte.com.mx/index.html
Email: info@danzarte.com.mx
Phone: 552 41889
Address: Amores 1618 – 101, Col. Del Valle CP.03100 Del. Benito Juárez, Mexico, , MX
Country: Mexico
Type: Ballet and Dance Company
Contact: Director Jos efsgfgsd
Social Media: www.facebook.com/AcademiaDanzarte

Delfos Danza Contemporánea
Website: www.delfosdanza.com
Email: infodelfos@yahoo.com
Address: Carnaval 37, Teatro, Centro Hist, MX
Country: Mexico
Type: Ballet and Dance Company
Touring Countries: USA, Italy

El Circo Contemporáneo
Website: www.elcircocontemporaneo.mx
Email: info@elcircocontemporaneo.com
Address: Espacio G1, Alhondiga 76-A, Col. San Javier, Col. San Javier, MX
Information: alternative email: elcircocontemporaneo.com@hotmail.com
Country: Mexico
Type: Ballet and Dance Company
Social Media: @ECCdm

Estudio 28 – Arte Físico Danza Contemporánea
Website:
Email: studio28@gmail.com
Phone: 228 817 4453
Address: Belisario Domínguez 28, Col. Centro, MX
Country: Mexico
Type: Ballet and Dance Company

ETERNO CARACOL DANZA
Website:
Email: ETERNOCARACOL@GMAIL.COM
Phone: 555 535 0325
Address: Tl, Col. Tlaxpana, MX
Country: Mexico
Type: Ballet and Dance Company
Contact: Director Ester Lopezllera
Social Media: http://es-la.facebook.com/eternocaracol

Eulalio Danza Contemporánea
Website:
Phone: 555 207 4675
Address: Col. Cuauht, MX
Country: Mexico
Type: Ballet and Dance Company
Social Media: www.facebook.com/EulalioDanzaContemporanea

Foramen M. Ballet
Website: www.fmbdanza.net/
Email: foramenmballet@gmail.com
Phone: 777 176 4428
Address: Nueva Tabachin no. 13, Col. Tlaltenango, Cuernavaca, MX
Country: Mexico
Type: Ballet and Dance Company
Contact: Director Marcos Ariel Rossi

Frecuencias Alteradas
Website:
Email: frecuenciasalteradas@hotmail.com
Phone: 553 202 4773
Address: Av. San Lorenzo n, Andador Flamingo Mz. 3, Edificio 7, Depto. 202, Col. Unidad Habitacional San Lorenzo Tezonco, MX
Country: Mexico
Type: Ballet and Dance Company

GineCEO
Website:
Phone: 523 338 268 119
Address: L, Col. Centro, MX
Country: Mexico
Type: Ballet and Dance Company
Contact: Directora Adriana Quinto

Grupo de Danza Convergencias de Texcoco
Website:
Phone: 525 959 545 239
Address: Lirios n, Col. Valle de Santa Cruz, MX
Country: Mexico
Type: Ballet and Dance Company
Contact: Directora Valentina Orozco

Grupo de Danza Minerva Tapia
Website:
Phone: 526 646 211 500
Address: Av. Las Palmas n, Col. Las Palmas, MX
Country: Mexico
Type: Ballet and Dance Company
Contact: Directora Minerva Tapia

Grupo de Experimentación artística Asaltodiario
Website:
Email: asaltodiario@hotmail.com
Address: Retorno Miguel Lantz Duret n, Col. Periodista, MX
Country: Mexico
Type: Ballet and Dance Company

Grupo Experimental Coreograf
Website:
Phone: 523 336 581 275
Address: Centro Cultural San Diego, Gonz, MX
Country: Mexico
Type: Ballet and Dance Company
Contact: Directora Rosa Olivia D

Grupo Gilberte Meunier
Website:
Phone: 522 814 0169
Address: Teresa Medina 10, Col. Centro, MX
Country: Mexico
Type: Ballet and Dance Company
Contact: Director Gilberte Meunier

Grupo Origen de Monterrey
Website:
Phone: 818 338 7702
Address: L, Col. La Monta, MX
Country: Mexico
Type: Ballet and Dance Company

Koreos Danza Teatro
Website: www.koreos.cjb.com
Email: koreos@yahoo.com
Phone: 951 36164
Address: José López Alavez #1002, Barrio de Xochimilco, MX
Country: Mexico
Type: Ballet and Dance Company
Contact: Director Gerardo IBAÑEZ
Social Media: http:// www.facebook.com/koreos.danzateatro

La Fábrica Danza
Website:
Email: lafabricadanzateatro@hotmail.com
Phone: 553 209 012
Address: viena 57 int. 301, MX
Country: Mexico
Type: Ballet and Dance Company
Contact: Directora Rosario Armenta
Touring Countries: USA, Venezuela, Cuba

Lah-chó
Website:
Phone: 525 556 587 288
Address: Los Talleres de Coyoac, Francisco Sosa n, Col. Del Carmen, Coyoac, MX
Country: Mexico
Type: Ballet and Dance Company

Nemian
Website: www.nemiandanza.com
Phone: 555 565 87788
Address: Fco. Sosa # 29, Del Carmen Coyoacán, MX
Country: Mexico
Type: Ballet and Dance Company
Contact: Director Isabel Beteta

Nucleodanza
Website:
Phone: 444 812 8191
Address: Col. El Pasco, MX
Country: Mexico
Type: Ballet and Dance Company
Contact: Director Federico Antonio Fuentes

Ojos Negros Danza Contemporánea
Website:
Phone: 525 555 164 451
Address: Gral. Salvador Alvarado n, Col. Escand, MX
Country: Mexico
Type: Ballet and Dance Company

Onírico
Website: www.onirico.com.mx
Email: oniricodanzateatrodelgesto@gmail.com
Phone: 555 594 5503
Address: Av. Acoxpa And. 58 Ent. I-2, Col. Villacoapa, MX
Country: Mexico
Type: Ballet and Dance Company
Social Media: www.facebook.com/oniricodanzateatrodelgesto

Pápura Danza Teatro
Website:
Phone: 555 677 3235
Address: Col. Belisario Dom, MX
Country: Mexico
Type: Ballet and Dance Company

Proyecto Bará
Website:
Email: proyectobara@hotmail.com
Phone: 555 590 3725
Address: Col. Moderna, MX
Country: Mexico
Type: Ballet and Dance Company

Proyecto Finisterra
Website:
Email: finisterra99@hotmail.com
Phone: 555 554 8347
Address: Col. La Fama, MX
Country: Mexico
Type: Ballet and Dance Company
Contact: Directora Isabel Romero
Touring Countries: Egypt, Canada

Quiatora Monorriel
Website: www.quiatoramonorriel.com/
Phone: 555 688 4019
Address: Xicoténcatl 176 C2, Del Carmen, Coyoacán, MX
Country: Mexico
Type: Ballet and Dance Company
Contact: Director Evo sdfs
Social Media: http:// www.facebook.com/groups/47720429946/

Rosa Romero Danza Contemporánea
Website:
Phone: 246 462 6426
Address: Col. Centro, MX
Country: Mexico
Type: Ballet and Dance Company

Taller de Danza contemporánea de la Universidad de Querétaro
Website:
Phone: 442 216 9022
Address: Av. Hidalgo s/n, Cerro de las Campanas, Centro Hist, MX
Country: Mexico
Type: Ballet and Dance Company

Taller de Danzas Helénica
Website:
Email: beasoc2002@yahoo.com.mx
Phone: 555 554 0137
Address: Col. Romero de Terreros, MX
Country: Mexico
Type: Ballet and Dance Company

Tandem Compaña de Danza
Website: www.tandemciadedanza.com/english
Email: hai.bridi.zain@gmail.com
Phone: 555 632 3798
Address: Col. Roma, MX
Country: Mexico
Type: Ballet and Dance Company
Contact: international Executive Aura López
Email: aura@tandemciadedanza.com

U.X. Onodanza
Website:
Email: uxdanzabizarra@aol.com
Phone: 555 594 5416
Address: Col. Villacoapa, MX
Country: Mexico
Type: Ballet and Dance Company
Touring Countries: Nicaragua, Germany, Korea (Seoul)

Umbral Danza Contemporánea
Website:
Phone: 998 801 460
Address: Guadalupe Victoria 150, Col. Unidad Donceles, MX
Country: Mexico
Type: Ballet and Dance Company

NEW ZEALAND

Black Grace
Website: www.blackgrace.co.nz
Email: admin@blackgrace.co.nz
Phone: 963 00835
Address: 14F Akepiro Street, Mount Eden, NZ
Information: One of New Zealand's leading contemporary dance companies. Black Grace is the most positive, living exPression of any New Zealand art. Founded by Neil Ieremia in 1995, Neil draws from his Samoan and New Zealand roots to create innovative dance works that reach across social, cultural and generational barriers. The work itself is highly physical, rich in the story telling traditions of the South Pacific and exPressed with raw finesse, unique beauty and power.
Country: New Zealand
Type: Ballet and Dance Company
Contact: founding Artistic Director Neil Leremia
Social Media: @BlackGraceNZ www.facebook.com/blackgracedanceco
Touring Countries: Noumea, Australia, Netherlands, New Zealand, North America

Footnote Dance
Website: www.footnote.org.nz
Email: footnote@footnote.org.nz
Phone: 438 47285
Address: 125 Cuba Street, NZ
Information: Footnote Dance is a significant part of the dance experience for thousands of Kiwis. Over the past 25 years, Footnote Dance has presented the fluid energy of dance as a real reflection of our New Zealand identity in the theatre, in schools and in the community.
Country: New Zealand
Type: Ballet and Dance Company
Contact: General Manager Richard Aindow
Email: richard@footnote.org.nz
office Manager Nik Jarvie-Waldrom
Social Media: @FootnoteDance www.facebook.com/footnotenewzealand
Venues: various/adaptable

Kahurangi New Zealand Maori Dance Trust
Website: www.kahurangi.com
Email: admin@kahurangi.com
Phone: 687 30041
Address: PO Box 1368, NZ
Information: The Kahurangi Maori Dance Theatre was at the forefront of the renaissance of Maori Performing Arts. Formed in the early 1980's by Tama Huata and a team who shared his vision to present Maori performing arts in a dynamic and contemporary manner, their touring teams have travelled the world promoting cultural understanding, and inviting audiences to participate in their programmes.
Country: New Zealand
Type: Ballet and Dance Company
Social Media: www.facebook.com/kahurangi.newzealand
Touring Countries: Australia, Canada, USA, China, Kuala Lumpur, India

Royal New Zealand Ballet
Website: www.nzballet.org.nz
Email: enquiry@rnzb.org.nz
Phone: 438 19000
Address: St James Theatre, 77-83 Courtenay Place, NZ
Information: The Royal New Zealand Ballet is a company of 34 dynamic dancers, performing an eclectic repertoire of outstanding dance for national and international audiences, whilst continuing to build a style that is ultimately unique to this company and Aotearoa, New Zealand.
Country: New Zealand
Type: Ballet and Dance Company
Contact: Executive Director Frances Turner
Artistic Director Francesco Ventriglia
Social Media: @nzballet www.facebook.com/nzballet
Touring Countries: Australia, China
Number of Performers: 34
Venues: Aotea Centre, Auckland 2256; St James Theatre Wellington 1550

Te Waka Huia
Website: www.maoriperformingarts.co.nz/wawcs012034
Email: tapeta.wehi@wananga.ac.nz

Phone: 098 337 787
Address: PO Box 70 090, NZ
Information: Te Waka Huia has set a standard from the very start, and has since gone on to set records admired and envied throughout the country in the history of traditional Maori performing art.
Country: New Zealand
Type: Ballet and Dance Company

PHILIPPINES

Ballet Manila
Website: balletmanila.com.ph
Email: info@balletmanila.com.ph
Phone: 252 55967
Address: 1915 Donada St., PH
Information: housed in its private compound equipped with three rehearsal studios, a music library, a warehouse for costumes and equipment, living quarters for dancers and visiting teachers, as well as a collection of ballet books and video for the continuing education of the dancers and students. A fully-staffed office takes care of its administrative, logistical and Marketing requirements and provides for all the training and performance needs of the dancers
Country: Philippines
Type: Ballet and Dance Company
Contact: ballet master Osias Barroso
Artistic Director Lisa Macuja-Elizalde
Social Media: www.facebook.com/pages/Ballet-Manila/40875734873
Venues: Cultural Centre of the Philippines 1800 (q.v.), Meralco Theatre 1000, University of The Philippines Theatre, 2200

Ballet Philippines
Website: ballet.ph
Email: info@ballet.ph
Phone: 283 23689
Address: 4th Floor Cultural Center of the Philippines, CCP Complex, Roxas Blvd., PH
Information: a resident dance company of the Cultural Center of the Philippines. The Phillipines' flagship company in ballet and contemporary dance. A cornerstone of Filipino cultural identity
Country: Philippines
Type: Ballet and Dance Company
Contact: Executive Director Jennifer Lee Bonto
Artistic Director Paul Alexander Morales
Associate Artistic Director Christine Crame
choreographer Alden Lugnasin
Social Media: @balletph www.facebook.com/balletphilippines
Venues: Cultural Centre of the Philippines 1800 (q.v.)

Bayanihan Philippines National Folk Dance Company
Website: www.bayanihannationaldanceco.ph
Email: bayanihan_mla@yahoo.com
Phone: 516 3028
Address: No.1742 Gen Malvar St., Taft Ave., PH
Country: Philippines
Type: Ballet and Dance Company
Contact: Executive Director Suzie M Bentiez
Chairman emeritus Helena Z. Benitez
Chairman Alfonso T. Yuchengo
Social Media: www.facebook.com/pages/Bayanihan-Philippine-National-Folk-Dance-Company/132995066739345?

Dagyaw Theatre and Dance Company
Website: www.oocities.org/inhs_iloilo/dagyaw.html
Email: iloilonhs_ph@yahoo.com
Address: Iloilo National High School, Luna Street, La Paz, PH
Information: see also Drama
Country: Philippines
Type: Ballet and Dance Company
Contact: Executive Director Riza Amaguin

Kalingawan Dance Troupe
Website:
Phone: 633 372 155
Address: West Visayas State University, La Paz, PH
Country: Philippines
Type: Ballet and Dance Company
Contact: choreographer Crisostomo Barrera

Leyte Kalipayan Dance Company
Website:
Phone: 533 699 212
Address: 22 Arellano Street, Tacloban City, PH
Country: Philippines
Type: Ballet and Dance Company
Contact: Artistic Director Teresita Pil

Philippine Barangay Folk Dance Troupe
Website:
Phone: 256 30179
Address: 131 Scout Fernandez St., PH
Country: Philippines
Type: Ballet and Dance Company
Contact: Artistic Director Eugenio Ticzon
founder & Director

Quezon City Ballet
Website:
Phone: 292 64071
Address: 1227 Quezon Ave, PH
Country: Philippines
Type: Ballet and Dance Company
Contact: Artistic Director Shirly Halili Cruz
Social Media: http:// www.facebook.com/pages/Quezon-City-Ballet/107683949255907

Ramon Obusan Folkloric Group
Website:
Phone: 283 10894
Address: 4 Chapel Road, NAIA Housing Area, PH
Country: Philippines
Type: Ballet and Dance Company
Contact: Artistic Director Roman A Obusan

Sanghiyas Folk Dance Troupe
Website:
Email: DirectorIV@phsa.edu.ph
Phone: 495 365 971
Address: Philippines High School for the Arts, National Arts Center, Mt. Makiling college, PH
Country: Philippines
Type: Ballet and Dance Company

Sining Kumintang ng Batangas
Website: www.siningkumintang.com
Email: pagcor_cordero@yahoo.com
Phone: 437 271 090
Address: c/o Bauan High School, San Pascual, Bauan, PH
Country: Philippines
Type: Ballet and Dance Company

U. P. Dance Company
Website:
Email: basiliov@mnl.sequel.net
Phone: 292 96963
Address: c/o U.P. College of Music, University of the Philippines Diliman, PH
Information: subsidized by the University of the Philippines; performs in the different campuses of the university system, and other provinces, plus occasionally cities in Asia Beijing, Hong Kong; its repertoire is made of international and local works
Country: Philippines
Type: Ballet and Dance Company
Contact: Artistic Director Basilio Esteban S Villaruz
Venues: U. P. Theatre, Abelardo Hall Auditorium

Vella C. Damian School of Ballet
Website:
Phone: 273 16226
Address: 390 Mayon Street, PH
Country: Philippines
Type: Ballet and Dance Company
Contact: Artistic Director Vella C Damian

SINGAPORE

Arts Fission Company, The
Website: www.artsfission.org
Email: admin@artsfission.org
Phone: 623 86469
Address: Cairnhill Arts Centre, 126 Cairnhill Road, #01-07/09, SG
Information: Set up in 1994, The ARTS FISSION COMPANY is the first full-time contemporary dance company in Singapore to incorporate itself as a company limited by guarantee. ARTS FISSION excels in cross-disciplinary creations and collaborations informed by Asian aesthetics and is dedicated to the creation and performance of original dance works that explore diverse issues connected to the everyday, including works that explores the effect of climate change on art, culture, and the environment.
Country: Singapore
Type: Ballet and Dance Company
Contact: rehearsal director Edwin Wee
Email: edwin.wee@artsfission.org
Social Media: www.facebook.com/artsfission.company
Touring Countries: Canada, Hungary, Jarkarta
Annual Performances: 4
Number of Performers: 6

Attitude Performing Arts Studio
Website: www.attitudearts.com
Email: apas29@singnet.com.sg
Phone: 646 79738
Address: No. 1 Jalan Anak Bukit, Bukit Timah Plaza, Unit 01-29 & 15, SG
Information: Since its inception in April 2001, Attitude Performing Arts Studio has been an Artistic hub that gathers dance enthusiasts of all ages from all walks of life. The school was founded with the aim to develop confident and virtuoso dancers for the stage both locally and internationally. It also aims to impart greater passion and deeper appreciation of performing arts.
Country: Singapore
Type: Ballet and Dance Company
Social Media: www.facebook.com/AttitudePerformingArtsStudio

Dance Ensemble Singapore Ltd
Website: www.des.org.sg
Email: desarts@des.org.sg
Phone: 633 47192
Address: 60 Waterloo Street, SG
Information: Dance Ensemble Singapore (DES), one of Singapore's most active Chinese cultural dance groups, officially opens its four-storey extension, the Arts Building, today. With their new facilities, DES plans to grow its student base and strengthen its position as a premier professional dance group
Country: Singapore
Type: Ballet and Dance Company
Contact: Artistic Director Yan Choong Lian
Email: desarts@des.org.sg
Social Media: www.facebook.com/DanceEnsembleSingapore
Number of Performers: 10
Venues: Victoria Theatre 904

ECNAD Project Limited
Website: www.ecnad.org
Email: info@ecnad.org
Phone: 622 66404
Address: 182 Cecil Street #04-05/06, Telok Ayer Performing Arts Centre, SG
Country: Singapore
Type: Ballet and Dance Company
Contact: Artistic Director Lim Chin Huat
co-founder and co-Artistic Director Tan How Choon
Touring Countries: Malaysia, Indonesia, New Zealand, Yugoslavia
Venues: Theatres, indoors and outdoors site-specific venues, experimental theatre spaces, and schools of various capacities

Frontier Danceland
Website: www.frontierdanceland.com
Email: info@frontierdanceland.com
Phone: 633 61526
Address: Goodman Arts Centre, 90 Goodman Road Block M #02-51/52, SG
Information: Founded in July 1991 by present Artistic Director, Low Mei Yoke and Tan Chong Poh, as an amateur dance company, Frontier Danceland gained professional status in 2011. Frontier Danceland aims to create a unique dance language.
Country: Singapore
Type: Ballet and Dance Company
Contact: Artistic Director Low Mei Yoke
Manager Sally Li Mei
Director Tan Chong Poh
Social Media: @frontierdancesg www.facebook.com/frontier.danceland
Touring Countries: USA
Venues: Esplanade Theatre Studio University Cultural Centre Theatre Kallang Theatre. Victoria Theatre Drama Centre Substation Guinness Theatre Tampines Cultural Centre

Odyssey Dance Theatre
Website: www.odysseydancetheatre.com
Email: odysseydancetheatre@gmail.com
Phone: 622 15516
Address: Aliwal Arts Centre #03 - 08, 28 Aliwal Street, SG
Information: Founded in 1999, Odyssey Dance Theatre Ltd (ODT), one of Asia Pacific's foremost full-time professional contemporary dance companies, is a strong advocate of local original dance works and has represented Singapore as cultural ambassador in numerous festivals, conferences, arts markets and cultural exchanges.
Country: Singapore
Type: Ballet and Dance Company
Contact: Chairman Koh Sauk Keow
Touring Countries: Asia Pacific, Europe and USA

Singapore Dance Theatre Ltd
Website: www.singaporedancetheatre.com
Email: fin_admin@singaporedancetheatre.com
Phone: 633 80611
Address: 201 Victoria Street, Bugis +, #07-02/03, SG
Information: More than a decade on, SDT continues to have the privilege to perform in a world-class performing arts venue, exhilarating audiences with a myriad of repertoires. In the course of each year, the company performs six seasons annually, with three full ballet performances at the stage of Esplanade Theatre.
Country: Singapore
Type: Ballet and Dance Company
Contact: Artistic Director Janek Schergen
Manager Paul Ang
Chairperson Laura Hwang
Touring Countries: Mexico, France, Australia, China, Hong Kong, London, Korea, ASEAN
Venues: Victoria Theatre 904, Kallang Theatre 1744, plus performances in the park; current performing home is the Theatre, Esplanade, Theatres on the Bay

Sri Warisan Som Said Performing Arts Ltd
Website: www.sriwarisan.com
Email: admin@sriwarisan.com
Phone: 622 566 070
Address: 47 Kerbau Road, SG

Information: Sri Warisan is a performing arts company founded by renowned cultural Medallion recipient, Madam Som Said. Sri Warisan, formed in 1997, and is one of the pivotal forces in Singapore's Malay dance scene. Blending rich traditional forms with contemporary techniques is Sri Warisan's trademark. Its performers are trained to excel in multi-disciplinary art forms such as dance, music, theatre and multi-media
Country: Singapore
Type: Ballet and Dance Company
Contact: Founder and Artistic Director Som Binte Mohamed Said
administrative Director Ahmad Sawal
Managing Director Adel Ahmad
admin Director Ahmad Sawal
Social Media: https:// www.facebook.com/groups/sriwarisan/
Touring Countries: Canada, China, Indonesia, Malaysia, Thailand, Philippines, Italy, Korea, Brunei, Belgium, Holland
Venues: Victoria Theatre 900, Drama Centre 300, Sri Warisan Studio 80, University Cultural Centre 1700

SRIWANA
Website: www.sriwana.com
Email: info@sriwana.com
Phone: 632 31956
Address: Goodman Arts Centre, 90 Goodman Road, Blk D #01-25, SG
Information: Sriwana was formed in 1950 as a Keron-cong Party (a traditional Malay Orchestra). Its activities were mainly to entertain guests at wedding parties and taking part in cultural shows organised by local educational bodies, especially the Malay Youth Literary Association (4PM), with whom Sriwana was affiliated.
Country: Singapore
Type: Ballet and Dance Company
Contact: President Fauziah Hanom Yusof
Email: fauziah@sriwana.com
Social Media: www.facebook.com/SRIWANA.SG
Number of Performers: 60
Venues: Victoria Theatre, UCC, SOTA, DBS ARTS THEATRE

SOUTH AFRICA

Cape Dance Company
Website: www.capedancecompany.co.za
Email: haley.capa@mweb.co.za
Phone: 217 010 599
Address: 7 A Bell Crescent, Westlake Business Park, Westlake, Tokai, ZA
Information: contemporary dance company working in neo-classical and neo-contemporary styles
Country: South Africa
Type: Ballet and Dance Company
Contact: contact Haley Sundelson
Email: haley.capa@mweb.co.za
administrative Director Marion Coxall
Email: coxallmc@mweb.co.za
Social Media: @CDC_SouthAfrica

TAIWAN

Address: 5F, 2-2, Sec2, Nan Ya Xi Road
Country: Taiwan
Type: Ballet and Dance Company
Contact: correspondent Chih-Chen Huang
Touring Countries: USA

Capital Ballet – Taipei
Email: cineplex@ms7.hinet.net
Phone: 228 351 491
Address: No.9-1, Lane 8, Yu-sheng St, Shihlin Distric
Country: Taiwan
Type: Ballet and Dance Company

Century Contemporary Dance Company
Website: www.ccdctw.com.tw
Email: ccdctw@yahoo.com
Phone: 223 944 354
Address: No.2, Lane 108, Sec 1., Nanchang Road, Da An District
Country: Taiwan
Type: Ballet and Dance Company
Contact: Artistic Director and choreographer Shu-Fen Yao

Cloud Gate Dance Theatre of Taiwan
Website: www.cloudgate.org.tw
Email: service@cloudgate.org.tw
Phone: 226 298 558
Address: No. 36, Ln.6, Sec. 1, Zhongzheng Rd, Tamsui District
Information: Acclaimed by the Times as "Asia's leading contemporary dance theatre," Cloud Gate Dance Theatre of Taiwan won the Stef Stefanou Award for Outstanding Company at the 19th National Dance Awards, UK on Feb 18th 2019 with Lin Hwai-min's 90th work, FORMOSA. Founded Cloud Gate Dance Theatre of Taiwan in 1973, Lin Hwai-min will step down at the end of 2019 from the position of Company's Artistic Director, and hand over the reins to CHENG Tsung-lung, who is the present Artistic Director of Cloud Gate 2

Country: Taiwan
Type: Ballet and Dance Company
Contact: Director of International Programs Joanna Wang
Email: joanna@cloudgate.org.tw
Social Media: www.facebook.com/cloudgate
Touring Countries: Worldwide: Australia, Austria, Brazil, Canada, China, Colombia, Czech Rep., England, Denmark, France, Germany, Greece, Holland, Israel, Italy, Japan, Korea, New Zealand, Norway, Russia, Switzerland, USA, Venezuela

Dance Forum Taipei
Website: www.danceforum.com.tw
Email: danceforum@crown.com.tw
Phone: 227 168 888
Address: No 151, Lane 120, Tun-hwa North Road
Country: Taiwan
Type: Ballet and Dance Company
Contact: Artistic Director Heng Ping
correspondent Shou-yuo Liu
Venues: Crown Theatre, other theatres up to 1000

Dance Theatre of Liao Mo-Si
Website: www.liao-mo-hsi.com.tw
Email: pontiac2@ms24.hinet.net
Phone: 623 68596
Address: No. 163, Lane 32, Section 2, Chang Rong Road
Country: Taiwan
Type: Ballet and Dance Company
Contact: Artistic Director Mo-Si Liao
Touring Countries: USA
Venues: Tai Nan City Culture Centre 2000

Formosa Aboriginal Song & Dance Troupe
Website: fasdt.yam.org.tw
Email: fasdt.dance@msa.hinet.net
Phone: 038 642 290
Address: No. 6, Lane 27, Chi Nan Road, section 2, , Chi Nan Cun, , Shou Feng Xiang,
Country: Taiwan
Type: Ballet and Dance Company

Grace Shiau Dance Theatre
Website:
Email: Moon.dance@msa.hinet.net
Phone: 225 605 724
Address: 3F No40-1, , Zhong Shan Bei Road, Section 2, Zhong Shan District,
Information: initiated in 1985
Country: Taiwan
Type: Ballet and Dance Company
Contact: Artistic Director and founder Grace Shiau

Hwa Kang Dance Troupe
Website: www.pccu.edu.tw
Email: crmspd@staff.pccu.edu.tw
Phone: 228 613 749
Address: No.55, Hwa Kang Rd, , Shi Lin District,
Information: members are mostly recruited from students or alumini in the Dance Dept. of the University of Chinese Culture or students from Hwa Kang Art School, see also Drama (Hwa Kang Theatre – different organisations under the same Director)
Country: Taiwan
Type: Ballet and Dance Company
Contact: direct Man-Li Wu
performing Manager Ai Qian Li
Artistic Director Rong Lan Chen
Touring Countries: Europe, USA
Venues: National Father Memorial Hall up 2500

Kaohsiung City Ballet
Website: www.kcb.org.tw
Email: Kcb15483@seed.net.tw
Phone: 777 15483
Address: 3F, No. 96, Si Wei er Road, , Si Wei er Road, , Ling Ya District,
Country: Taiwan
Type: Ballet and Dance Company

Ku & Dancers
Website: www.sites.google.com/site/kudancers/
Email: kudancers@gmail.com
Phone: 228 923 600
Address: No.71, Kaiming Street, , Beitou District
Country: Taiwan
Type: Ballet and Dance Company
Contact: correspondent Cynthia Wang

Lan-Yang Dancers
Website: www.lycc.org.tw
Email: lycc1966@ms33.hinet.net
Phone: 395 11161
Address: 189, Sec. 1, Beicheng Road, Luo Dong Zhen
Country: Taiwan
Type: Ballet and Dance Company
Contact: Artistic Director Mei Hong Lin
Touring Countries: Canada
Venues: Social and Educational Theatre 1200

Lee Tsai-E Dance Company
Website:
Email: tsaili01@ms18.hinet.net

Phone: 723 11991
Address: No. 10, Lane 65, , Zi Chiang Road one, , Qian Jing District,
Country: Taiwan
Type: Ballet and Dance Company
Contact: correspondent Chan-Chuan Huang

Legend Lin Dance Theatre
Website: www.legend-lin.org.tw
Email: legendlin.tw@gmail.com
Phone: 289 233 888
Address: 1F, No. 4, , Yung-jen Road, Yung-he District,
Country: Taiwan
Type: Ballet and Dance Company
Contact: Artistic Director Lee-chen Lin
Email: legendlin.tw@gmail.com
Social Media: https:// www.facebook.com/legendlin.tw

Neo-Classic Dance Company, The
Website: www.neo.org.tw
Email: neo@neo.org.tw
Address: 15F, No. 29, , Zhong Zheng North Road Section 2, , Dan Shui District,
Information: Dr. Liu Feng-Shueh founded Neo-Classic Dance Company in 1976. As Artistic Director, Dr. Liu attends to investigate the abstract concept and nature of dance, such as movement, time, space, and dynamics. She endeavors to reconstruct and exalt traditional Chinese materials, vocals, operas, and western and aboriginal cultures to present the works to their full majesty. Neo-Classic had been toured all over the world and obtained high praise by the audience.

Country: Taiwan
Type: Ballet and Dance Company
Contact: Artistic Director Feng-Shueh Liu
Email: neo@neo.org.tw
art administrator Tse-Hsuan LO
Email: neo@neo.org.tw
Touring Countries: U.S.A, France, Russia, China
Annual Performances: 12
Number of Performers: 20
Venues: National Theatre, Cultural Centre Hall

Sun-Shier Dance Theatre
Email: dans30@ms.hinet.net
Phone: 229 736 786
Address: 4F., No.102, Sec. 1, Chongsin Rd
Country: Taiwan
Type: Ballet and Dance Company

Tai-Gu Tales Dance Theatre
Website: www.taigu-tales.com
Email: taigutales@ms31.hinet.net
Phone: 223 927 805
Address: 1F, No. 72, , Ning Bo East Street,
Country: Taiwan
Type: Ballet and Dance Company
Contact: Artistic Director Xiu-Wei Lin
Touring Countries: Canada, France, Holland, Demark, USA, German, Hong Kong

Taipei Crossover Dance Company
Website: www.taipeicrossover.com
Email: mail@taipeicrossover.com
Phone: 202 773 0223
Address: 268 Kuang-Fu South Road, 5th floor
Country: Taiwan
Type: Ballet and Dance Company

Taipei Dance Circle
Website: www.taipei-dance-circle.imagecoffee.net
Email: td.circle@msa.hinet.net
Phone: 289 720 061
Address: No. 71, Kai Ming Street, , Bei Tou District
Information: founded in 1984. made up of mixture of dance graduates and individuals who have a passion for dance. winner of the Innovation Award for Performing Arts
Country: Taiwan
Type: Ballet and Dance Company
Contact: administrative Executive Shu-wen Fu
company Director Wan-Jung Jang
Artistic Director Shaw-Lu Liou
Touring Countries: Israel

Taipei Folk Dance Theatre
Website: www.tdance.org.tw
Email: tfdt@ms59.hinet.net
Phone: 285 096 695
Address: No. 15, Alley 8, Lane 578, , Bei An Rd, , Jong Shan District,
Information: first company created to spread Taiwan's traditional choreography around the country and the world
Country: Taiwan
Type: Ballet and Dance Company
Contact: Artistic Director Li-Hua Tsai
chief Director Wei-Jen Lee
Managing Director Hsiu-Hwa Ho

Taipei Lanyang Dancers
Website: www.lycc.org.tw
Email: lydancer@ms35.hinet.net

MUSO
COMMUNICATIONS

Digital & Print Publishing | Graphic Design
Web Development | Brand design | Marketing

info@musocommunications.com | www.musocommunications.com

Phone: 395 11161
Address: No.189, Sec. 1, Beicheng Rd., Luodong Town
Country: Taiwan
Type: Ballet and Dance Company
Contact: Artistic Director Hui-Ju Chen
Email: slimmamajessica@hotmail.com
Touring Countries: Japan, USA, Europe, South America

Water Reflection Dance Ensemble
Website: www.wrde.com.tw
Email: wrde@seed.net.tw
Phone: 222 575 312
Address: 220 New Road, 12F, No. 34-1, Taipei Itabashi
Country: Taiwan
Type: Ballet and Dance Company
Social Media: www.facebook.com/wrde.com.tw

UNITED STATES

Abhinaya Dance Company of San Jose
Website: www.abhinaya.org
Email: abdanceco@gmail.com
Phone: 408 871 5959
Address: 4950 Hamilton Avenue, Suite 105, US
Information: Abhinaya Dance Company of San Jose was founded in 1980 by Mythili Kumar to transmit classical South Indian bharatanatyam dance through training and presentations of the highest quality. Through multicultural collaborations, Abhinaya honors the tradition and fosters its stylistic evolution in the U.S
Country: United States
Type: Ballet and Dance Company
Contact: media contact Lisa Geduldig
Email: lisag@igc.org
Social Media: @AbhinayaDanceCo@AbhinayaDanceCo

African American Dance Ensemble
Website: www.africanamericandanceensemble.org
Email: aade@earthlink.net
Phone: 919 560 2729
Address: 120 Morris Street, US
Information: AADE's mission is to preserve and share the finest traditions of African and African American Dance and Music through research, education, performance and entertainment; to focus on the health and education of the community. The purpose is to help the youth become more active through dance and the arts
Country: United States
Type: Ballet and Dance Company
Contact: assistant Artistic Director Stafford C Berry Jr
Artistic Director & founder
Chuck Davis
Executive Director B. Angeloe Burch Snr.
Venues: Carolina Theater 1000

Alabama Ballet
Website: www.alabamaballet.org
Email: information@alabamaballet.org
Phone: 205 322 4300
Address: 2726 First Avenue South, US
Information: The Alabama Ballet began in 1981 as an outgrowth of the Birmingham Civic Ballet, the University of Alabama at Birmingham Ballet and Ballet Alabama. Under the co-Artistic direction of world-renowned dancers Dame Sonia Arova and Thor Sutowski, the company found status and recognition in the ranks of professional companies. Arova's and Sutowski's outstanding 15 year foundation set the stage for the leadership of Wes Chapman and Roger Van Fleteren, who came on board in 1996. In 2005, Tracey Alvey joined the Artistic team as Ballet Mistress
Country: United States
Type: Ballet and Dance Company
Contact: Artistic Director Tracey Alvey
development and office assistant Mary Reynolds Porter
Email: maryreynolds@alabamaballet.org
Venues: Wright Center 1200, Alys Stephens Centre 1800

Alaska Dance Theatre
Website: www.alaskadancetheatre.org
Email: info@alaskadancetheatre.org
Phone: 907 277 9591
Address: 550 East 33rd Ave, US
Information: Alaska Dance Theatre (ADT), founded in 1981, is the premiere nonprofit dance organisation in Alaska. It's mission is to promote dance through professional education, performance and advocacy in Alaska and to provide a recognized Artistic element within the dance community for local and visiting artists to expand their creative talent while nurturing discipline, confidence, fitness and the experience of movement. Believing that dance is for everyone, Alaska Dance Theatre strives to keep its programs affordable to a wide range of the population
Country: United States
Type: Ballet and Dance Company
Contact: Artistic Director Sarah Grunwaldt
Executive Director Codie Costello
Social Media: @AKDanceTheatre www.facebook.com/AlaskaDanceTheatre

Alban Elved Dance Company
Website: www.albanelved.com
Email: albanelveddancecompany@gmail.com
Phone: 336 409 5096

Address: PO Box 932, US
Information: Alban Elved Dance Company was founded in Berlin, Germany in 1997 by Artistic Director and choreographer Karola Lüttringhaus, to form an outlet for her diverse Artistic pursuits.
The group began performing in NC in 1999 and incorporated as a 501-c-3 non-profit organization in 2000. 'alban elved' is the Celtic name for the fall equinox, literally translating to "the light of the water" and water often finds a place in the company's works in actual or metaphorical form. The SARUS FESTIVAL was named after the sarus crane, Grus antigone, who had been a symbol for the company for years. The name "Sarus" has a Sanskrit origin and means "of water", "lake or wetland". In fact, in Tamil the term "Sarasa-naadanam" refers to graceful dancing
Country: United States
Type: Ballet and Dance Company
Contact: Artistic Director Karola Lüttringhaus
assistant Director Andrea Lieske

Albany Berkshire Ballet
Website: www.berkshireballet.org
Email: abballet@verizon.net
Phone: 413 445 5382
Address: 116 Fenn Street, US
Information: The Albany Berkshire Ballet was founded in 1960 by Artistic Director Madeline Cantarella Culpo as an outgrowth of her school, the Cantarella School of Dance, located in Pittsfield, Massachusetts. Originally known as the Berkshire Ballet Guild and later as the Berkshire Civic Ballet, it was originally intended as a performance outlet for the school's advanced students
Country: United States
Type: Ballet and Dance Company
Contact: Artistic Director & founder
Madeline Cantarella Culpo
Venues: Boland Theatre in the Berkshire Community College, Pittsfield, 510, Palace Theatre, Albany, NY 3000

All Nations Dance Company
Website: www.allnationsdance.org
Email: alnatdanco@aol.com
Phone: 724 716 4463
Address: PO Box 174, US
Information: All Nations Dance (AND) is a developing non-profit organisation and International Worship Arts Network, formed in January of 2007 under the leadership of D. Maximillion Elliott-Quinerly looking to equip and intergrate individuals and organisations from diverse backgrounds (race, age, denomination and social economic status), in an effort to meet its Mission and Vision
Country: United States
Type: Ballet and Dance Company
Contact: Director D.Maximillion Elliott-Quinerly
Touring Countries: China, South Africa

Allegro Ballet of Houston
Website: www.allegroballetofhouston.com/
Email: info@allegroballetofhouston.com
Phone: 281 496 4670
Address: 12680 Goar Road, US
Information: Allegro Ballet of Houston is a non profit organisation founded in 1951 by Emmamae Horn, and celebrates its 63rd Anniversary this year.
The company has been a member of Regional Dance America/SW since 1963, and is an honor company of the Southwest
Country: United States
Type: Ballet and Dance Company
Contact: co-Artistic Director Vanessa Brown
co-Artistic Director Peggy Girouard

Allyson Green Dance
Website: www.allysongreendance.com
Email: ag2011@allysongreendance.com
Phone: 619 269 9888
Address: 4364 60th Street, US
Information: ALLYSON GREEN choreographer and visual artist, grew up on the border of Mexico, in El Paso, Texas. She received a BFA cum laude in Visual Art (with Dance minor) from Washington University in St. Louis, Missouri. In 1999, Ms. Green was awarded the Jacob K. Javits Fellowship for graduate studies by the National Department of Education. She received her MFA in Choreography from the University of Wisconsin at Milwaukee in 2001, where she was named the Fine Arts Graduate student of the decade in 2005. Based in New York from 1986-2001, she performed with the companies of Yoshiko Chuma SOHK, Charles Moulton, Doug Varone, Randy Warshaw, and Bill Youn
Country: United States
Type: Ballet and Dance Company
Contact: Artistic Director Allyson Green
Touring Countries: Austria, Brazil, Belgium, Canada, France, Hungary, Macedonia, Portugal, Slovakia, Venezuela

Alonzo King's LINES Ballet
Website: www.linesballet.org
Email: info@linesballet.org
Phone: 415 863 3040
Address: 26 7th Street, US

Information: Alonzo King LINES Ballet is a celebrated contemporary ballet company that has been guided since 1982 by the unique Artistic vision of Alonzo King. Collaborating with noted composers, musicians, and visual artists from around the world, Alonzo King creates works that draw on a diverse set of deeply rooted cultural traditions, imbuing classical ballet with new exPressive potential. Alonzo King understands ballet as a science – founded on universal, geometric principles of energy and evolution – and continues to develop a new language of movement from its classical forms and techniques
Country: United States
Type: Ballet and Dance Company
Contact: project Manager Selby Schwartz
Email: selby@linesballet.org
Associate Artistic Director Robert Rosenwasser
Email: robert@linesballet.org
Artistic Director Alonzo King
technical Director Chris Griffin
Email: chris@linesballet.org
Executive Director Janette Gitler
Email: janette@linesballet.org
Social Media: @LinesBallet www.facebook.com/AlonzoKingLINESBallet
Venues: Center for the Arts Theater, SF 750

Alpha Omega Theatrical Dance Company
Website: www.alphaomegadance.org
Email: info@alphaomegadance.org
Phone: 212 749 0095
Address: 711 Amsterdam Ave, Suite 4E, US
Information: Alpha Omega Theatrical Dance Company creates, performs and educates through the art of dance. We explore, celebrate and provoke thoughts while connecting cultures and bridging audiences to contribute to life's infinite exPressions. Alpha Omega Theatrical Dance Company was founded in 1972 by Ronn Pratt, Dolores Vanison-Blakley, and Miriam Greaves to provide a platform for minority dancers and choreographers. A creative venue for artists and a safe haven for inner city youth it has served thousands for over four decades
Country: United States
Type: Ballet and Dance Company
Contact: Artistic Director Enrique Cruz DeJesus
Associate Director Clark Donna
Executive Director Dolores Vanison-Blakely
Email: vanison711@aol.com
Social Media: facebook.com/AOTDC

Alpha-Omega Theatrical Dance Company
Website: www.alphaomegadance.org
Email: alphaomegadance@aol.com
Phone: 212 749 0095
Address: 711 Amsterdam Avenue, Suite 4E, US
Information: Alpha Omega Theatrical Dance Company creates, performs and educates through the art of dance. We explore, celebrate and provoke thoughts while connecting cultures and bridging audiences to contribute to life's infinite exPressions. Alpha Omega Theatrical Dance Company was founded in 1972 by Ronn Pratt, Dolores Vanison-Blakley, and Miriam Greaves to provide a platform for minority dancers and choreographers. A creative venue for artists and a safe haven for inner city youth it has served thousands for over four decades
Country: United States
Type: Ballet and Dance Company
Contact: Executive Director Dolores Vanison-Blakely
Artistic Director Enrique Cruz DeJesus

Alvin Ailey American Dance Theater
Website: www.alvinailey.org
Email: info@alvinailey.org
Phone: 212 405 9000
Address: The Joan Weill Center for Dance, 405 W. 55th Street at 9th Avenue, US
Information: Alvin Ailey American Dance Theater grew from a now-fabled performance in March 1958 at the 92nd Street Y in New York City. Led by Alvin Ailey and a group of young African-American modern dancers, that performance changed forever the perception of American dance
Country: United States
Type: Ballet and Dance Company
Contact: General Manager Calvin Hunt
company Manager Dacquiri Smittick
Artistic Director Robert Battle
finance Director Pam Robinson
development Director Bennett Rink
Social Media: www.facebook.com/AlvinAileyAmericanDanceTheater
Venues: City Center Theater 2700; Joan Weill Centre for Dance (black box theatre) 295

American Ballet Theatre
Website: www.abt.org
Email: abt@abt.org
Phone: 212 477 3030
Address: 3rd Floor, 890 Broadway, US
Information: ABT isn't just a company. It's a collaboration. Dedicated, passionate people who come together to make sure that the commitment to the best in dance and movement is upheld, and available to all who seek it out

Country: United States
Type: Ballet and Dance Company
Contact: Director of Marketing James Timm
Executive Director Rachael Moore
Director of Press, public relations Kelly Ryan
Artistic Director Kevin McKenzie
Director of Productions and operations David Lansky
Social Media: @ABTBallet www.facebook.com/AmericanBalletTheatre
Venues: NYC Metropolitan Opera House 4000, NYC City Center 2684

American Indian Dance Theatre
Website: www.americanindiandancetheatre.org/
Email: info@americanindiandancetheatre.com
Phone: 323 463 1914
Address: 1703 South Delaware Ave., US
Information: American Indian Dance Theatre has been sharing the rich culture Native Americans with the world for 20 years
Country: United States
Type: Ballet and Dance Company
Contact: Producer Buddy Wilson

American Repertory Ballet
Website: www.arballet.org
Email: glustig@arballet.org
Phone: 732 249 1254
Address: 7 Livingston Ave, US
Information: American Repertory Ballet's mission is to bring the joy, beauty, artistry and discipline of classical and contemporary dance to New Jersey and nationwide audiences and to dance students through Artistic and educational programs. The organisation comprises: American Repertory Ballet professional company, the preeminent classical and contemporary ballet company in the state; Princeton Ballet School, one of the largest and most respected non-profit dance schools in the nation; and ARB's Access & Enrichment initiatives, including the long-running and acclaimed DANCE POWER program
Country: United States
Type: Ballet and Dance Company
Contact: Artistic Director Douglas Martin
Managing Director Christine Chen
school Director Mary Pat Robertson
Social Media: @ARBallet www.facebook.com/americanrepertoryballet
Venues: State Theatre (New Brunswick) 1840, McCarter Theatre (Princeton) 1100, New Jersey Performing Arts Center (Newark, NJ) 2700, Victoria Theater 500, Prudential Mall 2800, Joyce Theatre NYC

Amy Marshall Dance Company
Website: www.amymarshall.com
Email: chadlevy@amymarshall.com
Phone: 917 647 9477
Address: 28-43 41st Street, 2nd Floor, US
Information: Choreographer Amy Marshall and Executive Director Chad Levy co-founded the Amy Marshall Dance Company in 2000 in order to realise a vision of dance theater as a visual metaphor for the human spirit. Ms. Marshall's choreography pays tribute to both the beauty and tribulations of life's experiences through dramatic movement. The work's emotional structure explodes across the stage with dramatic confrontation and then suddenly resolves itself into a poignancy of classical dimensions. The virtuosic performance of the dancers leaves audiences awed and delighted
Country: United States
Type: Ballet and Dance Company
Contact: Artistic Director Amy Marshall
Email: amy@amymarshall.com
Executive Director Chad Levy
Email: chadlevy@amymarshall.com
Social Media: www.facebook.com/pages/Amy-Marshall-Dance-Company/116363793727

Anglo-American Ballet
Email: angloballet@aol.com
Phone: 212 307 5412
Address: 574 5th Ave, Floor 2, US
Information: The Anglo-American Ballet: A small professional company that performed at such venues as Lincoln Center – Houston International Festival – Edinburgh International Festival, Scotland – Boston First Night – the Colden Center for the Performing Arts – Queens Theatre in the Park and York College for the Performing Arts, NY. The Anglo-American Ballet also presented "Educational" and "Outreach" programs for such noted accredited organizations as the New York Department of Cultural Affairs, "On Stage Ltd" and Massachusetts Cultural Council. The appeal of the company was achieved through the diversity in its repertoire and dancers
Country: United States
Type: Ballet and Dance Company
Contact: Artistic Director, resident choreographer Catherine Kingsley
ballet master, company Manager Larry Crabtree

Anjani's Kathak Dance of India
Website: www.sundarkalakendra.org
Email: sundarkalakendra@aol.com
Phone: 909 468 9681
Address: 1934 Peaceful Hills Road, US
Information: Sundar Kala Kendra Foundation was established in 1985 to promote Indian classical Kathak dance in the USA. The foundation is an umbrella organisation for the Sundar Kala Kendra Kathak dance school and the Anjani's Kathak Dance of India the professional touring company. The foundation is an only such organisation in Southern California that promotes Kathak dance through teaching, performing, presenting artist and creating various Artistic Productions and presenting them at various venues in the greater Los Angeles area and in the USA
Country: United States
Type: Ballet and Dance Company
Contact: Artistic Director & choreographer Anjani Ambegaokar

Anthony Shay's AVAZ International Dance Theatre
Website: www.stanford.edu/group/psa/events/1998-99/avaz/index.utf8.html
Email: AVAZIDT@aol.com
Phone: 323 664 9041
Address: 3756 Aloha St, US
Information: Anthony Shay was choreographer and Artistic Director of the AVAZ International Dance Theatre, a group he founded in 1977. In this period he has choreographed over 150 works for both his own company and on commission to other groups. Currently performs contemporary full-length, narrative dance dramas based on themes from Persian literature
Country: United States
Type: Ballet and Dance Company
Contact: Artistic & Managing Director Anthony Shay
booking agent Gayle Hooks

Arc Dance Company
Website: www.arcdance.com
Email: info@arcdance.com
Phone: 206 352 0798
Address: 9250 14th AVE NW, US
Information: ARC Dance fosters the creative work of choreographers and dancers to produce moving contemporary ballet that engages and inspires a diverse audience and enriches cultural life. ARC brings the community closer to dance by presenting performances and educational programs in intimate settings as well as its own studio facility in the North Ballard/Crown Hill neighborhood of Seattle
Country: United States
Type: Ballet and Dance Company
Contact: Artistic Director Marie Chong
Social Media: @arcdance www.facebook.com/ARCDance?v=wall

ARKA Ballet
Website: www.arkaballet.org
Email: info@arkaballet.org
Phone: 301 587 6225
Address: PO Box 11561, US
Information: Under the direction of Artistic Director Roudolf Kharatian and Associate Director Jonathan Jordan, ARKA Ballet's performances feature a mix of old and new, including rarely-seen gems of the classical repertoire and new works by some of the areas up and coming choreographers
Country: United States
Type: Ballet and Dance Company
Contact: Artistic Director Roudolf Kharatian
Associate Artistic Director Jonathan Jordan

Art of Black Dance & Music, Inc.
Website: www.abdm.net
Email: deamabattle@yahoo.com
Phone: 617 666 1859
Address: 32 Cameron Ave, US
Information: Since its inception in l975, De Ama Battle and her troupe the Art of Black Dance & Music (ABDM) has studied, taught and performed the common history of humankind through the diverse cultural artistry of the African Diaspora. They reach people of all ages, cultural backgrounds, and those at various dance and music levels. They open the door to a world of dance, music and folklore as experienced through the performing arts
Country: United States
Type: Ballet and Dance Company
Contact: Director De Ama Battle

Aspen Santa Fe Ballet
Website: www.aspensantafeballet.com
Email: stacey@aspensantafeballet.com
Phone: 970 925 7175
Address: 0245 Sage Way, US
Information: Aspen Santa Fe Ballet's bold vision – top global choreographers, distinctive groundbreaking repertoire, and virtuoso dancers – has fostered a jewel of a dance company in the American West. The company's pioneering spirit arises from a dual set of home cities: Aspen, nestled in the Rocky Mountains, and Santa Fe, gracing the Southwestern plateau. Shaping the cultural landscape of these communities – and influencing the dance field at large – is a contemporary ballet company now two decades old
Country: United States
Type: Ballet and Dance Company
Contact: Artistic Director Tom Mossbrucker
Email: tom@aspensantafeballet.org
development Director Zander Higbie
Email: zander@aspensantafeballet.org
Executive Director Jean Phillipe Malaty
Email: jp@aspensantafeballet.org
Director of Marketing Jennica Deely
Email: jennica@aspensantafeballet.org
technical Director Eric Johnson
Email: eric@aspensantafeballet.org
Social Media: www.facebook.com/aspensantafebal
Venues: Wheeler Opera House

Atlanta Ballet Co
Website: www.atlantaballet.com
Email: publicrelations@atlantaballet.com
Phone: 404 873 5811
Address: 1695 Marietta Blvd NW, Michael C. Carlos Dance Centre, US
Information: Founded in 1929, Atlanta Ballet is one of the premier dance companies in the country and the official State Ballet of Georgia. Atlanta Ballet's eclectic repertoire spans ballet history, highlighted by beloved classics and inventive originals. After 87 years, Atlanta Ballet continues its commitment to share and educate audiences on the empowering joy of dance
Country: United States
Type: Ballet and Dance Company
Contact: Executive Director Artruro Jacobus
Email: ajacobus@atlantaballet.com
Marketing Director Tricia Ekholm
Email: teckholm@atlantaballet.com
Public Relations Manager Julia Berg
Email: publicrelations@atlantaballet.com
Artistic Director Gennadi Nedvigin
Social Media: @AtlantaBallet www.facebook.com/AtlantaBallet
Venues: The Fox Theatre 4500 Cobb Energy Performing Arts Centre 2750 Alliance Stage at the Woodruff Arts Centre 784

Augusta Ballet
Website: www.augustaballet.org
Email: info@augustaballet.org
Phone: 706 261 0555
Address: 1301 Greene Street, US
Information: Augusta Ballet is on a mission to foster a culture of dance appreciation and support across a diverse audience of all ages in the Augusta community and across the CSRA. They achieve this mission by presenting high-quality classical and contemporary ballet performances, offering free (or low cost) educational opportunities to local youth and offering unique events aimed at cultivating the next generation of ballet and dance audiences
Country: United States
Type: Ballet and Dance Company
Contact: founder Ron Colton
Social Media: @augustaballet www.facebook.com/augusta.ballet
Venues: Imperial Theatre 830

Avodah
Website: www.avodahdance.org
Email: jewelzkg@yahoo.com
Phone: 917 822 9665
Address: c/o HUC-JIR, One West 4th Street, US
Information: Avodah Dance is a New York City based non-profit 501(c) (3) modern dance company that has at the core of its mission the idea of a Jewish and universal value, Tikkun Olam, which means to "repair the world." Using dance as a tool for social change, Avodah Dance brings the art of dance to diverse populations with the goal of uplifting individuals and building community. Avodah Dance offers residencies, workshops, and performances in women's prisons, community centers, and synagogues, universities and public schools as well as traditional theater venues
Country: United States
Type: Ballet and Dance Company
Contact: Artistic Director Julie Gayer
Social Media: @avodahdance www.facebook.com/avodahdance
Venues: Hebrew Union College 140

AXIS Dance Company
Website: www.axisdance.org
Email: info@axisdance.org
Phone: 510 625 0110
Address: 1428 Alice Street, Suite 200, US
Information: AXIS Dance Company has become one of the world's most acclaimed and innovative ensembles of performers with and without disabilities. Founded in 1987, AXIS has paved the way for a powerful contemporary dance form called physically integrated dance. In 1997, Judith Smith led the company to new heights. Under her Artistic direction, AXIS expanded from in-house choreographers to various commissions from outside the company
Country: United States
Type: Ballet and Dance Company
Contact: Artistic Director Judith Smith

Email: judy@axisdance.org
Marketing and administrative assistant Christy Rotman
Email: info@axisdance.org
education Director Annika Presley
Email: annika@axisdance.org
Social Media: @AXISDanceCo www.facebook.com/
axisdancecomp

Ballet Arizona
Website: www.balletaz.org
Email: questions@balletaz.org
Phone: 602 381 0184
Address: 2835 E. Washington Street, US
Country: United States
Type: Ballet and Dance Company
Contact: school Manager Alison Morse
Email: school@balletaz.org
Director of Production Michael Panvini
Email: mpanvini@balletaz.org
Social Media: @BalletArizona www.facebook.com/
balletaz

Ballet Arkansas
Website: www.balletarkansas.org
Email: info@balletarkansas.org
Phone: 501 223 5150
Address: 1521 Merrill Dr, US
Information: A community, a city and a state thrives when it provides a well balanced atmosphere in which its citizens can partake. This well balanced atmosphere attracts businesses and strengthens the roots of the community. Ballet Arkansas is committed to providing the vital Artistic world of ballet. Whether it is through the performers or through the audience, the Productions of Ballet Arkansas promise to enrich the lives of all of those involved
Country: United States
Type: Ballet and Dance Company
Contact: Executive Director Lauren Strother
Social Media: @BalletArkansas www.facebook.com/
BalletAR
Venues: Robinson Centre Music Hall 2636, Wildwood Park for the Performing Arts 625

Ballet Austin
Website: www.balletaustin.org
Email: eugene.alvarez@balletaustin.org
Phone: 512 476 9151
Address: 501 West 3rd Street, US
Information: Founded in 1956 by Barbara Carson, the Ballet Austin Academy is the official ballet school of Ballet Austin, and one of the largest in the U.S. We're committed to providing the highest quality dance instruction to students, and currently the Academy has more than 800 students. Each area has a codified syllabus designed to facilitate the maximum physical, mental and emotional development appropriate to the age and physical ability of each student. Once a student enters the Lower School, the rigorous training of ballet technique begins. While the benefits of this training are all inclusive, the Academy's focus is to provide what is necessary for a professional career in dance
Country: United States
Type: Ballet and Dance Company
Contact: Executive Director Cookie Ruiz
Associate Artistic Director Michelle Martin
company manager Eugine Alvarez
Artistic Director Stephen Mills
Marketing Timothy Dillon
Social Media: @BalletAustin www.facebook.com/balle-taustin
Venues: Bass Concert Hall 3000

Ballet Chicago
Website: www.balletchicago.org
Email: info@balletchicago.org
Phone: 312 251 8838
Address: 17 North State Street, 19th Floor, US
Information: Ballet Chicago is an internationally recognized professional track school of ballet that creates exceptional dancers and people. Ballet Chicago believes every aspiring artist deserves the opportunity to explore his or her full potential, and strives to make classical ballet training accessible to all talented students who have the desire to dance. Ballet Chicago is dedicated to rigorous technical training in a culture that fosters personal growth and by teaching impeccable technique as well as fundamental life skills, their students go on to find success in dance and life
Country: United States
Type: Ballet and Dance Company
Contact: Artistic Director Daniel Duell
school Director Patricia Blair
Marketing Margo Ruter
Social Media: @BalletChicago www.facebook.com/
BalletChicago
Venues: various venues in Chicago area

Ballet Hawaii
Website: www.ballethawaii.org
Email: info@ballethawaii.org
Phone: 808 521 8600
Address: 777 South Hotel Street, Suite 101, US

Information: Ballet Hawaii has been enriching Hawaii's cultural environment by teaching, promoting, presenting, and producing dance since 1976. Originally a support group for the Honolulu City Ballet, this non-profit organisation provides opportunities for self-growth, while instilling self-esteem and pride in its students, patrons and audiences. Its classes are focused on building self-confidence through accomplishment, while its presentations of world-class performances provides the community with the priceless gift of professional quality dance
Country: United States
Type: Ballet and Dance Company
Contact: Executive Director John Parkinson
Email: John@ballethawaii.org
Artistic Director Pamela Taylor-Tongg
Email: Pam@ballethawaii.org
Social Media: www.facebook.com/BalletHI

Ballet Hispanico
Website: www.ballethispanico.org
Email: info@ballethispanico.org
Phone: 212 362 6710
Address: 167 West 89th Street, US
Information: Celebrating 42 years of dance and culture, Ballet Hispanico is recognised as the nation's premier Latino dance organization. Led by Artistic Director Eduardo Vilaro, the Company boasts a rich and diverse repertory of over 100 works by the foremost choreographers and emerging artists of our time. The works expand on founder Tina Ramirez's legacy of exploring the diversity of Latino culture through a fusion of classical, Latin, and contemporary dance powered by theatricality and passion
Country: United States
Type: Ballet and Dance Company
Contact: Executive Director Lee Koonce
Email: lkoonce@ballethispanico.org
Artistic Director Eduardo Vilaro
Email: evilaro@ballethispanico.org
Social Media: @BalletHispanicoww.facebook.com/
ballethispanico?ref=ts
Touring Countries: numerous appearances in major cities and festivals throughout the US, Europe and South America
Number of Performers: 13

Ballet Idaho
Website: www.balletidaho.org
Email: info@balletidaho.org
Phone: 208 343 0556
Address: 501 S. 8th Street, Suite A, US
Information: Ballet Idaho has been performing in Idaho since 1972. Currently it has an Artistic staff of 25 dancers, a professional teaching staff of ten, a professional costume designer, a Production staff of three, and an administrative staff of 6. Up to 40 musicians from the Boise Philharmonic and two pianists provide musical accompaniment for Ballet Idaho's performances, rehearsals and classes depending on the Production or project
Country: United States
Type: Ballet and Dance Company
Contact: Artistic Director Peter Anastos
Email: panastos@balletidaho.org
Executive Director Paul Kaine
Email: pkaine@balletidaho.org
Social Media: @BalletIdaho www.facebook.com/#!/
ballet.idaho
Annual Performances: 20
Number of Performers: 65
Venues: Morrison Center for the Performing Arts 2090

Ballet Magnificat!
Website: www.balletmagnificat.com
Email: info@balletmagnificat.com
Phone: 601 977 1001
Address: 5406 I-55 North, US
Information: Ballet Magnificat! was founded in 1986. Magnificat is Latin for "to magnify Him". It is derived from "Mary's Song" of praise in the 1st Chapter of the Gospel of Luke when she first learned she was to be the mother of the Messiah. Ballet Magnificat! is an arts organisation dedicated to presenting the good news of Jesus Christ to the whole world
Country: United States
Type: Ballet and Dance Company
Contact: founder & Director
Keith Thibodeaux
Artistic Director Kathy Thibodeaux
Social Media: @BalletMag www.facebook.com/pages/
Ballet-Magnificat/174161902975

Ballet Memphis
Website: www.balletmemphis.org
Email: karl@balletmemphis.org
Phone: 901 737 7322
Address: 7950 Trinity Road, US
Information: Identified as a "national treasure" by the Ford Foundation, Ballet Memphis annually produces more original work than any other company the size and continues to breathe new life into the classical ballets have long enjoyed

Country: United States
Type: Ballet and Dance Company
Contact: Artistic Director Dorothy Gunther Pugh
Associate Artistic Director Karl Condon
Social Media: @balletmemphis www.facebook.com/
balletmemphis
Venues: Orpheum Theatre 2200

Ballet New England and the Center for Dance Education
Website: www.gbadance.com
Email: common.gbad@gmail.com
Phone: 207 475 0110
Address: Great Bay Academy of Dance, One Route 236, US
Information: Great Bay Academy of Dance (GBAD) is the Seacoast's Non-Competition Dance Education Center for dancers of all ages. This means that they are focused on dance as an art form and as an education. Being a non-competition dance education center means that 100% of the time spent at GBAD is focused on learning and improving dance fundamentals and technique along with having fun. GBAD's strength is in the Vaganova technique of classical ballet
Country: United States
Type: Ballet and Dance Company
Contact: Executive Director Martha Lemire
Social Media: www.facebook.com/pages/GBADs-An-1836-Portsmouth-Nutcracker/206125712790012
Venues: The Music Hall 900; Newport Opera House 650; The Palace Theatre 880; The Capitol Center for the Arts, Concord 1250

Ballet NY Inc
Website: www.balletny.org
Email: balletny.Directors@gmail.com
Phone: 718 543 2760
Address: 4445 Post Road, #3H, US
Information: Ballet NY is the New York City-based ballet company, founded in 1997 by former New York City Ballet Principal Ballerina Judith Fugate and International Guest Artist Medhi Bahiri. It is a company of accomplished principal and soloist dancers. Foremost in Ballet NY's mission is to offer emerging choreographers the opportunity to create new works on accomplished dancers. The Company is committed to keeping ticket prices affordable in an effort to attract, cultivate and educate new audiences for dance
Country: United States
Type: Ballet and Dance Company
Contact: co-Artistic Director Judith Fugate
Social Media: @balletnyfacebook.com/medhi.bahiri
Touring Countries: USA, Mexico, Canada, Europe
Venues: Joyce Theater, The Ailey Citigroup Theater, j New York (470), Cowell Theater, San Francisco, University of CA, Santa Cruz, Cerritos Performing Arts Center (CA), The Egg, Albany, NY,

Ballet Oklahoma
Website: www.okcballet.com
Email: info@okcballet.com
Phone: 405 843 9898
Address: 7421 North Classen, US
Information: Oklahoma City Ballet inspires its audience through classical and contemporary dance performances, a strong educational program and community service. The company began under the Artistic direction of Ballet Russe de Monte Carlo dancers Yvonne Chouteau and Miguel Terekhov in the Science and Arts Foundation building on the Oklahoma City Fairgrounds
Country: United States
Type: Ballet and Dance Company
Contact: Artistic Director Robert Mills
Social Media: @okcballet www.facebook.com/Oklaho-maCityBallet
Venues: Civic Center Music Hall 2500

Ballet San Jose (Silicon Valley)
Website: www.balletsj.org
Email: lkopp@balletsanjose.org
Phone: 408 288 2820
Address: 40 North First Street, US
Information: Silicon Valley Ballet reflects the bold inventiveness of its high-tech home base – presenting groundbreaking programs that explore the digital-physical blur while enriching the community with brilliant artistry. As its widely inclusive engagement programs attract new audiences, SVB also honors its proud heritage as one of the two largest ballet companies in California, originally created as San Jose Cleveland Ballet in 1986, under founding Artistic Director, Dennis Nahat
Country: United States
Type: Ballet and Dance Company
Contact: Artistic & Executive Director
Stephanie Ziesel
Email: sziesel@balletsj.org
Director, Marketing & pr
Lee Kopp
Email: lkopp@balletsj.org
chief financial officer Sabrina Seiden
Email: sseiden@balletsj.org
Social Media: @balletsj www.facebook.com/BalletSJ

Ballet Tech
Website: www.ballettech.org
Email: questions@ballettech.org
Phone: 212 777 7710
Address: 890 Broadway, US
Information: Ballet Tech is a New York City public school offering its students a quality academic education and intensive and rigorous ballet training designed to develop professional dancers. The school is a collaboration between the NYC Department of Education and Eliot Feld's Ballet Tech Foundation. Unlike any other ballet school, the only criterion for enrollment is innate ability; Ballet Tech provides training and dance clothes to its entire student body free of charge
Country: United States
Type: Ballet and Dance Company
Contact: President, choreographer Eliot Feld
Director of operations Maggie Christ
Social Media: @eliotfeld
Venues: Joyce Theatre 452

Ballet Tennessee
Website: www.ballettennessee.org
Email: anna@ballettennessee.org
Phone: 423 821 2055
Address: 3202 Kelly's Ferry Road, US
Information: Based in Chattanooga since 1987, Ballet Tennessee embodies the spirit of community through dance by fulfilling its mission with professional track, outreach and educational programs, plus well-crafted performances. With the belief that "Everyone benefits from ballet, " all projects have strong elements of outreach to under-served audiences, youth-programming, and arts in education
Country: United States
Type: Ballet and Dance Company
Contact: Artistic Director Anna Baker-van Cura
Email: anna@ballettennessee.org
Executive Director Barry Van Cura
Email: barry@ballettennessee.org
Venues: Tivoli Theatre 1750, Roland Haze Concert Hall 500, Memorial Auditorium 3800

Ballet Theatre of New Mexico
Website: www.brtnm.com
Email: brt@brtnm.com
Phone: 505 888 1054
Address: 6913 Natalie NE, US
Information: For over twenty-five years, Ballet Repertory Theatre has been known as the ballet company at the KiMo. Ballet Repertory Theatre have worked hard to become the premiere ballet company for Albuquerque, integrating themselves into the community and — just like Albuquerque — truly being unique. Every year, the company expands its repertoire and reaches new audiences, joyously demonstrating its mastery of both classics and innovative works
Country: United States
Type: Ballet and Dance Company
Contact: Executive Director Katherine Giese
Artistic coordinator Alex Ossadnik

Ballet West
Website: www.balletwest.org
Email: info@balletwest.org
Phone: 801 869 6900
Address: 50 West 200 South, US
Information: Ballet West was established in Salt Lake City in 1963. Willam F. Christensen was the company's first Artistic Director, co-founding the company together with Utah's "First Lady of the Arts" Glenn Walker Wallace. In 1951, Christensen had established the first ballet department in an American university at The University of Utah and with the tireless assistance of Mrs. Enid Cosgriff this program grew into the Utah Civic Ballet, Ballet West's first incarnation. But this was not the first ballet company Willam Christensen's founded. Along with his brothers Lew and Harold, Christensen made history by establishing the oldest ballet company in the western United States, the San Francisco Ballet
Country: United States
Type: Ballet and Dance Company
Contact: music Director Terence Kern
Artistic Director Adam Sklute
Production Director David Heuvel
Executive Director Jóhann Jacobs
assistant conductor Jared Oaks
Social Media: @BalletWest1 www.facebook.com/BalletWestOfficialPage
Venues: Capitol Theatre 1900

BalletMet Columbus
Website: www.balletmet.org
Email: dance@balletmet.org
Phone: 614 229 4860
Address: 322 Mt. Vernon Ave., US
Information: Since 1978, BalletMet has brought incredible dance to theatres, studios and classrooms in Central Ohio and beyond. Located in the heart of downtown Columbus, BalletMet boasts an entire city block comprising a black box theatre performance space, seven dance studios, administrative offices and costume and scene shop
Country: United States
Type: Ballet and Dance Company
Contact: Artistic Director Gerard Charles
Executive Director Cheri Mitchell
Email: cmitchell@balletmet.org
Social Media: @BalletMet www.facebook.com/BalletMet
Venues: Ohio Theatre 2897, Capitol Theatre in the Vern Riffe Center 856, BalletMet Performance Space 250

Ballets Trockadero de Monte Carlo
Website: www.trockadero.org
Email: mail@trockadero.com
Phone: 212 865 7925
Address: Box 1325 Gracie Station, US
Information: Celebrating its 40th Anniversary season, Les Ballets Trockadero de Monte Carlo was founded in 1974 by a group of ballet enthusiasts for the purpose of presenting a playful, entertaining view of traditional, classical ballet in parody form and en travesti, Les Ballets Trockadero first performed in the late-late shows in Off-Off Broadway lofts. The TROCKS, as they are affectionately known, quickly garnered a major critical essay by Arlene Croce in The New Yorker, and combined with reviews in The New York Times and The Village Voice, established the Company as an Artistic and popular success
Country: United States
Type: Ballet and Dance Company
Contact: Artistic Director Tory Dobrin
Executive Director Eugene McDougle
Production Manager Isabel Martinez-Rivera
Social Media: @TrocksB www.facebook.com/thetrocks
Touring Countries: NY, Italy, Holland, Vienna and Paris

Baton Rouge Ballet Theatre
Website: www.batonrougeballet.org/home.html/home.html.html
Email: BRBTInfo@batonrougeballet.org
Phone: 225 766 8379
Address: PO Box 82288, US
Information: The Baton Rouge Ballet Theatre, under the direction of Molly Buchmann and Sharon Mathews, is a non-profit organisation chartered in 1960 to promote the development and advancement of ballet by maintaining a first rate dance company in the Baton Rouge area. Today, its scope has been extended to include communities outside the Baton Rouge area and to include other forms of dance as well as ballet
Country: United States
Type: Ballet and Dance Company
Contact: administrative Director Gayle Beard
Email: administrator@batonrouge.org
co-Artistic Director Molly Buchmann
Email: molly@batonrougeballet.org
co-Artistic Director Sharon Mathews
Email: sharon@batonrougeballet.org
Social Media: @BRBalletTheatre www.facebook.com/batonrougeballettheatre
Venues: Centroplex Theater for Performing Arts

Battery Dance Company
Website: www.batterydance.org
Email: battery@batterydance.org
Phone: 212 219 3910
Address: 380 Broadway, Fifth Floor, US
Information: Battery Dance Company performs on the world's stages, teaches, presents, and advocates for the field of dance. Battery Dance Company is dedicated to the pursuit of Artistic excellence and the availability of the Arts to everyone. An integral part of the fabric of New York City for 35 years, Battery supports the creative process; educates children in the New York City schools; enriches the General public through local programs and performances, national and international tours, and international arts exchange programs
Country: United States
Type: Ballet and Dance Company
Contact: Artistic Director and President Jonathan Hollander
Email: jonathan@batterydance.org
Social Media: @batterydance www.facebook.com/pages/Battery-Dance-Company/110799258955011
Venues: various outdoor venues throughout the city of New York, 3LD Arts& Technology Center

Bebe Miller Company
Website: www.bebemillercompany.org
Email: info@bebemillercompany.org
Phone: 212 777 1340
Address: 40 2nd Ave #404, US
Information: The Company celebrated its 25th year in 2010, and after two decades of operating as a traditional New York City touring company, the BMC family members now reside in various locations around the U.S. New work is developed over a period of years in long-term residencies that bring BMC dancers and project collaborators together for creative exploration, rehearsals, and community-based activities
Country: United States
Type: Ballet and Dance Company
Contact: company Director Caterina Bartha
Artistic Director Bebe Miller
Social Media: www.facebook.com/bebemillercompany
Venues: up to 4000

Big Dance Theater
Website: www.bigdancetheater.org
Email: mchickok@cs.com
Phone: 917 612 5381
Address: 303 Clinton Street, US
Information: Founded in 1991, Big Dance Theater is known for its inspired use of dance, music, text and visual design. The company often works with wildly incongruent source material, weaving and braiding disparate strands into multi-dimensional performance. Led by Co-Artistic Directors Annie-B Parson and Paul Lazar, Big Dance has delved into the literary work of such authors as Twain, Tanizaki, Wellman, Euripides and Flaubert, and dance is used as both frame and metaphor to theatricalize these writings
Country: United States
Type: Ballet and Dance Company
Contact: Artistic Director Annie B Parson
Producer and General Manager Aaron Rosenblum
Artistic Director Paul Lazar
Social Media: @BigDanceTheater www.facebook.com/bigdancetheater

Bill Evans Dance Co
Website: www.billevansdance.org
Email: don@billevansdance.org
Phone: 585 395 5134
Address: Benedict Beech, US
Information: William "Bill" Evans has led the development of Laban/Bartenieff-based dance technique for four decades. Almost 50 renowned dance educators have become certified in the Evans Method. 2016 will be the 40th anniversary of the Bill Evans Summer Institute of Dance, begun in Seattle in 1977 with such illustrious artist/teachers as Jim Coleman, Kitty Daniels, Regina DeCosse, William Evans, Peggy Hackney, Shirley Jenkins, Gregg Lizenbery, Daphne Lowell, Debbie Poulsen, Joana Mendl Shaw and Pam Shick
Country: United States
Type: Ballet and Dance Company
Contact: Manager Don Halquist
Email: don@billevansdance.org
Artistic Director Bill Evans
Email: billevansdance@hotmail.com
Venues: KiMo Theatre, Albuquerque 700, South Broadway Cultural Center Albuquerque 325, Rodey Theatre, University of New Mexico Center for the Arts Albuquerque 450

Bill T Jones/Arnie Zane Dance Company
Website: www.newyorklivearts.org/
Email: info@billtjones.org
Phone: 212 691 6500
Address: 219 West 19th Street, #1, US
Information: Founded in 1982, the Bill T. Jones/Arnie Zane Dance Company was born out of an 11-year collaboration between Bill T. Jones and Arnie Zane (1948–1988). During this time, they redefined the duet form and foreshadowed issues of identity, form and social commentary that would change the face of American dance. The Company has performed worldwide in over 200 cities in 40 countries on every major continent and is recognised as one of the most innovative and powerful forces in the dance-theater world
Country: United States
Type: Ballet and Dance Company
Contact: Executive Director Jean Davidson
Artistic Director Bill T Jones
Email: bill@billtjones.org
Social Media: @NewYorkLiveArts www.facebook.com/NewYorkLiveArts
Touring Countries: France, Italy, U.K., Germany, Portugal, Australia, Brazil
Venues: Joyce Theater 472, Brooklyn Academy of Music 2100

Bill Young and Dancers
Website: www.panix.com
Email: wgy@panix.com
Phone: 212 925 6573
Address: 100 Grand Street, 2nd floor, US
Information: Bill Young and Dancers reach toward the outermost extremes of physical dance – the movements topple over each other with the intensity and urgency of a white-water rapid – while forging a choreographic world full of emotional range and power. At once abstract and intensely felt, the dancing springs from an investigation of the immediacy of human interactions on stage, and a fascination with the inherent character and exPressive power of the purely physical impulse
Country: United States
Type: Ballet and Dance Company
Contact: Artistic Director Bill Young
booking Art Becofsky
management Catherine Peila
Artistic Director Colleen Thomas

Bodyvox
Website: www.bodyvox.com
Email: info@bodyvox.com
Phone: 503 229 0627
Address: 1201 NW 17 Avenue, US

Information: Based in Portland, Oregon, BodyVox's movement surges from a fascination with the endless possibilities of the human body in motion, informed by years of cross training and layers of experience. Hampton and Roland are distinguished artists on the world stage, formed by their years working as creators and performers with innovative dance companies Momix, ISO Dance, and Pilobolus. BodyVox builds upon this tradition of excellence with a unique voice that is equally influenced by its Northwest roots and world view
Country: United States
Type: Ballet and Dance Company
Contact: Artistic Director Ashley Roland
General Manager Una Loughran
Artistic Director Jamey Hampton
Social Media: www.facebook.com/bodyvox
Venues: Silva Concert Hall 700, Arlene Schnitzer Concert Hall 3000, Portland State University 400, Portland Opera 2500, other theaters 250-2500

Boston Ballet
Website: www.bostonballet.org
Email: info@bostonballet.org
Phone: 617 695 6950
Address: 19 Clarendon Street, US
Information: Boston Ballet maintains a repertoire of classical, neo-classical and contemporary works, ranging from full-length story ballets to new works by some of today's finest choreographers. Boston Ballet's second company, Boston Ballet II, is comprised of pre-professional dancers who gain experience by performing with the Company and independently, presenting lecture-demonstrations and special programs to audiences throughout the Northeast
Country: United States
Type: Ballet and Dance Company
Contact: Director of Marketing and communications Sharon Rice
Artistic Director Mikko Nissinen
Executive Director Valerie Wilder
Social Media: @BostonBallet www.facebook.com/bostonballet
Venues: Wang Theatre for Performing Arts 3600, Opera House 2600

Boston Liturgical Dance Ensemble, The
Website: www.blde.org
Email: blde@bc.edu
Phone: 617 552 6130
Address: 28 Commonwealth Avenue, US
Information: The Boston Liturgical Dance Ensemble is an Artistic company committed to the integration of dance and religious exPression. As a nonprofit organisation with outreach to the community, the company's work is threefold: performing of sacred dance works in theater and church venues, promoting educational workshops and classes in sacred and liturgical dance, and integrating dance ministry in liturgical prayer and worship
Country: United States
Type: Ballet and Dance Company
Contact: Associated Artistic Director Jamie Huggins
President & Artistic Director
Rev. Robert VerEecke
Managing Director Carol Coggio Faherty
Venues: Robsham Theater 591

Bowen McCauley Dance
Website: www.bmdc.org
Email: dance@bmdc.org
Phone: 703 910 5175
Address: 818 N. Quincy Street, Suite 104, US
Country: United States
Type: Ballet and Dance Company
Contact: Artistic Director Lucy Bowen McCauley
Email: lucy@bmdc.org
Executive Director Ricki Marion
Email: ricki@bmdc.org
music Director Larry Alan Smith
Social Media: @BMDCdance www.facebook.com/pages/Bowen-McCauley-Dance/35613804630

BREAK! The Urban Funk Spectacular
Website: www.loveProductions.com
Email: info@loveProductions.com
Phone: 212 714 9197
Address: 400 W 43rd Street, Suite 10R, US
Country: United States
Type: Ballet and Dance Company
Contact: contact Love Productions Inc
Venues: up to 15000

Bridgman|Packer Dance
Website: www.bridgmanpacker.org
Email: dancebp@gmail.com
Phone: 212 278 8111
Address: Pentacle, 75 Broad Street, #304, US
Information: Art Bridgman and Myrna Packer, Guggenheim Fellows in Choreography, are acclaimed for their innovative integration of choreography and video technology that explodes the partnering form into a magically populated stage where image and reality collide.
Representation: Pentacle, 75 Broad Street, #304 NY, NY 10004-2415

Country: United States
Type: Ballet and Dance Company
Contact: Artistic Director Art Bridgman
Artistic Director Myrna Packer
Social Media: www.facebook.com/pages/BridgmanPacker-Dance/98941984152
Touring Countries: USA, Ireland, Scotland, France, Switzerland, China, Singapore, Japan, El Salvador, Honduras, Panama, Canada, Mexico
Venues: Theaters both black box and proscenium, alternative performance spaces

Bruce Wood Dance Co.
Website: www.brucewooddance.com
Email: bruce.wood@brucedance.org
Address: 1300 Gendy Street, US
Country: United States
Type: Ballet and Dance Company
Contact: Artistic Director Bruce Wood
Email: bruce@brucewooddance.org
Venues: Charles W. Eisemann Center, 1, 700; Will Rogers Auditorium, 2, 800; Bass Performance Hall, 2, 000

Buglisi Dance Theatre
Website: www.buglisidance.org
Email: buglisi@buglisidance.org
Phone: 212 719 3301
Address: 229 West 42nd Street, Suite 502, US
Country: United States
Type: Ballet and Dance Company
Contact: Artistic Director Jacqulyn Buglisi
Email: buglisi@buglisidance.org
Executive Director Suzanne Konowitz
Email: buglisi@buglisidance.org
Social Media: www.facebook.com/buglisidancee
Venues: Joyce Theater 472

Butterworth Dance Company
Email: butterdanceco@gmail.com
Address: 4466 41st Street #6, US
Country: United States
Type: Ballet and Dance Company
Contact: Artistic Director Traves Butterworth
Venues: Don Powell Theatre San Diego State University 520, Various 1200-2000

California Ballet Company
Website: www.californiaballet.org
Email: info@californiaballet.org
Phone: 858 560 5676
Address: 4819 Ronson Court, US
Country: United States
Type: Ballet and Dance Company
Contact: Artistic and Executive Director Maxine Mahon
ballet mistress/education Director Judith Sharp
music Director and conductor John Stubbs
Venues: San Diego Civic Theatre 3000; others vary between Poway Performing Arts Centre 1, 800, Balboa Theater 1, 200, CBC Studio Theatre 100

California Riverside Ballet
Website: www.crballet.com
Email: crballet@sbcglobal.net
Address: 3700 6th Street, US
Country: United States
Type: Ballet and Dance Company
Contact: Executive Director Linda Jenkins
Artistic Director Mario Nugara
Venues: Riverside Municipal Auditorium 1678

Canton Ballet
Website: www.cantonballet.com
Email: cantonballet@cantonballet.com
Phone: 330 455 7220
Address: 1001 Market Avenue N, US
Information: Canton Ballet is a non-profit organization committed to fostering an appreciation of the art of dance within the local community and dedicated to providing the highest Artistic quality of instruction by operating a school for all age and skill levels, and a pre-professional company with performance opportunities for the serious or career oriented student at the advanced level.
Country: United States
Type: Ballet and Dance Company
Contact: Artistic & Executive Director
Cassandra Crowley
Venues: Canton Palace Theatre 1500

Carolina Ballet (affiliate of Columbia Music Festival Association)
Website: www.cmfaonline.com
Email: cmfa5678@aol.com
Phone: 803 771 6303
Address: 914 Pulaski Street, US
Country: United States
Type: Ballet and Dance Company
Venues: Township Auditorium 3100, Keenan Theatre 500, CMFA Artspace 250

Carolina Ballet Inc
Website: www.carolinaballet.com
Email: robertweiss@carolinaballet.com
Phone: 919 719 0800

Address: 3401-131 Atlantic Avenue, US
Country: United States
Type: Ballet and Dance Company
Contact: Artistic Director Robert Weiss
Social Media: @CarolinaBallet www.facebook.com/CarolinaBallet
Venues: Memorial Auditorium, A J Fletcher Opera Theater

Cedar Lake
Website: www.cedarlakedance.com
Email: info@cedarlakedance.com
Phone: 212 244 0015
Address: 547 W. 26th Street, US
Country: United States
Type: Ballet and Dance Company
Contact: Executive Director Greg Mudd
Artistic Director Benoit-Swan Pouffer
Venues: State Theatre

Celeste Miller & Co
Website: www.celestemiller.com
Email: millerceleste@yahoo.com
Phone: 404 625 4846
Address: P.O. Box 5227, US
Country: United States
Type: Ballet and Dance Company
Contact: company Manager, Artistic Director Celeste Miller
Venues: up to 1200

Chamber Dance Project
Website: www.chamberdance.org
Email: info@chamberdance.org
Address: PO Box 2360, US
Information: Chamber Dance Project, dancers & musicians, is a company of professional artists dedicated to redefining contemporary ballet in partnership with live music in intimate settings heightening the impact on audiences.
Country: United States
Type: Ballet and Dance Company
Contact: Artistic Director Diane Coburn Bruning

Charles Moore Dance Theatre
Website:
Email: cmdt397@aol.com
Phone: 718 254 0670
Address: 397 Bridge Street, 2nd Floor, US
Country: United States
Type: Ballet and Dance Company
Contact: Executive Director Faye Moore
Artistic Director Ella Thompson Moore
Social Media: http://www.facebook.com/pages/Charles-Moore-Dance-Theatre/245968312604
Venues: Peter Norton Symphony Space

Charleston Ballet Theatre
Website: www.charlestonballet.com
Phone: 843 723 7334
Address: 615 Johnnie Dodds Blvd, Mt. Pleasant, US
Country: United States
Type: Ballet and Dance Company
Contact: Executive Artistic Director Patricia Cantwell
Email: cbtpdc@aol.com
Artistic Director Don Cantwell
Venues: Gaillard Municipal Auditorium 2800

Charlotte Ballet
Website: charlotteballet.org
Email: lmcswain@ncdance.org
Phone: 704 372 0101
Address: 701 N. Tryon St., US
Information: formerly known as the North Carolina Dance Theatre, Charlotte Ballet is a world class repertory dance ensemble. It performs classic, contemporary and cutting-edge dance with virtuosity, energy, and Artistic excellence for local, statewide and national audiences
Country: United States
Type: Ballet and Dance Company
Contact: President & Artistic Director
Jean-Pierre Bonnefoux
Email: jpbonn@ncdance.org
Executive Director Douglas Singleton
Email: dsingle@ncdance.org
Director of Marketing & communications
Logan McSwain
Email: lmcswain@ncdance.org
Social Media: www.facebook.com/CLTballet
Venues: Belk Theater & Booth Playhouse at NC Blumenthal Performing Arts Center 2098

Chautauqua Ballet Company
Website: www.ciweb.org/dance-school
Email: boxoffice@ciweb.org
Phone: 716 357 6250
Address: PO Box 28, 1 Ames Ave., US
Information: visiting address: Chautauqua Dance Department, Camahan-Jackson Dance Studio, 67 Hedding Ave, Chautauqua, NY 14722, Tel: 716-357 6292
Country: United States
Type: Ballet and Dance Company
Venues: Chautauqua Amphitheater

BALLET AND DANCE COMPANIES

Chicago Festival Ballet
Website: www.chicagofestivalballet.com
Email: tim@chicagofestivalballet.com
Phone: 630 527 1052
Address: 1239 S. Naper Boulevard, US
Information: is a nonprofit organization for the presentation of musical and theatrical works; Joliet Studio address: 3039 Theodore Street, Joliet, IL 60431
Country: United States
Type: Ballet and Dance Company
Contact: Artistic honorary advisor Maria Tallchief
Artistic advisor Nathalie Krassorska
Director & founder
Kenneth Von Heidecke
Venues: up to 4000

Chicago Moving Company
Website: www.chicagomovingcompany.org
Email: cmc@enteract.com
Address: 3035 North Hoyne, US
Country: United States
Type: Ballet and Dance Company
Contact: Director of development and business Kay LsSota
co-Artistic Director/bookings/program Manager Cindy Brandle
founder/co-Artistic Director Nana Shineflug
Venues: various (perform in traditional theatres as well as alternative sites)

Christopher Caines Dance
Website: www.christophercainesdance.org
Email: info@christophercainesdance.org
Phone: 646 623 4433
Address: 639 West 204th Street 6D, US
Information: Canadian-born Christopher Caines has been called "the most musically sophisticated choreographer under 45 in the United States" (Dance View Times) and "One of the most musically erudite and articulate dance-makers around" (The New Yorker). Christopher Caines Dance is Caines's project-based chamber ballet company, performing with live music
Country: United States
Type: Ballet and Dance Company
Contact: Director of publicity and Marketing Diana Castelnuovo-Tedesco
Email: diana@fraichepr.com
Artistic Director and Choreographer Christopher Caines
Email: cc@christophercainesdance.org
Touring Countries: Any
Number of Performers: 15

Cincinnati Ballet
Website: www.cincinnatiballet.com
Email: info@cincinnatiballet.com
Phone: 513 621 5219
Address: 1555 Central Parkway, US
Country: United States
Type: Ballet and Dance Company
Contact: music Director Carmon DeLeone
Email: maestro@cballet.org
Artistic Director Victoria Morgan
Email: vmorgan@cballet.org
Managing Director Missie Santomo
Email: msantomo@cballet.org
Marketing Director Allie Honebrink
Email: ahonebrink@cballet.org
Venues: Music Hall 3400 (Nutcracker performances), Stanley J Arnoff Center for the Arts 2500 (regular season)

Cleo Parker Robinson Dance Ensemble
Website: www.cleoparkerdance.org
Email: cleodance@aol.com
Phone: 303 295 1759
Address: 119 Park Avenue West, US
Country: United States
Type: Ballet and Dance Company
Contact: Director of operations Mary Hart
Chief Operating Officer Malik Robinson
Executive Artistic Director & founder
Cleo Parker Robinson
Venues: up to 2600

Cohan/Suzeau Dance Company
Website: www.cohansuzeau.org
Email: suzeau@ku.edu
Address: Speaking of Dance...Inc, 1002 Avalon, US
Country: United States
Type: Ballet and Dance Company
Venues: Lied Center for Performing Arts (sitting 2000) and on tour (sitting varies)

Colorado Ballet
Website: www.coloradoballet.org
Email: info@coloradoballet.org
Phone: 303 837 8888
Address: 1278 Lincoln Street, US
Information: established in 1961, Colorado Ballet is a non-profit organisation that presents world-class classical ballet and superior dance in Denver. Colorado Ballet enhances the cultural life of Colorado through performances of the professional company, training at the Academy, and Education & Outreach programmes. Visit www.coloradoballet.org

Country: United States
Type: Ballet and Dance Company
Contact: music Director Adam Flatt
public relations Manager Sanya Andersen-Vie
Artistic Director Gil Boggs
Social Media: @ColoradoBallet http:// www.facebook.com/colorado.ballet
Annual Performances: 47
Number of Performers: 50
Venues: Ellie Caulkins Opera House (2000)

Columbia City Ballet
Website: www.columbiacityballet.com
Email: info@columbiacityballet.com
Phone: 803 799 7605
Address: 1545 Main St., US
Country: United States
Type: Ballet and Dance Company
Contact: Executive & Artistic Director
William Starrett
technical Director/lighting designer Barry Sparks
Venues: Koger Center for the Arts 2300

Commonwealth Ballet
Website: www.commonwealthballet.org
Email: adminstrator@commonwealthballet.org
Phone: 978 263 6533
Address: P.O. Box 892, US
Country: United States
Type: Ballet and Dance Company
Contact: Artistic Director Chip Morris
Venues: Community area school about 900

Concert Ballet of Virginia
Website: www.concertballet.com
Email: concertballetofvirginia@yahoo.com
Phone: 804 798 0945
Address: Box 25501, US
Information: short term contract
Country: United States
Type: Ballet and Dance Company
Contact: Executive Director Eleanor Rennie
Associate Director Scott Boyer
technical Director & designer
deVeaux Riddick
Artistic Director Robert Watkins
Venues: The Women's Club Auditorium home venue and others; capacities 450-1200

Conduit Dance, Inc.
Website: www.conduit-pdx.org
Email: info@conduit-pdx.org
Phone: 503 221 5857
Address: 918 SW Yamhill Avenue, 4th Floor, Suite 401, US
Country: United States
Type: Ballet and Dance Company
Contact: co-Director Tere Mathern

Connecticut Ballet
Website: www.connecticutballet.com
Email: ctballet@ix.netcom.com
Phone: 203 964 1211
Address: 20 Acosta Street, US
Country: United States
Type: Ballet and Dance Company
Contact: Artistic Director Brett Raphael
Social Media: www.facebook.com/connecticutballet
Annual Performances: 25
Number of Performers: 24
Venues: Stamford Center for the Arts, Bushnell Center for the Performing Arts

Contemporary Dance Oklahoma
Website: www.ou.edu/finearts/dance
Email: dance@ou.edu
Phone: 405 325 4051
Address: 560 Parrington Oval, Room 1000, US
Information: residence at the University of Oklahoma; all dancers are students at the university
Country: United States
Type: Ballet and Dance Company
Contact: coordinator for the Modern Dance department Austin Hartel
Email: ahartel@ou.edu
Venues: Rupel Jones Theatre and Donald W Reynolds Theatre

Contemporary Dance/Fort Worth
Website: www.cdfw.org
Email: cdfw@cdfw.org
Phone: 817 922 0944
Address: PO Box 11652, US
Information: the mission is to develop the art, artists, and audiences for Modern Dance through performance and education in schools and the community. Fort Worth's first professional modern dance company, Contemporary Dance/Fort Worth produces and presents innovative dance experiences
Country: United States
Type: Ballet and Dance Company
Social Media: www.facebook.com/Contemporary.Dance.Fort.Worth
Touring Countries: U.S., Mexico

Contemporary Motions
Email: mocany@yahoo.com
Phone: 718 857 8269
Address: 493 Lincoln Place, 4J, US
Country: United States
Type: Ballet and Dance Company
Contact: Artistic Director/founder Julio Enrique Rivera
Venues: Hope College

Dallas Black Dance Theatre
Website: www.dbdt.com
Email: admin@dbdt.com
Phone: 214 871 2376
Address: 2700 flora street, US
Country: United States
Type: Ballet and Dance Company
Contact: Executive Director Zenetta S Drew
Email: z.drew@dbdt.com
founder/Artistic Director Ann M Williams
Email: a.williams@dbdt.com
Social Media: @dallasblkdance www.facebook.com/dallasblackdance
Venues: Majestic Theatre 1500

Dana Tai Soon Burgess and Co
Website: www.dtsbco.com
Email: dtsbco@cs.com
Phone: 202 237 1352
Address: 2745 Arizona Ave, NW, US
Information: contemporary dance company; specializes in collaborative Productions which emphasises an Asian American sensibility
Country: United States
Type: Ballet and Dance Company
Contact: founding Artistic Director Dana Tai Soon Burgess
Touring Countries: Peru, Venezuela, Korea, China, Canada, Germany, Panama
Venues: Kennedy Center for the Performing Arts, 500-1600 , Lincoln Theatre 700

Dance Alive National Ballet
Website: www.dancealive.org
Email: dalive@bellsouth.net
Phone: 352 371 2986
Address: 1325 NW Second Street, Florida, US
Information: Represented by Siegel Artist Management www.siegelartist.com. Original choreography; Judy Skinner and Kim Tuttle have received 6 choreographic fellowships each from state of Florida; state touring company; original, traditional & Balanchine choreography;
Country: United States
Type: Ballet and Dance Company
Contact: Artistic Director/resident choreographer Kim Tuttle
resident choreographer Judy Skinner
Venues: Phillips Center for the Performing Arts, Gainesville , FL Through Southeast US. Capacities: Varies from 1800-300 seats, state of art to primitive venues.

Dance and Sculptural Costume
Website: www.shashahigby.com
Email: shasha@shashahigby.com
Address: PO Box 152, US
Country: United States
Type: Ballet and Dance Company
Contact: Artistic Director Sha Sha Higby

Dance Brazil
Email: dancebrazilpb@gmail.com
Phone: 212 382 0555
Address: 246 W. 38th Street – 8th Floor, 132 Prospect Pl, Suite 2R, US
Country: United States
Type: Ballet and Dance Company
Contact: Executive Director Margaret Wood
Artistic Director Jelon Vieira

Dance by Neil Greenberg
Website: www.neilgreenberg.org
Email: info@neilgreenberg.org
Phone: 212 982 1150
Address: 67 E 2nd Street, Suite 39, US
Country: United States
Type: Ballet and Dance Company
Contact: Artistic Director Niel Greenberg
booking contact Sophie Myrtil
Venues: The Kitchen 200

Dance Kaleidoscope
Website: www.dancekal.org
Email: dk@dancekal.org
Phone: 317 940 6555
Address: 4603 Clarendon Road, #32, US
Information: Indiana's premier professional contemporary dance company
Country: United States
Type: Ballet and Dance Company
Contact: Executive Director Janice Virgin
Email: janv@dancekal.org
Director of Marketing Paul Hansen
Email: paulh@dancekal.org
Artistic Director David Hochoy
Social Media: @dancekalDance Kaleidoscope

Dance Now NYC
Website: www.dancenownyc.org
Email: info@dancenownyc.org
Phone: 917 664 8065
Address: 527 Hudson Street, PO Box 20029, US
Information: offers choreographers year-round performance opportunities to increase their visibility and advance their career. Dance Now's residency and commissioning programmes encourage the exploration of the creative process and development of work
Country: United States
Type: Ballet and Dance Company
Contact: Executive Artistic Director and Producer Robin Staff
Email: robin@dancenownyc.org
Artistic Director and Producer Sydney Skybetter
Email: sydney@dancenownyc.org
Press officer Janet Stapleton
Email: janet@dancenownyc.org
Social Media: @DanceNOWNYC www.facebook.com/DanceNOWNYC

Dance Theatre of Harlem
Website: www.dancetheatreofharlem.org
Email: eschoelwer@dancetheatreofharlem.org
Phone: 212 690 2800
Address: 466 W. 152nd Street, US
Country: United States
Type: Ballet and Dance Company
Contact: Artistic Director Virginia Johnson
Email: vjohnson@dancetheatreofharlem.org
Executive Director Laveen Naidu
Email: lnaidu@dancetheatreofharlem.org
Social Media: @DTHBallet www.facebook.com/dancetheatreofharlem
Venues: City Centre Theatre NYC

Daniel Gwirtzman Dance Company
Website: www.gwirtzmandance.org
Email: Info@gwirtzmandance.org
Phone: 212 543 1367
Address: 720 West 181 Street, #31, US
Information: multi-generational Production
Country: United States
Type: Ballet and Dance Company
Contact: Artistic Director Daniel Gwirtzman

Danza Floricanto/USA
Website: www.danzafloricantousa.com
Email: floricanto@att.net
Phone: 626 796 2403
Address: 2758 E, Orange Grove Ave., US
Country: United States
Type: Ballet and Dance Company
Contact: Artistic/Managing Director Gema Sandoval
Venues: up to 3500

David Dorfman Dance
Website: www.DavidDorfmanDance.org
Email: info@daviddorfmandance.org
Phone: 212 677 2503
Address: 140 Second Avenue, #503, US
Information: work in prisons, homes, abuse shelters, schools and community centres of all kinds; managed by H-Art management (see agents and management)
Country: United States
Type: Ballet and Dance Company
Contact: Artistic Director David Dorfman
Email: david@daviddorfmandance.org
company Manager Ashley Richard
Email: ashley@daviddorfmandance.org
Social Media: @DorfmanDance www.facebook.com/daviddorfmandancepage
Touring Countries: North and South America, UK and Europe
Venues: Joyce Theatre NYC, BAM Next Wave Festival

David Parker & the Bang Group
Website: www.thebanggroup.com
Email: davidparker@thebanggroup.com
Phone: 212 337 9565
Address: 131 Perry St. #1A, US
Country: United States
Type: Ballet and Dance Company
Contact: company Manager Jeffrey Kazin
Artistic Director David Parker
Italy, Belgium, Canada, Croatia, Slovakia, France & Germany.
Venues: NYC: Dance Theatre workshop and Danspace Project St Mark's Church.

David Taylor Dance Theatre
Website: www.dtdt.org
Email: info@dawsonwallace.org
Phone: 303 789 2030
Address: PO Box 140699, US
Information: booking agent: Gary Lindsey Artist Services, 2700 15th Ave., San Francisco, CA 94127, Tel: 415-759 6410, Fax: 415-681 9801
Country: United States
Type: Ballet and Dance Company
Contact: Artistic Director James Wallace
Email: james@dawsonwallace.org

Touring Countries: Canada, Guatemala
Venues: Lakewood Cultural Center 320, City Center Englewood 2000

Dayton Ballet
Website: www.daytonballet.org
Email: dburke@DaytonBallet.org
Phone: 937 449 5060
Address: 140 N Main Street, US
Country: United States
Type: Ballet and Dance Company
Venues: Victoria Theatre 1137

Dayton Contemporary Dance Company
Website: www.dcdc.org
Email: contactus@dcdc.org
Phone: 937 228 3232
Address: 840 Germantown Street, US
Information: second company: Dayton Contemporary Dance Company II. Educational outreach programmes designed specifically for each tour. Agent: H-Art Management, info@h-artmanagement.com
Country: United States
Type: Ballet and Dance Company
Contact: Artistic Director Debbie Blunden-Diggs
Email: debbie@dcdc.org
Executive Director/CEO Ro Nita Hawes-Saunders
Email: ro_nita@dcdc.org
Venues: Victoria Theatre 1139

Delta Festival Ballet
Website: www.deltafestivalballet.com
Email: deltafestballet@aol.com
Phone: 504 888 0931
Address: 3351 Severn Avenue, Suite 303B, US
Information: also have a youth company: New Orleans Youth Ballet, 65 dancers
Country: United States
Type: Ballet and Dance Company
Contact: Artistic Director Joseph Giacobbe
Annual Performances: 9
Number of Performers: 200
Venues: Tulane University – Dixon Hall; Mahalia Jackson Theatre

Desert Dance Theatre
Website: www.desertdancetheatre.org
Email: info@desertdancetheatre.org
Phone: 480 962 4584
Address: PO Box 25332, US
Country: United States
Type: Ballet and Dance Company
Contact: vice President Lisa Chow
Venues: Herberger Theatre 800, Scottsdale Center for the Arts 700, Gammage Theatre 2500, Chandler Center 1500, Orpheum Theatre 1372

Diablo Ballet
Website: www.diabloballet.org
Email: diablo@diabloballet.org
Address: PO Box 4700, US
Information: Diablo Ballet is an award-winning internationally recognised professional performing dance company committed to enriching, inspiring, enlightening, and educating children and adults through the art of dance. The Company consists of dancers who have performed throughout the United States, Europe, and South America. email bookings: Marketing@diabloballet.org
Country: United States
Type: Ballet and Dance Company
Contact: stage Manager David Hartenstein
Artistic adviser Sally Streets
Artistic Director Lauren Jonas
Executive Director Susan Boreliz
Venues: Lesher Center for the Arts and Del Valle Theatre, Walnut Creek

Diavolo
Website: www.diavolo.org
Email: info@diavolo.org
Phone: 323 225 4290
Address: 616 Moulton Avenue, US
Information: DIAVOLO | Architecture in Motion® uses dance to explore the relationship between the human body and its architectural environment. Artistic Director Jacques Heim steers DIAVOLO's diverse team of dancers, designers, choreographers and engineers to create visceral and awe-inspiring works that reveal how they are affected emotionally, physically and socially by the spaces they inhabit. Meticulously designed bespoke architectural structures serve as the central inspiration for each work, activated by the stylistically varied and intensely physical choreography which has become the hallmark of this truly original company throughout its rich 25 year history. Member of ISPA
Country: United States
Type: Ballet and Dance Company
Contact: Chairman Mary Ellen Stuart
Artistic Director Jacques Heim
Executive Director Jennifer Cheng
chief operating Director Matt Wells
Social Media: @Diavolo_LA www.facebook.com/DiavoloLA
Venues: The Space

Dimensions Dance Theater
Website: www.dimensionsdance.org
Email: dimensionsdance@prodigy.net
Phone: 510 465 3363
Address: 1428 Alice Street, Suite 308, 3rd Floor, US
Information: special cross-cultural collaborations
Country: United States
Type: Ballet and Dance Company
Contact: administrative coordinator Latanya Tigner
Artistic Director Deborah Vaughan
Venues: Scottish Rite Center Theater 1500, Alice Arts Center 400

Donna Sternberg & Dancers
Website: www.dsdancers.com
Email: dsdancers@earthlink.net
Phone: 310 260 1198
Address: 911 9th Street, Suite 206, US
Information: (DS&D) is an interdisciplinary dance company whose mission is to build bridges between dance and science and to convey how the process of discovery is transformative. We use science as a framework to give shape and structure to our Artistic explorations connecting with audiences through the emotional and visceral power of dance
Country: United States
Type: Ballet and Dance Company
Contact: Artistic Director Donna Sternberg
Social Media: @DSDancers www.facebook.com/pages/Donna-Sternberg-Dancers/154932248078
Number of Performers: 6

Doug Elkins Choreography
Website: www.dougelkinschoreography.com
Email: dougelkinsdance@gmail.com
Address: c/o The Field, 161 Sixth Avenue, 14th Floor, US
Country: United States
Type: Ballet and Dance Company
Contact: Artistic Director Doug Elkins
General Manager Amy Cassello
Venues: major theatres up to 4000

Doug Varone & Dancers
Website: www.dougvaroneanddancers.org
Email: info@dougvaroneanddancers.org
Phone: 212 279 3344
Address: c/o Lisa Booth Management Inc, 1501 Broadway #1508, US
Country: United States
Type: Ballet and Dance Company
Contact: Executive Director Sarah Bodley
Email: sbodley@dougvaroneanddancers.org
tour Manager Eddie Taketa
Email: etaketa@dougvaroneanddancers.org
Social Media: @dovadance
Touring Countries: USA and abroad
Venues: 500 – 2500 seats

Douglas Dunn & Dancers
Website: www.douglasdunndance.com
Email: ddunn1019@aol.com
Phone: 212 966 6999
Address: Rio Grande Union Inc, 541 Broadway, 3rd Floor, US
Information: pieces from the past are available for revival, and current repertoire for immediate performance; Mr. Dunn is also available for teaching and setting work on modern and ballet companies
Country: United States
Type: Ballet and Dance Company
Contact: Artistic Director Douglas Dunn
Venues: in and outdoor performances

Duquesne University Tamburitzans
Website: www.duq.edu/tamburitzans
Email: tamburitzans@duq.edu
Phone: 412 396 5185
Address: 1801 Boulevard of the Allies, US
Information: Eastern European folk music and dance company. All live music, over 300 colorful costumes, 34 performers
Country: United States
Type: Ballet and Dance Company
Contact: Managing Director Paul G Stafura
Annual Performances: 50
Number of Performers: 29

eba Dance Theatre
Website: www.eba-arts.org
Email: ebadance@eba-arts.org
Phone: 518 465 9916
Address: 351 Hudson Avenue, eba Theater, US
Country: United States
Type: Ballet and Dance Company
Contact: Artistic Director Maude Baum
Email: mb@eba-arts.org
Venues: eba Theater 250, Empire Center, Albany 1000

Edith Stephen Electric Currents Dance Co
Website: www.edithstephen.webs.com
Email: edithstephenvideo@hotmail.com
Address: 55 Bethune St, Studio 630a, US
Country: United States
Type: Ballet and Dance Company

Eglevsky Ballet Company of Long Island
Website: www.eglevskyballet.org
Phone: 516 – 746 1115
Address: 999 Herricks Road, US
Information: a concert company
Country: United States
Type: Ballet and Dance Company
Venues: Tilles Center 2000

Eiko & Koma
Website: www.eikoandkoma.org
Email: info@eikoandkoma.org
Phone: 212 – 278 8111 x3
Address: c/o Pentacle, 246 West 38th Street, 4th Floor, US
Information: 1996 recipients of a MacArthur Fellows Program "genius grant", Award 2004: won Samuel Scripps American Dance Festival for lifetime achievement in modern dance, 2007 dance magazine award.
Country: United States
Type: Ballet and Dance Company
Contact: artist representative Ivan Sygoda
Artistic Directors Eiko
 & Koma

Elinor Coleman Dance Company
Website:
Email: Danse@nyct.net
Phone: 121 224 27640/7
Address: 10 West 18th Street, 2nd floor, US
Information: master classes, residencies
Country: United States
Type: Ballet and Dance Company
Contact: Managing Director Helena McDonagh
Artistic Director Elinor Coleman

Elisa Monte Dance
Website: www.elisamontedance.org
Email: info@elisamontedance.org
Phone: 212 868 4488
Address: 481 8th Avenue, Suite 543, US
Information: Domestic Booking Representative: Joanne Rile, Joanne Rile Artists Management, INC, 93 Old York Road, Suite 222 Jenkintown Commons, Jenkintown, PA 19046-3925, 212-885-6400, http://rilearts.com/ International Booking Representative: c/o Bernard Schmidt Productions, 461 W. 49th St. New York NY 10019 Tel: 212-307 5046 Fax: 212-397 2459 E-mail:bschmidtpd@aol.com
Country: United States
Type: Ballet and Dance Company
Contact: Director of operations Tiffany Rea-Fisher
Artistic Director Elisa Monte
Social Media: @ElisaMonteDance http:// www.facebook.com/elisamontedance
Number of Performers: 8
Venues: various, Joyce Theatre NYC 475

Ellen Webb Dance Studio
Website: www.ellenwebbstudio.com
Email: elweb@sbcglobal.net
Phone: 510 452 5919
Address: 2822 A Union Street, US
Country: United States
Type: Ballet and Dance Company
Contact: Artistic Director Ellen Webb
Venues: outdoor venues up to 500

Erica Essner Performance Co-op
Website: www.eecop.org
Email: essner@eecop.org
Phone: 646 335 5264
Address: 26 Berkeley Place, #1, US
Country: United States
Type: Ballet and Dance Company
Contact: Artistic Director Erica Essner
booking agent Janessa Clark

Eugene Ballet Company
Website: www.eugeneballet.org
Email: eballet@eugeneballet.org
Phone: 541 485 3992
Address: 1590 Willamette Street, US
Information: under the direction of choreographer Toni Pimble, this versatile ensemble can tour with repertory that can use from 6-28 dancers, plus does a wide range of educational works including native American-based repertoire
Country: United States
Type: Ballet and Dance Company
Contact: Managing Director Riley Grannan
Email: riley@eugeneballet.org
Artistic Director Toni Pimble
Email: toni@eugeneballet.org
financial Manager Denise Fearn
Email: finance@eugeneballet.org
Social Media: @EugeneBallet www.facebook.com/EugeneBalletCompany
Touring Countries: Canada, Taiwan, India, Sri Lanka, Bangladesh, Syria, Jordan, Tunisia
Venues: Hult Center for the Performing Arts (Eugene, Oregon) 2500; Morrison Center for the Arts (Boise, Idaho) 2, 100

Everett Dance Theatre
Website: www.everettdancetheatre.org
Email: info@everettdancetheatre.org
Phone: 401 831 9479
Address: 9 Duncan Avenue, US
Country: United States
Type: Ballet and Dance Company
Contact: Artistic Director Dorothy Jungels
co Artistic Director Aaron Jungels
Touring Countries: United States and Canada
Venues: 200 to 900 seat theaters

Evidence, A Dance Company
Website: www.evidencedance.com
Phone: 718 230 4633
Address: 80 Hanson Place, Suite 605, US
Country: United States
Type: Ballet and Dance Company
Contact: Artistic Director Ronald K. Brown
Touring Countries: USA, Europe

Felice Lesser Dance Theater
Website: www.fldt.org
Email: fldtny@aol.com
Phone: 212 594 3388
Address: 484 West 43rd Street, #9T, US
Country: United States
Type: Ballet and Dance Company
Contact: Artistic & Executive Director
 Felice Lesser
Social Media: Felice Lesser Dance Theater

Festival Ballet Providence
Website: www.festivalballet.com
Email: info@festivalballet.com
Phone: 401 353 1129
Address: 825 Hope St, US
Information: junior company & apprentice programme; the Company also has an Associated school and Summer Intensive program; for the most part the contract is 30 weeks, with add-on weeks possible for touring outside the terms of the regular season, and for those dancer
Country: United States
Type: Ballet and Dance Company
Contact: ballet mistress Milica Bijelic
Artistic Director Mihailo Djuric
 Marketing & public relations Manager
 Mark Fleisher
Managing Director Lisa LaDew
Venues: Providence Performing Arts Centre 3500, Veterans Memorial Auditorium 2200, Roberts Auditorium 800, Festival Ballet Providence Leach Grand Studio 90

Flamenco Vivo Carlota Santana
Website: www.flamenco-vivo.org
Email: santana@flamenco-vivo.org
Address: 4 West 43rd Street (Suite 608), US
Information: management services: Baylin Artists Management, 196 W. Ashland St, Suite 201Doylestown, PA 18901: 267-880 3750, E-mail: mbaylin@baylinarts.com
Country: United States
Type: Ballet and Dance Company
Contact: Artistic Director Carlota Santana
Email: santana@flamenco-vivo.org
Venues: touring varies 200 to 4000

Florida Ballet
Website: www.floridaballet.org/
Email: info@floridaballet.org
Phone: 904 353 7518
Address: 300 East State Street, US
Country: United States
Type: Ballet and Dance Company
Contact: Artistic Director Linda Reifsnyder Jenkins
Email: ljenkins@floridaballet.org

FLY Dance Company
Website: www.flydance.com
Phone: 713 523 3709
Address: 1922 Brunt St, US
Country: United States
Type: Ballet and Dance Company
Contact: fly Manager Mike Wood

Footworks Percussive Dance Ensemble
Website: www.footworks.org
Email: office@footworks.org
Phone: 410 897 9299
Address: PO Box 1760, US
Information: full time touring group; also provides instruction and Arts-In-Education
Country: United States
Type: Ballet and Dance Company
Contact: founder & Artistic Director
 Eileen Carson Schatz
Email: office@footworks.org
company Manager Lynda McIntyre
Email: office@footworks.org
Social Media: https:// www.facebook.com/pages/Footworks-Percussive-Dance-Ensemble/146239721383?ref=ts
Touring Countries: Great Britain, Canada, Finland, Japan
Venues: concert halls, outdoor festivals

Fort Wayne Ballet Inc
Website: www.fortwayneballet.org
Email: info@fortwayneballet.org
Phone: 260 484 9646
Address: 324 Penn Avenue, US
Information: student company only – no professionals at this time
Country: United States
Type: Ballet and Dance Company
Contact: business Manager Mary Johnson
Artistic Director Karen Gibbons-Brown
 Director of development & pr
 Melinda Perry
Venues: Performing Arts Center, Fort Wayne 700

Francisco Martinez Dancetheatre
Website: www.fmdt.org
Email: info@fmdt.org
Phone: 818 988 2192
Address: 6723 Matilija Avenue, US
Information: also school performances, residencies, parent workshops, teacher in-service, choreography
Country: United States
Type: Ballet and Dance Company
Contact: Artistic Director Francisco Martinez
Executive Director David Allen Jones
Venues: up to 1000

Gabrielle Lansner & Company
Website: www.gabriellelansner.com
Email: gabrielle_lansner_company@yahoo.com
Phone: 164 691 29741
Address: 470 West 24th Street, 17E, US
Country: United States
Type: Ballet and Dance Company
Contact: Artistic Director Gabrielle Lansner
company administrator Aimee McCabe

Gallim Dance
Website: www.gallimdance.com
Email: info@gallimdance.com
Phone: 718 622 2165
Address: The Church of St. Luke and St. Matthew, 520 Clinton Ave, US
Information: contemporary dance company dedicated to creating and performing original work by Andrea Miller, nurturing the careers of young artists, and stimulating the imagination of a diverse international audience
Country: United States
Type: Ballet and Dance Company
Contact: Artistic Director Andrea Miller
Email: andrea@gallimdance.com
Associate Director Francesca Romo
Email: francesca@gallimdance.com
operations Manager Matthew Martine
Email: matthew@gallimdance.com
Touring Countries: France, USA, Spain, Germany
Venues: Theatre National de Chaillot, Joyce Theater, Jacobs Pillow Dance Festival, Spoleto Festival, TANZ Bremen Festival, Madrid en Danza Festival

Garth Fagan Dance
Website: www.garthfagandance.org
Email: johanna@garthfagandance.org
Phone: 585 454 3260
Address: 50 Chestnut Street, US
Information: Have won five Bessie Awards
Country: United States
Type: Ballet and Dance Company
Contact: Marketing co-ordinator Johanna Lester
Artistic Director Garth Fagan
Executive Director Ruby Lockhart
Production/stage Manager Bets Quackenbush
company Manager Bit Knighton
Touring Countries: Recently: France and England
Venues: Jacob's Pillow, Joyce Theatre and Kennedy Centre for the Performing Arts

Gina Gibney Dance
Website: www.gibneydance.org
Email: info@ginagibneydance.org
Phone: 212 677 8560
Address: 890 Broadway, Studio 5-2, US
Country: United States
Type: Ballet and Dance Company
Contact: Artistic/Executive Director Gina Gibney
Social Media: @GibneyDance www.facebook.com/gibneydancepage

Grand Rapids Ballet
Website: www.grballet.com
Email: info@grballet.com
Phone: 616 454 4771
Address: 341 Ellsworth SW, US
Country: United States
Type: Ballet and Dance Company
Social Media: @grapidsballet www.facebook.com/grballet
Venues: The DeVos theatre 2400

Gus Solomons Company/Dance aka PARADIGM
Website: www.paradigm-nyc.org
Email: gus.solomonsjr@nyu.edu
Phone: 212 477 1321
Address: C/O Ken Maldonado, Zia Artists, 506 Fort Washington Avenue, 1H, US
Information: booking representative: Solomons Projects 5889 Broadway NY 10003-1217
Country: United States
Type: Ballet and Dance Company
Contact: Managing Director Ken Maldonado
Venues: large theatres, black box theatres, galleries

H.T. Chen & Dancers
Website: www.htchendance.org
Email: info@htchendance.org
Phone: 212 349 0126
Address: 70 Mulberry Street, 2nd Floor, US
Information: operates a community dance school and black-box theater in NYC; supports emerging dance artists through showcase opportunities and choreographic comissions
Country: United States
Type: Ballet and Dance Company
Contact: Artistic Director H T Chen
Associate Director/education Director Dian Dong
Touring Countries: China, Taiwan, Hong Kong
Venues: Joyce Theater 500, La Mama Annex 200

Halau Hula Ka No'eau Hawai'i Arts Ensemble
Website: www.artofhula.com
Email: HuliauDanceCo@aol.com
Phone: 180 828 45523
Address: PO Box 1907, US
Information: a formal Hawaiian dance academy and performing company
Country: United States
Type: Ballet and Dance Company
Contact: Director Michael Pili Pang

Hauser Dance
Email: nhdc@tcinternet.net
Phone: 612 871 9077
Address: 1940 Hennepin Avenue, US
Information: school offers modern dance technique, improvisation, guest artist workshops, instruction in Production, music for dance, and creative dance for children, cross-cultural workshops & exchanges, laban space-harmony technique, composition, repertory
Country: United States
Type: Ballet and Dance Company
Contact: Artistic Director Heidi Hauser Jasmin
General Manager Paul Jasmin
Venues: house theatre 100+, various up to 1000

Headlong Dance Theater
Website: www.headlong.comd
Email: info@headlong.comd
Phone: 215 545 9195
Address: 1170 South Broad Street, US
Country: United States
Type: Ballet and Dance Company
Contact: co-Director Amy Smith
founder Andrew Simonet
Touring Countries: USA, Dominican Republic, Poland, Italy

Heidi Duckler Dance Theatre (CDT)
Website: www.heididuckler.org
Email: animating.the.landscape@heididuckler.org
Phone: 818 784 8669
Address: 2934 Beverly Glen Circle, Suite 25, US
Country: United States
Type: Ballet and Dance Company
Contact: Artistic Director Heidi Duckler
administrator Vivian Babuts
Venues: site-specific performances

Helios Dance Theater
Website: www.heliosdancetheater.org
Email: laura@heliosdancetheater.org
Phone: 131 077 92131
Address: 1861 S. Midvale Ave. #5, US
Information: regular collaboration with up-and-coming young artists including composers, costumers, animators, filmmakers and photographers
Country: United States
Type: Ballet and Dance Company
Contact: founder/ Artistic Director & choreographer Laura Gorenstein Miller
Email: laura@heliosdancetheater.org
company Manager Melissa Painter
Email: melissand@earthlink.net
Touring Countries: Has performed across the US
Venues: Conjunctive Points Dance Center in Culver City 300

Houston Ballet
Website: www.houstonballet.org
Email: info@houstonballet.org
Phone: 713 227 2787
Address: 601 Preston Street, US

Information: classically trained company with a diverse repertory whose range includes the classics as well as contemporary works
Country: United States
Type: Ballet and Dance Company
Contact: PR Manager Sarah Lam
PR Associate Kimberly Cedeno
Social Media: @HoustonBallet www.facebook.com/houstonballet
Touring Countries: Canada, Australia, Europe, Asia
Number of Performers: 55
Venues: Brown Theater 2384, Cullen Theater 1066

Hubbard Street Dance Chicago (HSDC)
Website: www.hubbardstreetdance.com
Email: General@hubbardstreetdance.com
Phone: 312 850 9744
Address: 1147 West Jackson Blvd, US
Information: 17 dancers
Country: United States
Type: Ballet and Dance Company
Contact: Artistic Director Glenn Edgerton
Email: gedgerton@hubbardstreetdance.com
Executive Director Jason D. Palmquist
Email: jdpalmquist@hubbardstreetdance.com
Marketing and development officer Suzanne Appel
Email: sappel@hubbardstreetdance.com
Social Media: @HubbardStreet www.facebook.com/HubbardStreetDance

Ilka Doubek
Website: www.litchfielddance.com
Email: dancewithilka@aol.com
Phone: 843 237 7465
Address: PO Box 2577, US
Information: Ilka Doubek directs a youth ensemble called Litchfield Dance Company. Besides of a tour to Germany they also perform at Piccolo Spoleto Festivalin Charleston, SC; Pawleys Island Festival of Music and Art; invite guest dance artists.
Ilka Doubek is available as a master guest teacher.
Specialty: Ballet
Country: United States
Type: Ballet and Dance Company

Illstyle and Peace Productions
Website: www.pentacle.org
Email: marag@pentacle.org
Phone: 212 278 8111
Address: 75 Broad Street, Suite 304, US
Information: managed by Pentacle artists management (see Artists and Management)
Country: United States
Type: Ballet and Dance Company
Contact: Director Mara Greenberg
Email: marag@pentacle.org
founder/Director Ivan Sygoda
Email: ivans@pentacle.org
Associate Director, artist representative Anna Brady Nuse
Email: annan@pentacle.org
Director of booking and artist representation Harold Norris
Email: haroldn@pentacle.org

International Dance Festival of New York (a subsidiary of the Anglo-American Ballet)
Website: www.anglo-american-ballet.org
Email: angloballet@aol.com
Phone: 121 230 76909
Address: 250 West 54th Street, 4th floor, US
Country: United States
Type: Ballet and Dance Company
Contact: Director Catherine Kingsley
company Manager Larry Crabtree

Isadora Duncan International Institute
Website: www.idii.org
Phone: 212 753 0846
Address: 150 East 61st Street, Suite 11C, US
Country: United States
Type: Ballet and Dance Company
Contact: Artistic Director Jeanne Bresciani

Island Moving Co.
Website: www.islandmovingco.org
Email: info@islandmovingco.org
Phone: 401 847 4470
Address: PO Box 746, US
Information: Island Moving Co also works to establishing dance as a vital element in the education, motivation and growth of children
Country: United States
Type: Ballet and Dance Company
Contact: Artistic Director Miki Ohlsen
Venues: outdoors in summer, Rogers Auditorium at Christmas

James Sewell Ballet
Website: www.jsballet.com
Email: jsballet@aol.com
Phone: 612 672 0480
Address: 528 Hennepin Ave, Suite 205, US

Information: a small, mobile, flexible, affordable company, performing original dances by a living choreographer
Country: United States
Type: Ballet and Dance Company
Contact: Executive Director Gary Peterson
Artistic Director James Sewell
operations Manager Mary Jo Peloquin
development Director Tom McNamee
Venues: up to 1500

Jane Comfort and Company
Website: www.janecomfortandcompany.org
Email: jane@janecomfortandcompany.org
Phone: 212 226 5109
Address: 55 North Moore Street, US
Information: Agent: laurac@elsieman.org
Country: United States
Type: Ballet and Dance Company
Contact: Artistic Director Jane Comfort
artist representative Laura Colby
company Manager Leslie Cuyjet
Venues: up to 1000

Jazz Tap Ensemble
Website: www.jazztapensemble.org
Email: jtensemble@aol.com
Phone: 310 475 4412
Address: 1416 Westwood Boulevard, Suite 207, US
Information: available for residencies: lecture demonstrations, workshops, master classes
Country: United States
Type: Ballet and Dance Company
Contact: Managing Director Gayle Hooks
Artistic Director Lynn Dally
Venues: up to 2000

Jean Isaacs' San Diego Dance Theater
Website: www.sandiegodancetheater.org
Email: info@sandiegodancetheater.org
Phone: 619 225 1803
Address: 2650 Truxtun Drive, Suite 108, US
Information: 165K
Country: United States
Type: Ballet and Dance Company
Contact: Marketing Director tony robin
Artistic Director Jean Isaacs
Venues: Don Powell Theater

Jett
Website: www.jettejazz.org
Email: JetteJazz@excite.com
Phone: 190 839 71714
Address: 10 Raymond Terrace, US
Country: United States
Type: Ballet and Dance Company
Contact: Artistic Director Jay T Jenkins

Joe Chvala and The Flying Foot Forum
Website: www.flyingfootforum.com
Email: jchvala@flyingfootforum.com
Phone: 161 282 54291
Address: 3105 Garfield Avenue South, US
Country: United States
Type: Ballet and Dance Company
Contact: Artistic Director Joe Chvala
Venues: up to 4000

Joe Goode Performance Group
Website: www.joegoode.org
Email: info@joegoode.org
Phone: 415 561 6565
Address: 499 Alabama Street #150, US
Country: United States
Type: Ballet and Dance Company
Contact: Executive Director Dave Archuletta
Email: Dave@joegoode.org
Manager and operations Manager Alexander Zendzian
Email: alex@joegoode.org
Social Media: @JoeGoodeGroup www.facebook.com/JoeGoodePerformanceGroup
Venues: Centre for the Arts Yerba Buena Gardens 750, Sushi Gallery 250, University of Maryland at College Park 500

Joel Hall Dancers
Website: www.joelhall.org
Email: joel@joelhall.org
Phone: 773 293 0900
Address: 1511 West Berwyn Avenue, US
Country: United States
Type: Ballet and Dance Company
Contact: Managing Director Nancy Teinouitz
Artistic Director Joel Hall
Venues: Merle Reskin Theatre 1300, Athenacum Theatre 950, Harris Theatre

Joffrey Ballet, The
Website: www.joffrey.com
Email: Marketing@joffrey.com
Phone: 312 739 0120
Address: 70 East Lake Street, Suite 1300, US
Country: United States
Type: Ballet and Dance Company

71st ARD International Music Competition Munich

August 29 to September 16, 2022

Piano Trio
Voice
Wind Quintet
Oboe
Trumpet
Piano
Percussion
Viola
Clarinet
Flute
Violoncello
Bassoon
Trombone
Harp
French Horn
Piano Duo
String Quartet
Violin
Double Bass
Organ

Piano Trombone Flute String Quartet

Sébastian Jacot
1st prize 2015

Michael Buchanan
1st prize 2015

JeungBeum Sohn
1st prize 2017

Application deadline: March 31, 2022

Quatuor Arod
1st prize 2016

www.ard-musikwettbewerb.de

Contact: Director of Marketing and pr Elizabeth Burnham
Artistic Director Ashley Wheater
Executive Director Jon H Teeuwissen
Venues: The Auditorium Theatre of Roosevelt University

John Jasperse Company
Website: www.johnjasperse.org
Email: info@johnjasperse.org
Phone: 212 375 0187
Address: Thin Man Dance, Inc., 140 Second Ave, Suite 501, US
Country: United States
Type: Ballet and Dance Company
Contact: Artistic Director John Jasperse
Managing Director Barbara Bryan
Touring Countries: Chile, Spain

Joyce Trisler Danscompany, The
Website: www.danscompany.com
Email: regina@danscompany.com
Phone: 121 267 74351
Address: 333 E 13th Street, N, US
Information: community outreach programs are accessible
Country: United States
Type: Ballet and Dance Company
Contact: Artistic Director, choreographer, teacher Regina Larkin
producing Director Carmen De Lavallade
publicity Audrey Ross
Venues: Joyce Theatre 475

Kanopy Dance Company
Website: www.kanopydance.org
Phone: 160 825 52211
Address: 341 State Street, US
Country: United States
Type: Ballet and Dance Company
Contact: Artistic Director Lisa Andrea Thurrell

Kansas City Ballet
Website: www.kcballet.org
Email: kcbinfo@kcballet.org
Phone: 816 931 2232
Address: 1606 Broadway, US
Country: United States
Type: Ballet and Dance Company
Contact: General Manager Kevin Amey
Executive Director Jeffrey J Bentley
Marketing & communications Director Mike Alley
Artistic Director Devon Carney
Venues: Lyric Opera 1600, Midland Theatre 2200

Kathy Harty Gray Dance Theatre (KHGDT)
Website: www.khgdt.org
Phone: 703 413 3811
Address: PO Box 3291, US
Information: Dedicated to preserving, advancing and sharing Classic American Modern Dance. the company has spent over 20 years developing audiences and mentoring students of modern dance. Using a unique combination of lecture and dance, KHGDT presents programs that ed
Country: United States
Type: Ballet and Dance Company
Contact: Artistic Director Kathy Harty Gray
Touring Countries: Europe

KDNY
Website: www.kdnydance.com
Email: info@kdnydance.com
Phone: 646 529 6412
Address: Kathleen Dyer, Artistic Director, 132 E. 43rd Street, ste. 118, US
Country: United States
Type: Ballet and Dance Company
Contact: Artistic Director Kathleen Dyer
company Manager Heather Kemp

Khadra International Dance Theatre
Website:
Email: Khadrasf@aol.com
Phone: 415 337 2914
Address: 5809 Mission Street, US
Country: United States
Type: Ballet and Dance Company
Contact: Artistic Director Brooke Byrne

Koresh Dance Company
Website: www.koreshdance.org
Email: info@koreshdance.org
Phone: 215 751 0959
Address: 2020 Chestnut Street, US
Information: 10 dancers
Country: United States
Type: Ballet and Dance Company
Contact: Executive Director Alon Koresh
Artistic Director Roni Koresh
Social Media: http:// www.facebook.com/koresh.dance

Koroyar Bulgarian Music and Dance Ensemble
Website:
Email: rzuandk@juno.com
Phone: 195 168 50314 /
Address: c/o 5574 West Homecoming Pl., Unit B, US
Information: all material was collected in direct field research and/or verified by the leading Artistic institutions in the respective countries; the music portion of the programs often includes melodies from cultures few ensembles in the world do
Country: United States
Type: Ballet and Dance Company
Contact: assistant Director Loren Lichty
Executive Director & choreographer Richard Unciano
music Director Ron Muller
technical Director Rick Cofield

Kun-Yang Lin & Dancers
Website: www.kunyanglin.org
Email: Zia-Artists@nyc.rr.com
Phone: 212 928 6517
Address: c/o Zia Artists, 506 Fort Washington Avenue, 1H, US
Information: masterclasses, workshops
Country: United States
Type: Ballet and Dance Company
Contact: Artistic Director Kun-Yang Lin
Touring Countries: Southeast Asia, London, Austria and the USA

Lar Lubovitch Dance Company
Website: www.lubovitch.org
Email: Lubovitch@aol.com
Phone: 212 221 7909
Address: 229 West 42nd St., 8th Floor, US
Information: creating dances that are either performed by the Lubovitch company or taught to other companies; focus on creating new work for global distribution
Country: United States
Type: Ballet and Dance Company
Contact: Executive Director Richard Caples
Email: Lubovitch@aol.com
Artistic Director Lar Lubovitch
Social Media: @Lubovitch
Touring Countries: more than 30 countries as well as all 50 states of the U.S.
Annual Performances: 60
Number of Performers: 14
Venues: City Center Theater, New York 2684

Limón
Website: www.limon.org
Email: info@limon.org
Phone: 212 777 3353
Address: 307 W. 38th Street, Suite 1105, US
Country: United States
Type: Ballet and Dance Company
Contact: Artistic Director Carla Maxwell
Email: cmaxwell@limon.org
Executive Director Gabriela Poler-Buzali
Email: gpolerbuzali@limon.org
Venues: up to 2000

Lingo dancetheater
Website: www.lingodance.com
Email: kt@lingodance.com
Phone: 206 349 8772
Address: 1121 15th Avenue, US
Country: United States
Type: Ballet and Dance Company
Contact: Artistic Director KT Niehoff
Email: kt@lingodance.com

Liss Fain Dance
Website: www.lissfaindance.org
Email: info@lissfaindance.org
Phone: 415 380 9433
Address: 26 Seventh st, Floor 5, US
Country: United States
Type: Ballet and Dance Company
Contact: projects Manager and touring coordinator Megan Kurashige
Executive Director Ed Payne
Artistic Director Liss Fain
Social Media: @lissfaindance www.facebook.com/LissFainDance

Liz Lerman Dance Exchange
Website: www.danceexchange.org
Email: mail@danceexchange.org
Phone: 301 270 6700
Address: 7117 Maple Avenue, US
Country: United States
Type: Ballet and Dance Company
Contact: Managing Director and CEO Jane Hirshberg
founding Artistic Director Liz Lerman
Venues: various up to 1200

Lone Star Ballet
Website: www.lonestarballet.org
Email: info@lonestarballet.org
Phone: 806 372 2463
Address: 3218 Hobbs, US

Information: dancers are scholarship students, West Texas A & M University, scholarship money is provided by LSB; also presenting 2 companies and sharing 2 shows with them, 3 Productions & 1 guest; alternative e-mail: lonestarballet@reyne.net
Country: United States
Type: Ballet and Dance Company
Contact: Executive Director Craig Henderson
Email: craig@lonestarballet.org
Venues: Amarillo Civic Center Auditorium 2200

Loretta Livingston & Dancers
Website: www.livingstondance.com
Email: LLDances@aol.com
Phone: 213 300 7334
Address: PO Box 861949, US
Country: United States
Type: Ballet and Dance Company
Contact: Artistic Director, choreographer Loretta Livingston
Venues: unusual urban spaces such as libraries, outdoor plazas, subway stations and art galleries, as well as conventional theatres, both large and small

Lori Belilove Company
Website: www.isadoraduncan.org
Email: info@isadoraduncan.org
Phone: 212 691 5040
Address: 141 West 26th Street, US
Country: United States
Type: Ballet and Dance Company
Contact: Director of Marketing & communications Susan Brender
Artistic Director Lori Belilove
Touring Countries: England, Greece, Cyprus, Budapest, Korea, Brazil
Venues: Colleges and Universities worldwide

Los Angeles Ballet
Website: www.losangelesballet.org
Email: contact@losangelesballet.org
Phone: 310 477 7411
Address: Offices & Studios, 11755 Exposition Boulevard, US
Country: United States
Type: Ballet and Dance Company
Contact: Executive Director Julie Whittaker
Artistic Director Thordal Christensen
Artistic Director Colleen neary
Venues: Freud Playhouse ; Royce Hall, UCLA ; Alex Theatre, Glendale ; Redondo Beach Performing Arts Center; The Broad Stage, Santa Monica; Carpenter Performing Arts Center; Valley Performing Arts Center

Louisville Ballet
Website: www.louisvilleballet.org
Email: Info@louisvilleballet.org
Phone: 502 583 3150
Address: 315 East Main Street, US
Country: United States
Type: Ballet and Dance Company
Contact: Executive Director Jack R. Lemmon
Artistic Director Bruce Simpson
Venues: Whitney Hall, Kentucky Center for the Arts 2406, Brown Theatre

Lula Washington Dance Theater
Website: www.lulawashington.org
Email: mail@lulawashington.org
Phone: 323 292 5852
Address: 3773 S. Crenshaw Blvd., US
Country: United States
Type: Ballet and Dance Company
Contact: Associate Director Lula Washington
Executive Director & founder Erwin Washington
Associate Director Tamica Washington
Venues: up to 2000

Luna Negra Dance Theater
Website: www.lunanegra.org
Email: information@lunanegra.org
Phone: 312 337 6882
Address: 1016 N. Dearborn Parkway, US
Country: United States
Type: Ballet and Dance Company
Contact: founder & Artistic Director Eduardo Vilaro
Managing Director Brooke Manetti

Madison Ballet
Website: www.madisonballet.org
Email: information@madisonballet.org
Phone: 608 278 7990
Address: 160 Westgate Mall, Suite I, US
Country: United States
Type: Ballet and Dance Company
Contact: Artistic Director W Earle Smith
Email: esmith@madisonballet.org

Maida Withers Dance Construction Company
Website: www.maidadance.com
Email: m.withers@verizon.net
Phone: 202 994 0739

Address: 800 21st Street NW, Suite 227, US
Information: Withers creates work for other dance companies; directs site-specific events; residencies for improvisation; workshops on dance video as art
Country: United States
Type: Ballet and Dance Company
Contact: Artistic Director Maida Withers
Social Media: @MWDCCo
www.facebook.com/MaidaDance
Venues: Lisner Auditorium 1500, Marvin Theatre 450, Kennedy Center 600, Dance Place 130

Majikina Honryu Dance Co.
Website:
Email: majikina.dance@verizon.net
Phone: 310 475 3766
Address: 1738 Malcolm Avenue Suite 5, US
Information: traditional, classical & folk dances of Okinawa. Children's programmes. Will customise performances from 10-20 minutes to full theatrical programmes of 1 1/2 hours. Live musicians & taped music
Country: United States
Type: Ballet and Dance Company
Contact: Managing Director Heather C. Matsunaga
Email: majikina.dance@verizon.net
**Artistic Director; Executive Director Aiko Majikina

Malashock Dance and Company
Website: www.malashockdance.org
Email: info@malashockdance.org
Phone: 619 260 1622
Address: 2650 Truxtun Road, Suite 202, US
Country: United States
Type: Ballet and Dance Company
Contact: Artistic Director & founder
John Malashock
Executive Director Paloma Patterson
Venues: Old Globe Theatre 582, Lyceum Theatre 550

Manhattan Tap Inc.
Website: www.manhattantap.org
Email: hcornell@manhattantap.org
Phone: 845 480 1396
Address: PO Box 571, US
Information: for booking contact company directly
Country: United States
Type: Ballet and Dance Company
Contact: music Director/composer Keith Saunders
Touring Countries: United States, Canada, France, Germany, Spain, Switzerland, Brazil, Finland, The Netherlands, Czech Republic, Russia, Sweden, UK
Venues: up to 5000

Margaret Jenkins Dance Company
Website: www.mjdc.org
Email: info@mjdc.org
Phone: 415 861 3940
Address: 507 Polk Street, Suite 320, US
Information: dedicated to the making and touring of new work, international exchange, and programs that support process, choreographic mentorship and performance opportunities
Country: United States
Type: Ballet and Dance Company
Contact: Artistic Director Margaret Jenkins
Email: mj@mjdc.org
Social Media: @MJDanceCo www.facebook.com/mjdanceco
Venues: Centre for the Arts 750, Theater Artaud 300

Mark Morris Dance Group
Website: markmorrisdancegroup.org
Email: info@mmdg.org
Phone: 718 624 8400
Address: 3 Lafayette Avenue, US
Information: members of ISPA
Country: United States
Type: Ballet and Dance Company
Contact: Artistic Director Mark Morris
General Manager Huong Hoang
Email: huong@mmdg.org
Executive Director Nancy Umanoff
Email: nancy@mmdg.org
Venues: Brooklyn Academy of Music Opera House Brooklyn, NY, Zellerbach Hall Berkeley, CA, The New York State Theater, Lincoln Center New York, NY

Maude Baum & Company
Website: www.eba-arts.org
Email: ebadance@earthlink.net
Phone: 518 465 9916
Address: 351 Hudson Avenue, US
Country: United States
Type: Ballet and Dance Company
Contact: Artistic Director Maude Baum
Email: mb@eba-arts.org
Venues: eba Theatre 250, Empire Center 1000

Maura Nguyen Donohue/In Mixed Company
Website: www.inmixedcompany.com
Email: info@inmixedcompany.com
Phone: 917 207 5373
Address: 125 W 106 ST #2A, US
Country: United States

Type: Ballet and Dance Company
Contact: Artistic Director Maura N Donohue
Email: maura.donohue@gmail.com

Maximum Dance Company
Website: www.maximumdancecompany.com
Phone: 305 259 3160
Address: 3000 Biscayne Boulevard, suite 102, US
Country: United States
Type: Ballet and Dance Company
Contact: Artistic Director David Olds
Venues: Gusman Centre, Miami; Baily Concert Hall, St Lauderdale

Merce Cunningham Dance Company
Website: www.mercecunningham.org
Email: info@merce.org
Phone: 212 255 8240
Address: 55 Bethune Street, US
Information: 14 dancers, one year
Country: United States
Type: Ballet and Dance Company
Contact: archivist David Vaughan
Artistic Director Merce Cunningham
music Director Takehisa Kosugi
company manger Jeff Donaldson-Forbes
assistant to the choreographer Robert Swinston
Executive Director Trevor Carlson
Touring Countries: France, Belgium, North America, London and Australia during the 08 season
Venues: various

Meredith Monk
Website: www.meredithmonk.org
Email: info@meredithmonk.org
Phone: 212 904 1330
Address: 260 W. Broadway Suite #2, US
Information: composer, singer, Director/choreographer and creator of new opera, music theater works, films and installations
Country: United States
Type: Ballet and Dance Company
Contact: Artistic Director Meredith Monk
booking agent (usa) Rena Shagan

Miami City Ballet
Website: www.miamicityballet.org
Email: admin-fin@miamicityballet.org
Phone: 305 929 7000
Address: 2200 Liberty Ave., US
Information: Founded in 1986; Miami City Ballet School trains young dancers for entry into professional company; IMG phone: 212-774 6705
Country: United States
Type: Ballet and Dance Company
Contact: Executive Director Daniel J Hagerty
Email: dhagerty@miamicityballet.org
Artistic Director Lourdes Lopez
Venues: Carnival Center for the Performing Arts, Broward Center for the Performing Arts 2500, Kravis Center for the Performing Arts 2200, Naples Phil Concert Hall 1200

Miami Hispanic Ballet
Website: www.miamihispanicballet.org
Email: contact@miamihispanicballet.org
Phone: 305 549 7711
Address: 111 SW 5th Ave, US
Country: United States
Type: Ballet and Dance Company
Contact: Marketing Director Karen Eva Couty
founder & Director
Pedro Pablo Peña

Michael Mao Dance
Website: www.michaelmaodance.org
Email: Michael@michaelmaodance.org
Phone: 212 757 9669
Address: 130 West 56th Street, 7th floor, US
Country: United States
Type: Ballet and Dance Company
Contact: Artistic Director Michael Mao
business Manager Arthur Steinberg
Touring Countries: China, US, Mexico, France, Norway
Venues: New Century, Beijing 2100; Shanghai Art Theater 1850, Moterrey Opera House3000, Purchase, NY 850-Pepsico, Joyce 650 DTW 99 Kaye 550

Michael Minery's Tapaholics
Website: www.tapaholics.com
Email: tapaholics@fordance.org
Phone: 210 826 3498
Address: The Field, 161 Sixth Ave – 14 Floor, US
Country: United States
Type: Ballet and Dance Company
Contact: booking agent Suzy Zimmermann

Milwaukee Ballet
Website: www.milwaukeeballet.org
Email: 2thepointe@milwaukeeballet.org
Phone: 414 643 7677
Address: 504 West National Avenue, US
Information: residents at Marcus Center for the Performing Arts, Milwaukee
Country: United States

Mimi Garrard Dance Theatre
Website: www.mimigarrarddance.com
Email: mimimgdc@aol.com
Phone: 212 674 6868
Address: 63 Greene Street, Suite 506, US
Information: also video works
Country: United States
Type: Ballet and Dance Company
Contact: Artistic Director Mimi Garrard
Touring Countries: Peru
Venues: mostly colleges, universities, museums and festivals nation – and worldwide; online festivals

Minh Tran and Company
Website: www.mtdance.org
Email: info@mtdance.org
Phone: 503 998 0381
Address: 4110 SE Hawthorne Boulevard, PMB, #180, US
Country: United States
Type: Ballet and Dance Company
Contact: Artistic Director Minh Tran

Minnesota Ballet
Website: www.minnesotaballet.org
Email: office@minnesotaballet.org
Phone: 218 529 3742
Address: 301 W. First Street, Suite 800, US
Country: United States
Type: Ballet and Dance Company
Contact: Artistic Director Robert Gardener
Venues: The Decc 2600

Molissa Fenley and Company
Website: www.molissafenley.com
Email: molissa@molissafenley.com
Phone: 212 941 8911
Address: 260 West Broadway, Suite #1, US
Information: Molissa Fenley and Company present a one-week-long New York season each year, usually in the fall. During the spring of each year, Molissa is in residence at Mills College in Oakland, California and presents work there as well as other sites in California and the Pacific Northwest. The Company is based in New York throughout each summer and fall
Country: United States
Type: Ballet and Dance Company
Contact: Managing Director Mimi Johnson
Email: artservicesinc@mindspring.com
Artistic Director/choreographer Molissa Fenley
Email: molissa@molissafenley.com
assistant to Molissa Fenley Alyssa Wilmot
Email: alyssa@molissafenley.com
Social Media: @molissafenley www.facebook.com/molissa.fenley
Number of Performers: 5
Venues: theaters with 500 and less seats

Momenta
Website: www.momenta-dance.org
Email: info@momenta-dance.org
Phone: 708 848 2329
Address: 605 Lake Street, US
Country: United States
Type: Ballet and Dance Company
Contact: lighting design Mike Dutka
co-Director Stephanie Clemens
ballet master & choreographer
Valery Dolgallo
co-Director Larry Ippel
Venues: Home Theatre: Black Box 200

MOMIX
Website: www.momix.com
Email: momix@snet.net
Phone: 860 868 7454
Address: Box 1035, US
Country: United States
Type: Ballet and Dance Company
Contact: Artistic Director Moses Pendleton
Associate Director Cynthia Quinn

Monkey & the Waterfall Dance Theatre Co
Website: www.monkeywaterfall.org
Email: monkeywaterfall@hotmail.com
Phone: 808 737 9809
Address: 99-440 Aiea Heights Drive, US
Country: United States
Type: Ballet and Dance Company
Contact: co-Director Yukie Shiroma
co-Director Ben Moffat
Touring Countries: Scotland, Malaysia, Indonesia, Singapore, Canada

Montgomery Ballet
Website: www.montgomeryballet.org
Phone: 334 409 0522
Address: 2101 Eastern Blvd, Suite 223, US
Country: United States
Type: Ballet and Dance Company
Contact: Artistic Director Darren Christian McIntyre
Venues: Davis Theatre 1400, The Winton Blount Cultural Center; Carolyn Blount Theatre

Mordine & Company Dance Theatre
Website: www.mordine.org
Email: info@mordine.org
Phone: 312 654 9540
Address: 1016 N. Dearborn Parkway, US
Country: United States
Type: Ballet and Dance Company
Contact: Artistic/Executive Director Shirley Mordine
Email: mordine@mordine.org
Marketing Manager Suzy Grant
Email: Marketing@mordine.org
Venues: Dance Center of Columbia College, capacity 275 Millennium Park Pavilion Theatre, capacity 400 Store Front Theatre, Chicago, capacity 125 Site Specific Events, capacity open

Morphoses
Website: www.morphoses.org
Email: info@morphoses.org
Phone: 212 813 9818
Address: 800 Fifth Avenue, Suite 18B, US
Country: United States
Type: Ballet and Dance Company
Contact: Executive Director Lourdes Lopez

Muntu Dance Theatre of Chicago
Website: www.muntu.com
Email: info@muntu.com
Phone: 773 241 6080
Address: 7127 South Ellis Avenue, US
Country: United States
Type: Ballet and Dance Company
Contact: President Joan Gray
Email: joan@muntu.com
Artistic Director Amaniyea Payne
Email: amaniyea@muntu.com

Nai-Ni Chen Dance Company
Website: www.nainichen.org
Email: info@nainichen.org
Phone: 800 – 650 0246
Address: PO Box 1121, US
Country: United States
Type: Ballet and Dance Company
Contact: Artistic Director Nai-Ni Chen
Executive Director Andy Chiang
Touring Countries: USA, Canada, China, Europe, and other Asian countries
Venues: various, including New Jersey Performing Arts Center, major dance venues in New York, and touring to major theaters throughout the U.S.A.

Nancy Karp and Dancers
Website: www.nancykarp.org
Email: info@nancykarp.org
Phone: 415 516 8575
Address: 4250 Horton Street, Studio 6, US
Country: United States
Type: Ballet and Dance Company
Contact: Artistic Director Nancy Karp

Nashville Ballet
Website: www.nashvilleballet.com
Email: info@nashvilleballet.com
Phone: 615 297 2966
Address: 3630 Redman St, US
Country: United States
Type: Ballet and Dance Company
Contact: Artistic Director Paul Vasterling
Email: pvasterling@nashvilleballet.com
Executive Director Angie Adams
Email: aadams@nashvilleballet.com
Venues: James K Polk Theatre 1012, Andrew Jackson Hall 2442

Neta Dance Company
Website: www.netacompany.org
Email: neta@ufl.edu
Phone: 212 866 4626
Address: 449 West 125th Street Apt # 5D, US
Country: United States
Type: Ballet and Dance Company
Contact: Artistic Director Neta Pulvermacher
Email: neta@ufl.edu
company Manager Kristen Schifferdecker
Venues: Joyce Theatre, Dance Theatre workshop

Nevada Ballet Theatre
Website: www.nevadaballet.com
Email: info@nevadaballet.com
Phone: 702 243 2623
Address: 1651 Inner Circle, US
Country: United States
Type: Ballet and Dance Company
Contact: company Manager Geoffrey Stafford
Artistic Director Bruce Steivel
Executive Director Beth Barbre
finance Director Brooke Blake
Director of Marketing and pr Cindy Fox
ballet mistress Clarice Rathers
Touring Countries: Portugal
Venues: Judy Bayley Theatre, Univ. of Nevada, Las Vegas 550, Ham Hall, UNLV 1843, Samba Theatre, Casino Rio All-Suite Hotel 1500

New Jersey Ballet Company
Website: www.njballet.org
Email: info@njballet.org
Phone: 973 597 9600
Address: 15-17 Microlab Road, Suite 102, US
Country: United States
Type: Ballet and Dance Company
Contact: Director Carolyn Clark
Email: Director@njballet.org
assistant to Executive Director Paul H McRae
Email: paul@njballet.org
Venues: Mayo Performing Arts Center 1200, bergen Performing Arts Center 1500. 1200, NJ Performing Arts Centre (Prudential Hall) 2700, Kean University

New York Baroque Dance Company, The
Website: www.nybaroquedance.org
Email: sarahesther2000@yahoo.com
Phone: 212 662 8829
Address: 141 E. 3rd Street, Suite 2D, US
Information: touring and guest appearances are handled directly by the company. Also give workshops and lectures and stage direct operas; can supply full costumes for dancers, singers and chorus for our own Productions if the opera is already in company's repertoire
Country: United States
Type: Ballet and Dance Company
Contact: Artistic Director Catherine Turocy
Touring Countries: Germany, France, UK, Mexico, Canada, Japan
Annual Performances: 20
Number of Performers: 8
Venues: Florence Gould Hall 335; Alice Tully Hall, Lincoln Center 1096

New York City Ballet
Website: www.nycballet.com
Email: clanders@nycballet.com
Phone: 212 870 5656
Address: New York State Theater, 20 Lincoln Center, US
Country: United States
Type: Ballet and Dance Company
Contact: ballet master in chief Peter Martins
Venues: New York State Theater 2779, Saratoga Performing Arts Center (summer residency)

New York Theatre Ballet
Website: www.nytb.org
Email: admin@nytb.org
Phone: 212 679 0401
Address: 30 East 31st Street, US
Country: United States
Type: Ballet and Dance Company
Contact: Artistic Director, President, CEO Diana Byer
Email: dianabyer@nytb.org
Venues: Florence Gould Hall 400

Nicholas Leichter Dance
Website: www.nldnyc.org
Email: nld@aol.com
Phone: 718 797 4577
Address: 28 Old Fulton Street, THB, US
Information: Representation: Elsie management, www.elsieman.org. Organises masterclasses, workshops, residencies, lecture demonstrations, talkbacks and open rehearsals
Country: United States
Type: Ballet and Dance Company
Contact: Managing Director Christine Young
technical Director Christine Shallenberg
Artistic Director Nicholas Leichter
Social Media: www.facebook.com/nldnyc
Touring Countries: across the US, Canada, Germany, Russia and Taiwan
Venues: Cunningham Studio

Nina Winthrop and Dancers
Website: www.nwandd.com
Email: mail@NinaWinthropandDancers.org
Address: 161 Sixth Ave., 14th Fl., US
Country: United States
Type: Ballet and Dance Company
Contact: Artistic Director & choreographer Nina Winthrop
Managing Director Taimi Strehlow
Venues: Joyce SoHo 100, Flea Theater 150, Danspace Project 150

Northwest Florida Ballet
Website: www.nfballet.org
Email: toddericallen@cox.net
Phone: 850 664 7787
Address: 310 Perry Avenue, US
Country: United States
Type: Ballet and Dance Company
Contact: assistant Artistic Director Sharon Allen
Email: sallen@nfballet.org
Artistic Director/CEO Todd Eric Allen
Email: toddericallen@cox.net
ballet mistress Dorothy Daniels Lister
Email: lister_d@earthlink.net
office Manager Rhondra Starnes
Email: rstarnes@nfballet.org

Nutmeg Conservatory for the Arts Inc.
Website: www.nutmegballet.org
Email: office@nutmegconservatory.org
Phone: 860 482 4413
Address: 58 Main Street, US
Country: United States
Type: Ballet and Dance Company
Contact: founder & Executive Director Sharon Dante
Email: Sdante@nutmegconservatory.org
Artistic Director Victoria Mazzarelli
Email: vmazzarelli@Nutmegconservatory.org
ballet master & Production Manager Tim Melady
Email: tmelady@Nutmegconservatory.org
Social Media: TheNutmegBalletNutmegBallet
Venues: Bushnell Belding Theatre, Warner Theatre, Nancy Marine Studio Theater, Premier Studio Theatre

O-T-O Dance
Website: www.otodance.org
Email: anne@otodance.org
Phone: 520 624 3799
Address: PO Box 4605, US
Information: one of the few companies combining modern dance with the single point trapeze, other aerial apparatus, harness and silks in performance; studio address: 121 E 7th Street, corner of 7th St & 7th Avenue, Tucson, AZ 85705; alternative email: info@otodance.org.
Country: United States
Type: Ballet and Dance Company
Contact: technical Director Chuck Koesters
Email: chuck@otodance.org
Touring Countries: USA, Mexico, Central America, South America, Brittish Isles, Russia, Italy, Switzerland
Venues: various indoor and outdoor venues, festivals, small to proscenium theatre settings; able to create site specific thematic performance works

ODC/San Francisco
Website: www.odcdance.org
Email: lori@odcdance.org
Phone: 415 863 6606
Address: 351 Shotwell Street, US
Country: United States
Type: Ballet and Dance Company
Contact: Artistic Director Brenda Way
Executive Director Victor Gotesman
Email: victor@odcdance.org
Venues: ODC Theater (San Francisco); ODC Dance Commons (recently opened); others up to 2000. Based in San Francisco's historic Mission district

Oklahoma Festival Ballet
Website: www.ou.edu/finearts/dance
Email: dance@ou.edu
Phone: 405 325 4051
Address: 560 Parrington Oval, Room 1000, US
Information: The Oklahoma Festival Ballet is the resident ballet company of the University of Oklahoma. The company maintains a repertoire of over 33 short ballets and numerous full-length ballets in styles ranging from classical to romantic, abstract to contemporary and dramatic to comedic.
Country: United States
Type: Ballet and Dance Company
Contact: Director and regents professor Mary Margaret Holt
Email: marymholt@ou.edu
Touring Countries: regional tours the whole year
Venues: Rupel Jones Theater 600, Donald W. Reynold Performing Arts Center 600

Oregon Ballet Theatre
Website: www.obt.org
Email: info@obt.org
Phone: 503 227 0977
Address: 818 SE 6th Ave., US
Country: United States
Type: Ballet and Dance Company
Contact: Artistic Director Christopher Stowell
Venues: Keller Auditorium 3000, Newmark Theatre 872

Orlando Ballet
Website: www.orlandoballet.org
Email: kfabian@orlandoballet.org
Phone: 407 426 1733
Address: 1111 N. Orange Avenue, US
Information: Today, Orlando Ballet is Central Florida's only fully residential professional ballet company and performs its annual season at the Bob Carr Performing Arts Centre. The Company includes not only dancers from the United States, but also Brazil, Mexico, Japan, Korea, Romania and the Ukraine.
Country: United States
Type: Ballet and Dance Company
Contact: Artistic Director Robert Hill
Email: rhill@orlandoballet.org
Managing Director Katherine Fabian
Email: kfabian@orlandoballet.org
Director of Production Larry Rayburn
Email: lrayburn@orlandoballet.org
Venues: Dr. Phillips Performing Arts Center 2400

Oslund + Co/Dance
Website: www.oslundandco.org
Email: Director@oslundandco.org
Phone: 503 702 0514
Address: 918 sw yamhill, ste 401, US
Information: Oslund + Company/Dance reaches dance audiences through performances that are intellectually challenging, emotionally evocative and relevant to our times. The company's goal is to present work that engages viewers and participants in rewarding, insightful, and sophisticated exchange, and to create a relationship with audiences which deepens over time.
Country: United States
Type: Ballet and Dance Company
Contact: Artistic Director Mary Oslund

Pacific Northwest Ballet
Website: www.pnb.org
Email: Marketing@pnb.org
Phone: 206 441 2424
Address: 301 Mercer Street, US
Information: Enriching lives in the Pacific Northwest, considered a national treasure and acclaimed worldwide, PNB epitomizes excellence in the performing arts.
Country: United States
Type: Ballet and Dance Company
Contact: Artistic Director Peter Boal
Executive Director David Brown
Marketing Director Ellen Walker
Email: EllenW@pnb.org
Venues: McCaw Hall 3000

Palissimo
Website: www.palissimo.com
Email: office@palissimo.com
Address: US
Information: also offer workshops
Country: United States
Type: Ballet and Dance Company
Contact: Artistic Director Pavel Zustiak
Touring Countries: Czech Republic, Slovakia, Poland, Hungary, Italy, USA
Venues: Baryshnikov Arts Center, La MaMa, Performance Space 122, Ailey Citigroup Theatre, Dance New Amsterdam DNA, HERE Arts Center, Chashama, University Settlement

Parsons Dance Company
Website: www.parsonsdance.org
Email: info@parsonsdance.org
Phone: 212 869 9275
Address: 229 W. 42nd Street, 8th Floor, US
Information: an internationally renowned contemporary dance company based in New York City. Under the Artistic direction of David Parsons, the company presents uplifting, family-friendly contemporary dance to audiences around the world. It is the mission of Parsons Dance to deliver positive, affirming and life-enriching experiences to audiences worldwide, through dance and movement
Country: United States
Type: Ballet and Dance Company
Contact: Artistic Director David Parsons
Executive Director John Krasno
Email: john@parsonsdance.org
Venues: Joyce Theater

Pasadena Dance Theatre
Website: www.pasadenadance.org
Email: info@pasadenadance.org
Phone: 626 683 3459
Address: 1985 East Locust Street, US
Information: Pasadena Dance Theatre provides classical and innovative contemporary choreography through professional dance performance and offers the highest caliber of dance training through its conservatory.
Country: United States
Type: Ballet and Dance Company
Contact: Artistic Director Cynthia Young
Associate Artistic Director Laurence Blake
Venues: San Gabriel Civic Auditorium

Pat Cannon's Foot and Fiddle Dance Co
Website: www.footandfiddle.org
Email: info@footandfiddle.org
Phone: 845 753 6950
Address: 115 Johnsontown Road, US
Information: "Pat Cannon offers a creative mix of American Folk forms and Broadway pizzazz with her Foot & Fiddle Dance Company. An evening with Foot & Fiddle guarantees a good time for dancers and audiences alike." The New York times
Country: United States
Type: Ballet and Dance Company
Contact: Artistic Director Pat Cannon
Venues: concert halls, outdoor festivals

Pat Graney Company
Website: www.patgraney.org
Email: staff@patgraney.org
Phone: 206 329 3705
Address: 1419 S. Jackson, Studio 11, US
Country: United States
Type: Ballet and Dance Company
Contact: Executive/Artistic Director Pat Graney

Touring Countries: UK, Scotland, Japan, Brazil, Chile, Germany, Singapore
Venues: houses with seating up to 1400

Paul Taylor Dance Company
Website: www.ptdc.org
Email: ao@ptdc.org
Phone: 212 431 5562
Address: 551 Grand Street, US
Country: United States
Type: Ballet and Dance Company
Contact: Director of Marketing Alan Olshan
Artistic Director Paul Taylor
Executive Director John Tomlinson
Director of tour engagements Tim Robinson
Social Media: Paul Taylor Dance Company
Number of Performers: 16
Venues: Home: New York City Center, 1900 seats

Pearsonwidrig Dancetheater
Website: www.pearsonwidrig.org
Email: sarapatrik@pearsonwidrig.org
Phone: 212 433 0650
Address: 322 East 11th Street #11, US
Information: Sara Pearson and Patrik Widrig – Artistic Directors of PEARSONWIDRIG DANCETHEATER since 1987 – have gained an international following for work that transforms the familiar into the mysterious, the subversive, and the intimate.
Country: United States
Type: Ballet and Dance Company
Contact: Artistic Director Patrik Widrig
Artistic Director Sara Pearson
Touring Countries: Austria, Brazil, England, Germany, Greece, India, Italy, Japan, Mexico, New Zealand, Peru, Scotland, South Korea, Switzerland, United States, Wales

Pennsylvania Ballet
Website: www.paballet.org
Email: info@paballet.org
Phone: 215 551 7000
Address: 1819 JFK Blvd, Suite 210, US
Information: The mission of Pennsylvania Ballet is to maintain and nurture a financially sound, Philadelphia-based ballet company that presents the finest in artistry and performance to the widest possible audience, expands and diversifies its classical and contemporary repertoire and provides the highest caliber of instruction for aspiring professional dancers. Pennsylvania Ballet strives to enrich and expand the cultural lives of children and adults of the Greater Philadelphia region by educating its citizens about and through the art of ballet
Country: United States
Type: Ballet and Dance Company
Contact: ballet Director William DeGregory
ballet master Jeffrey Gribler
Artistic Director Roy Kaiser
Executive Director Michael Scolamiero
ballet mistress Tamara Hadley
choreogrpaher in residence Matthew Neenan
Social Media: @paballet www.facebook.com/pennsylvaniaballet
Venues: Academy of Music 2800, Merriam Theatre 1700

Pentacle
Website: www.pentacle.org
Email: marag@pentacle.org
Phone: 212 278 8111
Address: 75 Broad Street, Suite 304, US
Information: see also Promoters
Country: United States
Type: Ballet and Dance Company
Contact: Director Mara   Greenberg
Email: marag@pentacle.org
founder and Director Ivan Sygoda
Email: ivans@pentacle.org
Associate Director, artist representative Anna Brady Nuse
Email: annan@pentacle.org
Director of booking and artist representation Harold Norris
Email: haroldn@pentacle.org
Social Media: @PentacleDance www.facebook.com/pentacle.artist.rep

Pepatián
Website: www.pepatian.org
Email: pepatian@gmail.com
Phone: 917 300 8736
Address: PO Box 86, US
Information: umbrella organization for three programs: Bronx Artist Spotlight series (Jump It Up and Fall Into It), Pepon Osorio Projects and Merian Soto Dance & Performance
Country: United States
Type: Ballet and Dance Company
Contact: Director Jane Gabriels

Peter Pucci Plus Dancers
Website: www.pucciplus.com
Email: ellen@pucciplus.com
Phone: 914 666 8414
Address: 120 Byram Lake Road, US
Country: United States

Type: Ballet and Dance Company

Philadanco! Philadelphia Dance Company
Website: www.philadanco.org
Email: jmb@philadanco.org
Phone: 215 387 8200
Address: 9 North Preston Street, US
Country: United States
Type: Ballet and Dance Company
Touring Countries: Poland, Korea, Bermuda, Turkey, China, Italy
Venues: Kimmel Center 1000, Joyce Theater, NY 450

Pilobolus Dance Theatre
Website: www.pilobolus.org
Email: info@pilobolus.org
Phone: 860 868 0538
Address: PO Box 388, US
Information: Pilobolus is a modern performance company, founded in 1971, that to this day wears its revolutionary stripes on its sleeves. In keeping with its fundamentally collective creative process, Pilobolus Dance Theatre now curates and convenes groups of diverse artists.
Country: United States
Type: Ballet and Dance Company
Contact: Artistic Director Robby Barnett
Executive Director Itamar Kubovy
Touring Countries: USA
Venues: various up to 3000

Pittsburgh Ballet Theatre
Website: www.pbt.org
Email: inquiry@pittsburghballet.org
Phone: 412 281 0360
Address: 2900 Liberty Avenue, US
Country: United States
Type: Ballet and Dance Company
Contact: ballet master Steven Annegarn
Director of Marketing & pr
Ida D'Errico
Executive Director Harris Ferris
ballet mistress Marianna Tcherkassky
Artistic Director Terrence S Orr
Venues: Benedum Center 2800

Printz Dance Project
Website: www.printzdance.org
Email: info@printzdance.org
Phone: 415 927 3253
Address: 26 Mohawk Avenue, US
Information: Booking Agent: Kamstar Artist Management / Katherine Miller; Tel: 415-776 5522
Country: United States
Type: Ballet and Dance Company
Contact: Artistic Director Stacey Printz

Project in Motion
Website: www.projectinmotion.com
Email: PIMdance@gmail.com
Phone: 575 208 4413
Address: PO Box 112, US
Country: United States
Type: Ballet and Dance Company
Social Media: @projectinmotion www.facebook.com/ProjectInMotion

Raiford Rogers Modern Ballet
Website: www.raifordrogers.com
Email: lacb@earthlink.net
Phone: 310 477 9525
Address: 1222 S Westgate Ave Suite 102, US
Country: United States
Type: Ballet and Dance Company
Contact: Artistic Director Raiford Rogers
Venues: Luckmann Fine Arts Complex, L.A. 1200

Randy James Dance Works
Website: www.rjdw.org
Email: rjdwed@aol.com
Phone: 732 247 2653
Address: PO Box 4452, US
Country: United States
Type: Ballet and Dance Company
Contact: Artistic Director Randy James
Executive Director Ruth Lanza

Rebecca Kelly Ballet
Website: www.RebeccaKellyBallet.com
Email: RKballet@ix.netcom.com
Phone: 212 226 5738
Address: 579 Broadway No 4B, US
Information: bookings:RKB, New York, Tel: 212-431 8489; 8 dancers; during July/August call: 518-293 7608
Country: United States
Type: Ballet and Dance Company
Contact: Artistic Director Rebecca Kelly
General Manager Craig Brashear
Venues: Various theaters in New York City; Lake Placid Center for the Arts, Lake Placid; 350, New York

Rebecca Stenn Company
Website: www.rebeccastenncompany.com
Email: rstenn@verizon.net
Phone: 917 501 5239

Address: Rebecca Stenn Company, 425 West 24th Street #1B, US
Information: booking contact: Jodi Kaplan & Associates, 161 Sixth Avenue, 14th Floor, New York, NY 10013; jodi@bookingdance.com; www.bookingdance.com (212) 352 0400
Country: United States
Type: Ballet and Dance Company
Contact: booking agent Jodi Kaplan
Email: jodi@bookingdance.com
Artistic Director Rebecca Stenn
Touring Countries: Italy

Reggie Wilson/Fist and Heel Performance Group
Website: www.fistandheel.org
Email: info@fistandheel.org
Address: US
Country: United States
Type: Ballet and Dance Company
Contact: Director Reggie Wilson
Email: rwilson@fistandheel.org

Repertory Dance Theatre
Website: www.rdtutah.org
Email: rdt@rdtutah.org
Phone: 801 534 1000
Address: PO Box 510427, US
Information: visiting address: Rose Wagner Performing Arts Center; 138 West 300 South; Downtown Salt Lake City
Country: United States
Type: Ballet and Dance Company
Contact: Executive & Artistic Director
 Linda C. Smith
Venues: Rose Wagner Performing Arts Center: Jeann

Richmond Ballet, State Ballet of Virginia
Website: www.richmondballet.com
Email: bbonda@richmondballet.com
Phone: 804 344 0906
Address: 407 East Canal Street, US
Information: RICHMOND BALLET was founded in 1957, by local dance enthusiasts as a performance outlet for students in local dance programs. It existed for more than twenty years as a small, civic company until 1975, when the School of Richmond Ballet was created.
In 2000, Richmond Ballet moved into a newly renovated state-of-the-art Facility at 407 East Canal Street in the heart of downtown Richmond. The spectacular building boasts 53, 500 square feet.
Richmond Ballet's mission is to awaken and uplift the human spirit, both for audiences and artists/
It is dedicated to the promotion, preservation and continuing evolution of the art form of ballet. Richmond Ballet strives to keep meaningful works of dance alive and to produce and foster new works that remain true to these values.
Country: United States
Type: Ballet and Dance Company
Contact: Artistic Director Stoner Winslett
Managing Director Brett Bonda
Artistic Associate Malcolm Burn
Artistic Associate Judy Jacob
Annual Performances: 6
Number of Performers: 27
Venues: Dominion Energy Center

RIOULT Dance NY
Website: www.rioult.org
Email: booking@rioult.org
Phone: 212 398 5901
Address: 246 West 38th Street, 4th floor, US
Information: founded in 1994 and fast became an established name in modern dance with a reputation for creating and presenting the sensual, articulate, and exquisitely musical works of Pascal Rioult. Born into the American modern dance tradition, RIOULT is creating its own legacy of contemporary dance that speaks to the mind and heart. The company of ten dancers is based in New York City and presents an annual New York season, tours nationally and internationally and conducts community engagement activities in the tri-state area and while on tour
Country: United States
Type: Ballet and Dance Company
Contact: Marketing Manager Penelope Gonzalez
Email: penelope@rioult.org
Artistic Director/choreographer Pascal Rioult
Associate Artistic Director Joyce Herring
Managing Director/booking Amy Harrison
Email: booking@rioult.org
Social Media: @RIOULT https://www.facebook.com/pages/RIOULT-re-you/32329389169?ref=tn_tnmn
Touring Countries: USA, Europe and Mexico
Number of Performers: 10

Ririe-Woodbury Dance Company
Website: www.ririewoodbury.com
Email: info@ririewoodbury.com
Phone: 801 297 4241
Address: 138 W Broadway 300 South, US
Information: Ririe-Woodbury Dance Company furthers contemporary dance as an accessible and valued art form through performance and dance education

Country: United States
Type: Ballet and Dance Company
Contact: Artistic Director Daniel Charon
Managing Director Jena Woodbury
Email: jena@ririewoodbury.com
Venues: Capitol Theatre 2000, Rose Wagner Performing Arts Centre 500

River North Chicago Dance Company
Website: www.rivernorthchicago.com
Email: info@rivernorthchicago.com
Phone: 312 944 2888
Address: 1016 North Dearborn Parkway, US
Country: United States
Type: Ballet and Dance Company
Contact: Executive Director Gail Kalver
Email: gkalver@rivernorthchicago.com
Director of Marketing Alexis Jaworski
Email: ajaworski@rivernorthchicago.com
Artistic Director Frank Chaves
Email: fchaves@rivernorthchicago.com

Robin Becker Dance
Website: www.robinbeckerdance.org
Email: staff@robinbeckerdance.org
Phone: 212 316 2958
Address: 345 Riverside Drive, #5A, US
Country: United States
Type: Ballet and Dance Company
Contact: Artistic Director & choreographer
 Robin Becker

Rockford Dance Company
Website: www.rockforddancecompany.com
Email: info@rockforddancecompany.com
Phone: 815 963 3341
Address: Riverfront Museum Park, 711 N Main St, US
Country: United States
Type: Ballet and Dance Company
Contact: Managing Director Cindy Jo Savitski-Lantz
Artistic Director Matthew Keefe
Venues: Maddox Theatre, Rockford College 570, Corona-do Theatre 2400

Rod Rodgers Dance Company Inc
Website: www.rodrodgersdance.org
Email: rodrodgers.dance@verizon.net
Phone: 212 674 9066
Address: 62 East 4th Street, US
Country: United States
Type: Ballet and Dance Company
Contact: General Manager Rachel Lubell
Artistic Director Kim Grier
Executive Director Jason Rodgers
Venues: among others: La Mama experimental Theatre 200

Sacramento Ballet
Website: www.sacballet.org
Email: info@sacballet.org
Phone: 916 552 5800
Address: 1631 K Street, US
Country: United States
Type: Ballet and Dance Company
Venues: Community Center Theater 2400, CSUS main stage 450, Mondavi Center, 1800

Saint Louis Ballet
Website: www.stlouisballet.org
Email: info@stlouisballet.org
Phone: 636 537 1998
Address: 218 THF Blvd, US
Country: United States
Type: Ballet and Dance Company
Venues: up to 1200

San Francisco Ballet Association
Website: www.sfballet.org
Email: lwhite@sfballet.org
Phone: 415 861 5600
Address: 455 Franklin Street, US
Information: more than 60 dancers.
Country: United States
Type: Ballet and Dance Company
Venues: War Memorial Opera House, 301 Van Ness Avenue, San Francisco, over 3100

Sarasota Ballet of Florida
Website: www.sarasotaballet.org
Phone: 941 359 0099
Address: 5555 North Tamiami Trail, US
Country: United States
Type: Ballet and Dance Company
Venues: Van Wezel Performing Arts Hall 1756; Florida State University Center for Performing Arts 488

Sean curran company
Website: www.ichinohedance.org
Email: info@ichinohedance.org
Phone: 212 757 2531
Address: 159 West 53rd Street, US
Information: Over 35-year history, the Company has been performing in the U.S. in Asia and South America.
Country: United States

Type: Ballet and Dance Company
Touring Countries: Japan
Venues: Ailey City Group Theatre, Joan Weill Centre for Dance, Kennedy Centre Washington, New National Theatre Tokyo

Shapiro & Smith Dance
Website: www.shapiroandsmithdance.org
Email: info@shapiroandsmithdance.org
Phone: 612 879 0863
Address: Brooklyn Navy Yard, Building 280, Suite 220, US
Information: alternative email: laurac@elsieman.org
Country: United States
Type: Ballet and Dance Company
Venues: Joyce Theatre, Lincoln Center outdoors, Dance theatre workshop and Festival di Milano among others

Shreveport Metropolitan Ballet
Website: www.shreveportmetroballet.org
Email: info@shreveportmetroballet.org
Phone: 318 221 8500
Address: 6654 Saint Vincent Avenue, US
Country: United States
Type: Ballet and Dance Company
Venues: Civic Theater

Smuin Ballet
Website: www.smuinballet.org
Email: info@smuinballet.org
Phone: 415 556 5000
Address: 44 Gough Street, Suite 103, US
Country: United States
Type: Ballet and Dance Company
Contact: Executive Director Celia Fushille
company Manager JoEllen Arntz
Social Media: @smuinballetsmuinballet

Snappy Dance Theater
Website: www.snappydance.com
Email: info@snappydance.com
Phone: 617 718 2497
Address: PO Box 400075, US
Information: has been enriching the lives of audiences of all backgrounds and ages with its edgy yet accessible style of dance theater since 1997; blends dance with theater and acrobatics; takes audiences around the United States and abroad on a journey that's thought-provoking, often humorous, and always entertaining
Country: United States
Type: Ballet and Dance Company
Contact: Artistic Director Martha Mason
Email: mmason@snappydance.com
Executive Director Jurgen Weiss
Email: jweiss@snappydance.com
General Manager Philip Naulot
Email: pnaulot@snappydance.com

Spectrum Dance Theater
Website: www.spectrumdance.org
Email: staff@spectrumdance.org
Phone: 206 325 4161
Address: 800 Lake Washington Blvd., US
Information: founded in 1982 to bring dance of the highest merit to a diverse audience composed of people from different social, cultural, ethnic and economic backgrounds; principal objective is to make the art form of dance accessible through contemporary dance performances and high-quality dance training in a variety of dance styles
Country: United States
Type: Ballet and Dance Company
Contact: Artistic Director Donald Byrd
Executive Director Susie Purves
Venues: Moory Theater

Spoke The Hub Dancing, Inc.
Website: www.spokethehub.org
Email: spoke@spokethehub.org
Phone: 718 408 3234
Address: 748 Union Street, US
Country: United States
Type: Ballet and Dance Company
Contact: Artistic Director Elise Long
Space Rental Coordinanator Lori Jorgensen
Email: space@spokethehub.org

Springfield Ballet Company
Website: www.springfieldballetco.org
Email: info@springfieldballetco.org
Phone: 217 544 1967
Address: 420 S. 6th Street, US
Country: United States
Type: Ballet and Dance Company
Contact: Artistic Director Julie Guttas
Venues: Sangamon Auditorium 2018, Hoogland Center for the Arts 500

State Street Ballet
Website: www.statestreetballet.com
Email: contact@statestreetballet.com
Phone: 805 563 3262
Address: 2285 Las Positas Road, US
Country: United States
Type: Ballet and Dance Company

Stephen Petronio Company
Website: www.stephenpetronio.com
Email: info@stephenpetronio.com
Phone: 212 473 1660
Address: 140 2nd Avenue, Suite 504, US
Information: Europe Booking Agent: Damien Valette, 50 Rue Jean Pierre Timbaud, F-75011, Paris, France Tel: (+33) 0143 380333 Fax: (+33) 0143 389183
Country: United States
Type: Ballet and Dance Company
Contact: Artistic Director Stephen Petronio Managing Director June Poster
Venues: Joyce Theater 800

Susan Marshall & Company
Website: www.susanmarshallandcompany.org
Email: dance@sumacdance.org
Phone: 212 219 0005
Address: 63 Greene Street, Suite 506, US
Information: blends virtuoso athleticism, ordinary movement, gesture and pattern, and the spoken word; has a long history of multidisciplinary collaboration, with over 30 works made in collaboration with musicians, visual artists, and designers
Country: United States
Type: Ballet and Dance Company
Contact: Managing Director Jeremy Olson booking agent Rena Shagan choreographer/Artistic Director Susan Marshall
Touring Countries: USA, Europe and Far East

Talk Dance Theatre
Website: www.talkdance.org
Email: info@talkdance.org
Phone: 601 291 0158
Address: 6 Woodbridge Place, US
Country: United States
Type: Ballet and Dance Company
Contact: founder/Artistic Director/choreographer Stephen Wynne
Social Media: @talkdance/talkdance
Touring Countries: Germany, England, Canada, USA, Bulgaria, Greece, Russia, Poland

Tap Fusion
Website: www.tapfusion.com
Email: info@tapfusion.com
Phone: 212 505 6323
Address: US
Country: United States
Type: Ballet and Dance Company
Contact: Artistic Director Barry Blumenfeld

TazWood Dance Company
Website:
Email: mld@mtco.com
Phone: 309 367 9754
Address: 1 College Drive, US
Country: United States
Type: Ballet and Dance Company
Contact: Artistic Director Mary Dexter
Venues: Illinois Central College, East Peoria

Texas Ballet Theatre
Website: www.texasballettheater.org
Phone: 817 763 0207
Address: 6845 Green Oaks Road, US
Country: United States
Type: Ballet and Dance Company
Contact: music Director Jack Buckhannan Artistic Director Ben Stevenson ballet master Anna Donovan Associate Artistic Director Timothy O'Keefe
Venues: Fair Park Music Hall, Dallas 3400, Nancy Lee and Perry R. Bass Performance Hall, Fort Worth 1950

Trinity Irish Dance Company
Website: www.trinityirishdancecompany.org
Email: info@trinityirishdancecompany.org
Phone: 773 549 6135
Address: 2936 N Southport, US
Information: contracts negotiable
Country: United States
Type: Ballet and Dance Company
Contact: Artistic Director & founder Mark Howard Associate Artistic Director Deirdre Mahoney
Touring Countries: USA, Canada, Taiwan, Europe, Japan, Central America
Venues: up to 15.000

Trisha Brown Dance Company Inc
Website: www.trishabrowncompany.org
Email: b.dufty@trishabrowncompany.org
Phone: 212 977 5365
Address: 341 W. 38th Street, , Suite 801, US
Information: Trisha Brown Dance Company has presented the work of its legendary Artistic Director for over 40 years. Founded in 1970 when Trisha Brown branched out from the experimental Judson Dance Theater to work with her own group of dancers, TBDC offered its first performances at alternative sites in Manhattan's SoHo

Country: United States
Type: Ballet and Dance Company
Contact: Executive Director Barbara Dufty
Email: b.dufty@trishabrowncompany.org company Manager Dorothée Alémany
Email: d.alemany@trishabrowncompany.org development Director Monika Jouvert
Email: m.jouvert@trishabrowncompany.org
Social Media: @TrishaBrown www.facebook.com/trish-abrowndancecompany

Tulsa Ballet
Website: www.tulsaballet.org
Email: admin@tulsaballet.org
Phone: 918 749 6030
Address: 4512 S. Peoria Avenue, US
Country: United States
Type: Ballet and Dance Company
Contact: Artistic Director Marcello Angelini Marketing Director Todd Cunningham
Venues: Performing Arts Center, Tulsa 2400

Urban Ballet Theater
Website: www.urbanballettheater.org
Email: alex@urbanballettheater.org
Phone: 212 663 1830
Address: 5 West 102nd Street, Suite 5B, US
Country: United States
Type: Ballet and Dance Company
Contact: Executive Director Alex Erikson
Email: alex@urbanballettheater.org
Social Media: @UrbanBalletNYC http:// www.facebook.com/UrbanBalletTheater

Urban Bush Women
Website: www.urbanbushwomen.org
Email: info@urbanbushwomen.org
Phone: 718 398 4537
Address: 138 South Oxford St. #4B, Brooklyn, US
Information: Company is dedicated to encouraging cultural activity as an inherent part of community life. Representation: IMG Artists, jglawe@imgartists.com
Country: United States
Type: Ballet and Dance Company
Contact: Artistic Director Jawole Willa Jo Zollar Executive Director Amy Cassello
Touring Countries: Asia, Australia, Europe and South America
Venues: Jacob's Pillow, Lee Massachusetts, Lincoln Center

Vanaver Caravan Dance & Music Company
Website: www.vanavercaravan.org
Email: vcoffice@hvc.rr.com
Phone: 845 256 9300
Address: Waterstreet Market, 10 Main Street, Suite 322, US
Information: touring 'Pastures of Plenty' tribute to Woody Guthrie; offers workshops and masterclasses in international, ethnic and modern dance Represented by Siegel Artist Management www.siegelartist.com
Country: United States
Type: Ballet and Dance Company
Contact: Press & Artistic Director Livia Vanaver
Touring Countries: Europe

Verb Ballets
Website: www.verbballets.org
Email: info@verbballets.org
Phone: 216 397 3757
Address: 2140 Lee Road, Suite 218, US
Country: United States
Type: Ballet and Dance Company
Contact: Artistic Director Hernando Cortez Executive Director Dr Margaret Carlson

Visual Rhythm
Website: www.visualrhythm.com
Email: margie@visualrhythm.com
Phone: 140 828 87011
Address: 42 Race Street, US
Country: United States
Type: Ballet and Dance Company
Contact: Executive & Artistic Director Judy Pearson

Washington Ballet
Website: www.washingtonballet.org
Email: info@washingtonballet.org
Phone: 202 362 3606
Address: 3515 Wisconsin Avenue, NW, US
Information: originally founded as The Washington School of Ballet in 1944 by legendary ballet pioneer Mary Day and incorporated as a professional company in 1976, The Washington Ballet (TWB) is one of the pre-eminent ballet organizations in the United States. TWB built an international reputation presenting bold works by choreographers from around the world, including Choo-San Goh, Christopher Wheeldon, Mark Morris, Twyla Tharp and Nacho Duato, as well as Neoclassical masterworks and fresh stagings of 19th century classics
Country: United States
Type: Ballet and Dance Company

Contact: Artistic Director Septime Webre music Director Scott Speck
Social Media: @TWBalletTheWashingtonBallet
Annual Performances: 80
Venues: Kennedy Center – Eisenhower Theater 1100, Terrace Theater 475, Warner Theatre 1800

West Hawaii Dance Theatre
Website: www.whdt.org
Email: vh2dns4@ilhawaii.net
Phone: 808 329 8876
Address: 74-5626 Alapa Street, US
Country: United States
Type: Ballet and Dance Company
Contact: Artistic Director Virginia Holte

Westchester Ballet Company
Website: www.westchesterballet.org
Email: info@westchesterballet.org
Phone: 914 941 4532
Address: PO Box 694, 95 Croton Avenue, US
Country: United States
Type: Ballet and Dance Company
Contact: administrative Director Mary Levine Artistic Director Jean Logrea Artistic Director Beth Fritz-Logrea

Winifred R Harris' Between Lines
Website: www.betweenlines.org
Email: wrharris@betweenlines.org
Phone: 310 313 1647
Address: 5995 South Sepulveda Blvd, Suite 206, US
Country: United States
Type: Ballet and Dance Company
Contact: founder, Artistic Director, choreographer Winifred R Harris

Yoshiko Chuma & The School of Hard Knocks
Website: www.yoshikochuma.org
Email: info@yoshikochuma.org
Address: 201 East 4th Street, US
Information: downtown maverick world-class choreographer born in Osaka, Japan and based in New York City's East Village since 1980
Country: United States
Type: Ballet and Dance Company
Contact: Artistic Director Yoshiko Chuma management Bonnie Sue Stein at GOH Producti
Touring Countries: Japan, Estonia, UK, Germany, France, Czech Republic, Macedonia, Yugoslavia, Bosnia and Herzegovina, Lithuania, Sweden, etc

Zenon Dance Company and School, Inc.
Website: www.zenondance.org
Email: info@zenondance.org
Phone: 612 338 1101
Address: 528 Hennepin Avenue, Suite 400, US
Information: school offers courses in modern, ballet, jazz, hip hop and more for students of all levels and ages; a scholarship program with performance opportunities is also available
Country: United States
Type: Ballet and Dance Company
Contact: Artistic Director Linda Andrews
Email: linda@zenondance.org Managing Director Danielle Robinson-Prater
Email: danielle@zenondance.org Director of development Mara Winke
Email: mara@zenondance.org
Venues: Southern Theater, Theatre de la Jeune Lune, Illusion Theatre

Zvidance/ZGD Inc
Website: www.zvidance.com
Email: info@zvidance.com
Phone: 212 869 7429
Address: 65 West 106th St, Suite 1C, US
Country: United States
Type: Ballet and Dance Company
Contact: Executive Director Renee Robinson Artistic Director Zvi Gotheiner
Social Media: @zvidance www.facebook.com/ZviDance
Touring Countries: US, South America, Poland, Russia and Germany
Venues: The Kitchen, Joyce Theatre and Joyce Soho, DTW, Duke on 42nd Street

VIRGIN ISLANDS, U.S.

Caribbean Dance Company of The Virgin Islands
Website:
Phone: 340 773 8877
Address: PO Box 3065, 5 Church Street, Christiansted, VI
Information: dance school
Country: Virgin Islands
Type: Ballet and Dance Company
Venues: St Croix, St Thomas

THE CLIBURN

THE WORLD IS LISTENING

SIXTEENTH
VAN CLIBURN
INTERNATIONAL
PIANO
COMPETITION

2–18 JUNE, 2022
FORT WORTH, TEXAS USA

JURY

Marin Alsop, JURY CHAIRMAN
Alessio Bax
Jean-Efflam Bavouzet
Rico Gulda
Wu Han

Andreas Haefliger
Stephen Hough
Anne-Marie McDermott
Orli Shaham
Lilya Zilberstein

**WATCH THE ENTIRE
COMPETITION ONLINE
AT CLIBURN.ORG**

NOW BOOKING 2022 WINNERS
SDOAN@CLIBURN.ORG | 817.738.6536

Those listed in this section are dedicated to the performance of Early Music, and have been based on information received about engagements. We do not intend to pass judgement on quality.If you wish to be considered for inclusion, please send information regarding performances and touring engagements to the editor. **The entries are listed in alphabetical order with-in country.**

Ensembles de Musique Ancienne

Ceux qui sont énumérés dans la présente section sont dédiées à la performance de la musique ancienne, et sont fondées sur les renseignements reçus au sujet des missions. Nous n'avons pas l'intention de porter un jugement sur la qualité. Si vous désirez être inclus, veuillez nous envoyer des informations sur vos représentations et vos tournées. **Les entrée sont classés par ordre alphabétique dans le pays.**

Alte Musik

Diejenigen, die in diesem Abschnitt aufgeführt sind, um die Leistungsfähigkeit der Alten Musik gewidmet und haben Informationen über Engagements erhalten basiert. Wir beab-sichtigen nicht, ein Urteil über die Qualität passieren. Falls Sie Interesse daran haben, ebenfalls in dieser Rubrik aufgeführt zu werden, senden Sie uns bitte Informationen betreffend Ihrer Auftritte und Engagements. **Die Einträge sind für jedes Land alphabetisch sortiert.**

Ensemble di Musica Antica

Quelli elencati in questa sezione sono dedicati alla performance di musica antica, e sono stati sulla base delle informazioni rice-vute circa impegni. Non è nostra intenzione dare un giudizio sulla qualità. Se siete interessati ad essere inseriti in questa sezione vi preghiamo di inviare alla nostra redazione le infor-mazioni riguardanti il numero di spettacoli e/o di tournée effet-tuati dal vostro gruppo. **Le voci sono pubblicate in ordine alfabetico di paese.**

Conjuntos de Música Antigua

Los incluidos en esta sección se dedica a la realización de la música antigua, y se han basado en la información recibida acer-ca de los trabajos. No tenemos intención de emitir un juicio sobre la calidad. Si algún grupo quisiera ser incluido, rogamos envíe información sobre sus actuaciones y giras a nuestro edi-tor. **Las entradas se · muestran en orden alfabético dentro de cada país.**

performing arts
database

AUSTRALIA

Adelaide Baroque
Website: www.adelaidebaroque.com.au
Email: Manager@adelaidebaroque.com.au
Phone: 882 667 896
Address: 10 Clarence Avenue, AU
Information: For over 30 years Adelaide Baroque has fostered audiences for music of the baroque period through very well received concert programmes, workshops and master classes. Its aim is to excite contemporary audiences with the power of baroque music. Importantly, Adelaide Baroque has led the resurgence of interest in the presentation and promotion of historical performance practice nationally and internationally.
Country: Australia
Type: Early Music Ensemble
Contact: Chair Lynton Rivers
board member Frank May
Social Media: www.facebook.com/Adelaide-Baroque-444925635684280

Adelaide Baroque Inc.
Website: www.adelaidebaroque.com.au
Email: Manager@adelaidebaroque.com.au
Phone: 882 667 896
Address: 10 Clarence Avenue, AU
Information: Adelaide Baroque has been the training ground for many Australian musicians in the art of baroque performance practice through its workshops. Its commitment to best practice has seen Adelaide Baroque involved in nurturing the next generation of performers in an ongoing schools programs.
Country: Australia
Type: Early Music Ensemble
Contact: Chair Lynton Rivers
board member Frank May
Social Media: www.facebook.com/Adelaide-Baroque-Inc-390484520981392
Touring Countries: China, Australia, UK

AZERBAIJAN

Ensemble of Ancient Azerbaijan Instrument – Zuma, 'Alasgar Shekili'
Website:
Phone: 991 774 4498
Address: 6 Mammadsharif Harnidov Str, AZ
Country: Azerbaijan
Type: Early Music Ensemble
Contact: Director Vagif Kerimov

Ensemble of Ancient Music Instruments at the Museum of Musical Culture
Website: www.citisight.com/baku/musculture.html
Email: musculture@azdata.net
Phone: 124 986 972/4984
Address: 5 Rashid Behbudov Str., 1004, AZ
Country: AZ
Type: Early Music Ensemble
Contact: chief conductor Majnun Kerimov

CANADA

Aradia Ensemble
Website: www.aradia.ca
Email: info@aradia.ca
Phone: 647 960 6650
Address: 6 Castleview Ave, CA
Information: The Canadian Aradia Ensemble is one of the most exciting period instrument ensembles to emerge in recent years. Under the direction of Kevin Mallon, Aradia presents an innovative concert series in Toronto that incorporates old-world artistry and modern-day relevance.
Country: Canada
Type: Early Music Ensemble
Contact: Executive Director Samantha Little
Email: Executive.Director@aradia.ca
Artistic Director Kevin Mallon

Arion Orchestre Baroque
Website: www.arionbaroque.com
Email: info@arionbaroque.com
Phone: 514 355 1825
Address: 3950 rue Saint-Denis, CA
Information: Arion Baroque Orchestra, founded in 1981, is the only orchestra of early music on period instruments in Quebec and a leader in its field in North America. Led by the flamboyant vision of flautist Claire Guimond, the group winner of several awards and scholarships, Arion Baroque Orchestra presents a Montreal series of remarkable concerts, with the help of more than twenty passionate musicians and the participation of renowned guest conductors.
Country: Canada
Type: Early Music Ensemble
Contact: Artistic Director Claire Guimond
administrative Director Jeannie Lemieux
Email: jlemieux@arionbaroque.com
President Lise Rochette
vice President Daniel Binette
Social Media: @arionbaroque www.facebook.com/arionbaroque

Ensemble Anonymus
Website: www.anonymus.qc.ca
Email: ensemble@anonymus.qc.ca
Phone: 418 649 7141
Address: Bureau 128, 310, boulevard Langelier, CA
Information: It was in Quebec City in 1978 that Anonymus Ensemble was born, at the initiative of a group of young professional performers that gathered around Claude Bernatchez, founder and music Director of the ensemble. They have a deep passion and interest as the ancient music encourages them to revive the musical traditions of medieval Europe. Numerous shows and concerts as well as high-quality recordings testify today as much to the level of Artistic achievement achieved over the years as to the excellence of the Anonymus musicians.
Country: Canada
Type: Early Music Ensemble
Contact: Artistic Director Claude Bernatchez
Manager Sylvie Ouellet
Touring Countries: Canada, USA, Mexico, France

Les Boréades de Montréal
Website: www.boreades.com
Email: info@boreades.com
Phone: 514 634 1244
Address: 127, 17e Avenue, 127, 17 avenue, CA
Information: Founded by Francis Colpron in 1991, Les Boréades focuses on early music. The ensemble has chosen an interpretative approach in keeping with the spirit of the Baroque era, by adhering to the rules of performance practice of the past and playing on period instruments. Critics and audiences alike in Canada and abroad have been unanimous in hailing the group's energy and spontaneity as well as its theatrical, exPressive and elegant playing, indicative of a unique flair for Baroque aesthetics.
Country: Canada
Type: Early Music Ensemble
Contact: founder and Artistic Director Francis Colpron
Email: boreades@sympatico.ca
administrative Director and development Nicole Charbonneau
Email: nicoagenda@gmail.com
communications Director Samuel Lalande-Markon
Email: samuel@boreades.com
Artistic advisor François Filiatrault
President Sylvain Leith
Social Media: www.facebook.com/boreades.demontreal
Touring Countries: USA, Europe, Asia

Les Violons du Roy
Website: www.violonsduroy.com
Email: info@violonsduroy.com
Phone: 418 692 3026
Address: 995 Place d'Youville, CA
Information: The chamber orchestra Les Violons du Roy takes its name from the renowned string orchestra of the court of the French kings. The group, which has a core membership of fifteen players, was brought together in 1984 by founding conductor Bernard Labadie and specializes in the vast repertoire of music for chamber orchestra, performed in the stylistic manner most appropriate to each era. Although the ensemble plays on modern instruments, its approach to the works of the Baroque and Classical periods has been strongly influenced by current research into performance practice in the 17th and 18th centuries; in this repertoire Les Violons du Roy uses copies of period bows. The orchestra also regularly delves into the repertoire of the 19th and 20th centuries, as witnessed by its recordings of works by Piazzolla, Bartók, and Britten.
Country: Canada
Type: Early Music Ensemble
Contact: Executive Director Hugo Sanschagrin
Email: hsanschagrin@violonsduroy.com
Artistic administrator Laurent Patenaude
Email: lpatenaude@violonsduroy.com
orchestra personnel Director Claire-Émilie Calvert
Email: mhnault@violonsduroy.com
Social Media: @ViolonsduRoy www.facebook.com/violonsduroy
Touring Countries: Canada, USA, UK, France, Spain, Germany, Austria, Norway, Ecuador, Belgium, Morocco

Pacific Baroque Orchestra
Website: www.pacificbaroque.com
Email: contact@pacificbaroque.com
Phone: 160 421 50424
Address: Box 3215, Station Terminal, CA
Country: Canada
Type: Early Music Ensemble
Contact: General Manager Louise Woodward

Sine Nomine Ensemble for Medieval Music
Website: www.pims.ca/amici/sinenomine.html
Email: rosenfel@chass.utoronto.ca
Phone: 416 638 9445
Address: Pontifical Institute of Mediaeval Studies, 59 Queen's Park Crescent East, CA
Information: Sine Nomine (founded in 1991) performs the vocal and instrumental music of Europe transmitted in manuscripts from the tenth to the fifteenth century (or earlier, when it can be reasonably recovered).
Country: Canada
Type: Early Music Ensemble
Contact: Touring: Nationally and Internationally

Studio de musique ancienne de Montréal
Website: www.smamontreal.ca
Email: info@smamontreal.ca
Phone: 514 861 2626
Address: 1097, rue st Alexandre, bureau 407, CA
Information: The Studio de musique ancienne de Montréal has established a reputation as Montréal's finest early music vocal ensemble. Composed of 10 to 13 singers chosen for the remarkable clarity and purity of their voices, the Studio was founded in 1974 by Christopher Jackson, whose inspired leadership continues to this day. The Studio has brought more than 800 Renaissance and Baroque masterpieces before the public, and continues to reveal and share the vitality, sensuality, and emotional depth of early music.
Country: Canada
Type: Early Music Ensemble
Contact: Artistic Director Christopher Jackson
administrative Manager Simon Blanchet
communication and developement Elin Soderstrom
Email: elin.soderstrom@smamontreal.ca

Tafelmusik Baroque Orchestra
Website: www.tafelmusik.org
Email: info@tafelmusik.org
Phone: 416 964 9562
Address: 427 Bloor Street West, Box 14, CA
Information: size: 18 – 43; period instrument orchestra and chamber choir; performs 115 concerts a year in Toronto and on tour; over 80 recordings on Tafelmusik Media, Sony Classical, Analekta and CBC recordslabels; international and national touring 7-10 weeks per year, operates the annual Tafelmusik Baroque Summer institute to train young artists in period performance; orchestra for Opera Atelier productions; see also Orchestras
Country: Canada
Type: Early Music Ensemble
Contact: Director of Artistic Administration Beth Anderson
Email: banderson@tafelmusik.org
operations Manager Talia Harrison-Marcassa
Email: taliahm@tafelmusik.org
Managing Director Tricia Baldwin
Email: tbaldwin@tafelmusik.org
Social Media: @Tafelmusik www.facebook.com/tafelmusik.org
Touring Countries: Canada, USA, Europe, Asia
Touring: Nationally and Internationally China

Chinaart and Culture Co. Ltd
Website: www.artzj.com
Email: chinaart@vip.sina.com, zhangcac@gmail.com
Phone: 571 870 68831
Address: Room 203-205, 58 Longyou Road, Hangzhou, China
Information: China-art owns more than 100 famous signed artists worldwide. It hosts and undertakes Polish Cultural Festival and sets up "Chopin International Center of Music and Arts". It has many renowned cultural brand projects such as Global Musical Awards, China-art Music Hall, China-art Master Class, China-art Lecture hall, China-art Opera Stage etc. They organize foreign cultural festivals, music festivals, music drama, music competitions, film and TV, advertisements, exhibitions, lectures, classes etc
Country: CN
Type: Early Music Ensemble

JAPAN

Allegro Music Tokyo Inc
Website: www.allegromusic.co.jp
Email: opera@allegromusic.co.jp
Phone: 352 167 131
Address: Glück Heim 5002, Kioicho 3-29, Chiyoda-ku, JP
Information: Allegro Music Tokyo Inc. is a unique company of Japan that promotes concerts of early music musicians from overseas, introducing Japan to major and minor works not only from famous composers including C. Monteverdi, H. Purcell, A. Vivaldi, J.S. Bach, G.F. Handel and W.A. Mozart, but of lesser-known mediaeval and Renaissance composers as well.
Country: Japan
Type: Early Music Ensemble
Contact: Managing Director Kazuhiko Ogawa

Bach Collegium Japan
Website: www.bach.co.jp
Email: info@bach.co.jp
Address: 5-29-7-402, Sendagaya, Shibuya-ku, JP
Information: chamber orchestra using period instruments; has a chamber choir; many projects have included European artists
Country: Japan
Type: Early Music Ensemble
Contact: music Director Masaaki Suzuki
secretary General Kyoko Ohtomi

Danceries
Website: www3.ocn.ne.jp/~dancerie/
Email: zazie@skyblue.ocn.ne.jp
Phone: 798 510 321
Address: 3chome 14-7 nigawa cho, JP
Country: Japan
Type: Early Music Ensemble
Contact: Director Ichiro Okamoto
Touring Countries: France, Switzerland

Gagaku Music Society of Tenri University Tenri Gagaku
Website: gagaku.biz/tenri/
Email: univ@gagaku.biz
Phone: 743 634 945
Address: 1050 Somanouchi-chou, Tenri, JP
Information: Gagaku is Japanese ancient court music; in 1951 the club was founded as an extracurricular activity for the purpose of researching the Gagaku and acquiring its performance techniques and its prevalence
Country: Japan
Type: Early Music Ensemble
Contact: advisor Koji Sato

Kosei Gagakukai
Website: www.kosei-kai.or.jp
Email: y@kosei-kai.or.jp
Phone: 353 411 148
Address: c/o Fumonkan, 2-6-1 Wada, Suginami-ku, JP
Information: the group performs Japanese ancient court music; organised by Kosei Bunka Kyokai (q.v.)
Country: Japan
Type: Early Music Ensemble
Contact: Director Masaya Saito
President Hiroyasu Kanamori

Lute Song Duo
Website: www.linkclub.or.jp/~dowland/
Email: dowland@air.linkclub.or.jp
Phone: 429 556 652
Address: c/o Dowland & Company, 2-23-5-105, Irumagawa, Sayama, JP
Information: formed by lutenist Takashi Tsunoda and vocalist Mutsumi Hatano f in 1990; has 4 CDs; managed by Dowland & Company (q.v.)
Country: Japan
Type: Early Music Ensemble
Contact: leader & Producer
Takashi Tsunoda
vocalmezzo soprano Mutsumi Hatano
Touring Countries: UK, US

Reigakusha
Website: www.tokyo-concerts.co.jp
Email: info@tokyo-concerts.co.jp
Phone: 332 269 755
Address: c/o Tokyo Concerts, 6F Belx Shinjuku Bldg II, 23 Aizumi-cho, Shinjuku-ku, JP
Country: Japan
Type: Early Music Ensemble
Contact: music Director Sukeyasu Shiba
Touring Countries: USA, UK, Germany, Belgium, Norway, France, Italy, Switzerland, Finland, Holland and Morocco

Tablatura
Website: www.linkclub.or.jp/~dowland/
Email: dowland@air.linkclub.or.jp
Phone: 429 556 652
Address: c/o Dowland & Company, 2-23-5-105, Irumagawa, Sayama, JP
Information: formed in 1984; managed by DOWLAND & COMPANY; Tokyo Opera City Recital Hall 286 (q.v.); / formed by the lutenist Takashi Tsunoda in 1984; gained solid reputation for its free spirited arrangements and adventurous performance skills w
Country: Japan
Type: Early Music Ensemble
Contact: leader & Producer
Takashi Tsunoda

MEXICO

Ars Antiqua
Website:
Email: antiquamusica@hotmail.com
Address: Paseo del mirador No. 1481 Colinas de San Javier, MX
Country: Mexico
Type: Early Music Ensemble
Contact: contact Eduardo Arambula

Ars Nova
Website: www.arsnovamexico.com
Email: edna_butchart@hotmail.com
Phone: 667 753 9569
Address: Circuito Educadores 61, Cd Sat, MX
Country: Mexico
Type: Early Music Ensemble
Contact: Director Mario Aguilar

Capilla Virreinal de la Nueva España
Website:

Address: Escocia 29, dpt 109, Col. Parque San Andr, MX
Country: Mexico

Duo Slawinska-Duron
Website:
Phone: 555 672 7525
Address: Filipinas 1101-101A, Col Portales, MX
Country: Mexico
Type: Early Music Ensemble
Contact: contact Luisa Duron

La Fontegara México
Website: www.lafontegara.net
Email: walls@servidor.unam.mx
Phone: 555 616 5537
Address: San Luis Potos, MX
Information: María Díez-Canedo , recorder and baroque flute
Eunice Padilla , harpsichord and fortepiano
Eloy Cruz , baroque guitar and theorbo
Rafael Sánchez Guevara , viola da gamba
Country: Mexico
Type: Early Music Ensemble
Contact: Social Media: www.facebook.com/lafontegara

Los Tiempos Pasados
Website:
Email: lostiempospasados@hotmail.com
Address: MX
Country: Mexico
Type: Early Music Ensemble
Contact: contact Armando Lopez Valdivia

UNITED STATES

Alia Musica
Website: www.aliamusicapittsburgh.org
Email: alia.musica.pittsburgh@gmail.com
Phone: 412 427 6717
Address: 5 Clarendon Place, US
Information: ALIA MUSICA PITTSBURGH is dedicated to quality performances of challenging repertoire of contemporary music in all genres, focusing on Pittsburgh composers as well as major figures of the 20th and 21st centuries. A rigorous approach to the interpretation of these works resonates with audiences who expect the unexpected in our performances.
Country: United States
Type: Early Music Ensemble
Contact: Artistic Director Federico Garcia-De Castro
Social Media: @AliaMusicaPgh@aliamusicapgh
Touring Countries: All Europe, USA, and South America

American Bach Soloists
Website: www.americanbach.org
Email: info@americanbach.org
Phone: 415 621 7900
Address: 44 Page Street, Suite 403, US
Information: The American Bach Soloists ("ABS") is an American baroque orchestra dedicated to preserving the heritage of the music of Johann Sebastian Bach and his contemporaries through historically informed performances on period instruments. Founded in Belvedere, California in 1989 with the mission of introducing contemporary audiences to Bach's cantatas, co-founder and Artistic Director Jeffrey Thomas has since expanded the Artistic direction of the ensemble to include Bach's purely instrumental and larger choral masterpieces, as well as music of his contemporaries and that of the early Classical era
Country: United States
Type: Early Music Ensemble
Contact: music administrator Steven Lehning
Email: slehning@americanbach.org
Artistic Director Jeffrey Thomas
Executive Director Don Scott Carpenter
Email: dscarpenter@americanbach.org
Social Media: @AmericaBach www.facebook.com/americanbach

American Classical Orchestra
Website: www.americanclassicalorchestra.org
Email: info@aconyc.org
Phone: 212 362 2727
Address: 133 West 70th Street, US
Information: The American Classical Orchestra is devoted to preserving and performing the repertoire of 17th – to 19th – century composers, playing the works on original or reproduced period instruments. The musicians use historic performance practice techniques and pass these skills down to future generations through concert performances and educational programs
Country: United States
Type: Early Music Ensemble
Contact: founder & music Director
Thomas Crawford
Social Media: www.facebook.com/AmericanClassicalOrchestra

Apollo's Cabinet
Website:
Email: apolloscab@fuse.net
Phone: 513 662 8906
Address: 3523 Epworth Avenue, US
Information: Cincinnati's premier professional Baroque

ensemble, specialises in the performance of 17th and 18th century instrumental and vocal chamber music
Country: United States
Type: Early Music Ensemble
Contact: pr contact Barbara Lambert

Apollo's Fire (Cleveland Baroque Orchestra)
Website: www.apollosfire.org
Email: info@apollosfire.org
Phone: 216 320 0012
Address: 3091 Mayfield Road, Suite 217, US
Information: Apollo's Fire, The Cleveland Baroque Orchestra is a popular and critically acclaimed period-instrument ensemble specializing in early music (Renaissance, Baroque and early Classical) based in Cleveland, Ohio. The ensemble unites a select pool of early music specialists from throughout North America and Europe. Under the direction of Artistic Director Jeannette Sorrell, the ensemble has been praised internationally for a fresh and vibrant approach to baroque performance, and for creative and innovative programming
Country: United States
Type: Early Music Ensemble
Contact: Marketing Manager Sarah Blue
Email: sblue@apollosfire.org

Ars Antiqua
Website: www.arsantigua.net
Email: JerryFullerEsq@cs.com
Phone: 312 415 2391
Address: 2252 Orrington Avenue, US
Information: Ars Antiqua focuses on historically-informed performances using period instruments. In today's concert, they are shifting the focus just a bit to cross-culturally informed performances using indigenous instruments. They have crafted a program that consists of both western and oriental art music performed on Chinese pipa, along with the double bass, harp and violone from the western tradition
Country: United States
Type: Early Music Ensemble
Contact: Director Jerry Fuller
Email: JerryFullerEsq@cs.com

ARTEK
Website: www.artekearlymusic.org
Email: artekgwent@aol.com
Phone: 212 967 9157
Address: 170 West 73rd St, Suite 3C, US
Information: ARTEK is a New York State non-profit organisation that exists to present historically-informed concerts of music and educational activities, to stimulate interest and develop appreciation for early music in the society
Country: United States
Type: Early Music Ensemble
Contact: Artistic Director Gwendolyn Toth

Aston Magna Foundation for Music and Humanity Inc.
Website: www.astonmagna.org
Email: astonmagna@optonline.net
Phone: 413 528 3595
Address: P.O. Box 28, US
Information: Aston Magna seeks to interpret the music of the past as the composer imagined it. Original period instruments — or historically accurate reproductions – are essential performance elements. Performance techniques are appropriate to the period, national styles, culture and aesthetics of the time
Country: United States
Type: Early Music Ensemble
Contact: Artistic Director Daniel Stepner
Executive Director Susan Obel
Social Media: @AstonMagnaFesti

Baltimore Consort
Website: www.rile.com
Email: artists@rilearts.com
Phone: 215 885 6400
Address: Joanne Rile Artist Management, 93 Old York Road, Suite 222, US
Information: The Baltimore Consort has delighted audiences on both sides of the Atlantic and earned their CDs a place on the Billboard Magazine Top-Ten list. The Baltimore Consort's arrangements of early music from England, Scotland, France, Italy, and Spain speak to the heart as well as the mind, and their love for the early music of English/Scottish heritage has led them to delve into the rich trove of traditional balladry and dance tunes preserved in the Appalachian mountains and Nova Scotia
Country: United States
Type: Early Music Ensemble
Contact: Manager Joanne Rile
Touring Countries: France, Italy, and Spain

Baroque Band
Website: www.baroqueband.org
Email: info@baroqueband.org
Phone: 312 235 2368
Address: 30 East Adams Street, Suite 1204, US
Information: Chicago's Period-Instrument Orchestra. Ticket information is available at baroqueband.org or the

box office phone number at 312-235-2368

Country: United States
Type: Early Music Ensemble
Contact: Artistic Director Garry Clarke
Email: garry@baroqueband.org
Social Media: @baroqueband www.facebook.com/pages/Baroque-Band/267546737446
Touring: Nationally

Boston Baroque
Website: www.bostonbaroque.org
Email: info@bostonbaroque.org
Phone: 617 987 8600
Address: 10 Guest Street, Suite 290, US
Information: Boston Baroque is the first permanent Baroque orchestra established in North America and according to Fanfare Magazine, is widely regarded as "one of the world's premier period-instrument bands." The Boston-based ensemble produces lively, emotionally charged, groundbreaking performances of Baroque and Classical works for today's audiences performed on instruments and using performance techniques that reflect the eras in which the music was composed
Country: United States
Type: Early Music Ensemble
Contact: music Director Martin Pearlman
Executive Director Martha H. Jones
Email: mhjones@bostonbaroque.org
President David Friend
vice President Lee Carl Bromberg
Social Media: @BostonBaroque www.facebook.com/bostonbaroque
Touring Countries: Poland

Brandywine Baroque
Website: www.brandywinebaroque.org
Email: info@brandywinebaroque.org
Phone: 877 594 4546
Address: 1205 North Orange Street, US
Information: recordings available
Country: United States
Type: Early Music Ensemble
Contact: Social Media: www.facebook.com/Brandywine-Baroque

California Bach Society
Website: www.calbach.org
Email: info@calbach.org
Phone: 650 485 1097
Address: P.O. Box 1526, US
Information: The California Bach Society, a 35-voice chamber chorus, has established a reputation for its interpretations of Renaissance and Baroque choral music.
Country: United States
Type: Early Music Ensemble
Contact: Artistic Director Paul Flight
secretary Tony Mauro
board President Helen Barios

Castle Trio
Website: www.smithsonianchambermusic.org
Email: info@smithsonianchambermusic.org
Phone: 202 633 4174
Address: c/o Smithsonian Chamber Music Society, PO Box 37012, NMAH 4100, US
Country: United States
Type: Early Music Ensemble
Contact:

Chamber Music Program
Website: www.smithsonianchambermusic.org
Email: infos@mithsonianchambermusic.org
Address: PO Box 37012, NMAH/Room 4100 MRC 616, Smithsonian Institution, US
Information: Smithsonian Chamber Orchestra, Castle Trio, Axelrod String Quartet, Smithsonian Chamber Players
Country: United States
Type: Early Music Ensemble
Contact: Artistic Director Kenneth Slowik

Concert Royal
Website:
Email: concertroyal@aol.com
Address: 22 Southern Road, Hartsdale, US
Information: recordings with Nonesuch, Newport Classics; 3 series one of which is French baroque only; work in collaboration with the New York Baroque Dance Company
Country: United States
Type: Early Music Ensemble
Contact: Artistic Director James Richman
General Manager Karen Kenaston

Early Music Ensemble
Website: www.brandeis.edu/music
Email: mead@brandeis.edu
Phone: 781 736 3310 mus
Address: Department of Music, MS 051, Brandeis University, 415 South St, US
Information: also perform with the college's chamber choir
Country: United States

Type: Early Music Ensemble
Contact: Director Sarah Mead

Ensemble Musica Humana
Website: www.ensemblemusicahumana.com
Email: info@ensemblemusicahumana.com
Address: US
Information: specializes in performances of early music
Country: United States
Type: Early Music Ensemble
Contact: contact Corrine Byrne
Social Media: @EnsMusicaHumana www.facebook.com/EnsembleMusicaHumana

Ensemble Soleil
Website: www.esoleil.org
Email: info@esoleil.org
Phone: 180 289 94008
Address: PO Box 1048, US
Information: 3-8 members; multi-media theatrical events with live music, dancing, singing, art images on large screen, humanities narratives, concerts; 1997-99 grants NH council on Arts, NH humanities council; alternative address: Ensemble Soleil, P. O. Box 933, New L
Country: United States
Type: Early Music Ensemble
Contact: technical Director Peter Tourin
Artistic Director Jean Sawyer Twombly

Ensemble Voltaire
Website: www.ensemblevoltaire.com
Email: info@ensemblevoltaire.com
Phone: 313 665 4029
Address: c/o Elizabeth Humes, Artist's Representative, 505 East Huron, Suite 302, US
Information: CDs available; formerly Ensemble Ouabache
Country: United States
Type: Early Music Ensemble
Contact: founder Thomas Gerber
founder Barbara Kallaur

Florida State University Early Music Ensemble
Website: www.music.fsu.edu
Phone: 850 644 3890
Address: College of Music, Florida State University, US
Information: the FSA offers MA and PhD courses with strong emphasis on early music
Country: United States
Type: Early Music Ensemble
Contact: Director Charles E. Brewer

Folger Consort
Website: www.folger.edu
Email: consort@folger.edu
Phone: 202 544 4600
Address: Folger Shakespeare Library, 201 East Capitol Street SE, US
Country: United States
Type: Early Music Ensemble
Contact: Artistic Director Robert Eisenstein
Director of public programs Janet Griffin
Email: jgriffin@folger.edu

Fortune's Wheel
Website: www.fortuneswheel.org
Email: LHKnutson@aol.com
Phone: 781 643 0123
Address: 35 Johnson Rd, US
Information: devoted to rediscovering the riches of medieval musical traditions
Country: United States
Type: Early Music Ensemble
Contact: contact Lydia Knutson

Foundation for Baroque Music Inc
Website: www.baroquefestival.org
Email: impresario48@yahoo.com
Phone: 518 893 7527
Address: 165 Wilton Road, US
Information: CDs with FBM Records; the 16 musicians/vocalists make up various smaller ensembles; summer season only; also has an annual historical dance programme
Country: United States
Type: Early Music Ensemble
Contact: co-Artistic Director Kenneth Slowik
President & Artistic Director
Robert Conant

Handel and Haydn Society
Website: www.handelandhaydn.org
Email: info@handelandhaydn.org
Phone: 617 262 1815
Address: 300 Massachusetts Avenue, US
Information: (H&H) is considered America's oldest continuously performing arts organisation and will celebrate its Bicentennial in 2015. Its Period Instrument Orchestra and Chorus are internationally recognized in the field of Historically Informed Performance, using the instruments and techniques of the composer's time. Under Artistic Director Harry Christophers' leadership, H&H's mission is to perform Baroque and Classical music at the highest levels of Artistic excellence and to share that music with as large and diverse an audience as possible

Country: United States
Type: Early Music Ensemble
Contact: Executive Director and chief Executive officer Marie-Hélène Bernard
Email: mhbernard@handelandhaydn.org
Executive assistant Wei Jing Saw
Email: wjsaw@handelandhaydn.org
Director of Artistic planning and education Ira Pedlikin
Email: ira@handelandhaydn.org
assistant Director of education Bill Pappazisis
Email: bill@handelandhaydn.org
production Manager Jesse Levine
Email: jlevine@handelandhaydn.org
Director of development Mike Peluse
Email: mpeluse@handelandhaydn.org
Director of bicentennial and community engagement

Haydn by the Lake
Website: www.haydnbythelake.com
Email: mail@haydnbythelake.com
Phone: 847 869 9560
Address: 1563 Darrow Ave, US
Country: United States
Type: Early Music Ensemble
Contact: Artistic Director James Janssen

Indianapolis Baroque Orchestra
Website: indybaroque.org
Email: info@indybaroque.org
Phone: 317 808 2224
Address: 401 E Michigan Ave, US
Information: this company's mission is to enrich, inspire and educate the Indianapolis and Indiana communities with exuberant performances of 17th and 18th century music
Country: United States
Type: Early Music Ensemble
Contact: President Eric Edberg
Social Media: @IndyBaroque www.facebook.com/indybaroque

Istanpitta
Website: www.istanpitta.com
Email: avatar1@flash.net
Phone: 128 164 87885
Address: c/o Al Cofrin, 16018 Constitution, US
Country: United States
Type: Early Music Ensemble
Contact: Director Al Cofrin

King's Noyse
Website: www.noyseproductions.com
Email: daviddonglass@ameritech.net
Phone: 177 356 26889
Address: 6541 N. Bosworth Ave., US
Information: alternative website: www.harmoniamundi.com; 13 recordings on Harmonia Mundi USA; recipient of the Noah Greenberg Award
Country: United States
Type: Early Music Ensemble
Contact: Director David Douglass

Los Angeles Baroque Players
Website: www.home.earthlink.net/~labaroque
Email: rb@harpsichordcenter.com
Phone: 132 325 49613
Address: PO Box 41314, US
Country: United States
Type: Early Music Ensemble
Contact: contact Wm Neil Roberts

Magnificat
Website: www.magnificatbaroque.com
Email: contact@magnificatbaroque.com
Phone: 415 625 2983
Address: 50 Osgood Place, Suite 500, US
Information: offers audiences the chance to hear many significant works by well-known figures of the 17th Century while also uncovering forgotten masterpieces, including many modern premieres. With dramatic flair and sensitivity to historical context, Magnificat imbues each concert with an infectious joy and a delight in musical make-believe
Country: United States
Type: Early Music Ensemble
Contact: Artistic Director Warren Stewart
Email: contact@magnificatbaroque.com
Social Media: MagBaroque http://facebook.com/MagnificatBaroque

Music at Eden's Edge
Website: www.edensedge.org
Email: music@edensedge.org
Phone: 978 270 4463
Address: 94 John Wise Avenue, US
Information: a chamber music society which matches professional performances of the best of the chamber repertoire, old and new; with a broad audience needs of the North Shore of Massachusetts; concert series in elegant venues and outreach programs for school children
Country: United States
Type: Early Music Ensemble
Contact: Artistic Director Maria Benotti
media enquiries Ann Seamonds

Email: seamonds@seamonds.com

Music of the Baroque
Website: baroque.org
Email: baroque@baroque.org
Phone: 312 551 1415
Address: 111 North Wabash Ave., Suite 810, US
Information: under the direction of internationally acclaimed British conductor Jane Glover, Music of the Baroque occupies a special place in the rich cultural life of Chicago; long recognised as one of the area's top classical groups, the ensemble focuses on 18th-century works for chorus and orchestra
Country: United States
Type: Early Music Ensemble
Contact: music Director Jane Glover
Touring Countries: tours throughout Chicago

Music's Re-creation
Website: www.sfems.org/musicsre-creation
Email: jdrnbrg@saclink.csus.edu
Phone: 510 530 3202
Address: 3931 Linwood Avenue, US
Information: CD recordings on Centaur and Meridian
Country: United States
Type: Early Music Ensemble
Contact: contact John Dornenburg

Musica Angelica
Website: www.MusicaAngelica.org
Email: info@musicaangelica.org
Address: 1223 Wilshire Boulevard, #287, US
Country: United States
Type: Early Music Ensemble
Contact: music Director Martin Haselböck
Social Media: @MusicaAngelicLA
Touring Countries: Canada, Mexico, Brazil, Argentina

Musica Pacifica
Website: www.musicapacifica.org
Email: artists@rilearts.com
Phone: 215 885 6400
Address: 93 Old York Road, Suite 222, US
Country: United States
Type: Early Music Ensemble
Contact: Director Judith Linsenberg
Touring Countries: USA

New Orleans Musica da Camera
Website: www.nomdc.org
Email: mdc@nomdc.org
Phone: 504 895 1972
Address: 3705 Laurel Street, US
Information: Award winning, oldest early music ensemble in N. America; produce longest running early music radio program in world, on WWNO1 & WWNO2 89.9FM; includes women's vocal ensemble, Vox Feminae; Have recorded with Centaur, distributed by Qualiton Imports, with Belle Alliance, self distributed.
Country: United States
Type: Early Music Ensemble
Contact: co-Director Thais St Julien
Email: thais@nomdc.org
Associate Director Stuart Le Blanc
Email: stuart@nomdc.org
co-Director and founder Milton Scheuermann Jr
Email: milton@nomdc.org
Social Media: New Orleans Musica da Camera
Touring Countries: USA

New York Collegium, The
Website: www.nycollegium.org
Email: info@nycollegium.org
Phone: 212 717 9246
Address: 869 Lexington Avenue, US
Country: United States
Type: Early Music Ensemble
Contact: music Director Andrew Parrott
Executive Director Dorothea R. Endicott

New York Consort of Viols
Website: www.nyconsortofviols.org
Email: jdavidoff@nyconsortofviols.org
Phone: 212 580 9787
Address: 201 W 86th Street, Suite 905, US
Information: also do children's outreach concerts
Country: United States
Type: Early Music Ensemble
Contact: Artistic Director Judith Davidoff

Newberry Consort
Website: www.newberry.org
Email: consort@newberry.org
Phone: 312 255 3610
Address: The Newberry Library, 60 West Walton Street, US
Information: A constituent of the Newberry Library's Center for Public Programs; recordings with Harmonia Mundi and Noyse Productions
Country: United States
Type: Early Music Ensemble
Contact: Director David Douglass
Manager Ken Perlow

NYS Baroque
Website: www.nysema.com
Email: info@nysema.com
Phone: 607 533 4383
Address: 1220 Mecklenburg Road, Ithaca, US
Country: United States
Type: Early Music Ensemble
Contact: Artistic Director Heather Miller Lardin

Oberlin Baroque Ensemble
Website: www.oberlin.edu/con/summer/bpi/
Email: cathy.meints@oberlin.edu
Phone: 144 077 48221
Address: 170 Pyale Road, US
Country: United States
Type: Early Music Ensemble
Contact: professor of viola de gamba Catherine Meints

Opera Lafayette
Website: www.operalafayette.org
Email: operalafayette@operalafayette.org
Phone: 202 546 9332
Address: 921 Pennsylvania Ave SE, US
Information: an American period-instrument ensemble focused on the French 18th-century opera repertoire and its precursors, influences, and Artistic legacy
Country: United States
Type: Early Music Ensemble
Contact: Artistic Director Ryan Brown
Executive Director Diana Hossack
Email: dianahossack@operalafayette.org
Social Media: @operalafayette

Philomel Concerts Inc.
Website: www.philomel.org
Email: info@philomel.org
Phone: 215 487 2344
Address: PO Box 41055, US
Information: member of PennPAT roster (eligible for touring support, mid-Atlantic states); Joanne Rile Artists Management (tel: 215-664 8500)
Country: United States
Type: Early Music Ensemble
Contact:

Piffaro, The Renaissance Band
Website: www.piffaro.com
Email: info@piffaro.com
Address: 2238 Fairmount Avenue, US
Information: Recordings with Newport Classic, Deutsche Grammophon, Dorian.
Country: United States
Type: Early Music Ensemble
Contact: Artistic co-Director Robert Wiemken
Executive Director Shannon Cline
Email: shannonc@piffaro.com
Artistic co-Director Joan Kimball
Touring Countries: Germany, Spain, Belgium, Italy, England, Czech Republic, Austria, Switzerland, Columbia
Touring: Nationally and Internationally

Portland Baroque Orchestra
Website: www.pbo.org
Email: email@pbo.org
Phone: 503 222 6000
Address: 1020 SW Taylor Street, Suite 275, US
Country: United States
Type: Early Music Ensemble
Contact: Artistic Director Monica Huggett
Executive Director Abigail McKee

Quink Vocal Ensemble
Website: www.rile.com
Email: artists@rilearts.com
Phone: 215 885 6400
Address: c/o Joanne Rile Artists Management Inc., Jenkintown Commons, Suite 22, US
Information: a cappella ensemble (5 members)
Country: United States
Type: Early Music Ensemble
Contact: Manager Joanne Rile

REBEL
Website: www.rebelbaroque.com
Email: rebel@rebelbaroque.com
Phone: 914 734 9537
Address: 1116 Elm Street, US
Information: 1st prize, van Wassenaer Competition 1991 (The Netherlands); 2 recordings with Deutsche Harmonia Mundi, 3 recordings with Dorian, 1 on ATMA, 1 on H
Country: United States
Type: Early Music Ensemble
Contact: Director Karen Marie Marmer
Director J
Touring Countries: USA, Canada, Germany, The Netherlands, Belgium, Austria, France

Seattle Baroque Orchestra
Website: www.seattlebaroque.org
Email: info@seattlebaroque.org
Phone: 206 322 3118

Address: 911 Pime St, Suite 707, US
Country: United States
Type: Early Music Ensemble
Contact: music Director Ingrid Matthews
Executive Director Jeremy Johnsen

Sequentia
Website: www.sequentia.org
Email: info@aaronconcert.com
Phone: 212 665 0313
Address: c/o Aaron Concert, 331 West 57th St. #344, US
Information: CDs with German Harmonia Mundi, distributed worldwide through BMG Classics; Marc Aurel Edition (www.aurel.de), founded in 1977 by Benjamin Bagby and the late Barbara Thornton, Sequentia can look back on almost three decades of international concert tours
Country: United States
Type: Early Music Ensemble
Contact: Director Benjamin Bagby
Touring Countries: worldwide

Smithsonian Chamber Players
Website: www.smithsonianchambermusic.org
Email: info@smithsonianchambermusic.org
Phone: 202 633 4174
Address: PO Box 37012, US
Information: use the priceless treasures of the Smithsonian's collection of musical instruments to offer the public unique experiences and insights into the Western classical music of the past 400 years
Country: United States
Type: Early Music Ensemble
Contact: Artistic Director Kenneth Slowik

Southern California Early Music Consort
Website: SCEMC
Email: scemc@earthlink.net
Phone: 562 946 4001
Address: 11057 Valley View Avenue, US
Country: United States
Type: Early Music Ensemble
Contact: Director Thomas Axworthy

Tapestry
Website: www.shuppartists.com/Shupp/Artists/Tapestry.htm
Email: concerts@shuppartists.com
Phone: 631 928 1531
Address: Shupp Artists Management, 202 Michigan Avenue, US
Information: see also Orchestras & Choirs
Country: United States
Type: Early Music Ensemble
Contact: contact Erica Shupp (Shupp Artists Mgmt

The Boston Camerata, Inc.
Website: www.bostoncamerata.org
Email: Manager@bostoncamerata.org
Phone: 617 262 2092
Address: P.O. Box 120751, US
Country: United States
Type: Early Music Ensemble
Contact: General Manager Annie Vayner

Washington Bach Consort
Website: www.bachconsort.org
Email: contact@bachconsort.org
Phone: 202 429 2121
Address: 1010 Vermont Avenue NW, Suite 202, US
Information: also runs music education programs; see also Early Music
Country: United States
Type: Early Music Ensemble
Contact: board President David Condit
Executive Director Marc Eisenberg
music Director J. Reilly Lewis

Washington Cornett and Sackbutt Ensemble
Website: www.earlymusic.net/WCSE/
Email: holmesms@msn.com
Phone: 103 – 897 8990
Address: PO Box 386, US
Country: United States
Type: Early Music Ensemble
Contact:

Western Wind Vocal Ensemble Inc
Website: www.westernwind.org
Email: info@westernwind.org
Phone: 212 873 2848
Address: 263, West 86th Street, 3rd Floor, US
Information: 15 CDs with Nonesuch, Musical Heritage Society, Resmeranda, Newport Classics, Western Wind Records; do ensemble singing workshops while on tour; series for public radio; two workshops a year at Smith College, several others scattered around the country;
Country: United States
Type: Early Music Ensemble
Contact: Executive Producer William Zukof
Touring Countries: Italy, Germany, Switzerland, Taiwan, Singapore, Malaysia, Japan

This list comprises companies that spend all or much of their life presenting opera and/or operetta or music theatre. The companies are mainly building-based, but there are also a significant number of touring companies. **The entries are listed in alphabetical order within country.**

Opéra Musique Compagnies de Théâtre

Cette liste contient l'information de compagnies qui présentent surtout de l'opéra et/ou de l'opérette et du théâtre musical. Pour la plupart, les compagnies sont sédentaires mais un nom-bre significatif d'entre elles font des tournées. **Die Einträge sind für jedes Land alphabetisch sortiert.**

Oper und Musiktheater

In diesem Kapitel sind Opernensembles eingetragen, die sich vor allem mit Opern-, Operetten- oder Musiktheaterveranstaltungen befassen. Die Operngruppen haben hauptsächlich ein festes Haus, es gibt aber auch eine große Zahl von "Tourneegruppen". **Die Einträge sind für jedes Land alphabetisch sortiert.**

Opera e Teatro Musicale Societá

Questa sezione include compagnie che lavorano esclusiva-mente o quasi esclusivamente presentando opere liriche, operette e musicals. Le compagnie sono per la maggior parte stabili e con una loro sede fissa, esiste però un numero consid-erevole di compagnie 'di giro'. **Le voci sono pubblicate in ordine alfabetico di paese.**

Ópera y Música Teatro Empresas

Este listado se compone de compañías dedicadas principal-mente a la presentación de ópera,teatro musical y/o zarzuela.La mayoría de estas compañías son residentes de alguna sala de espectáculos, pero también aparece un número significativo de compañías itinerantes. **Las entradas se muestran en orden alfabético dentro de cada país.**

performing arts
database

OPERA/MUSIC THEATRE COMPANY

AUSTRALIA

Chamber Made
Website: www.chambermade.org
Email: info@chambermade.org
Phone: 390 907 095
Address: Meat Market, Office 22, 44 Courtney Street, AU
Information: CHAMBER MADE operates at the nexus of contemporary performance, music and sound to make intimate works that grapple with the resonant themes of our times. The company is renowned for redefining art-form boundaries and producing works that emerge from a deep collaborative dialogue across artform disciplines. Bringing contemporary composition and performance dramaturgy together in ever-shifting forms, our works have been presented in theatres, recital halls, lounge-rooms, galleries, on iPads and online.
Country: Australia
Contact: Artistic Director/CEO Tamara Saulwick
Email: Communications Manager Emilie Collyer
Email: Executive Producer Kylie McRae Operations & Finance Coordinator
Dan Sheehan
Social Media: @ChamberMadeOrg@ChamberMadeOrg
Touring: Belgium, Germany, Denmark, United States, United Kingdom, Hungary, Netherlands, Australia, etc.

Co-Opera Incorporated
Website: www.co-opera.com.au
Email: brian.chatterton@co-opera.com.au
Phone: 409 695 952
Address: PO Box 179, AU
Information: This is a professional Australian company which brings exciting productions of popular operas to new and existing audiences. Productions are designed to tour country regions throughout Australia and to attract new city audiences, through it's special style of cabaret.
Country: Australia
Contact: national touring administrator Helen Simpson
Email: helen.simpson@co-opera.com.aumembership officer Margaret Cannon
Email: friends@co-opera.com.au
Social Media: www.facebook.com/Operaonthemove
Touring: Australia, Singapore, Malaysia
Annual performances: 50
Annual productions: 2
Venues: Royal Adelaide Showground, Pirramimma Winery, Roxby Downs, Dubbo Reg Theatre, Penola Festival

Gold Coast City Opera
Email: barrywalmsley@ozemail.com.au
Address: PO Box 8800, Gold Coast Mail Centre, AU
Information: regular workshops; emphasis is on innovative productions of existing mainstream repertoire and new work
Country: Australia
Contact: founder & administrator
Barry Walmsley
Venues: from industrial sites to conventional performance spaces, including the Gold Coast Arts Centre

IHOS Opera
Website: www.ihosopera.com
Email: konstantinkoukias@gmail.com
Phone: 362 312 219
Address: 32 Pitt St North, AU
Information: IHOS Opera includes multiple art-forms, blending voice, dance and sound with installation art and digital technologies. IHOS has origins in the Greek-Australian tradition. The company was established in Hobart in 1990, by composer and Artistic Director Constantine Koukias, and production Director Werner Ihlenfeld. IHOS elaborates cross-cultural themes in modern Australia, and productions have been characterised by the use of unconventional industrial venues and dramatic language – ancient and modern forms of Greek, Hebrew, Mandarin and German, and alternative forms like braille, semaphore signalling and morse code.
Country: Australia
Contact: Artistic Director Constantine Koukias
Social Media: www.facebook.com/IHOS-Music-Theatre-and-Opera-16911292635
Venues: Standard theatre spaces, large warehouse spaces, site specific venues

Opera Australia
Website: www.opera.org.au
Email: enquiries@opera.org.au
Phone: 296 991 099
Address: 480 Elizabeth Street, Surry Hills, AU
Information:
Country: Australia
Contact: chief Executive officer Rory Jeffes
Email: Artistic Director Lyndon Terracini
Email: Chief Operating Officer Joe Martorana
Social Media: @OperaAust www.facebook.com/OperaAustralia
Venues: Sydney Opera House and Arts Centre Melbourne

Opera Queensland
Website: www.operaq.com.au
Email: info@operaq.com.au
Phone: 737 353 030

Address: 140 Grey Street, AU
Information: A Boundless Landscape of opera experiences reflects the richness, expanse and diversity of both the operatic art form and Queensland itself. Their mission to reflect, celebrate and enrich life in the communities, articulates the important role the arts play in contemporary Queensland life. One of Australia's major performing arts companies, OperaQ serves Metropolitan Brisbane and regional/remote Queensland through the development and presentation of opera projects that reflect their core values of excellence, community and adventure.
Country: Australia
Contact: Chair Sally Pitkin
Email: Director Kim Challenor
Email: Artistic Director Lindy Hume
Email: Executive Director Sandra Willis
Social Media: @operaqueensland www.facebook.com/OperaQueensland
Venues: Lyric Theatre, Brisbane 1986, Conservatorium Theatre Brisbane 607

Pinchgut Opera
Website: www.pinchgutopera.com.au
Email: info@pinchgutopera.com.au
Phone: 293 188 344
Address: PO Box 291, AU
Information: Pinchgut Opera rediscovers baroque and early classical opera masterpieces. Since 2002, Artistic Directors Antony Walker and Erin Helyard have led Pinchgut to present fourteen rarely performed operatic gems to audiences, in Sydney. Alongside the early music instrumentalists in the Orchestra of the Antipodes, Australian singers are frequently attracted from overseas careers to perform with this unique company. Pinchgut Opera's live recordings of the operas attract worldwide acclaim.
Country: Australia
Contact: Artistic Manager Alison Johnston
Email: operations Manager Andrew Johnston
Email: General Manager Sarah Gilchrist
Social Media: @Pinchgut www.facebook.com/PinchgutOpera?ref=hl
Venues: City Recital Hall Angel Place, Sydney Australia

Reckless Moments
Website: www.reckless.on.net
Email: Producers@reckless.on.net
Phone: 362 282 858
Address: PO Box 56, Battery Point Tasmania 7004
Information: Reckless Moments specialises in international co-productions, collaborations and tours. It also sponsors Creative Futures, an independent programme of intercultural performing arts projects involving artists & Producers from Australia, China and the UK. See also Dance and Theatre Companies.
Country: Australia
Contact: creative Producer Barry Plews
Email: barry.plews@reckless.on.netProducer + Interpreter/Translater Hu He
Email: hu.he@reckless.on.net

State Opera South Australia
Website: www.saopera.sa.gov.au
Email: info@saopera.sa.gov.au
Phone: 882 264 790
Address: 216 Marion Road, AU
Information: The State Opera of South Australia (SOSA) aspires to be the most exciting and innovative opera company in Australia, enhancing South Australia's reputation nationally and internationally. It was created as a Statutory Authority, under the State Opera of South Australia Act in 1976, to present, produce, manage and conduct theatrical and operatic performances that attracts a diverse local, national and, potentially, international audience. It is a flagship arts organisation in South Australia and has made a huge contribution to the operatic arts, not just in South Australia, but at a national level as well.
Country: Australia
Contact: Chair John Irving
Email: finance Director Nigel Bray
Social Media: www.facebook.com/STATEOPERASA
Annual productions: 3
Venues: Adelaide Festival Theatre 1800, The Opera Studio 250

West Australian Opera
Website: www.waopera.asn.au
Email:
Administration@waopera.asn.au
Phone:
892 788 999
Address: 825 Hay St, AU
Information: West Australian Opera was established in 1967 and will celebrate its 50th anniversary in 2017. It is Western Australia's only full-time, professional opera company. The company presents operas drawn from the mainstream operatic repertoire and increasingly is involved in the commissioning and development of new repertoire.
Country: Australia
Contact: General Manager Carolyn Chard
Email: Artistic Director Brad Cohen

Email: production Manager Mandy Farmer
Email: Chair Andrew Pascoe
Email: Artistic administrator Rebecca Kais
Social Media: @WAOpera www.facebook.com/waopera
Touring: New Zealang, Hong Kong, Singapore
His Majesty's Theatre, Supreme Court Gardens, Perth Concert Hall, Mandurah Performing Arts Centre

AZERBAIJAN

Azerbaijan State Academic Opera and Ballet Theatre
Website: www.tob.az/
Email: info@tob.az
Phone: 129 31651
Address: 8, 28 May str. 1000, AZ
Information: see also Dance Ballet Company of the Azerbaijan State Academic Opera and Ballet
Country: Azerbaijan

Azerbaijan State Theatre of Musical Comedy 'Shykhali Gurbanov'
Phone: 124 938 837
Address: 8 Azerbaijan Avenue, 4 1005, AZ
Information:
Country: Azerbaijan
Contact: chief conductor Nazim Hadjialibayov

Azerbaijan State Theatre of Song 'Rasid Beybutov'
Phone: 129 39710
Address: 12, Rashid Beybutov St. 1000, AZ
Information:
Country: Azerbaijan

Baku State Circus
Phone: 124 949 412
Address: 68, Samad Vurgun St., 1022, AZ
Information:
Country: Azerbaijan

Mugham Theatre
Phone: 124 924 998/085
Address: 9 Agabadji Rzayev str., 1004, AZ
Information:
Country: Azerbaijan
Contact: Director Arif Kasiyev

BRAZIL

Direção Cultura
Website: direcaocultura.com.br
Email: comunicacao@direcaocultura.com.br
Phone: 193 202 5400
Address: Rua Professor Frontino Guimarães 302, São Paulo, 04017-050, Brazil
Information: Cultural Producer located in the state of São Paulo who, since 1999, has been dedicated to the idealization and execution of cultural solutions, aiming mainly at the formation of the public and the democratization of culture.
Country: Brazil
Social Media: @direcaocultura www.facebook.com/direcaocultura

CAMBODIA

Khmer Arts Ensemble
Website: www.khmerarts.org
Email: veasna@khmerarts.org
Phone: 234 25780
Address: PO Box 2553, KH
Country: Cambodia
Contact: company Manager Chum Chanveasna
Email: veasna@khmerarts.orgArtistic Director Sophiline Shapiro
Email: sophiline@khmerarts.org

CANADA

Banff Centre, The
Website: www.banffcentre.ca
Email: arts_info@banffcentre.ca
Phone: 403 762 6100
Address: Office of the Registrar, Box 1020 Stn 28, , 107 Tunnel Mountain Drive, CA
Information: focus is on the development and production of new opera and song, dance and drama. Professional company residencies to produce new works are available. Member of ISPA
Country: Canada
Contact: President and CEO Janice Price
Email: chief financial officer Bruce Byford
Email: vice President Michael Code
Social Media: @banffcentre www.facebook.com/BanffCentre
Venues: Eric Harvie Theatre 959, Margaret Greenham Theatre 250, The Club 180

Battery Opera
Website: www.batteryopera.com
Email: info@batteryopera.com
Phone:

604 688 8583
Address:
703-1088 Quebec Street, CA
Information: Led by dancer/choreographer Lee Su-Feh and writer/singer David McIntosh, battery opera's "fearlessly iconoclastic" work interrogates the contemporary body as a site of intersecting and displaced histories and habits. Underlying the practice of battery opera is a dynamic dialogue and mutual attraction between opposing tensions, an exchange that is sensitive to the nuances of power and influence in the socio-political history we have inherited.
In battery opera, "brainy and bawdy" forms and traditions meet, merge and collide to celebrate the power and fragility of a human body that breathes, speaks, sings, thinks, moves, dances.
Country: Canada
Contact: Artistic Director Lee Suh-Fee
Email: Artistic Producer David McIntosh
Social Media: www.facebook.com/batteryoperaperformance

Calgary Opera
Website: www.calgaryopera.com
Email: info@calgaryopera.com
Phone: 403 262 7286
Address: Calgary Opera, 1315 – 7 Street SW, CA
Information: For 44 years, Calgary Opera has made a name for itself as a company that is committed to the development of Canadian talent and the development of new opera works, as well as bringing opera to all ages in the community on a broader scale.
Country: Canada
Contact: Chair Michael Brown
Email: Director Tina Antony
Email: finance Manager Don Swystun
Social Media: @CalgaryOpera www.facebook.com/calgaryopera
Venues: Jubilee Auditorium

Chants Libres
Website: www.chantslibres.org
Email: creation@chantslibres.org
Phone: 514 841 2642
Address: 1908, rue Panet, Bureau 303, CA
Information: in 1990, Pauline Vaillancourt founded Chants Libres, the lyric creation company, in association with Joseph Saint-Gelais and Renald Tremblay, with a mandate to bring all Artistic disciplines (music, theatre, visual arts, electronic media, video) together around the human voice
Country: Canada
Contact: Artistic and General Director Pauline Vaillancourt
Email: pauline@chantslibres.orgadministrative Director Stéphane Dumont
Email: stephane@dumontstpierre.caDirector of communications and development Nora Charifi
Email: communications@chantslibres.org
Social Media: @ChantsLibres www.facebook.com/ChantsLibres
Touring: France, Italy, The Netherlands, Germany, Venezuela

Edmonton Opera Association
Website: www.edmontonopera.com
Email: edmopera@edmontonopera.com
Phone: 780 424 4040
Address: 15230 – 128 Avenue, CA
Information: Edmonton Opera believes that art brings people together. Everyday, they bring artists and audiences together to celebrate shared experiences that resonate beyond the final note. Founded in 1963, Edmonton Opera is dedicated to producing great performances that showcase the powerful emotions of opera to their community. The seasons are designed to resonate with modern audiences. They challenge themselves to present familiar favourites in imaginative new productions, and take Artistic risks by featuring repertoire that audiences rarely get to experience live.
Country: Canada
Contact: General Manager / Artistic Director Tim Yakimec
Email: tim.yakimec@edmontonopera.com Marketing & communications Manager
Cameron Macrae
Email: cameron.macrae@edmontonopera.comchief financial officer Debra King
Email: debra.king@edmontonopera.comDirector of Artistic operations Ha Neul Kim
Email: haneul.kim@edmontonopera.com
Social Media: @edmontonopera www.facebook.com/EdmontonOpera
Annual performances: 9
Annual productions: 3
Venues: Northern Alberta Jubilee Auditorium 2700

Manitoba Opera
Website: www.manitobaopera.mb.ca
Email: mbopera@manitobaopera.mb.ca
Phone:
204 942 7479
Address: 1060-555 Main Street, CA
Information: Manitoba Opera was established in 1969 by Founding President Justice Kerr Twaddle and a group of individuals dedicated to presenting the great works of opera to Manitoban audiences

Country: Canada
Contact: Director of production Sheldon Johnson
Email: mbopera@manitobaopera.mb.ca General Director & CEO
Larry Desrochers
Email: Director of Administration Michael Blais
Email: chief financial officer Dale Sulymka
Social Media: www.facebook.com/pages/Manitoba-Opera
Venues: Manitoba Centennial Concert Hall 2305

Opera Atelier
Website: www.operaatelier.com
Email: oa@operaatelier.com
Address: St. Lawrence Hall, 157 King Street East, 4th Floor, CA
Information: average of 12 singers per production; orchestra size 31-36
Country: Canada
Contact: co-Artistic Director Jeannette Zingg
Email: opera.atelier@operaatelier.comco-Artistic Director Marshall Pynkoski
Email: opera.atelier@operaatelier.comExecutive Director Patricia Barretto
Email: patricia.barretto@operaatelier.com
Social Media: @OperaAtelier www.facebook.com/pages/Opera-Atelier
Touring: England, France, Japan, Singapore, South Korea, United States
Venues: Elgin Theatre 1485

Opera de Montreal
Website: www.operademontreal.com
Email: info@operademontreal.com
Phone: 514 985 2258
Address: 260 Boulevard de Maisonneuve Ouest, CA
Information:
Country: Canada
Contact: Artistic Director Michel Beaulac
Email: mbeaulac@operamontreal.comDirector of communications Pierre Vachon
Email: pvachon@operamontreal.comExecutive Director Pierre Dufour
Email: pdufour@operamontreal.com
Social Media: www.operademontreal http:// www.facebook.com/OperadeMontreal
Annual performances: 20
Annual productions: 5
Venues: Wilfrid-Pelletier Hall, Place des Arts 3000, Th

Opéra de Québec
Website: www.operadequebec.qc.ca
Email: operaqc@mediom.qc.ca
Address: 1220 avenue Taché, CA
Information: size of orchestra: 40-74
Country: Canada
Contact: General and Artistic Director Gregory Legendre
Email: operaqc@mediom.qc.ca pr & communications & development Director
Helen Hall
Email: Director of human rescources Fabien L'Heureux
Social Media: www.facebook.com/operadequebec
Venues: La Salle Louis-Frchette, Le Grand Thtre de Qubec 1796

Opera Hamilton
Website: www.operahamilton.ca
Email: info@operahamilton.ca
Phone: 905 527 7627
Address: 130 Jackson St East, 105 Main Street East, CA
Country: Canada
Venues: Great Hall, Hamilton Place 2115; Raffi Armenian Theatre, The Centre in the Square 1886

Opera in Concert
Website: www.operainconcert.com
Email: email@operainconcert.com
Address: 947 Queens Street East, 2nd Floor, CA
Information: Opera in Concert features new and rarely heard opera performed by up-and-coming young Canadian singers.
Country: Canada
Contact: Director of Marketing and publicity Henry Ingram
Email: chorus Director Robert Cooper
Email: chorus Manager Rory McGlynn
Email: General Director Guillermo Silva-Marin
Social Media: www.facebook.com/OperaInConcert
Venues: St. Lawrence Centre for the Arts, Jane Mallet Theatre

Opera Lyra Ottawa
Website: www.operalyra.ca
Email: frontdesk@operalyra.ca
Address: 2 Daly Avenue, Suite 110, CA
Information: from the two one-act operas in the York Street Theatre, OLO has grown steadily – now producing two fully staged operas in the National Arts Centre's Southam Hall and several second stage productions throughout the year
Country: Canada

Contact: General Director Jeep Jeffries
Email: jpjeffries@operalyra.caArtistic Director Tyrone Paterson
Email: ArtisticDirector@operalyra.caDirector of finance Carol Vahey
Email: cvahey@operalyra.caDirector of production Ron Ward
Email: rward@operalyra.caDirector of Marketing Vicky Marsolais
Email: vmarsolais@operalyra.ca
Social Media: @OperaLyraOttawa www.facebook.com/operalyraottawa
National Arts Centre's Southam Hall

Pacific Opera Victoria
Website: www.pov.bc.ca
Email: boxoffice@pov.bc.ca
Phone: 250 382 1641
Address: 1815 Blanshard ST, Suite 500, CA
Information:
Country: Canada
Contact: Artistic Director Timothy Vernon
Email: Executive Director Patrick Corrigan
Email: Director of Artistic Administration Ian Rye
Social Media: @PacificOperaVic www.facebook.com/pages/Pacific-Opera-Victoria
Venues: Royal Theatre 1400

Queen of Puddings Music Theatre
Website: www.queenofpuddingsmusictheatre.com
Email: info@queenofpuddingsmusictheatre.com
Phone: 416 203 4149
Address: The Historic Distillery District, 15 Case Goods Lane, Studio 206, CA
Information: committed exclusively to the creation and production of new Canadian music theatre/opera compositions and their presentation on the world stage
Country: Canada
Contact: Artistic Director Dairine Ni Mheadhra
Email: General Manager Claire Speed
Email: Artistic Producer Nathalie Bonjour
Social Media: www.facebook.com/queenofpuddings
Touring: Europe, USA

UWOpera Workshop
Website: www.music.uwo.ca
Email: music@uwo.ca
Address: Don Wright Faculty of Music, University of Western Ontario, CA
Information: Main Repertoire: Traditional and contemporary opera, student opera, voice majors
Country: Canada
Contact: department Chair Sophie Roland
Email: sroland2@uwo.ca
Venues: Talbot Theatre 375

Vancouver Opera
Website: www.vancouveropera.ca
Address: 835 Cambie Street, CA
Information:
Country: Canada
Contact: music Director Jonathan Darlington
Email: jwright@vancouveropera.caGeneral Director James W Wright
Email: jwright@vancouveropera.caDirector of finance Catriona Cheng
Email: ccheng@vancouveropera.caArtistic Director Tom Wright
Email: tomwright@vancouveropera.ca
Social Media: @VancouverOpera www.facebook.com/vancouveropera
Venues: Queen Elizabeth Theatre 2800

CHINA

Academy of Chinese Traditional Opera
Phone: 106 335 1122
Address: 400 Wanquansi, Xuan Wu District
Information: Academy of Chinese Traditional Opera is the only institute of its kind in China that offers both B.A., M.A. and M.F.A. degrees. Since the 1950s, its graduates have functioned as backbones in Chinese dramatic troupes, media arts, and filmmaking as well as theatrical education and criticism
Country: China

Bei Fang Kun Qu Opera Theatre
Website: www.beikun.com
Phone: 108 351 0663
Address: Taoranting Road, Xicheng District
Information: Kunqu (pronounced kwin chu) is one of the oldest and most refined styles of traditional Chinese theatre performed today. It is a synthesis of drama, opera, ballet, poetry recital, and musical recital, which also draws on earlier forms of Chinese theatrical performances such as mime, farce, acrobatics, ballad recital, and medley, some of which go back to the third century B.C. or even earlier.
Country: China
Contact: Managing Director/Artistic Director Fung-Yi Yang

Beijing Traditional Opera School
Address: No.8 Ma Jia Pu Dong Li, Feng Tai District

OPERA/MUSIC THEATRE COMPANY

Information: Peking Opera is being introduced to primary and middle school students in an effort to promote the traditional art to the younger generation
Country: China
Contact: principal Sun Yu Min
Email: vice-principal Wu Yi Ping

Chang Sha Opera Theatre
Phone: 731 855 51738
Address: 287 Yu Hua Road, Hu Nan
Country: China
Touring: Europe, South East Asia
Venues: Hu Nan Grand Hall 1488

China Central Song and Dance Ensemble of Nationalities
Address: No. 19, Zhong Guan Cun Nan (Da Jie) Main Street, Hai Dian District
Information: duplicate
Country: China
Contact: President Yu-Jie Bei
Email: foreign department Manager Tai-xiang Jiang

China Heaven Creation International Performing Arts Co. Ltd
Website: www.heaven-creation.com
Email: china-art@heaven-creation.com
Phone: 105 120 6986
Address: 18F Huasheng International Building, No.12, Yabao Road, Chao Yang District
Information: China Heaven Creation International Performing Arts Co., Ltd(CHC) was founded in 1999 with the approval of China National Ministry of Culture and China National Industrial and Commercial General Administration, which is a state-level performing arts company entitled with the right to import and export stage show productions, and the creative planning, producing, management and operating concerned
Country: China

China National Chinese Opera and Dance Drama Company
Website: www.coddc.com
Email: china_opera@163.com
Address: 1F No. 23, , Nan San Huan Eastern Road, Feng Tai District
Information: duplicate
Country: China
Contact: vice-President Yi-wei Jin
Email: President Wen-zeng Lin
Email: vice-President Ji-guang Jin
Email: pa to President /Manager of performances Yi Sun
Venues: Min Zhu Theatre, Bao Li Theatre

China National Opera House Company
Email: zhongguojingju@vrt.sina.com
Phone: 861 066 155 259
Address: 22 Xi Da Street, Ping An Li, Xi Cheng District
Information: Peking Opera
Country: China
Contact: Executive officer Hui-Jun Lu
Email: Managing Director Jiang Wu
Email: head of publicity Rui Zhou
Email: foreign affairs Min Liu
Touring: Korea
The People's Theatre 1470, Chang An Theatre 800

China National Theatre
Website: www.ntcc.com.cn
Email: ghyb1009@126.com
Address: No. 277, Di An Men Wai Da (Jie) Street, , Xi Cheng District
Information: duplicate
Country: China
Contact: President Zhou Zhiqiang
Touring: UK, Germany, USA
Venues: Dong Fang Xian Feng Theatre 300, Theatre of National Theatre Company 250

China Opera Theatre (China National Opera and Ballet Theatre)
Website: www.chinaopera.com.cn
Email: lh5658@126.com
Phone: 106 551 4787
Address: No. 115 Dong Zhong Street, Dong Cheng District Chao Wai,
Information: China Opera Theatre (China National Opera and Ballet Theatre) is a State-run opera company based in Beijing, China, and under the Chinese Ministry of Culture. CNOH consists of an opera troupe, a choir, a symphony orchestra and a stagecraft, costume and scenery departments. It is affiliated, through common direction under the Ministry of Culture, with the Shanghai Opera House company and other geju companies around China
Country: China
Contact: Director Feng Yu
Touring: USA

China Pingju Opera Theatre
Phone:
106 726 0380
Address: No.19, Fourth Section Xilou Yuan

Country: China
Contact: Director Hu Chun Ping
Email: Artistic Director Zhang Hong Wen

Dong Guan Cantonese Opera Troupe
Phone: 769 222 1505
Address: 151 Xin Feng Road
Information: Dong Guan Cantonese Opera Troupe plays an important role in the development and promotion of Cantonese opera in Dongguan. Along with the economic development, more and more people in Dongguan like Cantonese opera, especially the youth.
Country: China

Guang Dong Chao Opera Troupe
Phone: 867 521 5951
Address: No 6, Chaohu Road, Shan Tou
Information: Currently, the troupe is preparing to construct a performance plaza for Yuejue Opera with the synthesized function of creation and research, Artistic training, Artistic exchange, performance, museum, audio and video purposes to attract capable artists
Country: China
Venues: Shan Tou Chao Opera Art Centre

Guang Dong Han Opera Troupe
Phone: 753 223 4872
Address: Mei Xiang Road, Guang Dong
Information: Guangdong Han Opera was once called "Waijiang Opera." In 1927, Qian Rechu, a scholar in Dapu County in the late Qing Dynasty, changed its name to "Han Opera" according to the origins of Waijiang Opera. Han Opera is well known to the world. It is hailed as the "Peony of South China" and is one of the top three operas in Guangdong
Country: China
Venues: Mo Dang Theatre 300

Guang Dong Provincial Cantonese Opera Troupe
Email: yjy_xctj@163.com
Phone: 208 777 5095
Address: 703 Dong Feng East Road, Guang Dong
Information: Presents Cantonese opera
Country: China
Touring: USA, Canada, Singapore, Malaysia, Australia, Hong Kong, Macau, Taiwan

Peking Opera Theatre of Beijing
Phone: 106 726 7830
Address: No.30, Hai Hu Xi Li, Feng Tai District
Information: The Peking Opera Theatre of Beijing will bring a faithful rendition of Elegant Sounds of Good Times, based on the rare and exclusive scripts preserved in the Forbidden City. Theatre's experts strive to restore Peking Opera in its pristine form that every detail, ranging from stage setting to performing style, is meticulously attended to
Country: China
Touring: Australia, Japan, USA
Venues: Lin Yu Yuan Theatre 1100, Chang An Theatre, Hu Guang Hui Guan

Shan Xi Opera Troupe
Email: shaange@163.com
Phone: 298 785 4487
Address: No. 165, Wenyi Road
Information: Shan Xi Opera Troupe is an influential art group with a glorious history. Numerous drama masters and talents have gathered here, including winners of the Chinese Opera Plum Blossom Award. In 1959, the Shanxi Opera Troupe joined the Shanxi performance group and performed the traditional Shanxi Opera Visiting the West Lake and Chinese Orphan in Beijing
Country: China
Touring: Korea, Australia

Shanghai Huai Opera Troupe
Phone: 216 327 2637
Address: No. 50, Lane 155, Wei Hai Road
Information: Shanghai Huaiju group was established in 1953 May, Shanghai city is one of the earliest established National Theatre Arts groups. Served as the central leadership Mao Zedong , early labor leader , Zhou Enlai , a Red Army founder and leading General , Jiang Zemin and Hu Jintao , Wu Bangguo Comrades have watched Shanghai Huai theater performances
Country: China

Shanghai Municipal Performance Company
Email:
office@chinasmpc.com
Phone:
216 272 0234
Address: 18/F, No.211 Kang Ding
Information: Founded in 1985, Shanghai Municipal Performance Company (SMPC) is one of the earliest state-owned class-A performance corporations in China with independent legal status. The company is a professional agency with wide scope of business, including presenting all kinds of performances, performance advertising, stage production, exhibition, dance training and performance ticketing
Country: China
Touring: United States, Russia, UK, France, Germany, Japan, Italy, Australia, the Netherlands, Switzerland, Spain, Austria, Sweden, Thailand and Hong Kong SAR, Taiwan

Shanghai Peking Opera Theatre
Website: www.pekingopera.sh.cn
Email: jingju@pekingopera.com.cn
Phone: 216 433 3836
Address: 168 Yueyang Road
Information: As a prominent art company in China, Shanghai Jingju Company, established in March 1955 on the basis of Donghua Experimental Peking Opera Group and People Peking Opera Group, subordinate to CPC Shanghai Ministry of Propaganda, is one of ten national key Peking opera troupes entitled by China Ministry of Culture. Zhou Xinfeng, the first President, was a famous Peking Opera master himself.
Country: China

Sichuan Opera Theatre
Email: scdrama@sina.com
Phone: 288 665 8400
Address: 20 Zhuangyuan Jie, Sichuanhao Yang District
Information: The Sichuan Opera Theatre presents "Flaming Mountain, " a tale involving a traveling Buddhist monk and a Monkey King with magical powers, with plenty of acrobatics and costumes
Country: China
Venues: China Sichuan Opera Theatre

HONG KONG

Boom a Bliss Cantonese Opera
Phone: 852 337 3831
Address: 202 Mei Po House, Mei Tung Est, Kowloon, HK
Information: aims to promote Cantonese opera through-innovative progamming
Country: Hong Kong
Contact: Executive assistant Lai Wah Yuen F

Chinese Artists Association of Hong Kong
Website: www.hkbarwo.com
Email: hkbarwo@netvigator.com
Phone: 238 42929
Address: 4th Floor, Block A, Prospect Building, 493 Nathan Road, Yau Ma Tei, HK
Information: Chinese Artist Association of Hong Kong is a non-profit association of Cantonese opera groups and artists in Hong Kong, established in 1953. The association drives the development of Cantonese Opera through educational efforts. It organises training classes in traditional performing arts for teenagers and cooperates closely with the Vocational Training Council in offering opera courses. The association also holds regular performances by established artists
Country: Hong Kong
Contact: chief Executive officer Alisa Shum

Golden Phoenix Cantonese Opera
Phone: 235 79316
Address: Room 603, Perfect Commercial Building, 20 Austin Avenue, Tsim Sha Tsui, HK
Information: Led by Cantonese opera virtuosi Ng Chin-fung and Chan Ho-kau, the locally based Golden Phoenix Cantonese Opera will perform the new Cantonese opera "A Floating Life" and the classical work "Romance and Hatred" in December. Other performers include Sun Kim-long, Liu Kwok-sum, Lui Hung-kwong, Ko Lai and Wan Yuk-yu
Country: Hong Kong
Contact: General Director Ng Chin-fung

Jingkun Theatre Limited
Website: www.jingkun.org.hk
Email: jingkun@jingkun.org.hk
Phone: 280 52577
Address: Unit 18, 12/F, Metro Centre Ⅱ, 21 Lam hing St., Kowloon Bay, HK
Information: Founded in 1986, their scope of work includes performance production, popularisation, education and training, cultural exchanges, etc. They are a leading professional Beijing Opera troupe in Hong Kong who engage top artists from Hong Kong and mainland China. They have performances organised by Leisure and Culture Services Department Hong Kong. See also National Organisations
Country: Hong Kong
Contact: Artistic Director Yuen-ha Tang
Social Media: www.facebook.com/JingkunTheatre/

Ming Chee Sing Chinese Opera
Phone: 252 24699
Address: 72 Queen's Road Central, No.502, Parker House, HK
Information: Ming Chee Sing Chinese Opera is one of the top Cantonese Opera troupes in Hong Kong. The troupe was founded in 1990 by a Mrs Lau Kam Yiu to promote a young opera talent, the then Joyce Koi Ming Fai. Mr Lau himself, a retired businessman, later took over the management of Ming Chee Sing.
Country: Hong Kong
Contact: Chairman Koi Ming-fai

Opera Hong Kong

Website: www.operahongkong.org
Email:
enquiry@operahongkong.org
Phone: 223 40303
Address: Rm 1907, 19/F, Pacific Plaza, 410 Des Voeux Road West, HK
Information: Opera Hong Kong is the first opera company to have been established in Hong Kong. The company was formed in July 2003 as a non-profit organization. Since its inception, Opera Hong Kong has become a firmly established part of Hong Kong's cultural scene. Opera Hong Kong is committed to the mission of enhancing the appreciation of the art of opera in Hong Kong and promoting local music talents. They firmly believe that opera productions should be given a permanent niche in a culturally vibrant city such as Hong Kong. In addition to staging operas and other performances, Opera Hong Kong aims to make opera easy and fun to understand for the General public, especially the young, through a programme of education and outreach activities
Country: Hong Kong
Contact: Artistic Director Warren Mok
Email: General Manager Min Wong
Email: Chairman Moses Cheng
Social Media: www.facebook.com/OperaHongKongLimited/
Venues: Grand Theatre, Hong Kong Cultural Centre

ISRAEL

The Israeli Opera
Website: www.israel-opera.co.il
Phone: 369 27777
Address: The Israeli Opera, 19 Shaul Hamelech St., IL
Information: the Opera in Israel has aimed to develop its identity as an Israeli Opera by nurturing Israeli artists and soloists and to commission and perform original operas by Israeli composers. Runs workshops and the Young Artists Program; alternative phone contact: Opera Management 03-6927804
Country: Israel
Contact: Artistic Director Michael Eisenstadt
Email: music Director David Stern
Email: General Manager Hanna Munitz
Social Media: www.facebook.com/israeliopera

JAPAN

Bolshoi Circus Co Ltd
Website: www.bolshoicircus.com
Address: Bolshoi Circus Bldg., 2-14-5, Iidabashi, Chiyoda-ku, JP
Information:
Country: Japan
Contact: President Michiteru Azuma
Email: international div. Masanobu Nakayama

China Youth Opera Troupe
Website: www.china-art.co.jp
Email: cac@jg8.so-net.ne.jp
Phone: 356 168 822
Address: 8F, TKK Shinbashi Bldg., 1-17-8, Shinbashi, Minato-ku, JP
Information:
Country: Japan
Contact: Director Bo Cheng

Fujiwara Opera (The Japan Opera Foundation)
Website: www.jof.or.jp (japanese language only)
Email: jof@jof.or.jp
Phone: 354 663 185
Address: 8F Nishiazabu 28 Mori Bldg., 4-16-13 Nishi-Azabu, Minato-ku, JP
Information: a part of The Japan Opera Foundation (q.v.); established in 1934; performs mainly Italian operas; invites world-renowned singers; one of Japan's representative opera companies
Country: Japan
Contact: Artistic Director/contact Hiroyuki Okayama
Venues: Tokyo Bunkakaikan Hall 2303 (q.v.) Bunkamura Orchard Hall 2150 (q.v.)

Harmony Japan Co Ltd
Website: www.harmonyjapan.com
Email: inquiry@harmonyjapan.com
Phone: 334 093 345
Address: Harmony JAPAN Co., Ltd. 6-19-21, 7F Jingumae, Shibuya, Tokyo 150-0001 JAPAN
Information: Founded in 1988, over 25 years we have pursued live performing arts that truly move human minds, including "Disney on Classic", "Olympic Concert" in Japan, "Notre-Dame de Paris", "International Tchaikovsky Competition Laureates Gala Concert Japan Tour" and various jazz concerts such as Duke Ellington Orchestra, Pat Metheny, Chick Corea, Brad Mehldau, The Manhattan Transfer, Count Basie Orchestra, Sonny Rollins etc…
Country: Japan

Japan Operetta Society (2)
Website: www.operettahouse.com
Email: operetta@fa.mbn.or.jp
Phone: 334 791 535
Address: Les Fleurs Nishiazabu 104, 1-4-35 Nishi-Azabu, Minato-ku, JP

Information: aimed at disseminating operetta and contributing to the development of the arts in Japan by fostering Bel Canto singers who can act, dance and sing choral music
Country: Japan
Contact: Executive Director&Producer Masayoki Yoneta
Venues: New National Theatre Chu Gekijyo, Hokutopia Sakura Hall, Shinjuku Bunka Centre

Kansai Nikikai Public Interest Incorporated Association
Website: www.kansai-nikikai.com
Email: kansai-nikikai@pop17.odn.ne.jp
Phone: 663 604 649
Address: 2-3-11-601 Uchihommachi, Chuo-ku, JP
Information: The largest opera company outside Tokyo
Country: Japan
Venues: Archaic Hall 1820 (q.v.)

Kansai Opera
Email: kfacoper@pop07.odn.ne.jp
Phone: 669 434 567
Address: c/o Kansai Geijutsu Bunka Kyokai, 3F Uchihonmachi Green Bldg., 2-3-11, Uchihonmachi, Chuo-ku, JP
Information: founded in 1949; 3 subscription productions per year; well known for its enthusiasm to perform modern Japanese operas
Country: Japan
Contact: Chairman of bunka kyokai Shinichiro Ohkawa
Email: acting President of kagekidan opera Yoshiomi Kayamoto
Venues: Amagasaki Archaic Hall, etc

Kyodo Tokyo Inc
Website: www.kyodotokyo.com
Address: NBF Alliance 4F, 5-2-1 Minami Aoyama, Minato-ku, Tokyo 107-0062
Information: Kyodo Tokyo Inc. was founded in 1962. The Company's line of business includes providing live theatrical presentations, such as road companies and summer theaters.
Country: Japan
Contact: President and CEO Yoshito Yamazaki
Social Media: https://twitter.com/KyodoTokyo

Laughing Cats Co Ltd
Website: www.warauneko.com
Phone: 422 562 329
Address: 2-1-5 Midoricho, Musashino-shi, Tokyo 180-0012
Information: Laughing Cats Co Ltd has been promoting and coordinating a series of concerts, 'World Music Series' for 8 years, which includes music from Mongolia, the Silk Road, Tibet, Bolivia, Tanzania, etc. and manages folk music ensembles in the world and Japanese classical music artists.
Country: Japan

New National Theatre, Tokyo, Opera
Website: www.nntt.jac.go.jp
Phone: 353 525 733
Address: 1-1-1 Hon-machi, Shibuya-ku, JP
Information: see also Presenters & Venues
Country: Japan
Contact: Artistic Director opera Thomas Novohradsky
Venues: New National Theatre – The Opera House 1814 (q.v.), The Playhouse when proscenium style 1038 when open style 1010 (q.v.), The Pit 340-468 (q.v.)

Nihon Opera Kyokai
Website: www.jof.or.jp
Email: jof@jof.or.jp
Phone: 354 663 185
Address: 8F Nishi-Azabu 28 Mori Bldg., 4-16-13 Nishi-Azabu, Minato-ku, JP
Information: produces mainly original Japanese operas; managed by The Japan Opera Foundation (q.v.)
Country: Japan
Contact: General Director Hiroshi Ohga
Venues: New National Theatre: Middle Hall (q.v.), SHinjuku Bunka Centre (q.v.)

Nikikai Opera Foundation
Website: www.nikikai-opera.or.jp
Email: nikikai@mx3.alpha-web.ne.jp
Phone: 337 961 818
Address: 1-25-12, Sendagaya, Shibuya-ku, JP
Information: as Tokyo Nikikai Opera Theatre produces opera using singers of Niki-kai (q.v.) and guest singers; its activities also include educating and fostering singers, choirs and production staff, and promoting opera in Japan; one of Japan's representative opera c
Country: Japan
Contact: Chairman Yoshinobu Kuribayashi
Email: Managing Director Kingo Nakayama
Venues: Tokyo Bunka Kaikan Hall , New National Theatre

Opera Theatre Konnyakuza
Website: homepage2.nifty.com/konnyakuza/
Email:
JDQ01133@nifty.ne.jp
Phone:
334 127 202

Address: 101, 2-18-4 Komazawa, Setagaya-ku, JP
Information: aims to create 'Contemporary Japanese Opera' with emphasis on the nature of Japanese language
Country: Japan
Contact: Chairperson, music Director & composer Kyoko Hagi Artistic Director & composer Hikaru Hayashi
Email: music planning Director Satoshi Oishi
Email: public relations Azumi Tadachi
Venues: Setagawa Public Theatre and others

Suisei Musical
Website: suisei.m78.com
Email: suisei@m78.com
Phone: 423 708 035
Address: 788 Higashinaganuma, Inagi-shi, JP
Information:
Country: Japan
Contact: President Makoto Mizutani
Venues: Tokyo Metropolitan Art Space (q.v.) Aoyama Theatre (q.v.)

Takarazuka Revue Company
Website: www.chamber-opera.jp
Email: t-seisaku@hankyu.co.jp
Address: 1-1-57 Sakae-machi, Takarazuka City, JP
Information: all-female musical revue company; male roles are played by female actors; one of the many arms of the Hankyu Corporation; its first performance was in 1914 and the Company five troupes continues to produce mainly musicals and revues in Japanese
Country: Japan
Venues: Takarazuka Grand Theater 2527 (q.v.) Tokyo Takarazuka Theater 2, 069q.v. Takarazuka Bow Hall 500

Tokyo Chamber Opera Theatre, The
Website: www.chamber-opera.jp
Email: info@chamber-opera.jp
Phone: 356 422 267
Address: 7F Kabutocho Daini Bldg., 9-2 Kabuto-cho, Nihonbashi, Chuou-ku, JP
Information: founded in 1969 to produce chamber operas with Japan's representative artists; performs well-known works, neglected masterpieces and Japanese works; many world premieres; aims to contribute to the promotion of opera in Japan
Country: Japan
Contact: Chairman of Managing committee Yoshiaki Takezawa
Email: Artistic Director Hiroshi Wakasugi
Venues: Kioi Hall (q.v.) New National Theatre (q.v.) Meguro Persimmon Hall (q.v.)

Tokyo Opera Association (2)
Website: www.tokyo-opera.gr.jp/
Phone: 352 697 895
Address: 2-14-6-405 Shinjuku, Shinjiku-ku, JP
Information: presents Japanese operas all over the world, eg. 'Forgotten Boys – The Envoy of Tensho Era', written as a tribute to people and as a prayer for world peace; this opera features various traditional and modern music styles from both East and West, as well a
Country: Japan
Contact: music Director Katsu'umi Niwa
Email: counselor Masanobu Fukuoka representative & General Director Edward T Ishita
Email: Director Kayoko Ota pr & admin Mokoto Nozaki
Email: stage Manager Yu Kuriishi
Venues: The Tokyo Metropolitan Festival Hall 2303 (q.v.) Tokyo Metropolitan Art Space

Tokyo Opera Production (2)
Website: www.infoseek.livedoor.net/~operaproduce/
Email: operaproduce@jcom.home.ne.jp
Phone: 335 305 181
Address: 1F Meson du Mi Yai, 1-7-11 Tohshin-cho, Itabashi-ku, JP
Information: Japanese singers perform in original languages; often produces premiers of rarely-performed works; listed also in Agent
Country: Japan
Contact: Producer Fumiko Takenaka
Email: President Hiroshi Matsuo
Touring: Australia
Venues: New National Theatre (q.v.), Nakano Zero Hall (q.v.)

MEXICO

Compa
Website: mexico.udg.mx
Phone: 525 555 216 776
Address: Palacio de Bellas Artes, Av. Hidalgo 1, 3, Col. Centro, MX
Information: National Opera Company presents five productions a year with international cast
Country: Mexico
Contact: public relations Ester P
Email: General Director Gerardo Kleinburg

Temporada de Ópera de Guadalajara

Address: Conciertos Guadalajara A.C., Ex Convento del Carmen, MX
Country: Mexico
Venues: Teatro Degollado

NEW ZEALAND

Canterbury Opera
Website: www.canterburyopera.com
Email: info@canterburyopera.com
Phone: 643 366 9932
Address: Ropu Waitara o Waitaha, , 148 Gloucester Street, PO Box 176, NZ
Information:
Country: New Zealand
Contact: Artistic Director Brian Castles-Onion
Email: chief Executive officer Elizabeth Owens
Email: Chairman Richard Westlake
Venues: James Hay Theatre 1000

New Zealand Opera
Website: www.nzopera.com
Email: hello@nzopera.co.nz
Phone: 937 94020
Address: Level 3, 100 Mayoral Drive, NZ
Information: New Zealand Opera was formed in 2000 with the merger of the National Opera of Wellington and Opera New Zealand (Auckland), forming New Zealand's first fully professional national opera company. In 2012, Southern Opera merged with New Zealand Opera to form a truly national opera company and to ensure the long term future and viability of opera of an international standard in the South Island.
Country: New Zealand
Contact: General Director Stuart Maunder
Email: stuart@nzopera.co.nzDirector of music Wyn Davies
Email: wyn@polidori.co.ukExecutive Director Jane Clarke
Email: jane@nzopera.co.nz
Social Media: @NZOpera www.facebook.com/nzopera
Annual productions: 2
Venues: St James Theatre 1500 Wellington, ASB Theatre, Aotea Centre Auckland, The Edge

PHILIPPINES

Philippine Opera Company
Website: www.philippineopera.com
Email: phil_opera_co@yahoo.com.ph
Phone: 289 58097
Address: SJG Centre, Rockwell Drive corner Don Pedro Street, PH
Information:
Country: Philippines
Contact: Managing Director Karla Gutierrez
Email: Managing Director Jay Valencia Glorioso

SINGAPORE

Chinese Theatre Circle (CTC)
Website: www.ctcopera.com.sg
Email: ctcopera@yahoo.com
Phone: 632 34862
Address: 5 Smith Street, SG
Information: Established in 1981, the Chinese Theatre Circle (CTC) has been promoting the art of Chinese Opera, dance and music in Singapore and beyond. In March 1995, it became the first non-profit professional performing Chinese Opera company in Singapore and was subsequently awarded the Excellence for Singapore Award in 1997 for its efforts in promoting Chinese Opera in Asia and in the world.
Country: Singapore
Contact: Chairman Leslie Wong Sze Ying
Email: Artistic Director Joanna Wong Quee Heng
Social Media: www.facebook.com/chinesetheatrecirclesingapore
Touring: Australia, Belgium, Brazil, Canada, China, Egypt, England, France, Germany, Hong Kong, Hungary, Ireland, Italy, Japan, Korea, Malaysia, New Zealand, Romania, Scotland, Switzerland, The Netherlands, Turkey and the USA

Sing Sheng Philharmonic Society
Email: ongekse@singnet.com.sg
Phone: 628 28933
Address: 23 Lorong Lew Lian, 03-03, SG
Information: Sing Sheng Philharmonic Society aims to promote opera and choral music in Singapore, singing a wide variety of songs including Mandarin.
Country: Singapore
Contact: Director Cheryl Teh

Singapore Lyric Opera Ltd
Website: www.singaporeopera.com.sg
Email: gm@singaporeopera.com.sg
Phone: 633 61929
Address: Stamford Arts Centre, 155 Waterloo Street, #03-06, SG
Information: Singapore Lyric Opera's main objective is to promote and present western opera. Since its inaugural performance of Mozart's Die Zauberflöte in 1991, SLO has been active in presenting annual seasons of operas, concerts and musical events for the enjoyment of

Singaporeans from all walks of life. It gives opera fans opportunities to enjoy operas not frequently performed in the Asia-Pacific region
Country: Singapore
Contact: General Manager Anthony Tan
Email: anthonytan@singaporeopera.com.sgChair Toh Weng Cheong
Social Media: @sglyricopera www.facebook.com/singaporeopera
Venues: Victoria Theatre, Kallang Theatre

Tung On Wui Kun Cantonese Opera Troupe
Phone: 622 34416
Address: 21 Bukit Pasoh Road, SG
Information: Tung On Wui Kun Cantonese Opera Troupe aims to promote the art of Cantonese opera among the local community. The Tung On Opera Troupe is long-established and its performances are infrequent, with perhaps one full-length opera a year. However, in 1999 there were two: one was the well-known 'Emperor Kong Sui & Zhen Fei'.
Country: Singapore
Contact: secretary Chee Kin Foon
Email: Chairman Chow Chong Fatt

TAIWAN, PROVINCE OF CHINA

Chun-Mei Taiwanese Opera Troupe
Website: beam.to/chunmei
Email: Cheng_esther@hotmail.com
Address: No.397, Kai Xuan Road, Kaoshiung County
Information:
Country: Taiwan

Dafeng Musical Theatre
Website: dafengmusical.pixnet.net/blog
Email: tafen.jack@msa.hinet.net
Phone: 027 725 1889 / 9
Address: 2F – 3, No. 25, , Bo Ai Road, , Zhong Zheng District,
Information:
Country: Taiwan

Gang-a Tsui Theater
Email: nankuan@ms31.hinet.net
Phone: 222 539 712
Address: 6F-2, No. 486, , Wen Hua Road Section 2, , Ban Qiao District,
Information: has 8 full-time and 50 part-time actors & actresses; mainly produces traditional music records; devoted to the study of Nan-kuan music and opera originated in the southern Fukien province in the past few years; its goal is not only to preserve these class
Country: Taiwan
Contact: correspondent I-Chang Chou
Touring: Japan, Korea, Mexico, Singapore, USA

Holo Taiwanese Opera Troupe
Email: holonetl@ms7.hinet.net
Address: No.19, , Shin Sheng North Road Section 1,
Information:
Country: Taiwan
Contact: Producer Ning Meng Liu

Hsin-Chuan Taiwanese Opera Troupe
Website: hsinchuan.myweb.hinet.net
Email: hsin.chuan80@msa.hinet.net
Phone: 228 122 121
Address: 2F, No. 53, , Chong Qing North Road Section 4,
Information:
Country: Taiwan
Contact: Chairlady Shu Ru Huang
Email: head of development/Producer Zhi Ling Li

Hsin-Ho-Hsing Taiwanese Opera Troupe
Website: http://tw.myblog.yahoo.com/jw!mcX-CxIKeBRnCYrILMeL1rA--/article?mid=734&pre-v=748&l=f&fid=21
Email: lung1824@yahoo.com.tw / lung1824@hotmail.com
Phone: 048 826 462 / 09
Address: No. 26, Hong Nong 1st Street, , Bian Tou Li, , Zhang Hua County,
Information: winner of
Country: Taiwan
Contact: vice-President Shi-Chen Shi
Email: President Ching-Liu Jiang
villages & temples

Kae-Shyuan Cantonese Opera
Address: F5, No. 1, Lane 77, Tzu You Street, Yung Hor Town
Information: source of finance: Committee of Culture Construction, Ministry of Education, Culture Centre, Provincial Education Dept plus other government sources
Country: Taiwan
Contact: Managing Director Shao Zhen Liu
Email: playwright and Director Yin Lu
Email: deputy Director Yi Zhen Shi

Lan-Yang Taiwanese Opera Company
Website: www.ilccb.gov.tw
Email: lytoc@ilccb.gov.tw
Phone: 393 62542/333 4

Address: 2F, Jhong-Sang Rd
Information: traditional regional opera
Country: Taiwan
Contact: Managing Director Deng-Qing Chen
Email: Artistic diretor Chun Min Hang

Ming Hwa Yuan Taiwanese Opera Company
Website: www.twopera.com
Email: mhy.twopera@msa.hinet.net
Phone: 022 306 2121
Address: No. 132-7, , Da Li Street, , Wan Hua District,
Information: one of the well-known Taiwanese opera companies
Country: Taiwan
Contact: administrative Manager Li-Chun Tsai
Email: President Sheng-Fu Chen

Minkuan Taiwanese Opera Troupe
Website: http:// www.minkuan.org.tw/
Email: wusung03@ms64.hinet.net
Phone: 229 688 841 (mob
Address: 7F, No. 60, , Rui An Street, , Taipei County,
Information:
Country: Taiwan
Contact: correspondent Ching Chuan Lin

National Fu-Hsing Chinese Opera Theatre
Email: more203098@yahoo.com.tw
Address: No. 177, Section 2, Nei-hu Road
Information: presents traditional classics as well as contemporary creations of Chinese opera
Country: Taiwan
Contact: Director Tracy H L Chung
Email: contact Kun An Cheuq

National Guoguang Opera Company
Website: www.kk.gov.tw
Email: tzyung@kk.gov.tw
Phone: 229 383 567 409
Address: 5.F, No. 77, , Mu Zha Road Section 3, , Wun Shan District,
Information: with its basis in the traditional theatre and dramatic music, the company absorbs concepts of modern theatre and themes of contemporary urban societies; aims to modernize and popularize the art of Chinese Opera
Country: Taiwan
Contact: international communication T Z Yung Wang
Touring: not confirmed yet
Venues: National Chiang Kai Shek Cultural Centre ROC, National Theatre Concert Hall 1500

Rom Shing Hakka Opera Troupe, The
Website: hakkafans.myweb.hinet.net/
Email: hakka.fans@msa.hinet.net
Phone: 377 25099 / 37-
Address: No. 47-1, 4 Lin, New Eastern (Xin Dong) Road, , Feng Fu Li, , Hou Long Zhen,
Information:
Country: Taiwan
Contact: vice President Yueh-Ying Liang

Shiu-Kim Taiwanese Opera Troupe
Phone: 628 83672 / 939
Address: 14F.-1, No.66, , Chong Shan 1st Street, , East District,
Information: shiu530321@kimo.com.tw
Country: Taiwan
Contact: correspondent Hsiu Wan Huang
Email: shiuwan@mail2000.com.tw

Tang Mei Yun Taiwanese Opera Troupe
Website: www.meiyunt.org.tw/home.htm
Email: Meiyun.tang@msa.hinet.net
Phone: 229 495 005
Address: 2/F, No.1, Lane 464, Ching Ping Rd, Chunho City
Information:
Country: Taiwan
Contact: Executive Producer Jien Hua Xu

Wei Hai-Ming Chinese Opera Promotion Foundation
Email: weiming6@ms74.hinet.net
Address: 2/F, 32 Lane 295 Tunhwa South Road, Section 1
Information: aims to preserve and render the heritage of the Mei School repertory of Chinese opera
Country: Taiwan
Contact: Director Li Mei Jwo
Touring: mainland China

Yi-shin Taiwanese Opera
Website: yi-sin.myweb.hinet.net
Email: heart@cm1.ethome.net.tw
Phone: 227 971 811
Address: 2F., No.45, Lane 22, Wende Rd., Neihu District
Information:
Country: Taiwan
Contact: founder/Artistic Director Shiu Rung Huei

THAILAND

Opera Siam/Bangkok Opera
Website: www.operasiam.com
Email: intendant@bangkokopera.com
Phone: 022 315 273

Address: Production Office, 34 Soi Pipat 2, Silom Road, TH
Information:
Country: Thailand
Contact: Artistic Director Somtow Sucharitkul
Email: somtow@mindspring.comresident conductor Trisdee na Patalung
Email: trisdee@bangkokopera.comadministrative supervisor Pongsatorn Suraphab
Email: nowd_bass@hotmail.comDirector of development Nadaprapai Suchartkul
Email: drkiks@ymail.comassistant to Artistic Director Nath Khamnark
Email: nath.tbn@gmail.com
Social Media: bangkok opera www.facebook.com/OperaSiam
Touring: UK, USA, Gernany, Middle East, Czech Republic, Austria
Annual performances: 20
Annual productions: 5
Venues: Thailand Cultural Center

UNITED STATES

After Dinner Opera Company Inc.
Website: www.afterdinneropera.org
Email: bflusser23@nyc.rr.com
Phone: 212 477 6212
Address: 23 Stuyvesant St, US
Information: In 1949, Richard Flusser set out to change things by founding the After Dinner Opera Company. In doing this his objective was to produce opera, mostly American and mostly contemporary, and bring it to people all over this country and Europe. He wanted to make it possible for people to enjoy live opera in place where it had never been performed before
Country: United States
Contact: exec. Artistic Director Beth Flusser
Email: bflusser23@nyc.rr.com
Touring: Europe, Canada
Venues: various in NY City

Amarillo Opera Inc.
Website: www.amarilloopera.org
Email: amaopera_mila@amaonline.com
Phone: 806 372 7464
Address: 2223 S Van Buren St, US
Information: Amarillo Opera was founded in April 1988 by Mila Gibson, Opera Workshop and Vocal Professor at Amarillo College from 1982-2000. The company's first production, Giacomo Puccini's Madama Butterfly, starred Gibson who also served as Producer, Director, costumer and publicist. The success of that initial production led to the incorporation of Amarillo Opera with Dr. Merrill and Catherine Winsett, H.R. and Thelma Fulton and Gibson as Founding Directors and Gibson as General Director, with complete administrative and Artistic responsibility for the company
Country: United States
Contact: General and Artistic Director David O'Dell
Email: david.odell@amarilloopera.orgassistant to Artistic Director Rhanda Luna
Email: rhanda.luna@amarilloopera.org
Social Media: @amaopera www.facebook.com/amarilloopera
Venues: Amarillo Civic Centre Auditorium 2400

Amato Opera
Website: www.amoreopera.org
Email: info@amoreopera.org
Phone: 347 948 4588
Address: The Sheen Center, 18 Bleecker St, US
Information: The Amato Opera was an opera company located in the East Village neighborhood of the Manhattan borough of New York City. The company was produced by the husband and wife team of Anthony and Sally Amato and presented opera on a small scale with a reduced orchestra at low prices. Over its 61 years in existence, it encouraged and trained many young singers
Country: United States
Contact: Artistic Director Anthony Amato
Email: Executive Director Irene Freydel-Kim
Social Media: www.facebook.com/amoreopera
Venues: Residence Theater, 107 seats

American Musical Theater of San Jose
Email: amtsj@amtsj.org
Phone: 408 453 7123
Address: 1717 Technology Drive, US
Information: The American Musical Theatre of San Jose (AMTSJ), previously known as the San Jose Civic Light Opera (SJCLO), was a major professional non-profit musical theatre company in San Jose, California. It was founded in 1934 as the San Jose Light Opera Association. Prior to its demise in December 2008, it was the second largest theatre company in the Northern California
Country: United States
Contact: Director of communications & public affairs Steven Favreau
Email: Artistic Director Tim Bair President & Executive Producer
Michael Miller
Venues: San Jose Center for the Performing Arts 2540

American-International Lyric Theatre Inc.
Email: PPress322@aol.com
Phone: 212 662 3468
Address:
322 West Duke Ellingotn Boulevard, US
Information: American-International Lyric Theatre Inc. is a touring company; opera, operetta & dance shows for small or large audiences
Country: United States
Contact: Managing Director Paulette Singer
Email: Artistic Director Russell Miller
Venues: venues up to 25000

Anchorage Opera
Website: www.anchorageopera.org
Email: info@anchorageopera.org
Phone: 907 279 2557
Address: 1507 Spar Avenue, US
Information: Anchorage Opera is the center of Artistic creation, innovation and education through the presentation of opera and related events encouraging public collaboration and community engagement for the people of the State of Alaska. Founded by opera singer Marita Farrell and philanthropist Evangeline Atwood, Anchorage Opera began with the trailblazing work of this dynamic duo. The pair quickly secured financing, performers, and the Anchorage Symphony as their orchestra to produce a series of cameo performances, including Rigoletto and Faust. The company also recruited Willard Straight to direct and lead many full-length operas, including Carmen, Cosi Fan Tutti, and The Elixir of Love
Country: United States
Contact: General Manager Reed Smith
Email: treasurer Kathleen Cronen
Social Media: @AnchorageOpera www.facebook.com/AnchorageOpera
Venues: Discovery Theater 780, Atwood Theatre 2000

Annapolis Opera Inc
Website: www.annapolisopera.org
Email: admin@annapolisopera.org
Phone: 410 267 8135
Address: 801 Chase Street, Suite 304A, US
Information: Annapolis Opera has provided professionally staged operas and concerts for the mid-Atlantic region for 44 years. The mission is to support development of young professionals and to offer affordable operatic performances to local community
Country: United States
Contact: Artistic Director Ronald Gretz
Email: rjgretz@verizon.netAdministrative Assistant Victoria Brown
Email: admin@annapolisopera.orgGeneral Director Kathy Swekel
Email: GeneralDirector@annapolisopera.org
Social Media: www.facebook.com/pages/Annapolis-Opera-Inc/149923060209
Venues: Maryland Hall for the Creative Arts, 850.

Arizona Opera
Website: www.azopera.org
Email: info@azopera.com
Phone: 602 266 7464
Address: 1636 N. Central Ave., US
Information: Arizona Opera, now in its 44th Season, produces fully-staged operas, concerts, and collaborative programs throughout the state of Arizona each season. They are among only a handful of companies in the United States that regularly performs in more than one city. Arizona Opera elevates the transformative power of storytelling through music—cultivating community and strengthening a state and people as adventurous and diverse as the place they call home
Country: United States
Contact: General Director Ryan Taylor
Social Media: @azopera www.facebook.com/azopera
Venues: Phoenix Symphony Hall 2528, Tucson Convention Center Music Hall 2277, Orpheum, Gammag Auditorium Phoenix 3300.

Ash Lawn Opera
Website: www.ashlawnopera.org
Email: info@ashlawnopera.org
Phone: 434 293 4500
Address: PO Box 2498, US
Information: Ash Lawn Opera mission is to produce high quality opera and musicals at affordable prices, to provide training opportunities and experience for Young Artists and Interns, to provide educational nourishment for all sectors of the community, and to enrich the cultural vitality and quality of life in Virginia
Country: United States
Contact: President, board of Directors Anne L. Fife
Email: General Director Michelle Krisel
Social Media: @AshLawnOpera www.facebook.com/AshLawnOpera
Venues: The Paramount; 1, 100

Atlanta Opera
Website: www.atlantaopera.org
Email: info@atlantaopera.org
Phone:
404 881 8801
Address: 1575 Northside Drive, Blg 300, suite 350, US
Information: Founded in 1979, The Atlanta Opera is one of the finest regional opera companies in the United States producing mainstage opera productions and excellent arts education programs for all ages

Country: United States
Contact: General and Artistic Director Tomer Zvulun
Email: tzvulun@atlantaopera.org
Social Media: @TheAtlantaOpera www.facebook.com/TheAtlantaOpera
Cobb Energy Performing Arts Centre (see entry in Presenters & Venues)

Augusta Opera
Website: www.theaugustaopera.com/site/
Email: Director@augustaopera.com
Phone: 706 826 4710
Address: PO Box 240, US
Information: The mission of the Augusta Opera is to present opera and music theatre productions of the highest possible standards while encouraging growth of the art form through its educational programs and outreach. The Augusta Opera strives to create productions of the highest Artistic quality bringing together nationally recognised professionals, rising young professional artists, and talented youth and adults from the community. Through this unique collaboration of artists of all levels, The Augusta Opera enhances our community's quality of life and provides a platform for Artistic development for both local and national professionals
Country: United States
Contact: Managing Director Les Reagan
Email: Artistic Director Mark Flint
Email: President Dennis Sodomka
Venues: Imperial Theatre Augusta 820, St Pauls Church 750

Austin Lyric Opera
Website: www.austinlyricopera.org
Email: frontdesk@austinlyricopera.org
Phone: 512 472 5992
Address: 3009 Industrial Terrace, Suite 100, US
Information: the mission of Austin Opera is to produce operatic performances and educational programs that meet and preserve the highest standards of Artistic excellence that culturally enrich the lives of Texans. Originally founded in May 1986 as Austin Lyric Opera, the city's first professional opera company, Austin Opera has become a cultural touchstone for the fine arts community in the Central Texas region and has gained national acclaim as a Producer of great opera
Country: United States
Contact: General Director Joseph Specter
Email: jspecter@austinlyricopera.orgArtistic Director Richard Buckley
Email: rbuckely@austinlyricopera.org
Social Media: @AustinOpera www.facebook.com/Austin-LyricOpera
Venues: Bass Concert Hall University of Texas, City Coliseum 2860

Baltimore Opera Company
Website: www.baltimoreopera.com
Email: info@baltimoreopera.com
Phone: 410 625 6474
Address: 110 West Mount Royal Avenue, Suite 306, US
Information: The Baltimore Opera Company closed its doors in 2009, leaving Baltimore without a grand opera company. Since their demise, they are delighted that Lyric Opera Baltimore has launched and shows great promise for grand opera in Baltimore. Baltimore Concert Opera, an organization now entering its 6th year, continues to flourish and provide Baltimore with an entirely new way to experience opera. Baltimore is also surrounded by prominent companies in Washington, DC and Delaware
Country: United States
Contact: Artistic administrator Jim Harp
Email: General Director Michael Harrison
Social Media: @BaltimoreOpera www.facebook.com/pages/THE-BALTIMORE-OPERA-
Venues: Lyric Opera House 2400

Berkeley Opera
Website: www.westedgeopera.org
Email: info@westedgeopera.org
Phone: 510 841 1903
Address: 1700 Shattuck Avenue, Suite 312, US
Information: West Edge Opera believes that everyone, regardless of age, circumstance or background, can discover the excitement and relevance of opera in their lives. They look at the art form through a new lens, re-imagining tradition to connect with a modern audience. They create innovative experiences of the highest quality that respect the original spirit of the work
Country: United States
Contact: Artistic Director Mark Streshinsky
Email: musical Director Jonathan Khuner
Social Media: @westedgeopera www.facebook.com/westedgeopera
Venues: Julia Morgan Theater 350

Berkshire Opera Company
Website: www.berkshireopera.org

Email:
info@berkshireopera.org
Phone:
413 442 5995
Address: 297 North Street, US
Information: The mission of the BOC is to help bring world class professional opera to the Berkshires and especially to people who have never been exposed to it before. Recently, corporate sponsors helped bring the BOC to a number of area schools to expose kids to this exciting music. Founder Rex Hearn singlemindedly created this organization, trying duplicate the summer festivals of his native Great Britain
Country: United States
Contact: music Director Kathleen Kelly
Email: General Manager Marianne Juby
Email: conductor laureate Joel Revzen
Venues: Koussevitzky Arts Center, Berkshire Community College 510

Boheme Opera
Website: www.bohemeopera.com
Email: jrspucc@gmail.com
Phone: 609 581 9553
Address: PO Box 4157, US
Information: Boheme Opera was conceived and founded in 1981 as a musicians' guild in an unassuming parking lot of Trenton's St. Joachim's Church (today one of the two churches that comprises Our Lady of the Angels Parish, along with Immaculate Conception Church). The Company's evolution into a professional production company took place over the course of eight years, culminating in 1989 with its inaugural main stage season featuring fully staged productions of Verdi's La Traviata and Puccini's Tosca
Country: United States
Contact: Artistic Director Joseph R Pucciatti
Venues: Patriots Theater War Memorial 1800

Boston Lyric Opera
Website: www.blo.org
Email: boxoffice@blo.org
Phone: 617 542 4912
Address: 11 Avenue de Lafayette, US
Information: Boston Lyric Opera is the largest opera company in all of New England. Now in its 39th season, BLO celebrates the art of the voice through its mission of building curiosity, enthusiasm and support for opera by creating musically and theatrically compelling productions, events, and educational resources for the Boston community and beyond
Country: United States
Social Media: @BostLyricOpera www.facebook.com/BostonLyricOpera
Annual productions: 3
Venues: Tremont Street Boston 1522

Brooklyn Academy of Music (BAM)
Website: www.bam.org
Email: info@bam.org
Phone: 718 636 4123
Address: 30 Lafayette Avenue, US
Information:
Country: United States
Social Media: @BAM_Brooklyn www.facebook.com/BAMstage
Venues: Howard Gilman Opera House 2100, The BAM Harvey Lichtenstein Theatre 890, BAM Rose Cinema 750, BAM Cafe 250

Casa Italiana Opera Company
Website: www.casaitaliana.org
Email: mario@casaitaliana.org
Phone: 818 554 1291
Address: 1051 North Broadway, US
Information:
Country: United States
Contact: General Director and founder Mario E Leonetti
Email: Artistic Director Janet DeMay
Venues: Casa Italiana Theatre 250-500

Central City Opera House Association
Website: www.centralcityopera.org
Email: boxoffice@centralcityopera.org
Address: 400 S. Colorado Blvd., Suite 530, US
Information: see also Festivals
Country: United States
Contact: General/Artistic Director Pelham G Pearce
Email: Artistic Director emeritus John Moriarty
Email: Director of Marketing Valerie Hamlin Director of education & outreach
 Deborah Morrow
Email: Director of development Barbera Zarlengo
Email: music Director John Baril
Venues: Central City Opera House 550

Charleston Chamber Opera
Website:
www.charlestonchamberopera.com
Email:
info@charlestonchamberopera.com
Phone: 917 674 7277
Address: PO Box 12988, US
Country: United States

Contact: Executive Director Lara Wilson
Email: lara@charlestonchamberopera.comArtistic Director Patrice Tiedemann
Email: Patrice@charlestoncahamberopera.comDirector of development Thomas Trotter

Chautauqua Opera
Website: opera.ciweb.org
Email: Info@chautopera.org
Phone: 716 357 6286
Address: 412 West 42nd Street, Suite 4E4, US
Country: United States
Contact: Artistic/General Director Jay Lesenger
Email: Admin@chautopera.orgcompany Manager Gabriel Estin
Email: companyManager@chautopera.org
Social Media: www.facebook.com/chautopera

Chicago Opera Theater
Website: www.chicagooperatheater.org
Email: Marketingintern@chicagooperatheater.org
Phone: 312 704 8414
Address: 70 East Lake Street, Suite 815, US
Information: box office: 312-704-8414
Country: United States
Social Media: @ChicagoOpera https:// www.facebook.com/ChicagoOperaTheater?ref=hl
 Joan W & Irving B Harris Theatre for Music & Dance in Millennium Park, 1500

Cincinnati Opera Association
Website: www.cincinnatiopera.org
Email: info@cincinnatiopera.org
Phone: 513 768 5500
Address: 1243 Elm Street, US
Information:
Country: United States
Contact: Artistic Director Evans Mirageas
Email: Director of institutional advancement Rick Pender
Email: General Director/CEO Patricia K Beggs
Email: Director of communications Katie Syroney
Email: Director of Marketing and audience development Christopher Milligan
Venues: Music Hall 3417

Connecticut Grand Opera & Orchestra
Phone: 203 327 2867
Address: 15 Bank St, US
Information:
Country: United States
Social Media: www.facebook.com/pages/Connecticut-Grand-Opera-Orchestra/117525438273723
Venues: Palace Theatre Stamford 1580

Connecticut Opera
Website: www.connecticutopera.org
Email: info@connecticutopera.org
Phone: 860 527 0713
Address: 226 Farmington Avenue, US
Information:
Country: United States
Contact: Managing Director Linda Jackson
Email: Artistic Director Willie A Waters
Venues: The Bushnell 2740

Dallas Opera
Website: www.dallasopera.org
Email: info@dallasopera.org
Phone: 214 443 1043
Address: Winspear Opera House, 2403 Flora Street, Suite 500, US
Information: A fifty-three year tradition of Artistic excellence the Dallas Opera performs in the Winspear Opera House (see Venues)
Country: United States
Contact: General Director and CEO Keith Cerny
Email: music Director Emmanuel Villaume
Email: Artistic Director Jonathan Pell
Social Media: @thedallasopera www.facebook.com/dallasopera
Venues: Winspear Opera House 2, 200

Dan Froot
Website: www.danfroot.com
Email: danfroot@me.com
Phone: 310 766 4942
Address: 11405 Biona Drive, US
Information:
Country: United States
Contact: Artistic Director Dan Froot
Social Media: danfroot https:// www.facebook.com/pages/Whos-Hungry-Santa-Monica/170122700210

Dayton Opera
Website: www.daytonopera.org
Email: info@daytonopera.org
Phone: 937 228 0662
Address: 138 North Main Street, US
Information:
Country: United States
Contact: Marketing Director Shannon McClure
Email: General and Artistic Director Thomas Bankston
Venues: Schuster Performing Arts Center 2300

Des Moines Metro Opera

Website:
www.dmmo.org
Email:
dmmo@dmmo.org
Address: 106 West Boston Avenue, US
Information: number of singers approx 70; size of orchestra approx 50; three operas performed in repertory in one of America's most intimate theatres
Country: United States
Contact: Executive Director Thomas Smith
Email: business Manager Arlys Keller
Email: Artistic Director Robert L Larsen
Email: box office Manager Dennis Hendrikson Marketing & public relations Director
 Elizabeth Smith
Email: art Director Kimberly Udrovish
Email: production Director James Lile
Email: Artistic administrator Michael Egel
Email: development Director Robert Montana
Venues: Blank Performing Arts Center 488, Civic Center of Greater Des Moines 2750

Dicapo Opera Theatre
Website: www.dicapo.com
Email: dotproduction@aol.com
Phone: 121 228 89438
Address: 184 East 76th Street, US
Information: represented by: Vincent & Farrell Associates Inc., Tel: 212-541 7666. Young artists programme, by audition only age approx 20+. Childrens class age – 16. Seasonal programme also, for young artists to perform. subtitles available.
Country: United States
Contact: General Director Michael Capasso
Email: Artistic Director Diane Martindale
Touring: tour each production in New England area
Venues: up to a capacity of 204

Encompass New Opera Theatre
Website: www.encompassopera.org
Email: encompassopera@yahoo.com
Phone: 718 398 4675
Address: 138 South Oxford Street, Suite 1A, Brooklyn, , US
Information: create and develop new music theatre and contemporary opera
Country: United States
Contact: musical Director Mara Waldman
Email: Artistic Director Nancy Rhodes
Venues: Tribeca Performing Arts Center 300, Theatre Row 99

Eugene Opera
Website: www.eugeneopera.com
Phone: 541 485 3985
Address: PO Box 11200, US
Information:
Country: United States
Contact: Artistic Director Robert Ashens
Email: production Manager Jim Bradford
Email: Director of development Jaclyn LaRue
Venues: Hult Center for the Performing Arts 2400

Fargo-Moorhead Opera
Website: fmopera.org
Email: Director@fmopera.org
Phone: 701 239 4558
Address: Black Building – Skyway Level, 114 Broadway, Suite S1, US
Information:
Country: United States
Contact: office Manager Kay Weiss
Email: General Director David Hamilton
Venues: Festival Concert Hall, Reineke Fine Arts Center, N Dakota S.U. 980, Fargo Theatre 850

FBN Opera
Website: www.cmfa.net
Email: cmfa5678@aol.com
Phone: 803 771 6303
Address: 914 Pulaski St, US
Information:
Country: United States
Contact: Executive Director John Whitehead
Email: Artistic Director Ellen Schlaeffer
Venues: Township 3100, Artspace 200, Keenan Theatre 500

Festival Opera
Website: www.festivalopera.com
Email: info@festivalopera.com
Phone: 925 944 9610
Address: 675 Ygnacio Valley Road, Suite B215, US
Information:
Country: United States
Contact: Executive Director Sara Nealy Artistic & music Director
 Michael Morgan
Email: Chair James Bell
Venues: Hofmann Theater, Dean Lesher Regional Centre for the Arts 800

Florentine Opera Company
Website: www.florentineopera.org

Email: info@florentineopera.org
Phone: 414 291 5700
Address: 700 North Water Street, Suite 950, US
Information: children's productions; 4th oldest opera company in the USA
Country: United States
Contact: Director of finance Catherine Kiekhofer pr & Marketing Director
Amy Erato
Email: General Director William Florescu
Email: Director of production Noel Stollmack
Email: principal conductor and Artistic advisor Joseph Rescigno
Email: development Director Cindy Hosale
Venues: Uihlein Hall-Marcus Center for the Performing Arts

Florida Grand Opera
Website: www.fgo.org
Email: info@fgo.org
Phone: 305 854 1643
Address: Doral Center, 8390 NW 25th Street, US
Information:
Country: United States
Contact: Director for Marketing & communication Brendan Glynn
Email: music Director Ramon Tebar General Director & CEO
Susan T Danis
Email: Managing Director/Director of production Kevin Mynatt
Venues: Adrienne Arsht Center for the Performing Arts of Miami-Dade County/ Ziff Ballet Opera House

Fullerton Civic Light Opera
Website: www.fclo.com
Phone: 714 879 9761
Address: FCLO Music Theatre Administrative Offices, 218 W. Commonwealth, US
Information: orchestra size 20; performing musical comedy and Broadway musicals only (no opera). Third largest supplier of scenery and costumes in the US
Country: United States
Contact: Director of communications Marilyn Gianetti
Email: Producer Griff Duncan
Email: Artistic Director Jan Duncan
Social Media: www.facebook.com/fclomusictheatre
Venues: Plummer Auditorium 1300

Glimmerglass Opera
Website: www.glimmerglass.org
Email: info@glimmerglass.org
Phone: 607 547 0700
Address: PO Box 191, 7300 State Highway 80, US
Information:
Country: United States
Contact: Artistic Director Francesca Zambello
Email: fzambello@glimmerglass.orgManaging Director Linda Jackson
Email: ljackson@glimmerglass.org
Social Media: www.facebook.com/glimmerglassfestival
Venues: Alice Busch Opera Theatre

Goodspeed Musicals
Website: www.goodspeed.org
Email: info@goodspeed.org
Phone: 860 873 8664
Address: PO Box A, 6 Main Street, US
Information: three productions a year at The Goodspeed plus two-three at The Terris Theatre, home for new musicals. 22 singers per production; 8 members of orchestra per production, 10-13 weeks, 8 shows per week.
Country: United States
Contact: Director of development Nancy Altschuler
Email: naltschuler@goodspeed.orgDirector of finance William F. Nivison
Email: wnivison@goodspeed.orgGeneral Manager Rachel Tischler
Email: rtischler@goodspeed.orgproduction Manager Erica Gilroy
Email: egilroy@goodspeed.orgExecutive Director Michael Gennaro
Email: mgennaro@goodspeed.orgDirector of Marketing and public relations Dan McMahon
Email: dmcmahon@goodspeed.orgpublic relations Manager Elisa Hale
Email: ehale@goodspeed.org
Social Media: @goodspeedmuscl https:// www.facebook.com/GoodspeedMusicals
Venues: Goodspeed Opera House 398, The Norma Terris Theatre 200

Greensboro Opera Company
Website: www.greensboroopera.org
Email: opera2@bellsouth.net
Phone: 336 273 9472
Address: 1834 Pembroke Road 200 north davie street box 17, suite 315, US
Information: postal address: PO Box 29031, Greensboro NC 27429-9031.
Country: United States
Contact: Artistic Director t.b.a.
Email: General Director valery ryzkin
Email: Executive Director/ company Manager Elena De

Ngelis
Email: Marketing/development Director t.b.a
Venues: War Memorial Auditorium 2400

Guild Opera Company
Website: www.guildopera.org
Email: info@guildopera.org
Phone: 323 463 6593
Address: P.O. Box 4582, US
Information: most performances are for schoolchildren: runs in-school residency programs
Country: United States
Contact: Artistic Director Gabriel R. Pazos
Social Media: www.facebook.com/pages/Guild-Opera-Company/267051430010499
Venues: Thousand Oaks Performing Arts Center, Marsee Auditorium, Glendale Concert Auditorium up to 2000, various elementary schools within the LA, Orange and Ventura counties

Hawaii Opera Theatre
Website: www.hawaiiopera.org
Email: hotopera@hawaiiopera.org
Phone: 808 596 7372
Address: 848 S. Beretania St., Suite 301, US
Information: Hawaii Opera theatre's education programs reach over 13, 000 children and adults annually; programs include mainstage performances, touring programs, lecture series and intern programs; Marketing: La Reaux Communications
Country: United States
Contact: General & Artistic Director
Henry G Akina
Email: henry_akina@hawaiiopera.orghead of music Beebe Freitas
Email: b_freitas@hawaiiopera.orgExecutive Director Simon Crookall
Email: s_crookall@hawaiiopera.org
Social Media: @hawaiiopera www.facebook.com/HawaiiOpera
Venues: Neal Blaisdell Concert Hall 2017

Houston Grand Opera Studio
Website: www.houstongrandopera.org
Email: christine@elmorepr.com
Phone: 713 546 0200
Address: 510 Preston street, US
Information: the company is a subsidiary of the Houston Grand Opera Association, Inc.; international training programme for young artists with potential for major careers in the opera and music theatre profession; annual auditions November; no. of singers: 8
Country: United States
Contact: Press enquiries Christine Cantrell
Email: christine@elmorepr.com
Lillie & Roy Cullen Theatre 1063

Hub City Players
Website: hubcityplayers.com
Email: mlspin@gmail.com
Phone: 601 329 1104
Address: 81 Stones Throw Dr., Hattiesburg, MS 39402
Information: Winner of the 2018-19 American Prize in Musical Theatre, The Hub City Players have enjoyed success after success including intimate cabarets to fully-staged productions. Professional singers, actors, and dancers for regional performance opportunities.

Country: United States
Contact: Founding Director Mike Lopinto
Email: mlspin@gmail.comFounding Music Director Tammy Mansfield
Email: tammymansfield@bellsouth.net
Social Media: https:// www.facebook.com/HubCityPlayersHattiesburg https:// www.instagram.com/hubcityplayers/
Annual performances: 6-10
Annual productions: 0-5

Indianapolis Opera
Website: www.indyopera.org
Email: ticket@indyopera.org
Phone: 317 283 3531
Address: 250 East 38th Street, 4011 North Pennsylvania Street, US
Information:
Country: United States
Contact: Executive Director John Pickett
Email: Artistic Director Jim Caraher
Email: Artistic administrator Stephen Goldberg
Email: info@indyopera.orgeducation Director Patty Harvey
Venues: Clowes Memorial Hall of Butler University 2100

Intermountain Opera Association
Website: www.operabozeman.org
Email: ioaopera@montana.com
Phone: 406 587 2889
Address: PO Box 37, US
Information:

Country: United States
Contact: Artistic Director Linda Curtis
Email: office Manager Melissa Todd
Venues: Wilson Auditorium 1050

Kentucky Opera
Website: www.kyopera.org
Email: info@kyopera.org
Phone: 502 584 4500
Address: 323 West Broadway, , Suite 601, US
Country: United States
Contact: General Director David Roth
Email: david_roth@kyopera.orgDirector of development Frances Skolnick
Email: frances_skolnick@kyopera.orgDirector of production Chuck Schmidt
Email: chuck_schmidt@kyopera.org
Social Media: www.facebook.com/KentuckyOpera
Venues: Kentucky Center for the Arts-Whitney Hall 2400

Knoxville Opera Company
Website: www.knoxvilleopera.com
Email: hello@knoxvilleopera.com
Address: 612 East Depot Avenue, US
Information: no. of singers: 50; size of orchestra: 48; 2007-08 is 30th anniversary season
Country: United States
Contact: Executive Director and conductor Brian Salesky
Email: bSalesky@KnoxvilleOpera.comfinance Manager Marie Butler
Email: mbutler@KnoxvilleOpera.comproduction Manager/chorus master Don Townsend
Email: dtownsend@KnoxvilleOpera.comDirector of Marketing and public relations Michael Torano
Email: mtorano@KnoxvilleOpera.com
Social Media: @KnoxvilleOpera
Venues: Knoxville Civic Auditorium 2400, Tennessee Theatre 1650

La Gran Scena Opera Company
Website: www.granscena.org
Email: irasiff@aol.com
Phone: 212 460 9124
Address: 211 E. 11 St, No 9, US
Information:
Country: United States
Contact: art Director/vocal coaching Ira Siff
Venues: various internationally seating 500 up to 2000

Lake George Opera Festival (2)
Website: www.lakegeorgeopera.org
Email: lgopera@aol.com
Phone: 518 584 6018
Address: 480 Broadway, Suite 336, US
Information:
Country: United States
Contact: General Director t.b.a.
Venues: The Spa Little Theatre (Saratoga Springs)

Light Opera Works
Website: www.light-opera-works.org
Email: info@light-opera-works.org
Phone: 847 869 6300
Address: 927 Noyes Street, US
Information:
Country: United States
Contact: Artistic Director Rudy Hogenmiller
Email: General Manager Bridget McDonough
Venues: Cahn Auditorium, Evanston 1000, YMCA Childcare Center Auditorium 263

Long Beach Opera
Website: www.longbeachopera.org
Email: info@longbeachopera.org
Phone: 562 432 5934
Address: 507 Pacific Ave, US
Information:
Country: United States
Contact: General Director Andreas Mitisek
Email: Director of development Bill Eisentraut
Venues: Center Theater, Long Beach CA – Seating capacity – 825; Carpenter Center , Long Beach CA 1450 (seating capacity)

Los Angeles Opera
Website: www.laopera.com
Email: wehelpyou@laopera.com
Phone: 213 972 7219
Address: Dorothy Chandler Pavilion, 135 North Grand Avenue, US
Information: daytime customer service line: 213-972 8001
Country: United States
Contact: chief Executive officer Stephen D. Rountree
Email: General Director Plácido Domingo
Email: music Director James Conlon
Venues: Dorothy Chandler Pavilion 3054

Lyric Opera of Chicago
Website: www.lyricopera.org
Phone: 312 332 2244
Address: 20 N. Wacker Drive, US
Information:
Country: United States

Contact: Director of finance and admin Richard Dowsek
Email: Press relations coordinator Emily Lange
Email: General Director William Mason
Email: Artistic administrator Andreas Melinat
Email: Director of operations Nick Martin
Email: education Director Jean Kellogg
Email: music Director Andrew Davis
Email: Director of Marketing and communications Susan Mathieson Mayer
Email: Director of developement Mary Selander
Venues: Civic Opera House 3563

Lyric Opera of Kansas City
Website: www.kcopera.org
Email: whatsnew@ksopera.org
Phone: 816 471 4933
Address: 1029 Central, US
Information: number of singers: over 100 per season; size of Orchestra: maximum 63
Country: United States
Contact: General Director Evan R. Luskin
Email: Director of Marketing and public relations Virginia Long
Email: Artistic Director Ward Holmquist
Email: Director of production Tracy Davis
Email: Director of development Michelle LaPointe
Email: Director of education Paula Winans
Venues: Lyric Theatre 1600

Lyric Opera San Diego
Website: www.lyricoperasandiego.com
Email: comicop@hotmail.com
Phone: 619 231 5714
Address: 2691 university avenue suite 1, US
Information: specifically dedicated to regional southern California Singers
Country: United States
Contact: General Director Leon Natker
Email: Artistic Director J Sherwood Montgomery
Email: public relations Stephanie Thompson
Venues: North Park Theatre The Stephen and Mary Birch North Park Theatre Complex 800

Lyric Theatre of Oklahoma, Inc.
Website: www.lyrictheatreokc.com
Email: amy@lyrictheatreokc.com
Phone: 405 524 9310
Address: 1727 NW 16th St., US
Information:
Country: United States
Contact: Artistic Director Nick Demos
Email: Executive Director Paula Stover
Venues: Civic Center Music Hall 2500

Madison Opera
Website: www.madisonopera.org
Email: info@madisonopera.org
Phone: 608 238 8085
Address: 3414 Monroe Street, US
Information: Chorus: 50-80; principals as required; size of orchestra 70
Country: United States
Contact: General Director Allan Naplan
Email: Artistic Director John DeMain
Venues: Overture Hall 2200

Magic Circle Opera Repertory Ensemble Inc
Email: contact@magiccircleopera.org, www.magiccircleopera.org
Phone: 212 724 2398
Address: 200 West 70th St, Suite 6C, US
Information: all chamber opera 25 permanent members; commissions new work
Country: United States
Contact: coach Roger Malouf
Email: Executive Director Stephanie Weems
Email: dance and movement Liliana Morales
Email: Artistic Director/conductor/stage Director Ray Evans Harrell
Venues: Merkin Hall, 450;

Maine Grand Opera
Website: www.mainegrandopera.org
Phone: 123 723 01200
Address: PO Box 656, US
Information:
Country: United States
Contact: stage Director Beumont Glass
Email: Artistic Director Janna Hymes-Bianchi
Venues: Grand Auditorium 500, Hammond Hall 200

Metro Lyric Opera
Website: www.metrolyricopera.org
Phone: 732 531 2378
Address: 40 Ocean Avenue, US
Information: workshops and educational programmes
Country: United States
Contact: General & Artistic Director
Era M Tognoli
Venues: Paramount Theatre 1600

Metropolitan Opera
Website: www.metoperafamily.org
Email: sbillinghurst@metopera.org

Phone: 212 799 3100
Address: Lincoln Center, US
Information:
Country: United States
Contact: General Manager Peter Gelb
Email: principal conductor Fabio Luisi
Email: music Director James Levine
Email: Artistic Manager Sarah Billinghurst
Email: sbillinghurst@metopera.org
Social Media: @MetOpera https:// www.facebook.com/MetOpera
Venues: Metropolitan Opera House 3995

Michigan Opera Theatre
Website: www.michiganopera.org
Email: rjohnson@motopera.org (communications) laura@motopera.org
Phone: 313 961 3500
Address: 1526 Broadway, US
Information:
Country: United States
Contact: Director of production David Osborne
Email: Marketing Manager Michael Hauser
Email: General Director/Artistic Director David DiChiera
Email: Director of communications Laura Nealssohn
Email: Director of community programs Karen DiChiera
Email: assistant Artistic Director Roberto Mauro
Email: vice President/chief financial officer John Eckstrom
Detroit Opera House 2729; Ford Center for Arts & Learning

Minnesota Opera
Website: www.mnopera.org
Email: mnop@mnopera.org
Phone: 612 333 2700
Address: 620 North First Street, US
Information: In 2000, Artistic Director Dale Johnson articulated his Artistic philosophy, inspired by the early 19th-century Italian Bel Canto era and its ideals. Bel Canto, literally "beautiful singing," emphasizes intense emotional exPression supported by exquisite technique. As one manifestation of its philosophy, Minnesota Opera committed to producing one work from the early 19th-century Bel Canto period each season from 2000 through 2012, attracting luminary singers like Bruce Ford, Vivica Genaux, Brenda Harris and Sumi Jo to its stage. Minnesota Opera quickly became a destination for audiences and artists interested in Bel Canto-period operas. Today, regardless of what opera is on Minnesota Opera's stage, these Bel Canto values inform every aspect of the company's programs, from repertoire selection and visual design to casting and artist training
Country: United States
Contact: General Director Nina Archabal
Email: Artistic Director Dale Johnson Director of Marketing & communications
Kyle Clausen
Email: music Director Michael Christie
Venues: Ordway Centre for the Performing Arts

Mississippi Opera Association Inc
Website: www.msopera.org
Email: info@msopera.org
Phone: 601 960 2300
Address: PO Box 1551, US
Information:
Country: United States
Contact: interim Artistic Director Edward Dacus
Venues: Thalia Mara Hall 2360, others 200-1000

Mobile Opera, Inc.
Website: www.mobileopera.org
Email: info@mobileopera.org
Phone: 251 432 6772
Address: 257 Dauphin Street, US
Information: enrich the quality of life for all adults and children in diverse communities through the ultimate theatre experience of music as an exPression of the soul
Country: United States
Contact: General Director Scott Wright
Email: scottwright@mobileopera.org
Annual performances: 4
Annual productions: 2
Venues: Mobile Civic Center Theater 1950

Music Theatre of Wichita, Inc.
Website: www.musictheatreofwichita.org
Email: office@musictheatreofwichita.org
Phone: 316 265 3253
Address: 225 W. Douglas, Suite 202, US
Information: summer theatre, inhouse productions only.
Country: United States
Contact: producing Director Wayne Bryan
Email: patron services Director Bart Flickinger
Email: administrative Director David Frain
Venues: Century II Concert Hall 2141

Music-Theatre Group
Website: www.musictheatregroup.org
Email: diane@musictheatregroup.org
Phone: 718 797 1145
Address: 10 Jay Street, Suite 900, Brooklyn, US
Information: all original work commissioned by the

theatre
Country: United States
Contact: Chair Jeanie Chapin,
Email: President Diane Wondisford
Email: Treasurer Steven L. Krueger,

Musical Theatre Southwest
Website: www.musicaltheatresw.com
Email: info@musicaltheatresw.com
Phone: 505 265 9119
Address: 6320-B Domingo NE 87108, PO Box 81052, US
Information: non-profit organisation, volunteer operated, we have a large stock of costumes, props and backdrops from over 50 ears of musical theatre for rent.
Country: United States
Contact: Artistic Director working on voluntary basis
Venues: African American Performing Arts Centre 300

Nashville Opera Association
Website: www.nashvilleopera.org
Email: info@nashvilleopera.org
Phone: 615 832 5242
Address: Noah Liff Opera Center, 3622 Redmon Street, US
Information:
Country: United States
Social Media: @nashvilleopera www.facebook.com/nashvilleopera
Venues: Noah Liff Opera Center

Nautilus Music – Theater
Website: www.nautilusmusictheater.org
Email: ben@nautilusmusictheater.org
Phone: 651 298 9913
Address: 308 Prince Street, Suite 250, US
Information: monthly works-in-progress performance series Rough Cuts. Substantial workshop and professional development activity
Country: United States
Contact: Artistic Director Ben Krywosz
Venues: Southern Theater 150, various others up to 500

Nevada Opera Association
Website: www.nevadaopera.org
Email: info@nevadaopera.org
Phone: 775 786 4046
Address: 100 South Virginia Street, Pioneer Center for the, Performing Arts, US
Information: number of singers 65; size of orchestra 40; local educational outreach programs throughout Nevada
Country: United States
Contact: book keeper Janet Brown
Email: Artistic Director Michael Borowitz
Email: development Director Elisa Maser
Email: Executive Director William Russell
Venues: Pioneer Center for the Performing Arts 1500

Nevada Opera Theater
Phone: 702 699 9775
Address: 4080 Paradise Rd, Suite 15, US
Information:
Country: United States
Contact: General Director Eileen Hayes

New England Lyric Operetta
Phone: 203 655 0566
Address: 84 W. Park Place, US
Information:
Country: United States
Contact: Artistic Director William H Edgerton
Venues: Rich Forum 700

New Jersey State Opera
Website: www.njstateopera.org
Email: info@njstateopera.org
Phone: 973 928 5650
Address: 199 Scoles Avenue, US
Country: United States
Contact: Artistic Director Jason Tramm
Email: JTramm@njstateopera.org
Venues: New Jersey Performing Arts Centre 2700

New Jersey State Opera
Website: www.njstateopera.org
Email: info@njstateopera.org
Phone: 973 928 5650
Address: 199 Scoles Avenue, US
Information:
Country: United States
Contact: Artistic Director Jason Tramm
Email: JTramm@njstateopera.org
Venues: New Jersey Performing Arts Centre 2700

New Orleans Opera Association
Website: www.neworleansopera.org
Email: tcomfort@neworleansopera.org
Phone: 504 529 2278
Address: 616 Girod Street, Suite 200, US
Information: educational outreach is MetroPelican Opera; tours Louisiana and southern states; plays to 20,000 children per season
Country: United States
Contact: General and Artistic Director Robert Lyall
Email: robertlyall@neworleansopera.orgExecutive Director Timothy Todd Simmons

Email: tsimmons@neworleansopera.org
Venues: Mahalia Jackson Theatre of the Performing Arts 2317

New York City Opera
Website: www.nycopera.com
Email: Marketing@nycopera.com
Phone: 212 870 560 0557
Address: New York State Theater, 20 Lincoln Center Plaza, US
Information:
Country: United States
Contact: Executive Director Jane M. Gullong
Email: Associate producing Artistic Director General and Robin Thompson
Email: General and Artistic Director Gerard Mortier full-time from Se Director of Press & pr
Susan Woelzl
Email: Director of development Jennifer Zaslow Director of planning & Marketing
Claudia Keenan Hough
Email: Marketing assistant Jamie Morris
Email: music Director/maestro George Manahan

New York Gilbert & Sullivan Players Inc.
Website: www.nygasp.org
Email: info@nygasp.org
Phone: 212 769 1000
Address: 302 W 91 St, US
Information:
Country: United States
Contact: Artistic Director Albert Bergeret
Social Media: NYGASP https:// www.facebook.com/ nygasp
Touring: California, Mid-west, NH, NC, NJ, PA, NY
Venues: Symphony Space 700, City Center 2000

New York Grand Opera Company
Website: www.newyorkgrandopera.org
Email: info@nygrandopera.org
Phone: 212 245 8837
Address: 154 W. 57th Street, Suite 125, US
Information: summer opera productions fully-staged, performed free to the General public
Country: United States
Contact: Artistic Director Vincent La Selva
Email: Press representative Josephine Hemsing
Venues: Central Park Stage Summer 10000+, Brookdale Park at Montclair, NJ 10000+, Co-op City in the Bronx

Ohio Light Opera
Website: www.ohiolightopera.org
Email: ohiolightopera@wooster.edu
Phone: 330 263 2345
Address: College of Wooster, The Ohio Light Opera, 119 Beall Ave, US
Information:
Country: United States
Contact: Executive Director Laura Neill
Venues: Freedlander Theatre 394

Opera Birmingham
Website:
www.operabirmingham.org
Email: info@operabirmingham.org
Phone: 205 322 6737
Address: 3601 Sixth Avenue South, US
Country: United States
Contact: General Director John D. Jones
Social Media: @operabham www.facebook.com/Opera-aBirmingham
Venues: Samford University

Opera Brittenica
Website:
www.operabrittenica.com
Email: operabrittenica@gmail.com
Phone: 617 575 9610
Address: US
Information: devoted to exploring and performing the varied works of Benjamin Britten
Country: United States
Contact: Executive Director Joshua Collier
Email: Artistic Director David Sawicki
Email: Artistic advisor and Producer Aliana de la Guardia
Social Media: @OperaBrittenica https:// www.facebook.com/OperaBrittenica

Opera Carolina
Website: www.operacarolina.org
Email:
eclub@operacarolina.org
Phone: 704 332 7177
Address: 301 S. Tryon Street, Suite 1550, US
Information:
Country: United States
Contact: General Director and principal conductor James Meena
Email: james@operacarolina.orgDirector of client relations Natalija Martijan
Email: natalija@operacarolina.orgDirector of external relations Janet Dickinson
Email: janet@operacarolina.org

Social Media: @operacarolina www.facebook.com/operacarolina
Venues: North Carolina Blumethal Performing Arts Center, Belk Theater 2097

Opera Cleveland
Website: www.operacleveland.org
Email: info@operacleveland.org
Phone: 216 575 0903
Address: 1422 Euclid Ave, Ste 1052, US
Information: Opera Cleveland is the result of a merger between Cleveland Opera and Lyric Opera Cleveland
Country: United States
Contact: President of the board Peter Rubin
Email: Director of finance and Administration Shari Lash
Email: principal conductor Richard Buckley
Email: Executive Director Jeff Sodowsky
Email: Artistic Director Dean Williamson
Venues: State Theatre 3050

Opera Colorado
Website: www.operacolorado.org
Email: info@operacolorado.org
Phone: 303 778 1500
Address: 695 S. Colorado Boulevard, Suite 20, US
Information:
Country: United States
Contact: General Director Gregory Carpenter
Email: gcarpenter@operacolorado.orgBoard Member Michael Hughes
Email: mhughes@operacolorado.org Director of external affairs & Marketing
Camille Spaccavento
Email: cspaccavento@operacolorado.orgChairman of the Board of Director Mike Bock
Email: mike@petrie.com
Social Media: @OperaColorado www.facebook.com/operacolorado
Venues: Ellie Caulkins Opera House 2, 000

Opera Columbus
Website: www.operacolumbus.org
Email: info@operacolumbus.org
Phone: 614 461 8101
Address: 55 E. State Street, US
Information: produces, presents, and fosters high-quality opera in central Ohio, consistent with financially stable and sustainable operations
Country: United States
Contact: Managing Director & CEO
William Conner
Email: bconner@capa.comGeneral Manager Peggy Kriha Dye
Email: pkrihadye@operacolumbus.orgDirector of Marketing Kathy Karnap
Email: kkarnap@capa.com
Social Media: OperaColumbus www.facebook.com/OperaColumbus
Venues: Southern Theatre

Opera Company of Mid-Michigan (OCMM)
Website: www.ocmm.freeservers.com
Phone: 517 482 1431
Address: PO Box 13214, US
Information: OCMM coordinates with the Michigan State University School of Music
Country: United States
Contact: Artistic Director Terry Morris
Email: President Steve Zimmerman
Venues: Great Hall, Wharton Center 2500

Opera Company of Philadelphia
Website: www.operaphila.org
Email: tix@operaphilly.com
Phone: 215 893 3600
Address: 1420 Locust St, Suite 210, US
Information: offers educational outreach programmes and pre-opera lecture services; alternative email: info@phila.org
Country: United States
Contact: Director of Artistic & music Administration t.b.a. due to reorganisation
Email: Director of prodution Boyd Ostroff
Email: General and Artistic Director Robert B Driver
Email: Director of education t.b.a.
Email: t.b.a.
Venues: Academy of Music 2835

Opera Delaware
Website: www.operade.org
Email: lkimball@operade.org
Phone: 302 658 8063
Address: 4 South Poplar Street, US
Information:
Country: United States
Contact: Executive Director Julie Van Blarcom
Email: General and Artistic Director Leland P Kimball III
Email: Director of operations JulieAnne Cross
Email: production Manager Gina Scarnati
Venues: Grand Opera House 1100 Opera Studios 200

Opera Grand Rapids
Website: www.operagr.com
Email: hello@operagr.org

Phone: 616 451 2741
Address: 1320 East Fulton, US
Information: is the oldest opera company in Michigan; it serves a broad region in the western part of the state
Country: United States
Contact: Executive Director Anne Berquist
Email: aberquist@operagr.comArtistic Director Robert Lyall
Email: rlyall@operagr.com
Social Media: @operagr www.facebook.com/Opera.Grand.Rapids
Venues: De Vos Hall 2370

Opera Guild of Rochester
Website: www.operaguildofrochester.org
Email: operaguildofrochester@gmail.com
Phone: 585 334 232
Address: P.O. Box 92245, US
Information: Incorporated in 2004, Mercury Opera Rochester is the only professional opera company in Western New York. Now beginning its 6th season, the company typically produces three or four full opera productions per season with two performances of each productio
Country: United States
Contact: contact for lectures and education Agneta Borgstedt
Email: agneta.borgstedt@rochester.rr.comcontact for opera trips and tours Helga Strasser
Email: helgas@rochester.rr.com
Social Media: www.facebook.com/OperaGuildofRochester
Venues: Kodak Hall at Eastman Theatre 2400; Penfield High School 1000; Hochstein Performance Hall 950

Opera Idaho
Website: www.operaidaho.org
Email: info@operaidaho.org
Phone: 208 345 3531
Address: 513 South 8th St., US
Information: size of orchestra 34-56
Country: United States
Contact: General Director Mark Junkert
Social Media: www.facebook.com/operaidaho
Venues: The Egyptian Theatre

Opera in the Heights
Website: www.operaintheheights.org
Email: info@operaintheheights.org
Phone: 713 861 5303
Address: PO Box 7887, Lambert Hall, 1703 Heights Blvd., Houston, TX 77008, US
Information: regional company providing a stage for emerging opera performers since 1996
Country: United States
Contact: interim Managing Director Michael Branda
Email: Artistic Director William Weibel
Email: asst. General Director La Donna Jackson
Venues: Lambert Hall, 310 seats

Opera Memphis
Website: www.operamemphis.org
Email: david@operamemphis.org
Phone: 901 257 3100
Address: 6745 Wolf River Parkway, US
Information: A.I.R (Artists in Residence) program
Country: United States
Contact: education Director & Manager Jonathan Carter
Email: development Director Anne Barber
Email: General/Artistic Director Michael Ching
Email: accountant Michelle Thurlouth
Venues: Orpheum Theatre 2300

Opera North
Website: www.operanorth.org
Email: development@operanorth.org
Phone: 603 448 4141
Address: 20 West Park Street, US
Information:
Country: United States
Contact: Artistic Director Louis Burkot
Email: Executive Director Pamela A. Pantos
Venues: Lebanon Opera House 700

Opera Omaha
Website: www.operaomaha.org
Email: admin@operaomaha.org
Phone: 402 346 4398
Address: 1625 Farnam Street, Suite 100, US
Information: Heartland Opera Theatre is the resident touring company of Opera Omaha
Country: United States
Contact: Artistic Director & principal conductor Steward Robertson
Email: Director of maketing and public relation Kelly Blice
Venues: The Orpheum Theatre 2500

Opera Orchestra of New York
Website: www.operaorchestrany.org
Email: operaorchestrany@gmail.com
Phone: 212 906 9137
Address: 344 East 63rd Street, Suite B-1, US
Information:

OPERA/MUSIC THEATRE COMPANY

Country: United States
Contact: Executive Director Deborah Surdi
Venues: Carnegie Hall 2804 operas, Weill Recital Hall 268

Opera Parallèle
Website: www.operaparallele.org
Email: gfd@fd.co
Phone: 415 503 6279
Address: 50 Oak Street, US
Information: Opera Parallèle is a non-profit professional music organisation devoted to contemporary chamber opera and multidisciplinary projects at affordable ticket prices for San Francisco Bay area audiences
Country: United States
Contact: Artistic Director Nicole Paiement
Email: Executive Director Tod Brody
Email: General Manager Jacques Desjardins
Social Media: @OperaParallele www.facebook.com/operaparallele
Touring: North America, Australia, and Asia
Venues: San Francisco Conservatory of Music

Opera Roanoke
Website: www.operaroanoke.org
Email: mail@operaroanoke.org
Phone: 276 982 2742
Address: 1 Market Square SE, 2nd Floor, US
Information:
Country: United States
Contact: Director of operations Jenny Shelton General & Artistic Director
 Scott Williamson

Opera San José
Website: www.operasj.org
Email: boxoffice@operasj.org
Phone: 408 437 4450
Address: 2149 Paragon Drive, US
Information: Opera San José
Country: United States
Contact: music Director & principal conductor
 David Rohrbaugh
Email: corporate relations Manager Margot Helm
Email: General Manager Larry Hancock
Email: General Director Irene Dalis
Venues: California Theatre 1100

Opera San Luis Obispo
Website: www.operaslo.org
Email: operaslo@sbcglobal.net
Phone: 805 541 5369
Address: PO Box 14760, US
Information: size of orchestra 28; summer opera camp for 8-15 year olds in August, formerly known as the Pacific Repertory Opera.
Country: United States
Contact: Executive Director Sharon Dobson
Email: Artistic Director Brian Asher Alhadeff
Venues: Performing Arts Center 1150, Cal Poly Theatre 500

Opera Santa Barbara
Website: www.operasb.com
Email: info@operasb.com
Phone: 805 898 3890
Address: 1330 State Street, Suite 209, US
Information:
Country: United States
Contact: Artistic Director Jose Maria Condemi
Email: General Director Steven Sharpe
Venues: Lobero Theatre, 600

Opera Theater of Connecticut
Email: otcsings@aol.com
Phone: 860 669 8999
Address: Box 733, US
Information: perform for one week only in August in CT, one week in March in Sanibell Island, FL
Country: United States
Contact: administrative Director Kate Ford
Email: Artistic Director Alan Mann
Venues: Andrews Memorial Theater 500

Opera Theater of Pittsburgh
Website: otsummerfest.org
Email: info@otsummerfest.org
Phone: 412 621 1499
Address: 286 Main St, 3rd Floor, US
Information: a professional, non-profit organisation with 3 missions: development of new professional talent; education; building audiences for opera
Country: United States
Contact: Artistic Director Jonathan Eaton
Email: jeaton@otsummerfest.orgGeneral Manager Scott Timm
Email: stimm@otsummerfest.org
Social Media: @OperaTheaterPgh www.facebook.com/operatheaterofpittsburgh
Venues: on tour, OTP uses sponsor organization halls in Pittsburgh area

Opera Theatre of Saint Louis
Website: www.opera-stl.org

Email: info@opera-stl.org
Phone: 314 961 0171
Address: PO Box 191910, US
Information: see also Festivals
Country: United States
Contact: Executive Director Timothy O'Leary
Email: Artistic Director James Robinson
Email: Director of education and community programmes Allison Felter
Email: Director of Artistic Administration Paul Kilmer
Email: Director of development Nicole Ambos
Email: music Director Stephen Lord
Email: communications Director Maggie Stearns
Email: Director of operations Richard Barger
Venues: Loretto-Hilton Theater 987

OPERA! Lenawee
Website: www.aso.org
Email: info@aso.org
Phone: 517 264 3121
Address: 110 S. Madison St., US
Information:
Country: United States
Contact: music Director John Dodson
Email: Executive Director Susan Hoffman
Venues: Croswell Opera House 659, Dawson Auditorium 1200

OperaWorks
Website: www.operaworks.org
Email: info@operaworks.org
Phone: 818 898 9597
Address: 11862 Balboa Blvd. P.M.B. #391, US
Information: OperaWorks' highly acclaimed training provides one-of-a-kind performance and business skills, and world premiere productions in an extraordinary Artistic and individual experience. Courses include Advanced & Emerging Artists residencies; teacher training; master classes; and career planning.
Country: United States
Contact: Executive Director Ann Baltz
Email: Managing Director Gila Levi
Social Media: @OperaWorks https:// www.facebook.com/home.php#!/OperaWorks

PALA Opera Association
Phone: 121 276 98760
Address: 7 W. 81st Street, #12C, US
Information:
Country: United States
Contact: music Director Timothy Lindberg Producer & Artistic Director
 Elizabeth Falk
Venues: Town Hall NY 1500, Symphony Space 900, Players Theatre 150

Palm Beach Opera
Website: www.pbopera.org
Email: info@pbopera.org
Phone: 561 833 3709
Address: 415 S Olive Avenue, US
Information: 50 singers excluding chorus
Country: United States
Contact: General Director Daniel Biaggi
Email: dbiaggi@pbopera.orgManaging Director Greg Hirsch
Email: ghirsch@pbopera.org
Social Media: @palmbeachopera www.facebook.com/palmbeachopera
Venues: Kravis Center for the Performing Arts, West Palm Beach 2100

Paul Dresher Ensemble
Website: www.dresherensemble.org
Email: info@dresherensemble.org
Phone: 510 834 4102
Address: 333 Valencia St. #301, US
Information: The Paul Dresher Ensemble is represented exclusively by Bernstein Artists, Inc.: Bernstein Artists Inc., 282 Flatbush Ave. #101, Brooklyn NY 11217, Tel: 718-623 1214 Fax: 718-638 6110 email: BernsArts@aol.com; see also Orchestras
Country: United States
Contact: Managing Director Paul Dresher
Email: development Director Michele Fromson
Touring: produce and tour own works of collaboratively-created and experimental music theatre
Venues: Dinkelspiel Auditorium, Stanford University, University Theater, Holland Performing Arts Center, Lied Center for Performing Arts, Theater Artaud

Pensacola Opera
Website: www.pensacolaopera.com
Email: kyle@pensacolaopera.com
Phone: 850 433 6737
Address: PO Box 1790, US
Information:
Country: United States
Contact: Artistic Director Kyle Marrero

Piedmont Opera Inc
Website: www.piedmontopera.org
Email: info@piedmontopera.org
Phone: 336 725 7101

Address: 636 Holly Avenue, US
Country: United States
Contact: production Manager Bill Volz
Email: General Director James Allbritten
Venues: Stevens Center for the Performing Arts 1388

Pittsburgh Opera
Website: www.pittsburghopera.org
Email: info@pittsburghopera.org
Phone: 412 281 0912
Address: 2425 Liberty Avenue, US
Country: United States
Contact: General Director Christopher Hahn Director of Marketing & public relations
 Laura Willumsen
Email: music Director Antony Walker
Email: Artistic Director Christopher Hahn
Email: Director of education Marylin Michalka
Social Media: @PittsburghOpera www.facebook.com/pittsburghopera
Venues: Benedum Center for the Performing Arts 2770

Pocket Opera
Website: www.pocketopera.org
Email: info@pocketopera.org
Phone: 415 972 8930
Address: 469 Bryant Street, US
Information:
Country: United States
Contact: Executive Director Dianna Shuster
Email: Artistic Director Donald Pippin
Venues: Martin Myer Auditorium 400, Mountain View Center for the Performing Arts 585, California Palace of the Legion of Honour 300

Portland Opera
Website: www.portlandopera.org
Email: jfullan@portlandopera.org
Phone: 503 241 1407
Address: 211 SE Caruthers Street, US
Information:
Country: United States
Contact: Director of Marketing & public relations Jim Fullan
Email: Director of development Peter Bilotta
Email: production Director Laura Hassell
Email: music and education Sara Jane Patterson
Email: General Director Christopher Mattaliano
Email: Director of business operations Valeria Ramirez
Venues: Kaller Auditorium 3000

Portland Opera Repertory Theatre
Website: www.portopera.org
Email: portopera@aol.com
Phone: 207 879 7678
Address: PO Box 7733, US
Information:
Country: United States
Contact: public relations Gillian Britt
Email: General and Artistic Director Bruce Hangen

Prince Music Theater (2)
Website: www.princemusictheater.org
Email: info@princemusictheater.org
Phone: 215 972 1000
Address: 100 South Broad Street, Suite 650, US
Information: emphasis on new work; additional film series throughout the year
Country: United States
Contact: producing Artistic Director Marjorie Samoff
Venues: Prince Music Theatre 450

Sacramento Opera
Website: www.2intune.org/
Email: info@sacopera.org
Phone: 916 808 2000
Address: 1030 15th Street, Suite 200, US
Country: United States
Contact: General Director Rob Tannenbaum
Email: rtannenbaum@2inTune.orgdevelopment and Marketing Associate Ted Schaller
Email: tschaller@2inTune.org
Social Media: @SacOpera https:// www.facebook.com/SacOpera
Venues: Community Center Theater, Sacramento

San Diego Opera Association
Website: www.sdopera.com
Email: info@sdopera.com
Phone: 619 232 7636
Address: 1200 Third Ave., 18th Floor, US
Information: one of the largest education and outreach programs in the country, reaching in excess of 70k students and adults each year
Country: United States
Social Media: @SDOpera www.facebook.com/SanDiegoOpera
Venues: San Diego Civic Theatre 2885, Sherwood Auditorium 500 (recital only)

San Francisco Opera
Website:
www.sfopera.com
Email:
webmaster@sfopera.com

Phone: 415 861 4008
Address: 301 Van Ness Avenue, US
Information:
Country: United States
Contact: music Director Nicola Luisotti
Email: General Director David Gockley
Email: Associate Director of communications Julia Inouye
Email: chorus Director Ian Robertson
Social Media: @SFOpera www.facebook.com/SFOpera
Venues: War Memorial Opera House 3144

Santa Fe Opera
Website: www.santafeopera.org
Email: boxoff@santafeopera.org
Phone: 505 986 5955
Address: PO Box 2408, US
Information: number of singers: 40 principal seasonally; size of orchestra: 55 regular
Country: United States
Contact: Director of Administration Thomas Morris
Email: technical Director Paul Horpedahl Director of Press & public relations
Joyce Idema
Email: Director of development Carole Ely
Email: Artistic administrator Brad Woolbright
Email: Artistic Director Edo de Waart
Email: General Director Richard Gaddes (to end of 2007-08
Venues: Santa Fe Opera Theater 2126

Sarasota Opera Association (2)
Website: www.sarasotaopera.org
Email: info@sarasotaopera.org
Phone: 941 366 8450
Address: 61 N Pineapple Ave, US
Information: Presents a winter opera festival in Feb & Mar each year.
Country: United States
Contact: Executive Director Susan T Danis
Email: Artistic administrator G Michael Trupiano Artistic Director & principal conductor
Victor DeRenzi Marketing & public relations Director Darcy Ballew
Venues: Sarasota Opera House 1, 033

Seattle Musical Theatre
Website: seattlemusical.org
Email: smtoffice@seattlemusicaltheatre.org
Phone: 206 363 2809
Address: 7120 62nd Ave NE, US
Information: In 1977, a group of Seattle opera enthusiasts decided it was time to produce some lighter fare than what local companies were offering. Civic Light Opera was born and the music of German composer Johann Strauss, Jr., British composers Gilbert and Sullivan, and American Composer Victor Herbert filled the auditorium for the first two seasons.
Country: United States
Social Media: www.facebook.com/SeattleMusicalTheatre
Venues: Benedum Center 2837, Byham Theatre (Christmas) 1300, CLO Cabaret Theatre 250.

Seattle Opera
Website: www.seattleopera.org
Email: opera@seanet.com anna.percival@seattleoera.org
Phone: 206 389 7600
Address: PO Box 9248, 1020 John Street, US
Information:
Country: United States
Contact: General Director Speight Jenkins
Email: principal guest conductor Asher Fisch
Venues: Marion Oliver McCaw Hall

Shreveport Opera
Website: www. shreveopera.org
Email: ediller@shreveopera.org
Phone: 318 227 9503
Address: 212 Texas Street, Suite 101, US
Information: Shreveport opera ExPress: childrens operas and broadway musical revues
Country: United States
Contact: General/Artistic Manager Eric Diller
Venues: Civic Theatre 1737

Skylight Opera Theatre
Website:
www.skylightopera.com
Email:
info@skylightmusictheatre.org
Phone: 414 291 7811
Address: 158 N. Broadway, US
Information: the purpose of the Skylight Theatre, a non-profit making professional performing organisation, is to bring a full spectrum of musical and theatrical works to a wide and diverse audience; the Skylight Theatre strives to make a difference to people's lives
Country: United States
Contact: Managing Director Amy S. Jensen
Email: amyj@skylightmusictheatre.orgMarketing Manager Katie Behrend
Email: katieb@skylightmusictheatre.orgArtistic Director

Viswa Subbaraman
Email: viswas@skylightmusictheatre.org
Social Media: @skylightmusic1 www.facebook.com/skylightmusic1
Venues: Cabot Theater 358

Sorg Opera Company
Website: www.sorgopera.org
Email: sorgopera@core.com
Phone: 513 425 0180
Address: 65 South Main St, US
Information:
Country: United States
Contact: General Director Curtis Tucker Marketing & development Director
Charles Wente
Venues: Sorg Opera House 700

Squonk Opera
Website: www.squonkopera.org
Email: info@squonkopera.org
Phone: 141 282 49399
Address: 307 George Street, US
Information: multi-media performance – New Music Theatre
Country: United States
Contact: Artistic Director Steve O'Hearn
Email: steve@squonkopera.orgmusical Director Jackie Dempsey
Email: jackie@squonkopera.org
Touring: Europe
Venues: capacity up to 1200

Starlight Musical Theatre
Website: www.starlighttheatre.org
Email: info@starlighttheatre.org
Phone: 619 544 7827
Address: San Diego Civic Light Opera Association Inc., PO Box 3519, US
Information: alternative e-mail: Artistic@starlighttheatre.org
Country: United States
Venues: The Starlight Bowl (open air) 3800

Summer Opera Theatre Company, Inc.
Website: www.summeropera.org
Email: webmaster@summeropera.org
Phone: 202 526 1669
Address: c/o Music School – CUA, 620 Michigan Avenue, N.E., US
Information:
Country: United States
Contact: General Manager Deanne Giarrputo
Email: administrative Director Deanne Walter
Venues: Hartke Theatre, Catholic University of America 590

Syracuse Opera
Website: www.syracuseopera.com
Email: info@syracuseopera.com
Phone: 315 475 5915
Address: PO Box 1223, US
Information: educational programme throughout NY state
Country: United States
Contact: Director of development Eileen Price Director of Marketing & pr
Sue McKenna
Email: box office Manager outsourced to syracuse
Email: patron services/ company Manager Alana Munoz
Email: General Director/ Artistic Director Catherine Wolff
Email: Director of music Douglas Kinney Frost
Email: Director of operations Bari Wroblewski
Email: business Manager mathew dunn
Email: Associate Director of development/ensemble Manager Karin Falcone
Venues: Crouse-Hinds Concert Theater – John H. Mulroy Civic Center 2042

Tacoma Opera
Website: www.tacomaopera.com
Email: info@tacomaopera.com
Phone: 253 627 7789
Address: 917 Pacific Ave., Suite 407, US
Information:
Country: United States
Contact: General Director Noel Koran
Social Media: http:// www.facebook.com/TacomaOpera
Venues: Pantages Theater 1165

Toledo Opera Association
Website: www.toledoopera.org
Email: info@toledoopera.org
Phone: 419 255 7464
Address: 425 Jefferson Avenue, Suite 601, Ohio, US
Information:
Country: United States
Contact: education & outreach coordinator
Loviah Aldinger
Email: President, board of trustees Hussein Y Shousher
Email: General Director Renay Conlin
Venues: The Valentine Theatre 900, Peristyle Theatre 1700

Townsend Opera Players Inc
Website: www.townsendoperaplayers.com
Email: mbuckman@townsendoperaplayers.com
Phone:
209 523 6426
Address: 605 H Street, US
Information: orchestra size: 25-35; Camerata Chorus; Camerateens; Cameratini aged 6-12
Country: United States
Contact: Executive Director Matthew Buckman
Email: Artistic Director Dr. Joseph Wiggett
Email: business Manager Amy Sullivan
Venues: Modesto High School Auditorium 1100

Tri-Cities Opera Company
Website: www.tricitiesopera.com
Email: info@tricitiesopera.com
Phone: 607 729 3444
Address: 315 Clinton Street, US
Country: United States
Contact: General Director Susan S. Ashbaker
Email: GeneralDirector@tricitiesopera.comMarketing and events coordinator John Rozzoni
Email: Marketing@tricitiesopera.com
Social Media: @tricitiesopera www.facebook.com/pages/Tri-Cities-Opera/118978211488598
Venues: Forum Theatre, Binghamton 1, 515 Opera Center 245

Tulsa Opera, Inc.
Website: www.tulsaopera.com
Email: ccurry@tulsaopera.com
Phone: 918 582 4035
Address: 1610 S Boulder Avenue, US
Information: engaged in education program/reach 20, 000 students annually; free performances
Country: United States
Contact: Artistic Director Kostis Protopapas
Email: kprotopapas@tulsaopera.comMarketing and public relations Manager Thomas Golden
Email: tgolden@tulsaopera.comAdministration Charlotte Curry
Email: ccurry@tulsaopera.com
Social Media: www.facebook.com/TulsaOpera
Venues: Chapman Music Hall 2345

Utah Opera
Website: www.utahopera.org
Email: info@utahsymphonyopera.org
Phone: 801 533 5626
Address: Abravanel Hall, 123 W. South Temple, US
Information: extensive educational outreach programme; see also Utah Symphony
Country: United States
Contact: Director of Marketing Sara M. K. Neal
Email: Artistic Director for opera Christopher McBeth
Email: Chief Operating Officer David S. Green
Email: President and CEO Melia P. Tourangeau
Venues: Capitol Theater 1835

V. Abashidze State Theatre Music Comedy and Drama
Phone: 323 42773/347 7
Address: 182 Agmashenebeli ave., US
Information:
Country: United States
Contact: General Director Tinatin Rukhadze

Vermont Opera Theater
Website: www.vermontopera.org
Email: info@vermontopera.org
Phone: 180 278 54559
Address: P.O. Box 869, US
Information: touring company – opera, music theatre
Country: United States
Venues: opera houses, theatres, educational institutions

Vineyard Theatre (2)
Website: www.vineyardtheatre.org
Email: vineyard@vineyardtheatre.org
Phone: 212 353 3366
Address: 108 East 15th Street, US
Information: non-profit making organisation, off Broadway theatre
Country: United States
Contact: Artistic Director Douglas Aibel
Email: General Manager Rebecca Habel
Email: Executive Director Jennifer Garvey-Blackwell
Venues: Dimson Theatre 129

Virginia Opera Association
Website: www.vaopera.org
Email:
info@vaopera.org
Phone:
757 627 9545
Address: PO Box 2580, US
Information:
Country: United States
Contact: Director of education Laura Wigginton General Director & CEO
Paul A. Stuhlreyer, III,
Email: Director of production John Kennelly

Email: Artistic adviser Robin Thompson
Edythe C & Stanley L Harrison Opera House, Norfolk 1632, Carpenter Centre for Performing Arts (closed until 2009), Richmond 1981, George Mason University Centre for the Arts, Fairfax 1980

Vox Lumiere
Website: www.voxlumiere.com
Email: kevin@voxlumiere.com
Phone: 844 869 7625
Address: 1307 Hauser Blvd., US
Information: Vox Lumiere is an over-the-top mashup of music, dance, and technology bringing silent film classics to three-dimensional, high-decibel life.
Innovative productions blend old movies, new songs and powerful live performances into a showstopping spectacle that will have you on the edge of your seat as singers, dancers and musicians play off each other, the audience and the onscreen story in a magical exchange.
It's a riveting new kind of storytelling that will inspire you and haunt your dreams long after the curtain falls.
More than just a show, Vox Lumiere is an immersive, multimedia extravaganza that smashes the walls between stage and screen, with dazzling visuals, iconic stories and soul-pumping original music.
A captivating fusion of old Hollywood and modern music, Vox Lumiere redefines what it means to go to the theater.
Country: United States
Social Media: @voxlumiere http:// www.facebook.com/ voxlumiere

Washington Concert Opera
Website: www.concertopera.org
Email: info@concertopera.org
Phone: 202 364 5826
Address: 180 Connecticut Ave., NW, Suite 101, US

Information: concert performances in original languages with subtitles
Country: United States
Contact: Executive Director Judith M Gruber
Venues: Lisner Auditorium 1500

Washington National Opera
Website: www.dc-opera.org
Email: info@dc-opera.org
Phone: 202 467 4600
Address: 2700 F Street, US
Information:
Country: United States
Contact: President Michael M Kaiser
Venues: Kennedy Center Opera House 2200

West Bay Opera
Website: www.WBOpera.org
Email: GD@WBOpera.org
Address: Holt Building, 221 Lambert Avenue, Palo Alto, CA 94306, US
Information: 57 years of uninterrupted opera programming.
Country: United States
Contact: production Manager Michele Sullivan
Email: General Director Jose Luis Moscovich
Email: JoseLuis@WBOpera.org
Social Media: @WestBayOpera
Annual performances: 20
Annual productions: 3
Venues: Lucie Stern Theatre 430

West Coast Opera Theatre
Phone: 760 779 0061
Address: PO Box 166, US
Information:
Country: United States

Contact: musical Director Toni Spagnola General Manager & Artistic Director
Josephine Lombardo programme & publicity Director Roger Rogers
McCallum Theatre 1100, Annenberg Theatre, Palm Springs Museum concert 450, various church halls, senior centre halls & hotels
Wildwood Park
Website: www.wildwoodpark.org
Email: info@wildwoodpark.org
Phone: 501 821 7275
Address: 20919 Denny Road, US
Information: see also Venues
Country: United States
Contact: Executive Director Leslie Golden
Email: leslie@wildwoodpark.org
Social Media: @WildwoodPark www.facebook.com/ wildwoodparkforthearts
Venues: Lucy Lockett Cabe Festival Theatre 625

Wolf Trap Opera
Website: www.wolftrap.org
Email: wolftrap@wolftrap.org
Phone: 703 255 1900
Address: 1645 Trap Road, US
Information:
Country: United States
Contact: Chairman John C. Backus, Jr
Email: President and CEO Terrence D. Jones
Email: vice Chairman and secretary Lester L. Lyles
Venues: Barns of Wolf Trap 350, The Filene Center 3776, and on the lawn 3000

In the main this section includes only subsidised symphony or chamber orchestras, or those contracted to do regular recording work. Some orchestras are building-based, but also included are touring companies. **The entries are listed in alphabetical order within country.**

Orchestres, Ensembles Instrumentaux et Bandes

Dans son ensemble cette rubrique ne contient que des orchestres symphoniques ou de chambre qui sont subventionnés ou qui sont contactés pour faire des enregistrements à inter-valles réguliers. **Les entrée sont classés par ordre alphabé-tique dans le pays.**

Orchester, Bands und Instrumentalensembles

Hauptsächlich sind subventionierte Symphonie- oder Kammer-orchester aufgeführt, sowie Orchester, die regelmäßig Aufnahmen einspielen. Einige der aufgeführten deutschen und österreichischen Orchester arbeiten in Mehrspartentheatern und sind nich außerhalb des Theaters tätig. **Die Einträge sind für jedes Land alphabetisch sortiert.**

Orchestre, Bande e Gruppi Strumentali

Sono state inserite tutte quelle orchestre, sia sinfoniche che da camera, che ricevono un contributo statale o che hanno un contratto discografico. Le orchestre dei teatri dell'opera sono state incluse in questa sezione. **Le voci sono pubblicate in ordine alfabetico di paese.**

Orquestas, Bandas y Conjuntos Instrumentales

Por lo general sólo han sido incluidas las orquestas sinfónicas o de cámara subvencionadas y las orquestas que reciben con regularidad contratos de grabación. En cuanto a orquestas de ópera, los lectores deberán consultar la sección Ópera y Teatro Musical. **Las entradas se muestran en orden alfabético den-tro de cada país.**

performing arts

database

orchestre
dechambre
dePoris

© JEAN-BAPTISTE PELLERIN

Music brings
us together!

VILLE DE
PARIS

PRÉFECTURE
DE LA RÉGION
D'ÎLE-DE-FRANCE

orchestredechambredeparis.com

AUSTRALIA

Adelaide Symphony Orchestra
Website: www.aso.com.au
Email: aso@aso.com.au
Phone: 882 336 205
Address: 91 Hindley Street, AU
Information: With a reputation for vitality and versatility, the internationally acclaimed Adelaide Symphony Orchestra is South Australia's largest performing arts organisation, established in 1936. Across its 80 year history, the ASO has been there to corroborate life and contribute to South Australia's identity. Today the ASO plays a major role in Adelaide's cultural and economic vibrancy, and enriches the community through more than 70 world-class performances to more than 80, 000 diverse concertgoers each season.
Country: Australia
Contact: Executive administrator Shecky Leask
Email: Chair Colin Dunsford
Email: Managing Director Vincent Ciccarello

Australia Ensemble
Website: www.ae.unsw.edu.au
Email: australia.ensemble@unsw.edu.au
Phone: 293 854 874
Address: Music Performance Unit, Room G19, Robert Webster Building UNSW, AU
Information: The Music Performance Unit of the University of New South Wales is a small team responsible for the production of high quality classical music concerts on campus. A core of UNSW's cultural life, the Music Performance Unit manages several primary activities
Country: Australia
Contact: Director of music, art and culture Sonia Maddock
Email: s.maddock@unsw.edu.auoperations and Artistic coordinator Yvette Goodchild
Email: y.goodchild@unsw.edu.au
operations & communications Assistant Callum Bowles
Email: c.bowles@unsw.edu.au

Australian Art Orchestra (AAO)
Website: www.aao.com.au
Email: administrator@aao.com.au
Phone: 396 024 393
Address: Level 2, Mitchell House, 358 Lonsdale St, AU
Information: AAO primarily commissions and performs the work of Australian composers and has a strong interest in working with musicians from other music traditions and some of its most popular programmes come out of longstanding collaborations with South Indian and Australian Indigenous musicians. Mary Finisterer, Elena Katz Chernin, Howard Shore, Anthony Pateras, Paul Grabowsky, Sandy Evans, Alister Spence, Adrian Sherriff, Niko Schauble, Scott Tinkler, Philip Slater and Andrea Keller are among the many composers commissioned by the AAO to write works that have improvisation as a central component. Guru Kaaraikkudi Mani (IND) and the Young Wagilak Group from Arnhem Land, Northern Territory, Australia, are principal collaborators.The AAO has a long list of awards for excellence and has toured extensively. It's Principal Education Partner is Monash University, Melbourne and it is supported by the Australia Council for the Arts and Arts Victoria.
Country: Australia
Contact: Artistic Director Peter Knight
Email: administrator Brienna Macnish
Email: administrator@aao.com.au

Australian Brandenburg Orchestra
Website: www.brandenburg.com.au
Email: mail@brandenburg.com.au
Phone: 932 87581
Address: 142 New South Head Road, AU
Information: The Australian Brandenburg Orchestra, lead by charismatic Artistic Director Paul Dyer, celebrates music of the 16th, 17th and 18th centuries with excellence, flair and joy. Made up of leading specialists from all around Australia, the orchestra performs using original edition scores and instruments of the period, breathing fresh life and colour into baroque and classical masterpieces – as though the music has just sprung from the composer's pen.
Country: Australia
Contact: Chairman Greg Ward
Email: Artistic Director and co founder Paul Dyer

Australian Chamber Orchestra (ACO)
Website: www.aco.com.au
Email: aco@aco.com.au
Phone: 282 743 800
Address: Opera Quays, 2 East Circular Quay, AU
Information: One of the world's most lauded chamber ensembles, the Australian Chamber Orchestra is renowned for its inspired programming and unrivalled virtuosity, energy and individuality. Its unique programming extends across six centuries, spanning popular masterworks, adventurous cross-artform projects and pieces specially commissioned for the ensemble. Member of ISPA
Country: Australia
Contact: Artistic Director Richard Tognetti

Email: Chairman Guido Belgiorno-Nettis
Email: Managing Director Richard Evans
Email: Chief Operating Officer Alexandra Cameron-Fraser

Australian Opera & Ballet Orchestra
Website: opera.org.au
Email: customerservice@opera.org.au
Phone: 296 991 099
Address: 480 Elizabeth Street, AU
Information: Australia's national opera company was born when a band of idealists — butchers, pharmacists, newsagents — gave up their day jobs to celebrate the 1956 Mozart bicentenary with a season of four of his operas. Today, Opera Australia (OA) is Australia's largest arts employer, with annual seasons showcasing the world's great opera and music theatre repertoire, a touring programme staging works in regional Australia, and with performance broadcasts in cinemas and on national television and radio.
Country: Australia
Contact: chief Executive officer Rory Jeffes
Email: Artistic Director Lyndon Terracini
Email: Chief Operating Officer Joe Martorana

Australian String Quartet
Website: www.asq.com.au
Email: asq@asq.com.au
Phone: 883 133 748
Address: Room 111, Level 1, Hartley Building (Northern entrance), Gate 14, Kintore Avenue, AU
Information: For over 30 years, the Australian String Quartet (ASQ) has created unforgettable string quartet performances for national and international audiences. Dedicated to musical excellence with a distinctly Australian character. The purpose is to create chemistry and amplify intimacy through experiences that connect people with string quartet music.
Country: Australia
Contact: chief Executive Angelina Zucco
Email: Chairman Nicholas Callinan
Email: Marketing and Administration Helen Kearney
Email: Artistic Director Francesca Hiew
Email: Artistic Director Dale Barltrop

Australian Voices, The
Website: www.theaustralianvoices.com.au
Email: admin@theaustralianvoices.com.au
Phone: 731 75554
Address: 5/14 Mt Gravatt-Capalaba Rd, Upper Mt Gravatt, AU
Information: It is with a distinctive, fresh sound and high Artistic energy that The Australian Voices commission, perform and record the music of Australian composers. Since 1993 the ensemble has championed an astonishing flourish of new Australian vocal music, having commissioned hundreds of new works. Gordon Hamilton has been Artistic Director since 2009 and is considered one of Australia's most exciting young conductors and composers.
Country: Australia
Contact: Manager Tali Kellam-Pearson

Australian Youth Orchestra
Website: www.ayo.com.au
Email: info@ayo.com.au
Phone: 935 61400
Address: 19/285a Crown St, Surry Hills, AU
Information: The Australian Youth Orchestra (AYO) has a reputation for being one of the world's most prestigious and innovative training organisations for young pre-professional musicians. Our training pathway has been created to nurture the musical development of Australia's finest young instrumentalists across metropolitan and regional Australia: from the emerging, gifted, school-aged student, to those on the verge of a professional career. AYO presents tailored training and performance programmes each year for aspiring musicians, composers, arts administrators and music journalists aged 12 to 30.
Country: Australia
Contact: Artistic and Executive assistant Elena Phatak
Email: ElenaPhatak@ayo.com.aubusiness manager Kate O'Beirne
Email: KateOBeirne@ayo.com.auDirector of operations Warren Lenthall
Email: WarrenLenthall@ayo.com.auchief Executive officer Colin Cornish
Email: ColinCornish@ayo.com.au

Canberra Symphony Orchestra
Website: www.cso.org.au
Email: contact@cso.org.au
Phone: 262 479 191
Address: First Floor, 11 London Circuit, AU
Information: The Canberra Symphony Orchestra is the professional symphony orchestra of the nation's capital. Founded in 1950, the Canberra Symphony Orchestra has grown to become the largest professional performing arts organisation in Canberra and the surrounding region.
Country: Australia
Contact: communications Rachel Thomas
Email: chief Executive officer Sarah Kimball

artist & event engagement
Collusion
Website: collusion.com.au
Email: tour@collusion.com.au
Phone: 404 646 709
Address: 1/34 Oriel Rd, AU
Information: Collusion is Queensland's own original fine art music and dance ensemble. Together for 14 years, this group of award-winning chamber music musicians, in collaboration with composers and a choreographer and dancers, brings together exceptionally strong performances. Collusion is continuously developing new repertoires of very high quality while underpinning its programming with heart, beauty and warmth.
Country: Australia
Contact: Marketing and development Manager Alison Russell
Email: creative co-Director Benjamin Greaves

Darwin Symphony Orchestra
Website: www.dso.org.au
Email: dso@cdu.edu.au
Phone: 889 466 488
Address: Charles Darwin University, Casuarina Campus, AU
Information: The Darwin Symphony Orchestra (DSO), a not-for-profit organisation celebrating its 27th year in 2016. It is a treasured community icon throughout Darwin and the Northern Territory as a whole, comprising 65 volunteer musicians and a small professional core, who live and work within the Darwin community. The DSO is an orchestra of and for the community and the ensemble's identity as an accessible and essential community resource has resulted in concerts being held in some of the most remote places imaginable, with a diversity in programming that crosses all cultural boundaries. From floating on pontoons on the Katherine River to performing on a working barge on Darwin Harbour and becoming the first symphony orchestra to perform at Uluru, the DSO exemplifies the unique 'can do' attitude that is representative of the people of the Northern Territory.
Country: Australia
Contact: Artistic Director Matthew Wood

ELISION Ensemble
Website: www.elision.org.au
Email: daryl@elision.org.au
Address: 20 Balmoral Place, AU
Information: The ELISION Ensemble is a chamber ensemble specialising in contemporary classical music, concentrating on the creation and presentation of new works. The ensemble comprises a core of around 20 virtuoso musicians from Australia and around the world.
Country: Australia
Contact: Artistic Director Daryl Buckley
Email: daryl@elision.org.au

Melbourne Symphony Orchestra
Website: www.mso.com.au
Email: mso@mso.com.au
Phone: 386 461 106
Address: 22 Fanning St, AU
Information: The Melbourne Symphony Orchestra (MSO) was established in 1906 and is Australia's oldest orchestra. It currently performs live to more than 200, 000 people annually, in concerts ranging from subscription performances at its home, Hamer Hall at Arts Centre Melbourne, to its annual free concerts at Melbourne's largest outdoor venue, the Sidney Myer Music Bowl. The Orchestra also delivers innovative and engaging programmes to audiences of all ages through its Education and Outreach initiatives
Country: Australia
Contact: Director of human resources Miranda Crawley
Email: operations Director Gabrielle Waters
Email: Managing Director Sophie Galaise

Orchestra Victoria
Website: australianballet.com.au/music/orchestra-victoria
Email: orchestrainfo@australianballet.com.au
Phone: 396 943 600
Address: 25 Albert Drive Road, AU
Information: Orchestra Victoria is one of Australia's leading opera and ballet orchestras. Based in Melbourne, Orchestra Victoria works in partnership with Australia's premier arts companies delivering performances with The Australian Ballet, Opera Australia and Victorian Opera. They are the proud performance partner of Australia's premier performing arts companies, The Australian Ballet, Opera Australia and Victorian Opera, and also present concerts and education workshops in regional and outer metropolitan centres across the state.
Country: Australia
Contact: Artistic Director Nicolette Fraillon

Queensland Symphony Orchestra
Website: www.qso.com.au
Email: info@qso.com.au
Phone: 738 335 000
Address: 114 Grey Street, AU
Information: Queensland Symphony Orchestra is renowned for its high quality, breath-taking performances of both classical and modern compositions that engage

audiences of all musical tastes, interests and ages
Country: Australia
Contact: Artistic Administration Manager Michael Sterzinger
Email: chief Executive David Pratt
Email: chief financial officer Deb Houlahan

Sydney Camerata
Website: www.sydneycamerata.com
Email: sydneycamerata@outlook.com
Address: Level 1, The Arts Exchange, 18 Hickson Road, Millers Point, AU
Information: Sydney Camerata is home to a chamber orchestra and string quartet comprised of some of Australia's finest emerging talent. The organisation was formed with the intent to provide performance opportunities for Australia's emerging talented musicians and composers.
Country: Australia
Contact: Artistic Director Mathisha Panagoda
Email: m_panagoda@hotmail.com

Sydney Symphony
Website: www.sydneysymphony.com
Email: info@sydneysymphony.com
Phone: 282 154 600
Address: Clocktower Square, cnr Harrington & Argyle Streets, AU
Information: A permanent symphony orchestra is a sign of a city's musical maturity, and Sydney moved closer to achieving this when the Australian Broadcasting Commission was established. That was in 1932, the opening year of another symbol: the Sydney Harbour Bridge. The Sydney Symphony Orchestra had a promising predecessor. From 1919 to 1921 the orchestra of the New South Wales Conservatorium, conducted by the Belgian Henri Verbrugghen, gave regular professional symphonic concerts in Sydney, as well as touring Australia and New Zealand.
Country: Australia
Contact: General Manager John Horn
Email: Executive administrator Lisa Davies-Galli
Email: Executive Director Terrey Arcus

Symphony Services Australia Ltd
Website: symphonyinternational.net
Email: lidbetterk@symphonyinternational.net
Phone: 282 154 666
Address: Clocktower Square, Ground Floor, Shops 6-9, The 35 Harrington Street, AU
Information: Symphony Services International orchestrates musical excellence world-wide. It assists orchestras and classical musicians to perform at their best. All members of the global orchestral community can benefit from its products and services. Formerly Symphony Services Australia, it presents the ABC Symphony Australia Young Performers Awards and have set international benchmarks with its Conductor Development programme. It also holds the southern hemisphere's largest classical print music library, offering over 3, 500 programme notes and taking the headache out of tour management for visiting international artists.
Country: Australia
Contact: chief Executive officer Kate Lidbetter
Email: lidbetterk@symphonyinternational.netfinance Manager Dilek Henderson

Tasmanian Symphony Orchestra
Website: www.tso.com.au
Email: tso@tso.com.au
Phone: 362 324 444
Address: 1 Davey Street, AU
Information: This is Australia's most innovative, vibrant and flexible orchestra with a commitment to quality and excellence. The TSO will tailor programmes to fit any audience demographic and is able to perform a wide repertoire of work in a variety of forms.
Country: Australia
Contact: Managing Director Nicholas Heyward
Email: Executive assistant Fiona McAlpine
Email: Chair David Rich

West Australian Symphony Orchestra
Website: www.waso.com.au
Email: waso@waso.com.au
Phone: 893 260 000
Address: 445 Hay Street, AU
Information: The West Australian Symphony Orchestra (WASO) is Western Australia's largest and busiest performing arts organisation. With a reputation for excellence, engagement and innovation, WASO's resident company of full-time, professional musicians plays a central role in creating a culturally vibrant Western Australia. Member of ISPA.
Country: Australia
Contact: Chairman Richard Goyder AO
Email: chief Executive officer Mark Coughlan

West Australian Symphony Orchestra
Website: www.waso.com.au
Email: waso@waso.com.au
Phone: 893 260 000
Address: PO Box 3041, East Perth, AU
Information: the West Australian Symphony Orchestra

is the supporting orchestra for the West Australian Ballet and Opera companies; see also Presenters
Country: Australia
Contact: Executive Manager, Artistic planning Evan Kennea
Email: kenneae@waso.com.auExecutive Manager, orchestral management Keith McGowan
Email: mcgowan@waso.com.auorchestra Manager Alistair Cox
Email: coxa@waso.com.auExecutive Manager, Marketing Kelli Carnachan
Email: carnachank@waso.com.au

AZERBAIJAN

Azerbaijan State Capella of Azerbaijan State Philharmonic Society 'Muslim Magomayev'
Website: www.philarmonia.az
Email: info@philarmonia.az
Address: 2 Istiglaliyyat str., AZ
Country: Azerbaijan
Contact: chief conductor Mirbaji Imanova
Email: Director Melikov Akif Turan ogli

Azerbaijan State Chamber Orchestra 'Gara Garayev'
Phone: 124 972 905
Address: 2, Istiglaliyat St. 1001, Sabail, AZ
Country: Azerbaijan

Azerbaijan State Chamber Orchestra Named After Gara Garayev
Website: mct.gov.az
Email: mct@mct.gov.az
Phone: 124 934 398
Address: AZ
Country: Azerbaijan

Azerbaijan State Chamber Orchestra Named After Uzeyr Hajibeyli
Website: mct.gov.az
Email: mct@mct.gov.az
Phone: 124 934 398
Address: AZ
Country: Azerbaijan

Azerbaijan State Symphony Orchestra 'Uzeyir Hajibeyov'
Phone: 991 297 6231
Address: 2Istiglaliyat St. 1001, AZ
Country: Azerbaijan
Contact: Artistic Director t.b .a

Azerbaijan State Symphony Orchestra of Television and Radio 'Niyazi'
Phone: 991 293 1900
Address: 1, M. Huseyn St., AZ
Country: Azerbaijan
Contact: Artistic Director Ismail Hajiyev

Azerbaijan State Variety Orchestra 'Gaya'
Phone: 991 238 4315
Address: 5 kh Rzayeva St., AZ
Country: Azerbaijan
Contact: Artistic Director Teymur Mirzayev

Folk Orchestra of Ganja Philharmony
Phone: 992 256 5321/44
Address: 135 Atayev str.2000, AZ
Country: Azerbaijan

Initiative Center of Contemporary Music 'SONOR'
Address: 19 Rasul Rza street, AZ
Country: Azerbaijan

Natig Rhythm Group
Website: www.vokaliz.com
Email: booking@vokaliz.com
Address: AZ
Information: Natig Shirinov is recognized by many people as one of the greatest nagara players of our times. In 2001 he founded "Natig Rhythm Group". Besides nagara, he included traditional Azeri instruments such as zurna, balaban, tutek (whistle flute) to the group
Country: Azerbaijan
Contact: Booking Agent İlker Ersil

Seid Rustamov Folk Orchestra of AzerbaijanTelevision and Radio Company
Phone: 991 293 1900
Address: 9 Abdul Kerim Alizade, AZ
Country: Azerbaijan
Contact: Artistic Director Nariman Azimov

Symphony Orchestra of the Azerbaijan State Academic Opera and Ballet Theatre
Phone: 991 293 2067
Address: 28 May str. 8, AZ
Country: Azerbaijan

Variety Orchestra of the Azerbaijan State Television and Radio Company
Phone: 991 293 1900
Address: M. Huseyn St. 1, AZ

Country: Azerbaijan
Contact: Artistic Director Faig Sujadinnov

BRAZIL

Camerata Latino Americana
Email: cameratalatinoamericana@gmail.com
Phone: 119 895 11890
Address: BR
Information: The Camerata Latino Americana is a group formed by musicians that gather around the goal of promoting Brazilian and Latin concert music. Member of ISPA
Country: Brazil
Contact: Artistic Director Simone Menezes

Minas Gerais Philharmonic Orchestra
Website: www.filarmonica.art.br
Email: contato@filarmonica.art.br
Phone: 313 219 9000
Address: Rua Paraíba 330, BR
Information: managed by the Philharmonic Cultural Institute, the Minas Gerais Philharmonic Orchestra had its first concert in 2008. Member of ISPA
Country: Brazil
Contact: music Director Fabio Mechetti

Orquestra Sinfonica Brasileira
Website: www.osb.com.br/
Phone: 212 142 5800
Address: Av Rio Branco, 135, Salas 915 a 920, BR
Information: The Brazilian Symphony Orchestra (OSB) is the most traditional symphonic ensemble in Brazil and celebrated seven decades of continuous trajectory in 2010.
Country: Brazil
Contact: - Sandra Pinto
Email: sandra.pinto@osb.com.br

CANADA

Abbotsford Symphony Orchestra
Website: www.abbotsfordsymphony.com
Email: info@abbotsfordsymphony.com
Address: PO Box 573, CA
Information: Society is dormant
Country: Canada
Artistic Director & conductor
Johan Louwersheimer

Arcady
Website: www.arcady.ca
Email: info@arcady.ca
Phone: 519 428 3185
Address: PO Box 955, CA
Information: Arcady is an acclaimed ensemble dedicated to the mentorship of emerging artists and the performance of new Canadian music by Director Ronald Beckett and other Arcady composers. Arcady has performed three operas and produced three CDs of Beckett's work. The organization combines outstanding young Canadian performers with established professional instrumentalists and singers. The ensemble has also established a reputation for its energetic and imaginative performances of early music and is the regular chorus for Boris Brott's National Academy Orchestra of Canada.
Country: Canada
Contact: Artistic Director Ronald Beckett
Email: President Heather Fleming
Email: event coordinator Paula Thomas

Art of Time Ensemble
Website: artoftimeensemble.com
Email: info@artoftimeensemble.com
Phone: 647 344 2254
Address: 142 Fort York Blvd, CA
Information: Andrew Burashko formed Art of Time Ensemble in 1998 with the support of a small group of like-minded musicians and prominent figures in dance, theatre and other art forms, beginning with one-off concerts to small but enthusiastic audiences. Word quickly spread through Toronto's cultural scene. Today, Art of Time works with the best Canadian artists in the performing arts, film and literature, and noteworthy international musicians. Member of ISPA
Country: Canada
Contact: Artistic Director Andrew Burashko
Email: board member Ian Bandeen

Brantford Symphony Orchestra
Website: www.brantfordsymphony.com
Email: administrator@brantfordsymphony.ca
Phone: 519 759 8781
Address: PO Box 24012, 185 King George Road, CA
Information: Brantford Symphony Orchestra's aim is to provide enduring access to the best symphonic entertainment, giving people of all ages opportunities for musical growth and education
Country: Canada
Contact: co-President Joann Alho
Email: co-President Maureen Wills
Email: Director Joan Gould

Calgary Philharmonic Orchestra
Website: calgaryphil.com

Email: info@cpo-live.com
Phone: 403 571 0270
Address: Calgary Philharmonic Orchestra,
205 - 8th Ave SE, CA
Information: the CPO has been an integral part of our vibrant community for over fifty years and continues to celebrate the worlds greatest music with fans of all ages.
Country: Canada
President & CEO
Paul Dornian
Email: pdornian@calgaryphil.comDirector Doug Jones
Email: djones@calgaryphil.comAssociate Director
Jennifer MacDonald
Email: jmacdonald@cpo-live.com
Manager, education & outreach
Caroline Becq
Email: alewis@cpo-live.com

Chorale
Website: www.music.uwo.ca
Email: music@uwo.ca
Phone: 519 661 2111
Address: Don Wright Faculty of Music, University of Western Ontario, CA
Information: the Chorale is a select mixed choir made up of voice majors, instrumental majors, and non-music majors
Country: Canada
Contact: conductor Jennifer Moir

Choristes, Les
Website: www.music.uwo.ca
Email: music@uwo.ca
Phone: 519 661 2111
Address: Don Wright Faculty of Music, University of Western Ontario, CA
Information: Les Choristes is a dynamic women's choir comprised of students from across campus, most of whom are voice majors at the Don Wright Faculty of Music. The repertoire is diverse, and includes music of all eras and genres while specializing in music of the 21st century.
Country: Canada
Contact: Director Victoria Meredith

collectif9
Website: https:// www.latitude45arts.com/collectif9
Email: info@latitude45arts.com
Phone: 514 276 2694
Address: 107, boul. St-Joseph West
Information: Montréal's classical string band collectif9 has been attracting varied audiences since their 2011 debut. Known for energized, innovative arrangements of classical repertoire, the group performs "with an infectious energy and vigour that grabs an audience's attention" (The WholeNote). collectif9 has performed over 150 concerts across North America, Europe, and Asia.
Country: Canada

Edmonton Symphony Orchestra
Website: www.edmontonsymphony.com
Email: info@winspearcentre.com
Phone: 780 428 1414
Address: 9720 - 102 Ave NW, CA
Information: founded in 1952, the Edmonton Symphony Orchestra is one of Canada's orchestral ensembles. Its current roster includes 56 musicians from Canada and around the world, performing classical masterworks, pops and children's concerts
Country: Canada
Contact: Associate Executive Director Meghan Unterschultz
Email: munterschultz@winspearcentre.comArtistic administrator Rob McAlear
Email: rob.mcalear@winspearcentre.comExecutive Director Anne-Marie Petrov
Email: annemarie.petrov@winspearcentre.com

Esprit Orchestra
Website: www.espritorchestra.com
Email:
info@espritorchestra.com
Phone: 416 815 7887
Address: 174 Spadina Avenue, Suite 511, CA
Information: Founded in 1983 by Music Director and Conductor, Alex Pauk, Esprit's commitment to commissioning and advancing contemporary music has set it apart as one of the few organizations of its kind on a global scale. Esprit consistently collaborates with outstanding composers, and performs with first-class soloists and ensembles from Canada and abroad.
Country: Canada
Contact: operations Manager Rachel Gauntlett
Email: rachel@espritorchestra.com
Marketing & outreach coordinator
Amber Melhado
Email: amber@espritorchestra.compersonnel Manager
Christine Little Ardagh
Email: cardagh@espritorchestra.com

Fanshawe Chorus London
Website: www.choruslondon.com
Email:
GeneralManager@choruslondon.com

Phone: 519 433 9650
Address: 336 Sovereign Rd London, CA
Information: Fanshawe Chorus London comprises of 110 singers as well as 50 players in its own dedicated orchestra who operate as the Concert Players Orchestra
Country: Canada
Contact: Artistic Director David Holler
Email: General Manager April Voth

Fraser Valley Symphony
Website: www.fraservalleysymphony.org/
Email: fraservalleysymphony@gmail.com
Phone: 604 744 9110
Address: PO Box 122, CA
Information: founded in 1984, the Fraser Valley Symphony is an orchestra from the Fraser Valley Region. The Fraser Valley Symphony provides a forum for musicians to play a variety of orchestral music for the audiences in the Fraser Valley
Country: Canada
Contact: principal conductor Lindsay Mellor
Email: President Marg Deibert

Gerald Fagan Singers
Website: www.choruslondon.com
Email: info@choruslondon.com
Phone: 519 433 9650
Address: 336 Sovereign Rd, CA
Information: choir based in Canada. Also linked with the Fanshawe Chorus London
Country: Canada
Contact: conductor Gerald Fagan
Email: Manager Marlene Fagan

Hamilton Philharmonic Orchestra
Website: www.hpo.org
Email: communications@hpo.org
Phone: 905 526 1677
Address: 10 MacNab St. S., CA
Information: The Hamilton Philharmonic Orchestra was founded in 1884 as The Hamilton Orchestral Society and grew to become one of Canada's major professional orchestras. Today, the HPO is a leader in Hamilton's robust arts community where it provides professional orchestral services and music education programmes to address the needs of the community. The HPO continues to commission and premiere works and is one of the Artistic jewels of the Hamilton/Burlington area. The combined musical talents of its artists continue to enrich the community and enhance the quality of life for its residents.
Country: Canada
Contact: office administrator Gerry Custeau
Email: gcusteau@hpo.orgoperations and personnel Manager Neil Spaulding
Email: personnel@hpo.orgExecutive Director Diana Weir
Email: dweir@hpo.org

I Musici de Montréal
Website: www.imusici.com
Email: info@imusici.com
Phone: 514 982 6038
Address: 4672 B, rue Saint-Denis, CA
Information: founded in 1983 the orchestra is made up of 15 musicians whose repertoire ranges from baroque music to contemporary music. At every concert, I Musici strives to offer a unique musical experience that emphasizes passion and excellence but above all audacity and innovation.
Country: Canada
Contact: Executive Director Simon Gamache
Email: sgamache@imusici.comMarketing Manager Anna Bedic
Email: abedic@imusici.comArtistic Administration Solange Callejon
Email: scallejon@imusici.com

International Symphony Orchestra of Sarnia and Port Huron
Website: www.theiso.org
Email: iso@rivernet.net
Phone: 519 337 7775
Address: 251 North Vidal Street, CA
Information: The International Symphony Orchestra of Sarnia, Ontario and Port Huron, Michigan began in 1957. The Little Orchestra Society of Sarnia and the Port Huron String Ensemble came together and formed the Orchestra. The Orchestra is a non-profit organization and consists of around fifty-five musicians who are from both sides of the border between the United States and Canada. Many work full-time in the music profession. Other members are engineers, teachers, doctors, nurses, and homemakers, and all are well-trained musicians.
Country: Canada
Contact: Executive Director Anne Brown
Email: President Robert Dell

Kamloops Symphony
Website: www.kamloopssymphony.com
Email: info@kamloopssymphony.com
Phone: 250 372 500
Address: #6-510 Lorne Street, CA
Country: Canada
Marketing & community engagement coordinator

Ryan Noakes
Email: Ryan@kamloopssymphony.comvice President Michelle Chitsaz
Email: musical Director Dina Gilbert
Email: dina@kamloopssymphony.comExecutive Director Kathy Humphreys
Email: Kathy@kamloopssymphony.com

Kingston Symphony
Website: www.kingstonsymphony.on.ca
Email: info@kingstonsymphony.on.ca
Phone: 613 546 9729
Address: 11 Princess Street, Suite 206, CA
Information: The orchestra was founded in 1953 under the name the New Symphony Association of Kingston. It was renamed the Kingston Symphony in 1963 with the formation of its new umbrella organization, the Kingston Symphony Association. The KS is currently led by Evan Mitchell who has been principal conductor of the orchestra since September 2014.[1] The ensemble performs most of its concerts at The Grand Theatre
Country: Canada
Contact: General Manager Andrea Haughton
Email: ahaughton@kingstonsymphony.on.caoffice administrator Leslie O'Sullivan
Email: losullivan@kingstonsymphony.on.cadevelopment coordinator Cody Chretien
Email: cchretien@kingstonsymphony.on.capersonnel Manager Linda Craig
Email: kingstonsymphonypersonnel@gmail.comproduction Manager David Smith

Kitchener-Waterloo Chamber Orchestra
Website: kwchamberorchestra.ca
Email: info@KWChamberOrchestra.ca
Phone: 519 744 3828
Address: Ontario, CA
Information: The Kitchener-Waterloo Chamber Orchestra is comprised of a core of professional musicians, semi-professionals from our community, and highly skilled music students. Together, they share a love of music and a commitment to excellence in performance.
Country: Canada
music Director & conductor
Graham Coles
Email: kwchamberorchestra@on.aibn.com

Kitchener-Waterloo Symphony
Website: www.kwsymphony.ca
Email: info@kwsymphony.on.ca
Phone: 519 745 4711
Address: 36 King Street West, CA
Information: Since it was formed in 1945 by Dr. Glenn Kruspe to accompany a concert of the Grand Philharmonic Choir, the Kitchener-Waterloo Symphony has been the cultural centerpiece of Waterloo Region. In 1960, Frederick Pohl succeeded Glen Kruspe as Music Director and under his leadership a KWS Youth Orchestra was founded in 1966. In 1971 conductor Raffi Armenian joined the KWS. His position as Music Director for the Stratford Festival brought about the creation of the Canadian Chamber Ensemble, which attracted professional musicians to the orchestra. Maestro Armenian's tenure saw the KWS evolve into a fully paid professional orchestra with a core of 52 musicians that toured across Canada, Europe, South America and Asia, and made numerous recordings including several JUNO Award nominations.
Country: Canada
Contact: Executive Director Andrew Bennett
Email: Artistic administrator Olga Mychajluk
Email: omychajluk@kwsymphony.on.caDirector of audience engagement Kari Hueber
Email: khueber@kwsymphony.on.ca

Kitchener-Waterloo Symphony
Website: www.kwsymphony.on.ca
Email: mail@kwsymphony.on.ca
Address: 101 Queen Street North, CA
Information: see also Canadian Chamber Ensemble
Country: Canada
Contact: music Director Edwin Outwater
Email: Executive Director Genevieve Twomey
Email: Artistic administrator Olga Mychajluk
Email: omychajluk@kwsymphony.on.cadevelopment Manager Paul Pedersen
Email: ppedersen@kwsymphony.on.caDirector of operations Laurie Castello
Email: lcastello@kwsymphony.on.ca

Le Vent du Nord
Website: www.leventdunord.com
Email: info@leventdunord.com
Phone: 450 909 0940
Address: 200-1028 du Rivage, Saint-Antoine-sur-Richelieu, CA
Information: The award winning and highly acclaimed band Le Vent du Nord is a leading force in Quebec's progressive francophone folk movement. The group's vast repertoire draws from both traditional sources and original compositions, while enhancing it's hard-driving soulful music (rooted in the Celtic diaspora) with a broad range of global influences.
Country: Canada

ORCHESTRA, BAND AND INSTRUMENTAL ENSEMBLE

Contact: Manager Geneviève Nadeau
Email: genevieve@leventdunord.com

Les Violons du Roy
Website: www.violonsduroy.com
Email: info@violonsduroy.com
Phone: 418 692 3026
Address: 995 Place d'Youville, 4e etage, CA
Information: see also Early Music
Country: Canada
Contact: Artistic administrator Laurent Patenaude
Email: senior Manager – funding, Marketing and communications Hugo Sanschagrin
Email: music Director Bernard Labadie
Email: Managing Director Astrid Chouinard

Lethbridge Symphony Association
Website: www.lethbridgesymphony.org
Email: hello@lethbridgesymphony.org
Phone: 403 328 6808
Address: Box 1101, , Stn Main, CA
Information: the Lethbridge Symphony Orchestra provides opportunities for education in the community of Southern Alberta through collaborations with other organisations
Country: Canada
Contact: General Manager Melanie Gattiker
Email: melanie@lethbridgesymphony.orgmusic Director Glenn Klassen
Email: Administration Haley Neufeld
Email: finance Manager Mary Opyr
Email: mary@lethbridgesymphony.org

Manitoba Chamber Orchestra
Website: www.themco.ca
Email: info@themco.ca
Phone: 204 783 7377
Address: Unit Y300, 393 Portage Ave., CA
Information: The MCO is "Canada's tiny, perfect chamber orchestra" (Toronto Star). It has toured widely, commissions often, embraces a diverse repertoire, and collaborates regularly with the world's leading soloists, from James Ehnes to Marc-André Hamelin.
Country: Canada
Contact: music Director and conductor Anne Manson
Email: President Faye Warren
Email: Managing Director Vicki Young

McGill Chamber Orchestra
Website: www.ocm-mco.org
Email: info@ocm-mco.org
Address: 5459 Earnscliffe, CA
Information: Touring orchestra of Montreal.
Country: Canada
Contact: administrative Director Laurence Perle Barchichat
Email: laurence@ocm-mco.orgChairman Hans P Black Artistic Director & conductor
Boris Brott

Mississauga Philharmonic
Website: www.mississaugasymphony.ca/
Email: mail@mississaugasymphony.com
Address: c/o Orchestras Mississauga, 4141 Living Arts Drive, CA
Country: Canada
Contact: General Manager Eileen Keown
Email: eileen.keown@mississaugasymphony.caadministrator Susan Grohmann
Email: susan.grohmann@livingarts.on.caExecutive Director Mike Plaus
music Director & conductor
John Barnum
Email: info@mississaugasymphony.ca

Montreal Chamber Orchestra
Website: www.mco-ocm.qc.ca
Email: info@mco-ocm.qc.ca
Phone: 514 871 1224
Address: 5821 avenue de l'Esplanade, CA
Country: Canada
Conductor & Artistic Director
Wanda Kaluzny
Email: info@mco-ocm.qc.caChairman of the board
John D. Williams
Email: Executive Director Mona Awad

National Arts Centre Orchestra
Website: www.nac-cna.ca
Email: info@nac-cna.ca
Phone: 613 947 7000
Address: PO Box 1534, Station B, CA
Country: Canada
Contact: General Manager Marc Stevens
Email: marc.stevens@nac-cna.caPresident and chief Executive Officer Peter Herrndorf
Email: peter.herrndo@nac-cna.caManager of Artistic planning Daphne Burt
Email: daphne.burt@nac-cna.caManaging Director Christopher Deacon
Email: christopher.deacon@nac-cna.cacommunications officer Andrea Hossack
Email: andrea.hossack@nac-cna.camusic Director Pinchas Zukerman

Email: Director, music education and community engagement Geneviève Cimon
Email: genevieve.cimon@nac-cna.ca

National Youth Orchestra of Canada
Website: www.nyoc.org
Email: info@nyoc.org
Phone: 888 532 4470
Address: 59 Adelaide St. East, Suite 500, CA
Information: the NYOC's mission is to recruit Canada's best young classical musicians ages 16-28 and to train and mentor them for careers as professional orchestral musicians with great orchestras such as the Calgary Philharmonic, Edmonton Symphony, Toronto Symphony, Montreal Symphony and Vancouver Symphony and others across Canada and around the word; more than one-third of Canada's professional orchestral musicians are alumni of the NYOC; each year we audition about 500 top young musicians across Canada for 100 positions in the orchestra for our summer training institute and national concert tour; the NYOC bridges the gap between classical music education and orchestral music careers. We are Canada's premier institute to prepare young musicians for a productive, sustainable and realistic career in music and the arts. Performance is key, but the ability to build and sustain a career takes a well-rounded skill set that focuses on health, Marketing, and solid business skills; the NYOC has over 50 years of success creating career-ready performers
Country: Canada
Contact: operations Manager Bo Lee
Email: blee@nyoc.orgproduction and tour Manager Jonathan Welmers
Email: jwelmers@nyoc.orgExecutive Director Barbara Smith
Email: bsmith@nyoc.org

Newfoundland Symphony Orchestra
Website: www.nso-music.ca
Email: peter.gardner@nso-music.ca
Address: Arts & Culture Centre, Prince Philip Drive, PO Box 1854, CA
Information: semi-professional orchestra with a full time core including The Atlantic String Quartet, it's resident ensemble.
Country: Canada
Contact: music Director Marc David
Email: m.david@nso-music.comCEO Neil Edwards
Email: n.edwards@nso-music.comDirector of operations Sean Conway
Email: s.conway@nso-music.comcustomer relations Lynn Ann Pye
Email: l.pye@nso-music.com

Niagara Symphony Association
Website: www.niagarasymphony.org
Email: info@niagarasymphony.org
Phone: 905 687 4993
Address: 101 King Street, Unit 16, CA
Information: summer music camp at Ridley College, composer in the classroom and youth club for children
Country: Canada
Contact: office Manager Deborah-Marie Forrester
Email: info@NiagaraSymphony.orgManaging Director Candice Turner-Smith
Email: fundraising Manager Lauren Hundert
Email: Lauren.Hundert@NiagaraSymphony.orgeducation coordinator B. J. Armstong
Email: BJ.Armstrong@NiagaraSymphony.org

North Bay Symphony Orchestra
Website: www.northbaysymphony.org
Email: info@NorthBaySymphony.org
Address: 150 Main Street East, CA
Country: Canada
Contact: treasurer Kenneth Whitehead
Email: General Manager Rex Hiscock
Email: principal conductor Metro Kozak
Email: President Robert Palangio
Email: Associate conductor Mark Delouse

Nouvel Ensemble Moderne, Le
Website: www.lenem.ca
Email: info@lenem.ca
Phone: 514 343 5636
Address: 200, avenue Vincent-d'Indy, C.P. 6128, Succ. Centre-ville, CA
Information: contemporary orchestra ensemble from Montreal
Country: Canada
Contact: Artistic Director Lorraine Vaillancourt
Email: vaillal@sympatico.caGeneral Manager Normand Forget
Email: directionGenerale@lenem.caproduction coordinator Jenny Labonté
Email: j.labonte@lenem.ca

Oakville Symphony Orchestra
Website: www.oakvillesymphony.com
Email: oakville.symphony@cogeco.ca
Address: 310-200 North Service Road W, Ontario, CA
Information: community orchestra; OSO family christmas concert; outreach programme for children, private concerts for sponsors
Country: Canada

Contact: General Manager Peggy Steele
Email: oakville.symphony@cogeco.ca
music Director & conductor

Okanagan Symphony Society
Website: www.okanagansymphony.com
Email: admin@okanagansymphony.com
Address: PO Box 20238, CA
Information: performs in 3 communities and reaches an estimated audience of 16, 000 per season
Country: Canada
Contact: music Director Rosemary Thomson
Email: md@okanagansymphony.comMarketing coordinator Christina Ferreira
Email: Marketing@okanagansymphony.comExecutive Director Robert Barr
Email: ed@okanagansymphony.comadministrator Laurie Henderson
Email: laurie@okanagansymphony.com

Orchestra London Canada Inc
Website: www.orchestralondon.ca
Email: rgloor@orchestralondon.ca
Phone: 519 679 8558
Address: c/o Orchestra London Sales Office, 609 Wellington Street, , CA
Information: Orchestra London Canada has been sharing the magic of live, orchestral music for more than 60 years
Country: Canada
Contact: Executive Director Joe Swan
Email: jswan@orchestralondon.caChief Operating Officer Eadie Micks
Email: emicks@orchestralondon.caSales and Marketing Manager Terri Anne Moses
Email: tmoses@orchestralondon.caExecutive assistant Sharon Durston
Email: sdurston@orchestralondon.ca

Orchestra Toronto
Website: www.orchestratoronto.ca
Email: info@orchestratoronto.ca
Phone: 416 467 7142
Address: 131 Beecroft Road, #402, CA
Country: Canada
Contact: artist-in-residence Catherine Manoukian
Email: music Director Errol Gay
Email: Executive Director Wendy Limbertie

Orchestras Mississauga
Website: www.mississaugasymphony.ca
Email: mail@mississaugasymphony.com
Address: 4141 Living Arts Drive, CA
Information: Umbrella organization for Mississauga Symphony Orchestra, Sinfonia Mississauga chamber orchestra and Mississauga Philharmonic.
Country: Canada
Contact: Executive Director Mike Plaus
Email: music Director/conductor John Barnum
Email: info@mississaugasymphony.caGeneral Manager Eileen Keown
Email: eileen.keown@mississaugasymphony.caadministrator Susan Grohmann
Email: susan.grohmann@livingarts.on.ca

Orchestre Symphonique de Laval
Website: www.osl.qc.ca
Email: osl@osl.qc.ca
Address: 1535 Chomedey Blvd, P.O. Box 422, St-Martin, CA
Country: Canada
Contact: Executive Director Marie- Pierre Rolland
Email: mprolland@osl.qc.caArtistic Director Alain Trudel
Email: osl@osl.qc.caExecutive assistant Suzanne Chalifoux
Email: schalifoux@osl.qc.ca

Orchestre Symphonique de Montréal
Website: www.osm.ca
Email: General@osm.ca
Address: 260 Boulevard de Maisonneuve Ouest, 2, CA
Information: see also Festivals (Festival Int. de Lanaudi)
Country: Canada
Contact: Director of operations Paul Fortin
Email: Director of strategic planning Marie-Josée Desrochers
Email: musical Director Kent Nagano
Email: Director of personnel Michael Carpenter
Email: CEO Madelaine Careau

Orchestre Symphonique de Quebec
Website: www.osq.org
Email: billetterie@osq.qc.ca
Phone: 418 643 8486
Address: 401 Grande Allée Est, CA
Country: Canada
Contact: Artistic department Isabelle Lépine
Email: ilepine@osq.qc.caAdministration Denise St-Laurent
Email: dstlaurent@osq.qc.cacommunications and media Cecile Testud
Email: ctestud@osq.qc.caMarketing and finance Annie Bournival
Email: abournival@osq.qc.ca

Orchestre Symphonique de Sherbrooke
Website: www.ossherbrooke.com
Email: oss@abacom.com
Address: 1300, Boulevard de Portland, Domaine Howard Pavillion 1. C.P.610, CA
Country: Canada
Contact: communications assistant Anne-Marie Leblanc
Email: info@ossherbrooke.comGeneral Director Dominic Ferland
Email: dominicferland@ossherbrooke.com
Artistic Director & conductor
Stéphane Laforest
Email: stephanelaforest@ossherbrooke.com

Orchestre symphonique de Trois-Rivières
Website: www.ostr.ca
Email: orchestre@ostr.ca
Phone: 819 373 5340
Address: 1517, rue Royale, Case postale 1281, CA
Information: motivated by excellence and creativity, the company has more than twenty events each season, whether large concerts, recitals, youth activities or OSTR the contest for succession
Country: Canada
Contact: Executive Director Natalie Rousseau
Email: direction@ostr.caArtistic Director Jacques Lacombe
Email: directionartistique@ostr.caassistant to the Director General Carole Corbin
Email: Administration@ostr.caDirector of communications Julie Leblanc
Email: communications@ostr.ca

Orchestre Symphonique du Saguenay-Lac-St-Jean
Website: www.osslsj.com
Email: jrobert@osslsj.com
Address: 202 rue Jacques-Cartier Est, CA
Information: The Orchestre symphonique du Saguenay-Lac-Saint-Jean is the Producer and distributor of symphonic classical music professionally devoted mainly to the population of the Saguenay-Lac-Saint-Jean.
Country: Canada
Contact: technical Director Dominic Bédard
Email: dominicbedard@lorchestre.orgGeneral Director Christine Boily
Email: cboily@lorchestre.orgproduction assistant and librarian Angela Tremblay
Email: angeletremblay@lorchestre.orgArtistic Director Jacques Clément

Oshawa-Durham Symphony Orchestra
Website: www.odso.ca
Email: contact@odso.ca
Address: PO Box 444, CA
Information: Disbanded
Country: Canada
Contact: Chairman Edmond Vanhaverbeke
Email: music Director Marco Parisotto

Ottawa Symphony Orchestra
Website: www.ottowasymphony.com
Email: gm@ottawasymphony.com
Phone: 613 231 7802
Address: 250 - 2 Daly Avenue, CA
Information: the OSO presents a series of five concerts each season in Southam Hall at the National Arts Centre under Music Director and Conductor David Currie
Country: Canada
music Director & conductor
David Currie
Email: Marketing coordinator Yael Santo
Email: Marketing@ottawasymphony.comGeneral Manager L. Peter Feldman
Email: gm@ottawasymphony.com

Peterborough Symphony Orchestra
Website: www.thepso.org
Email: info@thepso.org
Phone: 705 742 1992
Address: PO Box 1135, LL 1, 311 George St. North, CA
Information: The Peterborough Symphony Orchestra (PSO) has championed the cause of orchestral music in Peterborough and surrounding areas for over 47 years. Their vision is of a community united by a love of music of many eras and genres, while advancing knowledge and appreciation of orchestral music throughout our community; the PSO pursues their vision through concerts, youth outreach, and partnering with other local organisations; also provides opportunities for residents and visitors to our community to enjoy high caliber orchestral concerts while providing talented local performers with an opportunity to learn and share their love of music with others. For more info about the PSO go to www.thepso.org/
Country: Canada
Contact: Executive Director Deanna Guttman
Email: production Manager Chris Reynard

Prince Edward Island Symphony Orchestra
Website: www.peisymphony.com
Email: peiso@peisymphony.com
Address: PO Box 185, CA

Information: The PEISO brings together players from different walks of life and experience, including professional musicians from the Island and other areas in the Maritimes
Country: Canada
Contact: administrator Natalie Williams Calhoun
Email: admin@peisymphony.compersonnel Manager and librarian Morgan Saulnier
Email: Marketing@peisymphony.commusic Director James Mark

Prince George Symphony Orchestra Society
Website: www.pgso.com
Email: admin@pgso.com
Phone: 250 562 0800
Address: 2880-15th Ave, CA
Country: Canada

Quatuor Bozini
Website: www.quatuorbozzini.ca/en/
Email: info@quatuorbozzini.ca
Phone: 514 667 0938
Address: 4816, rue Clark, CA
Information: since 1999, the Bozzini Quartet has been an original voice in new, contemporary, experimental and classical music
Country: Canada

Quatuor Bozzini
Website: www.quatuorbozzini.ca
Email: info@quatuorbozzini.ca
Phone: 514 667 0938
Address: 4816, rue Clark, CA
Information: Since 1999, the Bozzini Quartet has been an original voice in new, experimental and classical music. Their skew is radically contemporary, propelling the hyper-creative Montréal scene, and beyond. Not content to parlay received wisdom, the quartet cultivates an ethos of risk-taking, and boldly venture off the beaten track. With rigorous qualitative criteria, they have nurtured a vastly diverse repertoire, unbiased by the currents of fashion. This has led to over 180 commissioned pieces, as well as close to 300 other premiered works. A Bozzini Quartet concert is an art happening, with meticulous and sensuous attention to detail.
Country: Canada

Regina Symphony Orchestra
Website: www.reginasymphony.com
Email: info@reginasymphony.com
Address: 2424 College Avenue, CA
Country: Canada
Contact: Director of development Susanne Hamilton
Email: shamilton@reginasymphony.comoperations Manager Misty-Lee Selinger
Email: mselinger@reginasymphony.comMarketing and communications coordinator Alyssa Pittet
Email: apittet@reginasymphony.comExecutive Director Maxim Antoshin
Email: mantoshin@reginasymphony.ca

Saskatoon Symphony Orchestra
Website: www.saskatoonsymphony.org
Email: saskatoon.symphony@saskel.net
Address: 120-128 Fourth Avenue South, CA
Country: Canada
Contact: General Manager Jill Reid
Email: Artistic Director Douglas Sanford
Email: Director of Marketing Jacquie Berg
Email: musical Director Victor Sawa

Sault Ste Marie Symphony Orchestra
Website: www.saultsymphony.com
Email: info@saultsymphony.com
Phone: 705 945 5337
Address: 121 Brock Street, Suite 2, CA
Information: collaborate with the Algoma Fall Festival
Country: Canada
Contact: President Angela Rasaiah
Email: angela@saultsymphony.comprincipal conductor John Wilkinson
Email: info@saultsymphony.com

Sinfonia Mississauga
Website: www.mississaugasymphony.com
Email: mail@mississaugasymphony.com
Address: c/o Orchestras Mississauga, 4141 Living Arts Drive, CA
Country: Canada
music Director & conductor
John Barnum
Email: Executive Director Mike Plaus

St Cecilia Singers
Website: www.music.uwo.ca
Email: music@uwo.ca
Address: Don Wright Faculty of Music, University of Western Ontario, CA
Information: Student choir - Membership is by audition and is made up of both music and non-music majors from across campus
Country: Canada
Contact: conductor Gloria Gassi

Stick&Bow
Website: https://www.latitude45arts.com/stickbow
Email: info@latitude45arts.com
Phone: 514 276 2694
Address: 107, boul. St-Joseph West
Information: Stick&Bow, "The trailblazing Montreal duo that plays everything from Bach to Radiohead" (CBC Music's The Intro), unites Canadian marimba player Krystina Marcoux and Argentinian cellist Juan Sebastian Delgado. Classically trained musicians, they present a wide spectrum of musical styles, ranging from rock to gypsy-jazz and baroque to tango.
Country: Canada

Symphony Hamilton
Website: www.symphonyhamilton.ca
Email: info@symphonyhamilton.ca
Phone: 905 526 6690
Address: Box 89007, 991 King St. West, CA
Information: Symphony on the Bay is a community-based volunteer symphony orchestra serving Hamilton, Burlington and surrounding areas.
Country: Canada
Contact: General Manager Brenda Sandberg
Email: President Sydney Hassal
Email: librarian Graham Young
music Director & conductor
James R McKay

Symphony New Brunswick
Website: www.symphonynb.com
Email: symphony@nbnet.nb.ca
Phone: 506 634 0843
Address: Brunswick Square, Level III, 39 Kings Street, CA
Information: Free concerts for children.
Country: Canada
Contact: music Director and principal conductor Michael Newnham

Symphony Nova Scotia
Website: www.symphonynovascotia.ca
Email: CEO@symphonynovascotia.ca
Address: PO Box 218, 5657 Spring Garden Rd, Suite 301, CA
Information: CDs available
Country: Canada
Contact: Director of operations Mhiran Faraday
Email: operations@symphonyns.caDirector of Marketing and communiations Janice Fuller
Email: Marketing@symphonyns.caDirector of development Emma Penick
Email: development@symphonyns.capersonnel and production Manager Eric Mathias
Email: production@symphonyns.caCEO Erika Beatty
Email: CEO@symphonyns.ca

Tafelmusik Baroque Orchestra and Chamber Choir
Website: www.tafelmusik.org
Email: info@tafelmusik.org
Phone: 416 964 9562
Address: Trinity-St. Paul's Centre, 427 Bloor Street West, Box 14, CA
Information: Tafelmusik's vision is to be an international centre of excellence in period performance for generations to come. To sustain this vision, Tafelmusik is now creating artists and audiences for the future through artist training and audience development activities. Member of ISPA
Country: Canada
Contact: Managing Director William Norris
Director of Artistic Administration & operations
Beth Anderson
Email: banderson@tafelmusik.orgoperations coordinator Mara Brown
Email: mbrown@tafelmusik.org

Tambuco
Website: https://www.latitude45arts.com/tambuco
Email: info@latitude45arts.com
Phone: 514 276 2694
Address: 107, boul. St-Joseph West
Information: In their native Mexico and worldwide, Tambuco is known for its unique repertoire and breathtakingly vibrant performances. From body percussion, to sticks and stones, to modern percussion instruments, Tambuco's approach to sound and rhythm is virtuosic, visceral, and extraordinarily enjoyable.
Country: Canada

The Zodiac Trio
Website: https://www.latitude45arts.com/zodiac-trio
Email: info@latitude45arts.com
Phone: 514 276 2694
Address: 107, boul. St-Joseph West
Information: Over the past decade, the Zodiac Trio has established itself as the leading international trio of its kind, heralded by Radio France as "A breathtaking ensemble of virtuosity and sensitivity." Taking advantage of its unusual instrumentation of clarinet, violin and piano, the Zodiac Trio has been on the forefront of innovative programming, presenting 20th century masterpieces alongside new works and acclaimed original arrangements, offering the listener an immersive, musical

journey.
Country: Canada

Thunder Bay Symphony Orchestra
Website: www.tbso.ca
Email: info@tbso.ca
Address: PO Box 29192, CA

Timmins Symphony Orchestra
Website: www.timminssymphony.com
Email: info@timminssymphony.com
Address: PO Box 1365, CA
Information: runs the Timmins Symphony Geoffrey
James Lee School of Music
Country: Canada
Contact: conductor Matthew Jones
Email: President Kathy Vainio
Email: operations Manager Suzanne Robichaud

Toronto Philharmonia
Website: www.torontophilharmonia.com
Email: office@torontophil.on.ca
Address: 1210 Sheppard Ave East, Suite 109, CA
Information: fully professional orchestra, with both
international and Canadian guest artists
Country: Canada
music Director & conductor
Kerry Stratton
Email: Executive Director Linda Rogers

Toronto Symphony Orchestra
Website: www.tso.ca
Email: contactus@TSO.CA
Phone: 416 598 3375
Address: 145 Wellington St. W., , fifth floor (diagonally
southeast from Roy Thomson Hall), Suite 500, CA
Information: Founded in 1922, the Toronto Symphony
Orchestra is one of Canada's most important cultural
institutions, recognised internationally. Peter Oundjian,
now in his 13th season as the TSO's Music Director, leads
the Orchestra with a commitment to innovative pro-
gramming and audience engagement through a broad
range of performances that showcase the exceptional
talents of the Orchestra along with a roster of distinguished guest artists and conductors. Member of ISPA.
Country: Canada
Contact: chief Executive officer Matthew Loden
Email: Director of brand and communications Chris
Beard
Email: Artistic administrator David Dredla
Email: Director of public relations Francine Labelle

University of Calgary: Celebrity Series
Website: www.ffa.ucalgary.ca
Email: music@ucalgary.ca
Address: Dept of Music, U of C, 2500 University Drive
NW, CH F217, CA
Information: University music society performance.
Country: Canada
Contact: office assistant Susan Wong

Vancouver Recital Society
Website: www.vanrecital.com
Email: vrs@vanrecital.com
Phone: 604 602 0363
Address: 301 – 601 Cambie Street, Queen Elizabeth
Theatre Complex, CA
Information: The Vancouver Recital Society seeks to
foster and secure the future for classical chamber music
and recitals by engaging and enlightening audiences
through the presentation of the world's finest musicians,
both established and emerging. Member of IAMA
Country: Canada
Contact: Artistic Director Leila Getz
Email: leila.getz@vanrecital.comExecutive Director Sean
Bickerton
Email: sean@vanrecital.comMarketing and communica-
tions Manager Niamh Small
Email: niamh@vanrecital.com

Vancouver Symphony Orchestra
Website: www.vancouversymphony.ca
Email: reachus@vancouversymphony.ca
Phone: 604 684 9100
Address: 500 - 833 Seymour Street, CA
Information: Touring symphony orchestra at various
venues in Vancouver.
Country: Canada
Contact: chief development officer Leanne Davis
President & General Manager
Jeff Alexander
Director of Artistic operations & education
Joanne Harada
Email: Director of Marketing and Sales Alan Gove

Victoria Symphony (Society)
Website: www.victoriasymphony.ca
Email: Administration@victoriasymphony.ca
Address: 620 View Street Suite 610, CA
Information: the staff consist of both paid workers and
many volunteers. The musicians are 34 full-contract and
15 part-contract musicians. Each season the orchestra
gives more than 50 main series performances, as well as

a 2-week-long summer festival.
Country: Canada
Contact: Director of finance Pat Taylor
Email: Director of Marketing Bethany Wilson
Email: bethany@victoriasymphony.ca
personnel Manager & Artistic administrator
Peter Burris
Email: peter@victoriasymphony.caoffice administrator
Lynn Mesher
Email: Executive Director Mitchell Krieger
Email: mitchell@victoriasymphony.ca

Western Music - Don Wright Faculty of Music
Website: www.music.uwo.ca
Email: music@uwo.ca
Phone: 519 661 2111
Address: Don Wright Faculty of Music, Talbot College,
Room 210, CA
Information: student orchestra. Also has a choir
Country: Canada

Windsor Symphony Orchestra
Website: www.windsorsymphony.com
Email: shelley_sharpe@windsorsymphony.com
Phone: 519 973 1238
Address: 121 University Avenue, West, CA
Information: also organises family and educational
programs
Country: Canada
Contact: Marketing, communications and Sales Shelley
Sharpe
Email: shelley_sharpe@windsorsymphony.commusic
Director Robert Franz
Email: pwiebe@windsorsymphony.comExecutive Direc-
tor Sheila Wisdom
Email: swisdom@windsorsymphony.com

Winnipeg Symphony Orchestra
Website: www.wso.mb.ca
Email: wso@wso.mb.ca
Phone: 204 949 3999
Address: 555 Main Street, CA
Information: known for largest New Music Festival in
North America held annually, concerts 8 days, composer
competition
Country: Canada

CHINA

China National Symphony Orchestra
Website: www.cnso.com.cn
Email: cnsomail@126.com
Phone: 106 420 9692
Address: No. 11-1, He Ping (Jie) Street, Chao Yang District
Information: Since 1956, China's National Orchestra -
Central Philharmonic has been established, this art of
Chinese symphony "flagship" orchestra already stand the
forefront, sail over half a century, engraved in the history
of music under their own right into every monument.
Successive leaders and people of all circles at home
and abroad for the orchestra gave a warm concern and
support
Country: China

China Radio and Film Symphony Orchestra
Phone: 108 609 2785
Address: 26 Wen Hui Yuan Bei Road, Hai Dian District
Information: Over sixty years, along with the development of China's film and television music arts, the China
Radio and Film Symphony Orchestra has performed
music for nearly two thousand of films, TV dramas,
documentaries and special films. The Orchestra also
performed music in more than 40 countries and regions,
and played symphonic concerts, opera and ballets with
international conductors, composers, musicians and
dancers for many times to promote Chinese music development and international cultural exchange
Country: China

Chinese National Traditional Orchestra
Website: www.ccno.net
Phone: 106 491 3382
Address: No.15, Xiao Ying Road, Chao Yang District
Information: The China National Traditional Orchestra is
a state-level ensemble administered by China's Ministry
of Culture. It comprises a full orchestra and a chorus, all
members highly-esteemed both at home and abroad.
Carrying forward the cultural tradition of Chinese national music, CNO collects the essence of folk music as well
as contemporary works in performances at home and on
tour throughout Europe and the United States
Country: China

Guangzhou Philharmonic Orchestra
Phone: 208 771 1187
Address: 32 Shui Yin Si Heng Road, Sha He Ding
Information: After decades of Artistic growth, Guang-
zhou Philharmonic Orchestra becomes one of the most
prestigious orchestras in China
Country: China
Contact: principal conductor Liao Yuan
Email: Director Chen Shao-zhong

Guangzhou Symphony Orchestra

Website: www.gso.org.cn/en
Email: info@gso.org.cn
Phone: 203 758 8559
Address: 1 Haishan Street, Er Sha Island
Information: Since its founding in 1957, the Guangzhou
Symphony Orchestra (GSO) has developed into one of
China's most prestigious orchestras in its breadth of
organization and standard in performance. It is the first
and only Chinese symphony orchestra to have toured
and performed on five continents. The GSO is also one of
the very first orchestras in China to institute a profession-
al concert season
Country: China
Contact: Artistic Director Long Yu
Email: Foreign Department Cherry Chen

Shanghai Musicians Group
Email: elangao@hotmail.com
Phone: 216 555 5119
Address: c/o Gao Hua Xin, No. 2-1404, 630 Lane, Qu Yang
Road, Hong He District
Information: does not exist anymore
Country: China
Contact: Chairman Hua Xin Gao

Shanghai Philharmonic Orchestra
Email: spo@shphilharmonic.com
Phone: 216 252 3277
Address: 1498 Wuding Xi Road
Information: The Shanghai Philharmonic Orchestra (SPO)
is a professional symphony orchestra based in Shanghai,
China. It is under the Administration of the Shanghai Mu-
nicipal Administration of Culture, Radio, Film, and TV.The
current music Director is Muhai Tang and the deputy
Director is the young conductor Liang Zhang
Country: China

Shanghai Symphony Orchestra
Website: www.shsymphony.com
Email: shso105@sh163.net
Phone: 212 426 6128
Address: No.1380 Middle Fuxing Road
Information: The Shanghai Symphony Orchestra uses
music to communicate, connect and engage with audiences around the world. The symphony believes that
music – when exPressed in its essence – is an entirely different form of communication – a fourth way for humans
to communicate – beyond just the written word, spoken
language and body exPression. This music communi-
cates in a language that crosses all ethnic, social, cultural
and emotional boundaries
Country: China
Contact: performance Manager Ping Zhou

Shen Zhen Symphony Orchestra
Email: sso@21cn.net
Phone: 755 254 05114
Address: 2025 Huang Bei Road
Information: Shenzhen Symphony Orchestra (SSO) was
founded in 1982 and since then it has grown into one
of China's finest professional orchestras. The orchestra
has since distinguished itself as having a high level of
excellence and a rising international profile. Violinist Mr
Nie Bing is the current President of the orchestra
Country: China

Wu Promotion Co Ltd.
Website: www.wupromotion.com
Email: office@wupromotion.com
Phone: 105 165 0798
Address: B702, TYG Center, C2 Dongsanhuan Beilu
Information: Founded in Beijing in 1991 by Zezhou Wu
and Jiatong Wu, Wu Promotion is one of China's first and
leading performing arts promoters and event organisers.
Inspired by a deep passion and dedication to music,
Wu Promotion strives to enhance cultural exchange by
actively promoting the performing arts and capturing
the beauty and diversity of the world's culture through
unique events.
Country: China
Contact: Managing Director Jiatong Wu
Email: jiatong.wu@wupromotion.comsenior project
Manager Elena Piñuela
Email: elena.pinuela@wupromotion.comGeneral Manag-
er Maggie Zhen
Email: maggie.zheng@wupromotion.comProject Manag-
er for Greater China tours Xin Yu
Email: xin.yu@wupromotion.comDirector for Interna-
tional Tours Sherry Zhang
Email: sherry.zhang@wupromotion.comPR Media
Manager Donita Xie
Email: donita.xie@wupromotion.com
Social Media: www.facebook.com/WuPromotion www.
instagram.com/wupromotion

Xiamen Philharmonic Orchestra
Phone: 592 203 6307
Address: No. 67 Wen Yuan Road, Fujian Province
Information: The Xiamen Philharmonic Orchestra was
founded in 1998. The founder of the orchestra was Cai
Wanghuai, former Chairman of the Xiamen People's
Political Consultative Conference and currently the en-
semble's Honorary President. The Xiamen Philharmonic
Orchestra became the first private symphony orchestra

to exist without the support of State-run institutions
Country: China

Youth Symphony Orchestra
Website: www.ccom.edu.cn
Phone: 106 642 5662
Address: c/o Central Conservatory of Music, 43 Bao Jia Street, Xi Cheng district
Information: Established in 1940 as the National College of Music and merged with several music educational institutions in 1949, the Central Conservatory of Music (CCOM) is a specialized Chinese institution of higher education for nurturing high level music professionals
Country: China

COLOMBIA

Cuarteto de piano Altisonante
Website: cuartetoaltisonante.wix.com/4altisonante
Email: cuartetoaltisonante@gmail.com
Phone: 131 674 58392
Address: Cra 55 D # 175-31, CO
Information: female piano quartet from the Colombia National University (Universidad Nacional de Colombia - Sede Bogotá) playing 6 hand piano, 8 hand piano and 8 hand 2 pianos music pieces
Country: Colombia

GUAM

Guam Symphony Society
Website: www.guamsymphony.org
Email: symphony@ite.net
Phone: 671 477 1959
Address: PO Box 4069, GU
Country: GU
music Director & conductor
Stephen Bednarzyk
Email: President Donna Kloppenburg

HONG KONG

Academy Symphony Orchestra
Website: www.hkapa.edu
Email: PRDepartment@hkapa.edu
Phone: 258 48500
Address: Hong Kong Academy for Performing Arts, School of Music, 1 Gloucester Road, Wanchai, HK
Information: All orchestral instrument students participate in the Academy Symphony Orchestra. Weekly rehearsals cover standard symphonic literature as well as modern works. The Orchestra has performed under the batons of Sir Neville Marriner, Georg Tintner, Trevor Pinnock, Takuo Yuasa, Christoph Campestrini, Joseph Silverstein, and Francois-Xavier Roth, and has worked with famous soloists including Nigel Kennedy (violin), Julian Lloyd Webber (cello), Robert Holl (bass baritone), Andrew Marriner (clarinet), Guy Barker (trumpet), Paul Badura-Skoda (piano) and Malcolm Bilson (fortepiano)
Country: Hong Kong
Contact: dean of music Benedict Cruft

Asian Youth Orchestra (AYO)
Website: www.asianyouthorchestra.com
Email: ayo@asianyouthorchestra.com
Phone: 286 61623
Address: 15A, One Capital Place, 18 Luard Road, 18 Luard Road, HK
Information: This is Asia's premier pre-professional orchestra for advanced study, performance and international concert touring with celebrated artists and conductors
Country: Hong Kong
Contact: Chairman James Thompson
Email: founder and Artistic Director Richard Pontzious
Email: General Manager Keith Lau

China Philharmonic Orchestra
Website: www.chinaphilharmonic.org
Email: ayytzyn@126.com
Phone: 108 838 4159
Address: Room D1, 6/F, King's Vie Court, 901 King's Road, Quarry Bay, HK
Information: China Philharmonic Orchestra is a non-profit organisation which aims to promote cultural exchange between Hong Kong and China through joint performance of local and Chinese musicians. Its inaugural concert was held on December 16, 2000 and conducted by Artistic Director Long Yu. Their first season included the world premiere by Julian Lloyd Webber of the Cello Concerto No. 1 by Philip Glass and the symphonic Beijing opera Women Generals of the Yangs by Du Mingxin, their first commissioned symphonic work
Country: Hong Kong
Contact: artist Manager Zhao Yanan
Email: ayytzyn@126.com

Hong Kong Children's Choir
Website: www.hkcchoir.org
Email: info@hkcchoir.org
Phone: 271 56525
Address: 1/F, 1 Larch Street, Tai Kok Tsui, Kowloon, HK
Information: HKCC strives to develop children's Artistic

talents, their creativity and interests in arts, as well as to develop their inter-personal skills and cultivate their sensitivity to appreciate culture and the virtues of excellence
Country: Hong Kong

Hong Kong Chinese Orchestra
Website: www.hkco.org/
Email: inquiries@hkco.org
Phone: 318 51600
Address: 7/F Sheung Wan Municipal Services Building, 345 Queen's Road Central, HK
Information: The only professional, full-sized Chinese orchestra in Hong Kong. Its mission to promote and develop Chinese music. It has commissioned over 2400 new works in a variety of styles. The orchestra organises over 100 regular and outreach concerts as well as being invited to many international festivals.
Contact: Executive Director Celina Chin Man-wah
Email: Head of Programme, Education and Touring Patricia Sun Li-chuan
Social Media: www.facebook.com/pages/ Hong-Kong-Chinese-Orchestra/27447879125?fref=ts
Touring Countries: AT, AU, SG, JP, KZ, CN, NZ, IE, RU, BE, NO, TW, MO, CA, US, GB, DE, FR, CZ
Regular Venues: 0

Hong Kong Chinese Orchestra
Website: www.hkco.org
Email: inquiries@hkco.org
Phone: 318 51600
Address: 7/F Sheung Wan Municipal Services Building, 345 Queen's Road Central, HK
Information: This is the only professional Chinese orchestra in Hong Kong. It has commissioned thousands of new and arranged works, and presents free student concerts and outreach activities on a regular basis for all sectors of the community, as well as organising master classes and workshops
Country: Hong Kong
Contact: Executive Director Celina Chin Man-wah head of finance, personnel & Administration Vince Lau King Shan

Hong Kong Philharmonic Orchestra
Website: www.hkphil.org
Email: enquiries@hkpo.com
Phone: 272 12030
Address: Level 8, Administration Building, Hong Kong Cultural Centre, Tsim Sha Tsui, Kowloon, HK
Information: The mission of the Hong Kong Philharmonic Orchestra is to inspire and expand musical appreciation in Hong Kong, and to be a financially secure institution that brings distinction to the music world through its enriching performances and premier international standing
Country: Hong Kong
Contact: musical Director Jaap van Zweden
Email: Chairman Y. S. Liu
Email: chief Executive officer Michael MacLeod

Hong Kong Sinfonietta Limited
Website: www.hksl.org
Email: info@hksinfonietta.org
Phone: 283 63336
Address: 3/F Winsan Tower, , 98 Thomson Road, Wanchai, HK
Information: founded in 1990 by a group of local musicians, Hong Kong Sinfonietta is one of Hong Kong's flagship orchestras. With conductor Yip Wing-sie as Music Director, the orchestra has brought music closer to the community, and has achieved significant recognition locally and internationally for its passionate performances and innovative programming. Alternate email: enquiries@hksinfonietta.org. Member of IAMA
Country: Hong Kong
Contact: music Director Yip Wing-sie
Email: chief Executive officer Margaret Yang
Email: public relations and markerting Manager Amanda Mok

May Sing Chorus (permanently closed)
Email: greenhillmusic@yahoo.com.hk
Phone: 242 88996
Address: Flat B 26F Block 2 Kwai Chun Plaza, Kwai Fong, New Territories, HK
Information: May Sing Chorus is a non-profitmaking registered company.They perform in different venues
Country: Hong Kong
Contact: Manager Kei Fung Wong
Email: Chairman Wong Yin Lam

Pan Asia Symphony Orchestra
Phone: 226 87321
Address: 1F Wah Chi Mansion, 292 Temple Street, Kowloon, HK
Information: Pan Asia Symphony Orchestra is a highly organised orchestra aiming at promoting music among the General public especially the young generation in Hong Kong. In order to achieve its goal, the Orchestra has performed frequently in the Hong Kong City Hall, regional town halls and civic centres a few hundred times for more than 30 years. A number of internationally famous conductors and soloists have been invited to perform with it. By using the idioms of popular music and organizing concert talks, the Orchestra has success-

fully introduced serious music and Chinese orchestral music to the public, and at the same time, brought about an awareness of the indigenous culture of the people
Country: Hong Kong

The Hong Kong Philharmonic Society
Website: www.hkphil.org
Email: enquiries@hkphil.org
Phone: 272 12030
Address: Level 8, Administration Building, Hong Kong Cultural Centre, Tsim Sha Tsui, Kowloon, HK
Information: the mission of the Hong Kong Philharmonic is to inspire and expand musical appreciation in Hong Kong and beyond, and to be a financially secure institution that brings distinction to the music world through its enriching performances and premier international standing
Country: Hong Kong
Contact: Artistic Director Jaap van Zweden
Email: Artisticadmin@hkphil.org

Zero Zero Ensemble
Email: zzensemble@yahoo.com.hk
Phone: 856 226 1190
Address: 1528, On Pak House, Cheung On Estate, Tsing Yi, HK
Information: Zero Zero Ensemble performs contemporary dance
Country: Hong Kong
Contact: Artistic Director Force Chung Kuen Fong

INDONESIA

Bel Canto Productions
Email: belcanto@cbn.net.id
Phone: 831 6808
Address: no. 4, Menteng Dalam, ID
Information: produces a chamber-size concert from areas of operas to the 1950s sing-a-song; emphasis on vocal music; very up-market with expensive ticket prices
Country: ID
Contact: Producer Pooh Leow

Camerata di Musica Jakarta
Email: info@yayasanmusikjakarta.org
Phone: 216 398 596
Address: Jalan Kartini Raya, 53 AB-AD, ID
Country: ID

Depot Kreasi Seni Bandung (DKSB)
Phone: 622 272 05527
Address: Jl WR Supratman 57, ID
Country: ID
Contact: music Director Harry Roesli

Jakarta Arts Institute
Phone: 213 24807
Address: Dept. of Music, Institut Kesenia Jakarta-IKJ, TIM, J1. Cikini Raya 73, ID
Information: the institute is a home for young talented composers students who establish themselves in the national music scene; very keen to make international collaborations
Country: ID

Jakarta Philharmonia
Email: philharmonia_2000@yahoo.com
Phone: 622 158 41281
Address: Jl. HR Rasuna Said, Kuningan, ID
Information: a very recent venture of Jakarta Municipality to receive the classical music in the city; gradually will develop to be a string orchestra with 40 musicians, before enlarging to be a romantic orchestra (with string, brass and percussion played) by the end
Country: ID
Contact: music Director I G Bagus Wiswakarma
Email: Artistic Director Sulistyo Utomo

Nusantara Symphony Orchestra
Website: www.nusantaraorchestra.com
Email: nso@cbn.net.id
Phone: 217 397 869
Address: Kompleks Duta Mas Blok B2 No.16, Jl. RS Fatmawati No. 39, ID
Country: ID
Contact: Executive Director Aida Swenson
Email: music Director Otto Sidharta

Twilite Orchestra
Website: www.twiliteorchestra.org
Email: twilite@dnet.net.id
Address: Jl. Taman Pinang Nikel PR 35, Pondok Indah, ID
Information: a pops orchestra that tries to attract people by playing popular tunes including soundtrack while introducing a classical music to audiences including school children
Country: ID
music Director & conductor
Addie MS

Young Composer Week
Phone: 622 047 58202
Address: J1. Cipinang Timur, RT 004/RW 03, No. 10, ID
Information: once a regular, prestigious forum for young talents in the 1980s, the festival had been put on hold

香 港 中 樂 團
HONG KONG CHINESE ORCHESTRA
藝術總監：閻惠昌
ARTISTIC DIRECTOR : YAN HUICHANG

Hong Kong Chinese Orchestra
Anytime! Anywhere!

H K C O
NET CONCERT HALL

www.hkconetconcerthall.com

for 10 years due to funding problem: in 1998 it was just relived
Country: ID
Contact: contact Suka Hardjana

JAPAN

Bach Choir
Email: sangokaku@jcom.home.ne.jp
Address: 3-17-17 Nishi-Oizumi, Nerima-ku, JP
Country: Japan
Contact: conductor Hiroshi Kubota
Email: Director Yoko Kuwahara

Bach-Choir Tokyo
Website: www2.tky.3web.ne.jp
Email: bachchortokyo@aol.com
Address: 5-17-21-101 Funabashi, Setagaya-ku, JP
Country: Japan
Director & conductor
Emiko Omura

Bamboo Symphonia
Website: www.harmonyjapan.com
Email: artistsbox@aol.com
Phone: 334 111 233
Address: c/o Artist Box, 2-46-1 Komazawa, Setagaya-ku, JP
Information: consists of the more than 20 bamboo instruments of Japan and other Asian countries; instruments include: Shakuhachi, Shinobue, Sho, Pan-flute, Maui-marimba, Jegog-marimba, Bamboo-marimba, Angklung, Pinjakan, Romdemalam, etc.
Country: Japan
Artistic & Managing Director
Ozan Shibata

Central Aichi Orchestra
Website: www.caso.jp
Email: office@caso.jp
Phone: 525 813 851
Address: 6-15 Saikoh-dori, Atsuta-ku, Nagoya, JP
Information: medium-sized orchestra
Country: Japan

Century Orchestra Osaka
Website: www.century-orchestra.jp/
Address: 1-7 Hattori-Ryokuchi, Toyonaka, JP
Information: C.O.O. was established by the Osaka Prefectural Government in 1989 and it is managed by the Osaka Foundation of Culture (q.v.)
Country: Japan
Contact: secretary General Tetsuyuki Ideno
Email: chief conductor Kazuhiro Koizumi
Email: honorary conductor Uriel Segal
Email: President Michio Izuma
Email: conductor Seikyo Kim

Choir Kyo (Gasshodan Kyo)
Website: homepage3.nifty.com/choirkyo/en/index.htm
Email: thompay@mbe.nifty.com
Address: Ritsuyukai Office , 102 Haitsu Kuze, 2-28-4 Higashi Ikebukuro, Toshima-ku, JP
Information: regularly performs in annual concerts, radio and TV broadcasts and choral competitions; commissions new works; their highest technical level covers diversity of voice texture from bel canto to traditional Japanese singing
Country: Japan
Contact: 1st principal conductor Yoshinori Koba
Email: music Director Fumiaki Kuriyama
Email: chief Manager Kazuyuki Seki

Gunma Symphony Orchestra
Website: gunkyo.com
Email: office@gunkyo.com
Phone: 273 224 316
Address: 35-1 Takamatsu-cho, Takasaki-shi, JP
Country: Japan

Heinrich Sch
Website: www.collegium.or.jp/index_e.html
Email: office@collegium.or.jp
Phone: 669 290 792
Address: c/o Osaka Collegium Musicum, 2-11-17 Miyuki-cho, Miyakojima-ku, JP
Information: has wide repertoire and clear harmony
Country: Japan
President & conductor
Shuichi Tohma
Email: choir master Chikako Kurahashi
Email: Manager Akiko Okita

Hiroshima Symphony Orchestra
Email:
hirokyo@hiroshima-cdas.or.jp
Phone: 825 442 900
Address: 4F, Kokutaiji Shin-ai Bldg., 1-8-20 Kokutaiji, Naka-ku, JP
Information: its most important role is to appeal for peace as an orchestra in the city which has a tragic history of the atomic bombing in the past
Country: Japan
Contact: President Seisou Kitano
Email: Managing Director Hideto Ohno

Email: musical Director and permanent conductor Kazuyoshi Akiyama

Hyogo Performing Arts Center Orchestra
Website: www.gcenter-hyogo.jp
Phone: 798 680 203
Address: 2-22, Takamatsu-cho, Nishinomiya-City, JP
Information: 48 members; see also Venues (Hyogo Performing Arts Center)
Country: Japan
Contact: Artistic Director Yutaka Sado
Email: Associate conductor Yannick Pagel

Japan Chamber Orchestra
Website: www.japanarts.co.jp/
Phone: 334 998 090
Address: c/o Japan Arts Co-operation, 2-1-6 Shibuya, Shibuya-ku, JP
Country: Japan

Japan Philharmonic Orchestra
Website: www.japanphil.or.jp
Email: office@japanphil.or.jp
Phone: 353 786 311
Address: 1-6-1 Umezato, Suginami-ku, JP
Information: became a self-governing organisation in 1972; in 1973 the Japan Philharmonic Association was established to support the orchestra
Country: Japan
Contact: guest chief conductor Neeme J
Email: principal conductor Ryusuke Numajiri
Email: Managing Director Shuhei Deguchi
Email: founder conductor Akeo Watanabe
Email: music Director Kenichiro Kobayashi (to June 2008)
Email: music Director Alexander Lazarev (from Sept 2008)

Kanagawa Philharmonic Orchestra
Website: kanaphil.com
Email: kanaphil@mbf.sphere.ne.jp
Phone: 453 314 001
Address: 4-2 Hanamidai, Hodogaya-ku, Yokohama, JP
Information: as a symbol of the culture in Kanagawa prefecture, the Orchestra presents both concerts and accompanying music for ballet; also acts as a key orchestra for Kanagawa Arts Foundation's (q.v.) activities
Country: Japan
Contact: principal conductor Shigeo Genda
Email: Chairman Yutaka Hirano
Email: pops orchestra music Director Koichi Fujino
Email: vice General Director Ken Satoh
Email: guest chief conductor Hanns-Martin Schneidt

Kansai Philharmonic Orchestra
Website: www4.ocn.ne.jp/~kpo/
Email: kan-firu@fancy.ocn.ne.jp
Phone: 665 771 381
Address: 7F Nishi-kan, Orc 2-bangai, 1-2-4-700 Benten, Minato-ku, JP
Country: Japan
Contact: representative Noriyuki Inoue
Email: President conductor Sachio Fujioka
Email: secretary General Hideki Nishihama
Email: conductor David Howell
Email: principal conductor Taijiro Iimori

Kioi Sinfonietta Tokyo
Website: www.kioi-hall.or.jp
Email: kst@kioi-hall.or.jp
Phone: 352 764 500
Address: 6-5 Kioi-cho, Chiyoda-ku, JP
Information: resident orchestra of Kioi Hall (q.v.); both the Orchestra and the Hall are owned and managed by Nippon Steel Arts Foundation (q.v.); the Orchestra members are chosen from those who normally perform as soloists or as other ensemble players
Country: Japan
Contact: secretary-General Ryuichi Machida
Email: Chairman nippon steel arts foundation Akira Chihaya
Email: General Manager of production section Katsuto Takeshita
Email: orchestra honorary conductor laureate: Tadaa

Kobe Philharmonic
Website: www.kobephilharmonic.jp
Email: info@kobephilharmonic.jp
Phone: 782 227 105
Address: 5-3-1 Kumoi-dori, Chuo-ku, Kobe, JP
Country: Japan
Contact: music Director Chitaru Asahina

Kodo
Website: www.kodo.or.jp
Email: heartbeat@kodo.or.jp
Phone: 259 863 630
Address: Kodo Village, 148-1 Ogi Kanetashinden, JP
Information: world-famous Japanese traditional drum performance group; its objectives are the creation of new directions as well as the study and preservation of the tradition; active in cultural exchange through joint performances, festivals and workshops
Country: Japan

Contact: Managing Director Takao Aoki
Email: Artistic Director Tamasaburo Bando

Kohkyohgakudan Shin Tokyo Philharmonic
Website: www.tokyo-c-orch.co.jp
Email: office@tokyo-c-orch.co.jp
Phone: 339 827 237
Address: 2-12-2-403 Ikebukuro Honcho, Toshima-ku, JP
Information: owned by Tokyo Chamber Orchestra (q.v.)
Country: Japan
Contact: President Hatsue Kitsukawa

Konoe Kangen Gakudan
Phone: 337 140 811
Address: 5-21-12 Meguro-honcho, Meguro-ku, JP
Country: Japan
President & conductor
Hidetake Konoe

Kyoto Symphony Orchestra (KSO)
Website: www.city.kyoto.jp/bunshi/symphony/
Phone: 752 220 331
Address: 103 Tatemoto-cho, Izumoji, Kita-ku, JP
Country: Japan
General Director & mayor of kyoto
Yorikane Masumoto
Email: Manager Toko Aoyama
Email: chief conductor Junichi Hirokami (from April 2008
Email: Artistic Manager Mitsuru Yoshida
Email: assistant Manager Koji Miwa

Kyushu Symphony Orchestra
Website: orchestra.musicinfo.co.jp/~kyukyo
Email: kyukyo@par.odn.ne.jp
Phone: 928 228 855
Address: c/o Suenaga Culture Center, 1-11-50 Nanakuma, Jonan-ku, JP
Country: Japan
Contact: Chairman Toyohiko Goto
principal conductor & music advisor
Kazuyoshi Akiyama

Mito Chamber Orchestra (MCO)
Website: www.arttowermito.or.jp
Email: ankmr@arttowermito.or.jp
Phone: 292 278 118
Address: 1-6-8 Goken-cho, Mito, JP
Information: resident orchestra of Art Tower Mito (q.v.); its players, who are usually active internationally as other orchestra members and soloists, get together to hold concerts twice a year
Country: Japan
Contact: President Hanae Mori
Email: musical advisor Seiji Ozawa
General intendant & head of orchestra
Tatsuo Oguchi
Email: chief of Administration Takaki Yazawa
Email: Director of mito geijyutsu-kan Hidekazu Yoshida
Email: Administration Tetsuya Sekine

Nagoya Philharmonic Orchestra
Website: www.nagoya-phil.or.jp/english/
Email: meiphil@nagoya-phil.or.jp
Phone: 523 222 774
Address: Nagoya City Music Plaza 4F, 1-4-10 Kanayama Naka-ku, JP
Country: Japan
Contact: Chairman of the board Chiaki Yamaguchi
Email: honorary guest conductor Thierry Fischer
Email: music Director Kazuhiro Koizumi
Email: honorary conductor Moshe Atzmon
Email: conductor laureate Ken'ichiro Kobayashi
Email: resident conductor Kentaro Kawase

New Japan Philharmonic
Website: www.njp.or.jp
Email: info@njp.or.jp
Phone: 356 085 400
Address: Kinshi 1-2-3, Sumida-ku, JP
Information: a resident orchestra at Sumida Triphony Hall
Country: Japan

New Philharmony Orchestra Chiba
Website: homepage2.nifty.com/NPOC/
Email: LES07404@nifty.ne.jp
Phone: 432 224 231
Address: 11-2 Ichiba-cho, Chuo-ku, JP
Country: Japan
Contact: Chairman Akiko Doumoto

NHK Symphony Orchestra
Website: www.nhkso.or.jp
Phone: 357 938 111
Address: 2-16-49 Takanawa, Minato-ku, JP
Information: originally founded as the New Symphony Orchestra in 1926, the Orchestra changed its name to the NHK Symphony Orchestra in 1951 when it began receiving full financial assistance from NHK Japan Broadcasting Corporationq.v.; invites first-class musicians fro
Country: Japan
Contact: music Director, emeritus Charles Dutoit
Email: Chairman Kazuhiro Tabata

Email: permanent conductor Yuzo Toyama
Email: permanent conductor Hiroshi Wakasugi
Email: music Director Vladimir Ashkenazy
Email: honorary conductors Otmar Suitner, Horst Stein

Nissho Academy Chorus
Website: www2.odn.ne.jp/~aau86650
Email: nissho@par.odn.ne.jp
Phone: 337 914 088
Address: 1F Nakajima Bldg, 1-11-19 Ebisu Minami, Shibuya-ku, JP
Country: Japan
Contact: representative Yumio Kusumi
Email: permanent honorary music Director Kazuo Yamada
music advisor & composer
Bin Ebisawa
Email: conductor Hidetoshi Katano
Email: principal conductor Hiroshi Koizumi

Orchestra Asia
Website: www.seibun.or.jp
Email: center@seibun.or.jp
Phone: 332 956 147
Address: c/o Nihon Seishonen Bunka Center, 2-1-8 Sarugaku-cho, Chiyoda-ku, JP
Information: established in 1993 by musicians and Producers from China, Korea and Japan, for the purpose of making an Asian orchestra; consists of 27 Asian traditional instruments which play existing and new Asian works
Country: Japan
Contact: secretary General Tamio Tamura
Email: Artistic Director / conductor Park Bum Hoon
Email: planning Yasunori Ono
Email: production Yoshihiro Nara

Orchestra Ensemble Kanazawa
Website: www.oek.jp
Email: office@oek.jp
Phone: 762 320 171
Address: c/o The Ishikawa Orchestra Foundation, 20-1 Showa-machi, Kanazawa, JP
Country: Japan
Contact: deputy General Manager Florian Riem
Email: General Manager Masayuki Yamada
Email: principal guest conductor G

Orchestra Osaka Symphoniker
Website: www.sym.jp
Email: mail@sym.jp
Phone: 722 265 533
Address: 4F Toyo Bldg., 3-1-15 Kita Hanadaguchi-cho, Sakai, JP
Country: Japan
Contact: principal guest conductor Vladim
Email: President Hiroko Shikishima
music advisor & principal conductor
Heiichiro Ohyama
Email: General Manager Tetsuo Shikishima
Email: resident conductor Kiyotaka Teraoka

Osaka Collegium Musicum
Website: www.collegium.or.jp
Email: office@collegium.or.jp
Phone: 669 264 755
Address: Chuo-ku, Osaka Otedori 1-chome, 1-13 GI Pearl building 2F
Information: Osaka Collegium Musicum was founded by TOMA Shuichi in November 1975, to act upon the principles of the former 'colleguim musicum'. Since then they have been giving monthly concerts, and their orchestra and choir now give regular concerts five or six times a year. In addition, they have recently been giving some special concert performances including, 'The series of contemporary music' and 'The series of Japanese choral music'.
Country: Japan
Social Media: @Toma_Shuichi www.facebook.com/OsakaCollegiumMusicum

Osaka Philharmonic Chorus
Website: www.osaka-phil.com
Email: info@osaka-phil.com
Phone: 666 567 711
Address: c/o Osaka Philharmonic Orchestra, 1-1-44 Kishinosato, Nishinari-ku, JP
Country: Japan

Osaka Philharmonic Orchestra
Website: www.osaka-phil.com
Email: info@osaka-phil.com
Phone: 666 567 711
Address: 1-1-44 Kishinosato, Nishinari-ku, JP
Country: Japan
Contact: secretary General Shoji Onodera
Email: General music Director Eiji Oue

Pro Musica Nipponia
Website: www.promusica.or.jp/
Email: office@promusica.or.jp
Phone: 333 784 741
Address: 302 Takizawa Bldg., 3-17-1 Sasazuka, Shibuya-ku, JP
Information: since 1964, the ensemble has given performances in Japan of contemporary works using tradition-

al Japanese instruments; tours overseas extensively; see entries under National Organisations
Country: Japan
Contact: President Takuo Tamura

Saito Kinen Orchestra
Website: www.saito-kinen.com
Email: skftokyo@saito-kinen.com
Phone: 334 836 495
Address: 3F, 6-13-21 Seijo, Setagaya-ku, JP
Information: founded in 1984 when Seiji Ozawa organized a special concert series to commemorate the tenth anniversary of the death of Hideo Saito, the renowned Japanese educator who founded the distinguished Toho Gakuen School in Tokyo; under the leadership of Ozawa
Country: Japan
Contact: personnel Manager Yoshiko Shiga
Email: General Manager Yasuyuki Kurita
Email: conductor Seiji Ozawa

Sapporo Symphony Orchestra
Website: sso.or.jp
Email: info@sso.or.jp
Phone: 115 201 771
Address: c/o Sapporo Concert Hall, 1-15, Nakajima Koen, Chuo-ku, Sapporo, JP
Information: strives to reflect in its music the natural beauty and European climate of Japan's northernmost major island, the province of Hokkaido
Country: Japan
Contact: Principal Conductor Matthias Bamert
Email: Managing Director Kazuhito Torii
Email: Chairman of the board Masatoshi Murata

Sendai Philharmonic Orchestra
Website: www.sendaiphil.jp/
Email: info@sendaiphil.jp
Phone: 222 253 934
Address: 1-3-9 Nishiki-cho, Aoba-ku, Sendai, JP
Country: Japan
Contact: General Manager Tatsuo Kori
Email: Artistic Director Akihiro Nozaki

Symphonia Collegium Osaka
Website: www.collegium.or.jp
Phone: 669 290 792
Address: c/o Osaka Collegium Musicum, 2-11-17 Miyuki-cho, Miyakojima-ku, JP
Information: play with Heinrich Sch
Country: Japan
Contact: stage Manager Yoko Ono
Email: concert master Reiko Morita
President & conductor
Shuichi Toma
Email: Manager Akiko Okita

Telemann Chamber Choir
Website: www.telemann.ws
Email: nakahara@cafe-telemann.com
Phone: 663 451 046
Address: 2-1-17 Sonezaki Shinchi, Kita-ku, JP
Information: see also Telemann Institute Japan, Collegium Musicum Telemann, Telemann Chamber Orchestra
Country: Japan
Contact: music Director Takeharu Nobuhara

Telemann Chamber Orchestra
Website: www.telemann.ws
Email: nakahara@cafe-telemann.com
Phone: 663 451 046
Address: 2-1-17 Sonezaki Shinchi, Kita-ku, JP
Information: modern instruments ensemble; see also Collegium Musicum Telemann, Telemann Institute Japan, Telemann Chamber Choir
Country: Japan
music Director & conductor
Takeharu Nobuhara

Tokyo Chamber Orchestra
Website: www.tokyo-c-orch.co.jp
Phone: 339 827 237
Address: 2-12-2-403 Ikebukuro hon-cho, Toshima-ku, JP
Information: also has Kohkyohgakudan
Country: Japan
Contact: President Hatsue Kitsukawa

Tokyo City Philharmonic Orchestra
Website: www.cityphil.jp
Email: mail@cityphil.jp
Phone: 356 244 001
Address: 1-19-1-203 Sumiyoshi, Kohtoh-ku, JP
Information: its varied activities include regular concerts, youth concerts, religious music, opera, ballet, performances for radio, TV and recording
Country: Japan
Contact: Executive Director Keizo Kodama
Email: principal conductor Taijiro Iimori
Email: principal guest conductor Hikotaro Yazaki

Tokyo International Music Ensemble (TIME)
Website: www.tokyo-concerts.co.jp
Email: info@tokyo-concerts.co.jp
Phone: 332 269 755
Address: c/o Tokyo Concerts Inc., 6F Belx Shinjuku Bld II, 23 Aizumi-cho, Shinjuku-ku, JP

Information: plays contemporary music with mixture of Japanese traditional instruments and Western instruments; managed by Tokyo Concerts Inc (q.v.)
Country: Japan

Tokyo Kosei Wind Orchestra (TKWO)
Website: www.tkwo.jp
Email: office@tkwo.jp
Phone: 353 411 155
Address: Fumonkan, 2-6-1 Wada, Suginami-ku, JP
Information: established in 1960; commissions original works for wind orchestra from composers both in Japan and abroad; recorded over 180 CDs
Country: Japan
Contact: leader Hiroyasu Kanamori

Tokyo Metropolitan Symphony Orchestra
Website: www.tmso.or.jp
Email: tmsoinfo@tmso.or.jp
Phone: 338 220 727
Address: 1F Tokyo Bunka Kaikan, 5-45 Ueno Koen, Taito-ku, JP
Information: provides people in Tokyo with excellent concerts at affordable prices; has a concert series with features Japanese composer every year; CDs available
Country: Japan
Contact: honorary conductor Jean Fournet
Email: permanent conductor James DePriest
Email: General Director Akira kojima
Email: vice President Hiroichi Yamamoto
Email: chief guest conductor Kazuhiro Koizumi
intendant & Director
Kei Ohta

Tokyo Musical Ensemble
Website: www.d8.dion.ne.jp/~s_kimata
Email: s_kimata@d8.dion.ne.jp
Phone: 424 887 659
Address: 107, 4-23-47 Nishi-Tsutsujigaoka, Chofu, JP
Country: Japan
Contact: Director Sadao Kimata

Tokyo Philharmonic Chorus
Website: www.tokyo-concerts.co.jp/artist/f_artist.html
Email: kobayashi@tokyo-concerts.co.jp
Phone: 332 269 755
Address: 6F Belx-shinjuku Bld.2, 23 Aizumi-cho, Shinjuku-ku, JP
Information: founded in 1965; Japan's foremost independent professional group in the field; has enjoyed continuous concert and recording activities, performing works of various ages and genres from Palestrina to contemporary Japanese composers; both at home and abroad
Country: Japan

Tokyo Philharmonic Orchestra
Website: www.tpo.or.jp
Email: tophil@tpo.or.jp
Phone: 353 539 521
Address: 11F Tokyo Opera City Tower, 3-20-2 Nishi-Shinjuku, Shinjuku-ku, JP
Information: established in 1911; the oldest orchestra in Japan
Country: Japan
Contact: conductor laureate Kazushi Ono
Email: principal guest conductor Pascal Verrot
Email: conductor Kazumasa Watanabe
Email: permanent honorary conductor Kazuo Yamada
Email: honorary conductor Ondrej Lenard
Email: principal guest conductor Janos Kavacs
Email: special Artistic advisor Myung-Whun Chung
Email: principal guest conductor Vladimir Fedoseyev
Email: permanent conductor Yoichiro Omachi
Email: Chairman of the board Norio Ohga
Email: conductor laureate Tadaaki Otaka

Tokyo Symphony Orchestra
Website: www.tokyosymphony.com
Email: tokyosymphony@musicinfo.com
Phone: 333 626 764
Address: 2-23-5 Hyakunin-cho, Shinjuku-ku, JP
Information: since its foundation in 1946 the Orchestra has been energetically realizing activities such as giving premiere performances of many works of Japanese composers and also introducing works of composers world-wide; Kawasaki Office ; 5F MUZA Kawasaki Central
Country: Japan
Contact: permanent honorary conductor Arvid Jansons
Email: permanent honorary conductor Masashi Ueda
Email: President Tadashi Yokokawa
Email: music Director Hubert Soudant
Email: conductor laureate Kazuyoshi Akiyama
Email: public relations Midori Takase
Email: General Director Yoshihiko Yamashita
Email: permanent honorary conductor Shinji Touyama
Email: permanent conductor Naoto Otomo
Email: resident conductor Norichika Iimori

Tokyo Universal Philharmony Orchestra
Website: www.uniphil.gr.jp/
Email: info@uniphil.gr.jp
Phone: 337 660 876
Address: 6-5-17 Omori Nishi, Ota-ku, JP
Country: Japan

Contact: music Director Seiichi Mitsuishi
Email: President Takashi Kawamura

Usuki Masato World
Website: www.usuki-world.com
Email: info@usuki-world.com
Phone: 333 337 278
Address: 2-19-14 Takaido Higashi, Suginami-ku, JP
Information: has many fans for Usuki's charismatic performance notably among the young audience; aims to foster young talents and to disseminte classical music
Country: Japan
music Director & conductor
Masato Usuki

Yamagata Symphony Orchestra
Website: www.dewa.or.jp/~yamakyo
Email: yamakyo@dewa.or.jp
Phone: 236 252 203
Address: c/o Yamagataken Shinchiku Nishidohri Kaikan, 1-9-30 Midori-cho, Yamagata-shi, JP
Country: Japan
Contact: honorary conductor Hideomi Kuroiwa
Email: conductor Toshiyuki Kudo
founder & honorary conductor
Chiaki Murakawa
Email: General Manager Shiro Sagae
Email: Chairperson Takako Miyake
Email: permanent conductor Norichika Iimori

Yomiuri Nippon Symphony Orchestra
Website: yomikyo.yomiuri.co.jp
Email: yomikyo@k3.dion.ne.jp
Phone: 335 621 540
Address: 7F Daiichi Nurihiko Bldg., 2-9-2 Kyobashi, Chuo-ku, JP
Information: established in 1962 to contribute to the promotion and development of performing arts and culture in music; founded by three media companies: the Yomiuri Shimbun ((q.v.)), the Nippon Television Network Corporations ((q.v.)) and Yomiuri Telecasting Corpora
Country: Japan
Contact: honorary conductor Kurt Masur
Email: principal conductor Gerd Albrecht
Email: principal conductor Stanislaw Skrowaczewski
Email: General Manager Naohito Hazu
Email: Executive officer Shinzo Yoshida
Email: honorary guest conductor Tadaaki Otaka
Email: concertmaster Takumi Komoriya
Email: Director General Takao Ouchi

Za Ondekoza
Website: www.ondekoza.com
Email: taron@pop12.odn.ne.jp
Phone: 357 701 457
Address: c/o Victor Entertainment Inc., 1-14-5, Sendagaya, Shibuya-ku, JP
Country: Japan

Zampa Ufujishi Daiko
Email: ZAMPA@nyc.odn.ne.jp
Phone: 988 959 467
Address: c/o Zampa Ufujishi Daiko Jimkyoku Southern Press, Chimdon Stage, 718 Yagi, Nakagusu-ku, JP
Information: see entry under Ballet, Dance and Folk Art Companies
Country: Japan

REPUBLIC OF KOREA

ASIA Philharmonic Orchestra
Website: www.asiaphil.org
Email: apo@miracleofmusic.org
Phone: 274 50310
Address: Incheon & Arts, 9-1 Gahoe-dong, Jongno-gu
Information: consists of members from other orchestras in Japan, China, Korea, Singapore, Philippines, Vietnam, Thailand and Malaysia
Country: Republic of Korea
Contact: music Director/conductor Myung-Whun Chung

Bucheon Philharmonic Orchestra
Website: www.bucheonphil.org
Email: bucheonphil@naver.com
Phone:
326 258 330
Address: 788, Jung-dong, Builro 365, Wonmi-gu, Bucheon-si,
Information: since it was established in 1988, the Bucheon Philharmonic Orchestra has been highly recognized by classical music lovers for its concerts of fresh programs and repertory. Since Professor Hun-Joung Lim of Seoul National University was appointed as Permanent Conductor, it has grown into the Korea's leading orchestra, and can perform on domestic and international stages with exceptional individual skills and rich repertories
Country: Republic of Korea

Busan Metropolitan Traditional Music Orchestra
Phone:
516 244 737
Address: Busan Cultural Center, 848-4 Daeyeon4-dong,

Nam-gu
Country: Republic of Korea
Contact: Manager Ho-Seong Park

Busan Municipal Traditional Music Orchestra
Address: Busan Cultural Centre, 213-4 Daeyeon-dong, Nam-gu
Country: Republic of Korea

Busan Philharmonic Orchestra
Email: webmaster@busanphil.com
Address: Busan Cultural Centre, 848-4 Daeyeon4-dong, Nam-gu
Country: Republic of Korea

Changwon Symphony Orchestra
Website: www.changwonphil.com
Phone: 552 257 383
Address: Sungsan Arts Hall, Youngho-Dong 2, Changwon
Country: Republic of Korea
Contact: conductor Jong-Whi Park

Cheongju Municipal Kayagum Orchestra
Phone: 441 845 2855
Address: 562 Hoan-dong, Cheongju
Country: Republic of Korea
Contact: conductor Ky-Seol Lee
Email: management Il-Ro Yoon

Daegu Municipal Orchestra
Website: artcenter.daegu.go.kr
Phone: 536 066 111
Address: Daegu Culture & Arts Center, 187 Seong-dang-dong, Dalseo-gu
Country: Republic of Korea
Contact: conductor Hyun-Se Lee

Daejeon Philharmonic Orchestra
Website: www.dpo.or.kr
Email: dpo@dpo.or.kr
Phone: 426 102 266
Address: Daejeon Culture & Arts Center, 396 Manny-eon-dong, Seo-gu
Country: Republic of Korea
Contact: conductor Edmon Colomer

Euro-Asian Philharmonic Korea
Website: www.euroasianphil.com
Email: kate@euroasianphil.com
Phone: 222 328 744
Address: 6th Fl. DSI Bldg. 1450-2, Seocho3-dong, Seocho-gu
Country: Republic of Korea
planning & pr team / assistant Manager
Boyeon Kim
CEO & music Director
Nanse Gum

Gyeongbuk Philharmonic Orchestra
Phone: 539 502 272
Address: Culture & Sports Division, Gyongbuk Provincial Hall, 49 Dongho-dong, Buk-gu
Country: Republic of Korea
Contact: conductor Hyun-Gi Shin

Gyeonggi Provincial Philharmonic Orchestra
Website: orchestra.ggac.or.kr
Phone: 312 303 200
Address: Gyeonggi Arts Center, , 1117 Ingye-dong, Paldal-gu, Suwon
Country: Republic of Korea
Contact: conductor Nan-Se Gum

Hankook Symphony Orchestra
Website: www.koreasymphony.com
Email: spo88@hanmail.net
Phone: 259 38760
Address: 7-19 Yangjae1-dong, Seocho-gu
Country: Republic of Korea
Contact: music Director/conductor Sung-Ho Ha
Email: personnel Manager Ueun Young Chu

Incheon Symphony Orchestra
Email: imcso@hanmail.net
Phone: 324 387 772
Address: Incheon Multi Culture and Arts center, 1408 Kuwol 3-dong, Namdong-gu
Country: Republic of Korea
Contact: Director Kyung-Gu Lee

Jeonju Philharmonic Orchestra
Phone: 632 812 748
Address: 1220 Deokjin-dong 1-ka, Deokjin-gu, Jeongju
Country: Republic of Korea
Contact: conductor Seok-Hee Kang

KBS Symphony Orchestra
Website: kbsso.kbs.co.kr
Phone: 278 12240/2253/
Address: 18 Yeoido-dong, Youngdeungpo-gu
Information: see also Presenters & Venues
Country: Republic of Korea

Korean Chamber Ensemble
Website:
www.kce1965.com
Email: kce1965@hanmail.net
Phone: 259 25728
Address: #301 Bunsan Bldg, 97-3, Banpo-dong, Seocho-gu
Information: established in 1965; the oldest and most revered chamber ensemble of its kind in the Republic of Korea; released 7 CDs with both pure classical repertoire and standards; participated in many international festivals
Country: Republic of Korea
Contact: Artistic Director Min Kim
Email: Managing Director Michelle Kang

Korean Chamber Orchestra
Website: www.koreachamber.co.kr
Email: koreachamber@hanmail.net
Phone: 112 511 426
Address: 7-56 Chungjeonggro3-ga, Seodaemun-gu
Country: Republic of Korea
Contact: President Kyoung-Shik Park

Korean Festival Ensemble
Website: www.korfestival.or.kr
Phone: 250 18477
Address: 812 Union-Center Bldg., 837-11 Yeouk-sam-dong, Gangnam-gu
Information: organise Young Musicians Concerts in Oct; Spring Festival in April to explore a composer each year
Country: Republic of Korea
Contact: music Director Eun-Hee Park

Korean Philharmonic Orchestra
Email: kposkcho@hanmail.net
Phone: 287 47773
Address: 5F Suk-Yong Bldg., 41-1 Chang Chepng-dong, Seodaemun-gu
Country: Republic of Korea

Korean Symphony Orchestra
Website: www.koreansymphony.com
Email: kosym1@yahoo.co.kr
Phone: 252 36258
Address: 700 Seocho-dong, Seocho-gu
Information: established in 1985, residential orchestra at National Theatre, accompany the National Opera Company (q.v.), National Ballet Company (q.v.); largest orchestra not funded by the government
Country: Republic of Korea
Contact: Managing Director Young-Suck Choi
Email: General Manager Min Kim

Masan City Symphony Orchestra
Phone: 552 955 927
Address: 447 Yangdeok-dong, Masan
Country: Republic of Korea
Contact: conductor Jin-Hyun Baek

Nangye Traditional Korean Music Orchestra
Website: nangye.yd21.go.kr
Phone: 437 403 225
Address: c/o Cultural Promotion Dept., Yongdong Council, Buyong-ri, Yongdong-eup
Country: Republic of Korea
Contact: conductor Won-Sun Kim

National Choir Company
Website: www.nationalchorus.or.kr
Phone: 258 78111
Address: 2F Concert Hall - Seoul Arts Center, 700 Seo-cho-dong, Seocho-gu
Information: regular concerts and performances, Christmas concert with Messiah
Country: Republic of Korea
Contact: Director Myung-yup Kim

National Chorus of Korea
Website: www.nationalchorus.or.kr
Email: n-chorus@joyclassic.com
Phone: 258 78111
Address: Seoul Arts Center, Music House, 700 Seo-cho-dong, Seocho-gu
Information: presents regular concerts and opera performances, from renaissance to contemporary art; founded in 1973
Country: Republic of Korea
Contact: Manager Hong-shik Kim
Email: conductor, Artistic Director Myung-yup Kim

Seoul Ladies Singers
Website: www.choruscenter.co.kr
Email: webmaster@choruscenter.co.kr
Phone: 236 650 061
Address: Chorus Centre, 651-11 Naebalsan2-dong, Gangseo-gu
Country: Republic of Korea
Contact: music Director Hak-Won Yoon
Email: conductor Eui-Joong Yoon

Seoul Metropolitan Chorus
Phone: 239 91778
Address: Sejong Center for the Performing Arts, 81-3

Sejong-ro, Jongno-gu
Country: Republic of Korea
Contact: Director Jin-Sub Yeom

Seoul Metropolitan Korean Music Orchestra
Phone: 239 91630
Address: Sejong Centre for Performing Arts, 81-3, Sejong-ro, Jongro-gu
Information: resident company at Seoul Sejong Cultural Centre & funded by Seoul Metropolitan City Council
Country: Republic of Korea
Contact: President Teak-Joo Lee

Seoul Metropolitan Traditional Music Orchestra
Website: www.smtmusic.or.kr
Phone: 239 91188
Address: Sejong Center for Performing Arts, 81-3 Sejong-ro, Jongno-gu
Information: resident company at Seoul Sejong Cultural Centre & funded by Seoul Metropolitan City Council see also entry in Early Music
Country: Republic of Korea
Contact: Executive Director Sang-Jin Park

Seoul National Symphony Orchestra
Website: www.classicconcerts.co.kr
Phone: 221 651 288
Address: 20F Erye Bldg. 4 ga, Yangpyoung-dong, Youngdepungpo-gu
Country: Republic of Korea

Seoul Philharmonic Orchestra
Website: www.seoulphil.co.kr
Phone: 237 006 307
Address: Jongno-gu Sejong-daero 175
Information: the Seoul Philharmonic Orchestra presents a wide ranged repertoire from Mozart to Messaein featuring guest conductors and soloists
Country: Republic of Korea
Contact: Managing Director Byung Wook Lim

Seoul Pops Orchestra
Website: www.seoulpops.or.kr
Phone: 259 38760
Address: Dongseong Bldg., 7-19 Yangjae1-dong, Seocho-gu
Country: Republic of Korea
music Director & conductor
Sung-Ho Ha

Seoul Royal Symphony Orchestra
Website: www.srso.or.kr
Email: srso777@naver.com
Phone: 234 440 071
Address: 45-14 Janwon-dong, , Seocho-Gu
Country: Republic of Korea
Contact: conductor Pyung-Yong Lim

Seoul Sinfonietta
Website: www.seoul-sinfonietta.co.kr
Phone: 273 20990/1
Address: 4F, Daeha Bldg., 122 Samchung-dong, Jongno-gu
Information: first professional instrumental ensemble in Korea, established in 1987
Country: Republic of Korea
Contact: music Director Young-Zun Kim

Seoul Symphony Orchestra
Phone: 822 229 98702
Address: 144-7 Hangdang-dong, Sungdong-Gu
Country: Republic of Korea
Contact: music Director/conductor Jin-Kwon Lee

Seoul Tutti Ensemble
Email: stutti@hanmail.net
Phone: 235 52629
Address: 401 Geonsul Bldg, 8-1 Samsung-dong, Gangnam-gu
Country: Republic of Korea
Contact: music Director Ok-Hee Lee

Suwon Philharmonic Orchestra
Website: www.artsuwon.or.kr
Email: artsuwon@artsuwon.or.kr
Phone: 312 282 814/6
Address: Suwon Outdoor Concert Hall, 1128 Inkye-dong, Paldal-gu
Country: Republic of Korea
Contact: conductor Eun-Seong Park

MACAO

Macao Orchestra
Website: www.icm.gov.mo
Email: webmaster@icm.gov.mo
Phone: 283 66866
Address: Praça do Tap Seac, Edif. do Instituto Cultural, MO
Information: consisting of approximately 60 members from Asia, Europe, North America and Australia, the orchestra performs symphonic, chamber and educational concerts around Macau. The orchestra also tours mainland China 2 or 3 times per year and in 2007 performed in Jakarta, Indonesia. Member of ISPA
Country: MO

MALAYSIA

Hands Percussion Team
Website: www.hands.com.my
Email: mail@hands.com.my
Phone: 036 141 4480
Address: No. 18 Jalan S.B. Jaya 3, Tmn Industri Sungai Buloh, MY
Country: Malaysia
Contact: Team Manager Jonan Lim
Email: Marketing Manager Zoe Lee
Email: Artistic Director Bernard Goh

Kuala Lumpur Chamber Orchestra Players
Email: klcmp@tm.net.my
Phone: 325 44586
Address: 53, Jalan Terasek Tujuh, Bangsar Baru, MY
Country: Malaysia
Contact: Director James Vadiveloo

Malaysian Philharmonic Orchestra
Website: www.malaysianphilharmonic.com
Email: dfp_boxoffice@petronas.com.my
Phone: 603 205 17008
Address: Level 2, Tower 2, , Petronas Twin Towers, MY
Country: Malaysia
Contact: principal conductor Matthias Bamert
Email: Associate conductor Kevin Field
Email: chief Executive officer Juniwati Rahmat Hussin

National Symphony Orchestra
Website: www.istanabudaya.gov.my
Email: info@istanabudaya.gov.my
Phone: 340 265 555
Address: Jalan Tun Razak, MY
Country: Malaysia
Contact: General Director Mohamed Juhari Shaarani
Email: juhari@istanabudaya.gov.mysecretary Halimatun Md Nor

MEXICO

AMPRO Clásica
Website: www.amproclasica.com.mx
Email: beno.alcocer@me.com
Phone: 553 490 9643
Address: Centro Histórico, MX
Country: Mexico

Camerata de Coahuila
Website: cameratadecoahuila.org/inicio/
Email: contacto@cameratadecoahuila.org
Phone: 871 716 6812
Address: Zepeda 370 Sur Interior 1, Zona Centro, MX
Country: Mexico
Contact: vice-President Ricardo Santiba
Email: Artistic Director Ramon Shade

Camerata de la Emuaz
Address: Escuela de M, Av. Hidalgo 714, MX
Country: Mexico
Contact: music Director Alfonso V
Email: General Manager Alfredo Ibarra

Camerata de las Américas
Website: www.cameratadelasamericas.com/camerata/camerata.htm
Email: informes@cameratadelasamericas.com
Address: MX
Information: alternative email address: camerata@servidor.unam.mx
Country: Mexico

Consort Música
Website: www.consort.com.mx
Email: fguajardo@consort.com.mx
Phone: 818 366 6234
Address: Ave. Lázaro Cárdenas 2517-7 Ote. Garza García, NL, MX
Country: Mexico
Social Media: facebook.com/ConsortMusicaClasica/

Coro y Conjunto de C
Email: opera@mail.com
Phone: 525 555 233 699
Address: Benjam, Concepci, Col. Del Valle, MX
Country: Mexico

Ensamble Vocal Ars Cantata
Phone: 555 675 4787
Address: Camino Real al Ajusco 636-3, Tepepan-Xochimilco, MX
Country: Mexico
Contact: Artistic Director, conductor and Manager Marco Antonio Ugalde

ETHOS Trio
Email: ethos@prodigy.net.mx
Phone: 555 254 1594

Address: Av. Fuente de Aguilas 299, Col. Tecamachalco, MX
Information: also educational and outreach programmes; alternative email: ethosjazz@yahoo.com.mx
Country: Mexico

Grupo de M
Email: rfperz@uach.mx
Phone: 526 141 34239
Address: Instituto de Bellas Artes de Chihuahua, Rinc, Col. Rincones del Lago II, MX
Information: also classes of traditional musical instruments
Country: Mexico
Contact: contact Roberto Perez

Manuel M. Ponce Guitar Quartet
Website: increscendocuarteto.com/
Email: info@increscendocuarteto.com
Phone: 555 338 4075
Address: MX
Information: CDs available
Country: Mexico

Orquesta de Cámara de Bellas Artes
Website: www.palacio.bellasartes.gob.mx/index.php/gruposa/ocba
Email: gerenciapba@inba.gob.mx
Phone: 551 22593
Address: Juárez, Centro Histórico, MX
Country: Mexico
Contact: Manager Liliana Saldaña Lobera
Email: gerenciapba@inba.gob.mxdeputy Leonel Morgan Sotomayor
Email: internacionalespba@yahoo.com.mx

Orquesta de Cámara de la Ciudad de México
Website: www.occm.org.mx
Phone: 555 557 1506
Address: Dolorez Jiménez y Muro no. 2, Col. Periodista, MX
Country: Mexico

Orquesta de Cámara de la UAZ
Address: Av. Hidalgo 714, MX
Country: Mexico

Orquesta de Cámara de la Universidad Autónoma de Baja California
Website: www.uabc.mx
Address: Universidad Mexicali, MX
Country: Mexico

Orquesta del Nuevo Mundo
Email: newworldorchestra@terra.com.mx
Phone: 555 514 4954
Address: c/o Organizaci, Hamburgo 222-201, Colonia Ju, MX
Information: produced and managed by Organizaci
Country: Mexico
Email: Artistic Director Johannes Bruno Ullrich

Orquesta del Teatro de Bellas Artes - INBA
Website: www.bellasartes.gob.mx
Phone: 555 709 3300
Address: Regina 52, Planta Baja, Estudio O, Centro Hist, MX
Information: Resident orchestra of the National Opera company and National Ballet Company
Country: Mexico
Contact: Artistic Director Guido Mar
Email: General Manager Octavio Sosa
Email: principal guest conductor Alfredo Filipinni

Orquesta Filarmónica de la Ciudad de México
Email: ofcmexico@aol.com
Address: Periferico Sur 5141, Col. Isidro Fabela, Deleg. Tlalpan, MX
Country: Mexico

Orquesta Filarmónica de la UNAM
Website: www.ofunam.unam.mx
Email: saofunam@servidor.unam.mx
Phone: 555 622 7112
Address: Ciudad Universitaria, Sala de Conc, Col. Coyoacan, MX
Information: see also www.musica.unam.mx. Member of ISPA
Country: Mexico

Orquesta Filarmónica de Querétaro
Website: www.ofeq.org.mx
Email: informes@ofeq.org.mx
Phone: 442 214 0347
Address: Guerrero Sur 13, Col. Centro, MX
Country: Mexico

Orquesta Sinf
Phone: 525 557 021 249
Address: Rep, Col. Centro Hist, MX
Country: Mexico
Contact: Artistic Director and principal conductor Jorge Mester
Email: General Manager Mar
Email: Director Fernando Garc

Orquesta Sinf
Phone: 525 557 296 000
Address: Av. Instituto Polit, Col. Lindavista, MX
Country: Mexico

Orquesta Sinf
Website: www.elportalmexiquense.com/osem
Email: osem@edomex.gob.mx
Phone: 527 222 144 684/
Address: Jos, Primer Piso Co. Centro, MX
Country: Mexico
Email: subDirector art Virgilio Valle
Email: administrative Director Alfredo Higuera

Orquesta Sinf
Phone: 524 433 130 881
Address: Teatro Ocampo, Melchor Ocampo esq Guillermo Prieto, MX
Country: Mexico
Contact: Director art Alfredo Ibarra Garc

Orquesta Sinf
Phone: 521 228 0553
Address: Venustiano Carranza n, Centro Universitario, Tampico Madero, MX
Country: Mexico
Contact: Director Armando Vargas

Orquesta Sinfónica de Aguascalientes
Website: www.aguascalientes.gob.mx/cultura
Email: osa@aguascalientes.gob.mx
Phone: 449 917 2127
Address: Av. J. M. Chávez esq. Av., Venustiano Carranza 101, Col. Centro, MX
Country: Mexico

Orquesta Sinfónica de la Universidad Autonoma de Guadalajara
Website: www.uag.mx
Email: uag@uag.edu
Address: Av. Patria 1201, U.A. de Guadalajara, Oficina de la Orquesta, Edificio de la Nueva Recto, Col. Lomas del Valle, 3, MX
Country: Mexico

Orquesta Sinfónica de la Universidad de Guanajuato
Website: www.extension.ugto.mx/index.php/dec/osug
Email: osug@quijote.ugto.mx
Phone: 473 735 3700
Address: Meson de San Antonio Alonso No. 12, MX
Information: professional orchestra belonging to the University of Guanajuato
Country: Mexico

Orquesta Sinfónica de Mineria
Website: www.mineria.org.mx
Email: contacto@mineria.org.mx
Phone: 555 521 8878
Address: Felipe Carrillo Puerto #78, Col. Villa Coyoacan, MX
Country: Mexico

Orquesta Sinfónica del Estado de México
Website: www.edomexico.gob.mx/osem/index.html
Address: Praga y Trieste Fracc, Residencial las Torres, Unidad Mederos, MX
Country: Mexico
Contact: Artistic Director and principal conductor Felix Carrasco

Orquesta Sinfónica del Instituto Politécnico Nacional
Website: www.orquestasinfonica.ipn.mx
Email: mexicoclasico@hotmail.com
Address: Zacatenco, MX
Information: 6 CDs available
Country: Mexico

Philharmonic Orchestra of Jalisco - Orquesta Filarmónica de Jalisco
Website: www.ofj.com.mx
Email: info@ofj.com.mx
Phone: 333 030 9772
Address: c/o Teatro Degollado, Altos, Calle Degollado, between Av. Hidalgo and Calle Morelos, MX
Information: see also Festivals (Festival Cultural de Mayo)
Country: Mexico
Contact: Director Maria Claudia Parias

Quinteto de Alientos de la Ciudad de México
Email: quintmex@quintmex.com
Address: Milwaukee 44, MX
Information: dedicated to the promotion of contemporary works by international, Mexican and Latin American composers, 3 CDs available
Country: Mexico

Sinfonietta Ventus- Octeto de Alientos
Website: merhill.com/ventus/index.htm
Email: jonmarilyn@yahoo.com
Phone: 551 315 7407

Address: Cerrada del Colibrí No. 22, San Andrés Totltepec, MX
Country: Mexico
Contact: contact John Gustely

Solistas de México
Email: camerata@mail.internet.com.mx
Address: Veracruz 29, Col. H, MX
Country: Mexico

Tambuco - Percussion Ensemble
Website: www.tambuco.org
Email: info@tambuco.org
Phone: 555 674 8067
Address: Higuera 48 Bis, Villa Coyoacan, MX
Information: Four time GRAMMY Nominees, Tambuco is ranked among the finest and most innovative ensembles in the world, with the constant desire for perfection and unique, virtuoso performance. Tambuco has performed in 5 continents for more information, please visit www.tambuco.org
Country: Mexico
Contact: Artistic Director Ricardo Gallardo
Email: ricardogallardo@tambuco.org

NEW ZEALAND

Auckland Philharmonia Orchestra (APO)
Website: www.apo.co.nz
Email: apo@apo.co.nz
Phone: 962 31052
Address: Level 1 Auckland Town Hall, 301-303 Queen Street, NZ
Information: Auckland Philharmonia Orchestra is New Zealand's full-time professional metropolitan orchestra, serving the country's largest and most vibrant city with a comprehensive programme of concerts and education and outreach activities. In more than 50 mainstage performances annually, the APO presents a full season of symphonic work showcasing many of the world's finest classical musicians. The APO is also proud to support both New Zealand Opera and the Royal New Zealand Ballet in their Auckland performances, as well as working in partnership with Auckland Arts Festival and Michael Hill International Violin Competition.
Country: New Zealand
Contact: Artistic administrator Sam Torrens
Email: samt@apo.co.nzMarketing Manager Tracey Holdsworth
Email: traceyh@apo.co.nzpublicist Tiana Lyes
Email: tianal@apo.co.nz

Christchurch City Choir
Website: www.christchurchcitychoir.co.nz
Email: info@citychoir.co.nz
Phone: 334 80228
Address: 25 Harvard Avenue, Wigram, NZ
Information: A first-class symphonic choir, the Christchurch City Choir plays a significant role in the city's music and civic life, performing choral works of great beauty to loyal and new audiences each year. The City Choir has a long and proud history of contributing to the musical fabric of the city stretching back over 125 years, performing works from the established repertoire as well as lesser-known and contemporary works.
Country: New Zealand
Contact: Chair Philip Norman
Email: music Director John Linker

Christchurch Symphony
Website: www.cso.co.nz
Email: office@cso.co.nz
Phone: 394 37797
Address: Unit 2, 4 Klondyke Drive, NZ
Information: The orchestra actively contributes to the cultural diversity of the Christchurch community through a full and varied concert season, as the orchestra of choice for many touring artists and other arts organisations, through our extensive Community Engagement programme, and at civic events. Championing New Zealand composers and artists is hugely important to the CSO and we have, for many years, showcased and premiered New Zealand works and performed with the best of New Zealand talent.
Country: New Zealand

New Zealand String Quartet Trust
Website: www.nzsq.co.nz
Email: nzsq@nzsq.co.nz
Phone: 449 98883
Address: Level 2, Wakefield House, 90 The Terrace, NZ
Information: Acclaimed for its dynamic performing style, eloquent communication and beautiful sound, the New Zealand String Quartet has distinguished itself internationally for its imaginative programming and the championing of music from New Zealand.
Country: New Zealand
Contact: Manager Christine Argyle
Email: christine.argyle@nzsq.org.nz

New Zealand Symphony Orchestra
Website: www.nzso.co.nz
Email: info@nzso.co.nz

Phone: 480 12034
Address: 101 Wakefield Street, NZ
Information: The New Zealand Symphony Orchestra (NZSO) is a symphony orchestra based in Wellington, New Zealand

New Zealand Youth Choir & Voices NZ Chamber Choir
Website: www.choirsnz.co.nz
Email: choirs@choirsnz.co.nz
Phone: 449 90692
Address: PO Box 25025, Featherston Street, NZ
Information: The New Zealand Youth Choir has achieved considerable success since its formation in 1979. Performances around New Zealand and eight international tours have firmly established the choir's reputation for consistency, energy and excellence.
Country: New Zealand
Contact: operations Manager Emma Dowdle
Email: emma@choirsnz.co.nzcommunications administrator Murray Kirk
Email: comms@choirsnz.co.nzchief Executive Arne Herrmann
Email: CEO@choirsnz.co.nz

NZSO National Youth Orchestra
Website: www.nzso.co.nz
Email: nyo@nzso.co.nz
Phone: 480 13831
Address: Level 2, 101 Wakefield St, PO Box 6640, NZ
Information: duplicate
Country: New Zealand
Contact: music Director (nzso) James Judd
Email: Manager Pascale Parenteau

Orchestra Wellington
Website: www.wellingtonorchestra.co.nz
Email: margaretm@orchestrawellington.co.nz
Phone: 480 17810
Address: 13-27 Manners St, NZ
Information: While Orchestra Wellington has only been operating as an independent brand since 2013, the Wellington Regional Orchestra Foundation Inc. has been presenting concerts for more than 60 years in the region, making it the oldest city-based orchestra in the country. The Orchestra plays an extensive role in the cultural life of Wellington City and the wider region, presenting its own Subscription Series concerts, family and educational concerts and a developing array of outreach and community development activity.
Country: New Zealand
Contact: deputy Chair Francis Cooke
Email: deputy Chair Murray Newman

Orpheus Choir of Wellington Inc New Zealand
Website: www.orpheuschoir.org.nz
Email: administrator@orpheuschoir.org.nz
Phone: 458 63856
Address: PO Box 1306, NZ
Information: The Orpheus Choir of Wellington is New Zealand's leading symphonic choir, comprising of up to 150 voices. They perform regularly at major Wellington venues with highly regarded musicians and soloists, both international and local. The choir have also covered musical styles from Opera through Jazz to Broadway show music. Their singing has been described as "powerful", "polished" and possessing "razor-sharp ensemble and diction" and "verve". Orpheus can also provide small groups for corporate or private functions and for television or film work
Country: New Zealand
Contact: Chair Christine Pearce
Email: treasurer James Heslop

Southern Sinfonia
Website: www.southernsinfonia.org
Email: info@southernsinfonia.org
Phone: 347 75623
Address: 110 Moray Pl, NZ
Information: The Southern Sinfonia is Dunedin's only professional orchestra, and one of four regional orchestras in New Zealand's largest cities funded by Creative New Zealand. Annually, it presents a five-concert subscription series, plus schools, chamber and Proms concerts, and education programmes including masterclasses and workshops. It regularly accompanies productions by resident and touring opera, ballet, musical and choral companies.
Country: New Zealand
Contact: General Manager Philippa Harris
Email: philippa@southernsinfonia.orgMarketing and publicity officer Pieter du Plessis
Email: info@southernsinfonia.orgproduction Manager Arthur Bingham
Email: arthur@southernsinfonia.org

STRIKE Percussion Ltd
Website: www.strike.co.nz
Email: Manager@strike.co.nz
Phone: 211 322 570
Address: 234 Rongotai Road, NZ
Information: Founded in 1993, Strike is a high energy-drumming group made up of New Zealand's most outstanding percussionists. While working in a variety of

different styles, Strike specialises in movement-based or choreographed percussion. This concept of 'Percussion in motion' is developed in their stage shows. Strike is committed to working with New Zealand composers, as well as creating their own pieces

Voices New Zealand
Website: www.choirsnz.co.nz
Email: choirs@choirsnz.co.nz
Phone: 449 90692
Address: Level 4, 26 Brandon St, NZ
Information: Since its début at the 1998 New Zealand International Arts Festival, Voices New Zealand Chamber Choir has imPressed audiences and won awards in New Zealand and overseas. Drawing its members from the nation's best singers, Voices is flexible in size and in range and style of repertoire.
Country: New Zealand

Wellington Cathedral Choir
Website: wellingtoncathedral.org.nz/ music/choirs
Email: admin@wellingtoncathedral.org.nz
Phone: 447 20286
Address: cnr Hill and Molesworth Streets, PO Box 12-044, NZ
Information: The Wellington Cathedral of St Paul hosts frequent state services and events. Standing in the Parliamentary precinct the Cathedral is a visible symbol of the Anglican Church in New Zealand. The music and liturgy they provide is an important part of this function of the Cathedral. The Cathedral currently has three highly-trained choirs, a young and enthusiastic music staff, and an ever-expanding reputation for musical excellence. The Cathedral is enriching in a unique way the spiritual, musical and cultural life of both city and nation.
Country: New Zealand

PHILIPPINES

Ateneo de Manila University College Glee Club
Website: www.ateneocollegegleeclub.com
Email: Marketing@ateneocollegegleeclub.com
Phone: 329 244 601
Address: Marmaine Agbay, c/o Colayoo Hall, Ateneo de Manila University, Loyola Heights, PH
Information: is a choir based in the Ateneo de Manila University. It is distinguished as the oldest university chorale in the Philippines, having celebrated its 90th year in 2011. It has held concerts internationally, and has released several albums with songs genres ranging from Classical, Negro spiritual, Sacred choral works, as well as Pop, and OPM. The Glee Club remains active internationally through the performances it stages
Country: Philippines
Contact: General Manager Mikhael Fiorello C. Llado

Cebu Symphony Foundation
Address: Valez Hospital, PH
Country: Philippines
Contact: concert master Bonifacio Cabahug

Dela Salle University Chorale
Phone: 252 44611 loc.7
Address: c/o Rodolfo Delarmente, Cultural Arts Office, De La Salle University, 2401 Taft Avenue, PH
Country: Philippines
Contact: conductor Rodolfo Delarmente

Himig Singers
Email: bongav@dv.weblinq.com
Phone: 822 263 844
Address: c/o Alvin Aviola, 24-A, Aala Bldg., Anda St., PH
Country: Philippines
Contact: conductor Alvin Aviola

Las Pinas Boys Choir
Phone: 282 61856
Address: c/o Ricardo Maso, St. Joseph's Academy, Real St., Padre Diego Cera Ave., PH
Country: Philippines

Maguindanao Kulintang Ensemble
Phone: 632 837 3463
Address: c/o Aga Mayo Butocan, Blk. 17 Lot 10, Maharlika Village, General S.K. Pe, Upper Bicutan, PH
Country: Philippines
Contact: Artistic Director Aga Mayo Butocan

Manila Philharmonic Orchestra (MPO)
Email: mpoinc@info.com.ph
Phone: 270 51728/722 4
Address: Rm. 307, The Main Place Bldg, 190 N. Domingo St. corner Pinaglabanan St., San Juan, PH
Country: Philippines
Contact: music Director Rodel Colmenar

Monastery of the Transfiguration Boys Choir
Address: c/o Fr. Sabio Maria Siwcuan, OSB The Monastery of the Transfiguration, P.O.Box 11, PH
Country: Philippines

P.U.P. Banda Kawayan
Phone: 632 716 7832
Address: c/o Siegfredo Calabig, Polytechnic University of

the Philippines, Sta. Mesa, PH
Country: Philippines
Contact: Artistic Director Sieafredo Calabig

Pangkat Kawayan
Phone: 632 913 0837
Address: c/o Victor Toledo, 64 Luskot St., Galas, PH
Country: Philippines

Peace Philharmonic of the Philippines
Phone: 322 311 341/232
Address: c/p Salvador and Pilar Sala Foundation, 415 Gorordo Avenue, PH
Country: Philippines

Philippine Madrigal Singers
Phone: 272 17977
Address: c/o Prof. Andrea O. Veneracion, College of Music, University of the Philippines, Diliman, PH
Country: Philippines
Contact: choirmaster Andrea Veneracion

Philippine Normal University Chorale
Phone: 252 70377
Address: c/o Luzviminda Modelo, Philippine Normal University, Taft Avenue, PH
Country: Philippines
Contact: conductor Luzviminda Modelo

Philippine Philharmonic Orchestra
Website: www.culturalcenter.gov.ph
Email: ppo@culturalcenter.gov.ph
Phone: 283 21125
Address: c/o Cultural Centre of the Philippines, CCP Complex, Roxas Blvd., PH
Country: Philippines
Contact: principal conductor and music Director Eugene Castillo

U. P. Chamber Orchestra
Phone: 632 929 6963
Address: U.P. Abelardo Hall, U.P. Campus Diliman, PH
Country: Philippines
Contact: conductor Agripino Diestro

U. P. Cherubim & Seraphim
Phone: 632 921 7751
Address: c/o Elena Mirano, 15-A, Malinis St., U.P. Village, PH
Country: Philippines
Contact: conductor Elena Mirano

U. P. Concert Chorus
Phone: 292 96963
Address: c/o Janet Sabas Aracama, University of the Philippines, College of Music, Diliman, PH
Country: Philippines
Contact: conductor Janet Sabas Aracama

U. P. Jazz Ensemble
Phone: 632 929 6963
Address: c/o Rayben Maigue, College of Music, University of the Philippines, Diliman, PH
Country: Philippines

U. P. Musika Asya
Address: c/o Kristina Benitez, Dept. of Music Research, College of Music, University of the Philippines, Diliman, PH
Country: Philippines

U. P. Singing Ambassadors
Email: upsa@pacific.net.ph
Phone: 632 924 9378
Address: c/o Ed Manguiat, 722 Bldg., 7 Sikatuna Blies, Diliman, PH
Country: Philippines

UST Symphony Orchestra
Phone: 632 731 4022
Address: Prof. Herminigildo Ranera, Univ of Santo Tomas, UST Conservatory of Music, Espana, Sampaloc, PH
Country: Philippines
Contact: Artistic Director Erlinda Furle

SINGAPORE

Braddell Heights Symphony Orchestra
Website: www.bhso.org
Email: info@bhso.org
Phone: 628 81258
Address: Braddell Heights Community Club, 50 Serangoon Avenue 2, SG
Country: Singapore
Contact: Chairman Ng Kim Eng
Email: General Manager Daniel Heng
Email: deputy General Manager Samuel Kwan
Email: music Director Adrian Tan

ESO Symphony Orchestra
Email: emmanuelsymphonyorchestra@gmail.com

Address: Gnoh Hock Building (4th Floor), 469 MacPherson Road, SG
Information: The orchestra is founded by a team of committed members led by the President, Willy K.P. Ong, and first music Director, Tan York Sin

Keat Hong Chinese Orchestra (KHCO)
Website: www.khco.org
Email: contactus@khco.org
Phone: 676 91694
Address: Chua Chu Kang Community Club, 35 Teck Whye Ave., SG
Information: Keat Hong Chinese Orchestra (KHCO) was formed in 1974 and it is a cultural group under the Administration of Singapore Chua Chu Kang Community Club. With over 80 members, KHCO is a well-known amateur orchestra in Singapore, the orchestra has been actively developing young talents and contributing to the promotion of Chinese music in Singapore.
Country: Singapore
Contact: music Director Sim Boon Yew
Email: conductor Chin Yen Choong

OneHeartBeat Percussion
Website: www.oneheartbeat.com.sg
Email: experience@oneheartbeat.com.sg
Phone: 663 64815
Address: 69A Frankel Avenue, SG
Information: One HeartBeat Percussion comprises of a team of trained facilitators and passionate performers, who have been actively using rhythm centric activities as tools to create happy occasions and bring people together at various levels.
Country: Singapore

Philharmonic Chamber Choir, The (TPCC)
Website: www.tpcc.org.sg
Email: info@tpcc.org.sg
Phone: 646 61939
Address: Ghim Moh Post Office, PO Box 430, SG
Information: 2015 marks the twenty-first year since The Philharmonic Chamber Choir (TPCC) was formed by Lim Yau, its Artistic Director. It has excelled in giving voice to the great traditions of Western classical music: both a cappella, as well as large works for choir and orchestras, and has equally made its mark in performing the Asian a cappella repertoire.
Country: Singapore
Contact: Artistic Director Lim Yau
Email: assistant conductor Wong Lai Foon

Philharmonic Winds, The
Website: www.philharmonicwinds.org
Email: info@philharmonicwinds.org
Address: Goodman Arts Centre, 90 Goodman Road, Block D #01-23, SG
Information: Since its formation in 2000, The Philharmonic Winds has been presenting meaningful concerts of high standards. Each concert revolves around a theme, such as Sounds of Japan, All That Jazz, Absoluut Dutch, An American Portrait and Death and Life, amongst others. They have also presented works by Grainger and Varèse, wind serenades by Mozart, Dvořák and Strauss, as well as symphonies by Hindemith and Barnes. In addition, The Philharmonic Winds has participated in opera productions of Puccini's Madama Butterfly and Weill's Street Scenes.
Country: Singapore
Contact: Artistic Director / resident conductor Leonard Tan

Singapore Chinese Orchestra
Website: www.sco.com.sg
Email: sco@sco.com.sg
Phone: 655 74030
Address: 7 Shenton Way, Singapore Conference Hall, SG
Information: Inaugurated in 1997, the 85-musician Singapore Chinese Orchestra (SCO) is Singapore's only professional Chinese orchestra as well as a flagship local arts group. Since its inception, SCO has imPressed a broadening audience with its blockbuster presentations and is fast establishing itself among its counterparts around the world.
Country: Singapore
Contact: Executive Director Terence Ho Wee San
Email: Artistic Administration Loh Mee Jun
Email: senior Executive Lum Mun Ee

Singapore Indian Orchestra & Choir
Address: 9 EmPress Pl, SG
Information: Singapore Indian Orchestra & Choir is one of the few orchestras to have a choir to complement its performances. They have staged over 350 performances and are regularly invited to perform at local concerts of festivals in Singapore, Australia and Brunei.
Country: Singapore

Singapore National Youth Orchestra (SNYO)
Website: www.sso.org.sg/page.php?CategoryID=295
Email: corporate@sso.org.sg
Phone: 660 24200
Address: 80 Bencoolen Street, Level 8, NAFA Campus One Tower Block, SG
Information: The Singapore National Youth Orchestra

(SNYO) occupies a special place in Singapore's music community. It has produced a strong alumni, and contributes significantly to both seeding the Singapore Symphony Orchestra and other community orchestras in Singapore

Country: Singapore
Contact: chief Executive officer Chng Hak-Peng
Email: Chairman Goh Yew Lin
Email: Director Ang Chek Meng

Singapore Symphonia Company Limited
Website: www.sso.org.sg
Email: corporate@sso.org.sg
Phone: 660 24200
Address: 80 Bencoolen Street, Level 8, NAFA Campus One Tower Block, SG
Information: Singapore Symphonia Company Limited aims to enrich the local cultural scene, serving as a bridge between the musical traditions of Asia and the West, and providing Artistic inspiration, entertainment and education with a full-time professional orchestra of 96 members.
Country: Singapore
Contact: Chairman Goh Yew Lin
Email: Director Ang Chek Meng
Email: chief Executive officer Chng Hak-Peng

Singapore Wind Symphony (SWS)
Website: www.sws.sg
Email: contact@sws.sg
Phone: 677 97706
Address: #04-16 Inno Centre, Block 1003 Bukit Merah Central, SG
Information: The Singapore Wind Symphony (SWS) was founded in 1977 under the auspices of the National Theatre Trust, and was formerly known as the National Theatre Symphonic Band (NTSB). In 1992, it was renamed the Singapore Wind Symphony and embarked on a new era of excellence in music-making, winning local and international accolades, and establishing itself as one of the pinnacle ensembles of its kind in Singapore
Country: Singapore
Contact: Chairman Ho Chee Mun
Email: vice Chairman Wee Boon Chong
Email: board member Ang Ching Hong
Email: General Manager Mindy Lin
Email: production Manager Melvin Goh
Email: orchestra Manager Johan Ezran

SOUTH AFRICA

KwaZulu-Natal Philharmonic Orchestra - KZN
Website: www.kznphil.org.za
Email: kznphil@kznphil.org.za
Phone: 313 699 438
Address: 29 Acutt Street, 3rd floor, ZA
Information: the KZN Philharmonic is a professional orchestra which is comprised of around 70 multi-national musicians. The orchestra enjoys a reputation for excellence and innovation among South African orchestras, resulting in a loyal support base from the local community, regular concert subscribers and visitors to the province of KwaZulu-Natal. Member of ISPA
Country: South Africa

South African National Youth Orchestra Foundation
Website: www.sanyo.org.za
Email: team@sanyo.org.za
Phone: 832 722 117
Address: PO Box 95626, Waterkloof, ZA
Country: South Africa

TAIWAN, PROVINCE OF CHINA

(FLAGGED FOR DELETION) Pingtung Teacher's Chorus
Phone: 872 23052
Address: No.4-2 Minshen Road
Country: Taiwan
Contact: President Wen Rui Wen
Email: contact Miss Zheng
Email: conductor Zhen Ru Qiu

Academy of Taiwan Strings
Website: www.atstrings.com.tw
Email: ats.atstrings@gmail.com
Phone: 223 218 168
Address: B1, No.4-1, Ln75, Linyi St., Zhongzheng Dist.
Information: founded in 1990
Country: Taiwan

Amis Kakeng Musical Group
Email: Amis_kakeng@yahoo.com.tw
Address: 2F, 2, Alley 28, Lane450, Chunghsin Rd, Sec.2
Country: Taiwan
Contact: correspondent Saztoy Sajtay

Chai Found Music Workshop
Website: www.cfmw.com.tw
Email: cfmw@cfmw.com.tw
Address: 2F, No. 13, Lane 295, , Long Jiang Road, , Zhong Shan District,

Country: Taiwan
Contact: Artistic Director/ President Chen-Ming Huang
Email: chenming@cfmw.com.twassisrant to Artistic Director I-Hsien Lin
Email: music@cfmw.com.tw

Chang Xing Hakka Music Troupe
Website: www.hakka.gov.tw/mp.asp?mp=1
Email: K1024@mk.ks.edu.tw
Phone: 886 768 11423 /
Address: No. 23, Lane 259, , Tai Zhong Road, , Mei Nong District,
Country: Taiwan
Contact: correspondent Yi-Wen Hsieh

Chin-Yuan Chinese Ensemble, The
Website: chin-yuan.com.tw/mainhome.aspx
Email: linkujen@gmail.com
Address: 2/3F, , No. 29, , Bo Ai Road,
Information: established in Taipei in 1988
Country: Taiwan
Contact: Executive secretary Hsia-Yen O
founder & Artistic Director
Gu-Jen Lin

Contemporary Chamber Orchestra Taipei
Email: ccot1@ms4.hinet.net
Phone: 227 667 375
Address: 3F, 95, Kung Fu North Road
Information: regularly commissions local composers to produce new works and has performed programmes both abroad and in Taiwan
Country: Taiwan
Contact: music Director Chun-Fung Lee

Formosa Singers
Website: www.formosasingers.com.tw
Email: formosa.singers@msa.hinet.net
Phone: 225 919 422
Address: 2F, No. 61, , Min Quan Eastern Road Section 2, , Zhong Shan District,
Country: Taiwan
Contact: correspondent Julian Su

Forum Music
Website: www.musforum.com.tw
Email: fm@musforum.com.tw
Phone: 225 935 811
Address: No.4, Lane 187, , Min Zu West Road,
Country: Taiwan
Contact: correspondent Hsiao yu Lin

Han Tang Yuefu Ensemble, The
Email: info@hantang.com.tw
Phone: 228 080 683
Address: No.2, Alley 2, Lane 31, Bashih 1st St.
Country: Taiwan
Contact: Artistic Director Mei-o Chen

Hwa Kang Theatre
Website: www.hka.edu.tw
Email: ttl@mail.hka.edu.tw
Phone: 228 612 354
Address: No.8, Lane 73, Chien-Ye Road, , Si Lin District
Country: Taiwan

Ju Percussion Group
Website: www.jpg.org.tw
Email: bellaliu@mail.jpg.org.tw
Phone: 228 919 900
Address: 6F, No. 10, , Da Ye Road, , Bei Tou District,
Information: Ju Percussion Group Foundation manages Taipei International Percussion Convention (q.v.)
Country: Taiwan
Contact: programming coordinator Chien-ling Liu
Email: Artistic Director Tzong-Ching Ju
Email: Marketing Manager Pear Hsu
Email: Marketing coordinator Yen-Ting Hsu
Email: General Manager Shu-Kang Liu

Kaohsiung City Children's Chorus
Website: www.yacps.kh.edu.tw
Email: te103@mail3.yacps.kh.edu.tw
Phone: 752 10668 / 062
Address: No. 183, , Wu Fu Forth Road,
Country: Taiwan
chorus Director & principal
Guo-Chang Xie
Email: coach/Executive Shao-Kai Yuan

Kaohsiung City Chinese Orchestra
Website: www.kcco.org.tw
Email: kcso@ms.kcso.org.tw
Phone: 753 21666
Address: 5F, , No.99, , Ho-His Road,
Country: Taiwan

Kaohsiung City Symphony Orchestra
Website: www.kcso.org.tw
Email: kcso@ms.kcso.org.tw
Phone: 753 11000
Address: .4F, No.99, , Ho-His Road,
Country: Taiwan
Contact: conductor Pang-Hsing Hsiao

Lan-Yang Taiwanese Opera Company
Website: http://tw.myblog.yahoo.com/lanyang-opera
Email: lanyang.opera@yahoo.com.tw
Phone: 393 62542 / 333

Address: 2F, No. 482, , Zhong Shan Road Section 2,
Information: sister company of Lan-Yang Taiwanese Opera Troupe
Country: Taiwan
Contact: Managing Director Deng-Qing Chen
Email: Executive Shu Qin Zhang
Email: Artistic diretor Chun Min Hang

Little Giant Chinese Chamber Orchestra
Website: www.littlegiant.idv.tw
Email: giant.orchestra@gmail.com
Phone: 229 277 445
Address: 1F, No. 8, Alley 11, Lane 125, , Fu He Road, , Yong He District,
Information: the Little Giant Chinese Chamber Orchestra (gCO) was founded in October 2000 by its Artistic Director and conductor Chih-Sheng Chen. With ten years of experience, the gCO has matured into an ensemble of both technical and Artistic proficiency. A strong musical force in Taiwan, it represents a new generation of Chinese orchestral music. It strives to demonstrate the energy and passion of its dedicated musicians with every performance. Promoting Chinese music on the world stage. The gCO's repertoire ranges from the classics of Chinese traditional works to the latest contemporary compositions by Taiwanese and Chinese composers. It offers a full season at the prestigious National Concert Hall in Taiwan, presenting both the full orchestra of over one hundred musicians and smaller chamber ensembles throughout the year. In recent years, the orchestra has presented large-scale interdisciplinary projects, combining theatre and multimedia with orchestral music. Its international appearances include the Zentrum für Kunst und Medientechnologie (ZKM) at the 2007 Flying Circus Festival in Germany, the 2008 Hong Kong International Chinese Music Festival, the Edmonton Chinese Music Festival and a concert in Vancouver during its 2010 debut Canada Tour. In addition, the gCO's educational programmes have introduced thousands of young audience members to Chinese music
Country: Taiwan
Contact: Director Chih-Sheng Chen
Email: giant.orchestra@gmail.com

Musicians' Performing Group
Email: t196@ms16.hinet.net
Address: 4F, No.196, Shi-Ta Road
Information: consists of music teachers from various universities and colleges in Taiwan
Country: Taiwan
Contact: Director Wei Zhuang Cheng

National Chinese Orchestra
Website: nco.ncfta.gov.tw
Email: Use Website to contact
Phone: 223 435 252
Address: No. 21 - 1, , Zhong Shan Southern Road, , Zhong Shan Southern Road,
Country: Taiwan
Contact: orchestra Director Ming Shean Wang

National Taiwan Symphony Orchestra
Website: www.ntso.gov.tw
Email: Use Feedback on www.ntso.gov.tw/eng/service_en_feedback.aspx
Phone: 423 391 141
Address: No. 738 - 2, , Zhong Zheng Road, , Wu Feng District,
Information: oldest symphony orchestra in Taiwan
Country: Taiwan
Contact: Director Chi-Liang Ko
Managing Director & conductor
David Tscheng Hsiung Chen
Email: contact Jack Boh-Chung Chang

Philharmonia Moments Musicaux
Website: www.momentmusical.com.tw
Email:
muse@mmmu.org
Phone: 225 050 859
Address: No. 72, , Min Quan Eastern Road Section 3,
Country: Taiwan
Contact: Artistic Director and founder Po-Po Chiang
Email: correspondent Shiu-Chen Sun

Tainan City Traditional Orchestra
Website: tcto.ezgo.to
Email: tcto3367@mail.tncg.gov.tw
Phone: 622 89250
Address: No. 30, , Min Quan Road Section 2, , Zhong Xi District,
Information: part of Tainan City Government
Country: Taiwan

Tainan Symphony Orchestra
Website:
culture.tncg.gov.tw
Email: tso201099@yahoo.com.tw

Phone: 629 52150
Address: Culture Affairs Bureau, No. 30, , Min Quan Road Section 2,
Country: Taiwan
Contact: Artistic Director Joseph Huei-ming TWU

Taipei Century Symphony Orchestra
Website: www.century.org.tw/front/bin/home.phtml
Email: info@century.org.tw
Phone: 227 027 253
Address: 14F, , No.49, , He Ping East Road Section 3,
Information: also Youth Orchestra
Country: Taiwan
Managing & music Director
David Nian Fu Liao
Email: assistant Manager Bruce Lee

Taipei Chamber Singers
Website: www.tcschoir.org.tw
Email: singers.tcs@msa.hinet.net
Phone: 227 764 089
Address: 3F., No.159, , Dun Hua South Road, , Da An District,
Country: Taiwan
Contact: Artistic Director Yun-Hung Chen
Email: President Jenny Fang

Taipei Chinese Orchestra
Website: english.tco.taipei.gov.tw/MP_119042.html
Email: tco@tco.taipei.gov.tw
Phone: 223 832 170
Address: No.53, , Zhong Hua Road Section 1, , Zhong Zheng Dist.,
Information: also publishes the Taipei Chinese Music monthly; founded on September 1st, 1979 by Ministry of Education; plays role of "cultural ambassador" in Taipei City
Country: Taiwan
Contact: General Director Yiu-kwong Chung
Email: deputy Director Hsiao-Ping Chen

Taipei Grass-Mountain Folk Orchestra
Email: taipei.folk.music@gmail.com
Phone: 226 425 139 / 09
Address: 1F, No. 29, , Lane 129, Zhang Shu 1st Road, , Xi Zhi District,
Country: Taiwan
Contact: Artistic Director Tsun-Shin Huang

Taipei Male Choir
Website: www.taipeimalechoir.net.tw
Email: tmc.leiter@taipeimalechoir.net.tw
Phone: 223 644 825
Address: 11F-1, No. 171, , Luo Si Fu Road Section 1,
Country: Taiwan
Contact: Artistic Director Tien-Ming Tang

Taipei Percussion
Website: www.taipei-percussion.com.tw/
Email: tpperc@ms21.hinet.net
Phone: 287 723 745
Address: B1, No. 35, , Jian Guo South Road Section 1,
Country: Taiwan
Contact: Executive Director Hui-Yu You

Taipei Philharmonic Chorus & Chamber Choir
Website: www.tpf.org.tw
Email: mail@tpf.org.tw
Phone: 227 733 691
Address: No.28-B1, Lane 233, , Dun Hua Southern Road Section 1, , Da An District,
Information: members are selected annually to represent the TPC on international tours
Country: Taiwan
Contact: Artistic Director Dirk Hei Du
Email: Manager Ferdinand Ta-Ming Ting

Taipei Sinfonietta & Philharmonic Orchestra
Website: www.tspo.org.tw
Email: service@tspo.org.tw
Phone: 223 970 979
Address: B1, No 7, Sec. 1, Chi Nan Road
Country: Taiwan
Contact: Managing Director Wen Fu Lai
Email: head of development Yi An Chen
Email: Executive Director Bing-Ching Yu
Email: music Director Alexandr Rudin

Taipei Symphony Orchestra
Website: english.tso.gov.tw
Email: tso_service@mail.taipei.gov.tw
Phone: 225 786 731
Address: No. 25, Section 3, Bade Road, Songshan District, Taipei City, Taiwan 105
Information: Taipei Symphony Orchestra was founded in 1969, in the past 5 decades, it has evolved from a small group of musicians into a professional ensemble with over 100 members. TSO has graced the city with beautiful music since it was first founded, and its 50th anniversary also opened a brilliant new chapter in Taiwan's music history.
Country: Taiwan
Contact: Director Sung Wei-te
Social Media: www.facebook.com/TaipeiSympho-

nyOrchestra/
Touring Countries: AT, US, JP, FR, ES, DE, LA, LU, SG, CN, PH

Taipei Symphony Orchestra
Website: www.tso.taipei.gov.tw/
Email: tso_service@tso.gov.tw
Phone: 225 786 731
Address: 7F, No. 25, Bade Road Section 3,
Information: Taipei Symphony Orchestra was founded in 1969. at the time of its founding, TSO was just a small thirty-member organization, which today has grown to over a hundred members
Country: Taiwan

Taipei Wind Orchestra & Symphonic Band
Website: www.tsb.org.tw
Email: tsb@mail.tsb.org.tw
Phone: 223 223 654
Address: B1, No. 78-2, , Ning Bo Western street, , Zhong Zheng District,
Country: Taiwan
Contact: music Director Yui-Biau Hou
Email: administrative Director Yi-Wen Tu

Taiwan Chorus
Email: Simona50811@yahoo.com.tw
Phone: 772 17175
Address: 56, Lane 282, , Da Shun Third Road, , Ling Ya District,
Country: Taiwan
Contact: conductor Hung- Chang Wu
Email: correspondent Bin-Chen Hsih

Ten Drum Art Percussion
Website: www.ten-hsieh.com.tw/english/
Email: tenpc@ms43.hinet.net
Phone: 626 62225
Address: No.326, Sec. 2, Wenhua Rd., Rende Dist.
Information: the Ten Percussion Group was formed in March of 2000. The group is leaded by Shih Hsieh. Since it's culmination, the group has traveled to perform several times outside of Taiwan
Country: Taiwan
Contact: leader Hsieh Shih
Email: tenpc@ms43.hinet.net

Tone Melody Flute Ensemble
Email: mateki991@yahoo.com.tw
Phone:
227 727 299
Address: 10F-2, No.169, Zhong Xia East Road, Sec.4
Information: flute ensemble, also recording
Country: Taiwan
Contact: Executive secretary Wen Zhen Xu
Email: Director Qing Lin Chong
Email: Executive Director Wei Qing Lu

Yeh Shu Han Brass Quintet
Email:
yehbrass@iris.seed.net.tw
Phone: 022 362 1399
Address: 13F - 1, No. 4, , Xin Sheng Southern Road Section 3, , Da An District,
Information: Yeh Shu Han Brass Quintet was founded in 1986. In just a few years it has become the country's top performing groups
Country: Taiwan
President & Artistic Director
Shu Han Yeh
Email: General Manager I Sin Li

UNITED STATES

Abilene Philharmonic Orchestra
Website: www.abilenephilharmonic.org
Email: info@abilenephilharmonic.org
Phone:
325 677 6710
Address: 1102 North 3rd St. Suite C, US
Information: The Abilene Philharmonic has been enriching the cultural life of the "Big Country" in West Central Texas since 1950. Today, Music Director and Conductor David Itkin leads the orchestra in world class performances that draw audiences from more than 50 Texas cities. Its concert seasons include guest artists from the ranks of Van Cliburn competition winners and incredible programming such as the premiere of "Ansel Adams: America" by Dave and Chris Brubeck. The orchestra provides a classroom curriculum that follows with live performances for school children, master classes, a young artist competition, and its TicketReach effort enables a broad section of the community to experience inspiring entertainment.
Country: United States
Contact: Executive Director Kevin Smith
Email: ksmith@abilenephilharmonic.orgBox Office and Patron Services Manager Marisa Click Hackett
Email: mhackett@abilenephilharmonic.orgoperations Manager Daniel Ice
Email: dice@abilenephilharmonic.org

Absolute Ensemble
Website: www.absoluteensemble.com/
Email: bonnie@gohproductions.org
Phone:
646 808 0646
Address: 204 East 11th Street, Suite 223, US
Information: Absolute Ensemble is a multi-disciplinary electro-acoustic chamber band based in New York City. Created in 1993 by Conductor Kristjan Järvi (then a piano major at Manhattan School of Music), Absolute Ensemble has 18 key players hailing from across the Globe (Japan, Estonia, Australia, New Zealand, Switzerland, Holland, Bulgaria, Canada and the USA). Järvi's uncanny prescience for the future of classical music led him to create the band that the American Record Guide claims "may well be the most alluring and virtuosic of today's new music groups." An ebullient mix of jazz, classical and world music played with virtuosic flair, each project is created by the group from start to finish, drawing from their rich portfolios as composers, performers and improvisers
Country: United States
Contact: Press representative Christina Jensen
Email: christina@christinajensenpr.com

Acadiana Symphony Orchestra
Website: www.acadianasymphony.org
Email: fdesk@acadianasymphony.org
Phone: 337 232 4277
Address: 412 Travis St, US
Information: The Acadiana Symphony Orchestra is one of only two in the United States that is Associated with a Conservatory of Music. This unique partnership sets ASO apart from other symphony organizations in the country. The mission of the ASO, and its Conservatory is unified in order to achieve a cohesive approach in the development of high quality performances and educational programs
Country: United States
Contact: Executive Director Jenny Krueger
Email: Marketing Director Lana Carver
Email: President Anne Pyle

Adrian Symphony Orchestra
Website: www.adriansymphony.org
Email: info@adriansymphony.org
Phone: 517 264 3121
Address: 110 South Madison Street, US
Information: The Adrian Symphony Orchestra was founded in 1981 with the mission to create musical performances of the highest quality and to present activities that educate, enhance, and improve the quality of life for the citizens of Lenawee County and Southeast Michigan. Now in its 35th season, the ASO is committed to providing excellent Music for Everyone through diverse seasons of classical, pops, and school-day educational concerts
Country: United States
Contact: music Director John Dodson
Email: john@adriansymphony.orgExecutive Director Libby Watson
Email: libby@adriansymphony.orgcommunity relations Jee Pinsoneault
Email: jee@adriansymphony.org

Akron Symphony Orchestra
Website: www.akronsymphony.org
Email: Generalinformation@akronsymphony.org
Phone: 330 535 8131
Address: 17 North Main Street, US
Information: Widely recognised for musical excellence and performance versatility, the Akron Symphony Orchestra is committed to enhancing the quality of life of the community through educational and musical excellence
Country: United States
Contact: Executive Director Paul Jarrett
Email: pjarrett@akronsymphony.orgpersonnel Manager Jerome Miskell
Email: jmiskell@akronsymphony.org

Alabama Symphony Orchestra
Website: www.alabamasymphony.org
Email:
orchestra@alabamasymphony.com
Phone: 205 251 6929
Address: 3621 Sixth Avenue South, US
Information: The formation of the Alabama Symphony Orchestra (ASO) began with the first performance by a group of volunteer musicians in 1921. That group would evolve from a volunteer ensemble to the state's only full-time professional orchestra. Today, the ASO is continuing to make music and provide vital services to the residents of the state, serving nearly 100000 individuals a year through concert series, youth programs, and educational and community engagement efforts to fulfill our mission to change lives through music
Country: United States
Contact: Director of Artistic Administration Pierre Ruhe
Email: pruhe@alabamasymphony.comDirector of Marketing and communications Britney Elliott
Email: belliott@alabamasymphony.comstage Manager Barron Melton
Email: bmelton@alabamasymphony.comresident

conductor and principal pops conductor Christopher Confessore
Email: bill@alabamasymphony.comExecutive Director Curt Long
Email: clong@alabamasymphony.com

Albany Symphony Orchestra
Website: www.albanysymphony.org
Email: mwright@albanysymphony.org
Phone: 229 430 8933
Address: PO Box 70065, US
Information: The Albany Symphony Orchestra was organised as the Albany Symphonette in 1965 by a group of individuals who enjoyed playing good music and foresaw the potential for an orchestra in Albany. Conducted by Mr. E. L. Ziegler, the first concert held May 18, 1965, in the gym of Porterfield Methodist Church. In January, 1967, Dr. Edward A. Tarratus, Arts Division Chairman at Albany Junior College (now Darton State College), became conductor. During the 1967-1968 Season, under Dr. Tarratus leadership, and with the help of the Junior League of Albany, the orchestra was incorporated as a nonprofit organisation
Country: United States
Contact: music Director and conductor Claire Fox Hillard
Email: President Holland Wright

Albany Symphony Orchestra
Website: www.albanysymphony.com
Email: info@albanysymphony.com
Phone: 518 465 475
Address: 19 Clinton Ave, US
Information: The Albany Symphony is one of this region's most revered music and cultural institutions, having won numerous national awards for its adventurous concert programming, recording projects, composer residencies, and innovative educational efforts involving area schools throughout the region
Country: United States
Contact: Chairman Steve Lobel
Email: President Marisa Eisemann
Email: secretary Charles Buchanan
Email: music Director and conductor David Alan Miller

Alexandria Symphony Orchestra
Website: www.alexsym.org
Email: alex@alexsym.org
Phone: 703 548 0885
Address: 2121 Eisenhower Avenue, Suite 608, US
Information: Northern Virginia's premiere fully professional orchestra, the Alexandria Symphony Orchestra was founded in 1954 and has established a reputation for thematic and inter-arts programming that features a mix of classical and contemporary music. The ASO's move in 2002 to the critically-acclaimed Schlesinger Center established its reach and reputation as one of the region's leading arts institutions
Country: United States
Contact: Executive Director Jessica Goodyear Wisser
Email: wisser@alexsym.orgMarketing and operations Manager Karyn Garvin
Email: garvin@alexsym.orgstage Manager Craig B. Teer
Email: craigbteer@aol.com

Alhambra
Website: www.alhambragroup.com
Email: iganz@isabelleganz.com
Phone: 713 818 0386
Address: 2317 Southgate Blvd, US
Information: Alhambra was founded in 1981 by Dr. Isabelle Ganz to transcribe, record, and perform the vast treasures of Sephardic music which have been preserved by the descendants of the Jews of Spain. The ensemble has taped the songs of native singers (primarily at the Sephardic Home for the Aged in Brooklyn), worked with material transcribed by ethnomusicologists, and then arranged this music for performance on instruments appropriate to the folk cultures of the countries of origin. Their arrangements are foot-tapping and infectious
Country: United States
Contact: Artistic Director Isabelle Ganz
Email: iganz@isabelleganz.com

Allentown Symphony Orchestra
Website: www.allentownsymphony.org
Email: info@allentownsymphony.org
Phone: 610 432 7961
Address: 23 North 6th Street, US
Information: Under the musical leadership of Music Director/Conductor Diane Wittry, the Allentown Symphony performs five Subscription Concerts each year in Allentown's historic, 1200-seat Symphony Hall. Miller Symphony Hall is home to the Pennsylvania Sinfonia Orchestra, the Allentown Band, Repertory Dance Theatre's annual performance of the Nutcracker, among other musical institutions across the Lehigh Valley
Country: United States
Contact: Music Director/conductor Diane M Wittry
Email: Executive Director Sheila Evans
Email: sevans@allentownsymphony.orgfinance Ed Rice
Email: erice@allentownsymphony.orgDirector of Marketing Lucy Bloise
Email: lbloise@allentownsymphony.org

Altoona Symphony Orchestra
Website: www.altoonasymphony.org
Email:
aso.office@atlanticbbn.net
Phone: 814 943 2500
Address: 1331 12th Avenue, Suite 107, PO Box 483, US
Information: The Altoona Symphony Orchestra is looking forward to celebrating its 87th Season in 2015-16. This is an outstanding achievement in an era when many orchestras throughout the country cannot boast of such a history. Founded in 1928, the Gerhart String Ensemble has grown over the years to become a full orchestra. Once relying on community volunteers, even donating their own money to purchase music, the Symphony now employs over 75 professional musicians. The mission of the Altoona Symphony has always been to provide high-quality music to the residents of Central Pennsylvania. To this end, the Symphony has gained recognition for its musical diversity by performing both classical and popular works featuring talented local artists and nationally acclaimed musicians
Country: United States
Contact: Executive Director Pamela J. Snyder Etters
Email: aso.execdir@atlanticbbn.netoffice Manager Melissa Andre
Email: aso.office@atlanticbbn.net

Amarillo Symphony Inc
Website: www.amarillosymphony.org
Email: info@amarillosymphony.org
Phone: 806 376 8782
Address: 301 S Polk St, Suite #700, US
Information: Now in its 91st season, the Amarillo Symphony is under the direction of Jacomo Rafael Bairos as the organisation's 17th music Director and conductor. The appointment of Bairos marks the conclusion of an extensive two year search that amassed 213 applicants from 15 countries. Bairos, an imPressive conductor who is elegantly demanding, was selected to lead the organization into an era of exciting and inspiring orchestral music
Country: United States
Contact: music Director and conductor Jacomo Rafael Bairos
Email: Executive Director Susan White
Email: susan@amarillosymphony.org

American Classical Orchestra
Website: www.americanclassicalorchestra.org
Email: info@aconyc.org
Phone: 212 362 2727
Address: 133 West 70th Street, US
Information: The American Classical Orchestra is devoted to preserving and performing the repertoire of 17th- to 19th- century composers, playing the works on original or reproduced period instruments. The musicians use historic performance practice techniques and pass these skills down to future generations through concert performances and educational programs
Country: United States
founder & music Director
Thomas Crawford
Email: Director of development Glenn Askin

American Composers Orchestra
Website: www.americancomposers.org
Email: aco@americancomposers.org
Phone: 212 977 8495
Address: 244 West 54th Street, Suite 805, US
Information: American Composers Orchestra (ACO) is the only orchestra in the world dedicated to the creation, performance, preservation and promulgation of music by American composers. Founded in 1977, ACO pursues a singular mission by maintaining an unparalleled range of activities. ACO makes the creation of new opportunities for American composers and new American orchestral music its central purpose. ACO programs increase opportunities for American composers and generate broader awareness of their work. ACO's new approach generates further interest and programming by other music organizations. It also increases the audience for contemporary American orchestral music by influencing music decision makers
Country: United States
Contact: Director of development Barbara Burch
Email: Artistic Director Robert Beaser
Email: Executive Director Michael Geller
Email: conductor laureate Dennis Russell Davies

American Symphony Orchestra
Website: www.americansymphony.org
Email: info@americansymphony.org
Phone: 212 868 9276
Address: 263 West 38 Street, 10th Floor, US
Information: In 1962, Leopold Stokowski founded the American Symphony Orchestra with the imperative "to offer concerts of great music within the means of everyone." Thirty years later that imperative has expanded to rebuild audiences for orchestral music by connecting music to a wide range of interests and experiences. The mission of the ASO is to renew live orchestral music as a vital force in contemporary American culture. To this end, the ASO presents thematic programming, in which

musical works are curated around ideas drawn from a variety of disciplines such as history, visual arts, science, politics and literature. ASO pursues innovation in concert presentation and is devoted to the promotion of musical education
Country: United States
Contact: Executive Director Lynne Meloccaro
Email: lmeloccaro@americansymphony.org

American Wind Symphony Orchestra
Website: www.americanwindsymphonyorchestra.org/
Email: awso@consolidated.net
Phone: 724 799 8334
Address: 550 Plains Church Road, US
Information: Founded in 1957 by Mr. Boudreau, the American Wind Symphony has become an institution known for bringing its music to the masses via its floating arts center and stage. Mr. Boudreau has commissioned over 400 new musical compositions, which have been premiered during each season's concert tour. Each summer over the past half century, Maestro Boudreau, has motivated his top notch young musicians to perform at their highest capacity to the delight of concert goers
Country: United States
Contact: music Director Robert Austin Boudreau

Anchorage Symphony Orchestra
Website: www.anchoragesymphony.org
Email: aso@youraso.org
Phone: 907 274 8668
Address: 400 D Street, Suite 230, US
Information: The Anchorage Symphony Orchestra was founded in 1946, more than a decade before Alaska became a state, by a consortium of like-minded musicians looking for a musical outlet. Their first program collaborated with the Anchorage Little Theatre for a production of Charles Dickens' A Christmas Carol. From their original size of 17, the ASO grew through the 50's, hiring Peter Birch as conductor, and increasing to 32 members. Anchorage, however, continued to grow with the development of the City of Anchorage as the North Slope oil fields grew and with the continued military presence of Elmendorf Air Force Base, the ASO by the 1980s crossed the threshold as a semi-professional ensemble
Country: United States
Contact: music Director Randall Craig Fleischer
Email: Executive Director Sherri Burkhart Reddick
Email: Director, Marketing and pr Jennifer Cargile
Email: production Manager Lauren MacKenzie Miller

Anderson Symphony Orchestra
Website: www.andersonsymphony.org
Email: aso@andersonsymphony.org
Phone: 765 644 2111
Address: 1124 Meridian Plaza, Suite C, PO Box 741, US
Information: The Anderson Symphony Orchestra was organised in 1967 by leaders at Anderson University, with its very first performance made up largely of volunteers from the local community. Now 44 seasons later, the ASO is a proud assemblage of professional musicians, who for the most part, earn their living in the music arts. Maestro Richard Sowers has conducted the Symphony since 1989
Country: United States
Contact: Executive Director Dana E Stone
Email: administrative assistant RuthAnn Ginder

Ann Arbor Symphony Orchestra
Website: www.a2so.com
Email: a2so@a2so.com
Phone: 734 994 4801
Address: 22 East Huron, Suite 470, US
Information: The Ann Arbor Symphony Orchestra is passionately committed to enriching the culture of the region. They strive to attract, inspire and educate the most diverse audience possible, foster a growing appreciation for excellent music and regional talent, and provide imaginative programming through community involvement
Country: United States
Contact: Marketing Manager Stephanie Roose
Email: stephanie@a2so.comExecutive Director Mary Steffek Blaske
Email: mary@a2so.comeducation Director and General Manager Zac Moore
Email: zac@a2so.com

Annapolis Symphony Orchestra
Website: www.annapolissymphony.org
Email: info@annapolissymphony.org
Phone: 410 269 1132
Address: Maryland Hall for the Creative Arts, 801 Chase Street, US
Information: For over 50 years, the Annapolis Symphony Orchestra has proudly served as the leading performing arts organisation in Maryland's capital city. Formed in 1962, the ASO features 70 professional musicians who perform a variety of symphonic music for audiences of all ages. The vision is to be the best regional orchestra in the country, recognized as a jewel in the Washington/Baltimore area
Country: United States
Contact: Executive Director Katharene Snavely
Email: General Manager Marshall Mentz

Arapahoe Philharmonic
Website: www.arapahoe-phil.org
Email: ame@arapahoe-phil.org
Phone: 303 781 1892
Address: 2100 W. Littleton Blvd., Suite 250, US
Information: Founded in 1953, the Arapahoe Philharmonic is among the longest-established, continuously operating musical resources in Colorado

Arkansas Symphony Orchestra
Website: www.arkansassymphony.org
Email: hpace@arkansassymphony.org
Phone: 501 666 1761
Address: PO Box 7328, US
Information: The Arkansas Symphony Orchestra Society, Inc. exists to connect, enrich, inspire and advance Arkansas through the power of music. Incorporated in 1966, the ASO now performs over 60 concerts per season, which includes the Masterworks and Pops Concerts. In addition, the orchestra has a Chamber Series, River Rhapsodies, at the Clinton Presidential Center, ASO, I.N.C.: Intimate Neighborhood Concerts, plus a busy schedule of statewide touring, chamber music, and educational performances in numerous venues and collaborations with Ballet Arkansas and the Arkansas Repertory Theatre
Country: United States
Contact: music Director Philip Mann
Email: ehowell@arkansassymphony.org

Arlington Symphony
Website: www.symphonyarlington.org
Email: info@symphonyarlington.org
Phone: 817 385 0484
Address: PO Box 202051, US
Information: Under the baton of its founder, Maestro Robert Carter Austin, Symphony Arlington launched a successful debut season in 2000. Symphony Arlington's continued growth has taken it from Tarrant County College's 200 seat Roberson Theater in 2000, to University of Texas – Arlington's 400 seat Rosebud Theater the following season. In 2005 Symphony Arlington moved to the MetroCenter performance space with a 1750 seat capacity
Country: United States
Contact: General Manager Bethany Thomy
Email: gm@symphonyarlington.org

Asheville Symphony
Website: www.ashevillesymphony.org
Email: info@ashevillesymphony.org
Phone: 828 254 7046
Address: PO Box 2852, US
Information: The Asheville Symphony Orchestra performs and promotes symphonic music for the benefit, enjoyment and education of the people of Western North Carolina. The Asheville Symphony was established in 1960. At that time, all musicians performed on a volunteer basis and the Symphony was without a resident conductor or Manager
Country: United States
Contact: music Director and conductor Daniel Meyer
Email: Executive Director Steven Hageman
Email: Artistic administrator Sally Keeney

Ashland Symphony Orchestra
Website: https:// www.ashlandsymphony.org/
Email: symphony@ashland.edu
Phone: 419 289 5115
Address: 401 College Ave
Information: The mission of the Ashland Symphony Orchestra is to enrich the quality of life for all generations by presenting outstanding orchestral music, promoting community involvement, and encouraging music education.
Country: United States
Contact: Executive Director Martha Buckner
Email: symphony@ashland.edu
Social Media: https:// www.facebook.com/ashlandsymphonyorchestra https://twitter.com/AshlandSymphony https:// www.instagram.com/ashlandsymphonyorchestra/

Ashland Symphony Orchestra
Website: www.ashlandsymphony.org
Email: symphony@ashland.edu
Phone: 419 289 5115
Address: 401 College Avenue, US
Information: The Ashland Symphony Orchestra (ASO) is a professional orchestra located in the heart of Ashland County Ohio. Its mission is to enrich the quality of life for all generations by presenting outstanding orchestral music, promoting community involvement, and encouraging music education.
Country: United States
Contact: music Director and conductor Arie Lipsky
Email: personnel Manager Amanda Bekeny

Atlanta Symphony Orchestra
Website: www.atlantasymphony.org
Email: aso-info@woodruffcenter.org
Phone: 404 733 4900
Address: 1280 Peachtree St NE, US
Information: The Atlanta Symphony Orchestra and its affiliated members are committed to build on their foundation of Artistic excellence. They unite in the desire

to serve and to expand the audience through innovative programming, broader venues and increased educational opportunities while balancing Artistic growth with financial soundness. They share a heritage of passion for the music
Country: United States
Contact: President and CEO Stanley E. Romanstein

Augusta Symphony Orchestra
Website: soaugusta.org
Email: office@augustasymphony.org
Phone: 706 826 4705
Address: 1301 Greene Street, US
Information: Symphony Orchestra Augusta debuted on May 23, 1954, under the baton of its founding Director, Harry M. Jacobs. Setting the foundation for what would become a leading regional orchestra, three support groups followed: the Guild in 1957, the League in 1961 and Friends in 1981. With the addition of the Aiken Symphony Guild in 1986, the strong foundation was in place to allow SOA to fulfill its mission: to share the joy of great musical performance with the audience
Country: United States
Contact: Executive Director Mieko N. Hatano
Email: senior Director Jennifer Voth

Austin Symphony Orchestra
Website: www.austinsymphony.org
Email: acorroa@austinsymphony.org
Phone: 512 476 6064
Address: 1101 Red River Street, US
Information: the mission of the Austin Symphony Orchestra Society, Inc. is to enhance the cultural quality of life for the adults and young people of Austin and Central Texas by providing excellence in music performance and educational programming. Founded in 1911, the Austin Symphony Orchestra is Austin's oldest performing arts group. The ASO offers a complete season of musical and educational programming
Country: United States
Contact: Director of Marketing Jason Nicholson
Email: jnicholson@austinsymphony.orgExecutive Director Anthony Corroa
Email: acorroa@austinsymphony.orgassistant to the Director Shaler Wells
Email: swells@austinsymphony.org

Bakersfield Symphony Orchestra
Website: www.bakersfieldsymphony.org
Email: music@bakersfieldsymphony.org
Phone: 661 323 7928
Address: 1328 34th Street, Suite A, US
Information: Beginning in 1932 with a nucleus of determined, dedicated and talented individuals, and expanding over decades into the multi-faceted organisation it is today, the existence of the Bakersfield Symphony Orchestra is at once a tribute both to the individual contributions of its many players and to the community it serves. Further, the Orchestra is a manifestation of the ineffable power of music to foster and make tangible the highest ideals and spirit of that community
Country: United States
Contact: music Director John Farrer
Email: jfarrer@bakersfieldsymphony.orgGeneral Manager Oneida Rodenburg
Email: oneida@bakersfieldsymphony.org

Baltimore Chamber Orchestra
Website: www.thebco.org
Email: info@thebco.org
Phone: 410 685 4050
Address: 11 W. Mount Vernon Place Suite 2, US
Information: Baltimore Chamber Orchestra's first performance, led by Maestra Anne Harrigan, was on January 29, 1984. She introduced the audience to a classical orchestra offering virtuoso performances that touch the heart.From its beginning, Baltimore Chamber Orchestra has grown to occupy an essential niche in the thriving arts scene of greater Baltimore
Country: United States
Contact: music Director Markand Thakar
Email: Executive Director Lockwood Hoehl

Baltimore Symphony Orchestra
Website: www.baltimoresymphony.org
Email: ejackson@bsoatstrathmore.org
Phone: 410 783 8000
Address: 1212 Cathedral Street, US
Information: The Baltimore Symphony Orchestra (BSO) is internationally recognised as having achieved a preeminent place among the world's most important orchestras. Acclaimed for its enduring pursuit of Artistic excellence, the BSO has attracted a devoted national and international following while maintaining deep bonds throughout Maryland through innovative education and community outreach initiatives
Country: United States
Contact: music Director Marin Alsop

Bang on a Can
Website: www.bangonacan.org
Email: info@bangonacan.org
Phone: 718 852 7755
Address: 80 Hanson Place, Suite 301, US

Information: Bang on a Can is dedicated to making music new. Since its first Marathon concert in 1987, Bang on a Can has been creating an international community dedicated to innovative music, wherever it is found. With adventurous programs, it commissions new composers, performs, presents, and records new work, develops new audiences, and educates the musicians of the future
Country: United States
Contact: Executive Director Kenny Savelson
Email: kenny@bangonacan.orgArtistic Director Michael Gordon
Email: Artistic Director David Lang
Email: Artistic Director Julia Wolfe

Bangor Symphony Orchestra
Website: www.bangorsymphony.com
Email: symphony@bangorsymphony.com
Phone: 207 942 5555
Address: PO Box 1441, US
Information: Bangor Symphony Orchestra has been bringing the joy of live music to people throughout Maine since 1896, with concerts for many tastes and all ages. The Bangor Symphony Orchestra was a 2007 recipient of the National Endowment for the Arts award for Artistic Excellence
Country: United States
Contact: Marketing Director Johnna Lacey
Email: music Director and conductor Lucas Richman

Bartlesville Symphony Orchestra
Website: www.bartlesvillesymphony.org
Email: symphony@bartlesvillesymphony.org
Phone: 918 336 7717
Address: PO Box 263, US
Information: the Bartlesville Symphony is a treasured cultural jewel in Northeast Oklahoma. Under the direction of Maestro Lauren Green for the past 37 seasons, this community/professional orchestra in a town of 35000 has created for itself a unique niche in the cultural offerings of the region and in the symphonic world beyond. The symphony Generally rehearses on a weekly basis and presents a season of six subscription concerts. A variety of soloists are featured on these concerts, ranging from orchestra members and young competition winners to internationally-acclaimed artists
Country: United States
Contact: music Director-conductor Lauren Green
Email: lauren@bartlesvillesymphony.orgGeneral Manager Lee Grotholson
Email: lee@bartlesvillesymphony.org

Baton Rouge Symphony
Website: www.brso.org
Email: info@brso.org
Phone: 225 383 0500
Address: 7330 Highland Road, US
Information: founded in 1947, the Baton Rouge Symphony is the oldest arts organisation in the region and the oldest professional orchestra in the state. Its programs include a Symphony League, a Symphony Chorus, and the Louisiana Youth Orchestras. The mission of the Baton Rouge Symphony is to develop and maintain a financially-sound, first-class symphony orchestra with a regional and national profile which will provide education and cultural enrichment for the people of the greater Baton Rouge region and neighboring communities
Country: United States
music Director & conductor
Timothy Muffitt
Email: tmuffitt@brso.orgassistant conductor David Torns
Email: dtorns@brso.orgMarketing and pr Carrie Knight
Email: cknight@brso.org

Bay-Atlantic Symphony
Website: www.bayatlanticsymphony.org
Email: info@bayatlanticsymphony.org
Phone: 856 451 1169
Address: PO Box 481, US
Information: The Bay Atlantic Symphony was founded as the Bridgeton Symphony in 1983 in Bridgeton, New Jersey, by its first MusicDirector, Russell Meyer, and a group of dedicated music lovers. In 1993, the Symphony was named "Orchestra in Residence" at the Stockton Performing Arts Center at Stockton University in Pomona (20 miles west of Atlantic City). In 1995, the orchestra launched a national search for its next music Director and in 1997 selected Jed Gaylin to lead the orchestra into its next phase. The power of classical music is the cornerstone of the Bay Atlantic Symphony's programs. In addition, the Bay Atlantic Symphony strives to add to the region's cultural life by linking itself with important institutions and populations within the community
Country: United States
Contact: Executive Director Paul D. Herron
Email: music Director Jed Gaylin
Email: personnel Director Christopher Di Santo

Bellevue Philharmonic Orchestra
Website: www.bellevuephil.org
Email: info@bellevuephil.org
Phone: 425 455 9170
Address: 1805 136 Place NE #206, US
Information: The Bellevue Philharmonic was the only

professional orchestra in East King County and was founded by R. Joseph Scott as an all-volunteer community group in 1967. After thirty years of increasing professionalism and musicianship, the Board of Directors decided to transform the orchestra into a fully-professional organisation and launched an international search for a new music Director
Country: United States

Beloit Janesville Symphony Orchestra
Website: www.beloitjanesvillesymphony.org
Email: service@beloitjanesvillesymphony.org
Phone: 608 313 1200
Address: 444 E. Grand Avenue, Suite 100, US
Information: Beloit Janesville Symphony Orchestra is a professional orchestra offering three distinct concert series; classical, family pops, explorer. These distinct concerts reflect the interests of our communities and allow us to explore Artistic boundaries will also celebrating Artistic achievements
Country: United States
Contact: orchestra Manager Janis Johnson
Email: bjs.orchestraManager@gmail.comExecutive Director Rod Beaudoin
Email: BJSOBeloit@aol.com
music Director & conductor
Robert Tomaro
Email: tomaror@beloit.edu

Benedictine College - Atchison Community Orchestra
Website: www.benedictine.edu
Email: ruthk@benedictine.edu
Phone: 913 360 7301
Address: Benedictine College, 1020 North 2nd Street, US
Information: due to its location, Benedictine College has the unique opportunity to draw on a large number of accomplished musicians in a small area. To take advantage of this, the BC/Atchison Community Orchestra was formed, where locals from the area join Benedictine students to play great orchestra literature. Few other colleges can boast of such an organisation, which brings together the two communities and unites many great musicians
Country: United States
music Director & conductor
Alison Gaines
Email: Chairperson, music department Ruth Krusemerk

Berkeley Symphony Orchestra
Website: www.berkeleysymphony.org
Email: info@berkeleysymphony.org
Phone: 510 841 2800
Address: 1942 University Avenue #207, US
Information: Recognised nationally for its spirited programming, Berkeley Symphony has established a reputation for presenting major new works for orchestra alongside fresh interpretations of the classical European and American repertoire. It has been honored with an Adventurous Programming Award from the American Society of Composers, Authors and Publishers (ASCAP) in ten of the past twelve seasons
Country: United States
Contact: Executive Director René Mandel
Email: rmandel@berkeleysymphony.orgmusic Director Joana Carneiro
Email: Marketing Director Jenny Lee
Email: jlee@berkeleysymphony.org

Billings Symphony Orchestra and Chorale
Website: www.billingssymphony.org
Email: symphony@billingssymphony.org
Phone: 406 252 3610
Address: 2721 2nd Avenue North, Suite 350, US
Information: Founded as the Billings Symphony Society in May of 1951, the organisation's mission is to enrich lives through music. Today that mission remains the driving force behind the Billings Symphony Orchestra & Chorale. Each season, the BSO&C performs for tens of thousands people throughout south central and eastern Montana and northeastern Wyoming, and help introduce music to children, youth, adults, and seniors through Explore Music!, the BSO&C's music education and community engagement program
Country: United States
Contact: Executive Director Sandra Culhane
Email: sandra@billingssymphony.orgmusic Director Anne Harrigan
Email: orchestra personnel Manager Richele Sitton
Email: symphony@billingssymphony.org

Binghamton Philharmonic
Website: www.binghamtonphilharmonic.org
Email: info@binghamtonphilharmonic.org
Phone: 607 723 3931
Address: 71 State Street, Lower Level, US
Information: The Binghamton Philharmonic is a professional symphony orchestra dedicated to providing the region with performances of live classical music by artists of incomparable talent; they make great music accessible to all through innovative, engaging and affordable programming within and beyond the concert hall
Country: United States
Contact: development Director Sandra J. Griffiths
Email: sandy@binghamptonphilharmonic.orginterim Executive Director Jon Mosbo
Email: jmosbo@binghamptonphilharmonic.orgmusic Director Jose Luis Novo

Birmingham-Bloomfield Symphony Orchestra
Website: www.bbso.org
Email: bbso@bbso.org
Phone: 248 352 2276
Address: PO Box 1925, US
Information: The BBSO strives to cultivate interest in the musical arts for the entire family with emphasis on educational growth. Since its inception in 1975, the Birmingham-Bloomfield Symphony Orchestra, now under the music direction of John Thomas Dodson, has continued to serve the Detroit Metropolitan Area by presenting outstanding performances designed to please a wide range of musical tastes
Country: United States
Contact: Executive Director Dana Gill
Email: gill@detroitchamberwinds.org
principal conductor & music Director
Charles Greenwell
Email: Marketing Kelsey Browne
Email: browne@detroitchamberwinds.org
public relations & assistant Executive Director
Sebastian Kruger
Email: skruger@bbso.org

Bismarck-Mandan Orchestral Association Inc
Website: www.bismarckmandansymphony.org
Email: bmso@sdnet.com
Phone: 701 258 8345
Address: 215 North 6th St, US
Information: Bismarck-Mandan Orchestral Association began as the Bismarck-Mandan Council for the St. Paul Chamber Orchestra. In 1974 the Chamber Orchestra presented a successful three-day residency in Bismarck and wanted to make Bismarck their first Regional Home City. By late 1975 interest was growing to start an orchestra in the Bismarck-Mandan area. The Bismarck-Mandan Orchestral Association was formally organised in February 1976 as a non-profit tax-exempt corporation founded as a sponsoring organization for the Bismarck-Mandan Symphony Orchestra
Country: United States
Contact: music Director Beverly Everrett

Black Hills Symphony Orchestra
Website: www.bhsymphony.org
Email: contact@bhsymphony.org
Phone: 605 348 4676
Address: PO Box 2246, US
Information: The BHSO is administered by Black Hills Symphony Orchestra Society Inc., a non-profit organisation, and utilises approximately ninety musicians for typically five performances each season. The principal venue for the BHSO is the Performing Arts Center. The BHSO has partnered with many other local performing organizations, including Dakota Choral Union, Black Hills Dance Theater, Black Hills Community Theater, and Bells Of The Hills. The BHSO is currently conducted by Bruce Knowles; the concertmaster is Carol Knowles
Country: United States
Contact: conductor, music Director Jack Knowles

Bloomington Symphony Orchestra
Website: www.bloomingtonsymphony.org
Email: info@bloomingtonsymphony.org
Phone: 952 563 8573
Address: 1800 West Old Shakopee Road, US
Information: The Bloomington Symphony Orchestra (BSO) is a 75-member volunteer community orchestra located in the Twin Cities suburb of Bloomington, Minnesota. The BSO enriches the lives of our audiences and musicians with outstanding performances of challenging, educational, and thoughtfully selected repertoire.
Country: United States
Contact: General Manager Sara Kleinsasser Tan
Email: info@bloomingtonsymphony.orgMusic Director Manny Laureano
Email: info@bloomingtonsymphony.org

Boca Raton Philharmonic Symphonia
Website: www.bocasymphonia.org
Email: info@bocasymphonia.org
Phone: 561 376 3848
Address: 2285 Potomac Road, US
Information: The SYMPHONIA, a world class chamber orchestra, is dedicated to keeping classical music flourishing in South Florida. Founded in July 2004 as the Boca Raton Philharmonic Symphonia, The SYMPHONIA is called a "gem of an orchestra" by music critics because of the high caliber of its musicians, guest artists and programming. The mission of The SYMPHONIA is to enrich the South Florida community through distinctive musical performances and innovative educational outreach programs. Inspiring and engaging both existing and new audiences, The SYMPHONIA, is committed to the highest standards of Artistic excellence
Country: United States
Contact: President Steven L. Pomeranz
Email: administrator of the orchestra Annabel Russell
Email: orchestra Manager Jeffrey Kaye
Email: conductor Philippe Entremont

Boise Philharmonic
Website: www.boisephilharmonic.org
Email: info@boisephilharmonic.org
Phone: 208 344 7849
Address: 516 South 9th Street, US
Information: The mission of the Boise Philharmonic Association is to musically enrich, entertain and educate through community engagement and music performance at the highest level. As Idaho's largest and oldest performing arts organisation, (established as the Boise Philharmonic in 1960) the symphony performs for over 50000 people annually in concerts at the Morrison Center, NNU's Brandt Center in Nampa, in schools around the state, and in smaller recital halls and venues
Country: United States
Contact: Artistic Director/conductor Robert Franz
Email: Marketing Director Jimsi Kuborn
Email: jimsi@boisephilharmonic.orgExecutive Director Sandra Culhane

Boston Baroque
Website: www.bostonbaroque.org
Email: info@bostonbaroque.org
Phone: 617 987 8600
Address: 10 Guest Street, Suite 290, US
Information: Boston Baroque is the first permanent Baroque orchestra established in North America and according to Fanfare Magazine, is widely regarded as "one of the world's premier period-instrument bands." The Boston-based ensemble produces lively, emotionally charged, groundbreaking performances of Baroque and Classical works for today's audiences performed on instruments and using performance techniques that reflect the eras in which the music was composed
Country: United States
Contact: Executive Director Martha H. Jones
Email: mhjones@bostonbaroque.orgmusic Director Martin Pearlman
Email: President David Friend
Email: vice President Lee Carl Branberg

Boston Chamber Music Society
Website: www.bostonchambermusic.org
Email: info@bostonchambermusic.org
Phone: 617 349 0086
Address: 60 Gore Street, US
Information: The Boston Chamber Music Society, BCMS, presents the most extensive and longest-running chamber music series in New England. Founded in 1982 by cellists Bruce Coppock and Ronald Thomas with a group of enthusiastic music colleagues, BCMS is an ensemble of superb musicians who come together in different combinations to prepare and perform chamber music. Over the last thirty seasons, BCMS has built a reputation for impassioned performances, ripened over time by the long personal and professional histories of its member musician
Country: United States
Contact: Artistic Director Marcus Thompson
Email: President Stephen Friedlaender
Email: Managing Director Wen Huang
Email: whuang@bostonchambermusic.orgresearch and Marketing Associate Erica Schiller
Email: eschiller@bostonchambermusic.org

Boston Classical Orchestra
Website: www.bostonclassicalorchestra.org
Email: info@bostonclassicalorchestra.org
Phone: 617 423 3883
Address: Po Box 152, US
Information: Boston Classical Orchestra, performing orchestral masterpieces in Faneuil Hall for 34 years, marks the 20th Anniversary Season of Steven Lipsitt as Music Director. This year will be a celebration of all the things we do best: presenting orchestral masterpieces, collaborating with world-renowned guest soloists, and celebrating the birthdays of Verdi & Wagner (200) and Richard Strauss
Country: United States
Contact: music Director Steven Lipsitt
Email: info@bostonclassicalorchestra.org

Boston Philharmonic
Website: www.bostonphil.org
Email: info@bostonphil.org
Phone: 617 236 0999
Address: 295 Huntington Avenue, Suite 210, US
Information: The Boston Philharmonic is a 501(c)3 nonprofit organization dedicated to fulfilling a vision of "passionate music making without boundaries." The Boston Philharmonic Orchestra (BPO), founded by Benjamin Zander in 1979, features student, professional, and amateur musicians who present premier performances of top-notch classical music that is accessible and enjoyable for both music aficionados and the casual listener. The Boston Philharmonic Youth Orchestra (BPYO), founded in 2012, is a world-class, tuition-free ensemble that inspires passionate music-making in young musicians aged 12 to 21 and follow a motto of "shaping future leaders through music
Country: United States

Contact: conductor and music Director Benjamin Zander
Email: General Manager Elisabeth Christensen
Email: Executive Director Mark Cantrell

Boston Pops Orchestra
Website: www.bso.org
Email: customerservices@bso.org
Phone: 617 266 1492
Address: 301 Massachusetts Ave, US
Information: BSO founder Henry Lee Higginson had proposed this new series in the hope of re-creating the ambiance of summer evenings in Viennese concert gardens, while also providing summer employment for the members of the Boston Symphony, who at that point, had to search for other work six months out of the year
Country: United States
Contact: pr Bernadette Horgan
Email: conductor for pops Keith Lockhart
Email: Managing Director Mark Volpe
Email: Director of concert operations Christopher W. Ruigomez

Boston Symphony Chamber Players
Website: bostonsymphonychamberplayers.org
Email: BSCP@bso.org
Phone: 617 266 1492
Address: Symphony Hall, 301 Massachusetts Ave, US
Information: One of the world's most distinguished chamber music ensembles sponsored by a major symphony orchestra and made up of principal players from that orchestra, the Boston Symphony Chamber Players include first-Chair string and wind players from the Boston Symphony Orchestra. Founded in 1964 during Erich Leinsdorf's tenure as BSO music Director, the Chamber Players can perform virtually any work within the vast chamber music literature, expanding their range of repertoire by calling upon other BSO members or enlisting the services of such distinguished artists as pianists Leif Ove Andsnes, Emanuel Ax, and André Previn
Country: United States
Contact: orchestra Manager Ray Wellbaum
Email: Managing Director Mark Volpe

Boston Symphony Orchestra
Website: www.bso.org
Email: pr@bso.org
Phone: 617 266 1492
Address: 301 Massachusetts Avenue, US
Information: The Boston Symphony Orchestra (BSO) is an American orchestra based in Boston, Massachusetts. It is one of the five major American symphony orchestras commonly referred to as the "Big Five". Founded in 1881, the BSO plays most of its concerts at Boston's Symphony Hall and in the summer performs at Tanglewood. Andris Nelsons is the current music Director of the BSO. Bernard Haitink currently holds the title of conductor emeritus of the BSO, and Seiji Ozawa has the title of BSO music Director laureate
Country: United States
Contact: Managing Director Mark Volpe
Email: Artistic administrator Anthony Fogg
Email: public relations Associate Samuel Brewer

Boulder Philharmonic Orchestra
Website: www.boulderphil.org
Email: info@boulderphil.org
Phone: 303 449 1343
Address: Dairy Center for the Arts, 2590 Walnut Street, US
Information: under the vision and leadership of Music Director Michael Butterman, the Boulder Philharmonic Orchestra is celebrating its 55th season of providing outstanding orchestral music in our community. The Boulder Phil is a critically acclaimed professional orchestra, presenting performances nine months out of the year and employing a core of 72 of our region's most highly trained musicians
Country: United States
Contact: orchestra Manager Kim Peoria
Email: kpeoria@boulderphil.orgMarketing Holly Hickman
Email: holly@uptempoMarketing.orgpublicity and media relations Janet Braccio
Email: janetbraccio@comcast.netmusic Director Michael Butterman
Email: Executive Director Kevin Shuck
Email: kshuck@boulderphil.org

Bowling Green-Western Symphony Orchestra
Website: www.bgwso.org
Email: info@bgwso.org
Phone: 270 745 7681
Address: 500 East Main Street, US
Country: United States
Contact: conductor Jooyong Ahn
Email: music Director t.b.a. t.b.a.
Email: conductor@bgwso.org

Brazos Valley Symphony Orchestra
Website: www.bvso.org
Email: office@bvso.org
Phone: 979 696 6100
Address: PO Box 3524, US

Information: physical address: 2501 Earl Rudder Freeway S., College Station, Texas 77845
Country: United States
Contact: Office Manager Nika Hancock
Email: office@bvso.orgExecutive Director Mary Koeninger
Email: Executive@bvso.org

Brazosport Symphony Orchestra
Website: www.bcfas.org
Email: tcas@bcfas.org
Phone: 979 265 7661
Address: 400 College Blvd, US
Country: United States
Contact: President Bruce Story
music Director & conductor
Dr John Ricarte
Email: Manager Kay Jones

Breckenridge Music Institute Festival Orchestra
Website: www.breckenridgemusicfestival.com
Email: admin@breckenridgemusicfestival.com
Phone: 970 453 9142
Address: 217 S. Ridge Street Alley, PO Box 1254, US
Information: see also Festivals (Breckenridge Music Festival)
Country: United States
Contact: Director of Marketing Olivia Grover
Email: Olivia@BreckenridgeMusicFestival.comExecutive Director Marcia Kaufmann
Email: Marcia@BreckenridgeMusicFestival.com

Bremerton Symphony Orchestra and Chorale
Website: bremertonsymphony.wordPress.com/
Email: symphony@symphonic.org
Phone: 360 373 1722
Address: 532 Fifth St, Suite 16, PO Box 996, US
Country: United States
Contact: conductor Alan Futterman
Email: operations Director Mary-Cathern Edwards
Email: music Director Michael Woods
Email: Executive Director Gena Wales
Email: Marketing Director Joelle Jensen

Brevard Music Center
Website: www.brevardmusic.org
Email: bmc@brevardmusic.org
Phone: 828 862 2100
Address: 349 Andante Lane, US
Information: alternative postal address: P.O. BOX 312, Brevard, NC 28712; for contact with individuals refer to www.brevardmusic.org/about/contact; 7 week summer perf festival with 3 orchestras, employ guest soloists, educational institution and summer school for classical musicians; see also Festivals and Presenters
Country: United States
Contact: President/ chief Executive officer Larry Fogdall
Email: Artistic Director Keith Lockhart
Email: chief financial and administrative officer Claudia Hawkins
Email: Artistic administrator Jason Posnock

Brevard Symphony Orchestra
Website: www.brevardsymphony.com
Email: info@brevardsymphony.com
Phone: 321 242 2024
Address: 1500 Highland Avenue, US
Information: six concerts in Vero beach, Indian River, Florida october-april
Country: United States
music Director & principle conductor
Christopher Confessore
Email: Executive Director Fran S. Delisle
Email: Marketing Director Lesmarie Velez

Bronx Arts Ensemble
Website: www.bronxartsensemble.org
Email: info@bronnxartsensemble.com
Phone: 718 601 7399
Address: 80 Van Cortlandt Park South, Suite 7d-1, US
Country: United States
Executive & Artistic Director
William Scribner
Email: fundraising consultant Stephanie Rivers
Email: publicist and authors Manager Maggie Krupka
Email: fundraising consultant Eboni Banks

Brooklyn Philharmonic Orchestra
Website: www.brooklynphilharmonic.org
Email: info@brooklynphilharmonic.org
Phone: 718 488 5700
Address: 20 Jay Street, Suite M16, US
Country: United States
Contact: Artistic Director Alan Pierson

Buffalo Philharmonic Orchestra
Website: www.bpo.org
Email: dhart@bpo.org
Phone: 716 885 0331
Address: 499 Franklin Street, US
Information: The Buffalo Philharmonic Orchestra Society, Inc. provides a resident, professional, major symphony orchestra of Artistic excellence and integrity to enrich

the quality of life in Western New York through the presentation of live symphonic music and other musical events which educate and entertain the broadest possible audiences within and beyond the Western New York region.
Country: United States
Contact: music Director JoAnn Falletta
Email: Executive Director Daniel Hart
Email: dhart@bpo.orgDirector of orchestra and Artistic operations Lisa J Gallo

Bugs Bunny at the Symphony
Website: www.bugsbunnyatthesymphony.net
Email: mtaylor@imgartists.com
Phone: 212 994 3500
Address: Carnegie Hall Tower, 152 West 57th Street, 5th Floor, US
Country: United States
Contact: creator, conductor and Executive Producer George Daugherty
Email: Executive Producer David Ka Lik Wong

Butte Symphony
Website: www.buttesymphony.org
Email: buttesymphony@in-tch.com
Phone: 406 723 5590
Address: PO Box 725, 321 W. Broadway, US
Country: United States

California Symphony Orchestra
Website: www.californiasymphony.org
Email: info@californiasymphony.org
Phone: 925 280 2490
Address: 1475 North Broadway, Suite 420, US
Country: United States
Contact: Executive Director Walter Collins
Email: wcollins@californiasymphony.orgoperations Director Elaina Birnbaum
Email: elaina@californiasymphony.orgmusic Director Barry Jekowsky

Camellia Symphony
Website: www.camelliasymphony.org
Email: camelliaorch@aol.com
Phone: 916 929 6655
Address: PO Box 19786, US
Country: United States
Contact: General Manager/Executive Director Roberta McLellan
music Director & conductor
Allan Pollack

Canton Symphony Orchestra
Website: www.cantonsymphony.org
Email: azotta@cantonsymphony.org
Phone: 330 452 3434
Address: 2331 17th Street NW, US
Information: performs and presents live orchestral music to enrich, entertain, educate, and challenge diverse audiences in a variety of settings
Country: United States
Contact: Executive Director Michelle Mullaly
Email: mmullaly@cantonsymphony.orgorchestra Manager Michael G Koscso
Email: mkoscso@cantonsymphony.orgDirector of Marketing Irene Barker
Email: ibarker@cantonsymphony.org

Cape Ann Symphony
Website: www.capeannsymphony.org
Email: info@capeannsymphony.org
Address: Box 1343, US
Information: Founded in 1952, the Cape Ann Symphony is a flourishing regional orchestra, now acknowledged as one if the finest in the country.
Country: United States
Contact: business Manager David Benjamin
Email: music Director Yoichi Udagawa

Cape Cod Symphony Orchestra
Website: www.capesymphony.org
Email: tickets@capesymphony.org
Phone: 508 362 1111
Address: 1060 Falmouth Road, Suite A, US
Information: the Cape Cod Symphony Orchestra started as a community orchestra more than half a century ago. Since then, it has become one of the largest orchestral organisations in Massachusetts. Artistic Director and Conductor Jung-Ho Pak leads a polished and professional ensemble of 75 musicians, joined by emerging and world-class soloists to bring innovative and accessible programming to the community
Country: United States

Capistrano Valley Symphony
Website: www.capovalleysymphony.com
Email: info@capovalleysymphony.com
Phone: 949 240 8540
Address: 24681 La Plaza, US
Country: United States
Contact: conductor Carlo Spiga

Carmel Symphony Orchestra
Website: www.carmelsymphony.org
Email: cso@carmelsymphony.org

Phone: 317 844 9717
Address: 11 First Avenue NE, US
Country: United States
Contact: presdient and CEO Alan Davis
Email: Artistic Director David Bowden

Cascade Symphony Orchestra
Website: www.cascadesymphony.org
Email: musicDirector@cascadesymphony.org
Phone: 425 776 4938
Address: 8523 215th Street, US
Country: United States
Contact: music Director/conductor Michael Miropolsky

Catskill Symphony Orchestra
Website: www.catskillsymphony.org
Email: cso@oneonta.edu
Phone: 607 436 2670
Address: PO Box 14, US
Country: United States
Contact: Chair Martha Forgiano

Cayuga Chamber Orchestra
Website: www.ccoithaca.org
Email: info@CCOithaca.org
Phone: 607 273 8981
Address: Center Ithaca, Box 112, 171 East State Street, US
Country: United States
Contact: Executive Director Sheila Ossit
Email: ExecutiveDirector@CCOithaca.org

Cedar Rapids Symphony
Website: www.crsymphony.org
Phone: 319 366 8203
Address: 119 Third Ave SE, US
Country: United States
Contact: symphony school and education Director Rochelle Naylor

Central Iowa Symphony
Website: www.cisymphony.org
Email: info@cisymphony.org
Phone: 515 250 1121
Address: P.O. Box 1080, US
Country: United States
Contact: CIS conductor and music conductor Eric L. McIntyre
Email: mcintyr2@grinnell.edupersonnel Manager and orchestra member Brian Bunn
Email: bribunn@hotmail.com

Central Ohio Symphony
Website: www.centralohiosymphony.org
Email: mail@centralohiosymphony.org
Phone: 740 362 1799
Address: PO Box 619, US
Country: United States
Contact: Executive Director Warren Hyer
Email: mail@centralohiosymphony.orgmusical Director Jaime Morales-Matos

Central Wisconsin Symphony Orchestra
Website: www.cwso.org
Email: cwso@cwso.org
Phone: 715 345 2976
Address: PO Box 65, US
Country: United States
Contact: music Director Patrick Miles
Email: Executive Director Ann Huntoon

Chamber Orchestra of Philadelphia
Website: www.chamberorchestra.org
Email: info@chamberorchestra.org
Phone: 215 545 5451
Address: 1520 Locust St., Suite 500, US
Information: organises residency activities which include discussions, small programmes, workshops, master classes for different audiences; 30 - 35 musicians. Member of ISPA
Country: United States
Contact: conductor laureate Ignat Solzhenitsyn
Email: music Director Dirk Brossé

Champaign-Urbana Symphony Orchestra
Website: www.cusymphony.org
Email: music@cusymphony.org
Phone: 217 351 9139
Address: 701 Devonshire Drive, C-24, US
Country: United States
Contact: music Director Stephen Alltop
Email: Executive Director Jeffrey Farlow-Cornell

Chanticleer
Website: www.chanticleer.org
Email: info@chanticleer.org
Phone: 415 252 8589
Address: 44 Page Street, Suite 604, US
Information: Chanticleer is known around the world as "an orchestra of voices" for the seamless blend of its twelve male voices ranging from countertenor to bass and its original interpretations of vocal literature, from Renaissance to jazz, and from gospel to venturesome new music.
Country: United States

Contact: President, General Director Christine Bullin
Email: Director of operations and touring Curt Hancock

Charleston Symphony Orchestra
Website: www.charlestonsymphony.org
Email: info@charlestonsymphony.com
Phone: 843 723 7528
Address: 756 St. Andrews Blvd., South Carolina, US
Country: United States

Charlotte Symphony Orchestra
Website: www.charlottesymphony.org
Email: scottb@charlottesymphony.org
Phone: 704 972 2003
Address: 301 S. Tryon Street, US
Country: United States
Contact: President and chief Executive officer Robert Stickler
Email: roberts@charlottesymphony.orgDirector of Marketing Scott Belford
Email: scottb@charlottesymphony.org

Chattanooga Symphony & Opera
Website: www.chattanoogasymphony.org
Email: info@chattanoogasymphony.org
Phone: 423 267 8583
Address: 701 Broad Street, US
Country: United States
Contact: Orchestra Personnel Manager Eric Andersen
Email: eanderson@chattanoogasymphony.orgExecutive Director Samantha Teter
Email: steter@chattanoogasymphony.orgOperations Manager Kathy Allison
Email: kallison@chattanoogasymphony.orgCSOYO Manager Staci Spring
Email: csoyo@chattanoogasymphony.orgMusic Director and Conductor Kayoko Dan
Email: kdan@chattanoogasymphony.org

Chattanooga Symphony & Opera
Website: www.chattanoogasymphony.org
Email: csoinfo@chattanoogasymphony.org
Phone: 423 267 8583
Address: 701 Broad Street, US
Information: see also Opera
Country: United States
Contact: music Director and conductor Kayoko Dan
Email: kdan@chattanoogasymphony.orgExecutive Director Molly Sasse
Email: msasse@chattanoogasymphony.orgorchestra personnel Manager Eric Andersen
Email: CSOActingPM@aol.comMarketing and development assistant Sarah Marczynski
Email: smarczynski@chattanoogasymphony.orgDirector of Marketing Samantha Teter
Email: steter@chattanoogasymphony.orgDirector of development Michael Kull
Email: mkull@chattanoogasymphony.orgCSO youth orchestra conductor Gary Wilkes
Email: CSO youth philharmonic conductor Sandy Morris
Email: youth orchestras Manager Steve Tonkinson
Email: csoyo@chattanoogasymphony.org

Chautauqua Symphony Orchestra
Website: www.ciweb.org/entertainment/symphony
Email: boxoffice@ciweb.org
Phone: 716 357 6250
Address: PO Box 28, US
Information: summer festival orchestra; founded in 1929. See also Performing Companies (ballet), Venues
Country: United States

Cherish the Ladies
Website: www.cherishtheladies.com
Email: Joanie@cherishtheladies.com
Phone: 978 283 2883
Address: International Music Network, 278 Main Street, US
Information: Over the course of the past 27 years, Cherish the Ladies have risen to the top and are internationally recognized as one of the premier Celtic music and dance ensembles in the world.
Country: United States
Contact: booking agent Alycia Mack
Email: agent@cherishtheladies.com

Cheyenne Symphony Orchestra
Website: www.cheyennesymphony.org
Email: email@CheyenneSymphony.org
Phone: 307 778 8561
Address: 1904 Thomes Avenue, US
Country: United States
Contact: Executive Director Lindsey Bird Reynolds
Email: Lindsey@cheyennesymphony.org

Chicago Chamber Musicians
Website: www.chicagochambermusic.org
Email: info@chicagochambermusic.org
Phone: 312 819 5800
Address: 2 Prudential Plaza, 180 North Stetson Avenue, Suite 1330, US
Information: a society of musicians and music devotees committed to building an internationally recognised chamber music institution in Chicago. Since its inception,

CCM has launched a critically and popularly-acclaimed subscription series
Country: United States
Contact: Executive Director Kathleen Butera
Email: k.butera@chicagochambermusic.orgArtistic Director Meng-Chieh Liu
Email: Marketing Manager Keri Shane
Email: keri.shane@chicagochambermusic.org

Chicago Chamber Orchestra
Website: www.chicagochamberorchestra.org
Email: koberdieter@aol.com
Phone: 312 787 4570
Address: 126 East Chestnit Street, US
Information: second address; 01445 Radebeul-Dresden, Augustusweg 85, Germany, Tel/Fax: +49 351-830 3931
Country: United States
Contact: Executive Director Ryan Loeckel
Email: rloeckel@fourthchurch.orgmusic Director emeritus Kober Dieter
Email: KoberDieter@aol.compersonnel Manager David Tuttle
Email: music Director John Sherer
Email: JSherer@fourthchurch.org

Chicago Children's Choir
Website: www.ccchoir.org
Email: info@ccchoir.org
Phone: 312 849 8300
Address: 78 E. Washington Blvd., 5th Floor, US
Information: The Chicago Children's Choir is a multiracial, multicultural choral music education organisation, shaping the future by making a difference in the lives of children and youth through musical excellence; currently serving over 3000 children aged from 9-18
Country: United States
Contact: Artistic Director/President Josephine Lee
Email: CEO Misho Ceko
Email: Director of advancement Crystal Bowyer
Email: program Director Jocelyn Smith

Chicago Sinfonietta
Website: www.chicagosinfonietta.org
Email: dmacica@chicagosinfonietta.org
Phone: 312 236 3681
Address: 70 East Lake Street, Suite 226, US
Country: United States
Contact: Executive Director Jim Hirsch
Email: jhirsch@chicagosinfonietta.orgDirector of Marketing Camilla McClain
Email: cmcclain@chicagosinfonietta.org

Chicago Symphony Orchestra
Website: www.cso.org
Email: info@cso.org
Phone: 312 294 3345
Address: 220 South Michigan Ave, US
Country: United States
Contact: vice-President for Artistic planning Martha Gilmer
Email: vice-President for finance Isabel Goosen
Email: vice President for public relations Raechel Alexander
Email: President/CEO Deborah Card
Email: Director of orchestra personnel John Deverman
Email: music Director Riccardo Muti

Chinese Classical Orchestra
Website: chinesemusic.net
Email: syshen@megsinet.net
Phone: 630 910 1551
Address: PO Box 5275, US
Country: United States
Contact: concert and lecture Director Yuan-Yuan Lee
Email: Artistic administrator Billie Jefferson
Email: orchestra General Manager Kerry Leung
Email: music Director Sin-Yan Shen

Chippewa Valley Symphony
Website: www.cvsymphony.org
Email: Gordon@cvsymphony.org
Phone: 715 832 6366
Address: 316 Eau Claire St, US
Country: United States

Cincinnati Symphony Orchestra
Website: www.cincinnatisymphony.org
Email: publicrelations@cincinnatisymphony.org
Phone: 513 621 1919
Address: 1241 Elm Street, US
Country: United States
Contact: President Tony Devey
Email: vice President and General Manager Robert McGrath
Email: Director of Artistic Administration Naimah Bilal

Civic Orchestra of Chicago
Website: www.cso.org
Phone: 312 294 3000
Address: 220 S Michigan Avenue, US
Information: Training orchestra of the Chicago Symphony Orchestra
Country: United States

Contact: Manager Tabitha Fleger
Email: coordinator Blaine Inafuku

Clear Lake Symphony
Website: www.clearlakesymphony.org
Email: clsbob@aol.com
Phone: 281 486 0224
Address: PO Box 890582, US
Country: United States
Contact: Associate conductor Robert F Wall

Cleveland Chamber Symphony
Website: www.clevelandchambersymphony.org
Phone: 216 202 4227
Address: The Music School Settlement, 11125 Magnolia Drive, US
Information: the Cleveland Chamber Symphony (CCS) performs music of our time that dares to explore. It nurtures composers, musicians and audiences through professional performances, recordings, commissions, and educational experiences
Country: United States
Contact: Artistic Director Steven Smith

Cleveland Orchestra
Website: www.clevelandorchestra.com
Email: info@clevelandorchestra.com
Phone: 216 231 1111
Address: Severance Hall, 11001 Euclid Ave, US
Country: United States
Contact: Executive assistant Rosemary Klena
Email: rklena@clevelandorchestra.comExecutive Director Gary Hanson
Email: gh@clevelandorchestra.com

Colorado Music Festival Orchestra
Website: www.coloradomusicfest.org
Phone: 303 449 1397
Address: 900 Baseline Road, Cottage 100, US
Country: United States
Contact: Executive Director Catherine Underhill
Email: underhill@COmusic.orgmusic Director Michael Christie

Colorado Springs Philharmonic
Website: www.csphilharmonic.org
Email: information@csphilharmonic.org
Phone: 719 575 9632
Address: PO Box 1266, US
Country: United States
Contact: music Director Josep Caballé-Domenech
Email: concertmaster Michael Hanson

Colorado Symphony Orchestra
Website: www.coloradosymphony.org
Email: admin@coloradosymphony.org
Phone: 303 292 7979
Address: Boettcher Concert Hall, 1000 14th street, , #15, US
Country: United States
President & CEO
Gene Sobczak
Email: gsobczak@coloradosymphony.org

Columbus Indiana Philharmonic
Website: www.thecip.org
Email: info@thecip.org
Address: 315 Franklin Street, US
Country: United States
Contact: production coordinator Vanessa Edwards
music Director & conductor
David Bowden
Email: Executive Director Margaret Powers
Email: choral coordinator Beth Booth Poor

Columbus Symphony Orchestra
Website: www.csoga.org
Email: cbean@csoga.org
Phone: 706 323 5059
Address: PO Box 1499, 935 1st Avenue, US
Information: formed in 1855 and is the second orchestra founded in the nation. The CSO, under the direction of George Del Gobbo, has long been considered one of the Southeast's premier musical ensembles. The CSO is a tenant of RiverCenter for the Performing Arts. The Symphony's performance venue, Bill Heard Theatre, seats 2,000 and provides a state-of-the-art visual and acoustical experience. For more information about the CSO visit our website at www.csoga.org or call 706.323.5059
Country: United States
Contact: Executive Director Cameron Bean
Email: cbean@csoga.orgmusic Director and conductor George Del Gobbo
Email: delgobbo@csoga.orgMarketing Director Anna Bradley
Email: abradley@csoga.orgfinance Director Tammy Zitzelberger
Email: tammy@csoga.org

Columbus Symphony Orchestra
Website: www.columbussymphony.com
Email: cso@columbussymphony.com
Phone: 614 228 9600
Address: 55 East State Street, US
Information: www.picnicwiththepops.com lists the outdoor summer series
Country: United States
Contact: music Director Jean-Marie Zeitouni
Email: Managing Director and CEO William B. Connor Jnr.
Email: Executive assistant Arline Dimitri
Email: adimitri@capa.comGeneral Manager Pavana Stetzik
Email: pstetzik@columbussymphony.comorchestra personnel Manager Darren Fuster
Email: dfuster@columbussymphony.com

Concert Artists of Baltimore
Website: www.cabalto.org
Email: cab@cabalto.org
Phone: 410 625 3525
Address: 1114 St. Paul Street, US
Information: all-professional chamber orchestra and all-professional vocal ensemble
Country: United States
Contact: Artistic Director Edward Polochick
Email: Executive Director David Bielenberg

Connecticut Chamber Orchestra
Phone: 203 847 7724
Address: 18 Hills Lane, US
Information: CD of Mendelson Piano piece No 3 recorded with English Chamber Orchestra
Country: United States
Contact: Manager Sheila Gardiner
Email: music Director Sayard Stone

Core Ensemble, The
Website: www.core-ensemble.cc
Email: margot@core-ensemble.cc
Phone: 561 582 5388
Address: 1320 North Palmway, US
Country: United States
Contact: Executive Director Michael Parola
Email: Managing Director Margot Emery

Corpus Christi Symphony Orchestra
Website: www.ccsymphony.org
Email: ccso@ccsymphony.org
Phone: 361 882 2717
Address: 555 North Carancahua Tower II STE 410 PO Box 495, PAC at TX A&M Univ.-Corpus Christi 6300 Ocean Drive Corpus Christi T, US
Country: United States
Contact: music Director John Giordano
Email: President of the board Roger TenNapel

Dallas Brass
Website: www.dallasbrass.com
Email: mail@dallasbrass.com
Phone: 414 339 4275
Address: 4321 Clemson Drive, US
Country: United States
Contact: artist Manager Kevin Peters
Email: kevin@dallasbrass.com

Dallas Chamber Orchestra
Website: www.dallaschamberorchestra.org
Email: info@dallaschamberorchestra.org
Phone: 214 321 1411
Address: PO Box 600954, US
Country: United States
Contact: music Director Ronald Neal
Email: ronneal@dallaschamberorchestra.org

Dallas Symphony Orchestra
Website: www.DallasSymphony.com
Email: customerservice@dalsym.com
Phone: 214 692 0203
Address: 2301 Flora Street, US
Information: see also Venues (Winspear opera house)
Country: United States

Danville Symphony Orchestra
Website: www.danvillesymphony.org
Email: info@danvillesymphony.org
Phone: 217 443 5300
Address: 2917 North Vermillion Street, US
Country: United States
Contact: Executive Director Meda Bateman
Email: music Director Jeremy Swerling

Dayton Philharmonic Orchestra
Website: www.daytonphilharmonic.com
Email: clong@daytonphilharmonic.com
Phone:
937 224 3521
Address: Performance Place, 109 N Main Street Suite 200, US
Country: United States
Contact: Executive Director Curtis Long
Email: music Director Neal Gittleman
Email: Director of education Gloria Pugh
Email: Director of finance Peter Klosterman
Email: Director of development t.b.a
Email: Director of operations Matthew Borger
Email: Director Marketing David Bukvic
Email: communications Manager Joe Aiello

DeKalb Symphony Orchestra
Website:

www.dekalbsymphony.com
Email: dso@dekalbsymphony.com
Phone: 678 891 3565
Address: PO Box 1313, US
Information: Touring in North Georgia
Country: United States
Contact: music Director/conductor Fyodor Cherniavsky
Email: orchestra Manager Richard Rogers
Email: Executive Director Donna Peoples

Delaware Symphony Orchestra
Website: www.delawaresymphony.org
Email: dso@delawaresymphony.org
Phone: 302 656 7442
Address: PO Box 1870, US
Country: United States

Des Moines Symphony
Website: www.dmsymphony.org
Email: info@dmsymphony.org
Phone: 515 280 4000
Address: 221 Walnut Street, US
Information: alternative E-mail: cami@dmsymphony.org
Country: United States
music Director & conductor
Joseph Giunta
Email: Director of development Jim Dietz-Kilen

Detroit Chamber Winds & Strings
Website: www.detroitchamberwinds.org
Email: info@detroitchamberwinds.org
Phone: 248 559 2095
Address: 24901 Northwestern Highway, Suite 312, US
Country: United States
Contact: Director of communication Margo Strebig
Email: strebig@detroitchamberwinds.orgpr and Marketing Manager Jill Overacker
Email: overacker@detroitchamberwinds.org

Detroit Symphony Orchestra
Website: www.detroitsymphony.com
Email: j.woodward@dso.org
Phone: 313 576 5100
Address: 3711 Woodward Ave., US
Information: see also Presenters, Venues Orchestra Hall
Country: United States
Contact: Director of public relations Jill Woodward
Email: President and Executive Director Anne Parsons
Email: principal guest conductor and Artistic advisor Peter Oundjian
Email: music Director Leonard Slatkin (from Sept 2008)

Dubuque Symphony Orchestra
Website: www.dubuquesymphony.org
Email: info@dubuquesymphony.org
Phone: 563 557 1677
Address: 2728 Asbury Road, Suite 900, US
Country: United States
Contact: President, board of Directors Keith Bibelhausen
Email: Executive Director Jeff Goldsmith
Email: music Director/conductor William Intriligator
Email: operations and orchestra personnel Manager Victoria Molle

Duluth-Superior Symphony Orchestra
Website: www.dsso.com
Email: tickets@dsso.com
Phone: 218 733 7575
Address: 506 West Michigan Street, US
Country: United States
Contact: Executive Director Andrew Berryhill
operations & personnel Director
Nathan Carlsgaard
Director of Marketing & development
Barb Darland
Email: development Director Terry Dunham
Email: patron services Manager Christopher Cuhel

Durham Symphony Orchestra
Website: www.durhamsymphony.org
Email: office@durhamsymphony.org
Phone: 919 560 2736
Address: PO Box 1993, US
Country: United States
Contact: music Director and conductor Alan E Neilson

East Texas Symphony Orchestra
Website: www.etso.org
Email: info@etso.org
Phone: 903 526 3876
Address: PO Box 6323, US
Country: United States
Contact: Executive Director Nancy Wrenn
music Director & conductor
Per Brevig

Eastern Connecticut Symphony Orchestra
Website: www.ectsymphony.org
Email: ectsymphony@snet.net
Phone: 860 443 2876
Address: 289 State Street, US
Country: United States
Contact: Executive Director Isabelle Singer
music Director & conductor

Xiao-Lu Li

Eastern Philharmonic Orchestra
Website: www.easternmusicfestival.org
Email: info@easternmusicfestival.org
Phone: 336 333 7450
Address: c/o Eastern Music Festival and School, PO Box 22026, US
Information: plays in a 5 week seasonal series festival see Eastern Music Festival and School
Country: United States
Contact: President and CEO Thomas Philion
Email: Executive Director Stephanie Cordick
Email: principal conductor Gerard Schwarz

Eastman Philharmonia
Website: www.esm.rochester.edu
Phone: 585 274 1000
Address: Eastman School of Music, 26 Gibbs Street, US
Country: United States
Contact: conductor, eastman philharmonia Neil Varon
Email: concert Manager, eastman school of music Andrew Green
Email: Director, eastman school of music Douglas Lowry

El Paso Symphony Orchestra
Website: www.epso.org
Email: epsoorg@epso.org
Phone: 915 532 3776
Address: PO Box 180, US
Country: United States
Contact: music Director and conductor Bohuslav Rattay
Email: Executive Director Ruth Ellen Jacobson

Elgin Symphony Orchestra
Website: www.elginsymphony.org
Email: boxoffice@elginsymphony.org
Phone: 184 788 80404
Address: 20 DuPage Court, US
Country: United States
Contact: music Director Robert Hanson
Email: interim Marketing Director Ashley Mirakian

Elkhart County Symphony Orchestra
Website: www.elkhartsymphony.org
Email: ecsoadmin@elkhartsymphony.org
Phone: 157 429 31087
Address: PO Box 144, US
Information: youth orchestra, size 50, 2 perfs in season
Country: United States
Contact: board President Jenn Huddleston
Email: Executive Director Kristin D. Schwerha-Scott

Elmhurst Symphony Orchestra
Website: www.elmhurstsymphony.org
Email: Marketing@elmhurstsymphony.org
Phone: 630 941 0202
Address: PO Box 345, US
Country: United States
Contact: symphony Manager Jennifer Thompson
Email: music Director Stephen Alltop

Emerson String Quartet
Website: www.emersonquartet.com
Email: lpetrikova@imgartists.com
Phone: 212 994 3500
Address: 152 West 57th Street, 5th Floor, US
Information: the Emerson String Quartet stands alone in the history of string quartets with an unparalleled list of achievements over three decades: over thirty acclaimed recordings since 1987, nine Grammy® Awards (including two for Best Classical Album, an unprecedented honor for a chamber music group), three Gramophone Awards, the coveted Avery Fisher Prize and cycles of the complete Beethoven, Bartók, Mendelssohn and Shostakovich string quartets in the world's musical capitals
Country: United States
Contact: Managerial Associate Linda Petrikova
Email: lpetrikova@imgartists.comcellist Paul Watkins
Email: violinist Eugene Drucker
Email: violinist Philip Setzer
Email: violist Lawrence Dutton

Empire State Pops/Symphony/ Chamber Orchestras
Email: esconprod@aol.com
Phone: 914 723 2694
Address: 130 Garth Road, Suite 123, US
Country: United States
Contact: music Director Earl Groner
Email: Executive Director Gerald Marshall

Enid Symphony Orchestra
Website: www.enidsymphony.uniqhorns.com
Email: enidsymphony@sbcglobal.net
Phone: 580 237 9646
Address: 300 W Cherokee Avenue, Suite 100, US
Country: United States
Contact: Artistic Director, conductor Douglas Newell
Email: administrative Associate Nancy Walker Huey

Epic Brass
Website: www.epicbrass.com
Email: mail@epicbrass.com

Phone: 508 339 3742
Address: 146 Court Street, US
Information: heralded by the Press for their "virtuosity, versatility and verve, " Earl Raney's Epic Brass Quintet is one of the most dynamic chamber music groups on the concert stage today. Founded in 1983, this Boston-based ensemble combines elegant musical artistry with a youthful flair and brilliance, which captivates audiences worldwide
Country: United States

Epic Brass
Website: www.epicbrass.com
Email: mail@epicbrass.com
Phone: 508 339 3742
Address: 146 Court Street, US
Information: 7 recordings on Ars Nova Digital
Country: United States

Erie Philharmonic
Website: www.eriephil.org
Email: info@eriephil.org
Phone: 814 455 1375
Address: 609 Walnut St., US
Country: United States
Contact: Executive Director Eric Borenstien
Director of Marketing & public relations Karen Beardsley-Petit

Eugene Symphony Association
Website: www.eugenesymphony.org
Email: info@eugenesymphony.org
Phone: 541 687 9487
Address: 115 West 8th Avenue, Suite 115, US
Country: United States
Contact: Executive Director Paul Winberg
Email: music Director/conductor Giancarlo Guerrero

Evansville Philharmonic Orchestra
Website: www.evansvillephilharmonic.org
Email: evphil@evansvillephilharmonic.org
Phone: 812 425 5050
Address: PO Box 84, US
Country: United States
Contact: music Director/conductor Alfred Savia
Email: President Dick Arneson

Everett Symphony Orchestra
Website: www.everettsymphony.org
Email: info@everettsymphony.org
Phone: 142 525 81605
Address: 2710 Colby Avenue, US
Country: United States
Contact: music Director Paul-Elliott Cobbs
Email: Executive Director Jody Matthews

Exultate Choir & Orchestra
Website: www.exultate.org
Email: trossin@comcast.net
Phone: 651 707 0727
Address: P.O. Box 22314, US
Country: United States
Contact: Director Thomas Rossin
Email: trossin@comcast.net

Fairbanks Symphony/ Arctic Chamber Orchestra (ACO)
Website: www.fairbankssymphony.org
Email: symphony@fairbankssymphony.org
Phone: 907 474 5733
Address: PO Box 82104, US
Information: the Arctic Chamber Orchestra is the touring ensemble of the Fairbanks Symphony
Country: United States
Contact: operations Director Jenni Warren
music Director & conductor Eduard Zilberkant
Email: Executive Director Laura Bergh
Email: Marketing Director George Rydlinski

Fairfax Symphony Orchestra
Website: www.fairfaxsymphony.org
Email: info@fairfaxsymphony.org
Phone: 703 563 1990
Address: 3905 Railroad Ave., Suite 202 N., US
Information: resident orchestra at Shenandoah Valley Music Festival: also has a summer series of 35 concerts in the local parks
Country: United States
Contact: President and CEO Elizabeth Murphy
Email: music Director Christopher Zimmerman

Fargo-Moorhead Symphony
Website: www.fmsymphony.org
Email: info@fmsymphony.org
Phone: 121 823 38397
Address: 810 4th Ave. S., Suite #250, Townsite Center, US
Information: office: 810 4th Ave. South Moorhead, MN 56560
Country: United States
Contact: Executive Director Jeff vom Saal
Email: music Director Bernard Rubenstein

Flagstaff Symphony Orchestra
Website:

www.flagstaffsymphony.org
Email: info@flagstaffsymphony.org
Phone: 928 774 5107
Address: PO Box 122, US
Information: orchestra plays a series of concerts specifically destinated for school children. Also cross-over or fusion projects such as Native American music orchestrated & played with symphony.
Country: United States
Contact: Executive Director Laura Kelly

Flint Symphony Orchestra
Website: www.thefim.org
Email: cmooney@thefim.org
Phone: 810 238 1350
Address: 1025 E Kearsley St, US
Country: United States
Contact: Manager Tom Glasscock
Email: music Director Enrique Diemecke
Email: President Paul Torre
Email: Marketing Director Christina Mooney

Florence Symphony Orchestra
Website: www.florencesymphony.com
Email: Manager@FlorenceSymphony.com
Phone: 843 661 2541
Address: PO Box 3211, US
Country: United States
Contact: conductor Terry Roberts
Email: Executive Director Roger Malfatti
Email: Manager@florencesymphony.com

Florida Orchestra
Website: www.floridaorchestra.org
Email: admin@floridaorchestra.org
Phone: 727 892 3337
Address: 244 2nd Avenue North, Suite 420, US
Country: United States
Contact: principal guest conductor Stuart Malina
President & CEO
Michael Pastreich
Email: principal pops conductor Jeff Tyzik

Florida West Coast Symphony
Website: www.fwcs.org
Email: symphony@fwcs.org
Phone: 941 953 4252
Address: 709 N Tamiami Trail, US
Information: size of orchestra: 85; performances: 90; organise Sarasota Music Festival ((q.v.))
Country: United States
Artistic Director & conductor
Leif Bjaland
Email: chief financial officer Douglas Shanley
Email: Marketing Director Linda Joffe
Email: Executive Director Joeseph McKenna
Email: Director of education programs Roseanne McCabe
Email: Associate Marketing Director Laura M Scahill
Email: development Director Barbara Simon

Fort Collins Symphony Orchestra
Website: www.fcsymphony.org
Email: note@fcsymphony.org
Phone: 970 482 4823
Address: 214 S. College Avenue, US
Country: United States
Contact: principal conductor/music Director Wes Kenney
Email: Executive Director Carrie Newman

Fort Smith Symphony
Website: www.fortsmithsymphony.org
Email: fssymphony@fortsmithsymphony.org
Phone: 479 452 7575
Address: PO Box 3151, US
Country: United States
Music Director & Conductor
John Jeter

Fort Wayne Philharmonic
Website: www.fortwaynephilharmonic.com
Email: Marketing@fortwaynephilharmonic.com
Phone: 260 744 1700
Address: 2340 Fairfield Avenue, US
Country: United States
Email: assistant conductor Bradley Thachuk
Email: Director of development Christine Sand Maier
Email: Director of finance Christine Thompson
Email: Executive Director J L Nave
Director of education & community partnerships
Anna Ross
Email: Director of Marketing and public relations
Samantha Teter

Fort Worth Symphony Orchestra
Website: www.fwsymphony.org
Email: Administration@fwsymphony.org
Phone: 817 665 6500
Address: 330 East 4th Street, Suite 200, US
Country: United States
Contact: music Director Miguel Harth-Bedoya
Email: President Ann Koonsman
Email: development Director Amy Atkins
Email: Director of Artistic Administration Matthew Spivey

Email: operations Manager Ryan Bonisfas
Email: Director of finance Melinda Hayden
Email: Director of Marketing David Hadlock

Fox Valley Symphony
Website: www.foxvalleysymphony.com
Email: info@foxvalleysymphony.com
Phone: 920 968 0300
Address: 111 West College Avenue, Suite 550, US
Country: United States
Contact: Executive Director Marta Weldon
Email: music Director Brian Groner

Fremont Symphony Orchestra
Website: www.fremontsymphony.org
Email: info@fremontsymphony.org
Phone: 510 371 4860
Address: PO Box 104, Office: 3375 Country Dr. Fremont, CA 94536, US
Country: United States

Fresno Philharmonic
Website: www.fresnophil.org
Email: info@fresnophil.org
Phone: 559 261 0600
Address: 2377 West Shaw Avenue, Suite 101, US
Country: United States
Contact: development Director Karin Chao-Bushoven
Email: music Director Theodore Kushar
Email: Marketing Manager Mary-Frances Semsem
Email: Executive Director Don Reinhold

Gainesville Chamber Orchestra
Website: www.gcomusic.org
Phone: 135 233 65448
Address: PO Box 357011, US
Country: United States
music Director & conductor
Evans Haile

Gainesville Symphony Orchestra
Website: www.gsomusic.com
Email: boxoffice@gsomusic.com
Phone: 770 532 5727
Address: PO Box 162, US
Country: United States
Contact: music Director Gregory Pritchard
Email: Executive Director Pam Slaton

GAMAC Chamber Orchestra
Website: www.gamac.org
Email: aspainhour@gamac.org
Phone: 864 231 6147
Address: 907 North Main St. , Suite 12, US
Information: formed as an accompaniment Orchestra for the various GAMAC Chorales, the Chamber Orchestra has become the premiere instrumental performing group in the Anderson area; see also Presenters (Greater Anderson Musical Arts Consortium - GAMAC)
Country: United States
Contact: musical Director and conductor R. Alexander Spainhour, III

Garden State Philharmonic
Website: www.gardenstatephilharmonic.org
Email: gspmusic@earthlink.net
Phone: 732 451 0064
Address: 150 Brick Boulevard, US
Information: 3 youth orchestras; 1 community chorus
Country: United States
Artistic Director & conductor
Anthony LaGruth

Garland Symphony Orchestra
Website: www.garlandsymphony.org
Email: info@garlandsymphony.org
Phone: 972 926 0611
Address: PO Box 461204, US
Country: United States
Contact: music Director Robert Carter Austin
Email: General Manager - interim Stephanie Sunder
Email: production Manager Michael Hooper

Gateway Festival Orchestra of St. Louis
Website: gatewayfestivalorchestra.org
Email: iallen2@earthlink.net
Phone: 314 569 0371
Address: 722 Elkington Lane, US
Information: performs outreach concerts in the city of St. Louis for youths and adults
Country: United States
Contact: President Ivy Allen
Email: conductor/music Director James Richards

Glacier Symphony and Chorale
Website: www.glaciersymphonychorale.org
Email: info@glaciersymphonychorale.org
Phone: 406 257 3241
Address: PO Box 2491, US
Information: beside the main orchestra Glacier also has an adult choral of 80 voices, a choral ensemble of 24 voices, a string quartet, and a woodwinds quintet.
Country: United States
Contact: Executive Director Alan Satterlee
music Director & youth orchestra conductor

John Zoltek
Email: chorale and children's choir conductor Jim Stanard

Glendale Symphony Orchestra
Website: www.glendalesymphony.org
Email: info@glendalesymphony.org
Phone: 818 500 8720
Address: PO Box 1986, US
Country: United States
Contact: music Director Olivia Tsui
Email: Executive Director Diane Hedrick

Grand Junction Symphony Orchestra
Website: www.gjsymphony.org
Email: info@gjsymphony.org
Phone: 970 243 6787
Address: 225 North Fifth, Suite 120, US
Information: community, non-union orchestra
Country: United States
Contact: Executive Director Michael Schwerin
Email: music Director Kirk Gustafson

Grand Rapids Symphony
Website: www.grsymphony.org
Email: info@grsymphony.org
Phone: 616 454 9451
Address: 300 Ottawa Avenue NW, Ste. 100, US
Information: concert series are presented with performances designed to capture the imagination of young children and adults alike, featuring a wide range of music and performance styles. These series include the Richard and Helen DeVos Classical, Fox Motors Pops, Nestlé Gerber SymphonicBoom, Porter Hills Coffee Classics, Crowe Horwath Great Eras, Sacred Dimensions, PNC Lollipops, DTE Energy Foundation Family and the D&W Fresh Market Picnic Pops series, totalling more than 400 performances each year
Country: United States
Contact: Executive Director Peter T. Kjome
Email: pkjome@grsymphony.orgvice President for Marketing and communication Denise Borton
Email: dborton@grsymphony.org

Grant Park Musical Festival Orchestra and Chorus
Website: www.grantparkmusicfestival.com
Phone: 312 742 7638
Address: 205 East Randolph Drive, US
Information: the resident orchestra and chorus of the Grant Park Music Festival, a free summer festival funded by Chicago Park District: see also Festivals
Country: United States
Contact: principal conductor Carlos Kalmar
Email: chorus Manager Lee Lichamer
Email: Artistic and General Director James W. Palermo
Email: chorus Director Christopher Bell

Great Falls Symphony, Inc
Website: www.gfsymphony.org
Email: info@gfsymphony.org
Phone: 406 453 4102
Address: PO Box 1078, # 11 Third St. No., US
Country: United States
Contact: ensemble/youth orchestra Manager Jan Nerem
Email: choir Director Kathleen McIntosh
Email: music Director/conductor Gordon Johnson
Email: Executive Director Carolyn Valacich

Greater Anderson Musical Arts Consortium
Website: www.gamac.org
Email: aspainhour@gamac.org
Phone: 864 231 6147
Address: 907 N. Main St, Suite 12, US
Country: United States
Contact: Executive Director Dana Gencarelli
Email: dgencarelli@gamac.orgmusical Director R. Alexander Spainhour
Email: aspainhour@gmail.com

Greater Bridgeport Symphony Orchestra
Website: www.gbs.org
Email: operations@gbs.org
Phone: 203 576 0263
Address: 446 University Ave, 1489 South Main Street, 1489 South Main Street, US
Country: United States
Contact: Music Director Emeritus Gustav Meier
Email: Executive Director Alexander Morr
Email: operations@gbs.org

Greater Grand Forks Symphony Orchestra
Website: www.ggfso.org
Email: ggfso@und.edu
Phone: 701 777 3359
Address: 3350 Campus Drive, Mailstop 7084, US
Country: United States
Contact: Executive Director Jennifer Tarlin

Greater Lansing Symphony Orchestra
Website: www.lansingsymphony.org
Email: info@LansingSymphony.org
Phone: 517 487 5001
Address: 501 S. Capitol Ave., Suite 400, US
Country: United States
Contact: education and operations Manager Leanne

King
Email: Executive Director David Gross

Greater Trenton Symphony
Website: www.trentonsymphony.org
Email: info@trentonsymphony.org
Phone: 609 394 1338 adm
Address: 28 W State Street, Suite 202, US
Country: United States
Contact: music Director John Peter Holly

Greeley Philharmonic Orchestra
Website: www.greeleyphilharmonic.org
Email: greeleyphil1@gmail.com
Phone: 970 356 6406
Address: PO Box 1535, US
Information: the Greeley Philharmonic Orchestra grew out of concerts sponsored by the Fortnightly Music Club between 1908 and 1911. Enthusiasm grew, and in 1911, the Greeley Philharmonic Orchestra (GPO) was established. According to an early program, its "motive" was to provide pleasure and profit for local musicians, to give young people an opportunity for orchestral training and "to aid in raising the musical standards in our city." In time, it evolved into the cornerstone of Greeley's cultural structure. Although the founders of the GPO first set out to create a small yet viable community orchestra, the GPO has developed into a 65-piece professional orchestra that draws some of the most accomplished musicians from Northern Colorado and beyond.
Country: United States
Contact: administrative Coordinator Briana Harris
Email: greeleyphil1@gmail.comadministrative assistant and Marketing Logan Snook
Email: personnel Manager Becky Kutz Osterberg

Green Bay Symphony Orchestra
Website: www.greenbaysymphony.org
Email: info@greenbaysymphony.org
Phone: 920 435 3465
Address: PO Box 222, US
Country: United States
Contact: music Director Bridget-Michaele Reischl
Email: Executive Director Michael Stefiuk
Email: office Manager Aubrey Brennen

Greensboro Symphony Orchestra
Website: www.greensborosymphony.org
Phone: 336 335 5456
Address: 200 N. Davie St., Suite 328, US
Country: United States
Contact: Executive Director Lisa Crawford
Email: production Manager Vito Ciccone
Email: principal pops conductor Michael Berkowitz

Greenville Symphony Orchestra
Website: www.greenvillesymphony.org
Email: gso@greenvillesymphony.org
Phone: 864 232 0344
Address: 200 S. Main St., US
Country: United States
Contact: Marketing Director Carter Meadors
Email: operations Manager Anthony Marotta
Email: Executive Director Robert E. Howard
Email: music Director and conductor Edvard Tchivzhel

Greenwich Symphony Orchestra
Website: www.greenwichsym.org
Email: gsorch@verizon.net
Phone: 203 869 2664
Address: PO Box 35, US
Country: United States
Contact: President Mary Radcliffe
Email: music Director David Gilbert

Gulf Coast Symphony Orchestra, Inc.
Website: www.gulfcoastsymphony.net
Email: info@gulfcoastsymphony.net
Phone: 228 435 9800
Address: PO Box 542, US
Information: masterclasses for youth; also started Gulf Coast Youth Symphony Orchestra in 2001
Country: United States
Contact: music Director John W Strickler
Email: President Melanie Clark
Email: Executive Director Timothy James Borgman

Hamilton-Fairfield Symphony
Website: www.hfso.org
Email: info@hfso.org
Phone: 151 389 55151
Address: 23 South Front Street, US
Country: United States
Contact: music Director Paul Stanbery

Handel and Haydn Society
Website: www.handelandhaydn.org
Email: info@handelandhaydn.org
Phone: 617 262 1815
Address: 300 Massachusetts Avenue, US
Information: oldest continuously active performing arts organisation in USA; under the management of Columbia Artists Inc., NY: Arabesque CDs, London

Records/L'Oiseau Lyre
Country: United States
Contact: Executive assistant Lina Zhong
Email: lzhong@handelandhaydn.org
Director of Artistic planning Ira Pedlikin
Email: ira@handelandhaydn.org
production Manager Jesse Levine
Email: jlevine@handelandhaydn.org
Director of development Mike Peluse
Email: mpeluse@handelandhaydn.orgDirector of Marketing and communications Matthew Erikson

Harrisburg Symphony Orchestra
Website: www.harrisburgsymphony.org
Email: info@harrisburgsymphony.org
Phone: 717 545 5527
Address: 800 Corporate Circle, Suite 101, US
Country: United States
Contact: music Director Stuart Malina
Email: Executive Director Jeff Woodruff
Director of Marketing & patron services
Kent Wissinger

Hartford Symphony Orchestra
Website: www.hartfordsymphony.org
Email: info@hartfordsymphony.org
Phone: 860 246 8742
Address: 166 Capitol Ave, US
Country: United States
Contact: President and CEO David Fay
Email: david_fay@hartfordsymphony.orgDirector of Marketing and PR Katie Bonner Russo
Email: kbonner@hartfordsymphony.org

Helena Symphony Orchestra
Website: www.helenasymphony.org
Email: info@helenasymphony.org
Phone: 406 442 1860
Address: PO Box 1073, US
Country: United States
Contact: Executive Director Mary Williams
Email: President Joe Mavurek
Email: music Director and conductor Allan R Scott

Hendersonville Symphony Orchestra
Website: www.hendersonvillesymphony.org
Email: info@hendersonvillesymphony.net
Phone: 828 697 5884
Address: PO Box 1811, US
Information: offer master classes with guest artists for the schools; 1 youth orchestra, 1 newly formed Flute Choir, 3 youth ensembles; give performances of ""Carnival of the Animals"" to all 3rd grades and ""Peter and the Wolf"" to all 6th grades in the county
Country: United States
Contact: General Manager Deborah Anthony
Email: conductor Thomas Joiner

Hesperus
Website: www.hesperus.org
Email: mail@hesperus.org
Phone: 170 352 57550
Address: 3706 North 17th Street, US
Country: United States
Contact: co-Director Tina Chancey

Hollywood Bowl Orchestra (a project of the Los Angeles Philharmonic Association)
Website: www.hollywoodbowl.com
Email: bgrohl@laphil.org
Phone: 323 850 2060
Address: 2301 N Highland Avenue, US
Country: United States

Honolulu Symphony
Website: www.honolulusymphony.com
Email: info@honolulusymphony.com
Phone: 808 524 0815
Address: 650 Iwilei Road, Suite 202, US
Country: United States
Contact: principal conductor Andreas Delfs
Email: Marketing Manager Ryan Lum
Email: Executive Director Tom Gulick

Houston Symphony
Website: www.houstonsymphony.org
Email: office@houstonsymphony.org
Phone: 713 224 4240
Address: 615 Louisiana Street, Suite 102, US
Country: United States
Contact: General Manager Steven Brosvik
Email: Executive Director Mark Hanson
Email: music Director Andres Orozco-Estrada

Huntington Symphony Orchestra
Website:
www.huntingtonsymphony.org
Email: huntingtonsymphony@gmail.com
Phone: 304 781 8343
Address: PO Box 2343, 763 Third Ave., US
Country: United States
Contact: personnel Sandy White
Email: music Director Kimo Furumoto
Email: President Brandi Jacob-Jones

Huntsville Symphony Orchestra
Website:
www.hso.org
Email: hso@hiwaay.net
Phone: 256 539 4818
Address: Von Braun Center, 700 Monroe Street, US
Country: United States
Contact: Artistic administrator Evelyn Loehrlein
Email: Director of Marketing and development Jennifer Doss

Hutchinson Symphony Association
Website: www.hutchsymphony.org
Phone: 620 728 0246
Address: 400 Hyde Park Drive, US
Country: United States
Contact: music Director Dr Richard Koshgarian

Idaho Falls Symphony
Website: www.ifsymphony.org
Email: office@ifsymphony.org
Phone: 208 529 1080
Address: 450 A Street, US
Country: United States
Contact: Executive Director Tally Adler

Idaho State Civic Symphony
Website: www.thesymphony.us
Email: parkers@hostidaho.com
Phone: 120 823 41587
Address: PO Box 8099, US
Country: United States
Contact: conductor and music Director Chung Park
Email: President Carol Burnett

Illinois Philharmonic Orchestra
Website: www.ipomusic.org
Phone: 708 481 7774
Address: 377 Artists Walk, US
Country: United States
Contact: Marketing Director Corinne Johnston
Email: Executive Director Edmund Feingold
Email: music Director Carmon DeLeone

Illinois Symphony Orchestra Inc.
Website: www.ilsymphony.org
Email: cheryl@ilsymphony.org
Phone: 217 522 2838
Address: PO Box 5191, 524 1/2 East Capitol, US
Country: United States
Contact: music Director Karen Lynne Deal
Email: Executive Director Cheryl Snyder
Email: Director of operations Kamen Petkov

Immanuel and Helen Olshan - Texas Music Festival
Website: www.tmf.uh.edu
Email: tmf@uh.edu
Phone: 713 743 3167
Address: 3333 Cullen Blvd., Ste. 120, Houston, TX 77204-4017
Information: Classical music's rising stars align in Houston, joining an international faculty of performers, conductors, and soloists.
Country: United States
General & Artistic Director
Alan Austin
Email: tmf@uh.edu
Social Media: @TXMusicFestival@TexasMusicFestival.UH
Regular Venues: 0

Imperial Symphony Orchestra
Website: www.imperialsymphony.org
Email: info@imperialsymphony.org
Phone: 863 688 3743
Address: 1035 S Florida Ave, Suite 205, US
Country: United States
Contact: development Director Beth Mason
music Director & conductor
Mark Thielen

Indian Hill Music
Website: www.indianhillmusic.org
Email: info@indianhillmusic.org
Phone: 978 486 9524
Address: PO Box 1484, US
Country: United States
Contact: Executive Director Susan Randazzo
Email: music Director Bruce Hangen

Indianapolis Chamber Orchestra
Website: www.icomusic.org
Email: info@icomusic.org
Phone: 317 940 9607
Address: 4603 Clarendon Road, Suite 36, US
Country: United States
Contact: music Director Kirk Trevor
Email: Executive Director Elaine Eckhart

Indianapolis Symphony Orchestra
Website: www.IndianapolisSymphony.org
Email: iso@IndianapolisSymphony.org
Phone: 317 262 1100

Address: 32 East Washington Street, # 600, US
Information: recordings on Decca, Koss Classics and New World records; nationally syndicated radio series
Country: United States
Contact: chief Executive officer Gary Ginstling

Inland Empire/Riverside County Philharmonic
Website:
www.thephilharmonic.org
Email: thephilharmonic@thephilharmonic.org
Phone: 909 787 0251
Address: PO Box 1601, US
Information: also runs an education programme which includes 1 school district
Country: United States
Contact: Executive Director Barbara Lohman
Email: music Director Tomasz Golka

Ixtlan Artists Group
Website: www.ixtlanartists.com
Email: rtroup@ixtlanartists.com
Phone: 800 961 9601
Address: 47 Franklin Street, Wilkes-Barre, US
Country: United States
Contact: Director of operations Robin Troup
Email: rtoup@ixtlanartists.com
events coordinator & booking agent
Kate McDonnell
Email: agent@ixtlanartists.comperformer Kevin Locke
Email: kevinlocke@ixtlanartists.com

Jackson Symphony Orchestra
Website: www.jacksonsymphony.org
Email: jso@jacksonsymphony.org
Phone: 517 782 3221
Address: 215 West Michigan Avenue, US
Country: United States
Contact: music Director and conductor Stephen Osmond
Email: development Director Mary Spring

Jacksonville Symphony Orchestra
Website: www.jaxsymphony.org
Email: frontdesk@jaxsymphony.org
Phone: 904 354 5479 (ad
Address: 300 West Water Street, Suite 200, US
Country: United States
Contact: General Manager Richard Naylor
Email: public relations Director Paul Witkowski
Email: Director of Sales Katie Scales
Email: Executive Director Stacy Ridenour
Email: music Director Fabio Mechetti
Email: Director of development Kaye Glover
Email: Director of finance Holly Bryan

Jazz at Lincoln Center Orchestra
Website: www.jalc.org
Email: bwilson@jalc.org
Phone: 212 258 9800
Address: Broadway, 60th St, Frederick P. Rose Hall, US
Country: United States
Contact: Executive Director Adriann Ellis
Email: Director public relations Mary Fiance Fuss
Email: chief financial officer Caroline Cohen
Email: Artistic Director Wynton Marsalis

Jefferson Symphony Orchestra
Website: www.jeffsymphony.org
Email: info@jeffsymphony.org
Phone: 303 278 4237
Address: PO Box 546, US
Information: street address: 1204 Washington Ave., Suite 5, Golden, CO 80401-1736
Country: United States
Contact: Chairman of the board Calvin Winn
Email: principal conductor and music Director Willliam Morse
Email: Associate conductor J. Stephen Mallinson
Email: General Manager Jean Loucks
Email: office@jeffsymphony.org

Jewish Community Center Orchestra
Website: www.jccso.org
Email: sschallern@jccgw.org
Phone: 301 881 0100
Address: 6125 Montrose Road, Gildenhorn/Speisman Center for the Arts, US
Country: United States
Contact: music Director Sarah Schallern
Email: Manager Felice Kornberg

Johnson City Symphony
Website: www.jcsymphony.com
Email: elaine@jcsymphony.com
Phone: 423 926 8472
Address: PO Box 533, US
Country: United States
Contact: office Manager Elaine Pectol
Email: elaine@jcsymphony.commusic Director/conductor Robert J. Seebacher

Johnstown Symphony Orchestra
Website: www.johnstownsymphony.org
Email: info@johnstownsymphony.org
Phone: 814 535 6738

Address: 227 Franklin Street, Suite 304, US
Country: United States
Contact: music Director and conductor Istvan Jaray
Email: Executive Director Patricia Hofscher

Jupiter Symphony Chamber Players
Website: www.jupitersymphony.com
Email: admin@jupitersymphony.com
Phone: 121 279 91259
Address: 155 West 68th Street, Suite 319, US
Country: United States
Contact: founder Jens Nygaard

Kalamazoo Symphony Orchestra
Website: www.kalamazoosymphony.com
Phone: 269 349 7759
Address: 359 South Kalamazoo Mall, Suite 100, US
Information: The Kalamazoo Symphony Orchestra proudly celebrates 96 years of soul-prodding musical experiences and educational programming that stimulate audiences from the inside out. Founded in 1921, the KSO is the third largest professional orchestra in Michigan with a $2.5 million operating budget, and is recognised throughout the country as a regional orchestra of excellence. Member of ISPA.
Country: United States
Contact: music Director Julian Kuerti
Email: President and CEO Peter Gistelinck
Email: PGistelinck@kalamazoosymphony.comvice President Evan Menz
Email: EMenz@kalamazoosymphony.compersonnel Manager Frank Silva
Email: FSilva@kalamazoosymphony.com

Kansas City Symphony
Website: www.kcsymphony.org
Email: symphony-info@kcsymphony.org
Phone: 181 647 11100
Address: 1020 Central, Suite 300, US
Country: United States
Contact: Executive Director Frank Byrne
Email: General Manager Andrew Birgensmith
Email: Marketing Manager Jeff Barker
music Director & conductor
Michael Stern

Kennett Symphony of Chester County
Website: www.kennettsymphony.org
Email: info@kennettsymphony.org
Phone: 610 444 6363
Address: PO Box 72, US
Country: United States

Kentucky Symphony Orchestra
Website: www.kyso.org
Email: info@kyso.org
Phone: 859 431 6216
Address: PO Box 72810, US
Country: United States
Contact: music/Executive Director James R Cassidy
Email: General Manager Angela M Williamson

Knoxville Symphony Orchestra
Website: www.knoxvillesymphony.com
Email: info@knoxvillesymphony.com
Phone: 865 523 1178
Address: 100 S. Gay St. Ste. 302, US
Information: 21 concerts full-size 8 concerts, pops 7 concerts, chamber 5 and the superpops concert
Country: United States
Contact: Director of communications Stephanie Burdette
Email: Executive Director Rachel Ford
Email: music Director Lucas Richman

Kokomo Symphony
Phone: 765 455 1659
Address: PO Box 6115, US
Information: Principal $100 per service; principals $60 per service, $50 per service for the rest
Country: United States
Director concert & production
Jennifer Kirkman
Email: Executive Director June A Beck
Email: music Director t.b.a

Kronos Quartet
Website: www.kronosquartet.org
Email: office@kronosarts.com
Phone: 415 731 3533
Address: PO Box 225340, US
Information: For 40 years, San Francisco's Kronos Quartet—David Harrington (violin), John Sherba (violin), Hank Dutt (viola), and Sunny Yang (cello), have combined a spirit of fearless exploration with a commitment to continually re-imagining the string quartet experience. In the process, Kronos has become one of the world's most celebrated and influential ensembles, performing thousands of concerts worldwide, releasing more than 50 recordings, collaborating with many of the world's most eclectic composers and performers, and commissioning more than 800 works and arrangements for string quartet. Member of ISPA
Country: United States
Contact: Managing Director Janet Cowperthwaite
Email: Associate Director Laird Rodet

La Crosse Symphony Orchestra
Website:
www.lacrossesymphony.org
Email: lacrossesymphony@lacrossesymphony.org
Phone:
608 783 2121
Address: 3217 Commerce Street, US
Country: United States
Contact: music Director and conductor Amy Mills
Email: Executive Director Connie Knutson

La Jolla Symphony & Chorus
Website: www.lajollasymphony.com
Email: boxoffice@lajollasymphony.com
Phone: 858 534 4637
Address: 9500 Gilman Drive, UCSD 0361, US
Information: a community-based chorus and orchestra dedicated to bringing professional-quality music to the San Diego area - and beyond
Country: United States

La Porte County Symphony Orchestra
Website: www.lcso.net
Email: Executive@lcso.net
Phone: 121 936 29020
Address: PO Box 563, US
Country: United States
Contact: Executive Director Cheryl Ferguson
Email: music Director Philip Bauman

Lafayette Symphony Orchestra
Website: www.lafayettesymphony.org
Email: officeManager@lafayettesymphony.org
Phone: 765 742 6463
Address: PO Box 52, US
Information: physical address: 111 N 6th St Lafayette, IN 47901
Country: United States
Contact: Executive Director Kitty Campbell
Email: office Manager Erica Pence
Email: business Manager Rockie Allee

Lake Charles Symphony Orchestra
Website: www.lcsymphony.org
Email: info@lcsymphony.org
Phone: 337 433 1611
Address: PO Box 3102, US
Country: United States
Contact: Executive Director Debbie Reed

Lake Forest Symphony Assn Inc.
Website: www.lakeforestsymphony.org
Email: info@lakeforestsymphony.org
Phone: 847 295 2135
Address: 50 East Old Mill Road, US
Information: also operates a music school at 40 East Mill Road, Lake Forest; Summer internships available
Country: United States
Contact: interim Executive Director Joanne Bernstein
Email: Director of Marketing Pat Nissen
Email: Director of dev Stephanie Trautwein
Email: music Director Allan Heatherington

Las Colinas Symphony Orchestra
Website: www.lascolinassymphony.org
Email: info@lascolinassymphony.org
Phone: 972 252 4800
Address: PO Box 141446, US
Country: United States
Contact: President Todd Hill
Email: Executive Director Deborah Hawkins

Las Vegas Philharmonic
Website: www.lasvegasphilharmonic.com
Email: lvphil@anv.net
Phone: 702 895 2787
Address: 3271 S. Highland Dr., Suite 702, US
Information: contact services, ensemble outreach
Country: United States
Contact: administrative Manager Anita Meyer
Email: music Director David Itkin
Email: Director of development William Marion
Email: event coordinator Keith Neel

Las Vegas Sinfonietta
Website: LasVegasSinfonietta.com
Email: Taraskrysa@gmail.com
Phone: 312 451 6935
Address: 2419 Tottingham Road Henderson NV 89074
Information: The Las Vegas Sinfonietta (LVS) is a professional chamber orchestra based in vibrant Las Vegas, Nevada. LVS was founded by a passionate group of local musicians in 2019, dedicated to performing classical repertoire ranging from Baroque to Contemporary works. LVS is committed to sustained excellence in providing classical music performances to the diverse audiences.
Country: United States
Contact: Artistic Director TARAS KRYSA
Email: taraskrysa@gmail.com

Lexington Philharmonic Orchestra
Website: www.lexphil.org
Email: Marketing@lexphil.org

Phone: 859 233 422 688
Address: 161 North Mill Street, US
Country: United States
Contact: Marketing Director Chelsea Compton
Email: Executive Director Peter Kucirko
Email: music Director/conductor Scott Terrell

Lima Symphony Orchestra
Website: www.limasymphony.com
Email: deb@limasymphony.com
Phone: 419 222 5701
Address: PO Box 1651, US
Country: United States
Contact: conductor Crafton Beck
Email: conductor Dennis Kratzer
Email: office Manager Deb West
Email: Executive Director Marie Drum

Lincoln Orchestra Association
Website: www.lincolnsymphony.com
Email: info@lincolnsymphony.com
Phone: 402 476 2211
Address: 233 South 13th Street, B102, US
Country: United States
Contact: Executive Director Barbara Zach
Email: music Director Edward Polochick

Little Orchestra Society/Orpheon Inc.
Website: www.littleorchestra.org
Email: info@littleorchestra.org
Phone: 212 971 9500
Address: 330 West 42nd St., 12th Floor, US
Country: United States
Contact: Managing Director John Kordel
Email: Artistic administrator Alyce Mott
Email: music Director/conductor Dino Anagnost

Livermore-Amador Symphony
Website: www.livamsymph.org
Email: mcfannv@comcast.net
Phone: 192 537 36824
Address: PO Box 1049, US
Country: United States
Contact: Manager Virginia McFann
Email: musical Director/conductor Arthur Barnes

Livingston Symphony Orchestra
Phone: 197 363 58656
Address: PO Box 253, US
Country: United States
Contact: music Director/ principal conductor Istvan Jaray
Email: Manager E. Lois Cully

Livonia Symphony Orchestra
Website: www.livoniasymphony.com
Phone: 734 421 1111
Address: 37637 Five Mile Rd, #398, US
Country: United States
Contact: music Director Volodymyr Schesiuk

Long Beach Symphony Orchestra
Website: www.lbso.org
Email: lbso@lbso.org
Phone: 562 436 3203
Address: 555 E. Ocean Blvd, Suite 106, US
Country: United States
music Director & conductor
Enrique Arturo Diemecke
Email: Executive Director Robert C. Jones
Email: General Manager Janet Nyquist
Email: Director of Marketing and communications Rick Berry

Long Island Philharmonic
Website: www.liphilharmonic.org
Email: maral@liphilharmonic.org
Phone: 631 293 2223
Address: 1 Huntington Quadrangle, Suite 2C21, US
Information: extensive arts and education program
Country: United States
Contact: Executive Director Stephen Belth
Email: Director of education and community engagement Karen Beluso
Email: music Director David Wiley
Email: orchestra and production Manager Matthew Flood

Los Angeles Chamber Orchestra
Website: www.laco.org
Email: info@laco.org
Phone: 213 622 7001
Address: 350 S. Figueroa St., Suite 183, US
Country: United States
Contact: music Director Jeffrey Kahane
Email: Executive Director Rachel Fine

Los Angeles Master Chorale
Website: www.lamc.org
Email: lamc@lamc.org
Phone: 213 972 3110
Address: 135 North Grand Avenue, US
Information: seven commercial recordings; occasional appearances with the Los Angeles Philharmonic
Country: United States

Contact: Executive Director Terry Knowles
Email: music Director Grant Gershon
Email: publicist Libby Huebner

Los Angeles Philharmonic
Website: www.laphil.com
Email: Press@laphil.com
Phone: 213 972 7300
Address: 151 S. Grand Ave, US
Country: United States
Contact: President Deborah Borda

Louisiana Philharmonic Orchestra
Website: www.lpomusic.com
Email: info@lpomusic.com
Phone: 504 523 6530
Address: 1010 Common Street, Suite 2120, US
Country: United States
music Director & conductor
Klauspeter Seibel
Email: production Manager Cherie Pons Gunther
Email: Managing Director Barbara B. Mollere
Email: Associate Director of Marketing Annelise Cassar
Email: controller Joe Toups

Louisville Orchestra
Website: www.louisvilleorchestra.org
Email: nkoch@louisvilleorchestra.org
Phone: 502 587 8681
Address: 323 West Broadway Street, Suite 700, US
Country: United States
Contact: music Director Jorge Mester
Email: office administrator/Executive assistant Nathaniel Koch
Email: acting Associate conductor Jason Weinberger
Email: principal pops conductor Bob Bernhardt
Email: Marketing Manager Jamie Ingram

Lubbock Symphony Orchestra
Website: www.lubbocksymphony.org, Marketing@lubbocksymphony.org; rfruge@lubbocksymphony.org
Phone: 806 762 1688
Address: 601 av. k, US
Country: United States
Contact: conductor Tomasz Golke
Email: Executive Director Mary Saathoss
Email: Marketing Director Rose Fruge

Lynchburg Symphony Orchestra
Website: www.lynchburgsymphony.com
Email: lso@ntelos.net
Phone: 434 845 6604
Address: 621 Court St, US
Country: United States
music Director & conductor
Bruce Habitzruther
Email: General Manager Deirdre Serio
Email: President Jeannene Stephenson

Macon Symphony Orchestra
Website: www.maconsymphony.com
Email: mso@maconsymphony.com
Phone: 478 301 5300
Address: 400 Poplar Street, US
Country: United States
music Director & conductor
Adrian Gnam
Email: General Manager Doris M Wood

Madison Symphony Orchestra
Website: www.madisonsymphony.org
Email: info@madisonsymphony.org
Phone: 608 257 3734
Address: 222 W. Washington Ave. Suite 460, US
Country: United States
Contact: development Director Kathryn Rasmussen
Email: Executive Director Richard Mackie
Email: Marketing Director Ann Miller
Email: assistant conductor Beverly Taylor
music Director & conductor
John DeMain

Magic Valley Symphony Orchestra
Email: thadley@cableone.net
Phone: 120 873 31079
Address: PO Box 1805, US
Country: United States
Contact: music Director and conductor Ted Hadley

Mallarm
Website: www.mallarmemusic.org
Email: office@mallarmemusic.org
Phone: 919 560 2788
Address: Durham Arts Council, 120 Morris Street, US
Information: ecclectic innovative programmes and Artistic excellence
Country: United States
Contact: company Manager Kirsten Berlin
Email: Artistic Director Anna Ludwig Wilson

Manchester Symphony Orchestra
Website: www.manchestersymphonyorchestra.com/
Email: mso@manchester.edu
Phone: 260 982 5331

Address: PO Box 113, US
Country: United States
Contact: contact Scott Humphries
Email: CPHumphries@manchester.edu

Mankato Symphony Orchestra
Website: www.mankatosymphony.org
Email: mso@hickorytech.net
Phone: 507 625 8880
Address: PO Box 645, US
Country: United States
Contact: Executive Director Sara Buechmann

Mansfield Symphony Orchestra
Website: www.rparts.org
Email: rparts@rparts.org
Phone: 419 522 2726/ 41
Address: Richmond Performing Arts, 138 Park Avenue, PO Box 789, US
Country: United States
Contact: Marketing Director Barbara Byrd
Email: mso music Director Robert Franz
Email: chief Executive officer Terri Bergman

Marin Symphony Orchestra
Website: www.marinsymphony.org
Email: greatmusic@marinsymphony.org
Phone: 415 479 8100
Address: 4340 Redwood Highway, Suite 409 c, US
Country: United States
Contact: music Director Ann Krinitsky
Email: Executive Director Noralle Monestere

Marion Philharmonic Orchestra
Website: www.marionphil.com
Email: mpo@marionphil.com
Phone: 176 566 20012
Address: PO Box 272, , US
Country: United States
Contact: music Director Alexander Platt
Email: Executive Director Mary Kirby

Marshfield-Wood County Symphony Orchestra
Website: www.marshfield.uwc.edu
Email: ddelyser@uwc.edu
Phone: 715 389 6500
Address: 2000 West 5th Street, US
Country: United States
Contact: conductor Timothy McCollum
Email: Director of the music department David De Lyser

Maryland Symphony Orchestra
Website: www.marylandsymphony.org
Email: info@marylandsymphony.org
Phone: 301 797 4000
Address: 30 W Washington Street, US
Country: United States
Contact: music Director Elizabeth Schulze
Email: Executive Director Andrew Kipe
Email: Marketing Director Lisa Nielsen

Maui Symphony Orchestra and Festival
Website: www.mauisymphony.com
Email: info@mauisymphony.com
Phone: 808 877 2167
Address: 1135 Makawao Ave, PMB 284, US
Country: United States
Contact: music Director James French
Email: Paul Wells

McLean Orchestra
Website: www.mclean-orchestra.org
Email: info@mclean-orchestra.org
Phone: 703 893 8646
Address: PO Box 760, US
Information: also supports the McLean Youth Orchestra; 60 members aged 12-18; music Director Tina Anderson
Country: United States
Contact: concertmaster Regino Madrid
Email: Executive Director John Huling

Memphis Symphony Orchestra
Website: www.memphissymphony.org
Email: ryan.fleur@memphissymphony.org
Phone: 901 537 2500
Address: 585 S. Mendenhall Road, US
Country: United States
President & CEO
Ryan Fleur
music Director & conductor
David Lobel

Merced Symphony Orchestra
Website: www.mercedsymphony.org
Email: info@mercedsymphony.org
Phone: 209 383 3277
Address: Merced Symphony Hall, PO Box 894, US
Country: United States
Contact: orchestra Manager Barry Peiffer
Email: music Director Henrik Hul Jansen
Email: President Judy Edwina Smith

Meridian Symphony Orchestra
Email: mdnsymph@mississippi.net
Phone: 601 693 2224

Address: PO Box 2171, US
Country: United States
Contact: music Director/conductor Claire Fox Hillard
Email: General Manager Carolyn Fuchek-Abdella

Merling Trio
Website: www.merlingtrio.com
Email: susan.uchimura@wmich.edu
Phone: 269 387 4718
Address: School of Music, Western Michigan University, 1903 W. Michigan Ave, US
Country: United States

Miami Symphony Orchestra
Website: www.miamisymphony.org
Email: info@themiso.org
Phone: 305 275 5666
Address: 10689 North Kendall Drive, Suite 307, US
Information: the orchestra is a non-profit organisation funded by charities, governmental bodies, etc.
Country: United States
Executive & Artistic Director
Manuel Ochoa

Middletown Symphony Orchestra
Website: www.middletownsymphony.com
Email: mso@middletownsymphony.com
Phone: 151 342 42426
Address: PO Box 441, US
Country: United States
Contact: President Emily Koenig
Email: conductor Carmen DeLeone

Midland Symphony Orchestra
Website: www.mcfta.org
Email: dimond@mcfta.org
Phone: 989 631 5930
Address: 1801 West St Andrews Rd, US
Country: United States
Contact: music Director Bohuslav Rattay
Email: Managing Director Kimberly Dimond

Midland-Odessa Symphony & Chorale, Inc.
Website: www.mosc.org
Email: symphony@mosc.org
Phone: 432 563 0921
Address: PO Box 60658, 3100 LaForce Blvd, US
Country: United States
Contact: Executive Director Diane Hilbert
Email: Marketing Manager Lindsey Forrest
Email: operations Manager Rino Irving

Millikin-Decatur Symphony
Website: www.millikin.edu/music/Orchestral
Email: mluxner@mail.millikin.edu
Phone: 217 424 6211
Address: Millikin University, 1184 W Main St, US
Country: United States
music Director & conductor
Michael Luxner

Milwaukee Symphony Orchestra
Website: www.mso.org
Email: info@mso.org
Phone: 414 291 6010
Address: 1101 North Market Street, Suite 100, US
Country: United States

Minnesota Orchestra
Website: www.minnesotaorchestra.org
Email: info@mnorch.org
Phone: 612 371 5600
Address: Orchestra Hall, 1111 Nicollet Mall, US
Country: United States
Contact: music Director Osmo V
Email: Director of public relations Gwen Pappas
Email: assistant conductor Mischa Santora
Email: vice President and General Manager Robert Neu
President & CEO
Michael Henson (from Feb 2008)
Email: Marketing Manager Ronald J. Foster-Smith

Minot Symphony Orchestra
Website: www.minotsymphony.org
Phone: 701 858 4228
Address: 500 University Avenue West, US
Country: United States
Contact: Executive Director Paulette Baley
Email: music Director/conductor Dennis Simons

Mississippi Symphony Orchestra
Website: www.msorchestra.com
Email: mbeattie@msorchestra.com
Phone: 601 960 1565
Address: PO Box 2052, US
Country: United States
Contact: music Director Crafton Beck
Email: operations Director Richard Hudson
Email: Executive Director Michael Beattie
Email: finance Director Charlotte Smith

Missoula Symphony Orchestra
Website: www.missoulasymphony.org
Email: info@missoulasymphony.org
Phone: 406 721 3194

Address: PO Box 8301, US
Country: United States
Contact: music Director emeritus Joseph Henry
Email: Executive Director John Driscoll
Email: music Director Darko Butorac

Missouri Theatre Center for the Arts - Missouri Chamber Orchestra and Missouri Symphony Pops
Website: www.motheatre.org
Email: info@motheatre.org
Phone: 573 875 0600
Address: 203 South 9th Street, US
Information: the Missouri Chamber Orchestra & Missouri Symphony Pops are part of the Missouri Symphony Society, but they are active only during the summer June to first two weeks of August ; alternative email: kanani@ motheatre.org ; also Hot Summer Nights Music Festiv
Country: United States
Contact: Executive Director David A. White, III
Director of public relations & Marketing
Kanani May
Email: Director of audience development/arts education
Elaine Johnson
Email: production Manager Tyler Richardson

Modesto Symphony Orchestra
Website: www.modestosymphony.org
Email: info@modestosymphony.org
Phone: 209 523 0201
Address: 911 13th Street, US
Country: United States
interim President & CEO
Caroline Nickel
Email: cnickel@modestosymphony.org

Monmouth Symphony Orchestra
Website: www.monsym.org
Email: msoleague@monsym.org
Phone: 173 284 29000
Address: PO Box 1302, US
Information: community orchestra
Country: United States
Contact: General Manager Alice Rose Arnts
Email: musical Director Roy Gussman
Email: assistant conductor Steven Gosewisch

Monroe Symphony Orchestra
Website: www.monroesymphonyorchestra.com
Email: symphony2@bayou.com
Phone: 318 812 6761
Address: PO Box 4353, US
Country: United States
Contact: music Director/ conductor Clay Couturiaux
Email: Executive Director Vicky Valenzano
Email: vicky@monroesymphonyorchestra.com

Monterey Symphony
Website: www.montereysymphony.org
Email: info@montereysymphony.org
Phone: 831 624 8511
Address: PO Box 3965, US
Country: United States
Contact: President Janet McDaniel
music Director & conductor
Max Bragado-Darman
Email: Executive Director Joseph Truskot
Email: Director of operations Joan de Visser

Montgomery Symphony Orchestra
Website: www.montgomerysymphony.org
Email: montgomerysymphony@gmail.com
Phone: 334 240 4004
Address: PO Box 1864, US
Country: United States
Contact: Manager Helen Steineker
music Director & conductor
Thomas Hinds

Mount Hood Pops Orchestra
Website: www.mthoodpops.org
Email: pierikm@teleport.com
Phone: 503 666 6509
Address: PO Box 1641, US
Country: United States
Contact: conductor Ben Brooks
Email: orchestra Manager Marilyn Pierik

Muir String Quartet in Residence at Boston University
Website: www.bu.edu/cfa
Email: arts@bu.edu
Phone: 617 353 3350
Address: Boston University College of Fine Arts, 855 Commonwealth Avenue, Rm 230, US
Country: United States
Contact: Executive Director Ellen Carr

Muncie Symphony Orchestra
Website: www.munciesymphony.org
Email: emcdonald@bsu.edu
Phone: 765 285 5531
Address: Ball State University, 2000 University Avenue-EC112, US

Country: United States
Contact: Artistic Director Bohuslav Rattay
Email: administrative coordinator Claire Park
Email: Executive Director Elissa McDonald

Music Center of South Central Michigan
Website: www.musiccenterscmi.com
Email: musiccenter@musiccenterscmi.com
Phone: 269 963 1911
Address: PO Box 1613, US
Information: see also Presenters
Country: United States
Contact: music Director Brooks Grantier

Napa Valley Symphony
Website: www.napavalleysymphony.org
Email: info@napavalleysymphony.org
Phone: 707 944 9900
Address: 3379 Solano Avenue, Suite 1000, US
Country: United States
Contact: Executive Director Richard Aldag

Naples Philharmonic Orchestra
Website: www.thephil.org
Email: customerservice@thephil.org
Phone: 239 597 1900 (cu
Address: 5833 Pelican Bay Blvd, US
Country: United States
Contact: orchestra Manager Charles Gottschalk
founder, Chairman & CEO
Myra Daniels
Email: music Director/conductor Jorge Mester

Nashua Symphony
Website: www.NashuaSymphony.org
Email: nsa@NashuaSymphony.org
Phone: 603 595 9156
Address: 6 Church Street, US
Country: United States
Contact: Executive Director Eric Valliere
Email: music Director t.b.a

Nashville Symphony
Website: www.nashvillesymphony.org
Email: info@nashvillesymphony.org
Phone: 615 687 6400
Address: 1 Symphony Place, US
Information: The GRAMMY® Award-winning Nashville Symphony has earned an international reputation for its innovative programming and its commitment to performing, recording and commissioning works by America's leading composers. The Nashville Symphony has released 29 recordings on Naxos, which have received 24 GRAMMY® nominations and 13 GRAMMY® Awards, making it one of the most active recording orchestras in the country. The orchestra has also released recordings on Decca, Deutsche Grammophon and New West Records, among other labels. With more than 140 performances annually, the orchestra offers a broad range of classical, pops and jazz, and children's concerts, while its extensive education and community engagement programs reach 60, 000 children and adults each year.
Country: United States
President & CEO
Alan Valentine
Email: Manager of Artistic Administration Ellen Kasperek
Email: Vice President of Communications Jonathan Marx
Publicist & Communications Manager
Dave Felipe
Email: dfelipe@nashvillesymphony.org

National Philharmonic
Website: www.nationalphilharmonic.org
Email: office@nationalphilharmonic.org
Phone: 301 493 9283
Address: 5301 Tuckerman Lane, US
Country: United States
music Director & conductor
Piotr Gajewski
Email: piotr@nationalphilharmonic.orgchorale Artistic Director Stan Engebretson
Email: stan@nationalphilharmonic.orgAssociate conductor Victoria Gau
Email: victoria@nationalphilharmonic.orgDirector of Artistic operations Filbert Hong
Email: filbert@nationalphilharmonic.orgPresident Kenneth Oldham
Email: ken@nationalphilharmonic.orgDirector of public relations and Marketing Deborah Birnbaum
Email: deborah@nationalphilharmonic.orgDirector of development Leanne Ferfolia
Email: leanne@nationalphilharmonic.orgManager of development operations Katie Tukey
Email: katie@nationalphilharmonic.org

National Repertory Orchestra
Website: www.nromusic.com
Email: info@nromusic.com
Phone: 970 453 5825
Address: PO Box 6336, US
Country: United States
Contact: Executive Director Douglas W. Adams
Email: doug@nromusic.com
music Director & conductor
Carl Topilow

National Symphony Orchestra
Website: www.kennedy-center.org/nso
Phone: 202 416 8105
Address: John F Kennedy Center for the Performing Arts, 2700 F Street, US
Country: United States

New Amsterdam Singers
Website: www.nasingers.org
Email: info@nasingers.org
Phone: 121 284 21511
Address: PO Box 373, , Cathedral Station, US
Country: United States
Contact: music Director Clara Longstreth
Email: Manager Amy Harrison

New England Philharmonic
Website: www.nephilharmonic.org
Email: Manager@nephilharmonic.org
Phone: 161 786 81222
Address: 6 Hemenway Street, US
Information: community orchestra with composer in residence program with an annual young artist competition
Country: United States
Contact: acting President Jennifer Snodgrass
Email: music Director and conductor Richard Pittman

New Hampshire Music Festival
Website: www.nhmf.org
Email: info@nhmf.org
Phone: 603 279 3300
Address: 8 NH Route 25, US
Information: per service, professional musicians from around the country come together for 6 weeks of music each summer in concerts that feature exciting young soloists; during school year, guest artists give in-school residency sessions and free community concerts
Country: United States
Contact: Executive Director Frank Pesci
Email: fpesci@nhmf.orgbox office and accounting Juanita Cain
Email: jcain@nhmf.orgoperations Donna Mitchell
Email: dmitchell@nhmf.org

New Hampshire Philharmonic
Website: www.nhphil.org
Email: paul@nhphil.org
Phone: 160 364 76476
Address: 83 Hanover Street, US
Country: United States
Contact: Executive Director Paul Hoffman
Email: music Director and conductor Anthony Princiotti

New Haven Symphony Orchestra
Website: www.newhavensymphony.org
Email: ngallego@newhavensymphony.org
Phone: 203 865 0831
Address: PO Box 9718, US
Information: 4th oldest orchestra in the USA
Country: United States
Contact: Executive Director Elaine C. Carroll
Email: music Director and conductor William Boughton

New Jersey Symphony Orchestra
Website: www.njsymphony.org
Email: information@njsymphony.org
Phone: 973 624 3713
Address: 60 Park Place, 9th Floor, US
Country: United States
Contact: music Director Neeme J
Email: tPresident and CEO Andr
Email: vice President of development nicole kagan

New Mexico Symphony Orchestra
Website: www.nmso.org
Email: rstark@nmso.org
Phone: 150 588 19590
Address: 4407 Menaul Blvd. NE, US
Country: United States
Contact: Executive Director Kenneth Hopper
Email: music Director Guillermo Figueroa
Email: Director of development Joan Allen

New Philharmonic of New Jersey
Website: www.npnj.org
Email: npnj@earthlink.net
Phone: 973 267 0206
Address: PO Box 244, US
Country: United States
Contact: Associate conductor Karen Pinoci
Email: conductor, music Director Leon Hyman
Email: Executive Director Elizabeth Lehmann

New West Symphony
Website: www.newwestsymphony.org
Email: symphony@newwestsymphony.org
Phone: 805 497 5800
Address: 2100, East Thousand Oaks Blvd., Suite D, US
Information: noted for innovative youth education throughout the region
Country: United States
Contact: Director of Marketing John Baldon
Email: Executive Director Natalia Staneva

New World Symphony Inc. (America's Orchestral Academy)
Website: www.nws.org
Email: email@nws.edu
Phone: 305 673 3330
Address: 500 17th Street, US
Information: recordings available
Country: United States
Contact: vice President of Marketing Michael Frisco
Email: Artistic Director Michael Tilson Thomas
Email: President/ CEO Howard Herring
Email: senior vice President for musician advancement

New York Philharmonic
Website: www.nyphil.org/
Email: info@nyphil.org
Address: 10 Lincoln Centre plaza, US
Information: also have chamber ensemble groups
Country: United States
Contact: music Director Alan Gilbert
Email: Executive Director Matthew VanBesien
Email: Director of public relations Katherine E. Johnson

New York Pops
Website: www.newyorkpops.org
Email: info@nypops.org
Phone: 212 765 7677
Address: 333 West 52nd Street, Suite 600, US
Country: United States
Contact: music Director Steven Reineke
Email: Executive Director James M Johnson

New York Scandia Symphony
Website: www.nyscandia.org
Email: nyscandia@nyc.rr.com
Phone: 212 927 1596
Address: PO Box 583, FDR Station, US
Country: United States
Contact: Music Director Dorrit Matson,

New York Virtuosi Chamber Symphony
Website: www.nyvirtuosi.org
Email: jamesarts@worldnet.att.ne
Phone: 718 352 9115
Address: PO Box 604565, US
Country: United States
Contact: administrative advisor Jeffrey James
Email: music Director Kenneth Klein

Newton Symphony Orchestra
Website: www.newtonsymphony.org
Email: office@newtonsymphony.org
Phone: 617 965 2555
Address: 230 Central Street, US
Information: community volunteer orchestra with paid string-section leaders; subscription series of 4 concerts per season, including one opera, plus one family concert; annual concerto competition for school age residents of Newton, some additional concerts for hire
Country: United States
Contact: Artistic Director Jeffrey Rink
Email: Executive Director Letitia Stevens
Email: President of board Andris Vizulis

Nittany Valley Symphony
Website: www.nvs.org
Email: info@nvs.org
Phone: 814 231 8224
Address: PO Box 1375, US
Country: United States
Contact: music Director Michael Jinbo
Email: Executive Director Roberta Strebel

North Arkansas Symphony Orchestra
Website: www.nasymphony.org
Email: aburdick@nasymphony.org
Phone: 479 521 4166
Address: PO Box 1243, US
Information: visiting address: 123 North Block, Suite A, Fayetteville, AR 72702
Country: United States
Contact: development officer Karen Capella
music Director & conductor
Jeannine Wagar

North Carolina Symphony
Website: www.ncsymphony.org
Email: lcharlton@ncsymphony.org
Phone: 919 733 2750
Address: 3700 Glenwood Avenue, Suite 130, US
Information: performs extensively to about 50 different communities in NC playing in auditoriums and gymnasiums for both adult concerts with admission prices and free concerts to school children
Country: United States
Contact: President and chief Executive officer Sandi Macdonald
Email: smacdonald@ncsymphony.orgGeneral Manager Martin Sher
Email: msher@ncsymphony.orgDirector of communications Joe Newberry
Email: jnewberry@ncsymphony.org

Northbrook Symphony Orchestra

Website: www.northbrooksymphony.org
Email: jc@northbrooksymphony.org
Phone: 847 272 0755
Address: 899 Skokie Blvd, Suite LL12, US
Country: United States
Contact: Executive Director t.b.a.
Email: business Manager JC Wacholz
Email: music Director Lawrence Rapchak

Northeastern Pennsylvania Philharmonic
Website: www.nepaphil.org
Email: info@nepaphil.org
Phone: 570 341 1568
Address: 4101 Birney, Moosic, US
Country: United States
Contact: Executive Director Nancy Schmitt Farkas
Email: music Director Lawrence Loh

Northwest Indiana Symphony Orchestra
Website: www.nwisymphony.org
Email: info@nisorchestra.org
Phone: 219 836 0525
Address: 1040 Ridge Road, US
Country: United States
Contact: finance Director Chris McCabe
Email: intern Executive Director Dennise karkland
Email: Director of Marketing Tammie Miller
Email: music Director Kirk Muspratt

Norwalk Symphony Orchestra
Website: www.norwalksymphony.org
Email: info@norwalksymphony.org
Phone: 203 956 6771
Address: 83 Wall Street, Suite 1, US
Country: United States

Nova Vista Symphony
Website: www.novavista.org
Email: info@novavista.org
Phone: 408 624 1492
Address: PO Box 60312, US
Country: United States
Contact: music Director Anthony Quartuccio

NYS Baroque
Website: www.nysema.com
Email: info@nysema.com
Phone: 607 533 4383
Address: 1220 Mecklenburg Road, Ithaca, US
Information: see also Early Music
Country: United States
Contact: Artistic Director Heather Miller Lardin

Oak Ridge Symphony Orchestra
Website: www.orcma.org
Email: office@orcma.org
Phone: 865 483 5569
Address: 320 Robertsville Road, Suite 1, US
Information: non profit organisation
Country: United States

Oakland East Bay Symphony
Website: www.oebs.org
Email: admin@oebs.org
Phone: 510 444 0801
Address: 2201 Broadway, Suite 300, US
Country: United States
Contact: Marketing Director Debbi Hersh
Email: development Director Ken Ingraham
Email: Executive Director Jennifer Duston
Email: financial Director Maya Rath
Email: information systems Manager/web designer Patrice Hidu
Email: conductor Michael Morgan

Ocheami
Website: www.ocheami.org
Email: ocheami@earthlink.net
Phone: 206 329 8876
Address: PO Box 31635, US
Country: United States
Contact: Artistic Director Kofi Anang

Oklahoma City Philharmonic
Website: www.okcphilharmonic.org
Email: info@okcphilharmonic.org
Phone: 405 232 7575
Address: 428 West California Avenue, Suite 210, US
Country: United States
Contact: Executive Director Eddie Walker
Email: General Manager Kris Markes
Email: Marketing Manager Glynis Crawford

Olympia Symphony Orchestra
Website: www.olympiasymphony.com
Email: mbreselow@olympiasymphony.com
Phone: 360 753 0074
Address: 3400 Capitol Blvd. South, Suite 203, US
Country: United States
Contact: Executive Director Linda Spain
Email: music Director and conductor Huw Edwards

Omaha Symphony
Website:

www.omahasymphony.org
Email: boxoffice@omahasymphony.org
Phone: 402 342 3836
Address: 1605 Howard Street, US
Information: over 200 services, incl. chamber, education and outreach
Country: United States
President & CEO
Robert J Hallam
Email: General Manager Jennifer Barlament
Email: music Director Thomas Wilkins

Omaha Symphony
Website: www.omahasymphony.org
Email: jjohnson@omahasymphony.org
Phone: 402 342 3560
Address: 1605 Howard St, US
Country: United States
President & CEO
James M. Johnson
Email: Executive assistant Diane Coffin
Email: dcoffin@omahasymphony.org

Onix Ensemble
Website: www.onixensamble.com
Email: frontera.arts@gmail.com
Phone: 512 261 6979
Address: Lynn Fisher Manager, 3102 Lakeway Blvd, US
Information: a well known and acclaimed group of Mexican musicians dedicated to promote the best interpretations of Latin American contemporary music today. All members have an international career and the experience of soloists and virtuoso musicians. managed by Frontera Arts (see agents and management)
Country: United States
Contact: Artistic Director Alejandro Escuer
Email: info@onixensambel.com

Opera Orchestra of New York
Website: www.operaorchestrany.org
Email: operaorchestrany@gmail.com
Phone: 212 906 9137
Address: 344 East 63rd Street, Suite B-1, US
Country: United States
Contact: Executive Director Deborah Surdi

Orchestra Atlanta
Website: www.orchestraatlanta.org
Email: info@orchestraatlanta.org
Phone: 177 099 22559
Address: PO Box 566125, US
Country: United States
Contact: Executive and Artistic Director Brent Runnels
Email: General Manager Charles Little

Orchestra New England
Website: www.orchestranewengland.org
Email: info@orchestranewengland.org
Phone: 203 777 4690
Address: PO Box 200123, US
Country: United States
Contact: music Director James Sinclair
Email: Executive Director Junius Johnson
Email: personnel Director Joseph Russo

Orchestra of St Luke's
Website: www.oslmusic.org
Email: gjones@oslmusic.org
Phone: 212 594 6100
Address: 330 West 42nd Street, 9th Floor, US
Information: also have the St Luke's Chamber Ensemble
Country: United States
Contact: Director of Marketing Bill Rhoads,
Email: Vice President, Artistic Planning Elizabeth Ostrow,
Email: Director of Operations Angela DeGregoria
Email: Manager of School Partnerships Mark Caruso,

Orchestra of the Southern Finger Lakes
Website: www.osfl.org
Email: info@osfl.org
Phone: 607 936 2873
Address: PO Box 15, US
Country: United States
Contact: Executive Director Janet Newcomb
Email: conductor/music Director Toshiyuki Shimada

Oregon East Symphony
Website: www.oregoneastsymphony.org
Email: oes@uci.net
Phone: 541 276 0320
Address: po 1436, US
Information: currently developing youth orchestra
Country: United States
Contact: program Director Michelle Jakikawa
Email: music Director Kenneth Woods

Oregon Symphony
Website: www.orsymphony.org
Email:
symphony@orsymphony.org
Phone: 503 228 4294
Address: 921 SW Washington, Suite 200, US
Country: United States

Contact: vice President and General Manager Mary Crist
Email: President Elaine Calder
Email: music Director Carlos Kalmar
Email: vice President of development Gene Gregory
Email: vice President of Marketing Michael Kosmala
Email: resident conductor Gregory Vadja

Orlando Philharmonic Orchestra
Website:
www.orlandophil.org
Email: info@orlandophil.org
Phone: 407 896 6700
Address: 812 East Rollins Street, Suite 300, US
Information: series: Phil at Carr, Seranades at John and
Rita Lowndes Shakespeare Center, chamber & recitals,
Sound of Summer at A City Park, Ley Gardens
Country: United States
Contact: Executive Director David Schillhammer
Email: General Manager Mark Fischer
Email: music Director Christopher Wilkins
Email: personnel Manager Jim Ault

Orpheus Chamber Orchestra
Website: www.orpheusnyc.org
Email: info@orpheusnyc.org
Phone: 212 896 1700
Address: 490 Riverside Drive, 11th Floor, US
Information: As part of Orpheus' ongoing commitment
to new works by living composers, the American Notes
commissioning initiative seeks to engage composers
from diverse musical styles and backgrounds to create
musical pieces that explore the question of American
identity. Orpheus is proud to continue the American
Notes exploration over the next two years with compos-
ers Vijay Iyer and Shuying Li. Each of these imPressive
composers will begin with the complex question of what
defines the American spirit today – the characteristics,
experiences, communities, and relationships. Member
of ISPA
Country: United States
Contact: Executive Director Alexander Scheirle
Email: ascheirle@orpheusnyc.orgArtistic Director Laura
Frautschi
Email: lfrautschi@orpheusnyc.orgArtistic coordinator
James Wilson
Email: jwilson@orpheusnyc.org

Owensboro Symphony Orchestra
Website: www.owensborosymphony.org
Email: info@theoso.org
Phone: 270 684 0661
Address: 211 East 2nd Street, US
Country: United States
music Director & conductor
Nicholas Palmer
Email: Executive Director Bill Price

Pacific Symphony
Website: www.pacificsymphony.org
Email: info@pacificsymphony.org
Phone: 714 755 5788
Address: 3631 South Harbor Blvd, Suite 100, US
Information: has an award winning education and
outreach programme
Country: United States
Contact: President and Executive Director John E Forsyte
Email: vice President of development Katherine Akos
Email: vice President of Artistic and orchestra operation
Eileen Jeanette
Email: music Director Carl St Clair
Email: vice President of Marketing and public relations
Beth Brooks
Email: pr Director Jayce Keane

Paducah Symphony Orchestra
Website: www.paducahsymphony.org
Email: info@paducahsymphony.org
Phone: 270 444 0065
Address: 760 Broadway, US
Country: United States

Palm Beach Symphony Society Inc
Website: www.palmbeachsymphony.com
Email: info@palmbeachsymphony.com
Phone: 561 655 2657
Address: 44 Cocoanut Row, # M207B, US
Country: United States
Contact: assistant General Manager Monica Hidalgo
Artistic Director & General Manager
Ray Robinson
Email: music drector / conductor Ramon Tebar

Pasadena Symphony and Pops
Website: www.pasadenasymphony.org
Email: info@pasadenasymphony-pops.org
Phone:
626 793 7172
Address: 117 E. Colorado Blvd, Suite 200, US
Country: United States
Contact: music Director Jack Taylor
Email: chief Executive officer Paul Jan Zdunek

Paul Dresher Ensemble
Website:

www.dresherensemble.org
Email: info@dresherensemble.org
Phone: 510 834 4102
Address: 333 Valencia St. #301, US
Information: always seeking co-commissioner and
co-Producers: booking representation Bernstein Artists
Inc., 282 Flatbush Ave. #101, Brooklyn NY 11217, Tel:
718-623 1214 Fax: 718-638 6110 email: BernsArts@aol.
com; see also Opera
Country: United States
Contact: Managing Director Paul Dresher
Email: development Director Michele Fromson

Penfield Symphony Orchestra
Website: www.penfieldsymphony.org
Email: office@penfieldsymphony.org
Phone: 585 872 0774
Address: 1587 Jackson Road, US

Pennsylvania Sinfonia Orchestra
Website: www.pasinfonia.org
Email: pasinfonia@verizon.net
Phone: 610 434 7811
Address: 1524 West Linden Street, US
Information: Pennsylvania Sinfonia Orchestra celebrates
its 30th anniversary in the 2012-13 season. The Sinfonia
is a professional chamber orchestra that performs a
year-round schedule of concerts in the Lehigh Valley,
Pennsylvania. The Sinfonia is dedicated to making great
classical music interesting and approachable for listeners
of all ages
Country: United States
Contact: Executive Director Corliss Bachman
Email: pasinfonia@verizon.netmusic Director Allan
Birney

Pensacola Symphony Orchestra
Website: www.pensacolasymphony.com
Email: info@pensacolasymphony.com
Phone: 850 435 2533
Address: 205 East Zaragoza St., US
Information: also perform special concerts for children
in schools
Country: United States
Contact: patron services Maryette Harms

Peoria Symphony Orchestra
Website: www.peoriasymphony.org
Email: execdir@peoriasymphony.org
Phone: 309 637 2787
Address: 203 Harrison Street, US
Country: United States
Contact: music Director David Commanday
Email: Executive Director Judy Furniss

Philadelphia Orchestra
Website: www.philorch.org
Email: philadelphia_orchestra@philadelphiaorchestra.
org
Phone: 215 893 1900
Address: The Atlantic Building, 260 South Broad Street,
16th Floor, US
Country: United States
Contact: music Director Christoph Eschenbach (until
end of
Email: President and chief Executive officer James
Undercofler
Email: Artistic administrator and acting Director of
operations Bret Dorhout
Email: vp for Artistic planning Catheline van Bergen

Philadelphia Virtuosi Chamber Orchestra
Website: www.pvco.org
Email: PhilaVirtuosi@msn.com
Phone: 866 405 6844
Address: 1518 Walnut Street, Suite 401, , US
Country: United States
Contact: music Director Daniel Spalding
Email: Philavirtuosi@msn.comManaging Director Dennis
Krasnokutsky
Email: Dennis@pvco.org

Philharmonia Baroque Orchestra
Website: www.philharmonia.org
Email: jphillips@philharmonia.org
Phone: 415 252 1288
Address: 414 Mason Street, Suite 606, US
Information: America's Period-Instrument Orchestra;
2011 GRAMMY® Award Nominee; 2004 Ensemble of the
Year (Musical America); 21CDs with Harmonia Mundi
USA; Gramophone Award Winner; see also Orchestras
Country: United States
Contact: Executive Director Michael Costa
Email: mcosta@philharmonia.orgArtistic administrator
Jeffrey Phillips
Email: jphillips@philharmonia.org

Philharmonia Baroque Orchestra
Website: www.philharmonia.org
Email: jphillips@philharmonia.org
Phone: 415 252 1288
Address: 180 Redwood Street, Suite 200, US
Information: America's Period-Instrument Orchestra;
CDs with Harmonia Mundi USA; Gramophone Award

Winner; see also Early Music
Country: United States
Contact: Artistic administrator Jeffrey Phillips
Email: chorale Director Bruce Lamott
Email: Executive Director Peter Pastreich

Phoenix Symphony
Website: www.phoenixsymphony.org
Email: info@phoenixsymphony.org
Phone: 602 495 1117 (ad
Address: The Phoenix Symphony Administrative & Box
Offices, One North First Street, Suite 200, US
Country: United States
Contact: General Manager Andrew T. Kipe
Pine Bluff Symphony Orchestra, Inc.
Website: www.pinebluffsymphony.org
Email: william_fox@pbreynoldscenter.org
Phone: 870 536 7666
Address: 211 W. 3rd, Avenue, Suite 100, US
Country: United States
music Director & conductor
Charles Jones-Evans
Email: Executive Director William H Fox Jr

Pittsburgh Symphony Orchestra
Website: www.pittsburghsymphony.org
Email: customerservice@pittsburghsymphony.org
Phone: 412 392 4900
Address: 600 Penn Avenue, US
Country: United States
Contact: music Director Manfred Honeck (from autumn
2008)
Email: vice President hall management Carl Mancuso
President & CEO
Lawrence J Tamburri
Email: General Manager Marcie Solomon
Email: vice President Artistic Administration Robert B
Moir
Email: vice President of public affairs Jody Donerty

Plano Symphony Orchestra
Website: www.planosymphony.org
Email: info@planosymphony.org
Phone: 972 473 7262
Address: 5236 Tennyson Parkway, Ste. 200, US
Country: United States
Contact: music Director Hector Guzman
Email: Executive Director Debbie Watson

Plymouth Philharmonic Orchestra
Website: www.plymouthphil.org
Phone: 150 874 68008
Address: PO Box 3174, 16 Court Street, US
Country: United States
Contact: Executive Director Christopher Ford
Email: music Director Steven Karidoyanes

Pomerium
Website: www.pomerium.com
Email: blachly.3@nd.edu
Phone: 574 273 4022
Address: 1406 South Lake George Drive, US
Information: recordings with Nonesuch, Classic Masters,
Dorian, Deutsche Grammophon/Archiv Produktion, Pure
Classics, hold hard recording
Country: United States
Contact: conductor and Director Alexander Blachly

Pontiac-Oakland Symphony Orchestra
Email: ponder@oakland.edu
Phone: 248 334 6024
Address: PO Box 431174, US
Country: United States
Contact: acting President Laura Schartman
Email: Chairman of board Michael Ponder
Email: music Director David Daniels

Port Angeles Symphony Orchestra
Website: www.olypen.com/pasymphony
Email: pasymphony@olypen.com
Phone: 360 457 5579
Address: PO Box 2148, US
Country: United States
Contact: music Director, conductor Adam Stern

Portland Baroque Orchestra
Website: www.pbo.org
Email: email@pbo.org
Phone: 503 222 6000
Address: 1020 SW Taylor Street, Suite 275, US
Information: see also Early Music
Country: United States
Contact: Executive Director Thomas Cirillo
Email: Artistic Director Monica Huggett

Portland Symphony Orchestra
Website: www.portlandsymphony.com
Email: psobox@portlandsymphony.com
Phone:
207 773 6128
Address: PO Box 3573, US
Country: United States
music Director & conductor
Robert Moody

Email: Executive Director Ari Solotoff

Present Music
Website:
www.presentmusic.org
Email: newmusic@presentmusic.org
Phone: 414 217 0711
Address: 158 North Broadway, US
Country: United States
Contact: Managing Director Eric Lind
Email: Artistic Director Kevin Stalheim
Email: administrative coordinator Celeste Jantz
Email: senior management Associate Colleen O'Donnell

Prince George's Philharmonic Orchestra
Website: pgphilharmonic.org
Email: webmaster@pgphilharmonic.org
Phone: 301 446 3245
Address: PO Box 1111, US
Country: United States
Contact: Executive Director Brenton Benfield
Email: music Director Charles Ellis
Email: President of the board of Directors Mary Ann White

Prince William Symphony Orchestra
Website: www.pwso.org
Email: pr.pwso@gmail.com
Address: US
Country: United States
Contact: Executive music Director David Montgomery

Pro Arte Chamber Orchestra of Boston
Website: www.proarte.org
Email: info@proarte.org
Phone: 617 661 7067
Address: 99 Bishop Allen Drive, US
Country: United States
Contact: conductor emeritus Isaiah Jackson
Email: principal guest conductor Gunther Schuller

ProMusica Chamber Orchestra of Columbus Inc.
Website: www.promusicacolumbus.org
Email: info@promusicacolumbus.org
Phone: 161 446 40066
Address: 243 North 5th Street, Suite 202, US
Information: commissioned more than 30 works in 24 years; 80, world premieres
Country: United States
Contact: music Director Timothy Russell
Email: Director of Marketing and public relations Kristy Adams
Email: Executive Director Janet Chen

Psycho with Orchestra
Email: jchadwick@imgartists.com
Address: US
Country: United States
Contact: Manager Sam Weatherstone
Email: sweatherstone@imgartists.com

Pueblo Symphony Association
Website: www.thepueblosymphony.org
Email: pueblosymphony@hotmail.com
Phone: 719 545 7967
Address: 301 North Main, Suite 106, US
Country: United States
Contact: Executive Director June King
Email: music Director Dr Jacob Chi

Quad City Symphony Orchestra
Website: www.qcsymphony.com
Email: info@qcsymphony.com
Phone: 563 322 0931
Address: 327 Brady Street, US
Country: United States

Queens Symphony Orchestra
Website: www.queenssymphony.org
Email: qso@queenssymphony.org
Phone: 718 570 0909
Address: c/o Queens College, 65-30 Kissena Blvd., US
Country: United States
music Director & acting Executive Director Constantine Kitsopoulos
Email: ckitsopoulos@queenssymphony.org

Quincy Symphony Orchestra
Website: www.qsoa.org
Email: qsoa@adams.net
Phone: 217 222 2856
Address: 428 Maine Street, Suite 270, US
Information: community orchestra
Country: United States
Contact: conductor and music Director Bruce Briney
Email: General Manager Jane Polett

Raleigh Symphony Orchestra
Website: www.raleighsymphony.com
Email: Manager@raleighsymphony.org
Phone: 919 546 9755
Address: PO Box 25878, US
Country: United States
Contact: Executive Director Rachel M Parnell

Email: music Director Jim Waddelow

Rapides Symphony Orchestra
Website: www.rapidessymphony.org
Email: Manager@rapidessymphony.org
Phone: 318 442 9709
Address: 1101 Fourth Street, Suite 201, US
Country: United States
Contact: Manager Elizabeth Jarred
Email: music Director Joshua Zona

Reading Symphony Orchestra
Website: www.ReadingSymphony.org
Email: iinfo@readingsymphony.org
Phone: 610 373 7557
Address: 147 North 5th Street, Suite 4, US
Country: United States

Red Mountain Chamber Orchestra
Website: www.rmco.org
Email: suzanne@rmco.org
Phone: 120 225 43774
Address: 868 West 6th Street, US
Information: Red Mountain Chamber Orchestra is an all volunteer, community orchestra, affiliated with Birmingham Southern College
Country: United States
Contact: President Suzanne Beaudry
Email: conductor Leslie Fillmer
Email: conductor Robert Wright
Email: conductor Yurii Henriques

Redlands Symphony Orchestra
Website: www.RedlandsSymphony.com
Email: symphony@redlands.edu
Phone: 909 748 8018
Address: 1200 E. Colton Ave, PO Box 3080, US
Country: United States
Contact: chief Executive officer Paul Ideker
Email: music Director Jon Robertson

Reno Chamber Orchestra
Website: www.RenoChamberOrchestra.org
Email: scott@RenoChamberOrchestra.org
Phone: 775 348 9413
Address: PO Box 547, US
Country: United States
Contact: music Director and conductor Theodore Kuchar
Email: operations Manager Chris Morrison
Email: Executive Director Scott Faulkner
Email: business development Director Susan Olenwine

Reno Philharmonic Association
Website: www.renophilharmonic.com
Email: writeus@renophilharmonic.com
Phone: 775 323 6393
Address: 925 Riverside Dr., Suite 3, US
Country: United States
Contact: Executive Director Tim Young
Email: music Director Barry Jekowsky

Rhode Island Philharmonic Orchestra
Website: www.ri-philharmonic.org
Email: INFORMATION@RIPHIL.ORG
Phone: 401 248 7000
Address: 667 Waterman Avenue, US
Country: United States
Contact: Director of Marketing Pam Kennedy
Email: Executive Director David J. Beauchesne
Email: music Director Larry Rachleff
Director of operations & Artistic administator David Gasper
Email: Director of development Betty Ann Kearney

Richardson Symphony Orchestra
Website: www.richardsonsymphony.org
Email: info@richardsonsymphony.org
Phone: 972 234 4195
Address: 2100 North Collins Blvd, Suite 310, US
Country: United States
Contact: Director of development and community affairs Scot Wilkinson
Email: music Director Anshel Brusilow
Email: Executive Director George Landis

Richmond Philharmonic
Website: www.richmondphilharmonic.org
Email: rpo@richmondphilharmonic.org
Phone: 804 673 7400
Address: 8100 Three Chopt Rd, , Suite 238, US
Country: United States
Contact: music Director Robert Mirakian
Email: President J. Durwood Felton

Richmond Symphony
Website: www.richmondsymphony.com
Email: grichmond@richmondsymphony.com
Phone: 804 788 4717
Address: The Berkshire, 300 West Franklin St, Suite 103E, US
Country: United States
Contact: Executive Director David J.L. Fisk
Email: Director of finance and Administration Gail Richmond

Email: music Director Steven Smith
Director of Marketing & public relations
Teka Phan

Richmond Symphony Orchestra
Website: www.richmondsymphony.org
Email: rso@richmondsymphony.org
Phone: 765 962 5181
Address: PO Box 982, US
Country: United States
Contact: President Gail Clark
Email: musical Director/conductor Guy Victor Bordo
Email: rso@richmondsymphony.orgExecutive Director Olivia A. Miller

Ridgefield Symphony Orchestra
Website: www.ridgefieldsymphony.org
Email: email@ridgefieldsymphony.org
Phone: 203 438 3889
Address: 90 East Ridge Road, US
Country: United States
Contact: assistant conductor Petko Dimitrov
Email: Executive Director Lawrence Kopp
Email: music Director Gerald Steichen

River City Brass Band
Website: www.rivercitybrass.org
Email: info@rivercitybrass.org
Phone: 412 434 7222
Address: One Mellon Center, 500 Grant Street, Suite 2720, US
Country: United States
Contact: tour Manager Linda Reznik
Email: music Director Denis Colwell
Email: General Manager Joseph Zuback
Email: Marketing coordinator Di'Ray James

Riverside Symphony
Website: www.riversidesymphony.org
Email: nfo@riversidesymphony.org
Phone: 212 864 4197
Address: 225 West 99th St., US
Country: United States
Contact: Managing Director Joan Sher
Email: Artistic Director Anthony Korf
Email: music Director/conductor George Rothman

Roanoke Symphony Orchestra
Website: www.rso.com
Email: music@rso.com
Phone: 540 343 9127
Address: The Jefferson Center, 541 Luck Avenue, Suite 200, US
Information: pops and educational concerts offered in addition to main subscripton series and chamber orchestra series
Country: United States
music Director & conductor
David Wiley
Email: orchestra personnel Manager Julee Hickcox
Email: orchestra librarian John Smith

Robert Ashley Ensemble
Website: www.robertashley.org
Email: artservicesinc@mindspring.com
Phone: 212 941 8911
Address: 260 West Broadway, US
Country: United States
Contact: Artistic Director Robert Ashley

Rochester Philharmonic Orchestra
Website: www.rpo.org
Email: rpo@rpo.org
Phone: 585 454 7311
Address: 108 East Avenue, US
Information: also have a summer series at Constellation Brands- Marrin Sands Performing Arts Center
Country: United States

Rockford Symphony Orchestras, Inc.
Website: www.rockfordsymphony.com
Email: info@rockfordsymphony.com
Phone: 181 596 50049
Address: 711 North Main Street, US
Information: also have a youth orchestra, educational outreach, youth concerts, pre-concert lectures
Country: United States
Contact: music Director Steven Larsen
Email: Executive Director Brian Ritter
Email: rsyo conductor Alison Gaines

Rogue Valley Symphony
Website: www.rvsymphony.org
Email: office@rvsymphony.org
Phone: 154 155 26398
Address: 1250 Siskiyou Blvd, US
Country: United States
Contact: President Arline Borella
Email: music Director and conductor Arthur Shaw

Roswell Symphony Orchestra
Website: www.roswellsymphony.org
Email: rso@roswellsymphony.org
Phone: 505 623 5882
Address: 1717 West Second Street, Suite 112, US

Information: education programme to 18 schools in area, with up to 2700 children, run by volunteers from symphony board and guild
Country: United States
Contact: music Director John Farrer
Director of financial & office operations
Pam Satterfield
Email: Manager Jamie Elliott

Saginaw Bay Symphony Orchestra
Website: www.saginawbayorchestra.com
Email: info@saginawbayorchestra.com
Phone: 198 975 56471
Address: 201 vN. Washington, US
Information: non-profit organisation
Country: United States
Contact: financial Manager Dave P. Rupp
Email: production Manager Anna Leppert-Largent
Email: music Director and conductor Patrick Flynn

Saint Joseph Symphony
Website: www.saintjosephsymphony.org
Email: info@saintjosephsymphony.org
Phone: 816 233 7701
Address: 120 South 8th Street, US
Country: United States
Contact: Managing Director Ann Brock
Email: abrock@saintjosephsymphony.orgConductor/
Music Director Rico McNeela

Saint Louis Symphony Orchestra
Website: www.slso.org
Email: randya@slso.org
Phone: 314 533 2500
Address: Powell Symphony Hall, 718 North Grand Boulevard, US
Country: United States
Contact: vice President for Marketing Kristi Kovalak
Email: music Director David Robertson
Email: vice President of Artistic Administration Peter Czornyj
Email: Director of communications Jeff Trammel
Email: orchestra Manager Susan Lim

Saint Paul Chamber Orchestra
Website: www.thespco.org
Email: info@spcomail.org
Phone: 651 292 3248
Address: The Hamm Building, 408 St Peter Street, 3rd floor, US
Country: United States
Contact: Director of Marketing Jessica Etten
President & Managing Director
Dobson West
Email: production Manager Jason Piehl

Salina Symphony
Website: www.salinasymphony.org
Email: symphony@salinasymphony.org
Phone: 178 582 38309
Address: PO Box 792, US
Country: United States
Contact: music Director/conductor Ken Hakoda
Email: Executive Director Donna Holmes Antrim

Salisbury Symphony Orchestra
Website: www.salisburysymphony.org
Email: ljones@catawba.edu
Phone: 704 637 4314
Address: PO Box 4264, US
Country: United States
Contact: Executive Director Linda Jones
Email: music Director and conductor David Hagy

San Angelo Symphony Orchestra
Website: www.sanangelosymphony.org
Email: assistant@sanangelosymphony.org
Phone: 325 658 5877
Address: PO Box 5922, US
Country: United States
Contact: resident conductor David Phillips
Email: music Director Hector Guzman
Email: Executive Director Jennifer Odom

San Antonio Symphony
Website: www.sasymphony.org
Email: salazarp@sasymphony.org
Phone: 210 554 1000
Address: 222 E Houston Street, Suite 200, US
Country: United States
President & CEO
David Green
Email: vice President of Marketing Carolyn Bacon
Email: music Director Larry Rachleff (until end of 20

San Bernardino Symphony Orchestra
Website: www.sanbernardinosymphony.org
Email: sbsymphony1@aol.com
Phone: 909 381 5388
Address: 415 W. 2nd Street, US
Country: United States
Contact: Marketing Erin Brinker
music Director & conductor
Carlo Ponti Jr

San Diego Chamber Orchestra
Website: www.sdco.org
Email: stella.karl@orchestranova.org
Phone: 858 350 0290
Address: 11772 Sorrento Valley Rd., Suite #212, US
Country: United States
Contact: chief Executive officer Beverly Lambert
Email: Artistic Director Jung-Ho Pak

San Diego Symphony
Website: www.sandiegosymphony.org
Email: info@sandiegosymphony.org
Phone: 619 235 0800
Address: 1245 7th Ave, US
Information: Extensive education & outreach programs
Country: United States
Contact: Music Director Rafael Payare
Email: VP of Marketing and Communications Joan Cumming
Email: jcumming@sandiegosymphony.orgChief Executive Officer Martha Gilmer

San Francisco Ballet Orchestra
Website: www.sfballet.org
Email: tickets@sfballet.org
Phone: 141 586 52000
Address: 455 Franklin St, US
Information: the orchestra does not tour with the company. The company uses local orchestras in its tour venues; CDs include previously unrecorded works by Debussy and music for Lar Lubovitch's ballet 'Othello', Elliott Goldenthal, composer
Country: United States
Contact: orchestra personnel Manager Tracy Davis
Email: music Director and principal conductor Martin West

San Francisco Contemporary Music Players
Website: www.sfcmp.org
Email: info@sfcmp.org
Phone: 415 278 9566
Address: 55 New Montgomery Street, Suite 708, US
Country: United States
Contact: Artistic Director Steven Schick
Email: Executive Director Carrie Blanding

San Francisco Symphony
Website: www.sfsymphony.org
Email: messages@sfsymphony.org
Phone: 415 552 8000
Address: Davies Symphony Hall, 201 Van Ness Avenue, US
Information: the San Francisco Symphony sets the highest possible standard for excellence in musical performance at home and around the world; enriches, serves, and shapes cultural life throughout the spectrum of Bay Area communities; maintains financial stability and gains public recognition as a means of ensuring its ability to fulfill its mission. See also Festivals (San Francisco Symphony Summer Festival, San Francisco Symphony/SF Arts Commission Summer in the City)
Country: United States
Contact: Executive Director Brent Assink
Email: Director of Artistic planning John Mangum
Email: Director of public relations/communications Oliver Theil

San Luis Obispo Symphony
Website: www.slosymphony.com
Email: info@slosymphony.com
Phone: 805 543 3533
Address: 75 Higuera Street, Suite #160, US
Information: community orchestra; also small chamber orchestra
Country: United States
Contact: music education Director Edmund Feingold
Email: andrea@slosymphony.comcommunications Director Lisa Nauful
Email: lisa@slosymphony.com

Santa Barbara Symphony Orchestra
Website: www.thesymphony.org
Email: info@thesymphony.org
Phone: 805 898 9386
Address: 1330 State Street, Suite 102, US
Country: United States
Director of Marketing & education coordinator
Barbara Burger
Email: music Director Nir Kabaretti

Santa Cecilia Orchestra
Website: www.scorchestra.org
Email: info@scorchestra.org
Phone: 323 259 3011
Address: 2759 West Broadway, US
Information: offers free or affordable concerts in low-income Los Angeles communities
Country: United States
Contact: Artistic Director, conductor Sonia Marie De Leon de Vega

Santa Cruz County Symphony
Website: www.santacruzsymphony.org

Email: info@santacruzsymphony.org
Phone: 831 462 0553
Address: 307 Church Street, US
Country: United States
Contact: Marketing Director Benjamin Short
Email: Executive Director Jan Derecho,
Email: music Director and conductor John Larry Granger

Santa Fe Pro Musica
Website: www.santafepromusica.com
Email: office@santafepromusica.com
Phone: 505 988 4640
Address: PO Box 2091, US
Country: United States

Santa Fe Symphony Orchestra and Chorus, Inc
Website: www.santafesymphony.org
Email: symphony@santafesymphony.org
Phone: 505 983 3530
Address: PO Box 9692, US
Country: United States
Contact: administrative Director, box office Manager Yvonne Martinez
Email: operations Manager Diane Stengle
Email: General Director Gregory W. Heltman
Email: music Director Steven Smith
Email: President board of Directors Mick Ramsey
Email: fund development and pr administrator Kathrin Nun

Santa Rosa Symphony
Website: www.santarosasymphony.com
Email: info@santarosasymphony.com
Phone: 707 546 7097
Address: 50 Santa Rosa Avenue, Suite 410, US
Information: music education department - 4 youth ensembles, year-round string training
Country: United States
conductor & music Director
Bruno Ferrandis
Email: Executive Director Alan Silow
Email: Marketing Director Sara Obuchowski-Mitchell
Email: sara@santarosasymphony.com

Schuylkill Symphony Orchestra
Website: www.schuylkillsymphony.com
Email: orchestra@schuylkillsymphony.com
Phone: 570 628 2632
Address: PO Box 1310, US
Country: United States
Contact: music Director Donald Spieth

Scottsdale Symphony Orchestra
Website: www.scotsymph.org
Email: sso@scotsymph.org
Phone: 480 945 8071
Address: 3127 N 81st Pl, US
Country: United States
Contact: Executive Director Judith Vagis
Email: music Director Irving Fleming

Seattle Symphony Orchestra
Website: www.seattlesymphony.org
Email: info@seattlesymphony.org
Phone: 206 215 4700
Address: 200 University Street, US
Information: Director of Benaroya Hall: Patricia Isacsons
Sabee Tel: 206-215 4800; visiting address: 200 University Street, Seattle WA 98111-3906
Country: United States
Contact: music Director Gerard Schwarz
Email: Executive Director Thomas Philion

Seattle Youth Symphony Orchestras
Website: www.syso.org
Email: info@syso.org
Phone: 206 362 2300
Address: 11065 Fifth Ave NE, Suite A, US
Information: see also Presenters and Festivals (Marrowstone Summer Music Festival)
Country: United States
Contact: orchestra coordinator Janice Gatti
Email: music Director Stephen Radcliffe
Email: Executive Director Daniel Petersen
Email: finance Director Aimee Tan

SEM Ensemble
Website: www.semensemble.org
Email: pksem@semensemble.org
Phone: 718 488 7659
Address: 25 Columbia Place, US
Country: United States
Contact: Artistic Director Petr Kotik

Sheboygan Symphony Orchestra
Website: www.sheboygansymphony.org
Email: shebsym@sheboygansymphony.org
Phone: 920 452 1985
Address: 830 North Eighth Str., US
Country: United States
music Director & conductor
Kevin McMahon
Email: chorus Director Peter Dennee
Email: Managing Director Mary Schallhorn

ORCHESTRA, BAND AND INSTRUMENTAL ENSEMBLE

Shreveport Symphony
Website: www.shreveportsymphony.com
Email: office@shreveportsymphony.com
Phone: 318 222 7496
Address: PO Box 205, US
Country: United States
Contact: Executive Director Scott Green
Email: Associate conductor Kermit Poling
Email: music Director Mike Butterman

Signature Symphony
Website: www.signaturesymphony.org
Email: jim.fellows@tulsacc.edu
Phone: 918 595 7786
Address: Tulsa Community College, 10300 E 81st Street, Suite 6256A, US
Information: Signature combines pops with education; 5 classical performances, 5 pairs of pops, plus others.
Country: United States
Contact: orchestra Manager James Fellows
Email: jim.fellows@tulsacc.edumusic Director Andres Franco

Silk and Bamboo Ensemble
Website: chinesemusic.net
Email: syshen@megsinet.net
Phone: 630 910 1551
Address: Chinese Music Society of North America, PO Box 5275, US
Information: see also Chinese Classical Orchestra
Country: United States
Contact: music Director Sinyan Shen
Email: concert and lecture Director Yuan Yuan Lee
Email: Artistic administrator Billie Jefferson

Sinfonia da Camera
Website: www.sinfonia.uiuc.edu
Email: sinfonia@uiuc.edu
Phone: 217 244 4350
Address: 909 West Oregon St, suite 202, US
Country: United States
music Director & principal conductor Ian Hobson
Email: assistant Director Rebecca Riley

Sioux City Symphony Orchestra
Website: www.siouxcitysymphony.org
Email: info@siouxcitysymphony.org
Phone: 712 277 2111
Address: PO Box 754, US
Country: United States
Contact: operations Manager Trinette Patterson
Email: amusic Director/conductor Jungho Kim
Email: Executive Director Douglas Gerhart
Email: development Director David G. Krogh

Solisti New York Orchestra
Website: www.ransomwilson.com
Phone: 120 339 39158
Address: 180 Peck Hill Road, US
Country: United States
Contact: personnel Manager Adria Benjamin
Email: music Director/conductor Ransom Wilson

Sound Symphony Inc
Website: www.soundsymphony.org
Email: mail@soundsymphony.org
Phone: 631 827 9022
Address: P.O. Box 499, US
Country: United States
Contact: General Manager Lynda Reynolds,
Email: Personnel Manager Jennifer Haley,

South Arkansas Symphony
Website: www.southarkansassymphony.com
Email: sasomail@sbcglobal.net
Phone: 870 862 0521
Address: 315 East Oak Street, Suite 206, US
Country: United States
Contact: music Director Kermit Poling
Email: Executive Director Scott Watkins

South Bend Symphony Orchestra
Website: www.southbendsymphony.com
Email: Marketing@southbendsymphony.com
Phone: 574 232 6343
Address: 127 N. Michigan Street, US
Country: United States
Contact: music Director Tsung Yeh
Email: Marketing Manager Elisabeth Burnham
Email: Executive Director Jane Hunter

South Carolina Philharmonic
Website: www.scphilharmonic.com
Email: info@scphilharmonic.com
Phone: 803 771 7937
Address: 721 Lady Street, Suite B, US
Information: touring within South Carolina
Country: United States

South Dakota Symphony
Website: www.sdsymphony.org
Email: sdsymphony@sdsymphony.org
Phone: 605 335 7933

Address: 315 N. Main Avenue, Suite 204, US
Country: United States
Contact: Director of development Linda Clement
Email: Executive Director Thomas J Bennett

Southeast Iowa Symphony Orchestra
Website: www.seiso.us
Email: seiso@iwc.edu
Phone: 319 385 6352
Address: 601 North Main St, US
Country: United States
Contact: Executive Director Kathryn Gerst
Email: music Director Robert McConnell

Southeastern Ohio Symphony Orchestra
Website: www.seoso.org
Email: auditorium@coz.org
Phone: 740 826 8197
Address: PO Box 42, US
Country: United States
Contact: symphony Manager John Kunkel
Email: music Director/conductor Laura E. Schumann

Southwest Florida Symphony Orchestra and Chorus
Website: www.swflso.org
Email: info@swflso.org
Phone: 239 418 0996
Address: 12651 McGregor Blvd., Bldg. # 4-403, US
Country: United States
Contact: Artistic advisor Leif Bjaland
Email: Executive Director Frances H. Goldman

Space Coast Pops, Inc
Website: www.spacecoastpops.com
Email: popsorch@aol.com
Phone: 321 632 7445
Address: PO Box 3344, US
Information: visiting adress & tickets: 2150 Lake Drive, Cocoa, Florida 32926
Country: United States
Contact: General Manager Alyce Christ

Spokane Symphony
Website: www.spokanesymphony.org
Email: tickets@spokanesymphony.org
Phone: 509 624 1200
Address: 1001 W Sprague Ave, US
Information: the Spokane Symphony, founded in 1945, is the largest and most active professional performing arts organization in the Inland Pacific Northwest. The 70-piece professional orchestra performs approximately 60 concerts for more than 150, 000 listeners each season and provides a wide variety of exceptional educational experiences
Country: United States
Contact: Marketing and public relations Manager Audrey Overstreet
Email: audreyoverstreet@spokanesymphony.orgGeneral Manager Donald Nelson
Email: donaldnelson@spokanesymphony.orgDirector of development Kathleen Langenheim
Email: langenheim@spokanesymphony.orgDirector of finance Ellen Weigel
Email: ellenweigel@spokanesymphony.org

Springfield Symphony Association
Website: www.springfieldmosymphony.org
Email: info@springfieldmosymphony.org
Phone: 417 864 6683
Address: 1536 E Division St, US
Country: United States
Contact: music Director/conductor Ron Spigelman
Email: President Stan Arnoldy

Springfield Symphony Orchestra
Website: www.springfieldsymphony.org
Email: mjonnes@springfieldsymphony.org
Phone: 413 733 2291
Address: 1350, Main Street, US
Information: also do educational outreach programs
Country: United States
Contact: Executive Director Michael Jonnes
Email: musical Director Kevin Rhodes
Email: Marketing and pr Director Susan Bennett

Springfield Symphony Orchestra
Website: www.springfieldsym.org
Email: info@springfieldsym.org
Phone: 937 325 8100
Address: PO Box 1374, US
Information: six-concert subscription series, small ensemble visits to area schools, Concerts for Young People, the Springfield Youth Symphony and Springfield Youth String Ensemble, free outreach performances and two fundraisers
Country: United States
Contact: Executive Director David Deitrick
Email: music Director Peter Stafford Wilson

St Cloud Symphony Orchestra
Website: www.stcloudsymphony.com

Email: snadeau@stcloudsymphony.com
Phone: 320 252 7276
Address: PO Box 234, US
Country: United States
Contact: music Director Clinton Smith
Email: Executive Director Sandy Nadeau

St Olaf Band, Choir & Orchestra
Website: www.stolaf.edu/depts/music
Email: musicman@stolaf.edu
Phone: 507 786 3179
Address: St. Olaf College, 1520 St Olaf Avenue, Attn: Music Organizations, US
Information: Known worldwide, the St. Olaf Choir, St. Olaf Band and St. Olaf Orchestra tour annually around the US and regularly embark on international tours as well
Country: United States
Contact: Manager, music organisations B.J. Johnson
Email: musicman@stolaf.eduassistant Manager, music organisations Terra Widdifield
Email: widdifie@stolaf.edu

Stamford Symphony Orchestra
Website: www.stamfordsymphony.org
Email: office@stamfordsymphony.org
Phone: 203 325 1407
Address: 263 Tresser Boulevard, US
Information: Founded in 1919, the SSO achieved full professional status in the 1970's under the leadership of the legendary Skitch Henderson. From 1980 forward, Roger Nierenberg spent the next 24 years recruiting the New York metropolitan area's top players, crafting an ensemble of unparalleled caliber and remarkable versatility. In October 2005, Maestro Eckart Preu ascended our podium. Maestro Preu is an unpretentious, young and vibrant conductor bringing a fresh approach to classical music. His innovative programming is attracting new audiences and his style has been described as Serious Fun. Member of ISPA
Country: United States
Director, Marketing & communications Karine Jeanneret
Email: Marketing@StamfordSymphony.orgPresident and CEO Barbara J. Smith-Soroca
Email: BJSoroca@StamfordSymphony.orgoperations Manager Tony Melone
Email: Operations@stamfordsymphony.org

Stockton Symphony Association
Website: www.stocktonsymphony.org
Email: admin@stocktonsymphony.org
Phone: 209 951 0196
Address: 1024 W. Robinhood Dr., Suite 1, US
Country: United States
Contact: Executive Director Jane E. Kenworthy
Email: music Director Peter Jaffe

Sunriver Music Festival
Website: www.sunrivermusic.org
Email: srmusic@cmc.net
Phone: 541 593 1084
Address: PO Box 4308, US
Information: see also Festivals
Country: United States

Susquehanna Symphony Orchestra
Website: www.ssorchestra.org
Email: tonyawoody@msn.com
Phone: 410 838 6465
Address: PO Box 485, US
Information: non-profit community orchestra, providing education and entertainment for Harford County, Maryland
Country: United States
Contact: Marketing and publicity Manager Tonya Woody
Email: treasurer D. Henry Ruth
Email: President Susan Zollers
Email: founder / music Director Sheldon Bair

Symphony Inn C
Website: www.symphonyinnc.org
Email: symphony@symphonyinnc.org
Phone: 856 429 1880
Address: 41 South Hadden Avenue, Suite 7, US
Country: United States
Contact: assistant conductor Petko Dimitrov
Email: music Director Rossen Milanov
Email: President Trevor Orthmann
Email: resident composer Daniel Dorff

Symphony of Southeast Texas
Website: www.sost.org
Email: sost@sost.org
Phone: 409 892 2257
Address: 4345 Thelan, Suite 105, US
Country: United States
Contact: Executive Director Craig Escamilla

Symphony of the Americas
Website: www.symphonyoftheamericas.org
Email: info@sota.org
Phone: 954 335 7002

Address: 2425 East Commercial Boulevard, Suite 405, US
Information: every summer the orchestra has an international guest orchestra to perform in USA, Central and South America
Country: United States
Contact: Executive Director Renee LaBonte
Email: Artistic Director James Brooks-Bruzzese

Symphony of the Mountains Orchestra
Website: www.symphonyofthemountains.org
Email: info@symphonyofthemountains.org
Phone: 423 392 8423
Address: Kingsport Renaissance Center, 1200 East Center Street, US
Country: United States
music Director & conductor
Cornelia Kodkani-Laemmli
Email: Executive Director Ann L. Myers
Email: office Manager Jenny Smith

Symphony of the Southwest
Website: www.symphonyofthesouthwest.org
Email: symphonyofthesouthwest@gmail.com
Phone: 480 827 2143
Address: 122 North Macdonald Street, US
Information: formerly the Mesa Symphony Orchestra
Country: United States
Contact: music Director/conductor Cal Stewart Kellogg
Email: Executive Director Cathy Worcester

Symphony Silicon Valley
Website: www.symphonysiliconvalley.org
Email: info@symphonysiliconvalley.org
Phone: 408 286 2600
Address: PO Box 790, US
Country: United States
Contact: President Andrew Bales
Email: General Manager Jennifer Watkins

Synergy Brass Quintet
Website: www.brassquintet.org
Email: info@synergybrass.com
Phone: 617 797 7987
Address: PO Box 1136, US
Country: United States

Syracuse Symphony Orchestra
Website: www.syracusesymphony.org
Phone: 315 424 8222
Address: 411 Montgomery Street, Suite 40, US
Country: United States
Contact: Chairman Rocco Mangano
Email: General Manager Richard Decker
Email: music Director Daniel Hege
Director of Marketing & public relations
Marshall Whinney
Email: conductor emeritus Kazuyoshi Akiyama

Tacoma Symphony Orchestra
Website: www.tacomasymphony.org
Phone: 253 272 7264
Address: 738 Broadway, Ste 100, US
Country: United States
Contact: music Director Harvey Felder
Email: Executive Director Andy Bulow
Email: Director of Marketing and development Lisa Brown

Tallahassee Symphony Orchestra
Website: www.tallahasseesymphony.org
Email: operations@tallahasseesymphony.org
Phone: 850 224 0461
Address: 1020 East Lafaytte Street, Suite 207, US
Information: educational program with a youth orchestra performing at Ruby Diamond Auditorium
Country: United States
Contact: Executive Director Amanda Saure
Email: music Director / conductor Miriam Burns
Email: Director of operations Laura Figo

Tapestry
Website: www.shuppartists.com
Email: concerts@shuppartists.com
Phone: 631 928 1531
Address: Shupp Artists Management, 202 Michigan Avenue, US
Information: see also Early Music
Country: United States
Contact: contact Erica Shupp (Shupp Artists Mgmt

Terre Haute Symphony Orchestra
Website: www.thso.org
Email: info@thso.org
Phone: 812 234 6060
Address: 25 North Six Street, US
Country: United States
Contact: Executive Director Anne Lynk
Email: music Director/conductor youth symphony Chris Ludwa
Email: music Director/conductor David Bowden

Thayer Symphony Orchestra
Website: www.thayersymphony.org
Email: tsoDirector@thayersymphony.org

Phone: 978 466 1800
Address: 14 Monument Square 4th floor, US
Country: United States
Contact: program coordinator Deborah Brown
Email: conductor Toshimasa Francis Wada

The Bach Choir of Bethlehem
Website: www.bach.org
Email: office@bach.org
Phone: 610 866 4382
Address: 423 Heckewelder Place, US
Information: the oldest American Bach Choir; also hosts annual festival in May
Country: United States
Contact: Artistic Director and conductor Greg Funfgeld
Email: President David G. Beckwith
Email: Executive Director Bridget George

The Discovery Orchestra
Website: www.discoveryorchestra.org
Email: info@discoveryorchestra.org
Phone: 908 226 7300
Address: 50 Mt Bethel Road, PO Box 4064, US
Country: United States
Contact: Executive Director Virginia Johnston
Email: Artistic Director George Marriner Maull

The Met Orchestra
Website: www.metopera.org
Phone: 121 279 93100
Address: The Metropolitan Opera, Lincoln Center, US
Information: see also Opera
Country: United States
Contact: orchestra Manager Robert Sirinek
Email: music Director James Levine

Toledo Symphony
Website: www.toledosymphony.com
Email: music@toledosymphony.com
Phone: 800 348 1253
Address: PO BOX 407, US
Information: see also Presenters & Venues
Country: United States
Contact: Director of Marketing and public relations Ashley Mirakian

Topeka Symphony
Website: www.TopekaSymphony.org
Email: tso@TopekaSymphony.org
Phone: 785 232 2032
Address: PO Box 2206, US
Country: United States
Contact: General Manager Kathy Maag
Email: music Director John Strickler

Traverse Symphony Orchestra
Website: www.tso-online.org
Email: tso@tso-online.org
Phone: 231 947 7120
Address: 121 E. Front Street, Suite 301, US
Country: United States
Contact: Director of development Carleen McCall
Email: Executive Director Andrew Buelow
Email: admin Manager Linda Martin
Email: music Director Kevin Rhodes

Tucson Chamber Orchestra
Website: www.tucsonchamberorchestra.org
Email: elasansky@cox.net
Phone: 152 040 14369
Address: PO Box 13925, US
Country: United States
Contact: music Director and conductor Enrique Lasansky

Tucson Symphony Orchestra
Website: www.tucsonsymphony.org
Email: tmarshall@tucsonsymphony.org
Phone: 520 792 9155
Address: 2175 North 6th Avenue, US
Country: United States
Contact: music Director and conductor George Hanson
Email: Director of public relations/Marketing Terry Marshall
Email: acting Executive Director George Steele
Email: gsteele@tucsonsymphony.orgchief financial officer Robert Jennens
Email: rjennens@tucsonsymphony.org

Tulare County Symphony
Website: www.tcsymphony.org
Email: tcsymph@sbcglobal.net
Phone: 559 732 8600
Address: 208 W. Main Street, Suite 5A, US
Country: United States
Contact: music Director Bruce Kielsing

Tulsa Symphony Orchestra
Website: www.tulsasymphony.org
Email: info@tulsasymphony.org
Phone: 918 584 3645
Address: 117 N Boston Ave Suite 201, US
Information: Tulsa Symphony is a musician led and engaged per service orchestra drawing on a local, regional and national pool of 150 professional musicians. A wide

variety of outdoor and indoor concerts from chamber ensemble to large orchestra are presented each year. Tulsa Symphony's performance partners include the internationally acclaimed Tulsa Ballet, Tulsa Oratorio Chorus, Tulsa Project Theater and the Tulsa Opera Orchestra
Country: United States
Contact: Executive Director Ronald Predl
Email: ron.predl@tulsasymphony.orgAdministration Tom Stout
Email: tom@tulsasymphony.orgMarketing Todd Cunningham
Email: todd@tulsasymphony.org

Tupelo Symphony Orchestra
Website: www.tupelosymphony.com
Email: tso@tupelosymphony.com
Phone: 662 842 8433
Address: PO Box 474, US
Country: United States
Contact: orchestra Manager David East
Email: Chairman - board Peggy Oakes
Email: music Director/conductor Steven Byess
Email: President/Executive Director Margaret Anne Murphey

Tuscaloosa Symphony Orchestra
Website: tsoonline.org
Email: tso@tsoonline.org
Phone: 205 752 5515
Address: PO Box 20001, US
Country: United States
Contact: Executive Director Elisabeth McGuire

Tuscarawas Philharmonic
Website: www.tuscarawasphilharmonic.org
Email: genmgr@tuscarawaphilharmonic.org
Phone: 133 036 41843
Address: PO Box 406, US
Country: United States
Contact: General Manager Melanie Winn
Email: music Director and conductor Eric Benjamin
Email: finance Director Robert Henke

Utah Symphony
Website: www.utahsymphony.org
Email: info@utahsymphony.org
Phone: 801 533 5626
Address: Maurice Abravanel Hall, 123 West South Temple, US
Information: see also Utah Opera
Country: United States
Contact: music Director Thierry Fischer
senior vice President & interim CEO
David Green

Utica Symphony
Website: www.uticasymphony.net
Email: ExecutiveDirector@uticasymphony.net
Phone: 315 732 5146
Address: 505 Henry Street, US
Country: United States
Contact: Executive Director Mary Lee Ensijn
Email: music Director Charles A Schneider

Vallejo Symphony Orchestra
Website: www.vallejosymphony.org
Email: vallejosymphony@gmail.com
Phone: 707 643 4441
Address: PO Box 568, US
Information: visiting address: 3467 Sonoma Blvd, Suite 10, Vallejo CA 94590
Country: United States
Contact: conductor David Ramadanoff

Valley Symphony Orchestra and Chorale
Website: www.valleyorchestra.org
Email: administrator@valleyorchestra.org
Phone: 956 661 1615
Address: c/o South Texas Symphony Association, PO Box 2832, US
Information: visiting address: 1201 West University Drive, Suite 105, Edinburg
Country: United States
Contact: Executive Director Monica Folk
Email: music Director and conductor Peter Dabrowski

Venice Symphony
Website: www.thevenicesymphony.org
Email: venicesymphony@aol.com
Phone: 941 488 1010
Address: PO Box 1561, US
Country: United States
conductor & music Director
Kenneth Bowermeister

Vermont Symphony Orchestra
Website: www.vso.org
Email: info@vso.org
Phone: 802 864 5741
Address: 2 Church Street, US
Country: United States
Contact: Executive Director Alan Jordan
Email: music Director Jaime Laredo

Email: principal guest conductor Anthony Princiotti
Email: orchestra Manager Eleanor Long

Victoria Symphony Orchestra
Website: www.victoriasymphony.com
Email: victoriasymphony@sbcglobal.net
Phone: 361 576 4500
Address: 2112 North Navarro, US
Country: United States
Contact: Executive Director Michelle E Hall
Email: music Director and conductor Darryl One
Email: President Craig Calhoun

Virginia Symphony
Website: www.virginiasymphony.org
Phone: 757 466 3060
Address: 861 Glenrock Road, Suite 200, US
Country: United States
Contact: Associate conductor Benjamin Rous
Email: President and Executive Director Eric Borenstein
music Director & conductor
JoAnn Falletta

Waco Symphony Orchestra
Website: www.wacosymphony.com
Email: info@wacosymphony.com
Phone: 254 754 0851
Address: PO Box 1201, US
Information: season subscription concerts runs from
Sept through Apr; Nutcracker Ballet is presented
every-other year.
Country: United States
Contact: music Director/conductor Stephen Heyde
Email: stephen_heyde@baylor.edu

Walla Walla Symphony
Website: www.wwsymphony.org
Email: info@wwsymphony.org
Phone: 509 529 8020
Address: PO Box 92, US
Information: size: 80 members
Country: United States
Contact: General Manager Sharon Thompson
Email: CEO Mike Wenberg
Email: music Director, conductor Yaacov Bergman

Wallingford Symphony Orchestra
Website: www.wallingfordsymphony.org
Email: pventre@choate.edu
Phone: 203 697 2261
Address: PO Box 6023, US
Country: United States
Contact: music Director Philip Ventre

Washington Chorus, The
Website: www.thewashingtonchorus.org
Email: staff@thewashingtonchorus.org
Phone: 202 342 6221
Address: 2801 Upton Street, NW, US
Country: United States
Contact: Executive Director Diane Peterson
Email: music Director Julian Wachner

Washington Idaho Symphony
Website: www.washingtonidahosymphony.org
Email: symphony@pullman.com
Phone: 150 933 23408
Address: 115 NW State Street, US
Country: United States
Contact: music Director Jeremy Briggs Roberts
Email: orchestra Manager Rachel Gordon

Washington Metropolitan Philharmonic
Website: www.wmpamusic.org
Email: wmpa@earthlink.net
Phone: 703 799 8229
Address: PO Box 120, US
Information: approximately 80% of the Philharmonic
are semi-professional or professional musicians. The
orchestra is known for its adventuresome programming
Country: United States
music Director & conductor
Ulysses James
Email: wmpa@earthlink.net

Waterbury Symphony Orchestra
Website: www.waterburysymphony.org
Email: scollins@waterburysymphony.org
Phone:
203 574 4283
Address: 110 Bank Street, US
Country: United States
Contact: personnel Director T.D. Ellis
Email: Executive Director Steve Collins
music Director & conductor
Leif Bjaland

Waterloo/Cedar Falls Symphony Orchestra
Website:
www.wcfsymphony.org
Email: info@wcfsymphony.org
Phone: 319 273 3660
Address: Gallagher-Bluedorn Performing Arts Center,

8201 Dakota St, US
Country: United States
Contact: Executive Director Susan Munnik
Email: music Director Jason Weinberger

Waukesha Symphony Orchestra
Website: www.waukeshasymphony.org
Email: info@waukeshasymphony.org
Phone: 262 547 1858
Address: PO Box 531, US
Country: United States
Contact: music Director Alexander Platt
Email: Executive Director Christine Hansen

West Shore Symphony Orchestra
Website: www.wsso.org
Email: info@wsso.org
Phone: 231 726 3231
Address: 425 W Western Avenue, Suite 409, US
Country: United States
Contact: Marketing Manager Jim Lopez
Email: music Director Scott Speck
Email: President/CEO Carla Hill

West Virginia Symphony
Website: www.wvsymphony.org
Email: info@wvsymphony.org
Phone: 304 957 9876
Address: PO Box 2292, US
Country: United States
Contact: President Joe Tackett
Email: jtackett@wvsymphony.orgVice President of
Education and Operations Betty King
Email: bking@wvsymphony.orgMusic Director Lawrence
Loh

West Virginia Symphony Orchestra Inc.
Website: www.wvsymphony.org
Email: info@wvsymphony.org
Phone: 304 957 9876
Address: 4700 MacCorkle Avenue S.E., Suite 101
Information: The WV Symphony Orchestra has been
making great music to enrich and inspire everyone
in our region since 1939. We have a robust season of
symphonic masterworks and pops concerts in addition
to educational concerts and collaborations with the
Charleston Ballet for the Nutcracker.
Country: United States
Contact: Marketing Director Amanda McDonald
Email: amcdonald@wvsymphony.org
Touring Countries: US

Westchester Philharmonic
Website: www.westchesterphil.org
Email: info@westchesterphil.org
Phone: 914 682 3707
Address: 123 Main Street, US
Information: also runs edcational programmes for
young people, additionally performs free outdoor
summer concerts
Country: United States
Contact: Executive Director Joshua Worby
Email: Director, Marketing and Development Lenore
Eggleston,

Western New York Chamber Orchestra
Website: www.wnyco.org
Email: info@wnyco.org.
Phone: 716 673 3463
Address: 2162 Mason Hall, SUNY College at Fredonia, US
Information: mission: to bring classical music to the
Chantauqua region; strong education element
Country: United States
Contact: Executive Director Laura Koepke
Email: President Sandy Rotunda

Western Piedmont Symphony
Website: www.wpsymphony.org
Email: info@wpsymphony.org
Address: Arts Center of Catawba Valley, 243 Third Ave,
NE Suite 1N, US
Country: United States
Contact: music Director/conductor John Gordon Ross
Email: Executive Director Chis Brown

Western Wind Vocal Ensemble Inc
Website: www.westernwind.org
Email: info@westernwind.org
Phone: 212 873 2848
Address: 263, West 86th Street, 3rd Floor, US
Information: 15 CDs available: also do ensemble singing
workshops whilst on tour; workshops in summer at
Smith College New Hampshire, MA; see also Early Music
Country: United States

Westerville Civic Symphony
Website: www.westervillesymphony.org
Email: info@westervillesymphony.org
Phone:
161 489 05523
Address: PO Box 478, US
Information: also educational, outreach, childrens
programmes
Country: United States

Contact: operations Manager Claire Brock
Email: assistant conductor James Bates
Email: music Director Peter Stafford Wilson
Email: Managing Director Jerry Wade

Westfield Symphony Orchestra
Website:
www.westfieldsymphony.org
Email: wso@westfieldsymphony.org
Phone: 908 232 9400
Address: 224 East Broad Street, Suite 6, US
Country: United States
Contact: music Director David Wroe

Westmoreland Symphony Orchestra
Website: www.westmorelandsymphony.org
Email: info@westmorelandsymphony.org
Phone: 724 837 1850
Address: 951 Old Salem Road, US
Country: United States
Contact: Executive Director Morrie Brand

Wheeling Symphony Society, Inc
Website: www.wheelingsymphony.org
Email: wso@wheelingsymphony.org
Phone: 304 232 6191
Address: Wheeling's Capitol Theatre, 1015 Main Street,
US
Country: United States
Contact: Executive Director Bruce Wheeler
Email: music Director André Raphel

Wichita Falls Symphony Orchestra
Website: www.wfso.org
Email: ExecutiveDirector@wfso.org
Phone: 940 723 6202
Address: 1300 lamar, US
Country: United States
Contact: music Director Candler Schaffer
Email: Executive Director Janel Ponder Smith

Wichita Symphony Orchestra
Website: www.wso.org
Email: symphony@wso.org
Phone: 316 267 5259
Address: 225 W Douglas, Suite 207, US
Country: United States
Contact: operations Manager Anne Marie Brown
Email: Marketing and public relations coordinator Tara
Shaffer
Email: Executive Director Mitchell Berman
music Director & conductor
Andrew Sewell

William Ferris Chorale
Website: www.williamferrischorale.org
Email: requests@williamferrischorale.org
Phone: 773 508 2940
Address: 1032 W SHERIDAN RD, US
Country: United States
Contact: Artistic Director John Vorrasi
Email: artist in residence Thomas Weisflog
Email: music Director Paul French

Williamsburg Symphonia
Website: www.williamsburgsymphonia.org
Email: info@williamsburgsymphonia.org
Phone: 757 229 9857
Address: PO Box 400, US
Country: United States
Contact: Executive Director Carolyn Keurajian
Email: info@williamsburgsymphonia.org

Williamsport Symphony Orchestra
Website: www.williamsportsymphony.com
Email: info@williamsportsymphony.com
Phone: 157 032 20227
Address: 220 W 4th Street, US
Information: also have youth orchestra of 80 musicians:
Williamsport Symphony Youth Orchestra
Country: United States
Contact: principal conductor tba
Email: Marketing Manager John Blair
Email: Executive Director Valerie Whyman

Wilmington Symphony Orchestra
Website: www.wilmingtonsymphony.org
Email: info@wilmingtonsymphony.org
Phone: 910 791 9262
Address: 4608 Cedar Ave, Suite105, US
Country: United States
Contact: Interim Executive Director Lesa Broadhead
Email: Director@wilmingtonsymphony.org

Winston-Salem Symphony
Website: www.wssymphony.org
Email: info@wssymphony.org
Phone: 336 725 1035
Address: 201 N. Broad Street, US
Country: United States
Contact: operations and stage Manager Beverly Naiditch
Email: music Director Robert Moody
Email: box office/ office Manager Tina Baston
Email: Executive Director Merritt Vale

Email: Director of Marketing Hayden Barnes
Email: financial Director Selina Carter

Winter Park Bach Festival, Choir and Orchestra
Website: www.bachfestivalflorida.org
Email: info@bachfestivalflorida.org
Phone: 407 646 2182
Address: Rollins College, 1000 Holt Ave, PO Box 2763, US
Information: see also Festivals (Winter Park Bach Festival)
Country: United States
Contact: President Eric Ravndal
Email: Artistic Director and conductor John V Sinclair
Email: Executive Director Elizabeth Gwinn

Wisconsin Chamber Orchestra
Website: www.wcoconcerts.com
Email: wco@wcoconcerts.org
Phone: 608 257 0638
Address: PO Box 171, US
Country: United States
Contact: music Director Andrew Sewell
Email: operations Director Stephanie Miller-Lamb
Email: Executive Director Robert Sorge
Email: development Director Peter Schmeling

Wyoming Symphony Orchestra
Website: www.wyomingsymphony.org
Email: rachel@wyomingsymphony.org
Phone: 307 266 1478
Address: 225 S. David St, US
Country: United States
Contact: Executive Director Rachel Bailey
Email: rachel@wyomingsymphony.orgdeputy Director Makayla Moore
Email: makayla@wyomingsymphony.org

Yakima Symphony Orchestra
Website: www.yakimasymphony.org
Email: noel@yakimasymphony.org
Phone: 150 924 81414
Address: 32 N. 3rd St., Suite 333, US
Country: United States
Contact: music Director Helen N. Jewett
Email: music Director Brooke Creswell

Yale Symphony Orchestra
Website: www.yalesymphony.com
Email: brian.s.robinson@yale.edu
Phone: 203 432 4140
Address: Yale School of Music, 143 Elm Street, Room 202, US
Country: United States
Contact: Manager Brian Robinson
Email: brian.s.robinson@yale.edu

Young People's Chorus of New York City
Website: www.ypc.org
Email: information@ypc.org
Phone: 212 289 7779
Address: 1995 Broadway, Suite 305, US
Information: Concert Chorus Francisco J. Núñez, Conductor: award-winning performing ensemble of 44 young people ranging in age from 12-17; Intermezzo ChorusvElizabeth McKinney, Conductor: 75 boys and girls ages 11 and up; Young Men's Chorus Lauren Quigley, Conductor:
Country: United States
Contact: Artistic Director/founder Francisco J Nu
Email: production Manager Gina Vriens

Youngstown Symphony Orchestra
Website: www.youngstownsymphony.com
Email: symphony@youngstownsymphony.com
Phone: 330 744 4269
Address: 260 Federal Plaza West, US
Country: United States
Contact: music Director/conductor Isaiah Jackson until June 2006
Email: Executive Director Patricia Syak
Email: Marketing Director Liz Best

76ᵉ CONCOURS DE GENÈVE
INTERNATIONAL MUSIC COMPETITION
22 OCT–3 NOV 2022
Piano & Composition

COMPOSITION FINAL
26 OCT. CONSERVATOIRE, GENEVA
With the Neue Vocalsolisten Stuttgart

PIANO FINAL
3 NOV. VICTORIA HALL, GENEVA
With the Orchestre de la Suisse Romande

JURY CHAIR
PIANO – JANINA FIALKOWSKA
COMPOSITION – BEAT FURRER

CONCOURSGENEVE.CH

HINAKO TAKAGI
1ᵉʳ PRIX EX AEQUO COMPOSITION 2019
© MISA SHINSHI

MEMBER OF THE WORLD
FEDERATION OF INTERNATIONAL
MUSIC COMPETITIONS

Theatre Companies

This sections lists performing companies that spend all or much of their time presenting plays or theatre productions in a theatre setting.The companies are mainly building-based, but there are also a significant number of touring companies. **The entries are listed in alphabetical order within country.**

Compagnies de Théâtre

Cette section dresse la liste des entreprises les plus performantes consacrent tout ou une grande partie de leur vie présen-tant des pièces ou des pièces de théâtre dans un théâtre. Principalement les entreprises sont de construction à base, mais il ya un nombre important de sociétés plus tournées. **Les entrée sont classés par ordre alphabétique dans le pays.**

Theatergruppen

Dieser Abschnitt Listen erfolgreichsten Unternehmen alle oder einen Großteil ihres Lebens verbringen präsentiert Theaterstücke oder Theater-Produktionen im Theater. The Hauptsächlich Unternehmen sind Gebäude-basierte, aber es gibt eine beträchtliche Anzahl von Auch Gastensembles. **Die Einträge sind für jedes Land alphabetisch sortiert.**

Teatro Societá

Questa sezione elenca le aziende che svolgono spendono in tutto o in gran parte della loro vita presentare spettacoli teatrali o in un teatro impostata inizialmente Principalmente aziende stanno costruendo-based, ma ci sono un numero significativo di imprese anche itineranti. **Le voci sono pubblicate in ordine alfabetico di prodotto,paese e poi nome.**

Teatro Empresas

En esta sección se enumeran realizar las empresas que pasan toda o gran parte de su tiempo de la presentación de obras o producciones teatrales en algunas compañías de teatro. Son principalmente la construcción basada, pero también hay un número significativo de empresas de turismo. **Las entradas se muestran en orden alfabético dentro de cada país.**

performing arts
database

AUSTRALIA

2 Til 5 Youth Theatre Co-Op Ltd
Email: 2til5@arthunter.com.au
Address: Parry Street, AU
Country: Australia
Touring: No
Regular venues: Convent Garden Theatre 80

5 Angry Men
Website: www.flyingmonkey.com.au/5AM/flash/html/intro.html
Email: 5am@5angrymen.com
Address: Suite 904 37 Swanston Street, AU
Information: agent for Europe: Frans Brood Productions, Muinklaan 10, 9000 Gent, Belgium, Tel: +32 9-234 1212, Fax: +32 9-265 9650, E-mail: info@fransbrood.com, Internet: www.fransbrood.com
Country: Australia
Contact: Artistic Director Tomek Koman
Email: fiveangrymen@gmail.com
Touring Countries: Europe, UK, Russia, Japan, New Zealand
Touring: No
Regular venues: Outdoor performance

Araluen Centre for Arts & Entertainment
Website: www.araluencentre.com.au
Email: araluencentre.nreta@nt.gov.au
Phone: 889 511 122
Address: PO Box 3521, Larapinta Drive, AU
Information: see also Presenters
Country: Australia
Contact: Director Tim Rollason
publicity & promotions officer Rebecca Farrell
Contact: curator Kate Podger
Touring: No
Regular venues: 500 seat theatre; 4 galleries; community hire area approx. 200

Arena Theatre Company
Website: www.arenatheatre.com.au
Email: info@arenatheatre.com.au
Phone: 401 823 299
Address: 28 St Martin's Lane, AU
Information: Arena Theatre Company is powered by the twin drivers of art and audience: creating inspiring live performance known for genuine engagement with young people aged 5 – 25. High quality, original, Artistically ambitious theatre defines Arena's success. They believe in theatre's unique ability to provide a space of reflection, celebration and transformation for young people. They provide a theatrical space to which everyone is invited, on equal terms.
Country: Australia
Contact: Artistic Director Christian Leavesley
Email: christian@arenatheatre.com.au
Contact: Executive Producer Sheah Sutton
Email: sheah@arenatheatre.com.au
Contact: Artistic Associate Jolyon James
Email: jolyon@arenatheatre.com.au
Social Media: @arenatheatrecowww.facebook.com/arenatheatrecompany
Touring: No

Arena Theatre Company
Website: arenatheatre.com.au
Email: info@arenatheatre.com.au
Phone: 035 463 5160
Address: 208 Strickland Rd, Bendigo, VIC
Information: Arena produces high quality, original and Artistically ambitious theatre for young people. Our work is presented by Australia's major theatre Producers and arts centres and toured internationally. We believe in theatre's unique ability to provide a space of reflection, celebration and transformation for young people. Our aim is to speak to young people in languages they understand, in the spaces they occupy, but in ways they never thought possible.
Country: Australia
Contact: Program Manager Gayle McClure
Email: gayle@arenatheatre.com.au
Contact: Executive Director Sharon Custers
Email: sharon@arenatheatre.com.au
Social Media: facebook.com/arenatheatrecompanyinstagram.com/arenatheatreco

Arts Projects Australia Pty Ltd
Website: www.artsprojects.com.au
Email: apadmin@artsprojects.com.au
Phone: 882 711 488
Address: 12 King William Road, AU
Information: Arts Projects Australia is an independent Producer and event management company based in Adelaide. Since its establishment in 1997, APA has worked collaboratively with a range of festivals, Producers and cultural organisations on a diverse range of performing arts projects and tours.
Country: Australia
Contact: Director Ian Scobie
Contact: assistant Producer Daniel Vorrasi
Contact: Marketing Manager Nicola Prime
Touring Countries: Germany, Serbia, Ireland

Australian Dance Theatre
Website: www.adt.org.au
Email: adt@adt.org.au
Phone: 883 737 733
Address: 126 Belair Road, Hawthorn, AU
Information: Under the Directorship of Garry Stewart, Australian Dance Theatre creates dance that is an intelligent progression of the art form engaging audiences throughout the world over. Australian Dance Theatre is Australia's pre-eminent contemporary dance company and the longest running in the country. For 50 years Australian Dance Theatre has pioneered new work that has contributed to defining dance in this region.
Country: Australia
Contact: Artistic Director Gary Stewart
Contact: Executive Director Shaun Comerford
Contact: Chairman Kim Boehm
Social Media: @ausdancetheatrewww.facebook.com/AustralianDanceTheatre
Touring Countries: Europe, Ireland, Korea, Canada, Singapore, UK, Australia
Touring: No
ADT Studio 200; Playhouse, Adelaide Festival Centre 600; Scott Theatre 600; Her Majesty's Theatre 1000; Sydney Opera House 550, Victorian Arts Centre 850;

Australian Theatre for Young People (ATYP)
Website: www.atyp.com.au
Email: hello@atyp.com.au
Phone: 292 702 400
Address: Pier 4/5 Hickson Road, Walsh Bay, AU
Information: Australian Theatre for Young People specialises in integrating professional theatre practices with a supportive youth theatre process. It works with all levels of the arts industry, from the most celebrated national companies to the smallest youth theatres. It supports young people from their first theatre experience to their first professional production.
Country: Australia
Contact: General Manager Amy Maiden
Contact: Artistic Director Fraser Corfield
Contact: development Manager Andrew Deane
Contact: Chairman Mark Warburton
Social Media: @atyp_Sydneywww.facebook.com/AustralianTheatreforYoungPeople
Touring: No

Australian Theatre of the Deaf
Website: www.artsaccess.com.au/australian-theatre-of-the-deaf
Email: info@artsaccess.com.au
Phone: 396 998 299
Address: 222 Bank Street, AU
Information: Australian Theatre of the Deaf (ATOD) aims to make a unique contribution to Australian culture by creating daring and bi-lingual theatre for the hearing and the deaf. In so doing, it hopes to promote understanding and awareness of cultural difference and increase the audience for deaf cultural exPression.
Country: Australia
Contact: Chairman Brad Sadler
Contact: Executive Director Emma Dawson
Social Media: @ArtsAccessVicwww.facebook.com/artsaccessvictoria
Touring: No
Regular venues: small to medium-sized theatres and school venues

Back to Back Theatre
Website: www.backtobacktheatre.com
Email: info@backtobacktheatre.com
Phone: 352 212 029
Address: 60 Little Malop Street, AU
Information: One of Australia's few professional ensemble theatre companies, Back to Back Theatre is renowned for its work with actors who have an intellectual disability, creating work which is compelling and intriguing as it collaborates with artists, performing arts companies and communities.
Country: Australia
Contact: Artistic Director Bruce Gladwin
Contact: Executive Producer Alice Nash
Contact: markeing Manager Rebecca Kleindienst
Social Media: @Back2BackTheatrwww.facebook.com/backtobacktheatre
Touring: No
Regular venues: varies 100-350

Backbone Youth Arts Inc.
Website: www.backbone.org.au
Email: info@backbone.org.au
Phone: 733 918 239
Address: East Brisbane Bowls Club, 38 Lytton Road, AU
Information: BACKBONE now sits as the only metropolitan based multi-arts organisation with the specific mandate of working with young people in Queensland. With a 29-year legacy, BACKBONE is both a service and Artistic company. BACKBONE's program consists of a multifaceted web of activities including: festivals, events, performance works and workshops. We inspire children and young adults to develop confidence and personal power, to find their voice and sense of purpose, and to develop robust, versatile Artistic practices.
Country: Australia

Contact: Artistic Director and chief Executive Officer Katherine Quigley
Email: kath@backbone.org.au
Contact: program Manager Chris Beckey
Email: chris@backbone.org.au
Social Media: @BBoneYouthArts
Touring: No

Barking Gecko Theatre Company
Website: www.barkinggecko.com.au
Email: gecko@barkinggecko.com.au
Phone: 862 129 399
Address: 178 William St, AU
Information: Established in 1985 as Acting Out, it was renamed Barking Gecko Theatre Company in 1994 and is now a locally cherished, nationally significant professional theatre company specialising in creating productions for young people.
Country: Australia
Contact: CEO Helen Hristofski
Contact: financial Manager Joy Crocker
Contact: Marketing Manager Matt McEwen
Contact: Artistic Director Matt Edgerton
Social Media: @geckotweetswww.facebook.com/BarkingGeckoTheatreCompany
Touring: No
Regular venues: Subiaco Theatre Centre: Main Auditorium 302, Studio 90

Bell Shakespeare
Website: www.bellshakespeare.com.au
Email: mail@bellshakespeare.com.au
Phone: 282 989 000
Address: Level 1, 33 Playfair Street, AU
Information: Bell Shakespeare is an Australian theatre company specialising in the works of William Shakespeare, his contemporaries and other classics. It was founded in 1990 by John Bell. Bell Shakespeare is Australia's only national touring theatre company. The Bell Shakespeare vision is to create theatre that allows audiences of all walks of life to see themselves reflected and transformed through the prism of great writing.
Country: Australia
Contact: founding Artistic Director John Bell
Contact: Associate Artistic Director Peter Evans
Contact: Chair Anne Loveridge
Contact: General Manager Gill Perkins
Social Media: @bellshakespearewww.facebook.com/BellShakespeareCo
Touring: Nationally

Belvoir
Website: www.belvoir.com.au
Email: mail@belvoir.com.au
Phone: 296 983 344
Address: 18 & 25 Belvoir St, AU
Information: Belvoir sprang into being out of the unique action taken to save the Nimrod Theatre building from demolition in 1984. Belvoir presents an annual season of new Australian plays and re imagined classics.
Country: Australia
Contact: Artistic Director Eamon Flack
Contact: General Manager Brenna Hobson
Contact: Executive Director Sue Donnelly
Social Media: @BelvoirStwww.facebook.com/BelvoirSt
Touring: Nationally and Internationally
Regular venues: Upstairs Theatre 320-350, Downstairs Theatre 80

Bizircus
Website: www.bizircus.com
Email: bizircus@iinet.net.au
Phone: 403 347 452
Address: PO Box 999, AU
Information: Bizircus began 20 years ago as a collective of acrobats, artists, street performers and musicians. Since then the company has been dedicated to creating fresh new circus comedy shows, combining contemporary physical comedy with timeless acrobatic feats and to keep audiences swinging between fits of laughter and gasps of amazement.
Country: Australia
Contact: Manager Ross Vegas
Contact: contact Brendan Coleman
Social Media: www.facebook.com/Bizircus
Touring Countries: France, China, Hong Kong
Touring: No

Black Swan State Theatre Company
Website: www.bsstc.com.au
Email: information@bsstc.com.au
Phone: 862 129 300
Address: State Theatre Centre of WA, Level 1, 182 William Street, AU
Information: Since its inception in 1991, Black Swan has earned both critical and popular acclaim for its world premiere productions and highly distinctive reinterpretations of international theatre classics – all of which are infused with the unique culture of Western Australia. Its strength lies in artist development, encouraging access and engaging with the community. The company has seen enormous growth in building audiences, building capacity and establishing a benchmark for quality productions of scale in Western Australia.

Country: Australia
Contact: General Manager Natalie Jenkins
Email: natalie@bsstc.com.au
Contact: Marketing Manager Maria Sioulas
Email: maria@bsstc.com.au
Contact: Artistic Director Clare Watson
Contact: finance Manager Amanda Luke
Email: amanda@bsstc.com.au
Social Media: @BlackSwanSTCwww.facebook.com/
BlackSwanStateTheatreCompany
Touring Countries: China, Europe
Touring: No

Brink Productions
Website: brinkproductions.com
Email: info@brinkproductions.com
Phone: 882 116 565
Address: PO Box 3262 Rundle Mall, AU
Information: Brink has always existed to tell stories, but increasingly we find the methodology on which we've built the company has a greater flexibility, allowing our projects to begin from any number of starting points and take on any shape. Brink attracts major artists from across disciplines and across the country and the world, drawn to the company's vision of creating contemporary allegorical works that speak to a diversity of audiences.
Country: Australia
Contact: Artistic Director Chris Drummond
Contact: General Manager Karen Wilson
Social Media: @BrinkTheatrewww.facebook.com/brink-productions
Touring: No

Brisbane Multicultural Arts Centre
Website: www.bemac.org.au
Email: bemac@bemac.org.au
Phone: 733 914 433
Address: PO Box 7299, AU
Information: As Queensland's most dynamic Producer of multicultural arts, BEMAC has been successfully staging ground-breaking productions that fuel the diverse practice of artists from a variety of different cultural backgrounds for almost three decades. Established in 1987 by a group of passionate advocates and artists inspired to bring the creative work of a new generation of multicultural artists into the spotlight, BEMAC has grown to become the state's leading multicultural arts Producer, presenter and Artistic development organisation.
Country: Australia
Contact: General Manager Leanne Tu'ipulotu
Contact: programme coordinator Michelle Brown
Contact: artist development coordinator Simon Mula
Social Media: @BEMACpresentswww.facebook.com/
BEMACpresents
Touring: No

Canberra Youth Theatre Company
Website: www.cytc.net
Email: info@cytc.net
Phone: 262 485 057
Address: H Block, Gorman Arts Centre, Batman St, AU
Information: Canberra Youth Theatre (CYT) was established in 1972 and is an Australian not for profit youth arts company based in the ACT. We aim to develop curious and broad-minded theatre makers and theatre thinkers. We provide young people aged 7-25 years with the opportunity to explore, extend and develop their skills with emerging and professional artists. CYT is a place where young people's voices are heard, in a safe and accepting environment.
Country: Australia
Contact: Artistic Director Katie Cawthorne
Email: Artistic@cytc.net
Contact: General Manager Alicia Wyatt
Email: business@cytc.net
Contact: workshop coordinator Stefanie Lekkas
Email: workshops@cytc.net
Contact: administrative and Marketing Officer Jessica Baker
Email: info@cytc.net
Social Media: @CYT_Canberrawww.facebook.com/
CanberraYouthTheatre
Touring Countries: New Zealand
Touring: No
Regular venues: capacity 90

Circa Contemporary Circus LTD
Website: www.circa.org.au
Email: info@circa.org.au
Phone: 073 852 3110
Address: Judith Wright Centre of Contemporary Arts, Level 3, 420 Brunswick Street, AU
Information: Circa Contemporary Circus is one of the world's leading performance companies. Since 2004, from its base in Brisbane, Australia, Circa has toured the world – performing in 39 countries to over a million people. Circa's works have been greeted with standing ovations, rave reviews and sold-out houses across six continents.
 Circa is at the forefront of the new wave of contemporary Australian circus. Visit circa.org.au to find a Circa performance near you and discover why Circa has been hailed as nothing short of "... a revolution in the spectacle of circus." (Les Echos).

Country: Australia
Contact: Artistic Director Yaron Lifschitz
Email: yaron@circa.org.au
Contact: General Manager Charlie Cush
Email: charlie@circa.org.au
Contact: international representative europe Paul Tanguay
Email: paul.tanguay@sympatico.ca
Contact: technical director Jason Organ
Email: jason@circa.org.au
Contact: facilities Manager Evan Wright
Social Media: @CircaPresentswww.facebook.com/
circacontemporarycircus
Touring Countries: Mexico, Spain, Luxembourg, UK, Hungary, France
Touring: No
 indoor & outdoor performance venues

Circus Oz
Website: www.circusoz.com
Email: admin@circusoz.com.au
Phone: 396 760 300
Address: 50 Perry Street, AU
Information: Circus Oz was born in Melbourne, Australia in 1978. For 40 years the company has been putting up extraordinary shows and successfully touring them both nationally and internationally. From New York to South American rainforests, Madrid to outback Australia, Circus Oz has taken its self-crafted performances of wit, grace and spectacle to over 27 countries across five continents, to critical acclaim.
Country: Australia
Social Media: facebook.com/circusoz/www.instagram.
com/circusoz/
Touring: Nationally and Internationally

Cirkids Inc
Website: www.cirkidz.org.au
Email: circus@cirkidz.org.au
Phone: 883 465 735
Address: 27 Fifth Street, AU
Information: Cirkidz was founded in 1986 by artists Tony Hannan and Michael Lester, to provide meaningful recreation and community engagement opportunities for disadvantaged youth in Adelaide's industrial inner west. Tony and Michael believed circus skills training would enhance the young people's social, physical and creative development.

Country: Australia
Contact: General Manager Nick Skibinski
Email: General.Manager@cirkidz.org.au
Contact: Artistic Director Joshua Hoare
Email: Artistic.Director@cirkidz.org.au
Contact: Marketing Manager Judy Way
Email: Marketing@cirkidz.org.au
Social Media: @Cirkidzwww.facebook.com/Cirkidz
Touring: No

Company
Email: eulea@spirit.com.au
Phone: 612 624 72073
Address: Gorman House Arts Centre, PO Box 883, Civic Square, AU
Country: Australia
Contact: Artistic Director Eulea Kiraly
Touring: No

CONTACT Inc
Website: www.contact.org.au
Email: info@contact.org.au
Address: 10 Love Street, Queensland, AU
Information: Our vision: communities collaborating to shape their own futures Contact Inc. is a community cultural development organisation, working with people from diverse ages, cultures and backgrounds. Contact Inc. creatively collaborates with artists.
Country: Australia
Contact: Artistic Director Lenine Bourke
Touring: No

Corrugated Iron Youth Arts Inc.
Website: www.corrugatediron.org.au
Email: info@corrugatediron.org.au
Phone: 889 483 200
Address: 18 Bauhinia St, AU
Information: Corrugated Iron Youth Arts (CIYA) is the premier youth arts organisation in the top end of the Northern Territory, providing dynamic creative arts experiences that empower young people and develop young people's life skills, Artistic skills and confidence through an arts medium.
Country: Australia
Contact: Executive Producer Jane Tonkin
Email: jane@corrugatediron.org.au
Contact: Manager Fiona Carter
Email: accounts@corrugatediron.org.au
Social Media: www.facebook.com/corrugatediron
Touring: No

De Quincey Co
Website: www.dequinceyco.net
Email: info@DeQuinceyCo.net
Phone: 298 174 542

Address: A20 Woolley Building, Manning Road,, The Sydney University, AU
Information: De Quincey Co is one of Australia's most innovative and inspiring dance performance companies creating work at the intersection of dance, visual arts, theatre, music and performance. Led by Artistic Director Tess de Quincey, the company creates works of shifting scales for specific spaces – from a black box studio to a desert riverbed.
Country: Australia
Contact: Chair Antonia Seymour
Contact: General Manager Michael Huxley
Contact: secretary Tess de Quincey
Touring Countries: Scandinavia, Germany, France, UK
Touring: No
Regular venues: various, including site-specific spaces

DeckChair Theatre
Website: www.deckChairtheatre.com.au
Email: admin@deckChairtheatre.com.au
Phone: 894 304 771
Address: PO Box 130, AU
Information: closed company
 FREMANTLE'S DeckChair Theatre will close after its board ruled falling box office numbers, sponsorship and government support had rendered the 30-year-old company unviable. The company officially ceased trading yesterday. The company's board of Directors, Chaired by Dorothy Wardale, said the decision to wind up the award-winning Fremantle institution was "enormously difficult".
Country: Australia
Contact: finance officer Caron Brown
Email: admin@deckChairtheatre.com.au
Contact: Marketing and communications Manager Sian Roberts
Email: sroberts@deckChairtheatre.com.au
Contact: administrator Jasmyn Woodford
Email: jwoodford@deckChairtheatre.com.au
Contact: Executive Producer Michael Daly
Email: mdaly@deckChairtheatre.com.au
Contact: Artistic Director Chris Bendall
Email: admin@deckChairtheatre.com.au
Social Media: @deckChairfreohttp://www.facebook.
com/DeckChairTheatre
Touring: No

desoxy Theatre
Website: www.desoxy.customer.netspace.net.au/
contact.htm
Email: desoxy@netspace.net.au
Phone: 393 544 054
Address: c/o Auspicious Arts Projects, Level 1, 117 Sturt St Southbank, AU
Information: Desoxy Theatre is a project based theatre company based in Melbourne, Australia founded by Teresa Blake and Daniel Witton with the aim of creating original works for performance. Since 1990, Desoxy projects have included large scale works at major festivals, film and video, short pieces and independent seasons that have brought public and critical acclaim.
Country: Australia
Contact: co-Director Teresa Blake
Contact: co-Director Daniel Witton
Contact: technical Director Jon Davey
Touring Countries: Japan, Spain, Venezuela, Italy, Korea, England Ireland Scotland, The Netherlands, Austria and Belgium
Touring: No
Regular venues: small to medium up to 600

desoxy Theatre
Website: www.desoxy.customer.netspace.net.au/
Email: desoxy@netspace.net.au
Phone: 393 544 054
Address: c/o Auspicious Arts Projects, Level 1, 117 Sturt St Southbank, AU
Information: Since 1990, desoxy projects have included large scale works at major festivals, film and video, short pieces and independent seasons that have brought public and critical acclaim.
Country: Australia
Contact: Co-Director Daniel Witton
Contact: co-Director Teresa Blake
Touring Countries: Japan, Spain, Venezuela, Italy, Korea, England, Ireland, Scotland, The Netherlands, Austria and Belgium
Touring: No
Regular venues: small to medium up to 600

Doppio – Parallelo
Website: www.parallelo.on.net
Email: paola@parallelo.on.net
Phone: 882 310 070
Address: Lion Arts Centre, Corner North Terrace and Morphett Street, AU
Information: In today's Australian arts landscape, para//elo is one of a handful of performing arts organisations telling original Australian stories in the context of cultural diversity using cross-cultural practice and methodologies. For over twenty-one years para//elo has worked with diverse communities as the loam from which new Artistic works are born, many of which have toured nationally and internationally

Ensemble Theatre
Website: www.ensemble.com.au
Email: boxoffice@ensemble.com.au
Phone: 299 298 877
Address: 78 McDougall Street, AU
Information: The Ensemble Theatre aims to produce live theatre of the highest quality that entertains, educates, enlightens and challenges. The Ensemble Theatre believes that theatre can, and should be, a civilising influence in society. Ensemble Theatre in Kirribilli, Sydney is Australia's longest, continuously running professional theatre company and has constantly maintained the highest standards in theatrical presentation.
Country: Australia
Contact: Artistic Director Mark Kilmurry
Email: mark@ensemble.com.au
Contact: chief financial officer David Balfour Wright
Email: david@ensemble.com.au
Contact: casting and communications Manager Merran Doyle
Email: merran@ensemble.com.au
Contact: production coordinator Simon Greer
Email: simon@ensemble.com.au
Contact: front of house Manager James Birch
Email: jim@ensemble.com.au
Contact: accounts payable Anitza Vlahos
Email: anitza@ensemble.com.au
Contact: Marketing and Administration Assistant Emma Garden
Email: emmag@ensemble.com.au
Contact: production Manager Tom Blunt
Email: tom@ensemble.com.au
Contact: company Manager Claire Nesbitt-Hawes
Email: claire@ensemble.com.au
Social Media: ensemblesydneywww.facebook.com/ensemblesydney
Touring: No
Regular venues: Ensemble Theatre, Theatre Royal

Evolve Productions Australia
Website: www.evolveproductions.com.au
Email: info@evolveproductions.com.au
Phone: 293 006 002
Address: PO Box 263, AU
Information: Evolve Productions was established in 1993, and has since toured theatre shows internationally to critical acclaim, won international awards for animation and founded training programs that have gained respect in both corporate and performing arts fields.
Country: Australia
Contact: Director Michael Lindsey
Touring Countries: Singapore, United States
Touring: No

Flying Bookworm Theatre Company
Website: www.flyingbookworm.com.au
Email: enquiries@flyingbookworm.com.au
Phone: 393 101 146
Address: PO Box 8, AU
Information: With over thirty years experience in presenting theatre to tens of thousands of students across Victoria, The Flying Bookworm Theatre Company can proudly say that they know their audiences and their needs. The Flying Bookworm actors are knowledgeable on all aspects of OH and S and the codes of Professional Conduct and responsibilities that apply when working with children. With frequent contact with staff in schools, The FBTC is aware of the Pressures on staff and so ensures the administrative and booking processes are as simple as possible
Country: Australia
Contact: Director Jessikah Brown
Contact: Director Angus Brown
Touring: No
Regular venues: schools in-house

Flying Fruit Fly Circus, The
Website: www.fruitflycircus.com.au
Email: info@fruitflycircus.com.au
Phone: 260 430 777
Address: 605 Hovell Street, AU
Information: The Flying Fruit Fly Circus is Australia's National Youth Circus. They are renowned as both a centre of training excellence and an award-winning performing arts company, with a full-time training course, dedicated selective school and state-of-the-art facilities, catering for young people aged 8 to 18.
Country: Australia
Contact: Executive Director Richard Hull
Contact: Artistic Director Jodie Farrugia
Contact: Chair Lara Block
Social Media: @fruitflycircuswww.facebook.com/Fruit-FlyCircus
Touring Countries: Canada, America, New Zealand, Singapore, Australia, Japan, Nauru
Touring: No
Regular venues: Concert Halls, Theatres ,Circus Tents, Festivals indoors and out

Freewheels Theatre Co.
Email: freewheels@hunterlink.net.au
Phone:
249 585 244
Address: 83 Lakeview Street, AU
Information: Founded in Sydney in 1976 as a pilot theatre-in-education company, Freewheels came to Newcastle later that year. The company was committed to producing high quality programmes for a broad cross-section of the community, with the principle activity of the company being touring to schools.
Country: Australia
Contact: producing Director Debra Oswald
Touring: No

Genesian Theatre
Website: www.genesiantheatre.com.au
Email: gensiantheatre@hotmail.com
Phone: 292 676 646
Address: 420 Kent St, AU
Country: Australia
Contact: Director Sahn Millington
Social Media: @genesianswww.facebook.com/sharer/sharer.php?u=http%3A%2F%2Fwww.genesiantheatre.com.au%2Findex.php%3Fmode%3Dcontact%23.UHf-cOKB875k.facebook
Touring: No
Regular venues: capacity 135

Gravity Feed
Website: www.gravityfeed.org
Email: info@gravityfeed.org
Phone: 295 697 800
Address: Studio 22, 142 Addison Road,, AU
Information: Since 1992 Gravity Feed has evolved a unique architectural performance-theatre, employing large sets to create potent, subversive and densely atmospheric events. Its imPressive body of haunting work in which movement, objects, sound, light and the audience are equal partners traverses visual arts, architecture, and theatre.
Country: Australia
Touring: No

Gravity Feed
Website: www.gravityfeed.org
Email: info@gravityfeed.org
Address: Studio 22, Addison Road Centre, 142 Addison Road, Sydney, AU
Country: Australia
Touring: No

Griffin Theatre Company
Website: www.griffintheatre.com.au
Email: info@griffintheatre.com.au
Phone: 293 321 052
Address: 13 Craigend Street, AU
Information: Griffin is the only theatre company in the country entirely devoted to new Australian plays. Located in the historic SBW Stables Theatre, nestled in the heart of bustling Kings Cross, Griffin has been a permanent home for the exploration of Australian stories since 1978.
Country: Australia
Contact: Chair Bruce Meagher
Email: info@griffintheatre.com.au
CEO & Artistic Director
Declan Greene
Email: info@griffintheatre.com.au
Social Media: twitter.com/griffintheatrewww.facebook.com/GriffinTheatreCompanywww.instagram.com/griffintheatre/
Regular venues: 10999c08-dd85-4439-a7df-63bfd1ff-ca9d

Griffin Theatre Company
Website: www.griffintheatre.com.au
Email: info@griffintheatre.com.au
Phone: 293 321 052
Address: 13 Craigend Street, AU
Information: Located in the heart of Kings Cross—in the historic SBW Stables, Theatre—Griffin has been dedicated to bringing the best Australian stories to the stage for the better part of four decades. It's passionate about theatre that's written by Australians, about Australians, for Australians to enjoy. Iconic Aussie plays such as The Boys, Holding the Man and The Heartbreak Kid all had their world premieres at Griffin.
Country: Australia
Contact: Chair Bruce Meagher
Contact: Artistic Director Lee Lewis
Contact: project Manager Lyndell Droga
Social Media: @griffintheatrewww.facebook.com/GriffinTheatreCompany
Touring: No
Regular venues: The SBW Stables Theatre 105 seats

Grin and Tonic Theatre Troupe
Website: www.grinandtonictheatre.com.au
Email: kellie@grinandtonictheatre.com.au
Phone: 731 616 926
Address: 4 Lynwood Court, Ferny Hills, AU
Information: Grin and Tonic has been serving the State of Queensland in Australia for over forty years. At the helm of Queensland theatre, the company delivered the inaugural production of the Queensland Theatre Company in 1969, Peter Shaffer's The Royal Hunt of the Sun

Country: Australia
Contact: General Manager Kelli Lazarus
Contact: Artistic Director Jason Klarwein
Contact: assistant Director Travis Dowling
Social Media: www.facebook.com/grinandtonictheatretroupe/
Touring: No

Hayman Theatre Company
Website: haymantheatre.curtin.edu.au
Email: L.Brennan@curtin.edu.au
Phone: 892 667 088
Address: Kent Street, AU
Information: The Theatre Arts course opened in 1973 and was based in Hayman Hall at what was then WAIT (the Western Australian Institute of Technology). The course initially supported two resident theatre companies, a student company Theatregoround and a professional company WATC (the Western Australia Theatre Company). Both the course and the companies were originally led by Senior Lecturer and Artistic Director David Addenbrooke.
Country: Australia
Contact: Administration officer Leigh Brennan
Email: L.Brennan@curtin.edu.au
Social Media: @HaymanTheatrewww.facebook.com/HaymanTheatre
Touring: No
Regular venues: Theatre Upstairs 70

HotHouse Theatre
Website: www.hothousetheatre.com.au
Email: info@hothousetheatre.com.au
Phone: 260 217 433
Address: Gateway Island, Lincoln Causeway, AU
Information: Victoria's third largest professional theatre company, and is acknowledged as Australia's leading regional company. It conducts an annual subscription season and it aims to support the development of new Australian theatre. It manages a popular national residency project ' a month in the country' to support the development of new work.
Country: Australia
Contact: Chair Paul McGil
Artistic Director & co-CEO
Lyn Wallis
General Manager & co-CEO
Julie Amos
Social Media: @hothousetheatrewww.facebook.com/HotHouseTheatreAlburyWodonga
Touring: Nationally
Regular venues: Butter Factory Theatre, Gateway Island, Wodonga 167

Hoy Polloy Theatre
Website: hoypolloy.com.au
Email: hoypolloy@hotmail.com
Phone: 411 029 393
Address: AU
Information: Committed to staging plays that mainstream companies often ignore, Hoy Polloy also produce quality new works from Australian playwrights which engender a community spirit. We believe it is important to present plays which are vital, vibrant and challenging – not only for our audiences, but also for our casts and crews.
Country: Australia
Contact: Artistic Director Wayne Pearn
Contact: Associate Director Ben Starick
Social Media: @HoyPolloyProdwww.facebook.com/Hoy-Polloy-Theatre-795271413839328
Touring: Nationally
Regular venues: Mechanics Institute Performing Arts Centre

Ilbijerri Theatre Company
Website: ilbijerri.com.au
Email: info@ilbijerri.com.au
Phone: 393 299 097
Address: 5 Blackwood Street, AU
Information: ILBIJERRI's plays explore a range of complex and controversial issues from a uniquely Aboriginal and Torres Strait Islander perspective. Our work possesses the power to reach out and remind audiences of every person's need for family, history and heritage. Since commissioning and producing Jane Harrison's renowned classic STOLEN in 1992, the company has toured nationally and internationally, finding critical acclaim and resonance with both Indigenous and non-Indigenous audiences alike. Member of ISPA.
Country: Australia
Contact: Artistic Director Rachael Maza
Contact: company Manager Lauren Bok
Contact: finance Manager Jon Hawkes
Contact: Executive Producer Simeon Moran
Contact: President Gavin Somers
Social Media: @Ilbijerriwww.facebook.com/ilbijerri
Touring: No

Just Us Theatre Ensemble (JUTE)
Website: www.jute.com.au
Email: info@jute.com.au
Phone: 740 509 444
Address: 96 Abbott Street, AU

Information: JUTE came into being in 1992 when three passionate theatre makers living in Cairns met and creative sparks began to fly. JUTE's vision to enrich the world through theatre is put into practice every day as they flame the fires of creativity in regional theatre-makers, providing unfettered opportunities for the development and production of inspired new works that radiate the social space and ignite the imagination of the region.
Country: Australia
Contact: Artistic Director Suellen Maunder
Email: suellen@jute.com.au
Contact: Marketing Manager Peta Cooke
Email: peta@jute.com.au
Social Media: @JUTETheatrehttp://www.facebook.com/JUTETheatre
Touring: No
Regular venues: Centre of Contemporary Arts (CoCA)

Kinetic Energy Theatre Company Inc. & Kinetic Jazz
Website: www.kineticenergytheatre.org
Email: kineticenergy@iprimus.com.au
Phone: 296 656 489
Address: 1/54A, Mount St, Coogee, AU
Information: Kinetic Energy Theatre Company is a inter-disciplinary theatre company based in Sydney, Australia, and has been operational since 1975. It embraces all the arts as a platform for exploration, creation, performance and cultural engagement. The company tackles challenging subject matter and social justice issues, daring to marry the Artistic and the political. Committed to making a difference, Kinetic Energy looks for and indeed provides alternatives, both in its structure and its outreach. It's current workshop project OASIZ explores Deep Listening & healing through the arts.
Country: Australia
Contact: co-Director Jepke Goudsmit
Email: kineticenergygj@iprimus.com.au
Contact: co-Director Graham Jones
Social Media: www.facebook.com/KineticEnergyTheatreInc
Touring: No
St Luke's Hall Enmore

Kite Theatre
Website: www.qpac.com.au
Email: rti@qpac.com.au
Phone: 136 246
Address: Cnr Grey Street, AU
Information: KITE Program at QPAC is an early childhood arts education initiative of Education Queensland in partnership with QPAC. KITE delivers relevant contemporary arts education experiences for Prep to Year Three students and their teachers across Queensland.
Country: Australia
Contact: Associate Director Angela Slater
Contact: advertising Manager Judy Worsfold
Email: judy.worsfold@qpac.com.au
Social Media: @QPACwww.facebook.com/atQPAC
Touring: No
Regular venues: schools, theatres, outdoor venues

Kooemba Jdarra – Indigenous Performing Arts
Website: www.kooemba.com.au
Email: info@kooemba.com.au
Phone: 732 571 433
Address: 420 Brunswick Street, Fortitude Valley, AU
Information: Incorporated in 1993 and based in Brisbane, Kooemba Jdarra Indigenous Performing Arts produces contemporary performances that present the stories of Aboriginal Australians throughout Australia and internationally. Kooemba Jdarra is a not-for-profit organisation that receives funding from the government and corporate sponsors. Kooemba Jdarra also receives ongoing support from the Aboriginal community.
Country: Australia
Contact: Artistic Director Wesley Enoch
Touring Countries: United Kingdom, Switzerland, Korea
Touring: No
Regular venues: small to medium audience sizes

Kurruru Indigenous Youth Performing Arts Inc
Website: www.kurruru.org.au
Email: kurruru@chariot.net.au
Phone: 883 411 150
Address: 135 St Vincent Street, AU
Information: Kurruru Youth Performing Arts Inc (Kurruru) is one of Australia's leading Aboriginal and Torres Strait Islander youth performing arts programmes. It is committed to supporting the ongoing maintenance of culture, community and identity through the provision of quality performing arts opportunities for children, young people and their communities. Working through a diverse array of performing art forms including: dance, song, circus, music and comedy, informed by innovative community cultural development practices, Kurruru is a nationally recognised leader in the creation of contemporary Aboriginal and Torres Strait Islander performance.
Country: Australia
Contact: company Manager Diana Sautelle
Contact: Artistic Director Deon Hastie
Social Media:
www.facebook.com/kurruru
Touring: No

La Boite Theatre Company
Website: www.laboite.com.au
Email: info@laboite.com.au
Phone: 730 078 600
Address: The Works Level, 6-8 Musk Avenue, AU
Information: La Boite is a story of people, passion, purpose and place. They hold a unique place in the hearts and minds of artists and audiences in Brisbane. For the past nine decades La Boite has represented the adventurous and alternative. There has always been a strong focus on the development of new work and artists, and today it is no different. Theatre has the capacity to embrace difference in so many ways.
Country: Australia
Contact: Artistic Director David Berthold
Email: David@laboite.com.au
Contact: General Manager Rhys Holden
Email: rhys@laboite.com.au
Contact: Chair Julian Myers
Artistic Director & CEO
Todd MacDonald
Social Media: @LaBoiteTheatrewww.facebook.com/LaBoiteTheatreCompany
Touring: No
Regular venues: Roundhouse Theatre 400

Legs on the Wall
Website: www.legsonthewall.com.au
Email: admin@legsonthewall.com.au
Phone: 295 609 479
Address: 91 Canal Road, Lilyfield, AU
Information: The thriving heart of physical theatre in Australia, Legs are known nationally and internationally for their bold exuberance, and their stories told with depth, humour and intelligence. Celebrating and exploring the capacity of the physical body in motion, it uses physical metaphor to explore stories. Narrative text based stories, visual stories, abstract stories; all are linked by the body and its capabilities as the central vehicle for making work.
Country: Australia
Contact: admininstrator / venue coordinator Skadi Nova
Email: admin@legsonthewall.com.au
Contact: Senior Creative Producer Cecily Hardy
Email: Producer@legsonthewall.com.au
Contact: co Artistic Director Lee-Anne Litton
Contact: Co Artistic Director Joshua Thomson
Email: joshua@legsonthewall.com.au
Social Media: @LegsOnTheWallwww.facebook.com/pages/Legs-On-The-Wall/51529807530
Touring: No

Malthouse Theatre
Website: www.malthousetheatre.com.au
Email: admin@malthousetheatre.com.au
Phone: 396 855 111
Address: 113 Sturt St Southbank, AU
Information: At Malthouse Theatre they collaborate with local and international artists to create inventive performances that cut to the core of the human experience. Theatre has the power to interrogate, disrupt and to be an agent of change. At Malthouse Theatre the work they produce explores the world personally, socially and politically. Based in a dedicated venue, The Coopers Malthouse in Melbourne, they are a home for live experiences that entertain and provoke a dialogue with and within audiences.
Country: Australia
Contact: CEO Matthew Lutton
Contact: finance Manager Mario Agostinoni
Contact: General Manager Amanda Macri
Social Media: @MalthouseMelbwww.facebook.com/MalthouseTheatre
Touring Countries: China, India and Mexico
Touring: No
Regular venues: Merlyn Theatre up to 499, Beckett Theatre up to 198, Bagging Room up to 180 and Tower Room up to 100. Note :All dependent on the size of production.

Marguerite Pepper Productions
Website: www.mpproductions.com.au
Email: info@mpproductions.com.au
Phone: 412 231 313
Address: PO Box 7293, AU
Information: Founded by Marguerite Pepper in 1989, MPP is an independent production company based in Sydney, Australia. MPP is dedicated to supporting artists and ensembles in the creation of their work, from inception through to production and touring, in Australia and internationally.
Country: Australia
Contact: Managing Director Marguerite Pepper
Email: marguerite@mpproductions.com.au
Touring: No

Marian Street Theatre for Young People – MSTYP
Website: www.mstyp.org.au
Email: info@mstyp.org.au
Phone:
294 111 800
Address: Suite 214, 75 Archer St, AU
Information: MSTYP produces original plays for children, developed from classic fairy tales and contemporary stories

Melbourne Theatre Company
Website: www.mtc.com.au
Email: info@mtc.com.au
Phone: 386 880 800
Address: 140 Southbank Blvd, AU
Information: MTC is Melbourne's home of live storytelling, producing an annual mainstage season of up to 12 plays, NEON Festival of Independent Theatre, the Cybec Electric play readings series, an annual education programme, and more. MTC is one of the major performing arts companies in Australia, and one of the largest theatre companies in the English-speaking world. Founded in 1953, MTC is also the oldest professional theatre company in Australia, and currently exists as a semi-autonomous department of the University of Melbourne. Member of ISPA.
Country: Australia
Contact: Artistic Director Brett Sheehy
Contact: Chair Terry Moran
Contact: Executive Director Virginia Lovett
Contact: Executive administrator Annie Bourke
Social Media: @MelbTheatreCowww.facebook.com/MelbourneTheatreCompany
Touring: No
Regular venues: Southbank Theatre, The Sumner (500 seats); Southbank Theatre, The Lawler (150 seats); Arts Centre Melbourne, Playhouse (850 seats) and Arts Centre Melbourne, Fairfax Studio (350 seats).

Melbourne Writers Theatre
Website: melbournewriterstheatre.org.au
Email: melbournewriterstheatre@gmail.com
Phone: 417 912 718
Address: 349 Drummond St, AU
Information: The Melbourne Writers' Theatre's core activity is script development, which is furthered by means of panel discussions, readings and workshopping of plays by professional Directors and actors.
Country: Australia
Contact: Artistic Director Christine Croyden
Contact: stage Manager Mazz Ryan
Contact: company Manager Clare Mendes
Contact: Director Elizabeth Walley
Social Media: @melbwriters
Touring: No
Regular venues: Carlton Courthouse Theatre 100

Merrigong Theatre Company
Website: merrigong.com.au
Email: info@merrigong.com.au
Phone: 242 245 959
Address: 32 Burelli St, AU
Information: Merrigong Theatre Company manages one of Australia's busiest, most dynamic regional venues – Illawarra Performing Arts Centre (IPAC) in Wollongong is about an hour south of Sydney. The company also manages the city's key civic and community venue, the Wollongong Town Hall.
Since 2005, under Artistic Director Simon Hinton, Merrigong has developed into a vibrant theatre company in its own right, producing, presenting and touring exciting contemporary theatre and supporting the development of a wide range of theatre-makers. Member of ISPA
Country: Australia
Contact: Chairman Wayne Morris
Contact: CEO and Artistic Director Simon Hinton
Contact: General Manager Pauline Doyle
Social Media: @Merrigongwww.facebook.com/Merrigong
Touring Countries: USA, Ireland Canada
Touring: No

My Darling Patricia
Website: www.mydarlingpatricia.com
Email: info@mydarlingpatricia.com
Phone: 293 577 857
Address: PO Box 1711, AU
Information: My Darling Patricia's work is inspired by photographs and found objects; the detritus and residue of stories. The company name comes from one such find – a 60 year old secret love letter found inside the lining of an old vanity set. MDP creates work that pushes the boundaries of contemporary Australian theatre and invites audiences to step inside their inventive highly visual storytelling style.
Country: Australia
Manager & Producer
Marguerite Pepper
Email: marguerite@mpproductions.com.au
Contact: Artistic Director Clare Britton
Email: clare@mydarlingpatricia.com
Contact: Manager Julianne Campbell
Social Media: @MyDarlingPats
Touring: Nationally and Internationally

New Theatre
Website: www.newtheatre.org.au
Email: mail@newtheatre.org.au
Phone: 295 193 403
Address: 542 King Street, Newtown, AU
Information: New Theatre was set up in 1932 as the Sydney Workers Art Club, opening with the slogan "Art is a Weapon".

Country: Australia
Contact: theatre Manager Gemma Greer
Email: Manager@newtheatre.org.au
Contact: Artistic Director Louise Fischer
Email: Artistic@newtheatre.org.au
Contact: President Rosane McNamara
Email: President@newtheatre.org.au
Contact: publicist Alice Livingstone
Email: publicity@newtheatre.org.au
Social Media: @newtheatrewww.facebook.com/
NewTheatreSydney
Touring: No
Regular venues: New Theatre

Northern Rivers Performing Arts (NORPA)
Website: www.norpa.org.au
Email: info@norpa.org.au
Phone: 266 220 300
Address: 1 Bounty St, AU
Information: NORPA is a leading regional theatre company, based in the Northern Rivers region of NSW. It creates and produces its own work, as well as presenting dynamic theatre from some of Australia's best performing arts companies. Its home is the Lismore City Hall.
Country: Australia
Contact: Artistic Director Julian Louis
Contact: General Manager Patrick Healey
Contact: Chair David Wolff
Contact: vice Chair Peter Wood
Social Media: @NORPAOzwww.facebook.com/norpa.lismore
Touring Countries: UK
Touring: No
Regular venues: Lismore City Hall 664

Oxford Children's Live Theatre
Email: gypsy@gypsylefay.com
Phone: 398 983 248
Address: c/o Oxford & Station Streets, AU
Information: Oxford Children's Theatre is a theatre for everyone. It presents and produces a wide range of live performances.
Country: Australia
Contact: Artistic Director Joy Mudge
Touring: No

PACT centre for emerging artists
Website: www.pact.net.au
Email: pact@pact.net.au
Phone: 295 502 744
Address: 107 Railway Parade, AU
Information: PACT centre for emerging artists is the launching pad for the next generation of cultural leaders. It is at the forefront of innovation and groundbreaking performances. PACT is the nerve centre connecting artists, audiences, community and businesses. PACT works with and supports emerging artists working in contemporary and experimental performance. They define "emerging" as an artist in their first 5 years of professional practice. PACT is where artists build sustainable professional careers
Country: Australia
Contact: board member Dee Jefferson
CEO & Artistic Director
Katrina Douglas
Contact: General Manager Danielle Taylor
Contact: Chair Brer Adams
Social Media: @PACTSydneywww.facebook.com/pact-centreforemergingartists
Touring: No

Paperbag Theatre Company
Phone: 618 837 98030
Address: 26 Watson Street, AU
Information: specialising in history of Asian puppetry using lecture/demonstration suitable for schools and universities
Country: Australia
Contact: Artistic Director Karel Rehorek
Touring: No

Patch Theatre Company
Website: www.patchtheatre.org.au
Email: patch@patchtheatre.org.au
Phone: 884 700 165
Address: AU
Information: Patch Theatre Company has a diverse repertoire of acclaimed, tour-ready productions for 4-8 year olds and their families. The company is based in Adelaide, South Australia and has presented over 100 new productions to more than 1.8 million children and their families since it began in 1972.
Country: Australia
Contact: Artistic Director Geoff Cobham
Contact: Company Manager Penny Camens
Social Media: @patchtheatrecompany
Touring Countries: US, Canada, Singapore, Korea, Japan and New Zealand
Touring: Nationally and Internationally

Performing Lines Ltd
Website: www.performinglines.org.au
Email: Administration@performinglines.org.au
Phone: 293 190 066

Address: Suite 5, 245 Chalmers Street, AU
Information: Performing Lines Ltd draw on over 30 years of experience to foster innovation and creativity in live performance. They don't shy away from difficult, risky or Artistically challenging work, taking an adaptive rather than reactive approaches to all that they do.
Country: Australia
Contact: Executive Producer Marion Potts
Contact: General Manager Megan Roberts
Contact: Producer Narelle Lewis
Contact: Marketing Manager Thom Smyth
Social Media: @Performinglineswww.facebook.com/PerformingLines
Touring: No

Perth Theatre Company
Website: www.perththeatre.com.au
Email: contact@perththeatre.com.au
Phone: 862 129 399
Address: 178 William Street, AU
Information: Perth Theatre is a community theatre group, based in W.A. It aims to provide a platform for local community members to showcase their talents and get involved in creative theatre, drama and the arts. Each year Perth Theatre puts on two theatre performances. At the start of the year it has their adult show targeted at people aged 18+. At the end of the year they host their youth show targeted for ages 10—17. It prides itself on producing original productions and is constantly looking for people wanting to write or direct.
Country: Australia
Contact: Artistic Director Melissa Cantwell
Touring: No
Regular venues: Playhouse Theatre 427, and small contemporary venues in and around the city of Perth.

Q Theatre Company
Website: thejoan.com.au/about-us/the-q
Phone: 247 237 623
Address: PO Box 10, AU
Information: The Q is a contemporary theatre production programme based at the Joan Sutherland Performing Arts Centre, Penrith. The Q has evolved from the creative lineage of The Q Theatre Company and its more than fifty years of commitment to the presentation and production of new theatre works.
Country: Australia
Contact: Manager Emily Ayoub
Touring: No
Regular venues: Q Theatre 273

Queensland Theatre Company (QTC)
Website: www.queenslandtheatre.com.au
Email: mail@queenslandtheatre.com.au
Phone: 730 107 600
Address: 78 Montague Road, AU
Information: Queensland Theatre is the state's flagship professional theatre company. They present an annual season of plays every year featuring comedies, classics and new Australian work. They inspire and educate young people through school performances, workshops, and teacher training.
Country: Australia
Contact: Chairwoman Elizabeth Jameson
Contact: Artistic Director Sam Strong
Contact: Executive Director Sue Donnelly
Contact: finance Manager Valerie Cole
Social Media: @qldtheatrewww.facebook.com/qldtheatre
Touring: No
Regular venues: Cremorne Theatre 250, Playhouse Theatre 850, Bille Brown Studio 250

Ranters Theatre
Website: ranterstheatre.com
Email: info@ranterstheatre.com
Phone: 405 342 576
Address: Unit 6, 76-80 Grey St, St Kilda VIC 3182, Australia
Information: Established in 1994, Ranters Theatre was founded by graduates of the Victorian College of the Arts, Melbourne. Since that time the company has created over fifteen critically acclaimed productions, toured Europe extensively since 1999, and has been programmed in numerous international arts festivals. Member of ISPA.
Country: Australia
Contact: Artistic Director Adriano Cortese
Email: adriano@ranterstheatre.com
Contact: Executive Producer Robina Burton
Email: robina@ranterstheatre.com
Social Media: www.facebook.com/RantersTheatre/https://twitter.com/ranters_theatrewww.instagram.com/ranterstheatre/
Touring: Internationally

RIOT – Regionally Inspired Oz Theatre (formerly Mainstreet Theatre)
Website: www.mstc.com.au
Email:
mainstreet@dodo.com.au
Phone:
618 872 53015
Address:

PO Box 416, AU
Information: professional theatre company; produces dynamic, innovative, theatre informed and inspired by the region; workshops, touring shows, one-off performances and large scale community productions; visiting address: 'Varcoes', 12 Ferrers St, Mount Gambier SA 529
Country: Australia
Contact: Administration Fiona Rochow
Contact: business Manager Mark Stratford
Contact: Artistic Director t.b.a.
Contact: audience development officer Danni Jones
Touring: No

Riverland Youth Theatre
Website: ryt.org.au
Email: admin@ryt.org.au
Phone: 885 863 437
Address: 54 Ral Ral Ave, AU
Information: The Riverland Youth Theatre has a long history of engaging young Riverlanders in the ARTs, helping to enrich their lives whilst supporting and developing their creativity and Artistic exPression. Many of their region's community leaders today can tell a story or two of their involvement with the Riverland Youth Theatre during their formative years. In fact, the positive impact that the arts can have on young lives is well documented in providing vital support to build self-esteem, confidence, critical thinking skills and cultural understanding, as well as important skills to help shape the leaders of tomorrow.
Country: Australia
Contact: General Manager Danyon De Buell
Contact: Artistic Director Celeste Cody
Contact: Chairperson Cathy Schier
Contact: vice Chairperson Ed Cottam
Social Media: www.facebook.com/riverlandyouththeatre
Touring: No

Shakespeare Globe Centre Australia
Website: www.shakespeareglobe.org.au
Email: globeshakespeare@gmail.com
Phone: 293 515 231
Address: Old Teachers College, Room 426 The University Of Sydney, AU
Information: An educational and performance based organisation affiliated with Shakespeare's Globe in London.
Country: Australia
Touring: No

Shopfront Theatre for Young People
Website: www.shopfront.org.au
Email: hello@shopfront.org.au
Phone: 295 883 948
Address: 88 Carlton Parade, AU
Information: All young people have something to say and at Shopfront, they make sure everyone's voices are heard. Shopfront is a space where young people come together to exPress themselves. To learn, share and bring their imaginations to life. It is a space for celebrating the amazing ideas and creativity generated by young people and emerging artists.
Country: Australia
Contact: CEO Daniel Potter
Email: daniel.potter@shopfront.org.au
Contact: outreach Director Hannah Grant
Email: outreach@shopfront.org.au
Contact: creative Producer Natalie Rose
Email: natalie.rose@shopfront.org.au
Social Media: @shopfrontartswww.facebook.com/ShopfrontArts
Touring: No
Regular venues: capacity 150

Sidetrack Performance Group Ltd
Website: www.sidetrack.com.au
Email: info@sidetrack.com.au
Phone: 295 601 255
Address: 9/142 Addison Rd, AU
Information: The Sidetrack Theatre is a rustic and intimate 150-seat capacity performance space situated in the Inner-west's Addison Rd Centre Complex, Marrickville. The space has a large stage area (up to 8 x 9 metres) with excellent acoustics and sight lines. It is ideally suited to both small and medium theatrical productions and shows in development. It is also well set up to cater for community based productions. Sidetrack Theatre comes complete with onsite parking and a full support team behind each area, from ticketing through to Marketing & production.
Country: Australia
Social Media: www.facebook.com/pages/Sidetrack-Theatre/121568581206320
Touring: No
Regular venues: Sidetrack Studio Theatre 150

Slack Taxi
Website: www.slacktaxi.com.au
Email: jen@slacktaxi.com.au
Phone: 419 822 327
Address: PO Box 490, AU
Information: Don't be deceived by the name – Slack Taxi is a hard working production company and agent, able to offer your event some of Australia's best circus, stilt and street performers from Adelaide, Sydney, Mel-

bourne, Brisbane, Perth and Hobart
Country: Australia
Contact: Artistic Director Jen Martin
Email: jen@slacktaxi.com.au
Contact: Manager Meredith Banks
Email: Manager@slacktaxi.com.au
Social Media: @slacktaxiwww.facebook.com/slacktax-inews
Touring: No
mainly outdoors at major festivals & events

Southern Edge Arts
Website: www.southernedge.org.au
Email: seamail@southernedge.org.au
Phone: 898 416 002
Address: 77 Sanford Road, AU
Information: For the last 29 years, SEA has been a champion of creativity and quality arts practice in young people, building community and encouraging diversity. SEA has grown to become Western Australia's largest regional youth performance organisation and has developed a unique approach to skills development and performance making that encourages participation and validates the contribution of young people working with professional artists.
Country: Australia
Contact: Artistic Director Anne Sorenson
Contact: Chairperson Cathy Glen
Social Media: @southernedgeartwww.facebook.com/southern.edge
Touring: No

Southern Youth Theatre Ensemble (SYTE)
Website: www.syte.org.au
Email: russell@rdlj.net
Phone: 883 846 744
Address: 22 Gawler Street, AU
Information: Southern Youth Theatre Ensemble (SYTE) is a valued innovative and sustainable youth theatre ensemble committed to pursuing the principles of inclusion and best practice in a collaborative and professional environment.
Country: Australia
Touring: No
Regular venues: Noarlunga Community Arts Centre 120, Queens Theatre, various open space, schools

Spare Parts Puppet Theatre
Website: www.sppt.asn.au
Email: admin@sppt.asn.au
Phone: 893 355 044
Address: 1 Short St, Fremantle
Information: Spare Parts Puppet Theatre is Australia's flagship puppetry company dedicated to the development and creation of the art form. Through puppetry they share stories that celebrate what it is to be human; connecting audiences across generations.
Country: Australia
Contact: Artistic Director Philip Mitchell
Contact: Associate Director Michael Barlow
Social Media: www.facebook.com/sparepartspuppetstwitter.com/sparepartpuppetwww.instagram.com/sparepartspuppets/
Touring: Nationally and Internationally
Regular venues: acf09944-1f6b-4f50-b222-9ba31210f3f4

Sport for Jove
Website: www.sportforjove.com.au
Email: admin@sportforjove.com.au
Phone: 289 701 921
Address: 8 Marlborough St., AU
Information: Sport For Jove Theatre is dedicated to the production of passionate and innovative staging of the works of William Shakespeare and other classical theatre. Sport for Jove Theatre is the company behind the Sydney Hills Shakespeare in the Park (Nov/Dec), The Leura Shakespeare Festival (Jan) & Shakespeare in the Botanic Garden (Feb/March), as well as work in Sydney's established theatre venues.
Country: Australia
Contact: Chairman Gordon Stalley
Contact: Managing Director Damien Ryan
Contact: finance Director Gai Strouthos
Social Media: @SportforJovewww.facebook.com/sport-forjovetheatre
Touring: No

Stalker Theatre Company
Website: www.stalker.com.au
Email: admin@stalker.com.au
Phone: 290 436 908
Address: Level 2, 71-73 Chandos Street, AU
Information: Stalker Theatre is one of Australia's pre-eminent physical theatre companies. Founded in 1989, it celebrates over two decades of outstanding achievement in the production of innovative, inter-disciplinary, physical and visual theatre. Stalker makes high quality contemporary physical theatre in Australia across a range of cultural, social and political contexts, regions and nations, and delivers its work to extraordinarily diverse audiences. Its striking physical and visual productions communicate powerfully and imaginatively far beyond the constraints of traditional theatrical contexts.
Country: Australia

Contact: Director David Clarkson
Social Media: www.facebook.com/stalkertheatre
Touring: No
Regular venues: outdoor, site specific theatre spectacle, street theatre

State Theatre Company of South Australia (STCSA)
Website: www.statetheatrecompany.com.au
Email: info@statetheatrecompany.com.au
Phone: 884 155 333
Address: Fowlers Building, Corner Morphett Street and North Terrace, AU
Information: State Theatre Company of South Australia is the state's flagship professional theatre company performing an annual season of classic and contemporary Australian and international theatre works at its main performance home – the Dunstan Playhouse. The Company is a major community and cultural resource for all South Australians and is vital to Artistic life in the state.
Country: Australia
Contact: Artistic Director Geordie Brookman
Contact: Executive Director Jodi Glass
Contact: Chair Justin Jamieson
Social Media: @statetheatresawww.facebook.com/StateTheatreSA
Touring: No
Regular venues: Dunstan Playhouse, Space Theatre, The Amphitheatre

Sydney Theatre Company
Website: www.sydneytheatre.com.au
Email: mail@sydneytheatre.com.au
Phone: 925 01777
Address: Pier 4, Hickson Road, AU
Information: This leading Australian arts organisation has been a major force in Australian drama since its establishment in 1979. Sydney Theatre Company was formed in December 1978, following the closure of The Old Tote Theatre Company the month before. The then Premier, the Hon, Neville Wran, approached Elizabeth Butcher who had been seconded from NIDA to administer the Old Tote, and asked her to set up a new state theatre company, to perform in the Drama Theatre of the Sydney Opera House.
Country: Australia
Contact: Chair Ian Narev
Contact: Artistic Director Kip Williams
Contact: Executive Director Patrick McIntyre
Social Media: @SydneyTheatreCowww.facebook.com/SydneyTheatreCompany
Touring: No
Regular venues: Canberra Theatre Centre; Perth Festival; IPAC Wollongong; Riverside Parramatta ; Barking Gecko Theatre Company Perth; Adelaide Festival Centre and others

Tasmanian Theatre Company
Website: www.tastheatre.com
Email: info@tastheatre.com
Phone: 362 348 561
Address: Level 3, 77 Salamanca Place, AU
Information: The Tasmanian Theatre Company was launched on 27 May, 2008 by the Deputy Premier of Tasmania, the Hon, Lara Giddings MHA and luminous and internationally regarded actress, Essie Davis. The company produce and facilitate exceptional theatrical experiences and aim to inspire and entertain audiences, enrich and invigorate the community and support Tasmanian artists.
Country: Australia
Contact: administrator assistant Christine Bowling
Email: christine@tastheatre.com
Contact: Artistic Director / CEO Charles Parkinson
Email: charles@tastheatre.com
Contact: technical Manager Max Ford
Social Media: @tastheatrewww.facebook.com/tastheatre
Touring Countries: Korea, throughout Australia, regionally within Tasmania.
Touring: No
Some in-theatre & site-specific performances. Manage the Backspace Theatre – seats 120

Theatre Guild
Website: www.adelaide.edu.au/theatreguild
Phone: 883 035 999
Address: Level 5, Union House, University of Adelaide, AU
Information: The University of Adelaide Theatre Guild ('the Guild') is a not-for-profit community theatre company located at the University of Adelaide's North Terrace campus. The Guild is the second oldest amateur theatre company in South Australia, celebrating its 80th anniversary in 2018. This longevity in itself is exceptional but what is remarkable at the Guild is the pivotal role it has and continues to play in the development of both amateur and professional theatre in Adelaide and in Australia.
Country: Australia
Contact: board member Tim Allan
Touring: No

Tiny Top, The
Email: info@tinytop.com.au

Phone: 733 692 003
Address: 355 Simpsons Road, AU
Information: A hit at major festivals around Australia and South East Asia. Soon to tour Europe and the world. Affordable and popular. What goes on on the inside is a important what you see on the outside.
Country: Australia
Contact: Director Tony Rooke
Touring: No
Regular venues: We have our own venue. Chech our web site for details: www.tinytop.com.au

Urban Theatre Projects Ltd
Website: www.urbantheatre.com.au
Email: mail@urbantheatre.com.au
Phone: 297 072 111
Address: 5 Olympic Parade, AU
Information: Urban Theatre Projects creates distinctive new performances for Australian and international audiences that reflect stories and images of contemporary life. Engaging with diverse cultures and communities, the company explores new territory in contemporary theatre.
Country: Australia
Contact: Artistic Director Rosie Dennis
Social Media: @UTProjectswww.facebook.com/UT-Projects
Touring Countries: Canada, Belgium and South Africa
Touring: No

Van Egmond Group
Website: www.vanegmond.com.au
Email: admin@vanegmond.com.au
Phone: 398 674 333
Address: Level 1, 448 St Kilda Road, AU
Information: VEG and its Managing Director, Garry Van Egmond are synonymous with high quality and hugely successful shows, Marketing, logistics and production with a history built on relationships. An independent market leader for more than 40 years in touring, special events, event merchandising, Marketing, ticketing and promotion, they have a 'hands on' approach and have presented and produced some of Australia's largest entertainment events. Specialising in concerts, exhibitions, theatre, merchandising and special events, it has established itself as a leader in entertainment worldwide.
Country: Australia
Contact: commercial Director Christo Van Egmond
Contact: Managing Director Garry   van Egmond Europe, ew Zealand, China, Hong Kong, Singapore, Malaysia, Korea, Taiwan & Japan

Touring: No

Vitalstatistix National Women's Theatre
Website: www.vitalstatistix.com.au
Email: admin@vitalstatistix.com.au
Phone: 884 476 211
Address: Waterside Hall, 11 Nile Street, AU
Information: Vitalstatistix is a South Australian contemporary arts organisation with a focus on the development of multidisciplinary artworks, which experiment with ideas, forms and engagement. They provide a site for big ideas and intimate experiences, for long-term development and hothouse intensity, for contemporary art and community life.
Country: Australia
Contact: Director Emma Webb
Contact: production Manager Emma O'Neill
Contact: operations Manager Toby Nevill
Contact: Chair Narelle Walker
Social Media: @vitalstatistix_www.facebook.com/VitalstatistixArts
Touring Countries: Indonesia, North America, New Zealand
Touring: No
Waterside Hall. Flexible performance and rehearsal space, no fixed seating, 'old style community hall'. Maximum capacity 400.

Windmill Theatre
Website: www.windmill.org.au
Email: info@windmill.org.au
Phone: 882 107 200
Address: 2/234 Sturt Street, AU
Information: Empowered by a vision to be a leading centre for the creation of incredible theatrical works, Windmill is an ambitious and innovative company based in Adelaide, South Australia. It creates and presents unique and contemporary theatrical work for children, teens and families.
Country: Australia
Contact: Artistic Director Rosemary Myers
Contact: Executive Producer Kaye Weeks
Contact: business Manager Genevieve Booker
program & production Manager
Jason Warner
Marketing & development Manager
Adam Rossetto
Social Media: @WindmillTheatrehttp://www.facebook.com/windmilltheatre
Touring: No

Yirra Yaakin Aboriginal Corporation
Website: yirrayaakin.com.au
Email: yy@yirrayaakin.com.au
Phone: 893 803 040
Address: Subiaco Arts Centre, 180 Hamersley Rd, AU
Information: Yirra Yaakin (Yir-raarh Yaarh-kin] which means "Stand Tall" in Noongar language, is one of Australia's leading Aboriginal performing arts organisations producing award-winning, world-class theatre that is exciting, entertaining, educational, authentic and culturally appropriate. Established in 1993, the Year of Indigenous People, as Yirra Yaakin Noongar Theatre, they started off with one successful funding application, three staff members and the desire to provide the Aboriginal community with an Artistic outlet for positive self-determination.
Country: Australia
Contact: Artistic Director Kyle Morrison
Email: kyle@yirrayaakin.com.au
Contact: office Manager Judy Bone
Email: judy@yirrayaakin.com.au
Contact: Marketing Manager Andrea Fernandez
Email: Marketing@yirrayaakin.com.au
Contact: Chair Clem Rodney
Touring Countries: UK, China
Touring: No
Regular venues: varies from mainstage theatre to outdoor festivals

AZERBAIJAN

'YUGH' Theatre
Phone: 991 249 42890
Address: 83 Murtuz Muxtarov street, 1009, AZ
Country: Azerbaijan
Touring: No

Azerbaijan National State Theatre of Drama
Email: azdrama@azeurotel.com
Phone: 991 249 44939
Address: 1 Fizuli Square – 1000, AZ
Country: Azerbaijan
Contact: Director Makbet Bunyadov
Touring: No

Azerbaijan State Theatre for Young Spectators
Email: gtteatr@mail.ru
Address: 72 Nizami street, AZ
Country: Azerbaijan
Touring: No

Azerbaijan State Theatre of Russian Drama 'Samad Vurghun'
Website: www.rusdrama-az.com
Email: rdt@azdata.net
Phone: 124 934 048
Address: 7, Khagani St., 1000, AZ
Country: Azerbaijan
Contact: Director Aleksandr Sharovski
Touring: No

Azerbaijan State Youth Theatre
Phone: 991 249 32963
Address: 10 Hagani str.1000, AZ
Country: Azerbaijan
Contact: Director Huseynaga Atakishiyev
Touring: No

Ganja State Drama Theatre
Phone: 992 256 5888/18
Address: 54 A. Abbaszade Str. 2000, AZ
Country: Azerbaijan
Contact: Director Rafig Atakishiyev
Touring: No

Lyankaran State Drama Theatre
Phone: 991 715 4973
Address: 28 May St. 16, 4200, AZ
Country: Azerbaijan
Contact: Director Elshad Zeynalov
Touring: No

Mingyachevir State Drama Theatre
Phone: 991 475 2589
Address: 5 Gagarin St. 4500, AZ
Country: Azerbaijan
Touring: No

Nakchivan State Musical-Drama Theatre
Phone: 991 475 2589
Address: 2 Ahmad Javad str. 7000, AZ
Country: Azerbaijan
Touring: No

Poetry Theatre 'Nizamy'
Phone: 992 252 5188
Address: Baku St. 38, AZ
Country: Azerbaijan
Touring: No

Sheki State Drama Theatre
Phone: 991 773 661

Address: 174, Azadlyg St. 5500, AZ
Country: Azerbaijan

State Drama Music Theatre 'Arablinskiy'
Phone: 991 645 9121
Address: 21 Azerbaijan Ave, 5000, AZ
Country: Azerbaijan
Touring: No

State Theatre of Poetry 'Zardabi'
Phone: 992 256 4415
Address: 89 Zardabi Str., AZ
Country: Azerbaijan
Touring: No

Sumgait Music Drama Theatre
Phone: 991 645 9121
Address: 21, Azerbaijan Avenue 5000, AZ
Country: Azerbaijan
Contact: Director Shukurov Mehman
Touring: No

BRAZIL

Performas Produções
Website: www.performas.com.br
Email: contato@performas.com.br
Address: Rua Aureliano Coutinho 43/38, Vila Buarque, BR
Country: Brazil
Social Media: @performas_prodwww.facebook.com/performas
Touring: No

CANADA

2b Theatre Company
Website: www.2btheatre.com
Email: info@2btheatre.com
Phone: 902 453 6267
Address: 6068 Quinpool Road, CA
Information: strives to stimulate the mind and to awaken the spirit by producing theatre that is vital, innovative and challenging. Based in Halifax, Nova Scotia, 2b Theatre company creates, develops, and presents works for the regional, national, and international stages
Country: Canada
Contact: Artistic co-Director Christian Barry
Email: christian@2btheatre.com
Contact: Artistic co-Director Anthony Black
Email: anthony@2btheatre.com
Contact: Managing Director Colleen MacIsaac
Email: colleen@2btheatre.com
Social Media: @2btheatrewww.facebook.com/2btheatre
Touring: Nationally and Internationally
Regular venues: Neptune Theatre, Bus Stop Theatre

7 Fingers
Website: 7fingers.com
Phone: 514 521 4477
Address: 225, Roy E. Street, Office 205, CA
Information: The 7 Fingers is a collective that is at once unified and multi-faceted. In 2002, 7 circus artists came together and became The 7 Fingers. Over the course of 15 years, the collective has grown. Every year, projects have given way to new projects, as diverse as the very artists themselves. These include original productions, broadway shows, Artistic collaborations, project direction, custom designed events, performances for Olympic ceremonies, televised creations, immersive performance experiences and much more. Member of ISPA.
Country: Canada
Contact: Artistic Director Shana Carroll
Contact: chief Executive officer Nassib El-Husseini
Contact: administrative Director Richard Gagnon
Email: richard.gagnon@les7doigts.com
Contact: financial Director Lynne Ter Metz
Email: lynne.termetz@les7doigts.com
Contact: producing Director Luc Paradis
Email: luc.paradis@les7doigts.com
Social Media: @7doigtsdelamainwww.facebook.com/7doigts
Touring: No

Alberta Aboriginal Performing Arts
Website: albertaaboriginalarts.ca
Email: ababoriginalarts@gmail.com
Phone: 780 378 9609
Address: 8726 – 112 Avenue, CA
Information: ALBERTA ABORIGINAL ARTS is a registered, not-for profit Aboriginal Theatre and Performing Arts organization based in Edmonton, Alberta. Their mandate is to nurture and cultivate an Aboriginal arts scene in Edmonton by creating opportunities for Aboriginal artists, writers and performers to present their work to the public. They produce events that bring artists of multiple disciplines and Aboriginal traditions together. The goal is to encourage and inspire collaborations in art and performance in both contemporary and traditional styles and to bring these creations to audiences across Alberta. Member of ISPA
Country: Canada
Contact: Executive assistant Doreen Cardinal
Contact: Artistic Director Christine Frederick
Social Media: www.facebook.com/AlbertaAboriginalArts
Touring: No

Alberta Theatre Projects
Website: www.atplive.com
Email: info@atplive.com
Phone: 403 294 7475
Address: 220 – 9 Avenue SE, CA
Information: Alberta Theatre Projects is a Calgary-based, not-for-profit, professional theatre company that celebrates the art of live theatre. From its home in The Martha Cohen Theatre at Arts Commons, the company produces world-calibre shows with a focus on idea-driven new works, plays by Canadian playwrights, and contemporary theatre from around the world. It is also a national leader in new play development and dramaturgy.
Country: Canada
Director of finance & Administration Sharon Lensen
Email: slensen@ATPlive.com
Contact: Director of Artistic programming Laurel Green
Email: lgreen@ATPlive.com
Contact: Executive Director Vicki Stroich
Email: vstroich@atplive.com
Contact: Director of Marketing and communications Ashley Meller
Email: ameller@ATPlive.com
Social Media: @ATPlivewww.facebook.com/AlbertaTheatreProjects
Touring: No
Regular venues: Martha Cohen Theatre 400

Arts Club Theatre Company
Website: artsclub.com
Email: info@artsclub.com
Phone: 604 687 1644
Address: 203-162 W. 1st Avenue, CA
Information: The Arts Club Theatre Company, now in its 53rd season, is the largest theatre company in Western Canada. Each year, over a quarter of a million people experience the best in professional theatre at its three venues: the Stanley Industrial Alliance Stage, Granville Island Stage, and Revue Stage, as well as on tour throughout the province.
Country: Canada
Contact: Artistic Managing Director Bill Millerd
Email: ArtisticDirector@artsclub.com
Contact: Executive Director Peter Cathie White
Contact: Director of production Stephan Baeuml
Contact: Director of Sales and Marketing Bryan Woo
Social Media: @theArtsClubwww.facebook.com/theArtsClub
Touring: No
Regular venues: Stanley Industrial Alliance Stage 650; Granville Island Stage 450

Arts Commons
Website: www.artscommons.ca
Email: info@artscommons.ca
Phone: 403 294 7455
Address: 205 8th Avenue S.E., CA
Information: Arts Commons is an inspirational gathering place for all Calgarians and visitors alike. We are a space, both physical and metaphorical, that stimulate senses, trigger emotions, challenge assumptions, start conversations, and open minds. Member of ISPA
Country: Canada
Contact: CEO and President Johann Zietsman
Contact: Chair Henry Sykes
Social Media: @yycARTSwww.facebook.com/yycARTS
Touring: No

Belfry Theatre
Website: www.belfry.bc.ca
Email: hello@belfry.bc.ca
Phone: 250 385 6815
Address: 1291 Gladstone Avenue, CA
Information: a professional adult theatre company, dedicated to producing contemporary plays, with an emphasis on Canadian work, and to promoting Artistic, cultural, and educational events in the Greater Victoria Region
Country: Canada
Contact: production Manager Alex Currie
Email: alex.currie@belfry.bc.ca
Contact: General Manager Ivan Habel
Email: gm@belfry.bc.ca
Contact: Artistic Director Michael Shamata
Email: ad@belfry.bc.ca
Contact: financial officer Patricia O'Brien
Email: finance@belfry.bc.ca
Contact: Director of development Susan Stevenson
Email: susan.stevenson@belfry.bc.ca
Social Media: @BelfryTheatrewww.facebook.com/belfrytheatre
Touring Countries: USA, Australia, Europe
Touring: No
Regular venues: Mainstage Theatre 280, Studio Theatre 90-120, Rehearsal Hall 30

Black Theatre Workshop
Website: www.blacktheatreworkshop.ca
Email: info@blacktheatreworkshop.ca

Phone:
514 932 1104
Address: 432 – 3680 rue Jeanne-Mance, CA
Information: BTW aims to promote and produce black theatre that educates, entertains and delights its audiences. The company strives to create a greater cross-cultural understanding by its presence and the intrinsic value of its work
Country: Canada
Contact: Artistic Director Quincy Armorer
Email: ad@blacktheatreworkshop.ca
Contact: General Director Adele Benoit
Email: gm@blacktheatreworkshop.ca
Contact: President Jacklin Webb
Contact: vice President Clarence Bayne
Social Media: @TheatreBTWwww.facebook.com/Black-TheatreWorkshop
Touring: No
Regular venues: The Segal Centre for Performing Arts

Boca del Lupo
Website: bocadellupo.com
Email: info@bocadellupo.com
Phone: 604 684 2622
Address: 1422 William Street, CA
Information: Boca del Lupo's mission is to create and present extraordinary performances in unconventional spaces. The company consciously collaborates with artists diverse in culture and practice, and seeks to engage intergenerational audiences in the Metro Vancouver area. Member of ISPA
Country: Canada
Contact: Artistic Director Sherry J Yoon
Email: sjyoon@bocadellupo.com
Contact: Artistic Producer Jay Dodge
Email: jaydodge@bocadellupo.com
Contact: Managing Producer Dani Fecko
Email: dani@bocadellupo.com
Contact: Chair Miriam Aiken
Contact: vice Chair Lars Meyer
Social Media: @bocadellupowww.facebook.com/bo-cadellupo
Touring: No

Buddies in Bad Times Theatre
Website: www.buddiesinbadtimes.com
Email: info@buddiesinbadtimestheatre.com
Phone: 416 975 9130
Address: 12 Alexander Street, CA
Information: Buddies in Bad Times Theatre creates vital Canadian theatre by developing and presenting voices that question sexual and cultural norms. Built on the political and social principles of queer liberation, Buddies supports artists and works that reflect and advance these values.
Country: Canada
Contact: General Manager Shawn Daudlin
Email: shawn@buddiesinbadtimes.com
Contact: Artistic Director Brendan Healey
Email: brendan@buddiesinbadtimes.com
Contact: Head of Production Charissa Wilcox
Email: charissa@buddiesinbadtimes.com
Contact: Artistic Director Evalyn Parry
Email: evalyn@buddiesinbadtimes.com
Social Media: @buddiesTOwww.facebook.com/bud-diesinbadtimes
Touring: Nationally
Tallulah's Cabaret 150, Buddies Chamber 375

Canadian Stage Company
Website: www.canstage.com
Email: General@canstage.com
Phone: 416 367 8243
Address: 26 Berkley Street, CA
Information: Canada's largest non-profit contemporary theatre company, CanStage Play Development Program, develop and export Canadian plays and musicals internationally. Member of ISPA
Country: Canada
Contact: Artistic and General Director Matthew Jocelyn
Contact: Manager Gianna Ceci
Contact: co-Chair Alexandra Baillie
Social Media: @canadianstagewww.facebook.com/cdnstage
Touring: No
Regular venues: Berkeley Street Theatre

Canadian Vocal Arts Institute
Website: icav-cvai.ca
Email: info@icav-cvai.ca
Phone: 514 554 8822
Address: 200, avenue Vincent d'Indy, Bureau B-785, CA
Information: The Canadian Vocal Arts Institute was established in February 2004 by a group of people who care deeply about the emerging careers of our young opera singers and the standing of Montréal on the international vocal arts scene. The main objective of the Institute is to hold annually in Montréal an international training program for talented young singers eager to perfect their art. Member of ISPA
Country: Canada
Contact: General coordinator Catherine Fiset
Email: cfiset@icav-cvai.ca
Social Media: @ICAVCVAIwww.facebook.com/ICAV-Insti-tut-Canadien-dArt-Vocal-398603945592
Touring: No

Centaur Theatre Company
Website: www.centaurtheatre.com
Email: eloi@centaurtheatre.com
Phone: 514 288 1229
Address: Centaur Theatre Company, 453 St. François-Xavier, CA
Information: from classic to contemporary, Centaur Theatre Company produces theatre. In recent years, Centaur Theatre Company has produced and presented 19 world premiers of Montreal playwrights
Country: Canada
Contact: Artistic and Executive Director Eda Holmes
Contact: production Manager Howard Mendelsohn
Contact: General Manager Charles Childs
Contact: vice President Richard Pan
Social Media: @CentaurTheatrewww.centaurtheatre.com
Touring: No
Regular venues: 1250

Cirque du Soleil
Website: www.cirquedusoleil.com
Email: contact@cirquedusoleil.com
Address: Cirque du Soleil Inc., 8400, 2e Avenue, CA
Information: From a group of 20 street performers at its beginnings in 1984, Cirque du Soleil is a major Québec-based organization providing high-quality Artistic entertainment. The company has 5,000 employees, including more than 1,300 artists from more than 50 different countries. Cirque du Soleil has brought wonder and delight to more than 100 million spectators in more than 300 cities in over forty countries on six continents. Cirque du Soleil has 18 unique productions presented around the world in 2014.
Country: Canada
Contact: founder Guy Laliberte
Contact: President Daniel Lamarre
Contact: Marketing Manager Lyne Desroches
Social Media: @Cirquewww.facebook.com/Cirquedu-Soleil
Touring Countries: Europe. Belgium; Croatia; Germany; Poland; Russian Federation; Spain; United Kingdom. Americas. Argentina; Brazil; Canada; Costa
Touring: No

Cirque Éloize
Website: www.cirque-eloize.com
Email: eloize@cirque-eloize.com
Phone: 514 596 3838
Address: 417, rue Berri, CA
Information: Cirque Éloize has been creating performances since 1993. In addition to its tour performances, Cirque Éloize develops custom made concepts for international special events. To date, more than 4000 events have taken place. Member of ISPA
Country: Canada
Contact: Director, international development Sylvie Krauss Baumann
Social Media: @cirque_eloizewww.facebook.com/CirqueEloize
Touring: Nationally and Internationally

Corpus
Website: www.corpus.ca
Email: info@corpus.ca
Phone: 416 505 3193
Address: 805 Dovercourt Road, CA
Information: CORPUS is known for its precise and surrealist humour that combines movement with theatrical imagery
Country: Canada
 co-founder &Artistic Director
 David Danzon
Email: david@corpus.ca
 Artistic Producer & administrative Director
 Isorine Marc
Email: info@corpus.ca
Contact: President Jamie Piekarz
Social Media: @CORPUSdancewww.facebook.com/corpusdanceprojects
Touring: Nationally and Internationally
Number of Performers: 10

Dulcinea Langfelder & Co
Website: www.dulcinee.org
Email: info@dulcinee.org
Phone: 514 270 1050
Address: 5143, St-Laurent Blvd., 3rd floor, CA
Information: Dulcinea started dancing when she was 4 with "Miss Ronnie", who taught her Martha Graham Technique. At 13, she studied with Paul Sanasardo, who didn't like her habit of looking through the window at people walking down 6th ave during her barre exercises. He issued her an ultimatum: "You must chose between looking outside and the studio.
Country: Canada
Contact: Interim General Director Suzanne Bilodeau
Email: info@dulcinee.org
Contact: Founder Dulcinea Langfelder
Email: dulcy@dulcinee.org
Contact: Technical Director Vincent Santes

Email: dtech@dulcinee.org
Social Media: @DulcineeLangfel@dulcinee.org
Touring Countries: USA, China, Mexico
Touring: Nationally and Internationally

DynamO Théâtre
Website: www.dynamotheatre.qc.ca
Email: info@dynamotheatre.qc.ca
Phone: 514 274 7644
Address: 911, rue Jean-Talon Est, Bureau 131, CA
Information: DynamO Théâtre focuses on developing, producing and performing theatre of acrobatic movement and clowning productions for young audiences. Since it began 37 years ago, DynamO Théâtre created 23 productions, gave 4,500 performances in 29 countries on 5 continents for 1.5 million spectators.
Country: Canada
Contact: Co-Artistic Director Jacqueline Gosselin
Email: jackie@dynamotheatre.qc.ca
Contact: Co-Artistic Director Yves Simard
Email: ysimard@dynamotheatre.qc.ca
Contact: General Manager Chloé Besner
Email: cbesner@dynamotheatre.qc.ca
Contact: Touring and market development Kashia Malinowska
Email: kashia@dynamotheatre.qc.ca
Social Media: www.facebook.com/dynamotheatre1
Touring Countries: Europe, Asia, North and South America, Australia, Africa
Touring: No

Electric Company Theatre
Website: www.electriccompanytheatre.com
Email: info@electriccompanytheatre.com
Phone: 604 253 4222
Address: 1422 William St., CA
Information: Electric Company Theatre is a leading force in the Vancouver theatre scene, creating original work rich in spectacle and adventurous in form, strong in narrative and which reaches a diverse and growing audience
Country: Canada
Contact: Artistic Director Kim Collier
 company & financial Manager
 Jennifer Swan
Email: jennifer@electriccompanytheatre.com
Social Media: @theElectrics
Touring: No

Factory Theatre
Website: www.factorytheatre.ca
Email: info@factorytheatre.ca
Phone: 416 504 4473
Address: 125 Bathurst Street, CA
Information: Factory's mission is to enthrall audiences with the imagination of Canadian playwrights and develop the next generation of intercultural theatre artists. Since its founding in 1970, Factory has committed to exclusively produce Canadian plays. Factory has made it an Artistic priority to invest in, and showcase Canadian artists who bring their stories to the theatre in Toronto.
Country: Canada
Contact: Artistic Director Nina Lee Aquino
Email: nina@factorytheatre.ca
Contact: media relations Carrie Sager
Email: carrie@flip-publicity.com
Contact: company dramaturge Matt McGeachy
Email: matt@factorytheatre.ca
Contact: Managing Director Jonathan Heppner
Email: jonathan@factorytheatre.ca
Contact: administrator Ginger Scott
Email: ginger@factorytheatre.ca
Social Media: @FactoryToronto@FactoryTheatreTO/
Touring Countries: Europe
Touring: No
Regular venues: Mainstage 200, Studio Caf

Factory Theatre (Toronto)
Website: www.factorytheatre.ca
Phone: 416 504 4473
Address: 125 Bathurst Street, CA
Information: Founded in 1970 by Ken Gass and Frank Trotz, Factory Theatre was the first company to produce only Canadian plays. Its huge initial success led to the founding of the Alternate Theatre Movement which radically changed the face of Canadian theatre in favour of the Canadian voice. For more than 40 years, Factory has been known as the "Home of the Canadian Playwright" and has produced more than 300 new Canadian plays in mainstage productions and 600 more in workshop and other formats.
Country: Canada
Contact: Artistic Director Nina Lee Aquino
Email: nina@factorytheatre.ca
Contact: Production Manager Emma Alderman
Email: emma@factorytheatre.ca
 Marketing & Audience Development Manager
 Lauren Naus
Email: lauren@factorytheatre.ca
Contact: Managing Director Jonathan Heppner
Email: jonathan@factorytheatre.ca
Contact: Associate Producer Lucy Coren
Email: lucy@factorytheatre.ca
Contact: Patron Services Manager Himanshu Sitlani
Email: himanshu@factorytheatre.ca

Philanthropy & Partnerships Manager
Mark Aikman
Email: mark@factorytheatre.ca
Contact: Company Dramaturg Matt McGeachy
Email: matt@factorytheatre.ca
Contact: Studio Head Technician Lauren Dowell
Contact: Mainspace Head Technician Nick Mitanoff
Social Media: www.facebook.com/pages/Factory-Theatre/21482535223760twitter.com/factorytorontowww.instagram.com/factorytheatre/

Grand Theatre
Website: kingstongrand.ca
Email: grandtheatre2@cityofkingston.ca
Phone: 613 530 2050
Address: The Grand Theatre, 218 Princess Street, CA
Information: The Grand Theatre is a community-based, professionally managed civic asset that builds and fosters cultural vitality in Kingston. It creates a partnership between the City of Kingston and the community that sees arts and culture as an important component of everyday life in the City of Kingston. The Grand Theatre also facilitates and supports presentation and production, community development, artist support and the creation of partnerships and collaborations.
Country: Canada
Contact: theatre Manager Dianne Zemba
Email: dzemba@cityofkingston.ca
Contact: production supervisor Larry Stafford
Email: lstafford@cityofkingston.ca
Contact: box office coordinator Rebecca Brown
Email: rbrown@cityofkingston.ca
Contact: performing arts Manager Jayson Duggan
Email: jduggan@cityofkingston.ca
Contact: communications officer Bob Giarda
Email: bgiarda@cityofkingston.ca
Social Media: @Kingston_Grandwww.facebook.com/kingstongrandtheatre
Touring: No
Regular venues: The Grand Theatre 839, The McManus Theatre 150, The Poster Lounge 250-300, The McManus Studio 100

Green Thumb Theatre for Young People
Website: www.greenthumb.bc.ca
Email: info@greenthumb.bc.ca
Phone: 604 254 4055
Address: 5522 McKinnon Street, CA
Information: founded in 1975 to develop original Canadian plays. Since that time, Green Thumb has emerged as one of Canada's leading theatre companies for young people, producing material for audiences and artists, and contributing to the work in this field
Country: Canada
Contact: Artistic Director Patrick McDonald
Email: pmcdonald@greenthumb.bc.ca
Contact: Artistic Associate Shawn MacDonald
Email: ArtAssoc@greenthumb.bc.ca
Contact: General Manager Linda Gorrie
Email: gm@greenthumb.bc.ca
Social Media: @gr_thumbtheatrewww.facebook.com/GreenThumbTheatre
Touring Countries: Canada, United States, England, Scotland, Ireland, The Netherlands, Germany, Sweden, Hong Kong, Singapore, Australia, New Zealand and Mexico
Touring: Nationally and Internationally

Imago Theatre
Website: www.imagotheatre.ca
Email: info@imagotheatre.ca
Phone: 514 274 3222
Address: 5143 Boulevard St-Laurent, CA
Information: the company produces contemporary, socially relevant and alternative theatre
Country: Canada
Contact: Artistic and administrative Associate Erin Lindsay
Contact: Artistic and Executive Director Micheline Chevrier
Email: micheline@imago.ca
Social Media: @ImagoTheatre514www.facebook.com/ImagoTheatre
Touring: No

Infinitheatre
Website: www.infinitheatre.com
Email: info@infinitheatre.com
Phone: 514 987 1774
Address: 5413 St-Laurent Boulevard, suite 302, CA
Information: Infinithéâtre is an independent Anglophone theatre company in Montréal, founded in 1988 by Marianne Ackerman and Claire Shapiro as Theatre 1774. Over the course of the past ten years, in addition to its own work, Infinithéâtre has made a concerted effort to help younger and smaller companies and writers develop their projects and stage their productions.
Country: Canada
Contact: General Manager Simon Anthony Abou-Fadel
Email: Manager@infinitheatre.com
Contact: Artistic Director Guy Sprung
Email: Artistic@Infinitheatre.com
Social Media: @InfinitheatrewwwFacebook.com/InfinitheatreMontreal
Touring Countries: USA, Europe

Touring: No
Regular venues: Bain St-Michel 5300, rue St-Dominique approx: 110

L'Arsenal à musique
Website: www.arsenal.ca
Email: info@arsenal.ca
Phone: 514 738 0336
Address: 1511, chemin Canora, Mont-Royal, CA
Information: L'Arsenal's mission is to introduce concert music to a broad audience, and especially to young people, through bold and innovative interventions and concerts, as well as through the development of strategies for introducing the arts to school groups. member of IAMA
Country: Canada
Contact: General Manager Lorena Corradi
Email: lorenacorradi@arsenal.ca
Contact: Artistic Director Reggi Ettore
Email: reggiettore@arsenal.ca
Contact: project Manager Catherine Gay
Email: catherinegay@arsenal.ca
Contact: Executive assistant Lila Zarzi
Email: info@arsenal.ca
Social Media: @the_arsenalwww.facebook.com/larsenalamusique
Touring Countries: USA, Europe, Asia
Touring: No

Lemieux Pilon 4D Art
Website: www.4dart.com
Email: info@4dart.com
Phone: 514 284 5005
Address: 4123 Rue Drolet, CA
Information: Founded in Montreal in 1983-84, Lemieux Pilon 4D Art is a multidisciplinary company with more than 30 original productions to its credit. Internationally recognized for their mesmerizing fusion of dance, theatre, music, visual arts and film, Michel Lemieux and Victor Pilon are the dynamic duo who create unique hybrid productions that merge the real and the virtual, the performing arts and multimedia. Member of ISPA
Country: Canada
Contact: Executive Director Marie-Christine Dufour
Email: mcdufour@4dart.com
Contact: administrative Director Michel Maillochon
Email: micmail@4dart.com
Contact: extraordinary assistant coordinator Jean-Frédéric Bergeron
Email: jeanfrederic@4dart.com
Social Media: @4dartwww.facebook.com/lemieuxpilon4dart
Touring: Nationally and Internationally

Mermaid Theatre of Nova Scotia
Website: www.mermaidtheatre.ns.ca
Email: puppets@mermaidtheatre.ns.ca
Phone: 902 798 5841
Address: PO Box 2697, 132 Gerrish Street, CA
Information: Mermaid Theatre has been in continuous operation since it was founded in 1972 in Wolfville, Nova Scotia. They moved to the neighbouring town of Windsor in 1987, and helped to revitalise the historic town's downtown business core. Their extensive headquarters encompass production studios, administrative offices, rehearsal quarters, a versatile studio, and an elegant 400-seat performance facility known as The Mermaid Imperial Performing Arts Centre (MIPAC).
Country: Canada
Contact: Managing Director Sara Lee Lewis
Contact: administrator Cathy White
Contact: Artistic Director Jim Morrow
Social Media: @mermaidtheatrewww.facebook.com/MermaidTheatre
Touring: No
Regular venues: Mermaid Imperial Performing Arts Centre

Nightwood Theatre
Website: www.nightwoodtheatre.net
Email: info@nightwoodtheatre.net
Phone: 416 944 1740
Address: The Historic Distillery District, 15 Case Goods Lane, Studio 306, CA
Information: the oldest professional women's theatre company in Canada. Founded in 1979 by Cynthia Grant, Kim Renders, Mary Vingoe and Maureen White, Nightwood has produced, developed and toured landmark, award-winning plays
Country: Canada
Contact: Artistic Director Kelly Thornton
Email: kelly@nightwoodtheatre.net
Contact: Managing Director Beth Brown
Email: beth@nightwoodtheatre.net
Contact: Marketing coordinator Taylor Trowbridge
Email: Marketing@nightwoodtheatre.net
Social Media: @nightwoodtheatwww.facebook.com/nightwoodtheatre
Touring: Nationally and Internationally
Regular venues: Tapestry/Nightwood New Work Studio

One Man Lord of the Rings
Website: www.onemanlotr.com/

Email: sudds@slfa.com
Phone: 604 734 5945
Address: Justin Sudds, S.L Feldman & Associates, CA
Information: see also Performing Companies (One Man Star Wars)
Country: Canada
 booking, interview & media inquiries
 Justin Sudds
Email: sudds@slfa.com
Social Media: www.facebook.com/pages/One-Man-Lord-of-the-Rings/285605143733
Touring: No

One Man Star Wars
Website: www.onemanstarwars.com/
Email: sudds@slfa.com
Phone: 604 734 5945
Address: Justin Sudds, S.L Feldman & Associates, CA
Country: Canada
 booking, interview & media inquiries
 Justin Sudds
Email: sudds@slfa.com
Touring: No

Robbins Academy
Website: www.citadeltheatre.com/robbinsacademy
Email: citadel@citadeltheatre.com
Phone: 888 425 1820
Address: 9828 101A Avenue, CA
Information: the most comprehensive programme for creative development in professional theatre in Canada
Country: Canada
Contact: Artistic Director Bob Baker
Email: bbaker@citadeltheatre.com
Contact: Executive Director Penny Ritco
Email: pritco@citadeltheatre.com
Contact: play development Director Brian Dooley
Email: bdooly@citadeltheatre.com
Contact: technical Director Bill Heron
Email: bheron@citadeltheatre.com
Social Media: @citadeltheatrewww.facebook.com/citadeltheatre
Touring: No
Regular venues: Shoctor Theatre 663, Maclab Theatre 656, Rice Theatre 230, Zeidler Hall 240, Tucker Amphitheatre 120

Roseneath Theatre
Website: www.roseneath.ca
Email: natalie@roseneath.ca
Phone: 416 686 5199
Address: 651 Dufferin Street, CA
Information: creates and produces plays of enduring quality specifically for Student and Family Audiences. The company uses top professional theatre artists to create and perform fully produced, original plays for young people and their families all over the world. Roseneath Theatre gives over 300 performances per year to approximately 100,000 students, teachers and families making it the largest touring theatre in Ontario. Member of ISPA
Country: Canada
Contact: General Manager Natalie Ackers
Email: natalie@roseneath.ca
Contact: Artistic Director Andrew Lamb
Email: andrew@roseneath.ca
Contact: education and Marketing manage Gretel Meyer Odell
Email: education@roseneath.ca
Contact: production Manager Heather Landan
Email: heather@roseneath.ca
Contact: tour Manager Niki Poirier
Email: niki@roseneath.ca
Social Media: @RoseneathThtrwww.facebook.com/roseneaththeatre
Touring: No
Annual Performances: 300
Regular venues: Roseneath Theatre

Shaw Festival Theatre, Canada
Website: www.shawfest.com
Email: timj@shawfest.com
Phone: 905 468 2153
Address: 10 Queen's Parade, PO Box 774, Ontario, CA
Information: A theatre company inspired by the work of Bernard Shaw. The Festival produces plays from and about Shaw's era and contemporary plays that share his provocative exploration of society and celebration of humanity
Country: Canada
Contact: music Director Paul Sportelli
Contact: head of design William Schmuck
Contact: Artistic Director Jackie Maxwell
Contact: senior Manager, communications Laura Hughes
Email: lhughes@shawfest.com
Contact: Executive Director Tim Jennings
Contact: Director of human resources Dianne Gibbs
Email: diannegibbs@shawfest.com
Contact: Director of Marketing, Sales and Communications Valerie Taylor
Social Media: @Shawtheatrewww.facebook.com/shaw-festival
Touring: No
Regular venues: Festival Theatre, Royal George Theatre, Court House Theatre, Studio Theatre

Theatre & Company
Website: www.theatreandcompany.org
Email: boxoffice@theatreandcompany.org
Address: 36 King Street West, CA
Information: Theatre & Company is currently in its 18th season in downtown Kitchener an hour away from Toronto. We offer a wide range of programming including plays by Canadian playwrights, Harold Pinter, and family shows
Country: Canada
Contact: front of house and venue Manager Arthur Loik
Contact: Marketing coordinator Jes Brown
Contact: production Manager Anna Graham
Touring: No
Regular venues: The King Street Theatre Centre 383

Theatre Calgary
Website: www.theatrecalgary.com
Email: subscriptions@theatrecalgary.com
Phone: 403 294 7440
Address: 220 9th Ave SE, CA
Information: This is Calgary's largest professional theatre company. Theatre Calgary produces an eclectic mix of productions annually which stimulate, provoke, and delight. Member of ISPA
Country: Canada
Contact: Artistic Director Stafford Arima
Email: sarima@theatrecalgary.com
Contact: Chair Margo Randles
 Director of finance & Administration
 Kristen Dion
Email: kdion@theatrecalgary.com
Contact: Manager Susan McNair Reid
Email: smcnairreid@theatrecalgary.com
Contact: Director of communications Christopher Loach
Email: cloach@theatrecalgary.com
Social Media: @TheatreCalgarywww.facebook.com/theatrecalgary
Touring Countries: USA, Europe
Touring: No

Theatre for Living (Headlines Theatre)
Website: www.theatreforliving.com
Email: info@theatreforliving.com
Phone: 604 871 0508
Address: Suite 323 – 350 East 2nd Avenue, CA
Information: (Headlines Theatre) is a professional company which uses its award-winning and distinct theatre model to create audience interactive performances and workshops around the world that stimulate community dialogue about hard to discuss social issues. Theatre for Living developed out of Brazilian Director Augusto Boal's Theatre of the OpPressed
Country: Canada
Contact: outreach coordinator Liza Lindgren
Email: outreach@theatreforliving.com
Contact: Artistic and Managing Director David Diamond
Email: david@theatreforliving.com
Contact: office/production Manager and webmaster Dafne Blanco
Email: admin@theatreforliving.com
Contact: financial administrator Susan Shank
Email: finance@theatreforliving.com
Social Media: @theatre4livingwww.facebook.com/TheatreForLiving
Touring: No
Regular venues: various – community halls to mainstream venues

Theatre Gargantua
Website: www.theatregargantua.ca
Email: info@theatregargantua.ca
Phone: 416 260 4660
Address: 651 Dufferin St., CA
Information: Theatre Gargantua is one of Canada's leading multi-disciplinary theatre companies. Under the direction of Jacquie PA Thomas, the company has devised dynamic physical theatre for over 25 years. Each production melds daring physicality with striking designs, underpinned by live original music, provocative text and the innovative use of technology. To date, Gargantua has garnered dozens of nominations, awards and recognitions for categories including outstanding new play, direction, sound, set and lighting designs. Member of ISPA
Country: Canada
Contact: Artistic Director Jacquie Thomas
Email: jacquie@theatregargantua.ca
Social Media: @TGargantuawww.facebook.com/TheatreGargantua
Touring: No

Theatrefront
Website: www.theatrefront.com
Email: info@theatrefront.com
Address: 153 Maple Branch Path, CA
Information: Theatrefront is dedicated to stretching the boundaries of the human experience through theatre. Founded by Artistic Director Daryl Cloran, the company provides an environment for dramatic risks and for developing the trust and confidence for theatre professionals to push themselves to new emotional and physical limits.

Country: Canada
Contact: General Manager Kaija Corlazzoli
Email: kaija@theatrefront.com
Contact: Artistic Director Daryl Cloran
Email: daryl@theatrefront.com
Contact: Producer Sue Balint

Theaturtle
Website: www.theaturtle.com
Email: info@theaturtle.com
Address: CA
Information: Theaturtle was established in 1999 to create essential, ecstatic theatre that touches the earth and ignites the soul. Its name is derived from a story told in both Native Canadian and Jewish traditions that the world sits on the back of a turtle. They develop work slowly and carefully, plodding like the turtle. Then, they glide like a turtle into international waters to share their Canadian-made, physically and musically robust theatre. Member of ISPA
Country: Canada
Contact: Artistic Director Alon Nashman
Email: alon@theaturtle.com
Social Media: @lonsy
Touring: No

Threshold Theater
Website: www.thresholdtheater.ca
Email: mark@thresholdtheater.ca
Address: 109 Atlas Ave, CA
Country: Canada
Contact: co-Artistic Director Mark Cassidy
Email: mark@thresholdtheatre.ca
Contact: co-Artistic Director Suzanne Hersh
Email: suzanne@thresholdtheatre.ca
Social Media: @thresholdtheatr
Touring: No
Regular venues: small theatres up to 150

Volcano Theatre
Website: www.volcano.ca
Email: info@volcano.ca
Phone: 416 538 4436
Address: 251 Crawford Street, CA
Information: Volcano is an international award-winning live performance company based in Toronto. They explore compelling social and Artistic territories in innovative ways. Featured event – 'A Moveable Beast'. Member of ISPA
Country: Canada
Contact: General Manager Meredith Potter
Email: meredith@volcano.ca
Contact: Artistic Director Ross Manson
Email: ross@volcano.ca
Social Media: @volcanotheatrewww.facebook.com/volcanotoronto
Touring: Nationally

CHINA

Beijing People's Art Theatre
Website: www.bjry.com
Email: bjrenyi@126.com
Phone: 106 524 6789
Address: 22 Wang Fu Jing Avenue, Docheng District
Information: It was in 1907 that Chinese people put on the first western play, China then has its modern theatre called as hua ju (spoken drama). In the history of nearly 100 years, the prominent Chinese theatre professionals have devoted themselves to the career. Their dedication led to the emergence of a number of masterpieces, welcomed both at home and abroad. Beijing People's Art Theatre (BPAT), a first-rate national theatre company of China, its development in the last 50 years has been a miniature of the development of Chinese modern theatre
Country: China
Touring Countries: Japan, Canada, Singapore, Korea, Egypt, Hong Kong, Taiwan, Macao
Touring: No
Regular venues: Capital Theatre 970, Mini Theatre 400, Experimental Theatre 200-250

China Acrobat Troupe
Website: www.cncircus.com
Email: chinacircus@126.com
Phone: 106 780 2059
Address: Beijing Economic and Technological Development Zone, No.9,, Jian An Street,
Information: Founded in 1950, under the attention of the late premier Zhou Enlai, China National Acrobatic Troupe (CNAT) was the first national performing arts troupe established by the Central Government of China. Now CNAT has become an important company of Beijing Performances & Arts Group Co., Ltd. It covers a large variety of fields: Acrobatics, Aerial Acts, Farces, Magic, etc. The troupe is one of the best acrobatic circuses boasting of the largest scale and the most comprehensive programs in China.
Country: China
Touring: No
Regular venues: Tian Di Theatre, about 900

China National Chinese Opera and Dance Drama Company

Website: www.coddc.com
Email: china_opera@163.com
Address: 1F No. 23,, Nan San Huan East Road, Feng Tai District
Information: duplicate
Country: China
Contact: pa to President/Manager of performances Yi Sun
Contact: vice-President Yi-wei Jin
Contact: vice-President Ji-guang Jin
Touring: No
Regular venues: The Sky Bridge Theatre 1700

China National Theatre
Website: www.ntcc.com.cn
Email: ghyb1009@126.com
Phone: 108 306 9696
Address: No. 277, Di An Men Wai Da (Jie) Street,, Xi Cheng District
Information: China National Theatre is directly under the Ministry of Culture of People's Republic of China national arts groups. With strong Artistic resources and brilliant theatrical cultural traditions. China National Theatre to the creation and performance of high-quality, high-grade all outstanding theater productions responsibility; committed to creating quality, attention to personnel training, determined to open up the market
Country: China
Touring: No
Regular venues: Dong Dan Theatre 400, Hao Men Qiao Mini Theatre 300

Jinan – My Brothers and Sisters Performing Arts Troupe
Phone: 531 897 30839
Address: No.26, Qi Li Shan West Road
Information: This Art Troupe, founded in 1988, is made up of disabled persons to present a singing, dancing and music show. It is also one of the first local art troupes to play in the art palace of the Capital--Beijing. It has taken part in the China Culture and Art Festival, the "Asian and Pacific Decade of Disabled Persons show" and other national and international culture shows during these last years
Country: China
Touring: No

Shanghai Dramatic Art Centre
Website: www.china-drama.com
Email: publicity@china-drama.com
Phone: 216 473 8882
Address: 288 Anfu Road
Information: Shanghai Shanghai Dramatic Arts Center is the only national professional drama group, is one of China's most outstanding drama groups. Center not only has a large number of professional writers, Directors, actors, stage and other creative people, also has three sizes, full-featured professional theater performances, independent creation and exchange center each year to introduce colored show about 1000 games, to attract domestic and foreign audience ten million
Country: China
Touring Countries: Northern Ireland, England, Germany, Japan, Singapore, Turkey.
Touring: No
Regular venues: Shanghai Hua Ju Building, large theatre 500; tow small theatres 200 each.

Shanghai Opera House
Website: www.shanghaiopera.com.cn
Email: shgly@online.sh.cn
Phone: 216 248 5368
Address: No.10, Lane 100, Chang Shu Road
Information: Shanghai Opera House is the official government-funded western-style opera company of Shanghai, China, and the resident opera company at the new Shanghai Grand Theatre Shanghai Da Juyuan. Although the term "Opera House" is often applied to the building, both in English and Chinese texts, officially the building is not an opera house and the term "Shanghai Opera House" properly applies only to the performing company, not the building, as is also true for its senior sister company, the China National Opera House (CNOH) in Beijing
Country: China
Contact: Artistic Director/President Guo-yong Zhang
Touring: No
Regular venues: Shanghai opera theatre

COLOMBIA

Teatro Mayor Julio Mario Santo Domingo
Website: www.teatromayor.org
Email: prensa@teatromayor.com
Address: CO
Information: It has a capacity for 1,299 spectators and was built in order to present all kinds of opera and musical shows, concerts, classical ballet, contemporary dance and plays. Teatro Mayor Julio Mario Santo Domingo has three levels (Platea, First Balcony and Second Balcony) and a space designed so that all viewers have from any location an excellent view and sound reception.
 Member of ISPA
Country: Colombia

Social Media: @teatromayorwww.facebook.com/Teatro-MayorJulioMarioSantoDomingo
Touring: No

EGYPT

Noon Creative Enterprise
Website: www.meetphool.net
Email: info@meetphool.net
Phone: 111 791 1133
Address: EG
Information: seeks to work with professionals within the performing arts industry, civil society, youth and children and corporations through: 1) hosting a platform and space to support, promote, and showcase the work of professionals within the performing arts industry. 2) Introducing performing arts and other creative tools to civil society, youth and children for educational, capacity and skills development. Member of ISPA
Country: Egypt
Contact: concept and technical Manager Nada Sabet
Contact: research and outreach Iris Musel
Social Media: @meetphoolwww.facebook.com/Noon-CreativeEnterprise
Touring: No

HONG KONG

Chung Ying Theatre Company
Website: www.chungying.com
Email: info@chungying.com
Phone: 396 19800
Address: 10 Borrett Road, Mid-level, HK
Information: Chung Ying Theatre Company was founded in 1979, and is one of the most experienced local professional troupes. in 1982 they registered as a non-profit independent organization, and are currently funded by the HKSAR Government, and accept sponsorship of both private and commercial organizations to jointly promote the theatrical arts, theater education and outreach activities.
Country: Hong Kong
Contact: Artistic Director Tin-lung Ko
Contact: General Manager Dominic Cheung
Social Media: www.facebook.com/chungyingtheatre-fanpage
Touring: No

Ding Theatre
Email: dingtheatre@gmail.com
Phone: 289 63104
Address: Flat 1203, 12/F, Bright Way Tower, 33 Mongkok Rd, Mong Kok, HK
Information: Ding Theatre is a venue for different theatrical events in the area
Country: Hong Kong
Touring: No

Exploration Theatre Ltd
Website: www.etdrama.org.hk
Email: etdrama@yahoo.com.hk
Phone: 288 92132
Address: Rm. 401, 30 Pak Tin Street, Shek Kip Mei, Kowloon, HK
Information: A pioneering theatre company, Exploration Theatre has become a broad-based creative organization that uses innovative theatre and creative participation to engage people from all walks of life. Fundamental to Exploration Theatre is a belief in the transformative power of creativity through theatre. Exploration Theatre is committed to participation and learning. It explores different creative approaches to facilitate projects with young people through collaboration with business and educational partners
Country: Hong Kong
Contact: Chairman King NgFai Chung
Contact: vice Chairman Kwong Wah Tung
Contact: Director Koon Shing Wong
Contact: Artistic Director Karley Ng
Touring: No

Green Hill Anglo-Chinese Arts Performance Group
Website: www.greenhillmusic.org.hk
Email: greenhill107@yahoo.com.hk
Phone: 278 58807
Address: Unit A, 1st Floor, Smart A, Nos. 348-352, Prince Edward Road West, Kowloon, HK
Information: Founded in 1988, this government registered non-profit organization is for educating people, in order to promote, develop and improve the purpose of, and commitment to the art of music education in primary schools. It creates an organic combination between Pei Chun and School Education based on the specific circumstances of each school, organised by Chinese and Western musical instruments, dance, art training and Western orchestra formation and training
Country: Hong Kong
Contact: deputy head Li Yong
Contact: Chairman Huang Weida
Touring: No

Regular venues: Yi Zhi Xing Theatre, capacities about 150

Hong Kong Chorus
Website: www.hkcoc.org.hk
Email: hkchorus@netvigator.com
Phone: 241 16203
Address: Room C7, 7th Floor, How Ming Factory Building, 99 How Ming Street, Kwun Tong, HK
Information: Headed by Maestro Henry Shek as its Artistic Director, the Hong Kong Choir of Outstanding Children aims at providing professional and quality music education to children in a much diversified form. Young children who have potential in music and the performing arts are selected through open auditions to become members. The choir not only offers training in choral singing but also in music theory, ears training, instrument playing as well as drama and theatrical dancing
Country: Hong Kong
Contact: Chairman Ginny Shek
Social Media: www.facebook.com/hongkongchorus
Touring: No

Hong Kong Repertory Theatre
Website: www.hkrep.com
Email: enquiry@hkrep.com
Phone: 310 35930
Address: 4F Sheung Wan Municipal Services Building, 345 Queen's Road, Central, HK
Information: The Hong Kong Repertory Theatre is the longest standing and largest professional theatre company in the city, established in 1977 and incorporated in 2001. Financially supported by the Government of the Hong Kong Special Administrative Region, the Hong Kong Repertory operates under the guidance of its Governing Council, and employs a team of over 70 full-time professionals including the Artistic Director, resident Director, actors, technical and stage management staff as well as administrators
Since its establishment 36 years ago, it has presented more than 300 productions, many of which became timeless classics of the local theatre.
Country: Hong Kong
Contact: Artistic Director Anthony Chan
Email: ad@hkrep.com
Contact: resident Director Fung Wai Hang
Email: rd1@hkrep.com
Contact: Associate Director Roy Szeto
Email: rd2@hkrep.com
Social Media: www.facebook.com/HKREP
Touring Countries: China, Singapore
Touring: No
Number of Performers: 70
Regular venues: Black Box Theatre

PIP Cultural Industries
Website: www.pip-group.org
Email: info@pip-group.org
Phone: 810 04999
Address: 20, 11/F, Block B, Hi-Tech Industrial Centre, 491-501 Castle Peak Road, Tsuen Wan, HK
Information: PIP is all about "pleasure, imagination and play," so, in other words, they are fun. Formed in 1993 under the name Theatre Ensemble, the company rejected all forms of government subsidy in 2008 and renamed themselves the PIP Cultural Industries. As Hong Kong's first cultural industry, they are the mother of nine branches including PIP Theatre, and PIP Theatre Kids. Their popular theater productions, usually feature the company's Artistic Director, Jim Chim, and draw upon local and international news, trends and interests as inspiration, and shape them into tear-jerking jokes
Country: Hong Kong
Contact: Associate Artistic Director Jim Chim
Contact: co-Artistic Director Olivia Yan
Touring Countries: Japan, Taiwan
Touring: No
Regular venues: Shou Son Theatre, Hong Kong Arts Centre, 440

Sand and Bricks
Email: ribble@culturalfactory.org
Phone: 256 84507
Address: Flat B, 17/F, Block 9, Sea Crest Villa, Phase 3, 18 Castle Peak Road, HK
Country: Hong Kong
Contact: Chairman Ribble Chung
Touring: No

Theatre du Pif
Website: theatredupif.com
Email: thtdupif@netvigator.com
Phone: 290 42030
Address: Room 901-2, Hua Fu Commercial Buliding, 111 Queen's Road West, HK
Information: Theatre du Pif is a leading Hong Kong theatre company known for its cross-cultural heritage and bilingual productions performing in Cantonese, English or both. Using a workshop and devising process as well as collaborations with dramaturges and artists from other disciplines, they orchestrate movement, text and visual images to produce productions acclaimed both for

their power and their poetry. Member of ISPA.
Country: Hong Kong
Contact: co-Artistic Director Sean Curran
Contact: co-Artistic Director Bonni Chan
Touring Countries: China, Sweden, Germany, Japan
Touring: No

Zuni Icosahedron
Website: www.zuni.org.hk
Email: info@zuni.org.hk
Phone: 289 38704
Address: Room 203-4, 2/F., Cheong Tai Commercial Building,, 60-66 Wing Lok Street, Sheung Wan, HK
Information: Founded in 1982, is a Hong Kong based international experimental theatre company and a non-profit charitable cultural organization. Zuni is one of the nine major professional performing arts companies in Hong Kong, and has made venue partner with the Hong Kong Cultural Centre since 2009. As a premier experimental theatre company, Zuni has produced more than 200 original productions of alternative theatre and multimedia performances, and been invited to more than 60 cities around the globe for cultural exchange and performances
Country: Hong Kong
Contact: Chairperson Stanley Wong
Contact: secretary Glenis Wong
Social Media: www.facebook.com/??????-Zuni-Icosahedron-398430360213224
Touring Countries: Europe, United States, South Africa, China, Taiwan, Japan, Singapore and more
Touring: No

INDONESIA

Bengkel Teater
Address: Cipayung, Jawa Barat, Bojonggede, ID
Information: founded by W S Rendra as an alternative venue for performing arts in a village on the outskirts of Jakarta Cipayung Jaya.
Country: Indonesia
Contact: Artistic Director W.S. Rendra
Touring: No

Teater Garasi
Website: www.teatergarasi.org
Email: garasi@lycos.com
Phone: 622 744 15844
Address: J1 Bugisan Selatan 36A, Rt 01-08, Tegal Kenon-go, ID
Country: Indonesia
Contact: Artistic Director Yudi Ahmad Tajudin
Touring: No

Teater Koma
Website: www.teaterkoma.org
Email: info@teaterkoma.org
Phone: 217 350 460
Address: J1 Cempaka Raya No 15, Bintaro, ID
Information: founded in 1977; emphasis on plays by local playwrights including Nanois, also adapted Western plays by Brecht, Shakespeare and Miller
Country: Indonesia
Social Media: www.facebook.com/pages/Teater-Koma/33136550989
Touring: No

Teater Tetas
Website: www.welcome.to/teatertetas
Email: teatertetas@fcmail.com
Phone: 622 175 08729
Address: J1 Mangga 30 ART 001 RW 04, Gandaria Selatan, ID
Country: Indonesia
Contact: Director Ags Arya Dipayana
Touring: No

JAPAN

'Edo-Daikagura' Maruichi Senoh Troupe
Website: www.edo-daikagura.com
Email: senmaru@senmaru.info
Address: 1-3-17-706 Koishikawa, Bunkyo-ku, JP
Information: Reportedly, the original purpose of Daikagura was to serve as a talisman for the people, chasing away evil on behalf of Jingu (the grand Shintoism shrines). Thus, Daikagura was originally a very sacred and serious performance. Today, the performance is becoming people's entertainment. Senmaru wears a "kimono" and performs Japanese traditional tricks.
Country: Japan
Social Media: www.facebook.com/senmaru.mwww.instagram.com/senmaru01/

'Edo-Daikagura' Maruichi Senoh Troupe
Website: www.edo-daikagura.com
Email: office@edo-daikagura.com
Phone: 339 586 119
Address: 1-3-17-706 Koishikawa, Bunkyo-ku, JP
Country: Japan
Contact: contact Senmaru Kagami

Touring Countries: Canada, USA, UK, Germany, Austria, Switzerland, France, The Netherlands, Italy, Slovenia, Poland, Mexico, Ecuador, Colombia, Chile, Trinidad and Tobago, Singapore, Hong Kong, Japan
Touring: No

1980
Website: www.gekidan1980.cool.ne.jp
Email: ikhm-mc@mars.plala.or.jp
Address: 102, 3-40-5 Matsubara, Setagaya-ku, JP
Country: Japan
President & playwright & Director
Yoshiyuki Shibata
Touring: No

21 Seiki Kabuki Gumi
Website: www1.u-netsurf.ne.jp/
Address: c/o Omodaka Co., 206 Resupasu Yotsuya 3 cho-me, 20-3 Daikyo-cho, Shinjuku-kuTokyo, JP
Country: Japan
Contact: Director En'nosuke Ichikawa
Touring: No
Regular venues: Kabuki-Za, Shinbashi Enbujo

66, The Planning Group of Dramatic Performances
Address: 1-518 Kosugi-cho, Nakahara-ku, Kawasaki, JP
Country: Japan
leader & Director
Itsuroh Kobayashi
Touring: No
Regular venues: Jean-Jean (q.v.) Sogetsu Hall (q.v.) Aoyama Round Theatre (q.v.)

Academic Shakespeare Company ASC
Website: homepage2.nifty.com/asc_web
Email: asc_aya@nifty.com
Address: 4F, Sansei Bldg., 13-15, Odenma-cho, Nihon-bashi, Chuo-ku, JP
Country: Japan
Contact: co-Director Kazuhiro Kikuchi
Contact: Director Takayuki Ayanogi
Touring: No
Regular venues: Globe Tokyo 650-700 (q.v.), Tokyo Metropolitan Art Space small theatre 300 (q.v.)

Academy
Website: www.academy-kids.com
Email: info@academy-kids.com
Address: 1-28-6-202, Uemachi, Chuo-ku, JP
Country: Japan
Contact: Director Yohsuke Tsutsui
Touring: No

ACM Theatre
Website: www.arttowermito.or.jp
Phone: 292 278 111
Address: Mito Arts Foundation, 1-6-8 Goken-cho, Mito-shi, JP
Information: Art Tower Mito (ATM), symbolized by the 100-meter-tall metal tower that stands in its plaza, is a comprehensive cultural facility divided into three sections: a concert hall, a theater, and a gallery for contemporary art. Having opened in 1990 to commemorate the 100th anniversary of Mito's designation as an official city, the ATM complex has served as the venue for a wide variety of planned events, including musical concerts, dramatic productions, and art exhibitions featuring both Japanese and foreign artists. In addition, it has broadened the scope of its mission to act as a base for locally-produced cultural activities. In the future, ATM will continue to be a locus of creative activities, transmitting Artistic culture from Mito to the rest of the world.
Country: Japan
Social Media: @ACM_theatre@arttowermito
Touring: No
Regular venues: ACM Theatre

Ainu Museum, The
Website: www.ainu-museum.or.jp
Phone: 144 823 914
Address: 2-3-4 Wakakusacho, Shiraoi-cho, Shiraoi-gun, JP
Information: Ainu dance is designated as a National Living Treasure by the Japanese government
Country: Japan
Social Media: @ainu_museum@ainu.museum
Touring: No

Aki Isoda Office
Address: 401, 2-3-12 Naka-Meguro, Meguro-ku, JP
Country: Japan
Contact: President Aki Isoda
Contact: stage Director Tadashi Azuma
Contact: Producer Masami Hamada
Touring: No

Akira Miura Music Office & Shinryoku Theatre Company
Address: San'ei Bldg., 2-4-4 Nishihonmachi, Nishi-ku, JP
Country: Japan
Contact: Director Masatoshi Araya
Touring: No

Angel
Website: www.gekidan-angel.co.jp
Email: info@gekidan-angel.co.jp
Address: 1-21-5 Nakanokami-machi, Hachioji, JP
Information: productions; Marco Polo And His Travels, Gongitsune, etc
Country: Japan

AOITORI Theatre Company
Website: www.aoitori.org
Email: aoitori@happy.email.ne.jp
Phone: 334 867 727
Address: 301 KS House, 5-46-32 Jingumae, Shibuya-ku, JP
Information: all female company established in 1973
Country: Japan
representative, playwright, Director & actor
Saki Kasai
playwright & actor
Orime Amagi
playwright & actor
Mayumi Tenkoh
Contact: Producer Hatsumi Nagai
Director & actor
Ai Serikawa
Touring: No
Regular venues: Aoyama Round Theatre 300 (q.v.), Aoyama Spiral Hall , Theatre Trum

Araumaza
Website: www.araumaza.co.jp/
Email: arauma@araumaza.co.jp
Phone: 339 625 942
Address: 81-4 Shimizu-cho, Itabashi-ku, JP
Country: Japan
Contact: Director Takeshi Kanoh
Touring: No

Art Tower Mito
Website: www.arttowermito.or.jp/play/theatre-e.html
Email: webstaff@arttowermito.or.jp
Phone: 292 278 111
Address: Mito Arts Foundation, 1-6-8 Goken-cho, Mito-shi, JP
Information: see under Dance
Country: Japan
Artistic & Managing Director
Koshiro Matsumoto
Social Media: @art_tower_mito
Touring: No
Regular venues: ACM Theatre

Artist of Noh Kyogen-Ohkura School
Email: YATARO.09@a2.mnx.ne.jp
Address: 5-22-41-406, Shakujiidai, Nerima-ku, JP
Information: a school of Kyogen
Country: Japan
Contact: head master Yataro Ohkura
Touring: No
Regular venues: National Noh Theatre 591 (q.v.)

Atomu
Website: www.atomw.co.jp
Email: atomw@pop12.odn.ne.jp
Address: 4-23-22-A102, Naka-Ochiai, Shinjuku-ku, JP
Country: Japan
Contact: Director Hideaki Akiyama
Touring: No

Bitchu Kagura Kurashikisha
Phone: 818 642 82008
Address: c/o Fujiwara Syaryo, 886-2 Kasuyama, Kurashiki, JP
Country: Japan
Contact: Director Masao Matsui
Touring: No

Bun-raku Kyokai association
Website: bunraku.or.jp
Email: info@bunraku.or.jp
Address: c/o National Bunraku Theatre, 1-12-10 Nippon-bashi, Chuo-ku, JP
Country: Japan
Touring: No
Regular venues: National Theatre (q.v.), National Bunra-ku Theatre (q.v.)

Bungakuza
Website: www.bungakuza.com
Email: info@bungakuza.com
Address: 10 Shinano-machi, Shinjuku-ku, JP
Information: a Shingeki new drama troupe established in 1937
Country: Japan
Touring: No
Regular venues: Kinokuniya Southern Theater (q.v.), Kinokuniya Hall (q.v.), Bungakuza Atelier (q.v.)

Bungei
Address: 201 Aota Bldg., 3-1-9 Koenji-Kita, Suginami-ku, JP
Country: Japan
Contact: Director Haruo Muramatsu
Touring: No

Bunkaza
Website: www.bunkaza.com
Email: info@bunkaza.com
Phone: 338 282 260
Address: 3-22-12 Tabata, Kita-ku, JP
Country: Japan
Touring: No

Chijinkai
Website: www1.biz.biglobe.ne.jp/~CJK/
Email: chijinkai@mub.biglobe.ne.jp
Phone: 813 335 48308
Address: 7F, Maruki Bldg., 2-8-18 Shinjuku, Shinjuku-ku, JP
Country: Japan
Contact: Director Koichi Kimura
Contact: contact Emi Watanabe
Touring: No
Regular venues: Kinokuniya Hall (q.v.), Kinokuniya Southern Theatreq.v.

China Art Center
Website: www.china-art.co.jp
Email: info@china-art.co.jp
Phone: 356 168 822
Address: 1-22-6-1 Higashiayase, Adachi-ku , Tokyo 120-0004
Information: The China Cultural Arts Center (Taiyo International Co., Ltd.) includes artists in fields such as acrobatics, Kyoto drama, transformation, Shaolin martial arts, Niko and other performers and dancers selected from China's leading art groups. It has been formed and is developing performances and events at theaters, schools, hotels, shopping centers, etc. all over Japan.
Country: Japan

Choju Giga
Website: www.linkclub.or.jp/~giga/
Email: giga@acpv.ne.jp
Phone: 814 296 06000
Address: 4-4-3 Ohgidai, Iruma City, JP
Information: has transformed a number of Shakespeare's plays into their 'Kabuki Musicals'; hopes to tour abroad
Country: Japan
Contact: production Manager Megumi Nohara f
leader & Director & playwright & actor
Masafumi Chinen
Touring: No
Regular venues: Honda Gekijo 386 (q.v.), The Suzunari 200 (q.v.), Theatre Green 130 (q.v.)

Choryu
Website: www.gekidan-choryu.co.jp
Email: info@gekidan-choryu.co.jp
Phone: 666 582 315
Address: 1-6-17 Matsu, Nishinari-ku, JP
Country: Japan
Contact: Director Eiji Fujimoto
Touring: No
Regular venues: Hep Hall, Isshin-Ji Theatre

DAM Theatre
Website: homepage3.nifty.com/da-m/
Email: dam@mbh.nifty.com
Phone: 333 606 463
Address: 201 Inoue Bldg., 5-29-20 Higashi-Nakano, Nakano-ku, JP
Country: Japan
Contact: financial Manager Minako Saki f
Contact: house Manager Hijiri Yaegashi
representative & Director
Hiroshi Ohashi
Touring Countries: France, German, Hong Kong, Kyrgyzstan, Indonesia, Taiwan
Touring: No
Regular venues: Proto-Theater, Azabu. die pratze

Deaf Theatre of Japan
Website: www.totto.or.jp
Email: JTD@tokyo.email.ne.jp
Phone: 337 790 233
Address: 2-2-16 Nishi-Shinagawa, Shinagawa-ku, JP
Information: a deaf theatre troupe that uses Kyogen Noh farce; now our Memorial Book is available
Country: Japan
Contact: leader Akihiro Yonaiyama
Touring: No
Regular venues: National Noh Theatre (q.v.), Setagaya Public Theatre, Theatre X cai (q.v.)

Dohmu
Phone: 334 664 190
Address: 4-4-9 Kitazawa, Setagaya-ku, JP
Country: Japan
Contact: Director Goroh Kubota
Touring: No

Donkameza
Website: www.donkameza.com
Email: kameda@donkameza.com
Phone: 484 820 916
Address: 4-1-3, Nodera, Niiza, JP
Country: Japan
Director & playwright

Yukito Kameda
Touring: No

Dora Theatrical Company
Website: www.gekidandora.com
Email: gekidandora@pop12.odn.ne.jp
Phone: 339 371 101
Address: 1-1-4 Nakadai, Itabashi-ku, JP
Information: established in 1972
Country: Japan
Contact: Artistic Director Junji Ohmine
Contact: representative Director Shoichi Yamada
Contact: Head of Production dept. Motoko Tanabe
Touring Countries: Lithuania
Touring: No
Regular venues: Haiyuza Gekijo (q.v.)

Douke
Website: www.douke.co.jp/
Email: info@douke.co.jp
Phone: 929 229 738
Address: 4-2-7 Suzaku, Dazaifu, JP
Country: Japan
Contact: leader Shougo Shinozaki
Touring Countries: China, Thailand, South Korea
Touring: No

Dramatic Company Hakkiza
Website:
www2.infoweb.or.jp/PAJA/hakkiza/index-e.html
Email: hakkiza@m30.ctn.ne.jp
Phone: 333 897 671
Address: 1-10-5 Numabukuro, Nakano-ku, JP
Country: Japan
Contact: lighting Tomoyuki Nemoto
Contact: production Yoshiko Kijima f
Contact: actor representative Ken Ohara
 leader & Artistic Director
 Kazuo Sasaki
Touring: No
Regular venues: Ginza Miyukikan Gekijo 80 (q.v.)

Dramatic Company Souzo
Website: www.suyamapro.co.jp
Email: suyamapro@k4.dion.ne.jp
Phone: 524 523 111
Address: 20-15 Tsubaki-cho, Nakamura-ku, Nagoya, JP
Country: Japan
Contact: play writer Junko Suzuki f
Contact: President Kazuhide Suyama
Touring: No

EAST
Website: www.j28studio.com
Email: hirojboy@hotmail.com
Phone: 333 697 486
Address: B102, 7-2-10, Nishi-shinjuku, JP
Information: EAST&Hiroshi Jin's ""J.28 Teater
Group""have 3Groop!""East""is dance drama.""J-BOYS""is
entertainment.""Tokyo Trianglr""is dance.
Country: Japan
Contact: leader Hiroshi Jin
Touring: No

En Company
Website: www.en21.co.jp
Email: en@en21.co.jp
Phone: 358 280 654
Address: 5F Tawara-machi Centre Bldg., 1-2-3 Nishi
Asakusa, Taitoku, JP
Country: Japan
Contact: President Noboru Nakaya
Touring: No
Regular venues: Kinokuniya Hall 418 (q.v.), Theatre X
(q.v.), Stage En

Engeki Shudan Mitoh
Website: www1.biz.biglobe.ne.jp/~mitoh
Email: mitoh@mvc.biglobe.ne.jp
Phone: 338 800 034
Address: 1-9-1 Umejima, Adachi-ku, JP
Country: Japan
Contact: Director Yuzo Tachikawa
Touring: No

Engekijin Bhoukensha Ltd
Website: www.bhoukensha.co.jp
Email: info@bhoukensha.co.jp
Phone: 522 411 070
Address: 3F, Marubishi Bldg., 4-14-61 Ohsu, Naka-ku,
Nagoya, JP
Country: Japan
Contact: Director Misako Naito
Touring: No

Folk Group Onikenbai
Website:
www.f7.dion.ne.jp/~ragtime
Email: ragtime@f7.dion.ne.jp
Phone:
568 514 199
Address: c/o Ragtime, 1661-94 Tamano-cho, Kasugai, JP
Country: Japan
 secretary General & Producer

Yuko Yoshitomi f
President & Artistic Director
Yoshinori Iwase
Touring: No
Regular venues: Nagoya-shi Geijutsu Sohzoh Center Hall
640 (q.v.), Aichi-ken Kinroh Kaikan 1488 (q.v.), Artpia Hall

For-you
Website: www.gekidanforyou.com
Email: foryou-jm@mtg.biglobe.ne.jp
Phone: 422 465 461
Address: 3-30-9 Kichijoji Minami-cho, Musashino, JP
Country: Japan
Contact: Director Toshihiko Kojima
Touring: No

Fukidamari
Website: www2u.biglobe.ne.jp/~fuki/
Email: fukidamari@mwb.biglobe.ne.jp
Phone: 332 685 049
Address: 1F, Arai Bldg., 6-56 Kagurazaka, Shinjuku-ku, JP
Country: Japan
Contact: leader Nobuhisa Ohshima
Contact: deputy leader Ayako Minegishi f
Touring: No
Regular venues: Edo Tokyo Museum / Kouenji-kaikann
Hall

Furusato Caravan
Website: www.furucara.com
Email: furucara@alto.ocn.ne.jp
Phone: 423 816 721
Address: 6-5-3 Hon-cho, Koganei, JP
Information: performs original theatre pieces on the
road; supported by regional government
Country: Japan
Contact: composer Tateo Teramoto
Contact: President Yoshinobu Ouchi
Contact: chief Producer Junko Hiratsuka
 choreographer & actor
 Mie Amagi
 script writer & Director
 Katsuhiko Ishizuka
Contact: production stage Manager Mitsuyoshi Muray-
ama
Touring: No
Regular venues: Theater Apple 700 (q.v.), Tokyo Metro-
politan Art Space 841 (q.v.), Tokyo Geijutsu Gekijo

Gakugekidan Ichohza
Website: ichouza.com
Email: ichouza@h2.dion.ne.jp
Phone: 333 224 378
Address: 6-26-15-201 Matsubara, Setagaya-ku, JP
Information: also presents 'readers theatre'
Country: Japan
Contact: Director Yutaka Kameyama
Touring: No

Geijutsu Gekijo
Website: plaza.mdn.or.jp/~gekidangg/
Email: gekidangg@dream.com
Phone: 336 431 403
Address: Murabayashi Bldg., 1-8-7 Saga, Kohtoh-ku, JP
Country: Japan
Contact: Artistic Director Kazuki Kobayashi
Touring: No

Geikyo
Website: www.hinocatv.ne.jp/~wildcats/geikyo.htm
Phone: 425 872 136
Address: B1 Corpo Stable, 4-28-2 Toyoda, Hino, JP
Country: Japan
 leader & Director
 Takeshi Aono
 Artistic & stage Director
 Shizuo Arai
Contact: lighting designer Tsutomu Kawakami
Contact: set designer Hitoshi Sano
Touring: No
Regular venues: Eyepit Mejiro

Geinoh Yamashirogumi
Website: www.mahoroba.or.jp/~yama/
Phone: 333 664 741
Address: 1-22-3 Higashinakano, Nakano-ku, JP
Country: Japan
Contact: President Shoji Yamashiro
Touring: No

Gekidan Dainana Byohtoh
Phone: 338 091 431
Address: 6-47-3 Arakawa, Arakawa-ku, JP
Country: Japan
Contact: Director Renji Ishibashi
Touring: No

Gekidan Geiyuza
Website: www.geiyuza.com
Email: geiyuza@mri.biglobe.ne.jp
Phone: 424 894 555
Address: 2-28-4 Tamagawa, Chofu, JP
Country: Japan

Contact: Director Nirou Hiratsuka
Touring: No
Regular venues: Tokyo Metropolitan Art Space

Gekidan KAITAISHA
Website: www.kaitaisha.com
Email: gekidan@kaitaisha.com
Phone: 358 025 387
Address: 1F, Igarashi Bldg., 2-4-8 Yushima, Bunkyo-ku, JP
Information: founded in 1985
Country: Japan
Contact: company Manager Takeshi Hata
 representative & Director
 Shinjin Shimizu
Touring Countries: Germany, UK, Denmark, Croatia,
Singapore, HongKong, USA, Australia
Touring: No
Regular venues: Kampnagel300, ICA150, Chapter Arts
Centre100, Esplanade250

Gekidan Kazenoko
Website: www.kazenoko.co.jp
Email: all@kazenoko.co.jp
Phone: 426 521 001
Address: 1320-1 Miyama-cho, Hachioji, JP
Information: see also Gekidan Kazenoko-Hokkaidoq.v.,
Gekidan Kazenoko-Tokyoq.v. and Gekidan Kazenoko-Ky-
ushuq.v.
Country: Japan
Contact: General Manager Masami Miyashita
Touring Countries: Australia, Canada, and Korea in
recent 3 years
Touring: No
Regular venues: Honda Gekijo 386 (q.v.), Piccolo Theatre
396 (q.v.)

Gekidan Kazenoko-Hokkaido
Website: www.remus.dti.ne.jp/~Kazenoko/
Email: kazenoko@remus.dti.ne.jp
Phone: 117 263 619
Address: Nishi 11-chome, Kita 27-jo, Kita-ku, Sapporo, JP
Information: see also Gekidan Kazenoko (q.v.), Gekidan
Kazenoko-Tokyoq.v. and Gekidan Kazenoko-Kyushuq.v.
Country: Japan
Contact: Director Terumasa Narumi
Contact: stage Director Akane Nakajima f
Touring: No
Regular venues: Sapporo Children Theatre Yamabiko-za

Gekidan Kazenoko-Kyusyu
Website: www.kazenoko-kyushu.or.jp
Email: info@kazenoko-kyushu.or.jp
Phone: 928 417 889
Address: 5-5-13 Nishijin, Sawara-ku, JP
Information: performing with Korean Drama Company
for 4 years see also Gekidan Kazenokoq.v., Gekidan Kaze-
noko-Hokkaidoq.v. and Gekidan Kazenoko-Tokyoq.v.
Country: Japan
Contact: General Manager Yuichi Kariya
Contact: Yoichi Hayashi
Touring Countries: Australia, China Hong Kong, Korea,
India, Indonesia, US, Canada, Singapore
Touring: No

Gekidan Kazenoko-Tokyo
Website: www.kazenoko.co.jp/tokyo
Email: tokyo@kazenoko.co.jp
Phone: 334 668 339
Address: 4-21-19 Kitazawa, Setagaya-ku, JP
Information: see also Gekidan Kazenoko (q.v.), Gekidan
Kazenoko-Hokkaidoq.v. and Gekidan Kazenoko-Kyush-
uq.v.
Country: Japan
Contact: Administration Nobuko Takagaki
Contact: General Manager Toshiko Hosonuma
Contact: stage Director Tohru Tanaka
Touring: No
Regular venues: Honda Gekijo 386 (q.v.), Kitazawa Town
Hall 300 (q.v.)

Gekidan Magnet World
Website: www.soseisha.com
Email: soseisha-nigna@biglobe.ne.jp
Phone: 427 205 444
Address: 5-16-18, Morino, Machida, JP
Country: Japan
Contact: President Gai Sawamoto
Touring: No

Gekidan Toho Gendaigeki
Website: toho.co.jp
Phone:
332 018 100
Address: c/o Toho Co Ltd, Kita 15F, Yuraku-cho Denki
bldg, 1-7-1 Yuraku-cho, Chiyoda-ku, JP
Information: see also Toho Co Ltd
Country: Japan
Contact: dept. of foreign affairs Kazuhiko Matsuda
Contact: Manager Kuniaki Fujii
Touring: No
Regular venues: Imperial Theatre 1917 (q.v.), Geijut-
surzaq.v.

Gekidan Tosho

Phone:
333 777 483
Address: 1-50-6 Hon-cho, Shibuya-ku, JP
Information: established in 1925
Country: Japan
Contact: President Gennosuke Aiba
Touring: No
Regular venues: Mitsukoshi Gekijo 514 (q.v.)

Gekidan Urinko Theatre Troupe
Website: www.urinko.jp
Email: info@urinko.jp
Phone: 527 721 882
Address: 1-112 Hachimae, Meito-ku, Nagoya, JP
Information: has its own theatre; wishes to exchange the information about plays for children and youth; collaborated with Germany, Korea and Australia; please contact via email both Japanese and English
Country: Japan
Contact: representative Takeya Gotoh
Touring: No

Gekidan Wakakusa
Website: www.wakakusa.org
Email: g-wakakus@jcom.home.ne.jp
Phone: 333 336 821
Address: 3-3-16 Nishiogi-Minami, Suginami-ku, JP
Country: Japan
Contact: Director Midori Yaegaki
Touring: No
Regular venues: Wakakusa Atelier 100

Gekikohbo Rhyming
Website: www2.neweb.ne.jp.wd/rhyming/
Email: rhyming@mc.neweb.ne.jp
Phone: 334 437 358
Address: 302, 3-19-7 Takanawa, Minato-ku, JP
Country: Japan
Contact: leader Harumi Nakashima
Contact: actress ,Director harumi nakajima
Touring: No
Regular venues: Theatre Tops

Gekiza
Website: gekiza.fc2web.com
Email: gekiza@zd6.so-net.ne.jp
Phone: 527 330 444
Address: 4F, Imaike Chunichi Bldg., 5-3-2 Imaike, Chikusa-ku, Nagoya, JP
Country: Japan
Contact: Director Shizuo Amano
Touring: No
Regular venues: Meitetsu Hall

Gendaigeki Center Manatsuza
Website: www.manatsuza.com
Phone: 338 164 029
Address: 2F Akamon Abitation, 5-29-13 Hongo, Bunkyo-ku, JP
Country: Japan
Contact: Administration Satoshi Ono
Contact: leader Isshin Ikeda
Touring: No
Regular venues: Bunkyo Civic Hall 300 (q.v.)

Gifu Deaf Theatre Ibuki
Address: 301 Maison Nakagawa, 37-4 Oike-cho, JP
Country: Japan
 leader & Director
 Yoriko Kawai
Contact: assistant Director Shinobu Okuda f
Contact: lighting designer Kohzoh Asano
Contact: sound designer Nobuko Toki
Touring: No

Go Go Keronpa!
Website: www.mbird.ne.jp/isco/keronpa/index
Email: isco@bird.mbird.ne.jp
Phone: 357 224 231
Address: 3F, 2-2-6, Ebisu-minami, Shibuya-ku, JP
Information: established in 1997
Country: Japan
Contact: contact Takashi Endo
Touring: No

GRANDE OSTE
Email: onishi.noriko@dream.com
Phone: 338 160 157
Address: 6 San'yo Bldg., 1-5-17 Hongo, Bunkyo-ku, JP
Country: Japan
Contact: Producer Noriko Onishi
Contact: Noriko Onishi
Touring: No
Regular venues: Nippori Sunny Hall 400 (q.v.), Tokyo Metropolitan Art Space Mini Theater 200 (q.v.), Art Sphere (q.v.)

Gunma Chugei
Phone: 272 882 700
Address: 626-498 Akagiyama, Fujimi-mura, Seta-gun, JP
Information: The drama is mainly for children
Country: Japan
Contact: Executive Director Toshiko Ishikawa
Touring: No
Regular venues: Mirai Studio, primary schools around

Gunma area

Guy Foissy Theatre – Th
Website: www.ziocity.to.jp/hollywood/stage/1480/index.htmlg
Email: gytanima@t.toshima.ne.jp
Phone: 339 813 097
Address: 5-6-17 Higashi-Ikebukuro, Toshima-ku, JP
Country: Japan
Contact: Producer Masao Tani
Contact: auteur Guy Foissy
Touring: No
Regular venues: Theatre X cai (q.v.)

Haikyo
Website: haikyo.or.jp
Email: ghaikyo@jade.dti.ne.jp
Phone: 339 505 705
Address: 1-17-9 Kami-Ochiai, Shinjuku-ku, JP
Country: Japan
Contact: Director Toru Nishikawa
Touring: No
Regular venues: TACCS1179 Haikyo Hall

Haisho
Website: homepage2.nifty.com/haishou/
Email: haishou@nifty.com
Phone: 339 871 787
Address: B1F, Toto-Otsuka-Corpo, 2-7-3, Higashi-Ikebukuro, Toshima-ku, JP
Country: Japan
Contact: Director Shin Saito
Touring: No
Regular venues: Tokyo Art Theatre, Mini Theatre 300 (q.v.),

Hakken no Kai
Phone: 339 827 073
Address: Fukuda-so, 1-16-19 Ikebukuro Hon-cho, Toshima-ku, JP
Country: Japan
Contact: leader Ryosuke Uryu
Touring: No

Half Moon Theatre Company
Website: www.halfmoon-jp.com
Email: my@halfmoon-jp.com
Phone: 333 686 714
Address: A 308 Thanks Higashi Nakano, 1-32-1 Higashi Nakano, Nakano-ku, JP
Country: Japan
Contact: Artistic Director Masaharu Yoshiiwa
Touring: No
Regular venues: Geki Little Theatre 130 (q.v.), Eye Pit Mejiro (q.v.) Sanbyakunin Theatre 257, Kichijoji Theatre

Hanagumi Shibai
Website: www.hanagumi.ne.jp
Email: office@hanagumi.ne.jp
Phone: 337 099 430
Address: 1-19-6 Tamagawa, Setagaya-ku, JP
Country: Japan
Contact: Director Yukikazu Kano
Touring: No

Hasimoto Fusayo Mime Solo
Phone: 353 821 237
Address: 201 Nemoto-so, 2-19-23 Zenpukuji, Suginami-ku, JP
Country: Japan
Contact: mime Fusayo Hashimoto
Touring: No

Hihoukan Shoutendou Ichiza
Website: hiho.chanoyu.ne.jp/
Email: boogie@okym.enjoy.ne.jp
Phone: 862 315 915
Address: Boogie Studio, 3-20, Amaseminamimachi, JP
Information: established in 1992
Country: Japan
Contact: leader Tamatori Nyan Nyan
Contact: Manager chikara sumiyoshi
Contact: web Takashi Shirakami
 Russiawith ""beZen Koku""
Touring: No
Regular venues: Okayama Prefecture Culture Centre

Himawari Theatre Group
Website: www.himawari.net/
Email: produce@himawari.net
Phone: 334 760 011
Address: 2-12-12 Ebisu-Nishi, Shibuya-ku, JP
Country: Japan
Contact: Director Fujio Sunaoka
Touring: No

Hirosaki Gekijo
Website: www.hirogeki.co.jp
Email: office@hirogeki.co.jp
Phone:
177 764 102
Address: 36-2, Aza-Okada, Ohaza-Namioka, Namioka, JP
Information: production uses combinations of different languages, such as Chinese, French, English as well as the

standard Japanese and Japanese regional dialects, and visiting actors from overseas. And Hirosaki Gekijo took part in the world performing art festival in
Country: Japan
 Director & playwright
 Koji Hasegawa
Contact: Choichiroh Nakamura
Touring: No

Hosho Noh School
Website: www.hosho.or.jp
Email: info@hosho.or.jp
Phone: 338 114 843
Address: 1-5-9 Hongo, Bunkyo-ku, JP
Information: a school of Noh play managed by Hohshoh-kai (q.v.); has its own venue Hohshoh Nohga-kudo (q.v.)
Country: Japan
Touring: No

Hyogo Prefecture Art Culture Association
Website: hyogo-arts.or.jp
Email: kenminkaikan@hyogo-arts.or.jp
Phone: 783 212 131
Address: c/o Hyogo Kenmin Kaikan, Hyogo Geijutsu, 4-16-3, Shimoyamate-dori, Chuou-ku, Kobe, JP
Information: presented by Hyogo Arts & Culture Association
Country: Japan
Contact: Artistic Director Masakazu Yamazaki
Touring: No

ICANOF
Website: www.hi-net.ne.jp/icanof/top.htm
Email: mol@r66.7-dj.com
Phone: 178 459 247
Address: 14-18 Furujosenshita, Hachinohe, JP
Country: Japan
Contact: leader Shigeyuki Toshima
Touring: No

ISHINHA
Website: www.ishinha.com
Email: chiho@ishinha.com
Phone: 667 632 634
Address: 302, 6-4-16 Tani-machi, Chuo-ku, JP
Country: Japan
Contact: President Yukichi Matsumoto
 company Manager & planning
 Chiho Eto
Touring: No

Isseki Nicho
Website: www.isseki.com/
Email: kishimo@campus.ne.jp
Phone: 333 162 824
Address: 1F, Dai-ichi Shimura Bldg., 4-1-55 Narita-Higashi, Suginami-ku, JP
Information: established in 1986 by an ex-journalist
Country: Japan
Contact: Producer Keiko Takeuchi
Contact: production Masashi Kishimoto
 President & playwright & Director
 Toshinobu Kojo
Touring: No
Regular venues: Kinokuniya Theatre 418 (q.v.), Aoyama Round Theatre 376 (q.v.), THEATER/TOPS 155 (q.v.), Kinokuniya Southern Theatre 468 (q.v.)

Izumi School of Kyogen
Phone: 339 740 506
Address: 2-58-7 Toshin-cho, Itabashi-ku, JP
Information: teaches Kyogen in Paris
Country: Japan
Contact: the 20th head master Motoya Izumi
Contact: Chairman Setsuko Izumi f
Contact: kyogen actor Junko Izumi
Touring: No

Japan Mime Studio
Website: www009.upp.so-net.ne.jp/Nihon-MIME/
Email: hiro-s@bg7.so-net.ne.jp
Phone: 334 213 603
Address: 1-7-15 Komazawa, Setagaya-ku, JP
Information: with Etienne Decroux, and, in the summers, also studied "real mime"according to the Stanislavsky Method as taught by the distinguished Bella Reine. After returning to Japan he took over the Japan Mime Studio, and has worked unceasingly for over 53 years to promote mime and train aspiring mime artists
Country: Japan
Contact: Director Hiroyasu Sasaki
Touring: No
Regular venues: Edo Tokyo Hakubutsukan Hall; Theatre TRAM (q.v.)

Japanese Traditional Performers Association (JTP)
Website: www.dentougeinou.com
Email: info@dentougeinou.com
Phone:
453 243 421
Address: Yubinbango221-0822 Kanagawa Prefecture, Kanagawa-ku, Yokohama-shi Nishikanagawa 1-15-2

Information: Japanese Traditional Performers Association promotes Japanese popular culture, and present their projects locally and abroad. They deliver various performing arts with various flavours and specialize in the planning and production of traditional performing arts.
Country: Japan

Jitensha Kinqureat's Company
Website: www.jitekin.com/
Email: mail@jitekin.com
Phone: 354 894 434
Address: 901, 36-22 Udagawa-cho, Shibuya-ku, JP
Information: 4 actors plus guests, 2-3 productions per year
Country: Japan
Contact: Director Yumi Suzuki
Contact: playwright Sanae Iijima f
Touring: No
Regular venues: Haiyuza Gekijo, Space Zero

Kabugekidan Dengakuza
Website: www.valley.ne.jp/~dengaku/
Email: dengaku@valley.ne.jp
Phone: 265 783 423
Address: 9000 Tomigata, Ina, JP
Country: Japan
Contact: Manager Mitsuko Matsuda f
Contact: leader Michio Matsuda
Touring Countries: South Korea
Touring: No

Kageboushi Theater Company
Website: www.kageboushi.com
Email: office@kageboushi.com
Phone: 422 547 770
Address: 2-1-5 Midori-cho, Musashino, JP
Information: conducts international cultural exchange with people and organisations in theatre
Country: Japan
Contact: President Yasuaki Yamasaki
Contact: General Manager Junko Hashimoto
Contact: Director Toru Koda
Contact: Director of acting dept. Naoyuki Harada
Contact: stage Director Shinji Onohara
Touring: No

Kai
Website: www.gekidan-kai.com
Email: kai@gekidan-kai.com
Phone: 422 486 059
Address: 4-6-1 Kichijoji Minami-machi, Musashino, JP
Information: established in 1976; the best artists at Cultural Minisrty Art Festival perform plays by Japanese playwrights
Country: Japan
Contact: leader Koji Nakata
Touring: No

Kamonegi Shot
Website: www.jah.ne.jp/~kamonegi/
Email: kamonegi@po.jah.ne.jp
Phone: 333 689 021
Address: 4-22-33-13, Takadanobaba, Shinjuku-ku, JP
Country: Japan
Contact: actress Yu Yamagami
Director & playwright & actress
Ryoko Takami f
Contact: Manager Naomi Kikuchi
Director & actress
Keiko Tada
Touring: No
Regular venues: Theater/Tops 155 (q.v.), Aoyama Round Theatre 300 (q.v.), Theater Fonte 386 (q.v.), Art Sphere Sphere Mex 200 (q.v.)

Kansai Geijutsuza
Website: www.os.urban.ne.jp/home/kangei/
Email: kangei@os.urban.ne.jp
Phone: 666 612 112
Address: 2-10-2 Kishinosato Higashi, Nishinari-ku, JP
Country: Japan
Contact: Director Hiroshi Yamamoto
Touring: No
Regular venues: Kangei Studio

Kanze Noh School
Website: www.kanze.net
Phone: 357 664 520
Address: 6-24-4-1F Jingumae, Shibuya-ku, JP
Information: a school of Noh play
Country: Japan
Contact: head master Kiyokazu Kanze
Touring: No

Karagumi
Phone: 333 308 118
Address: 4-3-9, Yamato-cho, Nakano-ku, JP
Country: Japan
Contact: Director Juro Kara
Touring: No

Katoh Ken'ichi Jimusho

Website: homepage2.nifty.com/katoken/
Phone: 335 570 789
Address: 39-18 Sakae-cho, Nerima-ku, JP
Information: presents mainly translations of North American contemporary plays
Country: Japan
Contact: Producer Etsuko Abe f
Contact: representative Ken'ichi Katoh
Touring: No

Keihin Kyohdo Gekidan
Website: www.kinet.or.jp/keihin/
Email: keihin@kinet.or.jp
Phone: 445 114 951
Address: 2-109 Furuichiba, Saiwai-ku, Kawasaki, JP
Information: non-profit making company
Country: Japan
Contact: President Mamoru Shirotani
Contact: Director Toshiroh Hosoda
Touring: No
Regular venues: Space Keihin

Kinder Space
Website: www.kinder-space.com
Email: post@kinder-space.com
Phone: 482 554 342
Address: 1F Oku, Mansion Hiruma, 1-23-3, Nishi-Kawaguchi, Kawaguchi, JP
Information: holds workshops for professionals to beginners and also for local amateur theatre groups
Country: Japan
Contact: Director Kazuki Harada
Contact: Administration Hiromi Seta f
Touring: No
Regular venues: Kinder Space Atelier 50, Theater X, Sainokuni Saitama Art Theatre

Kita-ku Tsuka Kohei Gekidan
Website: www.tsuka.co.jp/
Email: mail@tsuka.co.jp
Phone: 359 241 126
Address: 4F Kyu Kitazono Shougakkou Nai, 3-6-1 Akabanekita, Kita-ku, JP
Country: Japan
Contact: Director Kohei Tsuka
Contact: administrator Maya Urata f
Touring: No
Regular venues: Hokutopia Tsutsuji Hall 402 (q.v.)

Kiyama Jimusho
Email: kiyama-co@hkg.odn.ne.jp
Phone: 359 580 855
Address: 3-17-11-201, Nishi-Ikebukuro, Toshima-ku, JP
Country: Japan
Contact: Producer Kiyoshi Kiyama
Contact: playwright Harue Tsutsumi
playwright & Director
Yoshiyuki Fukuda
Contact: Director Toshifumi Sueki
Touring Countries: UKLondon, USNew York, Poland, Taiwan etc
Touring: No
Regular venues: Haiyuza Gekijo 300 (q.v.)

Komaba Agora Theater
Website: www.komaba-agora.com
Phone: 334 672 743
Address: 1-11-13 Komaba, Meguro-ku, 153-0041, JP
Information: The Komaba Agora Theater "supports young theater companies through theaters". Since 2003, it has been prolific in innovating the way small theaters should be in Japan. The annual program is selected by young creators as program officers and led by Artistic Director Oriza Hirata.
Country: Japan

Komatsuza
Website: www.komatsuza.co.jp/
Email: webmaster@komatsuza.co.jp
Phone: 338 515 165
Address: 503, 1-30-5 Yanagibashi, Taitoh-ku, JP
Country: Japan
leader & playwright
Hisashi Inoue
Touring: No
Regular venues: Kinokuniya Hall 418 (q.v.)

Kongoh Noh School
Phone: 752 213 049
Address: Shijo Agaru, Muromachi-dori, Nakagyo-ku, JP
Information: a school of Noh play
Country: Japan
Contact: contact Ogamo Rebbeca Teele
Contact: head Hisanori Kongoh
Touring: No

Kosen Kagami Troupe
Website: www.interq.or.jp/www1/kanchang/daikagura/maruichi
Email: kosen@edo-daikagura.com
Phone: 338 136 220
Address: 706, 1-3-17 Koishikawa, Bunkyo-ku, JP
Information: we play at decoration parties
Country: Japan
Touring: No

Kukan Engi
Website: www3.plala.or.jp/koudai
Email: ko@lilac.plala.or.jp
Phone: 449 339 754
Address: c/o Okabe Kikaku, 1-12-7 Higashi Ikuta, Tama-ku, Kawasaki, JP
Country: Japan
President & playwright & Director

Kuromori Kabuki
Phone: 234 265 777
Address: 1-4-15 Naka-machi, Sakata, JP
Information: a farmers' Kabuki and has been handed down by the local people for nearly 270 years; play at Hiei Shrine on 15th/17th Feb every year
Country: Japan
Contact: leader Tsuyoshi Maeda
Touring: No
Regular venues: Hiei Shrine

Kurumiza
Phone: 757 912 191
Address: 21 Tanaka Asukai-cho, Sakyo-ku, JP
Country: Japan
Contact: Director Emiko Nakaguchi
Touring: No

Kyohgei
Website: www.kyogei.com
Phone: 503 385 3822
Address: 31-18 Nohso-Kitashirohori, Fushimi-ku, JP
Country: Japan
Contact: Director Sayoko Yamanaka
Touring: No

Kyorakuza
Website: www.kyorakuza.com
Phone: 335 450 931
Address: 1002,1-4-8,Tsukiji, Chuo-ku, JP
Country: Japan
Contact: President Kazuhisa Nakanishi
Contact: production Manager Fumino Tsukishima
Touring: No
Regular venues: Tokyo Metropolitan Art Space (q.v.), Theatre X cai (q.v.), New National Theatre (q.v.)

Kyu Shinkuukan
Phone: 333 231 513
Address: 2F, Sakamoto Bldg., 4-45-16 Akazutsumi, Setagaya-ku, JP
Country: Japan
Director & translator
Yumi Tominaga
Touring: No
Regular venues: Gekidan Kyu Shinkuukan, Shimo-Takaido Atelier 30

Lasenkan Theatre Company
Email: LasenkanTheatre@aol.com
Phone: 798 654 607
Address: 112, 5-3 Tozaki-cho, Nishinomiya, JP
Information: Spain Office: Apartat de Correus 136, 08360 Canet de Mar, Barcelona, Espa
Country: Japan
Director & production Manager
Saburo Shimada
Touring: No
Regular venues: Piccolo Theater 396 (q.v.), Centre Parroquial 200, Theater X (q.v.)

Libresen
Website: www.libresen.com
Email: office@libresen.com
Phone: 337 935 388
Address: 410, 1-5-10 Kami-Meguro, Meguro-ku, JP
Country: Japan
President & playwright & Director
Yasuhiko Ohashi
representative & playwright & Director
Yumiko Itoh
Contact: lighting designer Yoshiya Kawamata
Contact: stage Manager Mutsuo Aoki
Contact: Producer Naoko Ochiai
Touring: No
Regular venues: Honda Gekijo 386 (q.v.), Theater/Tops 155 (q.v.), The Suzunari 200 (q.v.), Ikebukuro Art Theatre

LIL-LIPUT ARMY II (Second)
Website: www.sa.netlaputa.com/~tama-sho
Email: tama-sho@sa.netlaputa.com
Phone: 669 443 380
Address: Tamatsukuri-Shogeki ten, 1F, 2-23-17, Tamatsukuri, Chuo-ku, JP
Country: Japan
Director & playwright
Efu Wakagi
Contact: sound coordinator Takayoshi Miyazaki
Contact: lighting designer Haruhiko Takayama
Touring: No
Regular venues: Wahha Hall, Honda Gekijo 400 (q.v.)

M.O.P.
Website: www.g-mop.com/
Email: staff@g-mop.com

Phone: 333 803 140
Address: c/o Nevula Project Co. Ltd, 5-2-1-3F Chuo, Nakano-ku, JP
Country: Japan
leader & playwright & Director
Nozomi Makino
Touring: No
Regular venues: Kinokuniya Hall

Michi
Phone: 118 838 545 offi
Address: N.A.C Talent Center Sapporo, 13-10, Hiraoka 2 jo, 1 cho-me, Kiyota-ku, Sapporo, JP
Information: founded in 1979
Country: Japan
Contact: leader Youichiro Kitagawa
Contact: General Manager/lecturer Hiromi Hosokawa f
Contact: assistant Chika Hosokawa
Touring: No
Regular venues: small to medium sized halls in Sapporo city

Mixed Media Art Communications MMAC
Phone: 333 112 461
Address: c/o NAP International, 4-21-4 Narita Higashi, Suginami-ku, JP
Information: organizes MMAC Festival in Tokyo (q.v.)
Country: Japan
Contact: Director Kyo Hoshino
Touring: No

MODE
Phone: 332 680 273
Address: No.203 Green-heights, 3-3, Sadohara-cho, Ichigaya, Shinjuku-ku, JP
Information: organize drama work shops throughout Japan
Country: Japan
representative & Producer
Osamu Matsumoto
Touring: No
Regular venues: Setagaya Public Theatre (q.v.)

Mumeijuku
Website: www.mumeijuku.net
Phone: 337 097 802
Address: 1-6-2 Okamoto, Setagaya-ku, JP
Information: own private non-profit & free acting school
Country: Japan
Contact: Artistic Director Kiyoto Hayashi
leader & actor
Tatsuya Nakadai
Touring: No
Regular venues: Le Theater Ginza 747 (q.v.), Sunshine Theater 832 (q.v.), Tokyo Geijutu Theater

Musical Company It's Follies
Website: www.allstaff.co.jp
Phone: 335 839 821
Address: Fontaine Bldg., 5-13-13 Roppongi, Minato-ku, JP
Information: founded in 1977
Country: Japan
Contact: Producer Gyo Ishikawa
President & General Producer
Yumi Tsuchiya
Contact: General Producer Joji Doi
Touring: No
Regular venues: Atelier Fontaine (q.v.), Kinokuniya Hall (q.v.), Haiyuza Gekijo q.v, Tokyo Metropolitan Art Theatre

NLT
Website: www.nlt.co.jp
Email: nlt@cello.ocn.ne.jp
Phone: 353 636 041
Address: 4F, Sugiyama Bldg., 13-10, Aizumi-cho, Shinjuku-ku, JP
Country: Japan
Contact: representative Shinji Kawabata
Contact: President Hiroshi Ogawa
Touring: No
Regular venues: Ginza Hakuhinkan Theater 388 (q.v.)

Nakama
Website: gekidan-nakama.com
Email: info@gekidan-nakama.com
Phone: 333 684 623
Address: 2-54-10 Chuo, Nakano-ku, JP
Country: Japan
Contact: Director Takeo Namai
Contact: production Yoshinobu Oda
Contact: stage Director Kiyoshi Takada
Contact: secretary General Hiroshi Miyake
Touring: No
Regular venues: Ikebukuro Art Hall, Kinokuniya Southern Theatre

Namidame Ginza
Website: www.namigin.com
Email: asai@k-factory.net
Phone: 337 702 242
Address: 7F Kotobukidougenzaka Bldg., 1-19-11 Dougenzaka, Shibuya-ku, JP
Country: Japan

Contact: lighting engineer Kimio Sato
Contact: Director Saburo Fukushima
Contact: sound engineer Takuhei Aoki
Contact: Press Mii Asai f
Contact: stage Director Takeshi Nihonmatsu
Touring: No
Regular venues: Theatre/Tops 155 (q.v.), Kinokuniya Hall 418 (q.v.)

New Art Theatre
Phone: 353 645 177
Address: 2-16-17, Koenji-Kita, Suginami-ku, JP
Country: Japan
Contact: representative Shozo Hisata
Contact: Manager Toshihiko Mashino
Touring: No

New National Theatre, Tokyo, Drama
Website: www.nntt.jac.go.jp
Phone: 353 525 738
Address: 1-1-1 Hon-machi, Shibuya-ku, JP
Information: see also Presenters
Country: Japan
Contact: Artistic Director drama Tamiya Kuriyama
Touring: No
Regular venues: New Natonal Theatre (q.v.), Playhouse 1010-1038, The Pit 340-468

Nezumiha Entokan Omega
Phone: 339 844 670
Address: 2-29-22 Nishi-Ikebukuro, Toshima-ku, JP
Country: Japan
Producer & Director
Seishi Miyashita
Touring: No
Regular venues: Nezumiha Entokan 30

Nijikko
Phone: 482 672 416
Address: 2-14-6 Shiba, Kawaguchi, JP
Country: Japan
Contact: Director Mineo Murase
Touring: No

Ninagawa Studio
Website: www.ninagawastudio.net
Email: info@ninagawastudio.net
Address: Minato-ku, JP
Country: Japan
Contact: Director Yukio Ninagawa
Touring: No
Regular venues: Meijiza, Misonoza Theatre q.v, Kintetsu Gekijo q.v, Setagaya Public Theatre

Nitosha
Website: www.nitosha.net
Email: info@nitosha.net
Phone: 356 384 587
Address: 2-17-12 Shin-Ohhashi, Koto-ku, JP
Country: Japan
Contact: company Manager Ai Nagai
Touring: No
Regular venues: Theatre Tram 220, Setagaya Public Theatre 600 Tokyo, Benisan Pit

NODA MAP
Website: www.nodamap.com
Phone: 337 977 993
Address: 5F, 2-1-13 Shibuya, Shibuya-ku, JP
Country: Japan
Contact: Director Hideki Noda
Contact: Producer Akiko Kitamura f
Touring: No
Regular venues: Bunkamura Theatre Cocoon 747 (q.v.), Kintetsu Gekijo 954 (q.v.)

NPO Dramatic Company Kyo
Website: gekidan-kyo.com
Email: gekidan_kyo1988@hotmail.com
Phone: 354 534 945
Address: 301 Haitsu 3, 3-30-3 Kitazawa, Setagaya-ku, JP
Information: Tokyo Novyi Repartory Theater
Country: Japan
representative & Director
Akiko Yagi
Contact: stage Hiroshi Okazaki
Contact: President Yuji Uehara
art & literature
Ko Sugasawa
Touring: No
Regular venues: Shimokitazawa Mini Theatre Kyo 42

NPO Gendaiza
Website: www.gendaiza.org
Email: info@gendaiza.org
Phone: 423 815 165
Address: 5-13-24 Midori-cho, Koganei, JP
Country: Japan
representative & playwright
Kai Kimura
Touring: No
Regular venues: Gendaiza Kaikan

NU! 21 Seiki Kabuki Gumi

Website: www1.u-netsurf.ne.jp/
Address: c/o Omodaka Co., 206 Resupasu Yotsuya 3 cho-me, 20-3 Daikyo-cho, Shinjuku-ku, JP
Country: Japan
Contact: Director En'nosuke Ichikawa
Touring: No
Regular venues: Kabuki-Za, Shinbashi Enbujo

NYLON 100oC
Website: www.sillywalk.com/nylon/
Email: sillywalk@sillywalk.com
Phone: 354 589 261
Address: c/o Silly Walk Co Ltd., 221 Shuwa Dai 2 Nanpeidai Residence, 12-13 Nanpeidai-cho, Shibuya-ku, JP
Country: Japan
leader & playwright & Director
Keralino Sandorovich
Contact: Producer Rie Hanazawa
Touring: No
Regular venues: Honda Gekijo 386 (q.v.)

Office Kousuke
Website: park.org/Japan/DNP/MTN/MN/home/index.html
Email: kousuke-@mub.biglobe.ne.jp
Phone: 357 666 051
Address: 3F, Yu Bldg., 3-12-12, Higashi, Shibuya, JP
Information: established in 1992 by Kyogen Noh farce performer, Kosuke Nomura; A.C.T. Japan is a collaborative network among people all over the world
Country: Japan
Contact: Director Kosuke Nomura Mannojo Nomura
Touring: No
Regular venues: National Noh-Gakudo

OM-2
Website: www.ask.ne.jp/~pratze/om-2/
Email: webmaster@pratze.ne.jp
Phone: 332 357 990
Address: c/o die pratze, 2-12 Nishi-Goken-cho, Shinjuku-ku, JP
Country: Japan
Contact: assistant Director Kohkichi Hagiwara
Contact: stage Manager Hiroshi Taguchi
Director & representative
Shigeo Makabe
Contact: production Shoko Muraoka f
Touring: No
Regular venues: die pratze 180 (q.v.)

Otona Keikaku
Website: www9.big.or.jp/~otona/
Email: otona@big.or.jp
Phone: 333 274 312
Address: 402 Kawano Matsubara Bldg., 1-46-9 Matsubara, Setagaya-ku, JP
Country: Japan
Director & playwright & actor
Suzuki Matsuo
Contact: production Manager Makiko Nagasaka f
Touring: No
Regular venues: Honda Gekijo 386 (q.v.) others

PAC Han Mime Kohboh
Website: www.xes.co.jp/pac/
Email: pac@xes.co.jp
Phone: 339 939 418
Address: 3-39-6 Hazawa, Nerima-ku, JP
Country: Japan
Contact: Director Han Arai
Touring: No
Regular venues: Studio PAC

Pappa Tarahumara
Website: www.pappa-tara.com
Email: info@pappa-tara.com
Phone: 333 852 066
Address: 1F Maruha Bldg., 1-1-5 Arai, Nakano-ku, JP
Information: Pappa TARAHUMARA is a Performing Arts company founded by the Director, Hiroshi Koike in 1982. They use dance, drama, music, and art.
Country: Japan
Contact: Artistic Director Hiroshi Koike
Contact: Executive Director Yuka Narasaki
Touring: No

Performance Troupe Taihen
Website: www.ne.jp/asahi/imaju/taihen
Email: taihen.japan@gmail.com
Phone: 663 200 344
Address: 1-15-15 Nishi-Awaji, Higashi-Yodogawa-ku, JP
Information: members are all physically handicapped
Country: Japan
Contact: leader/Artistic Director Manri Kim
Touring: No

Platina Papers
Website: www.platinum-papers.com
Phone: 356 006 211
Address: 3F, Yamagishi Bldg., 3-2-4 Shin-Ohashi, Kohtoh-ku, JP
Country: Japan
Director & playwright

Yasuyuki Tsutsumi
Touring: No
Regular venues: Space Zero q.v, Sun Mall

Play Project Team THE GAZIRA
Website:
www5d.biglobe.ne.jp/~cottone/
Email: cottone@msh.biglobe.ne.jp
Phone: 334 114 081
Address: c/o Office Cottone, 1F, 4-12-14 Ikejiri, Seta-
gaya-ku, JP
Country: Japan
Contact: Artistic Director Tatsuo Kaneshita
Touring: No
Regular venues: Kinokuniya Hall 418 (q.v.), Aoyama
Round Theatre 300 (q.v.), Theater/Tops 155 (q.v.), Seta-
gaya Public Theater 600 (q.v.)

Poplar Theater Company
Website: www.poplar21.jp
Email: office@poplar21.jp
Phone: 423 505 541
Address: 136-3 Sakahama, Inagi-shi, JP
Country: Japan
Contact: Director Yoshio Machinaga
Touring: No

Reclam-sha
Website: www.d5.dion.ne.jp/~ichiwaka/
Email: reclam@k3.dion.ne.jp
Phone: 334 100 606
Address: 02/04/2011, Taishido, Setagaya-ku, JP
Country: Japan
Contact: art Director t.b.a.
leader & Director
Ikko Suzuki
Contact: sound effect Director Keisuke Kawasaki
Contact: playwright Mikio Komatsu
Contact: stage Director Jirou Tatsumi
Contact: composer Yasushi Yamashita
Contact: lighting Director Seiji Moriwaki
Touring: No
Regular venues: Jean-Jean (q.v.), Theatre X cai (q.v.),
Setagaya Public Theatre (q.v.), Spark One

Ren'niku Kobo
Phone: 471 639 263
Address: 7-4-15 Kashiwa, Kashiwa, JP
Information: holds regular experimental workshops with
artists from various fields
Country: Japan
Contact: Director Shunji Suzuki
Contact: production Isao Hasegawa
representative & Artistic Director
Akira Okamoto
Contact: lighting Saburo Kaneko
Contact: sound Junji Umezu
Touring: No
Regular venues: Umewaka Noh Theatre 381 (q.v.),
Aoyama Round Theatre 300 (q.v.), Setagaya Public
Theatre

RINKOGUN
Website: www.alles.or.jp
Email: rinkogun@alles.or.jp
Phone: 334 266 294
Address: 202, 1-24-14 Umegaoka, Setagaya-ku, JP
Information: founded by Japanese playwright and
Director Yoji Sakate in 1983, has created a estimable
body of original work that grapples with a wide variety
of social and political issues in both modern Japan and
the world at large
Country: Japan
Contact: lighting Manager Isao Takebayashi
Contact: Administration Chiyo Kunimitsu
Contact: Administration Michihiro Furumoto
Contact: Director Yoji Sakate
Touring: No
Regular venues: Umegaoka Box, The Suzunari

Roba Music Theatre
Website: www.mmjp.or.jp/ROBAHOUSE/
Email: cx6m-mtmt@asahi-net.or.jp
Phone: 425 367 266
Address: Roba House, 6-22-32 Saiwai-cho, Tachikawa, JP
Country: Japan
Contact: leader Masataka Matsumoto
Touring: No
Regular venues: Shinjuku Culture Centre, Tokyo
Metropolican Art Hall

Romantica
Website: www.supertank.co.jp/romantica
Email: romantica@supertank.co.jp
Phone: 334 952 940
Address: 607 Gotanda Diamond Mansion, 6-25-2,
Nichi-Gotanda, Shinagawa-ku, JP
Country: Japan
Contact: Director Makiko Hayashi
Touring: No

Sankai Juku
Website: www.sankaijuku.com
Email: postman@sankaijuku.com

Phone: 334 989 622
Address: 401, 5-6-6 Minami Aoyama, Minato-ku, JP
Information: Sankai Juku which can be translated as
the studio of mountain and sea was founded in 1975
by Amagatsu; contact in Europe: Per Diem & Co. Tel/Fax:
+33-4-91-31-61-75 France
Country: Japan
Touring: No

Sapporo
Website: www.nn.iij4u.or.jp/~gekidan/sapporo/
Email: gekidan@nn.iij4u.or.jp
Phone: 116 636 259
Address: 4-14-8 Miyanosawa 3-jo, Nishi-ku, Sapporo, JP
Country: Japan
Contact: leader Kyoko Hasegawa
Contact: head of directing dept. Nobuyuki Iida
Touring: No

SCOT – Suzuki Company of Toga
Website: www.scot-suzukicompany.com
Phone: 334 458 013
Address: 2-15-24-201, Takanawa, Minato-ku, JP
Information: also have an office in Toga, address: 70-2
Kamimomose, Toga-mura, Nanto-shi, Toyama 939-2513.
TEL:+81 763-68-2356. FAX:+81 763-68-2912
Country: Japan
Touring: No
Regular venues: Toga Sanbo 350, Shin Toga Sanbo 500,
Open Air Theatre 700, Studio 100

Seinen Gekijo
Website: www.seinengekijo.co.jp
Email: info@seinengekijo.co.jp
Phone: 333 526 922
Address: 4F, Toikawa Bldg., 2-9-20 Shinjuku,
Shinjuku-ku, JP
Information: established in 1964
Country: Japan
Contact: representative Akio Fukushima
Touring: No
Regular venues: Kinokuniya Southern Theatre q. v.,
Kinokuniya Hall (q.v.)

Seinendan
Website: www.seinendan.org/
Email: info@seinendan.org
Phone: 333 699 107
Address: 1-11-13 Komaba, Meguro-ku, JP
Information: Komaba Agora Theatre 100 (q.v.) is their
home venue
Country: Japan
Contact: Director Oriza Hirata
Touring: No
Regular venues: Theatre Tram 200 (q.v.), Komaba Agora
Theatre 100 (q.v.),Kichijohji Theatre

Seinenza Theatre Company
Website: www.seinenza.com
Email: info@seinenza.com
Phone: 334 670 439
Address: 1-53-12 Tomigaya, Shibuya-ku, JP
Country: Japan
President & actor
Toshi Moritsuka
Contact: Press Sukeyoshi Mizuyachi
Touring: No
Regular venues: Kinokuniya Hall (q.v.), Kinokuniya
Southern Theatre (q.v.), Honda Gekijo (q.v.)

Seitoh
Website: www.seitoh.com
Email: ix@seitoh.com
Phone: 333 673 219
Address: 3-28-16 Kita-Shinjuku, Shinjuku-ku, JP
Information: established in 1980; the underlying theme
for the production is divinity and humanity; hoping to
envoke a kind of primordial sense of human being
Country: Japan
Contact: Director Toshio Furukawa
Touring: No
Regular venues: Space Across 70, Theater Apple 700
(q.v.)

Shakespeare Company Japan
Website: www.age.ne.jp/x/umi/
Email: umi@x.age.ne.jp
Phone: 222 234 668
Address: 106, 7-10 Otamayashita, Aoba-ku, Sendai, JP
Information: aims to build a replica of the Globe Theatre
on the coast of Sendai, northern Japan; has participated
in Edinburgh Festival
Country: Japan
Contact: Artistic Director Kazumi Shimodate
Contact: supervisor Tsunemoto Ohdaira
Contact: stage Manager Youko Ryougoku
Touring: No
Regular venues: L Park Sendai Studio Hall 190

Shakespeare Theater
Website: www2.odn.ne.jp/shkspr-thr/
Email: atelier@shkspr-thr.co.jp
Phone: 353 486 993
Address: 1F Tatsumi Heitz, 3-2-2 Higashi-Nakano,

Nakano-ku, JP
Information: play of Hamlet by Shakespeare, and New
Hamlet by Osamu Dazai in Feb 2002
Country: Japan
leader & Director
Norio Deguchi
Touring: No
Regular venues: The Globe Tokyo 650 (q.v.), Aoyama
Round Theatre 300 (q.v.)

Shanghai Taro Butou Koushi
Website: www.shang-bu.com
Email: info@shang-bu.com
Phone: 664 770 291
Address: 5F, Nishiyodo Bldg., 2-21-13 Hanakawa, Nishi-
yodogawa-ku, JP
Country: Japan
Contact: representative Taro Shanghai
Touring: No
Regular venues: Aoyama Round Theatre 376 (q.v.)

Shiki Theatre Company
Website: www.shiki.gr.jp
Phone: 459 031 141
Address: 1-24-7 Azamino, Aoba-ku, Yokohama, JP
Information: see also Venues & Presenters
Country: Japan
Contact: Director Keita Asari
Touring: No
Regular venues: Shiki Gekijo (q.v.)

Shimpa
Website: www.shochiku.co.jp/
Phone: 355 501 577
Address: c/o Engeki-bu, Shochiku Company, 4-1-1,
Tsukiji, Chuo-ku, JP
Country: Japan
Contact: Chairman Takeomi Nagayama
Touring: No

Shinjido
Website: www5b.biglobe.ne.jp/~shinjido/
Email: shinjido@mva.biglobe.ne.jp
Phone: 339 017 694
Address: 4-39-12 Shimo, Kita-ku, JP
Country: Japan
Contact: Director Nagaaki Takahashi
Touring: No
Regular venues: Tokyo Metropolitan Art Theatre (q.v.)

Shinjuku Ryozanpaku
Website: www5a.biglobe.ne.jp/~s-ryo/
Email: s-ryozanpaku@muc.biglobe.ne.jp
Phone: 333 857 971
Address: 1F Golden Mansion, 4-19-6 Kamitakada,
Nakano-ku, JP
Country: Japan
Contact: stage Manager Akihiko Muramatsu
Contact: company Manager Shinko Miura
leader & Director
Kim Sujin
Touring: No
Regular venues: Shinjuku Ryohzanpaku Purple Theater
tent 500, Suzunari 200 (q.v.), Kinokuniya Hall 418 (q.v.)

Shinkansen
Website: www.vi-shinkansen.co.jp
Phone: 353 613 027
Address: c/o Village Co Ltd, 5F Moriya Bldg., 7-1-10
Nishi-shinjuku, Shinjuku-ku, JP
Information: established by students at Osaka University
of Arts in 1980
Country: Japan
Touring: No
Regular venues: Theatre Drama City (q.v.), Sunshine
Theatre (q.v.), Theatre Apple (q.v.), Akasaka ACT Theatre,
Shinbashi Enbujo, Shochikuza

Shinseisakuza
Phone: 426 610 001
Address: 2-1419 Motohachioji-cho, Hachioji-shi, JP
Country: Japan
Contact: Director Miho Mayama
Touring: No

Shochiku Kabuki Company
Website: www.kabuki-za.co.jp
Email: kabuki-za@tokyo.email.ne.jp
Phone: 355 501 573
Address: 4-12-15, Ginza, Chuoh-ku, JP
Information: the traditional popular theater of Japan;
as its name implies Ka=singing, Bu=dancing, Ki=acting,
combines the three main theatrical arts into a perfor-
mance; see Shochiku Co Ltd
Country: Japan
Contact: Chairman Takeomi Nagayama
Touring: No

Sohgoh Geki Shudan Haiyukan
Website:
www.hi-you-can.com
Email: ttm-mr@ss.iij4u.or.jp
Phone: 522 038 721
Address: c/o Nagoya Butai Geijutsu Kyokai, 1-22-17
Sakae, Naka-ku, Nagoya, JP

Country: Japan
Contact: Director Tsutomu Mori
Touring: No
Regular venues: Artpia Hall

Sohsu Shimai
Website: www.duelsisters.com
Email: webmaster@duelsisters.com
Phone: 332 020 243
Address: 4F Waseda Ekimae Bldg., 74 Wasedamahi, Shinjuku-ku, JP
Country: Japan
Contact: leader Takemi Koike
Touring: No
Regular venues: Theater/Tops 155 (q.v.), Zenrosai Hall Space Zero 575 (q.v.), Kinokuniya Hall 418 (q.v.), Honda Gekijo 386 (q.v.), East Gallery

Sotoba Komachi
Website: www.sotobakomachi.com
Phone: 668 853 033
Address: 1F Maruyoshi Bldg., 1-12-24 Juso Higashi, Yodogawa-ku, JP
Country: Japan
Contact: leader Hajime Kitagawa
Touring: No
Regular venues: Hep Hall

SPAC Company
Website: www.spac.or.jp
Email: info@spac.or.jp
Phone: 542 084 000
Address: c/o Shizuoka Performing Arts Centre, 100-1, Hirasawa, JP
Information: resident company of Shizuoka Performing Arts Centre SPAC (q.v.); alternative address: 71-4, Ikeda, Shizuoka-shi, Shizuoka 422-8005 Tel: 54-203 5730 Fax: 54-203 5732; see more detailes in Presenters & Venues and Ministries
Country: Japan
Contact: Artistic Director Tadashi Suzuki
Touring: No

Studio Life
Website: www.studio-life.com
Email: info@studio-life.com
Phone: 333 195 645
Address: 1F Sunfuji Bld,1-38-10 Arai, Nakano-ku, JP
Information: agent & management Cube Inc: 8F, T & T Bldg. 3-25-10, Higashi Shibuya Tokyo; Tel: 3-5485 2233; Fax: 3-5485 2244; Producer: Hiroyuki Kitamaki, Noriko Takahashi [f], Manager: Mioko Kitazato [f]
Country: Japan
 playwright & Director
 Jun Kurata f
 Press & public relations Manager
 Keiji Fujiwara
Contact: President Kiichiro Kawauchi
Contact: theater Manager Yoshio Inada
Contact: lighting consultant Kazui Tsurisawa
Contact: company officer Kohji Ishitobi
Contact: production Manager Tsukihito Nakagawa
Touring: No
Regular venues: Westend Studio 120, Theatre Sunmall 300, Kinokuniya Hall, Art Sphere

Subaru
Website: www.bekkoame.ne.jp/~darts
Email: darts@bekkoame.ne.jp
Phone: 339 445 451
Address: 2-29-10 Honkomagome, Bunkyo-ku, JP
Information: has an active policy of international exchange, invites overseas Directors to work with it; a member of the Institute of Dramatic Arts (q.v.)
Country: Japan
Contact: President Hayaru Fukuda
Touring: No

Super Eccentric Theater
Website: movie.nifty.com/set/
Phone: 334 202 897
Address: Amuse Studio 2, 4-7-16 Setagaya, Setagaya-ku, JP
Country: Japan
Contact: leader Yuji Miyake
Touring: No

Super Ichiza
Website: www.infosite.ne.jp/super/
Email: super@infosite.co.jp
Phone: 522 625 955
Address: 3-23-1 Ohsu, Naka-ku, Nagoya, JP
Country: Japan
Contact: Director Shin'ichi Iwata
Touring: No

Suwaraji Gekien
Website: www.swa-raj.com
Email: office@swa-raj.com
Phone: 755 939 537
Address: 07-Sep, Yanagiyama-cho, Shinomiya, Yamashina-ku, JP
Country: Japan
Contact: Director / writer Shinji Kimura

Contact: lighting Director Kazushi Morimoto
Contact: dancer / actor Katsuya Kimura
Contact: actor Masao Inoue
Touring: No

T-Factory
Website: www1.odn.ne.jp/info/t_factory
Email: t_factory@syd.odn.ne.jp
Phone: 333 443 005
Address: 405, 3-5-12 Nishi-shinjuku, Shinjuku-ku, JP
Country: Japan
Contact: Press Yoshiko Hirai f
Contact: Director Takeshi Kawamura
Touring: No

Taichi Kikaku
Website: www7b.biglobe.ne.jp/~taichi-kikaku/TA-ICHI-KIKAKU/Top.html
Email: taichi-k@mub.biglobe.ne.jp
Phone: 353 859 137
Address: 4-44-14-409 Honcho, Nakano-ku, JP
Country: Japan
Contact: representative Lumiko Morimura
Touring Countries: worldwide
Touring: No
Regular venues: Noramlly 100~400 persons is best. but any type is OK.

Tamakko-ZA with drums and drama
Website: www.interq.or.jp/drums/tamakko
Email: tamakko@drums.interq.or.jp
Phone: 425 520 046
Address: 1346-2 Kumagawa, Fussa, JP
Information: both tradithional and original Japanese drums for children and adults
Country: Japan
Contact: Director Katsuyuki Suenaga
Touring Countries: Taiwan, South Korea
Touring: No

Tampopo
Website: www.gekidan.tampopo.com
Email: tampopo@gekidan.tampopo.com
Phone: 534 615 395
Address: Educational Drama Research Association Inc., 323-3 Koyasu-cho, Hamamatsu, JP
Country: Japan
Contact: Director Setsuko Kamiho
Touring: No

Teoriza
Email: headquarters1@teoriza.jp
Phone: 333 932 721
Address: 4-9-6 Narita-Higashi, Suginami-ku, JP
Country: Japan
Contact: Director Ayako Hosho
Contact: Executive Producer Hiromi Ozaki
Touring: No
Regular venues: Haiyuza Gekijo 300 (q.v.), Kinokuniya Hall 418 (q.v.), Sesi

Tessenkai (2)
Website: www.jade.dti.ne.jp/~tessen/
Email: tessen@jade.dti.ne.jp
Phone: 334 012 285
Address: 4-21-29 Minami-Aoyama, Minato-ku, JP
Information: see entry under Agent and Noh Laboratory Theater TESSENKAI
Country: Japan
Contact: secretary General Ken'ichi Kasai
Contact: President Tetsunojo Kanze
Touring: No
Regular venues: Hohshoh Nohgakudo 472 (q.v.), National Noh Theatre 591 (q.v.), Noh Laboratory Theater TESSENKAI 200 (q.v.)

The Operetta Company Tomoshibi
Website: www.tomoshibi.co.jp
Email: info@tomoshibi.co.jp
Phone: 333 520 231
Address: 4F, YM Bldg., 3-35-2 Shinjuku, Shinjuku-ku, JP
Country: Japan
Contact: General Director Yukinori Ohno
Contact: secretary Hiroshi Teratani
Touring: No

Theatre 2+1
Website: www.japan-artists.net/2plus1/
Email: 2plus1@japan-artists.net
Phone: 333 974 008
Address: 1-4-19 Nishiogi-Kita, Suginami-ku, JP
Country: Japan
Contact: Director Akihiko Nakahara
Touring: No

Theatre Academy
Website: www.theatre.co.jp
Email: info@theatre.co.jp
Phone: 359 835 001
Address: 3-14-16 Shimo-ochiai, Shinjuku-ku, JP
Information: has a youth theatre, Cosmos, which consists of members under 15 years old; see also Presenters
Country: Japan
Contact: leader Yasuhiko Asai

Touring: No

Theatre Company Caramel Box
Website: www.caramelbox.com/
Email: support@caramelbox.com
Phone: 353 860 220
Address: Daisan Nakano Bldg., 5-2-1 Chuou, Nakano-ku, JP
Information: established in 1985
Country: Japan
 leader & Director
 Yutaka Narui
Contact: Producer Masafumi Kato
Touring: No
Regular venues: Theater Apple 700 (q.v.), Sunshine Theater 832 (q.v.), Shin-Kobe Oriental Gekijo 639 (q.v.)

Theatre Company Erumu
Website: www.iris.dti.ne.jp/~erumu
Email: erumu@iris.dti.ne.jp
Phone: 332 050 029
Address: 804 Union Bldg., 1-6-16 Takadanobaba, Shinjuku-ku, JP
Information: productions are co-produced between Japan and South Korea
Country: Japan
Contact: General Director Kaichi Sato
Touring: No

Theatre Company Zinjanthropusboisei
Website: www.zinjan.jp/
Email: info@zinjan.jp
Phone: 542 508 337
Address: 8-1 Yachiyo-cho, Aoi-ku, Shizuoka city, JP
Information: Makoto Nakashima, Director, won the first prize at the Toga Directors' competition 2003
Country: Japan
Contact: Director Makoto Nakashima
Touring Countries: Korea Poland Germany
Touring: No

Theatre Echo
Website: www.t-echo.co.jp/
Email: info@t-echo.co.jp
Phone: 354 663 311
Address: Echo Bldg., 3-18-3 Higashi, Shibuya-ku, JP
Information: established in 1956
Country: Japan
Contact: President Naokazu Tadera
Touring: No
Regular venues: Ebisu Ecoh Gekijo, Haiyuza Gekijo 300 (q.v.), Kinokuniya Hall 418 (q.v.), Kinokuniya Southern Theatre (q.v.)

Theatre Freesize
Phone: 334 955 295
Address: 2F, Urban Meguro Bldg., 2-8-10, Meguro, Meguro-ku, JP
Country: Japan
Contact: leader Katsuya Hashizume
Touring: No

Theatre Group Ren
Phone: 985 289 369
Address: 1-46 Kirishima, JP
Country: Japan
Contact: lighting Tomoko Iiyama
Contact: actor Takako Inoue
 representative & Director
 Kenji Jitsuhiro
Contact: stage Manager Kenji Tarumizu
Contact: sound Taketoshi Fujimoto
Touring: No
Regular venues: Miyazaki Prefectural Arts Center (q.v.), Group Ren Theatre

Theatre KIO
Website: www.thekio.co.jp
Email: openmind@gold.ocn.ne.jp
Phone: 666 211 555
Address: 2-4-45, Abenosuji, Abeno-ku, JP
Country: Japan
Contact: leader Tomoyoshi Kikuta
Contact: Artistic Director Kouhei Nakadachi
Touring: No
Regular venues: Abeno LOXODONTA

Theatre KOORO
Website: www.kooro.com
Email: kouro@mks.or.jp
Phone: 666 956 401
Address: 2-4-7 Yata, Koen Minami, Higashi-Sumiyoshi-ku, JP
Information: plans to have readings, a drama school and seminars in the near future; formerly known as Nigat-su-Jidai; established for 40 years
Country: Japan
Contact: Director Chiyoko Yotsuhashi
Touring: No

Theatre Project Tokyo T.P.T.
Website: www.tpt.co.jp
Email: webmaster@tpt.co.jp
Phone: 336 341 351

Address: c/o Benisan Pit, 2-17-12 Shin-Ohashi, Kohtoh-ku, JP
Information: has an agreement of designers' exchange with Motley Theatre Design Course, London; invites young Directors and designers every year from all over the world; supported by Arts Plan 21: supported by government
Country: Japan
Contact: head of design Vicki Mortimer
Contact: Executive Producer Hitoshi Kadoi
Contact: Artistic Director David Leveaux
Touring: No
Regular venues: Benisan Pit 176 (q.v.)

Theatre Seigei
Website: www.seigei.com
Email: info@seigei.com
Phone: 492 435 560
Address: 327 Minami-Otsuka, Kawagoe, JP
Country: Japan
Contact: Director Hisashi Shimoyama
Touring: No

Theatre Toen
Website: www.t-toen.com
Email: info@t-toen.com
Phone: 334 192 871
Address: 1-30-13 Daita, Setagaya-ku, JP
Information: has presented works by both Japanese and overseas playwrights; established in 1959; has long history of working in Russia
Country: Japan
Contact: President Sumako Yamada
Contact: contact Isao Yokokawa
Touring: No
Regular venues: Kinokuniya Hall, Sanbyakunin Gekijo

Theatrical Company NYU-DOU-GU-MO
Website: www.nyudougumo.com
Email: info@nyudougumo.com
Phone: 339 648 321
Address: 39-9 Futaba-cho, Itabashi-ku, JP
Country: Japan
Contact: Director Yoshio Hoshikawa
Contact: production Takahiro Ito
Touring: No
Regular venues: Tokyo Metropolitan Art Space 700 (q.v.), Ginza Shogekijo 300 (q.v.)

Theatrical Troupe Mingei
Website: www.gekidanmingei.co.jp
Email: seisaku@gekidanmingei.co.jp
Phone: 449 877 711
Address: 649-1 Kurokawa, Asao-ku, Kawasaki, JP
Country: Japan
Contact: Executive Director Hideji Ohtaki
Touring: No
Regular venues: Kinokuniya Hall (q.v.), Kinokuniya southern Theatre (q.v.), Mitsukoshi Theatre

Third Stage
Website: www.thirdstage.com
Email: office1@thirdstage.com
Phone: 357 727 474
Address: 4F, 1-11-6, Sendagaya, Shibuya-ku, JP
Country: Japan
leader & playwright & Director
Shoji Kokami
Touring: No
Regular venues: Kinokuniya Hall 418 (q.v.), Sunshine Gekijyou 816 (q.v.)

Tobiraza
Website: www.tobiraza.co.jp
Email: cybertobiraza@tobiraza.co.jp
Phone: 332 210 530
Address: 703, 2-9-4 Iidabashi, Chiyoda-ku, JP
Country: Japan
Contact: leader Kensuke Yokouchi
Touring: No
Regular venues: Kinokuniya Hall 418 (q.v.)

Toh-hai
Website: www.g-tohai.co.jp
Email: komagome@g-tohai.co.jp
Phone: 339 415 526
Address: 1-37-13 Komagome, Toshima-ku, JP
Country: Japan
Touring: No

TOKIDOKI JIDO
Website: www.da.wakuwaku.com/
Email: tokidoki@da.wakuwaku.com
Phone: 335 439 595
Address: 5F, MK Bldg., 6-19-23, Tsukiji, Chuo-ku, JP
Country: Japan
Contact: Director Naoyuki Asahina
Touring: No
Regular venues: Theatre TRAM 248 (q.v.)

Tokyo Engeki Ensemble (1)
Website:
www.tee.co.jp
Email: tee@tee.co.jp

Phone: 339 205 232
Address: 4-35-17 Sekimachi Kita, Nerima-ku, JP
Information: has its own actor training academy; Brecht no Shibaigoya (q.v.) is its home theatre
Country: Japan
Contact: President Tsunetoshi Hirowatari
Touring: No
Regular venues: Brecht no Shibaigoya (q.v.)

Tokyo Engeki Shudan Kaze
Website: www.kaze-net.org
Email: info@kaze-net.org
Phone: 333 633 261
Address: 1-2-4, Higashi-Nakano, Nakano-ku, JP
Country: Japan
Contact: leader Yumiko Tsuji
Touring: No
Regular venues: Repertory Theatre Kaze

Tokyo Geijutsuza
Phone: 339 974 341
Address: 4-19-11 Shimo-Shakujii, Nerima-ku, JP
Information: performs for young audiences throughout Japan
Country: Japan
Contact: leader Kyoko Seki
Touring: No
Regular venues: Kinokuniya Southern Theatre, Haiyuza Theatre

Tokyo Kandenchi
Phone: 334 761 495
Address: 701 New Shibuya Co-oporus, 12-3 Udaga-wa-cho, Shibuya-ku, JP
Country: Japan
Contact: leader Yuji Ogata
Touring: No

Tokyo Kid Brothers
Phone: 334 025 339
Address: 2-3-26-302, Jingumae, Shibuya, JP
Country: Japan
Touring: No

Tomato-za
Website: www1.odn.ne.jp/tomatoza
Email: tomatoza@pop21.odn.ne.jp
Phone: 422 536 833
Address: 2-2-6 Yahata-cho, Musashino, JP
Country: Japan
Contact: Artistic Director Issei Dan
Contact: diector Toshiko Mizuuchif
Contact: General maneger Tsuyoshi Mizuuchi
Touring: No

Tsubakigumi
Email: tsubakigumi@nifty.com
Phone: 332 021 350
Address: 7-19-2 Shinjuku, Shinjuku-ku, JP
Country: Japan
Contact: leader Bunmei Tobayama
Touring: No
Regular venues: OFF.OFF Theatre (q.v.), Suzunari (q.v.), Hanazono Shrine Temple ground, Shimokitazawa geki Small Theatre

UPS – United Performers' Studio
Website: www.upsnews.co.jp
Email: info@upsnews.co.jp
Phone: 353 556 660
Address: B1 Mind Waa, 2-27-27 Izumi, Suginami-ku, JP
Country: Japan
Contact: President Yoko Narahashi
Touring: No

Warabiza
Website: www.warabi.jp
Email: info@warabi.or.jp
Phone: 187 443 939
Address: 430 Aza Waseda, Sotsuda, Tazawako, Senbo-ku-shi, JP
Country: Japan
Contact: Artistic Director Shohei Kikuchi
Contact: head of creative development Noriko Kanno
Contact: representative Katsuaki Kojima
Contact: Producer Mikio Korenaga
Touring: No
Regular venues: Warabi Theatre 730 (q.v.)

Yamanote Jijohsha Company
Website: www.eva.hi-ho.ne.jp/~yamanote/
Email: yamanotesan@yahoo.co.jp
Phone: 333 937 171
Address: 501, 4-33-5 Ogikubo, Suginami-ku, JP
Country: Japan
Contact: Chairman Masahiro Yasuda
Contact: Producer Keishi Okubayashi
Touring: No
Regular venues: Zenrosai Hall Space Zero 575 (q.v.), Toga Sanbo in Toyama

Yokohama Boat Theatre
Website: www.yokohama-boattheatre.com
Email: boattheatre@yahoo.com

Phone: 452 413 361
Address: Omorikita 1-11-11-404, JP
Country: Japan
Touring: No

Yorozu-Kyogen
Website: www.tmdnet.tv
Email: info@tmdnet.tv
Phone: 353 631 305
Address: c/o office Kousuke, 6F, 4-3, Yotsuya, Shinju-ku-ku, JP
Country: Japan
Contact: Director Manzo Nomura
Touring Countries: Ukraine, France, Germany, USA, Romania, Finland
Touring: No
Regular venues: National Noh-Gakudo

Yu-Kikai/Zenjido Theatre
Email: ykz@mba.sphere.ne.jp
Phone: 354 204 625
Address: 203, 2-28-7 Ebisu, Shibuya-ku, JP
Country: Japan
playwright & actor
Atsuko Takaizumi f
leader & Director
Akira Shirai
Touring: No
Regular venues: Aoyama Round Theatre 300 (q.v.), Zenrosai Hall Space Zero 575 (q.v.), The Globe Tokyo 650 (q.v.), Bunkamura Theatre Cocoon (q.v.), Setagaya Public Theatre 600 (q.v.)

Yuenchi-saisei-jigyodan
Website: www.u-ench.com
Email: u-ench@inter7.jp
Phone: 354 540 545
Address: c/o Ariko Nagai, 1-17-4-1B, Ohara, Setagaya-ku, JP
Country: Japan
Contact: Manager Ariko Nagai
President & playwright & Director
Akio Miyazawa
Contact: composer Keisuke Sakurai
Touring: No
Regular venues: Theatre Trum

Zazous Theatre
Phone: 354 303 841
Address: 301, 5-31-3 Daisawa, Setagaya-ku, JP
Country: Japan
Touring: No

Zenshinza Theatre Company
Website: www.zenshinza.com
Email: info@zenshinza.com
Phone: 422 490 770
Address: 3-13-2 Kichijoji Minami-cho, Musashino, JP
Information: alternative e-mail: zenshinza@mvb.biglobe.ne.jp
Country: Japan
Contact: theatre Manager Kiyoshi Ogura
Contact: Director Nobuko Nakamura
Contact: lighting Tokyo Stage Lighting Ltd.
Contact: Kiyoshi Ogura
Touring: No
Regular venues: Zenshinza Gekijo (q.v.), National Theatre, Tokyo (q.v.), Minamiza (q.v.), Chunichi Theatre (q.v.)

Zeppelin Theatre
Email: zeppelin@sepia.ocn.ne.jp
Phone: 335 050 215
Address: 2-210, Co-op Nomura Roppongi, 3-4-5 Roppongi, Minato-ku, JP
Country: Japan
Contact: President Yo Morishita
Touring: No

MALAYSIA

Actors Studio Malaysia
Website: www.theactorsstudio.com.my
Email: yuemay@theactorsstudio.com.my
Address: MY
Information: Over the years, The Actors Studio has been responsible for the nurturing and enabling of countless performing arts companies and individuals and is in no small way, responsible for the continuing growth of the Malaysian Performing Arts scene.
Country: Malaysia
Contact: General Manager Ian Chow
Email: ian@theactorsstudio.com.my
Contact: Press and media Ang Yue May
Email: yuemay@theactorsstudio.com.my
Social Media: @TAS_Malaysia @TheActorsStudio
Touring: No
Regular venues: own venue 153

Centre Stage Performing Arts Sdn Bhd
Address: 37-2A Mdn Bukit Indah Dua Taman, Bukit Indah, MY
Information: does stage design & TV production
Country: Malaysia
Contact: Director Normah Nordin

Touring: No

DramaLab
Website: www.dramalab.com.my
Email: dramalab@tm.net.my
Phone: 377 253 801
Address: 27-A Lorong Datuk Sulaiman 7, Taman Tun Dr Ismaili, MY
Country: Malaysia

MEXICO

Acroman
Phone: 281 71434
Address: Calle Froyl, Col. Plan de la Cruz, Zoncuantla, MX
Country: Mexico
Contact: Director Yocasta Gallardo Ramos
Touring: No

Agave Azul
Phone: 555 515 9777
Address: Sur 144, Col. Cove, MX
Country: Mexico
Touring: No

Agrupaci
Phone: 528 717 207 079
Address: Cerrada San Marcos 508, Col. Fuentes del Sur, MX
Country: Mexico
Contact: Director Jorge M
Touring: No
Regular venues: Teatro de C

Agrupaci
Phone: 525 555 231 059
Address: Jos, entre Jalisco y Revoluci, Col. Tabacalera, MX
Country: Mexico
Contact: Director Kuy Kendal
Touring: No

Alborde Teatro
Phone: 161 15095
Address: Teatro del Imss, Panama y 20 de Noviembre, MX
Country: Mexico
Contact: Director Marco Antonio Garcia Delgado
Touring: No

Amento
Address: Priv. Colonial 370-A, Col. Mar, MX
Country: Mexico
Contact: Artistic Director Mizraim Araujo
Touring: No

Arte M
Phone: 555 605 7391
Address: Pitagoras No. 1235-16, Col. del Valle, MX
Country: Mexico
Contact: contact Alfonso Obreg
Touring: No

Baúl Teatro
Website: www.baulteatro.com
Email: baul@prodigy.net.mx
Phone: 181 834 31491
Address: Padre Raymundo Jardón 910, Barrio Antiguo, MX
Country: Mexico
Touring: No

CAEN (Centro de Artes Esc
Address: Paseo de los H, Zona R, MX
Country: Mexico
Contact: Director Ignacio Flores de la Lama
Touring: No

Casa del Teatro, A.C.
Website: www.casadelteatro.com.mx/
Phone: 555 659 4238
Address: Vallarta No. 31-A, Plaza de la Conchita, Colonia Del Carmen, Coyoacán, MX
Country: Mexico
Contact: Director Luis de Tavira
Touring: No

Centro Cultural Los Arquitos
Email: icarquitos@yahoo.com.mx
Phone: 449 169 201
Address: Alameda, esq. Héroe de Nacozari, Barrio La Purísima, MX
Country: Mexico
Contact: Director Carmen Franco Alba
Social Media: www.facebook.com/pages/Centro-Cultural-Los-Arquito
Touring: No

Comicos de la Legua
Phone: 524 422 124 642
Address: Guillermo Prieto No. 7, Col. Centro, MX
Country: Mexico
Contact: Director Rene Barragan Mata
Touring: No

Compa
Phone:

526 461 771 195
Address: Foro Espacio, Narciso Mendoza No. 63, Fracc Bahia, MX
Country: Mexico
Contact: Director Fernando Rodr
Touring: No
Regular venues: Foro Espacio

El Corral de la Comedia
Phone: 443 312 0001
Address: Melchor Ocampo 239, Col. Centro, MX
Country: Mexico
Contact: Director Manuel Guizar
Touring: No

Escuela de Teatro de Filosofia y Letras
Phone: 818 342 8487
Address: Washingtong 201 Poniente, Esq. Con Colegio Civil, Col. Centro, MX
Country: Mexico
Contact: Director Sergio Garcia
Touring: No

Foro Shakespeare
Website: www.foroshakespeare.com
Email: contacto@foroshakespeare.com
Phone: 555 34642
Address: Zamora No. 7, Col. Condesa, MX
Information: PR contact: Fabian de la Cruz Polanco, fabian_polanco@yahoo.com.mx, www.efcomunica-ciones.com
Country: Mexico
Contact: Director Esther Grynberg
Social Media: @ForoShakespearehttp://www.facebook.com/foroshakespeare
Touring: No

Foro Silvia Pasquel
Email: foropasquel@hotmail.com
Phone: 555 211 4941
Address: AV. JUAN ESCUTIA # 96, COL. CONDESA, Entre Pachuca y Mazatlan, MX
Information: foropasquelacting@hotmail.com
Country: Mexico
Touring: No

Grupo 55
Website: www.grupo55.com
Email: info@grupo55.com
Phone: 555 408 1149
Address: Dr. Vertiz 1272-2, Col. Letr, Delegaci, MX
Information: Perform in Spanish, English; shows in French; also offer workshops, courses and consulting to cultural institutions, independent groups, schools and universities
 2nd email: lou_alzate@artManager.org
Country: Mexico
Contact: Artistic and General Director Larry Silberman
Contact: Artistic Director Jorge Ferro
Social Media: http://www.facebook.com/pages/Grupo-55/26747008545
Touring: No

Grupo a Trasluz
Phone: 222 242 5538
Address: 8 Oriente No. 401 Altos 3, Centro, MX
Country: Mexico
Contact: Directora Silvia Macip
Touring: No

Grupo Accion
Website: pagina.grupoformulayucatan.com.mx/genteenaccion.html
Email: ruthermi@hotmail.com
Phone: 199 992 068
Address: Calle 33-B # 513 x 6 y 8 Col, García Gineres, MX
Country: Mexico
Contact: Director Victor Belmont
Touring: No

Grupo Acoyani
Email: acoyani44@hotmail.com
Phone: 172 828 5218
Address: Peten 473, Col. Narvarte, MX
Country: Mexico
Contact: Director Elena Enciso
Touring: No

Grupo Actores del M
Phone: 525 555 531 383
Address: Av. Veracruz n, Col Condesa, MX
Country: Mexico
Contact: Director Ren f
Touring: No

Grupo Azul
Phone: 555 687 203
Address: Delegación Benito Juárez, Torres Adalid 517 Col, del Valle, MX
Country: Mexico
Contact: Director Cesar Pi
Touring: No

Grupo Bambalina
Phone: 998 806 624
Address: Calle Catarina No. 385, Costa del Sur, Super Manzana 51, MX
Country: Mexico
Contact: Directora Magdalena Hidalgo
Touring: No
Regular venues: Teatro El Forito 240, Teatro 8 de Octubre 80, Casa de la Cultura 300

Grupo Bochinche
Phone: 555 605 4887
Address: Luz Savinon n20 int8, Col.de valle, de Benito Juarez, MX
Country: Mexico
Contact: Director Carlos Corona
Touring: No

Grupo Camicpe
Phone: 555 551 7701
Address: Norte 88 No. 5616, Col. Gertrudis Sanchez, MX
Country: Mexico
Contact: Directore Dora Montiel
Touring: No

Grupo Cleta
Phone: 555 521 7602
Address: Donato Guerra No. 7, desp. 3, Col. Juarez, MX
Country: Mexico
Contact: Director Enrique Cisneros Lujan
Touring: No

Grupo Compa
Phone: 664 637 3122
Address: Av. Puerto del Sur No. 94, Col. Lomas Hipodromo, MX
Country: Mexico
Contact: Director Hebert Axel
Touring: No

Grupo Cootrarte Cooperativa de Trabajadores del Arte
Phone: 738 725 1835
Address: Guadalupe Victoria Sur No. 14, MX
Country: Mexico
Contact: Director Jorge Antonio Garc
Touring: No

Grupo Crisol
Phone: 951 515 2280
Address: Calle R, Unidad Habitacional, Ricardo Flores Mag, MX
Country: Mexico
Contact: Director Pedro G Castellanos Lemus
Touring: No

Grupo Cuerda – Grupo Cajon
Phone: 771 713 2668
Address: Cuauhtemoc 602 A-1, Col. Centro, MX
Country: Mexico
Contact: Director Mirna Vargas
Touring: No
Regular venues: Teatro de la Juventud 500, Foro Calsneeae 800, Foro Quetzalcoatl 500

Grupo Cultural Zero, A.C.
Phone: 777 314 0778
Address: Apartado Postal 1-111-8, MX
Country: Mexico
Touring: No

Grupo de Teatro de la Casa de la Cultura de Salamanca y/o Grupo Oodix
Phone: 464 648 0383
Address: Papaloapan No. 118, Col. Bella Vista, MX
Country: Mexico
Contact: Director Jaime Quiroga Lozano
Touring: No

Grupo de Teatro en Espiral
Phone: 555 665 5184
Address: Zamora n, Col. Condesa, MX
Country: Mexico
Contact: Directora Margarita Gonzalez
Touring: No

Grupo de Teatro Independiente Calmecac
Phone: 961 612 2383
Address: Primera Norte esq. Sexta Oriente, Col Xamaipac, MX
Country: Mexico
Contact: Director Dolores Montoya Galguerra
Touring: No

Grupo de Teatro Personare
Email: jocastro@becam.uacam.mx
Phone: 529 815 2218
Address: Privada 1, Lote 4, Fracc. Santa Cecilia, MX
Country: Mexico
Contact: Directora Lulu Avila
Touring: No

Grupo de Teatro Servicios Educativos del Estado de Chihuahua
Phone: 526 141 32026

Address: MX
Country: Mexico
Contact: Directora Rosa Saenz
Touring: No

Grupo de Teatro Zero U.A.N. Difusion Cultural
Phone: 311 212 0887
Address: Lerdo No. 71 Oriente Antigua Escuela de Medicina, Zona Centro, MX
Country: Mexico
Contact: Director Luis M
Touring: No

Grupo Delta Teatro
Email: flor-cosmica@yahoo.com
Phone: 669 985 0519
Address: Roosvelt 130, Centro, MX
Country: Mexico
Contact: Director Flor Villanueva
Touring: No

Grupo Derrumbe Teatro
Phone: 521 418 2266
Address: MX
Country: Mexico
Contact: Directore Cesar Cabrera
Touring: No

Grupo Drag
Phone: 555 543 9124
Address: Diagonal de San Antonio n, Col del Valle, MX
Country: Mexico
Contact: Director Eduardo Lopez Rojas
Touring: No
Regular venues: own venue cap. 60

Grupo Dromenon
Phone: 555 549 8815
Address: Futbol No. 75, Col. Country Club, MX
Country: Mexico
Contact: Director Gonzalo Blanco
Touring: No

Grupo Ecletico de Teatro
Phone: 866 633 7724
Address: Blvd. Juarez No. 112 Altos Depto. 1 Col. el Pueblo, MX
Country: Mexico
Contact: Director Jose Guadalupe Palacios
Touring: No

Grupo el Clan
Phone: 527 717 187 927
Address: Andador 1 Manz. I No. 202, Col. Plutarco Elias Calles, MX
Country: Mexico
Contact: Director Luis Carlos Cabrera
Touring: No

Grupo El Drag
Phone: 555 675 2432
Address: Av. Hidalgo No. 55, casa 1, Tepepan, Xochimilco, MX
Country: Mexico
Contact: Director Guillermo Murray Prisant
Touring: No

Grupo El Venero
Phone: 333 619 8301
Address: Gregorio D, Sector Hidalgo 5tm de Velarde, Col. Artesanos, MX
Country: Mexico
Contact: Director Javier Serrano
Contact: administradora/co-Directora Olga Valencia
Touring: No
Regular venues: Casa de Teatro El Venero 100

Grupo Ensamble Telemann
Email: telemann1234@aol.mx
Phone: 555 519 8616
Address: Concepci, Col. Atenor Sala, MX
Country: Mexico
Contact: Directora Consuelo Negrete
Touring: No

Grupo Entrop
Phone: 525 557 021 311
Address: Av. Instituto Tegnol, Col. Agricultura, MX
Country: Mexico
Contact: coordinador Arturo H Palafox
Touring: No

Grupo Espacio Vac
Phone: 526 188 110 105
Address: Constituci, Col. Centro, MX
Country: Mexico
Contact: Director Enrique Mijares
Touring: No
Regular venues: Auditorio Universidad

Grupo Fora Do Serio
Phone: 523 123 131 806
Address: Silvestre Revueltas 39, Lomas Vista Hermosa, MX

Country: Mexico
Contact: Director Augusto Albanez
Touring: No

Grupo Foro 1
Phone: 333 655 8104
Address: General Arteaga 434, Col. Artesanos, Sector Hidalgo, MX
Country: Mexico
Grupo Independiente de Teatro Escenica La Cachetada
Phone: 722 214 7378
Address: Pedro Ascencio Norte 103, Col. Centro, MX
Country: Mexico
Contact: Director Jose Manuel Hernandez
Touring: No

Grupo Inkualilwia El Buen Decir
Phone: 555 547 1625
Address: Naranjo 184, lote 1, Col. Santa Maria La Rivera, MX
Country: Mexico
Contact: Directora Araceli Sanabria
Touring: No

Grupo La Carrilla
Phone: 524 448 208 162
Address: Ignacio Ramirez 250, Col. Julian Carrillo, MX
Information: second address: Leon Garcia 735
Country: Mexico
Contact: Directora Martha Aguilar
Touring: No

Grupo La Estufa
Phone: 528 446 124 813
Address: Lucio Blanco 1211, Col Centro, MX
Country: Mexico
Contact: Director Jesus Valdez
Touring: No

Grupo La Mueca
Phone: 524 435 171 135
Address: Aquiles Serdan No. 797, Col. Centro, MX
Country: Mexico
Contact: Directore Ana Laura Diaz
Touring: No

Grupo La Otra Compa
Phone: 521 613 7168
Address: Claustro No. 826-2, Col. Nogales, MX
Country: Mexico
Contact: Director Octavio Trias
Touring: No

Grupo La Palomilla
Phone: 612 125 0486
Address: Altamirano No. 3880 entre Colima y Dunchy, MX
Country: Mexico
Contact: Director Jos Gonzalez
Touring: No

Grupo La Tar
Phone: 284 00752
Address: Apartado Postal No. 33, MX
Information: second address: Privada del Bosque No. 21, Col. Luz del Barrio 91028 Xalapa, Ver.
Country: Mexico
Contact: Director Carlos Converso
Touring: No

Grupo Lo'il Mixil Bromas de Monos
Phone: 967 678 3120
Address: Calle Tonala No. 3-A, Barrio de Serio, MX
Country: Mexico
Contact: Directore Ralph Lee
Touring: No

Grupo Marscara Entre Sombras
Phone: 555 512 3060
Address: Ayuntamiento Bucareli 128 C-1, Centro, MX
Country: Mexico
Contact: Director Pablo Spravkin
Touring: No

Grupo Me-Ximc-Co, A.C.
Phone: 555 683 6436
Address: Redenci, Col. San Jer, MX
Country: Mexico
Contact: Director Alvaro Hegenwich
Touring: No

Grupo Media Luna
Phone: 967 678 3037
Address: Fray Bartolom, Barrio de la Isla, MX
Country: Mexico
Contact: Director Miguel Arag
Touring: No

Grupo Musical Faros y Vulvas Multidisciplinarios
Phone: 555 120 2076
Address: Calle Bravo 201-21, Col. Valle de Arag, Cd. Nezahualcoyotl, MX
Country: Mexico

Contact: Director Saul Cortes
Touring: No

Grupo Palabra Viva
Phone: 333 641 6401
Address: Jos, Col. Providencia S.H., MX
Country: Mexico
Contact: Director Guillermo Covarrubias
Touring: No
Grupo Palleti
Phone: 525 556 681 029
Address: Leticia Negrete y Esmeralda Peralta, Camino al Desierto de los Leones No. 4710, MX
Country: Mexico
Touring: No

Grupo Palo de Lluvia
Phone: 555 610 0996
Address: Calle de Bufalo 159, depto 302, Col. del Valle, MX
Country: Mexico
Contact: Director Alejandro Calvillo
Touring: No

Grupo Piel de Papel
Phone: 555 584 7407
Address: Tonala 351, depto. 501, Col. Roma, MX
Country: Mexico
Contact: Director Guillermo Mendez
Touring: No

Grupo Punto y Raya
Phone: 555 604 7394
Address: Plaza De Los Heroes, Unidad Habitacional Santa Fe, MX
Country: Mexico
Contact: Directore Gilberto Guerrero
Touring: No

Grupo Rinoceronte Enamorado
Phone: 444 812 6498
Address: Altamirano 800, Barrio de Santiago, MX
Country: Mexico
Contact: Director Jes
Touring: No

Grupo Semillas H
Phone: 523 336 540 392
Address: Hermenegildo Bustos No. 4121, Col. Miravalle, MX
Country: Mexico
Contact: Director Jesus Esquivel Soto
Touring: No

Grupo Studio Odissea
Phone: 477 716 9865
Address: Trigo No. 126-6, Col. Cocillo, MX
Country: Mexico
Contact: Director Leopoldo Ibarra Saucedo
Touring: No

Grupo Taller Teatral Aristofanes A.C.
Phone: 664 685 9828
Address: Rio Jord, MX
Country: Mexico
Contact: Director Rafael Perez Barron
Touring: No

Grupo Tatuas
Phone: 667 717 1410
Address: Teofilo Noris No. 517 Nte., esq., MX
Country: Mexico
Contact: Director Rodolfo Arriaga
Touring: No

Grupo Teatral La Columna
Phone: 449 183 124
Address: Venustiano Carranza 101, 2f patio, Zona Centro, MX
Country: Mexico
Contact: Director Jes
Touring: No

Grupo Teatral Tehuantepec
Phone: 529 717 150 928
Address: Av. Juarez 3er. Callejon de Zaragoza, S/N Barrio Ja, MX
Country: Mexico
Contact: Director Marco Antonio Petriz
Touring: No

Grupo Teatro Ubu
Phone: 246 462 4792
Address: 1tm Privada, Rivera de Zahuapan n, Col. Adolfo Lopez Mateos, San Miguel Tlamahuco, MX
Country: Mexico
Contact: Director Jose Luis Castilla
Touring: No

Grupo Tequio
Phone: 834 315 0665
Address: Alfonso G. Rios No. 564, Fracc. Luis Quintero, MX
Country: Mexico

Contact: Director Medardo Trevi
Touring: No

Grupo Tradiciones
Phone: 555 605 1688
Address: Pirineos 157-A, Col Portales, MX
Country: Mexico
Contact: Director Jos Gonzalez
Touring: No

Grupo Truco Teatro Ritual de la Universidad de Colima
Phone: 523 123 143 380
Address: Universidad de Colima, MX
Country: Mexico
Contact: Directora Claudia Epriella
Touring: No

Grupo Tumaz
Phone: 834 315 0665
Address: Alfonso G. Rios No. 546, Fracc. Luis Quintero, MX
Country: Mexico
Contact: Director Ernesto Trejo Burgue
Touring: No

Grupo Utopia
Phone: 555 564 5732
Address: Tuxpan No. 83-4, Col. Roma Sur, MX
Country: Mexico
Contact: Director Marco Antonio Silva
Touring: No

Grupo Zumb
Phone: 555 532 2179
Address: Minas 183, int. 4, Col. Guerrero, Deleg. Benito Juarez, MX
Information: second address: Minas 183, int. 4, Col. Guerrero, M
Country: Mexico
Contact: Director Enrique Balleste
Touring: No

Imagen 2
Phone: 524 448 203 096
Address: Sand, Conjunto 5 de Mayo, MX
Country: Mexico
Contact: Director Antonio Trejo
Touring: No

Instituto Nacional de Bellas Artes
Website: www.bellasartes.gob.mx
Email: dsi@inba.gob.mx
Phone: 821 964
Address: Reforma y Campo Marte s/n, Col. Chapultepec Polanco, MX
Information: member of ISPA
Country: Mexico
Social Media: @bellasartesinbawww.facebook.com/INBAmx
Touring: No

Janet Pinela
Phone: 523 123 302 902
Address: Parotas 229, Fracc. Arboledas, MX
Country: Mexico
Touring: No

La Percha
Website: grupolapercha.blogspot.co.uk/
Email: grupolapercha@hotmail.com
Phone: 424 1557
Address: Sala La Percha, Entre Rios, MX
Country: Mexico
Contact: contact Leticia Parra
Touring: No

Liga Latinoamericana de Improvisaci
Phone: 555 514 0391
Address:
Durango 106, Col Roman, MX
Country: Mexico
Contact: Artistic Director Esteban Roel
Contact: administrator Karina Macias
Touring: No

Los Huizapoles
Phone: 612 124 6190
Address: Calle Baja California y Callej, MX
Country: Mexico
Contact: Director Raul Conde Peraza
Touring: No

Los Narradores Orales de Santa Catarina
Email: de_cuenteros@yahoo.com
Phone: 556 02058
Address: Francisco Sosa 202, Barrio de Santa Catarina, Ampl del Carmen, MX
Country: Mexico
Contact: contact Beatriz Fatero
Touring: No

Matraka Teatro
Email:

cutlopez@hotmail.com
Phone: 662 213 5208
Address: Gilberto Suarez 41, Col. Universitaria, MX
Information: second address: 1tm de Mayo No. 16, Col. Villa de Series, Hermosillo, Son.
Country: Mexico
Contact: Director Gerardo Gonzalez
Touring: No

Merlin
Phone: 555 639 8265
Address: Asociaci, Narradores de Cuentos Cl, Morena 710, Col. Narvarte, MX
Country: Mexico
Contact: Director Lidia Parnas
Touring: No

Mexicali a Secas, A.C.
Email: mexicaliasecas@hotmail.com
Address: Teatro del Imss, Av. Zaragoza y Calle F s/n, Col. Nueva, MX
Information: alternative mail: angelnorzagaray@hotmail.com
Country: Mexico
Contact: Director Angel Norzagaray
Touring Countries: Francia, Venezuela, United States, Cuba, Colombia, El Salvador, Spain
Touring: No
Regular venues: Teatro IMSS Mexicali

Mimus Teatro
Phone: 818 342 1722
Address: Matamoros 454 Pte., MX
Country: Mexico
Contact: Director Fernando Leal
Touring: No

Movimiento Teatral Tamaulipeco, A.C.
Phone: 831 232 4344
Address: Teatro del Imss, Boulevard Luis Echeverria 300 Sur, MX
Country: Mexico
Contact: Director Angel Alberto Lopez
Touring: No

ORTEUV – Organización Teatral de la Universidad Veracruzana
Email: divulart@uv.mx
Address: Zaragoza 12, Col. Centro, MX
Country: Mexico
Touring: No

OTIM – Organización de Teatros Independientes de México
Phone: 555 669 3589
Address: Arizona 156, Col. Napoles, MX
Country: Mexico
Touring: No

Programa de Teatro Callejero – I.A.P.
Phone: 552 614 6558
Address: AV. COYOACAN No. 739 5, COL. DEL VALLE, MX
Country: Mexico
Contact: Director Guillermo Diaz
Touring: No

Publik Teatro Contemporáneo
Phone: 281 88463
Address: Ursulo Galv, Col. Centro, MX
Country: Mexico
Touring: No

Rehilete
Phone: 818 355 6030
Address: Cedart Alfonso Reyes, Calle Madero No. 3500 Ote., MX
Country: Mexico
Contact: Director Gerardo Valdez Alejandro
Touring: No

S Teatro
Phone: 333 618 5304
Address: Justo Sierra 2494-1, Col Ladr, Secto Hidalgo, MX
Country: Mexico
Contact: Director Ricardo Delgadillo
Touring: No

Salamandra
Email: salamandra52@hotmail.com
Phone: 229 932 5075
Address: Venustiano Carranza 152, MX
Country: Mexico
Contact: Directora Selene Ariza Ortiz
Touring Countries: Norway, Aruba
Touring: No

Seña y Verbo
Website: www.teatrodesordos.org.mx
Email: info@teatrodesordos.org.mx
Phone: 555 521 16012
Address: Patricio Sanz 405 PB, Colonia Del Valle, MX
Information: for deaf and non deaf audience; also cours-

es, workshops, consultancy and studio
Country: Mexico
Touring Countries: Salvador, Costa Rica, Brasil, Venezuela, Austria, Germany, USA, China
Touring: No

SIBAN, A.C.
Phone: 555 282 5522
Address: Monte Camer, Barrilaco, MX
Country: Mexico
Contact: President Pepita Serrano

Sma Ktz' Ibajom 1
Phone: 967 611 2876
Address: La Caba, MX
Country: Mexico
Contact: Presidente Juan de la Torre Lopez
Touring: No

Taller de Produccion Teatral
Phone: 524 929 250 031
Address: Teatro Imss, Interior Alameda No. 145, Centro, MX
Country: Mexico
Contact: Director Salvador Castanedo
Touring: No

Taller de Teatro Actores y Mu
Phone: 525 552 075 180
Address: Palenque No. 272-1, Col. Narvarte, MX
Country: Mexico
Contact: Director Hector Avila
Touring: No

Taller de Teatro Anatómico
Phone: 312 314 5046
Address: Gabriel Rodriguez Valdez, Fracc. Villas del Rancho Blanco, MX
Country: Mexico
Touring: No

Taller de Teatro de la Universidad – Grupo a Camanche
Phone: 526 121 255 366
Address: Carretera al Sur KM 3.5, MX
Country: Mexico
Contact: Director Alejandro Merino
Touring: No

Taller de Teatro la Banda, A.C.
Phone: 555 254 5160
Address: Czda. Legaria esq. Lago Gran Oso, Col. Pensil, MX
Country: Mexico
Contact: Director Mario Lage
Touring: No

Taller de Teatro Sergio Magaña
Address: Grupo Esperpento rep de la UNAM plantel Acatlon, Centro Cultural Acatl, MX
Country: Mexico
Touring: No

Taller de Teatro Universitario D de la Universidad de Coahauila
Phone: 528 717 122 379
Address: Boulevar Revolucion y Comonfort, MX
Country: Mexico
Contact: Director Jorge Mendez Garza
Touring: No

Taller Teatral Independiente LOS MISMOS
Phone: 524 497 07136
Address: Av. Palmas No. 714, Fracc. Jes, MX
Country: Mexico
Contact: Director Concepci
Touring: No

Teatro al Cuadrado
Phone: 555 292 2385
Address: Apdo. Postal No. 41-861, Lomas de Chapultepec, MX
Country: Mexico
Contact: Directora Susana Wein
Touring: No

Teatro Alianza
Email: teatroalianza@alianza.edu.uy
Phone: 552 908 1953
Address: Sierra de los Angeles 606, Fracc. Villa Esperanza, MX
Information: second address: Penjamo No.149, Col. Mitras-Centro, 64460 Monterrey N.L.
Country: Mexico
Contact: contacto Angel Hinojosa
Touring: No

Teatro Cedart
Phone: 999 923 8674
Address: Ex-Penitenciaria Juarez, Calle 86 n, Parque de la Paz, MX
Country: Mexico
Contact: contact Toams Ceballos Campos
Touring: No

Teatro de Arena
Website: teatroarena.8m.com
Email: dedalus@teatroarena.8m.com
Phone: 555 530 9741
Address: MX
Information: alternative Email: dedalus@prodigy.net.mx
Country: Mexico
Contact: Directore Martin Acosta
Touring: No

Teatro de Ciertos Habitantes – Certain Inhabitants' Theatre
Website: www.ciertoshabitantes.com
Phone: 555 553 3052
Address: Cuernavaca 22-101, Colonia Dondesa, MX
Information: contact For United States and Canada: Arthur S. Waber, artsource@bellsouth.net; www.artsourcemanagement.com
Country: Mexico
Contact: Manager Fabrina Melón
Email: fabrina@ciertoshabitantes.com
Social Media: www.facebook.com/teatrodeciertoshabitantes
Touring: No

Teatro de La Rendija, A.C.
Phone: 555 536 0165
Address: Amores No. 806-GL, Col. del Valle, MX
Country: Mexico
Contact: Director Raquel Araujo
Touring: No

Teatro en Espiral, A.C.
Email: espiral19@hotmail.com
Phone: 555 577 3192
Address: Opalo 109-1 Col. Estrella, MX
Country: Mexico
Contact: Director Margarita Esther Gonz
Touring: No

Teatro Musical Juvenil
Email: jaimevalleteatro@yahoo.com
Phone: 555 651 5382
Address: Cóndor 388, col. Las Aguilas, D.F., MX
Country: Mexico
Contact: Director Jaime Valle
Touring: No
Regular venues: 100-500

Teatro Nojo D.F. Erectus
Phone: 555 516 9011
Address: Postes 106, Col. Jos, MX
Country: Mexico
Contact: Director Victor Trenado Rinc
Touring: No

Teatro Studio T
Email: teatrot@edg.net.mx
Address: Ignacio de la Llave 105, Plaza Manos, MX
Country: Mexico
Social Media: www.facebook.com/pages/Teatro-Studio-T/65921790173
Touring: No

Theater Frederik – C
Email: frederic@df1.telemex.net.mx
Phone: 525 556 171 637
Address: Guidorreni No. 15, Col. Alfonso XIII, Mixcoac, MX
Country: Mexico
Touring: No

Vision Actual
Phone: 555 536 3566
Address: Centro Cultural Arte en Movimiento, Pit, Col. Narvarte, MX
Country: Mexico
Contact: Director Lorena Vega Poncel
Touring: No

NEW ZEALAND

Auckland Theatre Company
Website: www.atc.co.nz
Email: atc@atc.co.nz
Phone: 930 90390
Address: Mt Eden War Memorial Hall, 487 Dominion Rd, NZ
Information: Auckland Theatre Company is one of Creative New Zealand's Arts Leadership organisations. It is also one of ten regional amenities considered an essential contributor to the well being of residents in the Auckland region and necessary to make the region a vibrant and attractive place to live in.
Country: New Zealand
Contact: Artistic Director Colin McColl
Email: colmccoll@atc.co.nz
Contact: General Manager Lester McGrath
Email: lester@atc.co.nz
Social Media: @AkldTheatreCowww.facebook.com/TheATC
Touring: No
Regular venues: Herald Theatre Aotea Centre, Maidment Theatre, University of Auckland, Sky City Theatre

Centrepoint Theatre
Website: www.centrepoint.co.nz
Email: centrepoint@centrepoint.co.nz
Phone: 635 45740
Address: 280 Church Street, PO Box 716, NZ
Information: Palmerston North's Centrepoint Theatre is the only professional theatre in New Zealand outside of the four main centres of Auckland, Wellington, Christchurch, and Dunedin

Country: New Zealand
Contact: business Manager Julie Barnes
Email: julie@centrepoint.co.nz
Contact: Artistic Director Jeff Kingsford-Brown
Email: jeffkb@centrepoint.co.nz
Social Media: @Centrepoint_PNwww.facebook.com/centrepointtheatre.manawatu
Touring: No
Regular venues: Centrepoint Theatre 135

Circa Theatre Company
Website: www.circa.co.nz
Email: circa@circa.co.nz
Phone: 480 17992
Address: 1 Taranaki St, NZ
Information: Circa's New Zealand-wide reputation for excellence is built on over 30 years of professional experience. And what a history! Champions of quality playwriting and performance since 1976, home and host to New Zealand's most influential theatre-makers, Circa continues to lead New Zealand theatre into the 21st Century.
Country: New Zealand
Contact: Administration and development Manager Caterina Smith
Contact: Sales and Marketing Manager Shalesh Vasan
Contact: Marketing assistant Georgia Latief
Social Media: @CircaTheatrewww.facebook.com/CircaTheatre
Touring: No
Regular venues: theatre up to 260, studio 102

Court Theatre, The
Website: www.courttheatre.org.nz
Email: info@courttheatre.org.nz
Phone: 396 30870
Address: Bernard Street, Addington, NZ
Information: The Court Theatre aims to enrich, support and sustain Christchurch and Canterbury audiences by providing theatre of the highest quality. The Court Theatre celebrates the New Zealand voice on stage, regularly programming original and established New Zealand theatre work as well as commissioning and developing original New Zealand plays.
Country: New Zealand
Contact: CEO Philip Aldridge
Email: CEO@courttheatre.org.nz
Contact: Artistic Director Ross Gumbley
Email: ross@courttheatre.org.nz
Contact: development Manager Steve Brooker
Email: steve.brooker@courttheatre.org.nz
Social Media: @courttheatrewww.facebook.com/TheCourtTheatre
Touring: No
Regular venues: Court I 291, Court II 115

Dragonfly Mime Theatre
Email: dragonflymime@hotmail.com
Phone: 044 763 771
Address: 37 Hathaway Avenue, Karori 5, NZ
Information: Choice of 5 shows with mime, mask, puppetry, dance; for all ages, venues & time frames. Workshops from 1hr – 1wk duration with theme or focus towards final performance.
Country: New Zealand
Contact: contact Katie Haines
Contact: contact Mark Turner
UK, Indonesia, Mexico, NZ, Korea & China
Touring: No

Fortune Theatre
Website: www.fortunetheatre.co.nz
Email: boxoffice@fortunetheatre.co.nz
Phone: 347 78323
Address: 231 Stuart Street, NZ
Information: Fortune Theatre is Otago & Southland's only professional theatre. Fortune Theatre's key driver is ensuring they contribute every day to the spiritual well-being of the community. Its thirteen full-time staff strive year-long to produce the highest quality work, to service their immediate community, along with the national and international visitors.
Country: New Zealand
Contact: Administration Manager Roz Hobbs
Email: admin@fortunetheatre.co.nz
Contact: Artistic Director Jonathon Hendry
Email: jonathonh@fortunetheatre.co.nz
Contact: Marketing Manager Lucy Summers
Email: Marketing@fortunetheatre.co.nz
Social Media: @fortunetheatrewww.facebook.com/fortunetheatre
Touring: No
Regular venues: Mainstage 214, Studio 120

Hagley Theatre Company
Website: www.hagleytheatreco.co.nz
Email: cameron.mattox@staff.hagley.school.nz
Phone: 336 45155
Address: The Open Stage, 510 Hagley Avenue, NZ
Information: Hagley Theatre Company is a self contained, independent training and performance programme attached to Hagley College in Christchurch, New Zealand

Country: New Zealand
Contact: Artistic Director Cameron Mattox
Email: ameron.mattox@staff.hagley.school.nz
Contact: Associate Artistic Director Darryl Low
Email: darryl.low@staff.hagley.school.nz
Social Media: www.facebook.com/Hagley-Theatre-Company-262399927113536
Touring: No
Regular venues: The Open Stage

Island Breeze
Website: www.islandbreeze.org.nz
Email: info@islandbreeze.org.nz
Phone: 754 48531
Address: PO Box 15-036, NZ
Information: Island Breeze is a ministry of Youth With A Mission (YWAM), an international missions organisation made up of Christians of many denominations, dedicated to presenting Jesus Christ to this generation through the training, equipping and mobilising of believers. Island Breeze mandate is 'To honour God and make Him known through His inherent gifts and exPressions within the nations'.
Country: New Zealand
Contact: Director Ray Totorewa
Touring: No

Pacific Underground
Email: pacific.underground@clear.net.nz
Phone: 990 87360
Address: 465 Mt Albert Rd, Mt Roskill, NZ
Information: Pacific Underground (PU) exists to tell stories of Pacific peoples living and growing up in Aotearoa through music, drama, film, events and entertainment. Established in 1994, PU has performed its own music and theatre shows all over New Zealand and the Pacific.
Country: New Zealand
Contact: Chair Posenai Mavaega
Contact: projects coordinator Tanya Muagututi'a
Social Media: www.facebook.com/pu.performingarts
Touring Countries: Samoa, Australia, and Fiji
Touring: No
Number of Performers: 15
Regular venues: varies

Taki Rua Productions
Website: www.takirua.co.nz
Email: tumuaki@takirua.co.nz
Phone: 438 53110
Address: PO BOX 106462, NZ
Information: main goal is to celebrate maori and pacific culture through theatre creations; touring throughout NZ to theatres and schools
Country: New Zealand
Contact: Artistic Director James Ashcroft
Contact: co-Producer Esther Green
Email: esther@takirua.co.nz
Touring: No

Taki Rua Productions (2)
Website: www.takirua.co.nz
Email: info@takirua.co.nz
Phone: 438 53110
Address: Level 1, Toi Poneke, 65 Abel Smith Street, PO Box 24 167, NZ
Information: multi-award winning national theatre company providing unique MAORI Theatre to New Zealand and International audiences; see also Agents & Producers
Country: New Zealand
Contact: creative Director James Ashcroft
Contact: business Manager Maria Gyles

NIGERIA

Thespian Family Theatre
Website: www.thespianfamilytheatre.com
Email: info@thespianfamilytheatre.com
Phone: 812 626 6895
Address: 10, Tahiru Olubani Street, Off Kudirat Abiola Road,, Oregun, NG
Information: promoting Nigerian culture through credible Nollywood stars. Member of ISPA
Country: Nigeria
Social Media: @ThespianFamilywww.facebook.com/thespianfamily
Touring: No

PHILIPPINES

Action for the Religious Theatre Ensemble (ARTE)
Address: Southeast sector MWSS, United, cor. Mayflower St., PH
Country: Philippines

Contact: Artistic Director Bong Ramos
Touring: No

Ang Nagkakaisang Anak Ng Kultura (Anak-Kultura)
Address: KPS-Youth Sector Drama Group, KPS Labangan, PH
Country: Philippines
Contact: Chairperson Regidor Abing
Touring: No

Artistang Biabasnong Eskaya (Abes)
Address: Bgy. Biabas Guindulman, PH
Country: Philippines
Contact: coordinator Clovis Nazareno
Touring: No

Arts Research & Training Institute in Southern Tagalog, Inc. (ARTIST Inc)
Website: www.artist-inc.org
Email: amosperez@artist-inc.org
Phone: 495 366 680
Address: 2558 Carbern Village, Brgy. Anos, Los Banos, PH
Information: non-stock, non-government institution which aims to popularize and develop people's art and literature from the Southern Tagalog region
Country: Philippines
Social Media: www.facebook.com/pages/ART-IST-Inc-Arts-Research-and-Training-Institute-in-Southern-Tagalog-Incorporated/109125215783535
Touring: No

Balintataw Theater Group
Phone: 632 407 637
Address: Ninoy Aquino Parks & Wild Life Office, Quezon Ave. Ext., PH
Country: Philippines
Contact: Artistic Director Cecilia Guidote-Alvarez
Touring: No

Barangay 2 Sarswelistas
Address: Bonifacio Street, Lacson Compound, PH
Country: Philippines
Contact: Director Cristina Fuentes
Touring: No

Barasoain Kalinangan Foundation Inc. – UHAY
Website: www.barasoainkalinangan.com/index.php
Phone: 927 648 6916
Address: Nicanor Abelardo Theater, Bulacan Capitol Complex Malolos, PH
Information: has two arms; UHAY-BKFI Repertory Company, Workshop – BKFI Theatre Laboratory
Country: Philippines
Contact: Chairman Dr. Virgilio Almario
Contact: President Dr. Mariano de Jesus
Contact: vice President Armando Sta Ana
Contact: secretary General and Executive Director Joseph Cristobal
Contact: treasurer Consolacion Gamboa
Touring: No
Regular venues: Nicanor Abelardo Theatre

Bayi Women's Theatre Collective
Email: wsrcdavaophils@gmail.com
Phone: 822 240 941
Address: Room 3E, Anda Corporate Center, F., Iñigo St. Quirino Ave., PH
Country: Philippines
Contact: Artistic Director Melinda Prieto
Touring: No

Bohol People's Art Development Theater Inc.
Address: 2F, Inson Bldg. Remolador cor., Borja Street, PH
Country: Philippines
Contact: Artistic Director Clovis Nazareno
Touring: No

BTD Arts Center
Phone: 725 534
Address: Pe, Elias Angeles, Naga City, PH
Information: caters for training, gallery exhibitions and productions
Country: Philippines
Contact: Executive Director Severino L. Mipa
Contact: Marketing Director Jose N Riuera
Contact: Chairman of the board Robert S Cledera
Contact: Director for performing arts Diosango R Badiola
Contact: Director for theatre operations Jesus A Ramirez
Touring: No

Carrascal Theater Arts Group (CATAG)
Address: Carrascal, PH
Country: Philippines
Contact: Chairperson Victorino Nimes
Touring: No

Children's Laboratory for Drama in Education Foundation
Email: childrenslaboratory@yahoo.com
Phone: 291 32983
Address: No. 5 V. Luciano St. Project 4, Parkway Village, Frisco, PH
Country: Philippines

Contact: Artistic Director Bing Baguioro
Email: childrenslaboratory@yahoo.com
Touring: No

Christian Community Theatre, Inc. (CCT)
Address: Zamora Street, PH
Country: Philippines
Contact: Chairman Armin Paredes
Touring: No

Collective Artistic of Surigao del Sur (CASS)
Address: Tandag, PH
Country: Philippines
Contact: Chairperson Noel Novo
Touring: No

Daba-Daba Theater Group
Address: 89 E. Quirino, PH
Country: Philippines
Contact: Artistic Director Mike Locsin
Touring: No

Dagyaw Theatre and Dance Company
Website: www.oocities.org/inhs_iloilo/dagyaw.html
Email: iloilonhs_ph@yahoo.com
Address: Iloilo National High School, Luna Street, La Paz, PH
Information: see also Dance
Country: Philippines
Contact: Executive Director Riza Amaguin
Contact: Artistic Director Edwin Duero
Touring: No

Darangan Cultural Troupe
Address: Mindanao State University, PH
Information: telefax: c/o
MSU President's Office +63-521 002
Country: Philippines
Touring: No

Diwata
Phone: 384 113 003
Address: 57 Belderol Street, PH
Information: childrens musical group of Sining Diwata; comprises different individual artists, whose aim is to promote indegenous culture of Higaonon Tribe
Country: Philippines
Contact: Chairperson Ann B Piquero-Dy
  melody & music arranger
  Webner Paul Remolados
Contact: instrumentation coordinator Danny Barbano
  visual art & performing coordinator
  Andrew Soliva
Contact: Artistic coordinator Egay C. Dy
Touring: No

Dramatis Personae (DP)
Phone: 632 725 7432
Address: Unit 302 Regency park Townhomes, Santolan Road, PH
Country: Philippines
Contact: President Lito Casaje
Touring: No

Dulaang Don Mateo Lopez (DUMALO)
Phone: 632 911 3724
Address: 17-B 9th Ave., Murphy, Cubao, PH
Country: Philippines
Contact: Artistic Director Sidney Dalanon
Contact: Chairman/President Julianito ""Boy"" Villsanta
Contact: production Manager Winda Abogado
Touring: No

Dulaang Maskara Theater Group (DMTG)
Address: 276 M. Santos St., Ugong, PH
Country: Philippines
Contact: President Jennette Bernardo
Touring: No

Dulaang Palanyag (DP)
Phone: 632 828 2128
Address: Lot 4, Block 4 Darwin St., BF Homes, PH
Country: Philippines
Contact: Artistic Director Winston Santiago
Touring: No

Gantimpala Theater Foundation Inc.
Phone: 897 9986
Address: 8005 – F. Tanguile cor. Kamagong Street, PH
Country: Philippines
Contact: Artistic Director Tony Espejo
Touring: No

Hablon-Dawani Society of Performing Arts
Phone: 528 111 485
Address: Cultural Outreach Office, Catanduanes State College, PH
Country: Philippines
Contact: stage Manager Sonia M Sorra
Contact: Director dance Estela T. Monjardin
Contact: drama Director Estrella S Placides
Contact: Artistic Director Efren T Sorra
Contact: choral trainer Cresencia Arcilla

Touring: No
Regular venues: school gymnasium, town plaza, street

Harlequin Theatre Guild
Email: harlequin@mail.dlsu.edu.ph
Phone:
632 504 4611
Address: 4F, Cultural Arts Office, SPS Bldg. De La Salle Unv., 2401 Taft Ave., PH
Country: Philippines
Contact: President htg Mariel de Guzman
Contact: coordinator for cultural arts Hiyoshi F Gregorio
Contact: dean of student affairs Monina Banaynal
Contact: Executive vice President htg Gerard Alexander B Fallarme
Contact: Director of cultural arts Renato V. Molano
Touring: No
Regular venues: Wiliam Shaw Theater, DLU 273, DLSU Ampitheater 100, SPS Rehearsal Hall, DLSU 100

Ibaan Literary Arts Workshop Organisation, Inc.
Address: 7935 Taylo St., PH
Country: Philippines
Contact: Artistic Director Manolito Sulit
Touring: No

Integrated Performing Arts Guild
Phone: 632 1633
Address: Mindanao State University, Iligan Institute of Technology, Tibanga, PH
Country: Philippines
Contact: Artistic Director Steven Patrick Fernandez
Touring: No

Kabpapagariya Ensemble
Address: c/o Romeo Narvaez, Mindanao State University, Tambler Campus, PH
Country: Philippines
Contact: Artistic Director Romy Narvaes
Touring: No

Kalingaw Repertory
Website: www.acabed.weblink.com
Phone: 344 344 56170 e
Address: Hiligaynon Theater ExPression, Center for Culture, West Negros College, Burgos St, PH
Country: Philippines
Contact: deputy Agmar Ceballos
Contact: head/resource building prog. Ella Mae Nayo
Contact: Artistic Director Joel Arbolario
  head/membership dev. & documentation
  Joseph Trey
  head/external liasoning & promotion
  Maricel Zamora
Touring: No
Regular venues: auditorium, public parks, other campus spaces

Kaliwat Theater Collective (Kaliwat-MCTN)
Phone: 638 229 62079
Address: 8 Mercury St, GSIS Heights, Matina, PH
Country: Philippines
Contact: program Director Nestor Horfilla
Touring: No

Kathara Theatre Collective
Address: 185 E. Anda St., PH
Country: Philippines
Contact: Artistic Director Elenita Dumalao
Touring: No

Katupis Dramatic Arts Guild
Address: Ibabao Arts Council of Calbayog, Inc., PH
Country: Philippines
Contact: Chairperson Jonas T Lim
Touring: No

Komedya ng San Dionisio (KSDS)
Phone: 282 66726
Address: San Dionisio Credit Cooperative Inc., 0554 Quirino Ave. Cor. Vidalez Street, San Dionisio, PH
Information: community based theatre
Country: Philippines
Contact: President Herminio C Herandez
Touring: No

KPS-Youth Sector Drama Group
Address: Labangan Gen. Santos Street, PH
Country: Philippines
Touring: No

Lanao Educational Arts for Development (LEAD)
Phone: 632 212 009
Address: Lead Center, Payag, Rosario Heights, Tubod, PH
Country: Philippines
Contact: Artistic Director Kim Oregenes
Touring: No

Magkasamang Sining Pananadem Magkasipan
Address: Iligan Capitol College, Mahayahay, PH
Country: Philippines
Contact: head Marlaw M Marmay
Touring: No

Makabugwas Theater Arts Organisation Makatao
Address: Riconee Site, Brgy, Capoocan, PH
Country: Philippines
Contact: Chairman Sally Roleda
Touring: No

Mindanao Community Theatre Network (MCTN)
Email: fereen@hamis.dohio.gw.ph
Phone:
888 584 000
Address: Blk. 1 Lot 2629, Villa Trinitas Subd., Bugo, PH
Information: a network of repertory groups, community based theater groups, actors' companies and indivisual theatre artists
Country: Philippines
Contact: board member Nestor Hortilla
Contact: Chairman Fe Remotique
Touring: No

Music & Dramatic Arts Theatre Phil. Inc.
Address: 17 Florencio Lerma St., Hilda Village, Tandang Sora, PH
Country: Philippines
Contact: Artistic Director Jennifer de Vera Catiis
Touring: No

Musical Theater Philippines
Phone: 638 092 760
Address: c/o Celeste Legaspi, 7 Washington Street, Midland Park, Manor II, Greenhills, PH
Country: Philippines
Touring: No

Naty Crame Rogers Philippine Drama Company
Phone: 632 631 963
Address: 40 Stella Maris, B.O. Capitol, PH
Country: Philippines
Contact: Artistic Director Naty Crame Rogers
Touring: No

NO USERNAME! Kalinangan Ensemble
Website: petatheater.com
Email: petafr@petatheater.com
Phone: 272 56244
Address: No 5 Eymard Drive, PH
Information: one of performance groups in Philippine Educational Theater Association PETA; its main function is to develop through research, training, experimentation and production; one of its major task includes the Playwright's Development Programme
Country: Philippines
Touring: No

NU! Tanghalang Batingaw
Website: lputbatingaw.blogspot.com
Email: tanghalangbatingaw.lpu@gmail.com
Address: Lyceum of the Philippines University, Real Corner Muralla Streets, Intramuros, PH
Information: the company undertakes to educate the people and enlighten them on multifarious social milieus and delusions. It recognises a powerful medium in theatre and has decided to use it as a catalyst than a mere source of Artistic articulation and entertainment. An educational theatre coupled with independent critical thinking, professionalism, discipline and deeper purpose for Artistic valuation
Country: Philippines
Social Media: www.facebook.com/pages/Tanghalang-Batingaw/122260223394
Touring: No

Philippine Educational Theater Association (PETA)
Website: petatheater.com
Email: petafr@petatheater.com
Phone: 272 56244
Address: No.5 Eymard Drive, New Manila, Quezon City, Metro Manila, PH
Information: see also National Organisations
Country: Philippines
Social Media: www.facebook.com/pages/PETA-Theatre-Centre/406341009405550
Touring: No
Regular venues: Rajah Sulayman Theater

Pia Puppet Theatre (Black Theatre of Manila)
Phone: 632 921 7941 lo
Address: PIA Bldg., Visayas Ave., PH
Country: Philippines
Contact: Director Lolita S Aquino
Touring: No

Repertory Philippines
Phone: 263 34821~24
Address: William J. Shaw Theater, 5th Level, Shangri-La Plaza, EDSA cor. Shaw Blvd., PH
Country: Philippines
Contact: Artistic Director Zeneida Amador
Touring: No

Samahang Makasining ng Santa Maria (Sama-Sama)
Phone: 639 764 10285 (
Address: 12 Jose Corason de Juses, Poblacion, Sta Maria, PH
Country: Philippines
Contact: President Ulysses Barcial
Touring: No

Samahang ng Mag – arral sa Edukasyon sa Pag-papapahalaga Out – Campus Chapter Organisation (SMEPOCCO)
Phone: 634 643 42764
Address: 132-C Gabak, Kawit, PH
Country: Philippines
Contact: President Romulo Conge Jr
Contact: Director Benedict Conge
Contact: advisor Rosemarie M Layola
Touring: No
Regular venues: PTA Alumni Hall

Samana Bay Cultural Group
Address: Teatro Pabrika, 282 Galguerra Drive, Sangandaan, Novaliches, PH
Country: Philippines
Contact: Artistic Director G Rowell Siena
Touring: No

Sanayan at Ugnayan sa Sining sa Ikauunlad ng Tayabas (SUSI)
Phone: 632 793 2317
Address: 28 Legaspi Street, Tayabas, PH
Information: a community based, non-profit theater group founded in 1987
Country: Philippines
Contact: Artistic Director Norman Ragudo
Contact: Chairman Mario Zarsuela
Touring: No

Sentro ng Kalinangan ng Bayan (Sengkaban)
Address: San Joaquin Multi-Purpose Building, National Shrine of St. Anne, Hagonoy, PH
Country: Philippines
Contact: Chairperson Thess Payongayong
Touring: No

Sining Kambayoka Ensemble (SKE)
Phone: – 521 002 c
Address: Mindanao State University, Lanao del Sur, PH
Information: second address: PO Box 5484, Iligan City, Lanao del Norte 9200
Country: Philippines
Contact: technical Director Eustess Guia
Contact: Artistic Director Sunnie Noel
Touring: No

Sining ng Bayan (SIBAY)
Address: Guadelupe, Esperanza, PH
Country: Philippines
Contact: President Carino Lor
Touring: No

Sining Pananadem
Address: UVS-MSU-Main Campus, Lanao Del Sur, PH
Country: Philippines
Touring: No

Sining Pandayan ng Nasugbu (Sinpana)
Phone: 634 393 11047
Address: 174 J.P Laurel Street, Nasugbu, PH
Country: Philippines
Contact: Artistic Director Rener Concepcion
Touring: No
Nasugbu Auditorium municipality's

Student Theatre Artist Foundation Inc.
Phone:
632 472 698
Address: DR. 2, Manila Metropolitan Theatre, Plaza Lawton, PH
Country: Philippines
Contact: Artistic Director Larry Simbol
Touring: No

Tanghalan Santa Ana (TSA)
Phone:
632 522 3335
Address: 2357 Daang Kalayaan, PH
Country: Philippines
Contact: President Lou Veloso
Touring: No

Tanghalang Apo Theatre Group & Community Theatre (Tatag-CT)
Phone: 634 722 32876
Address: 90-C Daang Corpuz West Tapinae, PH
Country: Philippines
Contact: Artistic Director Armante C Amante
Touring: No

Tanghalang Batingaw
Website: lputbatingaw.blogspot.com
Email: tanghalangbatingaw.lpu@gmail.com
Address: Lyceum of the Philippines University, Real Corner Muralla Streets, Intramuros, PH
Information: the company undertakes to educate the people and enlighten them on multifarious social milieus and delusions. It recognises a powerful medium in theatre and has decided to use it as a catalyst than a mere source of Artistic articulation and entertainment. An educational theatre coupled with independent critical thinking, professionalism, discipline and deeper purpose for Artistic valuation
Country: Philippines
Social Media:
www.facebook.com/pages/Tanghalang-Batingaw/122260223394
Touring: No

Tanghalang Gumaglaw (Tanglaw)
Phone: 632 619 666 loc
Address: 4F, SCC Chavalier Bldg., 3892 Roman Magsaysay Blvd., PH
Country: Philippines
Touring: No

Tanghalang Marilo
Address: Marilao, PH
Country: Philippines
Contact: leader Joel Palec
Touring: No

Tanghalang Pilipino (TP)
Phone: 283 23661
Address: 2F, Production Design Center, CCP Complex, Roxas Blvd., PH
Country: Philippines
Contact: Managing Director Ramon V Puno
Contact: Artistic Director Nonon Padilla
Contact: company Manager Joven G. Joven G.Reyes
Touring: No
CCP's Little Theater & Tanghalang Huseng Batute

Tanghalang Silangan (TS)
Address: Bisig Pagkakaisa – NAFLU, LGB 3F, Talipap, Quirino Highway, Novaliches, PH
Country: Philippines
Contact: Chairperson Connie dela Cruz
Touring: No

Teatro
Address: 131 Magallanes St., PH
Country: Philippines
Contact: Artistic Director Gamay Arkoncel-Dacanay
Touring: No

Teatro Balangaw
Address: Pook Bahaghari, Amoingon, PH
Country: Philippines
Contact: Artistic Director Danny Mandia
Touring: No

Teatro Dabawenyo (TD)
Address: Center for Women's Development, Rm 206 Chan Bldg., Burgos Street, PH
Country: Philippines
Contact: Chairperson Helen P Colmenares
Touring: No

Teatro Ibabang Nasunog (TIN)
Address: 3 Reodica Street, Luisiana, PH
Country: Philippines
Contact: President Samson L Igloria
Touring: No

Teatro Malaya (TEMA)
Address: Res: 4 Catelya Street, St. Michael Subd. II, PH
Information: second address: The Cardinal School, Pandayan, Meycauayan Bulacan 3020 Tel: 97-804 7547
Country: Philippines
Contact: Artistic Director Alvin Barcelona
Touring: No

Teatro Mulat Ng Pilipinas (TMP)
Phone: 292 19773
Address: 64 Mapagkawanggawa Street, Teacher's Village, PH
Information: second address: 27 Matimtiman St, Teachers Village, Quezon City, Metro Manila, Tel 2-928 7508
Country: Philippines
Contact: founder Amelia Lapena-Bonifacio
Touring: No

Teatro Pabrika
Address: 282 Galguerra Drive, Sangadaan Novaliches, PH
Country: Philippines
Contact: Chairperson Robert Mendoza
Touring: No

Teatro Rosario (TR)
Phone: 464 381 528
Address: Wawa II, Nawasa, Rosario, PH
Country: Philippines
Contact: founding Artistic Director Jasmin J Nolasco
Contact: advisor Rosalinda Buhain
Touring: No

Teatro Silencio Pilipinas
Phone: 292 91771
Address: 251, Tandang Sora Avenue, PH
Information: deaf dance theatre company

Country: Philippines
Contact: Artistic Director Jojo Lucila
Touring: No

Teatro Uhay
Address: Kasama Community, 5 M. de la Cruz Street, Krus na ligas Diliman, PH
Country: Philippines
Contact: Artistic Director Ronnie Salvador
Touring: No

Teatrong Balen (TB)
Phone: 455 961 4425
Address: 2390 Sto. Entierro Street, PH
Country: Philippines
Touring: No

Theater Academy for Street Kids, Ethnic and Disabled People (TASKED)
Phone: 297 11771
Address: 251 Unit-E, Tandang Sora Avenue, PH
Country: Philippines
Contact: project Director Irene M Calderon
Touring: No

Theatre Arts Guild (TAGUPCI)
Address: U.P. Visayas, Iloilo City, Iloilo 5000, PH
Country: Philippines
Touring: No

Tri-Media Exponents Inc.
Address: Unit 1123 Cityland Condominium V, South Superhighway, PH
Country: Philippines
Contact: Artistic Director Lorli Villanueva
Touring: No

Triumphant People Evangelistic Theater Society Inc. (TRUMPETS)
Phone: 632 725 7406/72
Address: A-1 Padilla Arcade, Greenhill Shopping Center, PH
Country: Philippines
Contact: President Auide Germora
Touring: No

Tropang Abril-Mayo NG Pasilag
Address: 1st Road Villa Silangan, St Cruz, PH
Country: Philippines
Contact: Chairperson Romeo Mendoza
Touring: No

University of CEBU – Theatre Workshop Company UC-TWC
Address: Student Cultural Service, University of Cebu, Sanciango St., PH
Country: Philippines
Contact: Chairman Rudy Aviles
Social Media: www.facebook.com/uctwc
Touring: No

SINGAPORE

ACT 3 International
Website: www.act3international.com.sg
Email: act3int@act3international.com.sg
Phone: 673 59986
Address: ONE-TWO-SIX Cairnhill Arts Centre, ACT 3 International, 126 Cairnhill Road, SG
Information: At ACT 3 Drama Academy, they open up worlds and start children on a journey of self-awareness, confidence and growth. Active, participatory and aesthetically rewarding, their drama programmes for children and young people are sensitive to the Artistic potential, emotional maturity and intellectual development of the very young from 18 months to teens who are eager to find their voice and contribute their ideas.
Country: Singapore
Contact: Artistic Director Ruby Lim-Yang
Social Media: www.facebook.com/act3international.com.sg
Touring: No
Regular venues: Drama Centre 326, University Cultural Centre 425

Actors Theatre Circle
Phone: 622 02009
Address: Blair Plain Conservation Area 35, 35 Blair Road, SG
Information: Actors Theatre Circle is a performing arts company based in Singapore. They perform theatrical shows in the area.
Country: Singapore
Touring: No

Drama Box Ltd
Website: www.dramabox.org
Email: weare@dramabox.org
Phone: 632 45434
Address: 14A – C Trengganu Street, SG
Information: Drama Box is a non-profit contemporary theatre company with charity status. Formed in 1990, it has since gained a respectable reputation for presenting works that raise social awareness and inculcate civic responsibility amongst Singaporeans. The productions are fun and entertaining, yet thought-provoking and reflective
Country: Singapore
Contact: Artistic Director Kok Heng Leun
Contact: Associate Artistic Director Koh Hui Ling
Social Media: @dramaboxwww.facebook.com/drama-box
Touring: No
Regular venues: Black Box Theatre

Dramaplus
Website: www.dramaplus.org
Email: dramaplus@pacificnet.sg
Phone: 629 90013
Address: 33 Kerbau Road, SG
Information: Dramaplus was originally a sole proprietorship, set up in 1992 by Roger Jenkins. It was incorporated as Dramaplus Arts, a non-profit company limited by guarantee, in 1995. Its mission is to present entertaining theatre that is contemporary, accessible, and relevant to Singapore yet universal in its themes. The website provides a brief history, information about their outreach and educational programmes to schools, courses and workshops for the young and old, facilities available for rental and links to related websites.
Country: Singapore
Contact: Artistic Director Roger Jenkins
Touring: No

Hi Theatre
Website: www.hi-theatre.org.sg
Email: info@hi-theatre.org.sg
Phone: 622 27450
Address: Raffles City Post office, PO Box 376, SG
Information: The theatre was formed in 1986 to further the interests of the hearing-impaired performers and craftsmen, thus giving the disabled a voice of their own. Its website gives information on its members and its local and international performances.
Country: Singapore
Contact: President Tommy Koh
Touring: No

Necessary Stage Ltd, The
Website: www.necessary.org
Email: admin@necessary.org
Phone: 644 08115
Address: 278 Marine Parade Road, #B1-02, Marine Parade Community Building, SG
Information: Formed in 1987 by the current Artistic Director Alvin Tan, The Necessary Stage (TNS) is a non-profit theatre company with charity status. The mission is to create challenging, indigenous and innovative theatre that touches the heart and mind. TNS has also been unwavering in its efforts to nurture new talents and local content, through platforms such as the Theatre for Youth Ensemble, Playwright's Cove, commissions at the Fringe Festival, Theatre for Seniors, and most recently, The Orange Playground (TOP). TOP is TNS' newest initiative in creative research and development, providing artists with an exploratory environment where risks can be freely taken within and with the creative process.
Country: Singapore
Contact: General Manager Melissa Lim
Contact: resident playwright Haresh Sharma
Contact: Artistic Director Alvin Tan
Contact: Chairperson Tan Chong Kee
Social Media: @tns_sgwww.facebook.com/thenecessarystage
Touring Countries: To be confirmed
Touring: No

Singapore Foochow Association Chinese Orchestra
Website: www.foochow.org
Email: sfa@foochow.org
Phone: 629 39852
Address: Foochow Bldg.,, 21 Tyrwhitt Road, #04-01, SG
Information: The Singapore FooChow Association Chinese Orchestra (SFACO) was established in 1983. The orchestra holds a strength of over 60 members comprising of students, NS men as well as working professionals. The orchestra is honoured to be under the baton of Singapore's renowned conductor, Mr Yeo Siew Mong, who is also the instructor of the pluckings section
Country: Singapore
Contact: musical Director Quek Ling Kiong
Touring: No
Regular venues: Auditorium Singapore Foochow Association 350

Singapore Repertory Theatre Ltd
Website: www.srt.com.sg
Email: office@srt.com.sg
Phone: 622 15585
Address: DBS Arts Centre, 20 Merbau Road, SG
Information: Singapore Repertory Theatre's (SRT) goal is to provide a platform for Asian artists both on and off stage and to give Singaporeans and visitors the opportunity to experience Broadway, the West End and the richness of Singaporean culture. SRT has established itself as one of Asia's leading English-language theatres. In addition to its repertoire of original work, the company has produced a number of highly popular and critically acclaimed productions of western classics starring Asian performers
Country: Singapore
Contact: Managing Director Charlotte Nors
Email: charlotte@srt.com.sg
Contact: admin Manager Deborah Foo-Ong
Contact: finance Manager Rosalind Lim
Contact: Chairman Robert Tomlin
Social Media: @SingaporeTheatrwww.facebook.com/singaporerepertorytheatre

Spell # 7
Website: www.spell7performance.org
Email: spell7performance@gmail.com
Phone: 639 21772
Address: 65 Kerbau Road, SG
Information: spell#7 is a Singapore-based performance company that creates intimate theatrical performances and environmental soundworks. Formed in 1997 by Kaylene Tan (Singapore) and Paul Rae (UK), the company has developed a distinctive and inventive focus on the ways history, culture and politics intersect in everyday life and experience.
Country: Singapore
Contact: Director Kaylene Tan
Contact: Director Paul Rae
Social Media: www.facebook.com/spellseven
Touring Countries: UK, Asia
Touring: No
Regular venues: Making Devised Theatre

SRIWANA
Website: www.sriwana.com
Email: info@sriwana.com
Phone: 632 31956
Address: Goodman Arts Centre, 90 Goodman Road, Blk D #01-25, SG
Information: duplicate
Sriwana was formed in 1950 as a Keroncong Party (a traditional Malay Orchestra). Its activities were mainly to entertain guests at wedding parties and taking part in cultural shows organised by local educational bodies, especially the Malay Youth Literary Association (4PM), with whom Sriwana was affiliated, to raise fund
Country: Singapore
Contact: President Fauziah Hanom Yusof
Email: Fauziah@sriwana.com
Contact: advisor Hamzah Rahim
Contact: secretary Harziana Hamid
Touring: Nationally and Internationally
Number of Performers: 60
Regular venues: Victoria Theatre 904, WTC Auditorium, schools

Teater Ekamatra
Website: www.ekamatra.org.sg
Email: General@ekamatra.org.sg
Phone: 663 56709
Address: 28 Aliwal Street, #02-10, SG
Information: Teater Ekamatra is an established and exciting Singapore arts company that spotlights contemporary experimental theatre. Teater Ekamatra has been commissioned by notable international arts festivals, such as the M1 Singapore Fringe Festival, Man Singapore Theatre Festival, and Esplanade Studio Series.
Country: Singapore
Contact: Artistic Director Mohd Fared Jainal
Contact: board of Director Tan Shou Chen
Social Media: @Ekamatra www.facebook.com/TeaterEkamatra
Touring: No
Regular venues: the substation

Teater Kami Limited
Email: teaterkami@hotmail.com
Phone: 673 38969
Address: One-Two-Six Cairnhill Arts Centre, 126 Cairnhill Road, SG
Information: Teater KAMi was founded on 5 June, 1989, by a group of enthusiastic young theatre practitioners who realised at a very early stage that theatre, as an art form, is one of the most effective tools for education and social awareness towards a better life. Teater KAMi firmly believes theatre as a form of Artistic practice can and should be a platform for producing productions that are educationally based in the context of cultural and real life education.
Country: Singapore
Contact: Manager Nordalisah Shahril
Contact: Artistic Director Atin Amat
Social Media: www.facebook.com/TeaterKami
Touring: No
Black Box Theatre company's own theatre venue

The Substation
Website: www.substation.org
Email: admin@substation.org
Phone: 633 77535
Address: The Substation, 45 Armenian Street, SG
Information: Founded in 1990 by the late Kuo Pao Kun, The Substation is Singapore's first independent contemporary arts centre. It is centrally located in the city's civic

district. The venues include a black box theatre, a gallery, a dance studio, Random Room and two multi-function classrooms. It presents and co-presents a wide range of artists and programmes, from traditionally trained dancers to local rock bands, established visual artists to young poets, publications to international short film festivals and experimental theatre to seminal conferences on Singapore arts and culture.
Country: Singapore
Contact: Chairperson Chew Kheng Chuan
Contact: Artistic Director Alan Oei
Contact: General Manager Samantha Segar
Social Media: @thesubstationwww.facebook.com/thesubstation
Touring: No
Regular venues: Substation Guiness Theatre 120, Mox 100-120, Play Den at the Arts House 120, Esplanade Theatre Studio 250, Theatre Studio Nafa 150

Theatre Arts Troupe
Website: www.theatreartstroupe.org
Email: theatreartstroupe@gmail.com
Phone: 632 46681
Address: Telok Ayer Performing Arts Centre (TAPAC), 182 Cecil Street #04-01, SG
Information: Theatre Arts Troupe is a non-profit, amateur arts troupe formed by a group of passionate art-lovers in promoting Chinese and Oriental arts culture. "Dances of the Orient" is the main concert series presented by the troupe. The concert series presents an array of classical, folk, ethnic, contemporary dances, music and songs, from Singapore, China and Asia.
Country: Singapore
Touring: No

Theatre Practice
Website: www.practice.org.sg
Email: ttp@practice.org.sg
Phone: 633 72525
Address: 155 Waterloo Street, SG
Information: Established in 1965 and slightly older than Singapore by more than a month, The Theatre Practice has etched out a pivotal and long-cherished spot in local theatre and cultural history. Through the years, The Theatre Practice has marched forward upon the strength of their bilingualism, while pursuing the ideals of "staying firmly rooted to the local, expanding awareness of the world at large, seeking commonalities yet accepting differences, and embracing one and all in harmony"
Country: Singapore
Contact: co-Chairman Daniel Goh
Contact: co-Chairman Samuel Seow
Social Media: www.facebook.com/thetheatrepractice
Touring: No
Regular venues: Victoria Theatre, Guinness Theatre substation, Community Centres

TheatreWorks (Singapore) Ltd
Website: www.theatreworks.org.sg
Email: tworks@singnet.com.sg
Phone: 673 77213
Address: 72-13 Mohamed Sultan Road, SG
Information: TheatreWorks is an independent, non-profit Singaporean theatre company that develops and nurtures professional arts skills. It supports Singapore artists, and articulates the Singapore arts through its various productions and developmental programmes. It promotes and produces Singapore writing, interdisciplinary performances, collaborations with international artists.
Country: Singapore
Contact: Artistic Director Ong Keng Sen
Contact: Managing Director Tay Tong
Contact: project Manager Mervyn Quek
Contact: administrator Ong Soo Mei
Touring: No
Regular venues: 72-13 is the new home of TheatreWorks see also Venues A converted rice warehouse, the space is flexible enough to be a gallery, a cinema and a theatre capacity of 250.

Toy Factory Theatre Ensemble
Website: www.toyfactory.com.sg
Email: info@toyfactory.com.sg
Phone: 622 21526
Address: 15A Smith Street, SG
Information: Founded in 1990, this theatre company is constantly seeking to create, innovate, and inspire, and is the heart of Toy Factory Productions Ltd (Toy). Having risen from humble puppetry beginnings to the theatrical giant that it is today, Toy has firmly established itself as Singapore's leading bilingual theatre company
Country: Singapore
Contact: General Manager Justin Wong
Contact: chief Artistic Director Goh Boon Teck
Contact: Administration Manager Larry Pham
Social Media: www.facebook.com/ToyFactoryProductions
Touring: No
Regular venues: Jubilee Hall 3880, Victoria Theatre 928, Toy Factory Theatre 17A Meth Street

Wild Rice Ltd
Website: www.wildrice.com.sg
Email: info@wildrice.com.sg

Phone: 629 22695
Address: 65 Kerbau Road, SG
Information: WILD RICE was founded in 2000 by Ivan Heng, an internationally acclaimed and award-winning theatre practitioner, and is recognised today as one of Singapore's leading professional theatre companies. The mission is to provide an open forum for the shared experience of theatre, celebrating their diversity, reflecting on the problems and possibilities of the times, and presenting productions that inspire, challenge and entertain.
Country: Singapore
Contact: Artistic Director Ivan Heng
Contact: co-Artistic Director Glen Goei
Social Media: @WILD_RICE_LTD
www.facebook.com/wildrice.sg
Touring: No

World-in-Theatre
Website: www.world-in-theatre.org
Email: priya@world-in-theatre.org
Phone: 812 89138
Address: 141 Cecil St, #08-03, SG
Information: World-in-Theatre is a theatre company founded in August 2002 by nine theatre practitioners. Inspired by the experience of working with the late Singapore theatre pioneer William Teo and his Asia-in-Theatre Research Centre, a group of his key performers set up World-in-Theatre to continue the vision and philosophy that Teo had developed. World-in-Theatre aims to bring to the Singapore stage, plays of universal significance. The theatre group draws inspiration from various performance traditions of the world and sees 'theatre' as a total performance art which is not about just the spoken word, but may also embrace dance, music and text
Country: Singapore
 Director & treasurer
 Guan Hou Heng
Email: hou@world-in-theatre.org
Social Media: @WorldInTheatrewww.facebook.com/Worldintheatre
Touring: No
Regular venues: The Substation, The Arts House

TAIWAN, PROVINCE OF CHINA

Assignment Theatre
Email: assignment.theatre@gmail.com
Address: No. 4 of 8, Lane 37,, Alley 230,, Bing Zhou Road Section 3,
Country: Taiwan
Touring: No

Bean Theatre
Website: www.bean.org.tw
Email: bean-theatre@mail.bean.org.tw
Phone: 755 05596
Address: No. 50,, Huaning Road,, Gu Shan District
Country: Taiwan
Contact: regimental commander YE Jun
Contact: theater Manager Fang Yuzhen
Contact: Administration Manager Li Jinlin
Touring: No

Contemporary Legend Theatre
Website: www.twclt.com
Email: admin@twclt.com
Phone: 223 923 868
Address: No. 72,, Ning Bo East Street,
Information: In 1986, when a group of opera actors realized that the traditional arts had no longer the advantage, they began to think seriously about how to integrate traditional opera with contemporary theater. Under the leadership of Artistic Director Wu Xing-kuo, the "contemporary legendary theater" was born. Since the establishment of the group, the contemporary legendary theater has been invited to perform abroad annually for many years. Member of ISPA
Country: Taiwan
Contact: Artistic Director Hsing-Kuo Wu
Touring Countries: UK, USA
Touring: No

Creative Society
Email: Creativ1@ms16.hinet.net
Phone: 227 237 305
Address: 8F No3, Lane 417,, Kuang-Fu South Rd,
Country: Taiwan
Touring: No

Godot Theatre Company
Website: www.godot.org.tw
Email: office@godot.org.tw / vick@godot.org.tw
Phone: 028 772 1867
Address: 5F, No. 102,, Guang Fu South Road,, Da An District,
Information: founded in 1988
Country: Taiwan
 founder & Artistic Director
 James Chi-Ming Liang
Contact: correspondent Ling-Yu Lin
Touring Countries: mainland China
Touring: No
Regular venues: National Theatre 1500, Sun Yat-sen Memorial Hall 2500, Taipei Social Educational Hall 1104,

National Arts Hall 700, cultural centers around Taiwan up to 2000

Golden Bough Theatre
Website: www.goldenbough.com.tw
Email: gbtmail@goldenbough.com.tw
Phone: 266 377 987 / 2
Address: No. 39-1, Lane 117,, Long Mi Road Section 2,, Ba Li District,
Country: Taiwan
Touring: No

Green Ray Theater
Website: www.greenray.org.tw
Email: greenray@greenray.org.tw
Phone: 223 956 838
Address: 1F, No. 59 of 2,,
Chong Qing South Road Section 2,
Information: promote original productions, see also National Organisations (Paper Windmill Cultural Foundation)
Country: Taiwan
Contact: Director Zu Ming Lang
Contact: Artistic Director Nian Zhen Wu
Touring: No

Healthy Growth Foundation Shiny Shoes Children's Theatre
Website: www.shoes.org.tw
Email: 50plusgrow@gmail.com
Phone: 227 000 657
Address: 2F, No. 1 Dong Fong Street,, Da An Distrcit
Country: Taiwan
Contact: Artistic Director Ming-Hua Lee
Contact: administrative Director Yun An Chen
Touring Countries: USA
Touring: No

Hwa Kang Art School
Website: www.hka.edu.tw
Email: hka.jason@gmail.com
Phone: 228 612 354
Address: No.8, Lane 73,, Jian Ye Road,, Yang Ming Mountain,
Country: Taiwan
Contact: principal Yong-Qing Ding
Touring: No

I Wan Jan Puppet Theatre
Website: ltlpuppet.pixnet.net
Email: ltl.puppet@msa.hinet.net
Phone: 226 369 174
Address: Taipei County Road 26, Girard Perregaux
Country: Taiwan
Touring Countries: Korea, Japan, Hong Kong, USA, Italy, France, Netherland, Germany, Canada, UK, Portugal, Moroco, Austria, Belgium, Mainland China
Touring: No

Ifkids Theatre Company
Website: www.ifkids.com.tw
Email: service@ifkids.com
Phone: 233 433 622
Address: 2F, No. 23,, Chong Ching South Road, Sec. 3
Country: Taiwan
Contact: correspondent Yi-ching Chen
Touring: No

Lan Ling Theatre Workshop
Email: boyun@saec.edu.tw
Phone: 223 325 445
Address: 2/F, No.1-A, Quan Zhou St.
Country: Taiwan
Touring: No

MAD Theatre
Website: www.mad-theater.com
Email: apdt22024759@yahoo.com.tw
Phone: 422 024 759
Address: 6F, No6, Hua Zhong Street, North District
Country: Taiwan
Contact: correspondent Gee-Tze Shih
Touring: No

Open Theater
Website: www.opentheater.org
Email: bigopen@ms28.hinet.net
Phone: 423 586 129
Address: B1, No. 107,, Tai Zhong Gang Road Section 3,, Xi Tun District
Country: Taiwan
Contact: General Manager Susu Cheng
Touring: No

Paper Windmill Theatre
Website: www.paperwindmill.com.tw/wind
Email: paper@seed.net.tw
Phone: 223 912 225
Address: 3F, No. 59-2,, Chong Qing South Road,, Section 2
Information: see also Paper Windmill Cultural Foundation in National Organisations; alternative Email: greenrey@ms32.hinet.net
Country: Taiwan

Contact: Executive Director Yung-feng Li
Touring: No

Performance Workshop
Website: www.pwshop.com
Email: admin@pwshop.com
Phone: 226 982 323
Address: 221 Xizhi, New Taipei City, 15th Floor, Hsin Tai Wu
Information: Performance Workshop exists to research and use experimental and creative methods
Country: Taiwan
Contact: Artistic Director Stan Lai
Contact: company Manager Ming-Chang Hsieh
Contact: administrative Director Nai-Chu Ding
Touring Countries: Singapore
Touring: No

Ping Fong Acting Troupe
Email: pingfong@pingfong.com.tw
Phone: 229 385 600
Address: B1, No. 111, Lane 43, Section 4,, Singlong Road,, Wen Shan District,
Country: Taiwan
Contact: Artistic Director Guo-Xiu Lee
Contact: administrative Director Xia Feng Lin
Contact: contact Shu Mei Xiao
Touring Countries: Hong Kong, Macau, UK, USA, Canada, Singapore
Touring: No

Shakespeare's Wild Sisters Group
Website: www.swsg95.com.tw
Email: swsg95@gmail.com
Phone: 223 010 950
Address: No.491, Sec.2, Jhonghua Rd, Jhongjheng District
Information: founded in the summer of 1995, Shakespeare's Wild Sisters Group owes its name to the fictional character in Virginia Woolf's novel A Room of One's Own, meaning to liberate women's talents from the opPression of patriarchy. Limiting itself to no specific issues or conventional aesthetics, SWSG takes materials from all arts inspiring to create original theatrical works, which have been brought to participate in many theater festivals in Taiwan as well as overseas for years.
Country: Taiwan
Touring: No

Song Song Song Children's Theatre
Website: www.9s.org.tw
Email: song@9s.org.tw
Phone: 227 389 859
Address: No.52, Lane 308,, He Ping East Road Section 3,, Da An District,
Information: financed by the government and private sector: promotes chinese folk culture; mixes Taiwanese folk art with mordern performing skills
Country: Taiwan
Contact: Managing Director/Artistic Director Shu Ming Zhu
Contact: Manager Tswei-Hwa Huang
Touring Countries: Japan, Korea, Europe
Touring: No

Spring Wind Art Theatre
Website: www.spring-wind.com.tw
Email: service@spring-wind.com.tw
Phone: 721 50211
Address: 2F, No. 107,, Zhong Xiao Road one,, Xin Xing District,
Country: Taiwan
Contact: Executive Director Ming-Chi Hsu
Touring: No

Tainaner Ensemble
Website: tainanerensemble.org/
Email: tainaner@tainanerensemble.org
Phone: 622 01719
Address: 321 Lane Art Settlement, 704 North Park Road
Country: Taiwan
Touring: No

Taipei Philharmonic Theater
Phone: 227 733 691
Address: B1, Lane 233,, Dun Hua South Road Section 1,, Da An District,
Information: alt email: tpf7@tpf.org.tw
Country: Taiwan
Contact: correspondent Shih-Chun Huang
Touring: No

Taipei Quiyi Troupe
Website: www.tqt.com.tw
Email: tqt@tqt.com.tw
Phone: 222 345 610
Address: No. 19,, Zhong shun Street Section 2,, Wen Shan District,
Information: founded august 1993
Country: Taiwan
Contact: regimental commander Patrick Kwok
Contact: deputy head Liu Nailing
Contact: pr Wang Xuan Chun
Touring: No

Taipei Story Theater
Website: storytheatre.pixnet.net/blog
Phone: 287 898 993
Address: 3/F, No.116-5 Tzu-Chiang Rd, Tamsui
Country: Taiwan
Contact: Producer Chung-I Chin
Social Media: www.facebook.com/tst.theatre
Touring: No
Regular venues: Culture Center 2000, black box 200

Taitung Theatre
Website: www.ttrav.org/taitungtheater
Email: ttdt@ms25.hinet.net
Phone: 893 46709
Address: 2F, 671, Kai-Feng Street
Country: Taiwan
Touring: No

U Theatre
Website: www.utheatre.org.tw
Email: utheatre@tpts8.seed.net.tw
Phone: 229 388 188
Address: B1., No. 72 Sec. 4, Xinglong Rd., Wenshan District
Country: Taiwan
Contact: founder/Artistic Director Ruoyu Liu
Touring: No

UNITED STATES

78th Street Theatre Lab
Phone: 212 873 9050
Address: 236 West 78th Street, US
Information: One of the few theaters left on the Upper West Side, the 78th Street Theatre Lab comprises a pair of Off-Off venues: a 30-seat space on the second floor and a 60-seat space on the third floor. It is currently home to the Drilling Company
Country: United States
Touring: No

A Noise Within
Website: www.anoisewithin.org
Email: boxoffice@anoisewithin.org
Phone: 626 356 3100
Address: 3352 E Foothill Blvd, US
Information: A Noise Within performs and promotes classical theatre as an essential means for the community to confront the universal human experience, expand personal awareness and challenge individual perspectives. A Noise Within's mission is to produce world-class performances of the great works of drama in rotating repertory with a resident company; to educate and inspire the public through programs that foster an understanding and appreciation of history's great plays and playwrights; and to train the next generation of classical theatre artists
Country: United States
Contact: producing Artistic Director Geoff Elliott
Email: ArtisticDirectors@anoisewithin.org
Contact: producing Artistic Director Julia Rodriguez-Elliott
Email: ArtisticDirectors@anoisewithin.org
Contact: Managing Director Michael Bateman
Email: mbateman@anoisewithin.org
Contact: General Manager Jennifer Potell
Email: jpotell@anoisewithin.org
Social Media: @anoisewithin @anoisewithintheatre
Touring: No
Number of Performers: 19

Actors Inc.
Website: www.actorsincorporated.com
Email: tickets@actorsincorporated.com
Phone: 978 984 3151
Address: 1660 Lakeview Avenue, US
Country: United States
Contact: Artistic Director Corinne Hickey
Email: corinne@actorsincorporated.com
Touring: No

Alliance Theatre
Website: www.alliancetheatre.org
Email: Holland.Baird@woodruffcenter.org
Phone: 404 733 4650
Address: Woodruff Arts Center, 1280 Peachtree St NE, US
Information: The Alliance Theatre puts world-class work on stage, but they are so much more than that. They have one of the most successful and respected acting education programs in the country. They are a community of artists, administrators, and business and civic leaders devoted to theatre, arts, and arts education
Country: United States
Contact: Artistic Director Susan V. Booth
Contact: Director of production Victor Smith
Email: victor.smith@woodruffcenter.org
Contact: Director of development Kristen Hathaway – Hansen
Email: kristen.hathaway-hansen@woodruffcenter.org
Contact: Director of educational programs Christopher Moses
Email: christopher.moses@woodruffcenter.org

Social Media: @alliancetheatre www.facebook.com/AllianceTheatre
Regular venues: Alliance stage 800, Hertz Stage 200

American Conservatory Theater
Website: www.act-sf.org
Email: tickets@act-sf.org
Phone: 415 749 2228
Address: 30 Grant Avenue, 7th Floor, US
Information: American Conservatory Theater (A.C.T.) is a large non-profit theater company in San Francisco, California, that offers both classical and contemporary theater productions.
Country: United States
Contact: Executive Director Ellen Richard
Contact: Artistic Director Carey Perloff
Social Media: @ACTSanFrancisco www.facebook.com/ACTSanFrancisco
Touring: No
Regular venues: The Geary Theater 1024

Berkshire Theatre Festival
Website: www.berkshiretheatregroup.org
Email: info@berkshiretheatre.org
Phone: 413 298 5536
Address: 83 East Main Street, US
Information: Berkshire Theatre Group was created in 2010 by the merger of two of Berkshire County's oldest cultural organizations, Berkshire Theatre Festival founded in 1928 in Stockbridge and The Colonial Theatre built in 1903 in Pittsfield. One of the largest and most exciting arts organizations in the area, BTG oversees the development, production and presentation of theatre, music and the performing arts on multiple stages
Country: United States
Contact: Director of productions Peter Durgin
Email: pete@berkshiretheatregroup.org
Artistic Director & CEO
Kate Maguire
Email: kate@berkshiretheatregroup.org
Social Media: @BrkshireThtrGrp www.facebook.com/berkshiretheatregroup
Touring: No

Brave New Workshop Comedy Theatre
Website: www.theatre.bravenewworkshop.com
Email: theatre@bravenewworkshop.com
Phone: 612 332 6620
Address: 824 Hennepin Ave S, US
Information: founded by Dudley Riggs in 1958, the Brave New Workshop Comedy Theatre is the oldest satirical and sketch comedy theatre in the United States
Country: United States
Contact: Marketing Manager Rachel Levitt
Email: rachel@bravenewworkshop.com
Contact: Artistic Director Caleb McEwen
Email: cmcewen@bravenewworkshop.com
Contact: box office Manager Rachael Davies
Email: info@bravenewworkshop.com
Social Media: @BNWImprov www.facebook.com/BraveNewWorkshop
Touring: No
Regular venues: The Brave New Workshop theatre storefront cabaret-style theatre capacity 200

Broadway Across America
Website: www.broadwayacrossamerica.com/
Email: special.services@broadwayacrossamerica.com
Phone: 800 448 6322
Address: Broadway in Orlando, 100 South Eola Drive Suite 101, US
Information: member of ISPA
Country: United States
Social Media: @BwayAmerica www.facebook.com/BroadwayAcrossAmerica
Touring: No

California Theatre Center
Website: www.ctcinc.org
Email: boxoffice@ctcinc.org
Phone: 408 245 2979
Address: PO Box 2007, US
Information: 20-30 actors
Country: United States
Contact: General Director Gayle Cornelison
Email: glc@ctcinc.org
Contact: administrative Director Susan Earle
Email: searle@ctcinc.org
Social Media: www.facebook.com/CaliforniaTheatreCenter
Touring Countries: China among others
Touring: Nationally and Internationally
Regular venues: Sunnyvale Community Center Theatre 200, Mayer Theatre at Santa Clara University 490

Capital Repertory Company
Website: www.capitalrep.org
Email: houseManager@capitalrep.org
Phone: 518 462 4531
Address: 111 North Pearl Street, US
Information: established in 1981 Capital Repertory Theatre has a rich, local history of excellent entertainment, offering a variety of shows throughout the year. The theatre currently includes a 286-seat theater, a cafe

space, a costume-making shop and a rehearsal hall. At the core of theREP's mission is "to create meaningful theatre with an authentic connection to the community we serve." Capital Repertory Theatre is a professional, not-for-profit cultural organization, and the only member of the League of Resident Theatres (LORT) within fourteen counties of the Upper Hudson-Mohawk Valley
Country: United States
Contact: producing Artistic Director Margaret Mancinelli-Cahill
Email: mcahill@capitalrep.org
Social Media: https://www.facebook.com/CapitalRep
Touring: No

Center Stage
Website: www.centerstage.org
Email: info@centerstage.org
Phone: 410 986 4000
Address: 700 North Calvert Street, US
Information: see also Presenters and Venues
Country: United States
Contact: Artistic Director Kwame Kwei-Armah
Contact: Managing Director Stephen Richard
Social Media: @CENTERSTAGE_MDwww.facebook.com/CENTERSTAGEMD
Touring: No
Regular venues: Pearlstone Theatre 541, Head Theatre 400

Central California Ballet
Website: www.livelyartsfoundation.com
Email: livelyarts2@aol.com
Phone: 877 608 5883
Address: 1379 Crown Drive, Alameda, US
Country: United States
Contact: Artistic Director Diane K. Mosier
Touring: No

Chicago Shakespeare Theater on Navy Pier
Website: www.chicagoshakes.com
Email: aszabo@chicagoshakes.com
Phone: 312 595 5656
Address: 800 East Grand Avenue, US
Country: United States
Contact: board Chairman Gary Gerst
Contact: Artistic Director Barbara Gaines
Contact: Executive Director Criss Henderson
Contact: Director of audience development Alida Szabo
Social Media: www.facebook.com/ChicagoShakespeare
Touring: No
Regular venues: main stage 510

Chicago Shakespeare Theatre World's Stage
Website: www.chicagoshakes.com
Email: customerservice@chicagoshakes.com
Phone: 312 595 5665
Address: 800 East Grand Avenue on Navy Pier, US
Country: United States
Contact: Artistic Director Barbara Gaines
Contact: Executive Director Criss Henderson
Social Media: www.facebook.com/ChicagoShakespeare
Touring: No

Cirque Le Masque
Website: www.cirquelemasque.com
Email: dennis@cirquelemasque.com
Phone: 516 455 9966
Address: 9363 Kenneth Ct., Boyton Beach, US
Country: United States
Contact: co-founder Dennis Schussel
Email: dennis@cirquelemasque.com
Contact: co-founder Bernie Schussel
Email: bernie@cirquelemasque.com
Touring: No

Contemporary Theatre ACT
Website: www.acttheatre.org
Email: act@acttheatre.org
Phone: 206 292 7660 (ad
Address: Kreielsheimer Place, 700 Union Street, US
Country: United States
Contact: Artistic Director Kurt Beattie
Contact: Managing Director t.b.a.
Contact: producing Director Joan Toggenburger
Contact: communications Director Karen Bystrom
Touring: No
Regular venues: The Falls 388, The Allen 412, The Bullitt 99, Busters 145

Dell'Arte International
Website: www.dellarte.com
Email: info@dellarte.com
Phone: 707 668 5663
Address: 131 High Street, PO Box 816, US
Information: has a nationally recognized arts in education program; also produces Mad River Festival and runs the International School of Physical Theatre; also has touring company Dell'Arte Company
Country: United States
Contact: producing Artistic Director Michael Fields
Contact: founding Artistic Director/master teacher Joan Schirle
Touring: No
Dell'Arte Studio Theatre 111, Dell'Arte/Rooney Amphitheatre 250

East West Players
Website: www.eastwestplayers.org
Email: info@eastwestplayers.org
Phone: 213 625 7000
Address: 4/F, 120 North Judge John Aiso Street, US
Country: United States
Contact: development Manager Lisa Tang
pr & Marketing Manager
Christine Huynh
Contact: Director of production Meg Imamoto
Contact: Artistic Director Tim Dang
Touring: No

El Teatro Campesino
Website: www.elteatrocampesino.com
Email: info@elteatrocampesino.com
Phone: 831 623 2444
Address: PO Box 1240, US
Country: United States
Contact: producing artist Director Kinan Valdez
Contact: Artistic Director Luis Valdez
Contact: business Manager Licha Muñoz
Touring: No
Regular venues: up to 150

Emelin Theatre for the Performing Arts
Website: www.emelin.org
Email: info@emelin.org
Phone: 914 698 0098
Address: 153 Library Lane, US
Country: United States
Contact: bookkeeper Bridget Bettke
Email: bridget.bettke@emelin.org
Contact: administrative assistane Susan Flink
Email: susan.flink@emelin.org
Contact: special assistant to the Director Harris Mercer
Email: harris.mercer@emelin.org
Contact: Executive Director Lisa Reilly
Email: lisa.reilly@emelin.org
Contact: graphic designer Jamie Lynn Weisinger
Email: jamielynnweis@emelin.org
Contact: company Manager Charles Zavelle
Email: charles.zavelle@emelin.org
Social Media: EmelinTheatrewww.facebook.com/EmelinTheatre
Touring: No
Regular venues: theatre 275

Ethnic Dance Theatre
Website: www.ethnicdancetheatre.com
Email: info@ethnicdancetheatre.com
Phone: 176 354 51333
Address: 4000 Winnetka Avenue North, US
Country: United States
Contact: Artistic Director Donald LaCourse
Contact: orchestra Director Dee Langley
Touring: No

Free Street: TeenStreet Chicago: MadJoy Theatrics
Website: www.freestreet.org
Email: gogogo@freestreet.org
Phone: 773 772 7248
Address: 1419 W Blackhawk, US
Information: Teenstreet is a jobs program for low-income Chicago youth that creates completely modern work; runs PANG program Producing Arts for the Next Generation; submit tapes/inquiries to: PANG, Free Street above address, E-mail: pang@freestreet.org
Country: United States
Contact: Artistic Director Ron Bieganski
Contact: Managing Director Bryn Magnus
Touring: No
Regular venues: TeenStreet Studio, Cetz Theater, Chicago

Geva Theatre
Website: www.gevatheatre.org
Email: gevatalk@gevatheatre.org
Phone: 585 232 1366(adm
Address: 75 Woodbury Blvd., US
Information: contemporary theatre, big theatre for little people, audiences in grades K-8, also offers a wide variety of educational, outreach and literary programs
Country: United States
Contact: Executive Director Nan Hildebrandt
Contact: company Manager Julie Madonia
Contact: Artistic Director Mark Cuddy
Contact: literary Manager/resident dramaturg Marge Betley
Contact: finance Director Alana Sansone
Contact: Managing Director Greg Weber
Touring: No
Regular venues: Geva Theatre 550, Next Stage 180, Elaine P. Wilson Mainstage 552

Goodman Theatre
Website: www.goodmantheatre.org
Email: info@goodmantheatre.org
Phone: 312 443 3800
Address: 170 North Dearborn St., US
Information: also outreach and educational programs; playwrights and Directors in residence programme
Country: United States
Contact: Artistic Director Robert Falls
Contact: Executive Director Roche Schulfer
Social Media: @GoodmanTheatrewww.facebook.com/GoodmanTheatre
Touring: No
Regular venues: Albert Ivar Goodman Theatre proscenium 840, Owen Bruner Goodman Theatre 400 flexible

History Theatre
Website: www.historytheatre.com
Email: pr@historytheatre.com
Phone:
651 292 4323
Address: 30 East 10th Street, US
Information: History Theatre commissions and produces plays and musicals that explore Minnesota's past and the diverse American experience. Its work provides a unique lens which links our past to the present, explores our common heritage, and illuminates our understanding of what it means to be American.
Country: United States
Contact: Marketing Director Rachel Flynn
Email: pr@historytheatre.com
Contact: Managing Director Karen Mueller
Email: kmueller@historytheatre.com
Contact: Artistic Director Ron Peluso
Email: rpeluso@historytheatre.com
Social Media: @HistoryTheatrefacebook.com/HistoryTheatre
Touring: No
Annual Performances: 115
Number of Performers: 100
Regular venues: 600

Human Race Theatre Company
Website: www.humanracetheatre.org
Email: contact@humanracetheatre.org
Phone: 937 461 3823
Address: 126 North Main Street, Suite 300, US
Information: celebrated 20th anniversary in 2006
Country: United States
Contact: Artistic Director Marsha Hanna
Contact: Executive Director Kevin Moore
Contact: Marketing Director Leigh Allan
Contact: technical Director Scott Kimmins
Touring: No
Regular venues: The Loft Theatre 219, Victoria Theatre 1100

Irondale Productions
Website: www.irondale.org
Email: irondalert@aol.com
Phone: 171 848 89233
Address: PO Box 150604, US
Information: various education and social programs in schools, prisons; also permanent research ensemble making ongoing investigations into the process of making theatre
Country: United States
Contact: Executive Director Terry Greiss
Artistic Director & co-founder
Jim Niesen
Contact: Associate Director Maria Knapp
Associate Artistic Director & scene designer
Ken Rothchild
Touring: No
Regular venues: various theatres up to 800

Jodi Kaplan & Associates (2)
Phone: 212 352 0400
Address: Jodi Kaplan & Associates, 161 Sixth Avenue, 14th Floor, New York, NY 10013, US
Country: United States
Contact: President Jodi Kaplan
Touring: No
Regular venues: Joyce Theatre 475

Kentucky Shakespeare Festival
Website: www.kyshakes.org
Email: info@kyshakes.org
Phone: 502 583 8738
Address: 1387 S. 4th St., US
Country: United States
Director of technology & design
Holly Johnson
Contact: Managing Director Doug Sumey
Contact: producing Artistic Director Curt L Tofteland
Contact: office Manager Jeanie Landers Thomas
Contact: assistant Director of education Regan Wann
Contact: Executive Director Steven Renner
Contact: educational outreach coordinator Heather Burns
Touring: No
Regular venues: Amphitheatre 1000

Lincoln Center Theater
Website: www.lct.org
Email: info@lct.org
Phone: 212 362 7600
Address: 150 West 65th St, US
Information: through tours, telecasts, films, publications, recordings and this website, the company reaches audiences across the nation and around the world
Country: United States

Contact: Artistic Director André Bishop
Contact: Executive Director Bernard Gersten
Contact: Managing Director Adam Siegel
Social Media: @LCTheaterwww.facebook.com/Lincoln-CenterTheater?_rdr=p
Touring: No
Regular venues: New House Theatre 290, Vivian Beamont Theatre 1000

Marneuli Drama Theatre Samshoblo
Phone: 992 572 91023
Address: US
Country: United States
Contact: Manager Nana Bokuchava

Meadow Brook Theatre
Website: www.mbtheatre.com
Email: kgentile@mbtheatre.com
Phone: 248 370 3310
Address: Oakland University, US
Country: United States
Contact: Artistic Director David L. Regal
Contact: technical Director Bryan Dambacher
Contact: Managing Director John Manfredi
Touring: No
Regular venues: capacity 585

Mixed Blood Theatre Company
Website: www.mixedblood.com
Email: info@mixedblood.com
Phone: 612 338 6131
Address: 1501 S Fourth Street, US
Country: United States
Contact: Artistic Director Jack Reuler
Contact: Director of touring Charlie Moore
Social Media: @mixed_blood
Touring: No
Regular venues: various including Mixed Blood Theatre 200

Mtskheta-Tianeti Regional Theatre
Phone: 329 86591
Address: US
Country: United States
Contact: Manager Rezo Mgeladze
Touring: No

Old Globe, The
Website: www.theoldglobe.org
Email: tickets@theoldglobe.org
Phone: 619 231 1941
Address: 1363 Old Globe Way, US
Information: produces a year round season of 15 plays and musicals on its 3 stages, including its highly-regarded Shakespeare festival
Country: United States
Contact: resident playwright Matthew Lopez
Contact: Executive Director Louis G. Spisto
Contact: Artistic Director emeritus Jack O'Brien
Contact: public relations Director Jeffrey Weiser
Touring: No
Regular venues: Old Globe 580, Cassius Carter Centre Stage 225, Lowell Davies Festival Theatre 612

Opera Saratoga
Website: www.operasaratoga.org
Email: info@operasaratoga.org
Phone: 518 584 6018
Address: 19 Roosevelt Dr, Ste 215 Saratoga Springs, NY 12866
Information: Opera Saratoga serves the communities of Saratoga Springs, the Lower Adirondack and New York State Capital areas by providing access to world-class opera through the production of an annual Summer Festival, as well as year-round activities including extensive educational programs, mentorship of emerging operatic artists, and unique opportunities for the public to experience opera in both our home theater and non-traditional venues that leverage and embrace the unique cultural, historic, and natu
Country: United States
Contact: Artistic and General Director Lawrence Edelson
Contact: Chair Robert Miller
Contact: President Rosemarie Rosen
Social Media: twitter.com/operasaratogawww.facebook.com/OperaSaratoga
Touring: Nationally and Internationally

Oregon Shakespeare Festival
Website: www.osfashland.org
Email: Administration@osfashland.org
Phone: 541 482 2111
Address: 15 South Pioneer Street, US
Information: variety of educational programs, lectures, backstage tours etc.
Country: United States
Contact: Artistic Director Bill Rauch
Contact: Executive Director Paul E Nicholson
Contact: media and Marketing Associate Robert Hackett
Touring: No
Regular venues: The Elizabethan Stage 1200, The Angus Bowmer Theatre 600, New Theatre 260-350

Pearl Theatre Co.
Website: www.pearltheatre.org

Email: info@pearltheatre.org
Phone: 212 505 3401
Address: 80 St. Mark's Place, US
Information: resident acting company with an art and education program
Country: United States
Contact: Marketing Director Michael Page
Contact: producing Director Mary Ann Ehlshlager
Contact: General Manager Shira Beckerman
Contact: Artistic Director Shepard Sobel
Touring: No
Regular venues: Theatre 80 with 160 seats

Portland
Center Stage
Website: www.pcs.org
Email: info@pcs.org
Phone: 503 445 3723
Address: 128 NW Eleventh Ave between Couch and Davis, US
Country: United States
Contact: Director of Marketing Synthia Furhman
Contact: Director of development Charlie Frasier
Contact: Managing Director Greg Phillips
Contact: Artistic Director Christopher Coleman
Contact: production Manager Tom Haygood
Touring: No
Regular venues: Gerding Theater at the Armory : main theatre 599; black box 200

Prince Music Theater
Website: www.princemusictheater.org
Email: info@princemusictheater.org
Phone: 215 972 1000
Address: 1412 Chestnut Street, US
Information: theatre address: 1412 Chestnut Street, Philadelphia PA 19102
Country: United States
Contact: producing Director Marjorie Samoff
Contact: producing Associate Bart Lynch
Social Media: @PrinceMusicTheawww.facebook.com/PrinceMusicTheater
Touring: No
Regular venues: Prince Music Theatre 450

Public Theater, The
Website: www.publictheater.org
Email: Press@publictheater.org
Phone: 212 539 8500
Address: 425 Lafayette Street, US
Information: see also Presenters
Country: United States
Contact: Artistic Director Oskar Eustis
Touring: No
Regular venues: Anspacher Stage Thrust Stage 275, Martinson Hall Set Black Box 199, Newman Stage Proscenium 299, Luesther Hall Loft Space 160, Shiva Theater Black Box 99

Repertorio Español
Website: www.repertorio.org
Email: info@repertorio.org
Phone: 212 889 2850
Address: 138 East 27th St, US
Information: founded in 1968 to introduce the best of Latin American, Spanish and Hispanic-American theatre in distinctive, quality productions, and to bring theatre to a broad audience in New York City and across the country, including seniors, students and Hispanics of all national backgrounds
Country: United States
Contact: Executive Director Robert Weber Federico
Contact: Artistic Director Rene Buch
dir. audience development & public relations Jose Antonio Cruz
Social Media: https://www.facebook.com/repertorionyc?directed_target_id=0
Touring Countries: Colombia, Bolivia, Portugal, Dominican Republic, Ecuador, Puerto Rico London UK
Touring: No
Regular venues: Spanish Repertory Theater 140

Roundabout Theatre
Website: www.roundabouttheatre.org
Email: info@roundabouttheatre.org
Phone: 212 719 9393
Address: 231 West 39th Street, Suite 1200, US
Information: see also Nottingham Playhouse (Venues) – UK, and Roundabout Theatre (venues)
Country: United States
Contact: Managing Director Harold Wolpert
Contact: Artistic Director Todd Haimes
Contact: Executive Director, external affairs Julia Levy
Social Media: @rtc_nycwww.facebook.com/RoundaboutTheatreCompany
Touring: No
American Airlines Theatre – Broadway,Studio 54 – Broadway, Harold & Miriam Steinberg Center for Theatre Laura Pels Theatre – Off-Broadway

Santa Monica Playhouse
Website: www.santamonicaplayhouse.com
Email: theatre@santamonicaplayhouse.com
Phone:

310 393 5573
Address: 1211 4th St., Suite 201, US
Information: now celebrating 53 years of continuous theatrical services, the Playhouse presents year-round Main Stage productions, family theatre musicals, workshops for all ages, parties, classes in public and private schools, international touring, and rental for productions, readings, lectures and more
Country: United States
Contact: co-Artistic Director Evelyn Rudie
Contact: co-Artistic Director Chris DeCarlo
Contact: Director of public relations Sandra Zeitzew
Social Media: @SMPlayhousefacebook.com/SantaMonicaPlayhouse

Sha Sha Higby Dance and Sculptural Costume
Website: www.shashahigby.com
Email: shasha@shashahigby.com
Phone: 415 860 6648
Address: PO Box 152, US
Information: international performance/sculptural artist, Sha Sha Higby is known for her evocative and haunting performances using the exquisite and ephemeral body sculpture she meticulously creates herself and moves. Elaborate sculptural costume, dance, and puppetry explore magic and emotion; creating an atmospheric world within the borders between death and life's Higby started out making dolls and pursued the art of puppetry and sculpture in her early years. Ms. Higby has performed her unique body of work throughout the United States, and internationally in Korea, Japan, Indonesia, Slovakia, Bulgaria, Singapore, Australia, Switzerland, England, Belgium, Germany and Holland. She is the recipient of numerous grants and awards including the National Endowment for the Arts Solo Theater Artist Fellowship, The Zellerbach Family Fund, and the California Arts Council New Genre Individual Artist Fellowship
Country: United States
Contact: Artistic Director Sha Sha Higby
Email: Shasha@shashahigby.com
Social Media: @Shashahigbywww.facebook.com/shashahigby
Touring: Nationally and Internationally

Shakespeare Theatre Company
Website: www.ShakespeareTheatre.org
Email: admin@shakespearetheatre.org
Phone: 202 547 1122
Address: Administrative Offices, 516 8th Street SE, US
Information: the mission of the Shakespeare Theatre Company is to present classic theatre of scope and size in an imaginative, skillful and accessible American style
Country: United States
Social Media: @ShakespeareinDCwww.facebook.com/ShakespeareinDC
Touring: No
Regular venues: Lansburgh Theatre, Sidney Harman Hall

Southern Theater
Website: www.southerntheater.org
Email: info@southerntheater.org
Phone: 161 234 01725
Address: 1420 Washington Avenue S, US
Country: United States
Contact: Managing Director Bonnie Schock
Marketing & communications Director Kate Nordstrum
Contact: Artistic Director Jeffrey Bartlett
Touring: No
Regular venues: capacity 150

Sundance Institute Theatre Programme
Website: www.sundanceresort.com
Email: institute@sundance.org
Phone: 435 658 3456
Address: PO Box 684429, US
Information: mission: The Sundance Theatre Programme, a professional not-for-profit organisation is dedicated to identifying and assisting emerging and established theatre artists and encouraging and supporting the development of new work for the stage
Country: United States
Contact: board President Robert Redford
Contact: producing Artistic Director Philip Himberg
Touring: No
Regular venues: Outdoor Eccles and King Stages at Sundance, Utah – Natural Mountain Amphitheatre

T. Daniel Productions
Website: www.tdanielproductions.org
Email: info@tdanielproductions.org
Phone: 773 743 0277
Address: 6619 N. Campbell Avenue, US
Information: the first Mime Company to perform "Le Boeuf sur le Toit" by music by Milhaud and pantomime by Cocteau. We wrote and performed a new pantomime to Kurt Weill's "Magical Night" for the American Premiere of the Music for the Ravinia Festival with James Conlon conducting the Chicago Symphony Orchestra
Country: United States
Contact: co-Artistic Director T. Daniel
Contact: co-Artistic Director Laurie Willets
Touring Countries: Canada, Puerto Rico, France, Spain, Canary Islands, Palma de Mallorca, Switzerland, Sweden, Austria, Turkey, Slovenia, Iran, Taiwan, Hong Kong,

Singapore, China
Touring: No
Regular venues: Cultural Centers PA series; Theatres (up to 3800); Concert Halls; Festivals (stages)

TanzTheater André Koslowski
Website: www.tanztheater-ak.com
Email: andre@tanztheater-ak.com
Phone: 814 883 6907
Address: 1829 Pine Hall Road, US
Information: Dance Theater Company performing works by German born Artistic Director and Choreographer Andre Koslowski
Country: United States
Social Media: @tanztheater_akwww.facebook.com/TanzTheaterAK
Touring: No
Annual Performances: 6

Tennessee Repertory Theatre
Website: www.tennesseerep.org
Email: bennett@tennesseerep.org
Phone: 615 349 3224
Address: 161 Rains Ave, Tennessee, US
Information: alternative email address: rene@tennesseerep.org
Country: United States
Contact: Executive Artistic Director David Alford
Contact: audience development Director Bennett Tarleton
Touring: No
Regular venues: Tennessse Performing Arts Center: Polk Theater 1

The Broad Stage
Website: www.thebroadstage.com
Email: info@thebroadstage.com
Phone: 310 434 3412
Address: 1310 11th Street, US
Information: the Eli and Edythe Broad Stage contribute to the cultural community through excellence in education, and will strive to promote Artistic excellence, creativity, collaboration and the free exchange of ideas in an open, caring community of learners
Country: United States
Contact: Director Dale Franzen
Contact: Artistic Chair Dustin Hoffman
Social Media: @TheBroadStagehttps://www.facebook.com/broadstage
Touring: No

The Perishable Theatre
Website: www.perishable.org
Email: info@perishable.org
Phone: 401 331 2695
Address: PO Box 23132, 95 Empire Street, US
Information: visiting address: 95 Empire Street, Providence, RI 02903
Country: United States
Contact: Artistic Director Venessa Gilbert
Contact: operations Manager Paul Ring
Touring: No
Regular venues: 75 seat black box

Theater at Lime Kiln (1)
Website: www.theateratlimekiln.com
Email: info@theateratlimekiln.com
Phone: 154 046 37088
Address: 2 West Henry Street, US
Information: Mailing address: PO Box 1244, Lexington, VA24450; Map address: 601 Borden Rd. Lexington. VA 24450. We produce professional and community theatre and present an eclectic music series from April to October.
Country: United States
Contact: Executive Director Tony Russell
Contact: box office Manager Alice Williams
Touring: No
Regular venues: The Kiln 388, The Bowl 600

Theatre IV
Website: www.theatreIV.org
Email: TheatreIVandBarksdale@gmail.com
Phone: 180 478 31688
Address: 114 West Broad Street, US
Country: United States
Contact: Artistic Director Bruce Miller
Contact: Managing Director Philip Whiteway
Touring: No
Regular venues: capacity 600

Triple EsPresso
Website: www.tripleesPresso.com
Email: dennis@tripleesPresso.com
Phone: 612 874 1100
Address: 12800 Industrial Park Blvd, Ste 252, US
Information: It's a 3-man stage-play with an over 20 year track record of making people laugh till their cheeks hurt! The full title is Triple EsPresso–a highly caffeinated comedy.
Contact: President and Executive Producer Dennis Babcock

Contact: Associate Producer Rosalie Miller
Email: rosalie@tripleesPresso.com
Contact: stage Manager and assistant production Manager Ben Netzley
Email: bennien@tripleesPresso.com
Touring: No

Trustus Theatre
Website: www.trustus.org
Email: trustus@trustus.org
Phone: 803 254 9732
Address: PO Box 11721, 520 Lady St., US
Information: theatre address: 520 Lady Street; Trustus Playwright's Festival in Aug annually
Country: United States
Contact: founder/Managing Director Larry McMullen
Artistic Director & founder Jim Thigpen
Contact: literary Manager/playwright in residence Jon Tuttle
Touring: No
Regular venues: capacity 134

Tsereteli Chiatura Drama Theatre
Phone: 992 795 2426/552
Address: 5 Chavchavadze str., US
Country: United States
Contact: Director Nana Demetrashvili
Contact: Manager Iza Jishkariani
Touring: No

Tsutsunava Ozurgeti Drama Theatre
Phone: 992 966 5321/66
Address: 1 Chavchavadze str., US
Country: United States
Contact: Artistic Director Otar Kutaladze
Contact: Manager Revaz Sarishvili
Contact: Artistic consultant Giorgi Sabo
Touring: No

Unexpected Productions Improv
Website: www.unexpectedproductions.org
Email: info@unexpectedproductions.org
Phone: 206 587 2414
Address: 1428 Post Alley, Market Theater – Pike Place Market
Information: Consistently voted Best Live Comedy in Western Washington, Unexpected Productions is the heart of improv in the Puget Sound. For 38 years we have focused on the art of storytelling in its work, taking suggestions from YOU & weaving them into stories & scenes. Before the pandemic, they perform 10 shows a week and are the home of the most established improv school and corporate training program in the Puget Sound. And are now perform 4 shows a week and again have live classes. Unexpected Productio
Country: United States
Touring: No
Annual Performances: 25-50
Number of Performers: 25-50
Regular venues: 0

Vazha Pshavela Telavi Drama Theatre
Phone: 992 503 1528/68
Address: 3 Freedom sq., US
Country: United States
Contact: Manager/Artistic Director Nukri Kantaria
Touring: No

Vineyard Theatre (1)
Website: www.vineyardtheatre.org
Email: vineyard@vineyardtheatre.org
Phone: 212 353 3366
Address: 108 East 15th Street, US
Information: nonprofit, off-Broadway theatre company
Country: United States
Contact: Artistic Director Douglas Aibel
Contact: Associate Artistic Director Sarah Stern
Contact: Executive Director Jennifer Garvey-Blackwell
Contact: General Manager Reed Ridgley
Touring: No
Regular venues: Dimson Theatre 120

Virginia Repertory Theatre
Website: www.va-rep.org
Email: vareptheatre@gmail.com
Phone: 804 783 1688
Address: 114 W. Broad St, US
Information: In 2012, Barksdale Theatre and Theatre IV, the Children's Theatre of Virginia, merged to become Virginia Repertory Theatre. We have the same staff and the same great seasons of productions on our four stages in Richmond and Hanover, Virginia, and we still tour educational programming to schools throughout the U.S.
Country: United States
Contact: box office Manager Janine Serresseque
Email: jsears@va-rep.org
Contact: Director of communications Susan Davenport
Email: susandavenport@comcast.net
production & technical Director Bruce Rennie
Email: brennie@va-rep.org
Contact: Artistic Director Bruce Miller
Email: bmiller@va-rep.org

Contact: Managing Director Phil Whiteway
Email: pwhiteway@va-rep.org
Social Media: @irginiaRephttp://www.facebook.com/BarksdaleTheatre
Touring: Nationally
Regular venues: capacity 240

Walnut Street Theatre (1)
Website: www.walnutstreettheatre.org
Email: pr@wstonline.org
Phone: 215 574 3550
Address: 825 Walnut Street, US
Information: America's oldest theatre; North America's largest subscriber base 54,000+
Country: United States
Contact: producing Artistic Director Bernard Havard
Contact: assistant to producing Artistic Director Kate Galvin
Contact: Managing Director Mark Sylvester
Contact: education Director Susan N. Quinn
Contact: production Manager Roy Backes
Contact: assistant to Managing Director Jessica Doheny
Contact: communications Manager Tom Miller
Contact: Director of institutional advancement Rebekah Sassi
Touring: No
Regular venues: Mainstage 1078, Studio 100

Washington Performing Arts
Website: www.washingtonperformingarts.org
Email: ticketservices@washingtonperformingarts.org
Phone: 202 833 9800
Address: 1400 K Street NW, Suite 500, US
Information: Washington Performing Arts provides the Washington area with high-quality performing arts presentations, supports performing artists and provides lifelong learning opportunities through arts education, youth involvement and community partnerships. Member of ISPA
Country: United States
Contact: President and CEO Jenny Bilfield
Email: President@washingtonperformingarts.org
Contact: Chairman Reginald Van Lee
Contact: Chief Operating Officer Allen Lassinger
Email: alassinger@washingtonperformingarts.org
Social Media: www.facebook.com/WashingtonPerformingArtsSociety/
Touring: No

Zachary Scott Theatre Center (ZACH)
Website: www.zachscott.com
Email: info@zachscott.com
Phone: 512 476 0594 (ad
Address: 1510 Toomey Road, US
Information: professional theatre company; member of Actor's Equity Association and Theatre Communications Group; has own Performing Arts School, Director – Cindy Vining, ext 236
Country: United States
Contact: musical Director Allen Robertson
Contact: development Director Michele Scherz Baylor
Contact: Managing Director Elisbeth Challener
Contact: Artistic Director Dave Steakley
Contact: Marketing/pr Director Jim Reynolds
Touring: No
Regular venues: The Kleberg Stage 230, John R. Whisenhunt Arena Stage 130, The Paramount Theatre Proscenium type 1200

The following is a list ordered alphabetically by products and services, and alphabetically within each country, useful to those who work in the performing arts.When the company name is,for example, Frank Smith PR, the indexing is done on the first name (Frank). **The entries are listed in alphabetical order by prod-uct, country and then name.**

Produits et Services

Ce qui suit est une liste ordonnée par ordre alphabétique des produits et des services, et par ordre alphabétique au sein de chaque pays, utile à ceux qui travaillent dans les arts de la scène. Lorsque le nom de la société est, par exemple, Frank Smith PR, l'indexation se fait sur le premier nom (Frank). **Les entrée sont classés par ordre alphabétique par produit, le pays et le nom**

Produkte und Dienstleistungen

Das Folgende ist eine Liste alphabetisch nach Produkten und Dienstleistungen, und alphabetisch innerhalb der einzelnen Länder, nützlich, um diejenigen, die in den darstellenden Künsten zu arbeiten. Wenn der Firma ist, ist beispielsweise Frank Smith PR, die Indizierung auf dem ersten Namen (Frank) getan. **Die Einträge sind alphabetisch nach Produkt, Land und Unternehmensnamen sortiert.**

Prodotti e Servizi

Di seguito è riportato un elenco in ordine alfabetico da prodotti e servizi, e in ordine alfabetico all'interno di ogni paese, utile per coloro che lavorano nelle arti dello spettacolo. Quando il nome della società è, per esempio, Frank Smith PR, l'indiciz-zazione viene eseguita sul nome (Frank). **Le voci sono pubbli-cate in ordine alfabetico di prodotto,paese e poi nome.**

Productos y Servicios

La siguiente es una lista ordenada alfabéticamente por pro-ductos y servicios, y por orden alfabético dentro de cada país, útil para aquellos que trabajan en las artes escénicas. Cuando el nombre de la empresa es, por ejemplo, Frank Smith PR, la indexación se realiza en el primer nombre (Frank).
Las entradas están organizadas en orden alfabético por producto, país y nombre de la empresa.

AUSTRALIA

John Paxinos & Associates Pty Ltd
Website: www.paxinos.com.au
Email: info@paxinos.com.au
Phone: 039 696 5085
Address: 117 Sturt Street, Southbank VIC 3006 Australia
Information: John Paxinos & Associates Pty Ltd works for a wide array of arts organisations and performing artists, offering financial, management and consulting services. They know the arts business better than any General recruitment firm in Australia and have extensive experience working with small, medium and large arts organisations.
Country: Australia
Contact: Director John Paxinos
Email: john@paxinos.com.au

Perth Theatre Company
Website: www.perththeatre.com.au
Email: admin@perththeatre.com.au
Phone: 892 439 054
Address: 51 Moores Drive, AU
Information: Perth Theatre aims to provide a holistic and professional design service for all aspects of equestrian lifestyle properties, equestrian businesses and rural lifestyle properties.
They provide a planning and design service, which covers all aspects of equestrian and country property planning, building and facility design, and assistance through construction.
Country: Australia

Symphony Services International
Website: www.symphonyinternational.net
Email: info@symphonyinternational.net
Phone: 280 147 625
Address: PO Box 435 Balmain NSW 2041, AU
Information: Symphony Services International is an international provider of services and products for symphony orchestras and classical musicians, conductors and soloists. The company supports talented musicians, both established and emerging and offers high quality orchestral music, products and services.
Country: Australia
Contact: Chief Executive Officer Kate Lidbetter
Email: lidbetterk@symphonyinternational.net
Phone: Artist Services Manager Tara Ende
Email: artists@symphonyinternational.net
Phone: Library Manager Vi King Lim
Email: limv@symphonyinternational.net
Phone: Library Coordinator Andari Anggamulia
Email: anggamuliaa@symphonyinternational.net
Phone: Finance Manager Dilek Henderson
Email: hendersond@symphonyinternational.net
Phone: Artist Finance Officer Teresa Majewski
Email: majewskit@symphonyinternational.net

CHINA

China National Publications
Website: www.cnpiec.com.cn
Email: cnpeak@cnpiec.com.cn
Phone: 105 066 6888
Address: No. 16, Gongti East Road, Chaoyang District, Beijing 100020 China
Information: China National Publications Import & Export (Group) Corporation (CNPIEC) is a large state-owned culture enterprise founded in 1949. In April 2002 it was incorporated into China Publishing Group Corporation as a member company. CNPIEC passed ISO9001 quality management system certification in 2009
Country: China
Contact: President Zhang Jichen
Phone: Chairman Liu Bogen

HONG KONG

International Fixer Ltd.
Website: www.internationalfixer.com
Email: hq@internationalfixer.com
Phone: 980 64900
Address: 15 Aberdeen Street, Central, HK
Information: International Fixer Ltd. is a live event specialist, providing General consultancy, production support, technical expertise and creative solutions for events, ranging from theatrical productions to rock concerts.
Country: Hong Kong
Contact: production Director Alex Ng

JAPAN

NHK Software Inc
Website:
www.nhk-sw.co.jp
Phone:
354 788 621
Address: 5-20 Kamiyama-cho, Shibuya-ku, JP
Information: the company's main activities include production of video software, programme supply for CATV, and copyright management of character goods
Country: Japan

Ongaku No Tomo Sha Corp
Website: www.ongakunotomo.co.jp
Email: home_ontomo@ongakunotomo.co.jp
Address: 6-30 Kagurazaka, Shinjuku-ku, JP
Information: a music publisher; operates its own halls, Ongaku no Tomo Hall (q.v.) in Tokyo and Ongaku no Tomo Hall-Shin-Osaka (q.v.); presents concerts for those halls; organizes classical music-related events for local authorities, business corporations, etc.
Country: Japan
Contact: Executive Director Tatsuo Takeishi
Phone: President Hiroshi Okabe

Orange Note Co Ltd
Website: www.orange-note.com
Phone: 642 138 180
Address: Hokkaido, Nayoro, Nishi 7 Jominami, 132-1277
Information: Orange Note Co Ltd. are involved in concert planning and help to organise events – anything from classical to rock.
Country: Japan

Pro Arte Musicae
Website: www.proarte.jp
Email: info@proarte.jp
Phone: 339 436 677
Address: Otowa 1-20-14-5F, Bunkyo-ku, JP
Information: Planning concerts, stage performances, production, management of artists (national and overseas artists), business management, planning and music festival, production, and publication. Pro Arte Musicae stands for "For Musical Arts" in Latin.
Country: Japan

To-on Kikaku Co.
Website: www.to-on.com
Phone: 339 441 581
Address: 1-15-1-5 Sugamo, Toshima-ku, Tokyo 170-0002 Japan
Information: a company that contributes to society through music
Country: Japan
Contact: President Nariyasu Fukuda

Tokyo Music Business Centre Co Ltd Toh On
Website: http:// www.tojc.co.jp
Email: info@tojc.co.jp
Phone: 337 660 355
Address: 1-21-1-1 Shinmachi, Hino-shi, Tokyo 191-0002 Japan
Information: With the cooperation of education-related people from all over the country, they interact with about 150, 000 students annually through appreciation events. They will provide opportunities for children to enjoy performing arts and contribute to the education of the minds of young people as well as the spread of culture and art.
Country: Japan
Contact: President Takashi Kawamura

SINGAPORE

Lushington Entertainments Pte Ltd
Website: www.lushington.com
Email: admin@lushington.com
Phone: 673 14895
Address: HPL House No. 08-01, 50 Cuscaden Road, SG
Information: Lushington enjoys the distinction of being Singapore's first and foremost rock, pop and jazz promoter. Formed in 1990 by a group of friends (B.S. Ong, B.H. Ong, Chan King Fook and S Gopal Krishna Pillay) as an independent affiliate of the publicly held HPL group of companies, Lushington pioneered the introduction of Singapore and S.E.Asia onto the major international touring map.
Country: Singapore

SOUTH AFRICA

Sheer Publishing
Website: www.sheerpublishing.co.za
Email: info@sheer.co.za
Phone: 114 387 000
Address: 75 Bram Fischer Drive, Randburg 2195, South Africa
Information: Sheer Publishing is one of Africa's largest independent Publishing houses and is currently looking to expand its client base within the African diaspora. Sheer Publishing's mission is to provide a comprehensive range of copyright services to our clients, both domestic, Continental and international.
Country: South Africa
Contact: CEO David Alexander
Email: licensing@sheer.co.za
Phone: General Manager Karabo Motijoane
Email: karabo@sheer.co.za

THAILAND

Media Transasia
Website: www.mediatransasia.com
Email:
info@mediatransasia.com
Phone: 220 42370

Address: 14 th Floor, Ocean Tower II, 75/10 Soi Sukhumvit 19, Sukhumvit Road, Klongtoeynue, Wattana, TH
Information: Media Transasia commands the entire gamut of publishing activities – from creating new markets to conceiving new publications, from editorial and design to colour separations and printing. The Group has grown from 2 cities in Asia to over 25 cities worldwide
Country: Thailand
Contact: newstand Rasina Uberoi
Email: rasina@mediatransasia.com
Phone: advertising Robert Gray Gray
Email: robert@mediatransasia.com
Phone: custom publishing Khun Egasith Chotpakditrakul
Email: egasith@mediatransasia.com

UNITED STATES

Allegro Corporation
Website: allegromusicparker.com
Email: Manager@allegromusicparker.com
Phone: 303 680 3915
Address: 11280 South Twenty Mile Road, Suite 110, Parker, CO 80134 USA
Information: Allegro Music is proud to service the needs of musicians & music educators in the Parker area. As Parker's only full service music store, Allegro provides great opportunities for students of all ages, as well as offering customers excellent values on a large variety of musical instruments, accessories & services. Allegro Music is locally owned & operated.Music education is a top priority at Allegro Music. The 6 lesson studios provide private one on one instruction and include a fully equipped percussion studio. The 6 lesson studios keep very busy. Allegro has a total of 22 teachers who teach up to 250+ students a week. The teachers and students are a great asset to Allegro and provide the entire foundation of the store.
Country: United States

GigSalad
Website: www.gigsalad.com
Email: gigs@gigbureau.com
Phone: 866 788 4447
Address: 2733 E. Battlefield Rd., Box 105, US
Information: GigSalad has all the ingredients you need to mix up a successful party, production, or event of any type or size. Find and book everything from bands, musicians, and DJs to entertainers, speakers, and event services. With tens of thousands of performers and professionals for hire across the U.S. and Canada, our marketplace provides an easy and secure way to create an extraordinary gathering, whether you're a first-time event host or a seasoned pro. Book something awesome!
Country: United States
Contact: CEO Mark Steiner

Koss
Website: www.koss.com
Email: customersupport@koss.com
Phone: 414 964 5000
Address: 4129 N Port Washington Rd, Milwaukee, WI 53212 usa
Information: Renowned for the invention of the world's first SP/3 Stereophone, Koss has been pioneering hi-fi since 1958 – three generations of American ingenuity, integrity and incomparable quality.
Country: United States
Contact: vice President Marketing Michael Koss

Musical America Worldwide
Website: www.musicalamerica.com
Email: info@musicalamerica.com
Phone: 609 448 3346
Address: PO Box 1330 Hightstown, NJ 08520
Information: Musical America is the critical resource for the business of the performing arts. Musical America provides news, analysis, forecast, insight, data and intelligence to successfully navigate the performing arts business.
Country: United States
Contact: advertising Sales Stephanie Challener Challener
Email: schallener@musicalamerica.com

Prima Donna Productions
Website: www.primadonnaproductions.com
Email: info@primadonnaproductions.com
Phone: 210 822 3552
Address: 6338 N. New Braunfels, #328 San Antonio, TX 78209
Information: Prima Donna Productions LLC is an independent company dedicated to providing General consumer services including Promotional & Event Services.
Country: United States
Contact: President Nikki Young

Red Poppy Music
Website: redpoppymusic.com
Email: info@redpoppymusic.com
Phone: 718 852 7755
Address: 80 Hanson Pl #301 Brooklyn, NY 11217 USA
Information: Red Poppy Music was founded in 1993 as the publishing company for the music of Michael Gordon, David Lang, and Julia Wolfe

giveo

Faster, easier, with Giveo. It's all in the app.

Give. Buy. Help. Waste Less. Save Planet.

Cashless donation fundraising and marketplace app

GIVEO is the new app that is revolutionising fundraising.

Download it for free right now for Apple and Android and start raising money right away.

"It's a very simple way to raise $100 or $100,000. It's just point and click and that's it."

Fundraising expert and arts leader Douglas Evans

Promoter, Producer, Presenter
The majority of the promoters, producers and presenters in this sec-tion are involved with music, opera, theatre and dance/ballet. **The entries are listed in alphabetical order within country.**

Promoteur, Producteur, Présentateur
La plupart des entrées qui apparaissent dans cette section s'occupent de musique, d'opéra, théâtre et de danse/ballet. **Les entrée sont classés par ordre alphabétique dans le pays.**

Promoter, Produzent, Moderator
Die meisten der in diesem Kapitel einträge befassen sich mit Musik, Oper, Theater und Tanz/Ballet. **Die Einträge sind für jedes Land alphabetisch sortiert.**

Promotore, Produttore, Presentatore
La maggior parte degli voci da noi elencati sono connessi con il mondo della musica, l'opera, teatro, il balletto e la danza. **Le voci sono pubblicate in ordine alfabetico di paese.**

Promotor, Productor, Presentador
La mayoría de organizaciones listados en esta sección trabajan específicamente en el mundo de la música, la ópera, teatro y la danza. **Las entradas se muestran en orden alfabético dentro de cada país.**

performing arts database

ARGENTINA

Ciudad Cultural Konex
Website: www.cckonex.org
Email: info@cckonex.org
Phone: 541 148 643 200
Address: 3131 Sarmiento, AR
Information: Multidisciplinary cultural space whose purpose is to stimulate and disseminate current art, bringing the vanguard movements closer to the community.. Member of ISPA
Country: Argentina

AUSTRALIA

Andrew Kay and Associates Pty Ltd
Website: www.akaaustralia.com.au
Email: pia@akaaustralia.com.au
Phone: 398 205 477
Address: Suite 1311 / 9 Yarra St, AU
Information: Andrew Kay has over 30 years experience in all aspects of the live entertainment industry. He started his working life as a professional actor prior to working for a government arts funding authority, then became General Manager of Australia's major theatre company (Melbourne Theatre Company) before finally becoming a commercial theatre Producer and concert promoter.
Country: Australia
Contact: Associate Producer Margot Teele
Email: margot@akaaustralia.com.au

Barry Crook Productions - Music Festivals Australia
Email: barryccrook@hotmail.com
Phone: 299 533 357
Address: 6/198 Kurraba Road, AU
Information: We offer tour management, festival organisation, TV, film & broadcasting, Press, national & international representation. Our visiting address is: 6/198 Kurraba Road, Neutral Bay NSW 2089. Also Nota Bene Productions (Barry Crook & Natalie Yuen).
Country: Australia
Contact: agent pa (theatre, tv, films) Emily Russell
Email: Managing Director Barry Crook

Brisbane Multicultural Arts Centre (BEMAC)
Website: www.bemac.org.au
Email: admin@bemac.org.au
Phone: 733 914 433
Address: 102 Main Street, AU
Information: As Queensland's most dynamic Producer of multicultural arts, BEMAC has been successfully staging ground-breaking productions that fuel the diverse practice of artists from a variety of cultural backgrounds for almost three decades. Established in 1987 by a group of passionate advocates and artists inspired to bring the creative work of a new generation of multicultural artists into the spotlight, BEMAC has grown to become the state's leading multicultural arts Producer, presenter and Artistic development organisation.
Country: Australia
Contact: Director Jo Pratt
Email: Producer Tanya-Hiroko Martin

Bunker Productions International Pty Ltd.
Website: bunkerproductions.com/Bunker.html
Email: louise@bunkerproductions.com
Phone: 413 330 776
Address: AU
Country: Australia
Contact: writer Director Louise Alston

Cre8ion
Website: www.cre8ion.com.au
Email: Cre8@Cre8ion.com.au
Phone: 419 421 398
Address: Po Box 5722, West End, AU
Information: Cre8ion is a dynamic and energetic company specialising in producing and touring theatrical shows and events of scale in Australia and internationally. The wealth of knowledge, experience and passion for creating, producing and bringing together innovative and vibrant teams to develop a diverse range of unique productions is at the core of Cre8ion's collaborations
Country: Australia
Contact: Producer Theresa Famularo
Email: Theresa@Cre8ion.com.au

Duet Entertainment Pty Ltd
Website: www.duetgroup.com
Email: harley@duetgroup.com
Phone: 299 092 188
Address: Suite 1605, Level 16, 122 Arthur Street, AU
Information: Found by legendary Promoter Kevin Ritchie in 1975, Duet represents the very best in Entertainment, worldwide. Today it is owned a operated by Harley Medcalf. Harley's career began in the local town halls in Australia in 1971, with acts including Billy Thorpe, Max Merritt, Tamum Shud, Sherbet & Hush, joing Duet in 1977.
Country: Australia
Contact: Managing Director Harley Medcalf
Email: harley@duetgroup.com

Edgley International
Website: edgley.com.au
Email: headoffice@edgley.com.au
Phone: 394 287 711
Address: 8 Chapel Street, AU
Information: Edgley International is a theatre and concert promotions company from Australia, first started in the 1930s. It has also been known as Edgley & Dawe Attractions, Edgley Ventures, and Michael Edgley International. The company is noted for bringing to Australia many foreign acts not previously seen in the country, particularly dance companies from Russia.
Country: Australia
Contact: Director Michael Edgley
Email: General Manager Jim Cranfield
Email: cranfield@edgley.com.auDirector Andrew Guild
Email: guild@edgley.com.au

Fresh Track Productions
Website: www.freshtrackproductions.com.au
Email: info@freshtrackproductions.com.au
Phone: 421 355 590
Address: 55 Thorngate Drive, AU
Information: This is a performing arts production company and includes events Marketing. It is based in Adelaide and Sydney. Details of current works, Directors profiles, and contact information provided.
Country: Australia
Contact: Associate Producer Tam Nguyen
Email: Managing Director Lee Cumberlidge
Email: Managing Director Torben Brookman
Email: Artistic Associate Geordie Brookman
Email: project Manager Kate Armstrong-Smith

Garage International, The
Website: www.thegarageinternational.com
Email: contact@thegarageinternational.com
Phone: 437 712 250
Address: PO Box 412, AU
Information: This is an arts management company that runs a venue in various festivals and offers the facilities for companies to present their show in the festival. Registration and management fees apply. This is not a presenting company.
Country: Australia
Contact: Managing Director Jorg Hacker
Email: technical Director Lucas Frazer
Email: technical Manager Mark Simpson

Hirano Productions
Website: www.hiranoproductions.com
Email: mail@hiranoproductions.com
Phone: 393 292 825
Address: Level 2, 66 Curzon St, AU
Information: Our mission is to create and foster exchange in the performing arts between Australia and Asia, through the development of reciprocal relationships with Asian presenters and Producers. The company has spanned activities in eight different countries.
Country: Australia

Hocking & Vigo
Website: www.hockingvigo.com
Email: davidvigo@hockingvigo.com
Phone: 396 024 344
Address: Clifford Hocking Pty Ltd, Level 2, 157 Toorak Road, PO Box 9109, AU
Country: Australia
Contact: Managing Director David Vigo

Macdonnell Promotions Ltd
Phone: 293 103 716
Address: 9 Telopea St, AU
Country: Australia
Contact: Managing Director Justin Macdonnell
Email: Producer Frank Madrid
Email: contact Mario Estrella

Marguerite Pepper Productions
Website: www.mpproductions.com.au
Email: info@mpproductions.com.au
Phone: 412 231 313
Address: PO Box 7293, AU
Information: Producers and Managers of Australian contemporary performance ensembles and independent creative Producer for festivals and organisations
Country: Australia
Contact: Managing Director Marguerite Pepper
Email: marguerite@mpproductions.com.au

McManus Entertainment
Website: www.mcmanusentertainment.com
Email: info@mcmanusentertainment.com
Phone: 394 816 377
Address: 460 Brunswick Street, AU
Information: Andrew McManus is a highly successful concert promoter professional currently serving as the owner and founder of McManus Entertainment out of Melbourne, Australia. He has enjoyed a large amount of success in an industry that is full of failure and difficult obstacles. Although he admits it freely, his career has not been without difficulty. However, Andrew McManus lives his life by the philosophy that giving up is not a viable option

Music Theatre Australia
Website: www.musictheatreaustralia.com.au
Email: enquiries@musictheatreaustralia.com.au
Phone: 386 796 055
Address: Lvl 1, 10 Dorcas St, AU
Information: Music Theatre Australia is a leading Australian entertainment agency and entertainment production company. MTA manages and represents a wide range of artists and acts including circus performers, celebrities, musicians, comedians, opera singers, MCs, jazz, street theatre and team building programs throughout Australia, Asia and the world.
Country: Australia
Contact: Marketing events Director Mandy Croker
Email: entertainment and event consultant Bob Burton
Email: Artistic Director Tania de Jong

Musica Viva Australia
Website: www.musicaviva.com.au
Email: contact@musicaviva.com.au
Phone: 283 946 666
Address: 757 Elizabeth St, AU
Information: Musica Viva is the largest presenter of chamber music in the world, a national company with offices in every Australian state and territory, reaching approximately 360, 000 people every year. Their story began in 1945 as a chamber music organisation focused on just one ensemble. Over the years they have evolved to embrace ensemble music of all styles and genres, presenting leading Australian and international artists to concert audiences and school students across the country. Today, our activities embrace digital technologies to reach a wider audience, and they are at the forefront of artist development.
Country: Australia
Contact: Artistic Director Carl Vine
Email: chief Executive officer Mary Jo Capps
Email: Director of Artistic planning Katherine Kemp
Email: Artistic coordinator Luke Iredale

Musicological Society of Australia
Website: www.msa.org.au
Phone: 261 256 514
Address: 35 Stirling Highway, AU
Information: MSA was founded in 1963 at the University of Sydney and achieved full national status in 1976. Its nine regional chapters (ACT, Hunter, Northern New South Wales, Queensland, South Australia, Sydney, Tasmania, Victoria and Western Australia) provide local activities, research networks and support groups for members.It is incorporated as an Association in the Australian Capital Territory (Associations Incorporation Act 1991), and is affiliated with the International Musicological Society (IMS), International Council for Traditional Music (ICTM) and the New Zealand Musicological Society (NZMS).
Country: Australia
Contact: treasurer Stephanie Rocke
Email: President Alan Davison
Email: secretary Daniel Bangert

Nexus Arts
Website: www.nexusarts.com.au
Email: nexusarts@netspace.net.au
Phone: 395 283 416
Address: PO Box 1009, AU
Information: Founded in Melbourne by Sue Russell over 35 years ago, Nexus Arts tours performers and presenters throughout Australia and New Zealand. The performers are carefully selected for their skill, passion for what they do, and their ability to entertain and inspire. They hope you find the information on their website a useful resource when choosing your future performers – particularly the feedback from schools.
Country: Australia
Contact: founder Sue Russell
Email: administrator Kirstie Armiger-Grant
Email: assistant Manager Robert Russell

ORiGiN Theatrical Pty Ltd
Website: www.origintheatrical.com.au
Email: enquiries@originmusic.com.au
Phone: 285 145 201
Address: PO Box Q1235, AU
Information: ORiGiN™ Theatrical is an Australian Independent music company and is the market leader in Australia and New Zealand for secondary market theatrical exploitation into amateur, community, schools, pro-am, small professional, fringe, regional, stock and repertory productions. Simply this means everything other than First Class Professional Productions. The world's leading theatrical rights owners trust ORiGiN™ Theatrical to strategically manage and exploit their properties to optimise the immediate and long term returns from their musicals and plays.
Country: Australia
owner & Manager
Phillip Walker
owner & Manager
Phillip Mortlock

Performing Lines Ltd
Website: www.performinglines.org.au
Email: Administration@performinglines.org.au

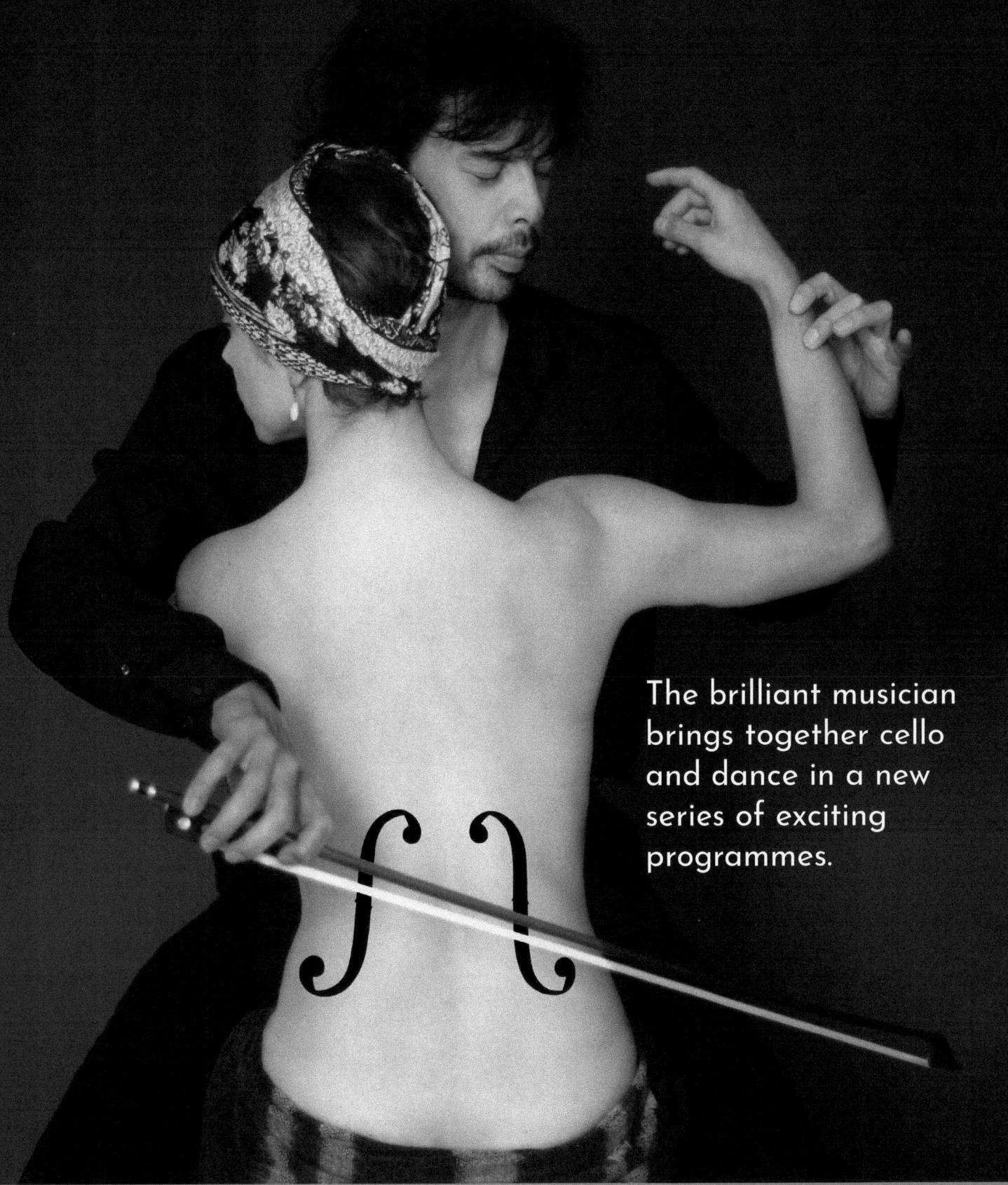

Phone: 293 190 066
Address: 5/245 Chalmers St, AU
Information: Performing Lines develops, produces and tours new and transformative Australian performing arts – regionally, nationally and internationally. They draw on over 30 years of experience to foster innovation and creativity in live performance. They don't shy away from difficult, risky or Artistically challenging work, taking an adaptive rather than reactive approach to all that they do. They make things happen, nurturing creativity, providing artists with access to broader audiences, and contributing to the enhancement of a distinctly Australian culture both in Australia and overseas.
Country: Australia
Contact: acting General Manager Karilyn Brown
Email: karilyn@performinglines.org.auproduction Manager Liz Young
Email: production@performinglines.org.auaccount coordinator Barbara Peters
Email: accounts@performinglines.org.auExecutive Producer Marion Potts
Email: marion@performinglines.org.auMarketing Manager Thom Smyth
Email: Marketing@performinglines.org.auadministrator Sarah Mott
Email: Administration@performinglines.org.auaccounts Barbara Peters
Email: accounts@performinglines.org.au

Really Useful Company Asia Pacific Pty Ltd
Website: www.reallyuseful.com
Email: info@reallyusefulcompany.com
Phone: 293 632 499
Address: Level 1/ 24 Bay St, Double Bay, AU
Information: Founded in 1977, The Really Useful Group exists to bring the work of Andrew Lloyd Webber to the world. They manage his complete catalogue including theatrical and symphonic works, a requiem mass and countless rock and pop songs. The Really Useful Group was also key in developing the casting by television format and has licensed numerous copyrights to be exploited in this way, introducing a new, younger, generation to musical theatre.
Country: Australia
Contact: owner Andrew Lloyd-Webber

Reckless Moments
Website: www.reckless.on.net
Email: Producers@reckless.on.net
Phone: 362 282 858
Address: PO Box 56, AU
Information: Reckless Moments specialises in international co-productions, collaborations and tours. It also sponsors Creative Futures, an independent programme of intercultural performing arts projects involving artists & Producers from Australia, China and the UK. See also Dance and Theatre Companies.
Country: Australia
Contact: creative Producer Barry Plews
Email: barry.plews@reckless.on.net

RMK Voice Productions
Website: www.rmk.com.au
Email: info@rmk.com.au
Phone: 299 221 300
Address: 6 Ridge Street, AU
Information: RMK 'Management is Australia's leading voice over agency representing voiCEOvers, voice actors, actors, presenters, crew and child talent.
Country: Australia
Contact: Managing Director Luke Downs
Email: luke@rmk.com.auGeneral Manager Jules Tyler
Email: jules@rmk.com.austudio Manager Otto Reitano
Email: otto@rmk.com.au

Rock Circuit Promotions
Website: www.rcp.com.au
Email: info@rcp.com.au
Phone:
293 628 801
Address: Level 1, 5 Goldman Lane, AU
Information: RCP are leading promotions and entertainment company that specialise in promoting local and international music, concerts and theatre throughout Australia. Established in the entertainment industry for over twenty years, RCP specialise in promoting and Marketing bands and music venues and also have extensive knowledge and experience in Venue Consultancy, Corporate Events, Club Entertainment and Promotions as well as Children's Entertainment.
Country: Australia

School Performance Tours
Website: www.schoolperformancetours.com.au
Email: spt@schoolperformancetours.com.au
Phone:
295 161 613
Address: 19 Shirlow Street, Marrickville, AU
Information: Formed in October 1987, they proudly believe School Performance Tours is the oldest continuously owned and operated Australian company promoting theatre in education (T.I.E.) productions to schools.
Country: Australia

Seed
Website: www.griffith.edu.au/music/popular-music/student-music/seed
Email: a.pages@griffith.edu.au
Phone: 737 356 632
Address: Griffith University, Gold Coast Campus, Parkland Drive, AU
Information: Seed is a compilation album featuring original music from independent artists. These Bachelor of Popular Music students are already forging their way in the Australian industry, with many touring the country regularly and releasing debut EPs.
Country: Australia

Short and Sweet Productions
Website: shortandsweet.org
Email: info@shortandsweet.org
Phone: 295 195 081
Address: PO Box 462, AU
Information: Short+Sweet is a global festival brand, presenting highly successful Theatre, Dance, Cabaret, and Song Festivals around the world. They provide audiences with exciting and contemporary works that challenge and entertain. Their mission is to build theatre-going audiences around the world. Beginning as a small festival of 10 minute plays in Sydney, they have now grown into a global organisation. It has made a huge impact on the Australian theatre scene through developing new, original work with emerging artists and providing a platform for established artists to showcase their talents.
Country: Australia
Contact: creator and founder Mark Cleary
Email: mark@shortandsweet.orgliterary Manager Pete Malicki
Email: pete@shortandsweet.orgpublicity and promotions Geoff Sirmai
Email: geoff@sirmai.com.auinternational coordinator Lexi Bartolome
Email: alexis@shortandsweet.orgtheatre festival Director Pete Malicki
Email: pete@shortandsweet.org

Simon Abrahams, Melbourne Fringe
Website: www.simonabrahams.com.au
Email: simon@simonabrahams.com.au
Address: AU
Information: Simon Abrahams is recognised as one of Australia's arts and cultural leaders, and is currently Creative Director & CEO of Melbourne Fringe and Chair of Theatre Network Australia, an organisation he co-founded in 2009. He is a programmer, creative Producer, performer and arts consultant. Member of ISPA
Country: Australia

Strut & Fret Production House
Website: www.strutnfret.com
Email: everything@strutnfret.com
Phone: 396 400 028
Address: GPO Box 1548, AU
Information: Strut & Fret has over twelve years experience within the arts industry, creating, producing, touring and Managing artists and productions throughout Australia and internationally. They also own and hire a number of touring venues including The Umbrella Revolution & Le Cascadeur. Please visit our website for further details.
Country: Australia

The Arts Centre
Website: ww.artscentremelbourne.com.au
Email: info@artscentremelbourne.com.au
Phone:
130 018 2183
Address: 100 St Kilda Rd, AU
Information: Sitting beneath one of the city's great symbols - the magnificent Spire - Arts Centre Melbourne is both a defining Melbourne landmark and Australia's largest and busiest performing arts centre. For over 30 years, they have played a leading role in showcasing the best local and international performing arts. They are host and partner to the national and state music, opera, theatre and dance companies, together with local companies, festivals and a multitude of commercial partners.
Country: Australia
Contact: senior publicist Jessica Bendell
Email: jessica.bendell@theartscentre.com.au

AZERBAIJAN

SS production
Email: ss.production@gmail.net
Phone: 124 970 947/948
Address: 16 Nizami str. 1000, AZ
Country: Azerbaijan
Contact: Executive Aysel Rajabli

BRAZIL

Aymberê Produções Artísticas
Website: www.aymbere.com.br
Email:
contato@aymbere.com.br
Address: São Carlos, BR

Information: provides consulting services and assistance to artists, programmers and curators interested in international development work in Brazil and or establish new partnerships in the country. Member of ISPA
Country: Brazil
Contact: Administration Patrícia Ceschi
Email: patricia@aymbere.com.brAdministration Gabriel Barone
Email: gabriel@aymbere.com.br

Boranda
Website: www.boranda.com.br
Email: contato@boranda.com.br
Phone: 112 362 9906
Address: BR
Information: Borandá acts on all of the music business branches, as record label, management and booking agency, promoter and publisher, using the internet as an important tool to connect artists with their public in Brazil and throughout the world. Member of ISPA
Country: Brazil
Contact: artist management, booking and label Fernando Grecco
Email: contato@boranda.com.br

CANADA

Across Oceans Arts
Website: www.acrossoceans.org
Email: info@acrossoceans.org
Address: CA
Information: Across Oceans Arts, based in Toronto Canada, has been facilitating international arts platforms in Canada and worldwide for over 25 years. Creation, Exchange and Development of exPression through arts collaboration between artists and communities of all genres and heritages. Signature projects: ti Krima! massive ensemble performance work for artists and communities; The Choreographic Marathon professional development and creation exchange; PREP for inclusive performance; 7 Days of Creation Residencies.
Country: Canada
Contact: Artistic and exectuive Director Maxine Heppner
Email: info@acrossoceans.org
 Administration & Outreach
Jennifer Watkins
Email: openarts@total.net

Agilo Arts
Website: www.agilo.ca
Email: info@agilo.ca
Phone: 604 418 1960
Address: Artscape Triangle Lofts, Suite 225, 38 Abell Street, CA
Information: supporting mid-sized companies, established and emerging independent artists, festivals and arts service organisations active in Ontario and other regions of Canada
Country: Canada
 consultant & Producer
Jessa Agilo
Email: jessa@agilo.ca

Ann Summers International
Website: www.sumarts.com
Email: sumintl@rogers.com
Phone: 416 362 1422
Address: 43 Bright Street, CA
Information: We represent international artists in their career development, as well as presenting and producing concerts, tours and events, whilst earning acclaim for innovative and creative ideas in audience development, and arts Marketing. Member of ISPA
Country: Canada
Contact: President Ann Summers Dossena

Arte Musica Foundation
Website: www.mbam.qc.ca
Email: webmaster@mbamtl.org
Phone: 514 285 2000
Address: The Montreal Museum of Fine Arts, P.O. Box 3000, Station "H", CA
Information: the Arte Musica Foundation, in residence at the Montreal Museum of Fine Arts, is proud to present its fourth musical season, with over eighty concerts slated for Bourgie Hall; enthralling and invigorating programming features remarkable homegrown talent while including a host of renowned musicians from far and wide, along with several from France, thanks to a new partnership with the Louvre; in September 2014, they are launching a project which will be realized over eight seasons: the concert presentation of the complete sacred cantatas by J. S. Bach, a first in Canada; this monumental undertaking will consolidate the partnerships the company has already established with Quebec's best musical ensembles
Country: Canada
Contact: General and Artistic Director Isolde Lagacé
Email: ilagace@mbamtl.orgadministrative Manager Marie-Hélène Dionne
Email: mdionne@mbamtl.orgCommunicatios Manager Alexandre Caron
Email: acaron@mbamtl.org

Atlantic Presenters Association
Website: www.atlanticpresenters.ca
Email: info@atlanticpresenters.ca
Phone: 902 892 6269
Address: Atlantic Presenters Association, Box 3, 115 Richmond Street, CA
Information: (APA) is the regional arts presenter's organisation for the four Atlantic Provinces: Newfoundland, Prince Edward Island, Nova Scotia and New Brunswick. It is a leader in the presentation of the performing arts and promo. Member of ISPA
Country: Canada
Contact: block booking coordinator Kate Gracey-Stewart
Email: kate@atlanticpresenters.caExecutive Director Laurie Gillis
Email: laurie@atlanticpresenters.capast President Tim Yerxa
Email: tim@theplayhouse.caPresident Darcy Campbell
Email: dcampbell@confederationcentre.comManager of programs and operations Jennifer Gillis
Email: jennifer@atlanticpresenters.ca

Attila Glatz Concert Productions
Website: www.salutetovienna.com
Email: glatz1@glatzconcerts.com
Phone: 416 323 1403
Address: 77 Bloor Street West, Suite 1801, CA
Information: Founded in 1987, Attila Glatz Concert Productions produces, promotes, and manages classical, jazz, folk, country, film and video game music performances worldwide.
Country: Canada
Contact: President Attila Glatz
Email: Stephanie Wright
Email: stephaniew@glatzconcerts.com

Calgary Pro Musica Society
Website: www.calgarypromusica.ca
Email: info@calgarypromusica.ca
Phone: 403 244 8277
Address: 5111 Northland Drive NW, CA
Information: Calgary Pro Musica is a non-profit organization that encourages and celebrates chamber music. Our concerts feature world renowned chamber ensembles performing in the beautiful Eckhardt-Gramatté Hall in the University of Calgary's Rozsa Centre (Calgary, Alberta, Canada). We contribute to our community through meaningful music outreach and learning programs. Calgary Pro Musica has been providing exceptional value to audiences and enriching Calgary's cultural life for over 38 years.
Country: Canada

Canadian Arts Presenting Association (CAPACOA)
Website: www.capacoa.ca
Email: mail@capacoa.ca
Phone: 613 562 3515
Address: 17 York Street, suite 200, CA
Information: The united, national voice of the Canadian performing arts presenting and touring sector. Member of ISPA
Country: Canada
Contact: Executive Director Sue Urquhart
Email: sue.urquhart@capacoa.caoperations Manager Melanie Bureau
Email: melanie.bureau@capacoa.caDirector of research and development Frederic Julien
Email: frederic.julien@capacoa.caPresident Michele Emslie
Email: michele.emslie@yac.ca

Dance Immersion
Website: www.danceimmersion.ca
Email: info@danceimmersion.ca
Phone: 416 203 0666
Address: 203-54 Wolseley Street, Toronto, CA
Information: Dance Immersion is a non-profit organisation that produces, promotes and supports dancers and dances of the African Diaspora. the organisation was founded in 1994 by Vivine Scarlett and was established to address the need for additional presentation, skill development, and networking opportunities for dance artists of African descent
Country: Canada

EMM Williams Productions
Website: www.emmwp.com
Email: info@emmwp.com
Phone: 514 577 7858
Address: 302 Rue de Saint Servan, CA
Information: EMM provide consultancy for there clients (promoters, festivals, event organisers, and governments) to help plan an event
Country: Canada

Joanne Morrow Arts Consulting Inc.
Email: morrow.arts.consult@gmail.com
Phone: 647 205 3638
Address: 1177 Yonge St., Suite 306, CA
Information: focusses on projects which assist performing arts creators, artists and ensembles in their development. Consults in cultural policy and research for arts councils and government

Country: Canada

John Lambert & Assoc.
Website: www.johnlambert.ca
Email: info@johnlambert.ca
Phone: 514 272 7532
Address: 5654 AVE DE L'ESPLANADE, CA
Information: provides international representation and career development for contemporary performing arts companies, specialising in theatre, circus and mixed media. The company fosters the development of long-term relationships between artists and presenters, including co-productions and financial investment in the creative process. Currently active in North America, Latin America, Europe, the Middle East and the Asia/Pacific. Member of ISPA
Country: Canada
Contact: President John Lambert

Kids' Entertainment, Inc.
Website: www.kidsentertainment.net
Email: info@kidsentertainment.net
Phone: 416 971 4841
Address: 460 College Street, 202, CA
Information: the mission statement of Kids' Entertainment is: "Kids' Entertainment is committed to bringing high quality, unique and diverse performing arts to young audiences. We will seek out the best through active relationships with professional organisations, international festivals and events, and management professionals. We will forge positive relationships with our artists from around the world by providing the means for them to promote and tour compelling art work, worthy of children's attention"
Country: Canada
Contact: Director Cheryle Hansen
Email: cheryle@kidsentertainment.netGeneral Manager Avril Helbig
Email: admin@kidsentertainment.netDirector of touring Tara Bailey
Email: tara@kidsentertainment.net

Latitude 45 Arts Promotion, Inc.
Website: www.latitude45arts.com
Email: info@latitude45arts.com
Phone: 514 276 2694
Address: 107, Boul. St-Joseph W., CA
Information: Latitude 45 represents a wide array of artists who work in the field of music. We represent singers, instrumentalists and composers from across our native Canada, coast to coast and from many corners of the globe in many styles and techniques. Latitude 45's artists engage audiences with the power of commitment and the joys of curiosity. Latitude 45, like the imagination, embraces the world.
Country: Canada
Contact: President Barbara Scales
Email: scalesb@latitude45arts.comagent and company Manager Eoin Ó Catháin
Email: eoin@latitude45arts.comUK agent John King
Email: kinjohn@latitude45arts.com

Mainstage Management Inc.
Website: mainstagemanagement.com/
Email: jack@mainstagemanagement.com
Phone: 604 488 9153
Address: PO Box 53503, CA
Country: Canada
Contact: Contact Jack Schuller
Email: jack@mainstagemanagement.com

Manifesto
Website: www.themanifesto.ca
Email: nfo@themanifesto.ca
Phone: 647 436 8404
Address: 37 Bulwer Street, CA
Information: through art exhibitions, dance competitions, workshops, free outdoor concerts, film screenings, networking opportunities, seminars, festivals, a pop-up arts market and much more, Manifesto creates powerful and engaging experiences, and provides opportunities for young artists to grow. Member of ISPA
Country: Canada

New Works
Website: www.newworks.ca
Email: info@newworks.ca
Phone:
604 893 887
Address: 303 - 3102 Main Street, CA
Information: New Works represents a small roster of dancers and dance companies to provide management, mentorship and technical support.
Country: Canada
Contact: Executive Director Joyce Rosario
Email: joyce@newworks.caArtistic administrator Andrea Hébert
Email: andrea@newworks.caMarketing and communications Diana Lee
Email: diana@newworks.ca
Office & Outreach Coordinator Jocelyn Coburn
Email: jocelyn@newworks.ca

Otter Bay Productions
Website: www.lostsound.com
Email: otterbay@lostsound.com
Address: P.O Box 72041, CA
Information: found sound and acoustic inventions. This acoustic Duo offers original music and performance that is compelling for sound art festivals, intimate venues, environmental programmes/conferences, children's festivals and acoustic film scores
Country: Canada
Contact: co-Artistic Director Robert Minden
Email: otterbay@lostsound.comco-Artistic Director Carla Hallett
Email: otterbay@lostsound.com

Philmultic Management and Productions Inc.
Website: www.philmultic.com
Email: info@philmultic.com
Phone: 514 482 6750
Address: 8191 Montview, CA
Information: talent management and record productions.
Country: Canada
Contact: Managing Director Risheng Risheng

Riverstreet Productions Inc
Email: riverstreetproductions@shaw.ca
Address: 721 - 54th Avenue SW, CA
Country: Canada
Contact: President John O'Reilly

Soundstreams
Website: www.soundstreams.ca
Email: info@soundstreams.ca
Phone: 416 504 1282
Address: 302-579 Richmond St W, CA
Information: A Toronto-based music presenter that commissions, develops, and showcases the work of contemporary Canadian composers and their international counterparts. Member of ISPA
Country: Canada
Contact: Artistic Director Lawrence Cherney
Email: Executive Director Ben Dietschi
Email: bend@soundstreams.caDirector of communications Peter Donato
Email: peterd@soundstreams.caPresident Daniel Weinzweig

Sulyma Productions Inc
Website: www.sulyma.com
Email: spi@sulyma.com
Phone: 780 448 5979
Address: 6620 – 124 Street N.W., CA
Information: independent arts and entertainment production company founded in 1987 by Michael H. Sulyma, Sulyma Productions Inc. (SPI) produces live performing arts, specials for television and international tours
Country: Canada
Contact: President/Producer Michael H. Sulyma
Email: spi@sulyma.com

The Theatre Centre
Website: www.theatrecentre.org
Email: info@theatrecentre.org
Phone: 416 534 9261
Address: The Theatre Centre Pop-Up, 1095 Queen St. West, CA
Country: Canada

Toyich International Projects (TIP)
Website: www.toyichinternationalprojects.ca
Email: boyanna@sympatico.ca
Phone: 416 922 0755
Address: 20 Prince Arthur Avenue, Suite17D, CA
Information: non-profit registered charity devoted to the professional/educational development of young Canadian musicians/teachers/adult amateurs.Programs include Monster Concerts, Master Classes and Summer Program for Canadian and international participants www.romesmarts.org in Rome, Italy
Country: Canada
President, CEO & Artistic Director Boyanna Toyich
Email: boyanna@sympatico.ca

CHINA

Ping Pong Productions
Website: www.pingpongarts.org
Email: info@pingpongarts.org
Phone: 106 593 6931
Contact: founder/Executive Director Alison M. Friedman
Email: General Manager, Associate Producer Vicki Si Yuan
Email: project coordinator Weina Zhang
Email: weina@pingpongarts.orgDirector of program operations Sophie Miyi Zhu

Poly Culture & Arts Co.
Website: www.polypm.com.cn/english/
Email: service@polyauction.com
Phone: 106 408 2277
Address: Floor 3, New Poly Plaza, 1 North Chaoyangmen Street, Dongcheng District

Country: China

UniArt Universal Culture & Media
Website: www.uniart-worldwide.com
Email: eva.liu@uniart-worldwide.com
Phone: 106 591 152 5806
Address: Suite805, E-Tower, China World Trade Center, C12 Guanghua Road
Information: promotes performing arts in mainland China, Hong Kong and Macao; promotes traditional Chinese performing arts around the world. Member of ISPA
Country: China

COLOMBIA

Fundación Gilberto Alzate Avendaño
Website: www.fgaa.gov.co
Email: atencionalciudadano@fgaa.gov.co
Phone: 128 29491
Address: Calle 10 # 3-16, CO
Information: develops and promotes Artistic practices and creative projects, promotes political culture, maintains a permanent cultural offer quality and participatory processes that link both Artistic field actors as citizens in the exercise of cultural rights in the Capital District. Member of ISPA
Country: Colombia

The Odeon Space (El Espacio Odeón)
Website: www.espacioodeon.com
Email: info@espacioodeon.com
Phone: 174 37064
Address: CRA. 5 # 12C - 73, CO
Information: The Odeon Space: Cultural Centre is an independent, nonprofit institution dedicated to promoting contemporary visual art and performing arts in Bogota
Country: Colombia

EGYPT

European-Egyptian Contemporary Music Society
Website: www.eecms-ebdaa.eu
Email: contact@eecms-ebdaa.eu
Address: EG
Information: The European-Egyptian Contemporary Music Society (EECMS) seeks to promote contemporary music in Egypt and foster creative dialogue by building relationships with cultural institutions and ensembles at a national and international level.
Country: Egypt

HONG KONG

Hong Kong Chopin Society
Website: www.chopinsocietyhk.org
Email: info@chopinsocietyhk.org
Phone: 286 83387
Address: No.2 Ice House Street, Central, HK
Information: this a non-profit company and is a well-established institution in Hong Kong, dedicated to the promotion of classical musical activities, including the organisation of public recitals and concerts, master classes and a major international piano competition
Country: Hong Kong
Contact: Chairman Andrew Freris

Serious Staging
Website: www.serious-staging.com
Email: info@serious-staging.com
Phone: 392 99555
Address: 603 Chao's Building, 143 Bonham Strand East, HK
Information: Having built a solid foundation on its event management and production experience, Serious Staging is best positioned to proactively identify potential for the creation of imaginative projects and extraordinary experiences. Serious Staging's venue opportunities and solutions service delivers more than just a vision – they create opportunities where none seem to exist to craft exceptional and out-of-the-ordinary proposals to clients looking for a one-of-a-kind venue and experience proposition. Service include identification of venue opportunities and provision of venue solutions. Member of ISPA.
Country: Hong Kong
Contact: Managing Director David Rule
Email: special projects Director John Binks
Email: technical Director Mark Taylor

The Hong Kong Institute for Promotion of Chinese Culture
Email: info@hkipcc.org.hk
Phone: 255 94904
Address: Unit L4-04, Jockey Club Creative Arts Centre, , 30 Pak Tin Street, Shek Kip Mei, Kowloon, HK
Information: non-profit making organisation receiving no government subsidy but supported by donations from prominent local individuals and organisations
Country: Hong Kong

INDONESIA

Gelar Nusantara PT
Website: www.gelar.co.id
Email: info@gelar.co.id

Phone: 812 901 88682
Address: Joglo Rempoa Art House, Jl. Gelatik Ujung 1D, Rempoa, Ciputat, ID
Country: Indonesia
Contact: Chairman Bram Kushardjanto
Email: bram@gelar.co.idCEO Kumoratih Kushardjanto
Email: kumo@gelar.co.id

ISRAEL

Incubator Theater
Website: www.incubator.org.il
Email: info@incubator.org.il
Phone: 026 543 004
Address: 18 Mesilat Yesharim St, IL
Country: Israel

JAPAN

Agora Planning Ltd
Website: www.komaba-agora.com
Email: info@komaba-agora.com
Phone: 334 672 743
Address: 1-11-13 Komaba, Meguro-ku, JP
Country: Japan

Allegro Music Tokyo Inc
Website: www.allegromusic.co.jp
Email: opera@allegromusic.co.jp
Phone: 352 167 131
Address: Glück Heim 5002, Kioicho 3-29, Chiyoda-ku, JP
Country: Japan
Contact: Managing Director Kazuhiko Ogawa

An Creative Inc
Website: www.ancreative.net/e/
Email: office@ancreative.net
Phone: 354 580 548
Address: 29-2 Sakuragaoka-cho, Shuwa Sakuragaoka Residence #510, Shibuya-ku, JP
Information: dance production/presentation/promotion company with a policy of furthering contemporary dance in Japan; represents Japanese dance companies/soloists, presents groups in Japan; plans and promotes festivals, conferences, events, performances, workshops
Country: Japan

Arte Esperanza Co. Ltd
Website: www.arte-esperanza.co.jp
Email: info@arteesperanza.jp
Phone: 334 736 044
Address: Rockwell House 1-3-3 Hiroo, Shibuya-ku, JP
Country: Japan

Aspen Incorporated
Website: www.aspen.jp
Email: info@aspen.jp
Phone: 354 670 081
Address: 20-16 Nishi-Azabu, 2 chome Minato-ku, JP
Information: Aspen Inc. manages top classical Japanese artists, produces concerts, and engages world renowned classical artists in classical music activities in Japan as well as other Asian regions. Since 1998, Aspen Inc. has been organising Ishikawa Music Academy inc. Member of IAMA.
Country: Japan
Contact: Director Mitsutoshi Kato
Email: Director Fumio Hayashi
Email: Chairman and CEO Masami Shigeta

Camerata Tokyo Inc.
Website: www.camerata.co.jp
Email: info@camerata.co.jp
Address: 2F, Wakho Bldg., 14-3, Motoyoyogi-machi, Shibuya-ku, JP
Information: commercial agent/concert management company; represents Japanese artists & presents foreign artists; well known as a record label
Country: Japan
Contact: President Hiroshi Isaka

Concert Service Co Ltd
Website: www.concert.co.jp
Email: chirashi@concert.co.jp
Address: 35 Kaitai-cho, Shinjuku-ku, JP
Information: established in 1994; management of Japanese artists & concerts; presents foreign artists in Japan & Asian countries
Country: Japan
President & CEO Shuetsu Sato
Email: vice President Mayumi Okura

Conversation & Company Ltd
Email: info@conversation.co.jp
Address: 2-1 Kanda - Ogawamachi, Chiyoda - ku, JP
Information: also present workshops, produce overseas concerts of Japanese musicians and dance companies, and cooperate with international arts festivals abroad
Country: Japan
Contact: General Director Shohachiro Haga

Dowland & Company
Website: www.linkclub.or.jp/
Email: dowland@air.linkclub.or.jp
Address: 2-23-5-105, Irumagawa, Sayama, JP
Information: artist management of soloists & ensembles; concert management & also produces CDs
Country: Japan
Contact: Managing Director Keiko Tsunoda
Email: Producer Takashi Tsunoda

Erato Music Office
Website: www.erato.musical.to
Email: erato@da3.so-net.ne.jp
Phone: 757 511 260
Address: c/o Kinki Chiho Hatsumei Centre, 14 Yoshida Kawara-cho, Sakyo-ku, JP
Information: mainly promotes Japanese musicians
Country: Japan
Contact: representative Takashi Tsugawa
Email: Administration Toyomi Umehara

Forte Music Office Inc
Address: 104 Asahi Plaza Umeda Higashi, 3-1-10 Nakazaki Nishi, Kita-ku, JP
Information: commercial promoter
Country: Japan
Contact: President Susumu Araki

Intermuse Tokyo Co Ltd
Email: intermu@aol.com
Address: 9-1-7 Akasaka, Minato-ku, JP
Information: classsical music promoter & management
Country: Japan
Contact: President Tomoya Ono

IVS Music Co Ltd
Email: ivsmusic@crocus.ocn.ne.jp
Address: 19-1 Haraikata-machi, Shinjuku-ku, JP
Information: promotes mainly classical music; also cooperates the management of Osaka International Chamber Music Competiton (q.v.) and its prizewinner's debut concerts in Japan; represents soloists, orchestras, chamber ensembles; manages concerts, recording of CDs
Country: Japan
Contact: Chairman Hisataka Saito
Email: President Ryoichi Yoshida

Japan Arts Link
Address: 3F, Nampeidai Heights, 4-13 Nampeidai-cho, Shibuya-ku, JP
Information: produces drama for Performing Arts Foundation of Hokkaido, Performing Arts Young Cultural of Sendai, and Hiroshima Cultural Foundation
Country: Japan
Contact: President/Producer Eiko Shibata

Japan Concert Bureau Co Ltd
Email: t-manai@rc5.so-net.ne.jp
Phone: 333 631 651
Address: 8F Musashino Bldg, 1-20-26 Hyakunin-cho, Shinjuku-ku, JP
Information: promotes mainly small groups or chamber orchestras with up to 20 members; wishes to bring more concerts to suburban/provincial towns and small islands; also an agent of pianists, violinists, chamber orchestras, piano trios
Country: Japan
Contact: Manager Yasuko Manai
Email: President Tsunekichi Manai

Japan International League of Artists
Website: www.jila.co.jp
Email: music@jila.co.jp
Phone: 333 564 033
Address: 2F Shinjuku Gyoen-mae Bldg , 1-34-8 Shinjuku, Shinjuku-ku, JP
Information: plans, produces, and manages concerts, organises auditions and competitions; works as an artists agent; represents foreign artists; publishes and sells CDs and sheet music; organises Tokyo International Competition for Chamber Music Chamber Music Composit
Country: Japan
Contact: secretary General Takeko Komiya
Email: composer/Producer/Director Kazuhiko Hattori

Japan Orchestral Society Ltd
Email: nikkyo@aurora.dti.ne.jp
Phone: 357 214 621
Address: 4F CI Bldg., 1-3-6 Ebisu Minami, Shibuya-ku, JP
Information: presents many foreign musicians from Europe and North America & coordinates concerts in Japan, other Far East & Southeast Asian countries; also represents Japanese artists
Country: Japan
Contact: President Yukio Mizota

Kajimoto Concert Management Co Ltd
Website: www.kajimotomusic.com
Email: concert@kajimotomusic.com
Phone: 335 740 969
Address: 8-6-25 Ginza, Chuo-ku, JP
Information: Kajimoto has been engaged in Managing leading classical artists and presenting concerts, tours

and events for over half a century

Kojima Concert Management Co Ltd.
Website: www.kojimacm.com
Email: kojimacm@ops.dti.ne.jp
Phone: 353 793 733
Address: 1-24-7-408 Shinjuku, Shinjuku-ku, JP
Information: also has an office in Osaka, see also Agents and Management
Country: Japan

Koransha
Website: www.koransha.com
Email: koransha_info@koransha.com
Address: 6F, Otowa NS Bldg., 2-10-2 Otowa, Bunkyo-ku, JP
Information: importer of artists, ballet, opera, circus, etc; stage planning & producing
Country: Japan
Contact: President Tadashi Nitta

Kyushu Ro-On
Email: ro-on@star.saganet.ne.jp
Address: 1-1-2 Tenjin, JP
Information: promoter
Country: Japan
Contact: Chairman Megumi Nakayama
Email: secretary General Chieko Kitamura
Email: Director of Marketing dept. Ryusuke Nakayama

Miho Project
Website: www.mihoproject.com
Email: info@mihoproject.com
Address: 311 Oikeno-cho, Muromachi-dori Oike-agaru, Nakagyo-ku, JP
Information: planning & producing of events, artists management; also represents some entertainment groups
Country: Japan
Contact: art Producer Miho Takechi

Muse Company
Website: www.musekk.co.jp
Email: MuseKK@aol.com
Phone: 334 798 535
Address: 4-6-10-101, Minami Aoyama, Minato-ku, JP
Information: plans & produces various workshops and community art projects; promotes and manages foreign artists & arts organisations
Country: Japan
Contact: President Yuko Ijichi

Musical Artists Guild
Email: m-arts@sa.il24.net
Address: No. 508, 1-13-1, Higashi, , Shibuya-ku, JP
Information: supporter of musicians' activities and promoter of their interests, including conditions of work; also promotes education for youth and international exchange; as an agent it represents soloists, chamber orchestras, etc.; plans and manages concerts
Country: Japan
Contact: Executive Director Tsutomu Momose

Nakatsubo Arts Service Co., Ltd
Website: www.nakatsubo.co.jp
Email: info@nakatsubo.co.jp
Address: 2005 Sky-Heights-Tokai, 1-13 Tomiya-cho, Kanagawa-ku, JP
Country: Japan
Contact: Manager international division Akiko Yanagisawa
Email: Executive vice-President Isao Nakatsubo

Nippon Artists, Inc
Website: www.nipponartists.jp
Email: info@nipponartists.jp
Phone: 359 783 311
Address: 5-5-7-2F TEL Koishikawa, Bunkyo-ku, JP
Information: International representation and management services for classical musicians incl. orchestral touring; concert promotion and the co-ordination of festivals
Country: Japan
Contact: Manager Kiyoshi Tamamura
Email: President Yusuke Terada

NPO Kaibunsha
Website: www.kaibunsha.net
Email: info@kaibunsha.net
Phone: 332 750 220
Address: 5F Kodama building, , 1-9-9 Nihonbashi Muromachi, Chuo-ku, JP
Information: promotes and produces drama, dance, contemporary music, Japanese traditional performing arts on an international level
Country: Japan
Executive Director & Producer Junko Hanamitsu

Osaka Collegium Musicum
Website: www.collegium.or.jp/
Email: office@collegium.or.jp
Phone: 669 264 755
Address: 1-13 1-chome, Chuo-ku, Osaka Otedori, JP
Country: Japan

Plankton Co Ltd
Website: www.plankton.co.jp/
Email: info@plankton.co.jp
Address: 5-28-10-1F, Jingu-mae, Shibuya-ku, JP
Country: Japan

Point Tokyo Co Ltd
Email: point@dssstage.co.jp
Address: 6B Roppongi International Bldg., 7-3-12 Roppongi, Minato-ku, JP
Information: production management, and support to importers and exporters of performing arts; presents The Ninagawa Company (q.v.)
Country: Japan
Contact: contact Misa Hayashi
Email: President Tadao Nakane

Second Line Co Ltd
Website: www.secondline.jp
Email: info@secondline.jp
Address: 1-7-21 Koenji Minami, Suginami-ku, JP
Information: event planning & production, stage management & direction, assignment of performers for events, promotion for various activities, organizing concert & promotion of tours, artist management, studio management, etc.
Country: Japan
Contact: President Akira Kuwabara

Shochiku Co Ltd
Website: www.shochiku.co.jp
Address: c/o Theatre Division, 18F, Tohgeki Bldg., 4-1-1, Tsukiji, Chuo-ku, JP
Information: major entertainment company; its operations include cinema production, distribution & all aspects of show business; Shochiku directly manages Kabukiza (q.v.), Shimbashi Embujo (q.v.), and Sunshine Gekijo (q.v.) in Tokyo, Shochikuza (q.v.) in Osaka as well
Country: Japan
Contact: vice Chairman Nobuyoshi Otani
Email: President Junichi Sakomoto
Email: Chairman Takeomi Nagayama

Station Co Ltd
Website: www.station.li
Email: info@station.li
Address: 2F, Sakuma Bldg., 11 Araki-cho, Shinjuku-ku, JP
Information: produces festivals, concerts and other events on national and international level
Country: Japan
Contact: President Mitsuo Tamura

Tate Corporation
Website: www.tate.jp
Email: susumu@tate.jp
Phone: 334 029 978
Address: 3-2-14-1F Jingu-Mae, Shibuya-ku, JP
Information: imports various kinds of performing arts such as dance, ballet, drama, concerts and musicals mainly from Europe, USA and Australia
Country: Japan
Contact: President Susumu Matahira

Tessenkai
Website: www.jade.dti.ne.jp
Email: tessen@jade.dti.ne.jp
Address: 4-21-29 Minami-Aoyama, Minato-ku, JP
Information: troupe/Producer of Noh plays; see entry under Drama and Noh Laboratory Theatre Tessenkai
Country: Japan
Contact: secretary General Ken'ichi Kasai
Email: President Tetsunojo Kanze

Toho Co Ltd
Website: www.toho.co.jp
Address: c/o Theatrical Division, 15F, Yurakucho Denki Bldg.-Kitakan, 1-7-1 Yuraku-c, Chiyoda-ku, JP
Information: major Producer of movies & theatricals in Japan, founded in 1932; the company operates Toho Musicals and Toho Gendaigeki; the former includes musicals in Japanese translation; it owns Imperial Theatre and Geijutsuza
Country: Japan

Tokyo Concert Produce
Phone: 339 827 239
Address: 2-12-2-403 Ikebukuro-honcho, Toshima-ku, JP
Country: Japan

Tokyo Ensoka Kyokai
Address: 302 Kyoei Bldg, 1-2-12 Higashi Ueno, Taito-ku, JP
Information: promotes chamber music concerts; represents mainly the Tokyo Solisten
Country: Japan
Contact: President Yoshiko Akamatsu

Tokyo Ongaku Bunka Centre
Phone: 335 019 188
Address: 1F, Dai-11 Mori Bldg., 2-6-4 Toranomon, Minato-ku, JP
Information: aimed at popularizing classical music by organising concerts of crossover between classical and

pop; also promotes tango music

Tokyo Opera Production
Website: operaproduce.web.fc2.com/english_version.htm
Email: operaproduce@jcom.home.ne.jp
Phone: 335 305 181
Address: 1F Meson du Mi Yai, 1-7-11 Tohshin-cho, Itabashi-ku, JP
Information: concert production and artist management; see also Opera
Country: Japan

Tokyo Pro Musica Co Ltd
Website: www.tokyopromusica.jp/
Email: promusica@mtf.biglobe.ne.jp
Address: New State Mener 1110, 2-23-1 Yoyogi, Shibuya-ku, JP
Information: commercial promoter which presents European singers and classical music artists
Country: Japan
Contact: President Masaru Arihara

Tsuka Kohei Jimusho
Website: www.tsuka.co.jp/
Email: mail@tsuka.co.jp
Address: Kyu Kitazono Shougakkou Nai 4F, Akabane-kita 3-6-1, Kita-ku, JP
Information: produces and promotes a drama company, Kita-ku Tsuka Kohei Geikidan
Country: Japan
Contact: Director Kohei Tsuka

KOREA, REPUBLIC OF

LUDI Company
Website: www.ludicompany.com/
Email: ludicompany@gmail.com
Phone: 270 30826
Address: #1607, LG Eclat Building, Seocho-dong, Seocho-gu
Country: Republic of Korea

Performance Planning MCT
Website: www.mctdance.com
Email: mctfeel@empal.com
Phone: 222 634 680
Address: 202 Samkyung Bldg, 62-11 Pil-dong 3-ga, Jung-gu
Country: Republic of Korea
Contact: President Sung-Heon Jang

PMC Production Co., Ltd
Website: www.i-pmc.co.kr/
Email: orientalmuse@nanta.co.kr
Phone: 269 207 747
Address: 11th FL., Daehak-ro, Jongno-gu
Information: NANTA is a comic musical non-verbal performance derived from the traditional Korean instrumental performance "Samulnori"; the kitchen is its backdrop, chefs its main characters; knives and other kitchen utensils are transformed into musical instruments in the hands of the performers; they thrill the audience with acrobatic cooking shows, a surprise wedding ceremony, and an exciting dumpling challenge; the highlight of the show is a "Water Drum Sequence" where drummers beat 5 standing kitchenware drums with water and LED lights
Country: Republic of Korea

SBS (Cultural Promotion Dept)
Website: www.sbs.co.kr
Email: webmaster@sbs.co.kr
Phone: 220 610 006
Address: 920 Mok1-dong, Yangcheon-gu
Country: Republic of Korea
Contact: President Keum-Ryul Ha

SBS Production
Website: www.sbspro.co.kr
Phone: 221 136 700
Address: 920 Mok1-dong, Yangcheon-gu
Country: Republic of Korea
Contact: President Woo-Kwang Kim

MALAYSIA

Betarecs Sdn Bhd
Website: www.betarecs.com.my/
Email: info@betarecs.sg
Phone: 209 255 1617
Address: 71-1 & 71-2, Medan Setia 1, Bukit Damansara, , MY
Country: Malaysia

Lee Wushu Arts Theatre
Website: www.wushuart.com/
Email: wushuarts@gmail.com
Phone: 751 13013
Address: No. 159-02, Jalan Bestari 1/5, Taman Nusa Bastari, MY
Information: Wushu (martial arts) management and promotion, (see also Agents and Management)
Country: Malaysia

MEXICO

Conciertos Guadalajara AC
Website: www.conciertosguadalajara.org/
Email: gorostiza@conciertosguadalajara.org
Phone: 333 613 2024
Address: Museo del Periodismo, Av. Alcalde #225, MX
Country: Mexico
Contact: Executive Director Martha Gonzalez
Email: matha@conciertoguadalajara.org

Latino Quality Productions
Address: Matamoros 40-A, Barrio de Santo Domingo, Tepoztlan, MX
Country: Mexico
Contact: contact Salvador López

Parnassós
Website: www.parnassos.com.mx
Email: parnassos@intercable.net
Phone: 818 356 9633
Address: Amazonas 300 Pte, Colonia del Valle, MX
Information: musical association that promotes music, dance and vocal artists. Organises concerts for New Young Talents amd Concerts for Ensembles of Young Talents among other activities. Also organises an International Piano Competition every two years and a National Piano Competition for Young pianists every year (see also Competitions)
Country: Mexico
Contact: President Myrtha Salazar

Pia Productions
Website: www.piaproducciones.org
Email: atencionaclientes@piaproducciones.org
Phone: 999 943 5212
Address: Fraccionamiento Jardines de Mérida, MX
Country: Mexico

Red Latinoamericana de Productores Independientes de Arte Contemporáneo
Address: Zamora 17, Col. Condesa, MX
Country: Mexico

NEW ZEALAND

Auckland Live
Website: www.aucklandlive.co.nz
Email: media@aucklandlive.co.nz
Phone: 930 92677
Address: Level 4, Aotea Centre, 50 Mayoral Drive, NZ
Information: Auckland Live is a leader in live arts and entertainment and an active contributor to the vibrancy and creativity of our city. They present live arts events at a number of prominent venues across Auckland, provide support to the arts and creative sector, and provide opportunities for people of all ages to engage with the arts. Member of ISPA
Country: New Zealand

Pacific Entertainment Ltd
Website: pacificentertainment.co.nz
Email: info@pacificentertainment.co.nz
Phone: 930 22070
Address: PO Box 108-069, Symonds Street, NZ
Information: specialised production and promotion of local and international concert and theatrical activities in New Zealand and the Pacific region, concentrating on overseas artists without neglecting local attractions; see also Presenters
Country: New Zealand
Contact: contact Robyn Alexander
Email: robyn@pacificentertainment.co.nzcontact Brendon Ham
Email: brendon@pacificentertainment.co.nzcontact Ian Magan
Email: ian@pacificentertainment.co.nz

The Human Agency
Website: www.thehumanagency.co.nz
Email: info@thehumanagency.co.nz
Phone: 937 86248
Address: 2nd Floor, 2 Fitzroy St, NZ
Country: New Zealand
Contact: Managing Director Shona McCullagh
Email: info@thehumanagency.co.nzsenior booker Anna Adam
Email: anna@thehumanagency.co.nzlive events Manager Vanessa Armstrong
Email: vanessa@thehumanagency.co.nzaccounts Liz van Dyk
Email: liz@thehumanagency.co.nz

SINGAPORE

Music and Movement Singapore Pte Ltd
Website: www.musicmovement.com.sg
Email: mm@musicmovement.com.sg
Phone: 622 77087
Address: 19 Kim Keat Road, #07-02 Fu Tsu Building, SG
Information: also artists management, music productions and publishing; see also Venues
Country: Singapore

Six Degrees
Email: admin@emilyhill.org
Phone: 656 222 1081 / 6
Address: 11 Upper Wilkie Road, SG
Country: Singapore
Contact: Admin Emily Hill

TAIWAN, PROVINCE OF CHINA

Management of New Arts
Website: www.mna.com.tw
Email: nemders@mna.com.tw
Phone: 266 369 168
Address: 9/F, No. 322, Sec. 1, Fusing South Road
Information: presenter and tour organizer
Country: Taiwan
Contact: President Xiao Hua Niu

New Aspect Promotion Corporation
Website: www.newaspect.org.tw
Email: service@newaspect.org.tw
Phone: 225 772 568
Address: 10F.-4, NO.20, SEC. 3, , Bade Rd, , Songshan District,
Information: mainly for Performing Arts and Visual Arts
Country: Taiwan
Contact: General Manager Fu-Fu Hsu
Email: Chairman Po-Yun Hsu
Email: confidential secretary Robin Chen
Email: Sunny Fan

UNITED STATES

2Luck Concepts
Website: www.2luck.com
Email: info@2luck.com
Phone: 518 781 3000
Address: Box 473, 70 Reardon York, US
Information: production, tour management, General management and booking for special projects and attractions; project development and production. Members of ISPA
Country: United States
Contact: Director Eleanor Oldham
Email: Director John Luckacovic

A.S.I.A. Group, The - American Stage in Asia
Website: www.theasiagroup.com
Email: info@theasiagroup.com
Address: 2101 L St NW, Suite 310, US
Information: The Asia Group provides full service strategic and business advisory services to the world's leading companies and organizations seeking to excel across Asia. With a team of dynamic and experienced professionals – from consultants and former senior government officials to lawyers and investment bankers – The Asia Group supports companies with end-to-end integrated strategies for market entry and expansion strategies to complex commercial dispute resolution initiatives.
Country: United States

Aaron Concert Artists, Inc.
Website: www.aaronconcert.com
Email: info@aaronconcert.com
Address: 331 W 57th St, Suite 344, US
Information: jaaron@aaronconcert.com
Country: United States
Contact: Managing Director Jon Aaron
Email: jaaron@aaronconcert.com

AEG Themestar LLC
Website: www.aegthemestar.com
Email: info@aegthemestar.com
Phone: 650 472 8100
Address: 1111 S. Figueroa Street, Suite 3100, US
Country: United States
Contact: CEO Mark Avery
Email: Executive vice President Eric Eisland

AGP Agency Inc.
Website: www.agpagency.com
Email: productions@agpagency.com
Address: 229 E 85th Street B. 36, US
Information: AGP Agency, Inc. is a New York based agency Managing talents in music, arts, sport, acting. With our diverse and unique client roster and strategic partnerships we provide specialised solution for Managing talents.
Country: United States
Contact: project Manager David Rasztovits
Email: drasztovits@agpagency.com

Alkahest Artists & Attractions, Inc
Website: www.alkahestartists.net
Email: info@alkahestartists.net
Phone: 888 728 8989
Address: Alkahest Artists and Attractions, Inc., P.O. Box 91236, US
Information: Alkahest Artists & Attractions, Inc. represents a diverse roster in the disciplines of music and theatre. Our emphasis is on developing and Managing regional and national tours of quality, affordable productions that have mainstream appeal.
Country: United States
Contact: President Elizabeth Bridges
Email: Elizabeth@alkahestartists.netDirector Lynn Billings Thomas
Email: billingstho@blomand.netExecutive assistant/media Keith S. Farley
Email: keith@alkahestartists.net

Allan Harris Productions
Website: www.allanharris.com/home
Email: elisabeth@bellaconcerts.com
Phone: 180 488 3331
Address: US
Country: United States
Contact: management/booking - US Pat Harris
Email: patharris@patharrisandAssociates.comPR Maureen McFadden
Email: maureen@dlmediamusic.com

Allied Concert Services, Inc.
Website: www.alliedconcertservices.com
Email: david@alliedconcertservices.com
Phone: 763 559 8019
Address: 3535 Plymouth Boulevard, Suite 212, Plymouth, US

America's Music Agency - Thomas Cassidy Inc
Website: www.americasmusicagency.com
Email: info@americasmusicagency.com
Phone: 520 751 4751
Address: PO Box 1311, US
Country: United States
Contact: President Thomas Cassidy
Email: tom@americasmusicagency.comvice President Susan Cassidy
Email: susan@americasmusicagency.com

American Conservatory of Music
Email: registrar@americanconservatory.edu
Phone: 219 931 2382
Address: 252 Wildwood Road, Hammond, US
Information: children's and pre-college preparatory programme
Country: United States

American Landmark Festivals
Website: www.americanlandmarkfestivals.org
Email: contact@americanlandmarkfestivals.org
Address: Federal Hall, 26 Wall Street, New York, US
Information: present international professional artists free to the public in national landmark buildings, cooperate with National Park Service; has presented concert series and special events for over thirty years: Founded in 1973 by Francis L. Heilbut, American Landmark Festivals is a nonprofit, tax-exempt organisation dedicated to the presentation of performing arts events in landmarks of historical, architectural and traditional significance
Country: United States

AMT Public Relations
Website: www.amtpublicrelations.com
Email: april@amtpublicrelations.com
Phone: 212 861 0990
Address: 440 East 79th Street, Suite # 9K, US
Information: specialises in promoting the performing arts industry including dance companies, orchestras and ensembles, music festivals, and individuals such as composers, musicians, dancers, and choreographers
Country: United States
Contact: Director April Thibeault
Email: april@amtpublicrelations.com

Anchorage Concert Association
Email: info@anchorageconcerts.org
Phone: 907 272 1471
Address: 430 West 7th Avenue, Suite 200, US
Information: Presenting the best entertainment and performing arts in Anchorage, Alaska
Country: United States

Arizona Friends of Chamber Music
Website: www.arizonachambermusic.org
Email: office@arizonachambermusic.org
Phone: 520 577 3769
Address: PO Box 40805, US
Information: Arizona Friends of Chamber Music (AFCM) was founded in 1948; a private nonprofit 501(c) organisation run by a volunteer board. They continue to bring to Tucson Evening Series of six concerts by the world's finest chamber musicians. They make every attempt to include a contemporary piece on most programs
Country: United States

Art Fegan Entertainment
Website: www.artfegan.com
Email: art@artfegan.com
Phone:
615 646 9606
Address: 131 North Second Street, The Historic Shuler Theater, US
Country: United States
Contact: Chief Operating Officer Stuart Hyatt
Email: stuart@artfegan.com

Artcore
Website: www.artcorewy.com
Email: artcorewyo@gmail.com
Phone: 307 265 1564
Address: PO Box 874, US
Information: visit website for forthcoming events and mailing list
Country: United States

Arthur Shafman's AAAArtistes International Ltd
Website: www.aaaartistes.com
Email: ashafman@aol.com
Phone: 212 799 4814
Address: 163 Amsterdam Avenue No.121, US
Information: personal management, concert management, theatrical producing, alternative web site: www. arthurshafman.com, Among Artists& Attractions represented include the following: Andrea Marcovicci, Sandra Reaves-Phillips, Karen Akers, Mark Nadler, Christine Andreas, KT Sullivan, Wesla Whitfield, Juile Budd, Andrea McArdle, Heather Mac Rae, Sally Mayes, Barbbara Brussell
Country: United States
Contact: President Arthur Shafman

Artists of Note Inc.
Website: www.artistsofnote.com
Email: jmurdock@artistsofnote.com
Phone: 630 557 2742
Address: PO Box 11, US
Country: United States
Contact: President Joann Murdock
Email: jmurdock@artistsofnote.com

Arts Brookfield
Website: artsbrookfield.com
Email: arts@brookfield.com
Phone: 212 417 7000
Address: Brookfield Office Properties / Arts Brookfield, 250 Vesey St., 15th Fl., US
Information: member of ISPA
Country: United States

Arts Marketing Insights
Website: www.artsMarketinginsights.com
Email: joanne@artsMarketinginsights.com
Address: 91 Meadowview Drive, US
Information: author: "Standing Room Only: Insights for Engaging Performing Arts Audiences, " publication April, 2014. Consultant in Marketing and management to arts organisations; professor, lecturer and author on arts management and Marketing; alternative e-mail: joannebernstein@ameritech.net
Country: United States
Contact: principal President Joanne Scheff Bernstein
Email: joanne@artsMarketinginsights.com

Arts Partnership of Greater Hancock County
Website: www.artspartnership.com
Email: event@artspartnership.com
Phone: 419 422 3412
Address: 618 South Main Street, US
Information: originally named the Findlay Area Arts Council, was founded in 1979 by a group of visionary community leaders. During its birth, the organization's mission was to encourage and stimulate the practice and appreciation of the arts locally and statewide. The founders included Mrs. E. A. Graham, Mrs. F. F. Flowers, W. T. Maddock, Alex Baluck, Mrs. J.S. Dimling, Mrs. T. A. Buis, E. L. Heminger, Jerry Osborn, Doug Salveson, C. R. Brown. In 1998, the organisation changed its name to The Arts Partnership of Greater Hancock County. The mission was modified to read: To provide, encourage and promote quality arts presentations, educational opportunities and entertainment. Although the organisation has grown and changed over the years, the core of its existence has always been to provide arts opportunities that strengthen our community
Country: United States

Arts Promotions Asia, Ltd
Website: www.artspromotionsasia.com
Email: darylries@aol.com
Phone: 212 877 1095
Address: c/o Daryl Ryes, 175 West 76th Street, 7D, US
Information: creative new work with east/west artists, dancers, musicians and visual artists; multi-media east-west productions
Country: United States
Contact: Director Daryl Ryes
Email: darylries@aol.com

Arts San Antonio
Website: www.artssanantonio.com
Email: artsafranc@aol.com
Phone: 210 226 2891
Address: 418 10th Street, US
Country: United States

ArtsEmerson: The World on Stage
Website: www.artsemerson.org
Email: artsemerson_news@artsemerson.org
Phone: 617 824 8030
Address: 120 Boylston St, US
Information: Built in 1903 as the second performance venue in Boston's historic Theatre District, the elegant architecture and impeccable acoustics of the Majestic were originally intended for opera performances. Over the years, the facility was also used for theatre, vaudeville and even movies. When Emerson College purchased the property in 1983, the building had severely deteriorated. After a magnificent restoration, made possible by Ted and Joan Benard-Cutler, the Cutler Majestic Theatre reopened in 2003 and now serves the Boston community by showcasing first-class performing arts groups in its exquisite 1, 186-seat auditorium. Recognized as a Boston Historic Landmark, the Cutler Majestic combines state-of-the-art theatre facilities with old world charm.
Member of ISPA
Country: United States
Contact: Artistic Director David Dower
Email: General Manager Bonnie Baggesen
Email: Executive Director David Howse

ARTSwego (Arts at Oswego)
Website: www.oswego.edu/arts
Email: artswego@oswego.edu
Phone: 315 312 3599
Address: Oswego State University of NY, 130A Tyler Hall, US
Country: United States

Associated Booking Corporation
Website: www.Associatedbooking.com/home.html
Email: musicbiz@mindspring.com
Phone: 212 874 2400
Address: 501 Madison Avenue, suite 603, US
Information: represents artists from diverse music genres ranging from blues to big bands to jazz to pop and rock and reggae
Country: United States
Contact: President Oscar Cohen

Association for Advancement of Creative Musicians (AACM)
Website: www.aacmchicago.org
Email: info@aacmchicago.org
Phone: 312 834 3390
Address: 410 S Michigan Avenue, Suite 943, US
Information: Internationally renowned for unparalleled contributions to modern music, the Association for the Advancement of Creative Musicians, Inc. (AACM) has been an inspirational leader within the cultural community since 1965. A non-profit organization chartered by the State of Illinois , the AACM is a collective of musicians and composers dedicated to nurturing, performing, and recording serious, original music. This collective of dynamic and visionary artists formed the AACM to meet their emergent needs to expose and showcase their original compositions and to create an outlet for the development and performance of their music.
Country: United States

Aviv Productions Inc
Website: www.aviv2.com
Email: itzik@aviv2.com
Phone: 480 659 1568
Address: 10418 East Meadowhill Drive, US
Information: international tours for artists, booking and management
Country: United States
Contact: President Itzik Becher
Email: itzik@aviv2.com

Bach Festival Concert Series
Website: www.bachfestivalflorida.org
Email: info@bachfestivalflorida.org
Phone: 407 646 2182
Address: Rollins College, 1000 Holt Ave, no 2763, Winter Park, US
Information: The Bach Festival Society is well known internationally and has enjoyed a long tradition of bringing world-class talent to Central Florida. Since its inception, the Society has expanded its offerings beyond the annual Bach Festival to include Choral Masterworks and Visiting Artists performances, as well as a variety of educational and community outreach programs to encourage participation in music at all levels.
Country: United States

Bang on a Can
Website: www.bangonacan.org
Email: info@bangonacan.org
Phone: 718 852 7755
Address: 80 Hanson Place, US
Information: with adventurous programmes, it commissions new composers, performs, presents, and records new work, develops new audiences, and educates the musicians of the future. Member of ISPA
Country: United States
Contact: Artistic Director Michael Gordon
Email: Artistic Director David Lang
Email: Artistic Director Julia Wolfe
Email: Executive Director Kenny Savelson

Email: kenny@bangonacan.org

Barbash Arts Consulting
Website: cathybarbash.com
Email: cbarbash@yahoo.com
Phone: 610 529 6286
Address: 269 Golf View Road, US
Information: Cathy Barbash is a specialist in public diplomacy, cultural policy, creative industry development, and corporate cultural sponsorships in the People's Republic of China. She expanded her practice to Cuba in September 2016. With over 30 years of experience Managing and consulting to leading NGO and government-related cultural organizations, Barbash provides strategy and advocacy services, represents and advises clients, provides appropriate high-level intervention for existing special projects, and assists in the development and identification of viable strategic partners and project opportunities. Barbash also advises on relations with government owned and operated cultural organizations. Member of ISPA
Country: United States
Contact: principal Cathy Barbash

Bernard Schmidt Productions Inc
Website: www.bernardschmidtproductions.com
Email: bschmidtpd@aol.com
Address: 16 Penn Plaza Suite 545, US
Information: cultural exchange projects between the USA and the world
Country: United States
Contact: President Bernard Schmidt
Email: bschmidtpd@aol.com

BesenArts LLC
Website: www.BesenArts.com
Email: Robert@BesenArts.com
Phone: 201 399 7425
Address: 7 Delaney Place, Tenafly, US
Information: BesenArts represents a select roster of chamber music ensembles and recitalists
Country: United States

Beth Morrison Projects
Website: www.bethmorrisonprojects.org
Email: info@bethmorrisonprojects.org
Phone: 646 682 7181
Address: 666 Ocean Ave, #D1 Brooklyn, US
Information: Founded in 2006 to identify and support the work of emerging and established composers and their multi-media collaborators, Beth Morrison Projects encourages risk-taking, creating a structure for developing new work that is unique to the artist. Member of ISPA
Country: United States
President & creative Producer
Beth Morrison
Email: info@bethmorrisonprojects.orgExecutive Director Jecca Barry
Email: jecca@bethmorrisonprojects.orgDirector of development Noah Stern Weber
Email: noah@bethmorrisonprojects.orgproduction Manager James Fry
Email: james.fry@bethmorrisonprojects.orgAssociate Producer Melanie Milton
Email: melanie@bethmorrisonprojects.org

bobby prince Music
Website: www.bpmusic.com
Email: bobby@bpmusic.com
Address: PO Box 1607, US
Country: United States

Brad Simon Organization Inc.
Website: www.bsoinc.com
Email: brad@bsoinc.com
Phone: 212 730 2132
Address: 445 East 80th Street, US
Country: United States

Cadence Arts Network Inc
Website: www.cadencearts.com
Email: rachel@cadencearts.com
Phone: 310 838 0849
Address: 10516 Clarkson Road, US
Information: Cadence Arts Network, inc. founded in 1989, offers consulting and networking services to members of the performing arts community. Known for advancing emerging and established performing artists in North America, Cadence also offers a variety of networking and consulting services to self-represented artists, agents, Managers and presenters. Member of ISPA
Country: United States
Contact: President Rachel Cohen
Email: rachel@cadencearts.comassistant Caitlin Heflin
Email: caitlin@cadencearts.com

Candlelight Concert Society, Inc.
Website: www.candlelightconcerts.org
Email: info@candlelightconcerts.org
Phone: 410 997 2324
Address: 8950 Route 108, Suite 115A, US
Information: Maryland based concert presenter, offering professional world-class chamber music concerts, children's programs, community outreach programs, master

classes, and pre-concert lectures and discussions
Country: United States

Celebrity Series of Boston, Inc.
Website: www.celebrityseries.org
Email: info@celebrityseries.org
Phone: 617 482 2595
Address: 20 Park Plaza, Suite 1032, US
Information: Our aim is to present the best in the per-
forming arts to the broadest possible audience, to create
new works that bring artists and audiences together,
and to engage young audiences in Artistic experiences
through performing arts-based education and commu-
nity service programs. Member of ISPA
Country: United States
Contact: President and Executive Director Garry Dunning
Email: Director of development Sara Curtis Robinson
Email: chief financial officer Edwin Derecho

Charles R Rothschild Productions, Inc.
Email: kidzlovemusic@aol.com
Phone: 212 421 0592
Address: 330 East 48th Street, US
Country: United States
Contact: President Charles R Rothschild

Colorado College - Great Performers and Ideas
Website: www.coloradocollege.edu
Email: President@coloradocollege.edu
Phone: 800 542 7214
Address: 14 E Cache La Poudre, US
Country: United States

Concert Artists Guild
Website: www.concertartists.org
Email: caguild@concertartists.org
Address: 850 Seventh Ave, PH-A, US
Country: United States
Contact: Executive vice-President Amy Frawley
Email: President Richard Weinert
Email: senior vice-President, artist Manager Steven D
Shaiman

Concordia College - Cultural Events
Website: www.concordiacollege.edu/Directories/offic-
es-services/cultural-events
Email: info@cord.edu
Phone: 218 299 4366
Address: Office of Cultural Events and Music Organiza-
tions, 901 8th St S, US
Information: sponsors several major events on campus,
including touring artist performances and the Faith,
Reason and World Affairs Symposium
Country: United States

Contemporary Record Society
Website: www.crsnews.org
Email: crsnews@verizon.net
Phone: 610 544 5920
Address: 724 Winchester Road, US
Information: services: artists representation; CD produc-
tion; publications; Artist Representation
Country: United States
Contact: Administration assistant Caroline Hunt
Email: President John Russo
Email: representative/ad Manager Jack M Shusterman

Crossover Media Inc.
Website: www.crossovermedia.net
Email: max@crossovermedia.net
Address: 400 West 43rd Street, Suite 206 t, US
Country: United States
Contact: President Max Horowitz
Email: max@crossovermedia.netcontact Vicky Thiel
Email: crossovermedia@frontier.comcontact Elizabeth
Miller
Email: elizabethmiller1@gmail.com

David Lieberman - Artist's Representative
Website: www.dlartists.com
Email: info@dlartists.com
Phone: 714 979 4700
Address: PO Box 10368, US
Information: member of ISPA
Country: United States
Contact: President David Lieberman
Email: david@dlartists.comDirector of touring Allen
Moon
Email: allen@dlartists.comDirector of operations Jay
Quantrill
Email: jay@dlartists.comDirector of Marketing Amanda
Bryant
Email: amanda@dlartists.com

David Rowe Artists
Website: www.davidroweartists.com
Email: DavidRowe@aol.com
Address: 24 Bessom Street, Suite 2, US
Country: United States
Contact: contact David Rowe

Diane Saldick, LLC
Website: www.dianesaldick.com
Email: diane.saldick@verizon.net
Address: 225 East 36th Street, US

Country: United States
Contact: Director Diane Saldick

dworkin & company
Website: www.dworkincompany.com
Email: elizabeth@dworkincompany.com
Address: PO Box 248, US
Information: management, public relations, special
events
Country: United States
Contact: owner Elizabeth Dworkin
Email: elizabeth@dworkincompany.comPR Associate
Susan Thames
Email: susan@dworkincompany.combooking Associate
Jacqueline Scoones
Email: jacquie@dworkincompany.com

EastCoast Entertainment
Website: www.eastcoastentertainment.com
Email: info@eastcoastentertainment.com
Phone: 828 232 5223
Address: 390 Merrimon Avenue, US
Information: Charleston Office: tel.:843-856 9922, fax:
843-856 8522, 1039 D Anna Knapp Boulevard, Mount
Pleasant, South Carolina 29464
Country: United States

Eastern Promotion Ltd
Website: www.easternpromotion.com
Email: eastern@caucasus.net
Phone: 329 90599
Address: 1 Meliqishvili str., US
Information: organises all types of promotion, foreign
and local artists' concerts, private events for local and
foreign companies, embassies, international presenta-
tions in Tbilisi and other Georgian cities
Country: United States

Encompass Arts LLC
Website: www.encompassarts.com
Email: kathy@encompassarts.com
Phone: 212 439 8055
Address: 119 West 72nd Street, US
Information: works with operatic, broadway, film and
stage talent to our agency; Encompass Arts has had
contracts with most every major theatre and orchestra in
the world today; Member of IAMA
Country: United States
Contact: founder/Director Katherine M. Olsen
Email: kathy@encompassarts.comManager / partner
Sandra Hormozi
Email: sandra@encompassarts.comManager / partner
Alex Moskvin
Email: alex@encompassarts.com

Encore Attractions
Website: www.encoreattractions.com
Email: jlonn@encoreattractions.com
Address: 9580 East Ranch Gate Road, US
Country: United States
Contact: Producer Jerry Lonn

ETB Productions
Website: www.etbproductions.com
Email: info@marceliot.com
Phone: 212 920 9516
Address: 1385 York Avenue, Suite 19F, US
Information: info@marceliot.com
Country: United States
Contact: President Marc Eliot

F Sharp Productions, Ltd
Website: www.sharpprods.com
Email: jimfsharpprods@sharpprods.com
Phone: 212 246 9146
Address: 35 W 81st Street, , Suite 11C, US
Information: music publishing, artists' representative
Country: United States
Contact: President Jim DiGiovanni

Hibernian Music
Website: www.susanmckeown.com
Email: suemckeown@yahoo.com
Phone: 212 260 2302
Address: 513 East 13th Street #3, US
Country: United States
Contact: Director Susan McKeown
Email: booking Lori Peters
Email: lori@madmissionagency.compublicist Hilary
Jackson
Email: hilary@susanmckeown.com

International Special Attractions Ltd
Website: www.isaattractions.com
Email: info@isaattractions.com
Phone: 310 553 7500
Address: 421 South Beverly Drive, 5th Floor, Suite 501,
US
Information: USA office: Northwoods Commerce Center,
108 Wintergreen Road, Building A, Branson (Missouri)
65616; tel: +1 417-336 0715; fax: +1 417 332 1031
Country: United States
Contact: secretary Katty Wang
Email: President Ge Hai Ping
Email: haiping.ge@isaattractions.comvice President/

General Manager Gary Fjelstad
Email: gary.fjelstad@isaattractions.com

J Cast Productions
Website: www.castproductions.com
Email: jcast@castproductions.com
Phone: 323 822 1999
Address: 2550 Greenvalley Road, US
Information: Producer of theatrical shows/come-
dies-musicals with Celebrity Names. Also packages
variety artists in events from one person shows to
concert engagements. Artists include Larry Hagman,
Susan Anton, Antonio Fargas, Jerry Van Dyke, Janet
Carroll, Soap Stars
Country: United States
Contact: President John Castonia

James Carter/Big Fish Productions
Website: www.bigfishproductioninc.com
Email: jcarter891@aol.com
Phone: 347 526 5211
Address: PO Box 782, Bronx, US
Country: United States
Contact: CEO James 'Prez' Carter

JMP Music Ltd
Website: www.jmpmusic.net/
Email: jad@jmpmusic.net
Phone: 961 454 3928
Address: Z.O.D Building, 4th Floor, US
Country: United States
Contact: Director Jad Mhanna
Email: jad@jmpmusic.net

Jumbie Records
Website: www.jumbierecords.com
Email: contact@jumbierecords.com
Address: US
Country: United States

Lisa Sapinkopf Artists
Website: www.chambermuse.com
Email: LSapinkopf@aol.com
Address: 9 Commodore Drive, Suite A309, US
Country: United States
Contact: Director Lisa Sapinkopf
Email: LSapinkopf@aol.com

Living Arts Inc.
Website: www.livingartsnyc.com
Email: info@livingartsnyc.com
Phone: 212 765 7777
Address: 52-23 39th Avenue, Sunnyside, US
Country: United States
Contact: President Peter Klein
Email: pkelin@livingartsnyc.comManaging Director
Jennifer Mcloughlin-Hoyt
Email: jmhoyt@livingartsnyc.com

Love Productions Inc
Website: www.loveproductions.com
Email: info@loveproductions.com
Phone: 212 714 9197
Address: 400 West 43rd Street, Suite 10R, US
Information: additional offices in Singapore, Indonesia
& Malaysia
Country: United States
Contact: President Steve Love

LVanHart Artist Productions
Website: www.lvanhart.com
Email: laura@ivanhart.com
Address: 45 Birch Street, Suite 12-H, US
Country: United States
Contact: President Laura Hartmann
Email: laura@ivanhart.com

MAPP International Productions
Website: www.mappinternational.org
Email: mapp@mappinternational.org
Phone: 646 602 9390
Address: 140 Second Avenue, Suite 502, US
Country: United States
Contact: Executive Director, Producer Ann Rosenthal
Email: ann@mappinternational.orgco-Director, Producer
Cathy Zimmerman
Email: cathy@mappinternational.orgDirector of develop-
ment Joyce Lawler
Email: joyce@mappinternational.orgadministrative
Manager Julia Gutierrez-Rivera
Email: julia@mappinternation.org

Mayfair Artists
Website: www.williamnoll.com
Email: mayfairnyny@aol.com
Address: 6888 Trail Blvd., US
Country: United States
Contact: Director William Noll

MCG Jazz
Website: www.mcgjazz.org
Email: akline@mcg-btc.org
Phone: 412 323 4000
Address: Manchester Craftsmen's Guild, 1815 Metropol-

itan Street, US
Information: MCG Jazz's mission is to preserve, present and promote jazz; besides live events also do their own recordings and organises own educational programs
Country: United States
Contact: Executive Producer Marty Ashby
Email: mashby@mcg-btc.orgMarketing Manager Amy Kline
Email: akline@mcg-btc.org

Melvin Kaplan Inc.
Website: www.melkap.com
Email: music@melkap.com
Phone: 802 658 2592
Address: 115 College Street, US
Country: United States
Contact: President Melvin Kaplan
Email: melvin@melkap.comartist Manager John Zion
Email: john@melkap.com
artist Manager & programs
Kate Barnes
Email: kate@melkap.compublicity Betsy Hoffmeister
Email: betsy@melkap.comAdministration Kim Kroeger
Email: kim@melkap.comfinance Tracy West
Email: tracy@melkap.com

MIA Management
Website: www.miaartists.com
Email: Info@MIAArtists.com
Phone: 646 620 1313
Address: 205 W. 88th St., 13A, US
Information: see also Agents & Management
Country: United States

Michael Herzlin
Email: mherzlin@aol.com
Phone: 516 297 6542
Address: 41 Winthrop Street, US
Information: French Horn player
Country: United States

Micocci Productions LLC
Website: www.micocci.com
Email: tony@micocci.com
Phone: 917 622 9817
Address: US
Information: Representing the work of significant theatrical and puppetry creators such as Lee Breuer, Basil Twist, Christopher McElroen, Julian Crouch, Stephen Earnhart and others. Also Assistant Directing Graduate Program in Arts Administration at the University of New Orleans.
Country: United States
Contact: President Tony Micocci
Email: tony@micocci.com

MidAtlantic Arts Foundation
Website: www.pennpat.org
Email: info@pennpat.org
Address: Pennsylvania Performing Arts on Tour, 230 South Broad Street, Suite 1003, US
Country: United States
Contact: Executive Director Katie West
Email: katie@pennpat.org
developing & Marketing Manager
Denise Flynn Buczko
Email: denise@pennpat.org

Nederlander Worldwide Entertainment
Website: www.nederlanderworld.com/
Email: info@NedlanderWorld.com
Phone: 212 822 4200
Address: 1450 Broadway, 20th Floor, US
Information: manages theatres and presents Broadway productions in emerging international markets, produces international productions for Broadway and elsewhere around the world, and undertakes cultural educational initiatives. The company's expertise covers theatre management and operations, along with all facets of live entertainment, including ticketing, management, promotion, Marketing, and advertising. See also Agents and Management. Member of IAMA
Country: United States
Contact: President Robert Nederlander
Email: General Manager Thom Schilling

New Amsterdam Presents
Website: www.newamsterdampresents.com
Email: info@newamsterdamrecords.com
Address: 98A Van Dyke St., US
Information: places new music in the public eye through the presentation of festivals, series, tours, and other live events
Country: United States

New York Stage Originals
Website: www.nystage.com
Email: lisa@nystage.com
Phone: 818 433 7191
Address: ., US
Country: United States
Contact: Executive Manager Philip Stern
Email: Director Lisa Hopkins

Octopus Theatricals
Website: www.octopustheatricals.com
Email: info@octopustheatricals.com
Address: 113 Adams Drive, US
Information: Octopus Theatricals, LLC is a company dedicated to producing and consulting in the performing arts. From experimental to commercial, they collaborate with artists and organizations to foster an expansive range of compelling theatrical works for local, national and international audiences. They eschew boundaries—aesthetic, geopolitical, institutional—and thrive on a nimble and rigorous practice. Member of ISPA
Country: United States
Contact: founder and Executive and creative Producer Mara Isaacs
Email: Associate Producer Ronee Penoi
Email: production coordinator Bryan Hunt

One Reel
Website: www.onereel.org
Email: info@onereel.org
Phone: 206 673 5060
Address: PO Box 9750, US
Information: the independent, not for profit Producer of the Northwest's premier arts events including Bumbershoot®: Seattle's Music & Arts Festival (bumbershoot.org), the Family 4th at Lake Union (family4th.org) and Emerald City Search (emeraldcitysearch.org).
Country: United States

Paul Szilard Productions, Inc.
Email: szilardpro@aol.com
Phone: 212 799 4756
Address: 2000 Broadway, Suite 2B, US
Country: United States
Contact: President Paul Szilard

Pentacle
Website: www.pentacle.org
Email: ivans@pentacle.org
Phone: 212 278 8111
Address: 75 Broad Street, Suite 304, US
Information: non-profit performing arts service organisation, see also Performing Companies
Country: United States

Phoenix Entertainment
Website: www.phoenix-ent.com
Email: info@phoenix-ent.com
Phone: 301 682 5944
Address: 5235 Westview Drive, Suite 100, US
Information: Seoul (Korea) office: #2510 Daelim Acrotel, 467-6 Dogok-dong, Gangnam-gu, Seoul 135-270, Korea, tel, 82 2-529 3530; fax: +82 2-529 3531, contact: Ellie Chung, Executive Producer, Asian Operations
Country: United States
Contact: Director Stephen Kane

Pro Musicis
Website: www.promusicis.org
Email: promusicis@aol.com
Phone: 212 787 0993
Address: 37 West 57th Street, US
Information: the aim of Promusicis is to share the Artistic inspiration of the world's finest concert artists
Country: United States
Contact: Executive Director John E. Haag

Producers Inc.
Website: www.Producersinc.com
Email: info@producersinc.com
Phone: 813 988 8333
Address: 11806 N 56th Street, US
Information: entertainment agency
Country: United States
Contact: President Craig Hankenson Jr
Email: vice President Kathy Hankenson
Email: entertainment consultant Kathy Smith
Email: kcsmith@Producersinc.com

R/J Productions
Website: www.rjprod.com
Email: rjprodmgt1@aol.com
Phone: 212 396 2666
Address: 401 E. 74 St, Suite 14S, US
Country: United States
Contact: joint Director Rich Aronstein
Email: joint Director Jerry Friedman

Ralph Pavone Productions
Website: www.ralphpavone.com
Email: pavprods@aol.com
Phone: 505 867 6500
Address: 7553 Mackenzie Drive NE, US
Country: United States
Contact: President Ralph Pavone Jr

Richard Frankel Productions
Website: www.rfpny.com
Email: lori@rfpny.com
Phone: 212 302 5559
Address: 729 7th Avenue, 12th Floor, US
Country: United States
Contact: contact Lori Steiger-Perry

Robert Friedman Presents
Website: www.rfpresents.com
Email: rf@rfpresents.com
Phone: 415 759 1992
Address: 451 30th Avenue, US
Country: United States
Contact: Director of operations Erin Maxwell
Email: President Robert Friedman

Robert M Gewald Management
Website: www.gewaldmanagement.com
Email: RobertGewald@hotmail.com
Phone: 212 753 0450
Address: 58 West 58th Street, US
Information: represents artists for colleges, universities, performing arts centers, festivals, state or county fairs, casinos, and many other venues throughout the county. Some of their artists are also available for workshops, residencies or special school performances (see also Agents and Management)
Country: United States
Contact: Director Robert Gewald
Email: RobertGewald@hotmail.com

Schwalbe and Partners Inc
Website: www.schwalbeandpartners.com
Email: info@schwalbeandpartners.com
Phone: 212 935 5650
Address: 170 East 61 Street #5N, US
Information: Schwalbe and Partners provide representation, management services, and promotional support in the fields of classical music and opera. For nearly 40 years it has devoted itself to providing personalised services to their artists, and to building strong relationships with presenters worldwide. Member of IAMA.
Country: United States
Contact: President Carrie Sykes
Email: artist services Director Debbie Colozzi
Email: founder Douglas Schwalbe
Email: Sales promotion Manager Melody Chan
Email: melody@schwalbeandpartners.com

Scott O'Malley & Associates
Website: www.somagency.com
Email: somagency@aol.com
Phone: 719 635 7776
Address: PO Box 9188, US
Country: United States
Contact: agent/management Scott O'Malley

Selby Artists Mgmt
Website: www.SelbyArtistsMgmt.com
Email: MSelby@SelbyArtistsMgmt.com
Phone: 212 382 3260
Address: 262 West 38th Street Suite 1701, NY, NY 10018
Information: SELBY/ARTISTS MGMT is a full service arts management company under the leadership of Margaret Selby. With a curated roster of award-winning and unique artists in the fields of dance, physical theater, and world music, SELBY/ARTISTS MGMT establishes and builds upon relationships with presenters across the globe.
Country: United States

SMI Production Inc
Website: www.josumi.com
Email: smi@josumi.com
Phone: 223 461 0976
Address: US
Information: also offices in Korea - see Agents and Management (SMI Entertainment Inc.)
Country: United States
Contact: President/CEO Youngjoon 'Jay' Jo
Email: youngjoon_jo@hotmail.com

Sundance Productions
Website: sundanceproduction.com
Email: info@sundanceproduction.com
Phone: 212 489 2203
Address: 630 9th Avenue, US
Information: Sundance Productions enters the world of film and television in its mission to create, develop, and produce marquee, award-winning and authentic programming
Country: United States
Contact: Administration Robert Redford
Email: Administration Laura Michalchyshyn

Taipei Cultural Center
Website: www.tpecc.org/
Email: tpecc@tpecc.org/
Phone: 212 697 630
Address: 1 East 42 street, Floor 7, US
Information: plans, promotes, and implements a variety of arts activities, as well as supervising the operation of Taipei Gallery and Taipei Theater
Country: United States
Contact: Executive cultural officer Ting-Chen Yang

Talent Center
Website: www.talentcenter.com
Email: info@talentcenter.com
Phone: 513 541 1257

Address: PO Box 23220, US
Information: alternative web page: www.Sunflower-Tones.net
Country: United States

Talent Productions
Website: www.talentproductions.com
Email: info@talentproductions.com
Phone: 877 365 0081
Address: 2404 26th Ave South, US
Information: alternative e-mail: talentpro@i29.net
Country: United States
Contact: President Larry Olson

Tanguero Productions
Website: www.tanguero.com
Email: tanguero@tanguero.com
Phone: 323 930 1244
Address: 8075 West 3rd St., Suite 410, US
Country: United States
Contact: office Manager Jayme Brown

Ted Schmidt & Associates, Inc.
Website: www.epluri.com/TedSchmidtResume.html
Email: tedschmidt@aol.com
Phone: 772 234 7200
Address: P.O. Box 643176, US
Country: United States
Contact: President Ted Schmidt

The Farber Foundry
Website: www.farberfoundry.com
Email: yael@farberfoundry.com
Phone: 917 386 5468
Address: PO Box 1948, US
Information: independent theatre production company founded by Yael Farber
Country: United States
Contact: Artistic Director Yael Farber
Email: yael@farberfoundry.comProducer Thomas O. Kriegsmann
Email: tommy@arktype.com

The Figueroa Music and Arts Project

Website: www.figueroaproject.org
Email: Info@figueroaproject.org
Phone: 505 850 4040
Address: P.O. Box 94596, US
Country: United States
Contact: creative Director Guillermo Figueroa
Email: figviolin@gmail.com

Traditional Arts Services
Website: www.tradarts.com
Email: john_ullman@tradarts.com
Phone: 206 545 4460
Address: 3661 Albion Place, North #2, US
Country: United States
Contact: co-owner John Ullman

Troika Entertainment
Website: www.troika.com
Email: mforrest@troika.com
Phone: 301 208 2080
Address: 818 West Diamond Avenue, Suite 250, US
Information: production company for touring musical theatre and Broadway shows
Country: United States
Contact: Executive Producer and CEO Randall A. Buck
Email: rbuck@troika.comGeneral Manager Roberta Roberts
Email: rroberts@troika.comMarketing Manager Courtney Davis
Email: cdavis@troika.com

Univeristy of Central Missouri Performing Arts Series
Website: www.ucmo.edu/pas
Email: pas@ucmo.edu
Phone:
660 543 4263
Address: Administration Building, Suite 196, University of Central Missouri, US
Country: United States
Contact: Director Jeff Imboden
Email: imboden@ucmo.edu

World Touring Productions
Website: www.worldtouringentertainment.com
Email: info@worldtouring.net
Phone: 631 724 4005
Address: 12 Nicola Lane, US
Country: United States

Zilker Theatre Productions
Website: www.zilker.org
Email:
zilkerinfo@yahoo.com
Phone: 512 479 9491
Address: P.O. Box 685093, US
Information: a non-profit organisation that provides pay-what-you-wish entertainment. Dedicated to the celebration and preservation of the Broadway musical, by mounting large-scale musical productions at the Beverly S. Sheffield Hillside Theater in Austin's Zilker Park
Country: United States

VIRGIN ISLANDS, U.S.

Double M Arts & Events, LLC/Michael Mushalla
Website: www.double-m-arts.com
Email: mushalla@gmail.com
Phone: 917 864 4137
Address: P.O. Box 793, Cruz Bay Station, St. John, VI 00831-0793
Information: Exclusive representative of the Mark Morris Dance Group, Scott Silven, Vox Motus, and The Abbey Theatre: The National Theatre of Ireland.
Country: VI
Contact: Founder and Creative Producer Michael Mushalla
Email: mushalla@gmail.com

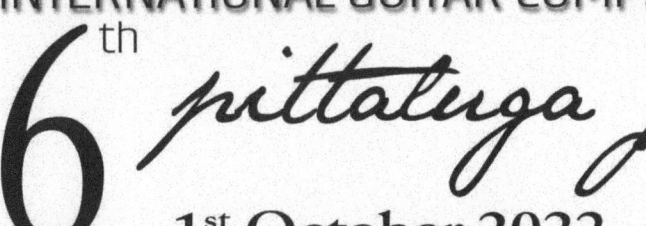

This section comprises producers of physical and digital recordings, with particular emphasis on offices where Artist & Repetoire (A&R) decisions are taken. It also includes producers of videos/films of performances and of performing arts documentaries. **The entries are listed in alphabetical order within country.**

Enregistrement

Cette rubrique inclue les producteurs de tous les médias de dif-fusion. Nous avons mis l'accent sur les bureaux ou les décisions A&R sont prises. Les producteurs de vidéos ou de films sur des représentations ainsi que de documentaires sur les arts vivants apparaîssent également. **Les entrée sont classés par ordre alphabétique dans le pays.**

Aufzeichnung

Dieses Kapitel umfaßt Produzenten von physische und digitale Aufnahmen. Besonders hervorgehoben werden die Abteilungen, die für A & R, Künstler- u. Repertoire- Entscheidungen verant-

wortlich sind. Eingeschlossen sind auch Produzenten von Videos und Dokumentarfilmen über darstellende Kunst. **Die Einträge sind für jedes Land alphabetisch sortiert.**

Registrazione

La sezione comprende i registrazioni fisiche e digitali con particolare risalto a quelle aziende che si occupano dell'intero svol-gimento delle registrazioni, dalle scelte artistiche al repertorio. Sono inclusi inoltre produttori di video e films di spettacoli o documentari d'arte scenica. **Le voci sono pubblicate in ordine alfabetico di paese.**

Grabaciónes

Esta sección incluye los registros físicos y digitales, con particu-lar interés en aquellas compañías donde se toman decisiones sobre A&R (artistas y repertorio).También aparecen productoras de grabaciones audiovisuales de espectacúlos y documentales sobre las Artes Escénicas. **Las entradas se muestran en orden alfabético dentro de cada país.**

performing arts
database

AUSTRALIA

ABC Country live
Website: https://radio.abc.net.au/stations/country/live
Address: GPO Box 9994, Sydney, NSW 2001, AU
Information: ABC Country best known for playing the best country music. ABC Country is distinctively and strongly Australian, reflecting contemporary country music culture.
Country: Australia
Social Media: https://twitter.com/abccountry

Australian Music Centre
Website: www.australianmusiccentre.com.au
Phone: 299 357 805
Address: PO Box N690, Grosvenor Place, NSW 1220, Australia
Information: The Australian Music Centre (AMC) is the national service organisation dedicated to the promotion and support of art music in Australia. Thei important work covers contemporary classical, contemporary jazz, improvised music, experimental music and sound art.
Country: Australia
Contact: chief Executive officer John Davis
Social Media: https://twitter.com/ausmusiccentre https://www.facebook.com/australianmusiccentre/ https://www.instagram.com/australianmusiccentre/

CAAMA Music
Website: www.caama.com.au/music
Phone: 889 519 778
Address: PO Box 2608, 101 Todd Street, AU
Information: The Central Australian Aboriginal Media Association (CAAMA) came to life in 1982 with the establishment of radio station 8KIN FM. Aboriginal-owned media was seen as being vital to the broad educational and community development aspirations of Aboriginal people in Central Australia.
Country: Australia
Social Media: www.facebook.com/caama.alicesprings https://twitter.com/caama https://www.instagram.com/caama_radio/

CPC Music Services Pty Ltd
Website: www.cpcmusic.com.au
Phone: 248 712 053
Address: PO Box 466 BOWRAL NSW 2576, AU
Information: Established in 1996, CPC Music Services is your central agency for music compilations, label copy, liner notes, royalty calculations, TV commercial and infomercial scripts, sourcing products and anything else that's too much trouble for you.
Country: Australia
Contact: Managing Director Chris Parry

Film Australia Ltd
Website: www.filmaust.com.au
Phone: 029 413 8777
Address: 101 Eton Road, Lindfield, NSW 2070 Australia
Information: Film Australia Ltd has many Australian documentaries suitable for use in schools, available for purchase or borrowing
Country: Australia
Social Media: https://twitter.com/ScreenAustralia http://www.facebook.com/screen.australia?v=wall

Fine Music Sydney
Website: https://finemusicsydney.com/
Phone: 294 394 777
Address: 72-76 Chandos Street St Leonards NSW 2065 Australia
Information: Fine Music Sydney (formerly known as 2MBS and Fine Music 102.5) is Australia's first stereo FM radio station. The station was officially opened on 1 February 1975 and they have now been on air for over 45 years.
Country: Australia
Contact: Chair Michael Morton-Evans Morton-Evans
Contact: station Manager Rebecca Beare
Contact: office Manager Sharon Sullivan
Contact: Production Coordinator Joe Goddard
Social Media: https://www.facebook.com/finemusicsydney https://www.instagram.com/finemusicsydney/ https://twitter.com/FineMusicSydney

Janda Music Pty Ltd
Website: n/a
Phone: 755 296 600
Address: Unit 4, 1 Distribution Avenue, AU
Information: Janda Music Pty Ltd is a distribution and record company specializing on classical music.
Country: Australia
Contact: national Sales Manager Andrew Steele

Melba Recordings
Website: www.melbarecordings.com.au
Phone: 395 345 004
Address: P.O. Box 415, Elwood, Victoria, AUSTRALIA 3184
Information: The Melba Foundation was established to promote Australia's finest classical musicians and artists in the national and international music world..
Country: Australia
Social Media: https://www.facebook.com/MelbaRecordings

Move Records
Website: www.move.com.au
Phone: 394 973 105
Address: 10 Glen Drive Eaglemont 3084 Victoria, Australia
Information: From its inception in 1968, Move has provided the means for Australia's best classical and innovative musicians to have their work recorded, published, and exposed to the public.
Country: Australia

Naxos of Australia
Website: www.savd.com.au
Phone: 282 874 882
Address: PO Box 691 Brookvale, 2100 Balgowlah, NSW, Australia
Information: Offering over 10, 000 titles, Naxos is the world's leading classical music label in terms of number of new releases and breadth of catalogue. Naxos produces over 200 exciting new recordings a year with exceptional talents in more than 30 countries.
Country: Australia
Social Media: https://twitter.com/Naxosrecords https://www.facebook.com/Naxos/
Main Focus: Classical, world, jazz, pop and rock

Newmarket Music
Website: www.newmarketmusic.com
Phone: 383 782 299
Address: 369 Macaulay Road, Kensington Victoria 3031, Australia
Information: Newmarket Music is a long-standing record label and distributor of fine Australian and internationally acclaimed music.
Country: Australia
Social Media: https://www.facebook.com/newmarketmusic https://twitter.com/Newmarketmusic

ORiGiN Recordings
Website: www.originmusic.com
Phone: 295 184 600
Address: PO Box Q1235 QVB Post Office, Sydney NSW, 1230 Australia
Information: The ORiGiN Music Group is an Australian independent music company owned by Philip Walker and Philip Mortlock
Country: Australia
Contact: Director Philip Walker
Email: philip@walsing.com
Contact: Director Philip Mortlock
Email: mortlock@originmusic.com.au

Tall Poppies Records
Website: www.tallpoppies.net
Phone: 244 651 259
Address: PO Box 6144. Kangaroo Valley NSW 2577. Australia
Information: Tall Poppies is a non-profit Australian record company which promotes Australian composers, musicians, graphic artists and poets. Founded in 1991, it was the first company in Australia to focus on the recording of solo and chamber music, with an emphasis on standard repertoire.
Country: Australia
Contact: owner Belinda Webster
Social Media: www.facebook.com/Tall-Poppies-174017485892/

Thompson Music Management
Website: thompsonmusic.com.au
Phone: 393 262 022
Address: 808 Mt Alexander Rd, Moonee Ponds VIC 3039, Australia
Information: Established in 1999, Thompson Music Management Pty. Ltd. is a fresh, highly motivated and innovative Record Label & Management Company.
Country: Australia
Contact: Managing Director Drew Thompson

Universal Music Publishing
Website: www.umusicpub.com
Phone: 292 070 500
Address: 3 Munn Reserve, Millers Point NSW 2000
Information: Universal Music Publishing Group is a leading global music publishing company home to the greatest artists, songwriters and song catalog in the world.
Country: Australia
Contact: Managing Director Robert Aird
Social Media: https://www.facebook.com/umusicpubau/ https://twitter.com/umusicpubau https://www.instagram.com/universalmusicpubau/

CANADA

Analekta
Website: https://www.analekta.com/
Phone: 514 939 0559
Address: 7889 boul. Saint-Laurent, bureau 201 Montréal (Québec) H2R 1X1, CANADA

Information: Founded in 1987, Analekta is the largest independent classical music production company in Canada. After 30 years, Analekta is today the largest classical music label in Canada, and is among the 15 largest independent classical labels in the world. With its outstanding production quality and constant exploration of new ways to reach a wider audience, Analekta's catalogue, artists, and very name have become synonymous with vitality and Artistic accomplishment. Members of ISPA
Country: Canada
Contact: President François Mario Labbé
Phone: 514 939 0559
Production & Event Coordinator: Amélie Cantin
Email: acantin@analekta.com
Phone: 514 939 0559 General Manager, Production Manager Julie M. Fournier
Email: jfournier@analekta.com
Phone: 514 939 0559
Social Media: https://www.facebook.com/analektamusique/ https://twitter.com/Analekta
Main Focus: Classical

BBC Worldwide Television
Website: www.bbcamerica.com
Address: 5th Floor, 409 King Street West, CA
Information: As COO, BBC Worldwide Canada Ltd., the commercial arm of the BBC conducting business in Canada, Hilary Read is responsible for all activities in the region with particular emphasis on programme and format Sales, digital syndication, co-productions, branded channels and BBC.com ad Sales.
Country: Canada
Contact: CEO Hilary Read
Social Media: https://twitter.com/BBCAMERICA https://www.facebook.com/BBCAmerica/ https://www.instagram.com/bbcamerica

CBC Records
Website: www.cbcshop.ca
Address: 250 Front Street West, Ground Floor Lobby, CA
Information: CBC Records now part of CBC Shop. CBCShop.ca is your connection to the licensed retailers offering a variety of products related to CBC and their programming.
Country: Canada
Contact: General Manager Randy Barnard
Social Media: @CBCSHOP https://www.facebook.com/cbcshopboutiqueradiocanada/ https://www.instagram.com/cbcshopboutiquetwitter.com/CBCSHOP

Centrediscs/Centredisques and Canadian Music Centre Distribution Service
Website: cmccanada.org
Phone: 416 961 6601
Address: 20 St. Joseph Street Toronto, ON, Canada M4y 1J9
Information: The Canadian Music Centre is the catalyst that connects you to the ever-evolving world of Canadian musical creation through performance, education, and promotion.
Country: Canada
Social Media: https://www.facebook.com/CanadianMusic https://twitter.com/cmcnational

DOREMI Classical Productions
Website: www.doremi.com
Address: 122 Alfred Avenue, CA
Information: DOREMI Classical Productions specializes in obscure and rare historic recordings.
Country: Canada
Contact: music Director Jacob Harnoy

Marquis Classics
Website: www.marquisclassics.com
Address: 30 Kenilworth Ave, Toronto, Canada M4L 3S3
Information: Established in 1981, Marquis Classics is one of Canada's leading independent record labels. It is owned by founder Earl Rosen and Dinah Hoyle.
Country: Canada
Contact: President Earl Rosen
Email: info@marquisclassics.com
Social Media: https://twitter.com/marquisrecords https://www.facebook.com/MarquisClassics

Rhombus International Inc
Website: www.rhombusmedia.com
Phone: 416 971 7856
Address: 662 King Street West, Suite 303 Toronto, Ontario M5V 1M7 Canada
Information: Rhombus Media is a leading Producer of theatrical feature films, TV drama, documentaries and performing arts programmes. Since its inception in 1979, Rhombus has released over 200 productions that h
Country: Canada
Contact: President Sheena Macdonald
Contact: Producer Niv Fichman
Contact: documentary maker Larry Weinstein
Contact: Director Barbara Willis – Sweete
Social Media: https://www.facebook.com/rhombusmedia https://twitter.com/rhombusmedia

Rhombus Media Inc
Website: www.rhombusmedia.com
Phone: 416 971 7856
Address: 662 King Street West Toronto, Suite 303, Ontario M5V 1M7, Canada
Information: Rhombus Media is a leading Producer of theatrical feature films, TV drama, documentaries and performing arts programmes. Since its inception in 1979, Rhombus has released over 200 productions that have been acclaimed by audiences around the world.
Country: Canada
Contact: Director Larry Weinstein
Contact: vice President Sheena Macdonald
Contact: Director Niv Fichman
Contact: Director/vice President Barbara Sweete
Social Media: https:// www.facebook.com/rhombusmedia https://twitter.com/rhombusmedia

Skylark Music
Website: www.skylark-music.com
Address: 4255 12th Ave W, Vancouver, BC – V6R2P8 Canada
Information: Skylark Music (est. 1982) has an imPressive catalogue of recordings by one of Canada's finest classical pianists, Jane Coop.
Country: Canada
Contact: vice-President George Laverock
Contact: General Manager Caroline Ewald
Email: skylark@skylark-music.com

Sony BMG Canada
Website: www.sonymusic.ca
Phone: 416 586 0022
Address: 150 Ferrand Dr Suite 300 Toronto, ON M3C 3E5
Information: The Canadian branch of Sony Music Entertainment.At Sony Music Entertainment, they fuel the creative journey. Played a pioneering role in music history, from the first-ever music label to the invention of the flat disc record.
Country: Canada
Contact: President Shane Carter
Contact: CEO sony bmg Rolf Schmidt-Holz
Social Media: https:// www.facebook.com/sonymusic-canada https:// www.instagram.com/sony_music_canada/ https://twitter.com/Sony_Music

Universal Music Canada
Website: www.universalmusic.ca
Phone: 416 718 4000
Address: 2450 Victoria Park Ave., Suite 1, CA
Information: Universal Music Canada (UMC) is Canada's leading music company, engaged in recorded music, music publishing, merchandising, and audiovisual content. Home to the most comprehensive catalogue of recordings and songs across every musical genre, UMC is committed to artistry, innovation and entrepreneurship in broadening opportunities for our artists on both the domestic and world stages as well as creating new experiences for fans.
Country: Canada
Social Media: @universalmusic https:// www.facebook.com/umusic https:// www.instagram.com/umusic/

HONG KONG

Bear Productions
Website: www.bear.com.hk
Phone: 277 18403
Address: Room 2, 10/F, Charm Centre, 700 Castle Peak Road, Kowloon, HK
Information: educational CDs & tapes with books for children; mainly distributes in Hong Kong, also own their own children choir for hiring and lending (public performance and broadcasting prohibited)
Country: Hong Kong
Social Media: @bearproduction www.facebook.com/BearChoir

BMG Music Publishing Asia
Website: www.BMG.com.hk
Phone: 852 721 8468
Address: Unit 215, 2/F, New East Ocean Centre, 9 Science Museum Road, HK
Country: Hong Kong
Contact: regional vice President David Loiterton
Contact: pa to vice President Fanny Ho

BMG Music Publishing HONG KONG Ltd
Website: www.BMG.com.hk
Phone: 348 80550
Address: Room B, 8/F, , Hang Lung House, , 184-192 Queen's Road Central, , HK
Information: Korea, Japan, China, Taiwan, Hong Kong, Phillipines, Malaysia, Singapore, Thailand, Indonesia, New Zealand, Australia, India, Middle East, South Africa
Country: Hong Kong
Social Media: @blackmediahk www.facebook.com/blackmedia.hk

EMI Hong Kong Ltd
Website: www.emimusic.com
Phone: 250 65668
Address: Rm 2705-9, Tower 6, The Gate Way, 9 Canton Road, Tsim Sha Tsui, HK
Information: EMI Hong Kong Ltd is part of EMI Music Asia. EMI Group Limited (originally an initialism for Electric and Musical Industries, also referred to as EMI Records Ltd. or simply EMI) was a British transnational conglomerate founded in March 1931 in London.
Country: Hong Kong
Contact: Sales Manager Ricky Ma

HNH International Ltd
Website: www.naxos.com.hk
Phone: 276 07818
Address: Level 11, Cyberport 1, 100 Cyberport Road, HK
Country: Hong Kong
a & r Director
 Matthew Freeman
Contact: Managing Director Klaus Heymann

Silk Road Music Company Ltd
Website: www.silkroadmusic.net
Phone: 279 30733
Address: Flat 1303A, 13F, B/K B, Hoi Luen Industrial Centre, 55 Hoi Yuen Road, Kwun Tong, Kowloon, HK
Information: Independent record company, based in Hong Kong, and was established in 1990 as Silk Road Music Co., Ltd., initially focused on the international music market.
Country: Hong Kong
Contact: Managing Director Desmond Chan
Social Media: www.facebook.com/silkroadmusichk/

Sony BMG Music Entertainment (Hong Kong) Ltd
Website: www.sonybmg.com.hk
Phone: 286 31783
Address: 24/F, Oxford House, Taikoo Place, Quarry Bay, HK
Information: own & distributed labels: RCA, Columbia, Epic, Zomba, Jive, etc. Alternative e-mail:nora.wong@sonybmg.com
Country: Hong Kong
promotion & product Manager
 Ellen Kong

Sony Music Entertainment Hong Kong Ltd
Website: www.sonymusic.com.hk
Phone: 277 14391
Address: Suites 2901-6, 29F, Tower 1, The Gateway, 25 Canton Road, TST, Kowloon, HK
Information: Played a pioneering role in music history, from the first-ever music label to the invention of the flat disc record. They've nurtured some of music's most iconic artists and produced some of the most influential recordings of all time.
Country: Hong Kong
Social Media: www.facebook.com/SonyMusicEntertainmentHK/

Universal Music Hong Kong Office
Website: www.universalmusic.com
Phone: 230 15888
Address: Level 28, Millennium City 6, 392 Kwun Tong, Kowloon, HK
Information: UMG embraces a vast array of artists covering a full spectrum of music around the world and is a leader in Local/Asia, International and Classical/Jazz repertoire
Country: Hong Kong
Social Media: www.facebook.com/UniversalMusicHongKong www.instagram.com/umwebzine/

INDONESIA

Aquarius Musikindo PT
Website: www.aquariusmusiconline.com
Phone: 213 807 236
Address: Jl. Batu Tulis XIII No.17, RT.7/RW.2, Kb. Klp., Kecamatan Gambir, Kota Jakarta Pusat, Daerah Khusus Ibukota Jakarta 10120, Indonesia
Information: Aquarius Musikindo is a Recording Company based in Jakarta, Indonesia, the story began in the late 60s when music is involved mainly in Aquarius cassette recording / reproduction. In addition to producing music in this country, we also became a manufacturer and authorized distributor for some of the album production WEA, EMI, JVC and PONYCANYON for Indonesia.
Country: Indonesia
Social Media: www.facebook.com/AquariusMusicOnli-netwitter.com/aqmusiconline

EMI Indonesia
Phone: 215 221 010
Address: Graha Aktiva, 5th Floor, Jl. HR, Rasuna, Said Blok X-1 Kav.3, ID
Country: Indonesia

Musica Studio (PT)
Website: www.musica-studios.co.id
Phone: 217 987 423
Address: Jalan Pancoran Timur Raya No. 3 Jakarta Selatan – Indonesia 12780
Information: Musica Studio's became the home and base camp of Indonesia's prominent artists.
Country: Indonesia
Social Media: www.facebook.com/MusicaStudios https://twitter.com/MusicaStudios https:// www.instagram.com/musicastudios/

PT Indo Semar Sakti
Website: na
Phone: 216 190 037
Address: jl. Tubagus Angke Raya no 2 Jakarta, Indonesia 11460
Information: Since the 1970s, Indo Semar Records has consistently produced and distributed quality music both international and domestic for you music lovers.
Country: Indonesia
Social Media: https://twitter.com/indosemarsakti https:// www.facebook.com/indosemarsakti

Sony BMG Music Entertainement Indonesia
Website: www.sonybmg.co.id
Phone: 857 192 87099
Address: Wisma GKBI, Jl. Jend. Sudirman No 28 South Jakarta, Jakarta, Indonesia 10210
Information: This company is the largest record company in Indonesia. This company is a subsidiary of Sony BMG Music Entertainment , which distributes music under the umbrella of Sony BMG Music Entertainment worldwide to Indonesia .
Country: Indonesia

JAPAN

ALM Records
Website: www.kojimarokuon.com
Phone: 035 397 7311
Address: 3-6-13, Asaya Minami, Suginami-ku, JP
Information: In 1974, Kojima Yukio, one of the founding members of Fontec Co., Ltd., established Kojima Recording. The company's label name is ALM RECORDS, and production of records begins. Since then, most of the discs have been making topical works that lead the times, with sound making with in-house recording. We aim to produce unique CDs that cherish the meticulous response and collaboration with musicians that can only be achieved with independent labels. In recent years, labels have been developed mainly for classical music, especially contemporary music, chamber music, old music, and Japanese music, and in particular, recording technology has received very high acclaim from various fields.
Country: Japan

Art Union Co Ltd
Website: www.artuniongroup.co.jp
Phone: 337 702 371
Address: 7F, Tosen Dogenzaka Bldg., 20-4 Maruyama-cho, Shibuya-ku, JP
Information: Art Union is a record production and distribution company that pursues works with uniqueness and foresight that are world-class, centered on independent music.
Country: Japan
Contact: Executive Director Taizo Fujii

Camerata Tokyo Inc.
Website: www.camerata.co.jp
Phone: 357 905 560
Address: 2F, Wakho Bldg., 14-3, Motoyoyogi-machi, Shibuya-ku, JP
Information: Camerata Tokyo is based on a new philosophy that integrates both record production and the music software industry such as concerts and music festivals, centered on Hiroshi Isaka, who has worked as a record Producer at JVC for more than a dozen years. It was established with the aim of becoming a content business that can be used not only in Japan but also internationally.
Country: Japan
Contact: President Hiroshi Isaka
Social Media: www.facebook.com/cameratatokyo

Columbia Music Entertainment
Website: www.columbia.co.jp
Phone: 335 848 265
Address: 4-14-14 Akasaka, Minato-ku, JP
Information: the oldest record company in Japan which is well known for its DENON label and its recording quality; dance, jazz, pop, world music
Country: Japan
Contact: Producer Yamakawa Atsushi
Contact: division President Nagata Isao
Social Media: www.facebook.com/NipponColumbia.Music https://twitter.com/nipponcolumbia

Fontec Inc
Website: www.fontec.co.jp
Phone: 333 930 183
Address: 5-22-5 Ogikubo, Suginami-ku, JP
Information: Fontech is a CD label focusing on classical music by Japanese musicians and contemporary music by Japanese composers. Since its founding in 1971, it has released more than 1, 000 titles. In particular, the abundance and high quality of catalogs in Japanese contemporary music have been highly evaluated both in Japan and overseas.

Country: Japan
Sales Manager & concert management div.
Sei'ichi Arita
Contact: President Sumio Yoshimura
Contact: Producer Akira Matsuda

King Record Co Ltd
Website: www.kingrecords.co.jp
Phone: 339 452 134
Address: 1-2-3 Otowa, Bunkyo-ku, JP
Information: King Records Co., Ltd. is a Japanese record company founded in January 1931 as a division of the Japanese publisher Kodansha. It initially began operating as an independent entity in the 1950s. It later became part of the Otowa Group
Country: Japan
Contact: General Manager international Susumu Morikawa
Contact: President Takehisa Koike
Contact: Executive Director Hide Toshi Shigematsu
Contact: export Manager Kenji Okazaki

Nami Records Co Ltd
Website: www.nami-records.co.jp
Phone: 334 405 542
Address: 2-11-3-205 Kami-Ohsaki, Shinagawa-ku, JP
Information: recorded predominantly by Japanese orchestras/artists but the number of recordings by foreign artists such as Israel String Quartet, Jan
Country: Japan
Contact: President Takashi Mitsukawa

Octavia Records Inc
Website: www.octavia.co.jp
Phone: 355 618 988
Address: 107-0052 Akasaka, Minato-ku, Tokyo 6-9-4 Japan
Information: Octavia Records Inc. is a record company that exclusively releases Classical and Jazz music. It was established in 1999 in Tokyo by Tomoyoshi Ezaki – a well-known and accomplished Producer and recording engineer.
Country: Japan
production dept a&r: Natsuko Samejima
Contact: production department Manager Miyuki Ito
Social Media: https:// www.facebook.com/octaviarecord/ https:// www.instagram.com/exton_recording/ https://twitter.com/octaviarecords

Pony Canyon Inc
Website: www.ponycanyon.co.jp
Phone: 364 309 700
Address: 2-5-10, Toranomon, Minato-ku, JP
Information: Pony Canyon Inc., also known by the short-hand form Ponican, is a Japanese company, established on October 1, 1966, which publishes music, DVD and VHS videos, movies, and video games. It is affiliated with the Japanese media group Fujisankei Communications Group.
Country: Japan
Contact: General Manager Yuji Takahashi

Sony Music Entertainment (Japan) Inc
Website: www.sonymusic.co.jp
Phone: 813 351 55050
Address: 4-5 Rokubancho, Chiyoda-ku, JP
Information: Sony Music Entertainment Japan was officially incorporated in March 1968 as a Tokyo-based 50/50 joint venture between Sony Corporation and U.S. conglomerate CBS to distribute the latter's music releases in Japan.
Country: Japan
Contact: representative Director/CEO Kazutomo Enomoto

Tokyo M-Plus Co. Ltd
Website: www.tokyo-m-plus.co.jp
Phone: 359 765 991
Address: 4-14-10 Sengoku Bunkyo-ku, Tokyo, Japan 1120011
Information: Tokyo M Plus Co., Ltd. is a music software import agency that handles CDs of classical music labels with rich overseas characteristics. We will deliver recommended music information such as new music information from overseas.
Country: Japan
Contact: President Tsutomo Miyazawa

Universal Music Ltd.
Website: www.universal-music.co.jp
Phone: 364 063 067
Address: 8-5-30 Akasaka, Minato-ku, JP
Information: Universal Music Publishing Group is a leading global music publishing company home to the greatest artists, songwriters and song catalog in the world.
Country: Japan
President & CEO
Keiichi Ishizaka

Victor Entertainment Inc (JVC)
Website: www.jvcmusic.co.jp
Phone:

354 237 777
Address: Paracio Tower, 3-6-7, Kita-aoyama, Minato-ku, JP
Information: Victor Entertainment started record production in 1928 as the music business division of Victor Company of Japan, Ltd. (currently JVC KENWOOD Corporation). Since becoming independent as a record company in 1972, as a comprehensive software company that has consistently played a central role in the entertainment business of the Victor Group (currently JVC KENWOOD Group), it has expanded its business centered on the planning, production, and Sales of music software.
Country: Japan
Contact: General Manager, western music Seigo Horiuchi
Contact: deputy General Manager, classical music Tomoo Nojima
Social Media: https:// www.facebook.com/jvcmusic https://twitter.com/VictorMusic

Ward Records, Inc
Website: www.wardrecords.com
Phone: 357 753 257
Address: 4F Kryakizaka, Terrace 6-15-1, Roppongi, Minato-ku, JP
Information: Japanese label, established in April 2001. Focusing on jazz, bossa nova, MPB, nu-jazz, club, rock and pop.
Country: Japan
Contact: label Manager Tanak Hidetoshi
Social Media: https:// www.facebook.com/wardrecords https://twitter.com/Ward_Rock

REPUBLIC OF KOREA

CNL Music
Website: www.cnlmusic.com
Phone: 252 21886
Address: 5F Seoduk Bldg., 1515-8 Seocho-dong, Seocho-gu
Information: Since its foundation by Sockgoo Choi and Tai Lee in 1990 as a distribution company, this Seoul (Korea) based company has focused in introducing and Marketing of high-class music products covering jazz, classical, new age, 1960~70's rock and world music.
Country: Republic of Korea
Contact: President Tae-Youn Lee

KBS Media Inc
Website: www.kbsmedia.co.kr
Phone: 278 18484/9
Address: 18 Yeoui-dong Yeongdeungpo-gu, Seoul, 07235 South Korea
Information: KBSMedia was founded in 1991 and has been actively licensing international and domestic rights of contents, distributing VOD contents, importing and dubbing foreign programs and carrying on various other businesses related to contents. KBS Media is and continues to be the company representing Korea's content industry.
Country: Republic of Korea
Contact: President Tae-Jin Jeong
Social Media: https:// www.instagram.com/kbsmedia. official/

Sony BMG Music Korea
Website: www.sonymusic.co.kr
Phone: 253 00900
Address: 1302-22, Seocho-dong, Seocho-gu
Information: Sony BMG Music Entertainment was an American record company owned as a 50–50 joint venture between Sony Corporation of America and Bertelsmann Music Group.
Country: Republic of Korea
Contact: Director Mun-Joon Yang
Social Media: https:// www.facebook.com/sonymusickorea https://twitter.com/sonymusickr_pop https:// www.instagram.com/sonymusickorea/

Warner/Chappell Korea
Website: warnerchappell.com
Phone: 252 73236
Address: No.911, Victoria Bldg., #705-1, Yoksam-dong, Gangnam-gu
Information: Warner/Chappell Music, the global music publishing company of Warner Music Group, is home to a wide array of legendary songwriters and a rich catalog of contemporary hits and influential standards.
Country: Republic of Korea
Contact: creative Manager Ki-Tae Lim

MALAYSIA

Life Records
Website: www.liferecords.com
Phone: 320 707 524
Address: 66-68, Jln Raja Chulan, Kuala Lumpur, 50200 Kuala Lumpur, Wilayah Persekutuan Kuala Lumpur, Malaysia
Information: Life Records reigns as the premier name in the Asian region for possessing one of the largest repertoire of Chinese or Mandarin pop, classical, folk, traditional, drama, opera and children's songs
Country: Malaysia

Contact: Director Cheong Hock Ng

MEXICO

Discos Musart S.A. de C.V.
Website: www.musart.com.mx
Phone: 555 341 9955
Address: Av Cuitlahuac no 2335, San Salvador Xochimanca, Azcapotzalco, MX
Information: Discos Musart is a Mexican record label founded in 1948. It is headquartered in Mexico City and remains one of the country's biggest labels, focusing on Mexican music, as well as international releases licensed from various labels around the world.
Country: Mexico
Contact: vice-President Andres Baptista
Contact: Director Eduardo Baptista Lucio
Contact: international Manager Pablo Camarena

Multimusic S.A. de C.V.
Website: prestashop.klak.mx
Phone: 527 19560
Address: Av Constituyentes 411, América, Miguel Hidalgo, 11820 Mexico City, CDMX, Mexico
Information: Multimusic, the largest independent record label in Mexico.
Country: Mexico
Contact: President Luis Alberto San Martin
Director/a&r
Olga San Martin
Social Media: www.facebook.com/Multimusicmx/ https://twitter.com/Multimusicmx

Sony Music Entertainment México
Website: www.sonymusic.com.mx
Address: Blvd. M. Avila Camacho 191-201, Col. Los Morales Polanco, MX
Information: Sony Music is a company dedicated to promoting important figures in Latin and international entertainment. This profile belongs to the Mexico offices and promotes artists signed with their labels, subsidiaries and licensees.
Country: Mexico
Social Media: https:// www.facebook.com/sonymusic-mexico https://twitter.com/sonymusicmexico https:// www.instagram.com/sonymusicmexico/ https:// www.facebook.com/sonymusicmexico https://twitter.com/sonymusicmexico https:// www.instagram.com/sonymusicmexico/

Universal Music México
Website: www.universalmusica.com
Phone: 526 35200
Address: Deleg. Miguel Hidalgo, CP 11580 Mexico City Mexico
Information: This is Universal Music's regional company in México founded in 1979 originally known as PolyGram Discos, SA De CV changing it's name in 1999 due to Seagram's acquisition of PolyGram and subsequently merged it with the Universal Music Group to form the world's largest recorded music business.
Country: Mexico
Contact: Director Marco Bissi

NEW ZEALAND

EMI Music New Zealand
Website: www.emimusic.co.nz
Phone: 935 61570
Address: 9th Floor, 15 Hopetoun Street, Ponsonby, PO Box 864, Shortland Street, NZ
Country: New Zealand
Contact: contact Morgan Donoghue
Main Focus: Other

Kiwi Pacific Records International Ltd
Website: www.kiwipacific.com
Phone: 687 60521
Address: PO Box 919, NZ
Information: NZ artists, South Pacific, Maori, Polynesia, NZ folk, NZ composers
Country: New Zealand
Contact: production Manager Murray Vincent

Loop Recordings Aot(ear)oa
Website: www.loop.co.nz
Phone: 480 33055
Address: PO Box 52097, Kingsland, NZ
Information: physical address: Level 7, 175 Victoria Street, Wellington, New Zealand
Country: New Zealand
Contact: label Manager Michael Tucker
Contact: Marketing Manager Phil Br
Social Media: loopcrewfacebook.com/looprecordings

Ode Records
Website: www.oderecords.co.nz
Phone: 963 01177
Address: PO Box 56 450, Dominion Rd, NZ
Information: classical, jazz, traditional, world music
Country: New Zealand
Contact: Managing Director Roger Marbeck
Social Media: @oderecords www.facebook.com/pages/Ode-Records/103252229733028
Main Focus: Other

Sony Music Entertainment New Zealand Ltd
Website: www.sonymusic.co.nz
Phone: 936 19300
Address: Level 1., 100 Ponsonby Road, Grey Lynn, NZ
Country: New Zealand
Social Media: @SONYMUSICGLOBAL www.facebook.
com/sonymusic

Triton AV
Website: www.tritonmusic.co.nz
Phone: 982 63520
Address: PO Box 15923, New Lynn, NZ
Country: New Zealand

PHILIPPINES

Bibliarch Inc.
Phone: 275 64582
Address: Ground Floor, Glorietta 3, Ayala Center, Makati
City, PH
Information: classical, jazz, latin, new music and world
music
Country: Philippines
Contact: Managing Director Jaime Daez

Dyna Music Productions
Phone: +632-632 1155
Address: Suite 901, The Orient Square, , Emerald Ave.,
Ortigas Center, Metro Manila, PH
Information: distributor, record company, music
publisher, merchandising, event promotions, Marketing,
AV production , advertising and promotions, content
developer
Country: Philippines
Contact: Managing Director Howard Dy
Contact: Howard Dy

SINGAPORE

Independent Classical Productions
Website: www.icp.mu
Phone: 644 40105
Address: 5000D Marine Parade Road, #10-16 Laguna
Park, SG
Country: Singapore
Contact: Recording engineer/Consultant Li Teo
Main Focus: Concert

TAIWAN, PROVINCE OF CHINA

Arc International Co Ltd
Phone: 882 231 44625
Address: Rm 506, 5F No.10 Chung-King South Road,
Sec. 1
Country: Taiwan
Contact: Managing Director Robert Chang

Aurora Music International
Website: www.aurora.ws
Phone: 229 992 811
Address: 4F, No. 12, Lane 609, , Sec. 5, Chung Hsin Rd., ,
San Chung Dist,
Information: classical, jazz, new age, traditional, world
music, folk also do vinyl, SACD, BD
artist manangerment, concert agent /concert promoter
Country: Taiwan
Social Media: http:// www.facebook.com/#!/AuroraTAS
Main Focus: Concert

Jingo Digital Inc.
Website: www.jingo.com.tw
Phone: 282 269 909
Address: 9F, Bldg A No. 736, Jung-Jeng Road, Jung He
City
Country: Taiwan
Contact: Manager, international department Yves Ye-
Shong Ho

Linfair Records Ltd
Website: www.linfairrecords.com
Phone: 223 941 828
Address: 12F, No.112 Chung Hsiao East Road, Section 1
Country: Taiwan
Contact: Managing Director Denver Chang
planning & Marketing, international dept.
Chin-Song Liao
Contact: pa to Managing Director Francen Chou
Contact: Director of classic dept. Jasmin Wang

Magnum Music Entertainment Pan China
Website:
www.magnum.com.tw
Phone: 287 717 739
Address: 2F, No 6-1, Lane 137, Yanji St
Country: Taiwan
Contact: international label Manager Alan Huang
Contact: promotion Ya Xin Tseng

Renaissance Music Society Ltd
Website:
www.rms-music.com
Phone: 227 460 683
Address: No.180, Sec. 6, , Jhong-shan N. Rd., , Shih-lin

District
Information: promotion of cultural events in Pan China,
cultural exchange between the West and East, organizer
of orchestral Concert Tours in the Far East
Country: Taiwan
Contact: international Manager Mike Yang
Contact: President Bob Chen

Sony BMG Music Entertainment (Taiwan) Ltd
Website: www.sonymusic.com.tw
Phone: 227 668 900
Address: 6F, No.35, Lane 11, Kwang-Fu North Road,
Chung Shan District
Information: also organises singing performances
Country: Taiwan
Contact: Chair/Producer Zhen Tong Cui

Welchen Publishing House Co Ltd
Website: www.welchenmusic.com
Phone: 227 066 825
Address: Guangfu South Road
Information: French, Spanish and World Music
Country: Taiwan
Contact: Managing Director Amy Cheng

Wind Records Company Ltd
Website: www.wind-records.com.tw
Phone: 222 185 881
Address: 5F, No.14, Lane 130, Min Chuan Road,
Hsin-Tien City
Information: alternative E-mail address: micp@ms4.
hinet.net/pc.greene@verizon.net USA; responsible for its
excellent reception in Germany, France, U.S.A., Canada,
U.K., Italy, Holland, Russia, Brazil, Argentina, mainland
China, Hong Kong, Japan, Singapore, Malaysia
Country: Taiwan
Contact: digital dep. Manager Yi-Kuei Yang
Contact: President Chin-Tsung Ken Yang

UNITED STATES

Albany Records
Website: www.albanyrecords.com
Phone: 518 436 8814
Address: 915 Broadway # 7, Albany, NY 12207, USA
Information: Albany Records is devoted to music by
American composers (with a few notable exceptions)
performed by the best of America's artists. From
premiere recordings of orchestral music by Roy Harris,
Morton Gould and Don Gillis to music by George Lloyd
and Andrei Eshpai, there is something for everyone on
Albany Records – provided your interests are just a bit
out of the ordinary.
Country: United States

Andante Corp.
Website: www.andante.com
Phone: 212 905 3420
Address: 56 West 22nd Street, 12th Floor, US
Information: the company's aim is to document and pre-
serve the world's recorded classical musical heritage and
to become the definitive online resource for information
about classical music and opera
Country: United States
Contact: President Alain Coblence
Contact: Chairman Pierre Berg

Angel Records
Website: www.angelrecords.com
Phone: 212 786 8600
Address: 150 5th Ave, New York, NY 10011, USA
Information: Angel Records was a record label founded
by EMI in 1953. It specialised in classical music, but
included an occasional operetta or Broadway score.
The Angel mark was used by EMI, its predecessors, and
affiliated companies from 1898.
Country: United States
President capitol classics & jazz
Bruce Lundvall
Contact: senior Director finance Michael Harris
Contact: vice-President Sales Brian Joosten
senior vice-President & General Manager
Tom Evered
Contact: Director publicity Matthew Amoroso

Arabesque Recordings, LLC
Website: www.arabesquerecords.com
Phone: 212 730 5000
Address: 5 International Drive, Suite 112 Rye Brook, NY
10573 USA
Information: Arabesque Records started out as a small
Classical Music Label in 1987 in NYC. Up until five years
ago, they had maintained a brick and mortar store in
NYC.
Country: United States
Contact: operations Manager Chaim Roberts
Contact: Managing member Marvin Reiss
Social Media: www.facebook.com/Arabesque-Record-
ings-LLC-1855985364424087/

Archer Records
Website: www.archer-records.com
Phone: 901 278 0300
Address: 1902 Nelson Ave, Memphis, TN 38114, United

States
Information: Archer Records is an independent record
label with notoriety in the classical guitar and Americana
genres. The label was founded in 2001 in downtown
Memphisby Ward Archer, who founded Cotton Row
Recording Studios in 1978 and is a former trustee of the
National Academy of Recording Arts and Sciences
Country: United States
Contact: President Ward Archer
Social Media: https:// www.facebook.com/archer-
records/

Arkadia Records
Website: www.arkadiarecords.com
Phone: 888 275 2342
Address: P.O. Box 77, Saugerties, NY 12477, USA
Information: Grammy Nominated Record and Video
label, offering the very best in Jazz and World Music
since 1996.They produce and present highly acclaimed,
and world-renowned Artists with a stellar catalog of
Award-Winning titles.
Country: United States
Contact: President Bob Karcy
Social Media: www.facebook.com/arkadiarecords/ www.
instagram.com/arkadiarecords/ https://twitter.com/
arkadiarecords

Ascencion Recordings Inc
Website: www.ascencionrecordings.com
Address: 5561 North Croatan Hwy, US
Information: After establishing Ascencion Recordings,
he and his wife Cathy released several recordings and
received airplay on 600+ radio stations worldwide.
Country: United States
Contact: Executive Producer Cathy Pescevich Kreplin
Contact: President Gordon Kreplin

BBC Worldwide Americas
Website: www.bbcworldwide.com
Phone: 212 705 9300
Address: 747 3rd Ave Fl 6 New York, NY 10017 USA
Information: BBC Worldwide Americas handles the
syndication of the
British Broadcasting Corporation programs in the U.S.
Country: United States

Bridge Records Inc.
Website: www.bridgerecords.com
Phone: 914 654 9270
Address: 200 Clinton Ave. New Rochelle, NY, 10801 USA
Information: incorporates a management division for
classical composers and performers; see also Agents and
Producers
Country: United States
Contact: artist Manager Becky Bridge Bridge
Email: becky@bridgerecords.com
Social Media: https://twitter.com/bridgerecords www.
facebook.com/BridgeRecordsInc

Cala Records Inc
Website: www.calarecords.com
Phone: 141 065 35900
Address: PO Box 89, Suite 750 2 Old Brompton Rd Lon-
don SW7 3DQ United Kingdom, US
Information: Producers of the London Sound series of
massed single-instrument ensembles. UK address: 17
Shakespeare Garden, N2 9LJ London, Tel: +44 (0)208 883
7306
Country: United States
Contact: vice President Jeremy Swerling
Contact: Artistic Chairman Geoffrey Simon

Cambria Music
Website: http:// www.cambriamus.com
Phone: 310 831 1322
Address: PO Box 374 Lomita, CA 90717 USA
Information: Founded in 1979, Cambria is an inde-
pendent American label specializing predominantly in
the classical repertoire. Our emphasis is on American
composers (including William Grant Still and David
Maslanka); women composers (including Germaine
Tailleferre, Florence Price and Elinor Remick Warren) and
historical re-issues.
Country: United States
Contact: classical division Director Lance Bowling
Email: cambriamus@aol.com

Cantaloupe Records
Website: www.cantaloupemusic.com
Phone: 718 852 7755
Address: 80 Hanson Place, Suite 301 Brooklyn,
NY 11217 USA
Information: Cantaloupe Music is the record label creat-
ed and launched in March 2001 by the three founders of
New York's legendary Bang on a Can organization—com-
posers Michael Gordon, David Lang and Julia Wolfe—
with Bang on a Can Managing Director Kenny Savelson.
Cantaloupe Music has made a massive impact in the
new music community, and has been recognized by
critics and fans worldwide for its edgy and adventurous
sounds.
Country: United States
Contact: label Manager Bill Murphy Murphy
Email: bill@cantaloupemusic.com

Social Media: https:// www.facebook.com/canta-loupemusic/ https://twitter.com/cantaloupeny

Cantilena Records
Website: www.cantilenarecords.com
Phone: 916 443 6877
Address: 1925 5th Ave Sacramento, CA 95818, USA
Information: Cantilena Records has a short but proud history. Jeroen de Boer is a common name in Amsterdam's restaurant, nightlife, and entertainment scene.
Country: United States
Contact: vice President Joan Bauerly
Contact: President Laurel Zucker
Social Media: www.facebook.com/Cantilena-Records-Publications-160582667357408

Cedille Records
Website: www.cedillerecords.org
Phone: 773 989 2515
Address: 1205 W Balmoral Ave Chicago, IL 60640 USA
Information: For more than two decades, Cedille has produced world-class recordings featuring outstanding classical musicians.
Country: United States
Contact: business Manager Cynthia Ross
Contact: President James Ginsburg Ginsburg
Contact: Director of operations Julia Nicols-Corry Nicols-Corry
Email: julia@cedillerecords.org
Contact: Marketing coordinator Madeleine Richter Richter
Email: madeleine@chicagoclassical.org
Social Media: www.facebook.com/CedilleRecords/ https:// www.instagram.com/cedillerecords/ https://twitter.com/cedillerecords

Celestial Harmonies
Website: www.harmonies.com
Phone: 520 326 4400
Address: PO Box 30122, US
Information: distributed in UK/Eire by DiscorD Distribution; distributed in Australia/New Zealand by Planet Imports
Country: United States
Contact: President Eckart Rahn

Centaur Records Inc
Website: www.centaurrecords.com
Phone: 225 336 4877
Address: 136 St Joseph St, Baton Rouge, LA 70802, USA
Information: Founded in 1976, Centaur is one of the oldest and largest independent classical labels in the U.S. Centaur recordings are available in major markets throughout the world.
Country: United States
Contact: v.p. production Daniel Cassin
Contact: President Victor E Sachse
Contact: accounts Executive Sally Wood
Social Media: www.facebook.com/Centaur-Records-Inc-140781766368 https://twitter.com/Centaur-Records

Chesky Records
Website: www.chesky.com
Phone: 212 586 7799
Address: 1650 Broadway, Suite 900 New York, NY 10019
Information: Audiophile record label specializing in Jazz, Classical, And Singer-Songwriter releases
Country: United States
Contact: President Norman Chesky
Contact: Artistic Director David Chesky
Social Media: www.facebook.com/cheskymusictwitter.com/cheskylabel www.instagram.com/cheskyrecords

Cobra Entertainment LLC
Website: www.cobra-entertainment.com
Phone: 310 268 1205
Address: 1663 Sawtelle Blvd, Los Angeles, CA 90025, USA
Information: Cobra Entertainment LLC is a music and video label which boasts an extensive and unique catalog of content. Their music catalog consists of a wide range of genres including classical, contemporary, nature, new age, Halloween and Christmas
Country: United States

Collegium Records
Website: www.collegiumrecords.com
Phone: 402 597 1240
Address: 35-41 72nd St, Flushing, NY 11372, USA
Information: They've been working at everything from concerts to large festivals since 1973 and are particularly familiar with Folk, Classical, and Jazz.
Country: United States
Contact: vice President Norma Schmidt
Contact: President Stanley Schmidt

Concord Music Group
Website: concord.com
Phone: 310 385 4229
Address: 10 Lea Ave, Nashville, TN 37210, USA
Information: Concord is the independent, worldwide leader in the development, management and acquisition of sound recordings, music publishing and theatrical performance rights.
Country: United States

Contact: vp international Sales/Marketing Peter Holden
Contact: General Manager Gene Rumsey

Crystal Records, Inc
Website: www.crystalrecords.com
Phone: 360 834 7022
Address: 28818 NE Hancock Rd, Camas, WA 98607, USA
Information: specialising in instrumental chamber music and solos, especially woodwind, brass, and strings. World class performers are featured, including international soloists and present and past members of major symphonies. The complete 12-CD box set of the 24 woodwind quintets of Anton Reicha was released in 2012, with the renowned Westwood Wind Quintet. In addition, the 300-CD catalog includes the largest collection of recordings by composer Alan Hovhaness, conducted or supervised by Hovhaness
Country: United States
Contact: founder Peter Christ
Social Media: https://twitter.com/crystal-records https:// www.facebook.com/Crystal-Records-1641370899408843/

Dick Clark Productions Inc.
Website: www.dickclarkproductions.com
Phone: 310 255 4600
Address: 2900 Olympic Blvd., US
Information: independent Producer of a wide range of television programming for broadcast networks, cable networks, distributors and advertisers, as well as a leader of award-winning communications experiences from live events and meetings to integrated Marketing
Country: United States
Contact: senior vice President of business operations and General counsel Michael Kohn
Contact: President Orly Adelson
Contact: Executive In charge of production Bob Bardo
Social Media: @dclarkp

Disk Eyes Productions/Time Pools Music
Website: www.diskeyes.com
Phone: 425 454 5359
Address: 816 Evergreen Point Way, #542 Medina, WA 98039 USA
Information: Disk Eyes is a boutique publishing, production and a sync music catalog company specializing in vintage music. We get our exclusive and fresh sound by organizing groups of diverse musicians and world class studios – combining talent in a session that might include members of the Grand Ole Opry teamed up with Tower of Power Horns. The synergy can be quite peculiar, and engaging.
Country: United States
Contact: licensing Carla Marrow
Email: carla@diskeyes.com
Contact: custom music production Donald Marrow
Social Media: www.facebook.com/diskeyesproductions/

E.R.M. Media
Website: www.ermmedia.org
Phone: 757 625 1212
Address: A & R Office:, 101 W. Plume Street, Suite 404, US
Country: United States
Contact: operations Manager Paul Harvey
  public relations/a & r
  Sherise Milton

ESS.A.Y Recordings
Website: www.essaycd.com
Phone: 203 778 5595
Address: 50 Woodcrest Lane, Danbury, CT, United States 06810
Information: Small classical label run by Richard Kapp, majoring in piano and violin music
Country: United States
Contact: contact Barbara Kapp

Fleur de Son Classics Ltd
Website: http:// www.fleurdeson.com/
Phone: 716 681 8106
Address: P.O. Box 132 Buffalo, New York 14225
Information: FLEUR DE SON CLASSICS, Ltd. Was founded, and is owned and operated by classical guitarists, Joanne Castellani and Michael Andriaccio, one of the foremost classical guitar duos in the world today.
Country: United States
Contact: President Joanne Castellani
  classical a & r Director
  Michael Andriaccio
Social Media: www.facebook.com/Fleur-De-Son-Classics-Ltd-133064610115531/wall/

G M Recordings Inc
Website:
http://www.gmrecordings.com/
Phone:
718 854 6727
Address: P.O. Box 894 Wingdale, NY 12594 USA
Information: GM Recordings, Inc., was founded by music icon Gunther Schuller (1925-2015) in Boston in 1981 to unite discerning and open-minded listeners with accomplished, innovative composers and musicians who might otherwise go unrecorded.
Country: United States
Contact: President Gunther Schuller

Contact: Manager Marc Lambert

Gothic Records
Website: www.gothic-catalog.com
Phone: 360 376 4175
Address: P.O. Box 414 Orcas, WA 98280 USA
Information: Loft Recordings was founded in 1999; in 2001, Loft purchased the assets of Gothic Records, a company which had been producing great organ and choral recordings for almost 25 years. Loft established "The Gothic Catalog" as a mail-order webstore where recordings from both companies could be showcased, alongside other recordings from third-party labels.
Country: United States

Harmonia Mundi USA
Website: www.harmoniamundi.com
Phone: 818 333 1500
Address: 1117 Chestnut St, Burbank, CA 91506, United States
Information: Since 1958, the label founded by Bernard Coutaz has not ceased to explore new repertoires and broaden its horizons, from early music to that of the 21st century, bringing together over 50 internationally renowned artists from all over the world.
Country: United States
Contact: General Manager Matthew Owen
Contact: vice President, Artistic Director Robina Young
Contact: Press Sarah Folger

Innova Recordings
Website: www.innovarecordings.com
Phone: 651 251 2823
Address: American Composers Forum, 332 Minnesota Street, Suite E 145, US
Information: Composer Service Organisation; alternative website: www.composersforum.org
Country: United States
Contact: Director Philip Blackburn

John Marks Records
Website: www.jmrcds.com
Phone: 401 782 6298
Address: 19 Wright Avenue, US
Information: distributed by Allegro in the USA
Country: United States
Contact: Director John Marks

Laurel Records
Website: www.laurelrecords.com
Phone: 510 525 3323
Address: 1018 Euclid Avenue, US
Country: United States
Contact: Producer, owner John C Gilbert

Lovely Music
Website: http:// www.lovely.com
Phone: 212 941 8911
Address: 260 West Broadway New York, NY 10013 USA
Information: The record label was founded by Johnson as an adjunct to the activities of Performing Artservices, Inc., a non-profit organization dedicated to the management and Administration of American avant-garde artists working in the fields of music, dance and theater.
Country: United States
Contact: Executive Director Mimi Johnson

Marston
Website: www.marstonrecords.com
Phone: 610 690 1703
Address: 206 Cheshire Circle, US
Information: restoration and preservation of historical releases
Country: United States
Contact: President Scott Kessler
Main Focus: Opera

MMC Recordings Ltd
Website: http:// www.mmcrecordings.com/
Phone: 781 944 0959
Address: 240 West Street Reading, MA , United States 01867
Information: MMC (Master Musicians Collective) makes eclectic mix of classical, jazz, alternative and children's music. Since its formation in 1992 by the renowned composer William Thomas McKinley (b. 1938), MMC Recordings has produced and released hundreds of orchestral works by the leading lights of contemporary classical music in addition to its rising stars.
Country: United States
Contact: President William Thomas McKinley

Mode Records
Website: www.mode.com
Phone: 212 979 1027
Address: PO Box 1262, US
Country: United States
Contact: President Brian Brandt
  a&r Director
  Alice Hom

Music and Arts Programs of America Inc.
Website:
www.musicandarts.com

Phone: 510 525 4583
Address: 2465 4th Street, Berkeley CA 94710 USA
Information: Music & Arts Programs of America, Inc. is an independent classical and jazz record label based in Berkeley, California.
Country: United States
Contact: Manager Frederick Maroth
Social Media: www.facebook.com/Musicandartsprogram stwitter.com/musicandartsinc https://www.instagram.com/musicandarts_inc/

Musika Records Inc
Website: www.musikainc.com
Phone: 201 944 7905
Address: 1285 Ave. of the Americas, 35th Floor, US
Country: United States
Contact: Director Alexander Lim
classical a&r Director
Yulee Choi

Naxos of America Inc
Website: www.naxos.com
Phone: 615 771 9393
Address: 1810 Columbia Ave, Suite 28, US
Information: offers high-quality streaming of the labels classical music recordings, as well as collections from several other independent classical music labels
Country: United States
Marketing & Sales Manager
Matt Whittier
Social Media: @naxosrecords www.facebook.com/NaxosUSA
Main Focus: Concert

New Albion Records
Website: http://www.newalbion.com/
Phone: 415 621 5757
Address: 584 Castro St, #525San Francisco, CA 94114, USA
Information: New Albion Records began in San Francisco in 1984. It was a record label that centered on modern art music, from a variety of styles. We released about five titles a year and have always searched for the most unusual and distinctive voices in composition.
Country: United States
Contact: Director Tom Welsh
Email: tom@newalbion.com
Social Media: www.facebook.com/newalbionrecords/ www.twitter.com/newalbion

New World Records
Website: www.newworldrecords.org
Phone: 212 290 1680
Address: 75 Broad St, Ste 2400 New York, NY 10004
Information: New World Records is a non-profit record label dedicated to the promotion of American music.
Country: United States
Contact: President Herman Krawitz
Contact: vice President Paul Tai

Newport Classic
Website: www.newportclassic.com
Phone: 401 848 2442
Address: 11 Willow St #4, New Providence, NJ 07974, USA
Information: Newport Classic approaches every recording session with a single goal: to capture the musical experience as accurately as possible. Producers collaborate closely with Newport Classic to ensure that you hear all the subtleties they put into the performance.
Country: United States
Contact: President Shelley Kraman
Contact: partner Larry Kraman

Odradek Records
Website: www.odradek-records.com
Phone: 785 842 2756
Address: 1040 New Hampshire Street, US
Information: member of IAMA
Country: United States
Social Media: @OdradekRecords www.facebook.com/OdradekRecords

Peter Rosen Productions, Inc.
Website: www.peterrosenproductions.com
Phone: 212 535 8927
Address: 245 W. 55th St. New York, New York 10019 USA
Information: has produced and directed over 100 full-length films and tv programs which have been distributed worldwide and have won awards at the major film festivals.
Country: United States
Contact: Producer/Director Peter Rosen

Polygram
Website: www.polygram.com
Phone: 212 333 8000
Address: Worldwide Plaza, 825 8th Avenue New York, New York 10019 USA
Information: Netherlands-based PolyGram N.V. is one of the world's largest entertainment companies and in 1997 remained the number one record company in the world. Over 80 percent of its income comes from the music business, specifically the acquisition, production,

Marketing, manufacture, and distribution of recorded music, along with music publishing
Country: United States

Putumayo World Music
Website: www.putumayo.com
Phone: 212 625 1400
Address: 413 Carpenter Road Charlotte, VT 054445-9280 USA
Information: Putumayo travels the world in search of exceptional songs from Congo to Cuba, Rome to Rio, New Orleans to Nova Scotia. Putumayo's meticulously researched and curated musical journeys are "guaranteed to make you feel good!
Country: United States
Contact: founder Dan Storper
Social Media: www.facebook.com/Putumayo/ https://www.instagram.com/putumayo_world_music/ https://twitter.com/PutumayoMusic

Sonora Productions
Website: www.sonoraproductions.com
Phone: 617 332 6142
Address: P.O. Box 415 Newton, MA 02459 USA
Information: Sonora Productions is a classical music record label based in Boston, Massachusetts. They are devoted to promoting the finest classical musicians, ensembles, and composers from Russia, Ukraine and the United States through our audiophile quality recordings and remastered historical recordings.
Country: United States
Contact: Managing Director Sofia Gilksberg

Sony Masterworks
Website: sonymusicmasterworks.com
Phone: 212 833 8200
Address: 25 Madison Ave, New York, NY 10010, United States
Information: Sony Music Masterworks is a record label, the result of a restructuring of Sony Music's classical music division. Before the acquisition of Bertelsmann's shares in the former Sony BMG, the label was known as Sony BMG Masterworks.
Country: United States
Contact: General Manager Alex Miller
Social Media: ww.facebook.com/SonyMasterworks www.instagram.com/sonymasterworks/twitter.com/sonymasterworks

Telarc International Corporation
Website: www.telarc.com
Phone: 216 464 2313
Address: 23307 Commerce Park Road, US
Information: The TELARC INTERNATIONAL brand is renowned for its technical innovations and audio excellence, most recently apparent with releases by Japanese piano sensation Hiromi, dynamic retro-modern-swing outfit Gordon Goodwin's Big Phat Band and legendary French composer Jacques Loussier.
Country: United States
Director international Sales & Marketing: Kajo Paulkert
Contact: chief engineer Jack Renner

Thirteen/WNET
Website: www.thirteen.org
Phone: 212 560 2888
Address: 825 8th AveNew York, NY 10019, USA
Information: THIRTEEN is one of America's most respected and innovative public media providers. A member of the WNET family of companies, THIRTEEN is a unique cultural and educational institution that harnesses the power of television and electronic media to inform, enlighten, entertain and inspire.
Country: United States
Director of culture & arts programmes
Paula Kerger
Contact: Executive Producer Margaret Similow
Social Media: www.facebook.com/thirteenwnet/ https://twitter.com/ThirteenWNET https://www.instagram.com/thirteenwnet/

V.I.E.W. Video & Music
Website: www.view.com
Phone: 845 246 9955
Address: 11 Reservoir Rd. Saugerties, NY 12477 USA
Information: Video label of Arkadia Entertainment Corp. who own Arkadia record label.
Country: United States
Contact: operations Svetlana Sukenik
Contact: President Bob Karcy

VAI Audio/VAI Distribution/Video Artists International
Website: www.vaimusic.com
Phone: 800 477 7146
Address: 109 Wheeler Ave Pleasantville, NY 10570 USA
Information: The leading independent DVD and CD label devoted to historic performing arts programming.
Country: United States
Social Media: www.facebook.com/VAI.News https://twitter.com/vaimusic https://www.instagram.com/vaimusic/

ZC Music/Premiere
Website: na
Phone: 570 775 4288

Address: 228 Maple Ridge Drive, US
Information: no longer exist
Country: United States

This list includes venues that present, and/or are available for hire/rent for a significant period of the year and/or interested in co-productions. The commercial theatres of London's West End and the boulevard private theatres of Paris are also included. **The entries are listed in alphabetical order within country.**

Lieux

Cette rubrique englobe les lieux qui accueillent des specta-cles et/ou qui sont disponibles à la location pour une certaine période de l'année et/ou qui s'interessent à des co-produc-tions. Les théâtres commerciaux du West End à Londres et les théâtres de Boulevard à Paris apparaissent dans cette liste. **Les entrée sont classés par ordre alphabétique dans le pays.**

Veranstaltungsorte

In diesem Kapitel werden Spielstätten gelisted, die entweder Konzerte usw. veranstalten oder Räumlichkeiten vermieten, sowie diejenigen, die sich mit Koproduktionen befassen. Die Londoner West End Theater und die privaten Boulevard Theater in Paris werden daher in diesem Kapitel aufgeführt. **Die Einträge sind für jedes Land alphabetisch sortiert.**

Luoghi

Questa sezione include tutti i teatri/auditorium/sale che pre-sentano, ospitano, che possono essere affittati o che sono interessati a co-produzioni di spettacoli. Sono inoltre qui inclusi i teatri commerciali londinesi del West End ed i teatri privati di Parigi. **Le voci sono pubblicate in ordine alfabeti-co di paese.**

Locales

Esta lista incluye salas que presentan espectáculos y/o que están disponibles para alquilar por un periodo significativo del año y/o que están interesadas en coproducciones. Los teatros comerciales del 'West End' de Londres o los teatros privados del 'Boulevard' de París también están incluidos en esta sección. **Las entradas se muestran en orden alfabético dentro de cada país.**

performing arts
database

ARGENTINA

Ciudad Cultural Konex
Website: www.cckonex.org
Email: hola@ciudadculturalkonex.org
Phone: 114 864 3200
Address: 3131 Sarmiento, Buenos Aires
Information: The Clorindo Testa y Asociados Studio was in charge of transforming the old oil pot into an original space, keeping the architectural details of the time intact. Today, the complex occupies a large part of the surface of the old property with a re-functionalization of its facilities where all kinds of Artistic exPressions coexist and interrelate with the common objective of providing cultural and Artistic enrichment to the community.
Country: Argentina
Social Media: https://twitter.com/CCKonex https://www.facebook.com/CIUDADCULTURALKONEX/ https://www.instagram.com/cckonex/
Capacity: 1000+
Annual Performances: 100+
Policies: All

AUSTRALIA

Abbotsford Convent Foundation
Website: https://abbotsfordconvent.com.au/
Email: info@abbotsfordconvent.com.au
Phone: 394 153 600
Address: 1 St Heliers Street, Abbotsford
Information: Just four kilometres from Melbourne's CBD and spread over 16 acres, the Abbotsford Convent, with its 11 historic buildings and gardens, is Australia's largest multi-arts precinct. The former Convent of the Good Shepherd, this ex-monastic site is now owned by the Abbotsford Convent Foundation (ACF), a not-for-profit organisation that operates the Abbotsford Convent on behalf of the public. Today, the Convent is home to over 100 studios, two galleries, cafes, a radio station, a school, and an abundance of green open space. Each year the Convent welcomes a diverse range of art projects, rehearsals, workshops, exhibitions, markets, events and festivals. Member of ISPA
Country: Australia
Contact: Fundraising officer Ali Murphy
Email: amurphy@abbotsfordconvent.com.au
Phone: 039 415 3607
Social Media: https://www.instagram.com/abbotsford-convent/ www.facebook.com/AbbotsfordConvent

ABC Southbank Centre
Website: http://about.abc.net.au/southbank/
studios&mediaproduction@abc.net.au

Phone: 139 994
Address: 120 Southbank Bvd, Melbourne, AU
Information: The current ABC Southbank Centre at 120 Southbank Boulevard looks very much 1990's with a strong street level bluestone edifice and dark recessed windows – not the most welcoming of buildings. Enter the new ABC Melbourne Accommodation Project (MAP) with its transparent facade that provides a highly visible internal environment when viewed externally.
Country: Australia
National Manager Productions, ABC Studios & Media Production
Julianne Goss
studios&mediaproduction@abc.net.au
Phone: 038 646 2220
Capacity: 501-1000
Policies: Rent and Present

Adelaide College for the Arts
Website: www.tafesa.edu.au/adelaide-college-of-the-arts
Email: info@tafesa.edu.au
Phone: 180 088 2661
Address: 39 Light Square, Adelaide, AU
Information: TheatresAC Arts has two main theatre spaces. These are used for in house performances and also for professional productions especially during the Adelaide Fringe and the Adelaide Festival.The 'Main Theatre' is a proscenium arch theatre that seats 220 and the 'X Space' experimental theatre that seats 110.
Country: Australia
Contact: Dean Joanne
Contact: Chairperson Joanne Denley
Contact: Chief Executive David Coltman
Phone: 088 207 8888
Social Media: https://twitter.com/ac_arts www.facebook.com/adelaidecollegeofthearts
Capacity: 251-500
Policies: Present and Produce

Adelaide Convention Centre
Website: https://www.adelaidecc.com.au/
Email:
Sales@avmc.com.au
Phone: 882 124 099
Address: 128 King William Street Adelaide
Information: Opened in June 1987, the Adelaide Convention Centre was the first purpose-built convention centre in Australia

Country: Australia
Contact: Director Simon Burgess
Contact: General Manager Coralie Cheney
Social Media: https://twitter.com/AdlConv www.facebook.com/AdelaideConventionCentre https://www.instagram.com/adlconv/

Adelaide Entertainment Centre
Website: www.theaec.net
Email: reception@theaec.net
Phone: 882 082 222
Address: Corner Port Rd and Adam St Hindmarsh, South Australia
Information: Adelaide's best concert and theatre venue. It is the most flexible venue of its type in Australia, boasting an arena and theatre. The unique operational capabilities and flexible labour hiring arrangements enable the Adelaide Entertainment Centre to offer the most competitive and accommodating venue hiring deals in Australia.
Country: Australia
Contact: General Manager Phil King
Phone: 088 208 2222
Social Media: www.facebook.com/AdelaideEntertainmentCentre
Disabled Access: Yes
Capacity: 1000+
Annual Performances: 25-50
Policies: Rent and Present

Adelaide Festival Centre
Website: www.adelaidefestivalcentre.com.au
Email: feedback@adelaidefestivalcentre.com.au
Phone: 882 168 600
Address: Adelaide Festival Centre, King William St, Adelaide SA 5000, Australia
Information: Adelaide Festival Centre is South Australia's principal performing arts venue and presenter of theatre, dance, music and exhibitions. It is a leading Asia Pacific cultural centre which offers a diverse programme of festival quality shows for a broad range of tastes and budgets throughout the year. Member of ISPA
Country: Australia
CEO & Artistic Director
Douglas Gautier AM
Chief Operating & Financial Officer
Carlo D'Ortenzio
Contact: Assistant Kim Thiel
Email: kim.thiel@adelaidefestivalcentre.com.au
Social Media: https://twitter.com/AdelaideFesCent www.facebook.com/FestivalCentre https://www.instagram.com/adelaidefescent/

Adelaide Town Hall
Website: www.adelaidetownhall.com.au
Email: townhall@adelaidecitycouncil.com
Phone: 882 037 590
Address: 128 King William Street, Adelaide
Information: Adelaide Town Hall is a landmark building on King William Street in Adelaide, South Australia, Australia. The Adelaide Town Hall was the venue on 1 August 1895 for the inaugural meeting of the Australasian Federation League of South Australia, this organisation having been formed at a meeting convened seven months earlier by the Australian Natives' Association in the colony.
Country: Australia
Social Media: https://www.instagram.com/adelaidetownhall/ www.facebook.com/AdelaideTownHall

Albany Entertainment Centre
Website:
www.albanyentertainment.com.au
Email: info@albanyentertainment.com.au
Phone: 898 445 005
Address: 2 Toll Place (off Princess Royal Drive), Albany, AU
Information: Albany Entertainment Centre, situated in Albany, Australia, is a perfect venue for all performing arts. It is available for hire and capable of hosting in a variety of configurations in the flexible and functional Kalyenup Studio or a cocktail function in the private and intimate Hanover Room.
Country: Australia
Social Media: https://www.instagram.com/albanyentertainment/ www.facebook.com/albanyentertainmentcentre

Albany Town Hall
Website: www.albany.wa.gov.au/utility/venues/townhall
Email:
arts@albany.wa.gov.au
Phone: 682 03850
Address: 217 York Street, Albany
Information: The Town Hall reopened to the public in early December 2020 and already the Ground Floor Galleries are fully programmed until December 2021 with staff onsite providing a concierge service. The City is excited to bring a broad range of exhibitions to the community, including the Great Southern Art Award. The first-floor hall will also be available for hire.
Country: Australia

Albert Hall
Website: ouralberthall.com
Email: events@ouralberthall.com
Phone: 026 213 0700
Address: 100 Commonwealth Ave, Yarralumla, AU
Information: Our aims are raising awareness of the national, historical, heritage, social, community, cultural and civic significance of Albert Hall and its Heritage Precinct. Advocating for community interest in the maintenance, conservation, accessibility and management of Albert Hall and its Heritage.Advocating for affordable community, cultural and civic use of Albert Hall and its Heritage. Encouraging creative and effective planning and management for a sustainable future for Albert H
Country: Australia
Social Media: www.facebook.com/Friends-of-The-Albert-Hall-151085081932759
Capacity: 251-500
Annual Performances: 100+
Policies: Rent and Present

Albury Entertainment Centre
Website: alburyentertainmentcentre.com.au
Email: entertainment@alburycity.nsw.gov.au
Phone: 260 435 610
Address: 525 Swift Street, Albury
Information: Albury Entertainment Centre is the city's premier function and performing arts venue. The venue is made up of two buildings joined by a covered walkway.
Country: Australia
Social Media: www.facebook.com/alburyentertainmentcentre

Alexander Theatre
Website: https://www.monash.edu/performing-arts-centres/our-venues/alexander-theatre/
Email: boxoffice@monash.edu
Phone: 399 051 111
Address: Building 7, Monash University, Wellington Road, AU
Information: The Alexander Theatre is one of three dedicated performance facilities at Monash University's Victorian campuses. Centrally located in the eastern suburbs it is a dynamic space that can be efficiently adapted to suit an array of performance purposes .
Country: Australia
Contact: event coordinator Sandy Coghill
Email: sandy.coghill@monash.edu
Capacity: 501-1000

ANU Arts Centre
Website: facilities.anu.edu.au/services/venue-hire
Email: venuehire@anu.edu.au
Phone: 261 255 111
Address: 105 Childers St, Acton ACT
Information: ANU Arts Centre has been working with National University Theatre Society (NUTS) and qualified student technicians to bring forward an array of significant concerns in relation to ANU Arts Centre. The Arts Centre is located next to the ANUSA Student Space in Union Court, and was historically used for ANU drama courses, which have now mostly been cut from the University's course offerings.
Country: Australia
Capacity: 1000+
Annual Performances: 100+
Policies: All

ANU Students Union
Website: www.anuunion.com.au
Email: gm@anuunion.com.au
Address: 3 Rimmer street Canberra
Information: The Union was set up in 1965 to provide a meeting place for students, graduates and staff. The Union evolved from the Student's Association. It concentrated on small scale activities such as debates, films, music, food and even art exhibitions. The events space can accommodate up to 300 guests for all occasions, and also has 2 x large outdoor courtyards.
Country: Australia
Contact: Chair Francis Claessens
Contact: Deputy Chair Nathalie RoSales-Cheng
Contact: Public Officer and General Manager Suranga Abeygunasekara
Social Media: https://www.facebook.com/AnuUnion https://www.instagram.com/anuunion/

Araluen Arts Centre
Website: artsandmuseums.nt.gov.au/araluen-cultural-precinct
Email: araluen@nt.gov.au
Phone: 889 511 122
Address: 61 Larapinta Drive, AU
Information: Araluen Arts Centre is the focal point of Alice Springs' performing and visual arts scene, incorporating galleries and a theatre. The annual theatre program includes performances by national touring companies and many high quality local productions. The theatre is also available for the presentation of corporate functions and conferences, in association with the function room and the galleries where suitable.
Country: Australia
Contact: Director Tim Rollason

Araluen Cultural Precinct
Website: https://araluenartscentre.nt.gov.au/
Email: araluen@nt.gov.au
Phone: 889 511 122
Address: 61 Larapinta Dr, Alice Springs,
Information: The Araluen Arts Centre operates as the visual art and performance hub of Central Australia, presenting an annual program of exhibitions, performances, and film. Known as the keeping place of stories, Araluen holds within its spaces some of the most significant works of art in Central Australia and brings to the stage world class performances from around the nation (and at times the world).
Country: Australia
Contact: Senior Director Felicity Green
Contact: Publicity And Promotions Manager Lisa-Marie Burgoyne
Social Media: www.facebook.com/araluenartscentre https:// www.instagram.com/araluenartscentre/

Ararat Performing Arts Centre (Town Hall Complex)
Website: http:// www.ararattownhall.com.au/
Email: townhall@ararat.vic.gov.au
Phone: 353 522 181
Address: corner of Barkly and Vincent Streets, Ararat, AU
Information: Housed in Ararat's stately old Town Hall, the PAC attracts a rich calendar of annual events. Here, local and guest artists stage regular performances, including national touring shows and festivals.
Country: Australia
Contact: Venue Manager Jacqueline Grenfell
Email: jgrenfell@ararat.vic.gov.au
Contact: Technical Manager Tim Lewis
Email: tlewis@ararat.vic.gov.au
Social Media: https:// www.facebook.com/ararattownhall/ https:// www.instagram.com/ararattownhall/?hl=en
Disabled Access: Yes
Capacity: 501-1000
Annual Performances: 11-25
Policies: Rent and Present

Arts Centre Melbourne
Website: www.artscentremelbourne.com.au
Email: info@theartscentre.net.au
Phone: 392 818 000
Address: 100 St Kilda Rd, Melbourne
Information: Sitting beneath one of our city's great symbols – our magnificent Spire – Arts Centre Melbourne is both a defining Melbourne landmark and Australia's largest and busiest performing arts centre.
Country: Australia
Contact: President Ian Carson
Contact: CEO Claire Spencer
Contact: Executive Director, Performing Arts Melanie Smith
Social Media: https://twitter.com/artscentremelb www.facebook.com/artscentremelbourne https:// www.instagram.com/artscentremelbourne/
Disabled Access: Yes
Capacity: 1000+
Annual Performances: 100+
Annual Productions: 0-5
Policies: All

Arts Centre, Warburton
Website: https:// www.yarraranges.vic.gov.au/Experience/The-Arts/Cultural-venues/Arts-Centre-Warburton
Email: boxoffice@yarraranges.vic.gov.au
Phone: 039 294 6511
Address: 3409 Warburton Hwy, AU
Information: The much loved Arts Centre, Warburton is a beautiful complex of historic buildings with a strong entertainment program, regular exhibitions and lively community gathering. It includes the wonderfully preserved art deco Mecca Theatre, which was built in 1934 and delivers state of the art digital cinema experience to audiences most of the week. The Mechanics Institute Hall which opened with a grand ball in 1913 remains a popular dance and performance space in the complex.
Country: Australia
Social Media: https:// www.facebook.com/artscentrewarburton/
Disabled Access: Yes
Capacity: 251-500
Policies: Rent and Present

Arts House
Website: www.melbourne.vic.gov.au/artshouse
Email: artshouse@melbourne.vic.gov.au
Phone: 393 223 720
Address: North Melbourne Town Hall, Level 1, 521 Queensberry Street, AU
Information: One of Australia's most exciting presenters of cutting-edge contemporary arts with programs of performance, live art, installation and multidisciplinary work – a range of national and international offerings that nurture, support and stimulate Melbourne's cultural impact. Arts House operates across two historic venues within the City of Melbourne: North Melbourne Town Hall and the Warehouse.
Country: Australia
Contact: business Manager Brian Horder
Email: brian.horder@melbourne.vic.gov.au
Contact: creative Producer Angharad Wynne-Jones
Email: angharad.wynne-jones@melbourne.vic.gov.au
Social Media: @artshousemelb www.facebook.com/ArtsHouseMelbourne
Policies: Present, produce, co-produce, Other

Arts Queensland
Website: www.arts.qld.gov.au
Email: reception@arts.qld.gov.au
Phone: 730 344 016
Address: Level 16, 111 George Street, AU
Information: Arts Queensland is the State Government body dedicated to building a strong and diverse arts and cultural sector that celebrates Queensland's unique identity and cultural heritage. Supports arts and cultural growth through partnerships, programmes and events.
Country: Australia
Social Media: https://twitter.com/artsqueensland https:// www.facebook.com/artsqueenslandAQ/
Capacity: 1000+
Annual Performances: 100+
Policies: All

Artslink (Queensland Arts Council)
Website: www.artslinkqld.com.au
Email: info@artslinkqld.com.au
Phone: 732 549 500
Address: 1F/24 Macquarie Street, AU
Information: Multi-arts, performing and visual arts touring. Large in-schools performing arts programme, arts training programme, community access programme servicing 63 local arts councils/branches state-wide.
Country: Australia
Contact: Artistic Director Arthur Frame
Social Media: @artslinkqld www.facebook.com/artslinkqueensland
Policies: Present and produce, Produce and co-produce, Other

ASM Global
Website: https://asmglobal.com/
Email: admin@aegogden.com
Phone: 733 633 666
Address: GPO Box 1040 Brisbane Qld 4001, AU
Information: ASM Global is responsible for the management of the largest network of venues in the Asia Pacific region, which includes a network of arenas, stadiums, conventions and exhibition centres, and theatres through Australia, Asia, and the Middle East.
Country: Australia
Contact: CEO Harvey Lister
Social Media: https:// www.facebook.com/ASMGlobalLive/ https:// www.instagram.com/asmgloballive/ https://twitter.com/asmgloballive/

Athenaeum Theatre
Website: www.athenaeumtheatre.com.au/
Email: info@athenaeumtheatre.com.au
Phone: 396 501 500
Address: 188 Collins Street Melbourne Victoria
Information: The Athenaeum or Melbourne Athenaeum is one of the oldest public institutions in Victoria, Australia, founded in 1839. Its building in the Melbourne City Centre consists of a main theatre hosting a range of theatre, comedy and music performances, a small studio theatre, and a subscription library.**Country: Australia**
Social Media: https:// www.facebook.com/athenaeumtheatremelb/
Capacity: 1000+
Annual Performances: 100+
Policies: Rent and Present

Bakehouse Theatre
Website: www.bakehousetheatre.com
Email: info@bakehousetheatre.com
Phone: 882 270 505
Address: 255 Angas Street Adelaide South Australia
Information: The Bakehouse is a charming, intimate live theatre at 255 Angas Street, near the east end (Hutt Street). Combine your theatre experience with dining or just a couple of drinks after the show. The Seven Stars pub is just down the road in Angas Street. The Hutt Street restaurant strip is around the corner and we are only five minutes walk to The Garden of Unearthly Delights during Fringe time.
Country: Australia
Contact: Artistic Director Pamela Munt
Email: pamela@bakehousetheatre.com
Contact: creative Producer Peter Green
Email: peter@bakehousetheatre.com
Contact: resident technical Manager Stephen Dean
Email: stephendean60@bigpond.com
Contact: resident stage Manager Andrew Zeuner
Email: Andrew.Zeuner@sa.gov.au
Social Media: www.facebook.com/pages/Bakehouse-Theatre/149954001683155
Capacity: 100-250
Annual Performances: 100+
Policies: Rent and Present

Belconnen Community Theatre
Website: https:// www.crcs.com.au/facility/bcs-theatre/
Email: contact@crcs.com.au
Phone: 262 640 200
Address: Belconnen Community Centre, 23 Swanson Court, AU
Information: Belconnen Community Theatre is a versatile, accessible, space within the Belconnen Community Centre. The theatre is used for performances, screenings, community forums, and corporate presentations and events.
Country: Australia
Social Media: https:// www.instagram.com/capital_region_cs/ www.facebook.com/BCSACT https://twitter.com/capital_rcs/
Disabled Access: Yes
Capacity: 100-250
Policies: Rent and Present

Belvoir Amphitheatre
Website: www.belvoir.net.au/amphitheatre
Email: admin@belvoir.net.au
Phone: 892 963 033
Address: 1177 Great Northern Highway, AU
Information: The Belvoir Amphitheatre is one of Perth's most outstanding venues, creating a unique atmosphere for any event. Etched into the landscape of Western Australia's famed Swan Valley, the Belvoir Amphitheatre is the ideal location for outdoor music and community festivals, just 35 minutes from the city centre.
Country: Australia
www.facebook.com/search/web/direct_search.php?q=-Belvoir%20Amphitheatre%20Australia&source=quickselect&sid=0.11538617557493114
Policies: Rent only, Open-air

Belvoir St Theatre
Website: www.belvoir.com.au
Email: mail@belvoir.com.au
Phone: 296 983 344
Address: 18 & 25 Belvoir St, AU
Information: When the Nimrod Theatre building in Belvoir Street, Surry Hills, was threatened with redevelopment in 1984, more than 600 people – ardent theatre lovers together with arts, entertainment and media professionals – formed a syndicate to buy the building and save this unique performance space in innercity Sydney.
Country: Australia
Contact: Artistic Director Ralph Myers
Contact: General Manager Brenna Hobson
Social Media: @BelvoirSt www.facebook.com/BelvoirSt
Policies: Present, produce, co-produce, Theatre

Bondi Pavilion Community Centre
Website: www.waverley.nsw.gov.au/recreation/places_of_interest/bondi_pavilion
Email: bondipav@ozemail.com.au
Phone: 908 38400
Address: Queen Elizabeth Drive, Bondi Beach
Information: The Bondi Pavilion hosts many activities in the centre throughout the year, including theatre productions, events, festivals, art exhibitions, regular classes to attend, pottery classes, workshops, screenings and much more.
Country: Australia
Capacity: 501-1000
Policies: Rent and Present

Brisbane Arts Theatre
Website: www.artstheatre.com.au
Email: info@artstheatre.com.au
Phone: 733 692 344
Address: 210 Petrie Terrace, Brisbane, AU
Information: Brisbane Arts Theatre was founded in 1936 as Brisbane Amateur Theatre by Jean Trundle and Vic Hardgraves. The company's name was changed in 1947. Its early seasons up until the early 1960s consisted of five productions, each with three-night seasons in venues such as All Saint's Hall, Princess Theatre, Theatre Royal and Albert Hall. It also presented 12 to 14 performances of an annual junior Shakespeare play and three one act plays throughout its season at various venues, including the Brisbane branch of the Royal Over-Seas League.
Country: Australia
Contact: Artistic Director John Boyce
Email: john.boyce@artstheatre.com.au
Contact: Admin Assistant Ava Moschetti
Email: ava.moschetti@artstheatre.com.au
Social Media: https://twitter.com/artstheatre www.facebook.com/artstheatre https:// www.instagram.com/artstheatre/
Capacity: 100-250
Annual Performances: 100+
Policies: Present and Produce

Brisbane City Hall
Website: www.brisbane.qld.gov.au/facilities-recreation/parks-venues/brisbane-city-hall
Email: enquiries@brisbane.qld.gov.au
Phone: 734 038 888
Address: 64 Adelaide St, Brisbane, AU
Information: Brisbane's first town hall was built in 1864, but this Town Hall was not opened until 1930. The magnificent clock and tower have recently been restored. The three-storey Brisbane City Hall holds a circular concert hall, with imPressive gallery seating, and great acoustics. Sit near the lions "on guard" at the front entrance and count the Corinthian columns across the facade.

Country: Australia
Capacity: 1000+
Annual Performances: 100+
Policies: Rent and Present

Brisbane Convention & Exhibition Centre
Website: www.bcec.com.au
Email: Sales@bcec.com.au
Phone: 733 083 000
Address: Cnr Merivale and Glenelg Streets, Brisbane Queensland, AU
Information: The Brisbane Convention & Exhibition Centre is a world-class purpose-built venue renowned for its operational and service excellence. The Centre is located in a unique urban cultural and entertainment precinct in the heart of Brisbane.
Country: Australia
Social Media: https://twitter.com/BCEC_Brisbane www.facebook.com/TheBCEC https://www.instagram.com/bcec_brisbane/
Disabled Access: Yes
Capacity: 1000+
Policies: Rent only

Brisbane Entertainment Centre
Website: www.brisent.com.au
Email: bec@brisent.com.au
Phone: 732 658 111
Address: 1 Melaleuca Drive, Boondall QLD
Information: The Brisbane Entertainment Centre is a multi-purpose arena located in Boondall, a Brisbane City suburb, in Queensland, Australia. It is managed by AEG Ogden. The arena has an array of seating plans which facilitate the comfort of its users, subject to performance. Specific seating plans are usually allocated, depending on the performance and the size of its audience.
Country: Australia
Social Media: www.facebook.com/BrisbaneEntertainmentCentre https://www.instagram.com/brisentcent/
Disabled Access: Yes
Capacity: 1000+
Annual Performances: 25-50
Policies: Rent and Present

Brisbane Jazz Club
Website: www.brisbanejazzclub.com.au
Email: info@brisbanejazzclub.com.au
Phone: 733 912 006
Address: 1 Annie St, Kangaroo Point, AU
Information: Brisbane's home of jazz! Back at our Kangaroo Point clubhouse with accessible entrance, toilets and upgraded bar.
Join us for LIVE JAZZ – every Thursday Friday, Saturday night and Sunday Sunset Session from 2.30pm!!!
Country: Australia
Contact: President Paul Day
Contact: vice President Alan Western
Contact: Artistic Director Malcolm Wood
Contact: Marketing Officer Naomi Doessel
Social Media: https://www.instagram.com/brisjazzclub/ https://www.facebook.com/BrisbaneJazzClub
Disabled Access: Yes
Capacity: 100-250
Annual Performances: 100+
Policies: Rent and Present

Brisbane Powerhouse Centre for the Arts
Website: www.brisbanepowerhouse.org
Email: info@brisbanepowerhouse.org
Phone:
733 588 622
Address: 119 Lamington Street, New Farm, AU
Information: Brisbane Powerhouse is Queensland's home for contemporary culture, a magnificent power station of the 1920s reborn as an arts centre on the Brisbane River.
With over 1, 250 performances and events each year, we are one of the busiest arts venues in the Asia-Pacific region. We offer a year-round program featuring events across music, comedy, Writers+Ideas, dance, film, visual arts, cabaret, circus, and theatre.
Country: Australia
Contact: Chair Valmay Hill
Email: info@brisbanepowerhouse.org
Contact: CEO Fiona Maxwell
Email: info@brisbanepowerhouse.org
Contact: RECEPTION
Email: info@brisbanepowerhouse.org
Phone: 733 588 622BOX OFFICE
Email: boxoffice@brisbanepowerhouse.org
Phone: 733 588 622FUNCTIONS
Email: events@brisbanepowerhouse.org
Phone: 733 588 622
Social Media: https://www.instagram.com/bris_powerhouse/ www.facebook.com/brisbanepowerhouse https://twitter.com/Bris_Powerhouse

Brown's Mart Community Arts
Website:
www.brownsmart.com.au
Email:
admin@brownsmart.com.au
Phone: 889 815 522
Address: 12 Smith Street Darwin City, Darwin, AU

Information: Housed in one of the most significant heritage buildings in the heart of Darwin city, Brown's Mart is an iconic, much loved performance space that has been the centre of community arts development for over 40 years. As a theatre resource and service organisation, the role is to offer professional support and affordable performance space to artists and arts organisations living and working throughout the Northern Territory.
Country: Australia
Contact: Artistic Director Sean Pardy
Contact: Chief Executive Officer Sophia Hall
Contact: venue Manager Kelly Blumberg
Disabled Access: Yes
Capacity: 100-250
Policies: Rent and Present

Bunbury Regional Entertainment Centre
Website: www.bunburyentertainment.com
Email: mail@bunburyentertainment.com
Phone: 979 23111
Address: 2 Blair Street, Bunbury, AU
Information: The Bunbury Regional Entertainment Centre is bringing the community the best of live theatre, music, comedy, contemporary dance, ballet, film, pantomime, drama, acrobatics, circus and much more.
Country: Australia
Contact: Executive Director Fiona de Garis
Contact: Event Manager Suzanne Clark
Social Media: https://twitter.com/brecbunbury/ https://www.instagram.com/brecbunbury/ https://www.facebook.com/brecbunbury/
Disabled Access: Yes
Capacity: 1000+
Annual Performances: 100+
Policies: All

Burdekin Theatre
Website: www.burdekintheatre.com.au
Email: burdekin.theatre@burdekin.qld.gov.au
Phone: 074 783 9880
Address: 161 Queen Street, Ayr QLD
Information: The Burdekin Theatre is the home of arts and entertainment in the Burdekin Region playing host to a diverse range of live performances, conferences, meetings, seminars, exhibitions and many local events.
Country: Australia
Social Media: https://www.instagram.com/burdekintheatre/ www.facebook.com/BurdekinTheatre
Capacity: 1000+
Annual Performances: 51-100
Policies: Rent and Present

Burnie Arts & Function Centre
Website: www.burniearts.net
Email: arts@burnie.net
Phone: 364 305 850
Address: 77-79 Wilmot Street, Burnie
Information: In 1976 the Burnie Civic Centre was officially opened and was the first purpose-built fully professional regional arts centre in Tasmania. The Centre incorporated a performing arts and functions venue and an art gallery. It is the only venue in the north west of the state, which is able to host large-scale indoor functions.
Country: Australia
Contact: General Manager Ben Turnbull
Email: arts@burnie.net
Social Media: www.facebook.com/pages/Burnie-Arts-Function-Centre/197439843607158 https://www.instagram.com/burniearts/

Cairns Civic Theatre
Website: https://www.cairns.qld.gov.au/CPAC
Email: events@cairnsperformingartscentre.com.au
Phone: 740 507 775
Address: Sheridan St & Florence St, PO Box 359, AU
Information: CPAC is Cairns Regional Council's leading performance arts venue. CPAC stands on the site of the former Cairns Civic Theatre which operated from 1974 – 2016.
Country: Australia
Contact: creative venues Manager Stephen Foster
Email: S.Foster@cairns.qld.gov.au
Social Media: www.facebook.com/CairnsCivicTheatre https://www.instagram.com/cairnsperformingarts/
Disabled Access: Yes
Capacity: 1000+
Annual Performances: 100+
Policies: Rent and Present

Canberra Theatre Centre
Website: www.canberratheatrecentre.com.au
Email: media@canberratheatrecentre.com.au
Phone: 262 752 700
Address: Civic Square, London Circuit, AU
Information: Canberra Theatre Centre includes the 1, 239 seat Canberra Theatre, The Playhouse seating 614 and The Courtyard Studio, an intimate rehearsal and performance space that seats up to 92 patrons. The Link connects the Canberra Theatre and The Playhouse and includes exhibition and function areas. The Centre also has a comprehensive technical workshop, backstage and dressing room areas, and is fully equipped with up-to-date lighting and audio facilities.
Country: Australia

Contact: Director Alex Budd
Email: alex.budd@act.gov.au
Contact: programming Manager Gill Hugonnet
Email: gill.hugonnet@act.gov.au
Contact: Technical Director Rohan Cutler
Email: rohan.cutler@act.gov.au
Discovery & Learning Program Manager Annabel Scholes
Email: annabel.scholes@act.gov.au
Contact: Marketing Manager Adriana Law
Email: adriana.law@act.gov.au
Social Media: https://www.twitter.com/canberratheatre?lang=en www.facebook.com/canberratheatrecentre https://www.instagram.com/canberratheatrecentre/
Disabled Access: Yes
Capacity: 1000+
Annual Performances: 100+
Policies: Rent and Present

Canberra Youth Theatre
Website: www.cytc.net
Email: info@cytc.net
Phone: 262 485 057
Address: H Block Gorman House, Batman St, AU
Information: Canberra Youth Theatre is for young creatives aged 7–25 who are passionate about theatre and the performing arts. Since 1972, we have provided high-quality productions and training courses with a focus on individual exPression.Our community produces intelligent theatre that is inspired by you – the youth of today. We challenge you to find your inner voice. We want you to be heard.
Country: Australia
Contact: Artistic Director Luke Rogers
Email: luke@storieslikethese.com
Social Media: https://twitter.com/cyt_canberra?lang=en www.facebook.com/CanberraYouthTheatre https://www.instagram.com/canberrayouththeatre/

Capella Cultural Centre
Website: www.capellaentertainment.com.au
Email: culturalcentre@bigpond.com
Phone: 749 849 300
Address: 89 Peak Downs St, Capella QLD
Information: International acts, big name entertainers, ballet, rock bands, eisteddfods, the latest release movies and more ! They all visit Capella and perform in the very well-appointed Capella Cultural Centre.
Country: Australia
Social Media: https://www.facebook.com/capellaqueensland/
Capacity: 501-1000
Policies: Rent and Present

Capital Venues and Events
Website: https://www.bendigoregion.com.au/arts-culture-theatres/space/the-capital
Email: bendigovenuesandevents@bendigo.vic.gov.au
Phone: 354 346 100
Address: 50 View Street, Bendigo
Information: Bendigo Venues & Events maintains some of the city's most important and historic venues including: The Capital, Bendigo Bank Theatre, The Engine Room, Dudley House, Ulumbarra Theatre and Bendigo Town Hall.The City of Greater Bendigo and Bendigo Senior Secondary College are proud to announce the name of the latest addition to Bendigo's thriving arts and cultural sector, Ulumbarra Theatre.
Country: Australia
Contact: Manager David Lloyd
Email: bendigovenuesandevents@bendigo.vic.gov.au
Social Media: https://www.instagram.com/capitalbendigo/?hl=en https://www.facebook.com/TheCapital-Bendigo

Capitol Theatre – Sydney
Website: www.capitoltheatre.com.au
Email: capitol@ctm.com.au
Phone: 293 205 000
Address: 13 Campbell St, AU
Information: Sydney's beautiful historic Capitol Theatre is host to world class musicals, theatre & ballet. Australian family owned & operated by Foundation Theatres.
Country: Australia
Head of Ticketing & Marketing ANASTASIA KOTYCHEVA
Contact: Executive Assisant KAREN MURPHY
Contact: Head of Patron Services KEVIN FOKES
Contact: Head of Venue Facilities MATT DANKS
Head of Food & Beverage Operations PAMELA WARING
Social Media: www.facebook.com/CapitolTheatreSydneytwitter.com/CapitolSydneyinstagram.com/capitoltheatresydney/
Disabled Access: Yes
Capacity: 1000+

Carnarvon Civic Centre
Website: https://www.carnarvon.wa.gov.au/Civic-Centre
Email: civiccentre@carnarvon.wa.gov.au
Phone: 899 414 200
Address: 1 Camel La Carnarvon, WA, Au

Information: The Carnarvon Civic Centre is located on the corner of Robinson Street and Camel Lane, Carnarvon, Western Australia. The Centre has two venues: The Camel Lane Theatre, a proscenium arch theatre, and digital surround sound cinema, with tiered seating for 300. And the Woolshed: A multipurpose hall with a maximum capacity of 450.
Country: Australia
Contact: Chief Executive officer Gary Martin
Email: martin.g@carnarvon.wa.gov.au
Phone: 089 941 0052 Executive Manager Development Services David Perry
Email: perry.d@carnarvon.wa.gov.au
Phone: 089 941 0005
Social Media: https:// www.facebook.com/carnarvon-civiccentre/

Casula Powerhouse Arts Centre
Website: www.casulapowerhouse.com
Email: reception@casulapowerhouse.com
Phone: 287 117 123
Address: 1 Powerhouse Road, Casula
Information: Casula Powerhouse Arts Centre is a cultural facility of the Liverpool City Council. As both Producer and presenter, they highlight the skill and creativity of local artists through music, exhibitions, performances and programs. Helping to grow the creative industry in South West Sydney, they provide opportunities for new, emerging and established artists in this region, alongside internationally and nationally renowned artists and companies. Supported by the NSW Government through Create NSW.
Country: Australia
Contact: Major Events Producer Nikki Akbar
Contact: Customer Relations and Visitor Experience Supervisor Sanja Vukelja
Contact: Director Craig Donarski
Social Media: twitter.com/CasulaArts www.facebook.com/casulapowerhouse www.instagram.com/casulapowerhouse/

Chaffey Theatre
Website: www.countryarts.org.au/venue-page/chaffey-theatre
Email: chaffey@countryarts.org.au
Phone: 885 861 800
Address: Seventeenth Street, PO Box 666, AU
Information: Chaffey Theatre is a prominent entertainment venue in Renmark with regular staging of entertaining events and movies. The historic location is ideal to catch the latest Hollywood flick or a little bit of the local talent. There is a licensed bar and facilities for disabled. The auditorium with a capacity of around 500 also hosts conferences and seminars.
Country: Australia
Contact: venue Manager Sharlene Martin
Social Media: www.facebook.com/ChaffeyTheatre
Policies: Theatre

Chapel off Chapel
Website: www.chapeloffchapel.com.au
Email: chapel@stonnington.vic.gov.au
Phone: 382 907 000
Address: 12 Little Chapel Street, Prahran, AU
Information: Chapel Off Chapel is an important venue that showcases talented local artists. The Chapel is an old church that has been converted into a theatre, the stage is flat to the floor and there is a raked seating bank. Consisting of two theatres and a welcoming foyer, Chapel Off Chapel has been described by Australian theatre and film stalwart Geoffrey Rush as "an industrious hotbed [for the arts]". Chapel Off Chapel has earned, both nationally and internationally, an excellent reputation as a progressive arts and live entertainment venue.
Country: Australia
Social Media: https://twitter.com/ChapelOffChapel www.facebook.com/ChapelOffChapel https:// www.instagram.com/ChapelOffChapel/
Disabled Access: Yes
Capacity: 251-500
Annual Performances: 51-100
Policies: Rent and Present

City Botanic Gardens
Website: www.brisbane.qld.gov.au/facilities-recreation/parks-and-venues/parks/city-botanic-gardens
Email: botanicgardens@brisbane.qld.gov.au
Phone: 734 038 888
Address: 147 Alice St, Brisbane, AU
Information: Events at the City Botanic Gardens include concerts, exhibitions and shows at the Riverstage and the Main Rotunda. The gardens also host a wide range of fitness activities and community and family orientated festivals.
Country: Australia
Disabled Access: Yes
Capacity: 1000+
Annual Performances: 11-25
Policies: Rent and Present

City Recital Hall Angel Place
Website: https:// www.cityrecitalhall.com/
Email: admin@cityrecitalhall.com
Phone: 282 562 222

Address: 2 Angel Place, Sydney
Information: Sydney has waited for many years for an intimate chamber music hall. Located just off Pitt Street in the city, this venue which is often referred to as "Angel Place" used to be the headquarters of the Liberal Party. City Recital Hall features a rectangular auditorium, with blond wooden flooring, two levels of encircling balcony seating and a high ceiling. As well as musical events, such as those that are part of the yearly Sydney Festival, the space is also suitable for lectures and meetings and is available for private hire.
Country: Australia
Contact: Chairwoman Renata Kaldor Ao
Email: admin@cityrecitalhall.com
Contact: deputy Chair Rachel Launders
Email: admin@cityrecitalhall.com
Social Media: https://twitter.com/cityrecitalhall https:// www.facebook.com/CityRecitalHall/ https:// www.instagram.com/cityrecitalhall/

Civic Theatre Newcastle
Website: www.civictheatrenewcastle.com.au
Email: civicinfo@ncc.nsw.gov.au
Phone: 249 742 166
Address: 375 Hunter Street Newcastle NSW
Information: The dramatic Civic Theatre is one of Australia's great historic theatres and hosts a wide range of concerts, musicals, plays, dances and other events. Of state significance, the Civic has been wowing audiences for more than 80 years.
Country: Australia
Contact: Manager major venues Vanessa Hutchins
Email: vhutchins@ncc.nsw.gov.au
Contact: technical production Lachlan Thomas
Email: lthomas@ncc.nsw.gov.au
Social Media: www.facebook.com/pages/Civic-Theatre-Newcastle/157484307616925 https:// www.instagram.com/civictheatrenewcastle/
Capacity: 1000+
Annual Performances: 100+
Policies: Rent and Present

Comedy Theatre
Website: https://marrinergroup.com.au/venues/comedy-theatre
Email: reception@marrinergroup.com.au
Phone: 130 011 1011
Address: 240 Exhibition Street, Melbourne
Information: Melbourne's Comedy Theatre retains a vital place in the city's vibrant live entertainment scene. Built in 1928, the theatre is a blend of European flavours. The exterior is a replica of a Florentine palace and the interior shows a strong Spanish influence. The Comedy Theatre still maintains a lot of its original characteristics including balcony seating, a generous foyer and an elegant staircase.
Country: Australia
Social Media: www.facebook.com/pages/Comedy-Theatre-Melbourne/135499599817248
Disabled Access: Yes
Capacity: 501-1000
Annual Performances: 25-50
Policies: Rent and Present

Cowra Civic Centre
Website: www.cowraregion.com.au/home/?id=2208
Email: civiccentre@cowra.nsw.gov.au
Phone: 263 402 130
Address: 77 Darling St, Cowra
Information: The Cowra Civic Centre regularly hosts live performances, cinema screenings, civic events, balls and seminars. The centre has two spaces – the main auditorium seating 335 people and the theatrette seating up to 80 people.
Country: Australia
Contact: Manager Jonathan Llewellyn
Email: jllewellyn@cowra.nsw.gov.au
Social Media: www.facebook.com/pages/Cowra-Civic-Centre/120215784708067 https:// www.instagram.com/cowraciviccentre/
Capacity: 251-500
Annual Performances: 100+
Annual Productions: 0-5
Policies: All

Cremorne Theatre
Website: www.qpac.com.au/visiting/our-venues/cremorne-theatre
Email: info@qpac.com.au
Address: corner of Grey and Melbourne Streets, South Bank, Brisbane
Information: The Cremorne Theatre is QPAC's most adaptable venue, being able to convert from traditional proscenium to theatre-in-the-round, concert, cabaret, cinema or flat floor modes, depending on the needs of the production. With a maximum seating capacity of 312, audiences and performers can get closer to each other, making the Cremorne ideal for creative productions, cabaret, intimate concerts, theatre, launches and conversations and lectures.
Country: Australia
Disabled Access: Yes
Capacity: 251-500
Policies: Rent and Present

Critical Path
Website: https:// www.facebook.com/criticalpath2/
Email: admin@criticalpath.org.au
Phone: 293 629 403
Address: The Drill, 1c New Beach Rd, Rushcutters Bay, AU
Information: Critical Path was established in 2005 to fill a recognised gap in the independent dance sector in NSW – providing a 'critical' pathway through which professional dance-makers could innovate their choreographic practice. Ten years on, Critical Path stands proud as a unique and significant contributor to the development of contemporary choreography in Australia.
Country: Australia
Contact: Director Claire Hicks
Contact: General Manager Laura Osweiler
Contact: Producer Ozlem Bekiroglou Aldogan
Social Media: https:// www.facebook.com/criticalpath2/
Capacity: 0-100
Policies: All

Crown Theatre Perth
Website: www.crownperth.com.au
Email: enquiries@crownperth.com.au
Phone: 180 055 6688
Address: Great Eastern Hwy, Burswood, AU
Information: Crown Perth is an entertainment complex located in Burswood, Western Australia, near the Swan River. The complex consists of a casino, convention centre with meeting rooms, theatre, two ballrooms and, previously, a golf course; along with a numerous restaurants and bars. It also features two hotels: the 405-room Crown Metropol Perth and 291-room Crown Promenade Perth.
Country: Australia
Social Media: www.facebook.com/CrownPerth/

Darebin Arts & Entertainment Centre
Website: http:// www.darebin.vic.gov.au/Discover-Darebin/Spaces-and-places/Darebin-Arts-Centre
Email: dac@darebin.vic.gov.au
Phone: 847 08282
Address: 274 Gower Street, Preston, AU
Information: Darebin Arts & Entertainment Centre is a splendid events centre located in central Preston. This state-of-the-art events venue comprises of several smaller event spaces that serve as function halls for conferences, seminars, training sessions, banquets and exhibitions. There's also a well-equipped theater on-site that plays host to dramas, comedies, concerts, gigs and music sessions. Several popular theater personalities and stalwarts from the music as well as corporate industry frequent the center quite often.
Country: Australia
Social Media: https:// www.facebook.com/DarebinArtsCentre/
Disabled Access: Yes
Capacity: 501-1000
Annual Performances: 25-50
Policies: Rent and Present

Darling Harbour
Website: www.darlingharbour.com.au
Email: info@shfa.nsw.gov.au
Phone: 292 408 500
Address: Darling Harbour, Sydney, AU
Information: Darling Harbour is Sydney's favourite destination for leisure and entertainment with more than 40 restaurants, 30 bars, cafes, museums, theatres, shops and parks. Proudly managed by Sydney Harbour Foreshore Authority.
Country: Australia
Social Media: https:// www.instagram.com/darlingharbour/ www.facebook.com/DarlingHarbourSydney https://twitter.com/darlingharbour
Capacity: 1000+
Policies: Rent only

Darwin Entertainment Centre
Website: www.yourcentre.com.au
Email: admin@yourcentre.com.au
Phone: 889 803 333
Address: 93 Mitchell Street Darwin
Information: Darwin Entertainment Centre is the premier entertainment venue in the Top End. Located in the heart of the city in the Mitchell Street entertainment district, this world-class venue plays host to a variety of local, national and international acts.
Country: Australia
Social Media: https://twitter.com/darwinentcentre www.facebook.com/yourcentre https:// www.instagram.com/darwinentertainmentcentre/
Capacity: 1000+
Annual Performances: 100+
Policies: Rent and Present

Derby Civic Centre
Website: www.sdwk.wa.gov.au/facilities/communitysportsfacilities/derbyciviccentre.html
Email: sdwk@sdwk.wa.gov.au
Phone: 891 910 999
Address: 30 Loch Street, Derby WA 6728, AU
Information: The Derby Civic Centre caters for a wide range of activities and functions. It is equipped with a stage, kitchen, bar and storage area. Tables and Chairs

are also provided

Don Russell Performing Arts Centre
Website: https:// www.gosnells.wa.gov.au/Lifestyle/
Leisure_Activities/Theatre_-_Don_Russell_Perform-
ing_Arts_Centre
Email: drpac@gosnells.wa.gov.au
Phone: 949 89414
Address: Lot 13, Murdoch Road, gosnells
Information: The Don Russell Performing Arts Centre is
located in Thornlie, with free parking, nearby restaurants
and is serviced by a bus route. The Centre presents
national touring shows, monthly Morning Melodies
performances and local theatre productions.
Country: Australia
Social Media: https:// www.facebook.com/drpac.cog/
Capacity: 100-250
Annual Performances: 51-100
Policies: Rent and Present

Dubbo Regional Theatre And Convention Centre
Website: www.drtcc.com.au
Email: info@drtcc.com.au
Phone: 268 014 378
Address: 155 Darling Street, Dubbo
Information: A venue for various events, Dubbo Re-
gional Theatre and Convention Centre is equipped with
a huge stage with a dressing room, a sound and light
control room and refreshment bar. The venue can be
used for various cultural events, workshops and musical
shows.
Country: Australia
Contact: operations co-ordinator Linda Christof
Email: linda.christof@dubbo.nsw.gov.au
Contact: technical and production co-ordinator David
Brown
Email: david.brown@dubbo.nsw.gov.au
Contact: front-of-house/functions co-ordinator Scott
McTiernan
Email: scott.mctiernan@dubbo.nsw.gov.au
Social Media: https://twitter.com/drtcc?lang=ga www.
facebook.com https:// www.instagram.com/drtcc/?hl=en
Capacity: 501-1000
Annual Performances: 100+
Policies: Rent and Present

Dunstan Playhouse
Website: https:// www.adelaidefestivalcentre.com.
au/venues/dunstan-playhouse/?v=Dunstan%20Play-
house&t=events&a=-1%2C19
Email: venue.Sales@adelaidefestivalcentre.com.au
Phone: 882 168 600
Address: Festival Dr, Adelaide
Information: An intimate venue, seating 590 people in
two levels. State Theatre of South Australia has been
based here since 1974 and uses the theatre, the rehearsal
rooms and the extensive production workshop also
housed in this second 'shell'.
Country: Australia
Disabled Access: Yes
Capacity: 501-1000
Policies: All

Eastbank Centre
Website: www.riverlinksvenues.com.au/venue_infor-
mation/eastbank_centre/
Email: admin@riverlinksvenues.com.au
Phone: 358 329 511
Address: 70 Welsford Street, AU
Information: With an extensive calendar of performanc-
es programmed for both Eastbank in Shepparton and
Westside in Mooroopna, Riverlinks has a reputation
for delivering one of the best arts and entertainment
programs in regional Australia.
Whether you are interested in experiencing some
live music, stand-up comedy, performing arts, or
family-friendly shows, you are sure to find an event at
Riverlinks.
Country: Australia
Social Media: www.facebook.com/riverlinks
Disabled Access: Yes
Capacity: 501-1000
Policies: All

Echuca Paramount Cinema and Performing Arts Centre
Website: www.echucaparamount.com
Email: cinemas@echucaparamount.com
Phone: 354 823 399
Address: 392 High Street, Echuca, Victoria
Information: A multipurpose venue that can hold
numerous events or functions. Located in the historic
river-port town of Echuca, offering both movies and live
entertainment. The Echuca Paramount is THE destination
for entertainment needs.
Country: Australia
Social Media: www.facebook.com/EchucaPara-
mount?ref=hl
Capacity: 501-1000
Policies: Present

Elder Hall
Website: music.adelaide.edu.au/concerts
Email: music@adelaide.edu.au
Phone:

883 135 995
Address: North Terrace, The University of Adelaide
Information: Known primarily as a concert and performance venue, Elder Hall is equipped with state-of-
the-art audiovisual capabilities and a range of flexible,
functional spaces that can be adapted to a variety of
needs. It has a capacity of 660 seats and is suitable for
professional, amateur and educational groups
Country: Australia
Social Media: https:// www.instagram.com/eldercon-
servatorium/ https:// www.facebook.com/ElderConserv-
atorium
Capacity: 501-1000
Annual Performances: 25-50
Policies: All

Emporium Function Centre
Website: www.emporiumfunctioncentre.com.au
Email: enquiries@emporiumevents.com.au
Phone: 297 085 555
Address: Level 1, 258 South Terrace Bankstown
Information: Emporium Function Centre is a venue for
various events like weddings, engagements, christen-
ings, corporate, school formals, special events, fundrais-
ers & outdoor catering.
Country: Australia
Social Media: www.facebook.com/emporiumfunction-
centre
Capacity: 251-500
Policies: Rent only

Enmore Theatre
Website: www.enmoretheatre.com.au
Email: boxoffice@centuryvenues.com.au
Phone: 295 503 666
Address: 118-132 Enmore Road, Newtown
Information: The Enmore Theatre is located in the New-
town Entertainment Precinct, Sydney's unique heartland
of live performance, music cinemas, restaurant, bars,
cafes and hotels. Historic King St and Enmore Rd play
host to this vibrant nightlife.
Country: Australia
Social Media: www.facebook.com/enmoretheatre
https:// www.instagram.com/enmore_theatre/
Disabled Access: Yes
Capacity: 1000+
Annual Performances: 100+
Policies: Rent and Present

Erindale Theatre
Website: https:// www.erindaletheatrecanberra.com.
au/
Email: info@erindaletheatrecanberra.com.au
Phone: 261 422 948
Address: McBryde Cres, Wanniassa, AU
Information: The Erindale Theatre opened as a part of
the Erindale Complex on June 24, 1979 with a gala per-
formance of the Australian Ballet. Since then, the theatre
has become a centre for both local community groups
and theatrical productions from the Tuggeranong and
Canberra region as well as interstate touring companies.
Country: Australia
Social Media: https://twitter.com/theatreerindale www.
facebook.com/ErindaleTheatre https:// www.instagram.
com/theatreerindale
Disabled Access: Yes
Capacity: 501-1000
Annual Productions: 100+
Policies: All

Esperance Civic Centre
Website: www.esperance.wa.gov.au/civic-centre
Email: civiccentre@esperance.wa.gov.au
Phone: 890 831 566
Address: Council Place Esperance, WA
Information: Situated in the heart of Esperance, just
a stones throw from picturesque Esperance bay, the
Esperance Civic Centre provides the focal point of
entertainment in the south east of Western Australia. An
undercover driveway affords patrons a sheltered access
to the well appointed Auditorium Foyer, complete with
refreshment bar and luxury seating.
Country: Australia
Social Media: www.facebook.com/esperanceciviccentre
Capacity: 501-1000
Annual Performances: 11-25
Policies: Rent and Present

Eugene Goossens Hall
Website: www.abc.net.au/studiosmediaproduction/
venue/eugene_goossens_hall.html
Email: rotziokos.maria@abc.net.au
Phone: 283 335 790
Address: 700 Harris St, Ultimo Sydney
Information: Includes large recording, studio will hold
full orchestra. Designed as a performance and recording
theatre it is 400m² and has its own comprehensive
support facilities including plush, raked seating for 300,
audio recording facilities, lighting grid, green room and
rehearsal spaces.Country: Australia
Contact: Venue Coordinator Maria Rotziokos
Email: rotziokos.maria@abc.net.au
Phone: 028 333 5790
 National Manager Productions, ABC Studios & Media

Production
 Julianne Goss
Events Centre at Maroochy
Website: maroochyrsl.com.au/welcome-events-centre
Email: enquiries@eventscentremaroochy.com.au
Phone: 754 432 211
Address: Memorial Avenue, Maroochydore, AU
Information: The Maroochy RSL Events Centre is a pur-
pose-built events centre, located on level one within the
award-winning Maroochy RSL, in the heart of Maroochy-
dore on the Sunshine Coast.
Country: Australia
Contact: President Michael Liddelow
Contact: Deputy President Len Thompson
Social Media: https:// www.facebook.com/rslmaroochy/
Capacity: 251-500
Annual Performances: 100+
Policies: Rent and Present

Everest Theatre
Website: www.seymourcentre.com/venues/ever-
est-theatre
Phone: 290 615 344
Address: Cnr Cleveland Street and City Road, AU
Information: Incorporating acoustic features to provide
optimum sound quality, as well as a removable forestage
that can vary the stage depth by over six metres, the
Everest can be used for music, dance and theatre
performances. It is also an ideal venue for conferences,
seminars and film-screenings.
Country: Australia
Capacity: 501-1000
Policies: Rent and Present

Exhibition Park in Canberra (EPIC)
Website: www.exhibitionparkincanberra.com
Email: infoepic@act.gov.au
Phone: 262 055 230
Address: Corner of Flemington Road and Northbourne
Avenue, Mitchell
Information: Exhibition Park In Canberra (EPIC) is a
Territory owned multi-purpose events facility, located at
the gateway to the National Capital. Establish, manage,
develop and maintain a multi-purpose exhibition
and event centre of national standard to meet the
requirements of our major clients and the community of
Canberra and the region.
Country: Australia
Contact: venue Manager Amal Davis
Email: amal.davis@act.gov.au
Contact: Events Operations Manager Kyle Robertson
Email: eventsepic@act.gov.au
Contact: Sales and Operations Manager Jacqueline Tudor
Email: infoepic@act.gov.au
Social Media: www.facebook.com/pages/Exhibi-
tion-Park-In-Canberra/144132665655605
Disabled Access: Yes
Capacity: 1000+
Policies: Rent only

Festival Hall
Website: www.festivalhall.com.au
Email: admin@festivalhall.com.au
Phone: 393 299 699
Address: 300 Dudley Street, Melbourne, AU
Information: Festival Hall is one of Melbourne's larger
concert venues and has hosted a variety of local and
international acts over many years. Festival Hall has been
used for black tie dinners, product launches, conferences, motivation sessions, art exhibitions, large Christmas
parties, religious and cultural events, and even as an
examination venue for Swinburne University. It's main
use continues to be hosting local and international
music acts.
Country: Australia
Social Media: https://twitter.com/festivalhall www.
facebook.com/FestivalHallMelbourne https:// www.
instagram.com/festivalhall/
Capacity: 1000+
Policies: Rent and Present

Fitzroy Town Hall (City of Yarra)
Website: www.yarracity.vic.gov.au/Services/Hall-book-
ings/Halls-available--costs/Fitzroy-Town-Hall-book-
ings/
Email: venuesandevents@yarracity.vic.gov.au
Phone:
920 55220
Address: 201 Napier Street, AU
Information: The Fitzroy Town Hall was rejuvenated to
its former glory in 2007. Heritage areas were sympathet-
ically restored, while modern improvements were added
including a lift, commercial kitchen, and heating and
cooling. This stunning venue is suited to many different
types of events including cocktail parties, balls and
formal dinners.
Country: Australia
Social Media: www.facebook.com/pages/Fitzroy-Town-
Hall/132950566744604
Policies: Rent only, Other

Footbridge Gallery, The
Website: https:// www.sydney.edu.au/engage/visit/
museums-theatres-galleries.html

Phone: 293 512 222
Address: The University Of Sydney, Parramatta Rd, AU
Information: The Footbridge Gallery currently offers three main 'living lab' spaces, as well as a stage for performances. The Footbridge Stage is a timber stage equipped with high-quality speakers, facing the grassed area outside the Old Geology Lecture Theatre.
Country: Australia
Capacity: 501-1000
Policies: Present

Footscray Community Arts Centre (FCAC)
Website: www.footscrayarts.com
Email: reception@footscrayarts.com
Phone: 393 628 888
Address: 45 Moreland Street, AU
Information: (FCAC) is a contemporary arts space engaging with and informed by community. All Artistic Outcomes that happen at the Centre are curated by FCAC's Programming Team. An Artistic Outcome is a programme, workshop and/or event that involves Artistic Practice. it defines Artistic Practice as a creative activity across any art form attended by the public or community of interest as either audience or participant. Rehearsal, workshop and studio spaces available.
Country: Australia
Contact: Chairperson Lyn Morgain
Contact: treasurer Neil Gardiner
Policies: Produce and rent, Arts centre

Forum Melbourne
Website: www.forummelbourne.com.au
Email: events@marrinergroup.com.au
Phone: 130 011 1011
Address: 154 Flinders St, AU
Information: Formerly the State Theatre, the Forum Theatre opened in 1929 with the largest seating capacity of any theatre in Australia. Since then the venue has been divided into two separate venues. Downstairs, Forum I is famous for its large stage, mesmerising proscenium and signature cabaret style booths. Upstairs, Forum II is a smaller venue with tiered seating, small stage, surround sound and cinema size screen.
Country: Australia
Social Media: www.facebook.com/forummelbourne/twitter.com/ForumMelbourne www.instagram.com/forummelbourne/

Frankston Arts Centre
Website: www.artscentre.frankston.vic.gov.au
Email: artscentre@frankston.vic.gov.au
Phone: 397 841 051
Address: 27-37 Davey Street, Frankston
Information: There are three Spaces at FAC in which to present peformances, Theatre-800 seats, Cube 37-200 seats and Function Centre 500 seats.
Country: Australia
Social Media: https://www.facebook.com/FrankstonArtsCentre https://twitter.com/the_fac https://www.instagram.com/the_fac/
Disabled Access: Yes
Capacity: 1000+
Annual Performances: 51-100
Policies: Rent and Present

Fremantle Arts Centre
Website: www.fac.org.au
Email: fac@fremantle.wa.gov.au
Phone: 894 329 555
Address: 1 Finnerty Street, AU
Information: FAC's prime function is as an Arts Centre. Fremantle Arts Centre grounds are open to the public 7 days a week from 10am to 5pm. The grounds and facilities are not available for weddings, meetings, or other private functions.**Country:** Australia
Contact: Director Jim Cathcart
Contact: General Manager Pete Stone
Social Media: @FreoArtsCentre www.facebook.com/fremantleartscentre
Policies: Rent only, Present and produce, Arts centre

Gasworks Theatre
Website: www.gasworks.org.au
Email: frontdesk@gasworks.org.au
Phone: 386 064 200
Address: 21 Graham Street, Albert Park VIC
Information: Gasworks Arts Park is a vibrant arts precinct producing a range of high-quality arts programs, workshops and activities for all ages. Situated in Albert Park, Melbourne, on the site of the former South Melbourne Gas Plant, Gasworks is just three kilometres from the CBD and the precinct houses four hectares of park, two theatres, three gallery spaces, a café, as well as function and workshop spaces.
Country: Australia
Contact: Chair James McCaughey
Contact: Chair Philippa Devine
Contact: Deputy Chair Michael Brett Young
Contact: Deputy Chair Janet Bolitho
Director & CEO
Tamara Jungwirth
Contact: Visual Arts Manager Tracey McIrvine
Contact: Marketing and Development Manager Devon Cartwright

Social Media: https://twitter.com/gasworksarts www.facebook.com/GasworksArtsPark
Disabled Access: Yes
Capacity: 251-500
Annual Performances: 25-50
Policies: Rent and Present

Geelong Performing Arts Centre
Website: www.gpac.org.au
Email: venuehire@gpac.org.au
Phone: 352 251 200
Address: 81 Ryrie Street, Geelong
Information: GPAC opened in 1981 with performing arts, functions, events and customer service in mind. With over nine spaces, it boasts two theatres, four conference and event spaces, a restaurant and cafe. Geelong Performing Arts Centre (GPAC) was built on the enthusiasm and commitment of the Greater Geelong Community with a need for a high quality facility for the benefit of the artists and audiences.
Country: Australia
Contact: youth and education programme coordinator Kelly Clifford
Email: kelly@gpac.org.au
Phone: 035 225 1207
Social Media: www.facebook.com/geelongperformingartscentre https://twitter.com/geelongarts https://www.instagram.com/geelongartscentre/
Capacity: 1000+
Annual Performances: 100+
Policies: Rent and Present

Genesian Theatre
Website: www.genesiantheatre.com.au
Email: gensiantheatre@hotmail.com
Phone: 130 023 7217
Address: 420 Kent St, Sydney, Australia
Information: Over the years the company has developed into a theatre providing a training ground for young theatre professionals and a place where those who love the theatre can meet, share, and extend their knowledge of the performing arts. The Genesian Theatre Company is one of Sydney's most active theatre companies. In addition to six main stage productions each year they run classes, workshops, and many other activities.
Country: Australia
Social Media: twitter.com/genesians/ www.facebook.com/pages/Genesian-Theatre/117135088344421 www.instagram.com/genesiantheatre/

George Jenkins Theatre
Website: www.artsonline.monash.edu.au/mapa/george-jenkins-theatre/
Email: georgejenkinstheatre@monash.edu
Phone: 039 904 4300
Address: Building 7, Alexander Theatre, Monash University, AU
Information: The George Jenkins Theatre, the Peninsula's Playhouse, is an intimate 426 seat venue ideal for plays, dance, concerts and conferences. Comprising a thrust stage with raked seating on three sides, this is one of those rare venues which really doesn't have a bad seat. Versatile stage access and five dressing rooms allow for movement of large casts while the seating configuration makes the venue equally ideal for conferences, lectures or other focused presentations.
Country: Australia
Contact: Theatre Manager Brett Wingfield
Capacity: 251-500
Policies: Rent and Present

Gladstone Entertainment Centre
Website: https://gladstoneentertainment.com/
Email: geccboxoffice@gladstonerc.qld.gov.au
Phone: 749 722 822
Address: 56 Goondoon Street Gladstone, QLD, Australia
Information: Gladstone Entertainment Convention Centre is Central Queensland's Premium business and entertainment venue, and central QLD's only fully integrated convention and entertainment centre.
Country: Australia
Social Media: @GladstoneECC www.facebook.com/GladstoneEntertainmentCentre https://www.instagram.com/liveatgecc/?hl=en
Capacity: 501-1000
Annual Performances: 25-50
Policies: Rent and Present

Glen Street Theatre
Website: www.glenstreet.com.au
Email: admin@glenstreet.com.au
Phone: 997 51455
Address: Corner of Glen Street & Blackbutts Road, Belrose
Information: The theatre comprises a comfortable 400-seat tiered auditorium configured in a slight fan-shape, which allows excellent sight lines from every angle. The stage is framed by a traditional proscenium arch and includes an orchestra pit which can be covered to provide a thrust stage. The theatre is equipped with substantial lighting and sound facilities to stage large and small productions, as well as access services including wheelChair seating and hearing loop facilities.
Country: Australia

Contact: Director Belinda Gibson
Email: belinda.gibson@glenstreet.com.au
Phone: 849 56598 technical Manager Nik Adams
Email: nik.adams@glenstreet.com.au
Phone: 849 56595House Operations Melissa Twells
Email: melissa.twells@glenstreet.com.au
Phone: 849 56597
Social Media: https://twitter.com/glenstreet www.facebook.com/GlenStreetTheatre https://www.instagram.com/glen.street.theatre/
Disabled Access: Yes
Capacity: 251-500
Annual Performances: 100+
Policies: Rent and Present

Golden Grove Arts Centre
Website: www.teatreegully.sa.gov.au/arts
Email: ggac@cttg.sa.gov.au
Phone: 839 77429
Address: 1 Tenison Place Golden Grove, SA,
Information: Golden Grove Arts Centre is the perfect place for events, functions, exhibitions or shows. The Centre is available for hire 7 days a week. Flexible multi-purpose venue available for a wide range of arts and cultural activities. Venue hire available.
Country: Australia
Social Media: ww.facebook.com/GGArtsCentre
Capacity: 501-1000
Policies: Rent and Present

Goldfields Arts Centre
Website: goldfieldsartscentre.com.au
Email: gac@ckb.wa.gov.au
Phone: 890 210 999
Address: 34 Cheetham Street, AU
Information: The Goldfields Arts Centre is the only multi-functional arts venue in the Goldfields region and one of only three A Class Art Galleries in regional Western Australia. The Goldfields Arts Centre was opened in November 1993 and has become a part of Kalgoorlie's landscape and lifestyle.
Country: Australia
Contact: Administration Donna Malec
Social Media: www.facebook.com/GoldfieldsArtsCentreKal
Policies: All, Multi-purpose

Gorman House Arts Centre
Website: http://www.agac.com.au/
Email: enquiry@agac.com.au
Phone: 261 820 000
Address: Gorman Arts Centre, 55 Ainslie Avenue Braddon,
Information: Gorman House Arts Centre is a significant heritage complex that has been adapted for arts use. It is occupied by some of the ACT's key arts organisations, smaller arts groups and individual artists. The Centre accommodates intimate performance spaces, dance studios and workshops, a gallery, artists' studios, small offices for arts business, meeting rooms and a weekend art, craft and second-hand market.
Country: Australia
Contact: Director Joseph Falsone
Email: joseph@agac.com.au
Contact: Business Manager Adelin Chin
Email: adelin@agac.com.au
Contact: Marketing Manager Kristi Monfries
Email: kristi@agac.com.au
Contact: Production Manager Bec Poulter
Email: rebecca.poulter@agac.com.au
Social Media: https://www.facebook.com/ainslieandgorman

Grant Street Theatre
Website: https://finearts-music.unimelb.edu.au/campus-experience/lionels-grant-street
Email: vcamcm-bookings@unimelb.edu.au
Phone: 390 359 129
Address: Grant Street, Melbourne, AU
Information: Grant Street Theatre, located in the "arts end" of town has undergone a radical revamp with a new destination bar, lounge and theatre space open to public, artists and audiences alike in Melbourne .
Country: Australia
Social Media: www.facebook.com/theartsend
Capacity: 100-250
Policies: Rent and Present

Griffith Regional Theatre
Website: www.griffithregionaltheatre.com.au
Email: theatre@griffith.nsw.gov.au
Phone: 269 628 444
Address: 1 Neville Place, PO Box 2283, AU
Information: Griffith Regional Theatre is a multi-purpose venue with two performance areas, a comfortable foyer with a licensed bar and is a perfect venue for your next night out, concert, production, conference, seminar, workshop, product launch or presentation.
Country: Australia
Manager theatre & gallery
Sarah Boon
Email: sarah.boon@griffith.nsw.gov.au
Contact: theatre coordinator Shannon King
Email: shannon.king@griffith.nsw.gov.au

Social Media: @GriffithTheatre www.facebook.com/
GriffithRegionalTheatre

Hamilton Performing Arts Centre
Website: www.hamiltonpac.com.au
Email: info@hamiltonpac.com.au
Phone: 355 730 429
Address: 113 Brown Street Hamilton
Information: Hamilton's major venue for a wide variety
of both touring and local performances, conferences,
exhibitions, meetings and social functions.
Country: Australia
Social Media: https:// www.facebook.com/hamiltonpac/
https:// www.instagram.com/hamiltonperformingarts/
Capacity: 501-1000

Her Majesty's Theatre
Website: www.hmt.com.au
Email: admin@hmt.com.au
Phone: 386 433 300
Address: 219 Exhibition Street Melbourne Victoria
Information: Her Majesty's Theatre, one of Melbourne's
iconic heritage theatres, and host to some of the world's
finest shows, can make your night out a royal affair.
Whether an intimate night for two, or a large corporate
event, our hospitality team offer a range of functions
and events designed to complete the perfect theatre
experience.
Country: Australia
Contact: Chair Mike Walsh
Contact: Executive Director Martin Gordon
Contact: Chief Operating Officer Nigel Hordern
Social Media: www.facebook.com/hmtmelb https://
www.instagram.com/hmt_melb/
Disabled Access: Yes
Annual Productions: 0-5
Policies: All

His Majesty's Theatre
Website: https:// www.ptt.wa.gov.au/venues/his-maj-
estys-theatre/
Email: hmt@ptt.wa.gov.au
Phone: 892 650 900
Address: 825 Hay Street, Perth, Western Australia
Information: The iconic His Majesty's Theatre, or the
Maj as it is affectionately known, is the only remaining
working Edwardian theatre in Australia and is home to
WA Ballet and WA Opera. It is the perfect venue to catch
a first class show ranging from comedy, drama, dance
and opera or an evening of cabaret DownStairs at the
Maj. Patrons can also submerge themselves in a treasure
trove of dazzling theatre history at the Museum of
Performing Arts.
Country: Australia
Contact: Venue Operations Manager Alex Lehmann
Email: Alex.Lehmann@ptt.wa.gov.au
Phone: 089 265 0905Functions Jane Duffield
Email: Jane.Duffield@ptt.wa.gov.au
Phone: 089 265 0900
Social Media: https://twitter.com/hismajestyt?lang=en
www.facebook.com/hismajestystheatre
Disabled Access: Yes
Capacity: 1000+
Annual Performances: 100+
Policies: All

Hopgood Theatre
Website: www.countryarts.org.au/venue-page/hop-
good-theatre
Email: noarlunga@countryarts.org.au
Phone: 087 009 4400
Address: Ramsay Place, Noarlunga Centre, South
Australia
Information: Named after Dr Don Hopgood and his
late wife, Raelene for their considerable services to the
community and art scene, the Hopgood Theatre is a
beautiful theatre in the south of Adelaide. Just 35
minute drive from the CBD, this theatre has housed
professional productions by the State Theatre Company,
Melbourne Comedy Festival, HIT Productions and Perth
Theatre Company, as well as many others. It is also a
great community based Venue, providing affordable
venue services to dance companies, community theatre
groups and schools. The Hopgood Theatre remains an
excellent and well-maintained Venue, and is currently
being managed by Country Arts SA.
Country: Australia
Contact: Arts Centres Leader Sussan Baldwin
Email: sussan.baldwin@countryarts.org.au
Contact: Administrative Officer Lauren Grant
Email: lauren.grant@countryarts.org.au
Contact: Theatre Technician Tom Bayford
Email: tom.bayford@countryarts.org.au
Social Media: www.facebook.com/hopgoodtheatre
Capacity: 251-500
Annual Performances: 51-100
Policies: Rent and Present

Hordern Pavilion
Website:
www.venues.playbillvenues.com/pages/view/
hordern-pavilion/overviews
Email:
vvents@playbillvenues.com.au
Phone: 299 215 333

Address: 1 Driver Avenue, AU

Information: For hire. Features: Tiered, retractable seating with accommodation for up to 3, 500 people; General admission capacity of up 5, 500; imPressive dome
ceiling; substantial rigging and catwalk facilities; fully
air-conditioned throughout; modular, portable stage;
modern Foyer / pre-function area; ample backstage facilities offer a mezzanine level Green Room, ground level
dressing rooms and offices; level loading dock access
directly into Pavilion; vehicle access; beverage service
outlets located in foyer and pavilion; high speed cable
broadband available.
Country: Australia
Social Media: @HordernPavilion www.facebook.com/
HordernPavilion
Policies: Rent only, Multi-purpose

HOTA Home of the Arts
Website: https://hota.com.au/
Email: hello@hota.com.au
Phone: 755 884 000
Address: 135 Bundall Rd, Gold Coast, QLD
Information: HOTA was first named 'The Keith Hunt
Community Entertainment and Arts Centre' and known
as 'The Centre'. It was officially opened in December
1986 and is owned and managed by the Gold Coast City
Council. With a second name change, it then became the
'Gold Coast Arts Centre' and this name remained until
March 2010.
Country: Australia
Contact: CEO Criena Gehrke
Contact: Chairman Ned Pankhurst
Contact: deputy Chair Kate Brennan
Social Media: https://twitter.com/hotagc/ www.
facebook.com/theartscentregc https:// www.instagram.
com/hotagc/
Disabled Access: Yes
Capacity: 1000+
Policies: All

Illawarra Performing Arts Centre
Website: www.merrigong.com.au
Email: info@merrigong.com.au
Phone: 242 245 999
Address: 32 Burelli Street, Wollongong,
Information: Located in the heart of Wollongong's
Arts Precinct, Illawarra Performing Arts Centre (IPAC)
is the region's most loved and respected venue for the
performing arts. Comprising three versatile spaces, it
plays host to a variety of events, from internationally
renowned theatre, music and comedy to a wide range of
community events.
Country: Australia
Contact: Production and Technical Manager Pip Rigter
Email: prigter@merrigong.com.au
Social Media: https:// www.instagram.com/Mer-
rigongTheatreCo/ https:// www.facebook.com/Mer-
rigong/ https://twitter.com/Merrigong

Independent Theatre
Website: www.theindependent.org.au
Email: independenttheatre@wenona.nsw.edu.au
Phone: 940 94462
Address: 269 Miller Street, North Sydney, Sydney
Information: Independent Theatre has been enthralling
Adelaide audiences with top quality theatre of strong
dramatic significance since it began almost 30 years ago
in 1984. Its work covers the gamut of theatrical writing,
from Ancient Greek tragedies to Australian and world
premieres of brand new plays.
Country: Australia
Contact: Artistic Director Rob Croser
Social Media: www.facebook.com/independent.theatre
Capacity: 251-500
Annual Performances: 51-100
Annual Productions: 0-5
Policies: All

International Convention Centre Sydney
Website: www.sydentcent.com.au
Email: events@sydentcent.com.au
Phone: 292 157 100
Address: 14 Darling Drive Sydney, NSW
Information: Darling Harbour, one of Sydney's most
popular pedestrian precincts, provides many location
options to make any event a success whether it be a
commercial activation, a cultural festival, or a community
activity. Attracting more than 25 million visitors per year
this entertainment, F&B, family and retail precinct is ideal
for many occasions and Place Management NSW is on
hand to work with you to deliver memorable occasions
in extraordinary locations.
Country: Australia
Social Media: https://twitter.com/darlingharbour www.
facebook.com/sydneyentertainmentcentre https://
www.instagram.com/darlingharbour/
Capacity: 1000+
Annual Performances: 100+
Policies: Rent and Present

Joan Sutherland Performing Arts Centre
Website: thejoan.com.au
Email: boxoffice@penrith.city

Phone: 472 37600
Address: 597 High Street, Penrith
Information: The Joan Sutherland Performing Arts
Centre was opened in 1990 with a community celebra-
tion and a Gala Concert performance by Dame Joan
Sutherland accompanied by Richard Bonynge. The
Centre initially housed the Penrith Conservatorium of
Music, the Richard Bonynge Concert Hall and the Allan
Mullins Studio but in 2005 it was upgraded to include
the Q Theatre, extended Conservatorium facilities and a
large atrium foyer.
Country: Australia
Contact: chief Executive officer Hania Radvan
Email: CEO@jspac.com.au
Phone: 024 723 7609Marketing Director Krissie Scudds
Email: kscudds@bigpond.net.au
Contact: Venue Coordinator Jolene Harris
Email: jolene.harris@penrith.city
Contact: PR Lisa Finn Powell
Email: Lisa.FinnPowell@penrith.city
Contact: Marketing Manager Malvina Tan
Email: malvina.tan@penrith.city
Phone: 024 723 7625
Social Media: https://twitter.com/_The_Joan www.face-
book.com/JoanSutherlandPerformingArtsCentre https://
www.instagram.com/the_joan/
Capacity: 1000+
Annual Performances: 100+
Policies: All

Judith Wright Centre of Contemporary Arts
Website: www.judithwrightcentre.com
Email: jwac@arts.qld.gov.au
Phone: 738 729 000
Address: Level 2, 420 Brunswick St (Cnr Berwick St), AU
Information: Named after the celebrated poet, the
Judith Wright Centre in Brisbane is home to a unique
blend of cabaret, circus, dance, music and contemporary
performance, located right in the heart of Fortitude
Valley's creative district.
Country: Australia
Contact: events Manager Tanya-Hiroko Martin
Arts & Program Development
Gennifer Gorzula
Social Media: www.facebook.com/JudithWrightCentre
https:// www.instagram.com/judithwrightcentre/
Disabled Access: Yes
Capacity: 251-500
Annual Productions: 11-25
Policies: Rent and Present

Keith Michell Theatre
Website: www.countryarts.org.au/venue-page/north-
ern-festival-centre
Email: northern@countryarts.org.au
Phone: 886 338 500
Address: 106 Gertrude St, Port Pirie
Information: The Northern Festival Centre is a fully
equipped multi-purpose arts centre and can accommo-
date a diverse range of conferences, performing arts,
film screenings, seminars and product launches. Within
the centre are the Keith Michell Theatre, The Ballroom
and meeting rooms (Barbara Welch Room and Council
Room).
Country: Australia
Contact: Manager Jenny Stephenson
Contact: Technical Manager Graham Johnston
Contact: Technical Manager Paul Schrader
Disabled Access: Yes
Capacity: 251-500
Annual Performances: 100+
Policies: Rent and Present

Kinselas
Website: www.kinselas.com.au
Email: info@kinselas.com.au
Phone: 028 080 7060
Address: 383 Bourke Street, Taylor Square, AU
Information: One of Sydney's most iconic venues,
Kinselas boasts an intriguing history. The Chapel, with
its high and ornate art deco ceilings, is a striking tribute
to the building's history as a funeral parlour. It was the
headquarters of Charles Kinsela from 1933 until 1982
before it was redeveloped to a pub.
Country: Australia
Social Media: www.facebook.com/kinselas https://
www.instagram.com/kinselas/
Capacity: 251-500
Annual Performances: 51-100
Policies: Rent and Present

Koorliny Arts Centre
Website: www.koorliny.com.au
Email: admin@koorliny.com.au
Phone: 946 77118
Address: 10 Hutchins Way Kwinana
Information: Maintained and well-equipped resource
with a versatile range of functions. It has three theatres
including a 1000 seat amphitheatre, a 256 seat proscenium arch theatre which doubles as a cinema, and a 92
seat intimate theatre, as well as a dance studio, a number
of multi-purpose studios and a courtyard which makes
it ideal for business functions, product releases, conferences and training programs. May also be referred to as

'Kwinana Community Arts Centre'.
Country: Australia
Contact: General Manager Kate McIntosh
Email: kate@koorliny.com.au
Contact: operations Manager Jon Lambert
Email: jon@koorliny.com.au
Contact: MARKETING OFFICER Monique Mulligan
Email: monique@koorliny.com.au
Social Media: https://twitter.com/koorlinyartswa www.
facebook.com/pg/koorlinyartscentre/ https://www.
instagram.com/koorlinyartswa/
Capacity: 251-500
Annual Performances: 100+
Annual Productions: 0-5
Policies: All

Kuranda Amphitheatre
Website: https://www.kurandaamphitheatre.org/
Email: info@kurandaamphitheatre.org
Phone: 740 939 311
Address: 5 Barron Falls Road, Kuranda, AU
Information: A community venture, which has been
created, built and managed by the people of Kuranda
since 1980, the Kuranda Amphitheatre is unique in North
Queensland. It is a sculptured botanical site set in the
rainforest with a main concert stage.
Country: Australia
Contact: President Liza Dewey
Contact: Secretary Sonya Richardson
Contact: Bookings John Dunne
Social Media: www.facebook.com/KurandaAmphitheatre/twitter.com/kurandaamphithe?lang=ca

Kyneton Town Hall
Website: https://www.mrsc.vic.gov.au/See-Do/Our-Facilities/Find-A-Venue/Kyneton-Town-Hall
Email: mrsc@mrsc.vic.gov.au
Phone: 354 211 431
Address: 129 Mollison Street, Kyneton
Information: The Kyneton Town Hall is a 400 seat art
deco theatre presenting a range of art and culture events
throughout the year. The venue is managed by Macedon
Ranges Shire Council, Arts & Culture Unit. The hall is also
available to hire for festivals, functions and events. The
venue is equipped with flexible seating that enables the
right atmosphere to be achieved for any event.
Country: Australia
Social Media: https://www.facebook.com/Kyneton-Town-Hall-100461940041749/
Disabled Access: Yes
Capacity: 251-500
Annual Performances: 11-25
Policies: Rent and Present

La Boite Theatre Company
Website: www.laboite.com.au
Email: info@laboite.com.au
Phone: 730 078 600
Address: The Works Level 5, 6-8 Musk Avenue, AU
Information: La Boite's Roundhouse Theatre is an
epic-intimate space and Australia's only purpose-built
theatre-in-the-round. It's also flexible enough to be
used as a thrust stage with the audience on three sides.
This 400-seat home stage offers a distinctive theatre
experience.
Country: Australia
Contact: VENUE HIRE
Email: venuehire@laboite.com.au
Contact: EVENT
Email: events@laboite.com.au
Contact: EQUIPMENT HIRE
Email: production@laboite.com.au
Social Media: www.facebook.com/LaBoiteTheatretwitter.com/LaBoiteTheatre www.instagram.com/laboitetheatre
Capacity: 251-500
Policies: All

La Mama
Website: www.lamama.com.au
Email: info@lamama.com.au
Phone: 393 476 948
Address: Level 1, 205 Faraday Street, AU
Information: La Mama Theatre is nationally and internationally acknowledged as a crucible for cutting edge,
contemporary theatre since 1967. Valued by artists and
audiences alike, La Mama is treasured for its continued
advocacy of those seeking to explore beyond mainstream theatre. As a not-for-profit association, La Mama
is producing work by theatre makers of all backgrounds
and encouraging works that deconstruct and critique
form, content and social issues
Country: Australia
 Artistic Director & CEO
 Liz Jones
Email: liz@lamama.com.au
Contact: La mama learning Producer Maureen Hartly
Email: maureen@lamama.com.au
Contact: Co-CEO and Company Manager Caitlin Dullard
Email: caitlin@lamama.com.au
 Marketing & Communications Coordinator
 Sophia Constantine
Email: sophia@lamama.com.au
Social Media: www.facebook.com/lamama.theatre

https://twitter.com/lamamatheatre https://www.instagram.com/lamamatheatre/

Latrobe Regional Performing Arts Centre
Website: https://www.latrobe.vic.gov.au/Home/Latrobe_Performing_Arts
Email: boxoffice@latrobe.vic.gov.au
Phone: 517 63333
Address: Cnr Breed and Grey Streets, AU
Information: The centre holds two different theatre
spaces. The venue is suitable, but not limited to, such
events as theatre productions, seminars, conferences or
film screenings.
Country: Australia
Contact: Theatre Technnican Brett Tippet
Email: brett.tippet@latrobe.vic.gov.au
Phone: 035 176 3351Venue Services Officer Naomi
Kokshoorn
Email: venueoperations@latrobe.vic.gov.au
Phone: 035 176 3331
Social Media: https://www.instagram.com/latrobeperformingarts/
Capacity: 251-500
Annual Performances: 51-100
Policies: Rent and Present

Laycock Street Theatre
Website: https://www.facebook.com/laycockstreet-theatre
Email: laycock.theatre@gosford.nsw.gov.au
Phone: 432 33233
Address: 5 Laycock Street, AU
Information: Laycock Street Community Theatre is
proudly owned and operated by Central Coast Council.
Designed to provide an unrivaled level of audience
comfort and technical excellence, Laycock Street
Community Theatre produces an annual subscription
season of hand-picked, international shows and touring
productions. It's also a popular performing arts venue
for professional and amateur organisations, orchestras,
bands, schools, concerts, comedies and Gosford Musical
Society.
Country: Australia
Social Media: https://www.facebook.com/laycockstreet-theatre/
Disabled Access: Yes
Capacity: 251-500
Policies: All

Lennox Theatre
Website: www.riversideparramatta.com.au/venue/lennox-theatre/
Email: office_riverside@parracity.nsw.gov.au
Phone: 288 393 399
Address: Corner market and Church Street, AU
Information: This venue is a multi-use performance
space with flexible seating which allows a large number
of seating configurations in both theatre or cabaret
style. The seating capacity depends on the configuration
chosen by the hirer.
Country: Australia
Contact: Director Robert Love
Email: rlove_riverside@parracity.nsw.gov.au
Contact: business Manager Sainesh Moss
Email: JAnkus@cityofparramatta.nsw.gov.au
 Marketing & Communications Manager
 Henri Marron
Email: hmarron@cityofparramatta.nsw.gov.au
Capacity: 100-250
Policies: Rent and Present

Lighthouse Theatre
Website: www.lighthousetheatre.com.au
Email: lighthouse@union.mq.edu.au
Phone: 355 594 999
Address: 185 Timor Street, Warrnambool
Information: Lighthouse Theatre is southwest Victoria's
leading creative hub for Performing Arts and Culture.
With programs showcasing the very best Theatre, Dance,
Music, Comedy, Cabaret and the unexpected; we bring
together audiences and artists to experience, to create
and to celebrate.The second venue, Lighthouse Studio is
a versatile, modern, multi-purpose venue that has been
designed to accommodate anything from intimate theatre and recitals through to catered banquets, receptions
and trade shows.**Country:** Australia
Contact: Service Manager Xavier Dannock
Phone: 035 559 4887
Social Media: www.facebook.com/LighthouseTheatre
https://www.instagram.com/lighthousetheatre/
Capacity: 501-1000
Annual Performances: 100+
Policies: Rent and Present

Lismore City Hall
Website: norpa.org.au/welcome-to-lismore-city-hall
Email: info@norpa.org.au
Phone: 266 220 300
Address: 1 Bounty Street, Lismore
Information: The Lismore City Hall is the premier
performing arts venue for the Northern Rivers region,
and the performance home of NORPA (Northern Rivers
Performing Arts).
Country: Australia

Contact: Artistic Director Julian Louis
Social Media: https://www.facebook.com/norpa.lismore
https://www.instagram.com/norpalismore/ https://twitter.com/NORPAOz

Little Theatre
Website: www.adelaide.edu.au/theatreguild/location
Email: theatreguild@adelaide.edu.au
Phone: 883 135 999
Address: Gate 10, Victoria Dr, Adelaide, AU
Information: The Little Theatre is a comfortable 120-seat theatre located on the University of Adelaide's
Lower North Terrace campus, in The Cloisters. This is
a colonnaded area clearly visible from Victoria Drive
on the western side of the pedestrian lights near the
University footbridge. The Little Theatre is located in the
south-western corner of The Cloisters.
Country: Australia
Social Media: https://www.facebook.com/UoATheatreGuild https://twitter.com/UoATheatreGuild
Capacity: 100-250
Policies: Rent and Present

Llewellyn Hall
Website: llewellynhall.anu.edu.au
Email: music.venues@anu.edu.au
Phone: 261 255 767
Address: 100 William Herbert Place, The Australian
National University, AU
Information: Named after the School of Music's
founding Director, Ernest Llewellyn, Llewellyn Hall is
Canberra's premier concert venue offering one of the
finest acoustics spaces in Australia to showcase musical
performance. Llewellyn Hall has comprehensive audio
visual facilities and audio and lighting production
capabilities for conferences, panel discussions, lectures
and interviews.
Country: Australia
Social Media: www.facebook.com/pages/Llewellyn-Hall-ANU-School-of-Music/165721686812319 https://twitter.
com/anullewellyn
Capacity: 1000+
Annual Performances: 100+
Policies: Rent and Present

LW Theatres
Website: https://lwtheatres.co.uk/
Email: customer.relations@lwtheatres.co.uk
Phone: 207 557 7300
Address: Drury Ln, Covent Garden, London, UK
Information: Since we started up back in 1977, our
passion and pride for what we do has seen us become
the largest operator of musical theatres in London. In
July 2018, we officially rebranded from The Really Useful
Theatres to LW Theatres, improving the look of our
website while finding new ways to step up our service.
Operates 7 theaters in the UK.
Country: Australia
Contact: Founder Andrew Lloyd Webber
Social Media: https://twitter.com/lwtheatres https://
www.instagram.com/lwtheatres/
Capacity: 1000+
Annual Performances: 100+
Annual Productions: 100+
Policies: All

Mackay Entertainment Centre
Website: https://www.themecc.com.au/
Email: mecc@mackay.qld.gov.au
Phone: 074 961 9777
Address: Cnr Alfred St & Macalister St Mackay, QLD,
Information: The Mackay Entertainment & Convention
Centre (MECC) is located in the heart of Mackay and is
just a short stroll away from a plethora of city centre
restaurants, an award-winning Regional Art Gallery,
hotels, a library, shopping precincts and our magnificent
blue water Pioneer River. The Centre is easily accessible
via foot, car, bike or bus and approximately 10 minutes
via taxi from the Mackay Airport.
Country: Australia
Social Media: www.facebook.com/THEMECC-C?rf=325516937512766twitter.com/the_mecc www.
instagram.com/the_mecc/

Malthouse Theatre
Website: www.malthousetheatre.com.au
Email: boxoffice@malthousetheatre.com.au
Phone: 396 855 111
Address: 113 Sturt Street Southbank, AU
Information: The Malthouse—home of Malthouse Theatre—houses two theatres, rehearsal studios, meeting
rooms, a bar and a café, all in the heart of Southbank.
The Malthouse is also used as an exciting alternative to
more conventional conference facilities and reception
centres, hosting conferences, events, product launches,
and AGMs for a range of clients.
Country: Australia
Contact: EDUCATION
Email: education@malthousetheatre.com.au
 SPONSORSHIP & DONATIONS
Email: development@malthousetheatre.com.au
Contact: MARKETING
Email: Marketing@malthousetheatre.com.au
Contact: CASTING
Email: companyManager@malthousetheatre.com.au

Contact: VENUE John Byrne
Email: jbyrne@malthousetheatre.com.au
Phone: 396 855 111TS Publicity – MEDIA Tatia Sloley
Email: tatia@tspublicity.com.au
Phone: 403 305 395
Social Media: www.facebook.com/MalthouseThe-atretwitter.com/MalthouseMelbinstagram.com/malthousetheatre
Disabled Access: Yes
Capacity: 501-1000

Malvern Town Hall
Website: https://www.stonnington.vic.gov.au/Com-munity/Venue-hire/Malvern-Town-Hall
Email: venues_booking@stonnington.vic.gov.au
Phone: 829 01213
Address: 1251 High Street, Malvern
Information: The Malvern Town Hall and Banquet Hall may be hired separately or together and each venue has its own toilet and entrance facilities. A public address system comprises microphones and a five-disk CD player. A commercial kitchen is available at no additional charge.
Country: Australia
Capacity: 501-1000
Policies: Rent and Present

Mandurah Performing Arts Centre
Website: www.manpac.com.au
Email: manpac@manpac.com.au
Phone: 895 503 900
Address: Ormsby Terrace, Mandurah
Information: Mandurah Performing Arts Centre is more than a performing arts centre. It's a hub for extraordinary, dynamic and creative ideas – a centre for the arts. ManPAC is a national leader in the curation and presentation of quality arts and cultural experiences that are relevant to local artists, audiences and the community.
Country: Australia
Social Media: www.facebook.com/mandurahperformingartscentre
Capacity: 501-1000
Annual Productions: 100+
Policies: Rent and Present

Manning Entertainment Centre
Website: https://mec.midcoast.nsw.gov.au/Home
Email: mec.production@midcoast.nsw.gov.au
Phone: 265 925 466
Address: 33 Manning River Dr, Taree
Information: The Manning Entertainment Centre is a 505 seat theatre in Taree, New South Wales. The theatre is regularly used by outside hirers including local dance schools, theatre groups and primary and high schools. The theatre is also hired by a wide variety of touring professional acts from ballet to pop music, stand up comedy and tribute acts.
Country: Australia
Contact: Theatre Manager Chris Tippett
Contact: Marketing Officer Kim MacDonald
Sales & Marketing Officer.
Helen Knight
Social Media: https://www.facebook.com/ManningEnt-Cent https://www.instagram.com/manningentcent/
Capacity: 501-1000
Annual Performances: 11-25
Policies: Rent and Present

Margaret River Cultural Centre
Website: www.artsmargaretriver.com
Email: info@artsmargaretriver.com
Phone: 089 780 5294
Address: 51 Wallcliffe Road, Margaret River
Information: Arts Margaret River manages the Shire of Augusta Margaret River owned Cultural Centre. This 350 (300 downstairs and 50 upstairs) raked seating venue can be configured for concerts, theatrical productions, conferences, and community celebrations.
Country: Australia
Contact: President Arts Margaret River Helen Whitbread
Contact: General Manager
Email: Manager@artsmargaretriver.com
Contact: Finance and Administration
Email: admin@artsmargaretriver.com
R&W Festival Creative Director
Email: creative@artsmargaretriver.com
R&W Festival Events Manager
Email: festival@artsmargaretriver.com
Social Media: https://www.facebook.com/artsmargaretriver https://www.instagram.com/artsmargaretriver/

Marian Street Theatre for Young People
Website: www.mstyp.org.au
Email: info@mstyp.org.au
Phone: 294 987 671
Address: 2 Marian Street, AU
Information: MSTYP acknowledges the Traditional Owners, the Gayamaygal, Garigal and the Wallamedegal and their Country on which we operate. We show our respect to all Aboriginal people. We acknowledge their Elders in the past and in the present, and acknowledge the spirits and ancestors of those that lived in our area.
Country: Australia
Contact: Artistic Director Nate Gilkes

Social Media: www.facebook.com/marianstreetthea-tre?ref=stream https://www.instagram.com/marian-sttheatreforyoungpeople/
Capacity: 251-500
Annual Productions: 0-5
Policies: All

Marrickville Town Hall
Website: https://www.innerwest.nsw.gov.au/explore/venues-for-hire/town-halls/marrickville-town-hall
Email: bookingsteam@innerwest.nsw.gov.au
Phone: 939 25000
Address: 303 Marrickville Road, Marrickville
Information: The Marrickville Town Hall was opened on 11 February 1922, a crowning glory of Marrickville Council Diamond Jubilee. The site on which the Marrickville Town Hall now stands was originally a market garden and nursery owned by Joseph Graham, mayor of Marrickville Council a record 9 times between 1868 and 1894. Marrickville Town Hall is one of our larger community venues hosting community events and programs and offering facilities for hire.
Country: Australia
Social Media: www.facebook.com/pages/Marrickville-Town-Hall-Marrickville/158003634230870
Disabled Access: Yes
Capacity: 501-1000
Annual Performances: 51-100
Policies: Rent and Present

Melba Hall
Website: mcm.unimelb.edu.au/melba-hall
Email: mcm-concerts@unimelb.edu.au
Phone: 383 447 830
Address: Gate 12, Royal Parade, The University of Melbourne, AU
Information: Renowned for the finest acoustics for chamber music in Melbourne, Melba Hall is located in the Conservatorium Building at the Melbourne Conservatorium of Music, a grand white building on Royal Parade, dating from 1909 and classified by the National Trust of Victoria. Melba Hall houses two of the finest Concert Steinways in Melbourne, and is a highly sought after venue for solo recitals and for professional recordings.
Country: Australia
Social Media: https://www.facebook.com/Mel-ba-Hall-120872491319934/
Capacity: 251-500
Annual Performances: 100+
Policies: All

Melbourne Convention and Exhibition Centre
Website: www.mcec.com.au
Email: enquiries@mcec.com.au
Phone: 392 358 000
Address: 1 Convention Centre Place, South Wharf, Victoria
Information: MCEC is Melbourne's home of unconventional. We host more than 1, 000 events each year, each one like no other. We have beautiful spaces, innovative menus and the best people in the business. Our team are not just the best at what they do, they're the best at doing things no-one else has done before. All this comes together for moments that will stay with you long after your event.
Country: Australia
Social Media: https://twitter.com/mcec?lang=en www.facebook.com/themcec https://www.instagram.com/mcec/?hl=en
Capacity: 1000+
Annual Performances: 100+
Policies: Rent and Present

Melbourne Olympic Parks
Website: www.melbournepark.com.au
Email: Sales@mopt.vic.gov.au
Phone: 392 861 118
Address: Batman Ave Melbourne, Australia
Information: Home of the Australian Open Tennis Championship and conveniently located in the heart of Melbourne city, Melbourne & Olympic Parks offers an array of flexible function spaces to create an unparalleled event experience. Set against the magnificent backdrop of the city skyline and the Yarra River, the Melbourne & Olympic Parks precinct comprises Rod Laver Arena, Melbourne Arena, Margaret Court Arena, AAMI Park, Tennis HQ and The Vista.
Country: Australia
Social Media: www.facebook.com/pages/Melbourne-Olympic-Park-Function-Centre/222670301176317?rf=527418143950547
Capacity: 1000+
Annual Performances: 100+
Policies: Rent and Present

Melbourne Recital Centre
Website: www.melbournerecital.com.au
Email: boxoffice@melbournerecital.com.au
Phone: 396 992 228
Address: 31 Sturt Street, Southbank,
Information: Melbourne Recital Centre is an acclaimed music destination combining architectural innovation and acoustic perfection within its two world-class performance spaces to showcase the best music, artists and ensembles from around the world.

Country: Australia
Contact: Director of corporate services Sarah MacPherson
Contact: Director of Marketing and customer relations Robert Murray
Contact: Chair Andrea Hull
Contact: CEO Euan Murdoch
Social Media: https://twitter.com/melbrecital www.facebook.com/Melb.Recital.Centre https://www.instagram.com/melbrecital/

Melbourne Town Hall
Website: https://www.melbourne.vic.gov.au/community/hubs-bookable-spaces/Pages/melbourne-town-hall-rooms-for-hire.aspx
Email: melbournetownhall@epicure.com.au
Phone: 039 658 9658
Address: 90-120 Swanston St, Melbourne, AU
Information: Located in the heart of the CBD, Melbourne Town Hall is the showcase destination for the city's cultural and civic life. It plays host to theatrical performances, weddings, receptions, exhibitions, corporate launches, school concerts, conferences and cocktail parties.
Country: Australia
Capacity: 1000+
Policies: Rent and Present

Merlyn Theatre
Website: https://www.malthousetheatre.com.au/venue-hire/
Phone: 396 855 111
Address: 113 Sturt Street, AU
Information: The Merlyn Theatre is the largest of the three theatres within The Coopers Malthouse and is named after Dame Merlyn Myer DBE to mark the generosity of the Sidney Myer Fund, The Myer Foundation, and the individual members of the Myer family who made the building conversion possible. The versatile venue offers a unique seating design and stage relationship which makes it ideally suited for drama, dance, music and opera – both contemporary and classical – as well as a unique venue for conferences, product launches and private functions.
Country: Australia
Disabled Access: Yes
Capacity: 251-500
Policies: Rent and Present

Metro Arts
Website: www.metroarts.com.au
Email: info@metroarts.com.au
Phone: 730 027 100
Address: 97 Boundary Street, West End
Information: The Metro Arts Building has a range of prime CBD-located offices and studios suitable for artists, small arts organisations and creative businesses. Venues can be hired from an hourly to a monthly basis to present performances, exhibitions, workshops and rehearsals.
Country: Australia
Contact: Chairman Michael Cottier
CEO & Creative Director
Jo Thomas
Contact: Producer Matt Seery
Social Media: https://twitter.com/metroartsau www.facebook.com/metroartsbrisbane https://www.instagram.com/metroarts/
Capacity: 100-250
Annual Performances: 100+
Annual Productions: 0-5
Policies: All

Metro Theatre
Website: www.metrotheatre.com.au
Email: bookings@centuryvenues.com.au
Phone: 029 550 3666
Address: 624 George Street, Sydney
Information: The Metro Theatre has long been Sydney's leading independent rock venue and has played host to some of the most memorable live gigs Sydney music fans have seen and heard. It is a landmark venue for both international and local acts, being a pivotal breakthrough venue for bands as they break on to the scene.
Country: Australia
Social Media: https://twitter.com/metro_theatre?lang=en www.facebook.com/themetrotheatre
Capacity: 1000+
Annual Performances: 51-100
Policies: Rent and Present

Middleback Theatre
Website: www.countryarts.org.au/venue-page/middle-back-theatre
Email: middleback@countryarts.org.au
Phone: 886 447 300
Address: 141a Nicolson Ave, AU
Information: Mobility impaired patrons can be comfortably seated in the theatre, and there are dedicated toilet facilities and car parking spaces; baby change tables are available; the Cinema has an Audio Loop that delivers clearer sound to patrons with hearing aids fitted with a 'T' switch.
Country: Australia
Contact: venue Manager Ryan Sutherland

Social Media: www.facebook.com/CountryArtsSA
Policies: Rent only, Rent and present, Theatre

Mildura Arts Centre
Website: www.milduraartscentre.com.au
Email: arts_centre@mildura.vic.gov.au
Phone: 350 188 330
Address: 199 Cureton Avenue, AU
Information: Mildura Arts Centre is the leading arts and culture hub of North West Victoria. Over the past few decades, our facilities have grown from a base at the Rio Vista Historic House, to include a dedicated regional art gallery, a performing arts theatre, heritage house and sculpture park, and ongoing cultural and creative programmes for everybody.
Country: Australia
Social Media: @milduraartscntr www.facebook.com/groups/36715005666/
Policies: Present, produce, co-produce, Arts centre

Montsalvat
Website: www.montsalvat.com.au
Email: montsalvat@montsalvat.com.au
Phone: 394 397 712
Address: 7 Hillcrest Ave, Eltham
Information: Montsalvat is also a place of welcome to all – old and young, committed and curious. Everyone is invited to find peace and pleasure in Montsalvat's lovingly tended gardens, enjoy Montsalvat's exhibitions, its restaurant and hospitality, and marvel at its complex of buildings that evoke a European past while exemplifying a very Australian trait of recycling and architectural inventiveness. ory.
Country: Australia
Contact: Arts Administrator Rachel Duffy
Email: artsadministrator@montsalvat.com.au
Social Media: https:// www.instagram.com/montsalvatartscentre/ https:// www.facebook.com/montsalvatartsandevents/

Mount Isa Civic Centre
Website: www.mietv.com.au/Civic-Centre.aspx
Email: civiccentre@mountisa.qld.gov.au
Phone: 474 73300
Address: 23 West Street Mount Isa
Information: The Mount Isa Civic Centre offers a range of products and services, with a diverse range of spaces available to suit each individuals particular needs. With our venue spaces allowing for diversity in production ranging from conferences to dramatic performance, comedy or music.
Country: Australia
Social Media: https:// www.facebook.com/IsaCivic/
Capacity: 100-250
Policies: Rent and Present

Naracoorte Town Hall
Website: https:// www.naracoortelucindale.sa.gov.au/services/townhalls/naracoortetownhall
Email: council@nlc.sa.gov.au
Phone: 088 760 1100
Address: 95 Smith Street, Naracoorte
Information: Located in the centre of Naracoorte at 95 Smith Street, the Naracoorte Town Hall is ideal for a wide range of events. Spaces available for hire at the Naracoorte Town Hall are the Auditorium, Supper Room or Meeting Room or a combination of the spaces. There is also a commercial kitchen that can be utilised by hirers.
Country: Australia
venues & tourism officer
Nigel Nisbett
Capacity: 251-500
Policies: Rent and Present

National Convention Centre
Website: www.nccc.com.au
Email: nccc.Sales@ihg.com
Phone: 262 765 200
Address: 31 Constitution Avenue, Canberra, AU
Information: The National Convention Centre (NCCC) has a total 15 individual meeting rooms which offer full flexibility and adaptability, suiting any conference program or meeting room design requirements. These include some of our larger areas such as the Royal Theatre, Exhibition Hall and Ballroom, with a further selection of breakout rooms, workshops rooms and tiered theatrettes also available – Canberra's largest, purpose-built meetings venue!
Country: Australia
Contact: General Manager Stephen Wood
Email: nccc.Sales@ihg.com
Social Media: https:// www.facebook.com/CanberraNCC/

National Institute of Dramatic Art (NIDA)
Website: www.nida.edu.au
Email: info@nida.edu.au
Phone: 296 977 600
Address: 215 Anzac Parade, Kensington, AU
Information: The National Institute of Dramatic Art (NIDA) is Australia's leading centre for education and training in the performing arts. Performers and audiences benefit from the proximity between stage and the back row, making it an ideal venue for intimate

performances, as well as larger productions.
Country: Australia
Contact: Chairman Noel Staunton
Contact: CEO Liz Hughes
Contact: General Manager Alistair Graham
Contact: Head of Marketing and Communications Laetitia Shepherd
Social Media: web.facebook.com/NIDAcommunity/

National Theatre Drama School
Website: www.nationaltheatre.org.au
Email: Marketing@nationaltheatre.org.au
Phone: 395 340 221
Address: 20 Carlisle Streets, St. Kilda, AU
Information: The School offers a nationally-accredited professional training course, the full-time Advanced Diploma of Acting and a part-time professional preparation programme, as well as a range of recreational programmes for both adults and children.
Country: Australia
Contact: Chair Susan Thacore
Contact: CEO Sarah Hunt
Email: sarah.hunt@nationaltheatre.org.au
Contact: MARKETING COORDINATOR Elizabeth Millington
Email: Marketing@nationaltheatre.org.au
Social Media: https:// www.facebook.com/nationaltheatremelbourne/ https:// www.instagram.com/thenationaltheatre/ https:// twitter.com/thenattheatre/
Capacity: 1000+
Annual Performances: 100+
Policies: All

New Fortune Theatre
Website: www.theatres.uwa.edu.au/venues/fortune
Email: bookings-theatres@uwa.edu.au
Phone: 648 86000
Address: The University of Western Australia, 35 Stirling Highway, Perth Crawley, AU
Information: Located within the Faculty of Arts, Business, Law and Education, the theatre makes a unique setting for dance, drama and music. The Theatre is most suited to daylight performances at weekends. The theatre can seat up to 340 patrons on three levels around the stage.
Country: Australia
Contact: theatre Manager Rob Lines
Email: rob.lines@uwa.edu.au
Phone: 864 882 441technical Manager David Hobbs
Email: david.hobbs@uwa.edu.au
Phone: 864 882 439
Capacity: 251-500
Policies: All

New Theatre
Website: www.newtheatre.org.au
Email: mail@newtheatre.org.au
Phone: 295 193 403
Address: 542 King Street, Newtown
Information: New Theatre was set up in 1932 as the Sydney Workers Art Club, opening with the slogan "Art is a Weapon". The first full-scale production in 1933 was The Ragged Trousered Philanthropists. The theatre helped galvanise opposition to Nazism in the 1930s and led the ultimately successful fight against stage censorship from the 40s to the late 60s, culminating in the now legendary staging of the banned America Hurrah in 1968. It has produced plays on important political and human rights issues through the struggles of anti-apartheid and black deaths in custody, to political satire on the Howard government.
Country: Australia
Contact: theatre Manager Gemma Greer
Email: Manager@newtheatre.org.au
Contact: Artistic Director Louise Fischer
Email: Artistic@newtheatre.org.au
Contact: President of the management committee Rosane McNamara
Email: President@newtheatre.org.au
Social Media: twitter.com/newtheatre www.facebook.com/NewTheatreSydney www.instagram.com/newtheatresydney/

Nexus Arts Centre
Website: nexusarts.org.au
Email: info@nexusarts.org.au
Phone: 882 124 276
Address: Lion Arts Centre, Corner North Terrace & Morphett St., AU
Information: Nexus Arts began as an artists' collective, the Multicultural Arts Workers Committee, which brought together culturally diverse artists during the early days of Australia's shift from a White Australia to a multicultural policy of immigration. The collective played a significant social and cultural role at the time by nurturing the Adelaide public's appreciation of culturally diverse arts and artists, while also assisting culturally diverse artists to settle in Australia.
Country: Australia
Contact: Artistic Director Emily Tulloch
Email: emily.tulloch@nexusarts.org.au
Phone: 882 124 276General Manager Blythe Chandler
Email: blythe.chandler@nexusarts.org.au
Phone: 882 124 276Media and Venue Manager Aaron

Schuppan
Email: media@nexusarts.org.au
Phone: 882 124 276
Social Media: www.facebook.com/NexusArts https:// twitter.com/nexusarts https:// www.instagram.com/nexusarts/
Policies: All

Northern Festival Centre
Website: www.countryarts.org.au/venue-page/northern-festival-centre/
Email: northern@countryarts.org.au
Phone: 886 338 500
Address: 106 Gertrude Street, Port Pirie , AU
Information: The Northern Festival Centre is a fully equipped multi-purpose arts centre and can accommodate a diverse range of conferences, performing arts, film screenings, seminars and product launches. In addition to being one of South Australia's most important industrial and commercial centres, it has a rich and historical base, with a number of heritage listed buildings and monuments throughout the city. The region offers visitors a myriad of activities and attractions in a district steeped in history and culture.
Country: Australia
Contact: Theatre Services Officer Bianca Roeters
Email: bianca.roeters@countryarts.org.au
Contact: Theatre Technician Paul Schrader
Email: paul.schrader@countryarts.org.au
Contact: Administration Officer Janet Jansen
Email: janet.jansen@countryarts.org.au
Disabled Access: Yes
Capacity: 1000+
Annual Performances: 25-50
Policies: Rent and Present

Octagon Theatre, UWA
Website: www.uwa.edu.au/theatres/venues/octagon-theatre
Email: bookings@theatres.uwa.edu.au
Phone: 864 887 407
Address: University of Western Australia, 35 Stirling Highway, AU
Information: The Octagon Theatre is a thrust stage venue, hosting opera, classical and popular music, as well as dance, theatre, stand-up comedy and seminars. It offers unparalleled intimacy for up to 758 patrons, with no patrons more than 12 meters from the stage.
Country: Australia
Social Media: www.facebook.com/pages/Octagon-Theatre-UWA/144178582294490
Disabled Access: Yes
Capacity: 501-1000

Odeon Theatre
Website: https:// www.odeontheatre.com.au/
Email: info@odeontheatre.com.au
Address: 67 Liverpool Street Hobart
Information: Built in 1916, the Odeon is Tasmania's premier 1200-capacity live music venue, hosting world-class artists including Queens of the Stone Age, Nick Cave, Laurie Anderson and Electric Wizard.
Country: Australia
Social Media: https:// www.facebook.com/theodeontheatre/
Capacity: 1000+
Annual Performances: 11-25
Policies: Rent and Present

Orange Civic Theatre
Website: www.orange.nsw.gov.au/site/index.cfm?display=181776
Email: council@orange.nsw.gov.au
Phone: 263 938 112
Address: 135 Byng Street Orange
Information: A multi-purpose venue located in the Central West of New South Wales. The theatre offers a diverse annual programme including many local, national and international touring productions. The 502 seat auditorium is a professional, user-friendly space with racked, continental seating plan. Outlined by a traditional proscenium arch, the stage is equipped to suit most technical requirements. The Orange Civic Theatre provides access for people with disabilities and ample off-street parking. Orange Civic Theatre has installed a hearing loop which covers the entire auditorium. WheelChair access to the auditorium is on the carpark side in Row E.
Country: Australia
Social Media: www.facebook.com/orangecivictheatre
Disabled Access: Yes
Capacity: 501-1000
Annual Performances: 51-100
Policies: Rent and Present

Ormond Hall
Website: https://ormondcollective.net.au/the-hall/
Email: office@ormondcollective.net.au
Phone: 437 004 372
Address: 557 St Kilda Road, Melbourne
Information: Built in 1891, this magnificent space is a heritage-listed dance hall and theatre that has distinctive

BYOM.academy

Make your music a business!

BYOM Academy- Be Your Own Manager

A Career Program for Classical Musicians

character, whilst still moving into the modern day. Originally refurbished in the 1920s and again in 2017, the Art Deco glamour touches have been retained, creating a neutral, yet nostalgic and captivating space.
Country: Australia
Capacity: 100-250
Policies: All

PAC Australia
Website: https://paca.org.au/
Email: admin@paca.org.au
Phone: 130 066 5263
Address: PO Box 456, Strawberry Hills, AU
Information: Our Vision is that all Australian communities are connected to stories that shape and reflect their lives, their culture and the places in which they live. Our Purpose is to unlock the potential of performing arts presenters and creators to transform and expand opportunities for audiences across Australia.
Country: Australia
Contact: Executive Director Katherine Connor
Contact: Programs Manager Lynda de Koning
Chair & Public Officer
Helen O'Neil
Contact: Vice President Simon Hinton
Social Media: https:// www.facebook.com/pacaustralia/ https:// www.instagram.com/pacaustralia/
Capacity: 1000+
Annual Performances: 100+
Annual Productions: 100+
Policies: All

Parks Arts & Functions Complex, The
Website: https:// www.parksrsc.ymca.org.au/theatre/
Email: parkstheatre@ymca.org.au
Phone: 088 406 2951
Address: 2-46 Cowan Street Angle Park
Information: Revitalised in 2014 with an extensive renovation, The Parks Theatre is the first YMCA managed venue and theatre company in Australia. Located between the City of Adelaide and Port Adelaide, the Theatre coordinates an extensive arts programme for all ages, including workshops, performing arts classes, performances, films, and artist in residences, facilitating ongoing arts participation by the community.
Country: Australia
Capacity: 251-500
Annual Performances: 100+
Annual Productions: 51-100
Policies: All

Perth Concert Hall
Website: www.perthconcerthall.com.au
Email: info@perthconcerthall.com.au
Phone: 892 319 900
Address: 5 St George's Terrace, Perth
Information: Perth Concert Hall's auditorium has a total capacity of 1731 plus 160 choir stall seats. The capacity is made up of 354 seat in the Upper Gallery, 260 in the Lower Gallery and 1117 in the Stalls. The auditorium features a thrust stage. A half thrust will see the exclusion of 75 seats (the equivalent of two rows), and full thrust reduces capacity by 194 seats, the equivalent of five rows. All seating is raked to optimise each delegate's view and is suitable for plenary sessions, vehicle launches, formal dinners, cocktail parties and special breakfasts.
Country: Australia
Contact: General Manager Brendon Elmer
Contact: deputy General Manager Lorraine Rice
Contact: Marketing Campaign Specialist Dharshini Murugiah
Contact: Events Manager Penelope Briffa
Social Media: twitter.com/perthconcerthal www.facebook.com/perthconcerthallwa www.instagram.com/perthconcerthall/

Perth Institute of Contemporary Arts (PICA)
Website:
www.pica.org.au
Email: info@pica.org.au
Phone:
892 286 300
Address: 51 James Street Northbridge, AU
Information: Housed in a large and striking heritage building in the heart of Perth, Western Australia, PICA is the city's focal point for those wishing to experience the best of Australian and international visual, performance and interdisciplinary art.
Country: Australia
Contact: Director Amy Barrett-Lennard
Email: Director@pica.org.au
Contact: General Manager Jeremy Smith
Email: business@pica.org.au
Contact: Communication Manager Ryan Sandilands
Email: communications@pica.org.au
Contact: Marketing Coordinator Leslie Rigot
Email: Marketing@pica.org.au
Social Media: https://twitter.com/pica_perth www.facebook.com/PICAARTS https:// www.instagram.com/pica_perth/
Capacity: 1000+
Annual Performances: 51-100
Annual Productions: 11-25

Policies: All

Perth Theatre Trust
Website:
https:// www.ptt.wa.gov.au/
Email:
Marketing@ptt.wa.gov.au
Phone: 892 650 900
Address: 852 Hay Street, Perth, AU
Information: Perth Theatre Trust is the Venue Manager for the Perth venues including His Majesty's Theatre, Perth Concert Hall, State Theatre Centre of Western Australia, Subiaco Arts Centre and the Albany Entertainment Centre.
Country: Australia
Contact: Chair Morgan Solomon
Social Media: https:// www.facebook.com/perththeatretrust/ https:// www.instagram.com/perththeatretrust/
Disabled Access: Yes
Capacity: 1000+
Annual Performances: 100+
Policies: All

Petersham Town Hall
Website: https:// www.innerwest.nsw.gov.au/explore/venues-for-hire/town-halls/petersham-town-hall
Email: bookingsteam@innerwest.nsw.gov.au
Phone: 293 352 222
Address: 107 Crystal Street, Petersham, AU
Information: Petersham Town Hall is a unique, Art Deco Town Hall located within Petersham where you can add your own style, flair and finishing touches for any event. Located upstairs within Petersham Town Hall is the Old Council Chambers, a set back in time with a look of grandeur that is perfect for a wedding ceremony and filming.
Country: Australia
Disabled Access: Yes
Capacity: 501-1000
Policies: Rent only

Pilbeam Theatre
Website: www.seeitlive.com.au/
Email: majorvenues@rrc.qld.gov.au
Phone: 749 274 111
Address: Victoria Parade, Rockhampton
Information: The Pilbeam Theatre is Central Queensland's performing arts centre – featuring National and International touring acts, local theatrical and musical productions and everything in between. Located on the riverfront on Rockhampton's Victoria Parade, the theatre provides regional access to arts and theatre, music and comedy lovers, school groups, children, and retirees.
Country: Australia
Social Media: www.facebook.com/PilbeamTheatre
Capacity: 501-1000
Annual Performances: 100+
Policies: All

Playhouse, The
Website: canberratheatrecentre.com.au/venue/the-playhouse
Email: venuehire@canberratheatrecentre.com.au
Phone: 262 752 700
Address: 180 London Circuit, Civic Square, Canberra
Information: The Playhouse design is based on Grecian and Elizabethan architectural principles offering superb sight lines from all three levels while maintaining an intimate atmosphere. The Playhouse has traditionally housed respected companies such as Bell Shakespeare Company and is a popular venue for comedy, drama, music and dance.
Country: Australia
Disabled Access: Yes
Capacity: 501-1000
Policies: Rent and Present

Plaza Theatre
Website: www.plazatheatre.com.au
Email: krsv@plazatheatre.com.au
Phone: 655 98755
Address: 47 Bold St, Laurieton
Information: The Plaza Theatre at Laurieton was built in 1959, before this date films were exhibited across the road in the School of Arts hall. The theatre was operated by George Hastorius and Bruce Longsworth. In the early 70's Bruce Longsworth bought the other partner out. After Bruce's death in 1972 the theatre was leased out to a variety of people.
Country: Australia
Capacity: 251-500
Policies: Present

Port Hedland Civic Centre
Website: www.porthedland.wa.gov.au
Email: council@porthedland.wa.gov.au
Phone: 891 589 300
Address: 13 McGregor Street, Port Hedland
Information: The beautiful Town of Port Hedland Civic Centre Gardens are located next to the town Civic Centre, overlooking the foreshore area of Port Hedland. The large grassed space is ideal for functions and events and is available for General usage and hire to the public. Facilities include toilets, a BBQ and picnic area. Whilst the Town of Port Hedland cannot grant exclusive use of

any park, the secluded location of this particular space makes it an ideal option for those hoping to keep their function or event semi-private.
Country: Australia
Disabled Access: Yes
Capacity: 1000+
Annual Productions: 100+
Policies: All

Portland Arts Centre
Website: https://portlandartscentre.com.au/
Email: enquiry@glenelg.vic.gov.au
Phone: 355 222 263
Address: 4 Glenelg St, Portland,
Information: Owned and managed by Glenelg Shire Council, Portland Arts Centre (PAC) is situated in the heart of Portland and houses a 144 seat proscenium arch theatre – for live theatre and cinema – and a community gallery foyer space. The Glenelg Shire Council's Arts Glenelg Program aims to provide a diverse range of professional national touring performances, catering for a range of age groups and interests.
Country: Australia
Social Media: https:// www.facebook.com/portlandartscentre/
Capacity: 100-250
Annual Performances: 11-25
Policies: Rent and Present

Princess Theatre
Website: www.theprincesstheatre.com
Email: harry@thetivoli.com.au
Phone: 721 114 705
Address: 8 Annerley Road, Brisbane
Information: The Princess Theatre is a stunning and well-appointed historical building in the heart of Woolloongabba. This prestigious venue can host many types of events including weddings ceremonies and receptions, fundraisers, private parties, theatre productions, film and photoshoots and corporate seminars and functions.
Country: Australia
Contact: venue Manager Harry Upton
Email: harry@thetivoli.com.au
Phone: 721 114 705
Social Media: www.facebook.com/princesstheatrebrisbane/

Princess Theatre (Marriner Group)
Website: http://eastend.melbourne/venues/princess-theatre
Email: venues@marrinergroup.com.au
Phone: 392 999 800
Address: 163 Spring Street, Melbourne, AU
Information: Melbourne's iconic Princess Theatre is regarded by many as Melbourne's most spectacular landmark. Dating back as far as 1854, the theatre was purchased by Marriner Theatres in 1986 and plans were put in place for its total refurbishment and to ensure its future viability as a live theatre venue.
Country: Australia
Social Media: https:// www.facebook.com/Princess.Theatre.Melbourne/ https:// www.instagram.com/princess_theatre/
Disabled Access: Yes
Capacity: 1000+
Annual Performances: 100+
Policies: Rent and Present

Quarry Amphitheatre
Website: www.quarryamphitheatre.com.au
Email: admin@quarryamphitheatre.com.au
Phone: 893 857 144
Address: 1 Waldron Drive City Beach , AU
Information: The Quarry Amphitheatre began its life as a working limestone quarry in 1834 when Henry Trigg was granted 500 acres of land. Over 180 years later the quarry has become one of Perth's premier outdoor performance venues. With its soaring limestone walls, manicured lawn terraces and views across the skyline and beyond, the venue is renowned for its peaceful ambience and magnificent natural bushland setting.
Country: Australia
Social Media: https:// www.facebook.com/quarryamphitheatre/ https:// www.instagram.com/quarryamphitheatre/
Capacity: 501-1000
Policies: Rent and Present

Queens Park Theatre
Website: https://qpt.cgg.wa.gov.au/
Email: qpt@cgg.wa.gov.au
Phone: 899 566 662
Address: 75 Cathedral Avenue, Geraldton, WA,
The Queens Park Theatre venue, including amphitheatre and surrounding gardens, are available for hire for various functions, events and conferences.
The theatre auditorium itself has a seating capacity of 656 which includes the box and circle seating, it also has two large foyers with bars, a reception room and mezzanine. The amphitheatre is a perfect outdoor venue with a capacity of 300 patrons and four access points from the upper stairs and ramp access to the lower part of the amphitheatre

Country: Australia
Contact: Venues Technical Team Leader Alexander Dick
Email: alexanderd@cgg.wa.gov.au
Phone: 089 956 6610
Acting Coordinator Events & Venues
Frederick Block
Email: frederickb@cgg.wa.gov.au
Phone: 089 956 6684
Treasury & Finance Officer
Email: carolined@cgg.wa.gov.au
Phone: 089 956 6625
Social Media: https:// www.instagram.com/queenspark-theatre/ www.facebook.com/QueensParkTheatre
Capacity: 501-1000
Policies: Rent and Present

Queensland Performing Arts Centre (QPAC)
Website: www.qpac.com.au
Email: info@qtix.com.au
Phone: 738 429 505
Address: Cnr Grey and Melbourne Sts, AU
Information: Queensland Performing Arts Centre (QPAC) is Queensland's entertainment destination and the leading presenter of performing arts in the Asia Pacific. Located on the banks of the Brisbane river, QPAC is one of four organisations that make up the state's Cultural Centre.
Country: Australia
Social Media: https://twitter.com/QPAC www.facebook.com/atQPAC https:// www.instagram.com/atqpac/
Disabled Access: Yes
Capacity: 1000+
Annual Performances: 100+
Policies: All

Redcliffe Cultural Centre
Website: www.moretonbay.qld.gov.au/events.aspx-?cid=4
Email: redcliffe.culturalcentre@moretonbay.qld.gov.au
Phone: 732 830 407
Address: Downs Street, AU
Information: The Redcliffe Cultural Centre is an exciting performing and creative arts space that caters for the cultural needs of local and regional audiences. Located in the heart of Redcliffe's Cultural Precinct, this venue plays host to touring productions, comedy shows, movies, musicals, conferences, civic functions, as well as a variety of community organisations and arts activities.
Country: Australia
Social Media: www.facebook.com/pages/Redcliffe-Cultural-Centre/102431139826210
Policies: Rent only, Rent and present, Multi-purpose

Regal Theatre
Website: www.regaltheatre.com.au
Email: admin@regaltheatre.com.au
Phone: 893 882 066
Address: 474 Hay Street Subiaco WA
Information: The Regal was placed on the State's heritage list of buildings in 1994. It is listed with the National Trust and is registered with the Australian Heritage Commission. The Regal was named after King George VI who, at the time of opening, had recently ascended the throne, and who was later acknowledged by the installation of a crown and lettering spelling out the cinema's name in neon over the front entrance.
Country: Australia
Contact: Manager Kim Knight
Email: kim@regaltheatre.com.au
Phone: 448 111 308technical Manager Raph Whittingham
Email: raph@regaltheatre.com.au
Phone: 402 211 034
Social Media: www.facebook.com/theregaltheatre
Capacity: 501-1000
Annual Performances: 51-100
Policies: Rent and Present

Regent Theatre and Plaza Ballroom
Website: www.marrinergroup.com.au/function-event-venues-plaza.php
Email: feedback@marrinergroup.com.au
Phone: 130 011 1011
Address: 191 Collins Street, Melbourne, AU
Information: A truly unique venue catering from grand gala dinners and cocktail functions to conferences, product launches and weddings. Renowned as one of Melbourne's most spectacular and imPressive events venues and situated in the heart of Collins Street at Melbourne's famous Regent Theatre, the prestigious Plaza Ballroom is a venue unmatched in history, elegance and grandeur.
Country: Australia
Social Media: https:// www.facebook.com/Regent. Theatre.Melbourne/
Capacity: 1000+
Policies: Rent and Present

Riverside Theatres
Website: www.riversideparramatta.com.au
Email: boxoffice_riverside@parracity.nsw.gov.au
Phone: 288 393 399
Address: Corner Church and Market Streets Parramatta
Information: Located on the banks of the Parramatta River, Riverside Theatres is nestled in the midst of the

Church Street Restaurant precinct. Pre-show dining and parking is ample, accessible and affordable. The Riverside Theatre, can house up to 761 patrons with comfortable, plush seating in a conventional proscenium arch stage with orchestra pit and fly tower. Larger scale productions including international acts are often seen on the Riverside stage including Shakespeare, comedy, drama, ballet, contemporary dance and musicals.
Country: Australia
Contact: Director Robert Love
Email: rlove_riverside@parracity.nsw.gov.au
Contact: business Manager Sainesh Moss
Email: JAnkus@cityofparramatta.nsw.gov.au
Contact: Program Manager Catherine Swallow
Email: cswallow_riverside@cityofparramatta.nsw.gov.au
Marketing & Communications Manager
Henri Marron
Email: hmarron@cityofparramatta.nsw.gov.au
Social Media: www.facebook.com/riversidetheatres
Capacity: 501-1000
Annual Performances: 100+
Policies: Rent and Present

Robert Blackwood Hall
Website: https:// www.monash.edu/performing-arts-centres/our-venues/robert-blackwood-hall/
Phone: 990 51111
Address: 49 Scenic Boulevard, Clayton, Melbourne, Victoria
Information: Named after Monash University's founding Chancellor, Sir Robert Blackwood, the Robert Blackwood Hall is Melbourne's most prestigious venue outside the CBD. Acoustically, it ranks with the best available in Australia and, as such, has been the venue for numerous commercial recordings for the ABC, Melbourne Symphony Orchestra and various film scores.
Country: Australia
Disabled Access: Yes
Capacity: 1000+
Policies: All

Rockhampton Showgrounds complex
Website: www.rockhamptonregion.qld.gov.au/FacilitiesRecreation/Showgrounds
Email: majorvenues@rrc.qld.gov.au
Phone: 493 74600
Address: Corner of Exhibition and New Exhibition Roads, AU
Information: Rockhampton Showgrounds Complex is Rockhampton's premier indoor/outdoor venue for just about anything. With an incredibly diverse program of events with everything from the Rockhampton Show and the Rocky Swap, to Beef Australia and Rodeos. The Rockhampton Showgrounds has something for everyone.
Country: Australia
Capacity: 501-1000
Policies: Rent and Present

Roma Street Parkland and Spring Hill
Website: www.visitbrisbane.com.au/roma-street-parkland-and-spring-hill
Email: info@cityparklands.com.au
Phone: 130 013 7468
Address: 1 Parkland Blvd, AU
Information: Roma Street Parkland, one of Brisbane's premier parks, is considered to be one of the best contemporary display gardens in Australia.Open seven days a week located in the heart of Brisbane city, Roma Street Parkland is an oasis of designer gardens and sprawling lawns that wind around 16 hectares of stunning parkland.
Country: Australia
Social Media: https:// www.facebook.com/romastreetparkland/
Disabled Access: Yes
Capacity: 1000+
Policies: Present

Royalty Theatre
Website: www.calisthenicssa.com.au/
Email: admin@calisthenicssa.com.au
Phone: 882 235 765
Address: 65 Angas Street, AU
Information: Royalty Theatre is the venue for different events like theatre plays, concerts, conferences and more.
Country: Australia
Social Media: www.facebook.com/pages/Royalty-Theatre/122646767790362
Policies: Theatre

Sale Memorial Hall
Website: https:// www.facebook.com/Sale-Memorial-Hall-338330159677333/
Phone: 351 442 337
Address: 88 MacAlister St, Sale, AU
Information: The Sale Memorial Hall is a multi-purpose building that can host events such as: Weddings, Debutant Balls, Cabarets, Dances, Parties, Eisteddfods, Speech & Award Nights, Concerts (including the Melbourne Symphony Orchestra) and Trivia Nights. The main hall is

capable of seating 650 people and the small hall will accommodate 150 people. The main hall includes a quality PA system suitable for speeches etc.
Country: Australia
Social Media: https:// www.facebook.com/Sale-Memorial-Hall-338330159677333/
Capacity: 501-1000
Policies: Rent and Present

San Remo Ballroom
Website: www.sanremoballroom.com.au
Email: functions@sanremoballroom.com.au
Phone: 393 474 000
Address: 365 Nicholson Street, AU
Information: San Remo Ballroom has been Melbourne's favourite function venue since 1963, providing a uniquely elegant setting for a host of corporate and social functions. San Remo Ballroom is a well-renowned and truly unique function venue situated just 2km from the heart of Melbourne's CBD. Recently renovated, our magnificent location exudes an unmatchable blend of old world charm and modern functionality designed to make any social or corporate function a wonderfully memorable occasion.
Country: Australia
Social Media: www.facebook.com/pages/San-Remo-Ballroom/138554542882105
Policies: Rent only, Multi-purpose

SBW Stables Theatre
Website: www.griffintheatre.com.au
Email: boxoffice@griffintheatre.com.au
Phone: 293 613 817
Address: 10 Nimrod Street, Sydney, AU
Information: Formerly the home of the now-defunct Nimrod Theatre Company, the Stables now host this state's foremost champion of new Australian writing for stage: Griffin Theatre Company. Renovated in 2010, the building nevertheless retains the original 120-seat theatre with its kite-shaped stage, one of the best venues for getting close to the action. Griffin Theatre Company produces between four and five shows each year, and hosts roughly the same number in its Griffin Independent program, showcasing independent and interstate companies.
Country: Australia
Contact: Chair Bruce Meagher
Contact: Executive Director and CEO Julieanne Campbell
Contact: undefinedArtistic Director and CEO Declan Greene
Social Media: www.facebook.com/GriffinTheatreCompany https://twitter.com/griffintheatre/ https:// www.instagram.com/griffintheatre/
Capacity: 100-250
Annual Performances: 100+
Annual Productions: 0-5
Policies: All

Scots' Church
Website: www.scotschurch.com
Email: admin@scotschurch.com
Phone: 396 509 903
Address: First Floor, 156 Collins Street, Melbourne,
Information: The Scots' Church Melbourne offers quality venues hosting groups as small as 3 people and up to 350 people. The venues have been utilised for concerts, personal development days, large and small team meetings, a base for school city experiences, and for registered and non-registered training courses.
Country: Australia
Contact: bookings admin Jonathan North
Email: admin@scotschurch.com
Social Media: https:// www.facebook.com/scotschurch-melbourne/
Disabled Access: Yes
Capacity: 1000+
Annual Performances: 51-100
Policies: All

Scott Theatre
Website: www.adelaide.edu.au/infrastructure/campus_services/services/scott/
Email: mark.karvelis@adelaide.edu.au
Phone: 883 033 620
Address: University of Adelaide, Kintore Avenue, AU
Information: Scott Theatre is a modern theatre facility located in the heart of Adelaide, in the grounds of the University of Adelaide. In 2010, the theatre underwent a $2 million upgrade, and now has seating capacity for 570 people, and wheelChair access to the ground floor foyer and auditorium levels.
Country: Australia
Policies: Theatre

Seymour Theatre Centre
Website: www.seymourcentre.com
Email: admin@seymour.sydney.edu.au
Phone: 029 061 5344
Address: Corner of City Rd and Cleveland St, AU
Information: The Seymour Centre, is a vibrant, 6-venue performing arts centre located in the heart of the University of Sydney.
Country: Australia
Contact: Artistic Director / General Manager Timothy

Jones
Contact: business Manager Colette Vella
Contact: Marketing Manager Elizabeth Maynard
Social Media: https://twitter.com/SeymourSydney www.facebook.com/seymoursydney https:// www.instagram.com/seymoursydney
Disabled Access: Yes
Capacity: 1000+
Annual Performances: 100+

Sidney Myer Music Bowl
Website: https:// www.artscentremelbourne.com.au/visit/theatres-and-spaces/sidney-myer-music-bowl
Email: info@artscentremelbourne.com.au
Phone: 130 013 0300
Address: Kings Domain Gardens, 21 Linlithgow Ave, Sidney, AU
Information: Come to the Sidney Myer Music Bowl, our versatile, multi-purpose, outdoor venue in the lush surrounds of Kings Domain, and join the annual magic as the Bowl lights up to the winking candles of Carols by Candlelight or groove to the beats of huge headline acts as they take to the massive stage in front of thousands of fans.
Country: Australia
Capacity: 1000+
Annual Performances: 100+
Policies: Rent and Present

Sir Robert Helpmann Theatre
Website: www.countryarts.org.au/venue-page/sir-robert-helpmann-theatre/
Email: helpmann@countryarts.org.au
Phone: 887 238 741
Address: 10 Watson Terrace, Gambier
Information: The theatre is named after the late Sir Robert Helpmann, a world renowned performer. He was born in Mount Gambier before pursuing an international career as an actor, dancer, choreographer and Director. The South East of South Australia is famed for its sparkling seas, fine Coonawarra wines, seafood fresh from the ocean, fascinating limestone caves and tall timber.
Country: Australia
Contact: venue Manager Frank Morello
Social Media: www.facebook.com/SirRobertHelpmannTheatre
Disabled Access: Yes
Capacity: 501-1000
Annual Performances: 100+
Policies: Rent and Present

Sleeman Sports Centre
Website: www.sleemansports.com.au
Email: info@sleemansports.org.au
Phone: 731 319 620
Address: Cnr Old Cleveland & Tilley Roads, AU
Information: The Sleeman Sports Complex is a centre of excellence for the development of elite athletes in Queensland. The complex offers a variety of aquatic and fitness activities, sports medicine programs and services as well as concerts, functions, conferences and trade shows.
Country: Australia
Social Media: https:// www.facebook.com/sleemansports https:// www.instagram.com/sleemansports/
Capacity: 1000+
Policies: Rent and Present

Somerville Auditorium
Website: www.theatres.uwa.edu.au/venues/somerville
Email: bookings@theatres.uwa.edu.au
Phone: 648 81732
Address: The University Of Western Australia 35 Stirling Highway, Crawley, AU
Information: In 1927, William Somerville conceived the idea of a venue defined by a cathedral
of Norfolk pine trees. Today the venue is best known for Perth Festival's annual
Lotterywest Film Season from November to April.
Country: Australia
Contact: Theatre Manager Rob Lines
Email: rob.lines@uwa.edu.au
Social Media: https:// www.facebook.com/somervilleauditorium/
Capacity: 1000+
Policies: Rent and Present

South Bank Parklands
Website: https:// www.visitbrisbane.com.au/south-bank?sc_lang=en-au
Email: vicsouthbank@cityparklands.com.au
Phone: 073 029 1797
Address: South Bank Parklands, AU
Information: South Bank is Brisbane's premier lifestyle and cultural destination. Located on the southern banks of the Brisbane River, its 17 hectares of lush parklands, world-class eateries, stunning river views and hundreds of delightful events all year round make it the perfect place to relax and unwind.
Country: Australia
Social Media: https://twitter.com/visitsouthbank www.facebook.com/VisitSouthBank https:// www.instagram.com/visitsouthbank/
Disabled Access: Yes
Capacity: 1000+

Annual Performances: 100+
Policies: Rent and Present

Space Theatre
Website: https:// www.adelaidefestivalcentre.com.au/venues/space-theatre
Email: venue.Sales@adelaidefestivalcentre.com.au
Phone: 882 168 600
Address: King William Rd, AU
Information: The Space Theatre is a General admission venue with no traditional stage or fixed seating, so that its configuration is completely flexible. It can be turned into a theatre in the round, a corner stage setting or a cabaret venue and depending on configuration seats anywhere between 200 to 350 people.
Country: Australia
Capacity: 251-500
Annual Performances: 100+
Policies: Rent and Present

St Martins Youth Arts Centre
Website: www.stmartinsyouth.com.au
Email: info@stmartinsyouth.com.au
Phone: 398 672 477
Address: 28 St Martins Lane, AU
Information: St Martins has been shaped by the many hands, hearts and minds that have made it what it is today, on the same site for 40 years. Our staff are award winning professional theatre makers whose primary interest is in making work for, and with, young people. They are committed to creating a space that's inclusive of all children and perspectives.
Country: Australia
Contact: Artistic Director Nadja Kostich
Email: info@stmartinsyouth.com.au
Contact: Marketing Coordinator Jason Cheetham
Email: jason@stmartinsyouth.com.au
Social Media: https://twitter.com/stmartinsyac www.facebook.com/stmartinsyouth https:// www.instagram.com/stmartinsyac/

Star Theatres
Website: www.startheatres.com.au
Email: office@mightygood.com.au
Phone: 882 341 800
Address: 145 Sir Donald Bradman Drive, Hilton
Information: Located on Sir Donald Bradman Drive at Hilton, Star Theatres incorporates two performance spaces. Both spaces are available for hire for a variety of activities and theatre applications.
Country: Australia
Social Media: www.facebook.com/pages/Star-Theatres/145585465502165
Capacity: 251-500
Annual Performances: 100+
Policies: Rent and Present

State Theatre
Website: www.statetheatre.com.au
Email: admin@statetheatre.com.au
Phone: 293 736 655
Address: 49 Market Street, Sydney, AU
Information: The State Theatre Sydney is an iconic performance theatre for comedians, bands, musicians, shows, music, dance, plays and a venue for weddings and events. The State Theatre has long been at the forefront of Sydney's Artistic and cultural life, the theatre is also responding to the changing needs and demands of its commercial patrons.
Country: Australia
Social Media: https://twitter.com/statetheatreau?lang=en www.facebook.com/StateTheatreAU https:// www.instagram.com/statetheatreau/
Capacity: 1000+
Annual Performances: 51-100
Policies: Rent and Present

State Theatre Centre of Western Australia
Website: https:// www.ptt.wa.gov.au/venues/state-theatre-centre-of-wa/
Email: stcwa@ptt.wa.gov.au
Phone: 862 129 200
Address: 174 – 176 William Street, AU
Information: The State Theatre Centre of Western Australia is a theatre complex located within the Perth Cultural Centre in Perth, Western Australia. The larger of three dedicated performance areas is known as the Heath Ledger Theatre in honour of Perth-born film actor Heath Ledger.
Country: Australia
Social Media: https:// www.instagram.com/perththeatretrust/ www.facebook.com/statetheatrecentreofwa
Disabled Access: Yes
Capacity: 1000+
Annual Performances: 100+
Policies: Rent and Present

Strawberry Hills Hotel
Website: www.strawberryhillshotel.com.au
Email: strawberryhillshotel@gmail.com
Phone: 296 993 355
Address: 453 Elizabeth Street, Surry Hills
Information: Why not hold your next birthday, gathering or special event at the strawberry hills hotel? we can

reserve a space in our outdoor beer garden to cater for events up to 210 guests. with a delicious and affordable canape menu, we have all the ingredients to ensure your night is all you hope it can be.
Country: Australia
Social Media: https:// www.facebook.com/officialstrawberryhillshotel/ https:// www.instagram.com/thestrawberryhillshotel/
Capacity: 100-250

Street Theatre
Website: www.thestreet.org.au
Email: street@thestreet.org.au
Phone: 262 471 223
Address: 15 Childers St, City West
Information: The Street is Canberra's leading creative Producer dedicated to contemporary performance and presenting bold work. Inspired by our geography and people, we champion creative process alongside finished work; rich dialogue with our community,
and in our city of ideas, inquisitive artists who have something to say about the world.**Country:** Australia
Contact: Arts Programs Producer Shelly Higgs
Contact: Artistic Director / chief Executive officer Caroline Stacey
Contact: Executive Producer Dean Ellis
Social Media: www.facebook.com/thestreettheatre https:// www.instagram.com/thestreetcbr/ https://twitter.com/thestreetcbr
Disabled Access: Yes
Capacity: 251-500
Annual Performances: 25-50
Annual Productions: 0-5
Policies: All

Subiaco Arts Centre
Website: ptt.wa.gov.au/venues/subiaco-arts-centre
Email: sac@ptt.wa.gov.au
Phone: 893 803 000
Address: 180 Hamersley Road, Subiaco
Information: Formerly known as the 'Subiaco Theatre Centre'. Performance areas including: Main Auditorium with a corner stage and raked seating three sides for 305; The Studio with an intimate performance area seating 115; Subiaco Theatre Gardens with a stunning Amphitheatre for outdoor concerts. Available to hire for functions and events.
Country: Australia
Contact: Acting Manager Natalie Di Risio
Email: natalie.dirisio@ptt.wa.gov.au
Phone: 893 803 000
Social Media: www.facebook.com/subiacoartscentre
Disabled Access: Yes
Capacity: 1000+
Annual Performances: 100+
Policies: Rent and Present

Sunken Garden – University of Western Australia
Website: www.theatres.uwa.edu.au/venues/sunken-garden
Email: bookings-theatres@uwa.edu.au
Phone: 864 887 407
Address: 35 Stirling Highway, Crawley, AU
Information: The Sunken Garden is an intimate amphitheatre with gardens, ponds and terraced lawns and is a beloved feature of the University's beautiful campus. For most of the year the Sunken Garden is an idyllic retreat for staff, students and wedding functions. The setting is one of the most beautiful in Perth. By the Swan River in Matilda Bay and nearby Kings Park, the Sunken Garden offers a stunning setting for all manner of events including wedding ceremonies, photographic sessions and filming.
Country: Australia
Disabled Access: Yes
Policies: Rent and Present

Sunshine Coast Events Centre Caloundra
Website: www.theeventscentre.com.au
Email: events@theeventscentre.com.au
Phone: 754 914 240
Address: 20 Minchinton Street Caloundra, QLD,
Information: The Events Centre, Caloundra is the Sunshine Coast's premier performing arts and conference centre. Be inspired by the diverse conferences, events, venue and hospitality services on offer. Be entertained by the kaleidoscope of concerts, music, dance, plays and shows for all ages. The Events Centre is one of the largest function centres on the coast with fine dining, high tech staging and equipment for large and small dinners, awards nights, conferences, theatre and special events.
Country: Australia
Contact: Chair Jeanette Burrows
Contact: Deputy Chair Fendall Hill
Social Media: www.facebook.com/theeventscentre
Capacity: 1000+
Annual Performances: 51-100
Policies: Rent and Present

Sutherland Entertainment Centre
Website: www.sutherlandshire.nsw.gov.au/Arts_Entertainment/Entertainment_Centre
Email: suthentcent@ssc.nsw.gov.au
Phone: 295 218 888
Address: 30 Eton Street, Sutherland

Information: The Sutherland Entertainment Centre is Sutherland Shire's premier entertainment and meeting facility located in the heart of the Shire. The Sutherland Entertainment Centre is a unique multi-purpose venue ideal for hosting a wide variety of events such as conferences, presentations, dinners, product launches, community and professional theatre and concerts.
Country: Australia

Social Media: https:// www.facebook.com/SutherlandEntertainmentCentre/ https:// www.instagram.com/entertainmentctre/
Capacity: 501-1000
Policies: Rent and Present

Sydney Comedy Store
Website: www.comedystore.com.au
Email: info@comedystore.com.au
Phone: 293 571 419
Address: 122 Lang Rd, Moore Park NSW
Information: The Comedy Store is Australia's premier stand up comedy club. Australia's home of comedy since 1981, presenting world class comedy every week. A night at The Comedy Store is a traditional authentic comedy club experience like no other. Two hard hitting hours of hilarity with a rotating line up of Australia's and the world's best comedians, all delivered by an expert host.
Country: Australia
Social Media: https:// www.instagram.com/comedystoresyd/ https:// www.facebook.com/comedystoresydney
Capacity: 251-500
Annual Performances: 100+
Policies: Rent and Present

Sydney Conservatorium of Music
Website: music.sydney.edu.au
Email: con.venues@sydney.edu.au
Phone: 293 511 222
Address: Cnr Bridge and Macquarie Street, AU
Information: Close to the Sydney Opera House and surrounded by the Royal Botanic Gardens, the Sydney Conservatorium of Music is located at the heart of Sydney's cultural precinct; features five performance venues and over 130 teaching and practice studios.
Country: Australia
Contact: Director, Media and PR Shehana Darda-Teixeira
Email: shehana.darda-teixeira@sydney.edu.au
Phone: 293 511 203Chancellor Belinda Hutchinson
Social Media: www.facebook.com/sydneycon https:// twitter.com/sydney_uni https:// www.instagram.com/sydney_uni/
Disabled Access: Yes
Capacity: 1000+
Annual Performances: 100+
Policies: All

Sydney Lyric Theatre
Website: www.sydneylyric.com.au
Email: admin@sydneylyric.com.au
Phone: 295 093 600
Address: Pirrama Road, Pyrmont, AU
Information: The Sydney Lyric opened in 1997 and has a history of welcoming legendary international performers and productions. Acquired by Foundation Theatres in 2011, it has now become a staple of the NSW musical theatre scene, hosting World Premieres, including Strictly Ballroom the Musical and Dream Lover, Australian Premieres including Legally Blonde the Musical, Beautiful: The Carole King Musical and Matilda the Musical, and successful runs of smash hit musicals such as Annie, Grease, War Horse, The Bo
Country: Australia
Contact: CHIEF EXECUTIVE OFFICER Graeme Kearns
Email: gkearns@sydneylyric.com.au
Contact: deputy General Manager Paul Rigby
Email: prigby@ctm.com.au
Social Media: https://twitter.com/sydneylyric?lang=en www.facebook.com/SydneyLyricTheatre https:// www.instagram.com/sydneylyrictheatre/?hl=en

Sydney Opera House
Website: www.sydneyoperahouse.com
Email: infodesk@sydneyoperahouse.com
Phone: 292 507 111
Address: GPO Box 4274, Royal Exchange, AU
Information: The Opera House is a World Heritage-listed masterpiece of 'human creative genius' that belongs to all Australians. It is the Country's number one tourist destination and its busiest performing arts centre, welcoming more than 10.9 million visitors a year on site and hosting more than 1, 800 performances attended by more than 1.4 million people.
Country: Australia
Contact: CEO Louise Herron
Contact: Programming Director Fiona Winning
Production & Events Director
Lou Oppenheim
Social Media: https://twitter.com/sydoperahouse www.facebook.com/sydneyoperahouse https:// www.instagram.com/sydneyoperahouse/
Disabled Access: Yes
Capacity: 1000+
Annual Performances: 100+
Annual Productions: 100+
Policies: All

Sydney Town Hall
Website: www.sydneytownhall.com
Email: mediateam@cityofsydney.nsw.gov.au
Phone:
292 659 333
Address: 483 George St, Sydney, AU
Information: Renowned for its high Victorian interiors and rich decoration, Sydney Town Hall is the largest and most ornate late 19th century civic building in Australia. Constructed primarily of Sydney sandstone, the landmark building is located on George Street, opposite the Queen Victoria Building and alongside St Andrew's Cathedral. Sited above the Town Hall station and between the city shopping and entertainment precincts, the steps of the Town Hall are a popular meeting place.
Country: Australia

Tandanya – National Aboriginal Cultural Institute
Website: www.tandanya.com.au
Email: tandanya@tandanya.com.au
Phone: 882 243 200
Address: 253 Grenfell Street, AU
Information: Tandanya offers an insight into the culture of the local Kaurna people, whose territory extends south to Cape Jervis and north to Port Wakefield. Inside are interactive visual-arts gallery spaces, plus a gift shop and a cafe.
Country: Australia
Contact: acting Artistic and cultural Director Tim Ritchie
Contact: venue coordinator Alison Hughes
Social Media: www.facebook.com/pages/Tandanya-National-Aboriginal-Cultural-Institute/155133834537136
Policies: Present and produce, Arts centre

The Concourse
Website: theconcourse.com.au
Email: theconcourse@centuryvenues.com.au
Phone: 280 758 100
Address: 409 Victoria Avenue, Chatswood
Information: An initiative of Willoughby City Council, The Concourse is the cultural home of the North Shore. It is one of Sydney's leading entertainment venues, home to a dynamic range of live arts and entertainment. The stunningly designed precinct includes two open green spaces, restaurants, cafés and retail stores, making The Concourse the perfect meeting place for all occasions.
Country: Australia
Social Media: https:// www.facebook.com/theconcourse/
Disabled Access: Yes
Capacity: 1000+
Annual Performances: 100+
Policies: Rent and Present

The Factory Theatre
Website: www.factorytheatre.com.au
Email: boxoffice@centuryvenues.com.au
Phone: 295 503 666
Address: 105 Victoria RdMarrickville NSW 2204, AU
Information: As a purpose built, dedicated live entertainment venue, the Factory hosts an array of live music and performances – from international rock concerts to intimate cabaret shows, film and dance. The Factory brings a breath of fresh air to Sydney's entertainment scene and a commitment to nurturing emerging performers and acts.
Country: Australia
Social Media: www.facebook.com/factorytheatre www.instagram.com/factory_theatre/
Disabled Access: Yes
Annual Performances: 51-100

The Landing at Dockside
Website: www.landingatdockside.com.au
Email: info@landingatdockside.com.au
Phone: 732 173 646
Address: 44 Ferry Street, Kangaroo Point, AU
Information: The Landing at Dockside is Brisbane's Premier Wedding and Function centre overlooking the Brisbane River. With three unique event spaces, The Landing at Dockside can cater for events ranging from 30-1500 guests. Offering both set and tailored packages, the experienced coordinators, impeccable service and award winning food will ensure your next event is one to remember.
Country: Australia
Social Media: www.facebook.com/pages/The-Landing-At-Dockside/233231746818382 https:// www.instagram.com/thelandingatdockside/
Capacity: 1000+
Policies: Rent only

The Pilbeam Theatre
Website: www.seeitlive.com.au
Email: pilbeamtheatre@rrc.qld.gov.au
Phone: 749 245 600
Address: Victoria Parade & Cambridge Street, AU
Information: Named after Rockhampton's former long-serving mayor, RBJ Pilbeam, the Pilbeam Theatre is located on the corner of Victoria Parade and Cambridge Streets, Rockhampton, overlooking the Fitzroy River. It is the focal point of a variety of events throughout the year including drama, dance, music, comedy and more. With seating for almost 1000 people (depending on configuration) the Pilbeam Theatre is the ideal venue for theatrical productions, small to large conferences, product demonstrations and launches, intimate cabarets and more.
Country: Australia
Policies: Present and produce, Multi-purpose

Theatre North
Website: www.theatrenorth.com.au
Email: admin@theatrenorth.com.au
Phone: 633 10052
Address: 57 Brisbane Street Launceston, Tasmania
Information: Theatre North Inc, trading as Theatre North at the Princess is an independent, non-profit organisation, established in 1995, and funded by the State Government and the City of Launceston.**Country: Australia**
Contact: General Manager Mandy Shepherd
Contact: Administration Finance Manager Linda Gleeson
Contact: technical Manager Malcolm Butters
Contact: President and Chair Natalie De Vito
Contact: undefinedVice Chair Annie Greig
Contact: Vice Chair David Rich
Social Media: https://twitter.com/theatrenorth@Theatre-North-Princess-Theatre-Earl-Arts-Centre https:// www.facebook.com/princesstheatrelaunceston/ https:// www.instagram.com/princesstheatrelaunceston/
Capacity: 1000+
Policies: Rent and Present

Theatre Royal
Website: www.theatreroyal.com.au
Email: admin@theatreroyal.com.au
Phone: 614 63300
Address: 29 Campbell St, Hobart
Information: The Theatre Royal is Australia's oldest working theatre and one of its most beautiful treasures. In 2012 it celebrated the 175th anniversary of the first performance in 1837. Leading Australian and international artists have performed here over the decades, including Laurence Olivier, Noel Coward, Lillian Gish, Marcel Marceau, Roy 'Mo' Rene, Ruth Cracknell, John Bell and Hugo Weaving. A contemporary centre for performing arts, the Theatre presents an annual program of live theatre, music, dance and entertainment.
Country: Australia
Contact: chief Executive Tim Munro
Email: tim@theatreroyal.com.au
Contact: Marketing and Business Development Manager Dale Tresidder
Email: dale@theatreroyal.com.au
Contact: program and operations Manager Don Hopkins
Email: don@theatreroyal.com.au
Social Media: https://twitter.com/TheatreRoyalHob www.facebook.com/theatreroyalhobart https:// www.instagram.com/theatreroyalhobart/
Capacity: 1000+
Annual Performances: 100+
Annual Productions: 11-25
Policies: All

Theatreworks
Website: www.theatreworks.org.au
Email: gm@theatreworks.org.au
Phone: 395 344 879
Address: 14 Acland St, Kilda VIC AU
Information: Theatre Works is a creative centre and venue in the heart of St. Kilda. It reaches out to the wider community; it supports innovative arts practitioners through collaborations, partnerships and the imaginative use of its space and resources.**Country: Australia**
Contact: front of house Manager Rachel Bostock
Contact: Box Office Manager Adam Gardner
Email: admin@theatreworks.org.au
Phone: 039 534 3388General Manager Dianne Toulson
Email: gm@theatreworks.org.au
Phone: 039 534 4879Production Manager Jacinata Anderson
Email: production@theatreworks.org.au
Phone: 039 534 4879Theatre Manager John Collopy
Email: tech@theatreworks.org.au
Phone: 039 534 4879
Social Media: https://twitter.com/theatre_works www.facebook.com/pages/Theatre-Works/ https:// www.instagram.com/theatreworksstkilda/
Capacity: 100-250

Thebarton Theatre
Website: www.thebartontheatre.com.au
Email: admin@thebartontheatre.com.au
Phone:
884 435 255
Address: 112 Henley Beach Road, Torrensville
Information: The medium-sized venue now seats 2000 people and is perfect for young bands breaking into the concert circuit, as well as more established bands that prefer the intimacy of the Thebby to huge and impersonal stadiums.**Country: Australia**
Social Media: https://twitter.com/ThebbyTheatre www.facebook.com/thebartontheatre https:// www.instagram.com/thebartontheatre/

Disabled Access: Yes
Capacity: 1000+
Annual Performances: 11-25
Policies: Rent and Present

Tivoli Theatre
Website: www.thetivoli.com.au
Email: hello@thetivoli.com.au
Phone:
738 521 711
Address: 52 Costin St, Fortitude Valley QLD
Information: In August 2019, The Tivoli opened What's Golden, a 300-person standing capacity performance space with a custom-built stage, sound system and lighting rig that sits within The Tivoli's central foyer, complementing the main auditorium of the iconic and much-loved Fortitude Valley venue.**Country: Australia**
Social Media: www.facebook.com/pages/The-Tivoli-Brisbane/149920008420221 https://www.instagram.com/thetivolibrisbane/
Disabled Access: Yes
Capacity: 251-500
Annual Performances: 51-100
Policies: Rent and Present

Townsville Civic Theatre
Website: www.townsville.qld.gov.au/facilities-and-recreation/theatres-and-galleries/townsville-civic-theatre
Email: performingarts@townsville.qld.gov.au
Phone: 074 727 9013
Address: 41 Boundary Street, South Townsville
Information: The Townsville Civic Theatre is North Queensland's premier cultural facility owned and managed by Townsville City Council. Since its opening in 1978, the theatre continues to be a dynamic centre of entertainment and provide an environment to further develop the performing arts in Townsville and the region.
Country: Australia
Capacity: 501-1000
Annual Performances: 51-100
Policies: Rent and Present

Tuggeranong Community Arts Centre
Website: www.tuggeranongarts.com
Email: info@tuggeranongarts.com
Phone: 629 31443
Address: 137 Reed Street, AU
Information: Tuggeranong Arts Centre, opened in 1998, was the first purpose-built multi-disciplinary arts centre in the ACT. The Centre, which is managed by Tuggeranong Community Arts Inc. hosts and presents a vibrant array of arts activities, engaging professional and community artists alike. Its dynamic youth programs continue to develop the skills, outlook and cultural awareness of young people in the Tuggeranong region and beyond.
Country: Australia
Contact: Chair Don Cumming
Contact: Vice Chair Jenny Hargreaves
Social Media: www.facebook.com/pages/Tuggeranong-Arts-Centre/233189360075720
Capacity: 251-500
Annual Productions: 6-10
Policies: All

Union House Theatre
Website: umsu.unimelb.edu.au/what-is-on/theatre/
Email: uht@union.unimelb.edu.au
Phone: 383 446 975
Address: Building 130 Union House, University of Melbourne, AU
Information: Union House Theatre is the hub for co-curricular student theatre and performance at the University of Melbourne. They program performances, workshops and events giving students a taste of professional practice. They have five staff members and manage two theatres – one is also a cinema – in Union House. They provide support to student playwrights, Directors, designers, performers and technicians.
Country: Australia
Contact: Artistic Manager Xanthe Beesley
Email: Artistic@union.unimelb.edu.au
Contact: Administration and development officer Erin Adams
Email: uht@union.unimelb.edu.au
Contact: Production and Venue Manager Khat Kerr
Email: production@union.unimelb.edu.au
Social Media: https://twitter.com/umsuunimelb?lang=en www.facebook.com/UMSU/ https://www.instagram.com/umsuunimelb/?hl=en

University of Melbourne, Facilities Hiring
Website: services.unimelb.edu.au/venuehire
Email:
uht@union.unimelb.edu.au
Address: Grattan Street, AU
Information: Venue Management in Academic Services manages the hire of shared teaching spaces to a variety of clients, including University departments, student clubs and external organisations. We control bookings in over 250 spaces varying in size from intimate 20 seat seminar rooms to large 500 seat fully equipped lecture theatres. We also manage the application process for

Wedding Photography Permits in the grounds of the University. With its grand old buildings and well-maintained gardens, the Univers
Country: Australia
Social Media: https://twitter.com/unimelb www.facebook.com/melbuni
Disabled Access: Yes
Capacity: 1000+
Annual Performances: 100+
Policies: All

University of Sydney – The Great Hall
Website: https://www.sydney.edu.au/engage/visit/places-of-interest/great-hall.html
Email: university.venues@sydney.edu.au
Phone: 293 511 537
Address: The University of Sydney, Science Rd, AU
Information: The Great Hall was officially opened to the public on the 18 July 1859. A grand festival of music was held over a week to commemorate the opening of the buildings on Grose Farm. Over the past 150 years the Great Hall has been used for a wide variety of events including, conferring of degrees, musical and dramatic productions, banquets, public lectures, book launches, balls, exams, commemoration, memorial services, antique fair, Chancellor's Committee annual book sale and so much more.
Country: Australia
Social Media: https://www.facebook.com/sydneyuni/ https://twitter.com/sydney_uni https://www.instagram.com/sydney_uni/
Disabled Access: Yes
Policies: Rent and Present

University Theatres
Website: www.theatres.uwa.edu.au
Email: bookings@theatres.uwa.edu.au
Phone: 864 882 691
Address: The University of Western Australia, 35 Stirling Highway, Crawley, AU
Information: The University of Western Australia boasts some of Australia's most distinctive and exciting venues, from the sumptuous Winthrop Hall to the magical Somerville Auditorium.
Country: Australia
Contact: theatre Manager Rob Lines
Email: rob.lines@uwa.edu.au
Contact: technical Manager David Hobbs
Email: david.hobbs@uwa.edu.au
Phone: 086 488 2439
Disabled Access: Yes
Capacity: 1000+
Annual Performances: 100+
Policies: All

UNSW Creative Practice Lab
Website: sam.arts.unsw.edu.au/
Email: cpl@unsw.edu.au
Phone: 293 855 684
Address: Io Myers Studio, UNSW, Gate 2, High St, Kensington, AU
Information: The space within Io Myers Studio was designed to allow for the creative mind to explore and execute works of every type. A fully flexible space, the studio hosts a wide range of activities, from students working on their first productions to Australia's premier performance artists. With recently upgraded equipment, the venue is suitable for live performance, video screenings and cross-media experimental works.
Country: Australia
Contact: Venue Hire and Administration Su Goldfish
Email: cpl@unsw.edu.au
Contact: technical equipment Manager Paul Matthews
Email: p.matthews@unsw.edu.au
Social Media: SAMUNSW https://www.facebook.com/samUNSW/
Policies: Rent only, Multi-purpose

Verbrugghen Hall
Website: music.sydney.edu.au/about/hire-scm-venues/verbrugghen-hall
Email: con.venues@sydney.edu.au
Phone: 293 512 222
Address: 1 Conservatorium Road, Sydney NSW 2000
Information: The Conservatorium of Music is home to five performance venues of outstanding acoustic and architectural quality. A world-class venue with exceptional acoustics, the Verbrugghen Hall is the largest performance space at the Conservatorium.**Country: Australia**
Capacity: 501-1000
Policies: All

Wagga Wagga Civic Theatre
Website: www.wagga.nsw.gov.au/civic-theatre
Email:
boxoffice@civictheatre.com.au
Phone:
269 269 688
Address: Burns Way (off Tarcutta Street), AU
Information: Based in the Civic Precinct on the banks of the Wollundry Lagoon, the Wagga Wagga Civic Theatre is a main focus of cultural activities within the communi-

ty. The theatre attracts a great variety of National and International Touring shows as well as many local events. The Wagga Wagga Civic Theatre boasts a 488 seat auditorium, lighting and sound systems, spacious foyers, fully appointed bar and balcony overlooking the beautiful Wollundry Lagoon.
Country: Australia
Social Media: @WaggaTheatre www.facebook.com/waggawaggacivictheatre
Annual Performances: 200
Policies: Rent only, Theatre

Wangaratta Arts Centre
Website: www.wangarattapac.com.au
Email: boxoffice@wangaratta.vic.gov.au
Phone: 357 228 105
Address: Cnr Ford & Ovens Streets Wangaratta
Information: Wangaratta Performing Arts & Convention Centre host 100+ live performances per year in a purpose built Theatre holding 512 patrons.**Country: Australia**
Contact: Venue Manager Tanya Camplin
Contact: Box Office Team Leader Allison Gillick
Contact: Technical Team Leader Matt Spiker
Social Media: https://www.facebook.com/WangPACC
Capacity: 501-1000
Annual Performances: 100+
Policies: Rent and Present

West Australian Ballet Centre
Website: www.waballet.com.au
Email: info@waballet.com.au
Phone: 892 140 707
Address: 134 Whatley Crescent Maylands
Information: In 1952, West Australian Ballet was established by Madame Kira Bousloff – the first ballet company formed in Australia that is still in existence today. West Australian Ballet's new state of the art facility features stunning new studios available for hire for dance classes, rehearsals workshops and auditions. The venue is also available for unique corporate and private events. Member of ISPA
Country: Australia
Contact: Artistic Director Aurelien Scannella
Email: info@waballet.com.au
Contact: head of operations Marcus Whelan
Email: info@waballet.com.au
Phone: 089 214 0752Executive Director Kellie Elia
Email: info@waballet.com.au
Phone: 089 214 0708Publicist Rosita Stangl
Email: info@waballet.com.au
Phone: 089 367 8884
Social Media: https://twitter.com/waballet?lang=en https://www.facebook.com/waballet/ https://www.instagram.com/waballet/?hl=en
Capacity: 1000+
Annual Performances: 100+
Policies: All

West Gippsland Arts Centre
Website: www.wgac.org.au
Email: artscentre@wgac.org.au
Phone: 356 242 456
Address: Corner of Smith and Albert Streets, Warragul
Information: The main auditorium has tiered seating for 492 patrons and a 14-metre stage with a proscenium arch and flytower. Other features include an orchestra pit to accommodate up to 40 musicians, a Yamaha concert grand piano, in-house audio loop, ample dressing room space and convenient backstage loading bay. The stage is masonite over a sprung hardwood floor.
Country: Australia
Social Media: www.facebook.com/westgippslandartscentre https://twitter.com/WGAC_Warragul/ https://www.instagram.com/westgippslandartscentre/
Capacity: 251-500
Annual Performances: 100+
Policies: Rent and Present

Western Australian Academy of Performing Arts (WAAPA)
Website: waapa.ecu.edu.au
Email: waapa@ecu.edu.au
Phone: 863 040 000
Address: ECU Mount Lawley Campus, 2 Bradford Street, AU
Information: The Western Australian Academy of Performing Arts (WAAPA) at Edith Cowan University operates as a Registered Training Organisation, provider number 4756. WAAPA is recognised nationally and internationally for the quality of its graduates. It provides the most comprehensive range of performing arts training in Australia. Most of the venues are available for hire (with the exception of the Geoff Gibbs and Roundhouse Theatres) depending on the current teaching and production timetables.
Country: Australia
Contact: Executive Dean David Shirley
Email: d.shirley@ecu.edu.au
Phone: 046 668 5852Marketing Manager Anton Mazandarani
Email: a.maz@ecu.edu.au
Phone: 863 046 817
Social Media: www.facebook.com/waapa.ecu

Western Australian Museum
Website: museum.wa.gov.au
Email: reception@museum.wa.gov.au
Phone: 130 013 4081
Address: Locked Bag 49, Welshpool DC,
Information: The Western Australian Museum's long and fascinating history reflects and documents the State's rich and diverse natural and cultural heritage. Established in 1891 in the old Perth gaol, it was known as the Geological Museum and its collections were geological, ethnological and biological. In 1897 it officially became the Western Australian Museum and Art Gallery.

Whitehorse Centre
Website: www.whitehorsecentre.com.au
Email: tickets@whitehorse.vic.gov.au
Phone: 926 26590
Address: 397 Whitehorse Road, Nunawading, Victoria
The Whitehorse Centre is the municipality's arts and cultural centre and is owned and run by Whitehorse City Council. The Whitehorse Professional Theatre and Music Season showcases some of the best professional theatre from around the country. It is also a popular venue for many of the City of Whitehorse's performing arts groups.
Country: Australia
Contact: coordinator Robyn McNicol
Email: robyn.mcnicol@whitehorse.vic.gov.au
Social Media: www.facebook.com/WhitehorseCentre
Capacity: 251-500
Policies: Rent and Present

Wilson Hall
Website: maps.unimelb.edu.au/parkville/building/151
Email: venue-management@unimelb.edu.au
Phone: 136 352
Address: 520 Wilson Hall Road Sumter, SC
Information: Wilson Hall was constructed following a fire in 1952 that destroyed the Joseph Reed's original Gothic Revival Wilson Hall (1879). The new building, designed by architects Bates, Smart and McCutcheon, was officially opened on 22 March, 1956. It is the university's main gathering space and is used for orations, examinations, graduations and other ceremonial occasions.
Country: Australia
Capacity: 1000+
Policies: Rent and Present

Winthrop Hall – University of Western Australia
Website: www.theatres.uwa.edu.au/venues/winthrop
Email: bookings@theatres.uwa.edu.au
Phone: 864 887 407
Address: University Theatres (M416), The University of Western Australia, 35 Stirling Highway, AU
Information: Built in 1932, the cathedral-like venue welcomes patrons with a marble and mosaic foyer and vaulted ceilings. The auditorium with its splendid pipe organ combines stained glass windows and Aboriginal motifs on the ceiling. Winthrop Hall has been used for many prestigious events including the Rally Australia Ball, productions by the West Australian Opera and Oz Opera, the Choir of Kings College, Cambridge, and the West Australian Symphony Orchestra.
Country: Australia
Policies: All

Wonthaggi Union Community Arts Centre
Website: https:// www.wonthaggiartscentre.com.au/
Email: basscoast@basscoast.vic.gov.au
Phone: 035 671 2470
Address: 96 Graham St, Wonthaggi, AU
Information: The Wonthaggi Union Community Arts Centre is the only one if its kind in Bass Coast and provides auditorium seating to over 400 guests for a variety of events. The Centre provides the Bass Coast community with a venue for local theatre, cinema, cultural programming, presentations, seminars, exhibitions and film. This great entertainment location is available for hire for community groups and commercial organisations.
Country: Australia
Team Leader, Arts & Culture
David Burrows
Email: david.burrows@basscoast.vic.gov.au
Phone: 035 671 2414 Bookings / Enquiries Margaret de Wolff
Email: margaret.dewolff@basscoast.vic.gov.au
Phone: 035 671 2470
Capacity: 251-500
Annual Performances: 51-100
Policies: Rent and Present

York Theatre
Website: www.seymourcentre.com/venues/york-theatre
Email: boxoffice@seymour.sydney.edu.au
Phone: 029 061 5344
Address: Cnr of City Rd and Cleveland St, The University of Sydney, AU
Information: The York Theatre is the largest theatre in the Seymour; a semi-circular amphitheatre configuration, featuring a thrust stage. Although the space is ideally suited to the presentation of theatre works, it can easily accommodate music, dance or concert style performances.
Country: Australia

Capacity: 501-1000
Policies: Rent and Present

Zenith Theatre & Convention Centre
Website: www.zeniththeatre.com.au
Email: paunit@willoughby.nsw.gov.au
Phone: 977 77547
Address: Mcintosh St & Railway St, Chatswood
Information: The Zenith Theatre & Convention Centre is a versatile, professional venue offering quality facilities and exceptional service

Country: Australia
Capacity: 251-500
Annual Performances: 51-100
Policies: Rent and Present

AZERBAIJAN

Azerbaijan State Philharmonia
Website: www.philharmonia.az
Email: info@philharmonia.az
Phone: 124 972 901/905
Address: 2 Istiglaliyat str, AZ
Information: The Azerbaijan State Philharmonic Hall was built between the years 1910–1912 at the request of the city elite and is designed in the Italian Renaissance (outside) and German Rococo (inside) architectural styles.
Country: Azerbaijan
Contact: Director Melikov Akif Turau
Contact: chief conductor Mirbaji Imanova
Capacity: 1100

Baku Jazz Centre
Website: www.bakujazz.com
Phone: 991 297 3100
Address: 19 Rashid Behbudov str., 1016, AZ
Information: Baku Jazz Centre was founded in the year of 2002. The goal of creating it was to improve and keep up the jazz culture in Azerbaijan. There are live jazz performances almost every evening. The centre has jazz musicians and performers working in different jazz styles and sometimes jazz concerts and movies are displayed on a large screen in the centre.
Country: Azerbaijan
Contact: Director Emil Ibragimov
Capacity: 500

Chamber and Pipe Organ Music Hall
Phone: 124 937 537
Address: 28 May St. 17, AZ
Country: Azerbaijan
Contact: Director Sevil Huseynova
Policies: Other

Folk Circus of Ropewalkers in Zagatala district
Phone: 991 745 5649
Address: 10 Nizami str., AZ
Country: Azerbaijan
Contact: Director Rashid Alekperov

Ganja State Philharmony 'F Amirov'
Phone: 992 305 65321/5
Address: 135 Atayev str., AZ
Country: Azerbaijan

Heydar Aliev Palace
Email: office@ha-saray.com
Phone: 124 988 925
Address: 35 Bul-Bul Ave, 1014, AZ
Country: Azerbaijan
Contact: Director Farhad Babayev

Ibrus Theatre
Phone: 124 922 168
Address: 18, Hasan Seyidbeyli str., Icheri Sheher, AZ
Country: Azerbaijan

Kapellhaus German-Azeri Cultural Assocation
Email: kapellhaus@azerin.com
Phone: 124 938 041
Address: 15/17, 28 May str. 15, AZ
Country: Azerbaijan
Contact: Chairman Robert Schultze

Karvan Jazz Club
Website: www.bakujazz.com
Phone: 129 39003
Address: 19, Rashid Behbudov str., 1016, AZ
Country: Azerbaijan
Contact: Director Emil Ibragimov

Nakchivan State Philarmony
Phone: 991 365 6898
Address: Azadlyg Avenue 1, AZ
Country: Azerbaijan
Contact: Director t.b.a.

Opera Studio 'Shovkat Mammadova'
Phone: 991 293 4668/93
Address: 19 Rashid Behbudov str., AZ
Country: Azerbaijan
Contact: Director Azad Aliev

Shakhriyar Baku Cultural Centre
Phone: 991 249 32583/4
Address: 3 Rashid Beybutov str., AZ
Country: Azerbaijan
Contact: Director Johar Hasanova

Sports and Concerts Complex
Phone: 991 249 07040/4
Address: 2 Abbas Sahhat str., 1000, AZ
Country: Azerbaijan
Contact: Director t.b.a.

Yugh Azerbaijan State Theatre
Phone: 124 943 982
Address: 83, M.Mukhtarov str., AZ
Country: Azerbaijan

BRAZIL

Zikzira Physical Theatre
Website: www.zikzira.com
Email: zz@zikzira.com
Phone: 313 047 6330
Address: Rua Laplace 18, Minas Gerais, BR
Information: Zikzira is a colaboration platform between various Artistic disciplines and between different national identities. Hosts workshops, lectures, as well as live events, installations and exhibitions
Country: Brazil
Social Media: @ZikziraTheatre www.facebook.com/ZikziraPhysicalTheatre
Policies: Rent and present, Theatre

CANADA

Acadia University Performing Arts Series
Website: www.artsacadia.acadiau.ca/acadia-performing-arts-series.html
Email: pas@acadiau.ca
Phone: 902 542 2200
Address: Acadia University, 15 University Avenue, CA
Information: This is a student drama company and venue. Alternative email address peter.smith@acadiau.ca
Country: Canada
Contact: Chair John Eustace
Email: john.eustace@acadiau.ca
Contact: lecturer Susan Barratt
Email: susan.barratt@acadiau.ca
Contact: Director Peter Smith
Email: peter.smith@acadiau.ca
Policies: Rent and present, Other

Alberta Jubilee Auditorium
Website: www.jubileeauditorium.com
Phone: 780 427 2760
Address: 11455 – 87 Avenue, CA
Information: Originally built between 1955 and 1957 as a gift to the people of Alberta, the mandate of the Alberta Jubilee Auditorium is to provide a place of celebration where community spirit and cultural enrichment thrive. Today, the rejuvenated Jubilee Auditorium continues its tradition of public service. In addition to playing host to the world through exciting performances, the Jubilee is Alberta's premier event space. Member of ISPA
Country: Canada
Contact: General Manager Leanne Smoliak
Email: leanne.smoliak@gov.ab.ca
Contact: Executive Director Brett Fraser
Email: brett.fraser@gov.ab.ca
Contact: senior Manager Bonnie Roche
Email: bonnie.roche@gov.ab.ca
Social Media: @itsallatthejube www.facebook.com/itsallatthejube
Capacity: 2538

Amis de la Musique de Richmond
Website: www.centredartderichmond.ca
Email: info@centredartderichmond.ca
Phone: 819 826 2488
Address: 1010 rue Principale Nord, CA
Information: Les Amis de la musique de Richmond, tenant of the Centre d'art de Richmond, is a not-for-profit organization whose mission is to make music and the arts accessible to the population of the Val-Saint-François regional county municipality. It is recognized by the Conseil des arts et des lettres du Québec as a multidisciplinary promoter
Country: Canada
Contact: Director Nancy Pelletier
Email: direction@centredartderichmond.ca
Contact: assistant Director Raphaelle Cadoret
Email: adj@centredartderichmond.ca
Social Media: @CentredArt www.facebook.com/pages/Centre-dArt-de-Richmond
Policies: Present and produce, Arts centre

Amphithéâtre-de-Trois-Rivières
Website: www.amphitheatrecogeco.com
Email: info@amphitheatre3r.com
Phone: 819 378 2009
Address: 100, avenue des Draveurs, PO Box 368, CA
Information: The Cogeco Amphitheatre offers covered seating for 3300 people (in addition to 204 seats in

the corporative boxes) and a grass esplanade that can accommodate up to 5500 people for a total of 9000 people. Its sophisticated outdoor stage equipment can meet the needs of even the largest local, national and international productions. The amphitheatre is located on one of the most prominent sites in the regional capital at the confluence of the St. Lawrence River and St. Maurice River, and is an engine of economic and touristic development for the entire area.
Country: Canada
Contact: General Manager Steve Dubé
Email: sdube@amphitheatre3r.com
Contact: communications Bineta Gueye
Email: bgueye@amphitheatre3r.com
Contact: communications officer Yvana Labouba
Email: ylabouba@amphitheatre3r.com
Contact: logistic support Jocelyn Pelletier
Email: jpelletier@amphitheatre3r.com
Social Media: @AmphitheatreTR www.facebook.com/amphitheatrecogeco
Policies: Rent and present, Open-air

Antigonish Performing Arts Series
Website: www.stfx.ca
Email: msteinit@stfx.ca
Phone: 902 867 3909
Address: St. Francis Xavier University, 1 West St., P. O. Box 5000, CA
Information: Immaculata Auditorium is a venue inside St. Francis Xavier University.
Country: Canada
Social Media: @stfxuniversity www.facebook.com/stfxuniversity
Annual Performances: 10
Annual Productions: 0
Policies: Present and produce, Concert hall

Arden Theatre, The
Website: www.ardentheatre.com
Email: posborne@stalbert.ca
Phone: 780 459 1542
Address: The Arden Theatre, 5 St Anne Street, CA
Information: Since opening its doors in 1984, the Arden Theatre has played host to some of the world's most renowned artists, from Celine Dion to Arlo Guthrie, as well as local musicians, dance schools, theatre troupes and school productions from their own community
Country: Canada
Contact: Marketing and pr coordinator Pamela Osborne
Email: posborne@stalbert.ca
Contact: Director Kelly Jerrott
Email: kjerrott@st-albert.net
Contact: theatre services coordinator Teri Tralnberg
Email: ttralnberg@stalbert.ca
Contact: Marketing coordinator Troy Funk
Email: tfunk@stalbert.ca
Social Media: @theardentheatre www.facebook.com/ardentheatre
Annual Performances: 315
Policies: Theatre

Arts & Culture Centre
Website: www.artsandculturecentre.com
Email: kgalliott@artsandculturecentre.com
Phone: 709 637 2581
Address: 11 University Dr, CA
Information: Committed to excellence and presenting the best to patrons, the Arts and Culture Centre offers a wide variety of programming from the best that Newfoundland has to offer to diverse artists from across Canada and abroad.
Country: Canada
Contact: regional Manager Karin Galliott
Email: kgalliott@artsandculturecentre.com
Contact: lighting technician Harry Tibbo
Email: htibbo@artsandculturecentre.com
Contact: chief technician Terry Jackman
Social Media: @ACC_CB www.facebook.com/pages/Joseph-R-Smallwood-Arts-and-Culture-Centre/231974050186328
Policies: All, Multi-purpose

Arts Commons
Website: https://artscommons.ca/
Email: info@artscommons.ca
Phone:
403 294 9494
Address: 205 8th Avenue S.E., CA
Information: Arts Commons is the home of Calgary's most innovative Artistic companies and partners, and is proud to present and promote creative collaboration within our city.
Country: Canada
President & CEO
Alex Sarian
Email: asarian@artscommons.ca
Contact: Director, Venue Operations Leslie Biles
Email: lbiles@artscommons.ca
Director, Marketing & Sales
Kaija Dirkson
Email: kdirkson@artscommons.ca
Social Media: https://www.instagram.com/yycarts www.facebook.com/yycARTS
Disabled Access: Yes

Capacity: 1000+
Annual Performances: 100+
Policies: All

Arts Court Theatre
Website: www.artscourt.ca
Email: info@artscourt.ca
Phone: 613 765 5555
Address: 2 Daly Avenue, suite 240, Ottawa
Information: Arts Court became Ottawa's central arts hub in 1988. Currently housed in the building are 19+ independent arts organizations

Country: Canada
Contact: arts court coordinator Monique Lachapelle
Social Media: https://twitter.com/artscourt www.facebook.com/artscourt https://www.instagram.com/artscourt/
Disabled Access: Yes
Capacity: 251-500
Policies: All

Banff Centre for the Arts
Website: www.banffcentre.ca
Phone: 403 762 6100
Address: 107 Tunnel Mountain Drive, PO Box 1020, CA
Information: the Banff Centre is the largest arts and creativity incubator on the planet. Our mission is inspiring creativity. Over 8, 000 artists, leaders, and researchers from across Canada and around the world participate in programmes at The Banff Centre every year
Country: Canada
Contact: President and CEO Janice Price
Email: Janice_Price@banffcentre.ca
Phone: 403 762 6139Vice President, Arts and Leadership Howard R. Jang
Email: Howard_Jang@banffcentre.ca
Phone: 403 762 6390
Social Media: https://twitter.com/banffcentre www.facebook.com/TheBanffCentre https://www.instagram.com/banffcentre/
Disabled Access: Yes
Capacity: 251-500
Annual Performances: 25-50
Annual Productions: 0-5
Policies: All

Bert Church Live Theatre
Website: www.thebertchurchtheatre.com
Email: bert.church@airdrie.ca
Phone: 403 948 8824
Address: 1000 E Lake Blvd SE, CA
Information: Located on the east side of Airdrie right next to Genesis Place and East Lake Park, Bert Church Live Theatre is a fully equipped, live performing arts facility.
The 377-seat facility provides audiences with a unique opportunity to experience world renowned performers in a local setting.
Country: Canada
Social Media: https://twitter.com/thebclt www.facebook.com/pages/The-Bert-Church-LIVE-Theatre https://www.instagram.com/thebertchurchlivetheatre/
Capacity: 251-500
Annual Performances: 11-25
Policies: Rent and Present

Brockville Arts Centre
Website: www.brockvilleartscentre.com
Email: bac@brockville.com
Phone: 613 342 7122
Address: 235 King St. West, CA
Information: Located on the St. Lawrence River in the world famous 1000 Islands region, the Brockville Arts Centre is recognised as one of the finest medium-sized historic theatres in Canada. Year after year we welcome thousands of theatre-goers to an experience that makes them feel close and connected to the performers on stage. The Brockville Arts Centre has one of the region's top art galleries, which is fully accessible and provides phonic in-ear devices for those with hearing disabilities. The theatre is air conditioned, has ample free parking and the lobby bar is licensed (LLBO).
Country: Canada
Contact: General Manager Peter Dunn
Email: pdunn@brockville.com
Contact: aministrative coordinator Jonathan Hanna
Email: jhanna@brockville.com
Contact: theatre technician Michael Sherman
Email: msherman@brockville.com
Social Media: www.facebook.com/thebrockvilleartscentre
Policies: Rent and present, Theatre

Canadian Museum of History
Website: www.historymuseum.ca
Email: information@historymuseum.ca
Phone: 819 776 7000
Address: 100 Laurier Street, CA
Information: The Museum's Theatre is suitable for a wide range of conferences and productions. Comprehensive technical information is available upon request. The Museum Box Office can assist with ticketing for all performing arts events.

Country: Canada
Social Media: @CanMusHistory www.facebook.com/CanMusHistory
Policies: Rent and present, Other

Capitol Centre
Website: www.capitolcentre.org
Email: boxoffice@capitolcentre.org
Phone: 705 474 1944
Address: 150 Main Street East, CA
Information: The property upon which the Capitol was built was purchased in 1927 by Louis Rosenbaum, a Sturgeon Falls businessman
Country: Canada
Contact: General Manager Dee Adrian
Email: dadrian@capitolcentre.org
Contact: Marketing Manager Katelyn Ricci
Email: kricci@capitolcentre.org
Social Media: @capitolcentre www.facebook.com/CapitolCentre
Policies: Rent and present, Arts centre

Carlu, The
Website: www.thecarlu.com
Email: events@thecarlu.com
Phone: 416 597 1931
Address: 444 Yonge Street, 7th Floor, Box 35, CA
Information: This architectural masterpiece, designated a National Historic Site, has been completely restored to its original 1930s splendour and glory, while boasting the very best in modern technology. The Carlu's one-of-a-kind surroundings and absolute multi-functionality, combined with its commitment to the ultimate sophistication and service will ensure the success of any event whether social, corporate or cultural.
Country: Canada
Contact: event specialist Morgan Bascom
Email: morgan.bascom@oliverbonacini.com
Contact: event specialist Natasha Ugarkovic
Email: natasha.ugarkovic@oliverbonacini.com
Social Media: @TheCarlu www.facebook.com/TheCarlu
Policies: Rent and present, Other

Centennial Theatre
Website: www.nvrc.ca/centennial-theatre
Email: ctcboxoffice@nvrc.ca
Phone: 604 984 4484
Address: 2300 Lonsdale Avenue, CA
Information: The largest multi-purpose performing arts venue on Vancouver's North Shore, Centennial Theatre is an ideal setting for a wide range of performances, special events, film screenings and workshops. With 658 seats, new state-of-the-art sound, lighting and projection systems, professional in-house technical staff and a versatile lobby space with a licenced concession, the theatre is an ideal rental venue for all kinds of touring acts and productions.
Country: Canada
Social Media: @Centennial_Thtr www.facebook.com/CentennialTheatre
Policies: Rent and present, Concert hall

Center in the Square
Website: centreinthesquare.com
Email: boxoffice@centreinthesquare.com
Phone: 519 578 5660
Address: 101 Queen Street North, CA
Information: The venue boasts a main hall which is acknowledged as a technical state-of-the-arts theatre, making it acoustically superior and widely regarded as one of the finest performance spaces in North America
Country: Canada
Contact: Chair Bruce Gordon
Social Media: @Centre_Square www.facebook.com/CentreInTheSquare
Policies: Rent and present, Other

Centre Communautaire Sainte-Anne
Website: www.centre-sainte-anne.nb.ca
Email: info@centre-sainte-anne.nb.ca
Phone: 506 453 2731
Address: 715 rue Priestman, CA
Information: Centre Communautaire Sainte-Anne offers a variety of cultural and community programmes, including performing arts for adults and youths, French films for the whole family, exhibitions, courses, workshops and more.
Country: Canada
Contact: Director General Thierry Arseneau
Email: tarseneau@centre-sainte-anne.nb.ca
Contact: Executive assistant Sylvette Drisdelle
Email: sdrisdelle@centre-sainte-anne.nb.ca
Contact: communications officer Anny Martel
Email: amartel@centre-sainte-anne.nb.ca
Contact: project officer Lôdvi Bongers
Email: lodvi@centre-sainte-anne.nb.ca
Social Media: @CCSAFred www.facebook.com/Centre.communautaire.Sainte.Anne/
Policies: Present and produce, Arts centre

Centre Culturel de Drummondville
Website: www.centre-culturel.qc.ca
Email: clahaie@centre-culturel.qc.ca
Phone: 819 477 5412

Address: 175, rue Ringuet, CA
Information: Centre Culturel de Drummondville is set in a modern destination and offers a range of theatre, music, comedy and lectures in a large stylish space.
Country: Canada
Contact: General Director Roland Janelle
Email: rjanelle@artsdrummondville.com
Contact: communications Director Claire Lahaie
Email: clahaie@artsdrummondville.com
Contact: co-Director Robert Fréchette
Email: rfrechette@artsdrummondville.com
Contact: public service Marie-Claude Lapierre
Email: mclapierre@artsdrummondville.com
Contact: technical Director Yves Daniel
Email: ydaniel@artsdrummondville.com
Social Media: @artsdrummond www.facebook.com/artsdrummondville
Annual Performances: 30
Annual Productions: 125
Policies: All, Other

Centre Culturel de Joliette
Website: www.spectaclesjoliette.com
Email: info@spectaclesjoliette.com
Phone: 450 759 6202
Address: 20, rue St-Charles-Borromée Sud, CA
Information: Established in 1979, this cultural center has the mission of presenting cultural activities. In particular, it broadcasts performances at the Salle Rolland-Brunelle and at the TELUS Cabaret. Now recognized for its diverse programming and exceptional subscriptions, it has become a must in the region.
Country: Canada
Contact: General Director Gilles Pitre
Social Media: @RollandBrunelle www.facebook.com/centre.culturel.joliette
Policies: Rent and present, Theatre

Centre culturel de l'Université de Sherbrooke
Website: www.centrecultureludes.ca
Email: dd-culture@USherbrooke.ca
Phone: 819 821 7742
Address: Centre culturel de l'Université, 2500, boul. de l'Université, CA
Information: located in the heart of the region, the Cultural Center of the University of Sherbrooke includes Salle Maurice-O'Bready, four fireplaces, two lounges and an Art Gallery
Country: Canada
Contact: General Director Mario Trépanier
Contact: communication Anne-Sophie Laplante
Email: anne-sophie.laplante@usherbrooke.ca
Contact: secretary Sophie Pouliot
Email: sophie.pouliot@usherbrooke.ca
Social Media: www.facebook.com/CentreCulturelUdeS
Policies: Multi-purpose

Centre culturel de Rivière-du-Loup
Website: www.centreculturelrdl.com
Phone: 418 867 6666
Address: Centre Culturel, 85 Rue Sainte-Anne, CA
Information: although it is rooted in the community, the Corporation allows organisations in the region to broadcast each year nearly forty activities in fields of arts such as classical music, creation, dance, song, humour or youth shows
Country: Canada
Contact: Managing Director and head of programming Pierre Lévesque
Contact: communications officer Marie Claude Durand
Social Media: @CCRDL www.facebook.com/pages/Centre-Culturel-Rivi%C3%A8re-du-Loup/265521276809795
Policies: Multi-purpose

Centre Culturel Franco-Manitobain
Website: www.ccfm.mb.ca
Email: ccfm@ccfm.mb.ca
Phone: 204 233 8972
Address: 340 Provencher Boulevard, CA
Information: Bent on discovery, creation, and surprise, the Centre culturel franco-manitobain (CCFM) offers a variety of activities to suit all ages and all tastes. Since 1974, the Centre has played an important role by featuring all forms of French-language, Artistic and cultural activities. It has given all Manitobans a chance to experience French-Canadian culture. Recognized as a cultural centre and crossroad for French cultural life in Manitoba, it implements a performing arts and visual arts programme as well as a community and educational programme for residents of Manitoba.
Country: Canada
Contact: Artistic programming coordinator Helene Molin-Gautron
Email: programmation@ccfm.mb.ca
Contact: programming assistant coordinator Daniel Girard
Email: dgirard@ccfm.mb.ca
Social Media: @CCFManitobain www.facebook.com/CCFManitobain
Policies: All, Multi-purpose

Centre for the Arts, Brock University
Website: brocku.ca/centreforthearts
Email: dslade@brocku.ca

Phone: 905 688 5550
Address: Brock University, 500 Glenridge Ave., CA
Information: the centre is split into two performance spaces which are the Sean O'Sullivan Theatre (533 seats) and the David S. Howes Theatre (500 seats)
Country: Canada
Contact: Director Debbie Slade
Email: dslade@brocku.ca
 Sales & Marketing coordinator
 Sara Palmieri
Email: sara.palmieri@brocku.ca
Contact: administrative assistant Deena Johnson
Email: djohnson@brocku.ca

Centre National des Arts du Canada
Email: info@nac-cna.ca
Phone: 613 947 7000
Address: 1 Elgin Street, CA
Information: The National Arts Centre collaborates with artists and arts organizations across Canada to help create a national stage for the performing arts, and acts as a catalyst for performance, creation and learning across the country. The NAC is also a pioneer in new media, using technology to teach students and young artists around the globe, by creating top-rated podcasts, and providing a wide range of NAC Orchestra concerts on demand. Member of ISPA
Country: Canada
Contact: Chair Adrian Burns
Contact: Executive Producer Heather Gibson
Email: heather.gibson@nac-cna.ca
Contact: Artistic Director Jillian Keiley
Email: EnglishTheatreAD@nac-cna.ca
Contact: President and CEO Peter Herrndorf
Email: peter.herrndorf@nac-cna.ca
Social Media: @CanadasNAC www.facebook.com/CanadasNAC.CNAduCanada
Policies: Arts centre

Centre Pierre-Péladeau
Website: www.centrepierrepeladeau.uqam.ca
Email: centrepierrepeladeau@uqam.ca
Phone: 514 987 4691
Address: Le centre Pierre-Péladeau, 300, boulevard de Maisonneuve Est, CA
Information: located in the centre of the Latin Quarter and part of the University of Quebec in Montreal, the Centre Pierre-Peladeau is available for the cultural community
Country: Canada
Contact: General Director Guy Vanasse
Email: vanasse.guy@uqam.ca
Contact: Administration David Perreault
Email: perreault.david@uqam.ca
Contact: technical Director Jean Paquette
Email: paquette.jean@uqam.ca
Policies: Rent and present, Multi-purpose

Centrepointe Theatre
Website: www.centrepointetheatre.com
Email: centrepointe.theatre@ottawa.ca
Phone: 613 580 2700
Address: 101 Centrepointe Drive, CA
Information: Centrepointe Theatre's grand opening took place on May 3, 1988, starring "local boy" and internationally renowned entertainer and imPressionist, Rich Little. Since then the theatre has hosted an extensive list of truly great artists performing to sold-out houses.
Country: Canada
Contact: booking services Christine Etherington
 Artistic Producer & Manager
 Allan Sansom
Social Media: @CentrepointeT www.facebook.com/centrepointetheatre
Policies: Rent and present, Theatre

Chan Centre for the Performing Arts – At the University of British Columbia
Website: www.chancentre.com
Email: chan.centre@ubc.ca
Phone: 604 822 9197
Address: University of British Columbia, 6265 Crescent Road, CA
Information: Since its opening in spring 1997, the Chan Centre for the Performing Arts has earned an international reputation for its striking design, stellar acoustics and exceptional programming. Artists, critics and audiences alike are unanimous in their praise of this multi-faceted facility, winning it a place among North America's premier performing arts centres. Member of ISPA
Country: Canada
Contact: rentals and programming assistant Laura Busby
Email: laura.busby@ubc.ca
Contact: co-Managing Director Joyce Hinton
Email: joyce.hinton@ubc.ca
Contact: programming Manager Wendy Atkinson
Email: wendy.atkinson@ubc.ca
Social Media: @chancentre www.facebook.com/chan.centre.ubc
Policies: All, Concert hall

Christ Church Cathedral Concert Series
Website: www.cathedralarts.com
Email:

info@cathedralarts.ca
Phone: 613 236 9149
Address: 414 Sparks Street, CA
Information: Christ Church Cathedral is the Anglican cathedral in Ottawa, Ontario, Canada. The church is located at 414 Sparks Street in the northwest section of the city's downtown at the western end of Sparks Street on top of a promontory looking down to the Ottawa River
Country: Canada
Social Media: @CathArtsOttawa www.facebook.com/cathedralartsottawa
Annual Performances: 10
Policies: Rent only, Other

Chrysler Theatre
Website: www.chryslertheatre.com
Email: theatreoperations@stclaircollege.ca
Phone: 519 252 6579
Address: St. Clair College Centre for the Arts, 201 Riverside Drive, CA
Information: The Chrysler Theatre is dedicated to bringing quality entertainment, as well as providing our local performing arts community with a venue designed to achieve excellence in the performing arts. Nestled within the St. Clair College Centre for the Arts, this venue provides the perfect space and atmosphere, not only for excellence in theatre events, but also a place to have meetings, conferences, weddings and banquets of up to 800.
Country: Canada
Contact: theatre Manager Veronica Mancini
Email: vmancini@stclaircollege.ca
Social Media: https://twitter.com/chryslertheatre https://www.instagram.com/ChryslerTheatre/
Disabled Access: Yes
Capacity: 501-1000
Policies: All

Citadel Theatre
Website: www.citadeltheatre.com
Email: citadel@citadeltheatre.com
Phone: 780 425 1820
Address: 9828 101A Avenue, CA
Information: The site constraints, complicated by an existing underground parking garage entrance, have been turned to advantage by embracing the arrival of cars from the street as part of the lobby prospect. The main theater is raised over the pedestrian mall with the underside of the seating forming a dynamic sculpted roof, as well as providing views between lobbies and mall.
Country: Canada
Contact: Artistic Director Bob Baker
Email: bbaker@citadeltheatre.com
Contact: Executive Director Penny Ritco
Email: pritco@citadeltheatre.com
Social Media: @citadeltheatre www.facebook.com/citadeltheatre
Policies: All, Multi-purpose

Conexus Arts Centre
Website: www.conexusartscentre.ca
Email: cac.admin@conexusartscentre.ca
Phone: 306 565 4500
Address: 200A Lakeshore Drive, CA
Information: The Conexus Arts Centre, known from 1970 until 2006 as the Saskatchewan Centre of the Arts, is a world class performing arts and theatre complex located within the heart of Wascana Centre in Regina, Saskatchewan. Constructed to commemorate Canada's centenary in 1967, it was opened by Governor General Roland Michener on August 24, 1970 to serve southern Saskatchewan as a centre for performing arts and exhibitions.
Country: Canada
Contact: client services coordinator Jim McCrum
Contact: chief Executive officer Neil Donnelly
Contact: theatre services Manager Shari Tourscher
Social Media: @conexusartscntr www.facebook.com/ConexusArtsCentre
Policies: Present, produce, co-produce, Theatre

Confederation Centre of the Arts
Website: www.confederationcentre.com
Email: info@confederationcentre.com
Phone: 902 628 1864
Address: 145 Richmond Street, CA
Information: Confederation Centre of the Arts is an excellent performance venue with the capacity to service virtually any requirement you may have. Located within walking distance of hotels, shops and restaurants, the Centre is a full-service rental facility.
Country: Canada
Contact: CEO Jessie Inman
Social Media: @ConfedCentre www.facebook.com/charlottetownfestival
Policies: All, Arts centre

Corporation Culturelle de Shawinigan
Website:
www.cultureshawinigan.ca
Email: corporationculturelle@shawinigan.ca
Phone:
819 539 1888
Address: 2100, boulevard des Hêtres, CA

Information: Corporation Culturelle de Shawinigan encourages and promotes the sustainable development of the arts, literature and culture in the territory of Shawinigan
Country: Canada
Contact: Artistic Director Louise Martin
Email: lmartin@shawinigan.ca
Contact: assistant Director Renée Vachon
Email: rvachon@shawinigan.ca
Social Media: @cultureshawi www.facebook.com/cultureshawi
Annual Productions: 150
Policies: Rent and present, Theatre

Corporation de la Salle Albert-Rousseau
Website: www.sallealbertrousseau.com
Email: billetterie@salle-a-rousseau.qc.ca
Phone: 418 659 6629
Address: Salle Albert-Rousseau 2410, chemin Sainte-Foy Québec
Information: An Italian-style performance hall, with a capacity of 1348 seats, the imPressive Salle Albert-Rousseau in Quebec City presents professional shows of variety, humor, song, theater and film conferences. Recognized as such by the various players in the entertainment industry and by public authorities, it is a major beacon for cultural art in all its forms.
Country: Canada
Contact: General Manager Claude Désormeaux
Contact: technical Director Michel Vezina
Contact: Director of programming and productions Julie Corriveau
Email: jcorriveau@salle-a-rousseau.qc.ca
Phone: 418 659 6629
Social Media: https:// www.facebook.com/sallealbertrousseau/ https:// www.instagram.com/salle_albert_rousseau/ https://twitter.com/salbertrousseau
Capacity: 1000+
Annual Performances: 100+
Policies: Rent and Present

Corporation Hector-Charland
Website: www.hector-charland.com
Email: hcharland@hector-charland.com
Phone: 450 589 9198
Address: 225, boul. de L'Ange-Gardien, CA
Information: Built on the site of one of Quebec's early academic halls, the Théâtre Hector-Charland became a key player in the cultural life of the Lanaudière region right from the start. The space is much sought after for its wonderful sense of intimacy in terms of acoustics and sight lines.
Country: Canada
Contact: General Artistic Director Claude de Grandpré
Email: cdegrandpre@hector-charland.com
Contact: deputy Director General Evelyne Chagnon
Email: echagnon@hector-charland.com
Social Media: @THCLAssomption www.facebook.com/pages/Théâtre-Hector-Charland/
Policies: Rent and present, Theatre

Corporation of Massey Hall and Roy Thomson Hall
Website: www.masseyhallandroythomsonhall.com
Email: contactus@mh-rth.com
Phone: 416 872 4255
Address: 178 Victoria Street, CA
Information: The Corporation of Massey Hall and Roy Thomson Hall is a not-for-profit charitable organization operating two of Canada's premier concert halls. Showcasing the world's greatest performers in all disciplines, the Halls are also prominent venues for diverse activities in the business and entertainment district of downtown Toronto. Member of ISPA
Country: Canada
Contact: Chair of the board Eileen Costello
Contact: President and chief Executive officer Deane Cameron
Social Media: @SOundboardTO www.facebook.com/soundboardTO
Policies: Rent and present, Concert hall

Cowichan Theatre
Website: www.cowichanpac.ca
Phone: 250 748 7529
Address: 2687 James Street, CA
Information: The Cowichan Performing Arts Centre (formerly known as the Cowichan Theatre) is a 731-seat proscenium arch theatre located in the Island Savings Centre, Duncan, BC. Opened in 1978, the Cowichan Performing Arts Centre serves the Cowichan region as a community theatre for local groups, as a roadhouse for touring professional artists, and as a conference and convention facility.
Country: Canada
Contact: technical Director Michael Schaefer
Email: mschaefer@cvrd.bc.ca
Contact: Manager Kristen Schrader
Email: kschrader@cvrd.bc.ca
Social Media: @CowichanPAC www.facebook.com/CowichanPAC
Policies: Rent and present, Theatre

Dance Victoria

Website: www.dancevictoria.com
Email: social@dancevictoria.com
Phone: 250 595 1829
Address: 2750 Quadra Street, CA
Information: Dance Victoria brings the world's best dance to the Royal Theatre and supports the development of new dance from its beautiful studios in Victoria's Quadra Village. Dance Victoria presents an annual subscription series at the Royal Theatre.
Country: Canada
Contact: Executive Producer Stephen White
Email: Producer@dancevictoria.com
Contact: General Manager Bernard Sauvé
Email: gm@dancevictoria.com
Contact: Marketing Manager Tracy Smith
Email: Marketing@dancevictoria.com
Contact: undefined
Social Media: https://twitter.com/dance_victoria https://www.instagram.com/dance_victoria/
Disabled Access: Yes
Capacity: 501-1000
Annual Performances: 25-50
Policies: All

Dancers' Studio West
Website: www.dswlive.ca
Email: communications@dswlive.ca
Phone: 403 244 0950
Address: PO Box 94097, RPO Elbow River, CA
Information: founded in 1980, DSW was opened as a dance community for Calgary. They know, produce and display a number of performances throughout the year
Country: Canada
Contact: Artistic Director Davida Monk
Email: davidamonk@dswlive.ca
Contact: President Megan Ballard
Social Media: @DSWTheatre www.facebook.com/pages/Dancers-Studio-West/302415829798850
Policies: Present and produce, Other

DanceWorks
Website: www.danceworks.ca
Email: info@danceworks.ca
Phone: 416 204 1082
Address: 15 Case Goods Lane, Studio 304, CA
Information: DanceWorks' matinees provide students with the experience of attending a professional contemporary dance show, followed by a lively question and answer period with dancers and choreographers. Attending a live performance offers students the opportunity to expand world perspectives and cultivates the skills to watch, analyze, feel, and appreciate a diversity of performance experiences. Workshops allow for further enrichment as students work directly with artists and explore movement, composition, and themes presented in our matinee presentations.
Country: Canada
Contact: General Manager Rosslyn Jacob Edwards
Email: rcj@danceworks.ca
Contact: dance curator Mimi Beck
Email: mbeck@danceworks.ca
Contact: programming and administrative assistant Julie McLachlan
Email: julie@danceworks.ca
Contact: education and outreach officer Kate Cornell
Email: education@danceworks.ca
Contact: President Tracy Hooey
Social Media: @DanceWorksMimi www.facebook.com/dance.danceworks
Policies: All, Arts centre

Diffusion Culturelle de Levis
Website: www.diffusionculturelledelevis.ca/
Email: info@diffusionculturelledelevis.ca
Phone: 418 838 6001
Address: 33 rue Wolfe, CP 60033, CA
Information: production company that produces plays
Country: Canada
Contact: coordinator Shanti Sarrazin
Contact: General Director Diane Blanchette
Contact: President Brigitte Duchesneau
Policies: Rent and present, Theatre

Early Music Vancouver
Website: www.earlymusic.bc.ca
Email: staff@earlymusic.bc.ca
Phone: 604 732 1610
Address: 1254 West 7th Avenue, CA
Information: performed on historical instruments; offers a winter and summer concert series, and summer workshops as part of the Vancouver Early Music Programme and Festival
Country: Canada
Contact: Managing Director Sarah Ballantyne
Email: staff@earlymusic.bc.ca
public relations & development
Deborah Jackson
Contact: Artistic Director Matthew White
Social Media: @EarlyMusicVan www.facebook.com/earlymusicvancouver
Policies: Rent only, Other

Elgin and Winter Garden Theatre Centre
Website: www.heritagetrust.on.ca/ewg

Email: ewg@heritagetrust.on.ca
Phone: 416 314 2901
Address: Elgin and Winter Garden Theatre Centre, 189 Yonge Street, CA
Information: primary rental: musicals, dramas, concerts; it is a national historic site; the complex is the last operating double-decker theatre in the world; spaces also available for corporate events, receptions, lectures and private functions**Country: Canada**
Contact: front of house Manager Lori MacLean
Contact: General Manager Brett Randall
Contact: Director of production Dana Johnston
Policies: Rent and present, Theatre

Firehall Arts Centre
Website: www.firehallartscentre.ca
Email: firehall@firehallartscentre.ca
Phone: 604 689 0691
Address: 280 East Cordova Street, CA
Information: dance festival: dancing on the edge festival; also production of 3-5 plays reflecting the cultural diversity in Canada
Country: Canada
Artistic Director & Artistic Producer
Donna Spencer
Email: dspencer@firehallartscentre.ca
Contact: technical Director Jamie Burns
Email: technicalDirector@firehallartscentre.ca
Contact: Associate Producer Caitlin MacKee
Email: cmckee@firehallartscentre.ca
Social Media: @FirehallArtsCte www.facebook.com/firehallartscentre
Policies: All, Arts centre

Flato Markham Theatre
Website: www.markhamtheatre.ca
Email: 305_show@markham.ca
Phone: 905 305 7469
Address: 171 Town Centre Blvd, CA
Information: Flato Markham Theatre is one of Canada's premier theatre houses serving the GTA and Markham residents. The theatre has over 300 live performances each year. Member of ISPA
Country: Canada
Social Media: @MarkhamTheatre www.facebook.com/MarkhamTheatre171
Policies: Rent and present, Theatre

Four Seasons Centre for the Performing Arts
Website: www.fourseasonscentre.ca
Email: info@fourseasonscentre.ca
Phone: 416 363 6671
Address: 145 Queen St. W, CA
Information: Four Seasons Centre for the Performing Arts is the first building of its kind in Canada; a theatre built specifically for opera and ballet performances. Owned and used primarily by the Canadian Opera Company (see performing companies)
Country: Canada
Contact: Chair Philip C. Deck
Social Media: @CanadianOpera www.facebook.com/canadianoperacompany
Policies: Rent and present, Concert hall

Fredericton Playhouse, The
Website: www.theplayhouse.ca
Email: admin@theplayhouse.ca
Phone: 506 458 8345
Address: Fredericton Playhouse Inc, 686 Queen Street, CA
Country: Canada
Social Media: @FredPlayhouse www.facebook.com/thefrederictonplayhouse

Friends of Chamber Music
Website: www.friendsofchambermusic.ca
Email: FCMtickets@yahoo.com
Phone: 604 437 5747
Address: PO Box 38046 RPO, King Edward Mall, CA
Information: a venue that puts on performances of chamber music throughout the year
Country: Canada
Social Media: www.facebook.com/pages/Friends-of-Chamber-Music-Vancouver-BC-Canada
Annual Performances: 10
Policies: Rent and present, Theatre

Georgian Music Series
Website: www.barrieconcerts.ca
Email: bruCEOwen@owendickey.com
Phone: 705 725 1070
Address: P.O. Box 452, CA
Information: present young Canadian musicians
Country: Canada
Contact: Director of artists' selection Bruce Owen
Policies: Rent only, Rent and present, Other

Glenn Gould Studio – Canadian Broadcasting Centre
Website: www.glenngouldstudio.com
Email: ggsinfo@glenngouldstudio.com
Address: 250 Front St West, CA
Information: performance hall and 48 digital track recording studio for concert performances; rental only

Country: Canada
Contact: senior Manager Shannon Spafford
Email: shannon.spafford@cbc.ca
Contact: assistant Manager Florence Ballard
Email: florence.ballard@cbc.ca
Contact: studio engineer Chris Jackson
Email: chris.jackson@cbc.ca
Contact: event coordinator Aimée Tobolka
Email: aimee.tobolka@cbc.ca
Social Media: www.facebook.com/pages/CBC-Glenn-Gould-Studio
Policies: Rent only, Theatre

Globe Theatre
Website: www.globetheatrelive.com
Email: onstage@globetheatrelive.com
Phone: 306 525 6400
Address: Globe Theatre, 1801 Scarth Street, CA
Information: disabled access lift to balcony and wheel-Chair access
Country: Canada
 Artistic Director & CEO
 Ruth Smillie
Email: ruths@globetheatrelive.com
Contact: Artistic Associate Andrew North
Email: andrewn@globetheatrelive.com
Social Media: @GlobeRegina www.facebook.com/pages/Globe-Theatre/33881883223
Annual Productions: 12
Policies: Present and produce, Theatre

Grand Falls Windsor Arts and Culture Centre
Website: www.artsandculturecentre.com
Email: rlodge@artsandculturecentre.com
Address: c/o Provincial Building, Cromer Avenue, CA
Information: operated and programmed by Newfoundland Department of Tourism, Culture & Recreation – Cultural Affairs Division**Country: Canada**
Contact: Manager Robert Lodge
Email: rlodge@artsandculturecentre.com
Social Media: @GPCFTA www.facebook.com/pages/Gordon-Pinsent-Centre-for-the-Arts
Annual Performances: 60
Policies: All, Arts centre

Grand Theatre
Website: www.kingstongrand.ca
Email: grandtheatre2@cityofkingston.ca
Phone: 613 530 2050
Address: The Grand Theatre, 218 Princess Street, CA
Country: Canada
Contact: cultural Director Colin Wiginton
Email: cwiginton@cityofkingston.ca
Contact: theatre Manager Dianne Zemba
Email: dzemba@cityofkingston.ca
Contact: production supervisor Larry Stafford
Email: lstafford@cityofkingston.ca
Contact: front of house coordinator Robert Downes
Email: rdownes@cityofkingston.ca
Contact: box office coordinator Rebecca Brown
Email: rbrown@cityofkingston.ca
Contact: performing arts Manager Jayson Duggan
Email: jduggan@cityofkingston.ca
Contact: communications officer Bob Giarda
Email: rgiarda@cityofkingston.ca
Contact: grand theatre foundation Carol Anne Muncaster
Email: camuncaster@cityofkingston.ca
Contact: Marketing Manager Julie Fossitt
Email: jfossitt@cityofkingston.ca
Contact: communications officer Amy Paauw
Email: apaauw@cityofkingston.ca
Social Media: @Kingston_Grand www.facebook.com/kingstongrandtheatre
Policies: All, Theatre

Grand Théâtre de Québec
Website: www.grandtheatre.qc.ca
Email: gtq@grandtheatre.qc.ca
Phone: 418 643 8131
Address: Grand Théâtre de Québec, 269, boulevard René-Lévesque Est, CA
Information: a building in Quebec containing various arts for the community
Country: Canada
Contact: CEO Marcel Dallaire
Contact: President Suzanne Gagné
Contact: vice President Lemay Alain
Social Media: @GrandTheatreQc www.facebook.com/grandtheatre?ref=search&s id=585916673.941688130..1
Policies: Theatre

Grande Prairie Live Theatre
Website: www.gplt.ab.ca
Email: box.office@gplt.ab.ca
Phone:
780 538 1616
Address: 10130-98 Avenue, CA
Information: plays, movies and concerts
Country: Canada
Contact: General Manager Wayne Ayling
Email: Manager@gplt.ab.ca
Contact: technical Director Bryan Strong

Email: technical.Director@gplt.ab.ca
Social Media: www.facebook.com/pages/Grande-Prairie-Live-Theatre
Annual Productions: 20
Policies: Rent and present, Theatre

Grant MacEwan College, John L Haar Theatre
Website: https:// www.macewan.ca/wcm/index.htm
Email:
info@macewan.ca
Phone:
780 497 4340
Address: Building 7, 10700, 104 Avenue NW Edmonton, Alberta
Information: Allard Hall is located on the western edge of McEwan University's downtown campus, right next to one of the most dynamic urban arts districts in the country.**Country: Canada**
Contact: theatre Manager Geoff Bacchus
Email: bacchusg@macewan.ca
Social Media: https://twitter.com/macewanu www.facebook.com/GrantMacEwanUniversity https:// www.instagram.com/macewanu/
Disabled Access: Yes
Capacity: 501-1000
Policies: All

Gros Becs, Centre de Diffusion de Théâtre Jeunesse
Website: www.lesgrosbecs.qc.ca
Email: info@lesgrosbecs.qc.ca
Phone: 418 522 7880
Address: 939 avenue, De Salaberry, CA
Information: professional theatre for a young audience (3-15 years old)
Country: Canada
Contact: Director Louise Allaire
Contact: co-Artistic Director Helen Blanchard
Contact: Director Renée Hudon
Social Media: @grosbecs www.facebook.com/grosbecs
Policies: Present and produce, Theatre

Hamilton Entertainment and Convention Facilities Inc
Website: www.hecfi.ca
Email: hectemp@hamilton.ca
Phone: 905 546 3100
Address: 10 MacNab St. South, CA
Information: home to four different venues – Copps Coliseum, Hamilton Place, Molson Canadian Studio and the Convention Centre
Country: Canada
Contact: Marketing/public relations officer Debra Vivian
Contact: Director of operations/events delivery Brad Calder
Contact: chief Executive officer Duncan Gillespie
Social Media: @HECFI_fans www.facebook.com/pages/Copps-Coliseum-Hamilton-Place-Hamilton-Convention-Centre
Policies: All, Multi-purpose

Hornby Festival Society
Website: www.hornbyfestival.bc.ca
Email: hornbyfestival@uniserve.com
Phone: 250 335 2734
Address: Hornby Festival Society, 2125 Sollans Road, CA
Information: Hornby Festival (q.v.) and other presentations
Country: Canada
Contact: interim Artistic Director Marc Atkinson
Contact: administrative Director Charmaine Logan
Social Media: www.facebook.com/HornbyFestival

Imperial Theatre
Website: www.imperialtheatre.nb.ca
Email: admin@imperialtheatre.nb.ca
Phone: 506 674 4100
Address: 24 King Square South, CA
Information: theatre that puts on shows and productions
Country: Canada
Contact: Executive Director Sharolyn Lee
Email: lee@imperialtheatre.nb.ca
Contact: assistant Executive Director Angela Campbell
Email: angela@imperialtheatre.nb.ca
Contact: operations Manager Jim Wilson
Email: jim@imperialtheatre.nb.ca
Contact: technical Director Shelley Brown
Email: shelley@imperialtheatre.nb.ca
Social Media: @ImperialTheatre www.facebook.com/ImperialTheatre
Policies: Rent and present, Theatre

Institut Canadien de Quebec
Website: www.institutcanadien.qc.ca
Email: courrier@icqbdq.qc.ca
Phone: 418 641 6788
Address: 350, rue Saint-Joseph Est, CA
Information: an organisation that makes art more accessible to the population of Quebec
Country: Canada
Contact: General Director Jean Payeur
Social Media: @ICQ_Quebec www.facebook.com/pages/LInstitut-Canadien-de-Qu%C3%A9bec/176468254731

Policies: Arts centre

Isabel Bader Centre for the Performing Arts
Website: www.theisabel.ca
Email: ibcpaboxoffice@queensu.ca
Phone: 613 533 6000
Address: 390 King Street West, Room 144, CA
Information: home for the creative arts at Queen's University and a hub of vibrant Artistic study, creation and exhibition in the community; provides learning experience to students studying at the university
Country: Canada
Contact: Director Tricia Baldwin
Email: jerry.doiron@queensu.ca
Kaméléart Matane
Website: www.kameleart.com
Email: kameleart@kameleart.com
Address: 616 avenue St Redempteur, CA
Information: Performing arts, primarily comedy venue.
Country: Canada
Contact: Artistic Director Marie-Claire Cot
Contact: programme Director Patsy Fournier
Contact: President Jeannine Desrosiers
Contact: treasurer Pierre Late
Social Media: http:// www.facebook.com/Kameleart
Policies: Other

Kay Meek Centre
Website: www.kaymeekcentre.com
Email: info@kaymeekcentre.com
Phone: 604 981 6335
Address: 1700 Mathers Avenue, West Vancouver, , CA
Information: member of ISPA
Country: Canada
Social Media: www.facebook.com/KayMeekCentre

Keyano Theatre & Arts Centre
Website: www.keyano.ca/theatre
Email: info@keyano.ca
Phone: 780 715 3921
Address: 8115 Franklin Avenue Fort McMurray
Information: Hosting hundreds of school, community, corporate and college events, the Keyano Theatre and Arts Centre is also available for rentals. This is a state-of-the-art facility with dance and music studios, rehearsal spaces, a 594-seat main stage theatre, a 194-seat recital theatre, an art gallery, and various reception opportunities.**Country: Canada**
Contact: Events Services Coordinator Diane Schuldt-Zundel
Social Media: https://twitter.com/keyanotheatre www.facebook.com/keyanotheatre https:// www.instagram.com/keyanotheatre/
Disabled Access: Yes
Capacity: 501-1000
Policies: Rent and Present

Kitchener-Waterloo Chamber Music Society
Website: www.k-wcms.com
Email: kwcms@yahoo.ca
Phone: 519 886 1673
Address: 57 Young St West, CA
Information: arrange concerts by other musicians, mostly touring. Present only chamber music and solo concerts
Country: Canada
Contact: President Jan Narveson
Email: kwcms@yahoo.ca
Annual Performances: 75
Policies: Present, produce, co-produce, Concert hall

La Maison Symphonique de Montréal
Website: www.adressesymphonique.gouv.qc.ca
Email: annie.legruiec@mcccf.gouv.qc.ca
Phone: 418 380 2363
Address: CA
Country: Canada
Contact: public relations officer Annie Legruiec
Email: annie.legruiec@mcccf.gouv.qc.ca

Labrador City Arts and Culture Centre
Website: https://artsandculturecentre.com/labwest/Online/default.asp
Email: support@artsandculturecentre.com
Phone: 709 944 7132
Address: 300 Hudson DriveLabrador City,
Information: A division of the Department of Tourism, Culture, Industry and Innovation, the head offices of the Arts and Culture Centres are located in the St. John's Arts and Culture Centre. Committed to excellence and presenting the best to patrons, the Arts and Culture Centres offer a wide variety of programming from the best that Newfoundland has to offer to diverse artists from across Canada and abroad. The Labrador West Arts and culture Centres first performance was held on February 14, 1986.
Country: Canada
Contact: Manager Chris Ball
Email: cball@artsandculturecentre.com
Phone: 709 944 7345
Social Media: https://twitter.com/ACCLabWest https:// www.facebook.com/ACC.Labrador.West/
Disabled Access: Yes
Capacity: 251-500
Annual Performances: 11-25
Policies: Rent and Present

Les Grands Ballets Canadiens de Montreal
Website: www.grandsballets.com
Email: info@grandsballets.com
Phone: 514 849 0269
Address: 4816 rue Rivard, CA
Information: since it was formed in 1957, Les Grand Ballets has remained loyal to the very essence of classical ballet and continues exploring new territory for dance lovers both near and far. Member of ISPA
Country: Canada
Contact: Executive Director Alain Dancyger
Contact: Director of touring and guest companies Corinne Jozsef
Contact: Artistic Director Gradimir Pankov
Social Media: @GrandsBallet www.facebook.com/lesgrandsballets
Policies: Theatre

Lester Centre of the Arts
Website: www.lestercentre.ca
Email: info@lestercentre.ca
Phone: 250 627 8888
Address: 1100 McBride St, CA
Information: also a venue for hire; the PRPAC being the only major venue in Prince Rupert
Country: Canada
Contact: General Manager Crystal Lorette
Email: CrystalL@lestercentre.ca
Social Media: @LesterCentre www.facebook.com/LesterCentreOfTheArts
Policies: All, Arts centre

Live Art Dance Productions
Website: www.liveartdance.ca
Email: info@liveartdance.ca
Phone: 902 420 0003
Address: PO Box 282 Halifax Central, 5183 Sackville St. 3rd. Floor, CA
Information: Atlantic Canada's only specialised presenter focusing on contemporary dance and movement related art. We present an annual season that features 7 productions by professional artists/companies at all career stages and from across Canada
Country: Canada
Contact: Executive Producer Paul Caskey
Email: Liveartpaul@eastlink.ca
Policies: Rent and present, Arts centre

Living Arts Centre in Mississauga
Website: www.livingarts.on.ca
Email: info@livingarts.on.ca
Address: 4141 Living Arts Drive, CA
Information: the Living Arts Centre is split into Hammerson Hall (1350) RBC Theatre (382) and a space called the Rogers Theatre (110)
Country: Canada
Contact: Manager of studio arts Gail Anderson
Email: Gail.Anderson@livingarts.on.ca
Contact: CEO Gerry Townsend
Email: gerry.townsend@livingarts.on.ca
Contact: customer service coordinator Megan Paul
Contact: performing arts Director Danna Evans
Contact: Director of Marketing Rob Hart
Email: rob.hart@livingarts.on.ca
Social Media: @livingartsctr www.facebook.com/livingartscentre
Policies: All, Multi-purpose

Maison de la Culture de la Vallée de la Gatineau
Website: www.mcvg.org/index.shtml
Email: mcvg_develculturel@bellnet.ca
Address: 181A rue Commerciale, CA
Information: Promotes culture in the area of la Vallée de la Gatineau
Country: Canada
Contact: President Michel Gauthier
Email: President@mcvg.org
Contact: co-ordinator Christiane Langevin
Email: infos@mcvg.org
Social Media: www.facebook.com/pages/Maison-de-la-culture-de-la-Vallée-de-la-Gatineau
Policies: Multi-purpose

McMaster University School of Art
Website: sota.humanities.mcmaster.ca
Email: sota@mcmaster.ca
Phone: 905 525 9140
Address: Togo Salmon Hall Room 414, 1280 Main St. West, CA
Information: University department.
Country: Canada
Contact: administrative coordinator Rose Mannarino
Contact: Associate professor, theatre and film Catherine Graham
Email: grahamca@mcmaster.ca
Contact: Associate professor, theatre and film Janice Hladki
Email: hladkij@mcmaster.ca
Social Media: @mcmasterhum http://www.facebook.com/mcmaster.humanities
Policies: Produce and co-produce, Other

Molson Canadian Ampitheatre
Website: www.molsonamp.com
Email: torontoinfo@livenation.com
Phone: 416 260 5600
Address: 909, boul. Lakeshore Ouest, CA
Information: Semi-enclosed outdoor concert venue in Toronto.**Country: Canada**
Policies: Open-air

Music in the Morning Concert Series
Website: www.musicinthemorning.org
Email: info@musicinthemorning.org
Phone: 604 873 4612
Address: PO Box 95024, Kingsgate RPO, CA
Country: Canada
Contact: Artistic Director June Goldsmith
Email: junegoldsmith@shaw.ca
Contact: Executive Artistic Director Barry Shiffman
Email: barryshiffman@musicinthemorning.org
Contact: General Manager Simone Doust
Email: simoned@musicinthemorning.org
Contact: production Manager Nicholas Jacques
Email: nicholasj@musicinthemorning.org

Music Toronto
Website: www.music-toronto.com
Email: admin@music-toronto.com
Address: Suite 1508, 67 Yonge Street, CA
Information: 16 chamber music concerts and piano recitals
Country: Canada
Artistic Producer & General Manager
Jennifer Taylor
Email: admin@music-toronto.com
Social Media: www.facebook.com/MusicToronto
Policies: All, Theatre

Myer Horowitz Theatre
Website: www.su.ualberta.ca
Email: theatre@su.ualberta.ca
Phone: 780 492 4764
Address: Students' Union Building, Room 2/900, University of Alberta, 8900 114 Street, CA
Information: University has various venues. Student Union Building: Myer Horowitz Theatre is the prominent arts venue
Country: Canada
Contact: technical supervisor Dennis Franz
Contact: Manager of entertainment and programming Christine Rogerson
Contact: operations Manager John Lovell
Contact: external communications and media advisor Simon Yackulic
Email: ecma@su.ualberta.ca
Contact: student union President Colten Yamagishi
Email: President@su.ualberta.ca
Social Media: @uasuevents www.facebook.com/UAlbertaSU
Policies: Multi-purpose

National Arts Centre / Centre national des Arts
Website: www.nac-cna.ca
Email: info@nac-cna.ca
Phone: 613 947 7000
Address: 1 Elgin Street, CA
Information: The National Arts Centre (NAC) is Canada's bilingual, multi-disciplinary home for the performing arts. The NAC presents, creates, produces, and co-produces performing arts programming in various streams—the NAC Orchestra, Dance, English Theatre, French Theatre, Indigenous Theatre, and Popular Music and Variety—and nurtures the next generation of audiences and artists from across Canada.
Country: Canada
Contact: President and Chief Executive Officer Christopher Deacon
Email: President@nac-cna.ca
Contact: Managing Director, English Theatre David Abel
Email: david.abel@nac-cna.ca
Contact: General Manager, Food and Beverage Nelson Borges
Email: nelson.borges@nac-cna.ca
Contact: Chief Technology Officer Martin Carbonneau
Email: martin.carbonneau@nac-cna.ca
Contact: Senior Director, Learning and Community Engagement Geneviève Cimon
Email: Genevieve.Cimon@nac-cna.ca
Social Media: www.facebook.com/CanadasNAC.CNAduCanadatwitter.com/canadasnacinstagram.com/NAC.CNA
Disabled Access: Yes
Policies: All

National Music Centre
Website: www.nmc.ca
Email: info@studiobell.ca
Phone: 403 543 5115
Address: 850 4 Street SE Calgary,
Information: The National Music Centre (NMC) is a national catalyst for discovery, innovation and renewal through music. In our new home at Studio Bell, we will preserve and celebrate Canada's music story and inspire a new generation of music lovers through programmes that includes on-site and outreach education programmes, performances, artist incubation and exhibitions.

Country: Canada
Contact: Chair Rob Braide
Contact: President and CEO Andrew Mosker
Email: andrew.mosker@nmc.ca
Contact: Chief of Staff and Senior Director Stephanie Pahl
Email: stephanie.pahl@nmc.ca
Contact: Director of Programs Adam Fox
Email: adam.fox@nmc.ca
Contact: Director of Marketing, Communications, and Visitor Experience Brandon Wallis
Email: brandon.wallis@nmc.ca
Social Media: https://twitter.com/nmc_canada www.facebook.com/NationalMusicCentre https:// www.instagram.com/nmc_canada/

New Dance Horizons Inc.
Website: www.newdancehorizons.ca
Email: office@newdancehorizons.ca
Address: 2207 Harvey St, CA
Information: Primarily a dance teaching facility.
Country: Canada
Contact: General Manager Amy Stevensen
Contact: Artistic Director Robin Poitras
Email: robrez@sasktel.net
Contact: office Manager Helen Coons-Schwark
Email: events@newdancehorizons.ca
Contact: administrative assistant Catherine Ready
Email: office@newdancehorizons.ca
Social Media: @NDH_Regina http:// www.facebook.com/newdancehorizons
Policies: Present and produce, Arts centre

Newfoundland Arts and Culture Centre Theatre Program
Website: www.artsandculturecentre.com
Email: mhaynes@artsandculturecentre.com
Address: Newfoundland Dept of Tourism, Culture & Recreation, PO Box 1854, CA
Information: The division operates the arts and culture centres at Gander, St John's, Stephenville, Corner Brook, Labrador West and Grand-Falls Windsor all
Country: Canada
Manager – programming & promotion
Richard J Stoker

Now Showing Live Arts
Website: www.candance.ca
Email: info@candance.ca
Address: Department of Theatre Arts, Faculty of Fine Arts, University of Lethbridge, 4401 University Drive, CA
Information: canadian network of dance presenters
Country: Canada
Contact: Chair Barb Clausen
Contact: vice-Chair Paul Caskey
Contact: treasurer Pierre Des Marais

Oakville Centre for the Performing Arts
Website: www.oakvillecentre.ca
Email: boxoffice@town.oakville.on.ca
Address: 130 Navy Street, CA
Information: The Mission of The Oakville Centre for the Performing Arts is to provide Oakville residents with a place to learn about themselves and the world around them through dance, music, storytelling and theatre.
Country: Canada
Marketing & development coordinator
Ronnie Brown
Email: rbrown@oakville.ca
Contact: technical supervisor Joe Henning
Email: jhenning@oakville.ca
Contact: theatre Manager Ken Coulter
Email: kcoulter@oakville.ca
Annual Performances: 260
Policies: All, Theatre

Orford Arts Centre
Website: www.arts-orford.org
Email: djoachim@arts-orford.org
Address: 3165 Chemin du Parc, CA
Information: Located in the Mont Orford national park, the Music Academy of international calibre is dedicated to its first mission: sustaining the development of emerging artists. To do so, the Arts Centre is committed to offering unique and enriching training activities with the assistance of devoted teachers of international renown. In addition to these activities, the Arts Centre proudly presents the Orford Festival, an unforgettable gathering of artists who, each summer, come from all over the world to bear witness of their love for arts and culture.
Country: Canada
Contact: financial Director Caroline Houle
Email: choule@arts-orford.org
Contact: Director François Tétreault
Email: ftetreault@arts-orford.org
Contact: administrative Director Josée Lambert
Email: jlambert@arts-orford.org
Social Media: www.facebook.com/caorford
Policies: All, Concert hall

Ovascène
Website: www.ovascene.com
Email: info@ovascene.com
Address: 919 route Saint-Martin, CA
Country: Canada

Contact: General Director André Lambert
Contact: technical Director Patrick Campagna
Contact: supervisor Louis Parent
Social Media: @ovascene www.facebook.com/pages/
Ovascène
Annual Performances: 50
Policies: Present and produce, Theatre

Peterborough Concert Association
Website: www.ptboconcert.ca
Email: jconley@pipcom.com
Phone: 705 740 0651
Address: 366 Applegrove Ave, CA
Country: Canada
Contact: President Jim Conley

Pro Musica Society
Website: www.promusica.qc.ca
Email: concerts@promusica.qc.ca
Phone: 514 845 0532
Address: 3505, rue Sainte-Famille, appt. 201, CA
Information: member of IAMA
Country: Canada
Contact: General Director Monique Dub
Contact: Artistic Director Pierre Rolland
Social Media: @ProMusicaMtl www.facebook.com/
societepromusica
Policies: Present and produce, Concert hall

Public Energy
Website: www.publicenergy.ca
Email: dancing@publicenergy.ca
Phone: 705 745 1788
Address: PO Box 2319, CA
Information: Formerly known as Peterborough New
Dance, since 1994 we have presented a mainstage
series of dance companies and independent choreog-
raphers drawn from across Canada, commissioned new
work in concert with other Canadian presenters on the
CanDance Network, and supported the development of
the local dance, theatre and performance community by
presenting area artists and arranging specialized classes
and workshops.
Country: Canada
Contact: Artistic Producer Bill Kimball
Email: bill@publicenergy.ca
Contact: General Manager Laurel Paluck
Email: admin@publicenergy.ca
Social Media: www.facebook.com/pages/Public-Energy
Policies: Rent and present, Multi-purpose

Queen Elizabeth Theatre Vancouver
Website: vancouver.ca/parks-recreation-culture/
queen-elizabeth-theatre
Email: vctinfo@vancouver.ca
Phone: 604 665 3050
Address: W Georgia St, CA
Information: Vancouver Opera and Ballet British Colum-
bia are the resident companies of the Queen Elizabeth
Theatre
Country: Canada
Contact: Director of vancouver civic theatres Rae
Ackerman
Contact: booking Manager Peter Kendall
Email: peter.kendall@vancouver.ca
Social Media: www.facebook.com/pages/Queen-Eliza-
beth-Theatre
Policies: All, Theatre

Red Deer College Arts Centre
Website: www.rdc.ab.ca/performing_arts
Email: roombookings@rdc.ab.ca
Phone: 403 342 3528
Address: Box 5005, CA
Information: college arts courses including music and
motion picture arts
Country: Canada
Contact: program assistant Dyane Lee
Email: dyane.lee@rdc.ab.ca
Contact: program Chair Dale Wheeler
Email: dale.wheeler@rdc.ab.ca
Contact: Marketing Manager Berni Hennebery
Email: berni.hennebery@rdc.ab.ca
Social Media: @RedDeerCollege www.facebook.com/
pages/Performing-Arts-at-Red-Deer-College
Policies: Arts centre

Rotonde, La
Website: www.larotonde.qc.ca
Email: info@larotonde.qc.ca
Address: 336, rue du Roi, suite 200, CA
Information: present international/national companies
as well as support local choreographers
Country: Canada
Contact: General Director Steve Huot
Social Media: @LaRotondeDanse www.facebook.com/
LaRotondeDanse
Policies: Present and produce, Theatre

Royal Conservatory of Music – Glenn Gould School
Website: www.rcmusic.ca
Email: rentals@rcmusic.ca
Phone: 416 408 2824
Address: 273 Bloor St, CA

Information: season consists of orchestral series, artist
series, Sunday family series, music appreciation series,
community talent, lecture series. Member of ISPA
Country: Canada
Contact: Chief Operating Officer Tony Flynn
Contact: President Peter Simon
Contact: Executive Director Mervon Mehta
Social Media: @the_rcm@theroyalconservatory
Policies: Present and produce, Concert hall

Salle Albert-Dumouchel Valspec Inc
Website: www.valspec.qc.ca
Email: info@valspec.qc.ca
Address: 169 rue Champlain, CA
Country: Canada
Contact: vice-President Jean-Pierre Leduc
Email: jpleduc@valspec.qc.ca
Contact: programme Director Clauderic Provost
Email: cprovost@valspec.qc.ca
Contact: technical Director Claude Lalonde
Email: clalonde@valspec.qc.ca
Contact: assistant technical Director Martin Primeau
Email: mprimeau@valspec.qc.ca
Social Media: @Valspec_SAD www.facebook.com/
valspec.sallealbertdumouchel
Annual Performances: 120
Policies: Present, produce, co-produce, Concert hall

Salle Dina-Bélanger
Website: www.reseaucentre.qc.ca/diffuseurs-que-
bec-sillery.html
Email: sdb@sdb.qc.ca
Address: 2047 Chemin Saint-Louis, CA
Information: Produces shows prioritising the niche of
music for the young and the General public in the region
of Quebec, while giving special support for emerging
artists and education audiences.
Country: Canada
Contact: General Director Jean-Guy Gingras
Contact: communications Director Mylene Feuiltault
Contact: ticket office Director Claire Gravel
Policies: Present and produce, Concert hall

Salle Pierre-Mercure
Website: www.centrepierrepeladeau.com
Email: reception@centrepierrepeladeau.com
Address: 300 Blvd de Maisonneuve, est, CA
Information: In addition to his theater with a capacity of
845 seats, the Centre Pierre-Peladeau has two rehearsal
studios, dressing rooms, administrative spaces and
public areas such as lobby, fireplaces, cloakroom, bar and
ticketing.
Country: Canada
Contact: Director Guy Vanasse
Email: vanasse.guy@uqam.ca
Contact: administrative technician David Perreault
Email: perreault.david@uqam.ca
Contact: customer service Alexe Lavigne-Descôteaux
Email: alexe.lavinge-descoteaux@uqam.ca
Policies: Rent and present, Theatre

Sanderson Centre for the Performing Arts
Website: www.sandersoncentre.ca
Email: sanderson@brantford.ca
Phone: 519 752 9910
Address: 88 Dalhousie Street, PO Box 1762, CA
Information: The Sanderson Centre for the Performing
Arts acts as a cultural focal point for the Performing Arts
in Brantford, Brant County and Southwestern Ontario
Country: Canada
Social Media: @SandersonCentre www.facebook.com/
sanderson.centre
Policies: Rent and present, All, Theatre

School for the Contemporary Arts, Simon Fraser University
Website: www.sfu.ca/sca
Email: ca@sfu.ca
Phone: 778 782 3363
Address: 149 West Hastings, Vancouver
Information: SFU's School for the Contemporary Arts of-
fers a unique curriculum in which studio classes in dance,
film, music/sound, theatre performance and production,
and visual art are integrated with the historical and
theoretical study of the arts.
Country: Canada
Contact: SCA Production Coordinator Gillian Hanemayer
Email: sca_production_coordinator@sfu.ca
Contact: Communications Brady Cranfield
Email: scaweb@sfu.ca
Phone: 778 782 9561Director's Assistant Samantha
Diamond
Email: scasec@sfu.ca
Phone: 778 782 3603
Social Media: https://www.facebook.com/SFUCon-
temporaryArts/ https://twitter.com/SFUContmpryArts
https:// www.instagram.com/sfucontemporaryarts/
Capacity: 251-500
Policies: All

Segal Centre Performing Arts
Website: www.segalcentre.com
Email: communications@segalcentre.org
Phone: 514 739 7944

Address: 5170 Côte-Ste-Catherine Montreal, Québec
Information: The Segal Centre for Performing Arts is a
not-for-profit theatre company dedicated to nurturing,
producing and presenting world-class English-language
theatre and to showcasing the best professional artists
from Montréal and beyond.
Country: Canada
Contact: Artistic and Executive Director Lisa Rubin
Email: lrubin@segalcentre.org
Social Media: https://twitter.com/segalcentre www.
facebook.com/segalcentre
Disabled Access: Yes
Capacity: 251-500
Policies: All

Shaw Performing Arts Centre
Website: www.mtyp.ca
Email: info@mtyp.ca
Phone: 204 947 0394
Address: Manitoba Theatre for Young People, 2 Forks
Market Road, CA
Information: home venue of Manitoba Theatre for Young
People q.v
Country: Canada
Contact: Artistic Director Leslee Silverman
communications & Marketing Manager
Alex Buchner
Contact: theatre school Director Kent Suss
Policies: All, Theatre

Société de musique contemporaine du Québec
Website: www.smcq.qc.ca
Email: smcq@smcq.qc.ca
Phone: 514 843 9305
Address: Centre Pierre-Péladeau, 300 Bld. de Maison-
neuve Est, CA
Information: resident ensemble: ensemble de la SMCQ;
also have a youth ensemble
Country: Canada
Contact: Artistic Director Walter Boudreau
Contact: General Director Aïda Aoun
Contact: assistant to the General Director Noémie Pascal
Contact: technical Director Marcello Delambre
Social Media: www.facebook.com/smcq.qc.ca
Policies: Produce and co-produce, Rent and present,
Concert hall

Société pour la promotions d'événements cul-turels du Haut-Richelieu Inc (SPEC)
Website: www.spec.qc.ca
Email: info@spec.qc.ca
Phone: 450 358 3949
Address: 75, rue Foch, CA
Country: Canada
Contact: President Claude Lef
Contact: Director General Guy Boulanger
Social Media: @SPECHR www.facebook.com/theatre-
desdeuxrives
Policies: Present, produce, co-produce, Theatre

Sony Centre for the Performing Arts
Website: www.sonycentre.ca
Email: info@sonycentre.ca
Phone: 416 386 6161
Address: 1 Front Street East, CA
Information: The Sony Centre, Toronto's first performing
arts centre, has played a defining role in the cultural life
of Toronto for more than 50 years; today, Sony Centre's
mission is to unite the global citizens of Toronto through
great Artistic experiences; the Sony Centre presents year-
round programming including concerts, musical theatre,
family entertainment, comedy, and dance; Toronto's
iconic Sony Centre has also proven to be an ideal venue
for product launches, town halls, holiday parties, and
fundraisers– it is truly where the world comes to play!
Country: Canada
Contact: interim CEO Mark Hammond
Contact: Director, sacility services Sandy Robinson
Contact: Associate Manager, promotions Jessica
Rashotte
Email: jessica@sonycentre.ca
Contact: corporate Sales Manager Scott North
Social Media: @SonyCentreTO www.facebook.com/
SonyCentreTO
Policies: Rent only, Present, produce, co-produce,
Theatre

St John's Arts and Culture Centre
Website: www.artsandculturecentre.com
Email: mhaynes@artsandculturecentre.com
Address: PO Box 1854, Prince Philip Drive, CA
Information: operated and programmed by Newfound-
land Department of Tourism, Culture & Recreation –
Cultural Affairs Division (q.v.)
Country: Canada
 Manager, programming & promotion
Aiden Flynn
Email: aflynn@artsandculturecentre.com
Contact: Director Doreen McCarthy
Email: mccarthyd@artsandculturecentre.com
Contact: public relations Kathryn Lear
Email: klear@artsandculturecentre.com
Contact: Administration Kelly Raymond
Email: kraymond@artsandculture.com

Contact: technical Director Karl Simmons
Email: ksimmons@artsandculture.com
Social Media: @ACCStJohns www.facebook.com/ACC.
St.Johns
Policies: Present, produce, co-produce, Theatre

St Lawrence Centre for the Arts
Website: www.stlc.com
Address: 27 Front Street E, CA
Information: As a focus of Canadian performing arts, the Centre will take a leadership role in providing Toronto residents, visitors and diverse cultural communities with a professional, service-oriented theatrical and entertainment facility. Varied and high quality cultural, Artistic and public events will be attracted, facilitated and presented continually.
Country: Canada
Contact: production co-ordinator Sean Tasson
Email: stasson@stlc.com
Contact: General Manager James Roe
Email: jroe@stlc.com
Contact: Director of finance Hayde Boccia
Email: hboccia@stlc.com
Contact: Director of Sales and Marketing Carol Henderson
Email: chenderson@stlc.com
Policies: Rent and present, Theatre

Stephenville Arts and Culture Centre
Website: www.artsandculturecentre.com
Email:
wcook@artsandculturecentre.com
Phone: 709 643 4571
Address: 380 Massachusetts Drive, CA
Information: operated and programmed by Newfoundland Department of Tourism, Culture and Recreation
Country: Canada
Contact: Manager Wanda Cook
Social Media: @ACC_SVILLE www.facebook.com/
ACCStephenville
Policies: All, Multi-purpose

Studio de l'Agora de la danse
Website: www.agoradanse.com
Email: info@agoradanse.com
Address: 840 rue Cherrier, CA
Information: box office: 514-525 1500
Country: Canada
Contact: General and Artistic Director Francine Bernier
Email: fbernier@agoradanse.com
Contact: digital communications officer Marie-Josée Beaubien
Email: mariejosee@agoradanse.com
Contact: administrative Director Christiane Dinelle
Email: Administration@agoradanse.com
Contact: communications and development Director Louise Duchesne
Email: louise@agoradanse.com
Social Media: @Agoradanse www.facebook.com/agoradeladanse?ref=mf
Annual Productions: 100
Policies: Rent and present, Theatre

Tangente-Laboratoire de Mouvements Contemporains
Website: www.tangente.qc.ca
Email: info@tangente.qc.ca
Address: 543 rue Sherbrooke est, CA
Information: international documentation centre on contemporary dance; see also National Organisations
Country: Canada
Contact: co Artistic/General Director Stéphane Labbé
Email: stephane@tangente.qc.ca
Contact: co Artistic/General Director Dena Davida
Email: dena@tangente.qc.ca
Contact: administrative Director Isabelle Scarfo
Email: isabelle@tangente.qc.ca
Contact: technical Director Paul Chambers
Email: chambers@tangente.qc.ca
Social Media: @tangentedanse www.facebook.com/
pages/TANGENTE-danse-contemporaine
Policies: Present and produce, Theatre

Tapestry New Opera
Website: tapestryopera.com
Email: information@tapestryopera.com
Phone: 416 537 6066
Address: 9 Trinity Street, Studio 316, Distillery Historic District, CA
Information: an international home for creators, developers and performers of new opera: all collaborators in telling stories that surprise, thrill and move audiences. Member of ISPA
Country: Canada
Contact: Managing/Artistic Director Wayne Strongman
Contact: business Director and coo Caroline Mackey
Contact: Artistic Director designate Michael Mori
Social Media: @TapNewOp www.facebook.com/pages/
Tapestry-new-opera-works
Policies: Produce and rent, Theatre

The Burlington Performing Arts Centre
Website: www.burlingtonpac.ca
Email: sadlerh@burlington.ca

Phone: 905 681 6000
Address: 440 Locust Street, CA
Information: a spectacular LEED (Leadership in Environmental Design) GOLD certified facility. The Centre is inclusive and respectful to all, combining accessibility with imaginative design and creativity, incorporating accessibility features wherever possible. The mission of The Burlington Performing Arts Centre is to provide the people of Burlington with a broad range of excellent performance opportunities that will both inspire and delight Three venues: Main Theatre (718 seats) Community Studio Theatre (200) and the Family Lobby.
Country: Canada
Contact: Executive Director Brian McCurdy
Email: Brian.McCurdy@burlington.ca
Contact: Executive assistant Susan Reeve
Email: Susan.Reeve@burlington.ca
Contact: Manager, operations and facility Sales Graham Frampton
Email: Graham.Frampton@burlington.ca
Social Media: @BurlingtonPAC www.facebook.com/
BurlingtonPAC
Policies: Rent and present, Theatre

The Concert Hall at Victoria Hall
Website: www.concerthallatvictoriahall.com
Email: concerthall@cobourg.ca
Address: 55 King Street West, CA
Information: The Concert Hall at Victoria Hall is available for rent for events including corporate meetings and seminars, lectures, exhibits, balls and receptions. It has hosted professional and amateur theatre companies.
Country: Canada
Contact: concert hall facilitator Beth Craig
Email: concerthall@cobourg.ca
Policies: Rent only, Concert hall

The Cultural Committee Mégantic
Website: https:// www.facebook.com/
Comit%C3%A9-culturel-M%C3%A9gan-
tic-Page-312230189371552/
Email: comiteculturelmegantic@hotmail.com
Phone: 819 554 6975
Address: CP 222, CA
Information: Tickets: Jean Coutu – Lac-Magantic branch 5256, rue Frontenac, tel:819-583 3303
Country: Canada
Social Media: https:// www.facebook.com/
Comit%C3%A9-culturel-M%C3%A9gan-
tic-Page-312230189371552
Capacity: 501-1000
Annual Performances: 25-50
Policies: Rent and Present

The Dance Centre
Website:
www.thedancecentre.ca
Email: info@thedancecentre.ca
Phone: 604 606 6400
Address: Scotiabank Dance Centre, Level 6, 677 Davie Street, CA
Information: has become a hub for dance activity, housing The Dance Centre's programmes, as well as rehearsals, classes, workshops, performances and events by dance artists and companies from Vancouver. Scotiabank Dance Centre generates an estimated 60, 000 visits annually
Country: Canada
Contact: Executive Director Mirna Zagar
Email: ExecutiveDirector@thedancecentre.ca
Contact: programming coordinator Raquel Alvaro
Email: programming@thedancecentre.ca
Contact: Marketing Manager Heather Bray
Email: Marketing@thedancecentre.ca
Contact: development Director Sheri Uquhart
Email: development@thedancecentre.ca
Social Media: @dancecentre www.facebook.com/thedancecentre
Policies: Rent only, Multi-purpose

The Grand Theatre
Website: www.kingstongrand.ca
Email:
grandtheatre2@cityofkingston.ca
Address: 218 Princess Street, CA
Information: One of the main cultural venues in the greater Kingston region, the City of Kingston's Grand Theatre serves as the prime performing arts venue for hundreds of professional and amateur performances annually including ballet, modern dance, theatre, variety
Country: Canada
Contact: administrative assistant to the cultural Director Elizabeth Cashman
Email: ecashman@cityofkingston.ca
Contact: theatre Manager Dianne Zemba
Email: dzemba@cityofkingston.ca
Contact: Marketing administrator Julie Fossitt
Email: jfossitt@cityofkingston.ca
Contact: grand theatre foundation: Executive Director Carol Anne Muncaster
Email: grandtheatrefoundation@cityofkingston.ca
Social Media: @Kingston_Grand www.facebook.com/
kingstongrandtheatre
Policies: All, Theatre

Théâtre de la Ville
Website:
www.theatredelaville.qc.ca
Email: infotheatre@theatredelaville.qc.ca
Phone: 450 670 1611
Address: 180 rue De Gentilly Est, CA
Information: The City Theatre has two theaters: the Pratt & Whitney Canada Hall and the Salle Jean-Louis Millette.
Country: Canada
Contact: General Director Danielle Bilodeau
Contact: Artistic Director Anne-Marie Provencher
Contact: technical Director Daniel Collette
Contact: communications Director Normand Desjardins
Social Media: www.facebook.com/theatredelaville.qc.ca
Policies: Theatre

Théâtre des Eskers
Website: www.ville.amos.qc.ca/FR/CITOYEN/THEA-
TRE_ESKERS
Email: spectacle@ville.amos.qc.ca
Phone: 819 732 9233
Address: 182, 1ère Rue Est, CA
Information: It offers its customers and Producers possibilities: cabaret, studio, cinema, conference, and of course, entertainment in Italian.
Country: Canada
Contact: theatre Director Alain Coulombe
Policies: Rent and present, Multi-purpose

Théâtre du cuivre
Website: www.ville.rouyn-noranda.qc.ca
Email: theatre.duculvre@ville.rouyn-noranda.qc.ca
Address: 145 rue Taschereau Ouest, CA
Information: rent the theatre to other organizations
Country: Canada
Contact: Director Jacques Matte
Email: jacques.matte@rouyn-noranda.qc.ca
Social Media: http:// www.facebook.com/pages/Théâ-
tre-du-cuivre/
Policies: Rent only, Theatre

Théâtre Périscope
Website: www.theatreperiscope.qc.ca
Email: info@theatreperiscope.qc.ca
Address: 939, rue Salaberry, CA
Information: Cradle unique theatrical adventure, it hosts each year daring productions from Quebec, Canada and Europe, many of which are among the most significant contemporary works of recent decades.
Country: Canada
Contact: acting Director Marie-Ève Dumont
Email: direction@theatreperiscope.qc.ca
Contact: Artistic Director Frédéric Dubois
Email: artistique@theatreperiscope.qc.ca
Contact: technical Director Steve Beaulieu
Email: technique@theatreperiscope.qc.ca
Social Media: @Le_Periscope www.facebook.com/
theatre.periscope
Policies: Produce and rent, Theatre

Toronto Centre for the Arts
Website: www.TOCentre.com
Email: kdell@tocentre.com
Phone: 416 733 9388
Address: 5040 Yonge St, CA
Information: owned and operated by City of Toronto. Home to other venues such as: Greenwin Theatre, Lyric Theatre, Studio Theatre
Country: Canada
Contact: General Manager Pim Schotanus
Contact: Director of operations Janette McDonald
Email: jmcdonald@tocentre.com
Contact: Director of finance and Administration Neil McGivney
Email: nmcgivney@tocentre.com
Contact: Director of production and facility services Kristopher Dell
Email: kdell@tocentre.com
Contact: booking coordinator Jannelle Armorer
Email: jarmorer@tocentre.com
Social Media: @TOcentre www.facebook.com/TOCentre
Policies: Rent only, Theatre

Toronto Early Music Centre
Website: www.torontoearlymusic.org
Email: frank.nakashima@gmail.com
Phone: 416 464 7610
Address: PO Box 714 Station P, CA
Information: historically informed musical performances played on original instruments or replicas
Country: Canada
Contact: President Frank Nakashima
Email: frank.nakashima@gmail.com
Contact: secretary Michael Lerner
Contact: treasurer Kathy Edwards
Social Media: @earlymusicTOToronto-Early-Music-Centre
Annual Performances: 5
Annual Productions: 1
Policies: Rent only, Present, produce, co-produce, Other

Toronto Operetta Theatre
Website: www.torontooperetta.com
Email: tot@torontooperetta.com

Address: 947 Queen Street East, Second Floor, CA
Information: see also Opera
Country: Canada
Contact: Director of Marketing and publicity Henry Ingram
Contact: General Director Guillermo Silva-Marin
Contact: administrative assistant Paul Niziol
Social Media: @TorontoOperetta http:// www.facebook.com/pages/Toronto-Operetta-Theatre
Policies: Concert hall

University of Guelph University Centre Programming
Website: www.uoguelph.ca
Email: sbaijal@uoguelph.ca
Phone: 519 824 4120
Address: University Centre Programming, UC Room 266, 50 Stone Road East, CA
Information: University establishment
Country: Canada
coordinator publicity & public relations Sam Baijal
Email: sbaijal@uoguelph.ca
Contact: dean college of arts Don Bruce
Social Media: @uofg www.facebook.com/uofguelph
Policies: Other

University of Saskatchewan Concert Series
Website: www.usask.ca/music
Email: music.uofs@usask.ca
Address: Music Department, 28 Campus Drive, CA
Information: University music department.**Country:** Canada
Contact: administrator Troy Linsley
Email: troy.linsley@usask.ca
Contact: department head Gerald Langner
Email: gerald.langner@usask.ca
Policies: Present and produce

Vancouver Civic Theatres
Website: vancouvercivictheatres.com
Email: vctinfo@vancouver.ca
Phone: 604 665 3050
Address: 649 Cambie St., CA
Information: Vancouver Civic Theatres is owned and operated by the City of Vancouver, and includes the VCT Board, which advises City Council on the operation, use, and improvement of the theatres. They are committed to developing, enhancing and promoting the city's vibrant arts scene, sharing with the world the astonishing breadth and depth of Vancouver's creative community and cultural entrepreneurs. Member of ISPA.
Country: Canada
Social Media: @Vancivictheatre www.facebook.com/VanCivicTheatres
Capacity: 2765

Vancouver New Music
Website: www.newmusic.org
Email: info@newmusic.org
Phone: 604 633 0861
Address: 837 Davie Street, CA
Country: Canada
Contact: Artistic Director Giorgio Magnanensi
Email: giorgio@newmusic.org
Contact: Managing Producer Jim Smith
Email: jim@newmusic.org
Social Media: @vannewmusic www.facebook.com/vannewmusic
Policies: Present, produce, co-produce, Present and produce, Produce and co-produce, Rent and present, Produce and rent, Other

Ville De L'île-Bizard
Website: www.ville.montreal.qc.ca/ibsg
Email: arribsg@ville.montreal.qc.ca
Address: 350, rue de L'Eglise, CA
Information: Ville De L'île-Bizard is the council, the theatre venue is la salle Pauline-Julien which is a 380 seat auditorium.
Country: Canada
Contact: Director General Jean-Paul Collinge
Policies: Theatre

Welland-Port Colborne Concert Association
Website: www.wellandportcolborneconcert.org
Email: stella.crouch@cogeco.ca
Phone: 905 735 7996
Address: c/o Stella Crouch, Artistic Director, 8 Clifford Street, CA
Country: Canada
Contact: Artistic Director Stella Crouch
Email: stella.crouch@cogeco.ca
Contact: technical Director Dave Colonico
Email: dcolonico@cogeco.ca
Policies: Produce and rent, Theatre

Whitehorse Concerts
Website: whitehorseconcerts.com
Email: concerts@navigonet.com
Address: Box 31451, CA
Country: Canada
Contact: programme co-ordinator Michele Emslie

Social Media: www.facebook.com/pages/Whitehorse-Concerts
Policies: Concert hall

Winnipeg's Contemporary Dancers (WCD) Studio Theatre
Website: www.winnipegscontemporarydancers.ca
Email: info@winnipegscontemporarydancers.ca
Phone: 204 452 0229
Address: 204 – 211 Bannatyne Avenue, Winnipeg
Information: Our venue is located in the heart of Winnipeg's historic Exchange District and could be the ideal location for your next event or function. The Rachel Browne Theatre is available to rent for dance, theatre and music performances, as well as workshops, lectures and fundraisers
Country: Canada
Contact: Artistic Director Jolene Bailie
Email: jbailie@winnipegscontemporarydancers.ca
Phone: 204 452 0229Chair Randal Newman
Contact: Administrator Iryna Kravchenko
Email: communications@winnipegscontemporarydancers.ca
Phone: 204 452 0229
Social Media: https:// www.instagram.com/wpgcontemps/ www.facebook.com/WpgContemps https://twitter.com/WpgContemps
Disabled Access: Yes
Capacity: 100-250
Annual Performances: 25-50
Annual Productions: 0-5
Policies: All

Yorkton Arts Council
Website: www.yorktonarts.ca
Email: yorktonartscouncil@sasktel.net
Phone: 306 783 8722
Address: 49 Smith St E, CA
Information: most bookings arranged through OSAC (see National Organisations). Venue is The Anne Portnuff Theatre, Yorkton Regional High School
Country: Canada
Contact: administrative assistant Cindee Massier
Email: yorktonartscouncil@sasktel.net
Contact: performing arts coordinator Debbie Hayward
Email: kdhayward53@yahoo.com
Policies: Rent only, Theatre

Yukon Arts Centre
Website: www.yukonartscentre.com/
Email: boxoffice@yac.ca
Phone: 867 667 8574
Address: 300 University Drive Whitehorse, Yukon
Information: Welcome to the Yukon Arts Centre (YAC), a vibrant, inclusive, creative space for artists and audiences. YAC has adapted rapidly to our COVID 19 reality and has found programming solutions to stay open, active, and connected to our community. The pandemic has re-enforced the importance of arts and exPression in our lives, but it has also moved us to develop new protocols which emphasize health and safety in all of our activities
Country: Canada
Contact: chief Executive officer Casey Prescott
Email: casey.prescott@yac.ca
Contact: CEO Casey Prescott
Email: casey.prescott@yac.ca
Phone: 867 667 8577
Marketing & Development Coordinator Mike Thomas
Email: mike.thomas@yac.ca
Phone: 867 667 8460Director of Visual Arts Mary Bradshaw
Email: mary.bradshaw@yac.ca
Phone: 867 667 8485
Social Media: https://twitter.com/YukonArtsCentre http:// www.facebook.com/YukonArtsCentre https://www.instagram.com/yukonarts/
Capacity: 251-500
Annual Performances: 100+
Policies: All

CHILE

Teatro Del Lago
Website: www.teatrodellago.cl/web/
Email: info@teatrodellago.cl
Phone: 295 70200
Address: Av. Philippi, CL
Information: a centre of Artistic excellence which encourages the development of culture and creativity in education through music and art; aims to be a benchmark at a regional, national and international level; the theatre is located in Chilean Patagonia and is wholly committed to the local community, to its traditions and the unique natural environment in which it is located
Country: Chile
Policies: Multi-purpose

Teatro NESCAFÉ de las Artes
Website: teatro-nescafe-delasartes.cl
Email: comunicaciones@teatro-nescafe-delasartes.cl
Phone: 223 63333

Address: Manuel Montt 032., Providencia, , CL
Country: Chile
Contact: Executive Director Alfredo Saint-Jean Domic
Email: alfredo@teatro-nescafe-delasartes.cl
Contact: promotion and programme Director Irene González Peña
Email: irene@teatro-nescafe-delasartes.cl
Social Media: @Teatro_NESCAFE http:// www.facebook.com/TeatroNESCAFE
Policies: Theatre

CHINA

Beijing Capital Theatre
Website: www.bjry.com
Email: bjrenyi@126.com
Phone: 106 523 3227
Address: 22 Wang Fu Jing Main Street, Dong Cheng District
Information: The Capital Theater was designed by the famous Chinese architect Lin Leyi to ensure the best sound effects, so that the audience can clearly and truly appreciate the language and music from the stage when sitting in any seat in the theater. There are drama bookstores, artist galleries and drama cafes in the theater hall, adding a heavy cultural connotation and Artistic atmosphere.
Country: China

Beijing Dance Academy
Website: www.bda.edu.cn
Email: international@bda.edu.cn
Phone: 008 610 689 37373
Address: No.1, Wanshousi Road, Hai Dian District
Information: Beijing Dance Academy is a full-time institution of higher learning with a commitment to developing excellent professional dancers, choreographers and dance researchers.**Country:** China
Contact: Director Guo Lei
Capacity: 1000+
Policies: Present and Produce

Beijing Working People's Cultural Palace
Website: www.bjwhg.com.cn
Phone: 106 525 2189
Address: East of Tian'anmen, Dongcheng District, Beijing
Information: Built in 1420, the Working People's Cultural Palace was once the Imperial Ancestral Temple in the Ming and Qing dynasties. It houses three great halls, including the ominously named Sacrificial Hall, with yellow-roof imperial architecture. When a new emperor ascended the throne or battles were won it was here that grand ceremonies to worship and give thanks would take place.
Country: China
Capacity: 1000+

Chang An Grand Theatre
Website: www.changandajuyuan.com
Phone: 400 600 4100
Address: Guanghua Chang'an Building, No.7 Jianguomen Inner St, Dong Cheng District
Information: Chang'an Grand Theater is a well-known Peking Opera performance theater. Chang'an Grand Theater is a perfect combination of classical national architectural style and modern architectural art, and its design and decoration have typical Ming and Qing styles.
Country: China

China Arts & Entertainment Group
Website: en.caeg.cn
Email: caeg@caeg.cn
Phone: 010 640 32702
Address: Floor16⊠17, EasyHomePlaza A3, Dongzhimen, SouthSt Beijing, China
Information: As China's only central state-owned cultural enterprise that has performance and exhibition business worldwide, CAEG has developed a nationwide market network of international performing arts, art exhibitions, and culture & tourism and theater operation, and set up branches in major cities in China and some European and American countries.
Country: China
Contact: Secretary of the Party Committee and Chairman Li Jinsheng
Contact: Director, General Manager and Deputy Secretary Li Baozong
Contact: Director and Deputy General Manager Qin Wenhuan
Capacity: 1000+
Annual Performances: 100+
Annual Productions: 100+

China Central Conservatory of Music
Website: www.ccom.edu.cn
Email: ccom@ccom.edu.cn
Phone: 106 642 5504
Address: No.43 Baojia Street, Xicheng District
Information: The CCOM is a magnet for music talents from all over the world. During its over 70 years of development, it has proudly maintained a strong team of faculty and administrative staff, including a number of outstanding specialists and scholars in music education,

composition, performance and research. Many aspiring young musicians have been attracted to further their professional training at CCOM.
Country: China
Contact: Vice President Qin Wenchen
Contact: Vice President Yu Hongmei
Social Media: www.facebook.com/Central-Conservatory-of-Music-389408427752098/

China Conservatory of Music
Website: en.ccmusic.edu.cn
Phone: 106 487 7114
Address: 1th AnXiang Road, Chaoyang District, Beijing, CN
Information: China Conservatory of Music was founded in 1964, which is a college based on studies of Chinese ancient civilization and equipped with unique music education style and research features

China National Children's Theatre
Website: www.cntc.org.cn
Email: cntc@cntc.org.cn
Phone: 400 101 6161
Address: 64 Dong An Men Da Jie, Dong Chen District
Information: CNTC has borne the responsibility of inheriting, developing, creating and presenting excellent theatrical performances for the youth, played an important role of representing, demonstrating and guiding in national children's drama. For more than half a century, CNTC has dedicated numerous classic and diverse dramas for the audience and cultivated a large number of distinguished and outstanding artists and performers for children's drama, many of whom are winners of various prestigious art awards in China.
Country: China
Contact: Dean and Deputy Secretary of the Party Committee Feng Li
Contact: Party Secretary and Vice President Yang Fan
Contact: Deputy Dean of China Children's Art Theater Zhao Hanbing
Contact: Deputy Dean of China Children's Art Theater Yu Xiaoyan
Capacity: 501-1000

Dongguan Theatre
Website: en.polytheatre.com/home/theaters/view/article_id/34.html
Email: yulantheatre@163.com
Phone: 769 228 37369
Address: Hongfu Road, Guangdong Province
Information: With a gross building area of 40257 m2, this theatre has a seating capacity of 1600 and a multi-functional experimental theatre with a seating capacity of 400. By adopting the mode of "government financial subsidy, objective management, independent management by Baoli Company with sole responsibility for profit &loss", it has created a special successful model of theatre management in China.
Country: China

Forbidden City Concert Hall
Website: theatrebeijing.com/concert_halls/forbidden_city_concert_hall/
Phone: 106 559 8285
Address: Inside Zhongshan Park, Xicheng District, Beijing
Information: Beijing Forbidden City Concert Hall is called "a pearl of music in China's royal garden", as it is situated inside one of Beijing's most beautiful parks, Zhongshan Park, and is surrounded by historic gardens and landmarks such as the Forbidden City and Tian'anmen Square. The Concert Hall is the major music festival venues of two Chinese famous orchestras China Philharmonic Orchestra and Beijing Symphony Orchestra as well as the major venue of Beijing International Music Festival.
Country: China
Capacity: 1000+

Guangzhou Opera House
Website: en.gzdjy.org/intro.html
Email: qiyedakehu@gzdhy.org
Phone: 203 839 2888
Address: No. 1, Zhujiang West Road, Zhujiang New Town, Tianhe District
Information: Guangzhou Opera House is rated as one of the "10 best opera houses around the world" (USA Today) and "The world's most spectacular theatres" (The Telegraph). Located in the center of CBD in Guangzhou, which is one of China's national core cities, as a cultural city icon, GOH contribute to strengthening the cultural content for canton area and the reform for cultural system in China by presenting performing arts of much diversity.
Country: China

Li Yuan Theatre
Website: www.liyuantheatre.cn
Email: contact@travelgreatwall.com
Phone: 135 525 27373
Address: 175 Yongan Road, Xicheng District, Beijing
Information: Drawing lavishly on many ways of Artistic exPression of the Chinese nation. Beijing Opera is a complex form of performing art consisting of music, singing, recitations, dancing, fine art, martial skills and acrobatics.
Country: China

Capacity: 501-1000
Annual Performances: 11-25

Macau Cultural Centre
Website: www.ccm.gov.mo
Email: enquiry@ccm.gov.mo
Phone: 853 287 00699
Address: Avenida Xian Xing Hai s/n
Information: The Macao Cultural Centre was founded in 1999 and remains a modern space that marks the cityscape surround it. Its several venues open for the Macao audience provide quality programmes, such as performances, conferences, exhibitions, among other projects organized by CCM or hirers
Country: China
Contact: Director Nelma Wong Morais Alves
Social Media: www.facebook.com/MacaoCulturalCentre?fref=ts
Policies: Multi-purpose

Majestic Theater
Website: www.228.com.cn/venue-143737.html
Phone: 216 217 4409
Address: 66 Jiangning Road, Jing'an District
Information: Majestic Theater is located at the junction of the prosperous Nanjing Road and Jiangning Road. Majestic Theater is an outstanding modern building in Shanghai. Its elegant and unique style combines the essence of modern and classical architecture. The entrance is a large circular tower with majestic momentum. The large crystal chandeliers are brilliant and colorful, the large and small light fountains are full of brilliance, and the bronze art sculptures are elegant.
Country: China

National Centre of the Performing Arts
Website: www.chncpa.org
Email: wangyue@chncpa.org
Phone: 106 655 0989
Address: No.2, West Chang An Street, Xi Cheng District
Information: The National Grand Theater always puts the pursuit of social benefits in the first place in its business philosophy. While taking into account economic benefits, it achieves the organic unity of social benefits and economic benefits.
Country: China
Contact: President of the NCPA Ning Wang
Contact: Vice President of the NCPA Jiachen Zhao
Contact: Vice President of the NCPA Tiechun Zhao
Contact: Vice President of the NCPA Jing Zhu
Contact: Vice President of the NCPA Zhixiang Li
Social Media: www.facebook.com/NationalCentreForThePerformingArts/

National Theatre of China
Website: www.ntcc.com.cn
Phone: 106 403 1009
Address: 277 Guang'anmen Outer St, Xicheng District, Beijing, CN
Information: National Theatre of China (NTC), affiliated to the Ministry of Culture, is a performing art organization with rich creative resources and a brilliant history. The theatre possesses a galaxy of senior artists, such as Ouyang Yuqian, Liao Chengzhi, Wu Xue, Shu Qiang, Jin Shan, and Sun Weishi who provided a solid foundation to the theatre's development.
Country: China
Contact: Dean of the National Theater of China Tian Qinxin
Contact: Secretary of the Party Committee of the National Theater of China Zhuge Yannan
Contact: Artistic Director of the National Theatre of China Ge Dali
Contact: Vice President of China National Theater Bai Xuefeng

People's Great Hall
Website: www.renmindahuitang.cn/index.asp
Phone: 010 830 84776
Address: Tian An Men Square, West Chang'an Street, Xicheng District, Beijing
Information: The construction of the Great Hall of the People originated from the 10th anniversary of the founding of the People's Republic of China in 1959. It is a majestic space with a "mountain"-shaped building plan, with two wings slightly lower, and the middle part slightly higher, with doors opening on all sides. **Country:** China

Sai Wan Ho Civic Centre
Website: www.lcsd.gov.hk/swhcc
Email: swhcc@lcsd.gov.hk
Phone: 825 318 45760
Address: G/F, 111 Shau Kei Wan Rd, Sai Wan Ho
Information: The Sai Wan Ho Civic Centre is conveniently situated above the Sai Wan Ho MTR station and easily accessible by public transport. The Centre is well equipped with integrated facilities, including a theatre, cultural activities hall, art studio and music practice rooms for a diverse range of activities. Since its opening in December 1990, the Centre has been providing spaces and facilities for people at Hong Kong East as well as all sectors of the community to stage cultural arts performances and community arts activities.
Country: China
Contact: Manager Nancy Chan

Capacity: 501-1000
Annual Performances: 100+
Policies: Rent and Present

Shanghai Art Theater
Website: www.yihaijuyuan.com
Phone: 216 256 8282
Address: No. 466, Jiang Ning Road, , Jing An District
Information: Shanghai Yihai Theater is located at the intersection of Jiangning Road and Wuding Road in Jing'an District, Shanghai's downtown area, adjacent to the business district of West Nanjing Road.Yihai Theater sincerely welcomes various performance groups and performance brokerage companies to come and perform.
Country: China

Shanghai Centre Theatre
Website: www.shanghaicentre.com
Email: leasing@shanghaicentre.com.cn
Phone: 216 279 8600
Address: West Office, Suite 710, 1376 Nanjing Road West, Shanghai
Information: Performing Arts. Corporate Functions. Product Launches. Special Events. Shanghai Centre offers everything you need under one roof with a variety of venues tied together within its fully-serviced complex. Whether it's the versatility of Shanghai's only internationally managed theatre; the spacious, open Atrium; the beautiful Terrace Garden; or the well-appointed ballrooms and function rooms of the five-star The Portman Ritz-Carlton, Shanghai.
Country: China
Contact: General Manager Richard Xu
Contact: Marketing Director Alex De Ceuster
Contact: EVP and Chief Operating Officer Byron Kan
Contact: Theatre Manager John Zhang
Contact: Administration Director Dehlia Jiang
Contact: Leasing Director Frances Hau
Social Media: www.facebook.com/pages/Shanghai%20Centre/135976026435366/

Shanghai Concert Hall
Website: www.shanghaiconcerthall.org
Email: contact@shanghaiconcerthall.org
Phone: 215 386 6666
Address: 523 Yan An Road East, Shanghai, CN
Information: As the first dedicated concert hall in China, Shanghai Concert Hall has been a landmark of Shanghai. It focus on chamber music with various music genres, including classical music, jazz, pop music and Chinese folk music, etc. Hailed as "a palace of classical music, a window for promoting the beauty of music and a base for popularizing music" by Shanghai citizens, the hall has been putting into practice its concept "Music for Everyone" by holding more than 500 top-notch concerts.
Country: China
Social Media: facebook.com/shanghaiconcerthall/

Shanghai Grand Theatre
Website: www.shgtheatre.com
Phone: 216 386 8686
Address: 300 Renmin Ave, CN
Information: The Shanghai Grand Theater is located in Shanghai People's Square with a total investment of 1.2 billion yuan. It is designed by French Chabangjie Architectural Design Company. It covers an area of 2.1 hectares, with a total construction area of 64, 000 square meters and a total height of 40 meters. theater. The whole building is like a crystal palace strung with musical notes. It adopts the most advanced fully automatic stage in the world.
Country: China
Capacity: 1000+
Policies: All

Shenzhen Concert Hall
Website: www.shenzhenconcerthall.com
Email: szyyt@shenzhenconcerthall.com
Phone: 755 828 41888
Address: 2016 Fuzhong 1st Rd
Information: Shenzhen Concert Hall is one of the most important symbolic cultural architectures in Shenzhen. Located in the central area of Futian District, it covers a surface area of 26345 square meters and a construction area of 41423 square meters. The architecture is designed by Arata Isozaki, a famous Japanese avant-grade architect, who enjoys a reputation in the international construction field. It is a modern and professional concert hall specifically designed and constructed for music performance.
Country: China
Contact: General Manager Xiaolan Guo
Contact: Deputy General Manager Guoliang Zhang
Contact: Deputy General Manager Yun He

Sichuan Conservatory of Music
Website: www.sccm.cn
Email: sccmws@126.com
Phone: 288 543 0270
Address: Xinsheng Road 6, Chengdu, Si Chuan Province
Information: Music and dance are the main focus of the

Sichuan Conservatory of Music, and the disciplines of art theory, drama and film and television, fine arts and design are developed in a comprehensive and coordinated manner.**Country: China**

Suzhou Culture and Arts Centre
Website: www.sscac.com.cn
Phone: 512 628 99700
Address: No.1, Guan Feng Street, , Suzhou Industrial Park
Information: The Suzhou Culture and Art Center has a construction area of nearly 150, 000 square meters, consisting of a grand theatre, performing arts hall, Jinji Lake concert hall, cinema, art gallery, cultural centre, training centre, and commercial centre. It is also the residence of Suzhou Symphony Orchestra and Suzhou Ballet, Arts School and Commercial Centre.
Country: China
Capacity: 1000+
Annual Performances: 100+
Tian Jin Conservatory of Music
Website: www.tjcm.edu.cn
Phone: 222 416 0078
Address: 57 Shi Yi Jing Road, He Dong
Information: Founded in 1958, the Tianjin Conservatory of Music was then called Hebei Conservatory of Music. It was set up on the base left behind by the Central Conservatory of Music when it moved fromTianjinto-Beijing. The current President of the conservatory is Yao Shengchang, who succeeded the former President, Miao Tianrui
Country: China
Disabled Access: Yes
Policies: Present and Produce

Xinghai Concert Hall
Website: www.concerthall.com.cn/about/
Phone: 203 758 2476
Address: No. 33 Qingbo Road, Ersha Island, Guangzhou, CN
Information: Xinghai Concert Hall, built in 1998, is one of the most influential performance venues in China and one of the professional concert halls with the best sound effects in China. This concert hall is located on Ersha Island on the banks of the Pearl River in Guangzhou. It is named after the famous Chinese musician Xian Xinghai.
Country: China
Social Media: www.facebook.com/xinghaiconcerthall/

EGYPT

Cairo Jazz Club
Website: www.cairojazzclub.com/
Email: admin@cairojazzclub.com
Phone: 106 880 4764
Address: 197A 26th July st, Agouza, 3rd floor, apt 33, EG
Country: Egypt
Social Media: @CairoJazzClub
Policies: Produce and rent, Other

HONG KONG

Academic Community Hall
Website: ach.hkbu.edu.hk/en/home/index.html
Email: ach@hkbu.edu.hk
Phone: 341 15182
Address: Oen Hall (Main Building), , Hong Kong Baptist University, 224 Waterloo Road, HK
Information: The Academic Community Hall has the seating capacity of 1, 346. It is suitable for classical concerts, orchestras, musicals, variety shows, ceremonies, religious functions and seminars, it also served as the competition venue for the Hong Kong Schools Music and Speech Festival for decades.
Country: Hong Kong
Contact: Manager Zoe Yim
Email: zoeyim@hkbu.edu.hk
Phone: 341 15189
Social Media: www.facebook.com/AcademicCommunityHalltwitter.com/hkbuach
Capacity: 1000+

Chinese University of Hong Kong
Website: www.cuhk.edu.hk/mus
Email: music@cuhk.edu.hk
Phone: 260 96510
Address: Room 201, Hu Yeung Shing Building, Chinese University of Hong Kong, Shatin, New Territories, HK
Information: Founded in 1965, the Department of Music has been providing practical and academic training in both Chinese and Western music for over half a century.
Country: Hong Kong
Contact: Department Chair Frederick Lau
Email: fredlau@cuhk.edu.hk
Phone: 394 33208Executive Director Chan Chi Chun
Email: cchan@cuhk.edu.hk
Phone: 394 36555
Social Media: www.instagram.com/thechineseuniversityofhongkong/ www.facebook.com/cuhkmusic
Disabled Access: Yes
Capacity: 501-1000

City University of Hong Kong Wei Hing Lecture Theatre
Website: www.cityu.edu.hk/wayfinder/en/Venue/2510/

Email: cpro@cityu.edu.hk
Phone: 344 27654
Address: 6 / F, Amenities Building, City University of Hong Kong, Tat Chee Avenue, HK
Information: Wei Hing Theatre is a theater located inside City University of Hong Kong. It is used for different activities for the students. City University of Hong Kong is open mostly to the University and local public and is a non-profit organisation
Country: Hong Kong
Social Media: www.facebook.com/cityuniversityhongkongtwitter.com/CityUHongKong www.instagram.com/cityuhongkong/

Hong Kong Academy for Performing Arts
Website: www.hkapa.edu
Email: aso.admission@hkapa.edu
Phone: 258 48500
Address: 1 Gloucester Road, Wanchai, HK
Information: The Hong Kong Academy for Performing Arts capitalises on its position within a dynamic and diverse cultural metropolis and its strong industry and community partnerships to provide students with an innovative, multidisciplinary and globally focused education.
Country: Hong Kong
Contact: Director Gillian Choa
Phone: 258 48598Head of Programme Development Robert Wells
Phone: 258 48642Administration Executive Lau Kitty
Phone: 258 48883
Social Media: www.facebook.com/HKAPA.edu/twitter.com/HKAPA/ www.instagram.com/HKAPA_edu/

Hong Kong Arts Centre
Website: hkac.org.hk
Email: hkac@hkac.org.hk
Phone: 258 20200
Address: 2 Harbour Rd, HK
Information: HKAC is a multi-arts centre that fosters Artistic exchanges locally and internationally, bringing the most forward creations to Hong Kong and showcasing homegrown talents abroad. HKAC stimulates innovation and promotes creativity. Being Hong Kong's only independent non-profit multi-arts institution, HKAC offers exhibitions, screenings and performances, connecting the arts of Hong Kong to the rest of the world through programmes and collaborations.
Country: Hong Kong
Contact: Executive Director Connie Lam Suk Yee
Contact: Assistant Manager, Executive Director's Office Peggie Fong Pui Che
Contact: Senior Research and Project Officer, Executive Director's Office Li Yu Ching
Contact: Personal Assistant to Executive Director Wendy Chiu Wai Man
Contact: Manager – Venue Operation Emily Wong Suk Mei
Contact: Assistant Manager – Venue Operation Joseph Lai Man Ho
Contact: Assistant Manager – Venue Operation Eva Wong King Yan
Contact: Officer – Ticketing Sita Lau Lai Yin
Social Media: www.facebook.com/HongKongArtsCentre www.instagram.com/hongkongartscentre/
Disabled Access: Yes
Policies: Rent and Present

Hong Kong Baptist University, MFA
Website: artsbu.hkbu.edu.hk
Email: artd@hkbu.edu.hk
Phone: 341 17197
Address: OEW 1100, Oen Hall Building (West), Ho Sin Hang Campus, HK
Information: The Faculty of Arts is an essential part of Hong Kong Baptist University, an institution that is firmly committed to being a leading liberal arts university in Asia for the world delivering academic excellence in a caring, creative and global culture.
Country: Hong Kong
Contact: dean Mette Hjort
Email: mettehjort@hkbu.edu.hk
Contact: senior administrative Manager Iris Chao
Email: ichao@hkbu.edu.hk
Contact: Associate Deans Wai Luen Kwok
Email: wlkwok@hkbu.edu.hk
Contact: Associate Deans Min-hua Liu
Email: minhualiu@hkbu.edu.hk
Contact: Associate Deans John Winzenburg
Email: jwinzenb@hkbu.edu.hk
Social Media: www.facebook.com/ArtsFacultyHKBU www.instagram.com/hkbuartsfaculty/

Hong Kong City Hall
Website: www.lcsd.gov.hk/hkch
Email: hkch@lcsd.gov.hk
Phone: 292 12840
Address: 5 Edinburgh Place, Central, HK
Information: Established in 1962, Hong Kong City Hall was the first fully fledged cultural venue in Hong Kong. Consisting of two unmistakeably sixties-styled blocks, the low block houses major facilities such as the Concert Hall, a theatre, an exhibition hall and restaurants, whilst the high block is home to an exhibition gallery, recital

hall, committee rooms and a marriage registry. City Hall is conveniently located in Central, and individuals and organisations can hire the venues for cultural and art activities
Country: Hong Kong
Contact: senior Manager Karen Law
Contact: Manager Barry Ng
Capacity: 1434

Hong Kong Coliseum
Website: www.lcsd.gov.hk/hkc
Email: stadiaMarketing@lcsd.gov.hk
Phone: 235 57234
Address: 9 Cheong Wan Road, Hung Hom, Kowloon, HK
Information: The Hong Kong Coliseum is a 12500 seat pillar-less arena, which takes the form of an inverted pyramid and is one of the major venues for world-class events in the city

Country: Hong Kong
Contact: senior Manager venue Francis Lai
Contact: senior Manager Marketing Maggie Pang
Capacity: 12500

Hong Kong Convention and Exhibition Centre
Website: www.hkcec.com
Email: info@hkcec.com
Phone: 258 28888
Address: 1 Expo Drive, Wanchai, HK
Information: Hong Kong Convention and Exhibition Centre (Management) Limited ('HML') is a professional private management and operating company. It is a conference and exhibition facility covering an area of 306, 000 square meters, providing 91, 500 square meters of leasable area.**Country: Hong Kong**
Contact: Managing Director Monica Lee-Müller
Social Media: www.facebook.com/HKCECofficial
Disabled Access: Yes
Capacity: 1000+
Annual Performances: 51-100
Policies: Rent and Present

Hong Kong Cultural Centre
Website: www.lcsd.gov.hk/hkcc
Email: hkcc@lcsd.gov.hk
Phone: 273 42009
Address: 10 Salisbury Road, Tsim Sha Tsui, Kowloon, HK
Information: Hong Kong Cultural Centre caters to performing arts of all varieties. The Centre is designed to house three major performing halls – the Concert Hall, the Grand Theatre and the Studio Theatre. There is also an Exhibition Gallery and four foyer exhibition areas. Other ancillary facilities include eleven rehearsal and practice rooms and two conference rooms
Country: Hong Kong
Contact: senior Manager Marketing Lo-mei Pang
Contact: senior Manager venue Bessie Tong
Policies: Rent only, Multi-purpose

Hong Kong Fringe Club
Website: www.hkfringeclub.com
Email: enquiry@hkfringeclub.com
Phone: 252 17251
Address: 2 Lower Albert Road, Central, HK
Information: For over 30 years since established, the Fringe Club has become a vibrant contemporary arts space where artists create and show their work, and those who enjoy the arts come to meet and see shows. Facilities for exhibitions and performances here are offered to both emerging and professional artists in Hong Kong and from overseas.
Country: Hong Kong
Contact: Chairman Wailee Chow
Contact: Sponsorship/ Donation Catherine Lau
Email: cat@hkfringeclub.com
Phone: 561 62162Advertising Kathy Chan
Email: kathychan@hkfringeclub.com
Phone: 252 51032Venue Hiring/ Party/ Showtime Supply Kathy Chan
Email: kathychan@hkfringeclub.com
Phone: 612 66637Exhibition
Email: ctingchan@hkfringeclub.com
Phone: 561 62133Theatre / Live Music Offy Leung
Email: offy@hkfringeclub.com
Phone: 561 62166
Social Media: www.facebook.com/hkfringeclub www.instagram.com/hkfringeclub/
Capacity: 100-250
Policies: All

Hong Kong Polytechnic University
Website: www.polyu.edu.hk/cpeo
Email: pccpeo@polyu.edu.hk
Phone: 276 67100
Address: Hung Hom, Kowloon, HK
Information: Located within the campus of The Hong Kong Polytechnic University, the Studio Theatre is adjacent to the Hong Kong Cross Harbour Tunnel and MTR Hung Hom Station, with Tsimshatsui commercial area in its vicinity and is easily accessible by various means of public transport.
Country: Hong Kong
Social Media: www.facebook.com/HongKongPolyUtwitter.com/HongKongPolyU www.linkedin.com/school/

hong-kong-polytechnic-university/

Jockey Club Auditorium
Website: www.polyu.edu.hk/cpeo/jca/index.php
Email: pccpeo@polyu.edu.hk
Phone: 852 276 67100
Address: Yuk Choi Rd, Hung Hom, HK
Information: Combining classical theatre interior design and modern external facade, Jockey Club Auditorium (JCA) has come into operation in 2000. Reminiscent of the grandeur of ancient classical theatre, the Auditorium, is elegantly set with balcony and main floor seating. The Jockey Club Auditorium provides not just a conducive environment for the development of culture on campus and in enriching campus life, but also a unique venue for events and corporates alike.
Country: Hong Kong
Disabled Access: Yes
Capacity: 1000+

Ko Shan Theatre
Website: www.lcsd.gov.hk/kst
Email: kst@lcsd.gov.hk
Phone: 274 09222
Address: 77 Ko Shan Road, Hunghom, Kowloon, HK
Information: Situated within the Ko Shan Road Park in Tokwawan, what was once an amphitheatre has been rebuilt to create the Ko Shan Theatre. Opened in October 1996, the air-conditioned block houses rehearsal facilities, committee rooms and exhibition facilities. The refurbished and upgraded auditorium can seat over 1000 people, and the Ko Shan Theatre is the major venue for local groups and, once a year, all the local bands gather together for their annual concert.
Country: Hong Kong
Disabled Access: Yes
Capacity: 501-1000

Ngau Chi Wan Civic Centre
Website: www.lcsd.gov.hk/ncwcc
Email: ncwcc@lcsd.gov.hk
Phone: 232 51970
Address: 2/F & 3/F, Ngau Chi Wan Municipal Services Buildin, 11 Clearwater Bay Rd, Kowloon, HK
Information: The Ngau Chi Wan Civic Centre, conveniently located in the heart of East Kowloon, has offered quality and diversified facilities for a wide range of cultural activities and other events since its opening on 23 April 1987. With the mission of enriching the lives of the community by providing more professional services and advanced facilities, the Centre has undergone a major improvement in 2002. In early 2004, the Exhibition Hall was also converted to a multi-purpose Cultural Activities Hall to suit the needs of the community
Country: Hong Kong
Contact: venue Manager Karen Lee
Capacity: 354

North District Town Hall
Website: www.lcsd.gov.hk/ndth
Email: ndth@lcsd.gov.hk
Phone: 267 14400
Address: 2 Lung Wan Stree, Sheung Shui, New Territories, HK
Information: Located at the centre of Sheung Shui, adjacent to MTR station, the Town Hall comprises an Auditorium and two Function Rooms, which are suitable for organising arts and cultural performances, ceremonies, exhibitions, conferences, seminars, receptions and training classes
Country: Hong Kong
Disabled Access: Yes
Capacity: 251-500
Annual Performances: 100+
Annual Productions: 100+
Policies: All

Queen Elizabeth Stadium
Website: https:// www.lcsd.gov.hk/en/qes/
Email: stadiaMarketing@lcsd.gov.hk
Phone: 259 11346
Address: 18 Oi Kwan Road, Wanchai, HK
Information: Opened in 1980, the Queen Elizabeth Stadium (the "Stadium") is Hong Kong's premier multi-purpose venue located in the heart of Wan Chai that provides the public with a chance to view and participate in sports, recreation and culture, all under the same roof. Apart from a 3500-seat arena, the Stadium houses a reception lobby, a VIP lounge, a multi-purpose hall, two function rooms, four committee rooms, three squash courts and a table-tennis playing area**Country:** Hong Kong
Contact: CEO Alex Kong
Capacity: 1000+

Serious Staging
Website: www.serious-staging.com
Email: info@serious-staging.com
Phone: 392 99555
Address: 8/F Bangkok Bank Building, 18 Bonham Strand West, HK
Information: Having built a solid foundation on its event management and production experience, Serious Staging is best positioned to proactively identify potential for the creation of imaginative projects and extraordinary

experiences. Serious Staging's venue opportunities and solutions service delivers more than just a vision – they create opportunities where none seem to exist to craft exceptional and out-of-the-ordinary proposals to clients looking for a one-of-a-kind venue and experience. Services include identification of venue opportunities and provision of venue solutions
Country: Hong Kong
Contact: Managing Director David Rule
Contact: special projects Manager John Binks
Contact: technical Director Mark Taylor
Capacity: 425

Sha Tin Town Hall
Website: www.lcsd.gov.hk/en/stth/index.html
Email: stth@lcsd.gov.hk
Phone:
269 42509
Address: 1 Yuen Wo Rd, Sha Tin, New Territories, HK
Information: Recognised as one of the Hong Kong's finest performing arts centres, Sha Tin Town Hall is also the heart of culture in the east of the New Territories. It is a well designed complex with integrated facilities giving people opportunities to enjoy culture and arts in relaxing surroundings. Whether for dance, drama and music activities, or for exhibitions and conferences, the Town Hall provides a complete range of performance and exhibition venues
Country: Hong Kong
Capacity: 1000+
Annual Performances: 51-100
Policies: Rent and Present

Sheung Wan Civic Centre
Website: www.lcsd.gov.hk/swcc
Email: swcc@lcsd.gov.hk
Phone: 285 32689
Address: 5/F, Sheung Wan Municipal Services Building, 345 Queen's Rd Central, HK
Information: The Sheung Wan Civic Centre is situated on the fourth to the seventh floors of the Sheung Wan Municipal Services Building. Since its opening in December 1989, the Centre's diversified facilities are available for hire by the public for organising cultural activities and other events. The facilities include, theatre, lecture hall, exhibition hall, rehearsal hall, dance practice room, art studios, music practice rooms and barrier free facilities.
Country: Hong Kong
Contact: Artistic adviser Gu Guanren
Disabled Access: Yes
Capacity: 251-500
Policies: Rent and Present

Sir Run Run Shaw Hall
Website: www.cuhk.edu.hk/srrsh
Email: srrsh@cuhk.edu.hk
Phone: 260 97852
Address: Chinese University of Hong Kong, Shatin, New Territories, HK
 The Shaw Hall of The Chinese University of Hong Kong was completed and opened in 1981. It is well-equipped and meets the professional stage specifications. It can accommodate 1438 spectators. It is the largest performance venue in the school with complete stage facilities.
Country: Hong Kong
Contact: Arts Administrator and Manager Chung Siu Mui Ribble
Contact: assistant arts administrator Tsang Shuk Ching Jane
Social Media: www.facebook.com/cuhkoaa/ www.instagram.com/cuhkoaa/

Sunbeam Theatre
Website: sunbeamtheatre.com
Phone: 285 60161
Address: 423 King's Road, North Point, HK
Information: For thirty years, "Sunbeam Theatre", in order to promote Chinese culture, arts and the promotion of cultural and Artistic exchanges between Hong Kong and the Mainland, has made a unique contribution to the public service. Ever since its opening, this theatre has been playing traditional Cantonese opera while attracting top performers, even though Cantonese opera is currently declining in popularity
Country: Hong Kong
Contact: Manager Man Pak Wipe
Capacity: 1033

Tai Po Civic Centre
Website: https:// www.lcsd.gov.hk/tpcc/
Email: tpcc@lcsd.gov.hk
Phone: 266 54477
Address: 12 On Pong Road, Tai Po Civic Centre, New Territories, HK
Information: Tai Po Civic Centre was officially opened in September 1985. Conveniently located at the centre of the Tai Po District on On Pong Road, you will see the Tai Po Civic Centre, a prominent purple-roofed pavilion surrounded by a garden and leading to a glazed-window building.**Country:** Hong Kong
Disabled Access: Yes
Capacity: 1000+
Annual Performances: 6-10
Policies: Rent and Present

Tsuen Wan Town Hall
Website: https:// www.lcsd.gov.hk/twth/
Email: twth@lcsd.gov.hk
Phone: 241 40144
Address: 72 Tai Ho Rd, Tsuen Wan, New Territories, HK
Information: Tsuen Wan Town Hall was inaugurated in 1980. It marked the first performing venue in the New Territories. The Town Hall was well-equipped with integrated facilities, including an Auditorium with 1420 seats which is ideal for wide range of performances while a Cultural Activities Hall with 260 seats which is best for small stage shows and screenings. It also has an Exhibition Gallery, a Lecture Room and a Conference Room which are suitable for exhibitions, conferences, receptions, training classes, etc.
Country: Hong Kong
Disabled Access: Yes
Capacity: 1000+

Tuen Mun Town Hall
Website: www.lcsd.gov.hk/tmth
Email: tmth@lcsd.gov.hk
Phone: 245 04202
Address: 3 Tuen Hi Road, Tuen Mun, New Territories, HK
Information: The Tuen Mun Town Hall is a well-equipped cultural complex managed by the department. Conveniently located in the heart of Tuen Mun and effectively served by a motorway network connecting all parts of the district as well as Yuen Long, Tsuen Wan and Kowloon, the Town Hall is the centre for cultural activities and performing arts in northwest New Territories since its opening in May 1987. To cope with Tuen Mun's rapid development, the Town Hall has been continually enhancing its facilities, improving its services and dedicating itself to promote the cultural activities in the region, with a vision to bringing to the local community a vibrant cultural milieu
Country: Hong Kong
Contact: Commanding Officer Ivy Leung Siu Han
Email: ishleung@lcsd.gov.hk
Phone: 245 15448**Manager Wai Han Chan
Email: fwhchan@lcsd.gov.hk
Phone: 245 04421
Disabled Access: Yes
Capacity: 1000+
Annual Performances: 100+
Policies: Rent and Present

University of Hong Kong
Website: www.hku.hk/music/
Email: music@hku.hk
Phone: 391 77045
Address: 11/F Run Run Shaw Tower, Centennial Campus, Pokfulam Road, HK
Information: The Music Department is a leading centre of research excellence in the region, with world-renowned scholars from across the globe who play a significant role in shaping the study of music today.
Country: Hong Kong
Contact: Chair Professor and Chairperson Daniel Chua
Email: dchua@hku.hk
Contact: Assistant Professor Youn Kim
Email: younkim@hku.hk
Contact: Director, Society of Fellows in the Humanities Giorgio Biancorosso
Email: rogopag@hku.hk
Capacity: 251-500
Policies: Present and Produce

INDONESIA

Bali Arts Centre
Phone: 361 227 176
Address: Jl. Nusa Indah – Abian Kapas, ID
Country: Indonesia

Blue Pacific Enterprises
Phone: 215 704 444 ext.
Address: Suite 310-312, Sahid Jaya Hotel, 86 Jalan Jenderal Sudirman, ID
Information: second address: 42 Jl Jaltan Hassamunin, Jakarta Pusat, Indonesia, Tel: 21-207 621/722 866
Country: Indonesia
Contact: vice-President Yumiati Nugruho

Erasmus Huis
Website: www.erasmushuis.or.id
Email: info@erasmushuis.or.id
Phone: 215 241 069
Address: Jl. HR. Rasuna Said Kav S-3, Kuningan, ID
Country: Indonesia
Contact: deputy Director Willem E. Meulenberg

Gedung Kesenian Jakarta
Website: www.gkj-online.com
Email: tu@gkj-online.com
Phone: 213 808 283/344
Address: Jalan Gedung Kesenian 1, ID
Country: Indonesia
Contact: Executive Director I.G. Kompiang Raka

Goethe Institut
Website: www.goethe.de/so/jak/deindex
Email: info@jakarta.goethe.org

Phone: 626 221 235 5002
Address: P.O.Box 3640, ID
Information: visiting address: Jl.Sam Ratulangi 9-15, Jakarta 10350
Country: Indonesia
Contact: head of cultural programme Marla Stukenberg

Jakarta Institute of the Arts
Phone: 622 743 71233
Address: Academic Administration Building, Jl. Parang Tritis Km 6.5, ID
Information: see also National Organisations
Country: Indonesia

Jakarta Playhouse
Website: www.gkj-online.com
Email: tu@gkj-online.com
Phone: 213 808 283
Address: Jalan Gedung Kesenian 1, ID
Information: an old venue from Dutch colonial era
Country: Indonesia
Contact: Executive Director I.G. Kompiang Raka

Polosseni
Website: www.goarchi.com/yp www.polosseni.com
Email: polos@goarchi.com
Phone: 361 975 869
Address: P.O. Box 56, Ubud, ID
Information: Specialising in Balinese Semar Pegulingan Gamelan and the accompanying Legong Kraton dances.
Country: Indonesia
Contact: Artistic Director I Made Djimat
Contact: administrator Ni Putu Sutarini
Contact: secretary Nyoman Sriani
Email: polos@goarchi.com
Policies: Other

Taman Ismail Marzuki Arts Center
Phone: 622 131 54087
Address: Kompleks Kesenian TIM, Jalan Cikini Raya, 73, ID
Information: This complex acquired its name from the great Indonesian musician, Ismail Marzuki, whose statue guards the entrance gate. It hosts the Institut Kesenian Jakarta Jakarta Institute for the Arts and Jakarta Planetarium. The arts institute is the only one of
Country: Indonesia

Teater Tanah Airku (TTA)
Phone: 622 187 793 369
Address: Jl Taman Mini Raya, ID
Information: equipped with an international standard lighting, sound and accoustic system, a 17 meter stage with capability to quickly change 60 tons of set, and multi media technology
Country: Indonesia
Contact: contact Budi Djohan

Teater Utan Kayu, Yayasan
Website: www.utankayu.org
Email: komunitasutankayu@yahoo.com
Phone: 218 573 388
Address: Jl. Utan Kayu No. 68 H, ID
Information: a vibrant, alternative arts complex; presents a regular monthly programme of theatre, music, dance, discussion and film screening; also have two-story arts gallery Galeri Lontar, cafe and book store; managed by Komunikas Utan Kayu Utan Kayu Community
Country: Indonesia
Contact: secretary Asty Leonast

ISRAEL

Incubator Theatre
Website: www.incubator.org.il
Email: info@incubator.org.il
Phone: 265 43004
Address: Messilat Yesharim 18, IL
Information: Member of ISPA
Country: Israel
Social Media: www.facebook.com/Incubator.Theater
Policies: Theatre

JAPAN

ACROS Fukuoka Symphony Hall
Website: www.acros.or.jp
Address: 1-1-1 Tenjin, Chuo-ku, JP
Information: A full-scale shoe-box hall with 2.0 second reverb at capacity. Movable stage with sound reflectors suitable for anything from world class full orchestra and chamber music to amateur recitals and performances. The hall is also suitable for non-musical use including academic conferences and lectures.
Country: Japan
Social Media: twitter.com/acros_shihainin www.facebook.com/%E3%82%A2%E3%82%AF%E3%83%AD%E3%82%B9%E7%A6%8F%E5%B2%A1-161116120570939/ www.instagram.com/acros_fukuoka/

ACT City Hamamatsu
Website: www.actcity.jp
Email: info@actcity.jp
Phone: 534 511 111

Address: 111-1 Itaya-machi, Hamamatsu, JP
Information: ACT CITY has both public and private occupancy. Keeping the idea of harmony between people and the environment in mind, ACT CITY is an attractive space in Hamamatsu city
Country: Japan
Contact: secretary General Umeo Suzuki
Contact: Managing Director Masayoshi Kawakami
Contact: Chairman of board of Director Takeshi Shoda
Policies: Multi-purpose

Aichi Prefectural Art Theatre
Website: www.aac.pref.aichi.jp
Phone: 971 5516
Address: 1-13-2 Higashi-Sakura, Higashi-ku, Nagoya, JP
Information: Three separate venues-the Theater, the Concert Hall, and the Mini Theater-were designed within the Art Theater employing the most sophisticated technologies, thereby enabling it to face the challenge of introducing the many to the performing arts
Country: Japan
Social Media: www.facebook.com/Aichi-Prefectural-Arts-Theater-1390709441154018/ https://twitter.com/APAT
Disabled Access: Yes
Capacity: 1000+
Annual Productions: 25-50
Policies: All

Aizu Fuugado
Website: www.aizu-bunka.jp
Email: info@aizu-bunka.jp
Phone: 242 270 900
Address: 12-1 Johtoh-machi, Aizu-Wakamatsu, JP
Information: presents its own productions; also available for hire. alternative contact number 0242 26 6661
Country: Japan
Contact: Director Nobuyoshi Iwasawa
Policies: Present and produce, Produce and co-produce, Rent and present, Produce and rent

Akigawa Kirara Hall
Website: www.akigawa-kirarahall.jp
Email: info@akigawa-kirarahall.jp
Phone: 425 597 500
Address: 1-16-1 Akigawa, Akiruno-shi, Tokyo
Information: Akikawa Kirara Hall is a hall built mainly for the performance of music, the quality of sound is outstanding.From full orchestra to solo, classical concert has been evaluated as optimum reverberation effect. Many are also used for concerts of top artists in Japan and abroad and for CD recording etc due to the good sound of the sound
Country: Japan
Contact: Honorary Advisor Bin Ebisawa
Disabled Access: Yes
Capacity: 501-1000
Annual Performances: 51-100
Policies: Rent and Present

Akita-shi Bunka Kaikan
Website: www.city.akita.akita.jp
Email: ro-edech@city.akita.akita.jp
Phone: 188 651 191
Address: 7-3-1 San-no, JP
Information: presents its own productions; venue is also available for hire
Country: Japan
Social Media: @akitacity
Policies: Produce and co-produce, Rent and present, Produce and rent

Alios Iwaki Performing Arts Centre
Website: www.iwaki-alios.jp
Email: info@iwaki-alios.jp
Phone: 246 228 111
Address: Misaki Flat 1, JP
Information: The Alios Iwaki Performing Arts Center is a newly built multipurpose city hall in Iwaki, Japan. The word "Alios" stands for Art, Life, Information, Oasis, and Sightseeing. The sound system that was installed in to this new build included 16 XTA DP448 audio management systems. Situated 300km east of Tokyo, the city of Iwaki is in the southern part of the Hamadori coastal region of Fukushima, Tohoku
Country: Japan
Social Media: @iwaki_alios www.facebook.com/iwakialios
Capacity: 1840

Amagasaki Cultural Centre – Archaic Halls
Website: www.archaic.or.jp
Phone: 664 823 503
Address: 2-7-16 Showa-dori, Amagasaki, JP
Information: The Amagasaki Cultural Center is a complex located in Amagasaki, Japan. The building, which opened in 1975, has three concerts halls. The "Archaic Hall" is the largest and seats 2030 people. Notable past performers include Roger Daltrey, Yes, The Smashing Pumpkins, and Alcatrazz
Country: Japan
Contact: Director Aya Shirai
Capacity: 2030

Anjo Shimin Kaikan – Salvia Hall
Website: www.city.anjo.aichi.jp
Phone: 566 751 151
Address: 18-28 Sakura-machi, Anjo, JP
Information: Since its opening in 1972, Anjo City Hall has been loved by the local people, including the people of Anjo City. In addition to the Salvia Hall with 1, 200 seats (including 6 wheelChair seats) named after the flower of Anjo City, Salvia, there are exhibition rooms, 5 meeting rooms, audiovisual rooms, lecture rooms, Japanese-style rooms, and other rooms that meet diverse needs. It is a facility equipped with.
Country: Japan
Social Media: twitter.com/Anjosiminkaikan

Aoba no Mori Park Arts and Culture Hall
Website: www.aobageibun.com
Email: aoba@cbs.or.jp
Phone: 432 663 511
Address: 977-1 Aoba-cho, Chuo-ku, JP
Information: Aoba no Mori Park Arts and Culture Hall contains 4 rooms with different specifications that can be used for various conferences and club activities, as well as a hall for full-scale concerts and lectures. Located in a quiet environment surrounded by Aobano-mori Park.
Country: Japan
Social Media: www.facebook.com/aobageibun/twitter.com/aobageibun

Aomori City Cultural Hall
Website: aobunkanko.com/facility/linkstationhall/
Email: aobunspo@actv.ne.jp
Phone: 177 737 300
Address: 1-chôme-4-1 Tsutsumimachi, JP
Information: Link Station Hall Aomori (Aomori City Cultural Hall) is a facility set up for citizens to appreciate, promote, lectures and conferences on cultural and Artistic activities. Currently, it is widely used by citizens as a base for local cultural activities, as a place for art appreciation in Japan and overseas, and as a venue for various conventions.
Country: Japan
Capacity: 1000+

Aoyama Ongaku Kinenkan – Baroque Saal
Phone: 753 930 011
Address: 9-1 Matsuo Dairi-cho, Nishikyo-ku, JP
Information: Aoyama Music Hall. Baroque rice is a classical music venue. The Aoyama Foundation runs its own chamber music show. They run a program for the performing arts support, and a prize for Aoyama Music Award
Country: Japan
Contact: Chairman Yoshimichi Aoyama
Capacity: 562

Aoyama Theatre
Website: www.aoyama.org
Phone: 337 975 678
Address: 5-53-1 Jingumae, Shibuya-ku, JP
Information: Housed in the building that also once hosted the Aoyama Round Theatre, this 1200-seat auditorium isn't super-distinctive, though its occasionally risky programming more than makes up for that fact. Aoyama Theatre's main stage structure includes 24 small risers, a sliding stage and a rotating stage. The Aoyama Round Theatre stage is made up of 44 independently movable risers. The performance areas of both theaters are adaptable to a wide variety of performance needs
Country: Japan
Policies: Rent and present, Theatre

Aqua Bunka Hall
Phone: 668 630 191
Address: 3-7-1 Sone Higashi-machi, Toyonaka, JP
Information: presents its own productions & available for hire
Country: Japan
Contact: Director Toshio Mizoguchi
Policies: Present and produce, Produce and co-produce, Rent and present, Produce and rent

Art Space Sunrise Hall
Phone: 339 853 986
Address: B1 Hinode Bldg, 4-19-6 Minami-Ikebukuro, Toshima-ku, JP
Information: Venue for different play. venue for hire
Country: Japan
Policies: Produce and co-produce, Rent and present, Produce and rent

Art Tower Mito (ATM)
Website: www11.arttowermito.or.jp
Email: webstaff@arttowermito.or.jp
Phone:
Address: 1-6-8 Goken-cho, Mito, JP
Information: Art Tower Mito (ATM), symbolized by the 100-meter-tall metal tower that stands in its plaza, is a comprehensive cultural facility divided into three sections: a concert hall, a theater, and a gallery for contemporary art. Having opened in 1990 to commemorate the 100th anniversary of Mito's designation as an official

city, the ATM complex has served as the venue for a wide variety of planned events, including musical concerts, dramatic productions, and art exhibitions featuring both Japanese and foreign artists
Country: Japan
Contact: Director General Hidekazu Yoshida
Contact: Executive Director of concert hall atm Ryosuke Hatanaka
Contact: General Manager of mito chamber orchestra Tatsuo Oguchi
Contact: Artistic Director of acm theatre Koshiro Matsumoto
Contact: advisor of acm theatre Sumio Yoshii
Capacity: 680

Asahi Seimei Hall
Website: https:// www.sunskyroom.jp/asahi/
Email: ash@sanko-inc.co.jp FAX 06-6202-7789
Phone: 362 023 919
Address: 4-2-16 Koraibashi, Chuo-ku, Osaka
Information: Equipped with a comfortable and calm atmosphere and abundant audio equipment, lighting equipment, and DCP projectors, it is ideal for events such as previews, lectures, company information sessions, Japanese music meetings, and piano presentations. You can also use the Yodoyabashi Sun Sky Room, which is a rental conference**Country:** Japan
Capacity: 251-500
Policies: Rent and Present

Asahikawa Shimin Bunka Kaikan
Website: www.city.asahikawa.hokkaido.jp/files/simin-bunka/
Email: siminbunka@city.asahikawa.hokkaido.jp
Phone: 166 257 331
Address: 9-chome, 7-jo-dori, Asahikawa, JP
Information: presents its own productions; also available for hire
Country: Japan
Policies: Present and produce, Produce and co-produce, Rent and present, Produce and rent

Ashiya Shimin Center – Luna Hall
Website: https:// www.city.ashiya.lg.jp/kouminkan/guide.html
Email: info@city.ashiya.hyogo.jp
Phone: 797 314 995
Address: 8-24 Narihira-cho, Ashiya, JP
Information: In the spring of 1970, the Luna Hall was completed as a hall for citizens on the banks of the Ashiya River, which is lined with cherry blossom trees. There are large and small halls that can be used for multiple purposes.
The large hall is used for various events such as music, theater, and various competitions. The small hall on the first basement floor is used for dance, ballet, and piano recitals, and the large hall is also used as a rehearsal room when using it.
Country: Japan
Capacity: 501-1000
Annual Performances: 25-50
Policies: Rent and Present

Atelier Fontaine
Phone: 238 216 619
Address: 2-6-13 Chuo, Yonezawa-shi, JP
Information: venue is also for hire
Country: Japan
Policies: Rent and present, Produce and rent

Atrion Ongaku Hall
Website: www.atorion.co.jp
Email: ongaku_atorion@kosei-buil.co.jp
Phone: 188 367 803
Address: 2-3-8 Naka-dori, JP
Information: Considering the hall itself as a "musical instrument", this hall was designed and constructed with the highest priority on the acoustic side, and the ceiling and walls are covered with "Akita cedar", and the warm and soft sound that makes use of the wood material is staged. It has been well received from the standpoints of both the above performers and the viewers in the audience.
Country: Japan
Contact: General Manager Hiroshi Nakatani
Contact: President Hiroshi Kato
Social Media: www.facebook.com/AtorionConcertHall. Akita/twitter.com/AtorionOngaku/

Ayase-shi Bunka Kaikan
Website: ayase-bunka.com
Email: info@ayase-manavi.net
Phone: 467 790 141
Address: 3838 Fukaya, Ayase, JP
Information: Ayase City Owens Cultural Center is used to carry out various projects aimed at improving the culture of Ayase citizens, with the aim of further revitalizing the cultural activities of Ayase citizens and contributing to raising the awareness of citizens' participation.**Country:** Japan

Banana Hall
Website: www.bananahall.co.jp
Email: ippan@bananahall.co.jp

Phone: 663 616 821
Address: 16-3 Dohyama-cho, Kita-ku, JP
Information: This is one of Osaka's best-known live houses and the reasons are easy to understand. To begin with, Banana Hall brings in a diverse selection of acts from around the world, representing many genres of live music. The Hall itself, with its high ceilings and excellent acoustics and lighting, also helps to ensure a quality performance. Patrons tend to be a diverse group, and change with the act
Country: Japan
Contact: Managing Director Kenji Takagi
Capacity: 578

Belle For
Website: www.tvt.ne.jp/~t-arts/bellforet.html
Email: t-arts@tvt.ne.jp
Phone: 868 312 525
Address: 7F, Alne-Tsuyama, 17, Shinuomachi, Tsuyama, JP
Information: presents its own productions, also available for hire; has a resident choir, Vocal Ensemble Tsuyama
Country: Japan
Contact: Director Minoru Kunitomi

Benisan Pit
Phone: 336 344 141
Address: 2-17-12 Shin-Ohashi, Kohtoh-ku, JP
Information: home of Theatre Project Tokyo T.P.T.q.v.
Country: Japan

Biwako Hall Center for the Performing Arts, Shiga
Website: www.biwako-hall.or.jp
Email: koho@biwako-hall.or.jp
Phone: 775 237 133
Address: 15-1 Uchidehama, Otsu, JP
Information: Opened in September 1998; the main theatre features one of Japan's largest quadruple stages, and all three theatres are equipped with advanced stage equipment and audience seating systems; run by Biwako Hall Foundation (q.v.)
Country: Japan
Contact: President Emi Uehara
Policies: Rent and present

Brahms Hall
Website: www.oclassic.net
Email: brahms@mx.biwa.ne.jp
Phone: 775 511 699
Address: 8-1-2 Tehara Ritto-cho Kurita-gun, Shiga, Ritto-city, JP
Country: Japan
Contact: Director Michiko Hagino

Buddhist Hall
Phone: 332 480 798
Address: c/o Tsukiji Honganji, 3-15-1 Tsukiji, Chuo-ku, JP
Information: a venue in a temple
Country: Japan

Bunkamura
Website: www.bunkamura.co.jp
Email: bunkamura@bunkamura.co.jp
Phone: 334 779 150
Address: c/o Tokyu Bunkamura Inc, 2-24-1 Dogenzaka, Shibuya-ku, JP
Information: run by Tokyu Bunkamura Inc; the facility includes 2 halls, 2o cinemas, a fine arts museum, an art gallery, rehearsal rooms and recording studios; international cultural exchange
Country: Japan

Bunkamura Orchard Hall
Website: www.bunkamura.co.jp/english/index.html
Email: bunkamura@bunkamura.co.jp
Phone: 334 779 150
Address: c/o Tokyu Bunkamura Inc, 2-24-1 Dogenzaka, Shibuya-ku, JP
Country: Japan
Contact: Producer Masashi Miyazawa

Bunkamura Theatre Cocoon
Website: www.bunkamura.co.jp
Email: bunkamura@bunkamura.co.jp
Phone: 334 779 150
Address: c/o Tokyu Bunkamura Inc, 2-24-1 Dogenzaka, Shibuya-ku, JP
Country: Japan
Contact: Artistic Director Yukio Ninagawa
Contact: Producer Kimiko Kurihara

Bunkaza Atelier
Website: bunkaza.com/
Email: info@bunkaza.com
Phone: 338 282 216
Address: 3-22-12 Tabata, Kita-ku, JP
Information: mainly presents Japanese Shin-geki drama
Country: Japan
Contact: Director Ai Sasaki

Chiba-ken Bunka Kaikan

Website: www.cbs.or.jp/kaikan/index.html
Email: chiba@cbs.or.jp
Phone: 432 220 201
Address: 11-2 Ichiba-cho, Chuo-ku, JP
Information: presents its own productions; also available for hire
Country: Japan
Contact: Director Misao Sase

Chiba-shi Bunka Centre Art-Hall
Website: www.ccf.chp.or.jp
Email: ccf-webmaster@chp.or.jp
Phone: 432 248 211
Address: 4 F Twin Bldg 2-gokan, 2-5-1 Chuo, Chuo-ku, JP
Information: presents its own productions; also available for hire
Country: Japan
Contact: Director Toshio Nakamura

Chigasaki Shimin Bunka Kaikan
Website: www.chigasaki-arts.jp/
Phone: 046 785 1123
Address: 1-11-1 Chigasaki, Chigasaki, Kanagawa Prefecture
Information: We carry out projects to promote cultural and Artistic activities and sports activities, and contribute to the formation and development of a healthy and vibrant area where Chigasaki citizens can lead a rich and fulfilling citizen's life.
Country: Japan
Contact: Chairman Teruo Inaoka
Contact: Vice Chairman Hiroshi Iwasawa
Contact: Vice Chairman Katsutoshi Kumazawa
Contact: Managing Director Shizuo Hisanaga
Capacity: 1000+
Annual Performances: 100+
Policies: Rent and Present

Chitose Shimin Bunka Centre
Website: www.city.chitose.hokkaido.jp/bunka/
Email: bunka-ch@city.chitose.hokkaido.jp
Phone: 123 261 151
Address: 2-2-11 Hokuei, Chitose, JP
Information: designed for classical music concerts
Country: Japan
Contact: Director Masaharu Ogawa

Chofu-shi Green Hall
Website: www.city.chofu.tokyo.jp
Email: mail001@city.chofu.tokyo.jp
Phone: 424 817 111
Address: 2-47-1 Kojima-cho, Chofu, JP
Information: presents both its own productions and co-productions
Country: Japan
Contact: General Manager Seiichiro Sugata

Chukyo TV Enterprise Co Ltd
Website: cte.jp/
Phone: 529 573 333
Address: 6F Yuraku-Kawai Bldg, 3-15-15 Nishiki, Naka-ku, Nagoya, JP
Information: Producer/presenter of foreign classical music groups in Japan
Country: Japan
Contact: President Kazutoshi Okita
Contact: Executive Director of cultural production div. Zen'ya Sakuma

Chunichi Theatre
Website: www.chunichi-theatre.com
Email: seisaku@chunichi-theatre.com
Phone: 522 637 171
Address: 9F Chunichi Bldg, 4-1-1 Sakae, Naka-ku, Nagoya, JP
Information: established in 1966; owned and directly operated by a newspaper company, Chunichi Shimbun
Country: Japan
Contact: President of chunichi shimbun Bungo Shirai

Clavia Hall
Phone: 276 752 331
Address: 1-17-56 Matsubara, Tatebayashi, JP
Country: Japan

Collabolative Music Workshop
Website: http:// www.gmaweb.net/npo/
Email: npo@gmaweb.net
Phone: 425 223 943
Address: 3F Kakuni Daini Bldg, 2-25-1 Akebono-cho, Tachikawa, JP
Information: We believe that the performer, the amateur choir, and the audience are all collaborating to make music. Here, the NPO "Ongaku Joint Workshop" was born, where musicians, choirs, and music fans work together to support young performers and proactively perform <orchestra works with chorus>, which is a treasure trove of classical music. ..
Country: Japan
Social Media: https:// www.facebook.com/kammersaal
Capacity: 100-250

Policies: Present and Produce

Collezione
Website: www.lacollezione.jp
Phone: 334 705 320
Address: 3F Collezione Bldg., 6-1-3 Minami-Aoyama, Minato-ku, JP
Country: Japan

Concert Hall ATM
Website: www.arttowermito.or.jp
Email: webstaff@arttowermito.or.jp
Phone: 292 278 111
Address: 1-6-8 Goken-cho, Mito-shi, JP
Country: Japan

Concert Hall Shizuoka
Website: www.aoi.shizuoka-city.or.jp
Email: info@aoi.shizuoka-city.or.jp
Phone: 542 512 200
Address: PO Box 251, Shizuoka Central Post Office, 1-9 Kurogane-cho, JP
Information: a shoebox type hall; presents its own productions; also available for hire
Country: Japan
Contact: Artistic Director Ichiro Nodaira

Concert Salon Andantino
Phone: 813 340 82006
Address: West 1F, Aoyama Twin Bldg, 1-1-1 Minami-Aoyama, Minato-ku, JP
Country: Japan

Cowbell Hall
Website: www.torikenmin.jp/a-cowbell/hall.htm
Phone: 858 531 621
Address: c/o Tohaku-cho, Nohkyo, 588-1, Tokuman, Tohaku-gun, JP
Information: produce competitions and festivals every year; available for hire
Country: Japan

Cremona Hall
Email: ropeway@334.co.jp
Phone: 138 233 105
Address: Hakodateyama Tenbodai, 1 aza-gotenyama, Hakodateyama, Hakodate, JP
Country: Japan
Contact: representative Takeshi Nishino

Daishi Hall
Website: www.daishi-bank.co.jp
Phone: 252 298 111
Address: 7-1071-1 Higashiborimae-dori, JP
Information: presents its own productions & available for hire
Country: Japan

Den-en Hall Ellora
Email: ellora@mud.biglobe.ne.jp
Phone: 489 921 001
Address: 3-14-6 Yumemino Higashi, Matsubushi-machi, Kita-Katsushika-gun, JP
Information: organized by Matsubushi-machi Furusato cultural Foundation Tel: 489-92 1001
Country: Japan
Contact: General Director Kimio Okuzumi

Den'en Hall Yahaba-cho Bunka Kaikan
Phone: 196 975 585
Address: 13-123 Oaza Minami-Yahaba, Yahaba-cho, Shiwa-gun, JP
Information: has rooms with sound facilities and glass windows attached to the hall for mother-and-child to enjoy music and a view in private
Country: Japan

Denki Hall
Website: www.denki-b.co.jp
Phone: 927 810 685
Address: 2-1-82 Watanabe-dori, Chuo-ku, JP
Country: Japan

Denryoku Hall
Website: www.d-biru.com
Phone: 222 252 251
Address: 7F Denryoku Bldg, 3-7-1 Ichiban-cho, Aoba-ku, Sendai, JP
Information: presents its own productions; also available for hire
Country: Japan

Die Pratze
Website: http://www.d-1986.com/index_d
Email: d-soko@d-1986.com
Phone: 358 115 399
Address: Higashinippori 6-19-7 Arakawa-ku, Tokyo, Japan
Information: The theater and the rehersal hall are rented out for theatre, dance, performance performances... We also carry out independent projects such as dance and theater festivals.Country: Japan

Contact: Artistic Director Shigeo Makabe
Email: d-soko@d-1986.com
Contact: Producer Hayashi Keiichi
Email: d-soko@d-1986.com
Social Media: https://twitter.com/d__soko https:// www.facebook.com/dsoko.theater/

Echizen-shi Bunka Center
Website: www.necsoft.co.jp/takefu/
Email: tbc@mitene.or.jp
Phone: 778 235 057
Address: 2-3-3 Takase, Echizen, JP
Information: venue for Takefu International Music Festival (q.v.)
Country: Japan
Contact: Artistic administrator Hiroshi Tanaka

Edogawa-ku Sohgoh Bunka Centre
Phone: 336 521 111
Address: 4-14-1 Chuo, Edogawa-ku, JP
Country: Japan

Ehime-ken Kenmin Bunka Kaikan
Phone: 899 235 111
Address: 2-5-1 Dohgo-cho, Matsuyama, JP
Information: presents its own productions; available for hire
Country: Japan
Contact: President Youzou Satoh

Ekimae Gekijo
Website: www.honda-geki.com/ekimae.html
Phone: 334 140 019
Address: 2-11-8-3F, Kitazawa, Setagaya-ku, JP
Country: Japan

Elisabeth University of Music Halls
Phone: 822 210 918
Address: 4-15 Nobori-cho, Naka-ku, JP
Information: Cecilia Hall: equipped with a pipe organ; Xavier Hall: suitable for ensembles and solo recitals
Country: Japan
Contact: chief educational affairs Yuji Kawano
Contact: govenor Jiro Kozaki

Enishi-an
Website: ikedayanet.com/
Email: rosso-mogu@i.email.ne.jp
Phone: 728 793 585
Address: 2-9-16 Nankoh, Shijohnawate-shi, JP
Information: a unique outdoor theatre with accommodation facility operated by Ikedaya; has an indoor space for performance as well
Country: Japan

EXPO Hall
Website: www.expo70.or.jp
Phone: 668 773 331
Address: c/o Commemorative Assoc for the Japan World Exposition, 1-1 Senri Banpaku Koen, Suita, JP
Information: large stage 22.5m x 19.0m and modern facilities
Country: Japan

Ezaki Hall
Phone: 542 552 231
Address: 8-20 Shichiken-cho, JP
Country: Japan
Contact: President Zenzaburo Ezaki

Festival Hall
Website: www.festivalhall.jp
Phone: 662 312 221
Address: 2-3-18 Nakanoshima, Kita-ku, JP
Information: Osaka International Festival (q.v.) is held at this venue
Country: Japan

Flanders Centre
Website: www.flanders.jp
Email: info@flanders.jp
Phone: 667 738 850
Address: 3F, International House Osaka, 8-2-6 Uehon-machi, Tenno-ji-ku, JP
Information: presents its own productions; available for hire
Country: Japan
Contact: Director Bernard Catrysse

Foundation Bunkyo Kaikan of Ishikawa Prefecture
Website: www.bunkyo.or.jp
Phone: 762 627 311
Address: 10-5 Oyama-cho, Kanazawa, JP
Country: Japan
Contact: Managing Director Yasuko Urabe
Contact: President Shigeki Fukuda

Fuchu Green Plaza – Keyaki Hall
Phone: 423 603 311
Address: 1-1-1 Fuchu-cho, Fuchu, JP
Information: presents its own productions; also available for hire

Country: Japan

Fuchu no Mori Theatre
Website: www.fuchu-cpf.or.jp/theater
Phone: 423 356 211
Address: 1-2 Sengen-cho, Fuchu, JP
Country: Japan

Fuji-shi Bunka Kaikan Ros
Website: rose-theatre.jp
Email: info@rose-theatre.jp
Phone: 545 602 510
Address: 1750 Tadewara-cho, Fuji, JP
Information: presents its own productions; also available for hire
Country: Japan

Fujisawa Lyra Hall
Website: www1.ttcn.ne.jp/~fujisawalyrahall
Phone: 466 222 721
Address: 5F 1-1-15 Ishigami, Kugenuma, Fujisawa, JP
Information: presents its own productions; also available for hire

Fujisawa Shimin Kaikan
Website: www.city.fujisawa.kanagawa.jp/
Phone: 466 232 415
Address: 8-1 Kugenuma-Higashi, Fujisawa, JP
Information: presents its own productions, also available for hire
Country: Japan
Contact: Director Katsuhisa Sekine

Fujisawa-shi Shonandai Bunka Centre – Shimin Theatre
Website: www.city.fujisawa.kanagawa.jp
Phone: 466 451 550
Address: 1-8 Shohnandai, Fujisawa, JP
Information: presents its own productions; also available for hire
Country: Japan
Contact: Director Hiroshi Watanuki

Fukagawa Museum Theatre of Edo Culture Replicas
Phone: 336 308 625
Address: 1-3-28 Shirakawa, Kohtoh-ku, JP
Country: Japan

Fukui-shi Bunka Kaikan
Phone: 776 205 010
Address: 2-7-1 Haruyama, JP
Information: presents its own productions; also available for hire, has a conference room
Country: Japan

Fukuno Bunka Sohzoh Centre (Helios)
Website: www.town.fukuno.toyama.jp/helios
Email: helios@city.nanto.lg.jp
Phone: 763 221 125
Address: 100, Yakata, Nanto-city, JP
Information: presents its own productions organized by World Music; also available for hire
Country: Japan
Contact: General Manager Tetsu Kitahori

Fukuoka Ginko Honten Dai-Hall
Phone: 927 232 131
Address: 2-13-1 Tenjin, Chuo-ku, JP
Information: presents its own productions; also available for hire
Country: Japan

Fukuoka Shimin Kaikan
Phone: 927 616 567
Address: 5-1-23 Tenjin, Chuo-ku, JP
Information: presents its own productions; also available for hire
Country: Japan
Contact: Director Ichiro Tanaka

Fukuoka Sun Palace Hall
Website: www.f-sunpalace.com
Phone: 922 721 123
Address: 2-1 Chikkoh Hon-machi, Hakata-ku, JP
Country: Japan

Fukushima-ken Bunka Centre
Website: www.culture-center.fks.ed.jp
Email: office@culture-center.fks.ed.jp
Phone: 245 349 191
Address: 5-54 Kasuga-cho, JP
Information: presents its own productions; also available for hire
Country: Japan
Contact: Director Toshiharu Takagi

Fukushima-shi Ongakudo
Website: www.f-shinkoukousha.or.jp
Phone: 245 316 221
Address: 1-1 Irie-cho, JP
Information: presents its own productions; also available for hire
Country: Japan

Fukuyama Geijutsu Bunka Hall – Reed'n Rose
Website: www.r-rose.jp
Email: rose@r-rose.jp
Phone: 849 281 800
Address: 2-1-10 Matsuhama-cho, Fukuyama, JP
Information: presents its own productions; also available for hire
Country: Japan
Contact: Director Shigeko Urabe

Fukuyama-shi Shimin Kaikan
Phone: 818 492 12151
Address: 1-10-1 Kasumi-cho, Fukuyama, JP
Information: presents its own productions; also available for hire
Country: Japan
Contact: Director Kazuyoshi Monden

Funabashi Shimin Bunka Hall
Website: www.city.funabashi.chiba.jp/shibunka/index.html
Email: shibunka@city.funabashi.chiba.jp
Phone: 474 345 555
Address: 2-2-5 Hon-cho, Funabashi, JP
Information: presents its own productions; also available for hire
Country: Japan
Contact: Director Toshio Kaneko

Galaxity Nishi-Arai Bunka Hall
Website: www.adachi.ne.jp/users/galaxy
Email: galaxy@adachi.ne.jp
Phone: 352 428 161
Address: 1-3-1 Kurihara, Adachi-ku, JP
Country: Japan

Geijutsuza
Website: www.toho.co.jp
Phone: 335 912 333
Address: 1-2-1 Yuraku-cho, Chiyoda-ku, JP
Information: operated by Toho Co Ltd (q.v.); recently undergone extensive renovation
Country: Japan

Gifu Shimin Kaikan
Website: www.city.gifu.gifu.jp/event/shimin/
Phone: 582 628 111
Address: 2-6 Mieji-cho, JP
Information: presents its own productions; also available for hire
Country: Japan
Contact: Director Masatoshi Kawade

Ginza Gas Hall
Website: www.tgud.co.jp/ginza_gashall/
Phone: 335 731 871
Address: 7-9-15 Ginza, Chuo-ku, JP
Country: Japan
Contact: Manager Shigeto Hasegawa

Ginza Hakuhinkan Theatre
Website: www.hakuhinkan.co.jp
Phone: 335 711 003
Address: 8-8-11 Ginza, Chuo-ku, JP
Country: Japan
Contact: Director Shota Higuchi
Contact: President Yoshifumi Ito

Ginza Miyukikan Gekijo
Phone: 335 726 792
Address: 6-5-17 Ginza, Chuo-ku, JP
Country: Japan

Ginza Shogekijo
Website: www.netlaputa.ne.jp/~gin-jel
Email: gin-jel@netlaputa.ne.jp
Phone: 335 625 510
Address: 3-8-4 Ginza, Chuo-ku, JP
Country: Japan

Globe Tokyo
Website: www.tglobe.net
Email: info-hall-rental@tglobe.net
Phone: 333 603 540
Address: 3-1-2 Hyakunin-cho, Shinjuku-ku, JP
Information: faithful replica of Shakespeare's Globe Theatre though it is equipped with advanced technology; also presents own Shakespeare productions
Country: Japan

Green Hall Sagamiohno
Website: www.hall-net.or.jp/green
Phone: 427 492 200
Address: 4-4-1 Sagamiohno, Sagamihara, JP
Country: Japan

Gunma Kenmin Kaikan
Website: www.manabi.pref.gunma.jp/kenmin/
Phone: 272 321 111
Address: 1-10-1 Hiyoshi-cho, Maebashi, JP
Information: presents its own productions; available for hire
Country: Japan
Contact: Director Tatsuo Kawashima

Gunma Music Centre
Phone: 273 224 527
Address: 28 Takamatsu-cho, Takasaki, JP
Information: presents its own music productions produced by Takasaki Municipal Government Office; also available for hire
Country: Japan

Gushikawa Shimin Geijutsu Gekijo
Website: www.city.gushikawa.okinawa.jp/
Phone: 989 734 400
Address: 175 aza Nakamine, Gushikawa, JP
Information: presents its own productions; also available for hire
Country: Japan
Contact: Director Seishun Yamashiro

Hachinohe-shi Kohkaido
Website: www.city.hachinohe.aomori.jp/shisetsu/kokaido
Email: kokaido@city.hachinohe.aomori.jp
Phone: 178 447 171
Address: 1-1-1 Uchimaru, Hachinohe, JP
Information: presents its own productions; also available for hire
Country: Japan
Contact: Director Hideo Tanaka

Hachioji Geijutsu Bunka Kaikan – Icho Hall
Website: www.hachiojibunka.or.jp
Phone: 426 213 001
Address: 24-1 Hon-cho, Hachioji-shi, JP
Information: presents its own productions; also available for hire
Country: Japan
Contact: Director Misao Takayama

Hadano-shi Bunka Kaikan
Website: navi.city.hadano.kanagawa.jp/b-kaikan/index.html
Phone: 463 811 211
Address: 82 Hirasawa, Hadano, JP
Information: presents its own productions; also available for hire
Country: Japan
Contact: Director Tomiko Inomata

Haiyuza Gekijo
Website: www.haiyuzagekijou.co.jp
Email: info@haiyuzagekijou.co.jp
Phone: 334 702 880
Address: 4-9-2 Roppongi, Minato-ku, JP
Country: Japan
Contact: contact Toshiji Takagi

Hakodate Shimin Kaikan
Website: www.zaidan-hakodate.com/kaikan/
Email: kaikan@zaidan-hakodate.com
Phone: 138 573 111
Address: 1-32-1 Yunokawa-cho, Hakodate, JP
Country: Japan

Hamarikyu-Asahi Concert Hall
Website: www.asahi.com/asahihall/
Phone: 355 418 710
Address: 5-3-2 Tsukiji, Chuo-ku, JP
Country: Japan
Contact: General Manager Yoshitaka Ohnoki

Hanamaki-shi Bunka Kaikan
Website: www.city.hanamaki.iwate.jp/bkkaikan
Email: bkkaikan@city.hanamaki.iwate.jp
Phone: 198 246 511
Address: 3-16-22 Wakaba-cho, Hanamaki, JP
Information: presents its own productions; also available for hire
Country: Japan
Contact: Director Shohzoh Takahashi

Harmony Hall
Phone: 263 472 004
Address: 4351 Shimauchi, Matsumoto, JP
Information: designed solely for classical music, in particular organ music, with design focus on compatibility of orchestral and organ music; A 43-stop organ is situated at frontal side of this shoebox-shaped hall
Country: Japan
Contact: Director Tsutomu Sakai

Harmony Hall Zama
Website: www.ny.airnet.ne.jp/harmony
Email: harmony@ny.airnet.ne.jp
Phone: 462 551 100
Address: 1-1-2 Midorigaoka, Zama-shi, JP
Country: Japan
Contact: Director Michiyoshi Matsushita

Hekinan-shi Geijutsu Bunka Hall – Emerald Hall
Website: https:// www.emerald-hall.jp/
Email: contact@emerald-hall.jp
Phone: 056 648 3731
Address: 1-70-1 Tsurumi-cho, Hekinan, JP
Information: The name Emerald Hall is derived from the

character "Midori" in Hekinan City. It is one of the leading music halls in Japan based on acoustic (live sound). The design also symbolically exPresses the trunk, branches and leaves of the tree. It presents the desire to convey the warmth of wood to the audience.
Country: Japan
Disabled Access: false
Capacity: 251-500
Annual Performances: 11-25
Policies: Rent and Present

Hibiya Koen Dai-Ongakudo Hibiya Yagai Ongakudo
Phone: 813 359 16388
Address: c/o Hibiya Kohkaido, 1-5 Hibiya Koen, Chiyoda-ku, JP
Country: Japan

Hibiya Koen Sho-Ongakudo
Phone: 335 016 429
Address: 1-6 Hibiya Koen, Chiyoda-ku, JP
Country: Japan
Capacity: 1070
Hibiya Kohkaido
Phone: 335 916 388
Address: 1-3 Hibiya Koen, Chiyoda-ku, JP
Country: Japan

Hikifune Bunka Centre
Phone: 336 163 951
Address: 1-38-11 Kyojima, Sumida-ku, JP
Country: Japan

Himeji-shi Bunka Centre
Website: www3.ocn.ne.jp/~bunka/
Email: bun-sou@theia.ocn.ne.jp
Phone: 792 988 011
Address: 426-1 Nishi-Nobusue, Himeji, JP
Information: presents its own productions; available for hire
Country: Japan
Contact: Director Makoto Ushio

Hino Shimin Kaikan
Phone: 425 852 011
Address: 1-12-1 Shinmei, Hino, JP
Information: presents its own productions; also available for hire
Country: Japan

Hino-cho Chohmin Kaikan – Watanuki Hall Niji
Phone: 748 533 233
Address: 1661 Matsuo, Hino-cho, Gamo'o-gun, JP
Information: presents its own productions; also available for hire
Country: Japan
Contact: Director Shuichi Noda

Hirosaki Shimin Kaikan
Website: www.hi-it.net/~shiminkai/
Phone: 172 323 374
Address: 1-6 oaza-Shimo-Shirogane-machi, Hirosaki, JP
Information: presents its own productions; available for hire
Country: Japan
Contact: Director Masahide Kudoh

Hiroshima Kenmin Bunka Centre Fukuyama
Phone: 849 219 200
Address: 1-21 Higashisakura-machi, Fukuyama, JP
Information: presents its own productions; also available for hire
Country: Japan
Contact: Director Hiromi Takata

Hiroshima Kohsei Nenkin Kaikan
Website: h-bkk.jp
Email: info@h-bkk.jp
Phone: 822 438 881
Address: 3-3 Kako-machi, Naka-ku, JP
Information: part of a congress complex, including hotel and banquet rooms, the hall is designed for conventions, popular music and classical music use; a movable orchestral shell is set up for concerts
Country: Japan
Contact: Director Norikatsu Miyachi
Policies: Congress centre

Hiroshima Yubin Chokin Hall
Website: www.mielparque.or.jp/
Phone: 822 236 367
Address: 19-1 Hakushima-Kita-machi, Naka-ku, JP
Information: presents its own productions; also available for hire
Country: Japan
Contact: General Manager Shigeki Tsuji

Hiroshima-shi Bunka Sohzoh-Nakakumin Bunka Centre Aster Plaza
Website: www.cf.city.hiroshima.jp/naka-cs/
Email: bunsou@cf.city.hiroshima.jp
Phone: 822 448 000
Address: 4-17 Kako-machi, Naka-ku, JP
Country: Japan

Contact: Director Shigeyuki Kageyama

Hisako Tsuji String Ensemble Hall
Website: www.mid.co.jp/panacreate
Phone: 669 272 289
Address: Tower Plaza Avenue, 5-13-4 Nakano-cho, Miyakojima-ku, JP
Information: presents its own productions; available for hire
Country: Japan
Contact: chief Manager Koji Sato

Hohshoh Nohgakudo
Website: www.hosho.or.jp
Email: info@hosho.or.jp
Phone: 338 114 843
Address: 1-5-9 Hongo, Bunkyo-ku, JP
Information: managed by Hohshoh-kai (q.v.)
Country: Japan
Contact: secretary General Masakatsu Takase
Contact: Chairman Fusateru Hohsho

Hokkaido Kohsei Nenkin Kaikan
Website: www.hokkaido-koseinenkin.com
Email: info@hokkaido-koseinenkin.com
Phone: 112 319 551
Address: Nishi-12-chome, Kita-1-jo, Chuo-ku, Sapporo, JP
Country: Japan

Hokutopia
Phone: 353 901 100
Address: 1-11-1 Oji, Kita-ku, JP
Country: Japan
Contact: Chairman of kita-ku cultural fondation Osamu Yamaguchi

Honda Gekijo
Website: www.honda-geki.com
Phone: 334 680 030
Address: 2-10-15 Kitazawa, Setagaya-ku, JP
Country: Japan

Hyogo Performing Arts Center
Website: www.gcenter-hyogo.jp
Email: pafh@gcenter-hyogo.jp
Phone: 798 680 223
Address: 2-22 Takamatsu-cho, Nishinomiya, JP
Information: see also Orchestras (Hyogo Performing Arts Center Orchestra)
Country: Japan
Contact: Artistic advisor Masakazu Yamazaki
Contact: Artistic Director Yutaka Sado

Hyuga-shi Bunka Kohryu Centre
Website: ww2.wainet.ne.jp/~hyugahch
Email: hyugahch@mb.wainet.ne.jp
Phone: 982 546 111
Address: 1-31 Naka-machi, Hyuga, JP
Information: presents its own productions; also available for hire
Country: Japan
Contact: secretary General Jinsuke Nakayama

Ibaraki Kenritsu Kenmin Bunka Centre
Website: www.net-ibaraki.ne.jp/kenbun
Email: kenbun@po.net-ibaraki.ne.jp
Phone: 292 411 166
Address: 697 Higashi-Kubo, Senba-cho, Mito, JP
Information: presents its own productions; available for hire
Country: Japan

Ichikawa-shi Bunka Kaikan
Website: www.city.ichikawa.chiba.jp/
Phone: 473 795 111
Address: 1-1-5 Ohwada, Ichikawa, JP
Information: presents its own productions; also available for hire
Country: Japan
Contact: Director Kenzo Nomura

ICU Sacred Music Center
Website: www.icuchurch.com
Email: smc@icu.ac.jp
Phone: 422 333 330
Address: 3-10-2 Ohsawa, Mitaka, JP
Country: Japan
Contact: Director icu sacred music center Masakata Kanazawa

Iida Bunka Kaikan
Website: www.city.iida.nagano.jp/bunkakaikan/
Email: ibunka@city.iida.nagano.jp
Phone: 265 233 552
Address: 5-5-1 Takaha-cho, Iida, JP
Country: Japan
Contact: Director Kunito Hara

Iino Hall
Website: www.iino.co.jp/hall
Phone: 335 063 251
Address: 7F Iino Bldg., 2-1-1 Uchisaiwai-cho, Chiyoda-ku, JP

Country: Japan

Iizuka-shi Bunka Kaikan – Iizuka Cosmos Common
Phone:
948 210 505
Address: 14-66 Iizuka, Iizuka, JP
Country: Japan

Ikeda Shimin Bunka Kaikan – Azalea Hall
Website: www.azaleanet.or.jp
Phone: 727 618 811
Address: 1-7-1 Tenjin, Ikeda, JP
Country: Japan
Contact: secretary General Masao Watanabe

IMA Hall
Website:
www.imasc.co.jp
Phone: 339 762 000
Address: 5-1-1 Hikarigaoka, Nerima-ku, JP
Country: Japan

Imperial Theatre
Phone: 332 137 221
Address: 3-1-1 Marunouchi, Chiyoda-ku, JP
Information: operated by Toho Co Ltd (q.v.)
Country: Japan

Institut Franco-Japonais du Kansai – Inabata Hall
Website: web.kyoto-inet.or.jp/people/ifjk606
Email: ifjk606@mbox.kyoto-inet.or.jp
Phone: 757 612 105
Address: 8 Yoshida Izumidono-cho, Sakyo-ku, JP
Country: Japan
Contact: Director Jean-Claude Deuthion

Iruma-shi Shimin Kaikan
Website: www.ictv.ne.jp/~shinko-sk
Phone: 429 642 411
Address: 3-10-10 Toyo-oka, Iruma-shi, JP
Information: acoustics well suited to classical music recordings
Country: Japan
Contact: head of management office Ken Nakazato

Isahaya Bunka Kaikan
Phone: 957 251 500
Address: 9-2 Uzu-machi, Isahaya, JP
Information: presents its own productions; available for hire
Country: Japan
Contact: Director Takio Nonaka

Isawa-cho Bunka Sohzoh Centre
Phone: 197 462 133
Address: 1-1 Aza Kagayachi, Natsuda, Isawa-cho, Isawa-gun, JP
Information: presents its own productions; available for hire
Country: Japan
Contact: Director Eiji Shirai

Isehara Shimin Bunka Kaikan
Phone: 463 922 300
Address: 348 Tanaka, Isehara, JP
Information: presents its own productions; available for hire
Country: Japan
Contact: Director Tadakatsu Shindo

Ishibashi Bunka Centre
Website: www2.ktarn.or.jp/~bunka
Phone: 942 332 27174
Address: 1015 Nonaka-machi, Kurume, JP
Country: Japan

Ishibashi Memorial Hall
Phone: 338 421 021
Address: 4-24-12 Higashi-Ueno, Taitoh-ku, JP

Ishihara Hall
Website: www.ishihara-hall.co.jp
Email: info@ishihara-hall.co.jp
Phone: 664 491 276
Address: Shin-Ishihara Bldg, 1-3-15 Edobori, Nishi-ku, JP
Information: a shoebox-shaped hall;
Country: Japan
Contact: Director Shintaro Sekiguchi

Ishikawa Prefectural Museum of Art Hall
Website: www.ishibi.pref.ishikawa.jp
Phone: 762 317 580
Address: 2-1 Dewa-machi, Kanazawa, JP
Information: presents its own programmes
Country: Japan
Contact: Director Susumu Shimazaki

Itabashi Kuritsu Bunka Kaikan
Phone: 335 792 222
Address: 51-1 Ohyama-Higashi-machi, Itabashi-ku, JP
Information: presents its own productions; available for hire

Country: Japan

Itami Aiphonic Hall
Website: hccweb1.bai.ne.jp/aiphonic
Email: aiphonic@hcc1.bai.ne.jp
Phone: 727 802 110
Address: 1-3-30 Miyanomae, Itami, JP
Country: Japan
Contact: Director Hiroshi Sakamoto

Itami Municipal Theater AI HALL
Website: www6.ocn.ne.jp/~aihall
Phone: 727 822 000
Address: 2-4-1, Itami, Itami, JP
Country: Japan
Contact: Producer Reiko Shiga
Contact: Producer Takashi Tsumura

Iwaki-shi Taira Shimin Kaikan
Website:
www.iwakich.jp
Phone: 246 259 144
Address: 1-6 Aza Misaki, Taira, Iwaki, JP
Information: presents its own productions; available for hire
Country: Japan
Contact: Director Kinichi Kanari

Iwakuni Shimin Kaikan
Phone: 827 241 221
Address: 1-15-3 Yamate-cho, Iwakuni, JP
Information: available for hire
Country: Japan

Iwate Prefectural Hall
Website: www.echna.ne.jp/~iwkenmin
Phone: 196 241 171
Address: 13-1 Uchimaru, Morioka, JP
Information: presents its own productions; available for hire
Country: Japan

Izumi Hall
Website: www.izumihall.co.jp
Email: office@izumihall.co.jp
Phone: 669 442 828
Address: 1-4-70 Shiromi, Chuo-ku, JP
Information: designed after Gro
Country: Japan
Contact: Director Takashi Mizuhata
Contact: Managing Director Junichi Itoh

Izumo Shimin Kaikan
Website: www.city.izumo.shimane.jp
Email: s-kaikan@local.city.izumo.shimane.jp
Phone: 853 241 212
Address: 2-15 En-ya Arihara-cho, Izumo, JP
Information: presents its own productions; available for hire
Country: Japan
Contact: Director Susumu Yasui

Japan Foundation Forum, Kokusai Kohryu Kikin Forum
Website: www.jfforum.jpf.go.jp
Phone: 355 620 699
Address: 4F, Mori Bldg., Akasaka 1-chome, 1-11-28, Akasaka, Minato-ku, JP
Country: Japan
Contact: secretary General Jun'etsu Komatsu

JELS Hall
Website: www.netlaputa.ne.jp/~gin-jel
Email: jelshall@netlaputa.ne.jp
Phone: 339 108 565
Address: B1F, Kitaohtsuka Bldg, 2-16-9 Kita-Ohtsuka, Toshima-ku, JP
Country: Japan

Joetsu Bunka Kaikan
Website: www.city.joetsu.niigata.jp/sisetu/jbreeze
Phone: 255 254 103
Address: 1-9-10 Shinko-cho, Joetsu, JP
Country: Japan
Contact: Director Tsugio Yamazaki

Joyo Geibun Centre
Website: www.joyonet.co.jp/~geibun
Phone: 292 316 611
Address: 1-5-18 Sannomaru, Mito, JP
Information: presents its own productions; available for hire
Country: Japan
Contact: Chairman Meishi Aoshika

JR Higashi-Nihon Art Centre Shiki Gekijo
Website: www.shiki.gr.jp
Phone: 354 054 330
Address: 1-10-48, Kaigan, Minato-ku, JP
Information: home theatre of Shiki Theatre Company (q.v.)
Country: Japan
Contact: Director Keita Asari

JT Art Hall Affinis
Website: www.jti.co.jp/JTI/arthall/index.html
Phone: 355 724 945
Address: 2F JT Bldg, 2-2-1 Toranomon, Minato-ku, JP
Information: owned by Japan Tobacco Inc.; presents a series of chamber music concerts ""JT Chamber Music""
Country: Japan

Jyoruri Theatre
Website: www.town.nose.osaka.jp/jyoruri/
Email: jyoruri@town.nose.osaka.jp
Phone: 727 343 241
Address: 30 Shukuno, Nose-cho, Toyono-gun, JP
Country: Japan

Kabuki-za
Website: www.shochiku.co.jp/play/kabukiza/theater/index.htm
Email: kabuki-za@tokyo.email.ne.jp
Phone: 335 413 131
Address: 4-12-15 Ginza, Chuo-ku, JP
Information: operated by Shochiku Co Ltd (q.v.)
Country: Japan

Kagawa Kohsei Nenkin Kaikan Hall
Website: www.kjp.or.jp/hp_33
Phone: 878 218 500
Address: 2-2-1 Fukuoka-cho, Takamatsu, JP
Country: Japan

Kagawa-ken Kenmin Hall
Website: www.kimai-net.gr.jp/kyouiku/kenminhall/hall.htm
Email: ahm55671@msd.biglobe.ne.jp
Phone: 878 233 131
Address: 9-10 Tamamo-cho, Takamatsu, JP
Country: Japan

Kagoshima Shimin Bunka Hall
Website: www.kagoshima-hall.or.jp
Phone: 992 578 111
Address: 2-3-1 Yojiro, JP
Country: Japan
Contact: Director Michiaki Sakamoto

Kagoshima-ken Bunka Centre
Website: www.minc.ne.jp/'~k_bunse
Phone: 992 234 221
Address: 5-3 Yamashita-cho, JP
Information: presents its own productions; available for hire
Country: Japan
Contact: Director Katsuharu Tokushige

Kaizuka Shimin Bunka Kaikan – Cosmos Theatre
Website: www.cosmostheater.or.jp
Phone: 724 365 031
Address: 1-18-1, Hatakenaka, Kaizuka, JP
Information: presents its own productions; available for hire
Country: Japan
Contact: Chairman Hirohisa Yamagata

Kamakura Noh Butai
Website: www.nohbutai.com/
Email: webmaster@nohbutai.com
Phone: 467 225 557
Address: 3-5-13 Hase, Kamakura, JP
Country: Japan
Contact: President Masao Kinoshita

Kamakura Performing Arts Centre
Website: www.city.kamakura.kanagawa.jp/geijyutu/top.htm
Phone: 467 485 500
Address: 6-1-2 Ohfuna, Kamakura, JP
Information: presents its own productions; available for hire
Country: Japan

Kameari Lirio Hall
Website: www.kccs.or.jp
Phone: 356 802 222
Address: 3-26-1 Kameari, Katsushika-ku, JP
Information: run by Katsushika Foundation for Culture and International Exchange (q.v.), see also Katsushika Symphony Hills (q.v.)
Country: Japan

Kamisu-machi Bunka Centre
Website: www.k-bssk.jp/bunka/
Email: bunka@k-bssk.or.jp
Phone: 299 905 511
Address: 4991-4 Mizoguchi, Kamisu-machi, Kashima-gun, JP
Information: presents its own productions; available for hire
Country: Japan
Contact: secretary General Hiroshi Noguchi

Kanagawa Kenritsu Kenmin Hall
Website: www.kanagawa-kenminhall.com
Phone: 456 625 901
Address: 3-1 Yamashita-cho, Naka-ku, Yokohama, JP
Information: presents its own productions & available

for hire; organizes International Arts Festival in Kanagawa (q.v.)
Country: Japan

Kanagawa Kenritsu Ongakudo
Website: www.kanagawa-ongakudo.com
Phone: 452 632 567
Address: 9-2 Momijigaoka, Nishi-ku, JP
Information: established in 1954 for the presentation of classical music concerts; well known for its wooden interior
Country: Japan
Contact: President Masazumi Ishii

Kanagawa Youth Centre Hall
Website: www.pref.kanagawa.jp/oshirase/tayori
Phone: 452 413 131
Address: 9-1 Momijigaoka, Nishi-ku, Yokohama, JP
Information: presents its own productions & available for hire
Country: Japan

Kanazawa-shi Bunka Hall
Website: www.bunka-h.gr.jp/
Phone: 762 231 221
Address: 15-1 Takaoka-machi, Kanazawa, JP
Information: presents its own productions; available for hire
Country: Japan
Contact: General Manager Kiyotaka Kurata

Kanazawa-shi Kanko Kaikan
Phone: 762 202 501
Address: 6-27 Shimo-Honda-machi, Kanazawa, JP
Country: Japan
Contact: Director Kiyotaka Kurata

Kanda Panthe (Panthe Hall)
Phone: 332 656 366
Address: 3-9-10 Nishi-Kanda, Chiyoda-ku, JP
Country: Japan

Kansho Kaikan
Address: 1-9-20 Nagasaki, Toshima-ku, JP
Country: Japan

Kanze Nohgakudo
Website: www.kanzekai.com
Phone: 334 695 241
Address: 1-16-4 Shohtoh, Shibuya-ku, JP
Information: first built in 1901; this venue is mainly used for performances by the famous Kanze Noh school
Country: Japan
Contact: Manager Ken Nakagawa

Kashima Kinroh Bunka Kaikan
Website: www.sopia.or.jp/kcs
Phone: 299 835 911
Address: 325-1 Kyuchu, Kashima, JP
Country: Japan
Contact: Director Minoru Arahara

Kasukabe Shimin Bunka Kaikan
Phone: 487 615 811
Address: 2-8-61 Kasukabe Higashi, Kasukabe, JP
Information: presents its own productions; available for hire
Country: Japan
Contact: Director Noboru Shibata

Katsushika Symphony Hills
Website: www.kccf.or.jp
Phone: 356 702 222
Address: 6-33-1, Tateishi, Katsushika-ku, JP
Information: managed by Katsushika Foundation for Culture and International Exchange (q.v.), see also Kameari Lirio Hall (q.v.)
Country: Japan

Kawai-cho Mahoroba Hall
Phone: 745 721 100
Address: 1-8-3 Takatsukadai, Kawai-cho, Kitakatsuragi-gun, JP
Information: presents its own productions; available for hire
Country: Japan

Kawamura Noh Butai
Website: www.kid97.co.jp/kawamura
Email: junko@mekiki.ne.jp
Phone: 757 228 717
Address: 14-320 Yanagizushichou, Kamidachiuri Agaru, Karasuma-dori, Kamigyo-ku, JP
Country: Japan
Contact: contact Junko Kawamura
Contact: President Teiji Kawamura

Kawasaki Nohgakudo
Phone: 442 227 995
Address: 1-37 Nisshin-cho, Kawasaki-ku, Kawasaki, JP
Information: organized by Kawasaki city cultural foundation
Country: Japan

Kawasaki-shi Asao Shiminkan
Website: www.city.kawasaki.jp/
Phone: 449 511 300
Address: c/o Asao Bunka Centre, 1-5-2 Manpukuji, Asao-ku, Kawasaki, JP
Country: Japan
Contact: Director Masami Morofushi

Kawasaki-shi Kyoiku Bunka Kaikan
Website: www.city.kawasaki.jp/88/88kyobun/home/index.htm
Phone: 442 336 361
Address: 2-1-3 Fujimi, Kawasaki-ku, Kawasaki, JP
Information: presents its own productions; available for hire
Country: Japan
Contact: Director Mieho Toyoda

Keihan'na Plaza – Sumitomo Hall
Website: www.keihanna-plaza.co.jp
Email: soumu@keihanna-plaza.co.jp
Phone: 774 955 111
Address: c/o Kabushiki Gaisha Keihan'na, 1-7 Hikaridai, Seika-cho, Sohraku-gun, JP
Country: Japan
Contact: President Yoshio Tateishi

Kenritsu Awaji Kinroh Centre – Viva Hall
Phone: 799 244 450
Address: 1788-1 Ubara, Sumoto, JP
Information: presents its own productions; also available for hire
Country: Japan

Ki no Atrium
Website: www.woodyland.go.jp/atoriumumoyouhou.htm
Email: keiri@oak.ocn.ne.jp
Phone: 336 992 533
Address: c/o Kantoh Shinrin Kanrikyoku Tokyo Bunkyo-ku, 6-2-11 Toh-yoh, Kohtoh-ku, JP
Country: Japan
Contact: planning section chief Ryuichiroh Nomura

Kid Airakku Art Hall
Phone: 333 225 564
Address: 2-43-11 Matsubara, Setagaya-ku, JP
Country: Japan

Kimitsu Shimin Bunka Hall
Website: www.protos.co.jp/bunka
Phone: 439 553 300
Address: 622 Minou, Kimitsu, JP
Information: presents its own productions; available for hire
Country: Japan
Contact: Director Yasuo Shigeta

Kinokuniya Hall
Phone: 333 540 141
Address: 3-17-7 Shinjuku, Shinjuku-ku, JP
Information: the venue is located in Kinokuniya, one of the largest bookstores in Japan; companies such as Bungakuza (q.v.), Mingei (q.v.), Seinenza (q.v.), Komatsuza (q.v.), Chijinkai (q.v.) perform there
Country: Japan
Contact: General Manager Kazuichiro Kaneko
Contact: deputy General Manager Yumiko Suzuki

Kinokuniya Southern Theatre
Website: www.kinokuniya.co.jp
Email: jg01@kinokuniya.co.jp
Phone: 353 613 321
Address: 7F Annex, Takashimaya Times Square Bldg, 5-24-2 Sendagaya, Shibuya-ku, JP
Information: opened in Oct '96; Kinokuniya Book Store's second venue for drama; see also Kinokuniya Hall (q.v.)
Country: Japan
Contact: General Manager Kazuichiro Kaneko
Contact: stage Manager Yoshikazu Araki
Contact: Manager Naoki Hata

Kintetsu Gekijo
Website: www.kintetsu.co.jp/theatre/index.html
Phone: 667 735 371
Address: 6-5-28 Uehon-machi, Ten-nohji-ku, JP
Information: presents its own productions; available for hire
Country: Japan
President & General Manager
Yoshitsugu Ikemura

Kioi Hall
Website: www.kioi-hall.or.jp
Phone: 352 764 500
Address: 6-5 Kioi-cho, Chiyoda-ku, JP
Information: the Hall has Kioi Sinfonietta Tokyo (q.v.) as its residential orchestra; promotes the cultural exchange between East and West
Country: Japan
Contact: secretary General Ryuichi Machida
Contact: President Akira Chihaya

Kirishima Kokusai Ongaku Hall
Website: www2.synapse.ne.jp/miyama
Email: miyama@po2.synapse.ne.jp
Phone: 995 788 000
Address: 3311-29 Takachiho, Makizono-cho, Aira-gun, JP
Information: presents its own productions; also available for hire; the venue for Kirishima International Music Festival and Courses (q.v.). Contact: Kagoshima-ken Bunkashinko-ka: 10-1, Kamoike-Shin-machi, Kagoshima 890-0064 Tel: 99-286 2111
Country: Japan
Contact: Director Shozaburou Kimura
Contact: Shozaburou Kimura

Kita Roppeita XIV Kinen Nohgakudo
Website: kita-noh.com
Email: info@kita-noh.com
Phone: 334 918 813
Address: c/o 14 Sei Roppeita Kinen Zaidan, 4-6-9 Kami-Osaki, Shinagawa-ku, JP
Information: managed by Roppeita XIV Commemorative Foundation; see also Kita Noh School
Country: Japan

Kitakata Plaza Bunka Centre
Website: www.kitakataplaza.jp
Email: info@kitakataplaza.jp
Phone: 241 244 611
Address: 2-1, Oshikiri, Kitakata, JP
Information: Currently, "Kitakata Plaza" is developing a business that supports the culture of the Kitakata region as a base for various cultural activities.
Kitakata Plaza has a large hall called the Seseragi Hall, a small hall that can be used for small-scale performances, and other conference rooms, and as a base for various cultural activities, we are developing businesses that support the culture of the Kitakata region.
Country: Japan
Disabled Access: Yes
Capacity: 1000+
Annual Performances: 100+
Policies: Rent and Present

Kitakyushu Shiritsu Hibiki Hall
Website: www.kicpac.org/hibiki/
Email: AEV24491@biglobe.ne.jp
Phone: 936 624 010
Address: 1-1-1 Hirano, Yahata Higashi-ku, Kitakyushu, JP
Information: shoe-box shape hall
Country: Japan
Contact: contact Masatoshi Sohshi
Contact: Director Shinichiro Tanaka

Kitakyushu Shiritsu Kokura Shimin Kaikan
Phone: 935 810 331
Address: 3-1 Johnai, Kokura-kita-ku, Kitakyushu, JP
Information: presents its own productions; available for hire
Country: Japan
Contact: Director Akinori Murata

Kitazawa Town Hall
Phone: 354 788 006
Address: 2-8-18 Kitazawa, Setagaya-ku, JP
Country: Japan

KOBE Art Village Center
Website: www.kavc.or.jp
Email: kavc@kavc.or.jp
Phone: 785 125 500
Address: 5-3-14, Shinkaichi, Hyogo-ku, Kobe, JP
Information: has gallery, conference room, rehearsal room & silk-screen studio; all facilities are available for hire; also presents its own productions and co-productions
Country: Japan
Contact: Director Fumiko Fukushima
Contact: Director Hitoshi Sakakibara
Contact: drama dept. officer Akiko Okano

Kobe Bunka Hall
Website: www.kobe-bunka.jp
Phone: 783 513 535
Address: 4-2-2 Kusunoki-cho, Chuo-ku, Kobe, JP
Country: Japan
Contact: President Eiji Tabuchi

Kobe Shimbun Matsukata Hall
Website: www.kobe-np.co.jp/matsukata
Email: m-hall@kobe-np.co.jp
Phone: 783 627 111
Address: 1-5-7 Higashi-Kawasaki-cho, Chuo-ku, Kobe, JP
Information: Kobe Shimbun a newspaper Cultural Foundation manages the venue; presents its own productions; available for hire
Country: Japan
Contact: Director Tsuguo Inagaki

Kochi Kenritsu Kenmin Bunka Hall
Website: www.kochi-bunkazaidan.or.jp/~hall
Email: hall@kochi-bunkazaidan.or.jp
Phone: 888 245 321
Address: 4-3-30 Hon-machi, JP
Country: Japan
Contact: represenative Takao Ogasawara

Contact: contact Kenji Morita

Kodaira Citizens Cultural Hall – Rune Kodaira
Website: www.runekodaira.or.jp
Phone: 423 455 111
Address: 1-8-5 Misono-cho, Kodaira, JP
Country: Japan
Contact: Manager Hiromi Sohma
Contact: Chairman of board of Directors Kunio Ozaki

Kohriyama City Cultural Centre
Website: www.city.koriyama.fukushima.jp/kc-center/
Email: bunka-ctr@city.koriyama.fukushima.jp
Phone: 249 242 491
Address: 1-2 Tsutsumishita-machi, Kohriyama, JP
Information: presents its own productions; available for hire
Country: Japan

Kohtoh-ku Bunka Centre
Phone:
336 448 111
Address: 4-11-3 Tohyo, Kohtoh-ku, JP
Information: presents its own productions; available for hire
Country: Japan

Kokubunji – Izumi no Sato Konzert Saal
Website: members.jcom.home.ne.jp/izuminosato-kzs
Email: izuminosato-kzs@jcom.home.ne.jp
Phone: 423 238 596
Address: 3-28-2 Higashi Moto-machi, Kokubunji, JP
Information: produces approx. 10 concerts every year
Country: Japan
Contact: President Tokuro Furuta

Kokugikan Arena
Website: www.sumo.or.jp
Phone: 336 235 111
Address: c/o Japan Sumo Association, 1-3-28 Yokoami, Sumida-ku, JP
Information: headquarters of Japan's national sport, Sumo; used usually for sumo tournament both professional and amateur but also availabe for classical music concerts, opera, etc.
Country: Japan
Contact: Chairman Toshimitsu Kitanoumi

Kokuritsu Yoyogi Kyogijo
Website: www.ntgk.go.jp
Phone: 334 681 171
Address: 2-1-1 Jin-nan, Shibuya-ku, JP
Country: Japan

Komaba
Website: www.komaba-eminence.com
Email: main@komaba-eminence.com
Phone: 334 851 411
Address: 2-19-5 Ohashi, Meguro-ku, JP
Country: Japan

Komaba Agora Gekijo
Website: www.komaba-agora.com
Email: info@komaba-agora.com
Phone: 334 672 743
Address: 1-11-13 Komaba, Meguro-ku, JP
Information: has accommodation, resources necessary for theatre production/promotion and printing facilities for the venue users; home of theatre company, Seinendan (q.v.)
Country: Japan
Contact: owner Keiko Hirata
Contact: Manager Oriza Hirata

Kongoh Nohgakudo
Address: Shijo Agaru, Muromachi-dori, Nakagyo-ku, JP
Country: Japan
Contact: President Hisanori Kongoh

Koshigaya Community Center Foundation Suncity Hall
Website: www.mesh.ne.jp/suncityhall
Email: suncityhall@mtf.biglobe.ne.jp
Phone: 489 851 111
Address: 1-2876-1 Minami-Koshigaya, Koshigaya, JP
Information: presents its own productions; available for hire
Country: Japan
Contact: General Director Takeshi Hirakawa

Kudan Kaikan Hall
Website: www.kudankaikan.or.jp
Phone: 332 615 521
Address: 1-6-5 Kudan-Minami, Chiyoda-ku, JP
Country: Japan

Kumamoto Civic Auditorium
Website: www.city.kumamoto.kumamoto.jp/
Phone: 963 555 235
Address: 1-3 Sakura-machi, JP
Country: Japan
Contact: General Director Hiroyuki Nakashima

KUMAMOTO Mielparque Hall

Phone: 963 556 334
Address: 15-11 Suido-cho, JP
Information: only for hire
Country: Japan

Kumamoto Prefectural Theatre
Website: www.kengeki.or.jp
Email: kikaku@kengeki.or.jp
Phone: 963 632 233
Address: 2-7-1 Ohe, JP
Information: Japan's first public-funded facility to house a concert hall and theatre in one structure; shape and seating plan of concert hall compensates for early and side reflections; presents its own productions; available for hire
Country: Japan
Contact: General Manager Yuhzo Kawamoto

Kunitachi College of Music Halls
Website: www.kunitachi.ac.jp
Email: peri@lib.kunitachi.ac.jp
Phone: 042 535 9500
Address: 5-5-1 Kashiwa-cho, Tachikawa-shi, Tokyo
Information: Kunitachi College of Music
aims to be a school for people who love music, believe in their commitment and dreams, and stick to their beliefs. Equipped with a large (1290 seats) and a small hall (500 seats) and plenty of rehearsal rooms
Country: Japan
Contact: Chairman Tadaaki Miyachi
Contact: President Susumu Shono
Social Media:
https://www.facebook.com/KunitachiCollegeOfMusic/
Disabled Access: Yes
Capacity: 1000+
Annual Performances: 51-100
Annual Productions: 51-100
Policies: Present and Produce

Kurashiki City Auditorium
Website: www.city.kurashiki.okayama.jp/bunka/shisetsu
Phone: 864 251 515
Address: c/o Kurashiki Shimin Kaikan, 17-1 Hon-machi, Kurashiki, JP
Information: available for hire
Country: Japan
Contact: Director Junichi Shibue

Kurashiki-shi City Kojima Cultural Center
Website: https://arsk.jp/
Phone: 864 731 250
Address: Yubinbango 711-0913 Kurashiki Kojimaajino
Information: The Kurashiki City Kojima Cultural Center rents out conference rooms in addition to the hall. It can be used according to its purpose, for music / drama performances, practice, classes / meetings, etc.
Country: Japan
Disabled Access: false
Capacity: 1000+
Annual Performances: 11-25
Policies: All

Kurashiki-shi Geibun-kan
Phone: 864 340 400 hall
Address: 1-18-1 Chuo, Kurashiki, JP
Information: presents its own productions; available for hire Website ; www.city.kurashiki.okayama.jp/bunka/shisetsu/index.html
Country: Japan
Contact: Director Yasuji Fujimoto

Kurashiki-shi Tamashima Bunka Centre
Phone: 865 252 611
Address: 1-6-27 Agasaki, Tamashima, Kurashiki, JP
Information: presents its own productions; available for hire
Country: Japan

Kusatsu Concert Hall
Phone: 279 888 686
Address: 54 Aza Shirane Kokuyurin, Oaza Kusatsu, Kusatsu-machi, Agatsuma-gun, JP
Information: presents its own production; also available for hire
Country: Japan

Kushiro Shimin Bunka Kaikan
Website: www13.plala.or.jp/bunkan/
Email: bunkan2@coral.broba.cc
Phone: 154 245 005
Address: 12-10 Shisui-cho, Kushiro, JP
Information: presents its own productions; available for hire
Country: Japan
Contact: Director Toshimitsu Ohta

Kyara Hall
Phone: 196 376 611 Hall
Address: c/o Morioka Cultural Foundation, 24-10-1, Nagai, Morioka, JP
Country: Japan

Kyoto Concert Hall

Website: www.kyotoconcerthall.org
Phone:
757 112 244
Address: c/o Kyoto City Foundation for the Promotion of Cla, 1-26 Hangi-cho, Shimogamo, Sakyo-ku, JP
Information: shoebox-shaped main hall is equipped with a German/French 90-stop pipe organ; presents its own productions; available for hire
Country: Japan
Contact: President Michio Okamoto
Contact: Producer Yasuyuki Suzuki

Kyoto Furitsu Bunka Geijutsu Kaikan
Website:
www.h6.dion.ne.jp/~bungei
Phone: 752 221 046
Address: Nishi Minami Kado, Kawaramachi-dori Hirokoji, Kamigyo-ku, JP
Information: presents its own productions; available for hire
Country: Japan
Contact: Director Seiji Ishizawa

Kyoto Furitsu Fumin Hall – ALTI
Phone: 754 411 414
Address: 590-1 Tatsumae-cho, Karasuma-dori Ichijo Sagaru, Kamigyo-ku, JP
Information: presents its own productions; available for hire
Country: Japan

Kyoto Kaikan Hall
Phone: 757 716 051
Address: 13 Okazaki Saishohji-cho, Sakyo-ku, JP
Information: available for hire
Country: Japan
Contact: Director Takao Mitsuno

Kyoto Kanze Kaikan
Phone: 757 716 114
Address: 44 Okazaki Enshoji-cho, Sakyo-ku, JP
Information: presents its own productions; available for hire
Country: Japan

Kyoto Kodomo Bunka Kaikan – Angel House
Phone: 754 640 356
Address: 431-1 Takigahana-cho, Ichijo-dori Naka-hon-matsu Nishi-Iru, Kamigyo-ku, JP
Information: presents its own productions; available for hire
Country: Japan

Kyoto-fu Nagaokakyo Kinen Bunka Kaikan
Phone: 759 555 711
Address: 4-1-1 Tenjin, Nagaokakyo, JP
Country: Japan

Kyoto-shi Avanti Hall
Phone: 756 718 188
Address: 9F Avanti Bldg., 31, Nishi-San-Noh-cho, Higashi Kujo, Minami-ku, JP
Information: available for hire
Country: Japan

Kyu Tokyo Ongaku Gakkoh Sohgakudo
Website: www.taitocity.net/taito/sougakudou
Phone: 338 241 988
Address: 8-43 Ueno Koen, Taito-ku, JP
Information: the hall is designated by the government as an Important Cultural Property
Country: Japan

Laforet Museum Harajuku
Phone: 334 750 411
Address: 6F, Laforet Harajuku, 1-11-6 Jingumae, Shibuya-ku, JP
Information: presents its own productions; available for hire
Country: Japan

Landmark Hall
Website: www.landmark.ne.jp
Phone: 452 225 050
Address: 5/F Landmark Plaza, 2-2-1-1 Minatomirai, Nishi-ku, Yokohama, JP
Information: presents its own productions & available for hire
Country: Japan
Contact: Director Akihiko Hattori

Lilia Main Hall/Lilia Concert Hall
Website: www.lilia.or.jp
Email: info@lilia.or.jp
Phone: 482 582 000
Address: 3-1-1 Kawaguchi, Kawaguchi, JP
Information: part of Kawaguchi Complex Centre of Culture-LILIA; presents its own productions; available for hire
Country: Japan
Contact: Chairman of the board Koushiro Okamura

Lovely Hall Kawachinagano Shiritsu Bunka Kaikan

Website: www.lovelyhall.com
Email: info@lovelyhall.com
Phone: 721 566 100
Address: 12-46 Nishidai-cho, Kawachinagano, JP
Information: produces an opera every two years; also organizes Kawachinagano World Music Festival (q.v.) every summer; Osaka Symphoniker (q.v.) is its resident orchestra
Country: Japan
Contact: Producer Tomoko Nishio
Contact: General Manager Shigeo Nagao

Lumi
Phone: 669 085 300
Address: 29-1 Suehiro-cho, Kadoma, JP
Information: multi-purpose halls with modern technology
Country: Japan
Contact: Producer Syosaku Sutoh
Contact: General Manager Masahiko Yamashita
Contact: Executive Director Yoshio Azuma

Lutheran Ichigaya Centre
Website: www.l-i-c.com
Email: info@l-i-c.com
Phone: 332 608 621
Address: 1-1 Ichigaya Sadohara-cho, Shinjuku-ku, JP
Information: has a pipe organ
Country: Japan
Contact: contact Akihiro Fujita

Lyric Hall
Website: www.nagaoka-caf.or.jp
Email: lyric@nagaoka-caf.or.jp
Phone: 258 297 711
Address: 315 Terajima-machi, Nagaoka, JP
Information: managed by Nagaoka Arts and Culture Foundation; see also Nagaoka Shiritsu Gekijo (q.v.); presents its own productions; available for hire
Country: Japan
Contact: Chairman Tamio Mori

Maebashi Municipal Culture Hall
Website: www.city.maebashi.gunma.jp
Phone: 272 241 111
Address: 2-12-1 Ote-machi, Maebashi, JP
Country: Japan
Contact: Director Mitsuru Mesaki

Maebashi Terrsa Hall
Website: www.maebashi-terrsa.or.jp
Phone: 272 241 111
Address: 2-5-1 Chiyoda-cho, Maebashi, JP
Information: presents its own productions; available for hire
Country: Japan

Mainichi Newspapers
Phone: 332 120 187
Address: Cultural Projects Dept, 1-1-1 Hitotsubashi, Chiyoda-ku, JP
Information: Producer/presenter; one of the leading newspaper companies; manages the Japan Music Competition
Country: Japan

Makuhari Messe
Website: www.m-messe.co.jp
Email: kikakukouhouka@m-messe.co.jp
Phone: 432 960 001
Address: 2-1 Nakase, Mihama-ku, JP
Information: presents its own productions; also available for hire
Country: Japan
Social Media: www.facebook.com/ChibaMakuhariMesse?fref=ts

Maruko-machi Bunka Kaikan – Seres Hall
Phone: 268 420 001
Address: 1488 Oaza-Kami-Maruko, Maruko-machi, Chiisagata-gun, JP
Information: presents its own productions; also available for hire
Country: Japan
Contact: Director Hideo Takano

Matsue-shi Sohgoh Bunka Centre – Plover Hall
Website: www.web-sanin.co.jp/matsue/plover
Email: plover@web-sanin.co.jp
Phone: 852 276 000
Address: 6-5-44 Nishi-Tsuda, Matsue, JP
Information: equipped with a pipe-organ made by Rudolf von Beckerath Orgelbau, Germany
Country: Japan
Contact: General Director Mizuya Ando

Matsuyama Shimin Kaikan
Website: www.maps.or.jp/
Phone: 899 318 181
Address: Horinouchi, Matsuyama, JP
Information: available for hire
Country: Japan

Matsuyama-shi Sohgoh Community Centre Camellia Hall
Website: www.city.matsuyama.ehime.jp/shisetsu/comcen/index.
Phone: 899 218 222
Address: 7-5 Minato-machi, Matsuyama, JP
Information: presents its own productions; available for hire
Country: Japan
Contact: secretary General Tadashi Akaboshi

Matsuzakaya Hall
Phone: 522 643 631
Address: 8F, Minami-Kan, Matsuzakaya Honten, 3-16-1 Sakae, Naka-ku, Nagoya, JP
Information: presents its own productions; available for hire
Country: Japan

Meguro-ku Kohkaido
Phone: 337 122 932
Address: 2-45-11 Naka-machi, Meguro-ku, JP
Country: Japan

Meijiza
Website: www.meijiza.co.jp
Email: meijiza@meijiza.co.jp
Phone: 813 366 03982 p
Address: 2-31-1 Nihombashi Hama-cho, Chuo-ku, JP
Country: Japan

Meitetsu Hall
Website: www.e-meitetsu.com/mds/main/hall/index.html
Phone: 525 857 811
Address: 1-2-1 Meieki, Nakamura-ku, Nagoya, JP
Information: presents its own productions; available for hire
Country: Japan

Melsa Hall
Website: www.melsa.co.jp
Phone: 582 663 030
Address: 1-15 Tetsumei-dori, JP
Information: presents its own productions; also available for hire
Country: Japan

Mie-ken Sohgoh Bunka Centre
Website: www.center-mie.or.jp/
Phone: 592 331 111
Address: 1234 Kohzubeta, Isshinden, Tsu, JP
Information: presents its own productions & available for hire
Country: Japan
Contact: Director Yoshihiro Kaji
Contact: Chairman Yasuo Takemura

Mielparque Hall
Website: www.mielparque.or.jp
Phone: 334 337 211
Address: 2-5-20 Shiba Koen, Minato-ku, JP
Country: Japan

Mielparque Hall Fukuoka
Website: www.mielparque.or.jp/
Phone: 925 250 771
Address: 4-14-52 Yakuin, Chuo-ku, JP
Information: available for hire
Country: Japan

Mielparque Hall Osaka
Website: www.mielparque.or.jp
Phone: 663 502 128
Address: 4-2-1 Miyahara, Yodogawa-ku, JP
Country: Japan

Min-On Concert Association
Website: www.min-on.or.jp
Email: info@min-on.or.jp
Phone: 353 623 400
Address: 8 Shinano-machi, Shinjuku-ku, JP
Information: presenter; see entry under National Organisation for details
Country: Japan
Contact: head of pr Yukio Yamaguchi

Minamiza
Website: www.shochiku.co.jp
Phone: 755 611 155
Address: Shijo Ohashi Higashizume, Higashiyama-ku, JP
Information: the oldest Kabuki theatre in Japan, designated as Cultural Property by the government; operated by Shochiku Co Ltd (q.v.)
Country: Japan
Contact: General Manager Takashi Yoshiura

Minoh Shiritsu Maple Hall
Website: www.kisweb.ne.jp/maple-h/toppage.htm
Email: maple-h1@mb1.kisweb.ne.jp
Phone: 727 212 123
Address: 5-11-23 Mino-o, Mino'o, JP
Information: presents its own productions; available for hire
Country: Japan

Misonoza Theatre
Website: www.misonoza.co.jp
Phone: 522 228 204
Address: 1-6-14 Sakae, Naka-ku, Nagoya, JP
Information: presents drama in co-operation with Mei-jiza (q.v.) and Toho Co Ltd (q.v.) in Tokyo; also presents Kabuki with Shochiku Co Ltd (q.v.) in Tokyo and Shin-Ka-bukiza (q.v.) in Osaka
Country: Japan

Mitaka City Arts Centre
Website: mitaka.jpn.org
Email: info@mitaka.jpn.org
Phone: 422 479 100
Address: 6-12-14 Kamirenjaku, Mitaka, JP
Information: shoebox-shaped hall has a partly adaptable stage; presents its own productions; available for hire
Country: Japan
Contact: Chairman Akira Mochida

Mitsukoshi Gekijo
Website: www.mitsukoshi.co.jp/gekijo
Phone: 332 748 675
Address: 1-4-1 Muro-machi, Nihonbashi, Chuo-ku, JP
Information: opened in 1927; located in the building of Nihombashi Mitsukoshi, a department store in Tokyo; presents its own productions
Country: Japan

Miyagi Kenmin Kaikan
Website: www1.neweb.ne.jp/wb/kenmin
Email: kenmin@mb.neweb.ne.jp
Phone: 222 235 591
Address: 3-3-7 Kokubun-cho, Aoba-ku, Aoba-ku, Sendai, JP
Information: presents its own productions; also available for hire
Country: Japan
Contact: representative Toshimitsu Yoshida

Miyazaki Prefectural Arts Centre
Website: www.miyazaki-ac.jp
Phone: 985 283 210
Address: 3-210 Funazuka, JP
Information: shoebox shaped Concert Hall equipped with a pipe organ; venue for Miyazaki Music Festival (q.v.); presents its own productions; available for hire
Country: Japan
Contact: President Kenji Aoki

Mizuho View Park Sky Hall
Phone: 425 577 070
Address: 2475 Hakonegasaki, Mizuho-machi, Nishita-ma-gun, JP
Information: available for hire
Country: Japan
Contact: head of social education dept. Eiichi Koike

Mizusawa-shi Bunka Kaikan – Z Hall
Website: www.isop.ne.jp/atrui/zhall.html
Email: zhall@rnac.ne.jp
Phone: 197 226 622
Address: 41 Aza Ishibashi, Sakurakawa, Mizusawa, JP
Country: Japan
Contact: contact Remi Ishizu
Contact: Chairman Yukio Murata

Modapolitica
Website: www.modapolitica.com
Email: office@modapolitica.com
Phone: 354 688 883
Address: 6-6-21 Minami Aoyama, Minato-ku, JP
Country: Japan

Mon'naka Tenjo Hall
Phone: 336 418 275
Address: 1-20-3 Monzen Naka-cho, Kohtoh-ku, JP
Country: Japan

Mori no Hall 21 Matsudo-shi Bunka Kaikan
Website: www.morinohall21.com
Phone: 473 845 050
Address: 646-4 Sendabori, Matsudo, JP
Information: the hall is in the cultural complex which consists of museum, library and large park; also has a rehearsal room
Country: Japan

Morioka Civic Cultural Hall
Phone: 196 215 100
Address: c/o Morioka Foundation for Cultural Activity, 5 F Malios, 2-9-1, Morioka-eki Nishi-dori, Morioka, JP
Information: small hall is equipped with pipe organ; presents its own productions; available for hire
Country: Japan

Morioka Theatre
Phone: 196 222 258
Address: c/o Morioka Cultural Foundation, 3-1, Mat-suo-cho, Morioka, JP
Information: Main Hall presents drama; presents its own

productions; available for hire
Country: Japan

Munakata Yurix
Website: www.yurix.munakata.com
Email: info@yurix.munakata.com
Phone: 940 371 311
Address: 400 Kubara, Munakata, JP
Information: presents its own productions; available for hire
Country: Japan

Muroran-shi Bunka Centre
Phone: 143 223 156
Address: 6-23 Saiwai-cho, Muroran, JP
Information: presents its own productions; available for hire website; www.city.muroran.hokkaido.jp/main/org9410/bunkagai.html
Country: Japan
Contact: Director Michitoshi Oshiba

Musashino Civic Cultural Hall
Website: www.musashino-culture.or.jp
Phone: 422 548 822
Address: c/o Musashino Cultural Foundation, 3-9-11 Naka-cho, Musashino, JP
Information: also promotes and invites artists from abroad
Country: Japan
Contact: standing Director Hideharu Miyazaki
Contact: chief Director Masatada Tsuchiya
Producer of classical & organ music
Kazuhiro Kurihara

Musashino Geino Gekijo
Phone: 422 553 500
Address: 1-15-10 Nakamachi, Musashino, JP
Information: presents its own productions; available for hire
Country: Japan

Musashino Music College Bach Saal
Website: www.musashino-music.ac.jp
Phone: 339 921 121
Address: c/o Public Relations & Planning Office, 1-13-1, Hazawa, Nerima-ku, JP
Information: the hall was designed for classical music concerts and opera practice; Hexagonal in shape, with one-floor seating plan
Country: Japan
Contact: President Naotaka Fukui
Contact: contact Tsuneo Sawamoto

Muse Hall
Phone: 878 330 013
Address: 2-6-40 Saiho-cho, Takamatsu, JP
Country: Japan

Musik Saal Akishino
Website: www.akishino-ongakudo.com
Phone: 742 357 070
Address: 2-4-1 Saidaiji Higashi-machi, JP
Information: presents its own productions; available for hire
Country: Japan

Muza Kawasaki Symphony Hall
Website: www.kawasaki-sym-hall.jp
Phone: 445 200 100
Address: Kawasaki City Cultural Foundation, 1310 Omi-ya-cho Saiwai-ku, JP
Information: Main hall has 1997 seats in vineyard style in which the audience sits in a circle with the stage at the center thus offering a 360-degree field of vision. Muza is equipped with various functions to secure reverberation time ideal for the classics as well
Country: Japan

Nagahama Shimin Kaikan
Phone: 749 623 095
Address: 1200 Miyashi-cho, Nagahama, JP
Information: presents its own productions; available for hire
Country: Japan

Nagano-ken Kenmin Bunka Kaikan
Website: business2.plala.or.jp/n-kenbun/
Phone: 262 260 008
Address: 1-1-3, wakasato, JP
Information: presents its own productions; available for hire
Country: Japan
Contact: Director Chisato Shinohara

Nagano-ken Matsumoto Bunka Kaikan
Phone: 263 347 100
Address: 69-2 Mizukuma, Matsumoto, JP
Information: one of the venues for Saito Kinen Festival (q.v.)
Country: Japan

Nagaoka Shiritsu Gekijo

Website: www.nagaoka-caf.or.jp
Email: lyric@nagaoka-caf.or.jp
Phone: 258 332 211
Address: 2-1-2 Saiwai-cho, Nagaoka, JP
Information: managed by Nagaoka Arts and Culture Foundation as newly-opened Lyric Hall (q.v.); presents its own productions; available for hire
Country: Japan

Nagasaki City Auditorium
Phone: 958 224 145
Address: 4-30 Uo-no-machi, JP
Information: the largest venue in Nagasaki city
Country: Japan
Contact: Director Shigenori Fushiki

Nagasaki Shimin Kaikan
Phone: 958 251 400
Address: 5-1 Uo-no-machi, JP
Country: Japan
Contact: representative Suketsugu Kabashima

Nagasaki-shi Chitosepia Hall
Phone: 958 422 700
Address: 5-1 Chitose-cho, JP
Information: available for hire
Country: Japan
Contact: Director Hidetoshi Higashikawa

Nagoya Citizen's Auditorium
Phone: 523 312 141
Address: 1-5-1 Kanayama, Naka-ku, Nagoya, JP
Country: Japan

Nagoya Civic Assembly hall
Phone: 527 317 191
Address: 1-1-3 Tsurumai, Showa-ku, Nagoya, JP
Information: presents its own productions; available for hire
Country: Japan

Nagoya-hs Geijutsu Sohouzoh Centre Hall
Website: culture.city.nagoya.jp
Phone: 529 311 811
Address: 1-3-27 Aoi, Higashi-ku, Nagoya, JP
Country: Japan

Naha Shimin Kaikan
Website: www.city.naha.okinawa.jp/out/kaikan/index.html
Phone: 988 555 081
Address: 1-2-1 Yorimiya, Naha, JP
Information: presents its own productions; available for hire
Country: Japan

Nakamura Shiritsu Bunka Centre
Phone: 880 354 887
Address: 2-1 Sakura-machi, Nakamura, JP
Information: presents its own productions & available for hire; also has a conference room
Country: Japan

Nakaniida Bach Hall
Email: bach-hall@town.kami.miyagi.jp
Phone: 229 637 367
Address: 101 Aza Ipponsugi, Kami-machi, Kami-gun, JP
Information: designed for acoustics; equipped with a pipe organ; commissions choral music and presents premier performance of it in August every year
Country: Japan
Contact: Director Sadao Takahashi

Nakano-ku Momijiyama Bunka Centre – Nakano ZERO Hall
Website: www.nices.or.jp/02guidance
Phone: 353 405 000
Address: 2-9-7 Nakano, Nakano-ku, JP
Country: Japan

Nara-ken Bunka Kaikan
Website: www4.kcn.ne.jp/~narabun
Phone: 742 238 921
Address: 6-2 Nobori-Ohji-cho, JP
Information: presents its own productions & available for hire
Country: Japan
Contact: Director Kazuchika Naka

Nara-ken New Public Hall
Website: www.shinkokaido.jp
Phone: 742 272 630
Address: 101 Kasugano-cho, JP
Information: Nara is the cradle of Kyogen and Noh; presents its own productions; available for hire
Country: Japan
Contact: Director Kenichi Fujii

Narashino Bunka Hall
Website: www.seaple-n.icc.ne.jp/~narabunh
Email: narabunh@seaple-n.icc.ne.jp
Phone: 474 791 212
Address: 1-16-1 Yatsu, Narashino, JP

Information: presents its own productions; available for hire
Country: Japan
Contact: Director Kenji Shimazaki

Narimasu Kumin Centre – ACT Hall
Phone: 359 986 881
Address: 3-11-3-405 Narimasu, Itabashi-ku, JP
Country: Japan

Narita Kokusai Bunka Kaikan
Phone: 476 231 331
Address: 303 Tsuchiya, Narita, JP
Information: presents its own productions & available for hire Website ; www.city.narita.chiba.jp/soshiki/nari-tabunka/index.html
Country: Japan
Contact: Director Takao Hirayama

National Bunraku Theatre
Website: www.ntj.jac.go.jp/bunraku/
Phone: 662 122 531
Address: 1-12-10 Nihonbashi, Chuo-ku, JP
Information: five Bunraku programmes are given per year: the Bunraku company also performs at the National Theatre (q.v.) in Tokyo; Bunraku bases its headquarters at two National Theatres in Osaka and in Tokyo; see also National Theatre
Country: Japan

National Children's Castle
Website: www.kodomono-shiro.or.jp
Phone: 337 975 666
Address: 5-53-1 Jingumae, Shibuya-ku, JP
Information: National Children's Castle is the name of the building complex which has two venues in it; Aoyama Theatre 1200 (q.v.) and Aoyama Round Theatre 300 (q.v.)
Country: Japan
Contact: President Kazuyo Takamine

National Engei Hall
Website: www.ntj.jac.go.jp
Phone: 813 326 57411
Address: 4-1, Hayabusa-cho, Chiyoda-ku, JP
Country: Japan
Capacity: 300

National Noh Theatre
Website: www.nntt.jac.go.jp
Phone: 334 231 331
Address: 4-18-1 Sendagaya, Shibuya-ku, JP
Information: see also National Theatre
Country: Japan
Contact: head of the theatre Kawai Hideya

National Theater of Japan
Website: www.ntj.jac.go.jp
Phone: 332 657 411
Address: 4-1 Hayabusacho, Chiyoda-ku, Tokyo
Information: The National Theater of Japan, the predecessor of the Japan Arts Council, was established in July 1966 with the aim of preserving and promoting traditional performing arts. In November of the same year, the National Theater, which performed Kabuki, Bunraku, dance, Japanese music, folk performing arts, statements, and Yagaku, opened as a base theater facility.
Country: Japan
Social Media: twitter.com/nt_tokyo www.instagram.com/nationaltheatre_tokyo/
Disabled Access: Yes

Nerima Bunka Centre
Phone: 339 933 311
Address: 1-17-37 Nerima, Nerima-ku, JP
Information: presents its own productions; available for hire
Country: Japan

New National Theatre, Tokyo
Website: www.nntt.jac.go.jp
Phone: 353 513 011
Address: c/o New National Theatre Foundation, 1-1-1 Hon-machi, Shibuya-ku, JP
Information: the first national theatre in Japan 1997 for modern performing arts including opera, ballet, contemporary dance and drama; there has been a national theatre for the traditional performing arts; see National Theatre in this section
Country: Japan
Contact: Artistic Director drama Tamiya Kuriyama
Contact: Artistic Director opera Thomas Novohradsky
Contact: President Toyama Atsuko
Contact: Executive Director Yoshikazu Hasegawa
Contact: Executive Director Makoto Ike
Contact: Artistic Director dance Asami Maki

New Pier Hall
Phone: 335 780 041
Address: 1-11-1 Kaigan, Minato-ku, JP
Country: Japan

NHK Enterprises 21 Inc
Website: www.nep21.co.jp

Phone: 334 817 800
Address: Dai-3 Kyodo Bldg., 4-14, Kamiyama-cho, Shibuya-ku, JP
Information: specializes in planning & production of events, TV programmes for NHK Japan Broadcasting Corporationq.v., development of multi-media software, etc.
Country: Japan
Contact: Director Shunichi Itaya

NHK Hall
Website: www.nhk-sc.or.jp/nhk_hall
Phone: 334 651 751
Address: 2-2-1 Jin'nan, Shibuya-ku, JP
Information: a home of NHK Symphony Orchestra (q.v.)
Country: Japan

NHK Service Centre
Website: www.nhk-p.co.jp
Phone: 334 640 200
Address: 4F, Dai'ichi Kyodo Bldg., 41-1 Udagawa-cho, Shibuya-ku, JP
Information: Producer/presenter
Country: Japan

Nihon Daigaku Casals Hall
Website: www.nu-casalshall.com
Phone: 332 941 229
Address: 01-Jun, Kanda Surugadai, Chiyoda-ku, JP
Information: planned and designed exclusively for chamber music and smaller ensembles
Country: Japan

Nihon Hall and Conference Room
Website: https:// www.nikkei-hall.com/
Email: nikkei-hall@nikkei-ps.co.jp
Phone: 036 256 7686
Address: General Project Dept, 15F, Mitsubishi Sohgo-hkenkyu Bldg., 2-3-6, Otemachi, Chiyoda-ku, JP
Information: Located on the 3rd to 5th floors of the Otemachi Nikkei Building, the Nikkei Hall is a multifunctional hall with 610 seats, adjoined to the conference room which can accommodate 400 people in a theater style**Country:** Japan

Nihon Kyoiku Kaikan Hitotsubashi Hall
Phone: 332 302 831
Address: 2-6-2 Hitotsubashi, Chiyoda-ku, JP
Country: Japan

Nihon Seinenkan Dai Hall
Phone: 334 752 455
Address: 15 Kasumigaoka, Shinjuku-ku, JP
Country: Japan

Nihonmatsu Shimin Kaikan
Phone: 243 235 121
Address: c/o Nihonmatsu-shi Bunka Centre, 1-92 Enoki-do, Nihonmatsu, JP
Information: available for hire
Country: Japan

Niigata Prefectural Civic Center
Website: www.niigata-bunka.jp/kenmin/
Email: jigyou@niigata-bunka.jp
Phone: 252 284 481
Address: 3-13 Ichibanbori-dori-cho, JP
Information: presents its own productions; available for hire
Country: Japan
Contact: Director Kazumasa Furukawa

Niigata-shi Ongaku Bunka Kaikan
Website: www.ryutopia.or.jp/onbun
Email: onbun@city.niigata.niigata.jp
Phone: 252 245 811
Address: 3-2 Ichibanbori-dori-machi, JP
Information: has 4 large size studios, 3 mid size studios, 6 small size studios
Country: Japan

Nippon Budokan
Website: www.nipponbudokan.or.jp
Phone: 332 165 100
Address: c/o Nippon Budokan Foundation, 2-3 Kitanomaru Koen, Chiyoda-ku, JP
Information: a national centre of traditional Japanese arts
Country: Japan

Nippori Sunny Hall
Website: www.tcn-catv.ne.jp/~acc
Phone: 338 073 211
Address: c/o Hotel Lungwood, 5-50-5, Higashi-Nippori, Arakawa-ku, JP
Country: Japan

Nirasaki-shi Bunka Hall
Website: www.nirasaki.net
Email: mail@nirasaki.net
Phone: 551 201 155
Address: 205 Sakai, Fujii-machi, Nirasaki, JP
Information: opened in Sept 1995; presents its own productions; available for hire
Country: Japan
Contact: President Sakyo Ohshiba

Nishinomiya Shimin Kaikan – Amity Hall
Website: amity.nishi.or.jp
Email: amity@nishi.or.jp
Phone: 798 333 111
Address: 10-11 Rokutanji-cho, Nishinomiya, JP
Information: presents its own productions; available for hire
Country: Japan
Contact: Director Yasuhide Tokugaki

Nissay Theatre
Website: www.nissaytheatre.or.jp
Email: y.niwa@nissaytheatre.or.jp
Phone: 335 033 122
Address: 1-1-1 Yuraku-cho, Chiyoda-ku, JP
Information: hosts annual Nissay International Family Festival in summer and Nissay Opera in autumn
Country: Japan
Contact: Executive Producer Yasuo Niwa
Contact: President Tsuyoshi Nahara

Nobeoka Sohgoh Bunka Centre
Website: www.wainet.ne.jp/~nsbc/
Email: jagajaga@ma.wainet.ne.jp
Phone: 982 221 855
Address: 611-2, Higashi Hamago-cho, Nobeoka, JP
Information: presents its own productions; available for hire
Country: Japan

Noh Laboratory Theatre – Tessenkai
Email: tessen@jade.dti.ne.jp
Phone: 334 012 285
Address: 4-21-29 Minami-Aoyama, Minato-ku, JP
Information: can accommodate other performing arts suitable to this theatre and its wooden floor; see also Drama & Agents
Country: Japan
Contact: Director Tetsunojo Kanze

Noto Engekido
Website: www.engekido.com
Email: engekido@nanaonet.jp
Phone: 767 662 323
Address: Ue-9 Nakajimamachi Nakajima, Nanao, JP
Information: opened in 1995; the venue for Noto Nakajima Drama Festival; presents its own productions; available for hire
Country: Japan
Contact: honorary Director Tatsuya Nakadai
Contact: General Manager Isao Miyashita
Policies: Produce and rent, Multi-purpose

Nova Hall
Website: www.tsukubacity.or.jp/
Phone: 298 525 881
Address: 1-10-1 Azuma, Tsukuba, JP
Information: used mainly as a concert hall; presents its own productions & available for hire
Country: Japan
Contact: Director Takashi Kataoka

Numazu Shimin Bunka Centre
Website: www.city.numazu.shizuoka.jp/sisetu/bunka/index.htm
Phone: 559 326 111
Address: 15-1 Miyuki-cho, Numazu, JP
Information: presents its own productions; available for hire
Country: Japan
Contact: Director Masahiro Yamada

Nyuzen Cosmo Hall
Website: www.town.nyuzen.toyama.jp/cosmo
Email: cosmo@town.nyuzen.toyama.jp
Phone: 765 721 105
Address: 3200 Nyuzen, Nyuzen-machi, Shimo-Niika-wa-gun, JP
Information: presents its own productions; also available for hire
Country: Japan

O'e Nohgakudo
Website: noh.fumi.org
Email: masa@fumi.org
Phone: 817 523 17625 M
Address: Yanaginobamba Higashi Iru, Oshikoji-dori, Nakagyo-ku, JP
Information: presents its own productions; available for hire
Country: Japan

OAG Hall
Phone: 335 827 744
Address: 7-5-56 Akasaka, Minato-ku, JP
Country: Japan

Obihiro Shimin Bunka Hall
Website: www.ma.megafit.net/~ocf-bunka/
Phone: 155 238 111
Address: 48-2, Minami-11-chome, Nishi 5-jo, Obihiro, JP
Information: presents its own productions; available

for hire
Country: Japan
Contact: Director Toshiaki Gotoh

Odawara Shimin Kaikan
Phone: 465 227 146
Address: 1-5-12 Hon-cho, Odawara, JP
Information: presents its own productions; available
for hire
Country: Japan
Contact: Director Yoshihiro Yamaguchi

OFF OFF Theatre
Website: www.honda-geki.com/offoff.html
Phone: 334 243 755
Address: 3F Taro Bldg, 2-11-8 Kitazawa, Setagaya-ku, JP
Country: Japan

Ohgaki City Suitopia Centre
Phone: 584 746 050
Address: 5-51 Murohon-machi, Ohgaki, JP
Information: presents its own productions; available for
hire; manages Ogaki Music Festival (q.v.)

Ohmi Hachiman-shi Bunka Kaikan
Phone: 748 338 111
Address: 366 De-machi, Ohmi Hachiman, JP
Information: presents its own productions; available
for hire
Country: Japan
Contact: Director Hayashi Teraoka

Ohtsuki Seiinkai Nohgakudo
Website: www.noh-kyogen.com
Phone: 667 618 055
Address: A-7 Uemachi, Chuo-ku, JP
Information: presents its own productions & available
for hire
Country: Japan

Oita Bunka Kaikan
Phone: 975 321 295
Address: 4-1 Niage-machi, JP
Information: preavailable for hire
Country: Japan
Contact: Director Kiyomi Takahashi

Oita Prefectural Art Hall
Phone: 975 520 077
Address: 1-61 Makimidori-machi, JP
Information: available for hire
Country: Japan

Oji Hall
Website: www.ojihall.com
Email: webmaster@ojihall.com
Phone: 335 640 200
Address: 4-7-5 Ginza, Chuo-ku, JP
Information: a shoebox-style hall designed for chamber
ensembles; seating capacity 315; refurbished in 2003;
commissions new works; rent, present
Country: Japan
Contact: production planning dept. international liaison
Masa Shibata
Contact: President Takao Ohtsubo

Okaya-shi Bunka Kaikan – Canora Hall
Website: www.lcv.ne.jp/~canora
Email: canora@po6.lcv.ne.jp
Phone: 266 241 300
Address: 8-1 Saiwai-cho, Okaya, JP
Information: main hall has good acoustics
Country: Japan
Contact: Director Norio Sato

Okayama Prefectural Museum of Art Hall
Website: www.pref.okayama.jp/seikatsu/kenbi/ho-ru.
htm
Phone: 862 254 800
Address: 8-48 Tenjin-cho, JP
Information: available for hire
Country: Japan

Okayama Shiritsu Shimin Bunka Hall
Phone: 862 730 395
Address: 1-1-30 Kobashi-cho, JP
Information: mainly for hire
Country: Japan
Contact: Director Mitsuo Asano

Okayama Symphony Hall
Website: http://www.okayama-symphonyhall.or.jp/
Email: j_info@okayama-symphonyhall.or.jp
Phone: 862 342 001
Address: 1-5-1 Omotecho, Kita-ku, Okayama-shi,
Okayama
Information: Since opening in September 1991, as a
base for art appreciation and cultural activities the hall
hosted Vienna Philharmonic performance, the NHK Sym-
phony Orchestra's regular concert, the performance of
Jose Carreras, one of the world's three major tenors, the
performance of the opera Wakahime...Country: Japan
Contact: Director Hideaki Tsuji
Email: j_info@okayama-symphonyhall.or.jp
Social Media: https:// www.facebook.com/hall.okaphil/

https://twitter.com/hall_okaphil https:// www.instagram.
com/hall_okaphil/

Okazaki Shimin Kaikan
Phone: 564 219 121
Address: 15-1 Aza Desaki, Rokku-cho, Okazaki, JP
Information: available for hire
Country: Japan

Okinawa Convention Center
Website: www.oki-conven.jp
Email: oki-conven@ocvb.or.jp
Phone: 988 983 000
Address: 4-3-1 Mashiki, Ginowan-shi, JP
Information: presents its own productions; also available
for hire
Country: Japan
Contact: Director Etsuko Higa

Okinawa Shimin Kaikan
Phone: 989 390 022
Address: 1-1-1 Yaejima, JP
Information: mainly for hire

Omigakudo
Email: matsukiart@nifty.com
Phone: 353 536 937
Address: 3F, Tokyo Opera City, 3-20-2, Nishi-shinjuku,
Shinjuku-ku, JP
Information: rents out as well as presents its own and
co-productions; has church like atmosphere
Country: Japan
Contact: President/matsuki art office co., ltd. Shogo
Matsuki

**Omiya Sonic City Hall Saitama-ken Sangyo
Bunka Centre**
Website: www.sonic-city.or.jp/
Phone: 486 474 111
Address: 5F Sonic-city Bld, 1-7-5 Sakuragi-cho, Omiya-ku,
Saitama, JP
Country: Japan
Contact: President t.b.a.
planning & customer relations dept.
Yoshiyuki Kuramochi

Omori Bellport Atrium
Website: www.omoribellport.com
Email: info@omoribellport.com
Phone: 354 711 439
Address: c/o Omori Bellport Co., Ltd., 6-26-2 Minami-Oi,
Shinagawa-ku, JP
Country: Japan
Contact: Director Masanori Yoda

Ongaku No Tomo Hall
Website: www.ongakunotomo.co.jp
Email: home@ongakunotomo.co.jp
Phone: 332 352 115
Address: 6-30 Kagurazaka, Shinjuku-ku, JP
Information: owned by music publishing company
Ongaku No Tomo Sha Corp.q.v.
Country: Japan
Contact: President Kumio Horiuchi

Ongaku No Tomo Hall, Shin-Osaka
Website: www.ongakunotomo.co.jp/hall/index.html
Email: home@ongakunotomo.co.jp
Phone: 663 970 335
Address: c/o Jigyo-bu, Sora Shin-Osaka 21, 2-1-3 Ni-
shi-Miyahara, Yodogawa-ku, JP
Information: well known for its acoustic; owned by a
publishing company in music, Ongaku No Tomo Sha
Corp. (q.v.); also has Ongaku no Tomo Hall (q.v.) in Tokyo
Country: Japan
Contact: President Hiroshi Okabe
Contact: vice President Takeshi Tatsuo

Open Theater EAST
Website: www.yomiuriland.co.jp
Phone: 449 661 111
Address: Yomiuri Land, 4015-1 Yanokuchi, Inagi, JP
Information: presents its own productions; available
for hire
Country: Japan
head of planning & Press dept
Toshio Sohara

Operetta Hall
Website: www.operettahouse.com
Email: operetta@fa.mbn.or.jp
Phone: 334 791 838
Address: B1F Les Fleurs Nishiazabu, 1-4-35 Nishi-Azabu,
Minato-ku, JP
Information: the only venue built for operetta perfor-
mance in Japan; also functions as a rehearsal room and a
venue for seminars, mini concerts
Country: Japan
President & art Director & Director
Hironori Terasaki
Contact: Producer Masayuki Yoneta

Osaka Kosei Nenkin Kaikan
Phone: 665 326 301
Address: 1-14-15 Shin-machi, Nishi-ku, JP

Country: Japan

**Osaka Municipal Labour Hall – Apio Osaka
Morinomiya Piroty Hall**
Phone: 669 441 151
Address: 1-17-5 Morinomiya Chuo, Chuo-ku, JP
Information: presents its own productions & available
for hire
Country: Japan

Osaka Nohgaku Kaikan
Phone: 663 731 726
Address: 2-3-17 Nakazaki-Nishi, Kita-ku, JP
Country: Japan
Contact: secretary General Jun'ichi Monkawa

Osaka Shochiku-za
Website: www.shochiku.co.jp
Phone: 662 142 211
Address: 1-9-19, Dohtombori, Chuo-ku, JP
Information: opened in March 1997, operated by Sho-
chiku Co Ltd (q.v.)
Country: Japan

OSAKA-JO HALL
Website: www.osaka-johall.com
Email: info@osaka-johall.com
Phone: 669 410 345
Address: 3-1 Osakajo, Chuo-ku, JP
Country: Japan
Contact: Chairman of the board Kazuo Yamahata

Otsu Shimin Kaikan
Website: www.city.otsu.shiga.jp/
Phone: 775 251 234
Address: 14-1 Shimanoseki, Otsu, JP
Country: Japan
Contact: representative , mayor of otsu Makoto Mekata
Contact: Manager Yoshiaki Kawaguchi

Palty Hall
Phone: 294 731 234
Address: 3210 Nakajo-machi, Hitachiohta, JP
Information: presents its own productions; also available
for hire
Country: Japan
Contact: Director Norimitsu Kurosawa

Parco Co Ltd
Website: www.parco-city.co.jp
Email: info@parco-city.co.jp
Phone: 334 775 857
Address: 15-1 Udagawa-cho, Shibuya-ku, JP
Information: produces/presents drama for its own
venues; see PARCO Theatre
Country: Japan
Contact: President Isamu Itoh

Parco Theatre
Website: www.parco-city.co.jp/play
Email: play@parco-city.co.jp
Phone: 334 775 858
Address: 15-1 Udagawa-cho, Shibuya-ku, JP
Information: PARCO is a department store which has
been presenting and providing new, unique, innovative
and sophisticated works; see also PARCO Co Ltd
Country: Japan
Contact: Director of development Koichi Yamazaki
Contact: President Isamu Itoh

Park Tower Hall
Website: www.ozone.co.jp/parktowerhall/index.html
Email: pt-hall@mail-ozone.jp
Phone: 353 226 633
Address: Shinjuku Park Tower, 3-7-1 Nishi-Shinjuku,
Shinjuku-ku, JP
Information: opened in 1994; owned by Tokyo Gas
Urban Development Company, a subsidiary of Tokyo Gas
Company and managed by Living Design Centre
Country: Japan

Parnassus Hall
Phone: 792 971 141
Address: 9-1-10 Tsujii, Himeji, JP
Information: presents its own productions; available for
hire; belongs to Himeji Hi-school
Country: Japan
Contact: representative Takafumi Yamamoto

Parthenon Tama
Website: www.parthenon.or.jp
Email: soumu@parthenon.or.jp
Phone: 423 751 414
Address: 2-35 Ochiai, Tama, JP
Information: main hall is a shoebox type; used by Virtu-
oso Ensemble Parthenon consists of young musicians for
their subscription concerts, as well as other artists
Country: Japan

Performing Arts Center – Tiara Koto
Website: homepage2.niffty.com/tiarakoto/
Email: tiarakoto@niffty.com
Phone: 336 355 500
Address: 2-28-36 Sumiyoshi, Kohtoh-ku, JP
Information: cooperation with Tokyo City Philharmonic

Orchestra (q.v.) and Tokyo City Ballet (q.v.); alternative website: www.kcf.or.jp
Country: Japan
vice Director & hall Manager
Osamu Ishihara
Contact: senior program officer Ryuichiro Mori
Contact: Director Naoki Shirahama

Philia Hall
Website: www.philiahall.com
Phone: 459 858 555
Address: 5F, South 1 Honkan, Aobadai Tokyu Square, 2-1-1 Aobadai Aoba-ku, JP
Information: a shoebox-shaped hall; presents its own productions & available for hire
Country: Japan
Contact: contact Reiko Tanaka

Phoenix Hall
Website:
http:// www.pcf.city.hiroshima.jp/icch/
Phone: 822 427 777
Address: 1-5 Nakajima-cho, Naka-ku, Hiroshima, JP
Information: The International Conference Center Hiroshima was established as a base facility in Hiroshima Peace Memorial Park, a sacred place for peace, in July 1989, the 100th anniversary of the enforcement of the city system.
Country: Japan
Contact: Chairman of the Board of Directors Steven Leeper
Contact: President Kazumi Matsui
Annual Performances: 51-100
Policies: Rent and Present

Phoenix Hall
Website: www.remus.dti.ne.jp
Email: phx-hall@remus.dti.ne.jp
Phone: 663 630 211
Address: 4-15-10 Nishi-Tenma, Kita-ku, JP
Information: opened in May 1995; an upper tier seating 133; both the front stalls and the stage are adaptable; the back of the stage is a large glass panel offering views across Osaka
Country: Japan
Contact: music Director Kyoko Edo

Phoenix Plaza
Phone: 776 205 060
Address: 1-13-6 Tawara, JP
Country: Japan

plan-B
Website: www.adguard.co.jp/artcamp/planb
Phone: 333 842 051
Address: B1, Monarc Nakano, 4-26-20 Yayoi-cho, Nakano-ku, JP
Country: Japan
Contact: contact Mr Takahashi

POCKET
Website: www005.upp.so-net.ne.jp/thepocket
Email: mitemite@gf7.so-net.ne.jp
Phone: 333 818 422
Address: 3-22-8, Nakano, Nakano-ku, JP
Information: rents out as well as presents its own productions; presents mainly drama but open to unique productions such as small scale opera etc.
Country: Japan
Contact: Manager Reiko Kasahara
Contact: President Hiroshi Kasahara

Puk Puppet Theatre
Website: www.puk.jp
Email: theatre@puk.jp
Phone: 333 703 371
Address: 2-12-3 Yoyogi, Shibuya-ku, JP
Information: PUPPET THEATRE PUK was founded by the late Toji Kawajiri, the elder brother of PUK's Artistic Director the late Taiji Kawajiri(1914-1994), in 1929, the same year as UNIMA foundation. PUK being an Artistic group based on free-exPression and anti-war ideals, its activities were mercilessly oPressed and perspected by the authorities of those days. PUK had to change its name several times and lost many of its members before and during the World War II. PUPPET THEATRE PUK started, right after the War , its free Artistic activities and then grew up to be a big groupe of more than eighty members and owing its Theatre House is actually the meeting place of puppeteers. PUPPET THEATRE PUK has three main sections – Puppet Troupe Section, Theatre House Section and TV Section. PUPPET THEATRE PUK started its creative activities with marionette technique. However, PUK soon enlarged its technical range adapting hand puppet, rod puppet, shadow puppet, Japanese traditional puppets and many others so as to puesue a wider possibility of theatrical exPression. As Japan has a long and various traditional and folk puppetry trends, PUK is very proud of making use of those cultural treasures in modern creation. English speaker:Haru Shimizu, Tamiko Onagi, Masami Sakurai
Country: Japan

Quest Hall

Website: www.harajuku-quest.com
Email: info@quest-hall.or.jp
Phone: 334 706 331
Address: 1-13-14 Jingumae, Shibuya-ku, JP
Country: Japan

Region Plaza Joetsu
Phone: 255 442 122
Address: 446-2, Oaza-Shimo-Monzen, Joetsu, JP
Information: presents its own productions; available for hire
Country: Japan
Contact: Director Ohichi Yamagishi

Rikkohkai Hall
Website: www.cts.ne.jp/~rikkokai
Email: rikkokai@east.cts.ne.jp
Phone: 334 713 425
Address: 2-32-3 Kita-Shinagawa, Shinagawa-ku, JP
Information: a small, but fully-equipped drama theatre located in 2nd floor basement
Country: Japan
Contact: Chairman Tatsuji Murabayashi

Saga Culture Hall
Phone: 952 323 000
Address: 1-21-10 Hinode, JP
Information: presents its own productions
Country: Japan

Saga Prefectural Art Museum Hall
Phone: 952 243 947
Address: 1-15-23 Johnai, JP
Information: website: www.pref.saga.lg.jp/ap-contents/kanko_bunka/k_shisetsu/hakubutu/index.html

Saitama Arts Theater
Website: www.saf.or.jp
Phone: 488 585 500
Address: 3-15-1 Uemine, Saitama-shi, JP
Information: opened in 1994; has 12 rehearsal rooms: 6 for theatrical and 6 for musical rehearsals; also has performing arts resource room and video editing room; presents its own productions; available for hire
Country: Japan

Saitama Kaikan
Website: www.saf.or.jp
Phone: 488 292 471
Address: 3-1-4 Takasago, Urawa-ku, Saitama-shi, JP
Information: the Main Hall designed with acoustic in mind; in the Small Hall seats are arranged in the arch shape surrounding the stage; presents its own productions & available for hire
Country: Japan
Contact: Director Fuminori Takeuchi

Saitama-shi Bunka Centre
Website: saitama-culture.jp
Phone: 488 663 171
Address: 1-7-1 Negishi, Minami-ku, Saitama-shi, JP
Information: presents its own productions & available for hire
Country: Japan
Contact: Director Seishi Matsuura

Sakata Shimin Kaikan
Phone: 234 223 527
Address: 2-2-45 Hon-cho, Sakata, JP
Country: Japan

Sakura Shimin Ongaku Hall
Phone: 434 616 221
Address: 1-16 Ohjidai, Sakura-shi, JP
Information: presents its own productions
Country: Japan
Contact: Director Masanobu Minowa

Salamanca Hall
Website: www.g-fureai.or.jp
Email: info@g-fureai.or.jp
Phone: 582 771 113
Address: c/o Gifu Prefecture Fureai Plaza Foundation, 5-14-53 Yabuta-Minami, JP
Information: this Renaissance-style hall is named after Catedral de Salamanca in Spain where its pipe organ was mended by an organ repairer from Gifu prefecture; equipped with a replica of the organ 45-stop Spanish; presents its own productions
Country: Japan

Sano-shi Bunka Kaikan
Phone: 283 247 211
Address: 508-5 Asanuma-cho, Sano, JP
Information: presents its own productions; also available for hire
Country: Japan

Sanseido Shinjuku Hall
Website: www1.sphere.ne.jp/SANSEIDO
Phone: 333 202 611
Address: 4-15-3 Nishi-Shinjuku, Shinjuku-ku, JP
Country: Japan
Contact: President Akihiko Eshima

Contact: business development dept. Tamiya Suzuki

Sapporo Concert Hall
Website: www.kitara-sapporo.or.jp
Email: hall@kitara-sapporo.or.jp
Phone: 115 202 000
Address: 1-15 Nakajima Koen, Chuo-ku, Sapporo, JP
Information: opened in July 1997; the main hall is designed in the form of a vineyard equipped with a French pipe organ and the chamber hall has a shoebox shape; the main hall is a venue for Pacific Music Festival (q.v.) and a home of Sapporo Symphony Orchestra (q.v.)
Country: Japan
Contact: General Director Kazuo Maye

Sapporo Shimin Kaikan
Phone: 112 419 171
Address: Nishi-1-chome, Kita-1-jo, Chuo-ku, Sapporo, JP
Information: available for hire
Country: Japan
Contact: General Director Akihiro Izumi

Sapporo-shi Kyoiku Bunka Kaikan
Phone: 112 715 821
Address: Nishi-13-chome, Kita-1-jo, Chuo-ku, Sapporo, JP
Information: presents its own productions & available for hire
Country: Japan

Sasebo Shimin Kaikan
Phone: 956 230 267
Address: 10-19 Hanazono-cho, Sasebo, JP
Country: Japan

Sayama-shi Shimin Kaikan
Email: sikaikan@city.sayama.saitama.jp
Phone: 429 539 101
Address: 2-33-1 Irumagawa, Sayama, JP
Information: website ; www.city.sayama.saitama.jp/kakuka/simin/sikaikan/index.htm
Country: Japan

Seinenza Gekijo
Website: www.seinenza.com
Email: info@seinenza.com
Phone: 334 670 439
Address: 1-53-12 Tomigaya, Shibuya-ku, JP
Information: home of Seinenza Theatre Company (q.v.)
Country: Japan

Seitoku University Kawanami Kinen Kohdo
Phone: 814 736 31401se
Address: c/o Seitoku University, 550, Iwase, Matsudo, JP
Information: presents its own productions; not available for hire
Country: Japan

Sembonzakura Hall
Email: senbonza@yk.rim.or.jp
Phone: 337 154 019
Address: Dai-san Esperance, 3-8-11 Takaban, Meguro-ku, JP
Information: also available to rent
Country: Japan
Contact: Director Jin Nakayama

Sendai City Youth Cultural Center
Website: www.bunka.city.sendai.jp/seinenbunka/index.html
Phone: 222 762 110
Address: 3-27-5 Asahigaoka, Aoba-ku, Sendai, JP
Information: presents its own productions; also available for hire
Country: Japan
Contact: Director Takao Ohsawa

Sendai-shi Izumi Bunka Sohzoh Centre – Sendai Izumity 21
Phone: 223 753 101
Address: 2-18-1 Izumi Chuo, Izumi-ku, Aoba-ku, Sendai, JP
Country: Japan

Sesi
Phone: 333 176 611
Address: 1-22-32 Umesato, Suginami-ku, JP
Country: Japan
Contact: President Toshio Ito

Setagaya Kuritsu Karasuyama Kumin Kaikan Hall
Phone: 333 263 511
Address: 6-2-19 Minami-Karasuyama, Setagaya-ku, JP
Country: Japan

Setagaya Kuritsu Kinuta Kumin Kaikan
Phone: 334 821 313
Address: 6-2-1 Seijo, Setagaya-ku, JP
Country: Japan

Setagaya Public Theatre
Website: www.setagaya-ac.or.jp/sept
Email: sept@setagaya-ac.or.jp

Phone: 354 321 526
Address: 4-1-1-5F Taishido, Setagaya-ku, JP
Information: also has a rehearsal room and a studio
Country: Japan
Contact: General Producer Hiroshi Takahagi

Shibata Shimin Bunka Kaikan
Website: www.city.shibata.niigata.jp/bunka/
Phone: 254 261 576
Address: 4-11-7 Chuo-cho, Shibata, JP
Information: presents its own productions; also available for hire
Country: Japan

Shibuya Kohkaido
Phone: 334 631 211 ext.
Address: 1-1 Udagawa-cho, Shibuya-ku, JP
Country: Japan

Shiga Kenritsu Nagahama Bunka Geijutsu Kaikan
Website: www.shiga-bunshin.or.jp/nagahama
Email: nagahama@shiga-bunshin.or.jp
Phone: 749 637 400
Address: 37, Ohshima-cho, Nagahama, JP
Information: unsuitable for classical music; presents its own productions; available for hire
Country: Japan
Policies: Rent and present, Theatre

Shigagin Hall
Phone: 775 260 005
Address: 1-38 Hama-cho, Otsu, JP
Country: Japan

Shimane Kenmin Kaikan
Email: culshimane@cul-shimane.jp
Phone: 852 225 503
Address: 158 Tono-machi, Matsue, JP
Information: presents its own productions; available for hire; operated by Shimane Perfecture Foundation for Cultural Promotion Tel: 852-22 5506
Country: Japan
Contact: Director Shuhji Okamoto

Shimbashi Embujo
Website: www.shochiku.co.jp/play
Phone: 335 412 600
Address: 6-18-2 Ginza, Chuo-ku, JP
Information: operated by the Shochiku Co Ltd (q.v.)
Country: Japan
Contact: General Manager Tamotsu Endo

Shimokitazawa Alley Hall
Website: member.nifty.ne.jp/alleyhall
Email: alleyhall@mbg.nifty.com
Phone: 334 681 086
Address: 3F Alley Bldg., 2-24-8 Kitazawa, Setagaya-ku, JP
Country: Japan
Contact: contact Mika Tsuboi

Shimonoseki Shimin Kaikan
Phone: 832 316 401
Address: 4-5-1 Takezaki-cho, Shimonoseki, JP
Country: Japan

Shimosuwa Sohgoh Bunka Centre
Phone: 266 280 018
Address: 4611-40 Nishi-Takano-machi, Shimosuwa-machi, Suwa-gun, JP
Country: Japan

Shin Toshi Hall
Website: www.yokohama-shintoshi.co.jp/hall
Phone: 454 652 001
Address: 9F Yokohama Shin Toshi Bldg., 2-18-1 Takashima, Nishi-ku, Yokohama, JP
Information: available for hire
Country: Japan
Contact: head of hall management Toshio Honda

Shin-Kabukiza
Phone: 666 312 121
Address: 4-3-25 Nanba, Chuo-ku, JP
Information: presents its own productions & available for hire
Country: Japan

Shin-Kobe Oriental Theater
Website: www.shin-oritheater.co.jp
Phone: 782 911 100
Address: 1-3 Kitano-cho, Chuo-ku, Kobe, JP
Information: Daiei, Japan's largest supermarket chain, operates the theatre; presents its own productions; available for hire
Country: Japan
Contact: Director Shinichi Goto

Shinagawa Kuritsu Sohgoh Kumin Kaikan – Kyurian
Website: www.shinagawa-culture.or.jp/curian/
Phone: 354 794 100
Address: 5-18-1 Higashi-Oi, Shinagawa-ku, JP
Country: Japan

Shinjuku Bunka Center
Website: www.shinjukubunka.or.jp
Phone: 333 501 141
Address: 6-14-1 Shinjuku, Shinjuku-ku, JP
Information: main hall is equipped with 5061-pipe organ by Alfred Kern & Fils. Caville-coll style; presents its own productions
Country: Japan
Contact: Director Yojiro Suma

Shinjuku Koma Gekijo
Website: www.koma-sta.co.jp
Phone: 332 028 111
Address: c/o Koma Stadium Inc., 1-19-1 Kabuki-cho, Shinjuku-ku, JP
Country: Japan

Shinjuku Meijiyasuda Seimei Hall
Website: www.meijiyasuda-life-hall.com
Email: office@meijiyasuda-life-hall.com
Phone: 333 426 705
Address: BIF Meijiyasuda Seimei Shinjuku Bldg., 1-9-1 Nishi-Shinjuku, Shinjuku-ku, JP
Information: presents its own productions & available for hire
Country: Japan
Contact: Director Kohtaro Igarashi

Shinjuku Theater Moli
Phone: 333 546 568
Address: 2F Shinjuku Moli, 3-33-10 Shinjuku, Shinjuku-ku, JP
Country: Japan
Contact: public relations Susumu Fujiwara
Contact: owner Shizuko Masuda
Contact: chief desk Yuko Arai
Contact: stage Manager Shuhzoh Hirano

Shinsei-cho Bunka Hall
Phone: 583 235 373
Address: 718 Karumi, Shinsei-cho, Motosu-gun, JP
Information: presents its own productions; available for hire
Country: Japan
Contact: Director Takuo Hirose

Shirakawa Hall
Website: www.shirakawa-hall.com
Email: desk@shirakawa-hall.com
Phone: 522 227 110
Address: 02/09/2015, Sakae, Naka-ku, Nagoya, JP
Information: opened in November 1994; this shoebox style hall is equipped with a mini orchestra pit and acoustic engineering
Country: Japan
Contact: General Manager Noritaka Endo
Contact: vice Manager Kaoru Endo

Shirane Tohgen Bunka Kaikan
Phone: 552 843 411
Address: 2971 Iino, Shirane-cho, Nakakoma-gun, JP
Information: presents its own productions; available for hire
Country: Japan
Contact: Chairman Michiyoshi Koike

Shizugin Hall Euphonia
Website: www.web-agora.com/euphonia
Phone: 542 508 777
Address: 7F Agora Shizuoka, 1-13 Ohte-machi, JP
Country: Japan
Contact: Managing Director Shigenobu Kataoka

Shizuka Hall
Website: www.tsuna-cho.jp/kankou/holl.htm
Phone: 799 622 001
Address: 5-4 Shizuki Niijima, Tsuna-cho, Tsuna-gun, JP
Information: reverberation time is 1.8 seconds when the hall is full; Shizuka Hall Viola Concours (q.v.) is held
Country: Japan
Contact: Director Shiro Miyama
Contact: contact Ichiro Kakihara

Shizuoka City Culture Hall
Website: www.chabashira.co.jp/~bnk1/index.html
Phone: 542 513 751
Address: 2-90 Sunpu-cho, JP
Country: Japan
Contact: Director Takeshi Suzuki
Contact: vice Director Motoyuki Unno

Shizuoka Performing Arts Centre (SPAC)
Website: www.spac.or.jp
Email: spac@spac.or.jp
Phone: 542 035 730
Address: 79-4 Ikeda Suruga-ku, JP
Information: Shizuoka Performing Arts Center (SPAC) was founded in 1995 by Shizuoka local government.
Country: Japan
Contact: General Artistic Director Tadashi Suzuki

Shobi Gakuen Vario Hall
Website: www.shobi.ac.jp/avi
Phone: 338 184 151

Address: 1-28-4 Hongo, Bunkyo-ku, JP
Country: Japan
Contact: Chairman Kenji Akamatsu

Showa Women's University, Hitomi Memorial Hall
Website: https://hall.swu.ac.jp/
Email: koudou@swu.ac.jp
Phone: 334 115 120
Address: 1-7-57 Taishido, Setagaya-ku, Tokyo
Information: The Hitomi Memorial Hall was built in April 1980 to commemorate the 60th anniversary of the founding of the school as a facility that embodies the founding spirit of Showa Women's University.**Country:** Japan
Contact: Chairperson Natsuko Ohara
Contact: President Mariko Band
Social Media: https://www.facebook.com/ShowaJoshi https://twitter.com/swu_official https:// www.instagram.com/insta_swu/
Disabled Access: Yes
Capacity: 1000+
Annual Performances: 100+
Annual Productions: 100+

Soeda Kohminkan – OAK HALL
Phone: 947 822 559
Address: 952 Oaza Sho, Soeda-cho, Tagawa-gun, JP
Information: presents its own production; mainly for hire
Country: Japan

Sogetsu Hall
Website: www.sogetsu.or.jp
Email: info@sogetsu.or.jp
Phone: 334 081 158
Address: 7-2-21 Akasaka, Minato-ku, JP
Information: owned by Sogetsu Foundation; available for hire
Country: Japan
Contact: secretary General Yujiro Arikawa
Contact: President Akane Teshigahara
Contact: Manager Masahide Morosaka

Sohtetsu Honda Theatre
Phone: 453 192 150
Address: 3F Sohtetsu Mu Bldg., 2-1-22 Minami-Saiwai, Nishi-ku, Yokohama, JP
Information: emphasis on presenting own productions
Country: Japan
Contact: Manager Keiko Shima
Contact: President Kazuo Honda

SPACE 107
Phone: 333 420 107
Address: B1, 1-8-5 Nishi-Shinjuku, Shinjuku-ku, JP
Country: Japan

Spiral Hall
Website: www.spiral.co.jp
Email: info@spiral.co.jp
Phone: 334 985 793
Address: Wacoal Art Center, 5-6-23 Minami-Aoyama, Minato-ku, JP
Information: part of the Wacoal Art Center; The Art Centre includes galleries, a hall, a theatre restaurant featuring music concerts & shops; The Spiral Hall regularly mounts its own productions; a multi-use open space with flat floor for drama, musicals
Country: Japan

Studio Akasaka Play Box
Website: members.tripod.co.jp/test000
Email: studioakasaka@hotmail.com
Phone: 357 705 121
Address: 1F/B1F Satoh Bldg., 8-12-12 Akasaka, Minato-ku, JP
Country: Japan

Subaru Hall
Website: www.tondabayashi-culture.org
Email: subaruhall@tondabayashi-culture.org
Phone: 721 250 222
Address: 2-8 Sakuragaoga-cho, Tondabayashi-shi, JP
Information: presents its own productions & available for hire
Country: Japan
Contact: Director satoshi Inoue

Suginami Nohgakudo
Phone: 333 812 208
Address: 1-55-9 Wada, Suginami-ku, JP
Country: Japan

Suita-shi Bunka Kaikan May Theater
Website: www.maytheater.jp/
Phone: 663 802 221
Address: 2-29-1 Izumi-cho, Suita-shi, JP
Information: presents its own productions
Country: Japan
Contact: President Tetsuo Inoue

Sumida Triphony Hall
Website: www.triphony.com
Email: sumida@triphony.com
Phone: 356 085 400

Address: 1-2-3 Kinshi, Sumida-ku, JP
Information: the main hall is shoebox type equipped with a German 66-stop pipe organ; The New Japan Philharmonic with its honorary Artistic Director, Seiji Ozawa, has become its resident orchestra
Country: Japan
Contact: President of sumida arts foundation Noboru Yamazaki

Sun Pearl Arakawa
Phone: 338 066 531
Address: 1-1-1 Arakawa, Arakawa-ku, JP
Country: Japan

Sun Plaza Hall
Website: www.sunplaza.or.jp
Phone: 333 881 151
Address: 4-1-1 Nakano, Nakano-ku, JP
Information: also runs: All Japan Concert Hall Association/Zenboku Hall Kyokai (q.v.)
Country: Japan

Sunbeam Yanai
Phone: 820 220 111
Address: Nishiushiroji, Yanai, JP
Information: well-known for its good acoustics
Country: Japan
Contact: Director Takashi Yoshimura

Sunshine Theatre
Website: www.sunshine-theatre.co.jp
Phone: 339 875 281
Address: P.O.Box 2200, 3-1-4 Higashi-Ikebukuro, Toshima-ku, JP
Information: operated by the Shochiku Co Ltd (q.v.); presents both its own productions and co-productions
Country: Japan
Contact: General Manager Seijiroh Kawashima
Contact: President Shigeru Kato

Suntory Hall
Website: www.suntory.co.jp/suntoryhall
Email: Yasumichi_Hayashi@suntory.co.jp
Address: 1-13-1 Akasaka, Minato-ku, JP
Information: Suntory Hall was groundbreaking in two respects when it first opened. One was the emphasis on achieving excellent acoustics as a dedicated concert hall. It was the first concert hall in Japan to adopt a vineyard-style seating arrangement, allowing the musicians and the audience to share an immersive music experience. The other was that the hall introduced new services that could be enjoyed pre-show and in the intervals to help embed a culture of concertgoing in Japan.
Country: Japan
Contact: President Tsuyoshi Tsutsumi
Social Media: https://twitter.com/SuntoryHall_PR
Disabled Access: Yes
Capacity: 1000+
Annual Performances: 51-100
Policies: All

Susono Shimin Bunka Centre
Phone: 559 939 300
Address: 586 Ishiwaki, Susono, JP
Country: Japan

Suzaka-shi Bunka Kaikan Mesena Hall
Website: www.janis.or.jp/users/mesena
Phone: 262 451 800
Address: 4-5-1 Sumisaka-minami, Suzaka, JP
Information: presents its own productions
Country: Japan

Suzuka Shimin Kaikan
Phone: 593 820 654
Address: 1-18-18 Kambe, Suzuka, JP
Country: Japan

Suzuka-shi Bunka Kaikan
Phone: 593 828 111
Address: 810 Iinojike-cho, Suzuka, JP
Country: Japan

Symphony Hall
Website: http:// www.symphonyhall.jp/
Phone: 664 531 010
Address: 2-3-3 Oyodominami, Kita-ku, Osaka
Information: The Symphony Hall, which Herbert von Karajan called "the best sound in the world, " was opened in 1982 and is "Japan's first classical music hall. Boasting the best environment for classical music with a reverberation of 2 seconds, this hall is loved by artists and audiences around the world as the "Classical Music Hall of Fame".
Country: Japan
Contact: President and CEO Toyonori Tanaka
Contact: Advisor Hiroshi Sakagami
Contact: Advisor Shizuichiro Kita
Social Media: https://www.facebook.com/thesymphonyhall https://twitter.com/thesymphonyhall https://www.instagram.com/the_symphony_hall/
Disabled Access: Yes
Capacity: 1000+

Annual Performances: 100+
Policies: All

Tachikawa-shi Shimin Kaikan – Amyu Tachikawa
Website: www.m-net.ne.jp/
Email: tachi-f@m-net.ne.jp
Phone: 425 261 311
Address: 3-3-20 Nishiki-cho, Tachikawa, JP
Information: presents its own productions; mainly concerts
Country: Japan
Contact: Chairman Kazuo Toyoda
Contact: contact Tamami Hashimoto

Tagajo Shimin Kaikan
Website: www.tagajocityhall.com
Phone: 223 680 131
Address: 2-27-1 Chuo, Tagajo, JP
Country: Japan

Taito Kuritsu Asakusa Kohkaido
Phone:
338 447 491
Address: 1-38-6 Asakusa, Taitoh-ku, JP
Information: presents its own productions; available for hire
Country: Japan

Takada Baba Rabinest
Website: http:// www.rabinest.com/
Email: staff@rabinest.com
Address: 3-27-4 Nishi-Waseda, Shinjuku-ku, JP
Information: Takada Baba Rabinest is a fully equipped multi-purpose hall.It can be used for photography, training, dance lessons, recitals, exhibitions, etc.
Country: Japan
Contact: Director Kyoji Yamaguchi
Social Media: https://twitter.com/rabinest
Capacity: 0-100
Policies: Rent and Present

Takamatsu Shimin Kaikan
Website: www.city.takamatsu.kagawa.jp
Phone: 878 392 888
Address: 1-8-22 Bancho, Takamatsu, JP
Country: Japan

Takarazuka Grand Theatre
Website: kageki.hankyu.co.jp/
Phone: 570 005 100
Address: 1-1-57 Sakae-machi, Takarazuka, JP
Information: the first performance was held in 1914; home stage in Osaka: Takarazuka Grand Theatre
Country: Japan
Contact: General Manager of revue business dept. Hiroshi Desaki
Contact: Managers of revue business Marketing of tokyo Tomotsugu Ogawa

Takarazuka Vega Hall
Website: www.hankyu.co.jp/kageki
Phone: 797 846 192
Address: 1-2-18 Kiyoshikohjin, Takarazuka, JP
Information: equipped with a Swiss-made pipe organ; organizes a domestic music competition and Takarazuka International Chamber Chorus Contest
Country: Japan
Contact: man dir of takarazuka foundation for culture prom Takashi Ohtsuka

Takayama Shimin Bunka Kaikan
Phone: 577 338 333
Address: 1-188-1 Showa-cho, Takayama, JP
Information: presents its own productions produced by Gifu Prefectural Government Office; also available for hire
Country: Japan

Takeo-shi Bunka Kaikan
Phone: 954 235 165
Address: 5538-1 Takeo, Takeo-machi, Takeo, JP
Information: presents its own productions; also available for hire
Country: Japan

Tanba Den'en Kohkyo Hall
Website: www.city.sasayama.hyogo.jp/denen/index.html
Phone: 795 523 600
Address: 41 Kitashin-machi, Sasayama-shi, JP
Country: Japan

Taniyama Southern Hall
Website: www.kagoshima-hall.or.jp
Phone: 992 602 033
Address: 1-4360 Taniyama Chuo, JP
Information: presents its own productions; available for hire
Country: Japan
Contact: Director Mariko Kojima

Tasaki Hall
Phone:
783 037 666

Address: 6-3-2 Minatojima-Naka-machi, Chuo-ku, Kobe, JP
Country: Japan
Contact: contact Nobuyuki Shibata

Teatre Fonte Izumi Kumin Bunka Center
Website: www.yaf.city.yokohama.jp/facilities/fonte/
Phone: 458 054 000
Address: c/o Yokohama Arts Foundation, 3F Izumi Chuoh Life, 3511-9 Izumi-cho, Yokohama, JP
Information: presents its own productions; available for hire
Country: Japan

Telepia Hall
Website: tokai-tv.com/event/telepia/index.html
Phone: 529 541 165
Address: c/o Tokai TV, 1-14-27, Higashi-Sakura, Higashi-ku, Nagoya, JP
Information: presents its own productions; available for hire
Country: Japan

Terpsichore
Email: terpsi@mac.com
Phone: 333 382 728
Address: 1F, 3-49-15 Nakano, Nakano-ku, JP
Information: Tokyo venue which often stages Butoh performances sometimes called the Mecca of butoh Tel ; 3-3383 3719 studio
Country: Japan
Contact: contact Yoshiko Hata

The College Operahouse
Website: www.daion.ac.jp/operahouse
Email: operahouse@hi-ho.ne.jp
Phone: 663 364 521
Address: 1-5-38 Shonai Nishi-machi, Toyonaka-shi, JP
Country: Japan
Contact: Director Tohru Kitano

The Suzunari
Website: www.honda-geki.com/suzunari.html
Email: suzunari@honda-geki.com
Phone: 334 690 511
Address: 1-45-15 Kitazawa, Setagaya-ku, JP
Information: presents its own productions; available for hire
Country: Japan
Contact: contact Yukie Futatsumori

Theater Green
Website: www.theater-green.com
Phone: 339 830 644
Address: 2-20-4 Minami-Ikebukuro, Toshima-ku, JP
Information: presents Theater Green Festival (q.v.)
Country: Japan
Contact: President Anjoh Asahina

Theater Sun-Mall
Website: www1.ocn.ne.jp/~sunmall/
Email: sunmall@poem.ocn.ne.jp
Phone: 333 525 577
Address: 1-19-10 Shinjuku, Shinjuku-ku, JP
Information: presents its own productions; available for hire
Country: Japan
Contact: administrator Aki Moriyama
Contact: President Kazue Ishitobi

Theater X (cai)
Website: www.theaterx.jp
Email: info@theaterx.jp
Phone: 356 241 181
Address: 2-10-14 Ryogoku, Sumida-ku, JP
Information: hosts Theatre X International Dance Festival (q.v.)
Country: Japan
Contact: Producer Misako Ueda

Theatre Academy
Website: www.theatre.co.jp
Email: info@theatre.co.jp
Phone: 359 835 001
Address: 3-14-16 Shimo-ochiai, Shinjuku-ku, JP
Information: has a youth theatre, Cosmos, which consists of members under 13 years old; see also Drama
Country: Japan

Theatre Apple
Website: www.theatre-apple.co.jp/
Phone:
332 090 222
Address: 1-19-1 Kabuki-cho, Shinjuku-ku, JP
Information: operated by Koma Stadium Inc Tel: 3-3202 8118, a company of Toho (q.v.) group; plans and produces not only its own musical productions but also works of other drama companies; has invited many foreign companiesmainly for presenting Broadway musicals
Country: Japan
Contact: theatre Manager Ken Sakai

Theatre Daikan'yama
Website: www.himawari.net/
Email: gekidan@himawari.net
Phone: 334 760 189
Address: 2-12-12 Ebisu-Nishi, Shibuya-ku, JP
Information: Himawari (q.v.) owns the venue
Country: Japan

Theatre Drama City
Phone: 663 773 888
Address: 19-1 Chaya-machi, Kita-ku, JP
Information: presents its own productions
Country: Japan
Contact: Executive Director t.b.a
Contact: t.b.a
Contact: Chairman Eiji Igata

Theatre TRAM
Website:
www.setagaya-ac.or.jp/sept
Email: sept@setagaya-ac.or.jp
Phone: 354 321 526
Address: 4-1-1 Taishido, Setagaya-ku, JP
Country: Japan

Theatre V Akasaka
Phone: 335 836 040
Address: 2-16-9 Akasaka, Minato-ku, JP
Information: presents its own productions; available
for hire
Country: Japan

Theatre/ Tops
Website: members.tripod.co.jp/theatertops
Phone: 333 509 696
Address: Tops House 4F, 3-20-8 Shinjuku, Shinjuku-ku, JP
Country: Japan

Tochigi Prefectural Culture Centre
Website: www.bunka-tochigi.jp
Email: so-bun@tochigi-syougai-bunkazaidan.or.jp
Phone: 286 431 000
Address: 1-8 Hon-cho, Utsunomiya, JP
Country: Japan
Contact: General Manager Akiko Yamamura

Toda-shi Bunka Kaikan
Website: www.city.toda.saitama.jp/bunka/index.html
Phone: 484 451 311
Address: 4-8-1 Kami-Toda, Toda, JP
Information: presents its own productions; available
for hire
Country: Japan

Toen Palata
Website: www.t-toen.com
Phone: 334 192 871
Address: 1-30-13 Daita, Setagaya-ku, JP
Information: presents its own productions
Country: Japan

Tokorozawa Shimin Bunka Centre – MUSE
Website: www.muse-tokorozawa.or.jp
Phone: 429 986 500
Address: 1-9-1 Namiki, Tokorozawa, JP
Information: produce its own concert programmes;
available for hire
Country: Japan

Tokushima Shiritsu Bunka Centre
Phone: 818 865 32185
Address: 1 Jonai, Tokushima-cho, JP
Country: Japan

Tokushima-ken Kyohdo Bunka Kaikan
Website: www.kyoubun.or.jp
Email: info@kyoubun.or.jp
Phone: 886 228 121
Address: c/o Tokushimaken Bunka Shinko Zaidan, 2-14
Aiba-cho, JP
Information: presents its own productions; available
for hire
Country: Japan
Contact: President Takeshi Aki

Tokyo Bay N.K. Hall
Website: www.nkhall.co.jp
Phone: 473 557 000
Address: 1-8 Maihama, Urayasu, JP
Country: Japan

Tokyo Engeki Ensemble
Website: www.tee.co.jp
Email: tee@tee.co.jp
Phone: 339 205 232
Address: 4-35-17 Sekimachi Kita, Nerima-ku, JP
Country: Japan
Contact: President Tsunetoshi Hirowatari

TOKYO FM Hall
Website: www.tfm.co.jp
Phone: 332 210 080
Address: 1-7 Kohji-machi, Chiyoda-ku, JP
Information: this hall has a square-plan, open stage

that can be divided into 8 parts, and removable seating
to accommodate a variety of uses from classical music
concerts to rock and electronic music and Butoh
Country: Japan

Tokyo International Forum
Website: www.t-i-forum.co.jp
Email: forumpr@t-i-forum.co.jp
Phone: 352 219 000
Address: 03/05/2001, Marunouchi, Chiyoda-ku, JP
Information: a large-scale multi-purpose cultural facili-
ties in Tokyo with five hall buildings; provides eight large
and small halls, the largest one with seating capacity as
many as 5000, exhibition space
Country: Japan
President & CEO
Iwao Toriumi

Tokyo Kohsei Nenkin Kaikan, WelCity
Website:
www.kjp.or.jp
Phone: 333 561 111
Address: 5-3-1 Shinjuku, Shinjuku-ku, JP
Country: Japan

Tokyo Metropolitan Art Space
Website: www.geigeki.jp
Phone: 353 912 111
Address: 1-8-1 Nishi-Ikebukuro, Toshima-ku, JP
Information: the Concert Hall can accommodate a
120-piece orchestra with a 200-member choir; also has a
revolving 126-stop Garnier pipe organ
Country: Japan
Contact: General Manager Tatsuo Izuno
Contact: Director Yuhshi Odashima

Tokyo Metropolitan Festival Hall
Website: www.t-bunka.jp
Email: bunka@sepia.ocn.ne.jp
Phone: 338 282 111
Address: 5-45 Ueno Koen, Taitoh-ku, JP
Information: the Hall which is known to the world as the
representative concert hall of Japan was established in
1961 in commemoration of the 500th anniversary of the
birth of the city of Tokyo
Country: Japan
Contact: Director General Norio Ohga

Tokyo Metropolitan Theatre
Website: www.geigeki.jp
Email: geigeki-info@geigeki.jp
Phone: 353 912 111
Address: Tokyo Metropolitan Foundation for History and
Culture, 1-8-1 Nishi-ikebukuro, Toshima-ku, JP
Information: Member of ISPA
Country: Japan
Contact: Artistic Director Hideki Noda
Contact: assistant Director Hiroshi Takahagi
Social Media: www.facebook.com/geigeki
Policies: Present and produce, Theatre

**Tokyo Opera City Concert Hall: Takemitsu
Memorial**
Website: www.operacity.jp
Email: hall@toccf.com
Phone: 353 530 788
Address: c/o Tokyo Opera City Cultural Foundation, 3-20-
2 Nishi-Shinjuku, Shinjuku-ku, JP
Information: opened in September 1997; the shoe-box
type Concert Hall has a pyramidal ceiling, two tiers of
balconies and acoustics designed to support all concert
forms; Toru Takemitsu was Artistic Director of the com-
plex; see also Competitions
Country: Japan
Contact: President Tsuyoshi Nahara
Contact: Managing Director of concert hall Naoki Ema

Tokyo Takarazuka Theatre
Website: kageki.hankyu.co.jp
Phone: 352 512 001
Address: 1-1-3 Yuraku-cho, Chiyoda-ku, JP
Information: all preformers are women; the first perfor-
mance was held in 1914; home stage in Osaka: Takarazu-
ka Grand Theatre operated by the Toho Co Ltd (q.v.)
Country: Japan
Contact: Director Takashi Saburi

Tomakomai Shimin Kaikan
Phone: 144 337 191
Address: 3-2-2 Asahi-Machi, Tomakomai, JP
Country: Japan

Tomakomai-shi Bunka Kaikan
Phone: 144 367 823
Address: 2-8-19 Asahi-cho, Tomakomai, JP
Country: Japan
Contact: Director Shunsuke Takahashi

Torii Hall
Website: www.toriihall.com/
Phone: 662 112 506
Address: 4F Kamigata Bldg, 1-7-11 Sen'nichimae, Chuo-
ku, JP
Country: Japan

Tosashimizu Shiritsu Shimin Bunka Kaikan
Phone: 880 823 300
Address: 11-1 Kotobuki-cho, Tosashimizu, JP
Information: presents its own productions & available
for hire
Country: Japan
Contact: Director Akira Kitadai

Tottori Kenritsu Kenmin Bunka Kaikan – Rika Hall
Website: www.torikenmin.jp
Email: bunka@torikenmin.jp
Phone: 857 218 700
Address: 101-5 Shohtoku-cho, JP
Information: the venue supports cultural activities, pro-
motes creative events & activities involving the public;
provides people in Tottori with quality performing arts
at affordable prices; presents its own productions &
available for hire
Country: Japan
Contact: facility Manager Yoji Fukushima
Contact: Director Katsuhumi Taketa
Contact: chief Manager Takayoshi Kawakami

Tottori Shimin Kaikan
Phone: 857 249 411
Address: 12 Kakede-cho, JP
Information: presents own productions & available for
hire
Country: Japan
Contact: General Manager Takamichi Kinoshita
Contact: deputy General Manager Masami Morihara

Toyama Kenmin Kaikan Hall
Website: www.kenminkaikan.com
Phone: 764 323 111
Address: 4-18 Shinsohgawa, JP
Country: Japan

Toyama-ken Kyoiku Bunka Kaikan
Phone: 764 418 635
Address: 7-1 Funabashi-Kita-machi, JP
Information: presents both its own production and
co-production programmes; the former has to be for the
artists who live in or are related to the prefecture
Country: Japan
Contact: Director Minoru Ohata

Toyama-ken Takaoka Bunka Hall
Phone: 766 254 141
Address: 13-1 Nakagawa Sono-machi, Takaoka, JP
Country: Japan
Contact: Director Yoshimi Neki

Toyonaka Shiritsu Rose Bunka Hall
Phone: 663 317 961
Address: 4-1 Noda-cho, Toyonaka, JP
Information: presents its own productions & available
for hire
Country: Japan
Contact: Director Junichi Naka

Toyono-cho Jubel Hall
Website: www.town.toyono.osaka.jp/jubel/index.htm
Email: jubel@mtj.biglobe.ne.jp
Phone: 727 387 700
Address: 1-2-5 Higashi Tokiwa-dai, Toyono-cho, Toy-
ono-gun, JP
Country: Japan
Contact: contact Ichiroh Kondoh

Tsu Region Plaza Oshiro Hall
Phone: 592 293 300
Address: 23-1 Nishi-Marunouchi, Tsu, JP
Country: Japan
Contact: Director Yasuo Kihira

Tsuda Hall
Website: tsudahall.com
Phone: 334 021 851
Address: 1-18-24 Sendagaya, Shibuya-ku, JP
Information: presents its own productions; available
for hire
Country: Japan

Tsuyama Bunka Centre
Phone: 868 227 111
Address: 68 Sange, Tsuyama, JP
Country: Japan

Tsuyazaki Bunka Kaikan – Camellia Hall
Phone: 940 523 321
Address: 458-1 Oaza Tsuyazaki, Tsuyazaki-cho, Munaka-
ta-gun, JP
Information: presents its own productions; available
for hire
Country: Japan
Contact: Director Yoshikata Nagase

TV Tokyo
Website: www.tv-tokyo.co.jp
Email: ir@tv-tokyo.co.jp
Phone: 334 321 212

Address: 4-3-12 Toranomon, Minato-ku, JP
Information: Producer/presenter; imports overseas material
Country: Japan

U-Port Kan'i Hoken Hall
Website: www.u-port.kfj.go.jp
Phone: 334 941 840
Address: 8-4-13 Nishi-Gotanda, Shinagawa-ku, JP
Country: Japan

Ueda Kanshohkai Nohgakudo
Website: www.pcct.zaq.ne.jp/feelnoh-kikaku/
Phone: 786 915 449
Address: 2-1-14 Ohtsuka-cho, Nagata-ku, Kobe, JP
Information: presents 7-8 professional & more than 10 amateur Noh play productions every year
Country: Japan
Contact: President Takahiro Ueda
Contact: secretary General Chizuru Ueda

Uji-shi Bunka Kaikan
Phone:
774 399 333
Address: c/o Uji-shi Bunka Centre, 1-1 Ori-idai, Uji, JP
Information: presents its own productions & available for hire
Country: Japan

Umeda Arts Theatre
Website: www.umegei.com
Phone: 663 773 800
Address: 19-1 Chaya-machi, Kita-ku, JP
Information: mainly presents its own productions; also available for hire
Country: Japan
Contact: Chairman Eiji Igata

Umewaka Nohgakudo (Umewaka Nohgaku Gakuin Kaikan)
Website: www.noh-umewaka.com
Email: office@noh-umewaka.com
Phone: 333 637 748
Address: 2-6-14 Higashi-Nakano, Nakano-ku, JP
Country: Japan
Contact: Director Rokuro Umewaka

Urayasu-shi Bunka Kaikan
Email: urayasu-bunka@jcom.home.ne.jp
Phone: 473 531 121
Address: 1-1-2 Nekozane, Urayasu, JP
Information: presents its own production & available for hire
Country: Japan
Contact: head of management Toshiaki Yonekura

Utsunomiya-shi Bunka Kaikan
Phone: 286 362 121
Address: 7-66 Akebono-cho, Utsunomiya, JP
Country: Japan
Contact: Director Akiichi Suda

Verde Hall Nakamachi Bunka Kaikan
Website: www.hk.sun-ip.or.jp/nakacho/verde
Email: verde@hk.sun-ip.or.jp
Phone: 795 321 300
Address: 135 Nakamura-machi, Naka-cho, Taka-gun, JP
Information: presents its own productions; available for hire
Country: Japan

Vieplan Theatre
Phone: 333 507 922
Address: B1 Seven Bldg, 2-8-1 Shinjuku, Shinjuku-ku, JP
Country: Japan

Wakayama Prefectural Culture Hall
Website: www.wacaf.or.jp/culturehall/index.html
Phone: 734 436 1331
Address: 1-1 Komatsubara-dori, JP
Information: presents its own productions & available for hire
Country: Japan

Wakayama Shimin Kaikan
Phone: 734 321 212
Address: 7 Minami-no-Cho, Denpobashi, JP
Country: Japan

Wako Shimin Bunka Centre – SUN AZALEA
Website: www.sunazalea.or.jp
Phone: 484 687 771
Address: 1-5 Hirosawa, Wako, JP
Information: presents its own productions & available for hire
Country: Japan
Contact: Director Harumi Hayasaka

Warabi Theatre
Website: www.warabi.or.jp
Email: gekijyo@warabi.or.jp
Phone: 187 443 915
Address: 430 Aza Waseda, Sotsuda, Tazawako-machi, Senboku-gun, JP

Information: the home of Warabiza (q.v.); not available for hire
Country: Japan
Contact: Manager Noriko Kanna

Washington Art
Website: www.washington-shoe.co.jp
Email: tkoba@washington-shoe.co.jp
Phone: 335 725 923
Address: 5-7-7 Ginza, Chuo-ku, JP
Country: Japan

Watanabe Memorial Hall
Phone: 836 317 373
Address: 8-1 Asahi-machi, Ube, JP
Country: Japan
Contact: Director Tomi Hamayasu

Yaizu-shi Bunka Centre
Phone: 546 273 111
Address: 1550 Sangamyo, Yaizu, JP
Information: presents its own productions & available for hire
Country: Japan
Contact: Director Tsutomu Misaki

Yakult Hall
Website: www.yakult.co.jp/hall
Phone: 335 747 255
Address: 1-1-19 Higashi-Shimbashi, Minato-ku, JP
Country: Japan

Yamagata Shimin Kaikan
Phone: 236 423 121
Address: 2-9-45 Kasumi-cho, JP
Country: Japan

Yamagata-ken Kenmin Kaikan
Phone: 236 227 133
Address: 3-1-23 Nanoka-machi, JP
Country: Japan

Yamaguchi Shimin Kaikan
Phone: 839 231 000
Address: 2-5-1 Chuo, Yamaguchi-shi, JP
Information: presents its own productions & available for hire
Country: Japan
Contact: Director Tadaharu Kubo

Yamaha Hall
Website: www.yamaha-hall.co.jp/
Phone: 335 723 139
Address: 7-9-14 Ginza, Chuo-ku, JP
Information: presents its own productions & available for hire
Country: Japan
Contact: President Mikiaki Ohbayashi

Yamanashi Kenritsu Kenmin Bunka Hall
Website: www.yamanashi-bunka.or.jp
Email: info@yamanashi-bunka.or.jp
Phone: 552 289 131
Address: 21-1 Kotobuki-machi, Kofu, JP
Country: Japan

Yarai Noh Stage
Website: www.kanze.com
Email: yarai@kanze.com
Phone: 332 687 311
Address: 60 Yarai-cho, Shinjuku-ku, JP
Information: presents its own Noh productions as well as rents out; managed by the Association ""Kyukokai"" which has over 20 Noh actors; its website is available in three languages; Japanese, English and French
Country: Japan
Contact: Chairman Yoshiyuki Kanze
Contact: foreign division Shizuko Kanze

Yasukuni Jinja Nohgakudo
Website: www.yasukuni.or.jp/event/index.html
Phone: 332 618 326
Address: 3-1-1 Kudan-Kita, Chiyoda-ku, JP
Information: out-door theatre
Country: Japan

Yatsugatake Kohgen Ongakudo
Website: www.yatsugatake.co.jp
Phone: 339 842 219
Address: c/o Ikebukuro Seibu Dai 2 Bldg, 1-17-4, Minami-Ikebukruo, Toshima-ku, JP
Information: hall address: Yatsugatake Kogen Lodge, Oaza Uminokuchi, Minamimaki-mura, Minamisaku-gun, Nagano 384-1302 Tel: 267-982 131 Fax: 267-983 133
Country: Japan
Contact: Chairman Masayuki Furuya

Yokkaichi-shi Bunka Kaikan
Website: www.city.yokkaichi.mie.jp/culture/index.html
Phone: 593 544 501
Address: 2-5-3 Yasujima, Yokkaichi, JP
Information: presents its own productions & available for hire
Country: Japan
Director & secretary General

Masahiro Aritake

Yokohama Arena
Website: www.iris.or.jp/~info-sh
Email: info-sh@iris.or.jp
Phone: 454 744 000
Address: 3-10 Shin-Yokohama, Kohoku-ku, Yokohama, JP
Country: Japan

Yokohama Doll Museum 'Akai Kutsu Puppet Theatre'
Website: www.welcome.city.yokohama.jp/doll/
Email: dolldoll@welcome.city.yokohama.jp
Phone: 456 719 361
Address: 18 Yamashita-cho, Naka-ku, Yokohama, JP
Information: the doll museum which exhibits 9000 dolls from 135 countries; presents puppetry and invites puppetry companies from abroad; wishes to promote international exchange
Country: Japan
Contact: Director Kaoru Kanetaka

Yokohama Minato Mirai Hall
Website: www.city.yokohama.jp/me/mmhall
Email: mmh@city.yokohama.jp
Phone: 818 145 682 202
Address: 2-3-6, Minato Mirai, Nishi-ku, JP
Information: shoe-box style with arena shape; organ: C.B.Fisk, 62 stops
Country: Japan
Contact: deputy Director General Yoshihiro Nagatsuka

Yokohama Museum of Art
Website: www.art-museum.city.yokohama.jp/
Phone: 452 210 300
Address: 3-4-1 Minato Mirai, Nishi-ku, Yokohama, JP
Information: exchanges Artistic and cultural interaction; presents own productions and co-production
Country: Japan
Contact: museum Director Koji Yukiyama
Contact: Chairman of the board Ryu Saito
Contact: promotion section Misuzu Matsui

Yokohama-shi Asahi Kumin Bunka Centre Sun Heart
Website: www.city.yokohama.jp/me/yaf/
Phone: 453 643 810
Address: 5F Futamatagawa Life, 1-3 Futamatagawa, Asahi-ku, Yokohama, JP
Country: Japan
Contact: contact Yukiko Kanei
Contact: General Director Hirotaka Uchida

Yokohama-shi Shimin Bunka Kaikan Kan'nai Hall
Website: www.city.yokohama.jp/me/yaf
Phone: 456 621 221
Address: 4-42-1 Sumiyoshi-cho, Naka-ku, Yokohama, JP
Information: available for hire
Country: Japan
Contact: Director Koushirou Tsuchida

Yokosuka Arts Theatre
Website: www.yokosuka-arts.or.jp
Email: theatre@yokosuka-arts.or.jp
Phone: 468 281 600
Address: 3-27 Hon-cho, Yokosuka, JP
Information: Yokosuka Art Theatre is mainly used for opera productions; equipped with the latest technology; Yokosuka Bayside Pocket is equipped with 21-piece movable stage-floor system
Country: Japan
Contact: President Ryoichi Kabaya

Yokosuka Bayside Pocket
Website: www.yokosuka-arts.or.jp/
Email: theatre@yokosuka-arts.or.jp
Phone: 468 281 600
Address: 3-27 Hon-cho, Yokosuka, JP
Information: situated in Yokosuka Art Theatre (q.v.); equipped with 21-piece movable stage-floor system
Country: Japan
Contact: President Ryoichi Kabaya

Yokosuka-shi Bunka Kaikan
Website: www.yokosuka-arts.or.jp/bunka
Phone: 468 232 950
Address: 50 Fukadadai, Yokosuka, JP
Information: presents its own productions & available for hire
Country: Japan
Contact: Director Ken Iwase

Yomiuri Hall
Website: www9.ocn.ne.jp/~yomihoru
Email: yomi3920@soleil.ocn.ne.jp
Phone: 332 310 551
Address: 1-11-1 Yuraku-cho, Chiyoda-ku, JP
Information: mainly for hire
Country: Japan
Contact: secretary General Seiichi Sangu

Yomiuri Shimbun
Email:
dy@yomiuri.com

Phone: 352 457 083
Address: Culture Promotion Dept, 1-2-1 Kiyosumi, Kohtoh-ku, JP
Information: Producer/presenter; one of the representative newspapers in Japan; also one of the three founding Press companies of Yomiuri Nippon Symphony Orchestra (q.v.)
Country: Japan
Contact: Manager of culture promotion dept. Shinzo Yoshida

Yonago-shi Bunka Hall
Phone: 859 354 171
Address: 58-6 Suehiro-cho, Yonago, JP
Information: presents its own productions & available for hire
Country: Japan

Yonago-shi Kohkaido
Phone:
859 223 236
Address: 2-61 Kakuban-cho, Yonago, JP
Information: available for hire
Country: Japan

Yorozu Studio
Website: www.yorozu-s.com
Email: otsuka@yorozu-s.com
Phone: 353 946 901
Address: 2-32-22 Kita-Ohtsuka, Toshima-ku, JP
Information: produces ""Back Up Series"" for upcoming drama companies; also available for hire
Country: Japan
Contact: Director Hirokazu Iimura

Yoyogi Yagai Stage
Phone: 334 696 081
Address: 2-3 Jin-nan, Shibuya-ku, JP
Country: Japan

Yurakucho Asahi Hall
Website: www.asahi-hall.jp/yurakucho/link
Phone: 332 840 131
Address: 11F Yurakucho Mullion, 2-5-1 Yuraku-cho, Chiyoda-ku, JP
Information: equipped with simultaneous translation system; presents its own productions & available for hire
Country: Japan
Contact: General Manager Hironobu Daido

Zenrosai Hall SPACE ZERO
Website: www.spacezero.co.jp
Email: info@spacezero.co.jp
Phone: 333 758 741
Address: Zenrosai Kaikan, 2-12-10 Yoyogi, Shibuya-ku, JP
Information: the Managing body of the Hall is Zenrosai, the cooperative insurance society; venue for Zenrosai Theatre Festival (q.v.)
Country: Japan
Contact: chief of business planning section Kohzoh Yoshida
Contact: President t.b.a.
Contact: Managing Director Hideki Nishiyama

Zenshinza Theatre
Website: www.zenshinza.com/
Email: zenshinza-gekijo@zenshinza.com
Phone: 422 490 300
Address: 3-13-2 Kichijoji Minami-cho, Musashino, JP
Information: see also Zenshinza Theatre Company (q.v.)
Country: Japan
Contact: lighting Manager Seiji Moriwaki
stage Director & sound Manager Yoshiyuki Endoh
Contact: theatre Manager Kiyoshi Ogura
Capacity: 500

REPUBLIC OF KOREA

Anyang Culture & Arts Center
Website: www.ayac.or.kr/main/main.asp
Phone: 313 895 200
Address: Anyang6-dong, Manan-gu Anyang
Country: Republic of Korea
Contact: President Yong-Kwan Lee

Arts Center Incheon
Website: https:// www.aci.or.kr/eng/
Email: artcenteric@korea.kr
Phone: 032 453 7700
Address: 222, Art Center-daero, Yeonsu-gu, Incheon
Information: Known for its globally recognized acoustic system, beautiful interior and exterior spaces, and unique external design inspired by a conductor's sophisticated hand gesture, with a breathtaking view of the ocean, 'Arts Center Incheon' suggests a vision for Incheon—a culture and art city with global competencies.
Country: Republic of Korea
Contact: CEO Lee Won Jae
Social Media: https:// www.facebook.com/aci.korea/ https:// www.instagram.com/artscenter.incheon/
Disabled Access: Yes
Capacity: 1000+

Annual Performances: 25-50
Policies: Rent and Present

Bucheon Boksagol Culture Center
Website: www.bcf.or.kr
Phone: 323 206 300
Address: 394-2 Sabg1-dong, Wonmi-gu, Bucheon
Country: Republic of Korea

Busan Catholic Center, Small Theatre
Phone: 514 621 870
Address: 81-1 Daecheong-dong 4-ga, Jung-gu
Information: presents concerts and short movies
Country: Republic of Korea

Busan Citizens' Hall
Website: https:// www.bscc.or.kr/citizen_eng/main/
Phone: 516 305 200
Address: 16, 133-beon-gil Jaseong-ro, Dong-gu, Busan
Information: Busan's first large-sized performance facility, which has grown with the people of Busan for over 40 years.
Country: Republic of Korea
Contact: Director Boo Choi Young
Disabled Access: Yes
Capacity: 1000+

Busan Culture Center
Website: https:// www.bscc.or.kr/eng/main/
Email: seryung@adzoom.net
Phone: 051 607 6222
Address: 848-4 Daeyeon4-dong, Nam-gu, Busan
Information: Busan Cultural Center is located in Daeyeondong, Nam-gu, dedicated to the role of fulfilling various cultural and Artistic needs of its citizens while creating a unique culture of Busan.
Country: Republic of Korea
Contact: CEO Yong Kwan Lee
Contact: Culture and Arts Division Director Chul Ho Park
Social Media: https:// www.facebook.com/vivabscc/ https:// www.instagram.com/vivabscc/ https:// twitter.com/vivabscc
Capacity: 1000+
Policies: Rent and Present

Chang Mu Arts Center
Website: https:// www.facebook.com/Changmuart/
Email: changmuart@naver.com
Phone: 704 264 8252
Address: 5-92 Changjeon-dong, Mapo-gu
Information: Comprehensive dance center opened in October 1992 with five sub-districts related to dance arts, including a small theater-post theater dedicated to dance, international cooperation organizations, Changmu International Arts Festival, Dance Monthly, and Changmu Association.
Country: Republic of Korea
Social Media: https:// www.facebook.com/Changmuart/
Capacity: 0-100
Policies: Present and Produce

Cheonan Culture & Arts Center
Website: https:// www.cnac.or.kr/
Phone: 156 60155
Address: 185 Seongnam-myeon, Seongnam-myeon, Dongnam-gu, Cheonan-si, Chungcheongnam-do,
Information: The Cheonan Arts Center has been proudly revealed in the Cheonan Recreation & Tourism Complex as a long-awaited wish of Cheonan City, which aims to become a cultural city with a rich scent of culture and arts.
Country: Republic of Korea
Contact: Director Seoyoung Lee
Contact: Director Miyeon Kang
Contact: Head of Cheonan Arts Center Jeon-bae Im
Email: 9191mbc@gmail.com
Phone: 041 901 6633
Capacity: 1000+
Annual Performances: 11-25
Policies: All

Cheongju Arts Centre
Phone: 432 794 609
Address: 755 Sagik1-dong, Heungdeuk-gu
Information: opened in 1995; operated by the city of Cheongju; own productions (10%), hire out (90%)
Country: Republic of Korea

Chuncheon Culture & Arts Center
Website: https:// www.cccf.or.kr:459/
Phone: 033 259 5800
Address: 13, Hyojasang-gil 5-beon-gil, Chuncheon-si, Gangwon-do
Information: Chuncheon Municipal Philharmonic Orchestra is resident orchestra; also present the International Mime Festival in May
Country: Republic of Korea
Capacity: 501-1000
Annual Performances: 51-100
Policies: Rent and Present

Chuncheon Puppet Theatre
Website: theatre.cocobau.com
Email: cococbau@cocobau.com
Phone: 332 428 450

Address: 327 Simil-ro, Chuncheon
Country: Republic of Korea
Contact: Managing Director Joon-Taek Kang

Chungju Cultural Center
Phone: 438 477 228
Address: 215 Seongnae-dong
Country: Republic of Korea
Capacity: 1000

Chungmu Art Hall
Website: http:// www.caci.or.kr/
Phone: 222 306 601
Address: 131-1 Heungin-dong, Jung-gu, Seoul
Information: A professional performance hall that performs world-class musicals, high-class classical music, ballet, and opera.
Country: Republic of Korea
Contact: CEO Jin-ho Yoon
Phone: 223 06606General Manager Ji Hyeon Seong
Phone: 223 06608Communication Media Team Leader Il-joo Jeong
Phone: 223 06630
Social Media: https:// www.facebook.com/chungmuartscenter/ https:// twitter.com/chungmuholic
Disabled Access: Yes
Capacity: 1000+
Annual Performances: 100+
Policies: Rent and Present

Daeduk Science & Cultural Center
Phone: 428 657 272
Address: 382 Doryong-dong, Yuseong-gu
Information: operated by Daeduk Science Town Foundation; mainly for rent
Country: Republic of Korea

Daegu Children
Website: https:// www.daegu.go.kr/woman/index.do?menu_id=00050228&servletPath=%2Fwoman
Phone: 537 600 609
Address: 176, Dongdaegu-ro, Suseong-gu, Daegu
Information: Provides a pleasant rest area in the city where children can always play to their heart's content. Operated as a nature learning center that the whole family enjoys. Consists of Daegu Science Education Center, Dream Nuri Building, Ookkori Theater, Outdoor facilities
Country: Republic of Korea
Capacity: 501-1000
Policies: All

Daegu Concert House
Website:
https:// concerthouse.daegu.go.kr/eng/index.do
Phone: 532 501 400
Address: 141 Taepyeong-ro(Taepyeong-ro 2-ga 1-1) Jung-gu, Daegu
Information: Daegu Concert House is a European theater that produces and supplies performances differently from the traditional concert hall.
 Under the slogan of "Everyone's Classics", Daegu Concert House is a place where performers from around the world, from classical music enthusiasts to amateurs
Country: Republic of Korea
Contact: Manager Seongnam Heun
Contact: Director Cheol-woo Lee
Contact: General affairs Manager Wonsoo Kim
Social Media: https:// www.facebook.com/daeguconcerthouse/ https:// www.instagram.com/daeguconcerthouse/
Disabled Access: Yes
Capacity: 1000+
Annual Performances: 100+
Policies: Present and Produce

Daegu Culture and Arts Centre
Phone:
536 066 114
Address: 187 Songdan-dong, Dalseo-gu
Country: Republic of Korea
Contact: Manager Jong-Heum Hong

Daegu Kkoekkori Theatre
Phone: 537 635 693
Address: San 136-2 Hwangkeum-dong, Suseong-gu
Country: Republic of Korea

Daegu Opera House
Website: www.daeguoperahouse.org
Email:
doh2013@hanmail.net
Phone: 536 666 000
Address: 15, Hoam-ro, Buk-gu, Daegu,
Information: Daegu Opera House stands at the center of Korea when it comes to opera. DOH has been not only producing and performing opera, but also fostering competent opera singers through its own education system.**Country:** Republic of Korea
Contact: President In Gun Park
Email: doh2013@hanmail.net
Phone: 536 666 001Director of Performing Art Division Sang Moo Choi
Email: doh2013@hanmail.net
Phone: 536 666 006Performance Planning Team Manag-

er Ah Me Kim
Email: doh2013@hanmail.net
Phone: 536 666 030Marketing Team Manager Soo Jung Kim
Email: doh2013@hanmail.net
Phone: 536 666 030
Social Media: https:// www.facebook.com/DaeguOpera
https:// www.instagram.com/daeguoperahouse/

Daejeon Artist's House
Website: https://dcaf.or.kr/web/page.do?menuIdx=446
Email: artisthouse@dcaf.or.kr
Phone: 424 801 0818
Address: 32 Jungang-ro, Jung-gu, Daejeon
Information: 'Daejeon Artist's House' is a cultural space where all citizens and local artists present and exhibit their creations, and sometimes citizens and artists meet and communicate by participating in creative activities together.
Country: Republic of Korea
Disabled Access: Yes
Capacity: 100-250
Annual Performances: 51-100
Policies: Rent and Present

Daejeon Culture and Arts Center
Website: www.djac.or.kr
Email: webmaster@djac.or.kr
Address: 89 Dunsandaero, Seo-gu
Country: Republic of Korea
Contact: chief Director Seok-Joon Jo

Dongsoong Arts Center
Website: www.dsartcenter.co.kr
Email: dsartcenter@dsartcenter.co.kr
Phone: 276 63390
Address: 122, Dongsung-gil, Jongno-gu, Seoul
Information: Once a space organized around performance and video culture, Dongsoong Arts Center is reborn as a complex cultural space with additions of exhibitions and education.
Country: Republic of Korea
Contact: Director Ock-Rang Kim
Capacity: 501-1000
Annual Performances: 100+
Policies: Rent and Present

Doosan Art Center
Website: www1.yonkang.co.kr/hall
Email: webmaster@yonkang.co.kr
Phone: 270 85001/3
Address: 270 Yeonji-dong, Jongno-gu
Country: Republic of Korea
Contact: Director Yong-Oh Park

Drama Center
Phone: 277 80261
Address: 8-19 Yejang-dong, Joong-gu
Country: Republic of Korea

Gangneung Culture & Arts Center
Phone: 336 494 127
Address: 408 Gyo 2-dong, Gangneung
Information: resident orchestra is Gangnung Philharmonic Orchestra
Country: Republic of Korea

Gimhae Arts and Sports Center
Website: http://english.gasc.or.kr/index.do
Email: gasc@gasc.or.kr
Phone: 553 201 234
Address: 1131 Naedong, Gimhae
Information: Gimhae Arts & Sports Center opened a new horizon in culture and arts with its majestic opening on November 25, 2005. As the most prized possession of the city of Gimhae, Gimhae Arts & Sports Center is equipped with three state-of-the-art theaters with seating for 2, 400 and hosts a variety of performing arts and cultural programs.
Country: Republic of Korea
Social Media: https:// www.facebook.com/gimhaeart
https:// www.instagram.com/gimhaeart/
Capacity: 1000+
Policies: Rent and Present

Gimje Cultural Arts Center
Phone: 658 540 3499
Address: 399-5 Seoam-dong
Country: Republic of Korea

Gongjichon Open-Air Stage
Phone: 332 503 593
Address: Samch'on-dong, Chuncheon
Country: Republic of Korea

Gongju Culture & Arts Center
Phone: 416 850 4467
Address: 283 Ungjin-dong, Gongju
Country: Republic of Korea

Goyang Aram Nuri Arts Complex
Website: www.artgy.or.kr
Email: friend@artgy.or.kr

Phone: 157 77766
Address: 777 Seongsa-dong, Deogyang-gu, Goyang-si, Gyeonggi-do
Information: Aram Nuri consists of three performance halls: Aram Theater (1, 887 seats), an opera theater, Aram Music Hall (1, 449 seats), which boasts the best architectural sound, and Sarasae Theater (304 seats), a state-of-the-art variable theater. In addition, there are Aram Art Museum with Gallery Nuri, a creative exhibition space, Norumok Outdoor Theater surrounded by the dense forest of Mt. Jeongbal, and Aram Masul with cultural and art lecture facilities and cafes and restaurants.
Country: Republic of Korea
Contact: Chairman Jaejun Lee
Contact: CEO Jaewal Jeong
Social Media: https:// www.facebook.com/artsgoyang
https://twitter.com/ArtsGoyang https:// www.instagram.com/artsgoyang/
Capacity: 1000+
Annual Performances: 51-100
Policies: Rent and Present

Gunsan Civic Centre
Website: culture.gunsan.go.kr
Phone: 634 629 301
Address: 790-3 Naun1-dong

Gwacheon Civil Center
Website: http:// www.gcart.or.kr/home/main/
Phone: 022 009 9743
Address: Gwacheon Civic Center 2nd floor, 5 Tongyeong-ro, Gwacheon-si, Gyeonggi-do
Information: The Gwacheon Cultural Foundation was established to enhance the quality of life for the citizens of Gwacheon through art.
Under the vision of a cultural city where citizens are the owners, of a culture that we create together, we will create the culture and arts of Gwacheon City with citizens.
Country: Republic of Korea
Contact: CEO Seongtaek Park
Contact: Chairman Jong-cheon Kim
Phone: 022 009 9710
Capacity: 1000+
Policies: All

Gwangju Civic Center
Website: https://gjcthall.modoo.at/
Email: gjcthall@gmail.com
Phone: 062 227 1971
Address: 15 Jungang-ro 107beon-gil, Nam-gu Gwangju
Information: The Gwangju Civic Center was built in 1971 at the request of citizens in Gwangju, where cultural space was scarce. From the 80s to the 90s, it was the first complex cultural facility in Gwangju, serving as a wedding hall, movie theater, and performance hall, staying near citizens.**Country:** Republic of Korea
Social Media: https:// www.instagram.com/gjct_hall/
https:// www.facebook.com/gjcthall/
Policies: Present and Produce

Gwangju Culture and Art Center
Website: art.gwangju.go.kr
Phone: 625 109 252
Address: 126 Unam-dong, Buk-gu
Information: also has a traditional music hall, gallery space and open-air sculpture garden
Country: Republic of Korea

Gyeonggi Arts Center
Website: www.ggac.or.kr
Email: webmaster@ggac.or.kr
Phone: 312 303 440
Address: 1117 Ingye-dong, Paldal-gu, Suwon
Country: Republic of Korea
Contact: Manager In-Geon Park

Gyeongsangnam-do Culture & Arts Center
Phone: 557 595 725
Address: 500-15 Chilam-dong, Jinju
Country: Republic of Korea

Hakchon Small Theatre
Website: www.hakchon.co.kr
Email: hakchon@hakchon.co.kr
Phone: 276 38233
Address: Samgwang Building, 46 Daehak-ro 12-gil, Jongno-gu, Seoul
Information: Hakchon, which started with the opening of the small theater Hakchon in Daehak-ro in March 1991, currently operates the Hakchon Blue Small Theater.
Country: Republic of Korea
Contact: President Min-Gi Kim
Social Media: https:// www.facebook.com/hakchon1991/ https://twitter.com/hakchon1991
Capacity: 100-250
Annual Performances: 100+
Annual Productions: 6-10
Policies: All

Hannam University Seongji Hall
Phone: 426 297 820
Address: 133 Ojeong-dong, Daedeok-gu
Country: Republic of Korea

Hyundai Arts Center

Website: www.hyundai-artscenter.co.kr
Phone: 522 306 131
Address: 101-1 Seobu-dong, Dong-gu
Information: multi purpose hall
Country: Republic of Korea
Contact: President Tae-Soon Kwon

Hyundai Hanmaeum Hall
Phone: 522 365 120
Address: 290-6 Jeonha-dong, Dong-gu
Country: Republic of Korea

Iksan Somri Cultural & Art Center
Phone: 638 584 830
Address: 58 Ma-dong
Country: Republic of Korea

Incheon Culture & Arts Center
Website: art.incheon.go.kr
Phone: 324 278 401
Address: 21569 Art-ro, Namdong-gu, Incheon
Information: Since its opening in 1994, Incheon Culture and Arts Center has established itself as a representative cultural space in Incheon.In addition to the high-quality performances of the Incheon City Arts Groups

Country: Republic of Korea
Capacity: 1000+
Annual Performances: 100+
Policies: Rent and Present

Jechon Cultural Center
Phone: 443 642 6410
Address: 415 Hwasan, Jecheon
Country: Republic of Korea

Jeju Culture & Arts Center
Phone: 647 545 231
Address: 852 Ildo 2-dong
Information: located in the grounds of Shinsan Park
Country: Republic of Korea

Jeolla Bukdo Educational and Cultural Center
Website: https://lib.jbe.go.kr/jec/index.do
Phone: 632 701 635
Address: 71 Andeokwon-ro, Deokjin-gu, Jeonju-si, Jeollabuk-do
Information: Our center operates a variety of differentiated curriculums to develop the hobbies and talents of the youth who will be the leading players in the future society, and plays a role as a regional education and culture center to provide lifelong learning opportunities for citizens.
Country: Republic of Korea
Contact: Director Kwang-Hwi Ko
Capacity: 1000+
Annual Performances: 100+
Policies: All

Jeolla Namdo Arts Center
Phone: 622 271 136
Address: 53 Daeeui-dong, Dong-gu
Country: Republic of Korea

Jeonbuk Art Hall
Phone: 632 844 445
Address: 104-5 Gyongwon-dong 1-ga, Wansan-gu
Country: Republic of Korea

Jeongdong Theatre
Website: http://jeongdongtheater.com/
Email: cs1500@jeongdong.or.kr
Phone: 275 11500
Address: 43 Jeongdong-gil, Jung-gu
Information: Founded on modern Artistic inspirations, Jeongdong Theater has featured numerous critically-acclaimed productions such as "Traditional Art Performance, ""Masters Exhibition" and "Art Frontier, " as well as programs like "Art Stage at Noon" that are geared toward the General public.
Country: Republic of Korea
Contact: Director Hyun-wook Jung
Social Media: https:// www.facebook.com/jeongdongtheatertw https:// www.instagram.com/jeongdongtheater/
Capacity: 251-500
Policies: Rent and Present

Jeongeup-sa Art Hall
Website: https:// www.ydpcf.or.kr/main/main.do
Phone: 635 377 567
Address: 596 Gukhoedae-ro, Yeongdeungpo-gu, Seoul
Information: Yeongdeungpo Art Hall, a multi-purpose space used for culture and arts with state-of-the-art facilities, has a large-scale performance hall accommodating large operas, ballets and musicals as well as various concerts on the first floor. Is operated to pursue a cultural space where people can participate through direct encounters and conversations with the works.
Country: Republic of Korea
Contact: Chairman Chae Hyeon-il
Capacity: 501-1000
Annual Performances: 25-50
Policies: Rent and Present

KAIST Grand Auditorium
Website: https://www.ksa.hs.kr/
Email: kaistcf@kaist.ac.kr.
Phone: 423 502 114
Address: 291 Daehak-ro, Yuseong-gu, Daejeon 34141
Information: A variety of cultural events hosted at KAIST all year round are open to the KAIST community as well as to the public. Events such as classical concerts, ballets, traditional Korean music and dance, musical, and rock concerts drew more than 500, 000 people since the start of the cultural event program in 1986.
Country: Republic of Korea
Contact: President Kwang Hyung Lee
Social Media: https://www.facebook.com/KAIST.official https://twitter.com/kaistpr https://www.instagram.com/official_kaist/
Capacity: 1000+
Annual Performances: 6-10
Policies: Present

KBS Changwon Hall
Website: https://kbsbiz.co.kr/kbs%ec%b0%b-d%ec%9b%90%ed%99%80/
Email: 055 280 7181
Phone:
552 807 180
Address: 376 Gonghang-daero, Gangseo-gu, Seoul
Information: KBS Changwon Hall is a multipurpose hall with 1, 807 seats as the center of culture and art in Gyeongsangnam-do. From concerts to concerts, group events, education and training, it is loved greatly. A place where culture and art breathe, a place where musicians and audiences communicate! KBS Changwon Hall presents memories and joy to all of you.
Country: Republic of Korea
Contact: Representative Eui-cheol Kim
Capacity: 1000+
Policies: Rent and Present

KBS Hall
Website: kbs.co.kr
Phone: 278 11000
Address: 18 Yeouido-dong, Yeoungdeungpo-gu
Country: Republic of Korea

KBS Media Enterprise Ltd.
Website: www.kbsmedia.co.kr
Phone: 278 18484/9
Address: 18 Yeoido-dong, Yongdeungpo-gu
Information: see also Recorded Media
Country: Republic of Korea
Contact: President Byung-Soon Lee

KBS Symphony Orchestra
Website: https://www.kbssymphony.org/eng/m/KBSSO/aboutKBSSO.php
Phone: 278 12240/2253/
Address: 18 Yeoido-dong, Youngdeungpo-gu
Information: The KBS Symphony Orchestra has been incredibly received by a wide range of audiences due to the diversity of its thrilling repertoires from symphony to chamber music. Audience levels have reached more than a hundred thousand and have been able to enjoy over a hundred performances every year, including regular concerts.
Country: Republic of Korea
Contact: President Jungok Park
Contact: Executive Nam
Contact: Concert Planning Director You Ri Son
Contact: Senior Manager Andy Kim
Contact: Manager Han Shin Lee
Contact: Manager Jung Yee Yoo
Contact: Manager Ji Min Kim

LG Arts Centre
Website: www.lgart.co.kr
Email: arts2005@lgart.com
Phone: 220 050 114
Address: 679 Yeoksam-dong, Gangnam-gu
Information: multi purpose stage; rent, present
Country: Republic of Korea
Contact: Manager Hyonjeong Lee
Contact: CEO Eui-Joon Kim

Lotte World Garden Stage
Website: www.lotteworld.com
Email: lotty@lotteworld.com
Phone: 241 12000
Address: 40-1 Jamshil-dong, Songpa-gu
Information: managed by Lotte World Entertainment Dept
Country: Republic of Korea
Contact: President Ki-Seok Jeong

Madang Cecil Theatre
Phone: 274 75773
Address: 192-18 Dongsoon-dong, Joongro-gu
Country: Republic of Korea

Mokpo Citizens Culture Center
Website: https://www.mokpo.go.kr/art/sports_center
Phone: 612 708 376
Address: 312, Buju-ro, Mokpo-si (Ogam-dong)
Information: Mokpo Culture and Arts Center was opened in July 1997 to improve the art level of Mokpo citizens and play a role as a cultural arts center. In the permanent exhibition room, the history, books, paintings and photographs of renowned local artists are permanently exhibited throughout the year, and high-quality performances and exhibitions continue, so you can fully enjoy the fragrant Namdo art
Country: Republic of Korea
Contact: Operating a literary facility management office Yongbeom Joo
Phone: 061 270 4031
Capacity: 1000+
Policies: Rent and Present

Nan Pa Academy of Music
Phone: 312 292 721
Address: 13-2 Namchang-dong, Paldal-gu, Suwon
Country: Republic of Korea

Naru Art Center
Phone:
220 494 700
Address: 227-344 Jayang3-dong, Gwangjin-gu
Country: Republic of Korea
Contact: CEO Pyung-Jun Park

National Gugak Center
Website: www.ncktpa.go.kr
Email: moon1025@korea.kr
Phone: 258 03300
Address: Seocho-dong 2364, Nambusunhwanno, Seocho-gu, Seoul
Information: The headquarters of traditional performing arts. A place where excitement, fashion, and marriage live. This is the National Gugak Center.Our center located at Seoul, as well as our branches located at the cities of Namwon, Jindo and Busan, has been trying to support the preservation, transmission and development of traditional music.
Country: Republic of Korea
Contact: Director Jae-won Lim
Social Media: https://www.facebook.com/gugak1951 https://twitter.com/gugak1951 https://www.instagram.com/gugak1951/
Annual Performances: 100+
Policies: Present and Produce

National Theatre of Korea
Website: www.ntok.go.kr
Email: ntok2010@naver.com
Phone: 222 804 114
Address: Jangchungdan-ro, Jung-gu
Information: opened in April 1950 for the purpose of developing indigenous culture and advancing the theatrical arts. The National Drama Company and the Changguk Company traditional opera are resident companies. Member of ISPA
Country: Republic of Korea
Contact: CEO Hosang Ahn
Social Media: @NTOK www.facebook.com/NTOKstory
Policies: Present and produce, Theatre

Pohang Arts Center
Website: https://culturalspace.phcf.or.kr/munhwaArtCenter/subMain.do
Phone: 054 289 7824
Address: 850 Hope-daero, Nam-gu, Pohang-si, Gyeongsangbuk-do
Information: It is a culture and art space that can perform various performances such as music, dance, theater, opera, and large-scale shows.The Grand Performance Hall of the Pohang Culture and Arts Center is a multi-purpose performance hall with 972 seats.The Small Performance Hall is a multi-purpose performance hall with 264 seats.The outdoor performance hall is a cultural and Artistic space with 300 seats.
Country: Republic of Korea
Capacity: 1000+
Policies: Rent and Present

Potato Blossom Studio
Email: potatostudio@hanmail.net
Phone: 234 485 338
Address: 333 Yigok-Ri, Pyeongchang
Country: Republic of Korea
Contact: President Sun-Chul Lee

Sadari Art Center
Website: www.sadariartcenter.com
Phone: 276 31355
Address: 163-25 Hyewha-dong, Jongno-gu
Information: Multi purpose arts centre for children
Country: Republic of Korea
Contact: CEO Hyun-Wook Jeong

Sangju Cultural Center
Website: http://www.sjcc.or.kr/
Phone: 545 376 215
Address: 235 Sansan Road, Sangju City
Information: Since 1990, Sangju Cultural Center has been hosting music events and lectures. Its grand hall can host 512 people, accompanied by small hall (80 seats) and exhibtion hall (250)
Country: Republic of Korea

Capacity: 501-1000
Annual Performances: 100+
Policies: Rent and Present

Sejong Center for the Performing Arts
Website: https://www.sejongpac.or.kr/eng/main/main.do
Phone: 239 91000
Address: 175 Sejong-daero (Sejongno) Jongno-gu, Seoul
Information: Sejong Center established by Seoul Metropolitan Government is a Seoul's representing culture and arts institution
Built in 1978 and reborn as a foundation in 1999, it has been dubbed the cradle of Korean performance culture and played an important role as a hub for Seoul's performance culture and arts.
Country: Republic of Korea
Contact: CEO Seung-yeop Lee

Seongnam Arts Center
Website: www.snart.or.kr
Phone: 317 838 000
Address: 757 Yatap-dong, Bundang-gu, Seongnam
Country: Republic of Korea
Contact: CEO Jong-Duk Lee

Seosan Cultural Center
Phone: 416 651 779
Address: 513 Eupnae-dong
Country: Republic of Korea

Seoul Arts Centre
Website: www.sac.or.kr
Email: webmaster@sac.or.kr
Phone: 258 01300
Address: Nambusunhwanro 2406, Seocho-gu
Information: operated by Seoul Arts Center Trust; regular events: Orchestra Festival, Opera Festival, Christmas Ballet; own productions (30%), hire out (70%)
Country: Republic of Korea
Contact: President Hyun-Taek Shin
Social Media: @I_Love_SAC www.facebook.com/SeoulArtsCenter.Korea

Seoul Foundation for Arts and Culture (SFAC)
Website: www.sfac.or.kr
Email: sns@sfac.or.kr
Phone: 923 290 7000
Address: 517 Cheonggyecheon-ro, Dongdaemun-gu, Seoul
Information: Seoul Foundation for Arts and Culture (SFAC) consists of venues such as the Seoul Theatre Centre, Namsan Arts Centre, Daehak-ro Creative Space and Namsan Creative Centre. Member of ISPA.
Country: Republic of Korea
Contact: Director Jong-Hwi Kim
Email: sns@sfac.or.kr
Contact: Chairman Gyeong-ja Lee
Email: sns@sfac.or.kr
Social Media: www.facebook.com/sfac2004 www.instagram.com/sfac2004/?fbclid=IwAR3X64XjjWT3cB-vDOLtczP0fZpXGLQ3ZkeqY4SwnxBx7wTu2OfCSkQE-BLQM

Seoul Nori Madang
Phone: 241 41985
Address: 47 Jamsil3-dong, Songpa-gu
Country: Republic of Korea

Sokcho Cultural Center
Phone: 392 631 1173
Address: 570-5 Yongnang-dong, Sokcho
Country: Republic of Korea

Sori Arts Center of Jeollabuk-do
Website: www.sori21.co.kr
Email: webmaster@sori21.co.kr
Phone: 632 707 800
Address: San 1-1 Deokjin-dong, Deokjin-gu, Jeonju
Country: Republic of Korea
Contact: CEO In-Kwon Lee

Suncheon Culture & Art Center
Website: https://www.suncheon.go.kr/scart/
Email: suncheonsi@hanmail.net
Phone: 617 493 516
Address: 16 Samsan-ro, Suncheon-si, Jeollanam-do
Information: We have improved the culture and arts to the central level by showing timely planned performances and more sophisticated performances that fit the sentiment of the Suncheon citizens to the citizens. In addition, we run a moving art group and go directly to the everyday life scene, and perform planned performances with citizens to ensure that there is no alienation between the classes of each region.
Country: Republic of Korea
Contact: Director Kang I – gu
Email: suncheonsi@hanmail.net
Phone: 061 749 8610Management Team Leader Chosun Hee
Email: suncheonsi@hanmail.net
Phone: 061 749 8614 Facility Team leader Seok-soon Cho
Email: suncheonsi@hanmail.net
Phone: 061 749 8619

Social Media: https:// www.facebook.com/suncheon.kr/
https:// www.instagram.com/suncheonsi/

Sungeui Music Hall
Phone: 275 28924
Address: 8-3 Yejang-dong, Joong-gu
Country: Republic of Korea

Suwon Citizens' Hall
Website: http://citizen.suwonsarang.com/mp01_de-fault/index.php
Phone: 312 442 161
Address: San 2-1, Maesan-ro 3-ga, Paldal-gu, Suwon-si
Information: Suwon Civic Center is located in the middle of Paldal Mountain. The 4 story building hosts events, performances, events, lectures, and academic research meetings.
Country: Republic of Korea
Disabled Access: Yes
Capacity: 251-500
Policies: Rent and Present

The Korean Children's Center
Website: www.children-center.or.kr
Phone: 222 046 028
Address: 18-11 Neung-dong, Gwangjin-gu

Uijeongbu Arts Center
Website: https:// www.uac.or.kr/uac.php
Phone: 318 285 841
Address: 1, Uijeong-ro, Uijeongbu-si, Gyeonggi-do
Information: The Uijeongbu Cultural Centre is a space for cultural and Artistic performances, educational academies, and exhibitions. It is a base for local culture and arts, and a space for cultural and Artistic communication in northern Gyeonggi Province.
Country: Republic of Korea
Contact: CEO Gyeongsik Son
Phone: 828 5830
Social Media: https:// www.facebook.com/uartcenter/
https:// www.instagram.com/uac65/

Ulsan Culture and Arts Center
Website: www.ucac.or.kr
Email: woo7458@ulsan21.net
Phone: 522 759 623/8
Address: 413-13 Dal-dong, Nam-gu
Information: the Centre includes exhibition hall, open-air performance space
Country: Republic of Korea
Contact: Manager Kwang-Oh Kim

Universal Arts Center
Website: www.uac.or.kr
Phone: 222 041 030
Address: 25 Neung-dong, Gwangjin-gu, Seul
Information: Universal Arts Center, is a performance venue in Seoul, South Korea. It is the home of the Universal Ballet, where the audience can enjoy dance and performing acts from various genres including ballet, opera, and award ceremonies.
Country: Republic of Korea
Contact: Head of Business Planning Dept Youngbo Lee
Email: hojojb@gmail.com
Phone: 070 712 41747Assistant Artistic Director Yoo Ji Yeon
Email: hojojb@gmail.com
Phone: 070 712 41712

Usong Arts Center
Email: solosun@hanmail.net
Phone: 426 296 363
Address: 155-3 Chayang-dong, Tong-gu
Country: Republic of Korea

Wonju Chiak Art Center
Website: http:// www.wcf.or.kr/culture/culture_art_1.php?tsort=2&msort=12
Phone: 033 760 9827
Address: 331 Seowon-daero, Wonju-si, Gangwon-do
Information: The Chiak Art Center is the oldest large-scale performance hall in Wonju and has held various performances, events, and exhibitions. There are 600-seat performance halls, underground installation halls, music practice rooms, General practice rooms, and dance practice rooms, and are provided to local residents, cultural artists, and culture and arts organizations who need a space for practice spaces and events.
Country: Republic of Korea
Capacity: 501-1000
Policies: Rent and Present

Woongjin Think Big Art Hall
Website: wj.i-pmc.co.kr
Phone: 256 90696
Address: 772 Yeoksam-dong, Gangnam-gu
Country: Republic of Korea
Contact: CEO Kwang-Ho Lee
Contact: CEO Seung-Hwan Song

Yeosu Civic Hall
Website: https://www.yeosu.go.kr/ www/sphere/mn55/yeosu.go
Phone: 061 659 3776
Address: 69 Jwasuyeong-ro (Gwangmu-dong), Yeosu-si,

Jeollanam-do
Information: Opening of the Citizens' Hall on June 28, 1987 (start of construction on July 22, 1983, completion on June 28, 1987). Remodeled in 2003**Country:** Republic of Korea

Yesul Madang Ukeumch'i
Phone: 422 542 620
Address: 202-19 Seonhwa 3-dong, Joong-gu
Country: Republic of Korea

Yongwol Culture and Arts Center
Phone: 333 702 545
Address: 961-2 Yongheung 4-ri, Yongwol-up
Country: Republic of Korea

Yonsei Centennial Memorial Hall
Website: https://ycac.yonsei.ac.kr/ycac/index.do
Email: concert@yss100.co.kr
Phone: 223 139 801
Address: Yonsei University, 134 Sinchon-dong, Seodae-mun-gu
Information: Just like all Yonsei culture and arts spaces, Yonsei Centennial Memorial Hall prioritizes its function as an educational space

Youngsan Art Hall
Website: www.youngsanarthall.com
Email: ysarthall@naver.com
Phone: 276 11587
Address: CCMM Bldg., Yeouido-dong, Youngdengpo-gu
Country: Republic of Korea

MACAO

Macao Cultural Centre
Website: www.ccm.gov.mo
Email: enquiry@ccm.gov.mo
Phone: 287 00699
Address: Avenida Xian Xing Hai s/n, MO
Information: the Macao Cultural Centre was founded in 1999 and remains a modern space that marks the cityscape surround it. Its several venues open for the Macao audience provide quality programmes, such as performances, conferences, exhibitions, among other projects organized by CCM or hirers. Member of ISPA
Country: Macao
Social Media: www.facebook.com/MacaoCulturalCentre
Policies: All, Multi-purpose

MALAYSIA

Auditorium MPSA Shah Alam
Website: http:// www.mbsa.gov.my/ms-my/mbsa/perkhidmatan/kemudahanawamtempahan/Halaman/tempahan_auditorium.aspx
Email: evaluation@mbsa.gov.my
Phone: 035 510 5133
Address: Majlis Perbandaraan Shah Alam, Wisma MPSA, Persiaran Perbandaran, Shah Alam, MY
Information: MBSA Auditorium Hall is located in Wisma MBSA building, Persiaran Perbandaran, Section 14 Shah Alam. The hall can accommodate up to 1, 400 people and is equipped with air conditioning facilities, a stage with 612 " x 543 " 30 " x 24 " projector screen and 8 dressing rooms. This hall is very suitable for formal and informal occasions such as seminars, talks and others.
Country: Malaysia
Capacity: 1000+
Policies: Rent and Present

Celestar Studio of Performing Arts
Website: http:// www.celestarstudio.com/
Email: celeste@celestarstudio.com
Phone: 013 371 0862
Address: 24B Jalan Memanda 4, Ampang Point, , MY
Country: Malaysia

Dewan Sri Pinang
Phone: 426 14700
Address: Lebuh Light, Pinang, MY
Country: Malaysia
Contact: supervisor Mansor Yacob

Dewan Theatreat
Phone: 676 59900
Address: Unit Pentadbir/Penyelia Bangunan, Tingkat Lima, Block A, Wisma Negeri, MY
Information: available for hire
Country: Malaysia
Contact: contact Encik Rani Haji Hashim

Five Arts Centre
Phone: 603 715 4858
Address: 27 Lorong Datuk Sulaiman 7, Taman Tun Dr Ismail, MY
Country: Malaysia

Istana Budaya Theatre
Website: www.istanabudaya.gov.my
Email: info@istanabudaya.gov.my
Phone: 340 265 555
Address: Jalan Tun Razak, MY
Country: Malaysia

Contact: Director General t.b.a.
Contact: deputy Director General (Artistic) Mohamed Juhari Shaarani
Contact: deputy Director General (operations) Fauzia Sabiri
Contact: Director, Marketing and public relations Zubaidah Mukhtar

Kadazan Dusan Cultural Centre
Phone: 887 17895
Address: c/o Kadazan Dusan Cultural Association, Sumu-ni Sdn Bhd, PO Box 408, MY
Country: Malaysia
Contact: Manager George Yapp

Kompleks Tun Abdul Razak (KOMTAR)
Phone: 426 21957
Address: Jalan Pinang, Pinang, MY
Information: capacity 300 (Auditorium A), 160 (Auditorium C & F), 1800 (Geodesic Dome)
Country: Malaysia
Contact: supervisor J Arfah Binti Abu Bakar

Kuala Lumpur City Hall (DBKL) Theatre
Phone: 329 16011
Address: High Court Building, Jalan Raja Laut, MY
Information: Mailing address: Unit Pengurusan Bangnan, Jabatan Pengurusan Oreanisai, Tingat 4, Bangunan DBKL, Jalan Raja, 50350 Kuala Lumpur
Country: Malaysia
Contact: Director of Administration and pr Izman bin Haji Ismail

Kuala Lumpur Performing Arts Centre (Pentas Seni KL)
Website: www.klpac.com
Email: marge@klpac.com
Phone: 603 404 79010
Address: Sentul Park, Jalan Strachan, MY
Information: opened May 2005
Country: Malaysia
Contact: Executive Producer Faridah Merican
Contact: Artistic Director Joe Hasham
Contact: theatre Manager Teoh Ming Jin
Contact: General Manager Marge Chew

Malaysian Tourist Information Centre (MATIC)
Phone: 326 43929
Address: 109, Jalan Ampang, MY
Country: Malaysia
Contact: Director Norhijjah Alias

MPS Hall
Phone: 676 23381
Address: c/o Culture and Arts Office, Jalan Yamtuan, Sereban, MY
Information: available for hire
Country: Malaysia
Contact: Director Tuan Haji Hassan bin Muhamed Z

Pan Urus Harta Sdn Bhd
Phone: 426 23705
Address: Tingat 32, Menara Komtar, Pinang, MY
Country: Malaysia
Contact: Director Chew See Jan

Panggung Bandaraya
Website: www.dbkl.gov.my/panggung/index.php
Email: dbkl@dbkl.gov.my
Phone: 326 179 000
Address: Sultan Abdul Samad Building, Jalan Raja, MY
Country: Malaysia

Petronas Philharmonic Hall – Dewan Filharmonik Petronas
Website: www.dfpmpo.com
Email: hamili@petronas.com.my
Phone: 320 517 008
Address: Level 2, Tower 2, Petronas Twin Towers, Kuala Lumpur City Centre, MY
Information: Malaysian Philharmonic Orchestra (q.v.) is the resident orchestra; alternative website: www.malaysianphilharmonic.com
Country: Malaysia
Contact: CEO Juniwati Rahmat Hussin
Contact: Marketing Manager Hamili Abdul Hamid
Contact: artist administrator Farha Mohamed Nor

Pusat Kebudayaan Suasana
Phone: 012 288 7508
Address: Suasana Cultural Centre, 42-1, Jln SL 1/3, Bandar Sungai Long, Batu 11, Jln Cheras, MY
Country: Malaysia

Putra World Trade Centre
Phone: 344 33999
Address: c/o Putrade Property Management Sdn. Bhd, Level 3, , Kompleks PWTC-UMNO, 41 Jalan Tun Ismail, MY
Country: Malaysia
Contact: reservation officer Nor Azmi Sulong

RTM Auditorium Tan Sri P. Ramlee
Phone: 822 48422
Address: Radio Televisyen Malaysia, Jalan P. Ramlee,

Kuching, MY
Country: Malaysia
Contact: Director of broadcasting Cik haj Norhayati

Sabah Foundation
Phone: 884 22211
Address: PO Box 11201, Kota Kinabalu, MY
Country: Malaysia
Contact: Director Datuk Musalman

Sabah Hall
Phone:
882 21854
Address: Tingkat 2, Wisma MUIS, PO Box 12233, Kota Kinabalu, MY
Country: Malaysia
Contact: Managing Director Jainal Sulai

Sanggar Teater Fauziah Nawi
Website:
www.fauziahnawi.com
Email: fauziah@fauziahnawi.com
Address: Fauziah Nawi (M) Sdn Bhd, 9B, Jalan Sulaiman 3, Taman Putra Sulaiman, MY
Country: Malaysia

Sarawak Indoor Stadium
Phone: 824 42286
Address: POX 2918, Jalan Stadium, Kuching, MY
Country: Malaysia
Contact: Chairman Hj Khaider Hj Ahmad

State Culture and Arts Centre, Kelantan
Phone: 976 43005
Address: c/o Kompleks Belia Dan Sukan Negeri Kelantan, Panji, Kota Bahru, MY
Country: Malaysia
Contact: Director Hj Saari Bin Salleh

State Culture and Arts Centre, Pahang
Email: pkknphg@hotmail.com
Phone: 955 55466
Address: c/o Ministry of Culture, Arts and Tourism, Lot 57100, Jalan Teluk Sisik, Kuantan, MY
Country: Malaysia
Contact: Director Encik Abdul Hamid Haji Muhamad

State Culture and Arts Centre, Perak
Phone: 525 44635
Address: Negeri Perak Pusat Kebudayaan + Pelancongan Wilaya, Taman Budaya Negeri Perak, Jalan Coldwell off Jala, MY
Country: Malaysia
Contact: Director Nawi Hj Adek

State Culture and Arts Centre, Pulau Pinang (Bahagian Auditorium)
Phone: 465 05199
Address: Pejabat Setiausaha Kerajaan, Aras 25, Komtar, Pinang, MY
Country: Malaysia
Contact: Director Yang Berhormat Datu Khalid Bin

Temple of Fine Arts
Phone: 227 43709
Address: Perbadanan Kesenian Malaysia, 114-116 Jalan Berhala, Brickfields, MY
Country: Malaysia

The Actors Studio Theatre Box
Website: www.theactorsstudio.com.my
Phone: 603 209 40400/14
Address: Level 3, New Wing, The Bangsar Shopping Centre, 285 Jln. Maarof, Bukit Bandaraya, MY
Country: Malaysia

University of Malaya Cultural Centre
Website: www.um.edu.my
Email: r1halim@umcsd.um.edu.my
Phone: 375 93454
Address: University of Malaya, Tingkat 1, Block E, Bangunan Perdana Siswa, Lembah Pantai, MY
Information: annual performing arts festival Nov Festival Seni
Country: Malaysia
Contact: Director of cultural centre Said Halim Nong
Contact: head of asian arts museum Othman Yatim
Contact: co-ordinator for music studies Sunetra Fernando
Contact: deputy Director/ co-ordinator for drama studies Hanafi Hussin

Wisma MCA Sdn Bhd
Phone: 326 18044
Address: 3F, 163 Jalan Ampang, MY
Country: Malaysia
Contact: contact Mr Antoni

MEXICO

Auditorio Carlos E. Mart
Phone: 528 444 173 003
Address: Universidad Aut, Domicilio Conocido, Col. Ex – Hacienda de Buenavista, MX

Country: Mexico
Contact: responsable Silvia P

Auditorio Cívico del Estado
Phone: 621 72969
Address: Planta Baja, Tehuantepec y Pedro Moreno, MX
Country: Mexico

Auditorio Municipal de Zapotiltic
Email: hayuntamientozap@prodigy.net.mx
Phone: 341 414 0442
Address: Ayuntamiento de Zapotiltic Council of Zapotiltic, Prol. Mariano Escobedo Anexo a la Casa de Cultura, Col. Centro, MX
Country: Mexico
Contact: responsable Agust

Auditorio Nacional Centro de Arte y Cultura
Website: www.auditorio.com.mx
Email: auditorio@auditorio.com.mx
Phone: 555 280 9250
Address: Paseo de la Reforma 50 esq Campo Marte, Col. Bosque de Chapultepec, MX
Information: alternative contact: 9138 1350
Country: Mexico
Contact: responsable Pedro Baranda Garc

Auditorio Telmex
Website: www.auditorio-telmex.com
Email: contacto@auditorio-telmex.com
Phone: 333 818 3800
Address: Obreros de Cananea 747, Complejo Belenes, MX
Country: Mexico
Social Media: @AuditorioTelmex www.facebook.com/AuditorioTELMEX
Capacity: 11500

Aula del Parque Infantil Tecaroca
Phone: 526 656 541 535
Address: DIF, Camino a la Aviaci, Col. Maclovia Herrera, MX
Country: Mexico

Café Los Artistas y de los Demás También
Address: Librería Don Quijote Plaza Fiesta, MX
Information: Capacity: 80 people.
Country: Mexico
Contact: responsable Norma Alicia Bustamante
Policies: Rent only, Theatre

Centro Cultural Alfa, Monterrey
Phone: 818 303 0001
Address: Av. Roberto Garza Sada No. 1000, Col. Carrizalejo, San Pedro Garza García, MX
Country: Mexico
Contact: Director Jos t.b.a
Policies: Other

Centro Cultural El Nigromante
Website: www.elnigromante.bellasartes.gob.mx/
Email: bellasartessma@hotmail.com
Phone: 415 152 0289
Address: Calle Hernández Macías 75, MX
Country: Mexico
Contact: Director Carmen Masip de Hawkins
Social Media: @bellasartessma www.facebook.com/el.nigromante
Policies: Present and produce, Multi-purpose

Centro Cultural Helénico
Website: www.helenico.gob.mx
Email: helenico@correo.conaculta.gob.mx
Phone: 415 50900
Address: Av. Revoluci, Col. Guadalupe Inn, MX
Country: Mexico
Social Media: @Helenico
Policies: All, Theatre

Centro Cultural Tijuana Cecut
Email: opina@cecut.gob.mx
Address: Paseo de los Heroes y Javier Mina s/n, MX
Country: Mexico
Contact: Director Lic. Teresita Vicencio Alvarez
Contact: festivals coordinator Lic. Teresa Trujillo
Policies: Arts centre

Centro Cultural y Deportivo Universitario de Campeche
Email: culturauac@uacam.mx
Phone: 981 816 2164
Address: Ciudad Universitaria, Av. Agustín Melgar s/n entre Juan de la Barrera y Calle 20, Col. Buenavista, MX
Country: Mexico
Contact: secretario General de la uac Jos t.b.a
Contact: Director de difusi Ricardo Encalada Argaez
Contact: rector de la uac Jos
Policies: Other

Chihuahua Institute of Culture
Website: www.ichicult.gob.mx
Phone: 614 214 4800
Address: Ave North Division and University Ave S, N, Col. Altavista, MX
Country: Mexico

Social Media: @ichicultchih www.facebook.com/ICHICULTCHIH

Cine Teatro ANDA
Website: www.anda.org.mx/
Address: Tlaxcala 2845 esq. Américas, Tlaxcala No. 2845 esq. Am, Col. Margaritas, MX
Country: Mexico
Contact: responsable Rafael Rodr
Social Media: @andaestadiorg
Policies: Other

Cine Teatro de Atlacomulco
Email: salpin@hotmail.com
Address: Av. Hidalgo Sur 8, Col. Centro, MX
Country: Mexico
Contact: contact Jos t.b.a
Policies: Theatre

Cine Teatro de la Casa de Cultura de Colima
Email: seculprom@hotmail.com.mx
Phone: 312 313 0608
Address: Secr. de Cultura del Gobierno del Estado Colima, Galv, Col. Centro, MX
Country: Mexico
Contact: Manager Hiram Mej

Concha Acústica de la Feria de Colima
Website: www.feriadecolima.com.mx/index.php?c=142
Email: informes@feriadecolima.com.mx
Address: Col. La Estancia, MX
Country: Mexico

Consejo Estatal para la Cultura y las Artes de Chiapas
Website: www.conecultachiapas.gob.mx
Email: informacion@conecultachiapas.gob.mx
Address: Blvd., Fracc. San Roque, MX
Country: Mexico
Contact: General Director Angelica Guadalupe Altúza Constantino
Email: direccion@conecultachiapas.gob.mx
Contact: artist coordinator Mabel García Espinosa
Email: coordinaciondeensenanza@conecultachiapas.gob.mx
Contact: Director of cultural promotion Cicerón Aguila Acevedo
Email: promocion@conecuktachiapas.gob.mx
Contact: assistant Manager Adolfo Raúl Pérez Ochoa
Email: administrativo@conecultachiapas.gob.mx
Policies: All, Other

Consejo Estatal para la Cultura y las Artes de Hidalgo
Website: www.hidalgo.gob.mx
Email: cecultah@e-hidalgo.gob.mx
Address: Palacio de Gobierno, Plaze Juárez, Col. Centro, MX
Information: see also Ministries, alternative Email address: cecultah@hotmail.com
Country: Mexico
Contact: General Director Lourdes Parga Mateos
Social Media: @gobiernohidalgoes-la.facebook.com/gobhidalgo
Policies: All, Multi-purpose

Consejo Estatal para la Cultura y las Artes de Nayarit
Email: corinaramirez@nayarit.gob.mx
Address: Av. Allende 329 Pte., MX
Information: alternative Email addresses: cecan@tepic.megared.net.mx, sarche@culturaspopulares.gob.mx
Country: Mexico
Contact: General Director Mtra. Alma Corina Ram

Consejo para la Cultura y las Artes de Nuevo León
Website: www.conarte.org.mx
Email: contacto@conarte.org.mx
Phone: 812 020 6705
Address: Antiguo Palacio Postal, Washington 648 Ote. piso 8, Col. Centro, MX
Country: Mexico
Policies: Congress centre

Cultural Institute of the State of Durango
Website: iced.durango.gob.mx
Email: webmaster@durango.gob.mx
Phone: 618 137 5807
Address: Nte 143 Constitution Street, MX
Country: Mexico
Social Media: @iceddgo www.facebook.com/cultura.durango
Policies: Other

Dirección de Cultura Municipal de La Paz
Email: culturaenlapaz@hotmail.com
Phone: 612 122 8784
Address: 16 de Septiembre y Belisario Dominguez, Palacio Municipal, MX
Country: Mexico

Dirección General de Culturas Populares
Website: www.difocur.gob.mx
Email: rgonzalezv_difocur@hotmail.com

Address: MX
Country: Mexico

El Forito Theater
Website: www.unicom.com.mx
Email: gwalls@unicom.com.mx
Phone: 998 880 4112
Address: El Forito/Unicom; Teatr, Av. Chich, Super Manzana 64, MX
Information: proscenium-style theatre; open year-round for performing arts presentations and other events requiring a theatre set up awards ceremonies, Sales presentations, speakers, debates etc.; outdoor garden for art exhibits, mime presentations etc.; alternative E
Country: Mexico
Contact: owner/administrator German Walls Rey advertising & website
Sharon Van Bramer
Contact: Sales Liz Brown

Embassy of the United States of America
Website: mexico.usembassy.gov
Email: embeuamx@state.gov
Address: Cultural and Information Department, Paseo de la Reforma 305, Col. Cuauht, MX
Country: Mexico
Contact: minister for cultural affairs William J Dieterich
Contact: deputy cultural attach Mark Glago
Contact: senior cultural affairs specialist Bertha Cea Echenique
Contact: cultural attach Robert E McDowell
Policies: Other

Escenario al Aire Libre del Teatro de la Ciudad
Email: rvillarreal@conarte.org.mx
Address: Juan Zuazua y Mariano Matamoros s/n, MX
Country: Mexico
Policies: Other

Foro al Aire Libre del Parque Griselda
Phone: 331 312 3898
Address: Av. 20 de Noviembre esq. Belisario Dom, Col. Centro, MX
Country: Mexico
Contact: contact Gloria Guillermina Araiza Torres
Policies: Other

Foro de Arte y Cultura de Guadalajara
Phone: 333 819 2397
Address: Secretar, Prol. Alcalde #1451, Col. Miraflores, MX
Country: Mexico
Contact: Director Jos dsfgrh
Policies: Other

Foro Rural en la Comunidad de Tepames
Phone: 312 321 0129
Address: Jardín Principal entre 16 de septiembre y Fco. Madero, Centro, Del, MX
Country: Mexico
Contact: contact Gloria Guillermina Araiza Torres
Policies: Other

Guerrero Institute of Culture
Website: www.institutoguerrerensedelacultura.gob.mx
Phone: 174 747 27051
Address: Av. Costera Miguel Alem, Fracc. Costa Azul, MX
Country: Mexico
Social Media: @Secugro www.facebook.com/Secretaria-DeCulturaDeGuerrero

Instituto Coahuilense de Cultura
Website: www.icocult.gob.mx
Phone: 844 410 2033
Address: Calle Juárez esquina con Hidalgo, Zona Centro, MX
Country: Mexico
Contact: ministry of culture Ana Sofia Garcia Camil
Policies: Multi-purpose

Instituto Cultural de Aguascalientes
Website: www.aguascalientes.gob.mx/ica/
Email: informacion.ica@gmail.com
Phone: 449 910 2010
Address: Venustiano Carranza 101, Colonia Centro, MX
Information: varied programme of musical and theatrical events
Country: Mexico
Social Media: www.facebook.com/InstitutoCultural
Policies: All, Multi-purpose

Instituto de Cultura de Baja California
Website: www.bajacalifornia.gob.mx/icbc
Email: mjacobo@baja.gob.mx
Phone: 686 553 5044
Address: Av.Alvaro Obregón 1209, Col. Nueva 2da Sección, MX
Country: Mexico
Contact: Director General Moisés Galindo Herrera
Email: mgalindo@baja.gob.mx
Contact: Director of Administration Víctor Manuel Aragón Molina
Email: varagon@baja.gob.mx
Policies: Multi-purpose

Instituto de Cultura de Campeche
Website: www.institutodecultura.gob.mx
Email: icc@campeche.gob.mx
Phone: 981 – 816 2957
Address: Calle 12 No. 173, Centro Histórico, San Francisco de Campeche, MX
Information: alternative Email address: iccampeche@prodigy.net.mx
Country: Mexico
Contact: secretary of culture Carlos A. Vidal Angles
Contact: deputy cultural and Artistic Director Joan E. Delgado Rodriguez
Contact: Director of cultural and Artistic education Alfredo Martínez Jiménez
Contact: assistant secretary for planning and Administration Sergio D. Coronado Bustos
Contact: Managing Director Sergio Rubén Silva Alemán
Policies: Multi-purpose

Instituto de Cultura del Yucatán
Website: www.culturayucatan.com
Email: icy@yucatan.gob.mx
Phone: 999 942 3800
Address: 25 Ginerés, Col. Garcia, MX
Country: Mexico
Contact: Director General Domingo Rodr

Mexican Institute of Culture
Website: www.edomexico.gob.mx/imc
Email: gemimcda@edomex.gob.mx
Phone: 172 227 41200
Address: 302 Boulevard Jesus Reyes, Delegacion San Buenaventura, MX
Information: see also International and National Organisations
Country: Mexico
Contact: Director General Ing. Agust
Policies: Rent and present

Museo de Arte Contemporáneo de Monterrey
Website: www.marco.org.mx
Email: informacion@marco.org.mx
Phone: 818 262 4500
Address: Zuazua y Jardón, Centro, MX
Country: Mexico
Social Media: @MuseoMarco www.facebook.com/museomarcomty
Policies: Other

Oaxaca, Musica y Cultura A.C.
Website: www.instrumenta.org
Email: juan@instrumenta.org
Phone: 555 286 4730
Address: Tlaxcala #173 Col Hipódromo de la Condesa, MX
Country: Mexico
Contact: Director Juan Ram
Policies: Other

Palacio de Bellas Artes
Website: www.bellasartes.gob.mx
Email: infoinba@inba.gob.mx
Phone: 528 21964
Address: Paseo de la Reforma and Campo Marte S / N, Col. Polanco, Chapultepec, , Del. Miguel Hidalgo, MX
Information: National Institute of Fine Arts, see also National Organisations (National Institute of Fine Arts-Centro Nacional de Bellas Artes: Dance Coordination; Music and Opera Coordination and Theatre Coordination)
Country: Mexico
Social Media: @bellasartesinba www.facebook.com/INBAmx
Policies: Arts centre

Queretano Institute of Culture and Arts
Website: www.culturaqueretaro.gob.mx
Email: lpedraza@queretaro.gob.mx
Phone: 442 251 9850
Address: And. Venustiano Carranza n, Centro Hist, MX
Country: Mexico
Contact: Director General Laura Gabriela Corvera Galvan
Social Media: @IQCA www.facebook.com/pages/Instituto-Queretano-de-la-Cultura-y-las-Artes/215102302059

Quintana Roo Institute of Culture
Website: www.secqr.gob.mx
Email: webmaster_cultura@qroo.gob.mx
Phone: 983 832 1350
Address: Av. Héroes No. 68, Col. Centro, MX
Information: see also International and National Organisations
Country: Mexico
Social Media: @cultura_qroo www.facebook.com/culturaqroo
Policies: Rent and present, Other

Sala de Arte del Instituto Cultural de Baja California
Phone: 664 683 5922
Address: Representaci, Av. Centenario #10151, Col. Zona R, MX
Country: Mexico
Contact: responsable Patricio Bayardo G

Sala de Espectáculos
Email: comunicacion@cecut.org.mx
Address: Centro Cultural Tijuana Tijuana Cultural Center, Av. Paseo de los Heroes, MX
Country: Mexico
Policies: Multi-purpose

Sala Esplandián
Email: ignaciozaragoza68@hotmail.com
Address: Av. González Ortega 930, Zona Centro, MX
Country: Mexico

Sala Ixcateopan
Phone: 762 622 2274
Address: Centro de Convenciones de Taxco, Av. Plateros #1, Col. Centro, MX
Country: Mexico
Contact: responsable Manuel Saire Prado

Sala Silvestre Revueltas
Email: ollinyoliztlidifusion@cultura.df.gob.mx
Phone: 555 606 4776
Address: Periférico Sur 514, Col. Isidro Fabela, Tlalpan, , MX
Country: Mexico
Policies: Other

Secretaría de Cultura del Estado de Jalisco
Website: cultura.jalisco.gob.mx
Email: ccomunic@jalisco.gob.mx
Address: Av. La Paz No. 875, Zona Centro, MX
Country: Mexico

Secretaría de Cultura del Estado de Michoacán
Website: www.michoacan.gob.mx/cultura
Email: scsecretario@michoacan.gob.mx
Address: Isidro Huarte 545, Col. Cuauhtémoc, MX
Country: Mexico

Secretaría de Cultura del Estado de Puebla
Website: www.sc.pue.gob.mx
Email: scultura@pue.gob.mx
Phone: 222 246 4885
Address: 3 Oriente 209, Centro Histórico, MX
Country: Mexico

Secretaría de Cultura del Gobierno de San Luis Potosí
Website: www.culturaslp.gob.mx
Email: cultura@culturaslp.gob.mx
Phone: 444 812 8512
Address: Jardín Guerrero 6, Zona Centro, MX
Country: Mexico
Policies: Multi-purpose

Secretaría de Cultura del Gobierno del Estado de Colima
Website: cenedic.ucol.mx/cultura
Email: info@culturacolima.gob.mx
Address: Calzada Galván y Ejército Nacional, Colonia Centro, MX
Country: Mexico
Social Media: @culturacolima www.facebook.com/culturacolima
Policies: Multi-purpose

Secretaría de Cultura DF
Website: www.cultura.df.gob.mx
Email: n_serratos@df.gob.mx
Address: Av. de la Paz 26, Colonio Chimalistac, MX
Country: Mexico

Secretaría de Cultura, Recreación y Deporte del Estado de Tabasco
Email: sriadecultura@prodigy.net.mx
Address: Colonia Centro, MX
Country: Mexico
Policies: Multi-purpose

Secretaría de las Culturas y Artes de Oaxaca
Website: www.oaxaca.gob.mx
Email: secretariadecultura@oaxaca.gob.mx
Phone: 951 516 4477
Address: MX
Country: Mexico
Policies: Multi-purpose

Sociculture
Phone: 555 535 7962
Address: Rivera de San Cosme Edif. Sur, arriba del Metro San Cosme n, Col. San Rafael, MX
Country: Mexico

Sociedad Artística del Tecnológico (SAT)
Website: sat.mty.itesm.mx
Email: sat.mty@itesm.mx
Address: Instituto Tecnológico, Auditorio Luis Elizondo, Col. del Tecnológico, MX
Information: see also Agents, alternative Email addresses: hugarza@itesm.mx, federico.sabre@itesm.mx
Country: Mexico
Policies: Multi-purpose

Sonoran Institute of Culture

Website: www.isc.gob.mx
Email: info@isc.gob.mx
Phone: 662 213 4411
Address: Instituto Sonorense de Cultura, Obregon #5 entre Yanes y Garmendia, MX
Information: see also International and National Organisations
Country: Mexico
Social Media: @ISCsonora www.facebook.com/iscsonora
Policies: Rent and present

State Institute of Culture of Guanajuato
Website: www.guanajuato.gob.mx/cultura
Email: jalcocerf@guanajuato.gob.mx
Phone: 147 310 22700
Address: Plazuela de Cata 1 y 2, Ex-Cava Domecq, Col. Mineral de Cata, MX
Country: Mexico

Teatro Aguascalientes del IMSS
Website: www.imss.gob.mx
Phone: 449 913 9050
Address: Instituto Mexicano del Seguro Social, Av. de la Convenci, Col. Lindavista, MX
Country: Mexico
Contact: contact Enrique Mendoza Terrones
Policies: Theatre

Teatro al Aire Libre Ángela Peralta
Email: alogarcia@miguelhidalgo.gob.mx
Address: Aristóteles s/n entre Emilio Castelar y Luis Urbina, Col. Polanco, MX
Country: Mexico
Policies: Theatre

Teatro al Aire Libre de Mexitlán
Phone: 663 84101
Address: Calle 2a. 8901-D, Benito Juárez, Col. Zona Centro, MX
Country: Mexico
Policies: Theatre

Teatro al Aire Libre de Rector
Phone: 686 552 9762
Address: Universidad Aut, Av. Alvaro Obreg, Col. Nueva, MX
Country: Mexico
Contact: responsable Maricela Jacobo Heredia

Teatro al Aire Libre de Tula de Allende
Phone: 773 732 0010
Address: Ayuntamiento de Tula de Allende, Domicilio conocido, Col. Centro, MX
Country: Mexico

Teatro al Aire Libre del Centro Comunitario Estudiantil
Phone: 686 566 0306
Address: Blvd. Benito Juárez s/n, Unidad Universitaria Campus Mexicali, MX
Country: Mexico
Contact: contact Maricela Jacobo Heredia
Policies: Other

Teatro al Aire Libre del Centro de Seguridad Social
Phone: 762 622 3510
Address: Instituto Mexicano del Seguro Social, Av. de los Plateros #330, Col. Centro, MX
Country: Mexico

Teatro al Aire Libre del Foro Lago
Phone: 777 318 8418
Address: Instituto de Cultura de Morelos, Av. Jos, Col. Centro, MX
Information: see also Cultural Institute of the State of Morelos
Country: Mexico

Teatro al Aire Libre del Parque Adolfo López Mateos
Email: perezperpuly@tecate.gob.mx
Phone: 665 654 9231
Address: Ayuntamiento de Tecate, Blvd. Universidad esq. Av. Piedra del Sol, Col. Militar, MX
Country: Mexico
Policies: Theatre

Teatro al Aire Libre del Parque Margarita Maza de Juárez
Phone: 665 654 9231
Address: Calle 5a núm. 214, Col. Benito Juárez, MX
Country: Mexico

Teatro al Aire Libre del Parque Municipal
Phone: 664 625 2470
Address: Parque Municipal Jos, Blvd. Insurgentes #16000, Col Libramiento Presa, MX
Country: Mexico

Teatro al Aire Libre Ignacio García Téllez
Email: rafael.puppo@imss.gob.mx
Phone: 612 123 6700
Address: Francisco I. Madero 315 y Héroes del 47, Esterito, MX

Country: Mexico
Policies: Theatre

Teatro al Aire Libre Netzahualcóyotl
Phone: 744 435 0130
Address: Av. Costera Miguel Alemán 4455, Col. Fracc. Costa Azul, MX
Country: Mexico
Policies: Theatre

Teatro al Aire Libre Vitro
Email:
clozano@vitro.com
Phone: 818 334 1772
Address: Grupo Industrial Vitro, Av. R, Col. Industria del Vidrio, MX
Country: Mexico

Teatro Alameda
Email: alerodri@aguascalientes.gob.mx
Phone:
449 975 0949
Address: Av. Convención #102 Esq. Alameda, MX
Country: Mexico
Contact: contact Hugo De Luna de Luna
Policies: Theatre

Teatro Alberto M. Alvarado
Email: mariogarza69@hotmail.com.mx
Phone: 871 750 1029
Address: Blvd. Miguel Alemán esq. Blvd, Francisco González de la Vega, Zona Centro, MX
Country: Mexico
Contact: contact Celia Rosario Uranga Garc
Policies: Theatre

Teatro Aldama
Phone: 555 546 1026
Address: Sindicato Nacional de Trabajadores de SAGARPA, , Rosas Moreno 71, , Col. San Rafael, MX
Country: Mexico
Contact: contact Benjamin Herrera
Policies: Theatre

Teatro Alvaro Carrillo
Website: www.oaxaca.gob.mx/ioc
Email: ioc@oaxaca.gob.mx
Phone: 951 514 6981
Address: Instituto Oaxaque, Calz. Madero esq. Av. Tecnol, Col. Centro, MX
Information: see also Cultural Institute of Oaxaca; theatre is temporarily closed
Country: Mexico

Teatro Ángela Peralta
Website: www.teatroangelaperalta.webpin.com/frameset.php?url=/intro.html
Address: Ayuntamiento de Allende Council of Allende, Col. Centro, MX
Country: Mexico

Teatro Ángela Peralta
Website: www.teatroangelaperalta.com
Email: prensa@teatroangelaperalta.com
Address: Council of Mazatlán, Av. Carnaval 1204, MX
Country: Mexico
Policies: Theatre

Teatro Antonio Leal y Romero
Website: www.cultura.gob.mx
Email: icags@infosel.net.mx
Phone: 449 916 4988
Address: Venustiano Carranza 101 Casa de la Cultura 1, Col. Centro, MX
Information: see also Instituto Cultural de Aguascalientes
Country: Mexico
Contact: responsable Alejandro Lozano Moreno

Teatro Auditorio Cívico Fray Ivo Toneck
Phone: 622 224 2626
Address: Calle 20 esq. Malpica, Col. Centro, MX
Country: Mexico
Policies: Theatre

Teatro Auditorio de la Casa de la Cultura Dr. V
Email: casaculturatux@prodigy.net.mx
Phone: 287 875 0144
Address: Conaculta / Instituto Nacional de Bellas Artes, Daniel Soto s/n, esq. Blvd. Benito Juárez, Col. Maria Luisa, MX
Information: see also Cultural Institute of Oaxaca
Country: Mexico
Contact: contact Reger Merl
Policies: Theatre

Teatro Axutla
Phone: 343 431 5176
Address: Parroquia de San Miguel, San Francisco 15, Col. Centro, MX
Country: Mexico
Contact: contact Domingo Huitr
Policies: Theatre

Teatro Benito Juárez
Email: tbenitojuarezcultura@yahoo.com.mx
Address: Ayuntamiento de El Oro Council of El Oro, Av. Ju, Col. Centro, MX
Country: Mexico
Social Media: @TEATROSDF www.facebook.com/teatrobenito.juarez
Policies: Theatre

Teatro Blanquita
Email: lcurbelo@cie.com.mx
Phone: 555 512 8264
Address: Eje Central Lázaro Cárdenas 16, , Col. Guerrero, MX
Country: Mexico
Contact: Manager Licelda Curbelo
Policies: Theatre

Teatro California
Website: isc.tectijuana.mx
Phone: 664 682 1624
Address: Instituto Tecnol, Calz. Tecnol, Col. Fracc. Tom, MX
Country: Mexico
Contact: responsable Manuela Monta

Teatro Campeche
Phone: 981 811 2910
Address: Instituto Mexicano del Seguro Social IMSS, Av. L, Col., MX
Country: Mexico
Contact: responsable Juan Palacios Figueroa

Teatro Centro Cívico de Jardines
Email: sistema_cultura_celaya@yahoo.com.mx
Phone: 461 175 4845
Address: Pirules s/n, Col. Jardines de Celaya, 2a, MX
Country: Mexico
Policies: Theatre

Teatro Ciudadela
Phone: 555 606 0700
Address: Subdirecci, Tres Guerras 9, Col. Centro, MX
Country: Mexico
Contact: contact Araceli Carrandi Garc
Policies: Theatre

Teatro Cuauhtémoc
Email: eduardo.iturbide@imss.gob.mx
Phone: 555 576 5908
Address: Av. 16 de Septiembre esq. Jardín, Col. Centro, MX
Country: Mexico
Policies: Theatre

Teatro de Aguascalientes
Email: teatroags@aguascalientes.gob.mx
Phone: 449 978 5414
Address: Instituto Cultural de Aguascalientes, Av. Aguascalientes Esq. Jos, Col. Jardines de Aguascalientes, MX
Information: see also Instituto Cultural de Aguascalientes q.v
Country: Mexico
Contact: contact Maria Elena Hermosillo Gonz
Social Media: http:// www.facebook.com/pages/Teatro-Aguascalientes/122782617749921
Policies: Theatre

Teatro de la ANDA
Website: www.anda.org.mx/
Email: andamty@hotmail.com
Phone: 818 372 7787
Address: Francisco I. Madero 1301 Pte, Centro, MX
Country: Mexico
Contact: contact Trinidad Delgado Valero

Teatro de la Casa de Cultura de Cos
Website: www.cultura.gob.mx
Email: buzon@aguascalientes.gob.mx
Phone: 458 987 0959
Address: Instituto Cultural de Aguascalientes, Madero Norte No 5, Col. Centro, MX
Information: see also Instituto Cultural de Aguascalientes
Country: Mexico

Teatro de la Casa de Cultura de Mexicali
Address: Av. Madero y Altamirano, Zona Centro, MX
Information: see also Instituto de Cultura de Baja California Norte q.v
Country: Mexico
Contact: contact Consuelo Barreiro Quintana
Policies: Theatre

Teatro de la Casa de Cultura de Rincón de Romos
Email: información.ica@aguascalientes.gob.mx
Phone: 465 951 1482
Address: Hidalgo 309, Col. Centro, MX
Country: Mexico
Policies: Theatre

Teatro de la Casa de Cultura de Tijuana
Phone: 664 687 2604

Address: Ave. París y Lisboa No. 5, Col. Altamira, MX
Country: Mexico
Contact: contact Grisel Aguirre Ruiz
Policies: Theatre

Teatro de la Ciudad
Phone: 555 510 2197
Address: Donceles 36 Centro, Cuauhtémoc, MX
Information: see also Cultural Institute of the State of
Morelos
Country: Mexico
Policies: Theatre

Teatro de la Ciudad de Camargo
Address: Instituto Chihuahuense de la Cultura, Av. Pablo
Ginther esq. Francisco Villa, Col. Árbol Grande, MX
Information: see also Cultural Institute of Chihuahua
Country: Mexico
Contact: contact Roberto Rodr
Policies: Theatre

Teatro de la Ciudad de Delicias
Address: Instituto Chiahuense de la Cultura, Av. Agricul-
tura y Río Conchos Oriente s/n, Col. Zona Centro, MX
Country: Mexico
Contact: contact Pablo Mu
Policies: Theatre

Teatro de la Ciudad de Ensenada
Website: www.bajacalifornia.gob.mx/icbc
Email: info@icbc.gob.mx
Phone: 646 177 0392
Address: Diamante s/n esq. Blvd. L, Col. Nueva Ensenada,
MX
Information: see also Cultural Institute of Baja California
Norte
Country: Mexico
Contact: contact Josefina Zavala Valle

Teatro de la Ciudad de La Paz
Email: teatrolapaz@hotmail.com
Phone: 612 125 0213
Address: Instituto Sudcaliforniano de Cultura, Navarro
entre Altamirano y H, Col. Pueblo Nuevo, MX
Information: see also Instituto de Cultura de Baja
California Norte
Country: Mexico
Contact: Directora Verna Alheida Pi

Teatro de la Ciudad de Monterrey
Email: teatro@teatrodelaciudad.org.mx
Phone: 818 343 8975
Address: Consejo para la Cultura de Nuevo Le, Zuazua y
Matamoros s/n, Col. Centro, MX
Country: Mexico
Contact: responsable Roberto Villareal Sep

Teatro de la Ciudad de Tapachula
Phone: 962 101 9207
Address: Ayuntamiento de Tapachula, Pista Antigua
Aeropuerto esq. Blvd. Independencia, Col. Solidaridad
2000, MX
Country: Mexico
Policies: Theatre

Teatro de la Ciudad Fernando Soler
Email: madelroblebarrett@terra.com.mx
Phone: 844 412 1947
Address: Instituto Coahuilense de Cultura, Xicot, Col.
Zona Centro, MX
Information: see also Instituto Coahuilense de Cultura,
alternative Email address: irmacaty@hotmail.com
Country: Mexico
Contact: responsable Gustavo Garc

Teatro de la Ciudad Francisco de Paula Toro
Address: Universidad Aut, Calle 12 n, Centro Hist, MX
Country: Mexico
Contact: contact Jorge Hurtado Oliver
Policies: Theatre

Teatro de la Ciudad Hermanos Domínguez
Phone: 967 678 3637
Address: Diag. Hermanos Paniagua s/n, Barrio de Fátima,
MX
Country: Mexico
Policies: Theatre

Teatro de la Ciudad Luis Donaldo Colosio
Phone: 938 382 6210
Address: Ayuntamiento del Carmen, Calle 26 A por 26,
Frente a la Calz. del Carmen, Col. Centro, MX
Country: Mexico

Teatro de la Ciudad San Francisco
Email: teatro@teatrosanfrancisco.com
Address: Teatro de la Ciudad San Francisco, Salamanca
S/N Col. Ex-Hacienda de Guadalupe, MX
Country: Mexico
Contact: contact Edith Cervantes Albarr
Policies: Theatre

**Teatro de la Escuela Preparatoria Federal Lázaro
Cárdena**
Email: epflc@lazarocardenas.edu.mx

Phone: 686 2701
Address: Paseo de los Heroes 11161, Zona Rio, MX
Country: Mexico
Policies: Theatre

Teatro de la Nación IMSS Ciudad Juárez
Website: www.imss.gob.mx/
Email: paul.davila@imss.gob.mx
Phone: 656 613 5930
Address: Panamá 477 , esquina con 20 de Noviembre,
Col. Partido Romero, MX
Country: Mexico
Policies: Theatre

Teatro de la Paz
Phone: 444 812 2698
Address: Villerías 206, , Centro Hstorico, , MX
Information: see also Cultural Institute of San Luis Potos
Country: Mexico
Contact: contact Jos hgfgdd
Social Media: http:// www.facebook.com/teatrodelapaz
Policies: Theatre

Teatro de los Héroes
Website: www.chihuahua.gob.mx/atach2/ichicult/up-
loads/teatrodelosheroes/inicioheroes.htm
Email: teatrodelosheroes@chihuahua.gob.mx
Address: Instituto Chihuahuense de Cultura, Divisi, Col.
Altavista, MX
Country: Mexico
Policies: Theatre

Teatro de Santa María del Obraje
Phone: 415 152 0116
Address: Calz. de la Presa 90, Col. Centro, MX
Country: Mexico
Policies: Theatre

Teatro Degollado
Website: www.degollado.gob.mx
Phone: 333 030 9770
Address: Belén Esq. Morelos S/n, Centro Historico, MX
Country: Mexico
Social Media: @Gob_Degollado www.facebook.com/
gobiernomunicipal.degolladojalisco
Policies: Theatre

Teatro del Estado
Website: www.bajacalifornia.gob.mx/icbc
Phone: 686 554 6419
Address: Blvd. L, Zona Centro, MX
Information: see also Cultural Institute of Baja California
Norte
Country: Mexico
Contact: responsable Rebeca Gilda Ulloa

Teatro del Estado Esperanza Iris
Website:
iec.tabasco.gob.mx/content/teatro-del-estado
Phone: 993 314 4210
Address: Periférico Carlos Pellicer Cámara s/n, zona
CICOM, Col. Centro, MX
Country: Mexico
Policies: Rent only, Theatre

Teatro del Ex Telar La Aurora
Email: bibsainz@hotmail.com
Phone: 985 856 2551
Address: Calle 42 esq. 35 s/n, MX
Country: Mexico

Teatro del Parque Víctor Sandoval Romero
Website: www.cultura.gob.mx
Email: icags@infosel.net.mx
Address: Av. López Mateos Esq. Paseo de la Feria, Col.
Centro, MX
Country: Mexico
Policies: Theatre

Teatro del Pueblo al Aire Libre
Email: cctarimoro@guanajuato.gob.mx
Phone: 466 664 1008
Address: Morelos 79, Col. Centro, MX
Country: Mexico

Teatro del Pueblo Alí Chumacero
Email: teatrotepic@hotmail.com.mx
Phone: 311 212 1623
Address: Av. Juan Escutia y Amado Nervo s/n, Col.
Centro, MX
Country: Mexico
Policies: Theatre

Teatro del Pueblo, Cuauhtémoc
Email: teatrodelpueblo.centro@gmail.com
Phone: 554 335 8036
Address: Rep. de Venezuela 72, Col. Centro, MX
Information: alternative email: caradelteatro@gmail.com
Country: Mexico
Policies: Theatre

Teatro del Pueblo, Jalpan
Phone: 524 412 960 285
Address: Ayuntamiento de Jalpan de Serra, Rivera del R,

Col. Centro, MX
Country: Mexico
Contact: responsable Gabriel Torres Sauceda

Teatro del Seguro Social
Email: mexicaliasecas@yahoo.com
Phone: 686 556 1434
Address: Instituto Mexicano del Seguro Social IMSS, Av.
Zaragoza s/n, Col. Nueva, MX
Country: Mexico
Contact: responsable Angel Norzagaray Norzagaray

Teatro Diana
Email: info@teatrodiana.com
Phone: 333 614 7072
Address: Av. 16 de Septiembre 710, Centro, Del, MX
Country: Mexico
Contact: contact Edmundo Ibarra Huerta
Social Media: @teatrodiana http:// www.facebook.com/
TeatroDiana
Policies: Theatre

Teatro en el Foro de El Lugar del Nopal
Website: www.lugardelnopal.com
Email: info@ellugardelnopal.com
Phone: 664 685 1264
Address: Privada 5 de Mayo 1328, MX
Information: independent cultural centre with kitchen,
gallery and concerts, also courses and studio Tango,
Salsa; guitar and piano; folk; alternative Email address:
nopalart@yahoo.com
Country: Mexico
Contact: contact Adelaida del Real Espinosa
Policies: Theatre

Teatro Ferrocarrilero
Phone: 618 811 2627
Address: Victoria 368 Nte., Col. Centro, MX
Country: Mexico

Teatro Foro La Puga
Email: ccarquitos@hotmail.com
Phone: 449 916 6098
Address: Col. La Estaci, MX
Information: see also Cultural Institute of Aguascalientes
Country: Mexico
Contact: responsable Marcela Duran Madrigal

Teatro Francisco Gabilondo Soler Cri-Cri
Phone: 449 978 5139
Address: Gobierno del Estado – Government, Blvd. Jos,
Parque H, MX
Country: Mexico

Teatro Francisco Javier Clavijero
Email: fomentocultural@terra.com.mx
Phone: 012 292 002 247
Address: Ayuntamiento de Veracruz, Emparan 166, Col.
Centro, MX
Country: Mexico
Contact: contact Alberto Mu

Teatro Fray Pedro de Gante
Phone: 477 713 2292
Address: Comunidad Franciscana de León, Héroes de la
Independencia 501, Anexo al Templo, Col. El Coecillo, MX
Country: Mexico
Contact: contact Mercedes I Aguilera

Teatro Gabriel Franzoni
Phone: 522 492 281 961
Address: Calle 6 Poniente #3904, Col. Aquiles Serd, MX
Country: Mexico

Teatro Galerías
Website: www.teatrogalerias.net
Phone: 333 631 0708
Address: Avenida Lapizlazuli 3445, Col. Residencial
Victoria, MX
Country: Mexico
Social Media: @teatrogalerias www.facebook.com/
pages/Teatro-Galerías/31688923771
Policies: Theatre

Teatro Griego
Address: Benem, Prol. Alcalde #1190,
Col. Sector Hidalgo, MX
Country: Mexico
Policies: Theatre

Teatro Hidalgo
Phone: 525 555 123 227
Address: Instituto Mexicano del Seguro Social IMSS, Av.
Hidalgo 23, Col. Centro, MX
Country: Mexico
Contact: contact Evangelina Gonzalez

Teatro Hidalgo Bartolom
Phone: 771 713 6767
Address: Consejo Estatal para la Cul. y Artes de Hidalgo,
Plaza Ju, Col. Centro, MX
Country: Mexico
Contact: responsable Lourdes Parga Mateos

Teatro Isauro Martínez
Website: www.teatroisauromartinez.com.mx
Email: informacion@teatroisauromartinez.com.mx
Phone: 871 192 0839
Address: Galeana 73 Sur, Col. Centro, MX
Country: Mexico
Policies: Theatre

Teatro Jorge Negrete ANDA
Email: oficialia@anda.org.mx
Phone: 555 535 2246
Address: Asociaci, Ignacio Altamirano 128, Col. San Rafael, MX
Country: Mexico
Contact: coordinator Sergio Reinoso Mart

Teatro José María Morelos
Email: cconvenciones@michoacan.gob.mx
Phone: 443 232 4400
Address: Av. Ventura Puente esq. Camelinas s/n, Col. Félix Ireta, MX
Country: Mexico
Policies: Theatre

Teatro Juan Ruiz de Alarc
Address: Centro de Capacitaci, Calle 49 D esq. 14, Col. San Mart, MX

Teatro Juárez de La Paz
Email: yosoyaltaira@hotmail.com
Phone: 612 122 2090
Address: Belisario Domínguez s/n entre 16 de Septiembre e Independencia, Col. Centro, MX
Country: Mexico
Policies: Theatre

Teatro Julio Castillo
Email: ccbgerencia@hotmail.com
Address: Conaculta / Instituto Nacional de Bellas Artes, Centro Cultural del Bosque, Paseo de la Reforma, esq. Campo Marte s/n, Col. Chapultepec Polanco, MX
Country: Mexico
Contact: coordinator Juan Jose Hernandez Rivas

Teatro Lírico
Phone: 555 512 5696
Address: Rep. de Cuba 54, Col. Centro, MX
Country: Mexico
Policies: Theatre

Teatro Manolo Fábregas
Website: www.manolofabregas.com
Email: produccfabregas@hotmail.com
Phone: 555 592 0751
Address: Velázquez de León 29, Col. San Rafael, MX
Country: Mexico
Policies: Theatre

Teatro Manuel Doblado
Website: www.leon.gob.mx/cultura
Email: erikatrujillomarin_1@hotmail.com
Phone: 477 716 9284
Address: c/o Instituto de Cultura del Estado de Guanajuato, Pedro Moreno 202, esq. Hermanos Aldama, MX
Country: Mexico

Teatro Metropolitan
Website: www.ocesa.com.mx
Email: mxmtocabl1@ocesa.com.mx
Phone: 555 518 3204
Address: Independencia #90, Col. Centro, MX
Information: alternative Email address: sbautista@ocesa.com.mx
Country: Mexico
Contact: contact Susuna Bautista Carbajal

Teatro Minerva al aire libre
Website: www.iqc.gob.mx
Email: iqcdir@prodigy.net.mx
Phone: 983 832 0223
Address: Instituto Quintanarroense de la Cultura, Av. Héroes 68, Col. Centro, MX
Information: see also Cultural Institute of Quintana Roo
Country: Mexico
Contact: contact Miguel Jim
Policies: Theatre

Teatro Morelos
Website: www.cultura.gob.mx
Email: icags@infosel.net.mx
Phone: 449 915 1941
Address: Nieto 113, Plaza de la Convenci, Col. Centro, MX
Information: see also Instituto Cultural de AguascalientesCountry: Mexico
Contact: responsable Elena Hermosillo Lopez

Teatro Morelos, Toluca
Address: Gobierno del Estado State Government / DIFEM, Plaza Morelos s/n, Col. Centro, MX
Country: Mexico
Contact: contact Carolina Monroy de Nemev

Teatro Nova
Email: c.rlopez@novaservicios.com.mx
Address: Av. del Bosque 139, Col. Cuauht, MX

Country: Mexico
Contact: contact Sim vsg
Policies: Theatre

Teatro Ocampo
Email: info@arte-cultura-morelos.com
Address: Instituto de Cultura de Morelos, Jard, Col. Centro, MX
Information: see also Cultural Institute of the State of Morelos
Country: Mexico
Contact: contact Yuridia Almanza Cabrera
Policies: Theatre

Teatro Principal de Puebla
Website: www.teatroprincipal.mx/
Email: teatroprincipalpuebla@gmail.com
Address: Gobierno del Estado de Puebla, Patronato del Teatro, Calle 8 Oriente esq. 6 Norte, Col. Centro, MX
Country: Mexico
Contact: Artistic Director Eduardo Ganime
Social Media: @TeatroPrincipal http:// www.facebook.com/pages/Teatro-Principal-de-Puebla/190242164354660
Policies: Theatre

Teatro Ramón López Velarde
Email: razzo@hotmail.com
Address: Av. La Encantada s/n, Col. Dif, MX
Country: Mexico
Policies: Theatre

Teatro Ricardo Castro
Email: sic.durango@hotmail.com
Phone: 618 811 4694
Address: Instituto de Cultura del Estado de Durango, Av 20 de Noviembre s/n, Col. Centro, MX
Country: Mexico
Contact: contact Victor Hugo J
Policies: Theatre

Teatro San Rafael
Phone: 555 592 2142
Address: Producciones Mafe, S.A. de C.V, Virginia Fábregas #40, MX
Country: Mexico
Contact: contact Rafaela Salinas Garc
Policies: Theatre

Teatro Tepic del IMSS
Email: carlos.ramosle@imss.gob.mx
Phone: 311 213 1170
Address: Instituto Mexicano del Seguro Social IMSS, Calz. de la Luz 14 esq., Col. Zona Centro, MX
Country: Mexico
Policies: Theatre

Teatro Tijuana
Email: alephteatro@yahoo.com.mx
Phone: 664 971 0019
Address: Instituto Mexicano del Seguro Social, Francisco C, Col. Aviaci, MX
Country: Mexico

Teatro Universitario de Mexicali
Address: Universidad Aut, López Rayón s/n, Col. Unidad Universitaria, MX
Country: Mexico
Contact: contact Salvador Sanchez Fajardo
Policies: Theatre

Teatro Universitario Escuela de Artes UABC Tecate
Email: educontkt@uabc.mx
Address: Universidad Aut, Calz. Universidad 1, Fracc. San Fernando, MX
Country: Mexico
Contact: contact Antonia Acevedo
Policies: Theatre

Teatro Universitario Rubén Vizcaíno Valencia
Website: www.uabc.mx
Email: tuopinion@uabc.mx
Phone: 664 979 7500
Address: Calz. Universidad 14418, Parque Industrial Internacional Tijuana, MX
Information: alternative email: sandra@uabc.edu.mxCountry: Mexico
Policies: Theatre

Teatro Xicohténcatl
Address: Av. Juárez 21, Col. Centro, MX
Country: Mexico
Policies: Theatre

Teatro-auditorio Dr. Samuel Ramos
Phone: 443 312 0161
Address: Universidad Michoacana de San Nicolás de Hidalgo, Av. Tata Vasco s/n, Centro, MX
Country: Mexico

Teatro-Auditorio Ricardo Chato Covarrubias
Phone: 613 132 0866

Address: Asoc Agr, Francisco I. Madero entre Rosaura Zapata yZaragoza, Col. Centro, MX
Country: Mexico
Contact: responsable Marco Antonio Cobarrubias Villa

Universidad Autónoma de Aguascalientes
Email: cvargas@correo.uaa.mx
Phone: 449 910 7400
Address: Av. Universidad 940, Ciudad Universitaria, MX
Country: Mexico

Universidad Autónoma de Baja California
Website: www.uabc.mx
Email: cuamea@uabc.edu.mx
Phone: 686 841 8200
Address: Benito Juárez S/N, Ex Ejidocoahuila, MX
Country: Mexico
Policies: Multi-purpose

Universidad Autónoma de Baja California Sur
Website: difusion.uabcs.mx
Email: jvaledith@uabcs.mx
Address: Carretera al Sur, Km 46, MX
Country: Mexico
Policies: Multi-purpose

Universidad Autónoma de Chiapas
Website: www.unach.mx
Phone: 962 620 1330
Address: Pista Principal Sn, Solidaridad, MX
Country: Mexico
Policies: Multi-purpose

Universidad Autónoma de Chihuahua
Phone: 614 439 1500
Address: Escorza 900, Zona Centro, MX
Country: Mexico
Policies: Multi-purpose

Universidad Autónoma de Ciudad Juárez
Phone: 656 688 2100
Address: Avenida Plutarco Elias Calles 1210, Fovissste Chamizal, MX
Country: Mexico
Policies: Multi-purpose

Universidad Autónoma de Coahuila
Phone: 448 438 1600
Address: Avenida Universidad SN, República Poniente, MX
Country: Mexico
Policies: Multi-purpose

Universidad Autónoma de Colima
Phone: 312 316 1000
Address: Av. Universidad 333, Colonia Las Víboras, MX
Country: Mexico
Policies: Multi-purpose

Universidad Autónoma de Hidalgo
Website: www.uaeh.edu.mx
Phone: 771 712 2000
Address: Carr Pachuca-Actopan km. 4, Edificio, MX
Country: Mexico
Contact: Director Luis Ramón Macías Pulido
Email: lrmacias@uaeh.edu.mx
Contact: webmaster Mauro Alberto Amador Lamb
Email: mauro@uaeh.edu.mx
Contact: web systems developer Mario Meneses Aguilar
Email: mariom@uaeh.edu.mx
Contact: systems designer and web applications Citlali Anahí Monzalvo López
Email: cmonzalvo@uaeh.edu.mx
Contact: designer and developer of 3D systems Nimrod Castillo Alcántara
Email: nimrod@uaeh.edu.mx

Universidad Autónoma de La Laguna
Phone: 871 718 5533
Address: Universidad Sin Asignación de Nombre de Colonia, Col. Chamilpa, MX
Country: Mexico
Policies: Multi-purpose

Universidad Autónoma de Nuevo León
Phone: 818 329 4000
Address: Pedro de Alba, Ciudad Universitaria, MX
Country: Mexico
Policies: Multi-purpose

Universidad Autónoma de Puebla
Phone: 222 229 5500
Address: 3 Oriente 4 sur no. 104, Col. Centro, Centro Histórico, MX
Information: organise musical presentations and festivals
Country: Mexico
Policies: Multi-purpose

Universidad Autónoma de San Luis Potosí
Phone: 444 811 8321
Address: Karakorum 1245, Lomas 4 Sección, MX
Country: Mexico

Policies: Multi-purpose

Universidad Autónoma de Sinaloa
Phone: 667 713 4043
Address: Ciudad Universitaria SN, MX
Country: Mexico

Universidad Autónoma de Sonora
Phone: 662 213 1581
Address: Luis Encinas y RoSales S/N, Col. Centro, MX
Country: Mexico
Policies: Multi-purpose

Universidad Autónoma de Tamaulipas
Phone: 834 318 1800
Address: 8 y 9 Matamoros s/n, Col. Centro, MX
Country: Mexico
Policies: Multi-purpose

Universidad Autónoma de Tlaxcala
Phone: 749 918 1151
Address: Ignacio Zaragoza 1 Centro, Av. Universidad n, MX
Country: Mexico
Policies: Multi-purpose

Universidad Autónoma de Zacatecas
Website: sistemas.uaz.edu.mx
Email: rectoria@uaz.edu.mx
Phone: 492 922 2001
Address: Jardín Juárez 147, Centro Histórico, MX
Country: Mexico
Policies: Theatre

Universidad Autónoma del Estado de Morelos
Website: www.uaem.mx
Email: webmaster2@uaem.mx
Phone: 777 329 7000
Address: Av. Universidad 1001, Col. Chamilpa, MX
Country: Mexico
Policies: Multi-purpose

Universidad de Guadalajara (UDG)
Website: www.fundacion.udg.mx
Email: cultura.udg@redudg.udg.mx
Phone: 333 044 4050
Address: "Juan Jose Arreola" State Public Library, Level No. 6, Periférico Norte #1695, Col. Belenes, MX
Information: member of ISPA
Country: Mexico
Social Media: @udg_oficial
www.facebook.com/UdG.Cultura?ref=stream&hc_location=stream
Policies: Other

Universidad de Guanajuato – Depto. Cultural
Website: www.ugto.mx
Email: mendiola@ugto.mx
Phone: 473 732 5702
Address: Calle de Alonso no 12, Mesón de San António, Zona Centro, MX
Country: Mexico
Contact: General Director Laura Gemma Flores García
Email: cultura_flores@ugto.mx
Policies: Other

Universidad de las Américas Puebla
Email: informes.nuevoingreso@udlap.mx
Phone: 222 229 2000
Address: Santa Catarina Mártir, MX
Country: Mexico
Policies: Multi-purpose

Universidad de Sonora
Website: www.uson.mx
Email: cartes@guaymas.uson.mx
Phone: 662 259 2115
Address: Blvd. Luis Encinas y RoSales S/N, , Col. Centro, MX
Country: Mexico
Contact: General administrative Director Rosa Elena Trujillo Llanes
Email: rtrujillo@sociales.uson.mx
Social Media: @buhosunison
Policies: Other

Universidad Juárez Autónoma de Tabasco
Website: www.ujat.mx
Phone: 993 358 1500
Address: Av. Universidad s/n, Zona de Cultura, MX
Country: Mexico
Policies: Multi-purpose

Universidad Juárez del Estado de Durango
Email: ujed@ujed.mx
Phone: 618 812 0044
Address: Constitución 404 sur., Zona centro, MX
Country: Mexico
Policies: Multi-purpose

Universidad Nacional Autónoma de México
Website: www.unam.mx
Email: Directorio@servidor.unam.mx

Address: Centro Cultural Universitario, Insurgentes Sur 3000, MX
Country: Mexico
Social Media: @unam_mx www.facebook.com/UNAM.MX.Oficial
Policies: Multi-purpose

Universidad Veracruzana
Website: www.uv.mx/
Email: jbarrera@uv.mx
Phone: 228 841 8900
Address: Lomas del Estadio S/N, Edificio A Piso 3, Col. Zona Universitaria, MX
Country: Mexico
Contact: international office María Alarcón
Email: maghernandez@uv.mx

NEW ZEALAND

Arena Manawatu
Website: www.arenamanawatu.co.nz
Email: office@arenamanawatu.co.nz
Phone: 635 61505
Address: 61 Pascal Street, NZ
Information: Arena Manawatu is the premier sports and recreation facility serving Palmerston North and the wider Manawatu region
Country: New Zealand
Contact: venues Manager John Lynch
Email: john@cetarena.co.nz
Contact: operations Manager Charles Foulds
Email: charles@cetarena.co.nz
Capacity: 15000

ASB Showgrounds
Website: www.asbshowgrounds.co.nz
Email: info@asbshowgrounds.co.nz
Phone: 963 89969
Address: 217 Greenlane Road West, NZ
Information: ASB Showgrounds is home to a truly world class events and exhibition centre. With over $30m spent on redeveloping their site in 2009, they have future proofed facilities to cater to any demand placed on them — whether indoor or outdoor. During the event planning process, you need to be sure that the event centre facilities you are looking at, have every angle covered. From the venue and its physical exhibition spaces, to event parking, there's a lot for you to consider.
Country: New Zealand
Contact: Marketing, Sales and events Manager Nicola Harris
Email: nicola@asbshowgrounds.co.nz
Social Media: www.facebook.com/ASB-Show-grounds-386303254758954
Capacity: 3500

Auckland University Students Association
Website: www.ausa.org.nz
Email: reception@ausa.org.nz
Phone: 930 90789
Address: 4 Alfred Street, NZ
Information: Auckland University Students' Association or AUSA was founded in 1891 to provide a united and representative voice to students of the University of Auckland and to deliver an expansive range of services and events that students want and need. The founding philosophy is student control of student affairs, and AUSA is run by students, for students.
Country: New Zealand
Contact: President Will Matthews
Social Media: @AUSAStudents www.facebook.com/AUSAStudents
Capacity: 104

BATS Theatre
Website: www.bats.co.nz
Email: bats@bats.co.nz
Phone: 480 24175
Address: 1 Kent Terrace, NZ
Information: BATS Theatre is New Zealand's leading venue for the development of new theatre practitioners and plays. The recently renovated venue has three intimate performance spaces and is located in the central city of the country's capital, Wellingtone.
Country: New Zealand
Contact: programmes Manager Cherie Jacobson
Social Media: https:// www.facebook.com/BATSTheatre/
Policies: Theatre

Baycourt Community and Arts Centre
Website: www.baycourt.co.nz
Email: baycourt@tauranga.govt.nz
Phone: 757 77189
Address: 38 Durham Street, NZ
Information: This is the premier performing arts facility in Tauranga. It is extensively used by local, regional, national and international performances, conferences and exhibitions. With three prominent spaces, the Centennial Theatre, the Exhibition Space and the Terrace Rooms, Baycourt is designed to suit every event.
Country: New Zealand
Contact: Manager Megan Peacock Coyle
Email: megan.peacockcoyle@tauranga.govt.nz
Contact: technical Manager Ben Hambling

Email: ben.hambling@tauranga.govt.nz
Contact: Marketing coordinator David Tauranga
Email: david.tauranga@tauranga.govt.nz
Policies: Rent and present, Theatre

Bruce Mason Centre
Website: www.aucklandlive.co.nz/venue/bruce-mason-centre
Email: info@bmcentre.co.nz
Phone: 948 82940
Address: 1 The Promenade, Takapuna Beach, NZ
Information: Located in Takapuna, a stone's throw away from the beach and with stunning views of Rangitoto, The Bruce Mason Centre is a short drive from Auckland's CBD and located in the heart of Takapuna's dining district. Bruce Mason Centre is named after one of New Zealand's greatest playwrights, Bruce Mason. Bruce was best known for a classic Kiwi play called 'The End of the Golden Weather'.
Country: New Zealand
Contact: Director Mohamed Mansour
Contact: Manager business development Josephine Godfrey
Contact: business development Executive Carol Gayagay
Annual Performances: 200
Policies: Rent and present, Produce and rent

Capital E – National Theatre for Children
Website: www.capitale.org.nz
Email: capitale@experiencewellington.org.nz
Phone: 491 33740
Address: 4 Queens Wharf, NZ
Information: Capital E is an award-winning not-for-profit organisation based in the cultural capital of Wellington, whose focus is children and their creativity. Capital E ignites the creative spark in young people, through digital workshops, live performance and events. It is a not-for-profit organisation based in Te Whanganui a Tara, Wellington providing quality experiences to schools and public.
Country: New Zealand
Contact: relationship development coordinator Hana Makin
head of programming & partnerships Melissa Conway
Social Media: @CapitalENZ www.facebook.com/Capital-Eforchildren
Policies: Theatre

Christchurch Convention Centre
Website: www.convention.co.nz
Email: bryan.pearson@vbase.co.nz
Phone: 333 93599
Address: 86-95 Kilmore Street, NZ
Information: Christchurch Convention Centre's proximity to the Christchurch International Airport and an abundance of good hotels around, makes it the right venue for conventions, exhibitions or gala dinners. The center's main hall can be split into three separate ones, as per the requirement, all of which are spacious and airy. The first floor houses seven breakout rooms, a board room and a bar, so visitors can chill out after or during the session.
Country: New Zealand
Contact: CEO Bryan Pearson
Capacity: 9000

Dunedin Centre
Website: www.dunedinvenues.co.nz/venues/dunedin-centre
Email: info@dunedinvenues.co.nz
Phone: 347 94396
Address: 1 Harrop Street, PO Box 5457, NZ
Information: The Dunedin Centre combines the very best heritage features with state of the art facilities. The grand baroque style of the Dunedin Centre makes an imPressive setting for any event. Located in the centre of the city you'll find the very best in conference, exhibition and performance facilities – it's the perfect blend of old-world style and modern convenience.
Country: New Zealand
Contact: business development Manager Kim Dodds
Social Media: www.facebook.com/Dunedincentre
Policies: Multi-purpose

Forum North Performance, Conference & Exhibition Centre
Email: forumnorth@wdc.govt.nz
Phone: 943 04244
Address: 7 Rust Ave, NZ
Information: Forum North, is Northland's top performance, conference and Expo centre, located just 2 hours from central Auckland. The venue is unrivalled in Northland for its versatility and our professional staff are happy to accommodate your every need, from setting up your event to Marketing it. Forum North in its entirety can be hired for large events like festivals and Expo's, or on a smaller scale for meetings and cocktails. Staging, lighting and all technical services are available for hire and we will do anything to make your event a success.
Country: New Zealand
Capacity: 594

Founders Theatre
Website: www.founderstheatre.co.nz

Email: clarencestreettheatre@gmail.com
Phone: 783 86600
Address: 221 Tristram Street, NZ
Information: Founders Theatre is owned and managed by H3, a unit within Hamilton City Council and is currently closed due to health and safety issues. The Council is currently undertaking public engagement and accepting submissions on the future of the venue. In the interim the experienced Founders team has been retained within H3 and continues to look after our clients' needs offering alternate options at Claudelands.
Country: New Zealand
Contact: Manager Sven Ladewig
Capacity: 1249

Hannah Playhouse
Website: www.hannahplayhouse.org.nz
Email: kathiy.watson@wmt.org.nz
Phone: 489 47412
Address: 12 Cambridge Terrace, NZ
Information: The Hannah Playhouse is a historic theatre and function venue located in one of Wellingtons busiest entertainment precincts. It is primarily used for theatre and performing arts experiences, but can also be hired as a function or conference venue.
Country: New Zealand
Contact: General Manager Kathy Watson
Email: kathiyw@experiencewellington.org.nz
Contact: front house administrator Ruby Harrison
Email: rubyh@experiencewellington.org.nz
Social Media: www.facebook.com/thehannahplayhouse
Capacity: 250

Hawke's Bay Opera House & Precinct
Website: www.hawkesbayoperahouse.co.nz
Email: danef@hdc.govt.nz
Phone: 687 15000
Address: 101 Hastings Street South, Hawkes Bay, NZ
Information: The plaza is the ultimate blank canvas waiting for you to bring your creative ideas to life. Whether you're planning a gala dinner, cocktail function, exhibition or product launch, it will be an event to remember at the Opera House Plaza.
Country: New Zealand
Contact: booking coordinator Charie Bowgett
Email: charieb@hdc.govt.nz
Social Media: @HB_OperaHouse www.facebook.com/hawkesbayoperahouse
Capacity: 980

Isaac Theatre Royal
Website: www.isaactheatreroyal.co.nz
Email: admin@isaactheatreroyal.co.nz
Phone: 336 66326
Address: 145 Gloucester Street, NZ
Information: The Isaac Theatre Royal, Christchurch is a 106 year old Historic Edwardian Heritage Theatre with up to 1292 seats over three levels.
The entire auditorium and foyer areas of the Theatre were rebuilt between 2012 – 2014, following the devastating earthquakes of 2011 which required deconstruction of those areas. Significant heritage fabric was retained including the magnificent original 1908 painted ceiling dome, the façade and the 1928 marble staircase amongst many other important heritage features. The Isaac Theatre Royal was rebuilt to 100% of new building codes following the earthquakes and is regarded as one of the safest, strongest and most spectacular performing arts venues in Australasia.
Country: New Zealand
Contact: chief Executive Neil Cox
Email: neil@itr.co.nz
Contact: event delivery and client relations Manager Freya Alexander
Email: freya@itr.co.nz
Contact: technical Manager Matthias Mard
Email: matt@itr.co.nz
Social Media: www.facebook.com/IsaacTheatreRoyal
Capacity: 1292

Maidment Theater
Website: www.maidment.auckland.ac.nz
Email: maidmentbooking@auckland.ac.nz
Phone: 930 82383
Address: 8 Alfred Street, NZ
Information: This well-appointed theatre is the pride of the Auckland University campus and is centrally located. With a wide range of performances throughout the year, the theatre helps bring together the University and the community. It is a twin theatre complex, fully air-conditioned and with easy access and facilities for the disabled.
Country: New Zealand
Social Media: @MaidmentTheatre www.facebook.com/maidmenttheatre
Capacity: 448

Marlborough Civic Theatre
Website: www.asbtheatre.com
Email: book@mctt.co.nz
Phone: 352 08558
Address: 2 Hutcheson Street, NZ
Information: The Marlborough Civic Theatre Trust was formed as a non for profit organisation on 16th No-

vember 1974 following the demolition of His Majesty's Theatre with the principal objective of establishing a new theatre for the Marlborough community to use.
Country: New Zealand
Contact: Chair Kevin Moseley
Contact: General Manager Andrew Scott
Social Media: www.facebook.com/asbtheatremarlborough
Capacity: 900

MT Smart Stadium
Website: www.mtsmartstadium.co.nz
Email: info@aucklandstadiums.co.nz
Phone: 936 62048
Address: 2 Beasley Avenue, Penrose, NZ
Information: New Zealand's premier outdoor concert and festival venue, Mt Smart Stadium hosts some of the world's best entertainment acts. As well as the main arena, Mt Smart features an international standard athletics facility, multi-purpose function spaces and a range of community-focused facilities catering for over 350000 visitors a year.
Country: New Zealand
corporate Sales & Marketing Manager
Jennifer Berthier
Social Media: @mtsmartstadium www.facebook.com/mtsmartstadium

MTG Century Theatre
Website: www.mtghawkesbay.com
Email: info@mtghawkesbay.com
Phone: 683 57781
Address: Tai Ahuriri, 1 Tennyson Street, NZ
Information: The MTG Theatre is a modernist masterpiece designed by architect Guy Natusch. Built in 1977 as a concert chamber to commemorate Napier's first Century as a city, MTG's 330 seat theatre is now an intimate setting for performing arts, film and lectures.
Country: New Zealand
Contact: Director Laura Vodanovich
Email: lvodanovich@mtghawkesbay.com
Contact: maori engagement Charles Ropitini
Email: charles.ropitini@mtghawkesbay.com
Social Media: www.facebook.com/mtghawkesbay
Policies: Present and produce, Theatre

Napier Municipal Theatre
Website: www.napiermunicipaltheatre.co.nz
Email: info@napiermunicipaltheatre.co.nz
Phone: 683 51059
Address: 119 Tennyson Street, Private Bag 6010, NZ
Information: The Napier Municipal Theatre is one of the best event venues in the country. It combines elegant art deco style with modern theatre facilities, making it a great choice when you need an event venue to hire. The large auditorium facilities and circular Pan Pac Foyer make it a flexible event and function venue with many options.
Country: New Zealand
Contact: venue Manager Glenys Fraser
Email: glenys.fraser@venues.co.nz
Contact: client relations Ian Reid
Email: ian.reid@venues.co.nz
Social Media: www.facebook.com/NapierMunicipalTheatre
Policies: Rent and present, All, Theatre

National Institute of Creative Arts and Industries – School of Music
Website: www.auckland.ac.nz/en/creative.html
Email: info-creative@auckland.ac.nz
Phone: 800 616 263
Address: Level 2, Building 421, 6 Symonds Street, NZ
Information: Students enjoy a musical education unmatched in New Zealand. With specialised facilities and expert staff, many of whom are world renowned, the university produces graduates of international calibre.
Country: New Zealand
Contact: communications coordinator Miranda Playfair
Email: m.playfair@auckland.ac.nz
Capacity: 880

Nelson School of Music
Website: www.nsom.ac.nz
Email: nsom@nsom.ac.nz
Phone: 354 89477
Address: 142a Collingwood Street, NZ
Information: The main auditorium is renowned for its acoustics and is considered to be one of the best auditoria in the Southern Hemisphere for chamber music. It is also home to the international Adam Chamber Music Festival every two years, and as well as being available for concert hire, the auditorium is also suitable for symposiums, lectures and conferences.
Country: New Zealand
Contact: office Manager Clare Monti
Contact: administrator Jan Sellers
Social Media: www.facebook.com/Nelson-School-of-Music-91650518659
Capacity: 380

Opera House, The
Website: www.pwv.co.nz/our-venues/opera-house/
Email: info@pwv.co.nz
Phone: 480 14207

Address: 113/111 Manners St, NZ
Information: History and heritage are words that are synonymous with the Opera House. An intimate and welcoming performance space that oozes antique charm and backstage drama, the Opera House has been a social and events venue for successive generations in Wellington. The Opera House hosts a wide variety of performances and events and is a place that springboards and showcases up-and-coming talent. It is also a popular choice for on-stage gala events, dining and programme launches.
Country: New Zealand
Policies: Theatre

Positively Wellington Venues
Website: venueswellington.com
Email: info@pwv.co.nz
Phone: 480 14231
Address: 111 Wakefield Street, PO Box 2199, NZ
Information: The collection of conference and performance venues combines heritage and character with state of the art technology. The diverse choice of meeting places and spaces offers versatility and flexibility, and the love to work with the clients to create innovative event set-ups that will deliver inspirational experiences.
Country: New Zealand
Contact: General Manager venues, Marketing and destination development David Perks
Social Media: @WgtnVenues www.facebook.com/positivelywgtnvenues
Policies: Multi-purpose

Regent on Broadway Theatre
Website: www.regent.co.nz
Email: Manager@regent.co.nz
Phone: 635 02100
Address: 53 Broadway, PO Box 1723, NZ
Information: Gear up to face some of the best national and international talents on stage at New Zealand's premier performing arts venue, The Regent, on Broadway. This eclectic theater came into existence in 1929 and was used for hosting movies and opera performances. Today, the refurbished theatre is host to concerts, theatre performances, dance shows, comedy and other plethora of cultural events throughout the year.
Country: New Zealand
Contact: General Manager Charles Forbes
Email: Manager@regent.co.nz
Contact: office administrator Julie Walker
Email: administrator@regent.co.nz
Social Media: @RegentTheatrePNRegent on Broadway
Policies: Theatre

Regent Theatre
Website: www.regenttheatre.co.nz
Email: warrent@regenttheatre.co.nz
Phone: 347 78597
Address: 17 The Octagon, PO Box 5036, NZ
Information: Originally a 2000 seat cinema, the Regent opened on 1 June 1928, and the interior is elaborately decorated in a revived baroque style, characteristic of the super cinemas of the time. The design is a variation of Robert Atkinson's for the 1921 Regent cinema in Brighton, England, which was demolished in 1974. There were comparable picture palaces in other cities in Britain and Australia, few of which now survive and, apart from the Dunedin building, none in their original form.
Country: New Zealand
Contact: Director Sarah Anderson
Email: saraha@regenttheatre.co.nz
Contact: Administration Manager Andrea Ford
Email: andreaf@regenttheatre.co.nz
Social Media: @RegentDunedin www.facebook.com/regentdunedin
Capacity: 1617

Royal Wanganui Opera House
Website: www.royaloperahouse.co.nz
Email: royaloperahouse@whanganui.govt.nz
Phone: 634 90511
Address: 69 St Hill Street, NZ
Information: This is New Zealand's last Victorian Theatre. It is 113 years old and has 830 seats, and is the the venue for many local, national and international events. These events include Grand Opera, Operetta, Tribute concerts, Piano recitals, Orchestral Concerts, School Events, Lectures, Graduations, Fashion Shows, Dance of all forms and Floral Theatre to name a few. Any function requiring a stage and auditorium style seating can be accommodated.**Country:** New Zealand
Contact: Manager John Richardson
Policies: Rent only, Theatre

St James Theatre
Website: www.venueswellington.com/venues/st-james-theatre/
Email: venues-Sales@WellingtonNZ.com
Phone: 4
80 14231
Address: 77-87 Courtenay Place, NZ
Information: Home of the Royal New Zealand Ballet, NZ Festival and the New Zealand Opera, the St James Theatre is the jewel in the crown of Wellington's theatre

scene. The Theatre hosts a variety of dance, drama, opera, comedy and cabaret every year. Designed and built in 1912 by Henry Eli White, the building has Category 1 Heritage status.

The St James Theatre is comprised of the St James Building (Auditorium and Stage House) and adjoining Counties (Ballet) Building.
Country: New Zealand
Disabled Access: Yes
Capacity: 1000+

Trafalgar Centre
Website:
www.trafalgarcentre.co.nz
Email: trafalgarevents@xtra.co.nz
Phone: 353 91301
Address: 7 Paru Paru Rd, NZ
Information: The Trafalgar Centre is the largest indoor multi-purpose events centre in the Nelson / Tasman Region. Built in the early 1970s as a sports stadium, the Centre also hosts major cultural and entertainment events and exhibitions. As well as the main stadium, it features the Victory Room, a popular venue for smaller events.
Country: New Zealand
Policies: Multi-purpose

TSB Bowl of Brooklands
Website: npeventvenues.nz/Venue-Hire/TSB-Bowl-of-Brooklands
Email: enquiries@npdc.govt.nz
Phone: 675 96060
Address: Brooklands Park Drive, NZ
Information: The iconic TSB Bowl of Brooklands is surrounded by a picturesque lake and the stunning backdrop of New Plymouth's Pukekura Park. The venue consists of an outdoor sound stage and a grass amphitheatre suitable for a variety of entertainers, as well as functions, concerts, corporate events, weddings and dinners.
Country: New Zealand
Social Media: www.facebook.com/TSB-Bowl-of-Brooklands-572280849523965
Policies: Theatre

TSB Showplace
Website: www.tsbshowplace.co.nz
Email: tsbshowplace@npdc.govt.nz
Phone: 675 96712
Address: 92 – 100 Devon Street West, NZ
Information: A heritage structure dating back to the late 19th Century, TSB Showplace is a major events center catering to events like conferences, drama, dance shows and concerts. This center is located close to the Waterfront in New Plymouth and has multiple venues that are available for hire.
Country: New Zealand
Contact: venue Manager Megan Brown
Email: megan.brown@npdc.govt.nz
Contact: business development officer Penny Burmester
Email: tsbshowplace@npdc.govt.nz
Social Media: @TSBShowplace www.facebook.com/TSB-Showplace-121263647936290
Policies: Multi-purpose

Vodafone Events Centre
Website: www.pacific.org.nz
Email: info@pacific.org.nz
Phone: 997 67777
Address: 770 Great South Road, NZ
Information: Vodafone Events Centre is a versatile event space located in Manukau City. The plush complex consists of indoor arenas for sporting events, community halls for weddings and reception as well as board rooms for corporate events, meetings and seminars, theater and concert space for cultural events and live performances. Business, art and entertainment form a heady cocktail at Vodafone Events Centre. The center is exceptionally well-maintained and well-equipped.
Country: New Zealand
Contact: Director Mike Hutcheson
Social Media:
www.facebook.com/vodafoneeventscentre
Policies: Multi-purpose

Wellington Cathedral of St Paul
Website: wellingtoncathedral.org.nz
Email: admin@wellingtoncathedral.org.nz
Phone:
447 20286
Address: cnr Hill and Molesworth Streets, PO Box 12-044, NZ
Information: Sixty one years went into designing and building the largest and most spectacular spaces in New Zealand. Commissioned in the early 1930s, it was to be a Gothic structure from stone or brick, but, after the Napier earthquake, the decision was made to build the cathedral out of reinforced concrete. One of the oldest cathedrals in Wellington, this, massive structure has been a source of pride for New Zealenders and comfort for believers of the faith.
Country: New Zealand
Contact: assistant Director of music Richard Apperley
Capacity: 1200

PHILIPPINES

Adamson University
Website: www.adamson.edu.ph
Email:
webmaster@adamson.edu.ph
Phone: 524 2011
Address: 900 San Marcelino st., Malate, PH
Information: Adamson University Theater hosts guests and university performing groups: Adamson University Brass Band, Adamson University Acoustic Band, Adamson University String Ensemble, Adamson University Folk Dance Troupe, Adamson University Chorale, Adamson University Chamber Singers, and Adamson University Acapellas whose members are all trained to be excellent performers.
Country: Philippines
Contact: President Marcelo V. Manimtim
Social Media: https:// www.facebook.com/AdamsonUniversity.Official/

Ateneo de Manila Theaters
Website:
http://www.ateneo.edu/about/facilities/theaters
Email: mpao@ateneo.edu
Phone: 426 6069
Address: Katipunan Avenue, Loyola Heights, PH
Information: The Henry Lee Irwin Theater is the Ateneo's premiere venue for the performance arts. With a seating capacity of 1, 131, it is also the ideal venue for conventions, corporate promotional activities, graduations, and movie premieres. Smaller, Fine Arts Theater is used for staging plays, dance performances, poetry reading, book launching programs and other art-related events.
Country: Philippines
Social Media: https://twitter.com/ateneodemanilau www.facebook.com/ateneodemanila https:// www.instagram.com/theateneo/
Capacity: 1000+
Policies: All

Bicol State University
Phone: 247 73320
Address: San Jose, PH
Country: Philippines

Cebu Coliseum
Address: 128 Sanciangko St, PH
Country: Philippines
Policies: Theatre

Cultural Centre of the Philippines (CCP)
Website: www.culturalcenter.gov.ph
Email: ccp@culturalcenter.gov.ph
Phone: 883 21125
Address: CCP Complex, Roxas Boulevard 1300 Pasay City, PH
Information: The Cultural Center of the Philippines (CCP) is the premiere showcase of the arts in the Philippines. Founded in 1969, the CCP has been producing and presenting music, dance, theater, visual arts, literary, cinematic and design events from the Philippines and all over the world for more than forty years.
Country: Philippines
Contact: Office of the President
Phone: 883 40468Office of the Vice President for Administration
Phone: 855 13737 Corporate Communications Division
Phone: 883 21125 Box Office
Phone: 883 23704 Production and Exhibition Department
Phone: 883 32125 Administrative Services Department
Phone: 883 23677
Social Media: www.facebook.com/culturalcenterofthephilippines/twitter.com/culturalctrph www.instagram.com/culturalcenterph/

De la Salle University Theatre
Phone: 253 60301
Address: De la Salle University, 2401 Taft Avenue, PH
Country: Philippines
Contact: contact Enrico Cordero
Capacity: 250

Far Eastern University Auditorium
Phone: 273 55621
Address: Far Eastern University, N Reyes St, PH
Country: Philippines
Contact: President Larry Rodriguez
Contact: theatre Manager/ contact Marie cayabyab
Capacity: 500

Francisco Santiago Hall
Phone: 632 818 1403
Address: PCI Bank Bldg, Horacio de la Costa St, PH
Country: Philippines
Contact: contact Amando Baltazar

Hiyas Ng Bulacan
Address: Bulacan Capitol Complex, Malolos, PH
Country: Philippines

Luzonian University

Address: University Site, Lucena City, PH
Country: Philippines

Manuel Quezon University Auditorium
Phone: 273 40121
Address: Manuel L. Quezon University, 916 R Hidalgo St, Quiapo, PH
Country: Philippines
Contact: Executive officer Viky Chan

Mindanao State University
Phone: 63 – 521 002 c
Address: Lanao del Sur, Marawi City, PH
Country: Philippines

NAC Open-Air Theatre (Tanghalang Maria Makiling)
Website: www.culturalcenter.gov.ph/venues/other-venues/tanghalang-maria-makiling-nac-theater
Email: contact_us@culturalcenter.gov.ph
Phone: 883 23704
Address: Los Baños, Laguna, Philippines
Information: Tanghalang Maria Makiling (NAC Theater) is an open theater that can accommodate up to 1, 000 audience complete with state of the art lights and sound system suitable for low, medium and large scale productions and performances, air-conditioned dressing rooms and office spaces
Country: Philippines
Social Media: www.facebook.com/culturalcenterofthephilippines/twitter.com/culturalctrph www.instagram.com/culturalcenterph/
Capacity: 501-1000

Philamlife Theatre
Phone: 526 9250
Address: Philamlife Bldg, U.N Avenue, PH
Country: Philippines
Contact: corporate affairs Manager Ariel del Mundo

Philippine High School for the Arts
Phone: 495 362 862
Address: National Arts Center, Mt. Makiling College, Los Ba, PH
Country: Philippines
Contact: Executive Director Fernando C Josef

Philippine Women's University Concert Hall
Phone: 252 68288
Address: Philippine Women's University, Taft Ave., PH
Country: Philippines
Contact: contact Myrna Allanza
Contact: Director Administration Jose S Eguerra

Pope Pius XII Catholic Centre Auditorium
Phone: 632 525 9126
Address: 1175 UN Ave., PH
Country: Philippines
Contact: accomodation coordinator Vicky Velasco
Capacity: 500

Sentrong Pangkultura ng Pilipinas
Website: www.ccpap.admw.edu.ph
Email: ccp@portalinc.com
Phone: 283 21125
Address: CCP Complex, Roxas Blvd, PH
Information: presents, co-produce; also houses Museum of Philippine Culture, Manila Film Center, gallaries, audio-visual room, library; resident companies are: Ballet Philippines, Philippine Philharmonic Orchestrra, Philippine Ballet Theater, Ramon Obusan Folkloric Gr
Country: Philippines
Contact: officer in charge public relations Irene O Rada
Contact: President Baltazar N Endriga
Contact: Associate Artistic Director Dennis N Marasigan

Smart Araneta Coliseum
Website: www.smartaranetacoliseum.com
Phone: 291 13101
Address: Araneta Centre, Cubao, PH
Information: the Smart Araneta Coliseum, known as The Big Dome is an indoor multi-purpose sports arena. It is one of the largest coliseums and indoor facilities in Asia, and it is also one of the largest clear span domes in the world. The Smart Araneta Coliseum is mostly used for sports such as basketball, it is the main venue of the Philippine Basketball Association. The Big Dome is also used for boxing, cockfighting, local and international concerts, circuses, religious gatherings, beauty pageants and more. It also houses different events ranging from entertainment events, business ventures, religious events to sports events
Country: Philippines
Social Media: @TheBigDome www.facebook.com/thearanetacoliseum
Policies: All, Multi-purpose

Southwestern University
Phone: 633 272 341
Address: Villa Aznar, PH
Country: Philippines

St Louis University
Email: kgb@burgos.slu.edu.ph

Phone: 744 422 001
Address: A Bonifacio St, PH
Country: Philippines
Contact: acting Director Laurel Bangaoet

University of Baguio
Address: General Luna St, PH
Country: Philippines

University of Manila Auditorium
Phone: 273 55098
Address: M.V. delos Santos St, PH
Country: Philippines
Contact: contact Emily de Leon

University of Mindanao Auditorium
Address: University of Mindanao, Botton St, Davao City, PH
Country: Philippines
Contact: senior vice President Paquita D Gavimo
Contact: exective vice President Saturrino R Detalcorin
Contact: President Dolores P Torres

University of San Agustin Little Theatre
Phone: 633 374 841
Address: University of San Agustin, General Luna St, PH
Country: Philippines
Contact: contact Emilio Sudaria

University of Santo Tomas
Phone: 632 731 3101
Address: Espa, PH
Country: Philippines
Contact: Director Melchor Saria

University of the East Theater
Phone: 632 735 5471
Address: University of the East, Claro M. Recto Ave., PH
Country: Philippines

University of the Philippines, Baguio
Email: dean@baguio.upcb.edn.ph
Phone: 744 423 888
Address: Gov Pack Road, PH
Country: Philippines
Contact: dean Jessica Carino
Contact: coordinator humanities div. Anne Christie Toves com, on culture & the arts
Beth Calirewegar

University of the Philippines, Diliman
Website: www.utheatre.upd.edu.ph
Email: pcca@nicole.upd.edu.ph
Phone: 632 920 53019
Address: Dilliman, PH
Information: alternative E-mail address: pcca@philon-line.com.ph
Country: Philippines
Contact: President Eil Q javier
Contact: President's comm on culture and the arts Chairman Jonathan Malicsi
Contact: chancellor Claro T Dr.Llaguno
Contact: supervisor Joaquin Jose Z Aranda

William Bernard Shaw Theatre
Phone: 263 34821
Address: Shangri-la Bldg, EDSA Cor. Shaw Blvd, PH
Country: Philippines
Contact: Manager Gidget Tolentino

SINGAPORE

72-13
Website: www.72-13.com
Email: tworks@singnet.com.sg
Phone: 673 77213
Address: 72-13 Mohamed Sultan Road, SG
Information: 72-13 ICAA is the home of TheatreWorks. A converted rice warehouse, the space is flexible enough to be a gallery, a cinema and a theatre. ICAA is a R&D Centre, a performance centre, a forum and a platform for Asia's exPression and its relationship to the rest of the world.
Country: Singapore
Contact: Artistic Director Ong Keng Sen
Contact: Chairperson Heman Chong
Contact: Board of Directors Kathy Lai
Contact: Board of Directors Noorlinah Mohamed
Contact: Board of Directors Ong Keng Sen
Social Media: www.facebook.com/pages/72-13/290366897730596 https://twitter.com/TWorkssg https://www.instagram.com/tworkssg/

Alliance Francaise
Website: www.alliancefrancaise.org.sg
Email: info.af@alliancefrancaise.org.sg
Phone: 673 78422
Address: 1 Sarkies Road, SG
Information: The theatre is an excellent space for organisations to rent either for rehearsals or performances. It is an intimate space that has been used in the past for lectures, talks, films, plays, concerts, musicals, and is booked by other organisations. Inclusive of stage lighting, amps, PA system with 4 normal microphones and CD player.
Country: Singapore

Contact: theatre Manager Aziz Ahmad
Email: aziz@alliancefrancaise.org.sg
Social Media: @AFSingapour www.facebook.com/AllianceFrancaiseSingapore
Capacity: 240

Arts House at Old Parliament
Website: www.theartshouse.com.sg
Email: enquiries@artshouse.sg
Phone: 633 26900
Address: 1 Old Parliament Lane, SG
Information: Occupying the almost 200-year-old building that was Singapore's first Parliament House, The Arts House has played an active role in the Singapore arts and creative scene. The House promotes and presents multidisciplinary programmes and festivals such as literary arts, film and performing and visual arts. Once the former Parliamentary Chamber, modeled after the House of Commons, the Chamber today boasts excellent acoustics and lighting suitable for events ranging from intimate performances to seminars and conferences.
Country: Singapore
Contact: CEO Sarah Martin
Contact: board Chair Christine Ong
Social Media: @The_Arts_House www.facebook.com/theartshouse
Capacity: 200

Centre for the Arts
Website: www.nus.edu.sg/cfa
Email: cfaMarketing@nus.edu.sg
Phone: 651 62492
Address: University Cultural Centre, 50 Kent Ridge Crescent, National University of Singapore, SG
Information: Located on the picturesque landscapes of Kent Ridge, the University Cultural Centre serves as a vibrant, innovative performing arts venue for high-quality events that reflect both the rich cultural heritage of Singapore and the best in international arts and entertainment. Performers and Producers can benefit from the state-of-the-art facilities and professional services of a standard previously unsurpassed in Singapore, and audiences of all ages, backgrounds and interests can indulge in a myriad of different cultural experiences through the performances.
Country: Singapore
Social Media: @NUSCFA www.facebook.com/nuscfa
Policies: Rent only, Multi-purpose

Drama Centre
Website: www.dramacentre.com
Email: enquiries.dc@artshouse.sg
Phone: 683 78400
Address: 100 Victoria Street, #05-01, National Library Building, SG
Information: The Drama Centre adds to Singapore's stable of world-class purpose built performing arts spaces with its 615-seat proscenium theatre. It also offers an intimate 120-seater black box, VIP lounge and function rooms to meet the demands of the diverse range of today's arts events – from the mid-sized theatrical presentation with stringent technical requirements, to intimate performances, talks and exhibitions.
Country: Singapore
Contact: Chairman Tan Wilson
Disabled Access: Yes
Capacity: 501-1000
Annual Performances: 100+
Policies: Rent and Present

Esplanade – Theatres on the Bay
Website: www.esplanade.com
Email: corporate@esplanade.com
Phone: 682 88377
Address: 1 Esplanade Drive, SG
Information: Esplanade is Singapore's national performing arts centre. The year-round line-up of about 3000 performances presented by Esplanade, brings together partners and hirers, and includes a diverse calendar of ticketed and non-ticketed programmes featuring dance, music, theatre, visual arts and more, making the arts accessible for everyone.
Country: Singapore
Social Media: www.facebook.com/EsplanadeSG
Annual Performances: 3000
Policies: Theatre

HarbourFront Centre
Website: www.harbourfrontcentre.com.sg
Email: rentals@harbourfrontcentre.com
Phone: 637 76311
Address: 1 Maritime Square, #09-72, SG
Information: Open from 10am to 10pm daily, Harbour-Front Centre is conveniently linked to an international cruise centre and VivoCity – Singapore's largest retail and lifestyle destination. Our exciting location creates a totally dynamic retail atmosphere for absolutely everyone.
Country: Singapore
Social Media: www.facebook.com/HarbourFrontCentreSG https://www.instagram.com/hfc_sg/
Capacity: 1000+
Policies: Rent and Present

Jubilee Hall – Raffles Hotel

Website: www.raffleshotel.com
Email: meet@raffles.com
Phone: 641 21341
Address: 1 Beach Road, SG
Information: The gracious setting of the Jubilee Hall is the ideal venue for corporate events including trade launches, lectures and award ceremonies. Equipped with the technology of a modern theatre and magnificent acoustics within the premise, the Hall presents a variety of plays, musicals, recitals, dances and films when night falls.
Country: Singapore
Contact: General Manager Simon Hirst
Social Media: www.facebook.com@raffleshotels
Capacity: 388

Kallang Theatre
Website: www.kallangtheatre.com
Email: enquiries@asiaartsculture.com
Phone: 634 87907
Address: 1 Stadium Walk, SG
Information: Kallang Theatre is a preferred venue for arts, events, seminars, exhibitions, corporate dinners and musical shows. Kallang Theatre hosted the inaugural launch of Asia Arts & Culture's maiden musical show, "Singapura – The Lion City".
Country: Singapore
Contact: Manager K C Ang

LASALLE College of the Arts
Website: www.lasalle.edu.sg
Email: venue@lasalle.edu.sg
Phone: 649 65000
Address: 1 McNally Street, SG
Information: Located within the city, the McNally campus is perfect for various performances, exhibitions, corporate events and product launches. The award-winning campus houses three major fully-equipped performance spaces – The Singapore Airlines Theatre, Flexible Performance Space and Creative Cube – as well as rehearsal rooms, dance studios and lecture theatres. Also available for hire are the outdoor spaces such as the Campus Green and Amphitheatre.
Country: Singapore
Social Media: www.facebook.com/lasalle.sg/twitter.com/lasallesg www.instagram.com/lasallesingapore/
Policies: Produce and Rent

Marina Bay Sands Pte Ltd
Website: www.marinabaysands.com
Email: inquiries@marinabaysands.com
Phone: 668 88868
Address: 10 Bayfront Avenue, SG
Information: This is one of the world's most desirable entertainment destinations. Marina Bay Sands® is a centre-piece in Marina Bay. Conceived by world-renowned architect, Moshe Safdie, this spectacular integrated resort combines the Marina Bay Sands hotel with three imPressive hotel towers and is crowned by the awe-inspiring one-hectare Sands SkyPark®, a grand event plaza on the waterfront, state-of-the-art theatres, the cutting edge lotus-inspired ArtScience Museum™, signature shopping and dining outlets, and the foremost MICE (Meetings, Incentives, Exhibitions and Conferences) facilities – all within one iconic landmark.
Country: Singapore
Social Media: @marinabaysands www.facebook.com/marinabaysands
Policies: Multi-purpose

Singapore Indoor Stadium
Website: www.sportshub.com.sg/venues/Pages/singapore-indoor-stadium.aspx
Phone:
633 35000
Address: 2 Stadium Walk, SG
Information: This magnificent structure by Kenzo Tange is a fine example of the blend of modern concepts with traditional and Asian architectural features. It is an indoor venue for sports, entertainment and community events. Since its opening in 1989, it has seen tennis tournaments, badminton matches, ice skating performances, circus acts and even pop concerts by Tina Turner and Elton John.
Country: Singapore
Social Media: @SGSportsHub www.facebook.com/sporesportshub
Capacity: 12000

Star Performing Arts Centre, The
Website: www.thestar.sg
Email: info@thestar.sg
Phone: 663 60055
Address: 1 Vista Exchange Green #04-01, SG
Information: The key venue of The Star Performing Arts Centre, The Star Theatre, is fitted with high-end audio, video and production lighting systems for an exceptional audio-visual experience. It heightens your enjoyment of a wide range of amplified music and speech events, as well as large-scale musical theatre and dance performances.
Country: Singapore
Contact: General Manager Jack Ho
Contact: Director of Sales and Marketing Sarah Lim
Contact: senior operations Manager Zailani Bin Ahmad

Social Media: @TheStarPAC www.facebook.com/The-StarPAC
Policies: Rent only, Multi-purpose

Substation
Website: www.substation.org
Email: admin@substation.org
Phone: 633 77535
Address: 45 Armenian Street, SG
Information: The Substation has various facilities available on its premises for rental to arts organisations, businesses, corporates and individuals. Arts practitioners, groups
and non-profit organisations may apply for rental subsidies as part of the Substation's mission to promote the arts in Singapore. The Substation Theatre hosts both high-profile, and small independent arts events, ranging from The Singapore Short Film Awards to gigs by local musicians, and performances by numerous local and international performing artists.
Country: Singapore
Contact: Artistic Director Alan Oei
Contact: General Manager Samantha Segar
Social Media: @thesubstation www.facebook.com/thesubstation
Policies: All, Arts centre

Suntec Singapore – International Convention & Exhibition Centre
Website: www.suntecsingapore.com
Email: Sales@suntecsingapore.com
Phone: 633 72888
Address: 1 Raffles Boulevard, SG
Information: Suntec Singapore International Convention & Exhibition Center is one of the busiest and most happening locations of the city. It is situated in the heart of the Central Business Distrcit of Singaore and is quite close to the Changi Airport. It houses convention halls, exhibition halls, galleries, theaters, ballrooms, meeting rooms, lobbies and more.
Country: Singapore
Contact: senior Director of operations Daniel Ang
Contact: chief Executive officer Arun Madhok
Contact: Executive assistant Carole Goh
Social Media: @SuntecSingapor www.facebook.com/suntecsingapora
Capacity: 6850

Victoria Theatre and Concert Hall
Website: www.vtvch.com
Email: enquiries.vtvch@artshouse.sg
Phone: 690 88810
Address: 9 EmPress Place, SG
Information: The Victoria theater has 614 seats and is referred to as the "grand old dame" of Singapore's performing arts scene. The Victoria Theatre and Concert Hall is home to the Singapore Symphony Orchestra. Built in 1862, the building re-opened in 2014 after a three year refurbishment. It retains its colonial architectural heritage while offering state of the art facilities for concerts and theatre performances.
Country: Singapore
Policies: Concert hall

Yong Siew Toh Conservatory of Music
Website: ystmusic.nus.edu.sg
Email: musGeneral@nus.edu.sg
Phone: 651 61167
Address: 3 Conservatory Drive, SG
Information: Officially opened in 2006, the Yong Siew Toh Conservatory of Music Building houses state-of-the-art facilities for training professional musicians. These include a 600-seat Concert Hall, 150-seat Orchestral Hall, sound-proof and temperature-controlled studios and practice spaces, a music library, smart classrooms, and one of the largest recording studios in Asia.
Country: Singapore
Contact: Dean Bernard Lanskey
Contact: Vice Dean Ho Chee Kong
Contact: Vice Dean Chan Tze Law
Contact: Vice Dean Brett Stemple
Contact: Associate Dean Rachel Tang
Social Media: https:// www.facebook.com/YSTConservatory/
Capacity: 501-1000
Annual Performances: 100+
Annual Productions: 100+
Policies: Present and Produce

SOUTH AFRICA

Artscape Theatre Centre
Website: www.artscape.co.za
Email: artscape@artscape.co.za
Phone: 214 109 800
Address: D F Malan Street, Foreshore, ZA
Information: venues: auditorium – seats 1487 with provision for two wheelChairs; stage – consists of the main stage, rear stage and two side stages; orchestra pit – consists of three lifts which can operate separately or as a combined unit; technical – the fly tower allows scenery to fly up to 21m above stage level. It houses 67 computerised décor battens including 3 cyclorama

battens. Member of ISPA
Country: South Africa
Contact: theatre Manager John Hawkins
Email: johnh@artscape.co.za
Contact: venue Director Guy Burbridge
Email: guyb@artscape.co.za
Social Media: @ArtscapeTheatre www.facebook.com/ArtscapeTheatre?ref=nf
Policies: All, Theatre

Playhouse Company, The
Website: playhousecompany.com
Email: MarketingManager@playhousecompany.com
Phone: 031 369 9456
Address: 29 Acutt Street, PO Box 5353, ZA
Information: the current theatre facade preserves two of the city's most famous landmarks, situated adjacent to each other in central Smith Street opposite the City Hall, first conceived as cinemas, namely the glamorous Prince's Theatre. It consists of three venues: The Drama Theatre, The Loft and The Opera Theatre. For more information and for hire contact artsadmin@playhousecompany.com or call +27 (031) 369 9461. Member of ISPA
Country: South Africa
Contact: Chairperson Thandiwe January-McLean
Contact: deputy Chairperson Judge Leona Theron
Social Media: @DurbanPlayhouse www.facebook.com/DurbanPlayhouse

South African State Theatre, The
Website: www.statetheatre.co.za
Email: info@statetheatre.co.za
Phone: 123 924 000
Address: 320 Pretorius Street, ZA
Information: the South African State Theatre is one of the best performing facilities in Africa as it is designed to house many different genres of performances under one roof such as dance, jazz, opera and musicals. Features other venues such as the Drama Theatre seating 640, the Arena seating 288, the Rendezvous seating 260, the Momentum seating 120 and the Intimate seating 100. Member of ISPA
Country: South Africa
Contact: front of house Manager Patrick Phala
Email: patrick@statetheatre.co.za
www.facebook.com/SouthAfricanStateThea-tre?ref=stream&hc_location=stream
Policies: Rent only, Theatre

TAIWAN, PROVINCE OF CHINA

Armed Forces Cultural Centre
Website: www.mnd.gov.tw
Email: a8894117@yahoo.com.tw
Phone: 223 774 228
Address: No.69 Section1, Zhong Hua Road
Information: also lectures; houses art archives
Country: Taiwan
Contact: chief Executive Su Zhen Hong

CHANGE CATEGORY Affiliated Orchestra of Taichung Hsien Cultural Centre, The
Website: www.tchcc.gov.tw
Email: lll@mail.tchcc.gov.tw
Phone: 425 260 136
Address: No.782, , Yuan Huan East Road, , Feng Yuan District,
Information: dedicates itself to the research and collection of motifs and elements of Chinese ethnic music
Country: Taiwan
Contact: administrative Director Ching Wen Huang
Contact: contact Yueh-Hsia Liao
Contact: Artistic Director Ju-Chi Chen

Crown Culture Group
Website: www.crown.com.tw
Email: danceforum@crown.com.tw
Phone: 227 168 888
Address: No.50, Lane 120, , Dun Hua North Road,
Country: Taiwan
Contact: Chairman Shin Tao Ping
Contact: Artistic Director Heng Ping
Contact: executiv Hui Jun Zhao

Kaohsiung Cultural Center
Website: www.khcc.gov.tw
Phone: 722 25136 to /8
Address: No. 67, , Wu Fu 1st Road, , Lian Ya district,
Country: Taiwan
Contact: contact Jing Wen Yue

Miaoli County Cultural Centre
Website: www.mlc.gov.tw
Phone: 373 52961 ext.
Address: No. 50, , Zi Zhi Road, , Miao Li District,
Country: Taiwan
Contact: contact Hui Zhu Li

National Chiang Kai-Shek Cultural Center
Website: https://npac-ntch.org/en/
Phone: 233 939 888
Address: No. 21-1, , Zhong Shan South Road,
Information: Completed in 1987, the NTCH marked Taiwan's grand entrance into the world of performing arts. The NTCH is a sophisticated international arts center in

Taiwan as well as an iconic contemporary theater in Asia.
Country: Taiwan
Contact: General and Artistic Director Yi-ruu Liu
Email: Director@mail.npac-ntch.org
Social Media: https:// www.facebook.com/ntch.tw

Novel Hall for Performing Arts
Website: www.novelhall.org.tw
Phone: 227 224 302
Address: No. 3, Song Shou Road, Xin Yi District,
Information: member of ISPA
Country: Taiwan
Contact: General Manager Huai-chun Ku

Tai Nan City, City Culture Centre
Website: tmcc.gov.tw
Phone: 626 92864
Address: No.332, Zhong Hua East Road, , Section 3
Information: The Tainan Municipal Cultural Center began construction in June 1980 and officially opened on October 6, 1984. The cultural center, after the merger of Tainan counties and cities into a municipality on December 25, 2010, was renamed Tainan City Tainan Cultural Center.**Country:** Taiwan
Contact: Director Min-Hua Fang
Phone: 062 692 864
Social Media: https:// www.facebook.com/tmcc.tw/ https://twitter.com/twtmcc
Disabled Access: Yes
Capacity: 1000+
Annual Performances: 100+
Policies: All

Tai Nan, City Library of Entertainment Hall
Website: www.tnml.tn.edu.tw
Email: promotion@mail.tmcc.gov.tw
Phone: 622 55146
Address: No.3, Park North Road, , Southern District,
Country: Taiwan

Taichung City Dadun Cultural Centre
Website: www.tccgc.gov.tw
Email: show001@tccgc.gov.tw
Phone: 423 727 311
Address: No. 600, , Ying Cai Road, , Western District,
Information: the Taichung City Dadun Cultural Centre offers exhibition and performance space, a library, and promotions and General affairs spaces
Country: Taiwan
Contact: Director Hsu Hsui-Lan

Taichung City, National Library of Public Information
Website: https:// www.nlpi.edu.tw/English/
Phone: 042 262 5100
Address: No.100, Wuquan S. Rd., Southern District
Information: The National Library of Public Information was founded in 1923 and is one of the earliest public libraries in Taiwan. It rents facilities for all kinds of performative arts.
Country: Taiwan
Contact: Director Chung-Ching Liu
Disabled Access: Yes
Capacity: 251-500
Policies: Rent and Present

Taichung County Cultural Center
Website: www.culture.taichung.gov.tw/home.asp
Email: facebook@culture.taichung.gov.tw
Phone: 422 289 111
Address: 89, Tai Zhong Gang Road Section 2, Xi Tun District,
Information: Taichung is known as a cultural city, with a prosperous style of writing, and a well-developed education. It spares no effort in promoting various cultural activities.
In 1965, the famous entrepreneur Mr. He Yong donated a cultural center on Shuangshi Road, the pioneer of Taiwan Cultural Center, and the Taichung Municipal Cultural Center on Tong Yingcai Road was established.
Country: Taiwan
Contact: Director Zhang Dachun
Social Media: https:// www.facebook.com/TaichungCulture
Capacity: 1000+
Annual Performances: 100+
Annual Productions: 100+
Policies: All

Taipei National Dr. Sun Yat-sen Memorial Hall
Website: www.yatsen.gov.tw
Email: sun@yatsen.yatsen.gov.tw
Phone: 227 588 008
Address: No.505, , Ren Ai Road Section 4, , Xin Yi District,
Information: also has a library, gallery space and an audio-visual center; able to hold conferences and award ceremonies; manages the Chung Shan Building
Country: Taiwan

Taipei National University of the Arts
Website: www.tnua.edu.tw
Email: master-p@performance.tnua.edu.tw
Phone: 228 961 000

Address: No. 1, Xueyuan Road, Beitou District, Taipei City
Information: Opened in 2005, Taipei National University of the Arts Concert Hall has a spectacle German-made organ and 500 seats. Concert Hall shall be satisfactory for all genres in music events. Taipei National University of the Arts also runs Experimental Theatre and Dance Theatre.
Country: Taiwan
Contact: President of the university Chen Kai-Huang
Email: President@ www.tnua.edu.tw
Phone: 022 893 8701Vice President Chia-Yi Lee
Email: v-President@tnua.edu.tw
Phone: 022 893 8709
Capacity: 1000+
Policies: All

Taitung County Culture Centre
Website: www.ccl.ttct.edu.tw
Email: public@mail.ccl.ttct.edu.tw
Phone: 893 20378
Address: 25 Nan-Ching Rd.
Information: promotes cultural activities
Country: Taiwan
Contact: Director Xin Lan Lai

UNITED STATES

171 Cedar Arts Center
Website: www.171cedararts.org
Email: Info@171CedarArts.org
Phone: 607 936 4647
Address: 171 Cedar Street, US
Information: 171 Cedar Arts Center is a dynamic organisation which enriches the community by offering excellent arts instruction, exhibiting today's artists and presenting live performances. Since first opening the Bruce House doors in 1968, 171 Cedar Arts Center has provided the community with a warm, friendly home in which to explore the arts. Over the years, with help from supporters and outstanding faculty they have grown into an award-winning organisation that provides top-quality programming and instruction
Country: United States
Contact: President Ann Nicholson
Contact: vice President Eric Elder
Social Media: @171CedarArts www.facebook.com/171cedararts
Policies: Present and produce, Multi-purpose

651 ARTS
Website: www.651arts.org
Email: info@651arts.org
Phone: 718 304 1045
Address: 1000 Dean Street, Suite 232, Brooklyn, US
Information: It is the mission of 651 ARTS to deepen the awareness and appreciation for contemporary performing arts and culture of the African Diaspora, and to provide professional and creative opportunities for performing artists of African descent
Country: United States
Contact: Chair Andrea Smith
Contact: vice Chair Obadele Davis
Social Media: @651ARTS www.facebook.com/651arts
Policies: Present, produce, co-produce, Arts centre

92nd Street Y
Website: www.92y.org
Email: webmaster@92Y.org
Phone: 212 415 5500
Address: 1395 Lexington Ave, US
Information: 92nd Street Y provide programmes across the spectrum of arts and culture, Jewish life and education, health and fitness and personal growth and travel. They also offer classes for adults, families and children. It is a nonprofit institution which serves over 300000 people annually, from newborns to centenarians. Member of ISPA
Country: United States
Contact: President Marc Lipschultz
Contact: Chairman of the board Stuart Ellman
Social Media: @92Y www.facebook.com/92nd-streetY?v=app_10442206389
Policies: Multi-purpose

A Noise Within
Website: www.anoisewithin.org
Email: Info@anoisewithin.org
Phone: 626 356 3100
Address: 3352 E Foothill Blvd, US
Information: A Noise Within's mission is to produce world-class performances of the great works of drama in rotating repertory with a resident company. Their aim is to educate and inspire the public through programmes that foster an understanding and appreciation of history's great plays and playwrights and to train the next generation of classical theatre artists.
Country: United States
Contact: President and board Chair Rebecca Elliott Bowne
Contact: board Director Molly Bachmann
Social Media: @anoisewithin www.facebook.com/pag-

es/A-Noise-Within-Theater-Company/49514622413
Policies: Produce and rent, Theatre

Abbey Church Events – Saint Martin's Abbey
Website: www.stmartin.edu/abbey
Email: oblates@stmartin.edu
Phone: 360 491 4700
Address: 5000 Abbey Way SE, US
Information: this space hosts an annual concert and lecture series plus Abbey Church Events. Saint Martin's also maintains collections of art, as well as a museum. Several prominent local artists have been commissioned to create liturgical objects in the worship space
Country: United States
Contact: Chair Neal Roth
Social Media: www.facebook.com/pages/Saint-Martins-Abbey
Policies: Present and produce, Rent and present, Concert hall

Abendmusik: Lincoln Fine Arts Series
Website: www.abendmusik.org
Email: info@abendmusik.org
Phone: 402 476 9933
Address: 2000 D Street, US
Information: Abendmusik will enrich Lincoln by sharing inspiring experiences with the world's finest music in the beautiful sanctuary of First-Plymouth
Country: United States
Contact: Artistic Director Tom Trenney
Email: tom@abendmusik.org
Contact: Executive Director Drew Duncan
Email: drew@abendmusik.org
Contact: President James Keim
Social Media: www.facebook.com/abendmusik
Policies: Present, produce, co-produce, Concert hall

Abilene Cultural Affairs Council, Paramount Performing Arts Series
Website: www.abilenecac.org
Email: acac@abilene.com
Phone: 325 677 1161
Address: 1101 North 1st Street, US
Information: the major goal of the Children's Performing Arts Series is to assure that each performance reaches children of all backgrounds. The Series was established to enable families of the Big Country to experience quality live entertainment without having to leave the area
Country: United States
Contact: Executive Director Lynn Barnett
Email: lynn@abilenecac.org
Contact: Director of operations Rebecca Armstrong
Email: operations@abilenecac.org
Social Media: @ArtfullyAbilene www.facebook.com/artfullyabilene
Policies: Present, produce, co-produce, Theatre

Academic & Cultural Events Series
Website: www.bvu.edu/aces
Email: steinfeld@bvu.edu
Phone: 712 749 2218
Address: Buena Vista University, 610 W. 4th Street, US
Information: ACES performances are open to the public and have three kinds of ACES events – cultural, scholarly and student life. Cultural events feature performances by touring groups or individuals. These could be theatre, vocal, dance or instrumental
Country: United States
Social Media: @BuenaVistaUniv www.facebook.com/bwaces?ref=stream
Policies: Present and produce, Multi-purpose

Academy of Early Music
Website: www.academyofearlymusic.org
Email: info@academyofearlymusic.org
Phone: 734 228 4338
Address: PO Box 7694, US
Information: Academy of Early Music presents a series of concerts each season that celebrate the richness of music from the Middle Ages to the Classical Era and feature artists and ensembles from around the world who specialise in period performances**Country:** United States
Contact: Executive Director Emily Solomon
Email: execDirector@academyofearlymusic.org
Social Media: www.facebook.com/AcademyOfEarly-Music
Policies: Present and produce, Other

Academy of Music
Website: www.academyofmusic.org
Email: rarmstrong@philorch.org
Phone: 215 893 1999
Address: 240 S Broad St., US
Information: the Academy is owned by The Philadelphia Orchestra Association and is managed by The Kimmel Center for the Performing Arts. Season tenants are Pennsylvania Ballet, Opera Company of Philadelphia and Philadelphia Orchestra. It is available for hire for coordinating corporate gatherings, hosting a concert and more
Country: United States
Contact: President and CEO Anne Ewers
Contact: senior vice President and cfo Rick Perkins
Contact: vice President of facilities and operations David

Thiele
Policies: All, Concert hall

Acadiana Arts Council
Website: acadianacenterforthearts.org/
Email: info@AcadianaCenterfortheArts.org
Phone: 337 233 7060
Address: 101 W. Vermilon St., US
Information: The AcA is located in the heart of Downtown Lafayette and functions as a cultural anchor for Acadiana. With over 38 years experience with outreach, arts funding and education, AcA serves an eight-parish region with community development, education performances and exhibits
Country: United States
Contact: Executive Director Gerd Wuestemann
Email: Gerd@AcadianaCenterfortheArts.org
Contact: office Manager Connie Petro
Email: Connie@AcadianaCenterfortheArts.org
Contact: Director of finance Vicki Chrisman
Email: Vicki@AcadianaCenterfortheArts.org
Social Media: @AcadianaArts www.facebook.com/acadiana.arts?ref=hl
Policies: Concert hall

Adrienne Arsht Center for the Performing Arts
Website: www.arshtcenter.org
Email: rentals@arshtcenter.org
Phone: 786 468 2000
Address: 1300 Biscayne Blvd. Miami, US
Information: Now gearing up for its 10th anniversary season, the Adrienne Arsht Center for the Performing Arts of Miami-Dade County is a cultural magnet offering great performances to entertainment-hungry audiences of all ages and backgrounds. It is vibrant, inventive and nurturing, serving as the catalyst for a new urban spirit in Miami's Town Square
Country: United States
Contact: President and CEO Johann Zietsman
Phone: 786 468 2201 Vice President, Communication Suzette Espinosa
Phone: 786 468 2221Marketing Georgiana Young
Phone: 786 468 2226Senior Director, Operations Jeremy G. Shubrook
Phone: 786 468 2205
Social Media: https://twitter.com/ArshtCenter https://www.facebook.com/AdrienneArshtCenter https://www.instagram.com/arshtcenter/
Disabled Access: Yes
Capacity: 1000+
Annual Performances: 51-100
Policies: Rent and Present

Agnes Scott College – Special Events & Conferences
Email: dparks@agnesscott.edu
Phone: 404 471 6043
Address: 141 E College Avenue, US
Information: Agnes Scott offers rental space in a beautiful campus setting with a variety rooms and lecture halls featuring advanced technology. They also provide catering services and the personalised attention needed for a successful event**Country:** United States
Contact: Director of special events and conferences office Demetrice Parks
Policies: Multi-purpose

Al Hirschfeld Theatre
Website: http:// www.alhirschfeldtheatre.org/
Phone: 212 560 2162
Address: 302 West 45th Street, New York, US
Information: Al Hirschfeld Theatre is a 1, 424 capacity Broadway theatre that has been entertaining audiences since 1924, when it opened with performances of Madame Pompadour! Named in honor of the late, great American caricaturist and illustrator Al Hirschfeld, known for his fantastic black and white portraits of celebrities and Broadway stars, the theatre has based its reputation on the quality of its productions, with many famous appearances over the years.
Country: United States
Social Media: https:// www.facebook.com/Fans-of-Al-Hirschfeld-Theatre-373122366361061/
Disabled Access: Yes
Capacity: 1000+
Annual Performances: 100+
Policies: Present

Al Ringling Theatre Friends, Inc
Website: www.alringling.com
Email: info@alringling.com
Phone: 608 356 8864
Address: 136 4th Avenue, PO Box 381, US
Information: The Al. Ringling Theatre in Baraboo, Wisconsin, United States, opened its doors in November 1915 and has been operating continuously ever since. Designed by the architectural firm Rapp and Rapp, it was built by Albert Ringling, one of the circus Ringling Brothers
Country: United States
Contact: board of Director Jonathan Beck

Contact: board of Director Charlene Flygt
Contact: board of Director Amber Giddings
Social Media: @TheatreAl www.facebook.com/alringlingtheater
Policies: Rent only, Concert hall

Alaska Center for the Performing Arts
Website: www.myalaskacenter.com
Email: fdesk@alaskapac.org
Phone: 907 263 2900
Address: 621 West Sixth Avenue, US
Information: the Alaska Center for Performing Arts offers great theater productions in music, dance and theatre from a wide variety of performers. As Alaska's premier performing arts center, patrons visiting the website can view the production calendar of events and get information about theater performances
Country: United States
President & coo
Nancy Harbour
Contact: Director of client services Cindy Hamilton
Email: chamilton@alaskapac.org
Contact: vice President Julie Millington
Email: jmillington@alaskapac.org
Social Media: @MyAlaskaCenter www.facebook.com/alaskapac
Policies: Rent only, Multi-purpose

Albany Concert Association, Inc, Concert Series
Website: www.albanyconcert.org
Email: PatronServices@AlbanySymphony.com
Phone: 518 694 3300
Address: 19 Clinton Ave Albany, NY, US
Information: The Albany Symphony is one of this region's most revered music and cultural institutions, having won numerous national awards for its adventurous concert programming, recording projects, composer residencies, and innovative educational efforts involving area schools throughout the region. As the premier professional orchestra based in the Capital Region, the Albany Symphony enriches a broad and diverse regional community in upstate New York, Western Massachusetts, and Southern Vermont.**Country: United States**
Box Office & Marketing Coordinator
Alayna Frey
Email: Alaynaf@albanysymphony.com
Director of Development & Marketing
Robert Pape
Email: robertp@albanysymphony.com
Social Media: https:// www.facebook.com/albanysym https:// www.instagram.com/albanysym/ https://twitter.com/albanysym
Capacity: 501-1000
Annual Performances: 11-25
Annual Productions: 0-5
Policies: All

Alberta Bair Theater
Website: www.albertabairtheater.org
Email: abt@albertabairtheater.org
Phone: 406 256 6052
Address: 2801 3rd Ave N, PO Box 1556, US
Information: Alberta Bair Theater is committed to enriching the lives of everyone in our community by providing a rich variety of exciting learning experiences in the arts for educators and their students
Country: United States
Contact: Executive Director Jan Dietrich
Email: jdietrich@albertabairtheater.org
Contact: President Brooke Murphy
Contact: box office Manager Travis Nilles
Email: tnilles@albertabairtheater.org
Social Media: @AlbertaBair www.facebook.com/AlbertaBairTheater
Policies: Theatre

Alden Theatre Series
Website: mcleancenter.org/alden-theatre
Email: george.sachs@fairfaxcounty.gov
Phone: 703 790 0123
Address: 1234 Ingleside Avenue, US
Information: Center facilities include the 386-seat Alden Theatre, the McLean Project for the Arts galleries, the Susan B. DuVal Art Studio, meeting and conference rooms, a rehearsal studio and a classroom/commercial kitchen. Local open clubs and organisations use the Center for their monthly meetings without charge. Center facilities may be rented for private functions such as business conferences, receptions, parties, and recitals. District residents and businesses pay reduced fees
Country: United States
Contact: Executive Director George Sachs
Social Media: @TheAldenVA www.facebook.com/mcleanvacenter
Policies: Multi-purpose

Alex Theatre
Website: www.alextheatre.org
Email: admin@alextheatre.org
Phone:
818 243 2539
Address: 216 N. Brand Blvd., US
Information: for more than 80 years, Glendale's Alex Theatre has been the centerpiece of the City's arts, culture and community programming. The programme offers a range of performances from classical, contemporary and world music concerts, to film screenings, live theatre and stand-up comedy. In addition, the Alex Theatre also hosts award shows, fundraisers and a variety of other special events and frequently serves as a location for television, commercials and film productions
Country: United States
Contact: General Manager Jack Allaway
Email: jack@alextheatre.org
Contact: business development and Sales Manager Nina Crowe
Email: ncrowe@glendalearts.org
Contact: CEO glendale arts Elissa Glickman
Email: eglickman@glendalearts.org
Contact: Director of Marketing and events Maria Sahakian
Email: msahakian@glendalearts.org

Alhambra, City of
Website: www.cityofalhambra.org
Phone: 626 570 5007
Address: 111 S First St, US
Information: Public art makes the places where we live, work and play more welcoming and beautiful – and creates a deeper interaction between the community and its environment.

Country: United States
Contact: cultural arts coordinator Helga Santiago
Contact: Executive Director Claudine Meeker
Policies: Congress centre

Alleghany Highlands Arts Council Performing Arts Series
Website: www.visitalleghanyhighlands.com/main/index.php?m=2&p=10
Email: artsco@aol.com
Phone: 540 962 6220
Address: PO Box 261, US
Information: Alleghany Highlands Arts Council Performing Arts S is committed to its mission of bringing the highest quality performing arts events to our residents as well as visitors to the Alleghany Highlands
Country: United States
Contact: Executive Director Tammy S Scruggs
Policies: Theatre

Allegheny College
Website: www.allegheny.edu
Email: rebecca.wiler@allegheny.edu
Phone: 814 332 3100
Address: 520 N Main Street, Allegheny College, US
Information: The Playshop Theatre at Allegheny College was inaugurated by Alice Huntington Spalding in 1929 with her production of Dear Brutus in Arter Hall. In the intervening 85 years, the Playshop has produced over 500 plays including classic works by Shakespeare, Molière, Shaw, Williams, O'Neill, Miller, Wilder, and Coward, contemporary playwrights such as Sam Shepard, Tom Stoppard, Suzan-Lori Parks, Wendy Wasserstein, Tina Howe, Tony Kushner, Caryl Churchill, and Paula Vogel, and musicals including The 25th Annual Putnam County Spelling Bee, The Pirates of Penzance and Carousel, as well as original works by faculty, students and visiting artist
Country: United States
Director of conference & events services
Rebecca Wiler
Policies: Theatre

Alliance for the Arts
Website: www.artinlee.org
Email: arts@artinlee.org
Phone: 239 939 2787
Address: School of Arts, Claiborne & Ned Fould Theatre, 10091 McGregor Blvd, US
Information: The Alliance for the Arts is the state designated arts agency for Lee County; a member supported non-profit with a passion to facilitate and nurture the creation, development, promotion, and education of arts and culture
Country: United States
Contact: Executive Director Lydia Black
Email: lblack@artinlee.org
Contact: pr Director Mike Kiniry
Email: publicity@artinlee.org
Contact: office Director Suzanne Croce
Email: Administration@artinlee.org
Social Media:
@ArtInLee www.facebook.com/artinlee.org
Policies: Arts centre

Alma College Performing Arts Series
Website: www.alma.edu
Email: admissions@alma.edu
Phone: 989 463 7304
Address: Heritage Center, US
Information: Alma College offers majors in art, music, theatre and dance, but rewarding opportunities to deepen involvement with the arts are open to students from all majors. In fact, more than one-quarter of all Alma students take part in at least one musical, theatre or dance performance each year
Country: United States
Contact: coordinator building Brian Tarasiewicz
Policies: Arts centre

Alys Stephens Performing Arts Center
Website: www.alysstephens.org
Phone: 205 975 9540
Address: 1200 Tenth Avenue South, US
Information: the mission of the Alys Stephens Center is to serve as a state-of-the-art center for the performance of live music, dance, theatre, comedy, and family entertainment. Dozens of community arts organizations choose to host their events and performances at the ASC each season. Member of ISPA
Country: United States
Contact: operations Director Bryan W Jones
Contact: interim Executive Director/senior Director of development Lili D Anderson
Contact: creative and Marketing Director Amber Allen-Parsons
Contact: technical Director Adam Stermer
Social Media: @ASCbham www.facebook.com/ASCbham
Policies: Theatre

American Theatre, The
Website: www.hamptonarts.net
Email: americantheatre@hampton.gov
Phone: 757 722 2787
Address: 125 East Mellen Street, US
Information: The American Theatre has a well-deserved reputation as a beautiful, yet comfortable venue. Featuring a fully equipped 392 seat auditorium, a lecture hall and art gallery, a dance studio, and ample lobby and dressing room spaces, the American Theatre is an ideal choice for performances, screenings, receptions, classes/workshops and events**Country: United States**
Contact: Artistic Director Jeffrey Stern
Email: jstern@hampton.net
Social Media: @AmericanTheatre www.facebook.com/pages/The-American-Theatre/233747765598
Policies: Rent and present, Theatre

American University Department of Performing Arts
Website: www.american.edu/cas/performing-arts/
Email: dpa@american.edu
Phone: 202 885 3420
Address: 4400 Massachusetts Ave., US
Information: Abramson Family Recital Hall At 213 seats, the Abramson creates an inviting space for performances both large and small. From orchestra and choral concerts, to small lectures and film screenings, this stunning space is host to many of the University's important events. The hall can accommodate patrons with accessibility needs. This space also has a full featured lighting and audio-visual system
Country: United States
Contact: General questions Richard Streeks
Email: streeks@american.edu
Policies: Concert hall

Anderson Center for the Arts
Website: anderson.binghamton.edu
Email: aburnet@binghamton.edu
Phone: 607 777 6802
Address: Binghamton University, State University of New York, PO Box 6000, US
Information: The complex is designed to meet the needs of every performing group – – soloists, chamber ensembles, symphonies, dance, or large theatrical productions complemented by a full-scale orchestra. The University's Fine Arts complex, which house the Anderson Center for the Arts, provides additional spaces for the academic departments in the form of two studio theaters and the Jean Casadesus Recital Hall used by the Theater and Music Departments, respectively. This combination of small studios and large theaters creates a versatile setting that is both intimate and spectacular, integrating music, dance, drama, and the visual arts, while serving the academic needs of the University as well as the region
Country: United States
Contact: Executive Director Garry Pedro
Email: gpedro@binghampton.edu
Contact: operations Director Annette Burnett
Email: aburnet@binghampton.edu
Contact: Marketing Director Roseanne Norris
Email: rnorris@binghampton.edu
Social Media: www.facebook.com/pages/Anderson-Center-for-the-Performing-Arts/54550928549?ref=ts
Policies: Concert hall

Annenberg Center
Website: www.annenbergcenter.org
Email: info@pennpresents.org
Phone: 215 898 3910
Address: 3680 Walnut Street, US
Information: The Annenberg Center is dedicated to the advancement of a diverse and thriving cultural community through the pursuit of excellence, innovation and intellectual engagement in the performing arts. As a destination and a resource, the Annenberg Center connects and engages artists, audiences, the University of Pennsylvania and the regional community through

shared experiences in its high quality venues. Member of ISPA
Country: United States
Executive & Artistic Director
Christopher Gruits
Email: gruits@upenn.edu
Artistic & education Manager
Caroline Leipf
Email: cleipf@ac.upenn.edu
Contact: General Manager Stuart Jasper
Email: jaspers@ac.upenn.edu
Social Media: @AnnenbergCenter www.facebook.com/AnnenbergCenter
Policies: Theatre

Annie Russell Theatre
Website: www.rollins.edu/annierussell/
Email: ohorn@rollins.edu
Phone: 407 646 2000
Address: 1000 Holt Avenue-2735, US
Information: The Annie Russell Theatre is a historic theater in Winter Park, Florida, United States. The theatre was named after the English-born actress Annie Russell. It was designed by the German-born architect Richard Kiehnel of Kiehnel and Elliott and constructed in 1931. It is located on the premises of Rollins College
Country: United States
Contact: producing Director, dept. Chair Thomas Ouellette
Contact: audience services coordinator Scottie Campbell
Contact: Director of dance dept W Robert Sherry
Contact: administrative assistant Olivia Horn
Policies: Concert hall

Appalachian State University Performing Arts Series
Website: www.pas.appstate.edu
Email: boxoffice@appstate.edu
Phone: 828 262 6084
Address: Office of Arts & Cultural Programs, ASU, PO Box 32057, US
Information: The Schaefer Center for the Performing Arts is a 1684-seat multi-use auditorium located on the campus of Appalachian State University in Boone, North Carolina. The Center features orchestra and balcony level seating and a proscenium stage. The Schaefer Center is also home to the Catherine J. Smith Gallery
Country: United States
Director of box office & patron relations
Sarah Heustess
Email: heustesss@appstate.edu
Contact: Director of Marketing Megan Stage
Email: stageme@appstate.edu
Contact: Director Denise Ringler
Email: weissbergdr@appstate.edu
Contact: Director of artist relations Sali Gill-Johnson
Email: gilljohnsons@appstate.edu
Social Media: @AppalachianArts www.facebook.com/appalachianperformingarts
Policies: Other

Appel Farm Arts & Music Center
Website: www.appelfarm.org
Email: applearts@aol.com
Phone: 856 358 2472
Address: 457 Sherley Road, PO Box 888, US
Information: Appel Farm also provides a unique, three-chambered noborigama wood-fire kiln to ceramic artists in the region, giving them the opportunity to advance their craft. Adults and children are able to take newly redesigned arts classes and workshops, and have the opportunity to study in well-equipped, on-site arts studios with professional working artists. Arts Lab, a community partnership with the Pittsgrove School District provides an opportunity for children to attend reduced cost classes each spring
Country: United States
Contact: Executive Director Mark E. Packer
Contact: Artistic Director Sean Timmons
Email: stimmons@appelfarm.org
Contact: Director of Marketing Heather Yelle
Email: hyelle@appelfarm.org
Policies: Open-air

Apple Hill Center for Chamber Music
Website: www.applehill.org
Email: info@applehill.org
Phone: 603 847 3371
Address: 410 Apple Hill Road, PO Box 217, US
Information: Founded in 1971 and situated on 100 acres of fields and woodlands in rural New Hampshire, Apple Hill is a center of chamber music performance and teaching. It is stewarded today by the organization's Director, Leonard Matczynski, and ensemble-in-residence, the Apple Hill String Quartet
Country: United States
Contact: Director Lenny Matczynski
Email: lenny@applehill.org
Contact: administrative coordinator Val Van Meier
Email: val@applehill.org
Policies: Arts centre

Arizona State University Public Events
Website: www.asupublicevents.com

Email: Press@asugammage.com
Phone: 480 965 3434
Address: 1200 South Forest Avenue, US
Information: Although part of Arizona State University, ASU Gammage operates under a self-sustaining business model. Ninety percent of its funding comes from its Broadway series and 10 percent comes from philanthropy. This self-sustaining business model, driven by private support and ticket Sales with no funding from the university or the state, runs like a business but with the heart of a nonprofit
Country: United States
Contact: Executive Director Colleen Jennings-Roggensack
Email: cjr@asu.edu
Contact: undefined
Director of Marketing & Communications
Theresa Dickerson
Email: Theresa.Dickerson@asu.edu
Social Media: https://twitter.com/OPerformingArts www.facebook.com/ASUGammageFan https://www.instagram.com/asugammage/
Capacity: 1000+
Annual Performances: 51-100
Policies: Rent and Present

Arkansas Tech University
Website: www.atu.edu
Email: jayne.jones@mail.atu.edu
Phone: 479 968 0389
Address: Music Department, Arkansas Tech University, 407 West Q St, US
Information: Lake Point Conference Center offers a variety of meeting rooms to meet your needs, from Executive Board room to the main conference room. All meeting and dining rooms have complimentary Wi-Fi available. The three meeting rooms are equipped with integrated audio/visual/computer equipment for presentation requirements all at no extra charge
Country: United States
Contact: vice President of development Jayne Jones
Contact: head of music department Dr. Cynthia Hukill
Social Media: @ArkansasTech www.facebook.com/arkansastech
Policies: Concert hall

Arlington County Cultural Affairs
Website: www.arlingtonarts.org
Email: arts@arlingtonva.us
Phone: 703 228 1850
Address: 1100 North Glebe Road, Suite 1500, US
Information: The Thomas Jefferson Theatre is a joint use facility with Arlington Cultural Affairs and Arlington Public Schools, and is used by several Arlington-based performing arts groups, producing theatre, opera, heritage arts festivals and dance
Country: United States
Contact: Director of cultural development Mary Briggs
Contact: Marketing Director Jim Byers
Social Media: www.facebook.com/arts.arlington
Policies: Theatre

Artpark
Website: www.artpark.net
Email: artpark@artpark.net
Phone: 716 754 4375
Address: 450 South 4th Street, Lewiston, US
Information: Artpark & Company produces and presents excellence in the performing and visual arts, and creates unique cultural experiences in a casual, natural setting. Artistic talent is nurtured and allowed to flourish in an atmosphere that is entertaining, educational and interactive for Artpark visitors
Country: United States
Contact: President Sofya Kozlova Clark
Email: sclark@artpark.net
Vice Presidents of Concerts & Marketing
Dave Wedekindt
Email: dwedekindt@artpark.net
Social Media: https://twitter.com/artparkny/ https://www.facebook.com/artparkny/
Capacity: 1000+
Annual Performances: 51-100
Policies: Rent and Present

Artpark
Website: www.artpark.net
Email: gosborne@artpark.net
Phone: 716 754 4375
Address: 450 South 4th Street, US
Information: ARTPARK is a park and a cultural institution located on the Niagara Gorge, USA. Established in 1974, Artpark is a collaboration between the New York State Parks and the cultural nonprofit institution Artpark & Company.
Country: United States
Contact: President Sonia Kozlova Clark Kozlova Clark
Email: sclark@artpark.net
vice President of concerts & Marketing
Dave Wedekindt Wedekindt
Email: dwedekindt@artpark.net

Social Media: twitter.com/artparkny www.facebook.com/artparkny www.instagram.com/artparkwny
Capacity: 1000+

Arts & Culture Alliance of Greater Knoxville
Website: www.knoxalliance.com
Email: info@knoxalliance.com
Phone: 865 523 7543
Address: 100 S. Gay Street, Suite 201, US
Information: Originally built in 1898, it re-opened following renovations during the summer of 2004. Located at 100 South Gay Street, the 28, 000 square feet of flexible use space houses multiple art galleries showcasing local and regional artists, the administrative offices of the Arts & Culture Alliance, and offices for numerous artists and cultural organisations. Additionally, the building houses studios for multiple artists and rehearsal, classroom and meeting space.
Country: United States
Contact: Executive Director Liza Zenni
Social Media: https:// www.facebook.com/KnoxArtAndCultureAlliance
Policies: All, Multi-purpose

Arts and Science Center for Southeast Arkansas
Website: www.asc701.org
Email: info@asc701.org
Phone: 870 536 3375
Address: 701 Main St, US
Information: ASC was founded in 1968, made a commission of the City of Pine Bluff in 1971, and accredited with the American Alliance of Museums (AAM) in 2001. ASC presents programming in the visual arts, performing arts, and the sciences through exhibits, performances, classes, and local partnerships
Country: United States
Contact: Director of operations Raven Harris
Email: rharris@asc701.org
Contact: Executive Director Lenore Shoults
Email: lshoults@asc701.org
Social Media: @ASC701 www.facebook.com/pages/Arts-Science-Center-for-Southeast-Arkansas/27054822755?ref=hl
Policies: Arts centre

Arts Commission of Greater Toledo
Website: www.acgt.org
Email: info@theartscommission.org
Phone: 419 254 2787
Address: 1838 Parkwood Avenue, Suite 120, Toledo, US
Information: The Arts Commission in Toledo, Ohio is the longest standing arts commission in Ohio, inspiring a vibrant Toledo since 1959 serving artists, arts organisations and art programming in NWO Northwest Ohio. The Franciscan Center is a beautiful, full-service, state-of-the-art theater and conference center located on the Franciscan Campus in Sylvania, Ohio. It features a full service theater, which seats 850 people, and two smaller conference rooms**Country:** United States
MARKETING & COMMUNICATIONS MANAGER
Crystal Phelps
Contact: COO Jennifer Jarrett
Email: jjarrett@theartscommission.org
Contact: President and Chief Executive Officer Marc D. Folk
Email: mfolk@theartscommission.org
Social Media: https:// www.facebook.com/ArtsCommission/ https://twitter.com/artscommission https:// www.instagram.com/theartscommission/
Capacity: 501-1000

Arts Council at Winston-Salem & Forsyth County
Website: www.infothearts.org
Email: info@infothearts.org
Phone: 336 722 2585
Address: 206 N Spruce Street, Suite 3, US
Information: Since its origin, The Arts Council has gained a reputation as an effective and efficient organisation to marshal support for the arts. Throughout the decades, The Arts Council has provided proactive leadership, sparked cultural growth and provided funds through grant programs to create a flourishing cultural environment
Country: United States
Contact: President and CEO Milton Rhodes
Email: mrhodes@intothearts.org
Policies: Arts centre

Arts Council Lake Erie West
Website: www.seven-eagles.com/home0.aspx
Email: martinnagy@aol.com
Phone: 419 531 2046
Address: 1700 N Reynolds Rd, US
Information: The Arts Council Lake Erie West (ACLEW), know as Common Space, is a regional not-for-profit community arts agency serving communities in the Lake Erie West Region of Northwest Ohio / Southeast Michigan. The grass roots agency was created in 1983 by entrepreneur: artists, educators and business persons to cultivate the arts with affordable artist work spaces and creative programs for the public
Country: United States
Contact: Executive Director Martin Nagy
Contact: program Director Leslee Wirick

Policies: Arts centre

Arts Council of Fairfax County
Website: www.artsfairfax.org
Email: info@artsfairfax.org
Phone: 703 642 0862
Address: 10604 Judicial Drive, US
Information: The Arts Council is the voice of the arts, dedicated to fostering dynamic and diverse local arts, ensuring that arts thrive by providing vision, leadership, capacity building services, advocacy, funding, education, and information
Country: United States
CEO & President
Linda Sullivan
Social Media: www.facebook.com/pages/Arts-Council-of-Fairfax-County/54717528726
Policies: Arts centre

Arts Council of Mississippi County
Website: www.artsmissco.org
Email: artsmissco@yahoo.com
Phone: 870 623 8460
Address: 306 W. Main Street, Blytheville, US
Information: The mission of the Arts Council of Mississippi County is to enhance the quality of life for the citizens in our area of service and to instill arts awareness and development through music, theatre, visual arts and dance.
Country: United States
Contact: President J.D. Harris
Contact: Coordinator David Lyttle
Contact: Vice President Candie Groves
Contact: undefinedSecretary Sarah Jackson
Capacity: 1000+
Annual Performances: 11-25
Annual Productions: 0-5
Policies: All

Arts Council of Tuscaloosa Bama Fanfare
Website: www.tuscarts.org
Email: Director@tuscarts.org
Phone: 205 785 5195
Address: 600 Greensboro Avenue, US
Information: Bama Theater is the venue of Arts Council of Tuscaloosa Bama Fanfare. The Bama Theatre is a historic theatre located in downtown Tuscaloosa surrounded by restaurants and night life. The theatre has been a Tuscaloosa feature since 1938 and continues as a venue for entertainment and art. The Bama Theatre is managed by The Arts Council and features the Bama Art House Film Series, Acoustic Nights, concerts and performances from local arts organisations
Country: United States
Contact: Executive Director Sandra Wolfe
Email: Director@tuscarts.org
Contact: publicity Kevin Ledgewood
Email: pr@tuscarts.org
Social Media: @tuscarts www.facebook.com/TheArtsCouncil.BamaTheatre.CAC
Policies: Theatre

Arts Place Inc.
Website: www.artsland.org
Email: artsland@artsland.org
Phone: 260 726 4809
Address: 131 East Walnut St, PO Box 804, US
Information: Arts Place nurtures the creative spirit by making arts experiences, education, and services accessible to the region's residents, artists and cultural organizations. Arts Place begins presenting summer performances in the new Hudson Family Park Amphitheatre in Portland. After two years of unresolved debate with the Indiana Arts Commission, Arts Place ends its relationship as a Regional Arts Partner to the state arts agency
Country: United States
Contact: Executive Director Eric Rogers
Contact: regional services and development Sue Burk
Contact: Marketing Director Jennifer Nixon
Social Media: @apjnixon www.facebook.com/pages/Arts-Place-Inc/76153718171?ref=ts
Policies: Concert hall

ArtsCenter
Website: www.artscenterlive.org
Email: info@artscenterlive.org
Phone: 919 929 2787
Address: 300-G East Main St, US
Information: The ArtsCenter exists in order to educate and inspire Artistic creativity and to enrich the lives of people of all ages. The vision of The ArtsCenter is to create an educational environment that provides opportunities, inspiration and tools to people of all ages and skill levels to participate in the arts
Country: United States
Contact: Executive Director Art Menius
Email: Director@artscenterlive.org
Contact: Director of development Julie Tomkovick
Email: development@artscenterlive.org
Social Media: @ArtsCenterLive www.facebook.com/artscenterlive
Policies: Present, produce, co-produce, Present and produce, Produce and co-produce, Produce and rent, Arts centre

ASNMSU Cultural Affairs Board Special Events
Website: panam.nmsu.edu
Email: cmeihlf@nmsu.edu
Address: PO Box 30001, Department 3SE, US
Information: The Pan American Center is the venue for ASNMSU Cultural Affairs Board Special Events, built in 1968 and renovated in 2006-07, is one of the finest arenas in the American Southwest. Seating 13140, the Pan Am hosts athletic events, including Aggie basketball and volleyball, as well as some of the top entertainers in America
Country: United States
Policies: Arts centre

Associated Students Inc., SJSU
Website: www.union.sjsu.edu
Email: Ted.Cady@sjsu.edu
Phone: 408 924 6350
Address: Students Union, Room 350, 1 Washington Square, US
Information: The Event Center Arena holds 4600 people for basketball, and more than 6500 people for concerts. It has hosted events such as Bruce Springsteen, Prince, Sting, Faith Hill. Sporting events include the SJSU Spartan Men's and Women's Basketball teams, and 2008 Pacific Rim Gymnastics Championships
Country: United States
Contact: Director of special events Ted Cady
Contact: Executive Director Cathy Busalacchi
Email: cathy.busalacchi@sjsu.edu
Social Media: @SJSU www.facebook.com/sanjosestate
Policies: Arts centre

Atlantic Center for the Arts
Website: www.atlanticcenterforthearts.org
Email: program@atlanticcenterforthearts.org
Phone: 386 427 6975
Address: 1414 Art Center Ave, US
Information: Atlantic Center for the Arts (ACA) is a nonprofit, interdisciplinary artists' community and arts education facility providing artists an opportunity to work and collaborate with contemporary artists in the fields of composing, visual, literary, and performing arts. Community interaction is coordinated through on-site and outreach presentations, workshops, and exhibitions
Country: United States
Contact: program and residency Manager Nick Conroy
Email: nconroy@atlanticcenterforthearts.org
Contact: co-Director Jim Frost
Email: jfrost@atlanticcenterforthearts.org
Contact: Marketing Kathryn Peterson
Email: kpeterson@atlanticcenterforthearts.org
Social Media: @Atlantic_Center www.facebook.com/atlanticcenterforthearts
Policies: Arts centre

Auditorium Theatre
Website: www.auditoriumtheatre.org
Email: info@auditoriumtheatre.org
Phone: 312 922 2110
Address: 50 East Congress Pkwy, US
Information: the Auditorium was built for a syndicate of businessmen to house a large civic opera house; to provide an economic base it was decided to wrap the auditorium with a hotel and office block. Hence Adler & Sullivan had to plan a complex multiple-use building
Country: United States
Contact: Executive Director Brett Batterson
Marketing & development officer
Judie Moore Green
Social Media: @AuditoriumChgo www.facebook.com/auditoriumtheatre
Policies: Theatre

Auditorium Theatre of Roosevelt University
Website: www.auditoriumtheatre.org
Email: info@auditoriumtheatre.org
Phone: 312 341 2300
Address: 50 E Congress Pkwy, US
Information: The Auditorium Theatre of Roosevelt University is an independent not-for-profit organization committed to presenting the finest in international, cultural, and community programming to Chicago and to the continued restoration and preservation of the National Historic Landmark Auditorium Theatre. Member of ISPA
Country: United States
Contact: Chairman John Svoboda
Social Media: @AuditoriumChgo www.facebook.com/auditoriumtheatre
Policies: Other

Aurora Fox Arts Center
Website: www.aurorafoxartscenter.org
Email: foxbox@auroragov.org
Phone: 303 739 1970
Address: 9900 E Colfax Avenue, PO Box 9, US
Information: the Aurora Fox offers the residents of Aurora and the metro area enjoyment of professional quality performances in a smaller, intimate, and accessible performing space. The goals are to bring new plays to the metro region for both the main stage and children's seasons, provide opportunities for children to perform in

a professional environment, and provide opportunities for minority performers and audiences in the community to be involved in the performing arts
Country: United States
Contact: Executive Producer Charles Packard
Email: cpackard@auroragov.org
Contact: Marketing Director Patricia Wells
Email: pwells@auroragov.org
Social Media: www.facebook.com/theaurorafox
Policies: Arts centre

Aurora University Guest Artist Series
Website: www.aurora.edu
Email: amanion@aurora.edu
Phone: 630 892 6431
Address: 222 Church Street, US
Country: United States
Contact: head of theatre Jeoffrey Baumgartner
Social Media: @AuroraU www.facebook.com/aurorauniversity
Policies: Arts centre

Austin Arts Center Trinity College
Website: www.trincoll.edu
Email: megan.fitzsimmons@trincoll.edu
Phone: 860 297 2000
Address: 300 Summit St, US
Information: The Trinity campus is alive with the arts. At large and intimate venues, you can attend music recitals, dance concerts, musical theater productions, small performance works, art exhibitions, and avant-garde cinema. Students and faculty regularly host exhibits and performances
Country: United States
Contact: Associate Director, calendar and special events Christine Guilmartin
Contact: publications assistant Lisa Hurley
Contact: Director Megan Fitzsimmons
Social Media: @trinitycolleg www.facebook.com/TrinityCollege
Policies: Concert hall

Austin Chamber Music Center
Website: www.austinchambermusic.org
Email: info@austinchambermusic.org
Phone: 512 454 0026
Address: 3814 Medical Parkway, US
Information: The Austin Chamber Music Center (ACMC) is dedicated to serving Central Texans by expanding knowledge, understanding, and appreciation of chamber music through the highest quality instruction and performance
Country: United States
Contact: business Manager Ora Shay
Contact: Executive Director Jeri DeAngelis
Contact: Artistic Director Michelle Schumann
Contact: assistant Director for education Eric Miller
Policies: Theatre

Austin Peay State University / Clarksville Community Concert Artist Series
Website: www.apsu.edu/creativearts
Phone: 931 221 7876
Address: Austin Peay State University, PO Box 4666, US
Country: United States
Contact: Director Feleecha johnson
Contact: Associate Director Marlon Crow
Contact: technical Director/house Manager Micheal Sorensen
Contact: secretary Jeanna Share
Social Media: @austinpeay www.facebook.com/austinpeay
Policies: Arts centre

Avalon Foundation
Website: www.avalontheatre.com
Email: info@avalontheatre.com
Phone: 410 822 0345
Address: 40 East Dover Street, US
Information: The Avalon Theatre is a historic theater located in downtown Easton, Maryland. Originally built as a cinema in 1921, The Avalon was billed as the "Showplace of the Eastern Shore." Today serves as the prime venue of the Mid-Shore area for performing arts, nationally and locally
Country: United States
Contact: Artistic Director Ellen General
Social Media: @AvalonTheatre www.facebook.com/pages/The-Avalon-Theatre/182300588529712
Policies: Theatre

Bach Dancing and Dynamite Society, Inc
Website: www.bachddsoc.org
Email: info@bachddsoc.org
Phone: 650 728 9436
Address: PO Box 302, US
Information: Bach brings a concert approach to a beachfront setting, with the intimacy of a club ambiance. There is a communal feeling to the Beach House and Concert Room, a room that brings the musicians and audience together in a special way. According to the musicians who have played there throughout the years,

the Douglas Beach House is "the best small venue in the United States
Country: United States
Contact: founder and concert Manager Pete Douglas
Contact: assistant to concert Manager Linda Goetz
Policies: Concert hall

Bailey Concert Hall
Website: baileyhall.org
Email: ntaver1@broward.edu
Phone: 954 201 6880
Address: 3501 SW Davie Road, US
Information: Bailey Hall, located on Broward College's central campus, is the cultural beacon for the arts community in Broward County. Beyond the rich academic experiences the college's students experience, the performance hall hosts the highest quality professional artists in a variety of disciplines
Country: United States
Contact: Bailey staff Natalie Taveras Rosario
Email: ntaver1@broward.edu
Contact: Bailey staff Frank Bolla
Email: fbolla@broward.edu
Policies: Concert hall

Baldwin Wallace College Academic & Cultural Events Series (ACES)
Website: www.bw.edu
Email: jhairsto@bw.edu
Phone: 440 826 2900
Address: ACES Office, 275 Eastland Road, Baldwin Wallace College, US
Information: The BW Conservatory of Music is a proven choice for students aspiring to perform with the best orchestras, operas and theatres; to gain acceptance to top graduate schools; and to land positions in teaching, arts management and music therapy
Country: United States
Contact: Director Jay T Hairston
Email: jhairsto@bw.edu
Policies: Concert hall

Ball State University – Emens Auditorium
Website: www.bsu.edu/emens
Email: emens@bsu.edu
Phone: 765 285 1539
Address: Ball State University, 2000 W. University Ave, US
Information: Emens Auditorium is Ball State's premier venue for arts and entertainment events. The auditorium seats more than 3000 people. Since its 1964 grand opening, many world-renowned artists, individuals, musicians, and shows have graced the Emens stage. Legendary events have included David Letterman, Stevie Wonder, Louis Armstrong, magician David Copperfield, comedian Adam Sandler, and the musicals Cats and Les Miserables, among many others
Country: United States
Social Media: www.facebook.com/emensauditorium
Policies: Theatre

Baltimore Museum of Art
Website: www.artbma.org
Phone: 443 573 1700
Address: 10 Art Museum Drive, US
Information: the beautifully renovated Baltimore Museum of Art is a unique venue with a variety of spaces that are ideal for events large and small – milestone celebrations, intimate dinner parties, wedding ceremonies and receptions, rehearsal dinners, bar/bat mitzvahs, corporate receptions, holiday parties, meetings, performances, film screenings, and much more
Country: United States
Contact: Director Doreen Bolger
Contact: Director of public relations Anne Mannix
Contact: Director of security Ron Haddaway
Social Media: @artbma www.facebook.com/artbma
Policies: Arts centre

Barbara B Mann Performing Arts Hall
Website: www.bbmannpah.com
Email: genmgr@bbmannpah.com
Phone: 239 481 4849
Address: 13350 Edison Parkway, US
Information: The Barbara B. Mann Performing Arts Hall is the premier place for Broadway musicals in Fort Myers. Located on the Edison Community College campus, it's the tallest building on campus, and the only theater in the area with the size and technology to host musicals like Guys and Dolls, as well as rock and jazz concerts. The Hall is also the home of the Southwest Florida Symphony from December through April
Country: United States
Contact: vice President programming Norbert Mongeon
Contact: General Manager Mary Bensel
Policies: Concert hall

Bardavon Opera House
Website: www.bardavon.org
Email: slamarca@bardavon.org
Phone: 845 473 5288
Address: 35 Market St, US
Information: The Bardavon Opera House was constructed in the year 1869, and since then continues to be one of the leading venues for operatic performances in the

city. Plays, dance recitals and music concerts also take to the stage here. Apart from these seasonal events, Bardavon organizes several major festivals through the year, such as the Hudson River Arts Festival and the Kids Expo
Country: United States
 Director, Marketing & pr
 Amy Manso
Contact: production Manager Stephen LaMarca
Contact: Executive Director Chris Silva
Policies: Concert hall

Bargemusic, Ltd
Website: www.bargemusic.org
Email: info@bargemusic.org
Phone:
718 624 4924
Address: Fulton Ferry Landing, US
Information: Since 1977, Bargemusic has presented chamber music in an unlikely and startlingly beautiful venue—a floating barge at the foot of the Brooklyn Bridge
Country: United States
 Executive & Artistic Director
 Mark Peskanov
Contact: founder Olga Bloom
Policies: Other

Barrington Area Arts Council
Email: baacouncil@aol.com
Address: PO Box 1266, 207 Park Avenue, US
Information: also publish the literary magazine 'Wetstone'; conduct writer workshops and have an Arts Forum; also organise and present an annual Summer Arts Fair which takes place every June
Country: United States
Contact: Executive Director Corinne Pierog
Social Media: www.facebook.com/pages/Run-for-the-Arts-Barrington-Area-Arts-Council/186108458120279
Policies: Open-air

Barrow Civic Theatre
Website: www.barrowtheatre.com
Email: john@barrowtheatre.com
Phone: 814 432 5196
Address: PO Box 1089, US
Information: theatre owned by Franklin Civic Operetta Association
Country: United States
Contact: technical Director Benjamin Geibel
Email: benta@barrowtheatre.com
Contact: General Manager Penny Gustavson
Email: pennygm@barrowtheatre.com
Social Media: @Barrow_Civic www.facebook.com/home.php?sk=group_21355792604
Policies: Theatre

Bartlesville Community Center
Website: www.bartlesvillecommunitycenter.com
Email: patd@bartlesvillecommunitycenter.com
Phone: 918 337 2787
Address: 300 SE Adams Blvd., US
Information: co-sponsor, mostly rent
Country: United States
Contact: Managing Director Val Callaghan
Email: vcallaghan@bartlesvillecommunitycenter.com
Contact: Marketing Director Jo Baughman
Email: jbaughman@bartlesvillecommunitycenter.com
Contact: administrative Director Sherry Gray
Email: sgray@bartlesvillecommunitycenter.com
Social Media: @BvilleCommCtr www.facebook.com/BartlesvilleCommunityCenter
Policies: Rent only, Theatre

Bartlesville Community Concert Association
Website: www.bccamusic.org/
Email: cswango@aol.com
Phone: 918 333 3313
Address: PO Box 651, US
Country: United States
Contact: concert Chairman Irvin Dunlap
Contact: treasurer Gail Barnett
Contact: President Carol Swango
Email: cswango@aol.com
Policies: Concert hall

Barton College Concert & Lecture Series
Website: www.barton.edu
Email: mdaughety@barton.edu
Phone: 252 399 6300
Address: Barton College, PO Box 5000, US
Country: United States
Contact: Chair, concert and lecture committee Morgan Daughety
Policies: Concert hall

Baruch Performing Arts Center
Website: www.baruch.cuny.edu/bpac
Email: PerformingArtsCenter@baruch.cuny.edu
Phone: 212 352 3101
Address: One Bernard Baruch Way, 25th Street between Lexington & 3rd Aves, New York, US
Information: Baruch Performing Arts Center convenes a conversation across the disciplines of art, science, and the humanities, as well as across the panoply of

world societies that are represented in Baruch's diverse student body. They do this by presenting and producing theater, music, dance, literary and spoken word, film, and discussions which inform through relevant content and engage through singular experiences, enriching the appreciation of Baruch students, faculty and alumni for culture in its broadest sense, while serving as a resource for all New Yorkers. Member of ISPA
Country: United States
Contact: Director Ted Altschuler
Email: ted.altschuler@baruch.cuny.edu
Contact: Marketing Manager Angela Renzi
Email: Angela.Renzi@baruch.cuny.edu
Phone: 646 312 4087production Manager Erick Creegan
Email: Erick.creegan@baruch.cuny.edu
Phone: 646 312 4086
Social Media: https://twitter.com/baruchpac www.facebook.com/BaruchPAC https://www.instagram.com/baruchpac/
Capacity: 501-1000
Annual Performances: 100+
Annual Productions: 51-100
Policies: All

Baryshnikov Arts Center
Website: www.bacnyc.org
Email: info@bacnyc.org
Phone: 646 731 3200
Address: Baryshnikov Dance Foundation, 450 W. 37th Street, Suite 501, US
Country: United States
Contact: Managing Director, foundation Christina Sterner
Contact: Artistic Director Mikhail Baryshnikov
Social Media: @bacnyc www.facebook.com/BACNYC
Policies: Arts centre

Bass Performance Hall
Website: www.basshall.com
Email: info@basshall.com
Phone: 817 212 4300
Address: 4th and Calhoun Streets, US
Information: operated by Performing Arts Fort Worth Inc, which co-promotes, and rents as necessary to accommodate any attraction suitable for its seat count
Country: United States
Contact: chief information officer Michael Cotham
Contact: Director of communications Carl Davis
Contact: Director of development Patricia H Schutts
Policies: Concert hall

Bay Arts Alliance Broadway Series
Website: www.BayArts.org
Email: info@bayarts.org
Phone: 850 769 1217
Address: 8 Harrison Avenue, US
Information: member of Florida Professional Presenters consortium; local artists – free concerts in the park; funded in part through the Florida State division of cultural affairs
Country: United States
Contact: Executive Director Jennifer Jones
Contact: Executive assistant Joy Adams
Contact: facility Manager Donald Schwartz
Social Media: www.facebook.com/bayartsalliance
Policies: Theatre

Bay Arts Council
Website: www.bayartscouncil.org/
Email: Director@bayarts.org
Phone: 989 893 0343
Address: 901 North Water Street, US
Country: United States
Contact: administrative assistant Carolyn White
Contact: Executive Director Tom Niemann
Policies: Concert hall

Bay Chamber Concerts
Website: www.baychamberconcerts.org
Email: info@baychamberconcerts.org
Phone: 207 236 2823
Address: 18 Central Street, Rockport, US
Information: Founded in 1960 by two brothers, pianist Andrew Wolf and flutist Thomas Wolf, Bay Chamber was created to model the former Curtis Institute of Music summer music colony in Rockport, Maine. The first 25 years were devoted to summer classical concert programs. In 1974, Bay Chamber began offering concerts year-round, adding jazz and world music to its program series.**Country:** United States
Contact: Artistic Director Manuel Bagorro
Email: manuel@baychamberconcerts.org
Contact: Executive Director Monica Kelly
Email: monica@baychamberconcerts.org
Contact: development Director Mackenzie Gassett
Email: Mackenzie@baychamberconcerts.org
Social Media: https://mobile.twitter.com/baychamber www.facebook.com/BayChamberME
Capacity: 251-500
Policies: Rent and Present

Bayfront Park Management Trust, City of Miami
Website: www.bayfrontparkmiami.com
Email: jsolano@miamigov.com

Phone: 305 358 7550
Address: 301 North Biscayne Boulevard, US
Country: United States
Contact: events coordinator Jose Solano
Email: jsolano@miamigov.com
Contact: Marketing Director Carol Cutt
Email: ccutt@miamigov.com
Contact: Executive Director Timothy Schmand
Email: tschmand@miamigov.com
Social Media: www.facebook.com/bayfrontparkmiami
Policies: Multi-purpose

Baylor University Distinguished Artist Series
Website: www.baylor.edu
Email:
kathy_g_johnson@baylor.edu
Address: School of Music, Box 97408, US
Information: soloist to chamber ensembles
Country: United States
Contact: series Manager Kathy Johnson
Social Media: www.facebook.com/pages/Bay-lor-University/61388081925
Policies: Concert hall

Beachfront Studio
Address:
575 Surfside Drive, US
Country: United States
Contact: cultural center Director Stephanie Birdsall
Policies: Other

Beasley Performing Arts Coliseum
Website: www.beasley.wsu.edu
Email: udy@maie.wsu.edu
Phone: 509 335 3525
Address: Washington State University, PO Box 641710, US
Country: United States
Contact: Director Leo Udy
Email: udy@mail.wsu.edu
Contact: assistant Director Russ Driver
Email: driver@wsu.edu
Policies: Other

Beaumont Music Commission BMC Inc
Email: bmc@exp.net
Address: PO Box 7469, US
Country: United States
Contact: Executive Director Cathy Theall
Policies: Other

Beck Center for the Arts
Website: www.beckcenter.org
Phone: 216 521 2540
Address: 17801 Detroit Avenue, US
Country: United States
Contact: Director of dance Lynda Sackett
Contact: Marketing assistant Fran Storch
Director of Marketing & external affairs
Yvette A. Hanzel
Contact: Artistic Director Scott Spence
Contact: Director of education Edward P. Gallagher
Social Media: @BeckCenter www.facebook.com/beck-center
Policies: Arts centre

Belasco Theatre
Website: www.telecharge.com
Email: tickets@telecharge.com
Phone: 212 239 6200
Address: 111 West 44th Street, US
Country: United States
Contact: vice President of theatre operations Peter Entin
Policies: Theatre

Belhaven College Preston Memorial Series
Email: cshelt@belhaven.edu
Address: Belhaven College, 1500 Peachtree Street, US
Country: United States
Contact: Chairman music department Christopher Shelt
Policies: Concert hall

Belknap Mill Society
Website: www.belknapmill.org/
Email: belknap@metrocast.net
Phone: 603 524 8813
Address: The Mill Plaza, 25 Beacon Street E, US
Country: United States
Contact: Manager Kathleen LaBranche
Contact: Executive Director Mary Rose Boswell
Social Media: www.facebook.com/pages/Historic-Belknap-Mill/153326591393153
Policies: Other

Belmont Abbey College Coffeehouse & Fine Arts Committee
Website: www.belmontabbeycollege.edu
Email: info@bac.edu
Phone: 888 222 0110
Address: 100 Belmont-Mt, Holly Road, US
Country: United States
Social Media: @BelmontAbbey www.facebook.com/belmontabbey

Benaroya Hall
Website: www.seattlesymphony.org
Email: BHMC@seattlesymphony.org
Phone: 206 215 4700
Address: PO Box 21669, US
Information: second address: 200 University Street, PO Box 21669, Seattle WA 98101; home of the Seattle Symphony Orchestra, music Director Gerard Schwarz; see also Orchestras
Country: United States
Contact: General Manager Jennifer Adair
Contact: Executive Director Simon Woods
Contact: music Director Ludovic Morlot
Social Media: @seattlesymphony/ www.facebook.com/seattlesymphony
Policies: Theatre

Benedictine College-Convocation-Arts Series
Website: www.benedictine.edu
Email: blaine@benedictine.edu
Address: Administration Bldg, Benedictine College, US
Country: United States
Contact: Chairman Blaine Schultz
Policies: Concert hall

Benedum Center for the Performing Arts
Website:
www.pgharts.org
Email: ciavarra@pgharts.org
Phone: 412 471 6070
Address: 802 Liberty Avenue, US
Information: presenting – rent and seasonal tenants: Pittsburgh Opera, Pittsburgh Ballet, Civic Light Opera, Pittsburgh Dance Council, Broadway Series – Cultural Trust/SFX
Country: United States
Contact: vice President of operations benedum center Gene Ciavarra
Contact: assistant Manager Susan Sternberger
Contact: pr Director Paul Kovach
Contact: administrative assistant Jacob Bacharach
Social Media: @CulturalTrust www.facebook.com/CulturalTrust?v=wall

Bennett College Academic & Cultural Enrichment Series (ACES)
Website: www.bennett.edu
Phone: 336 517 2100
Address: 900 E Washington St, US
Information: focus on educational programs rather than performing arts events
Country: United States
Contact: dean of student affairs Emilye Mobley
Social Media: @bennettcollege www.facebook.com/pages/Bennett-College/107254679356831
Policies: Concert hall

Bentley College
Website: www.bently.edu
Email: jmorris@bentley.edu
Phone: 781 891 2700
Address: SC 330 Bentley College, 175 Forest Street, US
Country: United States
Contact: coordinator, arts/lectures Jim Morris

Berea College Convocations
Website: www.berea.edu/convo
Email: randall_roberts@berea.edu
Phone: 859 985 3359
Address: CPO 2160, US
Country: United States
Contact: coordinator Randall Roberts
Email: randall_roberts@berea.edu
Social Media: @bereacollege www.facebook.com/bereacollege
Policies: Concert hall

Berkeley Rep
Website: www.berkeleyrep.org
Email: info@berkeleyrep.org
Phone: 510 647 2900
Address: 2025 Addison Street, Berkeley, US
Information: Berkeley Rep creates ambitious theatre that entertains and challenges its audiences, provokes civic engagement, and inspires people to experience the world in new and surprising ways.
Country: United States
Contact: Artistic Director Johanna Pfaelzer
Email: hr@berkeleyrep.org
Contact: Managing Director Susie Medak
Email: smedak@berkeleyrep.org
Contact: General Manager Theresa Von Klug
Email: hr@berkeleyrep.org
Social Media: twitter.com/berkeleyrep www.facebook.com/berkeleyrep www.instagram.com/berkeleyrep/

Berklee College of Music
Website: www.berkeley.edu/
Address: 1140 Boylston St, US
Country: United States
Contact: Director of performance center Cathy Horn
Social Media: @UCBerkeley www.facebook.com/UCBerkeley
Policies: Concert hall

Berks Arts Council
Website:
www.berksarts.org
Email: Info@BerksArts.org
Phone: 610 898 1930
Address: PO Box 854, US
Information: annual Berks Jazz Fest; Annual Bandshell Concert Series en plein air; Pagoda Awards
Country: United States
Contact: Executive Director Karen Haver
Email: Karen@BerksArts.org
Contact: production Manager Gary Spencer
Email: spencer@berksarts.org
Social Media: @BerksArtsCounci www.facebook.com/BerksArts4You
Policies: Concert hall

Bernhard Centre Special Events
Website: www.wmich.edu/studentcenter
Phone:
269 387 4860
Address: Bernhard Centre, 1903 W Michigan Ave, US
Information: The Bernhard Center, Western Michigan University's student center, offers the entire campus community many services, facilities and programs under one roof
Country: United States
Policies: Other

Bethany College
Website: www.bethanywv.edu
Email: rrose@bethanywv.edu
Phone: 304 829 7000
Address: Renner Union, PO Box 368, US
Country: United States
Contact: Director of communications Rebecca Rose
Policies: Other

Bethany College Second Century Performing Artists Series
Website: www.bethany.lb.edu
Address: 421 N. First St, US
Country: United States
Contact: Director Lorreen Emler
Policies: Concert hall

Bethel Woods Center for the Arts
Website: www.bethelwoodscenter.org
Email: info@BethelWoodsCenter.org
Address: PO Box 222, US
Information: not-for-profit Bethel Woods Center for the Arts, located at the site of the 1969 Woodstock festival in Bethel, NY, is not-for-profit cultural organization committed to inspiring exPression, creativity and innovation through the arts. Located just 90 minutes from New York City on 800 acres of manicured grounds, the center offers multiple stages featuring a diverse selection of popular artists and culturally-rich performances, an award-winning museum, and educational and community programmes that provide meaningful experience in arts, history and civic engagement
Country: United States
Contact: Director of development Audrey Garro
Email: agarro@bethelwoodscenter.org
Policies: Present, produce, co-produce, Present and produce, Produce and co-produce, Rent and present, Produce and rent, All, Arts centre

Bethune-Cookman University
Website: www.bethune.cookman.edu
Email: kershawc@cookman.edu
Phone: 386 481 2000
Address: 640 Dr. Mary McLeod Bethune Boulevard, US
Information: member of Florida Professional Presenters consortium
Country: United States
Director, cultural affairs & performance
Rebecca W Steele
Contact: Director, steel drum orchestra Pedro Orey
Contact: Director, jazz ensemble Hiram Powell
Contact: pr Manager Catherine Kershaw
Contact: operations Manager Cedric Evans
Policies: Concert hall

Bickford Theatre
Website: www.bickfordtheatre.org
Email: info@bickfordtheatre.org
Address: 6 Normandy Heights Road, US
Country: United States
Contact: technical Director Lewis Perlmutter
Contact: theatre Manager Laurel Smith
Contact: Artistic Director Eric Hafen
Contact: Executive Director Linda S. Moore
Social Media: @MorrisMuseumNJ www.facebook.com/MorrisMuseum
Policies: Theatre

Big Bear Lake Performing Arts Center
Website: www.citybigbearlake.com/
Email: bblpac@citybigbearlake.com
Phone: 909 866 4970
Address: PO Box 10000, 39707 Big Bear Blvd., US

Country: United States
Contact: theatre Director Donald B Gavitte
Policies: Arts centre

Bijou Theatre Center
Website: www.knoxbijou.com/
Email: bijoutc@aol.com
Phone: 865 522 0832
Address: PO Box 1746, 803 South Gay Street, US
Country: United States
Contact: General Manager Tom Bugg
Email: Tom@KnoxBijou.com
Contact: technical Director Lee Hamby
Email: Lee@KnoxBijou.com
Contact: assistant Manager Jeanine Fowler
Email: Jeanine@KnoxBijou.com
Social Media: @bijoutheatre www.facebook.com/BijouTheatre
Policies: Theatre

Biola University
Website: www.biola.edu
Email: admission@biola.edu
Phone: 562 903 6000
Address: 13800 Biola Avenue, US
Country: United States
Contact: Chair arts department Barry Krammes
Contact: Chair music department George Boespslug
Social Media: @biolau www.facebook.com/Biola
Policies: Concert hall

Birmingham Children's Theatre
Website: www.bct123.org
Email: reception@bct123.org
Phone: 205 458 8181
Address: P.O. Box 1362 Birmingham, US
Information: Three. We have a 250-seat theatre called the Wee Folks Theatre that is specifically designed for a more intimate, interactive experience. This theatre is Generally used by PreK-1st Graders. Our 950 seat Mainstage Theatre features stadium seating and a grand 70-foot proscenium stage. It accommodates 1st grade and up. The Charlotte Lane Dominick Studio Theatre seats 175 and is located in the BCT administrative offices wing of the BJCC. It is used for our Summer Series shows and Tiny Tyke Tales.
Country: United States
Contact: Associate Artistic Director Alex Ungerman
Email: alex@bct123.org
Phone: 205 458 8193 Executive Artistic Director Ashley Woods
Email: ashley@bct123.org
Phone: 205 458 8194
Sales & Office Manager
Stephen Pierce
Email: spierce@bct123.org
Phone: 205 458 8185
Social Media: https://twitter.com/BCT123org www.facebook.com/birminghamchildrenstheatre/ https:// www.instagram.com/bhamchildrenstheatre/
Capacity: 1000+
Annual Performances: 100+
Annual Productions: 6-10
Policies: All

Birmingham Music Club
Website: www.bhammusicclub.org
Phone: 205 253 1313
Address: PO Box 10486, Birmingham, US
Information: The Birmingham Music Club is not actually a club; it is a non-profit concert-presenting organization, known for presenting high-quality concerts for well over a century now. We retain our historical name, in order to honor our founders, and all those who have been so dedicated to keeping its good work going for all these years.
Country: United States
Contact: Executive Director Ron Bourdages
Contact: President Wyatt R. Haskell
Contact: Secretary Judy H. Wiggins
Social Media: www.facebook.com/bhammusicclub.org https://twitter.com/musicclubbham

Bloomsburg University Celebrity Artist Series
Website: www.bloomu.edu/CAS
Email: rPress@bloomu.edu
Phone: 570 389 4409
Address: Celebrity Artist Series, Bloomsburg University, 400 E 2nd Street, US
Information: Performed in the 2000-seat Mitrani Hall, Haas Center for the Arts, or the historic 600-seat K.S. Gross Auditorium, Carver Hall, the series has hosted hundreds of outstanding performances in its decades-long history. Acclaimed symphonies, opera, drama, comedy, world renowned dance companies, Tony award winning touring Broadway shows, Grammy winning solo performers in every genre and more… they've all been to Bloomsburg University and given their best
Country: United States
Contact: Director of performing arts facilities Randall Presswood
Social Media: @BloomsburgU www.facebook.com/celebartistseries
Policies: Concert hall

Blue Lake Fine Arts Camp
Website: www.bluelake.org
Phone: 231 894 1966
Address: Theatre Department, 300 East Crystal Lake Rd., US
Country: United States
Contact: President Fritz Stansell
Contact: camp Director Heidi Stansell
Policies: Other

Bluemont Concert Series
Website: www.bluemont.org
Email: info@bluemont.org
Phone: 540 955 8186
Address: PO Box 802, US
Information: Since 1976, the Bluemont Concert Series has presented more than 5, 000 high-quality events to a combined audience of more than 2 million in 68 communities in northwest and central Virginia. With steady growth, Bluemont has become a major public-private coalition of communities in the region.
Country: United States
Contact: President emeritus Peter Dunning
Email: peter@bluemont.org
Contact: Executive Director Lily Rose Dunning
Email: lily@bluemont.org
Contact: media coordinator Nathan Borger
Email: nathan@bluemont.org
artist-in-education program Manager & business Manager
Melissa W. Dunning
Email: melissa@bluemont.org
Social Media: www.facebook.com/BluemontConcertSeries
Policies: Theatre

Bluffton University Artist Series
Website: www.bluffton.edu/arts/series
Email: schatta@bluffton.edu
Phone: 419 358 3349
Address: 1 University Drive, US
Information: The Bluffton Artist Series brings to the campus each year a number of outstanding concert artists and ensemble groups
Country: United States
Contact: artist series Director Adam Schattschneider
Email: schatta@bluffton.edu
Social Media: @BlufftonU www.facebook.com/Bluffton-University
Policies: Present, produce, co-produce, Other

Blumenthal Performing Arts Center
Website: www.blumenthalarts.org/
Email: eesasky@ncbpac.org
Phone: 704 372 1000
Address: 130 N. Tryon St., US
Information: also has three galleries
Country: United States
Contact: President Tom Gabbard
Email: tgabbard@ncbpac.org
Contact: Marketing Wendy Oglesby
Email: woglesby@ncbpac.org
Social Media: @blumenthalarts www.facebook.com/NCBPAC
Policies: Present and produce

Bob Carr Performing Arts Centre
Website: www.drphillipscenter.org/explore/plan-your-visit/the-venues/bob-carr-theater.stml
Phone: 407 440 7000
Address: 401 West Livingston Street, US
Country: United States
Contact: Marketing division Manager Kirk Wingerson
Email: kirk.wingerson@cityoforlando.net
Social Media: @BobCarrPAC www.facebook.com/bob-carrpac
Policies: Rent only, Arts centre

Bob Jones University Concert, Opera and Drama Series
Website: www.bju.edu
Email: Finearts@bju.edu
Phone: 864 242 5100
Address: Bob Jones University, US
Country: United States
Contact: President Stephen Jones
Contact: dean of fine arts Darren Lawson
Annual Performances: 2
Annual Productions: 3
Policies: Concert hall

Booth Theatre
Website: www.telecharge.com
Email: tickets@telecharge.com
Address: 222 W 45th Street, US
Country: United States
Contact: vice President of theatre operations Peter Entin
Contact: management company The Shubert Org. Inc
Policies: Multi-purpose

Boston College
Website: www.bc.edu/robshaminfo
Email: howard.enoch@bc.edu

Address: Robsham Theater Arts Center, 140 Commonwealth Avenue, US
Information: have a professional ballet company in residence
Country: United States
Contact: office coordinator Bunny Doyle
Contact: Director Howard Enoch
Contact: assistant Director Sheppard Barnett
Policies: Theatre

Boston University College of Fine Arts School of Music
Website: www.bu.edu/cfa/music/
Email: csamusic@bu.edu
Phone: 617 353 8789
Address: 855 Commonwealth Ave, US
Country: United States
Contact: Director of school of music Robert K. Dodson
Email: jfilippi@bu.edu
Social Media: @BUArts www.facebook.com/BUArts
Policies: Concert hall

Bowlus Fine Arts Cultural Centre
Website: www.bowluscenter.org
Email: susan.raines@bowluscenter.org
Phone: 620 365 4765
Address: 205 E Madison St, PO Box 705, US
Country: United States
Contact: Executive Director Susan Raines
Email: susan.raines@bowluscenter.org
Contact: Marketing Director Candace McRae
Email: candacejayne@gmail.com
Contact: technical Director Jeff Jordan
Email: jeff.jordan@bowluscenter.org
Social Media: www.facebook.com/bowluscenter
Policies: Arts centre

Bradford Creative and Performing Arts Center
Website: www.bcpac.com
Email: arts@bcpac.com
Phone: 814 362 2522
Address: 10 Marilyn Horne Way, US
Information: visiting address: Seneca Building, 10 Marilyn Horne Way, Bradford
Country: United States
Contact: President James Guelfi
Social Media: www.facebook.com/pages/BCPAC/181293509590
Policies: Arts centre

Bradley University Activities Council Performing Arts Series
Website: www.bradley.edu
Email: khale@bradley.edu
Phone: 309 676 7611
Address: Student Center, 1501 W. Bradley Ave, US
Country: United States
Contact: Director Michelle Whited
Contact: President Kelcy Hale
Social Media: @bradkeyu www.facebook.com/BradleyUniversity
Policies: Other

Brandeis University Spingold Theater Center
Website: www.brandeis.edu
Email: spingold@brandeis.edu
Phone: 781 736 2000
Address: 415 South St, US
Country: United States
Contact: General Manager David Colfer
Social Media: @BrandeisU www.facebook.com/brandeisuniversity
Policies: Arts centre

Brattleboro Music Center Chamber Music Series
Website: www.bmcvt.org
Email: info@bmcvt.org
Phone: 802 257 4523
Address: Chamber Music Series, 38 Walnut Street, US
Country: United States
Contact: Managing Director Pam Lierle
Contact: education programs Director Carol Compton
Policies: Arts centre

Breakthrough
Address: PO Box 15425, US
Country: United States
Contact: office Manager Patricia McGivern
Policies: Other

Brevard Music Center
Website: www.brevardmusic.org
Email: bmc@brevardmusic.org
Phone: 828 862 2100
Address: 349 Andante Lane, US
Information: alternative postal address: P.O. BOX 312, Brevard, NC 28712; for contact with individuals refer to www.brevardmusic.org/about/contact; also Orchestras and Festivals
Country: United States
Contact: President/ chief Executive officer Larry Fogdall
Contact: Artistic Director Keith Lockhart
Contact: chief financial and administrative officer Claudia Hawkins

Contact: Artistic administrator Jason Posnock
Policies: Other

Brewton-Parker College – Fine Arts Council
Website: www.bpc.edu
Email: bteem@bpc.edu
Phone: 912 583 2241
Address: Brewton-Parker College, P.O BOX 197, US
Information: the new chapel also presents an arts lecture series, with 2 annual events a year
Country: United States
Contact: Director of public relations Terry Gaston
Social Media: @BrewtonParker www.facebook.com/brewtonparker
Policies: Concert hall

Briar Street Theatre
Website: www.blueman.com
Email: management@blueman.com
Phone: 773 348 4000
Address: 3133 N Halsted Street, US
Information: managed by Carol Fox & Associates
Country: United States
Contact: General Manager Chris Kantowicz
Contact: resident General Manager Laurie Viets
Contact: facilities Manager Phil Eickhoff
Policies: Theatre

Brigham Young University
Website: www.byu.edu
Email: kvcrossl@byugate.byu.edu
Address: A 410 Harris Fine Arts Centre, US
Country: United States
Contact: performing arts Manager Paul Duerden
Social Media: @byu www.facebook.com/byu
Policies: Concert hall

Brigham Young University – Idaho Center Stage Performing Arts Series
Website: www.byui.edu/centerstage
Email: sparhawkd@byui.edu
Phone: 208 496 3114
Address: 525 South Center Street, US
Information: The mission of Center Stage is to provide a wide variety of academic, cultural, social, and spiritual experiences in the performing arts to BYU-Idaho students, university employees and their families, and the local community.**Country:** United States
Contact: administrative Director Don Sparhawk
Email: sparhawkd@byui.edu
Annual Performances: 20
Policies: Theatre

Bristol Riverside Theatre
Website: www.brtstage.org
Email: susan@brtstage.org
Phone: 215 785 6664
Address: 120 Radcliffe Street, US
Information: Bristol Riverside Theatre (BRT) is an award-winning Equity theatre in Bucks County. Now in its 29 season, the theatre has grown to produce over 200 performance very year, including five Mainstage productions, special events and a summer musicale series.
Country: United States
Contact: producing Director/founder Susan Atkinson
Email: susan@brtstage.org
Contact: Artistic Director Keith Baker
Email: keith@brtstage.org
Contact: operations Manager Andrew Deppen
Email: andrewd@brtstage.org
Social Media: @brtstage www.facebook.com/BristolRiversideTheatre
Policies: Theatre

Broadhurst Theatre
Website: www.telecharge.com
Email: tickets@telecharge.com
Address: 235 W 44th Street, US
Country: United States
Contact: vice President of theatre operations Peter Entin
Contact: management company The Shubert Org. Inc
Policies: Theatre

Broadway Asia Company, The
Website: www.broadwayasia.com
Email: info@broadwayasia.com
Phone: 212 203 9986
Address: 250 West 52nd Street, 2nd Floor, US
Information: Management, production, licensing and consultation company concentrating on performing arts projects between the USA, Europe and Asia Pacific regions.
Country: United States
Contact: international licensing Manager Adam Gentle
Contact: Chairman Marc Routh
Contact: President Simone Genatt
Contact: Director tour management Maria Flotta
Policies: Theatre

Broadway Center for the Performing Arts
Website: www.broadwaycenter.org
Email: Administration@broadwaycenter.org
Phone: 253 591 5890
Address: 901 Broadway, US

Information: a non profit organization that manages and rents three theatres, a rehearsal hall and office building; also presents a performing arts season of 20-30 shows that vary from Broadway musicals and one-person shows, to acrobats and Celtic/jazz/big bands.
Country: United States
Contact: Marketing Manager Lacey Leffler
Email: laceyl@broadwaycenter.org
Contact: development Director Jane Bell
Email: jbell@broadwaycenter.org
Contact: events Manager Brenda Ramsey
Email: bramsey@boradwaycenter.org
Contact: Executive Director David Fischer
Email: dfischer@broadwaycenter.org
Social Media: @BroadwayCenter www.facebook.com/pages/Broadway-Center-for-the-Performing-Arts/51112013380
Policies: Arts centre

Broadway Theatre
Website: www.telecharge.com
Email: tickets@telecharge.com
Address: 1681 Broadway, US
Country: United States
Policies: Theatre

Broadway Theatre League
Website: www.broadwaytheatreleague.org
Email: info@broadwaytheatreleague.org.
Phone: 256 518 6155
Address: 700 Monroe Street, Suite 410 Huntsville, Alabama, US
Information: The purpose of the Broadway Theatre League of Huntsville is to provide professional live theatre for citizens of the Tennessee Valley area. Broadway Theatre League also strives to offer a well-rounded educational and cultural program to students of the Tennessee Valley through the Student Outreach Program.
Country: United States
Contact: Executive Director Andrew Willmon
Email: Andrew Willmon 256-551-2264
Phone: 256 551 2264
 Marketing & Development Director
 Wil Elrick
Phone: 256 551 2388membership Director Pennie Wood
Phone: 256 551 2378Patron Services Lisa Bollinger
Phone: 256 518 6155
Social Media: https:// www.facebook.com/Broadway-TheatreLeague/ https:// www.instagram.com/broadway-huntsville/
Disabled Access: Yes
Capacity: 1000+
Annual Performances: 100+
Annual Productions: 0-5
Policies: All

Broadway Theatre League
Phone: 719 545 4721
Address: 210 N. Santa Fe Avenue, US
Country: United States
Contact: Executive Director Maggie Divelbiss
Contact: President Ron Diodosio
Policies: All, Theatre

Broadway Theatre League of South Bend, Inc.
Website: www.broadwaytheatreleague.com
Email: info@broadwaytheatreleague.com
Phone: 574 234 4044
Address: 209 N. Main Street, Suite 201B, US
Country: United States
Contact: Executive Director Andrew Hoffmann
Policies: Theatre

Brookdale Community College Performing Arts Series
Website: www.brookdalecc.edu
Address: Brookdale Community College, US
Country: United States
Contact: programme Director Laurie Bender
Policies: Other

Brookhaven College Center For the Arts (CFA)
Website: www.bhc.dcccd.edu
Email: BCSA@dcccd.edu
Address: Brookhaven College, 3939 Valley View Lane, US
Country: United States
Contact: Executive dean Rodger Bennett
Policies: Concert hall

Brooklyn Academy of Music (BAM)
Website: www.bam.org
Email: info@bam.org
Phone: 718 636 4123
Address: 30 Lafayette Avenue, US
Information: produce Next Wave Festival: Autumn festival committed to the contemporary performing arts
Country: United States
Contact: Executive Producer Joseph V Melillo
Contact: President Karen Brooks Hopkins
Social Media: @BAM_Brooklyn www.facebook.com/BAMstage
Policies: Concert hall

Brooklyn Center for the Performing Arts

Website: www.BrooklynCenter.com
Email: Email@BrooklynCenter.com
Phone: 718 951 4600
Address: PO Box 100163, Ste 100, Bldg PAC, Campus Road and Hillel Place intersection, US
Information: special programming includes an acclaimed Children's programme, CinEvents featuring repertory classic films as well as Sneak Previews of new releases, and a Caribbean and Pop series. In addition, Community Showcase affords access to the facilities for the local community
Country: United States
 Executive dir., & General Manager
 Richarg Grossberg
Email: RchardG@BrooklynCenter.com
Contact: Managing Director Rick Berube
 dir., brooklyn center cinema & computer services
 Frank Angel
Social Media: @BrklynCtr
Annual Performances: 200
Annual Productions: 20
Policies: Present, produce, co-produce, Present and produce, Rent and present, Produce and rent, Theatre

Brooks Atkinson Theatre
Website: brooksatkinsontheater.com/
Phone: 212 719 4019
Address: 256 W 47th Street, US
Country: United States
Contact: management company
The Nederlander Org, Inc
Contact: house Manager Barbara Carellas

Brown County Civic Music Association
Website: www.bccivicmusic.org/
Email: civicmusic@aol.com
Phone: 920 338 1801
Address: PO Box 5243, US
Country: United States
Contact: President Amy L Kocha
Contact: Executive secretary Sandra Eberhardt
Policies: Theatre

Brownville Concert Series
Website: www.brownvilleconcertseries.com
Phone: 402 825 3331
Address: P.O. Box 52, 160 Atlantic, Brownville, US
Information: The mission of the Concert Series is to bring professional live performance to Southeast Nebraska.
Country: United States
Contact: programme Director James Keene
Policies: Present, produce, co-produce, Concert hall

Bryn Mawr College Performing Arts Series
Website: www.brynmawr.edu
Email: ngreaves@brynmawr.edu
Phone: 610 526 5000
Address: 10 N. Merion Avenue, US
Country: United States
Contact: coordinator, performing arts series Nicole Greaves
Social Media: @BrynMawrCollege www.facebook.com/BrynMawrCollege
Policies: Concert hall

Buckley Performing Arts Center
Website: www.massasoit.mass.edu/buckley
Email: swilhelm@massasoit.mass.edu
Phone: 508 588 9100
Address: Massasoit Community College, 1 Massasoit Blvd, US
Country: United States
Contact: Manager Sandy Wilhem
Email: swilhelm@massasoit.mass.edu
Policies: Arts centre

Bucks County Community College Department of Cultural Programming
Website: www.bucks.edu
Phone: 215 968 8000
Address: 275 Swamp Road, US
Information: family series; school program
Country: United States
Contact: coordinator Maria Cirillo-Lein
Policies: Arts centre

Bucks County Performing Arts Center
Website: www.bcpac.org/
Email: mary.bcpac@comcast.net
Phone: 215 493 3010
Address: 1140 Edgewood Road, US
Country: United States
Contact: secretary Joseph Eberhart
Contact: Executive Director Mary Borkovitz
Email: mary.bcpac@comcast.net
Contact: vice President and Marketing Pete Borkovitz
Contact: President Linda Strating
Social Media: www.facebook.com/pages/Bucks-County-Performing-Arts-Center-BCPAC/256604537700779
Policies: Concert hall

Buffalo Chamber Music Society
Website: www.bflochambermusic.org
Email: bcms@bflochambermusic.org

Phone: 716 462 4939
Address: P.O BOX 349, US
Information: member of Upstate New York Presenters
Country: United States
Contact: Executive Director Clementina Fleshler
Email: bcms@bflochambermusic.org
Annual Performances: 10
Policies: Rent only, Other

Burklyn Ballet Theatre / Burklyn Ballet Children's Program
Website: www.burklynballet.com
Email: info@BurklynBallet.com
Phone: 973 625 9300
Address: Johnson State College, 337 College Hill, US
Information: Summer Intensive where all students perform weekly. Students have 3 classes per day with world renowned master teachers. Performance opportunities also available at the Edinburgh Festival, Edinburgh Scotland.
Country: United States
Contact: Artistic Director Joanne Whitehill
Email: Burklyn@gmail.com
Social Media: @BurklynBallet www.facebook.com/Burklyn-Ballet-Theatre-1065330713478293
Policies: Other

Burlington Civic Music Association
Website: www.thehawkeye.com
Email: bwilson@thehawkeye.com
Phone: 319 754 8461
Address: Box 324, US
Country: United States

Bushnell Memorial Hall
Website: www.bushnell.org
Email: jennifer_gallager@bushnell.org
Phone: 860 987 6000
Address: 166 Capitol Avenue, US
Information: home to Connecticut Opera, Dance Connecticut and the Hartford Symphony; Bushnell presents 9 Broadway shows per season
Country: United States
Contact: Executive Director David Fay
Contact: senior Director of operations Kathleen Neidmann
Social Media: @thebushnell www.facebook.com/the-bushnell
Annual Performances: 9

Cain Park/City of Cleveland Heights
Website: www.cainpark.com
Email: cainpark@clvhts.com
Phone: 216 371 3000
Address: 40 Severance Circle, US
Information: conceived in the mid-30s, Cain Park is rich in history. The brainchild of Heights High School drama teacher Dr. Dina Rees Evans and Cleveland Heights Mayor Frank C. Cain, Cain Park's original purpose remains unaltered. Owned and operated by the City of Cleveland Heights, it is the living symbol of the City's commitment to nurturing quality programming in the arts for an area population that undeniably thrives on it
Country: United States
Contact: General Manager Erin Cameron
Email: cainpark@clvhts.com
Contact: public relations Manager Ksenia Roshchakovsky
Email: ksenia@clvhts.com
Contact: operations Manager Ian Hinz
Email: cainparkoperations@clvhts.com
Social Media: @CainPark www.facebook.com/CainPark
Annual Performances: 50
Annual Productions: 1
Policies: Present, produce, co-produce, Open-air

CAL Arts – School of Music
Website: www.music.calarts.edu
Email: musicinfo@calarts.edu
Phone: 661 255 1050
Address: California Institute of the Arts, 24700 McBean Pkwy, McBean Parkway, US
Information: performances by faculty and students
Country: United States
Contact: dean, school of music Susan Allen
Contact: production Manager, school of music Bob Clendenen
Social Media: @CalArts www.facebook.com/calarts

Cal Performances
Website: calperformances.org
Email: calperfs-info@calperformances.org
Phone: 510 642 0212
Address: University of California, Cal Performances, 101 Zellerbach Hall #4800, US
Information: We organise the biennial Berkeley Festival and Exhibition which is the largest early music festival in Northern America. Member of ISPA
Country: United States
Contact: General Manager Douglas Warrick
Email: dwarrick@calperformances.org
Contact: Director of public relations Christina Kellogg
Email: ckellogg@calperformances.org
Contact: Director of education and programs Laura Abrams
Email: labrams@calperformances.org

Contact: Director Matías Tarnopolsky
Email: mtarnopolsky@calperformances.org
Contact: development Director Sarah Sobey
Email: ssobey@calperformances.org
Social Media: @calperformances www.facebook.com/calperformances
Policies: Concert hall

Cal Poly Arts
Website: www.calpolyarts.org
Email: cparts@polymail.calpoly.edu
Address: California Polytechnic State University, 1 Grand Avenue, US
Country: United States
Contact: programme Manager Denise Leader Stoeber
Contact: Director Steven Lerian

Caldwell Fine Arts
Website: www.caldwellfinearts.org
Email: cfa@collegeofidaho.edu
Phone: 298 459 5783
Address: 2112 Cleveland Boulevard, US
Information: The auditorium is excellent for acoustic sound. Limited for theatre and dance productions by the wooden sound panels which surround, but turn, on the stage. Small agricultural and manufacturing community with Albertson College of Idaho, a liberal arts col
Country: United States
Contact: Executive Director Sylvia Hunt

Calico Theatre, UC Clermont College
Website: www.ucclermont.com
Email: community.arts@uc.edu
Phone: 513 732 5281
Address: 4200 Clermont College Drive, US
Information: art gallery displays local artists throughout the year
Country: United States
Contact: community arts coordinator Barbara Berner

California Center for the Arts, Escondido
Website: www.artcenter.org
Email: info@artcenter.org
Phone: 760 839 4138
Address: 340 North Escondido Blvd., US
Information: also rent; also has a visual arts Museum, art and dance studios, and a Conference Center containing meeting and banquet facilities
Country: United States
Contact: Director of performing arts Christian Wolf
Contact: technical Director Rob Collier
Contact: interim CEO Jon Teeuwissen
Social Media: www.facebook.com/theCCAE
Capacity: 1523

California Institute of Technology
Website: www.events.caltech.edu
Email: events@caltech.edu
Phone: 626 395 4652
Address: Caltech Public Events, Mail Code: 332-92, US
Information: alternative Email: dnn@caltech.edu
Country: United States
Contact: Manager Cara Stemen
Contact: assistant vice President for campus and community relations Denise Nelson Nash

California State Summer School for the Arts
Website: www.csssa.org
Email: application@csssa.org
Phone: 916 229 5160
Address: PO Box 1077, US
Country: United States
Contact: Executive Director Adrienne Luce
Social Media: www.facebook.com/csssa
Policies: Present and produce

California State University at Chico Public Events
Website: www.chicoperformances.com
Email: scummins@csuchico.edu
Phone: 530 898 5917
Address: California State University, Chico Performances, 400 West First Street, US
Information: is a broad spectrum campus unit within the division of University Advancement. With special responsibility for public event oversight, UPE manages the Chico Performances presenting program, the National Public Radio affiliate Northstate Public Radio KCHO & KFPR, the University Box Office, and the historical performance venue Laxson Auditorium
Country: United States
Contact: Director Stephen Cummins
Email: scummins@csuchico.edu
Policies: Present and produce

California State University Bakersfield Arts & Performing Arts Departments
Website: www.csub.edu
Email: ADupratt@csubak.edu
Phone: 166 165 42240
Address: 9001 Stockdale Highway, US
Country: United States

Contact: Chair, department of art Joyce Kohl
Contact: Chair, department of theatre Mandy Rees

California State University/Northridge Performing Arts Center
Website: www.valleyperformingartscenter.org
Email: vpac@csun.edu
Phone: 818 677 8800
Address: 18111 Nordhoff Street, US
Information: Now in its sixth season, VPAC's mission is to present a wide variety of performances that not only includes new and original work from the Los Angeles region, but also work from around the world that appeals to all of LA's rich and diverse communities
Country: United States
Social Media: @VPACatCSUN www.facebook.com/Valley-PerformingArtsCenter
Policies: Produce and rent

California Traditional Music Society
Website: www.ctmsfolkmusic.org
Email: info@ctmsfolkmusic.org
Phone: 818 817 7756
Address: 4924 Balboa Blvd #637, US
Information: organise Summer Solstice Folk Music, Dance and Storytelling Festival see Festivals
Country: United States
Contact: Executive Director Lisa Richardson

Calumet Theatre Company
Website: www.calumettheatre.com
Email: calumettheatre@choirtermi.net
Phone: 906 337 2166
Address: PO Box 167, 340 6th Street, US
Country: United States
Contact: Executive Director Jim Lowell

Cam-Plex Heritage Center
Website: www.cam-plex.com
Email: ticket@cam-plex.com
Phone: 307 682 0552
Address: 1635 Reata Drive, US
Information: The CAM-PLEX Heritage Center is a premiere performing arts center ideal for hosting a variety of events
Country: United States
Contact: theatre Manager Jaymi Gilmour-Crowley
Email: jaymi@cam-plex.com
Contact: Marketing Manager Sandra Bott
Email: sandra@cam-plex.com
Contact: General Manager Paul Foster
Email: paul@cam-plex.com
Social Media: @camplexevents www.facebook.com/camplexevents/
Capacity: 919

Canton Palace Theatre
Website: www.cantonpalacetheatre.org
Email: info@cantonpalacetheatre.org
Phone: 330 454 8172
Address: 605 North Market Avenue, US
Information: also an intermediate movie house showing art films, Hollywood hits and classics on the weekends; rental for live shows, movies and events
Country: United States
Contact: Executive Director Georgia Paxos
Email: georgia@cantonpalacetheatre.org
Social Media: @CantonPalaceThr www.facebook.com/CantonPalaceTheatre

Canyon Industries
Website: www.canyonentertainment.com
Email: simone@angelshq.com
Phone: 760 778 7966
Address: PO Box 256, US
Country: United States
Contact: Producer Valerie Hoffman
Contact: President Simone Sheffield

CAPA Columbus Association for the Performing Arts
Website: www.capa.com
Email: rcopley@capa.com
Phone: 614 469 1045
Address: 55 East State Street, US
Country: United States
Contact: facility rental Cory Pearson
  sponsorships & contributions
  Kimber Perfect
Contact: President Jennifer Kallaher
Contact: Bill Conner
Social Media: @CAPAColumbus www.facebook.com/CAPAColumbus
Policies: Present, produce, co-produce, Present and produce, Multi-purpose

Capitol Arts Center
Website: www.capitolarts.com
Email: info@capitolarts.com
Phone: 270 782 2787
Address: 416 East Main Street, US
Country: United States
Contact: Executive Director Steve Jones
Contact: Managing Director Kiri Barnett

Contact: Carrie Petrocelli
Contact: Kiri Petrocella

Capitol Center for the Arts
Website: www.ccanh.com
Email: friends@ccanh.com
Phone: 160 322 51111 e
Address: 44 South Main Street, US
Country: United States
Contact: Director of programming and events Kristin Ciccarelli

Capitol Civic Centre
Website: www.cccshows.org
Email: ccc@cccshows.org
Phone: 920 683 1937
Address: 913 S 8th Street, PO Box 399, US
Information: We are also the home stage to multiple regional performing arts groups, and available for General rental.
Country: United States
Contact: Executive Director Gian Paul Morelli

Capitol Theatre, Wheeling WV
Website: www.capitoltheatrewheeling.com
Email: info@capitoltheatrewheeling.com
Phone: 304 233 7000
Address: 1015 Main St, US
Information: Built in 1928, the Capitol Theatre has played a vital role in shaping Wheeling's economy and image. It was home of the legendary Jamboree USA broadcast over WWVA Radio since 1933 and to the Wheeling Symphony Orchestra.
Country: United States
Contact: BOOKING Dennis Magruder
Email: dmagruder@wesbancoarena.com
Phone: 304 233 7000BOX OFFICE MANAGER Doug Campbell
Email: pdcampbell@wesbancoarena.com
Phone: 304 233 7000MARKETING/ADVERTISING Sonya Fedorko
Email: sfedorko@wesbancoarena.com
Phone: 304 233 7000WEDDINGS AND BALLROOM RENT-ALS Cindy Johnson
Email: cjohnson@wesbancoarena.com
Phone: 304 233 7000MERCHANDISE Casey Tucker
Email: ctucker@wesbancoarena.com
Phone: 304 233 7000PRODUCTION Justin Malarkey
Email: jmalarkey@wesbancoarena.com
Social Media: www.facebook.com/Capitol-Theatre-Wheeling-WV-1425912254321544/twitter.com/CTWheelingWV

Caramoor
Website: www.caramoor.org
Email: info@caramoor.org
Phone: 914 232 1252
Address: PO Box 816, US
Information: Caramoor Center for Music and the Arts is a destination for exceptional music, captivating programs, spectacular gardens and grounds, and wonderful moments with friends and family. Visiting address: 149 Girdle Ridge Road, Katonah, NY 10536
Country: United States
Contact: Managing Director Paul Rosenblum
Email: paul@caramoor.org
Contact: chief Executive officer Jeffrey P Hayden
Email: jeff@caramoor.org
Social Media: @Caramoor www.facebook.com/Caramoor
Policies: Multi-purpose

Caramoor Center for Music and the Arts
Website: www.caramoor.org
Email: info@caramoor.org
Phone: 914 232 1252
Address: 149 Girdle Ridge Road, PO Box 816 Katonah, NY 10536 USA
Information: This performing arts center is located on a unique 90-acre setting of Italianate architecture and gardens in Westchester County, NY. It enriches the lives of its audiences with innovative and diverse musical performances. It involves various genres including Symphonic, Chamber Music, American Roots, American Songbook and Jazz. It also aims at mentoring young professional musicians and providing educational music programmes for young children. Audiences are invited to come early to explore the grounds, tour the historic Rosen House, enjoy a pre-concert picnic, and discover beautiful music in the relaxed settings the centre offers.
Country: United States
Contact: interim chief Executive officer Nina Curley Curley
vice President & Artistic Director
Kathy Schuman Schuman
vice President & chief financial officer
Tammy Belanger Belanger
Social Media: twitter.com/Caramoor www.facebook.com/Caramoor www.instagram.com/caramoor
Capacity: 1000+

Carlsbad Arts Office
Website: www.carlsbadca.gov
Email: arts@carlsbadca.gov
Phone: 760 434 2920

Address: 1200 Carlsbad Village Dr, US
Information: also has 'William Cannon Gallery' and a City Public Arts program
Country: United States
Social Media: @carlsbadcagov www.facebook.com/cityofcarlsbad

Carmel Music Society
Website: www.carmelmusic.org
Email: office@carmelmusic.org
Phone: 831 625 9938
Address: PO Box 22783, US
Country: United States
Contact: co-Presidents
Anne & Peter
Thorp

Carnegie Hall Corporation
Website: www.carnegiehall.org
Email: concertAdministration@carnegiehall.org
Phone: 212 247 7800
Address: 881 7th Ave, US
Information: visiting address: 154 W 57 Street, New York, NY 10019
Country: United States
Director of program planning & operations
Anna Weber
Executive & Artistic Director
Clive Gillinson
Contact: Director of public affairs Synneve Carlino
Contact: Director of Artistic planning Jeremy Geffen
Contact: Director of Marketing and creativer services Naomi Grabel

Carnegie Hall Inc
Website: www.carnegiehallwv.com
Email: info@carnegiehallwv.com
Phone: 304 645 7917
Address: 105 Church St, US
Country: United States
Contact: education Director Leah Trent
Contact: Artistic Director Lynn Creamer
Contact: Executive Director Susan Adkins

Carnegie Mellon Concerts
Website: www.music.cmu.edu
Email: dbarrett@andrew.cmu.edu
Phone: 412 268 3667
Address: Carnegie Mellon School of Music, 5000 Forbes Avenue, US
Information: The School of Music is one of five schools that comprise the College of Fine Arts. Teaching and rehearsal spaces are in the College of Fine Arts building and Margaret Morrison Carnegie Hall, as are two performance halls, Kresge Theatre and Alumni Concert Hall
Country: United States
Contact: special programs coordinator Daniel Barrett
Email: dbarrett@andrew.cmu.edu
Contact: Director of Marketing Emily Rybinski-Benish
Email: erb17@cmu.edu
Social Media: @CMUmusic www.facebook.com/CarnegieMellonMusic

Carolina Performing Arts
Website: www.carolinaperformingarts.org
Email: performingarts@unc.edu
Phone: 919 843 7776
Address: University of North Carolina at Chapel Hill, 100 Porthole Building, CB# 3233, US
Information: member of ISPA
Country: United States
Contact: Director of Marketing Don Smith
Email: jkreizman@unc.edu
Contact: Executive Director for the arts Emil Kang
Email: ctully@email.unc.edu
Social Media: @UNCPerformArts www.facebook.com/pages/Carolina-Performing-Arts/9560250967

Carolina Productions
Website: www.sa.sc.edu/cp
Email: sacp@mailbox.sc.edu
Phone: 803 777 7130
Address: Russell House, , Suite 318, US
Country: United States
Social Media: @usccp www.facebook.com/usccp

Carolina Theatre
Website: www.carolinatheatre.com
Email: boxoffice@carolinatheatre.com
Phone: 336 333 2600
Address: 310 S Greene St, US
Information: The Carolina Theatre, originally billed as "The Showplace of the Carolinas, " opened on Halloween night in 1927 as a 2, 200-seat vaudeville theater
Country: United States
Contact: Managing Director Brian Gray
Email: brian@carolinatheatre.com
Social Media: www.facebook.com/CarolinaTheatre

Carson-Newman College Concert Lecture Series
Website: www.cn.edu
Email: tteague@cn.edu
Phone: 865 471 3328
Address: PO Box 71987, Carson-Newman College, US
Country: United States

Contact: prof of music Thomas Teague

Carver Community Cultural Center
Website: www.thecarver.org
Email:
chris@thecarver.org
Phone: 210 207 2234
Address: 226 N Hackberry, US
Information: owned and operated by the City of San Antonio; also holds classes for youth in dance; free performances for schoolchildren; workshops and masterclasses
Country: United States
Contact: public information officer Chris Novosad
President & Director
William Lewis
Contact: program Manager Roland Mazuza

Casa Mañana
Website:
www.casamanana.org
Address: 3101 West Lancaster Avenue, US
Country: United States
Contact: Managing Director Leslie Bradford
Email: leslie.bradford@casamanana.org
Director of PR & Marketing
Darcy Koch
Email: darcy.koch@casamanana.org
President & Executive Producer
Wally Jones
Email: wally.jones@casamanana.org
Social Media: @CasaManana www.facebook.com/casafb
Policies: Present and produce, Theatre

Case Western Reserve University
Website: www.cwru.edu
Email: crb3@po.cwru.edu
Phone: 216 368 2679
Address: Thwing Center, 10900 Euclid Ave, US
Country: United States
Contact: Director Colleen Barker-Williamson

Caswell Council for the Arts – Caswell Performing Arts Series, Caswell Youth Series
Email: ccarts@caswell.k12.ec.us
Phone: 336 694 4591
Address: PO Box 609, US
Country: United States
Contact: Executive Director H. Lee Fowlkes

Catamount Film & Arts
Website: www.catamountarts.com
Email: catamount@kingcon.com
Phone: 802 748 2600
Address: 139 Eastern Avenue, Box 324, US
Country: United States
Contact: Executive Director Reginald Ainsworth

Cathedral Arts
Website: www.stjohndivine.org
Email: smith@stjohndivine.org
Phone: 212 316 7490
Address: Cathedral of St John the Divine, 1047 Amsterdam Avenue, US
Country: United States
Contact: production Alex Kanter

Cathedral Concert Series
Website: www.goccn.org/diocese/ccs/
Email: lgccso@intcomm.net
Phone: 361 888 6520
Address: 505 N. Upper Broadway, US
Information: concerts supported by advertisers, corporate sponsors, individual donors, and grants, all are no charge with the exception of one, being held at Richardson Auditorium, Del Mar College Campus
Country: United States
Contact: Executive Director Lee Gwozdz
Contact: administrative assistant Rachael Vasquez

Cedar City Music Arts
Email: Director@heritagectr.org
Phone: 435 865 4559
Address: PO Box 3371, US
Country: United States
Contact: Chairman of the board David Nyman
Contact: President Cindy Line

Cedar Crest College
Website: www.cedarcrest.edu
Email: rtamico@cedarcrest.edu
Phone: 610 606 4666 ext
Address: 100 College Drive, US
Country: United States
Contact: head of performing arts dept Roxanne Amico

Cedar Rapids Community Concerts Association
Email: bapdwingeo@aol.com
Phone: 131 936 24093
Address: 1017 F Ave NW, US
Country: United States
Contact: President George Baldwin
Contact: secretary Wilma Schadle

Cedarhurst Chamber Music
Website: www.cedarhurst.org
Email: sharon@cedarhurst.org
Phone: 618 242 1236
Address: Mitchell Museum at Cedarhurst, PO Box 923,
2600 Richview Road, US
Information: see John R and Eleanor R Mitchell Foundation, Mt Vernon, IL
Country: United States
Contact: Executive Director Sharon Bradham
Contact: Director of cedarhurst chamber music Randy
Winn
Contact: Executive assistant Linda Wheeler
Contact: Manager cedarhurst chamber music Brett Gibbs
Capacity: 300

Cedarville College Artist Series
Website: www.cedarville.edu/local/index.htm
Email:
vanloos@cedarville.edu
Phone: 937 766 7955
Address: 251 Main Street, US
Country: United States
Contact: assistant Director Jeff Beste
Contact: Director of student life centre Scott Van Loo

Celebrity Presentations Inc
Address:
PO Box 457, US
Country: United States
Contact: Director Sunny Charla Asch
Policies: Other

Centenary College Performing Arts Guild
Website: www.centenarystageco.org
Email: wallnau@centenarystageco.org
Phone: 908 979 0900
Address: 400 Jefferson St, US
Country: United States
Contact: Associate Artistic Director Catherine Rust
Contact: Artistic Director Carl Wallnau

Center for the Performing Arts @ Penn State
Website: www.cpa.psu.edu
Email: cfpa@psu.edu
Phone: 814 863 9494
Address: Eisenhower Auditorium, US
Information: nationally recognized commissioner of
Artistic works
Country: United States
Contact: Director George Trudeau
Email: gjt11@psu.edu
Contact: Sales and development services Director Tracy
Noll
Email: tqs4@psu.edu
Contact: Marketing and communications Director Laura
Sullivan
Email: lls19@psu.edu
Social Media: www.facebook.com/PSCPA
Policies: All

Center for Traditional Music & Dance
Website: www.ctmd.org
Email: traditions@ctmd.org
Phone: 212 571 1555
Address: 32 Broadway, Suite 1314, US
Country: United States
Contact: Director of artist management Kaisha S
Johnson
Contact: Artistic Director Ethel Raim
Contact: Executive Director Peter Rushefsky

Center Stage
Website: www.centerstage.org
Email: info@centerstage.org
Phone: 410 986 4000
Address: 700 North Calvert Street, Baltimore,
Maryland, US
Information: Baltimore Center Stage has been in its
historic Mt. Vernon home since 1975. In 2017, we
completed a $28 million renovation to create more
opportunities for art making and community building,
with new public spaces to gather in before and after
shows, and state-of-the-art performance spaces with the
best in theater design and technology. Since then, we
have hosted parties, company meetings, weddings, and
performances for those in the Baltimore community.
Country: United States
Contact: Artistic Director Stephanie Ybarra
Contact: Managing Director Michael Ross
Contact: Assistant Box Office Manager Grace Kennedy
Email: boxoffice@centerstage.org
Social Media: https://twitter.com/centerstage_md
www.facebook.com/CENTERSTAGEMD https:// www.
instagram.com/centerstagemd/
Capacity: 1000+
Annual Performances: 100+
Policies: Rent and Present

Central Florida Cultural Endeavors
Website: www.fif-lso.org
Email: fifcfce@fif-lso.org
Phone: 386 681 2410

Address: PO Box 1310, US
Information: CFCE concerts given September to May;
see also Florida International Festival; see also Festivals
Country: United States
Contact: General Manager Eric Lariviere

Central Methodist University Convocations
Website: www.centralmethodist.edu
Email: mkelty@centralmethodist.edu
Phone: 660 248 3391
Address: Central Methodist University, US
Country: United States
Contact: Chairman Mark Kelty

Central Michigan University
Website: www.cmich.edu
Email: ebner1rj@cmich.edu
Phone: 989 774 4000
Address: 1200 S. Franklin St, Michigan, US
Country: United States
Contact: university events Director Robert Ebner
Contact: assistant Director Keith Voeks
Social Media: @CMUniversity www.facebook.com/cmich

Central Ohio Technical College
Website: www.cotc.edu
Phone: 740 366 9494
Address: 1179 University Drive, US
Country: United States
Contact: Director of advancement Gay Jackson
Social Media: @COTCedu www.facebook.com/COTCCen-
tralOhioTechnicalCollege
Policies: Present, produce, co-produce, Present and
produce, Concert hall

Central Pennsylvania Friends of Jazz Concert Series
Website: www.friendsofjazz.org
Email: friends@friendsofjazz.org
Phone: 717 540 1010
Address: PO Box 10738, US
Information: Formed in 1980, CPFJ is a non-profit mem-
bership organisation serving a diverse community of jazz
lovers and students in South Central Pennsylvania.
Country: United States
Contact: Artistic Director Steve Rudolph
Contact: office Manager Sheila Ross
Email: cpfjoffice@gmail.com

Centre East Inc
Website: www.centreeast.org
Email: padams@nscpas.org
Phone: 847 673 6300/950
Address: 9501 Skokie Blvd, US
Information: alternative e-mail: roryrice@centreeast.org
Country: United States
Contact: Executive Director Phyllis Collen
Contact: Managing Director Rory Rice

Centre for Chamber Music Inc Great Artists Series
Website: www.centreforchambermusic.com
Phone: 203 661 6626
Address: PO Box 7888, US
Country: United States
Contact: Artistic Director Maureen M Walsh
Policies: Other

Centre for Cultural Exchange
Email: pon@maine.rr.com
Phone: 207 761 0591
Address: One Long Fellow Square, US
Country: United States
Contact: programme Director Ryan McMaken

Centrum
Website: www.centrum.org
Email: info@centrum.org
Phone: 360 385 3102
Address: Fort Worden State Park, Port Townsend, US
Information: Centrum's mission is to foster creative
arts experiences that change lives. We exist to present,
promote and honor:traditional and evolving arts
 Programs for a diverse array of learners that focus on the
intersection of the arts and creative education, residen-
cies that provide artists with precious time, space and
inspiration to develop innovative work
 Through inter-generational immersive workshops,
we bring together aspiring and master artists to ignite
creativity, find and provide mentorship...
Country: United States
Contact: Director of operations Lisa Waipio Werner
Email: lwerner@centrum.org
Contact: Executive Director John MacElwee
Email: jmacelwee@centrum.org
Contact: Marketing Manager Joe Gillard
Email: jgillard@centrum.org
Social Media: https://twitter.com/ptcentrum https://
www.facebook.com/ptcentrum
Disabled Access: Yes
Capacity: 1000+
Annual Performances: 51-100
Policies: All

Century Village Theatres

Website: www.centuryvillagetheater.com
Email: akoffler@cenrec.com
Phone: 561 451 1227
Address: 19296 Lyons Road, US
Country: United States
Contact: entertainment Director Abby Koffler

Cerritos Center for the Performing Arts
Website: www.cerritoscenter.com
Email: jthielke@cerritos.us
Phone: 562 916 8510
Address: 12700 Center Court Drive, US
Country: United States
Contact: Executive Director To Be Filled
Contact: technical Director Tom Hamilton
Email: thamilton@cerritos.us
Contact: management analyst Jeff Thielke
Email: jthielke@cerritos.us
Social Media: @cerritoscenter www.facebook.
com/pages/Cerritos-Center-for-the-Perform-
ing-Arts/69717809957?fref=ts
Policies: Rent and present, Arts centre

Chadron State College
Website: www.csc.edu
Email: lmacneill@csc.csc.edu
Phone: 308 432 6317
Address: Chadron State College, 1000 Main Street, US
Information: season September – April
Country: United States
Contact: Chairman of theatre Roger Mays
Contact: Chairman of arts Richard Bird
Contact: Chairman of music department Winkle
Contact: fine arts activities Director Loree MacNeill

Chamber 10
Website: www.marshall.edu
Email: music@marshall.edu
Phone: 130 469 63117
Address: Marshall University, Department of Music, 1
John Marshall Drive, US
Country: United States
Contact: Chair Jeffrey Pappas

Chamber Music at North Park
Website: www.northpark.edu
Email: KDickelman@northpark.edu
Phone: 773 244 5636
Address: 3225 West Foster Ave, Box 21, US
Country: United States
Contact: Artistic Director Elizabeth Buccheri
Contact: fine arts events Manager Karen Dickelman

Chamber Music at Rodef Shalom
Website: www.rodefshalom.org
Email: info@rodefshalom.org
Phone: 412 621 6566
Address: 4905 5th Avenue, US
Information: Music at Rodef Shalom is sponsored by
members of Rodef Shalom Congregation who have
donated monies towards this series. offer affordable
rental space to non-profit organizations for lectures and
concerts etc
Country: United States
Social Media: @rscpgh www.facebook.com/rscp-
gh?ref=ts
Capacity: 400

Chamber Music Cincinnati
Website: www.cincychamber.org
Email: admin@cincychamber.org
Phone: 513 939 2652
Address: PO Box 9013, US
Country: United States
Contact: President Joel Hoffman

Chamber Music Columbus
Website: www.columbuschambermusic.org
Email: info@columbuschambermusic.org
Phone: 614 267 2267
Address: PO Box 14445, US
Country: United States
Contact: President Robert Wilhelm
Contact: Chair, program committee Edmund King

Chamber Music Concerts
Website: www.sou.edu/cmc
Email: chamber-music@sou.edu
Phone: 541 552 6154
Address: Southern Oregon University, US
Country: United States
Contact: Executive Director Jody Schmidt

Chamber Music Conference and Composers' Forum of the East
Website: www.cmceast.org
Email: cmceast@cmceast.org
Phone: 212 927 5053 ·
Address: 900 W. 190th St., #11-O, US
Information: primarily for serious amateurs and
semi-professionals to advance their chamber music skills;
composers-in-residence for 3 weeks; participants need a
strong command of English; artist-faculty concerts
Country: United States

Contact: Executive Director Marilyn Bell
Contact: music Director Phillip Bush
Social Media: www.facebook.com/cmceast

Chamber Music Hawaii
Website: www.chambermusichawaii.com
Phone: 180 837 28236
Address: PO Box 61939, US
Country: United States
Contact: President James Moffitt
Contact: vice President Robert Nathanson

Chamber Music Houston
Website: www.chambermusichouston.org/home/
Email: cmh@rice.edu
Phone: 713 348 5400
Address: Rice University MS-532, 6100 Main Street, US
Information: Founded in 1960 by a group of chamber-music lovers, CMH (formerly Houston Friends of Chamber Music) has been a leader among mainstream presenters in Houston, and is the third oldest arts presenter in the city.
Country: United States
Contact: Executive Director Kerryn Barrera
Social Media: @ChamberMusicHou www.facebook.com/ChamberMusicHouston

Chamber Music in Napa Valley
Website: www.chambermusicnapa.org
Email: cmnv@napanet.net
Phone: 707 226 2190
Address: 4375 Atlas Peak Road, US
Country: United States
President, secretary & treasurer
John Kongsgaard

Chamber Music in Oklahoma
Website: www.cmok.org
Phone: 405 974 2415
Address: PO Box 54624, US
Information: all volunteers
Country: United States
Contact: President Richard Hollander
Contact: vice President Mary Jane Rutherford
Contact: Executive Director and treasurer Brad Ferguson
Contact: secretary Martha Royce Blane

Chamber Music Monterey Bay
Website: www.chambermusicmontereybay.org
Email: info@chambermusicmontereybay.org
Phone: 831 625 2212
Address: PO Box 221458, US
Country: United States
Contact: Executive Director Dana Werdmuller
Contact: President Amy Anderson
Policies: Other

Chamber Music PLUS
Website: www.chambermusicplus.org
Email: sanda@chambermusicplus.org
Phone: 520 400 5439
Address: 695 W. Annandale Way, US
Information: Presents unique programs that meld theater and classical music , for a complete and deepened sense of participation in the arts in the 21st Century. Produces a cutting edge arts in education program for grades 1 to 4 in the inner city schools in Hartford,
Country: United States
Contact: founding Director Sanda Schuldmann
Contact: Artistic Director Harry Clark
Contact: event Manager Susan Silverman
Social Media: www.facebook.com/CMPSW/

Chamber Music Society at Yale
Website: music.yale.edu
Email: concerts@yale.edu
Phone: 203 432 4158
Address: Yale School of Music, PO Box 208246, US
Information: YSM also presents an additional 250 free concerts in many classical genres, and a Duke Ellington Jazz Series.
Country: United States
Contact: Manager, concerts and public relations Dana Astmann

Chamber Music Society of Baltimore
Phone: 410 486 1140
Address: 2909 Woodvalley Drive, US
Information: programs comprise half contemporary music; commissions & premieres a new work each year
Country: United States
Contact: music Director Susan Foscher Weiss
Contact: Managing Director Anthony Stark

Chamber Music Society of Bethlehem
Website: www.cmsob.org
Email: mm04@lehigh.edu
Phone: 610 435 7611
Address: PO Box 447, US
Information: diverse programs of classical music for small groups
Country: United States
Contact: secretary Mardi Metzeger
Contact: President Jennifer Scavuzzo

Chamber Music Society of Detroit
Website: www.ChamberMusicDetroit.org
Email: Tickets@ChamberMusicDetroit.org
Phone: 248 737 9980
Address: 27655 Middlebelt Road, Suite 160, US
Information: one of the oldest and most prestigious chamber music presenters in the U.S. Through its 9-concert Signature Chamber Series and 3-concert Sunday Recital Series, the Chamber Music Society of Detroit brings the world's best artists and ensembles to the metro Detroit stage in outstanding performances which inspire thousands of audience members from across metro Detroit. In addition to its two flagship series at Seligman Performing Arts Center in Beverly Hills, the CMSD also presents a 6-concert inDepth Series in downtown Detroit and a new 4-concert series at Oakland University in Rochester, Michigan
Country: United States
Contact: President Steve Wogaman
Email: Steve.Wogaman@ChamberMusicDetroit.org
Contact: vice President, concert division Willa Walker
Email: Willa.Walker@ChamberMusicDetroit.org
Social Media: @CMSDetroit www.facebook.com/ChamberMusicDetroit
Annual Performances: 22
Policies: Rent and present, Concert hall

Chamber Music Society of Lincoln Center
Website: www.chambermusicsociety.org
Email: info@chambermusicsociety.org
Phone: 212 875 5775
Address: 70 Lincoln Center Plaza, 10th Floor, US
Information: The Chamber Music Society of Lincoln Center, (CMS) is one of eleven constituents of Lincoln Center for the Performing Arts
Contact: Artistic Director David Finckel
Contact: Executive Director Suzanne Davidson
Contact: Director of Marketing and communications Lauren Bailey
Email: lbailey@chambermusicsociety.org
Contact: Artistic Director Wu Han
Contact: Marketing Manager Emily Holum
Email: eholum@chambermusicsociety.org
Contact: Director of Artistic planning Valerie Guy
Email: vguy@chambermusicsociety.org
Contact: production Manager Mathieu Chester
Email: mchester@chambermusicsociety.org
Contact: public relations Manager Marlisa Monroe
Email: mmonroe@chambermusicsociety.org
Social Media: @chambermusic www.facebook.com/chambermusicsociety
Policies: Concert hall

Chamber Music Society of Logan
Website: www.cmslogan.org
Email: info@cmslogan.org
Phone: 143 575 25867
Address: PO Box 3620, US
Country: United States
Contact: Chairman Beth Saul

Chamber Music Society of Salt Lake City
Website: www.cmsofslc.org
Email: cms@cmsofslc.org
Phone: 801 561 3999
Address: PO Box 58192, US
Country: United States
Contact: President Jeannette Swent
Email: cms@cmsofslc.org
Contact: talent committee Chair Carter Foss
Email: ecfoss@comcast.net
Contact: publicity Chair Catherine Hamilton
Email: cms@cmsofslc.org

Chamber Music Society of St Cloud
Phone: 320 253 3683
Address: PO Box 205, US
Country: United States
Contact: contact Susan R. Dubin

Chamber Music Society of the North Shore
Website: www.cmsns.org
Email: iris@interaccess.com
Phone: 708 835 5084
Address: PO Box 470, US
Country: United States
Contact: President Iris Cosnow

Chamber Music Society of Utica
Website: uticachambermusic.org
Email: marietta@ntcnet.com
Phone: 315 822 4392 or
Address: 463 Partridge Hill Rd, US
Country: United States
Contact: President Marietta von Bernuth

Chamber Music Society of Williamsburg
Website: www.chambermusicwilliamsburg.org
Email: info@chambermusicwilliamsburg.org
Phone: 175 725 88555
Address: PO Box 1526, US
Country: United States
Contact: President Jim Coomer

Chamber Music Tulsa Inc
Website: www.chambermusictulsa.org
Email: ExecutiveDirector@chambermusictulsa.org
Phone: 918 587 3802
Address: 2210 South Main, US
Country: United States
Contact: Executive Director Bruce Sorrell
Policies: Other

Chamber Music West
Website: www.chambermusicwest.com
Email: monamyhre@chambermusicwest.com
Phone: 623 972 0478
Address: Suite 122E, 10451 W Palmeras Drive, US
Country: United States
Contact: Executive Director Nancy Root
Contact: Artistic advisory Chair Elsie Sterrenberg

Chandler Center for the Arts
Website: www.chandlercenter.org
Email: info@chandlercenter.org.
Phone: 480 782 2680
Address: 250 North Arizona Avenue, Chandler, US
Information: Chandler Center for the Arts is one of the most distinct multi-theatre performing arts and visual arts facilities in the country. The Center has a total seating capacity of 1, 500 with a unique design that allows for two rear sections of the Main Stage to rotate 180 degrees to become two intimate performance spaces — the 346-seat Hal Bogle Theatre and the 246-seat Recital Hall. **Country:** United States
Marketing & development
Judi Johnson
Phone: 480 782 2674General Manager
Michelle Mac Lennan
Email: michelle.maclennan@chandleraz.gov
Phone: 480 782 2683
Rental & Program Coordinator
Danielle Gojkovich
Email: danielle.gojkovich@chandleraz.gov
Phone: 480 782 2682
Social Media: https:// www.facebook.com/ChandlerCenterfortheArts https://twitter.com/chandlerarts https://www.instagram.com/chandlerarts/
Disabled Access: Yes
Capacity: 1000+
Annual Performances: 25-50
Policies: All

Chapman University Musco Center for the Arts
Website: https://muscocenter.org/
Email: info@muscocenter.org
Phone: 714 997 6812
Address: 1 University Drive, Orange, US
Information: The earliest incarnation of Chapman University was open to all people in the belief that every person should have access to an education. In fact, our first class included women and people of different ethnicities and faiths. Our heritage of diversity and inclusion provides us our strong foundation as we participate in building a more equitable future.
Country: United States
Contact: dean and proffesor Giulio M, Ongaro
Contact: Executive Director Richard T. Bryant
Social Media: https:// www.facebook.com/MuscoCenterfortheArts/ https://twitter.com/MuscoCenter/
Disabled Access: Yes
Capacity: 1000+
Annual Performances: 100+
Policies: All

Charles Ives Center for the Arts
Website: www.ivesconcertpark.com
Email: ivescenter@aol.com
Phone: 203 837 9226
Address: Western Connecticut State University Westside Campus, 43 Lake Avenue Ext., US
Country: United States
Contact: Executive Director Phyllis Cortese

Charleston Chamber Music Society
Website: www.charlestonchambermusic.org
Email: ndavids@aol.com
Phone: 304 344 5389
Address: PO Box 641, US
Country: United States
Contact: Executive Director NDavid Stern
Social Media: @CCMSWV

Charleston Community Music Association
Website: www.cmawva.org
Email: cmawva@cmawva.org
Phone: 304 744 1400
Address: PO Box 8008, US
Information: CCMA is a subscription based volunteer organization that host 5-6 performances each year in the Charleston, WV Municipal Auditorium. CCMA also hosts an annual New Year's Celebration with free performances at various venues Good Night.
Country: United States
Contact: President Joseph B Wollenberger

Charleston Concert Association
Website: www.charlestonconcerts.com

Email: chasconcertsassoc@aol.com
Phone: 843 571 7755
Address: PO Box 743, US
Country: United States
Contact: Director Jason Nichols

Charleston Heights Arts Center
Phone: 702 229 6383
Address: 800 S. Brush, US
Information: also rentals; season September-July
Country: United States
Contact: center co-ordinator Joanne Lentino

Charlotte Concerts
Website: www.charlotteconcerts.org
Email: Director@charlotteconcerts.org
Phone: 704 527 6680
Address: PO Box 11356, US
Information: formerly Carolina Concert Association. Charlotte Concerts has a dual mission to present world-renowned performing artists to local audiences, and to sponsor innovative arts education outreach initiatives in our local communities and schools.
Country: United States
Social Media: www.facebook.com/CharlotteConcerts

Charter Oak Cultural Center
Website: www.charteroakcenter.org
Email: cocc@charteroakcenter.org
Phone: 860 249 1207
Address: 21 Charter Oak Avenue, US
Country: United States
Contact: Executive Director Donna R Burman

Chautauqua Institution
Website: www.ciweb.org
Email: boxoffice@ciweb.org
Phone: 716 357 6250
Address: PO Box 28, US
Information: The Chautauqua Institution is a not-for-profit, 750-acre community on Chautauqua Lake in southwestern New York State, where approximately 7, 500 persons are in residence on any day during a nine-week season, and a total of over 100, 000 attend scheduled public events.
Country: United States
Social Media: @chq www.facebook.com/chq1874
Policies: All, Multi-purpose

Cheboygan Area Arts Council/Opera House
Website: www.theoperahouse.org
Email: jpl@nmo.net
Phone: 231 627 5432
Address: PO Box 95, 403 N Huron St, US
Country: United States
Contact: assistant to Executive Director Vicky Pyrzynski
Contact: Executive Director Joann Leal

Chester Fritz Auditorium University of North Dakota
Website: www.cfa.und.edu
Email: UND.info@UND.edu
Phone: 701 777 3076
Address: 3475 university avenue 9028, US
Information: The Chester Fritz Auditorium, a magnificent center for the performing arts, is considered the finest facility of its kind from Minneapolis to the West Coast. Since its opening, the Chester Fritz Auditorium has brought numerous nationally acclaimed performers to Grand Forks and to the University of North Dakota. The programming has varied from country western, opera, ballet, and symphonies, to Broadway Theatre shows. The Auditorium is also used for many University of North Dakota events.
Country: United States
Contact: Director Betty Allan
Email: betty.allan@und.edu
Social Media: @myUND www.facebook.com/Chester-Fritz-Auditorium-172827201630/
Capacity: 1132

Cheyenne Civic Center
Website: www.cheyenneciviccenter.org
Email: drohla@cheyennecity.org
Phone: 307 637 6364
Address: 2101 O'Neil Ave, US
Information: venue available for rent
Country: United States
Contact: Director Dru Rohla
Contact: administrative assistant to the Director Jeneane Buresh
Contact: box office Manager Vicky Wilkins
Contact: technical Director Dennis Madigan

Chicago Cultural Center
Website: www.chicagocenter.org
Email: culture@ci.chi.il.us
Phone: 312 744 6630
Address: Chicago Department of Cultural Affairs, 78 E Washington St, US
Country: United States
Manager, programs & exhibitions
 Rose Farina

Contact: commissioner Lois Weisberg
Contact: deputy commissioner of cultural programming Janet Carl Smith

Chicago Shakespeare Theater on Navy Pier
Website: www.chicagoshakes.com
Email: jfauver@chicagoshakes.com
Address: 800 East Grand Avenue, US
Information: home of dance companies Batsheva and Inbal (q.v.) and host to major festivals and competitions
Country: United States
Contact: board Chairman Hill Hammock
Contact: Executive Director Criss Henderson
Contact: public relations Manager Jeffrey Fauver
Social Media: www.facebook.com/ChicagoShakespeare
Policies: All, Multi-purpose

Chicago Theatre
Website: www.thechicagotheatre.com
Email: thechicagotheatre@theatredreams.com
Phone: 312 462 6363
Address: 175 North State Street, US
Country: United States
 Producer & entertainment Executive
 Lawrence J. Wilker

Children's Concert Society of Akron
Website: www.childrensconcertsociety.org
Email: ccs@uakron.edu
Phone: 330 972 2504
Address: Edwin J. Thomas Performing Arts Hall, 198 Hill St., US
Information: scholastic composers contest
Country: United States
Contact: President Diane Lazzerini

Children's Theatre, Inc – In-Theatre Series, Public School Series
Website: www.childrenstheatrews.org
Email: ctis4me@aol.com
Phone: 336 725 4531
Address: 610 Coliseum Drive, US
Information: working with the public school system to integrate performances into the curriculum
Country: United States
Contact: Executive Director Les Epstein

Chocolate Church Arts Center
Website: chocolatechurcharts.org
Email: info@chocolatechurch.com
Phone: 207 442 8455
Address: 804 Washington St, US
Information: art gallery attached to arts center; renovation to be completed in May 2010
Country: United States
Contact: Executive Director Barb Bowers

Christina Cultural Arts Centre Inc
Website: www.ccacde.org
Email: ccacde@aol.com
Phone: 302 652 0101
Address: 705 N Market Street, US
Country: United States
Contact: Executive Director Raye Avery

Churchill Arts Council
Website: www.churchillarts.org
Email: charts@phonewave.net
Phone: 775 423 1440
Address: PO Box 2204, US
Country: United States
Contact: presenting co-ordinator Valerie Serpa

Cincinnati Music Hall
Website: www.cincinnatiarts.org
Email: info@cincinnatiarts.org
Phone: 513 621 2787
Address: 650 Walnut Street, US
Information: Home of Cincinnati Symphony Orchestra, Cincinnati Pops Orchestra, Cincinnati Opera; disabled access; facilities for hard of hearing; occassional signed performances; hosts the Cincinnati May Festival. Founded in 1992, the Cincinnati Arts Association (CAA) is a not-for-profit organisation that oversees the programming and management of two of the Tri-state's finest performing arts venues – the Aronoff Center for the Arts and Music Hall – and is dedicated to supporting performing and visual arts,
Country: United States
Contact: Executive Director Steve Loftin
Contact: Director of operations Scott M. Santangelo
Social Media: @CincinnatiArts www.facebook.com/cincinnatiartsassociation

Cincinnati Playhouse in the Park
Website: www.cincyplay.com
Email: Administration@cincyplay.com
Phone: 513 345 2242
Address: 962 Mt. Adams Circle, US
Information: Nationally known for its excellence and commitment to new works and as an Artistic home for America's best actors, Directors and designers, the Playhouse always keeps its primary role at center stage — to serve the Tristate by producing the finest in classic and contemporary works: musicals, dramas, comedies

and recent hits.
Country: United States
Contact: Artistic Director Blake Robison
Contact: General Manager Suann Pollock
Contact: public relations Manager Connie Yeager
Email: pr@cincyplay.com
Social Media: @CincyPlay www.facebook.com/pages/Cincinnati-Playhouse
Policies: All, Theatre

Cincinnati Recreation Commission
Website: www.cincyrec.org
Email: info.crc@rcc.org
Phone: 513 352 4000
Address: 2 Centennial Plaza, 8th floor, 805 Central Avenue, US
Country: United States
Contact: Director Norman Merrifield

Circle in the Square Theater
Website: www.circlesquare.org
Email: circleinthesquare@att.net
Phone: 212 307 0388
Address: 1633 Broadway, US
Information: professional training Conservatory for actors and musical theatre actors; offers two year and summer intensive training with emphasis in acting or musical acting
Country: United States
Contact: Executive Director Colin O'Leary
Contact: Artistic Director Theodore Mann
Contact: President Paul Libin
Capacity: 604

Circle Theatre at Aquinas College Brink Hall
Website: www.circletheatre.org
Email: info@circletheatre.org
Phone: 616 632 1980
Address: 1607 Robinson Road SE, US
Country: United States
Contact: production Manager Tepper Lynne
Contact: Managing Director Joe Dulin
Contact: box office Manager Joni Hodsdon
Capacity: 1500

Citrus College – Haugh Performing Arts Center
Website: www.haughpac.com
Email: ghinrichsen@citruscollege.edu
Phone: 626 852 8046
Address: 1000 West Foothill Boulevard, US
Country: United States
Contact: production Manager/technical Director Dan Vilter
 Director of operations & Marketing
 Linda Graves
Contact: performing arts Director Greg Hinrichsen

City Center
Website: www.citycenter.org
Email: admin@citycenter.org
Phone: 212 247 0430
Address: 130 West 56th Street, US
Information: City Center produces, presents and makes its stages available for rental; theater entrance is at West 55th Street between 6th and 7th Aves
Country: United States
 Manager of Press relations & events
 Marisa Altamura
 vp, Marketing & communications
 Hawley Abelow
 President & CEO
 Arlene Shuler
 senio vp & Managing Director
 Mark Litvin
Contact: Director of Operations Andrey Shenin
Contact: building operations Manager Phil Schmeidl
 senior Director, facilities & capital planning
 David Ward

City of Chicago Cultural Affairs and Special Events
Website: www.cityofchicago.org/city/en/depts/dca.html
Phone: 312 744 3316
Address: Chicago Cultural Center, 78 E. Washington St., 4th Floor, US
Information: present the following festivals: Taste of Chicago, Chicago Gospel Festival, Chicago Blues Festival, Chicago Jazz Festival, Chicago Country Music Festival, Viva Chicago – Latin Music Festival, Celtic Festival, Chicago; special shows: Air and Water Show, Country: United States
Social Media: @ChicagoDCASE www.facebook.com/ChicagoDCASE/

Cityfolk
Website: www.cityfolk.org
Email: cityfolk@cityfolk.org
Phone: 193 722 33655
Address: 126 N Main Street, Suite 220, Ohio, US
Information: also organise and present the Cityfolk Festival: www.cityfolk.org/festival/festival.html
Country: United States

Contact: Director of programs and Marketing Dave Barber
Contact: Artistic and administrative Manager Holly Underwood
Contact: Executive Director John Harris

Civic Morning Musicals
Website: www.civicmorningmusicals.org
Email: syracusearts.net
Phone: 131 569 95856
Address: 124 Victoria Place, US
Information: also do an annual competition for young people: for singers and an instrumental competition in conjunction with the Syracuse Symphony; all volunteer organisation; promote a young peoples organisation Jr Pro Art
Country: United States
Contact: President/ program Chair John Spradling

Civic Music Association of Des Moines
Website: www.civicmusic.org
Email: info@civicmusic.org
Phone: 515 280 4020
Address: 900 Mulberry Street, Suite 203, US
Information: exists to engage, enrich and educate the central Iowa community through provocative, world-class musical performances by legends and rising stars. In its 89th year, Civic Music continues to be a unique and significant arts organization in Des Moines. The mission has not varied from its inception – to both present Artistic excellent performances and foster education. By bringing world-renowned artists to central Iowa, Civic Music not only offers audiences unforgettable fine arts experiences, but also builds awareness, understanding and respect for classical, world and jazz artistry
Country: United States
Contact: Executive Director Carrie Clogg
Social Media: @CivicMusic www.facebook.com/CivicMusicAssociation

Claremont Opera House, Inc
Website: www.claremontoperahouse.com
Email: info@claremontoperahouse.com
Phone: 603 542 0064 (ad
Address: Opera House Sqaure, PO Box 664, US
Country: United States
Contact: President John Bennett
Contact: acting Executive Director Louanne Lewit

Clarice Smith Performing Arts Center
Website: www.claricesmithcenter.umd.edu
Email: contact.theclarice@umd.edu
Phone: 301 405 7794
Address: University of Maryland, Suite 3800, US
Country: United States
Contact: Director of finance and Administration Robert Miller
Contact: Associate Director of communications Andrea Johnson
Contact: Executive Director Susie Farr
Director of Marketing & communication
Brian Jose
Contact: Director of cultural participation Ruth Waalkes
Social Media: @TheClariceUMD www.facebook.com/TheClariceUMD?_rdr=p

Clark Art Institute
Website: www.clarkart.edu
Email: info@clarkart.edu
Phone: 413 458 9545
Address: 225 South Street, US
Country: United States
Contact: Director Michael Conforti
Contact: public relations officer Sherrill Ingalls

Clark County Parks and Recreation Cultural Division
Website: www.clarkcountynv.gov/Depts/parks/Pages/default.aspx
Email: ccparks@ClarkCountyNV.gov
Phone: 702 455 8200
Address: 2601 East Sunset Road, US
Country: United States
Contact: programme supervisor Dorothy Wright
Contact: superintendant Joan Lolmaugh
Social Media: www.facebook.com/clarkcountyparks

Clark State Performing Arts Center
Website: www.clarkstate.edu/pac
Email: commonl@clarkstate.edu
Phone: 937 328 3841
Address: PO Box 570, 300 South Fountain, US
Information: Present a season of events and also provides a home for six resident art groups and community organizations
Country: United States
Contact: adminstrative assistant Lori Common
Contact: Director t.b.a.

Clemens Performing Arts Center
Website: www.clemenscenter.com
Email: TomW@clemenscenter.com
Phone: 607 733 5639
Address: PO Box 1046, US

Information: member of Upstate New York Presenters
Country: United States
Contact: Executive Director / Director of presenting Thomas Weidemann
Contact: Director of finance Robin Walter
Contact: Associate Executive Director Julie Kriston
Contact: Director of facilities Michael Kenna

Clemson University Brooks Center for the Performing Arts
Website: www.clemson.edu/brooks
Email: harderl@clemson.edu
Phone: 864 656 3043
Address: Room 221, Brooks Center for the Performing Arts, Box 340526, Clemson University, US
Information: The Brooks Center for the Performing Arts is the home for the performing arts at Clemson University. The state-of-the-art facility serves as a roadshow to many nationally and internationally acclaimed dance companies, theatre troupes, and music ensembles of all types. The center is comprised of a 968-seat proscenium theatre that serves as the main stage, a 100-seat black box theatre, and a 100-seat recital room
Country: United States
Contact: Chairman David Hartmann
Email: hartmad@clemson.edu
Contact: Director Lillian Harder
Email: harderl@clemson.edu
Contact: production Manager Woody Moore
Email: kmoore2@clemson.edu
Contact: technical coordinator Jim Breitmeier
Email: breitme@clemson.edu
Social Media: @BrooksCenterCU www.facebook.com/brookscentercu
Capacity: 968

Cleveland Chamber Music Society
Website: www.clevelandchambermusic.org
Email: information@clevelandchambermusic.org
Phone: 216 291 2777
Address: The Cleveland chamber music society, 2532 Lafayette Drive, US
Country: United States
Contact: President Mary Von Herrmann
Contact: Executive secretary Sharon Muskin
Contact: Chairman of programme committee Stephen Somach

Cleveland Institute of Music
Website: www.cim.edu
Email: Marketing@cim.edu
Phone: 216 791 5000
Address: 11021 East Boulevard, US
Information: Most concert performances free of charge
Country: United States
Contact: accounting Manager Kristen Kollar
Contact: Director, concerts and events production Lori Wright
Director of Marketing & communications
Susan Schwartz
Contact: Director of development Richard Buffett

Cleveland Museum of Art, Department of Performing Arts, Music & Film
Website: www.ClevelandArt.org/vivagala
Email: info@clevelandart.org
Phone: 216 421 7350
Address: 11150 East Blvd, US
Information: The Cleveland Museum of Art is renowned for the quality and breadth of its collection, which includes almost 45, 000 objects and spans 6, 000 years of achievement in the arts. Having recently completed an ambitious, multi-phase renovation and expansion project across its campus, the museum is a significant international forum for exhibitions, scholarship, performing arts and art education.
Country: United States
Contact: Associate Director, film John Ewing
Contact: Associate Director, music Thomas Welsh
Email: twelsh@clevelandart.org
production Manager, performing arts, music & film Kyra Burton
Contact: office Manager Michael McKay

Cleveland Public Theatre
Website: www.cptonline.org
Email: info@cptonline.org
Phone: 216 631 2727
Address: 6415 Detroit Avenue, US
Information: CPT invests in innovation and diversity, and has been recognized regionally and nationwide as a leader in the support and development of new work, the amplification of emerging voices, and for producing and presenting work from artists working outside of the theatrical mainstream.
Country: United States
Contact: Executive Artistic Director Raymond Bobgan
Email: rbobgan@cptonline.org
Phone: 216 631 272 7202Associate Artistic Director Beth Wood
Email: bwood@cptonline.org
Phone: 216 631 272 7206General Manager Denis M. Griesmer

Email: dgriesmer@cptonline.org
Phone: 216 631 272 7208technical Director Ashante Green
Email: agreen@cptonline.org
Phone: 216 631 272 7216
Social Media: https://twitter.com/CPTCLE www.facebook.com/ClevelandPublicTheatre https:// www.instagram.com/cptcle/
Capacity: 251-500
Annual Performances: 100+
Annual Productions: 0-5
Policies: All

Cliburn Concerts
Website: www.cliburn.org
Email: Generalinformation@cliburn.org
Phone: 817 738 6536
Address: c/o Van Cliburn Foundation, 2525 Ridgmar Blvd, Suite 307, US
Information: the Cliburn advances classical piano music throughout the world. Its international competitions, education programs, and concert series embody an enduring commitment to Artistic excellence and the discovery of new artists. Member of ISPA
Country: United States
Contact: President and CEO Jacques Marquis
Email: jmarquis@cliburn.org
Contact: Director of Artistic planning Sandra Doan
Email: sdoan@cliburn.org
Contact: Executive administrator Susan Henry
Email: shenry@cilburn.org
Social Media: @TheCliburn www.facebook.com/thecliburn

Clowes Memorial Hall of Butler University: Clowes Hall Series
Website: www.cloweshall.org
Email: klsteele@butler.edu
Phone: 317 940 9697
Address: 4600 Sunset Ave, US
Country: United States
Contact: Executive Director Elise J. Kushigian
Contact: operations Manager Karen Steele
Contact: education Manager cassandra Pixey
Contact: technology and communications coordinator Marketing Director

COA Auditorium
Website: www.albemarle.cc.nc.us/acadaff/finearts/schedule.h
Email: aswain@albemarle.cc.nc.us
Phone: 252 335 0821ext
Address: PO Box 2327, US
Information: venue available for hire
Country: United States
Contact: community center Manager Sam Johnson
Contact: box office Manager/administrative assistant Angela Swain

Coastal Carolina University – Wheelwright Series
Website: www.coastal.edu/wheelwright/index.html
Email: boxoffice@coastal.edu
Phone: 843 349 2787
Address: PO Box 26 1954, US
Information: Coastal Carolina University is a vital center for higher learning and cultural activity for South Carolina's Grand Strand region. A full cultural calendar complements the university experience for students as well as for the dynamic and diverse community surrounding the University
Country: United States

Cobb Energy Performing Arts Centre
Website: www.cobbenergycentre.com
Email: info@cobbenergycentre.com
Phone: 770 916 2800
Address: 2800 Cobb Galleria Parkway, US
Information: the Cobb Energy Performing Arts Centre is the first major performing arts facility built in metro Atlanta in four decades. it is a premier venue for Broadway shows, ballet, concerts, educational shows, family performances, opera, corporate meetings and events.
Country: United States
Director of Marketing & sponsorships
Tom Rowland
Social Media: @cobbenergypac
Policies: Rent and present

COCA Center of Creative Arts
Website: www.cocastl.org
Email: info@cocastl.org
Phone: 314 725 6555
Address: 524 Trinity Avenue, US
Country: United States
Contact: Executive Director Stephanie Riven
Contact: production Manager Kleye Page

Cochise College
Website: www.cochise.edu
Phone: 520 515 5360
Address: Sierra Vista Campus, 901 North Colombo Ave, US
Information: Cochise College provides accessible educa-

tional opportunities that are responsive to a diverse population and lead to constructive citizenship, meaningful careers and lifelong learning.
Country: United States
Contact: assistant dean student services Mark Boggie
Email: boggiem@cochise.edu
Social Media: @CochiseCollege www.facebook.com/CochiseCollege/
Policies: Other

Cocoa Village Playhouse
Phone: 321 636 5050
Address: 300 Brevard Avenue, US
Country: United States
Contact: General Manager/Executive Director Staci Hawkins-Smith

Coe College Marquis Series
Website: www.coe.edu
Email: publicrelations@coe.edu
Phone: 319 399 8581
Address: 1220 First Ave NE, US
Country: United States
Contact: Director of pr Rod Pritchard
Chair of marquis series & committee
Marc Falk

Coeur d'Alene Summer Theatre
Website: www.cdasummertheatre.com
Email: info@cdasummertheatre.com
Phone: 208 769 7780
Address: PO Box 1119, US
Country: United States
Contact: Artistic Director Roger Welch
Contact: box office Manager Kristin Kilmer

Coffeyville Community College
Website: www.coffeyville.edu
Email: nancyw@coffeyville.edu
Phone: 620 251 7700
Address: 400 W 11, US
Country: United States
Contact: Director humanities project Mark Frink

Colby-Sawyer College
Website: www.colby-sawyer.edu
Email: activities@colby-sawyer.edu
Phone: 603 526 3759
Address: Campus Activities, Ware Center, 541 Main Street, US
Country: United States
Contact: campus activities Director Sharon Williamson

Coleman Chamber Music Association
Website: www.coleman.caltech.edu
Email: info@colemanchambermusic.org
Phone: 626 793 4191
Address: 202 S Lake Ave, Suite 300, US
Information: also present the Coleman Chamber Ensemble Competition every April
Country: United States
Contact: Executive Director Kathy Freedland

College Community Arts Council Concert Series
Phone: 419 394 4575
Address: 7600 State Route 703 E, US
Country: United States
Contact: President Tim Bighand

College of Lake County
Website: www.clcillinois.edu
Email: gganther@clcillinois.edu
Phone: 847 223 6601 (ac
Address: 19351 W. Washington St, US
Country: United States
Contact: Director of performing arts building Gwethalyn J Bronner
Contact: activities Director Felicia Ganther

College of Marin Public Events
Website: www.marin.cc.ca.us
Email: Tara.Flandreau@marin.edu
Phone: 415 457 8811
Address: College of Marin, 835 College Avenue, US
Country: United States
Contact: Chair performing arts dept Tara Flandreau

College of Southern Maryland
Website: www.csmd.edu
Email: bxoffc@csmd.edu
Phone: 301 934 2251
Address: Fine Arts Center, PO Box 910, 8730 Mitchell Road, US
Information: The College of Southern Maryland is a public, regional community college
Country: United States
Contact: vice President of academic and career service Timothy Keating
Contact: arts presentation Director John Maerhofer
Social Media: @CSMHeadlines www.facebook.com/CollegeofSouthernMaryland

College of Staten Island – Center for the Arts
Website: www.csi.cuny.edu/arts
Phone:

718 982 2504
Address: 2800 Victory Boulevard, Building 1P, Room 116, US
Information: also available for hire
Country: United States
Managing & Artistic Director
Lisa B Reilly
theatre rental reservations & contracts office
Meredith Halsey-Kelly
Contact: administrative assistant Marlene Domina
Contact: box office Manager Hallie Smith DiLiberto
Contact: theatre operations Manager John Jankowski
Contact: Marketing Director Michele Maglio

College of The Arts and Letters
Website: www.arts.usm.edu
Email: arts@usm.edu
Phone: 601 266 4984
Address: Univ. of Southern Mississippi Box 5004, US
Information: guest artists are booked to perform as soloists with major performing ensembles such as Symphony Orchestra, Wind Ensemble, Jazz Band
Country: United States
Contact: dean college of the arts Elliot Pood

College of the Siskiyous
Website: www.siskiyous.edu
Email: info@siskiyous.edu
Phone: 530 938 4444
Address: 800 College Avenue, US
Country: United States
Contact: superintendant/President Randall Lawrence

College of Visual and Performing Arts, Masterpiece Season – James Madison University
Website: www.jmu.edu/arts
Email: weaverje@jmu.edu
Phone: 540 568 6358
Address: Forbes Center, 147 Warsaw Avenue, MSC 5602, US
Information: encore series, 12 performances
Country: United States
Contact: contact Jerry Weaver
Social Media: @JMUArts www.facebook.com/JMUArts/
Annual Performances: 12
Policies: Present and produce

College of William & Mary
Website: www.wm.edu
Email: ltwill@wm.edu
Phone: 175 722 14000
Address: Campus Center 203, US
Country: United States
Contact: President Taylor Reveley

Collins Center for the Arts
Website: www.collinscenterforthearts.com
Phone: 207 581 1755
Address: 5746 Collins Center for the Arts, University of Maine, US
Information: member of ISPA
Country: United States
Contact: art coordinator Karen Adrienne
Contact: technical Director Jeff Richards
Social Media: www.facebook.com/CollinsCenterfortheArts

Colonial Theatre
Website: www.thecolonial.org
Email: info@thecolonial.org
Phone: 603 357 1233
Address: PO Box 77, 95 Main Street, US
Country: United States
Contact: Director of production Kurt Steelman
Contact: Executive Director Alex Doyle
Contact: Director of audience services Jessica Reeves
Contact: Director of development Cindy Rodenhauser
Contact: Director of finance Gale Saleski

Colonial Theatre, The
Website: www.berkshiretheatregroup.org/
Email: info@thecolonialtheatre.org
Phone: 413 448 8084
Address: 111 South Street, US
Information: reopened in August 2006 after extensive restoration
Country: United States
Contact: Director of Marketing Rebecca Brighenti
Email: becky@berkshiretheatregroup.org
Contact: Artistic Director, CEO Kate Maguire
Email: kate@berkshiretheatregroup.org
Policies: All, Theatre

Colorado Springs Dance Theatre
Website: www.csdance.org
Email: info@csdance.org
Phone: 719 630 7434
Address: PO Box 877, US
Country: United States
Contact: partner Susan Wood-Ellis
Contact: contact Sherry Whitlock

Colorado Springs Fine Arts Center
Website: www.csfineartscenter.org
Email: info@csfineartscenter.org
Phone: 719 634 5581
Address: 30 W Dale St, US
Information: 4 annual musical performances for repertory season theater
Country: United States
Contact: performing arts Director Scott RC Levy
President & CEO
Sam Gappmayer

Columbia Theatre for the Performing Arts
Website: www2.selu.edu/NewsEvents/Columbia
Email: dganderson@selu.edu
Phone: 985 543 4366
Address: SLU 10797, US
Information: 900-seat performance hall, gallery and conference area, administrative offices, and sophisticated technical capabilities; venue for Fanfare festival in October (q.v.)
Country: United States
Contact: Associate Director for Marketing Tonya Lowentritt
Associate Director, operations & production
Pete Pfeil
Contact: administrative assistant Betsy Creel
Contact: Director Donna Gay Anderson
Contact: business Manager Carol Knott

Columbus Area Arts Council
Website: www.artsincolumbus.org
Email: caac@artsincolumbus.org
Phone: 812 376 2539
Address: 300 Washington Street, US
Information: Formed in 1972 as the Driftwood Valley Arts Council and renamed Columbus Area Arts Council in 1989, the Arts Council is a public, non-profit corporation supported by private donations, the City of Columbus, the Indiana Arts Commission, and the National Endowment for the Arts.
Country: United States
Contact: Executive Director G. Karen Shrode
Contact: programme coordinator Tami Sharp
Contact: resource development Director Stephanie Strothmann
Contact: Marketing and media Director Arthur Smith
Social Media: @artsincolumbus www.facebook.com/artsincolumbus
Policies: Present, produce, co-produce, Present and produce, Other

Columbus Arts Council Inc. – concert & artist series
Website: www.columbus-arts.com
Email: colombus_arts@yahoo.com
Phone: 662 328 2787
Address: PO Box 869, US
Country: United States
Contact: Executive Director Heather Rowland

Committee for African American History Observances
Phone: 843 546 1974
Address: PO Box 1507, US
Country: United States
Contact: board Chairman David H Drayton

Community Arts Music Association of Santa Barbara Inc. (CAMA)
Website: www.camasb.org
Email: info@camasb.org
Phone: 805 966 4324
Address: 2060 Alameda Padre Serra, Suite 201, US
Country: United States
Contact: Executive Director Mark Trueblood
concert & publicity Manager
Justin Rizzo-Weaver
Social Media: www.facebook.com/camasb
Policies: Present and produce, Other

Community Arts Partnership at the Peddie School
Website: www.peddie.org/capps
Email: bchevey@peddie.org
Phone: 609 490 7550
Address: Box A, South Main Street, US
Country: United States
Contact: Executive Director Bettsy Chevey

Community College of Baltimore County Essex Campus
Website: www.ccbcmd.edu
Email: nblack@ccbcmd.edu
Phone: 410 780 6572
Address: 7201 Rossville Blvd, US
Country: United States
Contact: secretary of student life Norma Black
Social Media: @CCBCMD www.facebook.com/ccbcmd

Community Concerts
Email: info@miamipianofest.com
Phone: 305 858 5016
Address: 2333 Brickell Ave, Suite 417, US

Country: United States
Contact: President and Managing Director Ruddy Garcia
Contact: Executive Director Agnes Youngblood
Contact: legal counsel Paul Sack

Community Concerts at Lackawanna College
Website: www.lackawanna.edu/news-events/
the-theater/community-concerts/
Email: GeorgeB@lackawanna.edu
Phone: 570 955 1455
Address: 501 Vine Street, US
Information: non-profit organisation dedicated to
bringing world-class jazz and classical performance to
northeastern Pennsylvania. formerly known as Scranton
Community Concerts
Country: United States
Social Media: @LackawannaEDU www.facebook.com/
communityconcerts

Community Series Inc
Website: www.communityseries.com
Email: jhicks@austincollege.edu
Phone: 903 813 2251
Address: 900 N Grand Ave., Suite 61602, US
Country: United States
Contact: assistant Manager Linda Williams
Contact: Manager Joe Hicks

Composers Conference & Chamber Music Center at Wellesley College
Website: www.composersconference.org
Email: admin@composersconference.org
Phone: 508 276 1011
Address: PO Box 5507, US
Country: United States
Contact: music Director Efrain Guigui
Contact: conference Director Mario Davidovsky
Contact: Executive Director Kathryn Welter

Concert Artists Guild New York Recital Series
Website: www.concertartists.org
Email: caguild@concertartists.org
Phone: 212 333 5200
Address: 850 Seventh Ave, PH-A, US
Information: see also Competitions
Country: United States
Contact: President Richard Weinert
Contact: booking Associate Cindy Hwang
Contact: senior vice President, artist Manager Steven
Shaiman
Contact: program Manager Patrick Hammond
Contact: Executive vice President Amy Roberts-Frawley

Concert Association of Florida, Inc
Website: www.concertflorida.com
Email: email@concertassociation.org
Phone: 305 532 9898
Address: 300 41st Street, Suite 214, US
Country: United States
Contact: Artistic Director Judy Drucker

Concerts at Grace Cathedral
Website: www.gracecathedral.org
Email: info@gracecathedral.org
Phone: 415 749 6300
Address: Grace Cathedral, , 1100 California Street, US
Information: organ recital series Sep-June
Country: United States
Contact: community events Manager Abby McKee

Concerts at One
Website: www.trinitywallstreet.org
Email: etucker@trinitywallstreet.org
Phone: 212 602 0768
Address: Trinity Church, 74 Trinity Place, US
Country: United States
Contact: Director trinity concerts Earl Tucker

Concerts at The Cloisters
Website: www.metmuseum.org
Email: communications@metmuseum.org
Phone: 212 650 2290
Address: The Cloisters, Ft Tryon Park, US
Country: United States
Contact: administrative assistant Emma Wegner
Contact: concert coordinator/assistant museum educator Nancy Wu

Concerts from the Library of Congress
Website: www.loc.gov/rr/perform/concert
Email: amcl@loc.gov
Phone: 202 707 5503
Address: Library of Congress, Music Division, US
Information: all concerts are free
Country: United States
Contact: chief, music division susan H vita
Contact: music specialist, Producer Michele L Glymph

Concerts International
Website: home.midsouth.rr.com/webs/ConcertsInternational
Email: barnett@midsouth.rr.com
Phone: 901 527 3067
Address: PO Box 770522, US

Country: United States
Contact: Executive Director Carol Barnett
Contact: Artistic Director Ralph Lake

Conejo Recreation and Park District Summer Concert Series
Website: www.crpd.org
Email: parks@crpd.org
Phone: 805 495 6471
Address: 403 W Hillcrest Drive, US
Information: each year, types of music change
Country: United States
Contact: recreational services Manager Steve Wiley
Contact: administrator Tom Hare

Connoisseur Concerts Association
Phone: 150 932 64942
Address: 315 W. Mission Ave #18, US
Information: annual Northwest Bach Festival-January;
Mozart on a Summer's Eve-July Series
Country: United States
Contact: Executive Director Gertrude Harvey
Contact: Artistic Director Gunther Schuller

Contemporary Arts Center
Website: www.cacno.org
Email: chamilton@cacno.org
Phone: 504 528 3805
Address: 900 Camp Street, US
Country: United States
Contact: Executive Director Jay Weigel
Contact: Marketing Director Melissa Weber
Contact: curator visual arts Dan Cameron

Contemporary Chamber Players of the University of Chicago
Website: music.uchicago.edu
Email: music@uchicago.edu
Phone: 773 702 8484
Address: Department of Music, Goodspeed Hall, 1010 E
59th Street, US
Information: artists in residence: Pacifica String Quartet,
8th Blackbird
Country: United States

Cooperstown Concert Series Inc.
Website: www.cooperstownconcertseries.org
Phone: 607 547 1812
Address: PO Box 624, US
Information: also do a children series
Country: United States
Contact: co-Director Richard Brown

Coral Ridge Presbyterian Concert Series
Website: www.crpc.org
Email: charlesboateright@crpc.org
Phone: 954 771 8840
Address: 5555 N Federal Highway, US
Information: The Coral Ridge Concert Series seeks to
present captivating music in a beautiful space to the
people of South Florida
Country: United States
Contact: concert series Director Charles Boatright
Social Media: @coralridgepc www.facebook.com/
coralridgechurch

Coral Springs Centre for the Arts
Website: www.coralspringscenterforthearts.com
Email: info@coralspringscenterforthearts.com
Phone: 954 344 5999
Address: 2855 Coral Springs Drive, US
Information: member of Florida Professional Presenters consortium; the Coral Springs Museum of Art also
belongs to the City Centre
Country: United States
Social Media: @cstheater www.facebook.com/Coral-
SpringsCenterForTheArts
Policies: All, Arts centre

Corcoran Gallery of Art
Website: www.corcoran.org
Email: education@corcoran.org
Phone: 202 639 1700
Address: Public Programs, 500 17th Street NW, US
Information: year round programming
Country: United States
Contact: vp of communications and Marketing Kristin
Guiter
Contact: Director of special events Allie Gallo

Cornell College Music Mondays Concert Series
Website: www.cornellcollege.edu
Email: mhearne@cornellcollege.edu
Phone: 319 895 4320
Address: 600 First Street W, US
Country: United States
Contact: music series Director Martin Hearne
Contact: coordinator Cathy Schonhorst

Cornell Concert Series, Cornell University
Website: www.cornellconcertseries.com
Email: info@cornellconcertseries.com
Phone: 607 255 4363

Address: 101 Lincoln Hall, US
Country: United States
Contact: concert Manager Tokiko Nobusawa

Cornell University
Email: theatre@cornell.edu
Phone: 607 254 2700
Address: Department of Theater, Film & Dance, Schwartz
Center for the Performing Arts, 430 College Avenue, US
Information: member of New York Presenters consortium
Country: United States
Contact: department Chair Mr Goetc
Contact: General Manager Tanja Grove
Contact: Artistic Director David Feldshuh

Corning Painted Post Civic Music Association
Website: www.corningcivicmusic.org
Email: info@corningcivicmusic.org
Phone: 800 531 3679
Address: PO Box 1402, US
Information: the Corning-Painted Post Civic Music
Association is a non-profit organization dedicated to
presenting some of the premier musical talent of today
and the rising stars of tomorrow in a world-class live
performance venue. Subscripton based, at present 750
subscribers; member of Arts of Southern Fingerlakes
and APAP
Country: United States
Contact: President Bob Paul

Corpus Christi Chamber Music Society Inc.
Email: jallison@the-i.net
Phone: 136 185 50264
Address: PO Box 60124, US

Information: visiting address: 4709 Curtis Clark, Corpus
Christi TX 78411
Country: United States
Contact: secretary Judy Mellenburch
Contact: treasurer Rebecca Brackett
Contact: vice President John Latimer
Contact: President David Parker
Contact: programme Director Joan Allison

Corpus Christi Community Concert, Inc.
Phone: 136 198 01949
Address: 5319 St. Andrews, US
Country: United States
Contact: President Doris Daner
Contact: secretary Marilynn Yankee

Cort Theatre
Website: www.telecharge.com
Phone: 121 294 43700
Address: 138 West 48th Street, US
Country: United States
Contact: management company The Shubert Org. Inc
Contact: vice President of theatre operations Peter Entin
Capacity: 1083

Cottey Lecturers and Artists Super Series
Website: www.cottey.edu
Email: kkorb@cottey.edu
Phone: 417 667 8181
Address: Cottey College, 1000 W. Austin Blvd., US
Information: all women's college
Country: United States
Contact: coordinator of campus activities and calendar
Kris Korb
Social Media: @CotteyCollege
Policies: Other

Council for the Arts of Greater Lima
Website: www.limaartscouncil.org
Email: General@limaartscouncil.org
Phone: 419 222 1096
Address: PO Box 1124, US
Information: see also Festivals
Country: United States
Contact: operations Manager Eric Pepple

Count Basie Theatre
Website: www.countbasietheatre.org
Email: info@countbasietheatre.org
Phone: 732 224 8778
Address: 99 Monmouth St, US
Country: United States
Contact: Marketing Director Diana St. John
Contact: CEO Numa Saisselin

County College of Morris
Website: www.ccm.edu
Email: clally@ccm.edu
Phone: 973 328 5060
Address: 214 Center Grove Road, US
Country: United States
Contact: cultural affairs coordinator Christine Lally

Crawford County Community Concert Association
Phone: 419 562 3719
Address: PO Box 469, US
Country: United States

Contact: President Bob Slater

Creighton University Department of Fine & Performing Arts
Website: ccas.creighton.edu
Email: info@creighton.edu
Phone: 402 280 2700
Address: 2500 California Plaza, US
Information: home of Nebraska Shakespeare Festival; the Lied Center is also utilised by non-University organisations, including traveling arts groups
Country: United States
Social Media: @Creighton www.facebook.com/creightonuniversity

Crocker Art Museum Music Series
Website: www.crockerartmuseum.org
Email: cam@cityofsacramento.org
Phone: 916 264 7000
Address: 216 O St, US
Country: United States
Contact: Director of Marketing and communications Robin Koltenuk

Crooked Tree Arts Center
Website: www.crookedtree.org
Email: info@crookedtree.org
Phone: 231 347 4337
Address: 461 E Mitchell St, US
Country: United States
Contact: cultural coordinator Mary Wiklanski
Contact: Director of development Liz Ahrens
Contact: education Director Gail Lambert
Contact: Liz Ahrens

CSB/SJU Fine Arts Programming
Website: www.csbsju.edu/finearts
Email: mdarnall@csbsju.edu
Phone: 320 363 5030
Address: 37 South College Avenue, US
Information: Four Art Galleries between the two campuses. College of Saint Benedict and Saint John's University
Country: United States
Contact: production Manager Jack Dempsey
Contact: Director of operations Mary Darnall
Contact: Mary Darnall
Contact: Director fundraising and Marketing Nicole Gram

Cultural Activities Center Inc
Website: www.cacarts.org
Email: cac@cacarts.org
Phone: 254 773 9926
Address: 3011 North 3rd St, US
Country: United States
Contact: Executive Director Terri Matthew
Contact: technical Director Byron Lovelace
Contact: Marketing Director James Boon

Cultural Events
Website: www.lvc.edu
Email: j_evans@lvc.edu
Phone: 717 867 6165
Address: Lebanon Valley College, US
Country: United States
Contact: Director of student activities Jen Evans
Contact: secretary, student activities, multicultural affairs Debra J. Bishop

Cultural Events Series
Website: http://ces.frostburg.edu
Email: wmandicott@frostburg.edu mplummer@frostburg.edu
Phone: 301 687 4411
Address: Frostburg State University, 101 Braddock Road, US
Country: United States
Contact: Director William Mandicott

Cultural Foundation
Phone: 818 349 2789
Address: 20941 Hackney St., US
Country: United States
Contact: Executive Director Ross Hopkins

Cultural Resources Council Youth Theatre Series
Website: www.cspot.org
Email: rdwyer@cspot.org
Phone: 315 435 2155
Address: J H Mulroy Civic Center, 411 Montgomery St, US
Information: alternative E-mail: lkrandall@culturalresourcescncl.org
Country: United States
Contact: interim Director Patrick O'Connor
Contact: youth theater programme Director Robert Dwyer

Culver Academies Concert Series
Website: www.culver.org
Email: covenr@culver.org
Phone: 574 842 8255
Address: Culver Academies, C E F Suite 152, 1300 Academy Rd, US

Information: tend to specialise in small productions able to be performed as one-off's one-night events
Country: United States
Contact: theatre Director Richard Coven
Contact: events coordinator and technical Director Marsha Coven

Curtis M Phillips Center of the Performing Arts at the University of Florida
Website: www.performingarts.ufl.edu
Email: mblachly@performingarts.ufl.edu
Phone: 352 392 1900
Address: Curtis M. Phillips Center, 3201 Hull Road, PO Box 112750, US
Information: member of Florida Professional Presenters Consortium, APAP & ISPA; also has wide variety of lectures. For rental inquiries please contact the UFPA Operations Director at 352-273-2474 or mcox@performingarts.ufl.edu
Country: United States
Contact: Director of Marketing Amy Douglas
Email: adouglas@performingarts.ufl.edu
Contact: Phillips Center rentals Matt Cox
Email: mcox@performingarts.ufl.edu
Contact: Director Michael Blachly
Email: mblachly@performingarts.ufl.edu
Social Media: @ufPerformArts www.facebook.com/UFPA1
Capacity: 843

Curtis Theatre
Website: www.curtistheatre.com
Email: curtistheatre@ci.brea.ca.us
Phone: 714 990 7722
Address: City of Brea Cultural Arts, 1 Civic Centre Circle, US

Cynthia Woods Mitchell Pavilion
Website: www.woodlandscenter.org
Email: info@woodlandscenter.org
Phone: 281 364 3010
Address: 2005 Lake Robbins Drive, US
Information: a Live nation venue
Country: United States
Contact: President and CEO Jerry MacDonald
Contact: vp of operations Jeff Young
Marketing & pr
Mandi Hunsicker-Sallee

Da Camera of Houston
Website: www.dacamera.com
Email: boxoffice@dacamera.com
Phone: 713 524 5050 / 7
Address: 1402 Sul Ross, US
Information: We offer a broad range of repertoire and musical styles in innovative concerts of outstanding musical excellence. Da Camera, founded in 1987, was created with the intention to produce a series of thematically programmed chamber music and jazz concerts designed to attract new listeners to the concert hall. Under the Artistic leadership of Sarah Rothenberg since 1994, Da Camera maintains a commitment to the highest caliber of musicianship in the performers and ensembles brought together to perform in its Houston-based subscription series presented primarily at the Wortham Theater Center and The Menil Collection, and in its extensive education and outreach activities, recordings and touring productions. Member of ISPA
Country: United States
Contact: Artistic and General Director Sarah Rothenberg
Email: srothenberg@dacamera.com
Director of Marketing & audience development Leo Boucher
Email: lboucher@dacamera.com
Contact: General Manager Ab Sengupta
Email: asengupta@dacamera.com
Contact: Director of production Charlotte Craff
Email: ccraff@dacamera.com
Social Media: @dacamerahoustonfacebook.com/dacamera

Da Camera Society
Website: www.dacamera.org
Email: kellyagarirson@yahoo.com
Phone: 213 477 2929
Address: Mount St. Mary's College, 10 Chester Place, US
Information: events complement great music with fine architecture and history – every event takes place in a historic/striking venue
Country: United States
Contact: music education Manager Sean Bradley
Contact: Director Kelly Garrison
Contact: box office and client services Manager Carol Krause
Contact: administrative Director Sherrill Herring

Dallas Chamber Music Society, Inc.
Website: www.dallaschambermusic.org
Email: info@dallaschambermusic.org
Phone: 214 864 1993
Address: 3630 Harry Hines BLVD Dallas, US
Information: Dallas Chamber Music Society's mission is to develop and sustain a love for great chamber music as interpreted by today's most prestigious ensembles – both established and emerging – from around the world.

Serving the North Texas area, Dallas Chamber Music Society presents concerts and related educational events in order to provide opportunities to hear these outstanding groups perform great music in the classical tradition.
Country: United States
Contact: Executive Director Mary Anna Salo
Social Media: https:// www.instagram.com/dalchamber/ https:// www.facebook.com/dallaschambermusicsociety
Disabled Access: Yes
Capacity: 1000+
Annual Performances: 6-10
Policies: Present and Produce

Dana Centre, Saint Anselm College
Website: www.anselm.edu/dana
Email: dana@anselm.edu
Phone: 603 641 7700
Address: Dana Centre for Humanities, 100 St Anselm Drive, US
Country: United States
Contact: asst. vice President for public relations Tracy Manforte Sweet
Contact: Director Robert Shea
Contact: technical/assistant Director Joe Deleault

Dance Affiliates
Website: www.dancecelebration.org
Email: info@dancecelebration.org
Phone: 215 636 9000
Address: 4701 Bath Street Bldg 46B, US
Information: large educational and outreach programs
Country: United States
Contact: project educational Director Anne-Marie Mulgrew
Contact: Artistic Director Randy Swartz
Email: randy.schwartz@danceaffiliates.org
Contact: Director of development Jane Bensignor
Email: jane@danceaffiliates.org
Social Media: www.facebook.com/pages/Dance-Affiliates/98
Policies: All, Arts centre

Dance Center of Columbia College
Website: www.dancecenter.org
Email: preynolds@colum.edu
Phone: 312 369 8300
Address: 1306 S. Michigan Ave, US
Country: United States
Contact: academic coordinator Jyl Fehrenkamp
Contact: Executive Director Phil Reynolds
Contact: community outreach and education coordinator Alycia Scott
Contact: Chair Bonnie Brooks
Contact: Marketing Director Ligia Himebaugh

Dance Place
Website: www.danceplace.org
Email: ideas@danceplace.org
Phone: 120 226 91600
Address: 3225 8th Street N.E., US
Information: weekly performances and daily classes for all ages and abilities
Country: United States
Contact: Founding Director Carla Perlo
Contact: Communications Director Carolyn Kamrath
Email: carolynk@danceplace.org
Social Media: DancePlace http:// www.facebook.com/DancePlaceDC
Policies: All, Theatre

Dance St Louis
Website: www.dancestlouis.org
Email: muthoff@dancestlouis.org
Phone: 314 289 4101
Address: 3547 Olive Street, US
Information: outreach program to schools and colleges
Country: United States
Contact: Executive Director Michael Uthoff
Contact: public relations Manager Barbara MacRobie
Contact: General Manager Laura Burkhart
Contact: Director of development Maureen Manget
Contact: Director of finance Berrien Tedford

Dance Theater Workshop
Website: www.dtw.org
Email: dtw@dtw.org
Phone: 212 691 6500
Address: 219 W 19th Street, US
Country: United States
Contact: Executive Director Stephen Greco
Contact: Artistic Director Carla Peterson
Social Media: @NewYorkLiveArts www.facebook.com/NewYorkLiveArts
Policies: Rent only, Other

Dance Umbrella
Website: www.danceumbrella.com
Email: dance@austinfree.net
Phone: 512 450 0456
Address: PO Box 1323, US
Information: presents contemporary dance/movement; physical address: 3710 Cedar #288, Austin, Texas 78705
Country: United States
Contact: Executive Director Phyllis Porreca Slattery

Email: phyllis@danceumbrella.com
Policies: Rent only, Multi-purpose

Dance Umbrella, Boston
Website: www.danceumbrella.org
Email: bmcguire@danceumbrella.org
Phone: 617 482 7570
Address: 515 Washington St., 5th floor, US
Information: contemporary/avant-garde and culturally diverse world dance and performance
Country: United States
Contact: Artistic Director/ Producer Jeremy Alliger

DanceCleveland
Website: www.dancecleveland.org
Email: jsherman@dancecleveland.org
Phone:
216 861 2213
Address: 1148 Euclid Ave, Suite 311, US
Information: dance education workshops and classes, dance therapy workshops and classes, in school education and classes
Country: United States
Contact: Executive Director Pamela Young

Dancing in the Streets, Inc.
Website:
www.dancinginthestreets.org
Email: info@dancinginthestreets.org
Phone: 212 625 3505
Address: 545 Eighth Avenue, Suite 8SE, US
Information: innovative and site specific work
Country: United States
Contact: Executive Director, Dancing in the Streets Aviva Davidson

Danspace Project
Website: www.danspaceproject.org
Email: info@danspaceproject.org
Phone: 212 674 8112
Address: 131 E. 10th Street, US
Country: United States
Contact: administrative and program Associate Abby Harris
Contact: Marketing Associate Rennica Johnson
Contact: Executive Director Guy Yarden

Danville Area Association for the Arts & Humanities Performing Arts Series
Phone: 434 792 6965
Address: PO Box 3581, US
Country: United States
Contact: Executive Director Arlyne McDowell

Danville Concert Association
Website: www.danvilleconcert.org
Phone: 143 479 29242
Address: P.O. Box 2584, US
Country: United States
Contact: contact Jo Silvers

Darius Milhaud Society – Music by Darius Milhaud
Phone: 121 692 14548
Address: 15715 Chadbourne Road, US
Information: initiate and coordinate rather than produce; obtain music by serving as liaison with publishers; can provide listings of repertoire by category; publish the Darius Milhaud Newsletter
Country: United States
Contact: President Katharine Warne

Darke County Center for the Arts
Website: www.centerforarts.net/
Email: dcca@centerforarts.net
Phone: 937 547 0908
Address: Box 718, US
Information: arts and education program in schools of Darke County
Country: United States
Contact: Artistic Director Keith Rowlins

Darke County Center for the Arts
Website: www.centerforarts.net/contact-us.htm
Email: dcca@centerforarts.net
Phone: 937 547 0908
Address: Box 718, US
Country: United States
Contact: Artistic Director Keith Rawlins
Contact: production Director Mary Frances Shultz
Contact: Executive Director Julie Strait
Policies: Rent only, Other

David A Straz Jr Center for the Performing Arts
Website: www.strazcenter.org
Email: Bonniejean.Paulish@strazcenter.org
Phone: 813 222 1000
Address: 1010 N MacInnes Place, US
Information: The Straz Center is a member of the Florida Professional Presenters Consortium and the League of American Theatres and Producers. The state-of-the-art complex is the largest performing arts center in the Southeastern United States. Member of ISPA
Country: United States

Contact: office administrator Bonniejean Paulish
Email: Bonniejean.Paulish@strazcenter.org
Contact: Marketing Director Heather Chamberlain
Email: Heather.Chamberlain@strazcenter.org
Contact: Director of corporate giving and sponsorship Marc Brechwald
Email: marc.brechwald@strazcenter.org
Contact: Director of foundations and public funding Donna McBride
Email: donna.mcbride@strazcenter.org
Contact: Director of special events Sharon McDonald
Email: sharon.mcdonald@strazcenter.org
Social Media: @StrazCenter www.facebook.com/StrazCenter
Policies: Multi-purpose

David H Koch Theater
Website: www.davidhkochtheater.com
Email: Artistic@nycOpera.com
Phone: 212 870 5500
Address: David H. Koch Theater, 20 Lincoln Center, US
Information: Formerly known as the New York State Theater now reopened after renovations, under the new name David H Koch Theater.
Country: United States
Policies: All, Theatre

Daytona Beach Community College
Website: www.dbcc.cc.fl.us
Email: web_services@falconmail.dbcc.edu
Phone: 386 254 3042
Address: 1200 W International Speedway Blvd, US
Country: United States
Contact: cultural coordinator Kenneth Walker

Daytona Beach Symphony Society
Website: www.dbss.org
Email: info@dbss.org
Phone: 386 253 2901
Address: PO Box 2, US
Country: United States
Contact: Executive Director Carol Anderson-McLean
Contact: President, board of Directors Skip Diegal
Policies: Other

Dean Lesher Regional Center for the Arts
Website: www.dlrca.org
Email: dlrca@dlrca.org
Phone: 925 295 1400
Address: 1601 Civic Drive, US
Information: see also in this section Centre Repertory Co.
Country: United States
Contact: production services coordinator Toni Kilcoyne
Contact: audience services coordinator Courtney Egg
Contact: arts centre Manager Scott Denison

Dearborn Highlands Arts Council
Website: www.dearbornhighlandsarts.org
Email: dearbornarts@comcast.net
Address: 331 Walnut Street, US
Country: United States
Contact: Executive Director Marilyn Bower
Policies: Arts centre

Deerfield Academy Events Series
Website: www.deerfield.edu
Email: copyright@deerfield.edu
Phone: 413 772 0241
Address: Deerfield Academy, 7 Boyden Lane, US
Country: United States
Contact: Chairman of academy events committee David Howell

Defiance College Schomburg Series
Website: www.defiance.edu
Email: defiance@defiance.edu
Phone: 419 784 4010
Address: 701 N Clinton St, US
Country: United States
Contact: contact Douglas Fiely

Del Norte Association for Cultural Awareness
Website: www.dnaca.net
Email: dnaca@harborside.com
Phone: 707 464 1336
Address: PO Box 1480, US
Information: bringing performing artists to the north coast each year since 1983
Country: United States
Contact: Executive Director Holly O Austin

Delaware State University Cultural Programs for the Community
Website: www.desu.edu
Email: dparks@desu.edu
Phone: 302 857 6697
Address: Arts Centre/Gallery, 1200 N Dupont Highway, US
Information: also a historical black institution
Country: United States
Contact: Director of arts centre/gallery Donald A Parks

Denison University Vail Series

Website: www.vailseries.org
Email: wales@denison.edu
Phone: 740 587 6539
Address: Denison University, US
Information: non profit organisation; concerts are free to campus community
Country: United States
Contact: Director Lorraine A Wales

Dennos Museum Center
Website: www.dennosmuseum.org
Email: ejenneman@nmc.edu
Phone: 231 995 1055
Address: Northwestern Michigan College, 1701 East Front Street, US
Information: see also Northwestern Michigan College
Country: United States
Contact: performing arts Manager Eugene Jenenman
Email: ejenneman@nmc.edu
Contact: museum Director Eugene Jenneman
Social Media: @TheDennos
Policies: All, Concert hall

Denver Arts & Venues
Website: www.ArtsandVenues.com
Email: Kent.Rice@denvergov.org
Phone: 720 865 4220
Address: 1345 Champa St., US
Information: Denver Arts & Venues owns and operates some of the Rocky Mountain West's highest-profile facilities, including Red Rocks Park & Amphitheatre, the Denver Performing Arts Complex, Colorado Convention Center, Denver Coliseum and McNichols Civic Center Building

Country: United States
Director, Marketing & communications
Brian Kitts
assistant Director, Marketing & communications
Jordan Bishop
Social Media: @denverarts www.facebook.com/ArtsandVenuesDenver
Policies: All

Denver Center for the Performing Arts
Website: www.denvercenter.org
Email: info@dcpa.org
Phone: 303 893 4000
Address: 1101 13th St., US
Information: DCPA is the nation's largest not-for-profit theatre organization dedicated to creating unforgettable shared experiences through beloved Broadway musicals, world-class plays, educational programs and inspired events
Country: United States
Contact: chief Marketing officer Jennifer Nealson
Contact: Chairman and chief Executive Daniel L. Ritchie
Social Media: @denvercenter www.facebook.com/DenverCenter
Capacity: 1000

Denver Theatres and Arenas
Website: www.artscomplex.com
Email: Kent.Rice@denvergov.org
Phone: 720 865 4220
Address: Denver's Division of Theatres & Arenas, 1245 Champa Street, US
Information: mainly rent; small amount of presenting
Country: United States
Contact: Director Kent Rice
Contact: booking information Jeanette Murrietta
Contact: Marketing Director Erik Dyce

Department of Cultural & Public Affairs, City of Slidell
Website: www.slidell.la.us
Email: kbergeron@cityofslidell.org
Phone: 985 646 4375
Address: PO Box 828, US
Information: will provide technical assistance
Country: United States
Contact: Director Kim Bergeron

Detroit Chamber Winds & Strings
Website: www.detroitchamberwinds.org
Email: info@detroitchamberwinds.org
Phone: 248 559 2095
Address: 24901 Northwestern Highway, Suite 312, US
Information: Detroit Chamber Winds & Strings (DCWS) has become a champion of administrative collaboration in pursuit of Artistic excellence.**Country:** United States
Marketing & pr
Jill Overacker
Email: overacker@detroitchamberwinds.org
Contact: Executive Director Maury Okun
Email: okun@detroitchamberwinds.org
Contact: Director of communication Margo Strebig
Email: strebig@detroitchamberwinds.org
Social Media: @DetChamberWinds www.facebook.com/DetroitChamberWinds

Detroit Cultural Affairs
Website: www.ci.detroit.mi.us

Phone: 313 224 3470
Address: 1240 Coleman A Young Municipal Center, US
Information: do not present events – act more as a promoter for programmes to introduce community groups and youth groups to cultural institutions; see also National & Regional Ministries
Country: United States
 grants & technical assistant
 James Heart
Contact: Director Marilyn Wheaton

District Curators Inc
Website: www.jazzarts.org
Email: paul@jazzarts.org
Phone: 202 723 7500
Address: 6925 Willow Street NW 22, US
Information: the Jazz Art Festival is the primary presenting season between June & August
Country: United States
Contact: Executive Director Bill Warrell

Dona Ana Arts Council
Website: www.daarts.org
Email: info@daarts.org
Phone: 505 523 6403
Address: 211 North downtown mall, US
Information: also sponsor the Dona Ana Arts Council Renaissance Crafts Fair and Street Fair
Country: United States
Contact: Executive Director Amy Johnson-Bassford

Donna and Marvin Schwartz Center for Performing Arts
Website: www.schwartzcenter.emory.edu
Email: boxoffice@emory.edu
Phone: 404 727 5050
Address: 1700 North Decatur Road, Suite 251, US
Information: a 90, 000-square-foot (8, 400 m2) multi-discipline performing arts facility on the campus of Emory University in Atlanta, Georgia.Completed in early 2003, the Schwartz Center provides a multidisciplinary teaching and performance center for the performing arts programs at Emory including dance, music, and theater
Country: United States
Contact: Managing Director, arts center project Randy Fullerton
Contact: Associate vp for arts and sciences development John Ingersoll
Contact: media relations, public relations, and Marketing Sally Corbett

Door Community Auditorium
Website: www.dcauditorium.org
Email: boxoffice@dcauditorium.org
Phone: 920 868 2728
Address: PO Box 397, US
Country: United States
Contact: Executive Director Cari Lewis
Email: Director@dcauditorium.org
Social Media: www.facebook.com/DoorCommunity. Auditorium
Policies: Concert hall

Downers Grove Concert Association Artists Showcase West
Website: www.dgconcerts.org
Phone: 630 968 7162
Address: 917 Kenyon, US
Information: an all volunteer organization; members of the Chicago Area Presenters Network, the Illinois Presenters Network
Country: United States
Contact: concert impresario Ruth L Burson

Downey Civic Theatre
Website: www.downeytheatre.org
Email: koconnor@downeyca.org
Phone: 562 904 7230
Address: 8435 Firestone Blvd, US
Country: United States
Contact: Director Kevin O'Connor
Contact: theatre supervisor Noreen Kimura

Downtown Crossing Association
Website: www.downtowncrossing.org
Email: info@downtowncrossing.org
Phone: 617 482 2139
Address: 101 Arch Street, Suite 160, US
Country: United States
Contact: President Anne Meyers

Downtown Music Productions
Website: www.downtownmusicproductions.org
Email: dmpmimi@msn.com
Phone: 212 477 1594
Address: 310 East 12 Street, US
Country: United States
Contact: Artistic Director/conductor/pianist Mimi Stern-Wolfe

Drawer 2
Website: www.earlham.edu/events
Email: knighly@earlham.edu
Phone: 765 983 1373

Address: Earlham College, US
Country: United States
Contact: events coordinator Lynn Knight

DSU, the Celebrity Concert Series
Website: www.celebrityconcertseries.com
Email: lemmon@dixie.edu
Phone: 435 652 7994
Address: 225 South 700 East, US
Information: Dixie State College Celebrity Concert Series (CCS) was formally organized in 1958 with Dr. Ron Garner as Manager. Seven professional and non-professional concerts were presented that year
Country: United States
 Programming & Marketing
 Steve Lemmon
Email: lemmon@dixie.edu
Social Media: @DSUCulturalArts www.facebook.com/dsuculturalarts

Duke University Institue of the Arts
Website: www.dukeperformances.org
Email: aaron.greenwald@duke.edu
Phone: 919 660 3356
Address: Duke Performances, Box 90685, US
Country: United States
Contact: interim Director Aaron Greenwald

Duluth Depot – St Louis County Heritage & Arts Center
Website: www.duluthdepot.org
Email: info@duluthdepot.org
Phone: 218 727 8025
Address: 506 W Michigan St, US
Country: United States
Contact: operations Manager Mary Karl

Dumbarton Concerts Inc
Website: www.dumbartonconcerts.org
Email: office@dumbartonconcerts.org
Phone: 202 965 2000
Address: Historic Dumbarton Church, 3133 Dumbarton Street, NW, US
Country: United States
Contact: Executive Director Constance Zimmer
Contact: Managing Director Mimi Newcastle

Duncan Theatre @ Palm Beach Community College
Website: www.pbcc.edu/arts/duncan
Email: alexanmp@pbcc.edu
Phone: 561 868 3314
Address: 4200 Congress Ave, MS #62, US
Information: member of Florida Professional Presenters consortium, Association of Performing Arts Presenters, International Association of Performing Arts for Young People
Country: United States
Contact: Managing Director Mark Alexander

DuPont Theatre
Website: www.duponttheatre.com
Phone: 302 656 4401
Address: 1007 North Market Street, US
Information: theatre for hire, different events
Country: United States
Contact: General Manager Annmarie O'Hara-Townsend
Contact: box office Manager Diane Angeline

Early Music Foundation
Website: www.EarlyMusicNY.org
Email: info@EarlyMusicNY.org
Phone: 212 749 6600
Address: 10 West 68th Street, US
Information: presents 'EARLY MUSIC NEW YORK – FREDERICK RENZ, Director, ' touring internationally & annual NYC concert series, recording label – "Ex cathedra Records;" services to the historically informed performance field – "New York Early Music Central."
Country: United States
Contact: Director Frederick Renz
Email: info@EarlyMusicNY.org
Policies: Multi-purpose

Early Music Guild of Seattle International Series
Website: www.earlymusicguild.org
Email: emg@earlymusicguild.org
Phone: 206 325 7066
Address: 2366 Eastlake Avenue E, Suite 325, US
Information: 200 – 300k $ total income per year
Country: United States
Contact: Executive Director August Denhard
Contact: assistant to Director Ann Stickney

Early Music in Columbus
Website: www.earlymusicincolumbus.org
Email: info@earlymusicincolumbus.org
Phone: 614 861 4569
Address: 1 College and Main, US
Information: the Early Music in Columbus (OH/USA) concert series presents professional artists who specialize in the music of the Medieval, Renaissance and Baroque Periods. The series is in its 34th season
Country: United States
Contact: programmes Director Sarah Hixon

Email: info@earlymusicincolumbus.org
Social Media: www.facebook.com/earlymusiccbus/

Early Music Now
Website: www.earlymusicnow.org
Email: info@earlymusicnow.org
Phone: 414 225 3113
Address: 759 N Milwaukee St – Suite 420, 759 N Milwaukee Street, Suite 420, US
Information: Early Music Now is dedicated to the creation of lively connections with the past through historically informed presentations of music composed before 1800.
Country: United States
Contact: founder Thallis Hoyt Drake
Contact: General Manager Charles Q Sullivan
Social Media: https:// www.facebook.com/pages/Early-Music-Now/115097775178095
Policies: Multi-purpose

East Carolina University Performing Arts Series
Website: www.ecu.edu/cs-cfac/SRAPAS.cfm
Email: theatre@ecu.edu
Phone: 252 328 4788
Address: 207 Mendenhall Student Center, East Carolina University, East Fifth Street, US
Information: Arts Smart and Family Fare Series music, dance, theater, Travel-Adventure Film Series. alternate phone: +125-23285386
Country: United States
Social Media: @ECUPerformArts www.facebook.com/SRAPAS

East County Performing Arts Center
Website: www.ecpac.com
Email: ecpac@ecpac.com
Phone: 619 440 2277/ 44
Address: 210 E Main St, US
Information: books a series of 30-40 diverse performers; also for rent
Country: United States
Contact: facilities Manager Melissa Hill
Contact: production Manager Kathy Wright
 President & CEO
 not existing anymore
Contact: paul russell from artbeat mana

Eastern Iowa Community College District
Website: www.eicc.edu
Email: eiccd@eicc.edu, hbedell@eicc.edu
Phone: 563 336 3300
Address: 306 West River Drive, US
Country: United States
Contact: Director Vic McAvoy

Eastern Kentucky University Centerboard
Website: www.eku.edu
Email: mark.cross@eku.edu
Phone: 859 622 1225
Address: Eastern Kentucky Univ, 202 Perkins Building, 521 Lancaster Avenue, US
Country: United States
Contact: Director special programmes/marketting and pr Mark Cross

Eastern Michigan University
Website: www.emich.edu/campuslife
Email: campus.life@emich.edu
Phone: 734 480 1927
Address: Office of Campus Life, McKenny Union, US
Country: United States
Contact: programme coordinator Melissa Ginotti
Contact: Director of office of campus life Glenna Miller
Social Media: @EMUcampuslife www.facebook.com/EMUcampuslife

Eastern New Mexico College of Fine Arts
Website: www.enmu.edu
Email: dagerig@gmail.com
Phone: 575 562 2373
Address: Eastern New Mexico University, Station 16, US
Country: United States
Contact: dean, college of fine arts David Gerig
Contact: Chair, dept of music Dustin Seifert
Contact: Chair, dept of theatre and dance Janeice Scarbrough

Eastman School of Music
Website: www.esm.rochester.edu
Email: concerts@esm.rochester.edu
Phone: 585 274 1110
Address: 26 Gibbs St, 60 Gibbs Street Rochester, NY 14604, US
Country: United States
Contact: Director of concert operations Andrew Green
Contact: assistant Director of concert operations Serin Hong

Eau Claire Regional Arts Council
Website: www.eauclairearts.com
Email: ecrac@charter.net

Phone: 715 832 2787
Address: 316 Eau Claire Street, US
Country: United States
Contact: Executive Director Peter Provost

Edgar H Smith Fine Arts Series
Website: www.wou.edu
Email: fineart@wou.edu
Phone: 503 838 8333
Address: 345 N. Monmouth Ave, US
Information: total artists' fees: between 40-70k $ per year; some international touring groups
Country: United States
Contact: Director Carole Orloff

Edinboro University – Concert and Lecture Series
Website: webs.edinboro.edu/pubrel/arts/performin-garts.html
Email: barbaro@edinboro.edu
Phone: 814 732 2518
Address: Music Department, Room 109, Heather Hall, Pennsylvania, US
Information: recently renovated Louis C. Cole Auditorium has a state of the art sound shell
Country: United States
Contact: office for the performing arts series Cosmo Barbaro

Edison Theatre at Washington University
Website: www.edisontheatre.wustl.edu
Email: edison@artsci.wustl.edu
Phone: 314 935 7362
Address: Campus Box 1119, One Brookings Drive, US
Information: Edison Theatre is the only fully technically equipped, proscenium thrust theater at Washington University in St. Louis and plays a varied role on campus.
Country: United States
Contact: Executive Director Charlie Robin
Contact: operations Manager Bill Larson
Email: alarson@wustl.edu
Social Media: @EdisonTheatre www.facebook.com/EdisonTheatre
Capacity: 656

Egg
Website: www.theegg.org
Email: info@theegg.org
Phone: 518 473 1061 / b
Address: PO Box 2065, US
Country: United States
Contact: Executive Director Peter Lesser operations & production Manager Bill Darcy
Contact: production coordinator Justin Testo

Eisenhower Hall Theatre
Website: www.ikehall.com
Email: gary.keegan@usma.edu
Phone: 845 938 2782
Address: West Point, US
Country: United States
house Manager & theatre Director Gary F. Keegan
Contact: stage services Manager George Plank
Contact: Marketing/public relations Richard Storey

El Camino College Center for the Arts
Website: www.elcamino.edu
Email: lkirst@elcamino.edu
Phone: 131 053 23670
Address: 16007 Crenshaw Blvd, US
Country: United States
Contact: Executive Director Bruce Spain
Contact: administrative assistant Louise Kirst

El Paso Arts Resources Department, City of
Website: www.artsandculture.org
Email: mcad@elpasotexas.gov
Phone: 915 541 4481
Address: 2 Civic Center Plaza, 1st Floor, US
Information: aims to create links between Mexican and American culture
Country: United States
Contact: Director Yolanda Alameda

El Paso Pro Musica
Website: www.elpasopromusica.org
Email: info@elpasopromusica.org
Phone: 915 833 9400
Address: 6557 N. Mesa St., US
Information: presents a 3 week Chamber Music Festival in January
Country: United States
Contact: festival Director Zuill Bailey
Contact: Executive Director Kathrin Berg Pettit

El Teatro Campesino
Website: www.elteatrocampesino.com
Email: info@elteatrocampesino.com
Phone: 831 623 2444
Address: 705 Fourth Street, PO Box 1240, San Juan Bautista, US
Information: Founded by Luis Valdez in 1965 as the cultural arm of the UFW movement, ETC functions as a multi-generational theatre company that has been at the forefront of using theatre as an Artistic generator of social change
Country: United States
Contact: Artistic Director Luis Valdez
Social Media: https:// www.facebook.com/elteatrocampesino/ https://twitter.com/teatrocampesino
Capacity: 100-250
Annual Performances: 100+
Annual Productions: 0-5
Policies: Present and Produce

Elgin Community College
Website: www.elgin.edu/arts
Email: sduchrow@elgin.edu
Phone: 847 214 7421/ 78
Address: Visual & Performing Arts Center, 1700 Spartan Drive, US
Country: United States
Contact: Director Steve Duchrow

Elon University
Website:
jclark28@elon.edu
Email:
troxlerg@elon.edu
Phone: 336 278 5607/05
Address: 2800 Campus Box, US
Information: every semester have performances representing each of the performing arts
Country: United States
Contact: assistant to the dean Patti Gross dean of cultural & special programs George Troxler

Embassy Centre Foundation Inc
Website: www.fwembassytheatre.org
Email: info@fwembassytheatre.org
Phone: 260 424 6287
Address: 125 West Jefferson Blvd, US
Country: United States
Contact: Executive Director Kelly Updike

Emelin Theatre for the Performing Arts
Website: www.emelin.org
Email: emelin98@aol.com
Phone: 914 698 3045
Address: 153 Library Lane, US
Country: United States
Contact: bookkeeper Bridget Bettke
Email: bridget.bettke@emelin.org
Contact: administrative assistant Susan Flink
Email: susan.flink@emelin.org
Contact: Marketing assistant Harris Mercer
Email: harris.mercer@emelin.org
Contact: Marketing Director Ashley Prymas
Email: ashley.prymas@emelin.org
Contact: Executive Director Lisa Reilly
Email: lisa.reilly@emelin.org
Contact: graphic designer Jamie Lynn Weisinger
Email: jamielynnweis@emelin.org
Contact: company Manager Charles Zavelle
Email: charles.zavelle@emelin.org
Social Media: @EmelinTheatre www.facebook.com/EmelinTheatre
Policies: Rent and present, Theatre

EMMA Concert Association
Email: luisfog@aug.com
Phone: 904 829 3013
Address: c/o Yolanda Garcia-Fernandez, 20 Nelmar Ave., US
Country: United States
Contact: President Eva Doolittle

Emmanuel Music
Website: www.emmanuelmusic.org
Email: music@emmanuelmusic.org
Phone: 617 536 3356
Address: 15 Newbury Street, US
Country: United States
Contact: Executive Director and Artistic administrator Leonard Matczynski
Contact: Artistic Director Craig Smith

Empire State Plaza
Website: www.empirestateplaza.org
Email: sponsorships@empirestateplaza.org
Phone: 877 659 4377
Address: 279 Madison Ave, US
Information: festivals and concerts; free to the public. Run by the NY State Office
Country: United States
Social Media: @PlazaEvents www.facebook.com/EmpireStatePlaza

Emporia Arts Council
Website: www.emporia.com/eac
Email: artscncl@osprey.net
Phone: 620 343 6473
Address: PO Box 1227, US
Information: has artist in residence and education programmes

Country: United States
Contact: Executive Director Melissa Windsor

Englewood Performing Arts Series
Email: onkor@sunline.net
Phone: 941 473 2787
Address: PO Box 1304, US
Information: member of Florida Professional Presenters consortium
Country: United States
Contact: programme Director Orville Splitt
Contact: President Judy Moore

Ensemble Music Society of Indianapolis
Website: www.ensemblemusic.org
Email: pamela.steele@comcast.net
Phone: 131 725 48915
Address: PO Box 40188, US
Country: United States
Contact: President Pamela Steele

Enumclaw Arts Commission
Website: www.cityofenumclaw.net
Email: garylaturner@ci.enumclaw.wa.us
Phone: 360 802 0239
Address: 1339 Griffin Avenue, US
Information: also have a public arts program
Country: United States
Contact: cultural programmes coordinator Gary LaTurner

Erie Civic Music Association
Website: www.eriecivicmusic.com
Email: butchvick@aol.com
Phone: 814 864 5681
Address: P.O. Box 143, US
Country: United States

Ethel Barrymore Theatre
Website: www.telecharge.com
Phone: 212 944 3700
Address: 243 West 47th Street, US
Country: United States
Contact: management company The Shubert Org. Inc
Contact: reception Margo B
Contact: vice President of theatre operations Peter Entin
Capacity: 1096

Etherredge Center, USCA
Website: www.usca.edu/ec
Email: janes@usca.edu
Phone: 803 648 6851
Address: 471 University Parkway, US
Country: United States
Contact: Executive Director Jane Schumacher
Contact: technical Director Chet Longley

Eugene O'Neill Theatre
Website: www.eugene-oneill-theater.com
Phone: 212 239 6200
Address: 230 West 49th Street, US
Country: United States
Contact: Director Paul Monte

Evangel University Artist Series
Website: www.evangel.edu, lochnerb@evangel.edu
Phone: 417 865 2815 ext
Address: 1111 N Glenstone, US
Country: United States
Contact: Chairman Michael Buesking
Contact: Executive secretary Elaine Tate
Contact: pr Brenda Lochner

F M Kirby Center
Website: www.kirbycenter.org
Phone: 570 823 4599
Address: 71 Public Square, US
Country: United States
Contact: Director of programming Will Beekman
Contact: Director of operations Drew Taylor
Social Media: @FMKirbyCenter www.facebook.com/fmkirbycenter
Policies: Rent and present, Arts centre

Fairbanks Concert Association
Website: www.fairbanksconcert.org
Email: info@fairbanksconcert.org
Phone: 907 474 8081
Address: PO Box 80547, US
Information: visiting address: 794 University Ave, Suite 104, Fairbanks AK99709
Country: United States
programme selection & Executive Director Anne Biberman
Contact: board President Scot McCrea

Fairfield Center for Creative Arts
Website: www.fairfield.ca.gov
Email: tgrames@fairfield.ca.gov
Phone: 707 428 7469
Address: 1035 Texas Street, US
Information: Fairfield City Hall 1000 Webster Street, CA 94533
Country: United States
Contact: contact Todd Grames

Fairleigh Dickinson University Performing Arts Series
Phone: 973 443 8636
Address: 285 Madison Ave, US
Country: United States
Contact: Chairman Elliet Hoffman
Contact: Chairman of the performing arts department Richard Wallace
cultural & performing arts Director
t.b.a.
Contact: Director of theatre program Steven Hollis

Feldman Chamber Music Society
Website: www.feldmanchambermusic.org
Phone: 175 755 21630 (
Address: PO Box 6144, US
Country: United States
Contact: President Patrick Deams

Ferst Center for the Arts at Georgia Tech
Website: www.arts.gatech.edu
Email:
info@arts.gatech.edu
Phone:
404 894 2787
Address: 349 Ferst Drive NW, US
Information: 970 seat venue located on university campus. Lobby also available for rental.
Country: United States
Contact: Event Coordinator Rachel Haage
Email: rachel.haage@arts.gatech.edu
Contact: Marketing Specialist Elizabeth Geiger
Email: elizabeth.geiger@arts.gatech.edu
Policies: Rent and present, Arts centre

Festival Chamber Music Society
Website: www.festivalchamber.org
Email: fchamber@aol.com
Phone: 212 678 6970
Address: PO Box 1773, US
Information: all concerts take place at: Merkin Hall in the Abraham Goodman House, 129 West 67th Street, New York City
Country: United States
Contact: Director Ruth Sommers

Festival Dance & Performing Arts
Website: www.festivaldance.org
Email: cindy@festivaldance.org
Phone: 120 888 33267
Address: University of Idaho, PO Box 442403, US
Country: United States
Contact: Executive Director Cindy Barnhart

Festival of Orchestras
Website: www.festivaloforchestras.com
Phone: 407 896 2451
Address: 1353 Pallmetto Avenue, Suite 100, US
Information: member of Florida Professional Presenters consortium
Country: United States
Contact: Executive Director Susan Cohn Lackman

Fine Arts Center of Kershaw County
Website: www.fineartscenter.org
Email: jpeterson@fineartscenter.org
Phone: 803 425 7676
Address: 810 Lyttleton Street, US
Information: Founded in 1974 by three independent groups (Camden Art Association, Camden Music Association, and the Camden Community Theatre), the Fine Arts Center was intended to be the cultural focus of the county and to serve as the local arts agency and an umbrella organization for affiliate clubs
Country: United States
Social Media: @FACofKC www.facebook.com/Fine-ArtsCenter
Capacity: 284

Fine Arts Council of Trumbull County
Website: www.trumbullarts.org
Email: bbrown@trumbullarts.org
Phone: 330 399 1212
Address: PO Box 48, 347 N. Park Ave., US
Country: United States
Contact: Director Roberta Brown

First Night Providence Inc
Website: www.firstnightprovidence.org
Email: info@firstnightprovidence.org
Phone: 401 521 1166
Address: 10 Dorrance Street, Suite 920, US
Information: New Year's Eve festival of the arts
Country: United States
Contact: Executive Director Doris Stephens
Contact: assistant Director Annette Robinson
Contact: Artistic Director Kathleen Pletcher

Fitchburg State College Performing Arts
Website: www.fsc.edu
Email: sfranzen@fsc.edu
Phone: 978 345 2151
Address: Campus Center, 160 Pearl St, US

Country: United States
Contact: campus center Director Tullio Nieman

Fitzgerald Theater, The
Website: www.fitzgeraldtheater.org
Email: fitzgerald@mpr.org
Phone: 651 290 1200
Address: 10 East Exchange Street, US
Country: United States
Contact: General services Manager Shane Wethers
Contact: production Manager Thomas Campbell
Contact: audience services assistant Jude Mitchell

Flint Center for the Performing Arts
Website: www.flintcenter.com
Email: pdavis@flintcenter.com
Phone: 408 864 8820
Address: Flint Center for the Performing Arts, 4th Floor, 21250 Stevens Creek Blvd, US
Information: also rent San Jose Symphony 35-40 concerts, San Francisco Symphony 7-8 concerts
Country: United States
Contact: General Manager Paula Davis
Email: pdavis@flintcenter.com
Contact: event coordinator Nora Whiting
Email: nwhiting@flintcenter.com

Flint Institute of Music, The
Website: www.thefim.com
Phone: 810 238 1350
Address: Dort Music Center, 1025 E Kearsley St, US
Information: see also Orchestras (Flint Symphony Orchestra), music Director & conductor: Enrique Diemecke; Flint School of Performing Arts is one of the largest community arts schools in the USA
Country: United States
Contact: President Paul Torre
Contact: Manager flint symphony orchestra Tom Glasscock
Contact: development Director Carol Hartley
Contact: Marketing Director Christina Mooney
Contact: Director of audience services Linda Scott
Contact: Director flint school of performing arts Davin Pierson Torre

Florence Gould Hall at the French Institute Alliance Francaise
Website: www.fiaf.org
Email: wlaurent@fiaf.org
Phone: 212 355 6100 Eve
Address: 22 E 60th St, US
Information: venue address: 55 East 59th, New York. bet. Park & Madison; FIAF presents French & Francophone Performing Arts
Country: United States
Contact: Director of Sales Wendy Laurent

Florida Atlantic University
Website: www.fau.edu
Email: cox@fau.edu
Phone: 561 297 3810
Address: Department of Theatre, 777 Glades Road, P. O. Box 3091, US
Information: opened in 1994; three-building complex, includes the University Theater, a multimedia lecture hall, rehearsal studios, a fully equipped flexible 200-seat auditorium, a 500-seat proscenium theatre and the 100 seat small auditorium
Country: United States
theatre supervisor & Chairperson Richard Gamble
Contact: administrator Christie Cox

Florida Atlantic University – Dept. of Music
Website: www.fau.edu
Email: music@fau.edu
Phone: 561 297 3820
Address: Department of Music, 777 Glades Road, PO Box 3091, US
Country: United States

Florida Dance Association
Website: www.floridadanceassociation.org
Email: info@floridadanceassociation.org
Phone: 786 397 7717
Address: 111 SW 5th Avenue, US
Country: United States
Contact: Executive Director Bill Doolin

Florida Keys Community College
Website: www.fkcc.edu
Email: twfacdanny@aol.com
Phone: 305 296 9081
Address: Tennessee Williams Fine Arts Center, 5901 College Road, US
Country: United States
Contact: Chair of fine arts division Lynne Bentley Kemp
Contact: theater Director Franck Wood

Florida Southern College Festival of Fine Arts
Website: www.flsouthern.edu/festival-of-fine-arts.aspx
Phone: 863 680 4111
Address: 111 Lake Hollingsworth Drive, US
Information: Continuing a tradition of more than fifty

years, the Festival of Fine Arts has planned an exciting new season filled with diverse, vibrant events showcasing the arts.
Country: United States
Contact: Executive Director Lawrence Burke
Contact: coordinator Robert MacDonald
Contact: house Manager Tony Harris
Social Media: @FLSouthern www.facebook.com/FloridaSouthern

Florida State College at Jacksonville-The Artist Series
Website: www.artistseriesjax.org
Email: artistseries@fscj.edu
Phone: 904 632 3228
Address: 501 W State St, Suite 141, US
Information: member of Florida Professional Presenters Consortium, Association of Performing Arts Presenters, Southern Arts Federation and The League of American Theatres and Producers
Country: United States
Contact: Executive Director Milton A. Russos

Florida State University Campus Entertainment
Website: www.union.fsu.edu
Email: oglesby@admin.fsu.edu
Phone: 850 644 6710
Address: A305 Oglesby Union, US
Information: The Oglesby Union is a diverse and engaging community that fosters individual and collective learning by providing outstanding services and opportunities for involvement.
Country: United States
Contact: concert Director Adam Sterritt
Social Media: @OglesbyUnion www.facebook.com/FSUOglesbyUnion

Florida Theatre Performing Arts Center
Website: www.floridatheatre.com
Email: info@floridatheatre.com
Phone: 904 355 5661
Address: The Florida Theatre, 128 East Forsyth Street, US
Information: member of Florida Professional Presenters consortium
Country: United States
Contact: President Numa Saisselin
Email: numa@floridatheatre.com
Contact: house Manager Jennifer Dobrowolski
Email: jennifer@floridatheatre.com
Contact: Director of Marketing Kathryn Wills
Email: kathryn@floridatheatre.com
Contact: technical Director Saul Lucio
Email: saul@floridatheatre.com
Social Media: @FloridaTheatre www.facebook.com/FloridaTheatre
Capacity: 1918

Flynn Center for the Performing Arts
Website: www.flynncenter.org
Email: amalina@flynncenter.org
Phone: 802 652 4500
Address: 153 Main Street, US
Country: United States
Contact: Executive Director Andrea Rogers
Contact: Director of programming Arnie Malina
Contact: chief financial officer Diana Petrovs
Contact: Marketing Director tba

Folger Shakespeare Library
Website: www.folger.edu
Email: webmaster@folger.edu
Phone: 202 544 4600
Address: 201 E. Capitol Street SE, US
Information: publishes the illustrated, completely re-edited Folger Editions of Shakespeare's plays, award-winning exhibition catalogs, and the journal Shakespeare Quarterly; public programs include plays, concerts, literary readings, family activities, and exhibitions, as well as numerous K-12 and college programs for students and teachers. Advanced scholars participate in a variety of Folger Institute seminars and colloquia
Country: United States
Contact: public programmes Director Janet Alexander Griffin
Contact: head of external relations Garland Scott
Contact: Marketing Manager Peter Eramo
Email: peramo@folger.edu
Social Media: @FolgerLibrary www.facebook.com/folgershakespearelibrary
Policies: Arts centre

Folly Theater
Website: www.follytheater.com
Email: rental@follytheater.com
Phone: 816 842 5500
Address: PO Box 26505, US
Information: also available for rent, physical address 300 W. 12th Street, Kansas City, MO 64105
Country: United States
Contact: Executive Director Douglas Tatum

Fontana Chamber Arts
Website: www.fontanachamberarts.org
Email: aberquist@fontanachamberarts.org
Phone: 269 382 7774

Address: 359 South Kalamazoo Mall, Suite 200, US
Information: presentation of quality chamber music performances, community outreach & collaboration with other arts organizations; 50 events annually, fall/winter season Sept – May; see also Festivals (Fontana Chamber Arts Festival of Music & Art)
Country: United States
Executive & Artistic Director
Anne Berquist
Contact: administrative assistant Difei Li

Fontana Performing Arts Center
Email: w www.fontanarecreation.org
Phone:
909 428 8390
Address: 9460 Sierra Ave, US
Country: United States
Contact: Executive Director Larry Watson

Ford Community & Performing Arts Center
Phone: 313 943 2354
Address: 15801 Michigan Avenue, US
Information: see also Festivals (Dearborn Homecoming Festival)
Country: United States
Contact: Director fine art Jack Raeburn
Contact: deputy Director, dance, festival Eric Peterson

Fort Hays State University Encore Series
Email:
cbrock@fhsu.edu
Phone: 785 628 5801
Address: Memorial Union, US
Country: United States
Contact: coordinator of special events Carol Brock

Fort Myers Community Concert Association
Website: www.fortmyerscommunityconcerts.org
Phone: 123 993 93236
Address: PO Box 606, US
Country: United States
Contact: President Franklin B. (Mary Lee) Mann
Contact: treasurer Kay Holloway
Contact: secretary John Tyrer
Contact: vice President Mr. David Carleton Hall

Fort Worth Opera
Website: www.fwopera.org/
Email: dkwoods@fwopera.org
Phone: 817 731 0726
Address: 1300 Gendy St., US
Country: United States
Social Media: @FortWorthOpera www.facebook.com/FortWorthOpera

Foundation for Baroque Music/Festival of Baroque Music
Website: www.baroquefestival.org
Email: impresario48@yahoo.com
Phone: 518 893 7527
Address: 165 Wilton Rd, US
Information: a pool of 30 musicians – own performers; produce CDs; see also Early Music
Country: United States
Contact: President and Artistic Director Robert Conant
Contact: co-Artistic Director Kenneth Slowik

Four Seasons Concerts
Website: www.fsarts.org
Email: fsa@fsarts.org
Phone: 510 845 4444
Address: Four Seasons Arts, Inc., 2930 Domingo Avenue, #190, US
Country: United States
Contact: concert Associate Janet Warzyn
Contact: President and Director Jesse W Anthony

Fox Associates
Website: www.fabulousfox.com
Phone: 314 534 1678
Address: 527 N Grand, US
Country: United States

Fox Cities Performing Arts Center
Website: www.foxcitiespac.com
Email: info@foxcitiespac.com
Phone: 920 730 3782
Address: 400 W College Ave Appleton, WI 54911, USA
Information: nonprofit organization located in downtown Appleton, provides a premier venue for live performing arts. The Center proudly serves as a gathering place for the community to engage in educational opportunities while enhancing a greater understanding and appreciation of the live performing arts.. Member of ISPA
Country: United States
Contact: President Maria van Laanen
Social Media: twitter.com/foxcitiespac www.facebook.com/FoxCitiesPerformingArtsCenter www.instagram.com/foxcitiespac
Capacity: 1000+

Fox Theatre – Delta International Series
Website: www.foxtheatre.org

Email: helpdesk@foxtheatre.org
Phone: 404 881 2100
Address: 660 Peachtree Street NE, US
Information: The theatre is primarily a rental facility. The Delta International Series performances are the only shows the theatre presents Total of 7-10 shows.
Country: United States
Contact: General Manager Allan Vella

Francis Marion University
Website: departments.fmarion.edu/finearts
Email:
jsallenger@fmarion.edu
Phone: 843 661 1385
Address: Department of Fine Arts, PO Box 100547, US
Information: The Francis Marion University Department of Fine Arts and Artist Series provide free public drama and chamber music performances in campus venues (100 to 800 seat)
Country: United States
Contact: Manager, arts centre Joseph Sallenger
Contact: Chair, fine arts Lawrence Anderson
Capacity: 800

Franciscan Center
Website:
www.franciscancenter.org
Email: Director@franciscancenter.org
Phone: 419 885 1547
Address: 6832 Convent Boulevard, US
Information: also rental; the Franciscan Center also has 3 concert rooms
Country: United States
Contact: technical Director Mark Morales
Contact: Executive Director Penny Marks

Franklin & Marshall College – Sound Horizons
Website: www.fandm.edu/arts.xml
Email: matthew.weaver@fandm.edu
Phone: 717 358 4490
Address: PO Box 3003, US
Country: United States
Contact: concert coordinator Matthew Weaver

Frauenthal Center Presents
Website: www.frauenthalcenter.org
Email: lmedema@cffmc.org
Phone: 231 722 9750
Address: 425 W. Western, US
Information: home of the West Shore Symphony Orchestra, Western Michigan's Cherry County Playhouse
Country: United States
Contact: operations Manager Macey Meyer

Fraze Pavilion for the Performing Arts
Website: www.fraze.com
Email: fraze@ketteringoh.org
Phone: 937 296 3300
Address: 695 Lincoln Park Boulevard, Lincoln Park Center, US
Country: United States
Contact: General Manager Karen Durham
Contact: technical Director John Rensel

French Institute Alliance Fran
Website: www.fiaf.org
Email: reception@fiaf.org
Phone: 212 355 6100
Address: 22 East 60th St, US
Information: is an American private, non-governmental, not-for-profit organization. Its mission is to promote and enhance the knowledge and appreciation of French and Francophone culture, to increase the knowledge of the French language, and to encourage interaction a
Country: United States
Contact: Director of Sales Wendy Laurent

Frick Art & Historical Center
Website: www.frickart.org
Email: agillen@frickart.org
Phone: 412 371 0600
Address: 7227 Reynolds St, US
Information: also present summer outdoor series: First Friday, free concert featuring American folk singers, opera, jazz, blues, new music etc.
Country: United States
Contact: Director of visitor services Sue Martin
Contact: Executive Director William Bodene

Frick Collection
Website: www.frick.org
Email: info@frick.org
Phone: 212 288 0700
Address: 1 East 70 St, US
Information: broadcast concerts WQXR-FM
Country: United States
Contact: concert coordinator Joyce Bodig

Friends of Chamber Music (CO)
Website: www.friendsofchambermusic.com
Email: info@friendsofchambermusic.com
Phone: 303 388 9839
Address: 191 University Blvd., 974, US
Information: The mission of Friends of Chamber Music is

to present the finest chamber music performances to the Denver metropolitan area for the enrichment of diverse audiences; to introduce chamber music to new audiences; and to provide education and outreach programs for children and adults in the community.
Friends of Chamber Music annually offers a series of concerts including string quartets, piano trios, soloists, and mixed chamber ensembles. Artists and ensembles are the best available on the international concert scene.
Country: United States
Contact: President Alix Corboy
Email: alixcorboy@gmail.com
Social Media: @FCMDenver
Annual Performances: 10
Policies: Rent and present, Concert hall

Friends of Chamber Music (MO)
Website: www.chambermusic.org
Email: Marketing@chambermusic.org
Phone: 816 561 9999
Address: 4635 Wyandotte, Suite 201, US
Country: United States
Contact: Executive Director Cynthia Siebert
Director of Marketing & public relations
Dan Billingsley
Contact: box office Manager Amanda Smith
production Manager & community development
Christina Lenon
Contact: development Director Julia Scherer

Friends of Chamber Music OR
Website: www.focm.org
Email: pat@focm.org
Phone: 503 224 9842
Address: 222 NW Davis St, Suite 405, US
Country: United States
Contact: Executive Director Pat Zagelow
Email: pat@focm.org
Social Media: www.facebook.com/focm.org
Policies: Multi-purpose

Friends of Good Music
Website: www.friendsofgoodmusic.com
Email: fogm@friendsofgoodmusic.com
Phone: 171 637 52494
Address: PO Box 222, US
Information: member of Upstate New York Presenters consortium; volunteer organisation, all mail to be sent to the Program Chairperson
Country: United States
Contact: vice-President Sylvia Lynch
Contact: President Nancy Consedine
Contact: corresponding secretary Carol Gallo

Friends of Historic Boonville
Website: www.friendsofhistoricboonville.org
Email: fohb@sbcglobal.net
Phone: 660 882 7977
Address: 614 East Morgan, PO Box 1776, US
Information: see also Missouri River Festival of the Arts
Country: United States
Contact: Executive Director Holly Peterson

Friends of the Arts
Website: www.fotapresents.org
Email: info@fotapresents.org
Phone: 516 922 0061
Address: PO Box 702, US
Information: presents Long Island Jazz Festival, The Summer Festival, and Beethoven Festival, also concerts at Coe Hall, children's carousel; designs and implements arts-in-education programs in Long Island schools
Country: United States
Contact: Director of audience services Lis Sinniger
Contact: Executive Director Maryann Beaumont

Fulton Opera House
Website: www.thefulton.org
Email: admin@thefulton.org
Phone: 717 394 7133
Address: PO Box 1865, US
Information: producing theatre; rent out opera house
Country: United States
Contact: Managing Director Aaron Young
Contact: Artistic Director Michael D Mitchell

Gainesville Arts Council Pearce Series
Website: www.theartscouncil.net
Email: gladys@theartscouncil.net
Phone: 770 534 2787
Address: PO Box 1632, US
Country: United States
Contact: Executive Director Gladys P Wyant

Gaithersburg Council for the Arts, City of
Website: www.gaithersburgmd.gov
Email: artsbarn@gaithersburgmd.gov
Phone: 301 258 6394
Address: 311 Kent Square Road, US
Country: United States
Contact: cultural arts Director Denise Kayser
Contact: President Julius Persensky

Gallagher-Bluedorn Performing Arts Center

Website: www.gbpac.com
Email: carignan@uni.edu
Phone: 319 273 3660
Address: 8201 Dakota St, US
Country: United States
Contact: Executive Director Steve Carignan
Contact: Programming Associate Amy Hackenmiller
Contact: public relations/development Director Joanne Wzontek
Contact: Marketing Director Janelle Durst

Galvin Fine Arts Center
Website: www.sau.edu/galvin
Email: lsadlek@saunix.sau.edu
Phone: 563 333 6251
Address: St Ambrose University, 518 W. Locust St, US
Information: have an annual competition held in March: Competition of Federal Music Teachers of Iowa
Country: United States
Contact: Director Lance Sadlek

Garde Arts Center
Website: www.gardearts.org
Email: info@gardearts.org
Phone: 860 444 7373
Address: 325 State Street, US
Information: founded in 1985, The Garde Arts Center, Inc. is a non-profit professional performing arts center nationally recognized for its unique architecture and multi-faceted programming serving Southeastern Connecticut.
Country: United States
Contact: Marketing Director Jeanne Sigel
Email: jsigel@gardearts.org
Contact: Executive Director Steve Sigel
Social Media: @gardeartscenter www.facebook.com/

Garden City Chamber Music Society
Email: marijastroke@earthlink.net
Phone: 212 787 7088
Address: 201 West 89th St, Suite 9F, US
Information: perform 8 concerts per year
Country: United States
Contact: Artistic Director Marija Stroke
Contact: Artistic Director Bruce Adolphe

Garden State Arts Foundation
Website: www.gsafoundation.org
Email: csantiago@turnpike.state.nj.us
Phone: 732 442 9200
Address: PO Box 5013, US
Country: United States
Contact: arts centre coordinator Carolyn Santiago

Garth Newel Music Center
Website: www.garthnewel.org
Email: office@garthnewel.org
Phone: 540 839 5018
Address: PO Box 240, US
Information: educational programmes
Country: United States
Contact: Director of operations Georgia Tennant
Contact: Executive Director Richard Riley
Contact: Artistic Director Evelyn Grau

Geffen Playhouse
Website: www.geffenplayhouse.com
Phone: 310 208 6500
Address: 10886 Le Comte Avenue, US
Information: Temporary physical location Brentwood Theatre, 11301 Wilshire Blvd. Building 211, West LA, California, 90073
Country: United States
Contact: Artistic Director Randall Arney
Contact: Managing Director Ken Novice

General Concert and Lecture Series
Email: sfonte1049@aol.com
Phone: 318 274 2205
Address: PO Box 1172-GSU, 403 Main St, US
Country: United States
Contact: Director Stephen Fontenot

Geneva Concerts Inc.
Website: www.genevaconcerts.org
Email: info@genevaconcerts.org
Phone: 131 578 97716
Address: PO Box 709, US
Country: United States
Contact: President Ford Weiskittel

George Mason University Center for the Arts
Website: www.gmu.edu/cfa
Email: stagecfa@gmu.edu
Phone: 703 993 8888
Address: 4400 University Drive, MS 2F5, US
Information: offers highly capable performance, conference, and reception venues
Country: United States
Social Media: @GMU_CFA www.facebook.com/gmucfa
Policies: Rent and present, Concert hall

George Washington University Lisner Auditorium
Website: www.lisner.org
Email: lisner@gwu.edu

Phone: 202 994 6800
Address: 730 21st St NW, US
Country: United States

Georgetown University
Website: performingarts.georgetown.edu
Email: lignellr@georgetown.edu
Phone: 202 687 3838
Address: Dep of Performing Arts, Davis Performing Arts Center, Box 571063, US
Country: United States
Contact: Administrative Director, Dept of Performing Arts Ron Lignelli

Georgia Perimeter College Guest Artist Series
Phone: 404 299 4145
Address: 555 N. Indian Creek Drive, US
Country: United States
Contact: music performance co-ordinator Tommy Joe Anderson

Georgia State University Concerts Committee
Website: www.gsu.edu
Phone: 404 463 9088
Address: Student Activities, GSU, University Plaza, Suite 380, University Centre, US
Country: United States
Contact: Chair Cherrell Thomas

German Society of Pennsylvania
Website: www.germansociety.org
Email: info@germansociety.org
Phone: 215 627 2332
Address: 611 Spring Garden Street, US
Country: United States
Contact: office Manager Catherine Fuller

Germantown Performing Arts Centre
Website: www.GPACweb.com
Email: info@GPACweb.com
Phone: 901 751 7500
Address: 1801 Exeter, US
Information: in addition to its many popular programs, GPAC is home to the IRIS Chamber Orchestra under the direction of Michael Stern
Country: United States
Contact: assistant Director Carrie Corbett
Contact: Executive Director Tania Castroverde-Moskalenko

Gershwin Theatre
Website: www.nederlander.com
Phone: 212 840 5577
Address: 222 West 51st Street, US
Country: United States
Contact: management company The Nederlander Org, Inc
Contact: General Manager Mr Kay
Capacity: 1933

Gila Valley Arts Council
Website: www.gvac.org
Email: tomgreen1953@outlook.com
Phone: 928 428 0081
Address: David M. Player Center for the Arts Safford, US
Information: Gila Valley Arts Council is a non-profit organization dedicated to the presentation of the performing arts in Graham County, Arizona, with special emphasis on sharing the artists with the school children with special student concerts and workshops.Country: United States
Contact: President Tom Green
Email: tomgreen53@msn.com
Contact: Artistic Director Jack Kukuk
Social Media: https://www.instagram.com/gilavalley-yartscouncil/ https://www.facebook.com/GilaValle-yArtsCouncil/
Capacity: 251-500
Annual Productions: 6-10
Policies: All

Gilder Lehrman Hall at The Morgan Library & Museum
Website: www.themorgan.org
Email: media@themorgan.org
Phone: 212 685 0008
Address: 225 Madison Avenue, New York, US
Information: In 1924 J. P. Morgan, Jr. gave his father's extraordinary library to the public. The most influential financier in this country's history, Pierpont Morgan was also a voracious collector. He bought on an astonishing scale, collecting art objects in virtually every medium, including the rare books, manuscripts, drawings, prints, and ancient artifacts that are the core of The Morgan Library & Museum's holdings.
Country: United States
Contact: Communications and Marketing Noreen Khalid Ahmad
Email: nkahmad@themorgan.org
Contact: undefined
Director of Communications & Marketing Michael Reid
Email: mreid@themorgan.org
Contact: Manager of Communications Adam Mrlik
Email: amrlik@themorgan.org

Social Media: https://www.facebook.com/morganlibrary https://twitter.com/morganlibrary https://www.instagram.com/themorganlibrary/
Annual Performances: 100+
Policies: Rent and Present

Gina Bachauer International Piano Foundation
Website: www.bachauer.com
Email: info@bachauer.com
Phone: 801 297 4250
Address: 138 W. Broadway, Suite 220, US
Information: see also Agents & Producers and Competitions
Country: United States
Contact: Chairperson Kary Billings
Contact: vice Chairman Brad Beagles
Contact: secretary Arlo McGinn
Contact: treasurer Nathan Morgan
Social Media: www.facebook.com/ginabachauer
Policies: All, Other

Glema Mahr Center for the Arts
Website: www.glemacenter.org
Email: bradley.downall@kctcs.edu
Phone: 270 824 8650
Address: Madisonville Community College, 2000 College Drive, US
Country: United States
Contact: Director Brad Downall

Glendale Community College
Website: www2.gccaz.edu/
Email: robert.albury@gccaz.edu
Phone: 162 384 53000
Address: 6000 West Olive Avenue, US
Country: United States

Gloucester County College
Website: www.gccnj.edu
Email: help@gccnj.edu
Phone: 185 646 85000/4
Address: 1400 Tanyard Rd, US
Country: United States
Contact: college activities co-ordinator Eoin Kinnarney

Golden West College Community Theatre
Website: www.gwctheater.com
Email: tamen@gwc.cccd.edu
Phone: 714 895 8150
Address: 15744 Golden West St, US
Country: United States
Contact: Director Tom Amen

Goliard Concerts
Website: www.goliardconcerts.com
Email: info@goliardconcerts.com
Phone: 171 872 88927
Address: 21-65 41st St, US
Information: presenting organisation with resident ensembles and performers; occasionally guest artists
Country: United States
Contact: Artistic Director Arielle Levioff

Goodman Banks Series Kingswood-Oxford School
Website: www.kingswoodoxford.org
Email: pierce.w@k-o.org
Phone: 860 233 9631
Address: 170 Kingswood Rd, US
Country: United States
Contact: Director Wayne Pierce

Goodman Theatre
Website: www.goodmantheatre.org
Email: info@goodmantheatre.org
Phone: 312 443 3800
Address: 170 North Dearborn St., US
Information: Goodman Theatre, Chicago's oldest and largest not-for-profit theater, has won international renown for the quality of productions, the depth and diversity of Artistic leadership, and the excellence of its many community and educational programs. For rental info email RentalInfo@GoodmanTheatre.org
Country: United States
Contact: Artistic Director Robert Falls
Contact: Executive Director Roche Schulfer
Social Media: @GoodmanTheatre www.facebook.com/GoodmanTheatre
Policies: Present and produce, Theatre

Gordon Center for Performing Arts
Website: www.gordoncenter.com
Email: gordoncenter@hotmail.com
Phone: 410 356 7469
Address: 3506 Gwynnbrook Avenue, US
Country: United States
Contact: Director Nancy Goldberg

Goucher College Concert Series
Website: www.goucher.edu
Email: lweiss@goucher.edu
Phone: 410 337 6148
Address: 1021 Dulaney Valley Road, US
Information: combination of professional and high grade student presentations; lecture recitals; master-

classes
Country: United States
Contact: Manager Lisa Weiss

Governors Chamber Music Series
Phone: 206 281 8292
Address: 205 McGraw St, US
Country: United States
Contact: Artistic Director Judith Cohen

Grand 1894 Opera House, The
Website: www.thegrand.com
Email: thegrand@thegrand.com
Phone: 409 763 7173
Address: 2020 Postoffice Street, US
Information: rent
Country: United States
Contact: stage Manager Jeff Pye
Contact: Executive Director Maureen Patton

Grand Canyon University Chamber Music Series
Website: www.grand-canyon.edu
Email: music@grand-canyon.edu
Phone: 602 589 2482
Address: 3300 W Camelback, US
Country: United States

Grand Opera House
Website: www.thegrandwilmington.org
Email: grandopera@grandopera.org
Phone: 302 652 5577
Address: 818 N Market Street, US
Information: entertains and engages its communities through exceptional, diverse live performances and educational outreach; committed to broad accessibility and sound financial management
Country: United States
Contact: Managing Director Stephen Bailey
Email: sbailey@grandopera.org
Contact: Executive Director Mark Fields
Email: mfields@grandopera.org
Contact: Director of Administration Christine Molino
Email: cmolino@grandopera.org
Contact: operations Manager Julia Dougherty
Email: jdougherty@grandopera.org
Contact: special projects Manager Amy Bish
Email: awbish@grandopera.org
Contact: Director of development Meredith Mitchell
Email: mmitchell@grandopera.org
Contact: Director of Marketing Terry Cruz
Email: tcruz@grandopera.org
Contact: Director of operations Jaime Bohn
Email: jbohn@grandopera.org
Social Media: @thegrandwilm www.facebook.com/thegrandwilmington
Policies: All, Theatre

Grand Opera House
Website: www.grandoperahouse.org
Email: grandinfo@grandoperahouse.org
Phone: 920 424 2355
Address: 100 High Avenue, PO Box 1004, US
Country: United States
Contact: President and chief Executive officer Joseph Ferlo
Email: joef@grandoperahouse.org
Contact: development and community relations Manager Jeff Potts
Email: jeffp@grandoperahouse.org
Contact: office Manager Anna Pistohl
Email: annp@grandoperahouse.org
Contact: administrative assistant Nicki Scovronski
Email: nickis@grandoperahouse.org
Contact: operations Manager David Lange
Email: davidl@grandoperahouse.org
Contact: box office and events Manager Shawna Terry
Email: shawnat@grandoperahouse.org
Contact: technical Director Tom Hanson
Email: tomh@grandoperahouse.org
Policies: Rent and present, Theatre

Grand Opera House – A Performing Arts Center of Mercer University
Website: www.mercer.edu/thegrand
Email: Lambert_KJ@Mercer.edu
Phone: 478 301 5463
Address: 651 Mulberry Street, US
Information: also rent
Country: United States
Contact: Managing Director Karen Lambert

Grand Performances
Website: www.grandperformances.org
Email: comments@grandperformances.org
Phone: 213 687 2190
Address: 350 South Grand Ave, Suite A4, US
Country: United States
Contact: Artistic Director Michael Alexander
Contact: Director of programming Leigh Ann Hahn

Grand Rapids Community College-Theatre Dept
Website: www.grcc.edu/theater
Email: theater@grcc.edu
Phone: 616 234 4000

Address: 143 Bostwick Avenue NE, US
Country: United States
Contact: Spectrum Theatre Program Director Tom Kaechele
Email: tkaechel@grcc.edu
Contact: theatre Manager Michelle Urbane
Email: murbane@grcc.edu
Social Media: @grcc www.facebook.com/grandrapidscc

Grand Valley State University Lunchbreak Series
Website: www.gvsu.edu
Email: phippsda@gvsu.edu
Phone: 616 331 2581
Address: Grand Valley State University 1300 PAC, US
Country: United States
Contact: Lunchbreak series coordinator Pablo Mahave-Veglia

Grayson County College Humanities Series
Email: hicksjoe@grayson.edu
Phone: 903 463 8706
Address: 6101 Grayson Drive, US
Country: United States
Contact: Manager Joe Hicks

Greater Anderson Musical Arts Consortium (GAMAC)
Website: www.gamac.org
Email: dgencarelli@gamac.org
Phone: 864 231 6147
Address: 907 North Main St. , Suite 12, US
Information: GAMAC, a unique arts umbrella organization, resides in a small 30, 000 people Southern U.S. town, a former textile center, now diversified into various forms of manufacturing; see also Orchestras (GAMAC Chamber Orchestra)

Greater Augusta Arts Council
Website: www.augustaarts.com
Email: arts@augustaarts.com
Phone: 706 826 4702
Address: PO Box 1776, US
Country: United States
Contact: Executive Director Brenda Durant

Greater Columbus Arts Council's Artists-in-Schools Program
Website: www.gcac.org
Phone: 614 224 2606
Address: 55 E State Street, US
Information: produce and present Columbus Arts Festival, offer grants
Country: United States
Contact: Director of educatoin Tim Katz
Contact: President Bryan W. Knicely

Greater Hartford Jewish Community Center
Website: www.mandelljcc.org
Email: thejcc@mandelljcc.org
Phone: 860 236 4571
Address: 335 Bloomfield Avenue, US
Country: United States
Contact: Executive Director David Jacobs
Email: djacobs@mandelljcc.org
Contact: Marketing Director Renee St. Louis
Email: rstlouis@mandelljcc.org
Contact: visual and performing arts Director Jill Ziplow
Email: jziplow@mandelljcc.org
Social Media: @MandellJCC_CT www.facebook.com/MandellJCC

Green Mountain Festival Series
Website: www.greenmountainfestivalseries.com
Email: info@greenmountainfestivalseries.com
Phone: 802 875 4473
Address: PO Box 561, US
Information: arts-in-education programme
Country: United States
Contact: vice President Cynthia Knowles
Contact: President George Thomson

Green Music Center
Website: gmc.sonoma.edu/connect/media
Email: gmccommunications@sonoma.edu
Phone: 707 664 3813
Address: 1801 East Cotati Avenue, US
Information: the aim is to create transformative experiences in the arts and education that promote active learning. It is a world-class performing arts complex and consists of multiple performance venues, a music education wing, sprawling outdoor spaces, an on-site restaurant and much more. Member of ISPA
Country: United States
Contact: Executive Director Larry Furukawa – Schlereth
Contact: Artistic Director Emmanuel Morlet
Social Media: @greenmusicctr www.facebook.com/greenmusiccenter?v=wall
Policies: Present and produce, Multi-purpose

Greenwich House Arts
Website: www.gharts.org
Email: gharts@gharts.org
Phone: 212 242 4770
Address: 46 Barrow St, US
Country: United States

Contact: assistant Executive Director of programs Gerri Matusewitch
Contact: CEO and Executive Director Roy Levitt

Greenwood-Lander Performing Arts
Website: www.lander.edu/glpa
Email: glpa@lander.edu
Phone: 864 388 8326
Address: Lander University, US
Country: United States
Contact: Executive Director Beverly Psomas

Gretna Music
Website: www.mtgretna.com/music
Email: music@mtgretna.com
Phone:
717 361 1508
Address: 1 Alpha Drive, US
Information: see also Festivals
Country: United States

Gulf Shores Entertainment Series, Special Events Div, City of
Website: http:// www.gulfshoresal.gov
Email: events@gulfshoresal.gov
Phone: 251 968 1172
Address: PO Box 299, US
Country: United States
Contact: program coordinator Teri Westbrook

Gusman Center for the Performing Arts
Website: www.gusmancenter.org
Email:
info@gusmancenter.org
Phone: 130 537 42444
Address: 174 E. Flagler Street, US
Information: member of Florida Professional Presenters consortium; office address 169 E. Flagler Street, Suite 837, Miami, FL 33131
Country: United States
Contact: theatre Director Margaret Lake
Contact: box office Manager Miguel Aleman

Gustavus Adolphus College Artist Series
Website: www.gustavus.edu
Email: al@gac.edu
Phone: 507 933 7363
Address: 800 W. College Ave, US
Country: United States
Contact: Director fine arts programmes Alan Behrends

Guthrie Arts and Humanities Council
Website: www.thepollard.org
Phone: 405 282 2800
Address: Box 38, US
Country: United States
Contact: President Donald Coffin

Guthrie Theater
Website: www.guthrietheater.org
Email: webmaster@guthrietheater.org
Phone: 612 225 6000 (ad
Address: 818 South 2nd Street, US
Country: United States
Contact: Managing Director Jacques Bruntswick
Contact: Director of communications Melodie Bahan
Contact: Director Joe Dowling

Gwinnett Civic & Cultural Center
Website: www.gwinnettcenter.com
Email: info@gwinnettcenter.com
Phone: 770 623 4966
Address: 6400 Sugarloaf Parkway, Bldg 100, US
Country: United States
Contact: Sales Manager Chris Muller
Director Sales & Marketing
Cheryl Ann-Gee

Hancher
Website: www.hancher.uiowa.edu
Email: tim-meier@uiowa.edu
Phone: 319 335 1160
Address: 317 Seashore Hall West, US
Country: United States
Contact: Director of patron services Connie Tipsword
Email: connie-tipsword@uiowa.edu
Contact: Director of Marketing and communications Rob Cline
Email: rob-cline@uiowa.edu
Contact: Executive Director Charles Swanson
Email: charles-swanson@uiowa.edu
Contact: secretary Tim Meier
Email: tim-meier@uiowa.edu
Contact: programming Director Jacob Yarrow
Email: jacob-yarrow@uiowa.edu
Social Media: http:// www.facebook.com/#!/pages/Hancher/89683214316
Policies: Present, produce, co-produce, Other

Harborside Complex
Website: www.fmharborside.com
Email: Rrundle@cityftmyers.com
Phone: 239 321 8110
Address: PO Box 9204, US

Information: member of Florida Professional Presenters Consortium; now mainly conventions, trade shows and banquets; the venue is for rent
Country: United States
Contact: Director Rose Rundle
Contact: event services Manager Rhonda Decherd

Harding University Arts&Life Series
Website: www.harding.edu/concertsseries
Email: jwalls@harding.edu
Phone:
501 279 4630
Address: 915 E. Market, HU 10767, Harding University, US
Information: small series in a small community; tries to book attractions of General interest
Country: United States
Contact: Concert Series Director Jay Walls
Email: jwalls@harding.edu
Social Media: @HardingU/@HardingU
Annual Performances: 6
Annual Productions: 6
Policies: Concert hall

Harkness Dance Center
Website:
www.92y.org/harkness
Email: webmaster@92y.org
Phone: 212 415 5555
Address: 92nd Street Y, 1395 Lexington Ave, US
Information: see also 92nd Street Y, Tisch Center for the Arts; Dance Education Lab teacher training course, lectures ; full range of classes for adults and children/teens; workshops
Country: United States
Contact: Director Joan Finkelstein

Harlem Dance Foundation Inc
Phone: 212 662 2057
Address: 144 West 121st Street, US
Country: United States
Contact: General Manager/Executive Director Olive Adams
Contact: Artistic Director Carolyn Adams

Harlem Stage / Aaron Davis Hall Inc.
Website: www.harlemstage.org
Email: gshanck@harlemstage.org
Phone: 212 281 9240
Address: The Gatehouse, 150 Convent Ave, US
Country: United States
Contact: Executive Director Pat Cruz
Contact: Managing Director Gregory S Shanck
Contact: Director of programming Brad Learmonth

Harlingen Community Concert Association
Phone: 956 748 3020
Address: PO Box 707, US
Country: United States
Contact: President James Hough

Harriet and Charles Luckman Fine Arts Complex, California State University
Website: www.luckmanarts.org
Email: info@luckmanarts.org
Phone: 323 343 6610
Address: The Harriet & Charles Luckman Fine Arts Complex, California State University, 5151 State University Drive, US
Information: also presents visual arts at the Luckman Gallery
Country: United States
Contact: Executive Director Wendy Baker
Contact: Marketing Director Nicholas Viski Mestas

Harriman-Jewell Series
Website: www.hjseries.org
Email: info@hjseries.org
Phone: 816 415 5025
Address: 500 College Hill #1015, US
Information: venues are located in downtown Kansas City, Missouri
Country: United States
Contact: Artistic Director Richard Harriman
Contact: Marketing Manager Tim Ackerman
Contact: Executive Director Clark Morris
Contact: ticketing services Manager Ann Reed
Contact: events Manager/Marketing Associate Heather Forbis

Harris Theater
Website: www.harristheaterchicago.org
Email: communications@harristheaterchicago.org
Phone: 312 334 7777
Address: 205 E. Randolph Drive, US
Information: Harris Theater, a 1500-seat venue in downtown Chicago's Millennium Park, hosts a diverse range of local, national, and international artists and ensembles. Member of ISPA
Country: United States
Social Media: @HarrisTheater www.facebook.com/harristheater
Capacity: 1500

Harrisburg Area Community College

Website: www.hacc.edu
Phone: 717 780 2545
Address: 1 HACC Drive, US
Country: United States
Contact: performing artist series Director Teri Guerrisi

Hartwick College Foreman Creative and Performing Arts Series
Website: www.hartwick.edu
Email: markusonc@hartwick.edu
Phone: 607 431 4034
Address: Hartwick College, US
Information: member of Upstate New York Presenters; also present the New York State Music Festival annual, summer months
Country: United States
Contact: Director of events planning Cira P Markuson

Harvard Musical Association in Boston
Phone: 617 523 2897
Address: 57A Chestnut Street, US
Country: United States
Contact: General award librarian Manager Craig Hanfon

Harvey B. Gantt Center for African-American Arts + Culture
Website: www.ganttcenter.org
Email: info@ganttcenter.org
Phone: 704 547 3700
Address: 551 South Tryon Street, US
Information: celebrates the contributions of Africans and African – Americans to American culture and serves as a community epicenter for music, dance, theater, visual art, film, arts education programs, literature and community outreach
Country: United States
Contact: Chief Operating Officer Bonita Buford
Contact: President and CEO David Taylor
Social Media: @HBGanttCenter www.facebook.com/pages/Harvey-B-Gantt-Center-for-African-American-Arts-Culture/177279726856
Policies: Multi-purpose

Helen Hayes Theatre
Website: www.helenhayestheatre.com
Phone: 212 944 9450
Address: 240 West 44th Street, US
Country: United States
Contact: management company Little Theatre Group

Helena Presents
Website: www.myrnaloycenter.com
Email: myrnaloycenter@aol.com
Phone: 406 443 0287
Address: Myrna Loy Center, 15 N Ewing, US
Country: United States
Contact: Director Ed Noonan

Henderson Parks and Recreation Department, City of
Website: www.cityofhenderson.com
Email: Sue.Kohl@cityofhenderson.com
Phone: 702 267 4055
Address: Cultural Arts Office, P.O. Box 89009, US
Country: United States
Contact: assistant recreation coordinator Sue Kohl
Contact: Sue Kohl

Hendrix College Special Events
Website: www.hendrix.edu/specialevents
Email: specialevents@hendrix.edu
Phone: 180 027 79017
Address: Hendrix College, 1600 Washington Avenue, US
Information: the Hendrix Special Events Committee bring 4-6 performers/groups to campus each year; promoting fine and performing arts
Country: United States
Contact: co-Chair Jim Wiltgen
Contact: co-Chair Robert Hessling

Henry Ford Community College Fine Arts Department
Website: www.henryford.cc.mi.us
Phone: 313 845 9634
Address: 5101 Evergreen, US
Information: alternative website: ww.hscc.com
Country: United States
Contact: division Director Rick Gower
Contact: performing arts Manager t.b.a

Herberger Theater Center
Website: www.herbergertheater.org
Email: laustin@herbergertheater.org
Phone: 602 254 7399
Address: 222 E Monroe St, US
Information: resident dance and theater companies
Country: United States
Contact: Executive assistant Catherine Hinkle
Contact: President Richard Bowers

Here Arts Center
Website: www.here.org
Email: info@here.org
Phone: 212 647 0202

Address: 145 Sixth Ave., Ground Floor, US
Information: in addition to producing and presenting a number of their own projects annually, HERE offers artists creative work space at subsidized, below-market rates
Country: United States
Contact: General Manager Abby Marcus
Contact: co-founder, Executive Director Kristin Marting
Contact: producing Director Kim Whitener

Heritage Center Theater
Website: www.heritagectr.org
Email: Dallenolcott@gmail.com
Phone: 435 865 2890
Address: 105 North 100 East, US
Information: Large performing arts space showcasing classical music, choirs, dance & seasonal performances.
Country: United States
Contact: Managing Director Jason Clark
Contact: front of house Manager Dallen Olcott

Hermosa Civic Center
Website: www.hermosabch.org
Phone: 310 318 0280
Address: 710 Pier Ave, US
Country: United States
Contact: recreation supervisor Lisa Lynn
Contact: Director community resources Mary Rooney

Hershey Theatre
Website: www.hersheytheatre.com
Email: htheatre@hersheytheatre.com
Phone: 717 534 3405
Address: PO Box 395, 15 E Caracas Ave, US
Country: United States
Contact: Executive Director Marta Howell
Contact: Director od community relations Diane Paul

Hesston-Bethel Performing Arts Series
Website: hesstonbethel.org
Email: matthews@hesston.edu
Phone: 620 327 8144
Address: PO Box 3000, 325 S. College Ave., US
Information: HBPA uses four venues: Bethel College Memorial Hall, Capacity 1800. Hesston College Yost Center, Capacity 1500. Hesston Mennonite Church, Capacity 650. Bethel College Krehbiel Auditorium, Capacity 440
Country: United States
Contact: hbpa Director Matthew Schloneger
Social Media: www.facebook.com/pages/Hesston-Bethel-Performing-Arts/144652665576484
Annual Performances: 5
Policies: Present and produce, Concert hall

Heymann Performing Arts Center
Email: hpacc@eatel.net
Phone: 337 291 5540
Address: 1373 S. College Road, US
Country: United States
Contact: General Manager Frank Bradshaw
Contact: ticket Manager E. Plumbar

High Point Theatre
Email: louisa.hart@high-point.nc.us
Phone: 336 883 3401
Address: PO Box 230, US
Information: also rent
Country: United States
Contact: Director Louisa Hart

Historic Paramount Foundation/ Joseph B. Gould Family Paramount Theatre
Website: www.historicparamounttheatre.com
Phone: 303 623 0106
Address: 1621 Glenarm Place, US
Country: United States
Contact: Executive Director and General Manager Jim Sprinkle

Hobby Center for the Performing Arts
Website: www.thehobbycenter.org
Phone: 713 315 2400
Address: 800 Bagby Street, Suite 300, US
Country: United States
Contact: Director of Marketing Sheri Johnson
Email: sheri@thehobbycenter.org
Contact: box office Manager Elizabeth McClees
Email: elizabeth@thehobbycenter.org
Contact: ticketing services Manager Sheri Voight
Email: svoight@thehobbycenter.org
Contact: Managing Director of Uniquely Houston Series Annalisa Minnitti
Email: annalisa@thehobbycenter.org
Contact: Senior Director Russell Buonasera
Email: russell@thehobbycenter.org
Contact: Director of finance Lynne Earll
Email: lynne@thehobbycenter.org
Contact: technical Director Michael Metzdorf
Email: michael@thehobbycenter.org
Contact: audience services Manager Judi Stallings
Email: judi@thehobbycenter.org
Social Media: @hobbycenter
Policies: Rent and present, Theatre

Holland Area Arts Council Performing Arts Series

Website: www.hollandarts.org
Phone: 616 396 3278
Address: 150 East 8th Street, US
Country: United States
Contact: project coordinator Andrew Snyder
Contact: Director Norma Freestone

Honeywell Foundation, Inc
Website: www.honeywellcenter.org
Email: ticket@honeywellcenter.org
Phone: 260 563 1102
Address: 275 W. Market Street, US
Country: United States
Contact: Executive Director Tod Minnich

Hopkins Center
Website: www.hop.dartmouth.edu/Online/default.asp
Email: hopkins.center@dartmouth.edu
Phone: 603 646 2422
Address: Dartmouth College, 4 East Wheelock Street, US
Information: member of ISPA. various venues; auditoriums, theaters and recital halls
Country: United States
Social Media: @HopkinsCenter www.facebook.com/hopkinscenter
Policies: Arts centre

Horowitz Center
Website: www.howardcc.edu/discover/arts-culture/horowitz-center/
Email: JBroderick@howardcc.edu
Phone: 443 518 1490
Address: 10901 Little Patuxent Parkway, US
Information: As an educational and production venue, the Horowitz Visual and Performing Arts Center offers community members the opportunity to engage with the arts as patrons and as students
Country: United States
Social Media: @HowardCC www.facebook.com/horowitzcenter
Policies: Multi-purpose

Horton Grand Theatre
Website: www.sdmt.org/visit/the-horton-grand-theatre
Email: info@sdmt.org
Phone: 833 428 0947
Address: 444 Fourth Ave, US
Information: The historic Horton Grand Theatre is located in the heart of downtown San Diego's vibrant Gaslamp Quarter. This beautiful 240-seat theatre is located within easy walking distance to dozens of terrific restaurants, bars, and shopping.
Country: United States
Contact: founder and President Erin Lewis
Contact: Artistic Director Jill Townsend
Policies: Theatre

Hot Springs Village Property Owners Association
Website: www.hsvwoodlands.com
Email: kglauck@hotmail.com
Phone: 501 922 4231
Address: Ponce de Leon Centre, 1101 Desoto Boulevard, US
Country: United States
Contact: contact Karen Lauck

Houghton College Artist Series
Phone: 585 567 9400
Address: Houghton College, US
Information: member of Upstate New York Presenters
Country: United States
Contact: Director Robert Galloway

Hult Center for the Performing Arts
Website: www.hultcenter.org
Email: marcia.a.james@ci.eugene.or.us
Phone: 541 682 5087
Address: One Eugene Centre, US
Country: United States
Contact: cultural services Director Laura Niles
Contact: programming Manager Carol Philips
Marketing & pr Manager
Billie Moser

Humboldt State University CenterArts
Website: www.humboldt.edu/centerarts
Email: Roy.Furshpan@humboldt.edu
Phone: 707 826 4411
Address: Humboldt State University, 1 Harpst Street, US
Country: United States
Contact: Director Roy Furshpan

Huntington Arts Council
Website: www.huntingtonarts.org
Email: info@huntingtonarts.org
Phone: 631 271 8423
Address: 213 Main Street, US
Information: member of the Association of Performing Arts Presenters (APAP) and Americans for the Arts; summer season only; see also Festivals
Country: United States
Contact: Executive Director Diana J Cherryholmes
Email: dcherryholmes@huntingtonarts.org

Social Media: @HuntingtonArts www.facebook.com/HuntingtonArts

Huntsville Chamber Music Guild
Website: www.uah.edu\music
Email: music@uah.edu
Phone:
256 824 6436
Address: Music Dept, University of Alabama, 301 Sparkman Drive, US
Country: United States
Contact: Associate Professor; Department Chair Director of Jazz Studies, Director of Musi Don Bowyer

Idaho Falls Civic Auditorium
Website: www.idahofallsidaho.gov/city/the-civic-auditorium.html
Phone: 120 861 28396
Address: 501 S Holmes, US
Information: rent only, do not produce
Country: United States
Contact: Manager Ed Morgan

Illinois Central College – Performing Arts Center
Website:
www.artsaticc.com
Email: info@icc.edu
Phone: 309 694 5136
Address: 1 College Drive, US
Information: Arts at ICC presents more than 500 performances, lectures, rehearsals, meetings, master classes, clinics, seminars, receptions, orientations, forums, auditions and tournaments annually.
Country: United States
Social Media: @ArtsAtICC www.facebook.com/IllinoisCentralCollege

Illinois State University's Braden Auditorium 'Stars on Stage' Series & 'Performing Arts' Series
Website: www.bsc.ilstu.edu/bsc
Email: infocentre@ilstu.edu
Phone: 309 438 4636
Address: Bone Student Center, Illinois State University, Campus Box 2640, US
Country: United States
Contact: General Manager Jeremy Schenk
Contact: box office Manager Pat Shupe
Contact: technical Director Andrew Gordon

Imperial Theatre
Website: www.imperialtheatre.com
Email: info@imperialtheatre.com
Phone: 706 722 8241
Address: 749 Broad Street, US
Information: venue available for rent
Country: United States
Contact: Executive Director Charles Scavullo
Email: charles@imperialtheatre.com
Contact: box office Manager Melanie Rivera
Email: boxoffice@imperialtheatre.com
Contact: technical Director Tim Campbell
Social Media: @AugustaImperial www.facebook.com/imperialaugusta
Policies: Present and produce, Theatre

Imperial Theatre
Website: www.shubertorganization.com/theatres/imperial.asp
Email: tickets@telecharge.com
Address: 249 West 45th Street, US
Country: United States
Policies: Rent and present, Theatre

Independent Presbyterian Church November Organ Recital Series
Website: www.ipc-usa.org
Email: jmclelland@ipc-usa.org
Phone: 205 933 1830
Address: 3100 Highland Ave, US
Information: non-profit organisation
Country: United States
Contact: music Director Jeff McLelland

Indian Wells Valley Concert Association
Website: www.iwvca.tripod.com
Email: iwvca@hotmail.com
Phone: 760 375 5600
Address: PO Box 1802, US
Information: stage limitations at current venue preclude many types of dance, as well as opera/drama needing more than bare-bones stage
Country: United States
Contact: business Manager Carl Helmick Jr
Contact: President Greg Morrow

Indiana State University Convocation Series
Email:
devmeyer@isugwi.indstate.edu
Phone: 812 237 2336
Address: Erickson Hall, Room 125, US
Country: United States
Contact: Director Allen Varner

Indiana University Auditorium

Website: www.iuauditorium.com
Email: tickets@indiana.edu
Phone: 812 855 9528
Address: 1211 E 7th Street, US
Country: United States
Contact: Director Doug Booher
Contact: facility/events Manager Deena Brown

Indiana University Jacobs School of Music
Website: www.music.indiana.edu
Email: musics@indiana.edu
Phone:
812 855 9846
Address: Office of Pre-College and Special Programs, Merrill Hall 006, US
Country: United States
Contact: Director of Marketing and publicity Alain Barker

Indiana University of Pennsylvania
Website: www.iup.edu/theater
Email: destefan@iup.edu
Phone: 724 357 2315
Address: Arts & Entertainment, Ackerman Hall 101, 911 South Drive, US
Country: United States
Contact: Associate Director Frank DeStefano

Indy Parks Arts Services
Email: pnorman@indygov.org
Phone:
317 327 7417
Address: Garfield Park Art Center, 2432 Conservatory Drive, US
Information: MacAllister Center available to rent
Country: United States
Contact: arts services Manager Paul Norman

Institute of Outdoor Theatre
Website: www.outdoor-theatre.org/
Phone: 252 328 5363
Address: Institute of Outdoor Theatre East Carolina University, College of Fine Arts and Communication, 201 Erwin Building Mail Stop 528, US
Country: United States
Social Media: www.facebook.com/instituteoutdoortheatre/

Inter-Media Art Center Inc (IMAC)
Website: www.IMACtheater.org
Email: michael@imactheater.org
Phone: 631 549 9666
Address: 370 New York Ave, New York, US
Information: non-commercial professional TV production facility
Country: United States
Contact: Executive Director Michael Rothbard

Interlochen Center for the Arts
Website: www.interlochen.org
Email: admissions@interlochen.org
Phone: 231 276 7200
Address: PO Box 199, US
Information: see also Festivals
Country: United States
communications & engagement
Steve Hoffman
Contact: Director of Marketing t.b.a.
coordinator of conferences & tours
Barbara Sandys

Intermedia Arts Minnesota
Website: www.intermediaarts.org
Email: info@IntermediaArts.org
Phone: 612 871 4444
Address: 2822 Lyndale Ave. S, US
Information: focus on interdisciplinary and cross-cultural performance and visual arts
Country: United States
Contact: Marketing Manager Katrina Roth
Contact: Executive Director Daniel Gumnit
Contact: Artistic Director Theresa Sweetland

International Artists Series
Phone: 305 643 9821
Address: PO Box 012661, US
Country: United States
Contact: Associate Director Shirley Evans
Contact: Director A Robert Owens

International Chamber Music Series
Website: icmsonline.org
Email: info@icmsonline.org
Phone: 864 370 9560
Address: PO Box 162, US
Country: United States
Contact: President Falls L Harris
Contact: programs John Beckford
Contact: publicity Clifford Hackett

International Series
Phone: 305 642 8000
Address: 59 NW 25 Ave, US
Country: United States
Contact: Managing Director Francis Mayville

Iowa State Center – Stephens Series
Website: www.center.iastate.edu
Email: center@center.iastate.edu
Phone:
515 294 3347
Address: Scheman Building, Suite 4, Iowa State University, US
Information: also rent; alternative email address: mnorth@center.iastate.edu
Country: United States
Contact: Director of Marketing Sara Barr
Contact: Director of programming Mark E Miller
Contact: Director of performing arts Mark North

Irvine Barclay Theatre
Website:
www.thebarclay.org
Email: info@thebarclay.org
Phone: 949 854 4607
Address: 4199 Campus Drive, Suite 680, US
Country: United States
Contact: General Manager Christopher Burrill
Director of communications & program development
Karen Drews Hanlon
Contact: President Douglas C Rankin

Isabella Stewart Gardner Museum Concerts
Website: www.gardnermuseum.org
Email:
concerts@isgm.org
Phone: 617 278 5102
Address: 2 Palace Rd, US
Country: United States
Contact: music Director Scott Nickrenz
Contact: public relations Manager Katherine Armstrong

Islip Arts Council Chamber Music Series
Website: www.islipartscouncil.org
Email: iacouncil@aol.com
Phone: 631 224 5420
Address: 50 Irish Lane, US
Country: United States
Contact: founding Director Lillian Barbash
Contact: Artistic Director Amy Tuttle Donaghy
Contact: Executive Director Dawn Kraus

Ithaca College Concerts
Website: www.ithaca.edu/music
Email: ekibelsbeck@ithaca.edu
Phone: 607 274 3171
Address: 3322 Whalen Center, Ithaca College, US
Information: Member of Association of Performing Arts Presenters (APAP)
Country: United States
Social Media: @IthacaMusic www.facebook.com/IthacaMusic/
Policies: Concert hall

Jackson Community College
Website: www.jccmi.edu
Phone: 517 787 0800
Address: 2111 Emmons Road, US
Country: United States
Director of events & college selections
Cindy Allen

Jacksonville University
Website: www.ju.edu
Phone: 904 745 7370
Address: 2800 University Boulevard North, US
Information: member of Florida Professional Presenters consortium; managed by Professional Facilities Management, 220 Weybosset St, Providence, RI 02903 Tel: 401-421 2997 Fax: 401-421 5767
Country: United States
Contact: Chair of music Robert Tudor
Contact: Director of dance Brian Palmer
Contact: Director artist series/dean college of fine arts Bill Hill

James W Miller Auditorium
Website: www.millerauditorium.com
Phone: 269 387 2311
Address: Western Michigan University, 1903 W Michigan Avenue, US
Information: rent also
Country: United States
Contact: Director Elaine M. Williams
Contact: Associate Director Rob Pennock
Director of Marketing & development
Tracey Lawie
Contact: business Manager Faith Wicklund
Contact: technical director Guy Barks

Jamestown Concert Association
Website: www.jamestownconcertassociation.org
Email: stluke@madbbs.com
Phone: 171 648 71522
Address: 315 North Main Street, Suite 200, New York, US
Country: United States
Contact: President R. Richard Corbin
Contact: vice President Sally Ulrich

Japan Society
Website: www.japansociety.org
Email: info@japansociety.org
Phone: 212 832 1155
Address: 333 East 47th St, US
Information: programs focus on Japanese and Japanese American performing arts and collaborations with American artists or works inspired by Japanese performing arts
Country: United States
Contact: Director, performing arts Yoko Shioya
Contact: President Richard J Wood
Contact: sr. production coordinator Futoshi Miyai

Japanese American Cultural and Community Center Oratori-Japan America Theatre
Website: www.jaccc.org
Email: info@jaccc.org
Phone: 213 628 2725
Address: 244 South San Pedro Street, Suite 505, US
Information: currently closed for repairs and upgrades
Country: United States
Contact: chief Executive officer Chris Iraire

Jasmine Hill Gardens and Outdoor Museum
Website: www.jasminehill.org
Email: admin@jasminehill.org
Phone: 334 567 6463
Address: P.O. Box 6001, US
Country: United States
Contact: administrator Jason Snowgraw

Jasper Community Arts Commission – Performers Series, Backstage Series
Website: www.jasperarts.org
Email: jasperarts@psci.net
Phone: 812 482 3070
Address: 951 College Avenue, US
Jay Pritzker Pavilion
Website: www.millenniumpark.org
Email: dcase@cityofchicago.org
Phone: 312 742 1168
Address: Millennium Park, 201 E Randolph St, US
Information: Pritzker Pavilion serves as the centerpiece for Millennium Park and is the new home of the Grant Park Symphony Orchestra and Chorus and the Grant Park Music Festival, the nation's only remaining free outdoor classical music series. It also hosts a wide range of music series and annual performing arts events. Performers ranging from mainstream rock bands to classical musicians and opera singers have appeared at the pavilion. All rehearsals at the pavilion are open to the public
Country: United States
Contact: media relations Karen Ryan

Jazz Club of Sarasota
Website: www.jazzclubsarasota.org
Email: admin@jazzclubsarasota.com
Phone: 941 366 1552
Address: 330 S Pineapple Ave, STE 111, US
Information: Many events are free to the community. Jazz at Two Friday's and Annual Sarasota Jazz Club Festival March 1, 2015 to March 7, 2015
Country: United States
Contact: President Dave Walrath
Email: davewalrath@msn.com
Social Media: www.facebook.com/Jazz-Club-of-Sarasota-207675489252054/
Policies: Present, produce, co-produce, Other

JCC of Metropolitan New Jersey/Maurice Levin Theater
Website: www.jccmetrowest.org
Phone: 973 736 3200
Address: 760 Northfield Avenue, US
Country: United States
Contact: Director of cultural arts Julie Rossi
Contact: Director of public relations/Marketing Melissa M.Allen

Jefferson Academy of Music Chamber Music – Sunday Afternoons
Phone: 614 292 2693
Address: Ohio State University Campus, 1866 North College Road, US
Information: children's concerts; concerts for community organizations, retirement communities, schools, workshops and masterclasses
Country: United States
Contact: Executive Director Ruth Triplett Haddock

Jefferson Community College Cultural Affairs Committee
Website: www.sunyjefferson.edu
Email: becky_small-kellog@sunyjefferson.edu
Phone: 315 786 2200
Address: Jefferson Community College, Outer Coffeen St., US
Country: United States
Contact: book keeper Yvonne Brown
Contact: scanlon learning Director Rebecca Small-Kellog

Jefferson Performing Arts Society
Website: www.jpas.org

Email: info@jpas.org
Phone: 504 885 2000
Address: 1118 Clearview Pkwy, US
Information: JPAS annually provides a wide range of theatrical performances that appeal to many interests and age groups. Most seasons include a selection of grand opera, musical theater, dance and music. JPAS strives to network and partner with national and international artists and companies to bring new and diverse programming to the Southern Region.
Country: United States
Contact: Executive/Artistic Director Dennis Assaf
Email: MaestroDGA@gmail.com
Contact: technical Director Matt Foglia
Email: td@jpas.org
Contact: Marketing/pr Joshua Frederick
Email: joshua@jpas.org
Contact: Production/Company Manager Nicholas Frederick
Email: production@jpas.org
Social Media: @JPASnola www.facebook.com/jpasnola/

Jewish Arts Foundation
Website: www.palmbeachjewishfilm.org
Email: jewisharts18@aol.com
Phone: 561 659 1156
Address: 230 Royal Palm Way, Suite 207, US
Information: all attractions are related to Jewish Arts; annual film festival Dec; classical music scholarship competition event
Country: United States
Contact: Executive Director Karen Davis

Jewish Community Center of Greater Washington
Website:
www.jccgw.org
Email: sschallern@jccgw.org
Phone: 301 881 0100
Address: Gildenhorn/Speisman Center for the Arts, 6125 Montrose Road, US
Information: present, rent, produce
Country: United States
Contact: cultural arts Director Maida Barron
Contact: music Director Sarah Schallern
Contact: Executive Director Arnie Sohinki

Jewish Community Center of Metropolitan Detroit
Website: www.jccdet.org
Email: info@jccdet.org
Phone: 248 661 1000
Address: 6600 West Maple Road, US
Information: supports Jewish unity, ensures Jewish continuity and enriches Jewish lives while conveying the importance of well-being within the Jewish and General community and the people of Israel
Country: United States
Contact: Executive Director James Issner
Email: jissner@jccdet.org
Social Media: www.facebook.com/jcc.detroit

Jewish Museum
Website: www.thejewishmuseum.org
Phone: 212 423 3200
Address: 1109 Fifth Avenue, US
Country: United States
Contact: Director Joan Rosenbaum

John Addison Concert Hall – Harmony Hall Regional Center
Website: www.pgparks.com
Phone: 301 203 6070
Address: 10701 Livingston Rd, US
Country: United States
Contact: acting Director Lawrence J Knowles

John Brown University Lyceum Artists Series
Email: nnethert@jbu.edu
Phone: 479 524 7154
Address: 2000 West University, Box 3004, US
Country: United States
Contact: contacts Becky Pohle

John Drew Theater at Guild Hall
Website: www.guildhall.org
Email: joshgladstone@guildhall.org
Phone: 631 324 0806
Address: 158 Main Street, US
Country: United States
Contact: Artistic Director Josh Gladstone
Policies: All, Theatre

John F. Kennedy Center for the Performing Arts
Website: www.kennedy-center.org
Email: tkennedy@kennedycenter.org
Phone: 800 444 1324
Address: The John F. Kennedy Center for the Performing Arts, 2700 F St NW, US
Information: The Kennedy Center, located on the banks of the Potomac River near the Lincoln Memorial in Washington, D.C., opened to the public in 1971. Its roots date back to 1958, when President Dwight D. Eisenhower signed bipartisan legislation creating a National Cultural Center. To honor Eisenhower's vision for such a facility,

one of the Kennedy Center's theaters is named for him. The National Cultural Center Act authorized the Center's construction, spelled out an Artistic mandate to present a wide variety of both classical and contemporary performances, specified an educational mission for the Center, and stated that the Center was to be an independent facility, self-sustaining, and privately funded. Member of ISPA
Country: United States
Contact: Chairman David Rubenstein
Contact: President Deborah Rutter
Contact: music Director Gianandrea Noseda
Social Media: @kencen www.facebook.com/Kennedy-Center
Policies: Multi-purpose

John Golden Theatre
Phone: 212 944 3700
Address: 252 West 45th Street, US
Country: United States
Contact: management company The Shubert Org. Inc
Contact: vice President of theatre operations Peter Entin

John Harms Center for the Arts
Website: www.johnharms.org
Phone: 201 567 5797
Address: 30 North Van Brunt St, US
Information: also rent theater for 30 productions
Country: United States
Contact: pr Manager Ed Kirchdoesser
General Director & Director of programming
Jessica Finkelberg

John J. Cali School of Music
Website:
www.montclair.edu/music
Email: music@mail.montclair.edu
Phone: 973 655 7212
Address: Montclair State University,
One Normal Avenue, US
Country: United States
Contact: Director Robert Cart
Contact: concert Manager Martha Learner
Contact: secretary Andrew Pecota
Social Media: @montclairstateu www.facebook.com/calischoolofmusic
Policies: Present and produce, Other

John Lyman Center for Performing Arts
Website: www.lyman.southernct.edu
Email: tomascakL1@southernCT.edu
Phone: 203 392 6154
Address: Southern Connecticut State University, 501 Crescent Street, US
Country: United States
Contact: Associate Director David Starkey
Contact: Director Larry Tomascak
Contact: assistant Director Vincent Ferrie

John Michael Kohler Arts Center
Website: www.jmkac.org
Email: rkohler@jmkac.org
Phone: 920 458 6144
Address: 608 New York Avenue, PO Box 489, US
Information: Intertwining three historic landmarks with dramatic contemporary architecture and captivating art, the John Michael Kohler Arts Center sets the stage for a unique and memorable experience. The lively art-filled environment includes acclaimed changing exhibitions, outdoor sculpture gardens, and world famous artist-created washrooms.
Country: United States
Contact: Director Ruth De Young Kohler
Email: rkohler@jmkac.org
Contact: senior Manager Ann Brusky
Email: abrusky@jmkac.org
Social Media: @JMKAC www.facebook.com/jmkac
Capacity: 1000

John R and Eleanor R Mitchell Foundation,
Website: www.cedarhurst.org
Email: mitchellmuseum@cedarhurst.org
Phone: 618 242 1236
Address: Cedarhurst Chamber Music, , Mitchell Museum School Programs, PO Box 923/Richview Road, US
Information: see Mitchell Museum at Cedarhurst
Country: United States
Contact: Executive Director Sharon Bradham
Social Media: @CedarhurstArts www.facebook.com/Cedarhurst

Johns Hopkins University
Website: www.jhu.edu/gcpa
Phone: 443 287 9900
Address: Office of Government Relations, 901 S Bond Street, Suite 540, US
Country: United States
Contact: Executive Director of facilities Larry Kilduff

Johnson County Community College – The Carlsen Center
Website: www.jccc.net
Email: malley@jccc.net
Phone: 913 469 4450

Address: 105 Carlsen Center, 12345 College Blvd, US
Country: United States
Contact: Director carlsen center Charles R Rogers
Sales & Marketing Director
Mike Alley
Contact: arts education Angel Mercier

Joseph Meyerhoff Symphony Hall
Website: www.baltimoresymphony.org
Email: webmaster@baltimoresymphony.org
Phone: 410 783 8126
Address: 1212 Cathedral Street, US
Information: The Baltimore Symphony Orchestra (BSO) is internationally recognized as having achieved a preeminent place among the world's most important orchestras. Acclaimed for its enduring pursuit of Artistic excellence, the BSO has attracted a devoted national and international following while maintaining deep bonds throughout Maryland through innovative education and community outreach initiatives.
Country: United States
Social Media: @BaltSymphony www.facebook.com/BSOmusic

Joyce Theater
Website: www.joyce.org
Email: staff@joyce.org
Phone: 212 691 9740
Address: 175 Eighth Avenue, US
Country: United States
Contact: Executive Director Linda Shelton
Contact: Director of development Marie-Louise Stegall
Contact: Director of Marketing Elizabeth Fort
Contact: Director of programming Martin Wechsler
Contact: production Manager Richard Koch
Contact: finance Director Margaret Hollenbeck

Judson College Artist Series
Website: http:// www.judson.edu
Email: lmcmanus@judson.edu
Phone: 800 447 9472
Address: Music Department, 302 Bibb St, US
Country: United States
Contact: Manager Lanny McManus

Juilliard School, The
Website: www.juilliard.edu
Email: admissions@juilliard.edu
Phone: 212 799 5000 ext
Address: 60 Lincoln Center Plaza, US
Country: United States
vice President for development & public affairs
Anthony J. Newman
Contact: Associate dean for admissions Lee Cioppa
Contact: pr Manager Gloria Gottschalk
Contact: Director of educational outreach Alison Scott-Williams
Contact: Director of communications Janet Kessin
Contact: dean Ara Guzelimian

Julia Morgan Center for the Arts
Website: www.juliamorgan.org
Email: hanah@berkeleyplayhouse.org
Phone: 510 845 8542
Address: 2640 College Avenue, US
Country: United States
Contact: Executive Director Jerry R. Foust

Juneau Arts and Humanities Council
Website: www.jahc.org
Email: info@jahc.org
Phone: 907 586 2787
Address: 350 Whittier Street, US
Information: The Juneau Arts & Humanities Council (the Council) incorporated in 1973. It is the formal arts agency for the Capital City of Juneau, Alaska and operates the Juneau Arts and Culture Center (JACC), a vibrant community center; providing a location for concerts and events, rotating gallery, and a lobby gift shop. postal address: P.O. Box 20562, Juneau, AK 99802
Country: United States
Contact: Executive Director Nancy DeCherney
Social Media: www.facebook.com/juneau.arts

Juneau Jazz & Classics
Website:
www.jazzandclassics.org
Email: info@jazzandclassics.org
Phone: 907 463 3378
Address: PO Box 22152, US
Information: present 16 day festival of classical, jazz & blues concerts, workshops & master classes
Country: United States
founder & Artistic Director
Linda Rosenthal
Contact: Executive Director Sandy Fortier

Juniata College Artists Series
Website: www.juniatapresents.com
Email: herzog@juniata.edu
Phone: 181 464 13608
Address: 1700 Moore Street, US
Information: multi disciplinary

Country: United States
Contact: Director of artists series Chad Herzog

Kahilu Theatre Foundation
Website: www.kahilutheatre.org
Email: janet@kahilutheatre.org
Phone: 808 885 6017
Address: PO Box 549, US
Country: United States
Contact: operations Director Alva Kamalani
Contact: Managing Director Janet Coburn

Kansas State University
Website:
www.ksu.edu/mccain
Email: mccain@ksu.edu
Phone: 785 532 6425
Address: McCain Auditorium, US
Country: United States
Contact: Director Tod Holmberg

Kauffman Center for the Performing Arts
Website: www.kauffmancenter.org
Email: contact@kauffmancenter.org
Phone:
816 994 7222
Address: 1601 Broadway, US
Information: offer diverse performing arts experiences; represents three exceptional resident companies – the Kansas City Ballet, the Lyric Opera of Kansas City, and the Kansas City Symphony, our Broadway presenter, Theater League, and Harriman-Jewell Series.
Country: United States
Contact: President and CEO Jane Chu
Social Media: @kauffmancenterfacebook.com/kauffmancenter
Policies: Rent and present, Arts centre

Kaye Playhouse at Hunter College
Website: kayeplayhouse.hunter.cuny.edu
Email: kayeinfo@hunter.cuny.edu
Phone: 212 772 5207
Address: 68st Street betw. Park+Lexington, US
Country: United States
Contact: Manager Nancy Dodds

Kean University
Website: www.keanstage.com
Email: lgambini@kean.edu
Phone: 908 737 4081
Address: Kean Stage, 1000 Morris Ave, US
Information: Kean Stage presents professional theatre, dance companies, concert artists, and family-focused shows all year round via Wilkins Theatre, Enlow Recital Hall and Premiere Stages
Country: United States
Contact: Director of arts programming John J Wooten
Social Media: @KeanStage www.facebook.com/kean-stage
Policies: Present and produce

Keene State College – Redfern Arts Center
Website: www.keene.edu/arts/redfern/
Email: smayers@keene.edu
Phone: 603 358 2167
Address: Keene State College, US
Information: The Main Theatre of the Redfern Arts Center at Keene State College is a 572 seat proscenium with a stage that allows for the presentation of most professional touring shows; seating in the Main Theatre is divided into three sections; the Orchestra section, closest to the stage, seats 170; the Loge section in the centre of the house seats 100; the Balcony section comprises the rear of the house and seats 302; a steep rake in the Loge and Balcony section provides these seats with excellent sightlines, and allows patrons to be closer to the stage; wheelChair seating is provided in the Orchestra section and at the sides of the Loge section.
Country: United States
Contact: Director Shannon Meyers
Email: smayers@keene.edu
Contact: assistant Director Sharon Fantl
Email: sfantl@keene.edu
Contact: Marketing and business Manager Jackie Hooper
Email: jhooper@keene.edu

Kenan Center Inc
Website: www.kenancenter.org
Phone: 716 433 2617
Address: 433 Locust St, US
Country: United States
Contact: Executive Director Susan Przybyl

Kennedy Center for the Performing Arts, The
Website: www.kennedy-center.org
Phone: 800 444 1324
Address: 2700 F Street, NW, US
Information: the Kennedy Center is America's living memorial to President Kennedy and it presents the greatest performers and performances from across America and around the world, nurturing new works and young artists, and serving as a leader in arts education
Country: United States
Contact: Chairman David M Rubenstein

Contact: President Michael M. Kaiser
Contact: music Director Christoph Eschenbach
Social Media: @kencen www.facebook.com/Kennedy-Center
Annual Performances: 200
Policies: Present and produce, Rent and present, Concert hall

Kent School – Performing Arts Series
Website: www.kent-school.edu
Email: brodyl@kent-school.edu
Phone: 860 927 6000
Address: PO Box 2006, US
Country: United States
Contact: coordinator Lisa Brody

Kentucky Center for the Arts
Website: www.kentuckycenter.org
Email: info@kentuckycenter.org
Phone: 502 562 0100
Address: 501 West Main Street, US
Information: residents and rentals
Country: United States
Contact: Director of Marketing Kim Baker
Contact: Director of event operations Vickie Dorsey

Kerrville Performing Arts Society (KPAS)
Website: www.kpas.org
Phone: 183 089 65727
Address: PO Box 291884, US
Country: United States
Contact: President Ilse Bailey
Contact: Artistic Chair Greg Talford

Kimmel Center for the Performing Arts
Website: www.kimmelcenter.org
Email: aewerf@kimmelcenter.org
Phone: 215 790 5800
Address: 1500 Walnut Street, Floor 17, US
Information: Located in the heart of Center City, Philadelphia, The Kimmel Center's mission is to operate a world-class performing arts center that engages and serves a broad audience through diverse programming, arts education, and community outreach. The Kimmel Center campus is comprised of the Kimmel Center for the Performing Arts (Verizon Hall, Perelman Theater, SEI Innovation Studio, and the Merck Arts Education Center), the Academy of Music (owned by the Philadelphia Orchestra Association), and the University of the Arts Merriam TheaterCountry: United States
Contact: President, CEO Anne Ewers
Contact: Executive vice President J. Edward Cambron
Social Media: @KimmelCenter www.facebook.com/KimmelCenterPhilly

KiMo Theatre
Website: www.cabq.gov/kimo
Email: KiMotheatre@cabq.gov
Phone: 505 768 3522
Address: Albuquerque Cultural Services Department, 423 Central Avenue NW, US
Country: United States
Contact: cultural services department Director Velia Silva
Contact: theatre Manager Craig Rivera

Kings Point Theatre
Email: kingspointclubhouse@wcicommunities.com
Phone: 813 634 9229
Address: Kings Point Theatre, 1900 Clubhouse Dr, US
Information: member of Florida Professional Presenters Consortium; events exclusively for members of the Sun City Centre community
Country: United States
Contact: assistant Director Donna Trommer
Contact: special events program Manager Chris Lenkiewicz

Kingsborough Community College – Event Technical Services
Website: www.kingsborough.edu
Email: pwinnick@kingsborough.edu
Phone: 718 368 5028
Address: 2001 Oriental Blvd, US
Country: United States
Contact: Director, event technical services Paul Winnick

Kirkland Art Center
Website: www.kirklandartcenter.org
Email: kacinc@centralny.twcbc.com
Phone: 315 853 8871
Address: PO Box 213, US
Information: member of Upstate New York Presenters consortium
Country: United States
Contact: Executive Director Annette Clarke
Contact: program Director Matt Mielnick

Kirkland Fine Arts Center, Millikin University
Website: www.millikin.edu/kirkland
Email: bpearson@millikin.edu
Phone: 217 424 6253
Address: 1184 W Main Street, US
Country: United States
Contact: technical Director Bryan Diver

Contact: Director Berry Pearson
Contact: box office Jan Traughber

Kirtland Center for the Performing Arts
Website: www.kirtland.edu/kcpa
Email: kcpa@kirtland.edu
Phone: 989 275 5000 ext
Address: 10775 N St Helen Road, US
Country: United States
Contact: Director Gary Carton

Kitchen, The
Website: www.thekitchen.org
Email: info@thekitchen.org
Phone: 212 255 5793
Address: 512 W 19th Street, US
Country: United States
Contact: Director of communications and public programmes Blake Zideill
Contact: Executive Director, curator Debra Singer
Contact: Associate Director Kerry Scheidt

Knox College Lectures & Concert Series
Website: www.knox.edu
Email: csouther@knox.edu
Phone: 309 341 7303
Address: K-Box 228, US
Country: United States
Contact: Director student activities Trish Hurst

Kodiak Arts Council
Website: www.kodiakarts.org
Email: kodiak-arts-council@gci.net
Phone: 907 486 5291
Address: PO Box 1792, US
Country: United States
Contact: Executive Director Katie Oliver
Contact: President Michael Wall
Contact: programs coodinator Erin Starr-Hallow
Social Media: @KodiakArts www.facebook.com/kodiak-artscouncil/

Koger Center for the Arts
Website: www.kogercenterforthearts.com
Email: KogerCenter@sc.edu
Phone: 803 777 7500
Address: 1051 Greene St., US
Information: As the gateway to The Vista, the capital city's vibrant hub of dining and entertainment, the Koger Center for the Arts stands out as Columbia, South Carolina's premier center for the arts.Country: United States
Contact: Marketing Director Chip Wade
Contact: Director Nate Terracio
Social Media: @kogercenter@Koger Center for the Arts
Policies: All, Arts centre

Krannert Center for the Performing Arts – Krannert Marquee Series
Website: www.krannertcenter.com
Email: kran-tix@illinois.edu
Phone: 217 333 6700
Address: 500 South Goodwin Avenue, US
Information: Krannert Center for the Performing Arts is dedicated to the advancement of education, research, and public engagement through the pursuit of excellence and innovation in the performing arts. Embracing the art of the past as well as the art of our time, the Center supports the belief that creativity is a core human characteristic and that the arts hold uniquely transformative potential. Through its multiple and integrated roles as classroom, laboratory, and public square, Krannert Center serves as a touchstone for the exploration and expansion of human experience. Member of ISPA
Country: United States
Contact: Director Mike Ross
Email: mikeross@illinois.edu
Social Media: @KrannertCenter www.facebook.com/KrannertCenter
Capacity: 4000

Kupferberg Center – Queens College
Website: www.kupferberg.org
Email: V.Charlop@kupferberg.org
Phone: 718 544 2996
Address: 65-30 Kissena Blvd, US
Information: also rent; recording facilities
Country: United States
Contact: Executive Director Vivian Charlop
 Marketing & pr
 Patricia Price
Contact: technical Director Anthony Fitsch
Contact: operations Manager Michael Kelleher
Contact: theatre Manager Renee Jones
 Director of grants & contributions
 Dedi Firestone

Kutztown University Performing Artists Series
Website: www.kutztown.edu/activities/kupas
Email: kupas@kutztown.edu
Phone: 161 068 34511
Address: Office of Cultural Affairs, Kutztown University, US
Country: United States

Contact: Director Ellen Finks
Contact: office of cultural affairs Amy Botwright

Kuumbwa Jazz Center
Website: www.kuumbwajazz.org
Email: tim@kuumbwajazz.org
Phone: 831 427 2227
Address: 320-2 Cedar St, US
Information: Producers of jazz; venue also used by other promoters to present a variety of acoustic music
Country: United States
Contact: Director Tim Jackson
Contact: Marketing Director Sandy Sloan

L'Ermitage Foundation
Email: drearlcherniak@aol.com
Phone: 310 472 3330
Address: PO Box 491698, US
Information: charitable foundation – no fees provided but hotel acomodation provided to performers/no charge; venue address: Bel Age Hotel 1020 No. San Vicente Blvd, West Hollywood CA 90069
Country: United States
Contact: Executive Director Ren

LA Arts – Performance Series
Website: www.laarts.org
Email: mail@laarts.org
Phone: 207 782 7228
Address: 221 Lisbon St, US
Information: arts and education programs. L/A Arts' mission is to engage and inspire a vibrant community through arts and culture
Country: United States
Social Media: www.facebook.com//pages/LA-Arts/74894226731

La Guardia Community College
Website: www.lagcc.cuny.edu
Phone: 718 482 5151
Address: La Guardia Performing Arts and Conference Center, 31-10 Thomson Ave, US
Information: school time series for elementary school; family series
Country: United States
Contact: assistant Artistic prod Handan Ozbilgin
Contact: General Manager Steven Hitt

La Jolla Music Society
Website: www.ljms.org
Phone: 858 459 3724
Address: 7946 Ivanhoe Ave, Suite 309, US
Information: La Jolla Music Society carries forward a distinguished tradition reaching back to the Musical Arts Society of La Jolla founded in 1941 by Nikolai Sokoloff, former conductor of the Cleveland Orchestra.
Country: United States
Contact: Marketing Director Kristen Sakamoto
Email: ksakamoto@ljms.org

La Mirada Theatre for the Performing Arts
Website: www.lamiradatheater.com
Email: lmoore@lamiradatheatre.com
Phone: 156 294 47977
Address: 14900 La Mirada Boulevard, US
Country: United States
Contact: Artistic Director Brian Kite
Contact: secretary Laura Moore

La Pena Cultural Center
Website: www.lapena.org
Email: info@lapena.org
Phone: 510 849 2568
Address: 3105 Shattuck Avenue, US
Information: also rent venues for bigger occasions
Country: United States
Contact: publicity coordinator Fernando Torres
Contact: Executive Director Paul B Chin
Contact: programme coordinator Nyla Moujaes

Lafayette College Performance Series
Website: www.lafayette.edu/williamscenter
Email: fingercenter@lafayette.edu
Phone: 610 330 5010
Address: Williams Center for the Arts, US
Information: alternative e-mail: williamscenter@lafayette.edu
Country: United States
Contact: operations Director Allison Quensen Blatt
Contact: Director of cultural program Ellis Finger

Lafayette Community Concerts
Phone: 131 823 31035
Address: PO Box 2465, US
Country: United States
Contact: President Charles Yolebert

Lake County Community Concert Association
Phone: 184 750 27312
Address: 814 Keith Ave, US
Country: United States
Contact: contact Patti O'Dell

Lake Michigan College Mendel Center Mainstage
Website: www.themendelcenter.com
Email: boxoffice@lakemichigancollege.edu
Phone: 269 927 8700
Address: 2755 E Napier Ave, US
Information: alternative website: www.mendelmainstage.org
Country: United States
Social Media: @LMCMendel www.facebook.com/mendelcenter

Lake Placid Center for the Arts
Website: www.LakePlacidArts.org
Email: inf@lakeplacidarts.org
Phone: 518 523 2512
Address: 17 Algonquin Drive, US
Country: United States
Contact: Director Nadine Duhaime

Lake Superior Big Top Chautauqua
Website: www.bigtop.org
Email: info@bigtop.org
Phone: 715 373 5552
Address: PO Box 455, 101 West Bayfield Street, US
Information: Lake Superior Big Top Chautauqua provides entertaining and educational cultural activities with an emphasis on performances that celebrate history and the environment.
Country: United States
Contact: operations Manager Phil Anich
Email: pranich@bigtop.org
Contact: Executive Director Terry Meyer-Matier
Email: terry@bigtop.org
Contact: General Manager Patrick Grace
Email: patrick@bigtop.org
Social Media: @BigBlueTent www.facebook.com/bigbluetent

Lake Superior State University Cultural Events
Website: www.lssu.edu
Email: jwilkinson@gw.lssu.edu
Phone: 906 635 2265
Address: Lake Superior State University, US
Country: United States
Contact: Chair cultural affairs John Wilkinson

Lake-Sumter Community College Performing Arts Series
Website: www.lscc.edu
Phone: 352 787 3747
Address: Paul P Williams Fine Arts Centre, 9501 US Highway 441, US
Country: United States
Contact: President Charles Mojock
Contact: theatre Manager Greg Cumba
Contact: events coordinator t.b.a.

Lakeland Center Youkey Theatre
Website: www.thelakelandcenter.com
Email: mike.lapan@lakelandgov.net
Phone: 863 834 8100
Address: 701 West Lime St, US
Information: Member of Florida Professional Presenters Consortium, IAVM, FFMA
Country: United States
Contact: Executive Director Mike LaPan
Contact: assistant Director Scott Sloman
Contact: Marketing Manager Erica Smith
Contact: information systems and accounting controller Steven Collazo
Policies: Present, produce, co-produce, Multi-purpose

Lakeland College Krueger Fine Art Series
Website: www.lakeland.edu
Email: lakeland@lakeland.edu
Phone: 920 565 1536
Address: PO Box 359, US
Country: United States
Contact: coordinator Deb Fale
Contact: Chair, fine arts dept Martin Ulrich

Lakeside Association
Website: www.lakesideohio.com
Email: sstary@lakesideohio.com
Phone: 419 798 4461
Address: 236 Walnut Ave, US
Information: see also Festivals
Country: United States
Contact: music Director Shirley Stary
Contact: choral Director Craig Dieterich
Contact: Marketing Director Reea Bishoff

Lancaster Festival Inc
Website: www.lanfest.org
Email: lanfest@lanfest.org
Phone: 740 687 4808
Address: PO Box 1452, US
Information: Lancaster Festival; see also Festivals
Country: United States
Contact: Artistic Director Gary Sheldon
Contact: Executive Director Lou Ross

Lancaster Opera House
Website: www.lancopera.org

Email: lancasteroperahouse@aol.com
Phone: 716 683 1776
Address: 21 Central Avenue, US
Information: member of APAP, LHAT
Country: United States
Contact: Artistic Director David Bondrow
Email: dbondrow@lancopera.org
Contact: technical Director Kirkland Gilmer
Email: Kirkland@lancopera.org
Social Media: @LancOperaHouse www.facebook.com/LancasterOperaHouse/

Lancaster, City of Performing Arts Center
Website: www.lpac.org
Email: jkerpa@cityoflancasterca.org
Phone: 661 723 5945
Address: 44933 Fern Ave, US
Information: also available to rent
Country: United States
Policies: Rent and present, Theatre

Lange Trust
Email: ernst@bex.net
Phone: 419 625 8380
Address: 1402 Columbus Ave, US
Information: concerts are free for the county community
Country: United States
Contact: Chair Diane Ernst
Policies: Concert hall

Las Vegas Arts Council
Phone: 505 425 1085
Address: PO Box 2603, US
Information: organize People's Fair arts & crafts every August, annual International Juried Art Exhibition ""Faces of Woman""; and annual Film Festival ""Las Peliculas""
Country: United States
Contact: project Director Maggie Romigh

Las Vegas Cultural and Community Affairs Division Cultural Season, City of
Website: www.ci.las-vegas.nv.us
Phone: 702 229 6792
Address: 749 Veterans Memorial Dr, US
Country: United States
Contact: administrator Nancy Deaner
Contact: cultural coordinator Priscilla Romer

LaSalle Bank Theatre
Website: www.broadwayinchicago.com
Email: customerservice@broadwayinchicago.com
Phone: 312 977 1700/977
Address: c/o Broadway In Chicago, 17 North State Street, Suite 810, US
Country: United States
Contact: President, broadway in chicago Lou Raizin

Lawrence University – Performing Arts at Lawrence
Website: www.lawrence.edu
Email: jillian.l.jonhnson@lawrence.edu
Phone: 920 832 6585
Address: Office of communications, PO Box 599, US
Country: United States
Contact: Manager of conservatory performances Jillian Johnson

LEAP – Leadership Education Asia Pacific
Website: www.leap.org
Email: leap@leap.org
Phone: 213 485 1422
Address: 327 East Second St, Suite 226, US
Information: Leadership Education for Asian Pacifics, Inc. (LEAP) is a national non-profit organization founded in 1982 to achieve full participation and equality for Asian Pacific Americans. Achieve full participation and equality for Asian Pacific Americans through
Country: United States
President & CEO
J.D. Hokoyama
Contact: vice President of resource/business development Linda Akutagawa
Contact: Executive assisant June Berk
Contact: vice President of finance and Administration Grace Toy

Lebanon Opera House
Website: www.lebanonoperahouse.org
Email: lebanon.opera.house@valley.net
Phone: 603 448 0400
Address: PO Box 384, US
Country: United States
Contact: Executive Director Partridge Boswell

Lee Civic Center
Website: www.leeciviccenter.com
Phone: 239 543 8368
Address: 11831 Bayshore Road, US
Information: only rent, present trade shows & concerts
Country: United States
Contact: General Manager Alta Mosley

Lee University School of Music
Website: www.leeuniversity.edu
Email: music@leeuniversity.edu

Phone: 423 614 8240
Address: PO Box 3450, US
Information: serves well over 300 music majors in undergraduate and graduate programmes, as well as 700 students involved weekly in some aspect of music performance. Ensemble opportunities abound, with 7 instrumental ensembles and 8 vocal ensembles, providing diversity in style, including jazz, opera, choral and orchestral masterworks, world music, contemporary worship, urban gospel, and musical theatre
Country: United States
Contact: recruitment coordinator Christina Reynolds
Email: creynolds@leeuniversity.edu
Contact: coordinator of music events Kristi Vanoy
Email: kvanoy@leeuniversity.edu
Social Media: @LeeUSOMfacebook.com/leeuniversity-schoolofmusic
Policies: Concert hall

Leeds Center for the Arts
Website: www.leedscenter.com
Email: Leedscenter@Bellsouth.net
Phone: 859 744 6437
Address: PO Box 836, US
Information: live performances at fundraisers, visual arts shows & receptions
Country: United States
Contact: President of board of Directors Fara Fox-Tyree
Contact: Marketing Director Sara Sharffer

Leigh University Music Department
Website: www.lehigh.edu/~lnmsc
Phone: 610 758 3835
Address: 356 Zoellner Arts Centre, 420 E Packer Avenue, US
Country: United States
Contact: professor and Chair of department Paul Salerni
Contact: professor Nadine Sine

Leo Yassenoff Jewish Community Center
Website: www.columbusjcc.org
Email: jsaltman@columbusjcc.org
Phone: 614 231 2731
Address: Cultural Arts Department, 1125 College Avenue, US
Country: United States
Contact: Executive Director Carole Folkerth
Contact: Director of special events/corporate sponsorships Sheila Cline
Contact: cultural arts Director Jared Saltman

Lesher Center for the Arts
Website: www.dlrca.org
Email: dlrca@dlrca.org
Phone: 925 295 1400
Address: 1601 Civic Drive, US
Information: The Lesher Center for the Arts is home to various theatres with a capacity of up to 785 people.
Country: United States
Contact: General Manager Scott Dennison
Social Media: @LesherCenter www.facebook.com/LesherCenter
Capacity: 785

Leventhal-Sidman JCC
Website: www.lsjcc.org
Email: initialname@lsjcc.org
Phone: 161 724 48290 e
Address: 333 Nahanton St, US
Information: for more information contact Barrie Keller
Country: United States
Contact: performing arts Director Susan Tovsky

Lexington Center Corporation
Website: www.lexingtoncenter.com
Email: Sales@lexingtoncenter.com
Phone: 859 233 4567
Address: 430 W Vine St, US
Information: also have sport entertainment facilities
Country: United States
Contact: Director of sports entertainment Carl Hall
Contact: performing artist Luanne Franklin

Lied Center for Performing Arts
Website: www.liedcenter.org
Email: cbethea2@unl.edu
Phone: 402 472 4700
Address: 12th and R Street, PO Box 880151, US
Country: United States
Contact: Executive Director Charles Henry Bethea

Lied Center of Kansas
Website: www.lied.ku.edu
Email: tvanleer@ku.edu
Phone: 785 864 3469
Address: University of Kansas, 1600 Stewart Drive, US
Country: United States
Contact: Director of public relations Karen Lane Christilles
Contact: Director Tim van Leer

Lime Kiln Arts
Website: www.theateratlimekiln.com
Email:

info@theateratlimekiln.com
Phone: 540 463 7088
Address: Lime Kiln Theater, PO Box 1244, US
Country: United States
Contact: Executive Director Tony Russell

Lincoln Center – City of Fort Collins
Website: www.lctix.com
Email: lcinfo@fcgov.com
Phone: 970 221 6735
Address: 417 W Magnolia St, US
Information: The Lincoln Center is one of Colorado's largest and most diverse presenters of professional theatre, dance, music, visual arts and children's programs. It features two performing art spaces (a 1, 180-seat performance hall and a 220-seat theatre), three galleries, and an outdoor sculpture/terrace/performance garden. It also has two conference/special events rooms available for rentals
Country: United States
Social Media: @FoCoLincolnCtr www.facebook.com/pages/Lincoln-Center-for-the-Performing-and-Visual-Arts-Fort-Collins/206370565050
Policies: Rent and present, Multi-purpose

Lincoln Center Theater
Website:
www.lct.org
Email: info@lct.org
Phone:
212 873 7600
Address: 150 West 65th St, US
Country: United States
Contact: Executive Producer Bernard Gersten
Contact: Artistic Director André Bishop
Contact: Managing Director Adam Siegel
Policies: Present and produce, Theatre

Lincoln Friends of Chamber Music
Website: www.lfcm.org
Email: info@lfcm.org
Phone: 140 243 55454
Address: 1551 Sunburst Lane, Nebraska, US
Country: United States
Contact: head of artist selection Gunter Hofmann

Lincoln Theater – University of Hartford
Website: www.hartford.edu
Email: harttpr@hartford.edu
Phone: 860 768 4454
Address: 200 Bloomfield Avenue, US
Information: Lincoln Theater welcomes outside bookings, as well as campus-based activities. It is used for commencements, lectures, concerts, theatre and music theatre performances, solo performances, symphonies, concerts, and a variety of other activities. Many of Hartt's main-stage productions take place here. Lincoln Theater seats 716, has a thrust stage 65 feet at its widest, 52 feet from the back wall to the front edge of thrust and a full orchestra pit. It has computerized sound and lighting equipment. The dressing rooms easily accommodate up to 50 performers.
Country: United States
Social Media: @harttschool www.facebook.com/UniversityofHartford
Capacity: 716

Lincoln University Performing Arts Series
Email: trickey@lincolnu.edu
Phone: 573 681 5000
Address: PO Box 29, US
Country: United States
Contact: Chairman Harry Trickey
Contact: secretary Candace Hawkins

Lindsborg Arts Council
Website: www.lindsborgarts.org
Email: lindsborgarts@sbcglobal.net
Phone: 785 227 3032
Address: 402 N. Roosevelt, US
Country: United States
Contact: Executive Director Angela Janzen

Links Hall
Website: www.linkshall.org
Email: info@linkshall.org
Phone: 773 281 0824
Address: 3435 N. Sheffield, 2nd Floor, US
Country: United States
Contact: Executive Director CJ Mitchell
Contact: Managing Director Jennifer Thornton
Contact: administrative coordinator Erica Mott

Lippes Concert Hall in Slee Hall
Website: www.slee.buffalo.edu
Email: rehard@buffalo.edu
Phone: 716 645 2921
Address: 105 Slee Hall Department of Music, University at Buffalo, US
Country: United States
Contact: concert Manager Philip Rehard
Policies: Concert hall

Live Nation

Website: www.clearchannel.com
Phone: 917 421 95100
Address: 220 W 42nd Street, US
Information: world's largest diversified promoter, Producer and venue operator for live entertainment events; owns, partially or entirely, and/or operates 116 venues; also develops and manages touring Broadway shows
Country: United States
President & CEO
Michael Rapino

Lively Arts Foundation Inc
Website: www.livelyarts.org
Email: livelyarts2@aol.com
Phone: 877 608 5883
Address: 1379 Crown Drive, US
Information: supports resident Central California Ballet; non-profit presenting and producing organization
Country: United States
Contact: Artistic Director Diane K Mosier

Lobero Theatre Foundation
Website: www.lobero.com
Email: dasbell@lobero.com
Phone: 805 966 4946
Address: 33 E. Canon Perdido St, US
Information: the Lobero is California's oldest continuously operating theatre
Country: United States
Contact: Executive Director David Asbell

Long Beach Ballet
Website: www.LongBeachBallet.com
Email: admin@LongBeachBallet.com
Phone: 562 426 4112
Address: 1122 East Wardlow Road, US
Country: United States
Contact: Artistic Director David Wilcox

Long Center for Performing Arts, The
Website: thelongcenter.org
Email: info@thelongcenter.org
Phone: 512 457 5100
Address: 701 W. Riverside Drive, US
Information: Our mission is to be a community gathering place where creativity happens—a premier performing arts center that enriches lives by connecting audiences and artists.
member of ISPA
Country: United States
Social Media: @longcenter www.facebook.com/long-centeraustin

Longacre Theatre
Website: www.telecharge.com
Email: tickets@telecharge.com
Phone: 212 944 3700
Address: 220 West 48th Street, US
Country: United States
Contact: vice President of theatre operations Peter Entin
Contact: management company The Shubert Org. Inc
Capacity: 1095

Longwood Gardens Performing Arts
Website: www.longwoodgardens.org
Phone: 610 388 1000 ext
Address: c/o Performing Arts Department, PO Box 501, US
Information: runs ongoing series of festivals according to the season
Country: United States
Contact: peforming arts leader Thomas Warner
Contact: performing arts technical co-ordinator Kenneth Homer
Contact: performing arts coordinator Dara Schmoyer

Los Alamos Concert Association
Website: www.losalamosconcert.org
Email: annsmcl@aol.com
Phone: 505 662 9000
Address: PO Box 572, US
Information: LACA is an all-volunteer non-profit presenter of a classical concert series in Los Alamos, New Mexico. We have been presenting world-class artists since 1946.
Country: United States
Contact: Artistic Director Ann McLaughlin
Email: annsmcl@aol.com
Annual Performances: 5
Policies: Theatre

Los Angeles County Museum of Art, Music Programs Department
Website: www.lacma.org
Email: music@lacma.org
Phone: 323 857 6115
Address: Los Angeles County Museum of Art, 5905 Wilshire Blvd, US
Information: music area does not include pop, only classical and jazz
Country: United States
Contact: music programs coordinator Ryan Zwahlen

Louisburg College Concert Series
Website: www.louisburg.edu

Phone: 919 496 2521
Address: 501 North Main Street, US
Country: United States
cultural affairs advisor & Director
Robert Pool

Louisiana State University – Lively Arts
Website: www.lsu.edu/upc/livelyarts
Email: khavar1@lsu.edu
Phone: 225 578 5964
Address: LSU Union, PO Box 25123, US
Country: United States
Contact: Chair Kristian Havard
Contact: publicity Perry Poussard

Louisiana State University – Shreveport Theatre Series
Phone: 318 797 5348
Address: Student Activities, One University Place, US
Information: attractions vary by season
Country: United States
Contact: assistant Director Kathrine Grimmet

Louisiana Tech Concert Association
Website: www.latech.edu
Phone: 318 257 2930
Address: PO Box 8608, US
Country: United States
Contact: Director of performing arts Ken Robbins
Contact: coordinator of theatre Cherrie Sciro

Loveland Civic Music Association
Phone:
197 066 39420
Address: PO Box 952, US
Country: United States
Contact: President Hank Thode

Lower Manhattan Cultural Council
Website: www.lmcc.net
Email: info@lmcc.net
Phone: 212 219 9401
Address: 125 Maiden Lane, 2nd Floor, US
Information: (LMCC), a 501(c) nonprofit, has been a leading voice for arts and culture Downtown and throughout New York City for 40 years, producing cultural events and promoting the arts through grants, services, advocacy, and cultural development programmes
Country: United States
Contact: President Andrew Hamingson
Email: ahamingson@lmcc.net
Contact: Executive vice President Diego Segalini
Social Media: @LMCCfacebook.com/LMCCNYC
Policies: Present, produce, co-produce, Present and produce, Produce and co-produce, Other

Lowndes/Valdosta Arts Commission
Email: lvac@surfsouth.com
Phone: 229 794 0058/561
Address: Turner Center for the Arts, 527 N Patterson St, US
Country: United States
Contact: Chairman of I/vac Katharine Courson
Contact: vice Chairman Bob Harrison
Contact: grants Ann Schutt

Lubbock Arts Alliance Inc.
Website: www.lubbockarts.org
Email: mail@lubbockarts.org
Phone: 806 744 2787
Address: PO Box 5092, US
Country: United States
Contact: Executive Director Libby Camp

Lunt-Fontanne Theatre
Website: www.nederlander.com
Phone: 212 840 5577
Address: 205 West 46th Street, US
Country: United States
Contact: management company The Nederlander Org, Inc
Contact: theatre operator Kip Makkonen
Capacity: 1492

Lutcher Theater Inc
Website: www.lutcher.org
Email: lutcher@exp.net
Phone: 409 886 5535
Address: PO Box 2310, US
Country: United States
Contact: Managing Director Jim Clark

Luther College Center Stage Series
Website: www.luther.edu
Email: gertta01@luther.edu
Phone: 563 387 1536
Address: 700 College Drive, US
Country: United States
Contact: Director of campus programming Tanya Gertz

Lyceum Theatre
Website: www.telecharge.com
Phone: 212 944 3700

Address: 149 West 45th Street, US
Information: other: theatre
Country: United States
Contact: management company The Shubert Org. Inc
Contact: vice President of theatre operations Peter Entin
Capacity: 924

Lycian Centre
Phone: 845 469 7412
Address: PO Box F, US
Information: visiting address: 1351 King Highway, Chester NY
Country: United States
Contact: theatre Manager Susan Logothetis
Contact: Executive Director Richard Logothetis

Lynchburg Community Concert Association
Phone: 143 423 91281
Address: PO Box 1332, US
Country: United States
Contact: President Jean P Eberhardt

Lyric Theatre, The
Website: www.lyrictheatre.com
Email: info@lyrictheatre.com
Phone: 772 286 7827 (bo
Address: 59 SW Flagler Avenue, US
Information: named to the National Register of Historic Places
Country: United States
Contact: pr/Marketing Denise Belizar
Contact: Executive Director John Loesser
Capacity: 500

Mabel Tainter Memorial Theater
Website: www.mabeltainter.com
Email: mtainter@mabeltainter.com
Phone: 715 235 9726
Address: PO Box 250, 205 Main Street, US
Country: United States
Contact: Executive Director Laura Reisinger
Contact: public relations Gerry Schuster

Macomb Center for the Performing Arts
Website: www.macombcenter.com
Email: macombarts@macomb.edu
Phone: 586 286 2141
Address: 44575 Garfield Road, US
Country: United States
Contact: program administrator Christine Guarino
Contact: Marketing specialist Mary Jo Heft
Contact: education outreach coordinator Marie Rees operations Manager, rental & event coordinator Nancy Kramarczyk
Contact: development Manager Lois Jackman

Madame Walker Theatre Center
Website: www.walkertheater.com
Email: mwtcPresident@aol.com
Phone: 317 236 2099
Address: 617 Indiana Avenue, US
Information: Performing Arts Series; Jazz on the Avenue; family performing arts series and a film festival
Country: United States
Contact: President Cynthia Bates

Madison-Morgan Cultural Center
Website: www.madisonmorgancultural.org
Email: info@madmorg.org
Phone: 706 342 4743
Address: 434 South Main Street, US
Information: some student performances
Country: United States
Contact: Executive Director tba
Contact: membership and special events Elsie Monks

Magic Valley Arts Council, KMVT TV, CSI Continuing Education Arts on Tour
Website: www.magicvalleyartscouncil.org
Email: carolyn@twinfallscenter.org
Phone: 208 734 2787
Address: PO Box 1158, US
Information: local school residencies
Country: United States
Contact: program Director Carolyn White

Mahaffey Theater at the Progress Energy Center
Website: www.mahaffeytheater.com
Email: info@mahaffeytheater.com
Phone: 172 789 25798
Address: 400 First Street South, US
Information: managed by SMG
Country: United States
Contact: General Manager David Rovine
Contact: Marketing Manager Nicole Landry

Maine Center for the Arts
Website: www.mainecenterforthearts.org
Email: brett.zeigler@umit.maine.edu
Phone: 207 581 1804
Address: University of Maine, 5746 Maine Center for the Arts, US
Information: currently closed for renovations; performances staged in communities around the state

Country: United States
Contact: Executive Director John Patches
Contact: Associate Director Adele Adkins
Contact: assistant Brett Zeigler

Majestic Theatre
Website: www.newyorkcitytheatre.com/theaters/majestictheater/theater.php
Email: tickets@telecharge.com
Phone: 212 944 3700
Address: 247 West 44th Street, US
Information: The Majestic Theatre is a Broadway theatre located at 245 West 44th Street in midtown Manhattan. It is one of the largest Broadway theatres with 1, 645 seats, and traditionally has been used as a venue for major musical theatre productions.
Country: United States
Contact: vice President of theatre operations Peter Entin
Contact: management company The Shubert Org. Inc
Policies: Rent and present, Produce and rent

Majestic Theatre
Website: www.majesticempire.com
Email: kfeldman@majesticempire.com
Phone: 210 226 5700
Address: PO Box 390, US
Country: United States
Contact: Executive Director Kirk Feldmann
Contact: Director of booking Isabelle Rodriguez

Manhattanville College
Website: www.mville.edu
Email: Francis.Brancaleone@mville.edu
Phone: 914 694 2200
Address: Department of Music, 2900 Purchase St, US
Country: United States
dance & theatre Director
Michael Posnick
Contact: music Director Carmelo Comberiati

Mann Center for the Performing Arts – Summer Outdoor Facility
Website: www.manncenter.org
Phone: 215 546 7900/893
Address: 52nd Street & Parkside Avenue, West Fairmount Park, US
Information: Philadephia Orchestra Summer Festival: 5 weeks mid – – June-late July
Country: United States
President & CEO
tba

Marble Collegiate Church – Music at Marble
Website: www.marblechurch.org
Email: staff@marblechurch.org
Phone: 212 686 2770
Address: 1 W 29 St, US
Country: United States
Contact: Chair of music committee Claire Zack
Contact: music Director Kenneth Dake

Marcus Center for the Performing Arts
Website: www.marcuscenter.org
Email: Info@marcuscenter.org
Phone: 414 273 7206
Address: 929 N Water Street, US
Information: the premier arts entertainment destination for Milwaukee and Wisconsin. It provides a vibrant setting for outstanding cultural experiences, where the arts come to life every day. Located in the heart of the Downtown Theater District, the Marcus Center offers live performance of opera, ballet, children's theater, symphony, Off Broadway, comedy, drama, dance, jazz and national touring productions of Broadway shows. Home of the Milwaukee Ballet. Admin address: 123 E State Street, Milwaukee, WI 53202**Country:** United States
Contact: President and CEO Paul Mathews
vp Sales & Marketing
Heidi Lofy
Contact: Director of facility relations Jerold Fox
Email: jfox@marcuscenter.org
Social Media: @marcuscenter www.facebook.com/MarcusCenter.org
Policies: All, Arts centre

Maricopa Community Colleges – Office of Fine Arts Development
Website: http://mcli.maricopa.edu/
Email: randy.wright@cgcmail.maricopa.edu
Phone: 480 731 8630
Address: 2411 W 14th St, US
Country: United States
Contact: fine arts development co-ordinator Josh Rathkamp
Contact: acting Director academic affairs, support programs Eric Leshinskie

Marin Center-Marin County Fair
Website: www.marincenter.org
Email: jfarley@co.marin.ca.us
Phone: 415 499 6400
Address: 10 Avenue of the Flags, US
Information: also rent
Country: United States
Contact: Manager Jim Farley

Marin Community Playhouse
Website: www.playhousesananselmo.com
Email: info@PlayhouseSanAnselmo.org
Phone: 141 545 68555
Address: 27 Kensington Road, US
Country: United States
Contact: Manager George Barcos

Marina Civic Center of Panama City
Website: www.marinaciviccenter.com
Phone: 850 769 1217
Address: 8 Harrison Avenue, US
Information: run by Bay Arts Alliance
Country: United States
Contact: Executive assistant Joy Adams Executive Director & facilities co-ordinator Chris Cockriol

Marion Cultural and Civic Center
Website: www.marionccc.org
Email: marionccc@verizon.net
Phone: 618 997 4030
Address: PO Box 51, US
Country: United States
Contact: Director Mike Bennet
Contact: Director admin Julie Johnston
Capacity: 1065

Market Square Concerts
Website: www.marketsquareconcerts.org
Email: info@marketsquareconcerts.org
Phone: 717 221 9599
Address: Post Office Box 1292, US
Information: For 32 years, Market Square Concerts has been dedicated to the presentation of a wide repertoire of chamber music performed by distinguished professional artists, both established and emerging, and to the education and engagement of the General public
Country: United States
Contact: Artistic Director Peter Sirotin
Contact: Executive assistant Darlene Richter
Email: drichter@marketsqaureconcerts.org
Social Media: @MarketSquareC www.facebook.com/MarketSquareConcerts/
Policies: Present and produce

Marquis Theatre
Website: www.nederlander.com
Phone: 212 840 5577
Address: 1535 Broadway, US
Country: United States
Contact: management company The Nederlander Org, Inc
Contact: Manager David Calhoun
Capacity: 1584

Marsh Symphony on the Prairie Series
Website: www.indyorch.org
Email: iso@indyorch.org
Phone: 317 262 1100
Address: 32 East Washington Street, Suite 600, US
Information: Hosts the festival series for 8 weeks during the summer, starts at the end of June
Country: United States
Contact: music Director Jack Everly
Contact: Executive Producer Ty Johnson

Marshall Artists Series
Website: www.marshall.edu/muartser
Email: watkins@marshall.edu
Phone: 304 696 6656
Address: c/o Jomie Jazz Center, 1 John Marshall Drive, US
Information: also organise the Huntington International Film Festivals twice annually spring, autumn
Country: United States
Contact: Marketing Director Angela Jones
Contact: Director Penny Watkins

Marshall Regional Arts Council Performing Arts Series
Website: www.marshallartscouncil.org
Email: info@marshallartscouncil.org
Phone: 903 935 4484
Address: PO Box C, US
Country: United States
Contact: Director Joyce Weekly

Martha's Vineyard Chamber Music Society
Website: www.mvcms.vineyard.net
Email: mvcms@vineyard.net
Phone: 508 696 8055
Address: PO Box 4189, US
Country: United States
Contact: Artistic Director Delores Stevens

Martin E. Segal Theatre Center
Website: www.thesegalcenter.org
Email: mestc@gc.cuny.edu
Phone: 212 817 1860
Address: The Graduate Center, The City University of New York, 365 Fifth Avenue, US
Country: United States
Contact: Executive Director Daniel Gerould

Contact: Managing Director Rebecca Sheahan

Martin Luther King Jr Concerts
Website: brooklynconcerts.com
Email: brooklyncommunityevents@yahoo.com
Phone: 718 802 3700/469
Address: Brooklyn Concerts, 209 Joralemon Street, US
Country: United States
Contact: Executive Director Debra Garcia

Martin Luther King Jr Performing & Cultural Arts Complex
Website: www.kingartscomplex.com
Email: yxu@kingartscomplex.com
Phone: 614 645 5464
Address: 867 Mt Vernon Avenue, US
Information: literary series, performances for youth/children, visual arts
Country: United States
Contact: Executive Director Demetries J. Neely
Email: dneely@kingartscomplex.com
Contact: Marketing Associate Yifan Xu
Email: yxu@kingartscomplex.com
Contact: facilities Director Darla Reid
Email: dreid@kingartscomplex.com
Social Media: @KingArtsComplex www.facebook.com/king.arts.complex

Mary D'Angelo Performing Arts Center
Website: www.mercyhurst.edu
Email: mfuhrman@mercyhurst.edu
Phone: 814 824 3000
Address: Mercyhurst College, 501 E 38th Street, US
Information: hold 3 film series, 24-25 films a year: documentaries, foreign films, etc
Country: United States
Contact: Director Michael Fuhrman
Contact: assistant Director Bruce Parkhurst
Contact: production Manager Greg Clepper

Maryland National Capital Park and Planning Commission
Website: www.pgparks.com
Email: website@pgparks.com
Phone: 301 454 1450
Address: Art and Cultural Heritage Division, 6611 Kenilworth Ave, Suite 200, US
Country: United States
Contact: division chief Barbara Funk
Contact: Director publick playhouse Curlen Lee
Contact: Director, arts/harmony hall regional center Lawrence Knowles
Contact: joint arts specialist Christel Stevens
Contact: joint arts specialist Stewart Seal
Contact: Director montpelier cultural/arts center Richard Zandler

Maryland Theatre
Website: www.mdtheatre.org
Email: tix@mdtheatre.org
Phone: 301 790 3500/200
Address: 21-27 South Potomac Street, US
Information: Maryland Symphony Orchestra is resident; venue was built in 1915; presents country artists, comedians, orchestra concerts, children's shows, musicians, recitals, stage shows, and others
Country: United States
Contact: President of the board Patricia Wolford

Masonic Temple Theatre Series
Website: www.nederlanderdetroit.com
Phone: 313 832 5900
Address: 500 Temple Ave, US
Information: present mainly Broadway musicals; also ballet and concerts
Country: United States
Contact: Managing Director Alan Linchtenstein

Massachusetts Institute of Technology Guest Artist Series
Website: web.mit.edu/mta/ www
Email: mta-request@mit.edu
Phone: 617 542 2394
Address: 77 Massachusetts Avenue, 14N 207, US
Country: United States
Contact: concerts office Director Clarise E Snyder
Contact: assistant Matthew Agoglia

Mateel Community Center Inc
Website: www.mateel.org
Email: office@mateel.org
Phone: 707 923 3368
Address: PO Box 1910, 59 Rusk Ln, US
Information: primarily a venue for local presenters; provide a summer arts and music faire, and a winter faire; major fundraiser is a three day Concert Reggae on the River
Country: United States
Contact: General Manager Justin Crellin

Maui Arts & Cultural Center
Website: www.mauiarts.org
Email: macc@mauiarts.org
Phone: 808 242 2787
Address: One Cameron Way, US
Information: 45 to 60 Attractions, 100 to 150 Performances; all cultures represented: Indian, Jewish, Japanese, Korean, Hawaiian, Okinawan, European; for booking information call 808-242 2787/265
Country: United States
President & CEO
Art Vento
Contact: Marketing Director Karee Carlucci

Maui Philharmonic Society
Email: sandramaul@aol.com
Phone: 808 244 3771
Address: 95 Mahalani Street, US
Country: United States
Contact: Executive Director Sandra L McGuinness

Maverick Concerts Inc
Website: www.maverickconcerts.org
Email: maverickmuse@aol.com
Phone: 845 679 8217
Address: P.O. Box 9, 120 Maverick Road, US
Information: alternative e-mail: fairchildmary@gmail.com
Country: United States
Contact: music Director Alexander Platt
Contact: Director of public relations Mary Fairchild
Contact: Chairperson of the board David Segal
Annual Performances: 25
Policies: Concert hall

Max M. Fisher Music Center
Website: www.detroitsymphony.com
Email: jwoodward@dso.org
Phone: 313 576 5100
Address: 3711 Woodward Ave, US
Information: home of Detroit Symphony Orchestra (q.v.)
Country: United States
Contact: Director of public relations Jill Woodward
President & Executive Director

Mayville State University Fine Arts Series
Website: www.masu.nodak.edu
Email: thein@badlands.nodak.edu
Phone: 701 786 4035
Address: 330 Third Street NE, US
Country: United States
Contact: Associate Director fine arts series Neal Nelson
Contact: Director fine arts series Anthony Thein

McAninch Arts Center at College of DuPage
Website: www.atthemac.org
Email: raffel@cod.edu
Phone: 630 942 3008
Address: 425 Fawell Blvd, US
Information: The MAC is dedicated to giving residents of west suburban Chicago continued access to engagement with the arts — now celebrating the grand re-opening after a $35 million renovation
Country: United States
Contact: Marketing Manager Roland Raffel
Contact: Director Diana Martinez
Social Media: @AtTheMAC www.facebook.com/AtTheMAC
Capacity: 1200

McCallum Theatre for the Performing Arts
Website: www.mccallumtheatre.com
Email: information@mccallum-theatre.org
Phone: 760 346 6505
Address: McCallum Theatre for the Performing Arts, 73000 Fred Waring Dr, US
Information: The McCallum Theatre's mission is to entertain and educate the public by offering a variety of performing arts experiences that reflect the diversity of people, interests, and tastes of the communities and constituents served by the Theatre.
Country: United States
Contact: facilties superintendent Dan Rose
Contact: Executive Director Ted Giatas
Contact: Director of presentations Mitch Gershenfeld
Contact: Director of Marketing Rick Darius

Meany Center for the Performing Arts
Website: meanycenter.org
Email: meany@uw.edu
Phone: 206 543 4880
Address: 1313 NE 41st Street, US
Information: Meany Center for the Performing Arts (formerly UW World Series) at the University of Washington fosters innovative performances that advance public engagement, cultural exchange, creative research and learning through the arts. Meany Center provides opportunities for diverse artists, community, students and faculty to connect in the discovery and exploration of the boundless power of the arts to create positive change in the world. Member of ISPA
Country: United States
Contact: Executive and Artistic Director Michelle Witt
Email: mwitt@uw.edu
Contact: Managing Director Rita Calabro
Email: rcalabro@uw.edu
Contact: Director of Artistic engagement Elizabeth Duffell
Email: eduffell@uw.edu
Social Media: @MeanyCenter www.facebook.com/

meanycenter
Capacity: 1206

Merced College
Website: https:// www.mccd.edu/
Email: webmaster@mccd.edu
Phone: 209 384 6000
Address: Arts Division, 3600 M St, US
Information: Eligible persons or groups may use District buildings or grounds designated as the Civic Center for public, literary, scientific, recreational, or educational meetings, or for
discussion of matters of General or public Interest, subject to this procedure.Country: United States
Contact: arts Chairman John P. Graulty
Social Media: https:// www.facebook.com/mercedcollege/ https://twitter.com/MercedCollege https:// www.instagram.com/themercedcollege/
Capacity: 1000+
Policies: Rent only

Meridian Community College Arts and Letters Series
Website: www.mcc.cc.ms.us
Email: mthames@mcc.cc.ms.us
Phone: 601 484 8696
Address: 910 Highway, 19 North, US
Country: United States
Contact: coordinator Michele Thames

Merkin Concert Hall at Kaufman Center
Website: www.kaufman-center.org
Email: info@kaufman-center.org
Phone: 212 501 3340
Address: Goodman House, 129 West 67th Street, US
Country: United States
Contact: Executive Director, kaufman center Lydia Kontos
Contact: Director of Marketing and communications

Merrick-Bellmore Community Concert Association
Phone: 516 623 6618
Address: PO Box 174, US
Country: United States
Contact: vice President Ruth Weissman
concert Chairman & publicity
Ruth Silverman
Contact: President Gerald Silverman

Mesa Arts Center
Website: www.mesaartscenter.com
Email: artscenterinfo@mesaartscenter.com
Phone: 148 064 46501
Address: PO Box 1466, US
Information: also exhibition spaces and art studios; visiting address: 1 East Main Street; Mesa, AZ 85201
Country: United States
Contact: Executive Director Cindy Ornstein
Contact: Director Randy Vogal

Mesa County Community Concert Association
Phone: 197 024 52083
Address: 1155 Lakeside Drive, No. 801, US
Country: United States
Contact: President Paul Schneider
Contact: secretary Jackie Porter

Messiah College Cultural Series
Website: www.messiah.edu
Phone: 717 691 6027
Address: Messiah College, US
Country: United States
Contact: Director of pr Carla Gross

Metropolis Performing Arts Centre
Website: www.metropolisarts.com
Email: info@metropolisarts.com
Phone: 847 577 2121
Address: 111 W Campbell Street, Suite 203, US
Country: United States
Contact: Executive Director Tim Rater

Miami Civic Music Association
Website: www.miamicivicmusic.org
Email: info@miamicivicmusic.org
Phone: 877 733 3031
Address: 5360 S W 87th Avenue, US
Country: United States
Contact: President and Artistic Director Rosalina Sackstein

Miami Light Project, Inc
Website: www.miamilightproject.com
Email: bboone@miamilightproject.com
Phone: 305 576 4350
Address: PO Box 1048, US
Information: Founded in 1989, Miami Light Project is a not-for-profit cultural organization which presents live performances by innovative dance, music and theater artists from around the world; supports the development of new work by South Florida-based artists; and offers educational programs for students of every age.
Country: United States
Artistic & Executive Director

Elizabeth Boone
Email: bboone@miamilightproject.com
Contact: Managing Producer Rebekah Lanae Lengel
Email: rlengel@miamilightproject.com
Social Media: @mialightproject http:// www.facebook.
com/miamilightproject
Policies: All, Other

Miami University Performing Arts Series
Website: www.fna.muohio.edu/pas
Email: swoffoph@muohio.edu
Phone: 513 529 6333
Address: 102 Hall Auditorium, US
Country: United States
Contact: Director Patti Hannan Swofford

Miami University, Hamilton, Artists Series
Website: www.ham.muohio.edu/Artistseries
Email: epsteihr@muohio.edu
Phone: 513 785 3000
Address: 1601 University Boulevard, US
Country: United States
Contact: series Director Howard Epstein

Miami-Dade Community College
Website: www.culture.mdcc.edu
Email: caffairs@mdcc.edu
Phone: 305 237 3010
Address: Cultural Affairs Department, 300 NE Second
Avenue, Suite 5501-3, US
Country: United States
Contact: contact Georgiana Pickett

Michigan Theater
Website: www.michtheater.com
Email: info@michtheater.org
Phone: 734 668 8397
Address: 603 East Liberty, US
Country: United States
Contact: technical Director J. Scott Clarke
 Director of operations & programming
 Tara McComb
 Marketing & development Director
 Lee Berry
Contact: facility Director Arthur McViccar
Contact: annual gifts/membership Director Laura Barnes

Mid-Atlantic Center for the Arts
Website: www.capemaymac.org
Email: mstewart@capemaymac.org
Phone: 609 884 5404
Address: PO Box 340, 1048 Washington St., US
Information: also tours of cultural importance
Country: United States
 Director of Marketing & communication
 Jean Barraclough
Contact: Director Michael Zuckerman
Contact: chief outreach officer Mary Stewart

Mid-Hudson Civic Center
Website: www.midhudsonciviccenter.com
Phone: 845 454 9800
Address: 14 Civic Center Plaza, US
Information: non profit organisation
Country: United States
Contact: Executive Director Susan Du Moulin

MidAmerica Productions
Website: www.midamerica-music.com
Email: leconomou@midamerica-music.com
Phone: 212 239 0205
Address: 70 W. 36 Street, Suite 305, US
Country: United States
Contact: program development Director Sara Bong
Contact: Executive Director Norman Dunfee
Contact: General Director, Artistic Director Peter Tiboris
 Director of public relations & publications
 Elizabeth Economou
Contact: Director of audience development Molly
Waymire

MidAmerican Center for the Contemporary Music
Website: www.bg www.bgsu.edu/musical-arts/maccm.
html
Email: kdoles@bgsu.edu
Phone: 419 372 2685
Address: College of Musical Arts, Bowling Green SU, US
Information: focus is on contemporary music; annually
presents New Music and Art Festival Oct, all new music,
Digital Arts Concert Series and Music at the Forefront
Series
Country: United States
Contact: Director Kurt Doles
Email: kdoles@bgsu.edu
Contact: coordinator Adam Zygmunt
 department of musicology, composition & theory
 Marilyn Shrude

Middlebury College Center for the Arts
Website: www.middlebury.edu/arts
Email: carroll@middlebury.edu
Phone: 802 443 5697
Address: Middlebury College, 72 Porter Field Rd, US
Information: museum of art and music library on site

Country: United States
Contact: events Manager Allison Coyne Carroll
Contact: performing arts series Director Paul Nelson

Middlesex County College Fine Arts Committee
Website: www.middlesex.cc.nj.us
Email: mcglincy@middlesex.cc.edu
Phone: 732 906 2569
Address: Middlesex County College, 20600 Woodbridge
Avenue, US
Country: United States
Contact: assistant Director Pat Daly

Middletown Commission on the Arts (MCA)
Website: arts2go.org
Email: stephan.allison@middletownct.gov
Phone: 860 638 4510
Address: 100 Riverview Center-Suite 140, 245 deKoven
Drive, US
Information: primarily a year-round resource for local
arts organisations/artists while presenting on a small
scale usually during summer months, outdoors
Country: United States
Contact: arts and culture coordinator Stephan Allison

Midland Center for the Arts Theatre Guild
Website: www.mcfta.org
Email: sabin@mcfta.org
Phone: 989 631 5930
Address: 1801 W St Andrews Rd, US
Information: home of the Midland Symphony Orchestra;
alternative e-mail: winslow@mcfta.org
Country: United States
Contact: Artistic Director museums and exhibits Linda
Basque
Contact: Managing Director professional programs
Phyllis Sabin
Contact: Managing Director museums and exhibits
Bruce Winslow

Midwestern State University Artist-Lecture-Series
Website: www.mwsu.edu
Email: jane.leishner@mwsu.edu
Phone: 940 397 4219
Address: 3410 Taft Blvd, US
Country: United States
Contact: administrative assistant advisor Trevor Clifton
Contact: Associate vice President for student affairs Jane
Leishner

Mifflin-Juniata Concert Association
Email: alevin@acsworld.net
Phone: 717 247 3577
Address: PO Box 231, US
Country: United States
Contact: Director emeritus Allen Levin

Milledgeville-Baldwin County Allied Arts
Email: alliedarts@alltil.net
Phone: 478 452 3950
Address: John Marlor Arts Center,
201 North Wayne St, US
Information: no rock
Country: United States
Contact: Executive Director Randy Cannon

Millennium Centre
Website: www.millenniumevents.ws
Email: lgcarlyle@gmail.com
Phone: 336 723 3700
Address: 101 West 5th Street, Winston, US
Information: The Millennium Center is a privately owned
full service venue located in the heart of downtown
Winston-Salem. They can provide casual or fine dining
amenities, full bar service, decorations, audio/visual
services.
Country: United States
Capacity: 1028

Miller Fine Arts Series
Website: www.friends.edu
Email: plinsc@friends.edu
Phone: 316 295 5877
Address: 2100 University, Friends University, US
Country: United States
Contact: Manager Cecil Riney

Miller Outdoor Theatre
Website: www.milleroutdoortheatre.com
Email: Lydia@ltbaehr.com
Phone: 832 487 7102
Address: 6000 Hermann Park Drive, US
Information: Houston's Miller Outdoor Theatre in
Hermann Park is unique in the United States, offering an
eight month season of professional entertainment that is
Artistically excellent, culturally diverse and always FREE
of charge to the public. This is the largest "always free"
program of its kind in the country.
Country: United States
Contact: Managing Director Cissy Segall Davis
 Director of finance & operations
 Reg Burns
Contact: public relations Lydia Baehr
Email: Lydia@ltbaehr.com

Social Media: @MillerOutdoor www.facebook.com/
milleroutdoor/?ref=ts

Miller Plaza
Website: www.downtownchattanooga.org
Email: cpritchard@thecdp.org
Phone: 423 265 0771
Address: 850 Market St., 2nd Floor Miller Plaza, US
Information: alternative e-mail: cpritchard@thecdp.org
Country: United States
Contact: Executive Director Carla Pritchard

Miller Theatre at Columbia University
Website: www.millertheatre.com
Email: miller-arts@columbia.edu
Phone: 212 854 1633
Address: 2960 Broadway, MC 1801, US
Country: United States
Contact: Director Mellisa Smey
Contact: Marketing and communications Manager
Christine Pill

Mimbres Region Arts Council
Website: www.mrac.cc
Email: arts@mrac.cc
Phone: 505 538 2505
Address: PO Box 1830, US
Country: United States
Contact: Executive Director Faye McCalmont

Minnesota Orchestral Association
Website: www.mnorch.org
Email: info@mnorch.org
Phone: 612 371 5600
Address: 1111 Nicollet Mall, US
Information: additional internet address: www.minneso-
taorchestra.org
Country: United States
Contact: President and CEO Tony Woodcock

Minnesota State University – Moorhead Perform-
ing Arts Series
Website: www.mnstate.edu/perform/
Email: wigtil@mnstate.edu
Phone: 1218 – 477 2271
Address: 1104 7th Ave S., US
Country: United States
Contact: performing arts series Managing Director
Elizabeth Evert
Contact: performing arts series Director Amber Gamradt
Contact: Craig Ellingson

Minskoff Theatre
Website: www.nederlander.com
Phone: 212 840 5577
Address: 200 W 45th Street, US
Country: United States
Contact: management company
The Nederlander Org, Inc
Capacity: 1700

Mississippi State University Lyceum Series
Website: www.msstate.edu/dept/lyceum
Phone: 662 325 7454
Address: PO Drawer HY, US
Country: United States
Contact: series' administrator Brenda Neubauer
Contact: performing arts Chair Maridith Geuder

Missouri Valley Folklife
Phone: 181 669 18717
Address: PO Box 5916, US
Country: United States
Contact: contact Valerie Andruss

Mitchell Museum at Cedarhurst
Website: www.cedarhurst.org
Email: mitchellmuseum@cedarhurst.org
Phone: 618 242 1236
Address: PO Box 923, 2600 Richview Road, US
Information: see John R and Eleanor R Mitchell Founda-
tion, Mt Vernon, IL
Country: United States
Contact: Executive Director Sharon Bradham

Moberly Area Council on the Arts
Website: www.macc.cc.mo.us
Email: info@macc.edu
Phone: 660 263 4110 ext
Address: Moberly Area Community College, 101 College
Ave., US
Country: United States
Contact: contact Jackie Jorgensen

Mobile Chamber Music Society
Website: www.mobilechambermusic.org
Email: music@mobilechambermusic.org
Phone: 251 476 8794
Address: 4159 Carmel Drive North, Mobile, , US
Country: United States
Contact: Executive Director, vice President of program-
ing Daniel Silver

Mobile Civic Center Complex
Website: www.mobilecivicctr.com

Email: mlmccrory@mobilecivicctr.com
Phone: 125 120 87261
Address: 401 Civic Center Dr., US
Country: United States
Contact: General Manager/booking Jay Hagerman

Modlin Center for the Arts
Website: modlin.richmond.edu
Email: modlinarts@richmond.edu
Phone: 804 289 8980
Address: Modlin Center for the Arts 453 Westhampton Way University of Richmond, , US
Information: In 1992, the University began working on a plan for an expanded arts center to improve the performance, rehearsal and exhibition venues, classrooms, and studios for the visual and performing arts, and to provide room for continued growth. The plan was for the new building to connect to the existing Modlin Fine Arts building with an archway above Keller Road similar to the archway in North Court. The existing Emily Gardner Room and the Keller Gymnasium would be a converted for use by the art and art history department. The area occupied by Crenshaw pool would become part of a new theater complex that would house a new theater and dance venue and related shop space. Camp Theater would become a concert hall. Member of ISPA
Country: United States
Contact: Executive Director Deborah Sommers
Email: dsommers@richmond.edu
Contact: Marketing Director Jonathan Gunter
Email: jgunter@richmond.edu
Phone: 804 287 6893administrative coordinator Beverly Bradshaw
Email: bbradsha@richmond.edu
Social Media: www.twitter.com/modlincenter www.facebook.com/modlincenter www.instagram.com/modlincenter/
Capacity: 501-1000
Annual Performances: 100+

Mohave Community College
Website: https://www.facebook.com/mohavecc/
Email: mcc@mohave.edu
Phone: 928 757 4331
Address: 1971 Jagerson Ave, Mohave, US
Information: We bring passion and energy to our work by dreaming big, being bold, having fun, and fostering a caring environment. Celebrating each other and our results with enthusiasm makes our work meaningful and exciting. Our individual differences and backgrounds strengthen our teams, where we seek input and ensure every voice is heard. We amplify our impact when we empower each other to take ownership and work together toward common vision.
Country: United States
Social Media: https://www.instagram.com/mohavecc/ www.facebook.com/mohavecc https://twitter.com/mohavecc

Mohawk Trail Concerts/Music in Deerfield
Website: www.mohawktrailconcerts.org
Email: info@mohawktrailconcerts.org
Phone: 413 625 9511
Address: PO Box 75, US
Information: additional web address: www.musicindeerfield.org a non-profit making organisation
Country: United States
Contact: office Manager Karen Sandquist

Mondavi Center
Website: www.mondaviarts.org
Email: tickets@ucdavis.edu
Phone: 530 754 5000
Address: Mondavi Center Admin Bldg, One Shields Ave, University of California, US
Information: also lecture programme
Country: United States
Contact: Director of development Debbie Armstrong
Contact: Director of programming Jeremy Ganter
Contact: Executive Director Don Roth
Contact: Director of arts education Joyce Donaldson
Contact: Director of Marketing Rob Tocalino

Monday Musical Club, Inc
Website: www.mondaymusical.com
Email: info@mondaymusical.com
Phone: 330 743 2717
Address: Stambaugh Auditorium, #3, 1000 5th Avenue, US
Information: fund scholarships, competitions, community projects
Country: United States
Contact: Manager Kathy Doyle

Monmouth County Park System
Website: www.monmouthcountyparks.com
Email: info@monmouthcountyparks.com
Phone: 732 842 4000
Address: 805 Newman Springs Rd, US
Country: United States
Contact: cultural services Manager Angela Knox
Contact: recreation supervisor Patty Conroy

Monmouth University
Website: www.monmouth.edu/performingarts

Email: vpeck@monmouth.edu
Phone: 732 571 3554
Address: 400 Cedar Avenue, New Jersey, US
Country: United States
Contact: counselor/coordinator of arts programing/promotio Vaune Peck

Montalvo Center for the Arts
Website: www.montalvoarts.org
Email: info@montalvoarts.org.
Phone: 408 961 5800
Address: 15400 Montalvo Rd. Saratoga, US
Information: Montalvo Arts Center's mission is to engage the public in the creative process, acting as a catalyst for exploring the arts, unleashing creativity, and advancing different cultural and cross-cultural perspectives. We achieve our mission by creating and presenting arts of all types, nurturing artists, and using our historic property in innovative ways.
Country: United States
Contact: Executive Director Angela McConnell
Contact: Managing Director Kelly Hudson
Social Media: https://www.facebook.com/montalvoarts https://www.instagram.com/montalvoarts/ https://twitter.com/montalvoarts
Capacity: 1000+
Annual Performances: 100+
Policies: Rent and Present

Montclair State University School of the Arts
Website: www.montclair.edu
Email: gambinil@mail.montclair.edu
Phone: 973 655 5366
Address: c/o Alexander Kasser Theater, 1 Normal Avenue, US
Information: children's programming and cultural series; professional theatre
Country: United States
Executive Director, arts & cultural programming

Montgomery County Community College
Website: www.mc3.edu
Email: hhaves@mc3.edu
Phone: 215 641 6518
Address: Box 400, 340 De Kalb Pike, US
Information: speakers series and art shows; run archival film festival
Country: United States
Contact: assistant Director cultural affairs Jennifer Merritt
Contact: Director cultural affairs Helen Haves

Montgomery County, Performing Arts Society
Website: www.mcpas.org
Email: twoforgolf@aol.com
Phone: 193 676 02787
Address: PO Box 1714, US
Country: United States
Contact: President Elizabeth Pease

Monticello Opera House
Website: www.monticellooperahouse.org
Email: Office@MonticelloOperaHouse.org
Phone: 850 997 4242
Address: Monticello Opera House, Inc., 185 West Washington Street, PO Box 518, US
Information: 1890's restored Opera House
Country: United States
Contact: Executive Director Fran Litton
Email: fran@monticellooperahouse.org
Policies: Concert hall

Moraine Valley Community College Fine and Performing Arts Center
Website: www.morainevalley.edu/fpac/
Email: adduci@morainevalley.edu
Phone: 708 974 4300
Address: 9000 W. College Pkwy., US
Information: The Fine and Performing Arts Center offers an array of music, dance, theater, and art for all ages. Home to the Dorothy Menker Theater, the John and Angeline Oremus Theater, and the Robert F. DeCaprio Art Gallery, the center opened its doors in 1994. The center prides itself as a showcase for performances, a catalyst for budding artists to practice their art, a center for academic preparation for two-year degrees and transfer programs, and a resource for all who love the arts and want to learn more.
Country: United States
Social Media: @MVCCFPAC www.facebook.com/MVC-CFPAC

Morganton Municipal Auditorium
Website: www.ci.morganton.nc.us
Email: comma_d@ci.morganton.nc.us
Phone: 828 433 7469
Address: PO Box 3448, US
Country: United States
Contact: Executive Director Bill Wilson

Morrison Artists Series
Website: morrison.sfsu.edu/
Email: raf@sfsu.edu
Phone: 415 338 1051
Address: San Francisco State University, Music Department, 1600 Holloway Ave, US

Country: United States
Contact: Artistic Director Richard Festinger
Email: raf@sfsu.edu

Morton Theatre
Website: www.mortontheatre.com
Email: admin@mortontheatre.com
Phone: 706 613 3770admi
Address: PO Box 1724, US
Information: is a government-owned/ non-profit corporation-managed rental facility; occasionally co-sponsors or co-produces selected events throughout the year
Country: United States
Contact: technical Director Erwin Greene
Contact: Executive Director Robert L. Herman
Contact: theatre assistant Megan K. Rocks

Mostly Music at Northeastern Illinois University
Website: www.neiu.edu/Celebration_Arts
Email: C_Vohs@neiu.edu
Phone: 773 442 4978
Address: 5500 Norh St Louis Avenue, US
Information: 80 senior citizen concerts, 4 fine arts series and special events
Country: United States
Contact: Artistic Director Christie Vohs

Mount Baker Theatre
Website: www.mountbakertheatre.com
Email: info@mountbakertheatre.com
Phone: 360 733 5793
Address: 104 N Commercial St, US
Information: disabled access; facilities for the hard of hearing signed performance; education program reaching 20, 000 students per year
Country: United States
Contact: Executive Director Brad Burdick
Email: burdick@mountbakertheatre.com
Contact: Marketing Director Amy Guerra

Mount St Mary's University Artists Lectures & Performers Series
Website: www.msmary.edu
Email: blaugher@msmary.edu
Phone: 301 447 5308
Address: Mount St Mary's University, Visual and Performing Arts, 16300 Old Emmitsburg Road, US
Country: United States
Contact: Chair Kurt E Blaugher

Mount Vernon Nazarene College Lecture Artist Series
Website: www.mvnc.edu
Email: bcochran@mvnc.edu
Phone: 740 392 6868
Address: 800 Martinsburg Rd, US
Country: United States
Contact: Chairman of the mvnu lecture artist series Virginia Cameron

Mountain Laurel Centre for the Performing Arts
Website: www.mlcpa.org
Email: info@mlcpa.org
Phone: 570 588 5800
Address: Bushkill Falls Road, P.O.Box G, US
Information: MLC offers on-site studies, lectures and seminars as well as workshops and one to one sessions with world-renowned artists
Country: United States
Contact: President/ chief Executive officer t.b.a.
Contact: vice President Edward E Sader
Contact: Director of development Amy E Rue
Contact: finance Director Sandra L Argeanas

Mountain View Center for the Performing Arts
Website: www.mvcpa.com
Email: performingarts@mvcpa.com
Phone: 650 903 6565
Address: City of Mountain View, PO Box 7540, US
Information: Rental House only
Country: United States
Marketing & public relations Manager Michele Roberts
Contact: business Manager Cindy Miksa
Contact: operations Manager Patrick Skelton
Contact: Executive Director W. Scott Whisler

Movement Theatre International
Email: mapedretti@aol.com
Phone: 215 337 9100
Address: 50 Bernard Drive, US
Information: MTI theatre available to groups to self-produce
Country: United States
Contact: Artistic Director Michael A Pedretti

MTU/ Great Events Series
Website: www.greatevents.mtu.edu
Email: mkmorell@mtu.edu
Phone: 906 487 2844
Address: The Rozsa Center for the Performing Arts, Michigan Tech Univ, 1400 Townsend Drive, US
Information: Principal series: Great Events Series; also home for Keweenaw Symphony Orchestra; Rentals; alternative web: www.rozsa.mtu.edu

Country: United States
Contact: Director, great events series Director, Rozsa Center
Contact: Michael Morelli
Contact: Valerie Pegg

Munson-Williams-Proctor Arts Institute
Website: www.mwpi.org
Email: bmoortis@mwpi.org
Phone: 315 797 0000
Address: Performing Arts Division, 310 Genesee Street, US
Information: member of Upstate New York Presenters, Association of Performing Arts Presenters, International Society for the Performing Arts, International Association of Assembly Managers
Country: United States
Contact: Director of performing arts Bob Mortis

Murphy Theatre Community Center Inc.
Phone: 937 382 3643
Address: 50 W Main St, US
Information: also rentals
Country: United States
Contact: consultant and Director Doug Lynn

Murray Civic Music Association
Address: US
Country: United States
Contact: vp for programming Sonya Baker

Museum of Fine Arts Chamber Music Concerts Series/Concerts in the Courtyard
Website: www.mfa.org
Email: concerts@mfa.org
Phone: 617 267 9300
Address: 465 Huntington Avenue, US
Country: United States

Music & Performing Arts at Trinity Cathedral
Website: www.mandpa.org
Email: dhathaway@dohio.org
Phone: 216 579 9745
Address: 2230 Euclid Avenue, US
Information: encourage neighbourhood residencies
Country: United States
Contact: Artistic Director Daniel Hathaway

Music at the Meeting House
Website: www.glastonburyfirst.org
Email: firstchurch@glastonburyfirst.org
Phone: 860 633 4641
Address: 2183 Main St, US
Country: United States
Contact: Director of music ministries Angela R Salcedo

Music Before 1800
Website: www.mb1800.org
Email: MB1800@aol.com
Phone: 212 666 0675
Address: 529 W 121 St, US
Country: United States
Contact: Executive Director Louise Basbas

Music Box Theatre
Website: www.telecharge.com
Email: tickets@telecharge.com
Phone: 212 944 3700
Address: 239 West 45th Street, US
Country: United States
Contact: vice President of theatre operations Peter Entin
Contact: management company The Shubert Org. Inc
Capacity: 1010

Music Center / Performing Arts Center of Los Angeles County
Website: www.musiccenter.org
Email: General@musiccentre.org
Phone: 213 972 7211
Address: 135 North Grand Avenue, US
Information: resident companies: Los Angeles Philharmonic (q.v.), Center Theatre Group, Los Angeles Opera (q.v.) and Los Angeles Master Chorale
Country: United States
Contact: Vice President for Education Mark Slavkin
Contact: Managing Director Michael Solomon
Contact: Artistic Director Barbara Leonard

Music Center of South Central Michigan
Website: www.musiccenterscmi.com
Email: musiccenter@musiccenterscmi.com
Phone: 269 963 1911
Address: PO Box 1613, US
Information: includes symphony orchestra, Boys' Choir, Girls' Chorus, Community Music School Community Chorus & Pops Ensemble; see also Orchestras
Country: United States

Music Conservatory of Westchester
Website: www.musicconservatory.org/
Email: info@musiced.org
Phone: 914 761 3715
Address: 216 Central Avenue, US
Information: also offers comprehensive, exciting

programs in music instruction, opera, musical theater, drama, TV commercials, and music therapy
Country: United States
Contact: Director of communications Jon Chattman
Email: Jon@musiced.org
Contact: Executive Director Jean Newton
Email: Jean@musiced.org
Social Media: @musicmatters914 www.facebook.com/pages/Music-Conservatory-of-Westchester/60177972469

Music for Montauk
Phone: 631 668 3290
Address: Box 2209, US
Country: United States
Contact: treasurer Tom Bogdan

Music for Mt Lebanon
Website: www.musicformtlebanon.org
Email: wcfraser12@verizon.net
Phone: 412 264 3354
Address: P.O. Box 1305, Moon Township, US
Information: emphasize the variety of popular and classical music; visiting address: 2016 Worcester Drive, Pittsburgh PA 15243-1542
Country: United States
Contact: Artistic Director Richard Pinkerton
Policies: Concert hall

Music Foundation of Spartanburg (USA)
Website: www.sparklenet.com/musicfoundation
Email: music@teleplex.net
Phone: 864 948 9020
Address: Box 1274, US
Country: United States
Contact: General Manager Dana Gencarelli

Music from Salem
Website: www.musicfromsalem.org
Email: info@musicfromsalem.org
Phone: 518 232 2347
Address: 25 E. Main Street Cambridge, New York, US
Information: Music from Salem explores, with equal intensity, the variety of musical exPression in masterworks from the 18th and 19th century to pieces by seldom heard contemporary composers. This adventurous and diverse repertory imparts an energy, excitement and sense of exploration to every performance. It is firmly grounded in the genius of the past and open to exciting new forms of musical exPression.
Country: United States
Contact: Artistic Director Lila Brown
Social Media: https:// www.facebook.com/musicfromsalem/ https:// www.instagram.com/musicfromsalem/
Capacity: 0-100
Annual Performances: 25-50
Annual Productions: 0-5
Policies: All

Music Guild
Website: www.themusicguild.com
Email: info@themusicguild.com
Phone: 131 055 83500
Address: 3637 Motor Avenue, Suite 240, US
Information: 30 children's concerts
Country: United States
Contact: Executive/Artistic Director Eugene Golden

Music Hall
Website: www.themusichall.org
Email: info@themusichall.org
Phone: 603 433 3100
Address: 104 Congress Street, US
Information: theatre address: 28 Chestnut Street, Portsmouth NH 03801
Country: United States
Contact: Artistic Director Jane Forde
Contact: Executive Director Jeffrey Gabel

Music Hall Center for the Performing Arts
Website: www.musichall.org
Email: info@musichall.org
Phone: 313 963 7622
Address: 350 Madison Ave, US
Country: United States
President & Artistic Director
Vince Paul
Contact: Director of events Karen McBride

Music in the Air
Website: www.musicintheair.org; www.hotribscooljazz.org
Email: mita@columbus.gov
Phone: 614 645 7995
Address: 1111 E. Broad St. STE 101, US
Information: also present Festival Latino and Jazz & Rib Fest
Country: United States
Contact: Managing Director Paul Hoy
Contact: Artistic Director Ed Myers

Music in the Mountains

Website: www.musicinthemountains.com
Email: info@musicinthemountains.com
Phone: 970 385 6820
Address: 1063 Main Avenue, US
Country: United States
Contact: Artistic Director Gregory Hustis
Contact: music Director Guillermo Figueroa

Music Mountain
Website: www.musicmountain.org
Email: info@musicmountain.org
Phone: 860 824 7126
Address: PO Box 738, US
Information: The Steinway Piano is the official piano of Music Mountain
Country: United States
Contact: President board Manager Nicholas Gordon

Music Programs – LACMA
Website: www.lacma.org
Email: publicinfo@lacma.org
Phone: 323 857 6000
Address: 5905 Wilshire Blvd, US
Information: primarily multi centuries repertoire
Country: United States

Music Society of the Midland Center for the Arts
Website: www.mcfta.org
Phone: 989 631 5930
Address: 1801 W St Andrews Drive, US
Country: United States
Contact: Artistic Director Jim Hohmeyer
Contact: Managing Director James F Hohmeyer
Contact: Robb Woulfe

Music Worcester Inc.
Website: www.musicworcester.org
Email: music@musicworcester.org
Phone: 508 754 3231
Address: 323 Main Street, US
Information: Music Worcester was formed through a merger between the 'International Artist Series' and 'Worcester County Music Association'
Country: United States
Contact: Executive Director Stasia Hovenesian
Contact: Marketing Director Andrea Ehrenreich

Music/Theatre Workshop
Email: musictheatre@earthlink.net
Phone: 773 973 7266
Address: 7359 N Greenview, US
Information: tour through Illinois; theatre productions are all new works; assist youth with the creation and presentation of work; working in collaboration with the Field Natural History Museum and Cook County Juvenile Detention Centre
Country: United States
Contact: Executive Director Robert T Carter
Contact: programme coordinator Chiara Liberatore
Contact: Artistic Director Meade Palidofsky

Musicians from Marlboro
Website: www.marlboromusic.org
Email: info@marlboromusic.org
Phone: 212 581 5197
Address: 201 W 54 St, US
Information: touring program of the Marlboro Music School and Festival
Country: United States
Contact: Associate Frank Salomon

Muskingum College Fine Arts Series
Website: www.muskingum.edu
Email: jmartin@muskingum.edu
Phone: 740 826 8211
Address: Muskingum College, 163 Stormant Street, US
Country: United States
Contact: special events Jerry Martin
Contact: Director of public relations Janice McCloud

Nantucket Musical Arts Society
Phone: 508 228 1287
Address: PO Box 897, US
Information: summer series
Country: United States
Contact: President Eva-Maria Tausig

Napa Valley Opera House
Website: www.napavalleyoperahouse.org
Email: info@nvoh.org
Phone: 707 226 7372
Address: 1030 Main Street, US
Information: historic venue, built in 1879, re-opened August 2003 following $14 million renovation, located in heart of California wine country
Country: United States
Contact: interim Artistic Director Chris Smith
Contact: Marketing Director Julie Dalrymple
Contact: development coordinator Mary Ann Moffitt

Naperville-North Central College Perf. Arts Association
Phone:
630 369 5595
Address: 1240 Royal St George, US
Country: United States
Contact: vice President for programming Patricia Hagmeyer

Nashua Community Concert Association
Website: www.gran-net.com/ncc
Email: ncca@aspi.net
Phone: 160 388 26840
Address: c/o Ernest D. Berube, 31 Cushing Avenue, US
Country: United States
Contact: stage Manager Chris Buswell
Contact: President Ernest D Berube

Nassau County Department of Recreation & Parks
Website: www.co.nassau.ny.us
Email: doreenbanks@mail.co.nassau.ny.us
Phone: 516 572 0252
Address: Eisenhower Park, Admin Bldg, US
Country: United States
Contact: commisioner Doreen Banks
Contact: Director of performing arts Brenda Spezio
Contact: regional supervisor Andrew Hardwick

National Building Museum – Music in the Great Hall
Website:
www.nbm.org
Email: cabrams@nbm.org
Phone: 202 272 2448
Address: 401 F Street NW, US
Country: United States
Contact: vp of communications and Marketing Carol Abrams

National Council for the Traditional Arts
Website: www.ncta.net
Email: info@ncta.net
Phone: 301 565 0654
Address: 1320 Fenwick Lane, Suite 200, US
Information: produce 5 major festivals annually
Country: United States
Contact: Executive Director Julia Olin
Policies: Other

National Technical Institute for the Deaf (NTID)
Website: www.rit.edu
Email: jmo5601@rit.edu
Phone: 585 475 6250
Address: Performing Arts Program – Robert F Panara Theatre, 52 Lomb Memorial Drive, US
Information: all NTID productions and guest artists must be accessible to both deaf and hearing audiences
Country: United States
 coordinator & General Manager
Jim Orr
Contact: Artistic Director Bonnie Meath-Lang
Contact: dance programmes Thomas Warfield
Contact: Chairperson Joseph Bochner

National-Louis University
Website: www.nl.edu
Email: tfrank@nl.edu
Phone: 847 256 5150 ext
Address: Evanston Campus, 2840 Sheridan Rd, US
Country: United States
Contact: facility Manager Terri Frank

Navajo Dine College
Website: www.dinecollege.edu
Email: wjensen@ncc.cc.nm.us
Phone: 928 724 6741
Address: Office of Student Programs, One Circle Drive, Route 12, US
Information: specialise in Native American music and dance
Country: United States
Contact: student programmes Director Walter Jensen

Nazareth College Arts Center
Email: nlpeet@nac.edu
Phone: 585 389 2175
Address: 4245 East Ave, US
Information: member of Upstate New York Presenters
Country: United States
Contact: arts center Director David Ferrell
Contact: Director of programmes Joseph Baranowski
assistant Director & operations Manager
Terrence Meyer
Contact: publicity Manager Lee Ann Brind'Amour
Contact: technical Director David LaDue

Nederlander Theatre
Website: www.nederlander.com
Phone: 212 840 5577
Address: 208 W 41st Street, US
Country: United States
Contact: management company The Nederlander Org, Inc

Capacity: 1203

Neil Simon Theatre
Website: www.nederlander.com
Phone: 212 840 5577
Address: 250 West 52nd Street, US
Country: United States
Contact: management company The Nederlander Org, Inc
Contact: house Manager Victor Irving
Capacity: 1450

New England Conservatory
Website: www.newenglandconservatory.edu
Email: admissions@newenglandconservatory.edu
Phone: 617 585 1101
Address: 290 Huntington Avenue, US
Country: United States
Contact: Manager of performing services Bryan Yankee
Contact: public relations Manager Ellen Pfeifer
Contact: President Tony Woodcock

New Horizons – Children's National Medical Center
Email: tlassite@cnmc.org
Phone: 202 884 3465
Address: 111 Michigan Avenue NW, US
Information: arts education & cultural enrichment programs in children's hospital
Country: United States
Contact: Managing Director – new horizons Tina Lassiter

New Orleans Ballet Association (NOBA)
Website: www.nobadance.com
Email: muebelacker@nobadance.com
Phone: 504 522 0996
Address: 5813 Citrus Boulevard, Suite 203, US
Country: United States
Contact: Marketing Manager Megan Uebelacker
Contact: Executive Director Jenny R Hamilton

New Orleans Friends of Music
Website: www.friendsofmusic.org
Email: nofom@tulane.edu
Phone: 150 489 50690
Address: 1035 Eleonore Street, US
Country: United States
Contact: President Julianne Nice

New Orleans Public Schools Cultural Resources
Email: aienops@acadiacom.net
Phone: 504 304 3815
Address: 3510 General DeGaulle, US
Country: United States
Contact: secretary Sharon Isaac
Contact: coordinator Janet Johnson

New Victory Theater
Website: www.newvictory.org
Phone: 646 223 3000
Address: c/o The New 42nd Street, 229 W 42nd Street, 10th Floor, US
Information: presenting venue; offers complete education program
Country: United States
Contact: President Cora Cahan
Contact: programming Associate Carrie DuBois
Contact: Director of programming Mary Rose Lloyd

New York City College of Technology
Website: www.citytech.cuny.edu
Email: fdezego@citytech.cuny.edu
Phone: 718 260 5000 ext
Address: 300 Jay St, US
Country: United States
Contact: contact Frank De Zego
Contact: Director of communications Eileen Fischer

New York University Program Board
Website: www.osa.nyu.edu
Email: adam.ebnit@nyu.edu
Phone: 212 998 4997
Address: 60 Washington Square South, Suite 704, US
Country: United States
Contact: coordinator of campus programming Adam Ebnit

Newark Symphony Hall
Website: www.newarksymphonyhall.org
Phone: 973 643 4550
Address: 1020 Broad Street, US
Country: United States
Contact: General Manager Oscar James
Contact: development/Marketing officer Catherine J Lenix-Hooker
Contact: Executive Director Roslyn L Lightfoot

Newport Performing Arts Centre
Website: www.coastarts.org
Email: occa@coastarts.org
Phone: 541 265 9231
Address: 777 W Olive Street, PO Box 1315, US
Information: various film festivals throughout the year; taking international bookings
Country: United States

Contact: Executive Director Catherine Rickbone

Nicholls State University
Email: angela.hammerli@nicholls.edu
Phone: 985 448 4273
Address: Artists and Lectures Committee, PO Box 2038, Louisiana, US
Country: United States
Contact: head, artists and lectures series Angela Hammerli

Nicolae Bretan Music Foundation
Email: miki2@cox.net
Phone: 703 893 5871
Address: 8542 Georgetown Pike, US
Information: see also Competitions (The Nicolae Bretan Competition for Vocal Interpretation)
Country: United States
Contact: President Judit Bretan

Norris Cultural Arts Center
Website: www.norrisculturalarts.com
Email: info@norrisculturalarts.com
Phone: 630 584 7200
Address: 1040 Dunham Road, US
Information: school, community events. other email: businessoffice@norrisculturalarts.com
Country: United States
Contact: Director of operations Jo Anne Granquist
Email: businessoffice@norrisculturalarts.com

Norris Theatre for the Performing Arts
Website: www.palosverdesperformingarts.com/
Email: Marketing@pvperformingarts.com
Phone: 310 544 0403
Address: 27570 Norris Center Drive, Norris Center Drive Rolling Hills Estates, US
Information: Established in 1983, the 450-seat Norris Theatre offers tiered seating with outstanding visibility from any seat in the house
Country: United States
Contact: Artistic Director James W. Gruessing
Contact: President and acting Executive Director Julie Moe-Reynolds
Contact: Office Manager Vicky Mar
Social Media: https://twitter.com/PV_Perf_Arts https://www.facebook.com/palosverdesperformingarts https://www.instagram.com/pvpanorristheatre/
Disabled Access: Yes
Capacity: 251-500
Annual Performances: 100+
Annual Productions: 11-25
Policies: All

North Carolina Central University – Lyceum Series
Website: www.nccu.edu/academics/universitycollege/devsup/lyceum.cfm
Phone: 919 530 6100
Address: 1801 Fayetteville St., US
Information: the mission of the North Carolina Central University Lyceum Series is to promote and enhance the intellectual, cultural, and aesthetic aspects of student growth and development through a series of outstanding lectures, recitations, concerts, dramas, and exhibitions
Country: United States

North Carolina State University Center Stage
Website: www.ncsu.edu/arts
Email: artsncstate@ncsu.edu
Phone: 919 513 1800
Address: Campus Box 7306, US
Information: Arts NC State advocates on behalf of an exciting and diverse collective of visual and performing arts programs. By fostering collaboration, coordination, shared resources, cross-promotion, and mutual support among these programs, Arts NC State enriches the lives of students while serving the community, region and state. The programs of Arts NC State are the Crafts Center, the Dance Program, the Gregg Museum of Art & Design, the Music Department, NC State LIVE, and University Theatre
Country: United States
Contact: Executive Director Rich Holly
Email: rtholly@ncsu.edu
Social Media: @artsncstate www.facebook.com/artsncstate/?fref=ts

North Iowa Area Community College – On Stage
Website: www.niacc.edu
Email: slavetim@niacc.edu
Phone: 641 422 4274
Address: 500 College Drive, US
Country: United States
Contact: auditorium Manager Tim Slaven

North Metro Arts Alliance
Website: www.nmarts.net
Email: aholmes@adams50.org
Phone: 303 429 1999
Address: PO Box 1043, US
Country: United States
Contact: vice President Peggy Boccard

Contact: President Becky Silver

North Orange County Community Concerts Association
Website: www.northocconcerts.org
Email: membership@northocconcerts.org
Phone: 714 535 8925
Address: 623 South Clara St, 114 No. Pomona Ave., Fullerton CA 92832, US
Country: United States
Contact: vice President John Jackson
Email: jackandeileen2002@yahoo.com
Annual Performances: 5
Policies: Rent and present, Other

North Shore Music Theatre
Website: www.nsmt.org
Email: pr@nsmt.org
Phone: 978 232 7200
Address: 62 Dunham Road, US
Country: United States
Contact: communications Manager Julie Arvedon
Contact: contact Mike Ceceri
Artistic director & Executive Producer Jon Kimbell until end of Janu

Northeast Ohio Jazz Society
Website: www.neojazz.org
Phone: 121 642 69900
Address: 4614 Prospect, Suite 533, US
Information: free-standing concerts, full range of jazz; also offers educational courses and workshops
Country: United States

Northeastern State University Allied Arts
Website: www.nsuok.edu
Email: robinska@nsuok.edu
Phone: 918 456 5511 ext
Address: ., US
Country: United States
Contact: Director Katherine Robinson

Northeastern University Center for the Arts – Arts Performance Series
Website: www.centerforthearts.neu.edu
Email: de.arias@neu.edu
Phone: 617 373 4472
Address: 102 The Fenway, 118 Cushing Hall, US
Country: United States
Contact: Director Del Lewis
Contact: Director of public relations Susan Jaeger
Contact: Del Lewis

Northern Arizona University Performing Arts Series
Website: www.nau.edu/cal/theatre/events
Email: artsandletters@nau.edu
Phone: 928 523 3781
Address: 317 W Tormey Dr, PO Box: 5064, US
Information: two state-of-the-art stages, the 300-seat Clifford E. White and the Studio Theater a highly flexible space has been transformed into the round, tennis court, modified thrust, and various configurations over the years, allowing our students to experience a variety of audience actor dynamics.**Country:** United States
Contact: Chair Kathleen M. McGeever
Email: Kathleen.McGeever@nau.edu
Phone: 928 523 4500
Social Media: https:// www.facebook.com/NAUTheatre https:// www.instagram.com/nautheatre/
Capacity: 501-1000
Annual Performances: 100+
Policies: All

Northern Illinois University Programming & Activities
Website: www.niu.edu/cab
Email: cabfinearts@niu.edu
Phone: 815 753 1580
Address: Campus Life Building, 539 Lucinda Ave, Room 150, US
Country: United States
asst Director – univ. programming & activities Mary Tosch

Northern Michigan University Cultural Events Series
Website: www.mnu.edu
Phone: 906 227 1481
Address: Northern Michigan University Art Museum, US
Country: United States
Contact: cultural affairs co-ordinator Wayne Francis

Northland College Arts and Letters Series
Website: www.northland.edu
Email: shall@northland.edu
Phone: 715 682 1679
Address: 1411 Ellis Avenue, US
Country: United States
Contact: senior coordinator t.b.a.

Northwestern Michigan College
Website: www.nmc.edu
Email: cmuma@nmc.edu
Phone: 123 199 51399 c

Address: 1701 E Front St, US
Information: see also Dennos Museum Center
Country: United States
Contact: contact Cathy Muma

Northwestern State University of Louisiana
Website: www.nsula.edu
Email: brent@nsula.edu
Phone: 318 357 4522
Address: Creative and Performing Arts, 140 Central Ave., US
Country: United States
Contact: Director, school of creative and performing arts Bill Brent

Northwestern University School of Music
Website: music.northwestern.edu
Email: nusmweb@northwestern.edu
Phone: 847 491 7575
Address: 711 Elgin Road, US
Country: United States
Contact: department of music studies Chair Richard Ashley
Contact: music performance studies co-Chair Karen Brunssen

Norton Center for the Arts, Centre College
Website: www.center.edu
Email: hoskins@center.edu
Phone: 859 236 4692
Address: 600 W Walnut St, US
Country: United States
Contact: Managing Director George Foreman

Notre Dame de Namur University Ralston Concert Series
Website: www.music.ndnu.edu
Email: mschmitz@ndnu.edu
Phone: 650 508 3429
Address: 1500 Ralston Avenue, US
Country: United States

Nyack College Program of Cultural Events
Website: www.nyackcollege.edu
Phone: 914 358 1710
Address: 1 South Boulevard, US
Country: United States
Contact: contact Marion Howe

NYK Productions Inc
Website: www.nykconcerts.com
Email: info@nykconcerts.com
Phone: 954 457 9100
Address: 215 N. Federal Highway, Hallandale Beach, US
Country: United States
Contact: public relations/General coordinator Mayumi Hasegawa
Contact: President Arie Kaduri
Contact: talent coordinator Alison Chaplin

O'Shaughnessy Auditorium/O'Shaughnessy Presents!
Website: www.stcatherine.college.edu
Email: plynch@stkate.edu
Phone: 651 690 6701
Address: 2004 Randolph Avenue, US
Country: United States
Contact: Managing Director Jamie Ryan

Oakeside Bloomfield Cultural Center
Email: oakside240@aol.com
Phone: 973 429 0960
Address: 240 Belleville Ave, US
Information: art shows for youth
Country: United States
Contact: Director Kim Rylly

Oakwood University Arts and Lectures
Email: music@oakwood.edu
Phone: 256 726 7278musi
Address: 7000 Adventist BLVD, US
Information: supports the college's mission of providing students with the broadest possible access to quality music instruction, opportunities, and services.
Country: United States

Oberlin College Conservatory of Music Artist Recital Series
Website: www.oberlin.edu/arseries
Email: marci.alegant@oberlin.edu
Phone: 440 775 8926
Address: Oberlin Conservatory of Music, 77 West College St, US
Country: United States
Contact: presenter of recital series Nita Karpf
Contact: Associate dean Marci Alegant

Oglebay Institute Fine Arts Department
Website: www.oionline.com
Email: inspire@oionline.com
Phone: 304 242 7747
Address: 1330 National Road, US
Information: also have ballet, jazz, tap and modern dance classes; drama classes; shows independent and art films

Country: United States
Contact: Director performing arts Kate Crosbie
Contact:
Director of Marketing and communication Misty Klug
Social Media: www.facebook.com/oglebayinstitute

Ohio Northern University Artist Series
Website: www.onu.edu
Email: ed-williams@onu.edu
Phone: 419 772 2151 Mus
Address: 525 South Main Street, US
Country: United States
Contact: Director honors program Patrick Croskery
Contact: communication arts department Nils Reiss
Contact: music department Ed Williams

Ohio Theatre
Email: info@ohioballet.org
Phone: 419 241 6785
Address: 3114 Lagrange Street, US
Information: also rent
Country: United States
Contact: General Manager Jim Stitulski

Ohio University Performing Arts Series
Website: www.ohio.edu/performingarts
Email: performingarts@ohio.edu
Phone: 740 593 1780
Address: Ohio University Performing Arts Series, Baker Center 339, US
Country: United States
Contact: Director Gretchen Stephens
Social Media: @ouperformingart www.facebook.com/OU-Performing-Arts-22446717913

Ohio Wesleyan University Performing Artists Series
Website: www.owu.edu
Email: dgvander@owu.edu
Phone: 740 368 2000
Address: 61 S Sandusky St, US
Country: United States
Contact: music Nancy Gamso
Contact: jazz Marty Kalb
Contact: theatre, dance Glen Vanderbilt

Oklahoma City University – School of American Dance and Arts Management
Website: www.okcu.edu/dance_amgt
Email: ado@okcu.edu
Phone: 405 521 5322
Address: The American Spirit Dance Co., 2501 N Blackwelder, US
Information: all productions are originated by Oklahoma City University; does not book outside organisations and performers; dance company The American Spirit Dance Company conducts domestic USA and international tours
Country: United States
Contact: dean John Bedford
Contact: Director Jo Rowan

Oklahoma State University Allied Arts
Website: alliedarts.okstate.edu
Email: joe.ray@okstate.edu
Phone: 405 744 7509
Address: 030 Student Union, Oklahoma State University, US
Country: United States
Contact: coordinator (special events) Joe Ray

Old First Concerts
Website: www.oldfirstconcerts.org
Email: staff@oldfirstconcerts.org
Phone: 415 474 1608
Address: 1751 Sacramento St, US
Country: United States
Contact: Director Kathy Barr
Contact: program Associate Rick Bahto

Omaha Performing Arts
Website: www.omahaperformingarts.org
Email: info@omahaperformingarts.org
Phone: 402 345 0202
Address: 409 South 16th St. (Orpheum Theater), 1200 Douglas Street (Holland Performing Arts Center), Omaha, US
Information: The largest arts institution in Nebraska. The organisation is dedicated to enriching the lives of the citizens of Omaha and surrounding communities. In its two venues: the Orpheum Theater and Holland Performing Arts Center, the organisation presents the best of Broadway, jazz, blues, dance, comedy, family and popular entertainment, along with a range of educational programmes and free community events
Country: United States
Contact: President Joan Squires
Email: Jsquires@omahaperformingarts.org
Contact: senior vice President Arnold Reeves
Email: Areeves@omahaperformingarts.org
Contact: Associate Director of Marketing and Digital Lee Turkovich
Social Media: https://twitter.com/OPerformingArts www.facebook.com/OmahaPerformingArtsOrg https://

www.instagram.com/Operformingarts/
Disabled Access: Yes
Capacity: 1000+
Annual Performances: 100+
Policies: Rent and Present

Omni Foundation for the Performing Arts
Website: www.omniconcerts.com
Email: info@omniconcerts.com
Phone: 415 242 4500
Address: 236 W. Portal Avenue #1, US
Country: United States
Contact: Executive Director Richard Patterson

On Stage
Phone: 256 764 1881/ 76
Address: 123 North Seminary Street, US
Information: non-profit organisation founded in 1936
Country: United States
Contact: President Van Morgan
Contact: programme Chairman Harriet Edwards

On the Boards – New Performance Series, Northwest New Works
Website: www.ontheboards.org
Email: info@ontheboards.org
Phone: 206 217 9886 (ad
Address: PO Box 19515, US
Information: visiting address: 100 West Roy, Seattle, WA 98119
Country: United States
Contact: Artistic Director Lane Czaplinski
pr & Marketing Director
Laurie Rose
Contact: Managing Director Diane Ragsdale

Onion River Arts Council
Website: www.onionriverarts.org
Email: orac@sover.net
Phone: 802 229 9408
Address: 39 Main St # 1, US
Information: arts in education program brings arts to schools and makes it easier for children to go to see performances
Country: United States
Contact: Director Diane Manion

onStage at Connecticut College
Website: www.conncoll.edu/events/concerts
Email: onstage@conncoll.edu
Phone: 860 439 2787
Address: onStage at Connecticut College, 270 Mohegan Ave, PO Box 5216, US
Country: United States
Contact: Director Robert A. Richter

OPAS at Texas A & M University
Website: www.mscopas.org
Email: anne@msc.tamu.edu
Phone: 979 845 1661
Address: MS 1237, Texas A&M University, US
Information: Founded in 1972, OPAS at Texas A&M University – an organization of the Memorial Student Center – presents professional productions of theatre, music and dance programs that enlighten, entertain and inspire audiences of the Brazos Valley. OPAS programs are funded entirely by revenue generated from ticket Sales and contributions.
Country: United States
Contact: Executive Director Anne Black
Email: anne@msc.tamu.edu
Contact: business co-ordinator Terri Becker
Email: terri@msc.tamu.edu
Contact: Marketing and development co-ordinator Becky Wade
Email: becky@msc.tamu.edu
Contact: communications coordinator Shanna Wright
Email: swright@msc.tamu.edu
Social Media: @mscopas www.facebook.com/MSCOPAS

Opera Columbus
Website: www.operacolumbus.org
Email: info@operacolumbus.org
Phone: 614 461 8101
Address: 55 E. State Street, US
Information: The mission of Opera Columbus is to enrich central Ohio by producing high quality opera, nurturing emerging talent, and cultivating exposure to opera in ways that feed the souls of our residents, bolster the cultural economy, and make central Ohio a great place to live, work and play.
Country: United States
Contact: assistant Executive Director and Director of development Susan Ropp
Email: sropp@operacolumbus.org
Contact: Director of Artistic and educational programming Peggy Kriha Dye
Email: pkrihadye@operacolumbus.org
Contact: Executive Director Chad Whittington
Email: cwhittington@capa.com
Social Media: @OperaColumbus www.facebook.com/OperaColumbus/
Policies: Present, produce, co-produce, Theatre

Opera House Fund Inc – Broadway Live at the Opera House
Website: www.lexingtonoperahouse.com
Email: mail@lexingtonoperahouse.com
Phone: 859 233 4567
Address: Lexington Center Corp, 430 West Vine St, US
Country: United States
Contact: performing arts department Sally Noger

Opera House Of Sandwich
Website: www.sandwichoperahouse.com
Email: operahouse@sannauk.com
Phone: 815 786 2555
Address: 140 East Railroad St, US
Information: also rent
Country: United States
Contact: Executive Director Sandra Black

Opera Music Theatre International
Website: www.omti.org
Email: info@omti.org
Phone: 120 268 37874
Address: 1300 Pennsylvania Ave, NW #700, US
Information: see also Marjorie Lawrence International Vocal Competition and Festival
Country: United States
Contact: President and General Director James K McCully

Orange Coast College
Website: www.occtickets.com
Email: gblanc@cccd.edu
Phone: 714 432 5916
Address: 2701 Fairview Road, US
Country: United States
Contact: communications and business George Blanc
Contact: dean, visual and performing arts Joseph Poshek

Orange County Community College – Arts & Communication Department
Email: mstrunsky@sunyorange.edu
Phone: 845 341 4787
Address: 115 South St, US
Country: United States
Contact: Chairperson Mark Strunsky
Contact: music advisor Chris Parker
cultural affairs & lyceum coordinator Dorothy Szefc

Orcas Center
Website: www.orcascenter.org
Email: info@orcascenter.org
Phone: 360 376 6822
Address: PO Box 567, 917 Mt Baker Rd, US
Country: United States
Policies: Present, produce, co-produce, Produce and rent, Arts centre

Ordway Center for the Performing Arts
Website: www.ordway.org
Phone: 651 282 3000
Address: 345 Washington Street, US
Information: The Ordway, recognized as one of the U.S.'s leading not-for-profit performing arts centers, is home to a wide variety of performances throughout the year that encompass the finest in American musical theater, world music, dance, and vocal artists in its Music Theater and Concert Hall. Each year the Ordway presents its Flint Hills International Children's Festival and serves over 50, 000 children and adults through its Ordway Education programs. Since the Ordway opened, it has become known as Saint Paul's most inviting performance venue, attracting audiences from throughout the region to its diverse range of presentations.Member of ISPA
Country: United States
Contact: President and CEO Jamie Grant
Contact: vice President of advancement Diane Nixa
Contact: Executive vice President and cfo Christine Sagstetter
Social Media: @theordway www.facebook.com/ordway-center
Capacity: 2206

Oregon Symphony Association
Website: www.orsymphony.org
Email: symphony@orsymphony.org
Phone: 503 228 4294
Address: 921 S. W. Washington Street, Suite 200, US
Information: see also Orchestras (Oregon Symphony)
Country: United States
Contact: vice President of Marketing Michael Kosmala
Contact: interim President Gerald R Hulsman

Oroville Community Concert Association
Website: www.chamberorganizer.com/orovillechamber
Email: swedin@cncnet.com
Phone: 153 058 90836
Address: 29 Orchard Hill Drive, US
Country: United States
Contact: President Sharon Wedin

Osprey Productions, University of North Florida
Website: www.unf.edu
Email: osprod@unf.edu

Phone: 904 620 2460
Address: 4567 St Johns Bluff Rd S, US
Information: 2 outdoor festivals
Country: United States
Contact: arena Manager Becky Purser

Ottawa Municipal Auditorium Entertainment Series
Website: www.grapevine.net/~omalive
Email: omalive@grapevine.net
Phone: 785 242 8810
Address: PO Box 462, US
Information: receive tours
Country: United States
Contact: administrative Manager Shande Stitt

Otterbein College Artist Series
Website: www.otterbein.edu
Phone: 614 823 1600
Address: Cellar House, 141 W Park St, US
Country: United States
Contact: Director Patricia Kessler
Contact: office Manager Barbara Brown

Overture Center for the Arts
Website: www.overturecenter.com
Email: info@overturecenter.com
Phone: 608 258 4141
Address: 201 State St, US
Information: Overture Center for the Arts is a stunning architectural landmark in the heart of Madison's thriving cultural arts district. In addition to housing ten resident organizations and presenting more than 200 performances, art exhibitions, and educational and community events each year, Overture offers a variety of venues for performances, corporate meetings, conventions, trade shows, weddings, banquets, and receptions. member of ISPA
Country: United States
President & CEO
Ted DeDee
Email: President@overturecenter.org
Contact: Marketing Director Heather Harris
Email: hharris@overturecenter.org
Contact: finance Manager Chris Vogel
Email: cvogel@overture.org
Social Media: @OvertureCenter www.facebook.com/overturecenter
Policies: All

Oxnard Performing Arts Center
Website: https:// www.oxnardperformingarts.com/
Email: info@oxnardperformingarts.com
Phone: 805 385 8147
Address: 800 Hobson Way, Oxnard, US
Information: As one of the larger theater's in western Ventura County, the Oxnard Performing Arts & Convention Center provides outstanding entertainment opportunities to Ventura County residents and visitors. Consisting of 1, 604 seats, the theater provides a convenient location for numerous cultural, educational and entertainment opportunities.A combination of distinctive features makes the Oxnard Performing Arts & Convention Center the ideal Complex for business meetings, trade shows, seminars...
Country: United States
Contact: Chairperson Gary Blum
Contact: Vice Chair Carol Flores-Beck
Contact: Executive Director Carolyn Merino Mullin
Social Media: https:// www.facebook.com/OxnardPerformingArts/ https:// www.instagram.com/oxnardpacc/ https://twitter.com/oxnardpacc
Capacity: 1000+
Annual Performances: 51-100
Policies: All

OZ Arts Nashville
Website: www.ozartsnashville.org
Email: info@ozartsnashville.org
Phone: 615 350 7200
Address: 6172 Cockrill Bend Circle, US
Information: OZ Arts supports the creation, development and presentation of significant performing and visual art works by leading artists whose contribution influences the advancement of their field. Member of ISPA
Country: United States
Contact: founder Cano Ozgener
Contact: President and chief Executive officer Tim Ozgener
Contact: Artistic Associate Kate Abrams
Contact: technical Director Tyler Axt
Contact: accounting Manager Jaime Lassiter
Social Media: @OZNashville www.facebook.com/OZArtsNashville
Policies: Multi-purpose

Pabst Theater
Website: www.pabsttheatre.org
Email: gwitt@pabsttheatre.org
Phone: 414 286 3665
Address: 144 E Wells St, US
Information: present and rent
Country: United States
Contact: pr Director Cecilia Hrobsky

Contact: Executive Director Gary Witt

PACE Performing Arts/Community & Education
Website: www.pacefl.org
Email: rs@pacefl.org
Phone: 305 895 5488
Address: 7538 South West 64th St, US
Information: a non-profit making performing arts group and events coordinator
Country: United States
Contact: Executive Director Rod Glaubman

Pace University Performing Arts Series
Website: www.pace.edu
Email: ncatalano@pace.edu
Phone: 914 923 2653
Address: Dow Hall, Rm 114, Elm Road, US
Country: United States
Contact: Director Nicholas Catalano
Contact: assistant Director Joyce Farrell

Pacific Arts Councils Network (PAC)
Website: www.prel.org
Email: phillipl@prel.org
Phone: 808 441 1300
Address: Pacific Resources for Education and Learning, 900 Fort Street Mall, Suite 1300, US
Country: United States
Contact: Executive Director Lori Phillips

Pacific Composers Forum
Website: www.composersforum.com
Email: info@composersforum.com
Address: 2054 Midvale Avenue, US
Information: all new music, mostly premieres
Country: United States
Contact: Executive Director Mark Ruttle

PACT, Inc – Ruth Eckerd Hall
Website: www.rutheckerdhall.com
Email: lpoppens@rutheckerdhall.net
Phone: 727 791 7060
Address: 1111 McMullen Booth Road, US
Information: member of Florida Professional Presenters consortium; member of ISPA, Southern Arts Presenter
Country: United States
Contact: Director of Marketing/communications Lex Poppens
Contact: Director of entertainment Bob Rossi
Contact: Executive Director/CEO Robert Freedman

Palace Theatre
Website: www.palacetheatre.org
Email: info@palacetheatre.org
Phone: 603 668 5588
Address: 80 Hanover Street, 6 Parmenter Road, US
Information: The Palace Theatre is a non-profit performing arts center that hosts its own professional company, youth and teen program and presenting acts.
Country: United States
Contact: President and chief Executive officer Peter Ramsey
Email: peterramsey@palacetheatre.org
Contact: Artistic Director Carl Rajotte
Email: carlrajotte@palacetheatre.org
Contact: Director of individual development Tina Kelly
Email: tinakelly@palacetheatre.org
Contact: Director of corporate development Tammi Graff
Email: tammigraff@palacetheatre.org
Contact: production Manager Whit Privette
Email: whitprivette@palacetheatre.org
Contact: youth theatre administrator Megan Quinn
Email: pyt@palacetheatre.org
Contact: grant writer Heather Merrill
Email: heathermerrill@palacetheatre.org
Social Media: @PalaceTheatre www.facebook.com/pages/The-Palace-Theatre/30277326381
Policies: All, Theatre

Palace Theatre
Website: palacetheatreonbroadway.com/
Email: customerservice@nederlander.com
Phone: 212 840 5577
Address: 1450 Broadway, US
Country: United States
Policies: Theatre

Palm Beach Community College Glades Campus/ Dolly Hand/ Cultural Arts Center
Website: www.pbcc.edu/arts
Email: woodhaml@pbcc.edu
Phone: 561 994 1160
Address: 1977 College Dr, US
Information: member of Florida Professional Presenters consortium
Country: United States
Contact: Manager Leigh Woodham

Palm Springs Desert Museum – Annenberg Theater
Website: www.psmuseum.org
Email: info@psmuseum.org
Phone: 760 322 4800
Address: 101 Museum Drive, US

Information: season runs from October to April
Country: United States
Contact: Director of Marketing communications Bob Bogard
Contact: Executive Director Steven Nash
Contact: pDirector of Administration and operations Lisa Vossler

Panama City Music Association
Website: www.panamacitymusicassoc.org
Phone: 185 023 61260
Address: PO Box 133, US
Information: booking address: 709 E Beech Drive, Panama City, FL 32401
Country: United States
Contact: vice President for talent/Artistic Director Joanne Cox
Contact: President Dr. Mimi Bozarth

Paramount Arts Center
Website: www.paramountartscenter.com
Phone: 606 324 3175
Address: PO Box 1546, US
Country: United States
Contact: Executive Director Kathleen Timmons
Contact: Marketing Director Tyson Compton

Paramount Arts Centre
Website: www.paramountarts.com
Email: boxoffice@paramountarts.com
Phone: 630 896 7676
Address: 23 East Galena Boulevard, US
Country: United States
Contact: chief Executive officer Tim Rater
Contact: Marketing Jamie Gronwick
Contact: Artistic Director Jim Corti

Paramount Center for the Arts
Website: www.paramountcenter.org
Email: Tickets@paramountcenter.org
Phone: 914 736 9585
Address: 1008 Brown St, US

Paramount Theatre for the Performing Arts
Website: www.austintheatrelliance.org
Email: pbeutel@austintheatrelliance.org
Phone: 512 472 2901
Address: PO Box 1566, US
Information: also show many classic films
Country: United States
Contact: Director of programming Paul Beutel

Park Theatre Performing Arts Center
Website: www.parkpac.org
Email: kashe@parkpac.org
Phone: 201 865 6980
Address: 560 32nd St, US
Information: present, rent, produce
Country: United States
Contact: technical Director Jim Foster
Contact: Executive Director emeritus Kevin Ashe
Contact: Executive Director John Penn Lewis

Parker Playhouse/Fort Lauderdale Broadway Series
Website: www.parkerplayhouse.com
Email: info@parkerplayhouse.com
Phone: 954 764 1441
Address: 707 North East 8th St, US
Country: United States

Parrish Art Museum
Website: www.thehamptons.com/museum
Email: fergusone@parrishart.org
Phone: 631 283 2118
Address: 25 Job's Ln, US
Country: United States
Contact: pr Erik Ferguson
 Director public progams & education
 Cara Conklin

Pasco-Hernando Community College Performing Arts Series
Website: www.phcc.edu
Phone: 727 847 2727
Address: 10230 Ridge Road, US
Country: United States
Contact: Executive Director of foundation David Barzelay
Contact: President of college Robert W Judson

Pasquerilla Performing Arts Center – Mainstage and Family Fun Series
Website: office.upj.pitt.edu
Email: nevali@pitt.edu
Phone: 814 269 7200
Address: University of Pittsburgh at Johnstown, 450 Schoolhouse Road, US
Country: United States
Contact: box office/Administration Beverly Walerysiak
Contact: technical Director Thomas Brubakar
Contact: Manager Patricia Carnevali

Patty Granville Arts Center
Website: www.garlandarts.com/gov/eg/arts/default.asp

Email: arts@garlandtx.gov
Phone: 972 205 2780
Address: PO Box 469002, US
Country: United States
Contact: Director of cultural facilities Patty Granville
Social Media: @GarlandArts www.facebook.com/GranvilleArtsCenter
Policies: Rent only

Paul Mellon Arts Center
Website: www.choate.edu
Email: rbrandt@choate.edu
Phone: 203 697 2396
Address: 333 Christian Street, US
Information: Secondary prep boarding school. Main Stage Theater capacity 760. Chapel Theater capacity 100. Experimental Theater capacity 168.
Country: United States
Contact: contact Randi Brandt
Policies: Present, produce, co-produce, Present and produce, Theatre

PCA – Great Performances
Website: www.pcagreatperformances.org
Email: pcabox@pcagreatperformances.org
Phone: 207 773 3150
Address: 477 Congress St, US
Country: United States
Contact: Executive Director Aimee Petrin
Contact: Director of development Mary Campbell
Contact: Director of Marketing and audience development Tom Ayres

Peace Center for the Performing Arts
Website: www.peacecenter.org
Email: mriegel@peacecenter.org
Phone: 864 467 3030
Address: 101 Broad Street, US
Country: United States
Contact: President Megan Riegel
Contact: Executive vice President for Marketing Carol May

Pend Oreille Arts Council
Website: www.artinsandpoint.org
Email: kim@artinsandpoint.org
Phone: 208 263 6139
Address: PO Box 1694, US
Country: United States
Contact: Executive Director Kim Queen

Peninsula Arts Appreciation Council Entertainment Series
Website: www.vistatheater.org
Email: paac@vistatheater.org
Phone: 190 647 57188
Address: 218 Iron Street, US
Country: United States
Contact: Executive Director Alfred L Keefer

Pennyroyal Arts Council
Website: www.pennyroyalarts.org
Email: paci@bellsouth.net
Phone: 270 887 4295
Address: PO Box 1038, US
Country: United States
Contact: Executive Director Carol Barta

Pensacola Junior College Music and Theatre Department
Website: www.pjc.edu
Email: kryan@pensacolastate.edu
Phone: 850 484 1000
Address: 1000 College Boulevard, US
Country: United States
Contact: administrative assistant Kelly Ryan
Contact: box office Manager Rhoda Moya

Pentangle Council on the Arts
Website: www.PentangleArts.org
Email: info@pentanglearts.org
Phone: 802 457 3981
Address: 31 The Green, US
Information: alternative e-mail: Pentarts@sover.net
Country: United States
Contact: Executive Director Sabrina Brown

People's Symphony Concerts
Website: www.pscny.org
Email: jennifer@franksalomon.com
Phone: 212 581 5197
Address: 201 West 54th Street, Suite 4C, US
Country: United States
Contact: Manager Frank Salomon
Contact: programme Manager Jennifer Flores

Peoria Civic Center
Website: www.peoriaciviccenter.com
Email: CustomerService@peoriaciviccenter.com
Phone: 309 673 8900
Address: 201 SW Jefferson Ave, US
Country: United States
Contact: Marketing Manager Dan Aspell
Email: daspell@peoriaciviccenter.com
Contact: General Manager Anne Clayton

Email: AClayton@PeoriaCivicCenter.com
Social Media: @peoriaciviccntr www.facebook.com/
PeoriaCivicCenter
Policies: Rent only

Peoria Park District
Website: www.peoriaparks.org
Email: smith1202@aol.com
Phone: 309 688 3667
Address: 2218 N Prospect Rd, US
Information: also present the Arts and Enter Section
Festival (July), annual; all events are free
Country: United States
Contact: fine arts coordinator Linda Elegant Huff

Pepperdine University Center for The Arts
Website: www.arts.pepperdine.edu
Email: rebecca.carson@pepperdine.edu
Phone: 131 050 64522
Address: 24255 Pacific Coast Highway, US
Information: also present the Parkening International
Guitar Competition (June) every three years; next in 2012
Country: United States
Contact: theatre operations Manager Todd M. Eskin
Contact: technical production Manager Kirk Pierron
Contact: Managing Director Rebecca Carson

Performance on 42nd
Website: www.whitney.org
Phone: 917 663 2551
Address: Whitney Museum of American Art at Philip
Morris, 120 Park Avenue at 42nd Street, US
Information: 6-7 Visual Art Exhibitions per year
Country: United States
Contact: Manager/Producer Shamin Momin
Contact: Howie Chen

Performance Riverside
Website: www.performanceriverside.org
Phone: 909 222 8100
Address: 4800 Magnolia Ave, US
Country: United States
Performance Space 122
Website: www.ps122.org
Email: info@performancespacenewyork.org
Phone: 212 477 5829
Address: 150 First Avenue 4th Floor New York, NY, US
Information: Performance Space New York provides
incomparable experiences for audiences by presenting
and commissioning artists whose work challenges
boundaries of live performance. Performance Space New
York is dedicated to supporting the creative risks taken
by artists from diverse genres, cultures and perspectives.
We are an innovative local, national and international
leader in contemporary performance. Formerly known
as ps122
Country: United States
Contact: Executive Artistic Director Jenny Schlenzka
Contact: deputy Director Pati Hertling
Email: Pati@performancespacenewyork.org
Contact: Press Blake Zidell
Email: blake@blakezidell.com
Contact: undefined
Social Media: https:// www.facebook.com/performanc-
espacenewyork
Disabled Access: Yes
Capacity: 251-500
Annual Performances: 100+
Policies: All

Performing Arts Association of St Joseph Inc
Website: www.paastjo.org
Email: info@paastjo.org
Phone: 816 279 1225
Address: 719 Edmond Street, US
Country: United States
Contact: Managing Director Mary Fahey

Performing Arts at Hamilton
Website: www.hamilton.edu
Email: mreiserm@hamilton.edu
Phone: 315 859 4331
Address: 198 College Hill Road, US
Country: United States
Contact: Director of performing arts Michelle Reis-
er-Memmer

Performing Arts Center – Purchase College
Website: www.artscenter.org
Email: center@purchase.edu
Phone: 914 251 6200
Address: 735 Anderson Hill Road, PO Box 140, Purchase
College, US
Information: the Performing Arts Center, Purchase
College, a four-theatre complex, is the major profession-
al, non-profit arts presenter. Each theatre is specifically
designed for the optimum presentation of a different
type of performance, enabling the presentation of any
kind of event
Country: United States
Contact: Director Harry McFadden
Email: harry.mcfadden@purchase.edu
Contact: Administration Karl Duchek
Email: karl.duchek@purchase.edu

Contact: Administration Gilbert Leib
Email: gilbert.leib@purchase.edu
Contact: accountant Teresa Milne-Davis
Email: teresa.milne-davis@purchase.edu
Contact: Administration Coni Guhl
Email: constance.guhl@purchase.edu
Social Media: @PurchasePAC www.facebook.com/
pages/The-Performing-Arts-Center-Purchase-Col-
lege/239798119185
Policies: Present and produce, Theatre

Performing Arts Center – University at Albany
Website: www.albany.edu/pac
Email: pferlo@csc.albany.edu
Phone: 518 442 3995 (di
Address: PAC-266, University at Albany, 1400 Washing-
ton Avenue, US
Country: United States
Contact: Director Patrick Ferlo
Contact: department secretary Cathy Baker
Contact: assistant Director Kim Engel

Performing Arts Center at Georgia Southern University
Website: georgiasouthern.edu/pac
Email: pac@georgiasouthern.edu
Phone: 912 478 7999
Address: 847 Plant Drive, US
Country: United States
Contact: Executive Director Carol Thompson
Social Media: @ThePACatGSU
Policies: Rent and present

Performing Arts Council of Toledo
Email: pact@accesstoledo.com
Phone: 419 241 3777
Address: 1838 Parkwood Avenue, Suite 420, US
Information: First Night 31 Dec – Festival in Toledo;
organises Musa Machine Arts Program in schools and
Season Sampler a reduced ticket system for arts events
in the area
Country: United States
Performing Arts Foundation, Inc
Website: www.grandtheater.org
Email: joconnell@grandtheater.org
Phone: 715 842 0988
Address: 401 Fourth Street, US
Country: United States
Contact: Executive Director Jim O'Connell
Contact: General Manager/Associate Director Merry
Little
Email: mlittle@grandtheater.org
Annual Performances: 100
Policies: Rent and present, Theatre

Performing Arts Series Youth & Adult
Website: www.cityofelgin.org
Email: hemmens@cityofelgin.org
Phone: 847 697 3616
Address: The Hemmens Cultural Center, 150 Dexter
Court, US
Information: the Cultural Center also contains exhibition
hall, art gallery & banquet facilities
Country: United States
Contact: technical supervisor Butch Wilhelmi
Contact: front of house supervisor Bill Folk
Contact: Bill Folk

Performing Arts Society of Acadiana
Website: www.pasa-online.org
Email: pasajll@aol.com
Phone: 377 237 2787
Address: PO Box 52979, US
Country: United States
Contact: Executive Director Jackie Lyle

Pershing Auditorium
Website: www.pershingauditorium.com
Email: info@pershingauditorium.com
Phone: 402 441 7500
Address: 226 Centennial Mall S., US
Country: United States
Contact: Manager Tom Lorenz
Contact: Marketing Director Derek Andersen

Peter B Lewis Theater
Email: www.Guggenheim.org
Phone: 121 242 33500
Address: Solomon R Guggenheim Museum, Sackler
Center for Arts Education, 1071 Fifth Avenue at 89th
Street, US
Country: United States
Capacity: 299

Philadelphia Chamber Music Society
Website: www.pcmsconcerts.org
Email: mail@pcmsconcerts.org
Phone: 215 569 8587
Address: 1528 Walnut Street, Suite 301, US
Information: PCMS presents an annual season of 55+
concerts by world-renowned artists. PCMS was created
so leading international artists would share their talents
each season in Philadelphia, and be enjoyed by all audi-
encesCountry: United States

Contact: Executive Director Philip Maneval
Email: pmaneval@pcmsconcerts.org
Contact: Artistic Director Anthony Checchia
Email: achecchia@pcmsconcerts.org
Contact: Artistic Director Miles Cohen
Email: mcohen@pcmsconcerts.org
Social Media: @pcmsconcerts www.facebook.com/
pcmsconcerts

Philharmonic Center for the Arts
Website: www.thephil.org
Email: info@thephil.org
Phone: 239 597 1111
Address: 5833 Pelican Bay Boulevard, US
Information: member of Florida Professional Presenters
consortium
Country: United States
Contact: CEO/Chairman Myra Daniels

Philharmonic Society Orange County
Website: www.philharmonicsociety.org
Email: contactus@philharmonicsociety.org
Phone: 949 553 2422
Address: 2082 Business Center Drive, Suite 100, US
Information: presents the Eclectic Orange Festival Sept –
June, see also Festivals
Country: United States
Contact: President and Artistic Director Dean Corey
Contact: Director of patron services Jonathan Mariott
Contact: Director of education Rita Major
Contact: Director of Marketing and pr Chantel Chen

Phillips Collection Concert Series
Website:
www.phillipscollection.org
Email: communications@phillipscollection.org
Phone:
202 387 2151
Address: 1600 21 Street NW, US
Country: United States
Contact: Director Dorothy Kosinski

Phoenix Chamber Music Society
Website: www.phoenixchambermusicsociety.org
Email: jcrummhorn@cox.net
Phone: 160 225 20095
Address: PO Box 34235, US
Country: United States
Contact: Executive Director Janet Green

Phoenix Parks Recreation & Library Department Cultural Programs
Website: www.phoenix.gov
Phone: 602 262 4627
Address: Phoenix Centre for the Arts, 1202 N Third St, US
Country: United States
Contact: Director of cultural programs Carmela Ramirez

Pick-Staiger Concert Hall – Northwestern Univer-sity, School of Music
Website: www.northwestern.edu
Email: pick-staiger@northwestern.edu
Phone: 847 491 5441
Address: 50 Arts Circle Drive, US
Country: United States
Contact: Director of concert activities Richard Van Kleeck

Pierre Monteux School for Conductors and Orchestra Musicians
Website: www.monteuxschool.org
Email: admin@monteuxschool.org
Address: 13 Captain Bill Road – Suite 2, PO Box 457, US
Information: a training programme to enable conduc-
tors to competently handle any conducting situation,
to help instrumentalists meet the many demands of
orchestral playing by studying and performing a large
and varied repertoire over the course of its six-week pro-
gramme. 2014 Summer Season is June 16 through July
27 Online application deadline is February 10, 2014
Country: United States
Contact: Executive Director Ron Schwizer
Email: admin@monteuxschool.org
Social Media: www.facebook.com/monteuxschool
Policies: Present and produce

Pikes Peak Center
Website: www.pikespeakcenter.com
Phone: 719 477 2121
Address: 190 S. Cascade Avenue, US
Information: owned by El Paso County and operated by
the Colordo Springs World Arena
Country: United States
Contact: General Manager Dorothea Lischick
Contact: Director of Marketing, Sales and promotions
Andrea Nyquist
Contact: Director of event services Dennis Lucero

Pima Community College
Website: www.pima.edu
Email: cfa@pima.edu
Phone: 520 206 6986
Address: Center for the Arts, 2202 W Anklam Road, US
Information: Pima is the 5th largest multi-campus com-

MUSO
COMMUNICATIONS

Digital & Print Publishing | Graphic Design
Web Development | Brand design | Marketing

info@musocommunications.com | www.musocommunications.com

munity campus in the country
Country: United States
Marketing & pr
Chris Cunningham
Contact: dean of arts division Frank Pickard

Pinal County Fine Arts Council, Arts in the Desert Series
Website: www.centralaz.edu
Email: public.events@centralaz.edu
Phone: 520 494 5223
Address: Signal Peak Campus, 8470 N. Overfield Rd, US
Country: United States
Contact: Marketing Director Daniel Bush

Pitman Theatre
Website: www.alverno.edu
Email: boxoffice@alverno.edu
Phone: 414 382 6150
Address: Alverno College, Alverno Presents, 3401 S 39th Street, PO Box 343922, US
Country: United States
Contact: alverno presents Director David Ravel

Pittsburgh Center for the Arts Exhibitions and Programs
Website: www.pittsburgharts.org
Phone: 412 361 0873
Address: 6300 5th Avenue, US
Information: offers studio art classes and workshops; exhibits work by contemporary regional artists; promotes and sells artists' work; provides school-and community-based education programs
Country: United States
Contact: interim Director Charlie Humphrey

Pittsburgh Chamber Music Society
Website: www.chambermusicpittsburgh.org/
Email: info@pittsburghchambermusic.org
Phone: 412 624 4129
Address: 315 South Bellefield Avenue, Room 305, US
Country: United States
Contact: Executive Director Kristen Linfante
Email: Director@chambermusicpittsburgh.org
Contact: Marketing and program coordinator Alisa Cullison
Email: alisa@chambermusicpittsburgh.org
Social Media: @chambermusicpgh www.facebook.com/chambermusicpittsburgh
Policies: Other

Pittsburgh Cultural Trust
Website: www.pgharts.org
Email: mail@pgharts.org
Phone: 412 471 6070
Address: 803 Liberty Avenue, US
Information: see also National Organisations
Country: United States
Contact: programming Manager Darcy Kucenic
Contact: President J Kevin McMahon
Contact: public relations Manager Veronica Corpuz
Contact: technical Director Bernard M. Bloom
Contact: theater services Director Susan Sternberger
Contact: Executive assistant to the President Ann M Ungar
Contact: operations Manager John Mumper
Contact: Associate production Manager Evan H. Stein

Pittsburgh Dance Council
Website: www.pgharts.org
Email: mail@pgharts.org
Phone: 412 471 1916
Address: 803 Liberty Avenue, US
Country: United States
Contact: Executive Director Paul Organisak
Contact: programming Manager Darcy C. Kucenic

Pittsburgh Symphony Heinz Hall
Website: www.pittsburghsymphony.org
Email: cmancuso@pittsburghsymphony.org
Phone: 412 392 4900
Address: Heinz Hall, 600 Penn Avenue, US
Information: alsorent; home of Pittsburgh Symphony
Country: United States
Contact: Manager of performing arts Carl Mancuso
Social Media: @pghsymphony www.facebook.com/PittsburghSymphonyOrchestra

Placitas Artists Series, Inc.
Website: www.PlacitasArts.org
Email: scoro9451@aol.com
Phone: 505 867 2471
Address: PO Box 944, US
Country: United States
Contact: Artistic Director Sally Curro
Contact: President Jackie Ericksen
Contact: secretary Gary Libman
Contact: treasurer Tim long

Playhouse Square Foundation – Broadway Series, Children's Theatre Series, Discovery Theatre Series
Website: www.playhousesquare.org
Phone: 216 771 4444

Address: 1501 Euclid Ave, Suite 200, US
Information: not-for-profit performing arts centre
Country: United States
Contact: Director of Marketing Adam Kaser
Contact: President Art J Falco
Contact: Director of education Carling Porter

Plymouth State College Silver Cultural Arts Center
Website: www.plymouth.edu/psc/cac
Email: djeffrey@mail.plymouth.edu
Phone: 603 535 2874 (di
Address: Main Street Suite 36, 17 High Street, US
Information: season September-April
Country: United States
Contact: Director Diane Jeffrey
Contact: house Manager Virginia Fisher
Contact: events coordinator Karen Weldon

Poetry Center and Cultural Affairs Department
Website: www.pccc.edu/poetry
Email: mgillan@pccc.edu
Phone: 973 684 6555
Address: Passaic County Community College, 1 College Blvd, US
Country: United States
Contact: assistant Director Aline Papazian
Contact: Executive Director Maria Mazziotti Gillan

Point Loma Nazarene College Cultural Events Series
Website: www.pointloma.edu
Email: paulkenyon@pointloma.edu
Phone: 619 849 2325
Address: 3900 Lomaland Drive, US
Country: United States
Contact: Chairman music dpet Paul Kenyon

Polk Community College Special Performances Series
Website: www.polk.cc.fl.us
Email: sbevis@polk.cc.fl.us
Phone: 863 297 1050
Address: 999 Avenue H, NE, US
Country: United States
Contact: cultural events assistant Sharon Bevis
Contact: Associate vice President William Ryan

Portland Institute for Contemporary Arts
Website: www.pica.org
Email: pica@pica.org
Phone: 503 242 1419
Address: 224 NW 13th, #305, US
Country: United States
Contact: guest Artistic Director Mark Russell
Contact: Executive Director Victoria Frey
Contact: performing arts program Director Erin Boberg

Portland Piano International
Website: www.portlandpiano.org
Email: info@portlandpiano.org
Phone: 503 228 1388
Address: 222 NW Davis St, Suite 405, US
Information: Portland Piano International presents a recital series of at least 6 pianists and a summer festival of at least 5 pianists performing recitals, master classes and lectures
Country: United States
Contact: Executive Director Pat Zagelow

Post Street Theatre
Website: www.poststreettheatre-sf.org
Phone: 141 532 12900
Address: 450 Post Street, US
Information: formerly known as Theatre on the Square
Country: United States

Poughkeepsie Riverfront Amphitheatre
Website: www.bardavon.org
Phone: 845 473 5288
Address: 35 Market Street, US
Information: also rent; promote festivals
Country: United States
Contact: Managing dr of production Stephen Lamarca
Contact: Managing Director of theater Lucia S. Edgcomb
Contact: Executive Director Chris Silva

Poway Center for the Performing Arts
Website: www.powayarts.org
Email: powayarts@aol.com
Phone: 858 668 4797
Address: 15498 Espola Rd, US
Information: presenting done by private Poway Center for the Performing Arts Foundation
Country: United States
Contact: Marketing and development Manager Michael Putnam
Contact: Executive Director Michael Rennie
Contact: administrative assistant Lynn Wolsey

Prairie Center for the Arts
Website: www.prairiecenter.org
Email: rpileckis@ci.scaumburg.il.us
Phone: 847 895 3600

Address: 201 Schaumburg Ct, US
Country: United States
Contact: technical supervisor Ethan Goldspiel
Contact: production supervisor Rob Pileckis
Contact: Director Betsy Armistead

Premiere Performances
Website: www.premiereperformances.org
Email: gkohn@umsl.edu
Phone: 314 516 5814/577
Address: University of Missouri – St. Louis, #1 University Drive, US
Information: alternative e-mail: klbmezzo@umsl.edu
Country: United States
Contact: production Associate Gloria Kohn
Contact: Artistic Director Katharine Lawton Brown

Presbyterian College
Website: www.presby.edu
Email: lwshealy@presby.edu
Phone: 864 833 8523
Address: Office of Cultural Events, 503 South Broad, US
Information: most events free admission; spaces used for college music department events and community events
Country: United States
Contact: Director of cultural events Laura Shealy

Princess Theatre Center for the Performing Arts
Website: www.princesstheatre.org
Email: lindy@princesstheatre.org
Phone: 256 350 1745
Address: 112 2nd Ave NE, US
Country: United States
Contact: Technical Director Penny Linville
Contact: Executive Director Lindy Ashwander
Contact: Office Manager Debbie Nieberlein

Princeton University Concerts
Website: www.princeton.edu/sites/puconcerts
Email: pucmail@princeton.edu
Phone:
609 258 4239
Address: The Woolworth Center, Princeton University, US
Information: Since 1894, the music of history's most revered composers has been performed by the world's most celebrated artists at Princeton University. In its 123-year history the series has presented many of the classical music world's most important musicians, including violinist Isaac Stern, cellist Yo-Yo Ma, the Budapest String Quartet and pianist Vladimir Ashkenazy. Today, an extraordinary roster of musicians make their Princeton debuts each season and join this pantheon. Among them are some of the most highly regarded artists of our time...young musicians on the cusp of sensational careers...and riveting performers pioneering new forms of exPression. Member of ISPA
Country: United States
Contact: Artistic Director Nathan Randall
Capacity: 900

Pro Musica
Website: www.promusicajoplin.org
Email: promusica@festfreedom.net
Phone: 417 625 1822
Address: 402 S. Main Street, Suite 502, US
Information: Pro Musica was founded by Cynthia Schwab in 1981. Pro Musica's mission is "to foster interest in, appreciation for, and enjoyment of world-class, live classical music in Joplin and the four-state area". Pro Musica has been the leader in providing culturally rich, classical music programming for Joplin, Missouri and the surrounding area.
Country: United States
Contact: Executive Director Cynthia Schwab
Social Media: @ProMusicaJoplin

Proctor's Theatre
Website: www.proctors.org
Email: info@proctors.org
Phone: 518 382 3884
Address: 432 State Street, US
Information: ongoing movie series see website
Country: United States
Contact: Director of operations Robert Warlock
Director of Marketing & pr
Kathy Jarvis
Contact: production Manager Dan Sheehan
Contact: chief Executive Director Ci Philip Morris
Contact: Director of finance Kathleen Cetnar

Providence Office of Cultural Affairs
Website: www.caparts.org
Email: info@caparts.org
Phone: 401 621 1992
Address: 65 Weybosset Street, #39, Suite 68, US
Information: see Festivals Providence World Music Festival, Capitol Arts Jazz Festival; Convergence International Arts Festival
Country: United States
Contact: public programming Director Bob Rizzo

Providence Performing Arts Center
Website: www.ppacri.org

Email: pjprokop@ppacri.org
Phone: 401 421 2997
Address: 220 Weybosset St, US
Information: The Providence Performing Arts Center presents a full roster of touring Broadway theatricals and contemporary engagements.
Country: United States
Contact: Director of Marketing P.J. Prokop
Contact: General Manager Alan J Chille
Contact: President J.L. "Lynn" Singleton
Social Media: ProvPacRIProvPacRI
Capacity: 3100

Public Theater, The
Website: www.publictheater.org
Email: Press@publictheater.org
Phone: 212 539 8500
Address: 425 Lafayette Street, US
Information: see also Drama
Country: United States
Contact: Executive Director Andrew D. Hamigson
Contact: Artistic Director Oskar Eustis
Director of production & facilities
Ruth E. Sternberg
Contact: joint Associate Producer Mandy Hackett
Contact: joint Associate Producer Peter DuBois

Purdue Convocations
Website: www.convocations.org
Email: convocations@purdue.edu
Phone: 765 494 9712
Address: Purdue University, ENAD 112, 400 Centennial Mail Drive, US
Country: United States
Contact: Director Todd Wetzel
Contact: assistant Director Laura Clavio
Contact: Marketing Director Addy EDDY

Pyramid Arts Center
Website: www.pyramidarts.org
Email:
pyramid1@frontiernet.net
Phone: 585 461 2222
Address: 302 North Goodman Street, US

Queensborough Professional Performing Arts Center
Website: www.visitqpac.org
Email: VTicali@qcc.cuny.edu
Phone: 718 631 6311
Address: Box Office, Queensborough Community College, 222-05 56th Avenue, US
Information: The cornerstone of the Performing Arts Center is the annual Professional Performing Arts Series. The Series was created to bring a high level of accessible world-class entertainment to the community at large. Throughout its over 50-year history, QPAC has successfully produced over 1, 200 performances and served over 1 million individuals in its intimate 875-seat theater
Country: United States
Contact: Executive and Artistic Director Susan Agin
Email: SAgin@qcc.cuny.edu
Contact: technical Director John Funke
Email: JFunke@qcc.cuny.edu
Contact: production Manager Vinny Ticali
Email: VTicali@qcc.cuny.edu
Social Media: @VisitQPAC www.facebook.com/Queensborough-Performing-Arts-Center-QPAC-313801112247/
Capacity: 875

Quick Center for the Arts
Website: www.quickcenter.com
Email: info@quickcenter.com
Phone: 203 254 4242
Address: Fairfield University, 1073 North Benson Rd., US
Information: Serving the intellectually hungry and perpetually curious, the Quick Center provides a home for the exploration of remarkable and inspiring performing arts opportunities for the community at large. Member of ISPA
Country: United States
Contact: Executive Director Peter Van Heerden
Contact: Director of programming and audience development Lori Jones
Contact: business/operations Manager Kurt Leon
Contact: Manager of business development Marni Smith Katz
Social Media: @FairfieldQuick www.facebook.com/FairfieldQuickCenter
Policies: Multi-purpose

Quincy Civic Music Association
Email: kirby@adams.net
Phone: 217 223 4617
Address: PO Box 1165, US
Country: United States
Contact: President Kirby Eber
Contact: talent committee Chairman Mowbray Allan

Radford University – Cultural Concert Series
Website: www.radford.edu
Email: jscartel@radford.edu
Phone: 540 831 5000
Address: Dean, College of Visual and Performing Arts, Radford University, US

Country: United States
Contact: Chair Joseph Scartelli

Raleigh Chamber Music Guild
Website: www.rcmg.org
Email: rcmg@juno.com
Phone: 919 821 2030
Address: PO Box 2059, US
Information: periodically commission new works; conduct masterclasses for young musicians; ensemble mini-residencies
Country: United States
Contact: Executive Director Nancy Lambert

Ramsey Regional Activity Center
Website: ramsey.wcu.edu
Phone: 828 227 7677
Address: Western Carolina University, 1601 Ramsey Center, US
Country: United States

Rapid City Concert Association
Phone: 605 721 3914
Address: PO Box 9211, US
Country: United States
Contact: General Manager John Ellison
Contact: Chairman of the membership Donna Peppers

Ravinia Festival
Website:
www.ravinia.org
Email:
ravinia@ravinia.org
Phone: 847 266 5000
Address: 418 Sheridan Road, US
Country: United States
Contact: Artistic Director, jazz at ravinia Ramsey Lewis
President & CEO
Welz Kauffman
Contact: General Manager Pat Sanders
Contact: music Director James Conlon
Contact: Associate Director of communications Amy Schrage

Raymond F Kravis Center for the Performing Arts Inc
Website: www.kravis.org
Email: kravis@kravis.org
Phone: 561 833 8300
Address: 701 Okeechobee Boulevard, US
Information: member of ISPA, IAAM, and Florida Professional Presenters consortium
Country: United States
Contact: Director of Marketing and public relations Linda Birdsey
Contact: senior Director of programming Lee Bell
Contact: chief financial officer Kyle Roberts-Ruge
Contact: chief Executive officer Judith Mitchell
Social Media: KravisCenter www.facebook.com/kravis-center

Rea Enterprises
Email: reabsld@aol.com
Phone: 631 261 1576
Address: 5 Yorktown Place, US
Country: United States
Contact: administrative assistant Claudia Dunmille
Contact: President Rea Jacobs
Contact: vice-President Joseph Jacobs

Redlands Bowl
Website: www.redlandsbowl.org
Email: info@redlandsbowl.org
Phone: 909 793 7316
Address: 25 Grant St. Redlands, CA 92373
Information: Redlands Bowl hosts the Redlands Bowl Summer Music Festival, America's longest continuously running summer music festival with no admission charge, and various music events throughout the year. see also Festivals
Country: United States
Contact: Executive Director Beverley Noerr
Email: bnoerr@redlandsbowl.org
Contact: programme Director Valerie Peister
Email: vpeister@redlandsbowl.org
Contact: Operations Director Kristi Marnell
Email: kmarnell@redlandsbowl.org
Disabled Access: Yes
Capacity: 1000+
Policies: Present and Produce

Redwood Arts Council
Website: www.redwoodarts.org
Email: racmusic@sonic.net
Phone: 707 874 1124
Address: PO Box 449, US
Country: United States
Contact: Director Candace Rossman

Reed Whipple Art Center
Phone: 702 229 6211
Address: 821 Las Vegas Boulevard North, US
Country: United States
Contact: contact Alice Rice

Regional Arts at the Kravis Center
Website: www.kravis.org
Email: kravis@kravis.org
Phone: 561 833 8300
Address: 701 Okeechobee Bvld, US
Country: United States
Contact: regional arts programming Associate Sharon McDaniel

Reif Arts Council
Website: www.reifcenter.org
Email: dmarty@reifcenter.org
Phone:
218 327 5780
Address: 720 Conifer Drive, US
Information: The Reif Performing Arts Center is a facility in which a wide variety of arts are experienced, exhibited and taught. It is a regional attraction drawing people from over 100 miles for regular performances. Each year, the Reif Center hosts about 40 national and international touring performances, representing a diverse range of Artistic disciplines, including country music artists, rock tributes, classical musicians, classical and contemporary dance, musical theater, children's theater, comedy
Country: United States
Contact: President David Marty
Email: dmarty@reifcenter.org
Social Media: @ReifCenter www.facebook.com/Reif-Center/
Annual Performances: 42
Annual Productions: 3
Policies: All

Renaissance & Baroque Society of Pittsburgh
Website:
www.rbsp.org
Email: Director@rbsp.org
Phone:
141 236 12048
Address: 5530 Penn Avenue, US
Country: United States
Contact: Executive Director Ann Felter Mason

Reno Performing Arts Center Series
Website: www.pioneercenter.com
Email: admin@pioneercenter.com
Phone: 775 686 6610
Address: Pioneer Center for the Performing Arts, 100 S Virginia Street, US
Country: United States
Contact: Executive Director Willis Allen
Contact: accounting/youth programs Terrie Schulte
Contact: Marketing Director Samantha Fleischer
Contact: technical Director Lou Manganello
Contact: house Manager Bernie Bronov
Contact: guest services Director Dennyse Daniels

Rensselaer Polytechnic Performing Arts Series
Website: www.union.rpi.edu
Email: union@rpi.edu
Phone: 518 276 6505
Address: 15th Stage Avenue, US
Country: United States
Contact: coordinator of student activity Cameron McLean

Res MusicAmerica Inc.
Phone: 141 088 93939
Address: 211 Goodwood Gardens, US
Country: United States
Contact: Artistic Director Vivian Adelberg Rudow

Results Unlimited
Phone: 412 344 7477
Address: 421 Cochran Road, US
Country: United States
Contact: contact Helen Trautman

Rhode Island College
Website: www.ric.edu/artseries
Phone: 401 456 8194
Address: 301 Roberts Hall, 600 Mount Pleasant Ave, US
Country: United States
Contact: theatre Director Jamie Taylor
Contact: music Director Rob Franzblau
Contact: performing arts series Director Michael Ducharme
Contact: dance Director Dante Del Giudice

Rhythm Foundation Inc
Website: www.rhythmfoundation.com
Email: info@rhythmfoundation.com
Phone: 305 672 5202
Address: PO Box 398567, US
Information: non-profit organization
Country: United States
Contact: Director Laura Quinlan

Rialto Square Theatre
Website: www.rialtosquare.com
Email: rgreen@rialtosquare.com
Phone: 815 726 7171
Address: 15 E Van Buren St, US

Information: available for hire; theatre address: 102 North Chicago Street
Country: United States
Contact: General Manager Randall Green

Richard B. Fisher Center for the Performing Arts
Website: fishercenter.bard.edu
Email: fishercenter@bard.edu
Phone: 845 758 7900
Address: Bard College, 60 Manor Ave., US
Country: United States
Contact: Producer for opera and music programs Susana Meyer
Contact: Director of Communications Mark Primoff
Email: pr@bard.edu
Social Media: Bard_FisherCtr www.facebook.com/FisherCenterforthePerformingArtsAtBardCollege

Richard Rodgers Theatre
Website: www.nederlander.com
Phone: 212 840 5577
Address: 226 W 46th Street, US
Country: United States
Contact: management company
The Nederlander Org, Inc
Capacity: 1368

Richland Performing Arts
Website: www.rparts.org
Email: marthaf@rparts.org
Phone: 419 522 2726
Address: PO Box 789, US
Information: visiting address: 138 Park Avenue W, Mansfield
Country: United States
Contact: CEO Thomas J. Carto
Contact: Director of Sales Lori Waters
Contact: Director of Marketing Martha Fort
Contact: Director of finance Alison Crabb
Contact: Director of development Shelley Mauk
Contact: Director of operations Darlene Taylor

Ritz Theatre
Website: www.ritztheatre.org
Email: nancy@ritztheatre.org
Phone: 419 448 8544
Address: 30 S Washington Street, US
Information: recently renovated 1928 Vaudeville theatre
Country: United States
Contact: business Manager Nancy Betz
Contact: Executive Director Michael Strong
Contact: production Manager John Spahr
Contact: Marketing Manager Bruce Hannam
Contact: box office Manager Carlene Hitchcock
Contact: comunity relations Carolyn Daughenbaugh

River Center for the Performing Arts
Website: www.rivercenter.org
Email: emorris@rivercenter.org
Phone: 706 653 7993
Address: PO Box 2425, US
Information: home of Columbus Symphony and Schwob School of Music; also features a media technology center, Columbus Public Broadcasting, organized in partnership with Georgia Public Broadcasting; also runs an education and outreach program
Country: United States
Contact: Executive Director and project Manager Enich Morris
Contact: business Manager Pat Phillips
Contact: volunteer coordinator Sandy Mullins
Contact: finance and Marketing Manager Janina McPherson
Contact: technical Director Steve Sweet

River Park Center
Website: www.riverparkcenter.org
Email: info@riverparkcenter.org
Phone: 270 687 2770
Address: 101 Davies Street, US
Information: RiverPark Center is a non-profit Regional performing arts and civic center that entertains and educates nearly 200, 000 people – including 25, 000 children – annually through nearly 800 events.
Country: United States
Contact: Director of Marketing and Development Faith Holley
Email: fholley@riverparkcenter.org
Contact: Executive Director Roxi Witt
Email: rwitt@riverparkcenter.org
Social Media: @rpcgm
Policies: Present, produce, co-produce, Produce and rent, Arts centre

Riverside Fine Arts Association
Website: www.riversidefinearts.org
Email: info@riversidefinearts.org
Phone: 904 389 – 6222
Address: 1100 Stockton Street, US
Information: present outstanding national and international artists; ensembles that complement church atmosphere

Country: United States
Contact: Executive Director Stacey Aubrey

Robert E Parilla Performing Arts Center Montgomery College
Website: www.montgomerycollege.edu
Email: debra.fyodorov@montgomerycollege.edu
Phone: 301 251 7536
Address: 51 Mannakee St, US
Country: United States
Contact: Manager Debra Fyodorov

Rochester Broadway Theatre League
Website: www.rbtl.org
Email: mail@rbtl.org
Phone: 585 325 7760
Address: Auditorium Theatre, 885 East Main St, US
Information: Built in 1928, the Auditorium Theatre has become the Greater Rochester area's home for large-scale Broadway musicals such as The Phantom of the Opera, Miss Saigon, The Producers, Disney's THE LION KING and Wicked. In addition, The Auditorium Theatre hosts a variety of rock, classical, comedy, R&B, dance and children's shows. The Theatre is owned and operated by the Rochester Broadway Theatre League (RBTL).
Country: United States
Contact: Executive vice President Linda Glosser
Social Media: @rbtl www.facebook.com/rbtledu

Rochester Chamber Music Society
Website: www.rochesterchambermusic.org
Email: rcmsociety@gmail.com
Phone: 802 767 9008
Address: PO Box 834, US
Information: The purpose of chamber music is to create a rapport between its performers and their listeners. With its excellent acoustics, Christ United Methodist Church offers a conducive environment for such an experience. The informality of the musicians explaining their music further creates a bond, making the music personal and accessible for the listeners and the performers
Country: United States
Contact: Artistic Director Horacio Nuguid
Contact: Executive Director Joan Smith

Rochester Civic Theatre
Website: www.rochestercivictheatre.org
Email: info@rochestercivictheatre.org
Phone: 507 282 8481
Address: 20 Civic Center Dr SE, , US
Information: The Rochester Civic Theatre is southeastern Minnesota's premier Producer and presenter of professional and community theater, live music, and dance. Established in 1951, the Rochester Civic Theatre has matured into an award-winning, multidisciplinary theater and performing arts resource for the City of Rochester and the entire Southeast Minnesota tri-state area
Country: United States
Contact: Executive Director Gregory Stavrou
Email: gstavrou@rochestercivictheatre.org
Contact: education Director Denise Ruemping
Email: denise@rochestercivictheatre.org
Contact: Artistic Director Greg Miller
Email: greg@rochestercivictheatre.org
Social Media: @RCTMN www.facebook.com/RochCivicTheatre

Rochester Office of Special Events
Website: www.cityofrochester.gov/specialevents/
Email: specialevents@cityofrochester.gov
Phone: 585 428 6690
Address: 30 Church Street, US
Information: The Office of Special Events showcases the vitality of Rochester by hosting, promoting, or sponsoring cultural programs that enhance a strong sense of community and attract visitors.**Country:** United States
Contact: Director of cultural affairs Margaret Reichert
Email: Margaret.Reichert@cityofrochester.gov
Social Media: @CityRochesterNY www.facebook.com/CityofRochesterNY

Rockefeller Arts Center
Website: www.fredonia.edu/rac
Email: arts.center@fredonia.edu
Phone: 716 673 3217
Address: 280 Central Ave., US
Information: houses faculty offices for the Department of Visual Arts and New Media and the Department of Theatre Arts and Dance, as well as classrooms, rehearsal halls and spacious, well-equipped art studios, dressing rooms, scenery and costume shops
Country: United States
Contact: centre Director Jefferson Westwood
Email: westwood@fredonia.edu
Contact: assistant Director Patrick Rocheleau
Email: patrick.rocheleau@fredonia.edu
Contact: operations Manager/technical Director Eric Hadley
Email: hadley@fredonia.edu
Contact: public relations assistant Douglas Osborne-Coy
Email: douglas.osborne-coy@fredonia.edu
Social Media: www.facebook.com/RockefellerArtsCenter?ref=ts
Policies: Rent and present, Theatre

Roger L Stevens Centre North Carolina School of the Arts
Website: www.uncsa.edu/performances/stevens-center/
Phone: 336 770 399
Address: 405 W Fourth Street, US
Information: Originally a 1929 silent movie theatre the Stevens Center is a magnificently restored neoclassical theatre located in downtown Winston-Salem, NC. Reopened in April 1983, the Stevens Center is the primary performance space for the University of North Carolina School of the Arts as well as the Winston-Salem Symphony, Piedmont Opera Theatre, and several other local and state arts organizations
Country: United States
Social Media: @UNCSchoolofArts www.facebook.com/uncschoolofthearts/

Rogue Music Theatre
Website: www.mind.net/rmt
Email: rmt@valleysoftisp.net
Phone: 541 479 2559
Address: PO Box 862, US
Information: present regionally its own show
Country: United States
Contact: administrative assistant Penny King
Contact: Artistic Director Richard Jessup
Contact: financial assistant Jo Yarrish

Rolande Tower
Website: www.ococean.com
Email: ocpr@ococean.com
Phone: 410 289 8311
Address: 4001 Coastal Highway, US
Country: United States
Contact: Executive Director Michael Noah
Contact: media services Manager Donna Abbott

Ross Ragland Theater
Website:
www.rrtheater.org
Email: rrt@rrtheater.org
Phone: 541 884 0651
Address: 218 N 7th Street, US
Information: programme of children's theatre and workshops during the summer
Country: United States
Contact: Executive Director Cari McMahon

Roundabout Theatre
Website: www.roundabouttheatre.org
Email: info@roundabouttheatre.org
Phone: 212 719 9393
Address: 231 West 39th Street, Suite 1200, US
Information: see also Nottingham Playhouse (Venues) – UK, and Roundabout Theatre (Performing companies)
Country: United States
Contact: Artistic Director Todd Haimes
Social Media: @rtc_nyc www.facebook.com/RoundaboutTheatreCompany

Royale Theatre
Website: www.telecharge.com
Email: tickets@telecharge.com
Phone: 212 944 3700
Address: 242 West 45th Street, US
Country: United States
Contact: vice President of theatre operations Peter Entin
Contact: management company The Shubert Org. Inc

Rushmore Plaza Civic Center
Website: www.gotmine.com
Phone: 605 394 4115
Address: 444 Mt Rushmore Rd N, US
Information: the Plaza also promotes dog shows, basketball games, rock concerts, broadway shows
Country: United States
Contact: General Manager Brian Maliske

Russian River Chamber Music
Website: www.russianriverchambermusic.org
Email: admin@russianriverchambermusic.org
Phone: 170 752 48700
Address: 401 Center St. #100, US
Country: United States
Contact: Artistic Director Gary McLaughlin
Contact: President Richard Kagel

Rutgers University Newark Campus University Series
Website: www.rutgers.edu
Email: idwatson@andrommeda.rutgers.edu
Phone: 973 353 5119
Address: 110 Warren Street, Room 213, Bradley Hall, US
Information: presenter of attractions, own choir
Country: United States
Contact: Chairperson of the dept. of visual and perf arts Ian Watson

Saco River Festival Association
Website: www.sacoriverfestival.org
Email: srfa@psouth.net
Phone: 207 625 7116
Address: PO Box 610, US

Information: at least one concert each season that is something different; past years have included choral music, chamber orchestras, jazz, early music
Country: United States
Contact: Artistic advisor Judith Ingram
Contact: Executive Director Frank Glazer
Contact: President Jim O'Neil
Contact: Press, board member David F Bower
Contact: Janet Topkin

Sacramento Community Concert Association
Website: www.saccca.org
Email: concertdorothy@aol.com
Phone: 191 697 41357
Address: PO Box 254825, US
Country: United States
Contact: Executive secretary Dorothy Alden

Saddleback College
Website: www.saddleback.edu
Email:
genglish@saddleback.edu
Phone:
949 582 4413
Address: Performing Arts Program, 28000 Marguerite Pkwy, US
Country: United States
Contact: dean Bart McHenry
Contact: Director of performing arts Kate Realista
Contact: ticket office Manager Harry Snowden
Contact: public information officer Nina Welch

Saenger Theatre
Website: www.pensacolasaenger.com
Email:
dlee@cityofpensacola.com
Phone: 850 595 3882
Address: PO Box 13666, 118 South Palafox Place, US
Country: United States
Contact: General Manager Douglas Lee
Contact: Director of Marketing Kathy Summerlin
Contact: box office Manager Deanna Willis
Policies: Theatre

Saenger Theatre
Website: www.mobilesaenger.com
Email: saengertheatre@cityofmobile.org
Phone: 251 208 5600
Address: 6 South Joachim St, US
Country: United States
Contact: Chairman Mike Rogers
Social Media: @SaengerMobile
Capacity: 1921

Saginaw Choral Society
Website: www.saginawchoralsociety.com
Email: info@saginawchoralsociety.com
Phone: 517 753 1812
Address: 326 S Jefferson Avenue, US
Information: a non-profit organisation
Country: United States
Contact: President William Millar
Contact: Director of development and Marketing Tamara Grefe
Contact: business Manager Lee E. Wright
Contact: conductor Robert C. Sabourin

Saint Mary College Community/Cultural Program
Website: www.stmary.edu
Phone: 913 682 5151
Address: 4100 S Fourth Trafficway, US
Country: United States
Contact: President of the college Diane Steele
Contact: Director of fine arts Williams Krusemark

Saint Mary's College
Website: www.saintmarys.edu
Phone: 574 284 4625
Address: Moreau Center for the Arts, Saint Mary's College, US
Country: United States
Contact: Director dance programme Indi Dieckgrafe
Contact: Director of special events Richard Baxter
Contact: Chair department of music Nancy Menk

Saint Mary's University of Minnesota
Website: www.pagetheatre.org
Email: julsmith@smumn.edu
Phone: 507 457 1714
Address: School of the Arts;, 700 Terrace Heights #67, US
Country: United States
Contact: General Manager Smith Julie

Salem Community College
Website: www.salemcc.org
Email: harrison@salem.cc.edu
Phone: 856 351 2621
Address: 460 Hollywood Avenue, US
Country: United States
Contact: co-ordinator of cultural events Terri Harrison

Salina Arts & Humanities
Website: www.salinaarts.com
Email: sahc@salina.org

Phone: 785 309 5770
Address: PO Box 2181, US
Information: A department of the City of Salina that provides a wide variety of cultural arts programs and services which also includes the nationally accredited Smoky Hill Museum and the Smoky Hill River Festival.
Country: United States
Contact: Executive Director Brad Anderson
Email: brad.anderson@salina.org
Contact: Marketing coordinator Kay Quinn
Email: kay.quinn@salina.org
Social Media: www.facebook.com/salinaarts/?ref=hl

Salisbury University Performing Arts Series
Website: www.salisbury.edu
Email: tppfeiffer@salisbury.edu
Phone: 410 543 6030
Address: Salisbury State University, US
Information: also have an art gallery; produces a series of lectures, annually
Country: United States
Contact: Chairman music department Richard Johnson
Contact: symphony orchestra Director Jeff Sehoien
Contact: theatre Director Paul Pfeiffer
Contact: dance company Director Victoria Hutchinson
Contact: cultural affairs Director June Salgado

Salmon Arts Council
Website: www.salmonartscouncil.org
Email: salmonartscouncil@gmail.com
Phone: 208 756 2987
Address: 200 Main Street, US
Country: United States
Contact: Executive Director Mary Cerise

Salt Lake County Performing Arts Center
Website: www.arttix.org
Phone: 801 323 6800
Address: 50 W 200 South, US
Information: Music Theatre and Broadway Musicals at the Capitol Theatre; Chamber Music at the Abranavel Hall
Country: United States
Contact: Director Marian Iwasaki

Salvatore Martirano Memorial Composition Award, The
Website: www-camil.music.uiuc.edu/comptheory/index.html
Email: zbrownin@uiuc.edu
Phone: 217 333 2620
Address: 2136 Music Building, University of Illinois, 1114 W Nevada St, US
Information: $1k first place award for composers' competition; see also under Competitions and Awards
Country: United States
Contact: Director, martirano composition award Zack Browning

Samford University Wright Center
Website: www.samford.edu
Email: dvhartle@samford.edu
Phone: 205 726 2011
Address: Wright Center Concer Hall, Samfor University, 800 Lakeshore Drive, US
Information: Box office line: 205-726 2462
Country: United States
Contact: corordinator David V. Hartley

Sammons Center for the Arts
Website: www.sammonsartcenter.org
Email: info@sammonsartcenter.org
Phone: 214 520 7788
Address: 3630 Harry Hines Boulevard, US
Information: features local artists
Country: United States
Contact: Executive Director Joanna St Angelo
Contact: assistant Director Michael Cook

San Antonio Chamber Music Society
Website: www.sacms.org
Email: drdaleb@aol.com
Phone: 210 408 1558
Address: PO Box 12702, US
Country: United States
Contact: President Dale Bennett

San Diego Concourse
Website: www.sdccc.org
Phone: 619 525 5000
Address: 202 C St, MS 57, US
Information: only rent
Country: United States
Contact: President Carol Wallace

San Diego Early Music Society
Website: www.sdems.org
Email: sdems@sdems.org
Phone: 619 291 8246
Address: PO Box 82008, US
Information: 2 concert series : 1. International Series ; 2. Recital Series
Country: United States
Contact: vice President Laurent Planchon
Contact: President Mark Lester

Policies: Concert hall

San Diego State University Cultural Arts Series
Website: www.sdsu.edu
Email: jamie.cochran@sdsu.edu
Phone: 619 594 6487
Address: Aztec Centre, Aztec Mesa, Room 108, 5500 Campanile Drive, US
Country: United States
Contact: programs coordinator Jamie Lynn Cochran
Social Media: @SDSU www.facebook.com/SanDiegoState

San Francisco Conservatory of Music
Website: www.sfcm.edu
Email: admit@sfcm.edu
Phone: 415 864 7326
Address: 50 Oak Street, US
Country: United States
Contact: President David H Stull
Contact: dean Mary Ellen Poole
Contact: assistant to the dean Alice Beckett
Contact: senior Manager, communications Joseph Sargent
Social Media: @SFConservMusic www.facebook.com/SanFranciscoConservatoryOfMusic
Policies: Concert hall

San Francisco Performances
Website: www.sfperformances.org
Email: info@sfperformances.org
Phone: 415 398 6449
Address: 500 Sutter Street, Suite 710, US
Information: San Francisco Performances has been a leader in the Bay Area cultural scene since our founding in 1979. We have introduced hundreds of classical music, jazz and contemporary dance artists to audiences, including world-renowned performers like Yo-Yo Ma, the Juilliard String Quartet, Philip Glass, and the Paul Taylor Dance Company. With a strong curatorial vision, great Artistic taste and adventurous programming, we are the city's premier presenter of intimate concerts, solo recitals and dance. Member of ISPA
Country: United States
Contact: Founder / President Ruth Felt
Email: ruth@sfperformances.org
Contact: Director of development Michele Casau
Email: michele@sfperformances.org
Contact: Director of Marketing Will Crockett
Email: phil@sfperformances.org
Contact: Director of education programmes Christine Lim
Email: christine@sfperformances.org
Contact: Director of finance/Administration Christian Jessen
Email: christian@sfperformances.org
Contact: Director of communications Nancy Bertossa
Email: nancy@sfperformances.org
Social Media: https://twitter.com/sfperformances www.facebook.com/sfperformances https:// www.instagram.com/sfperformances/
Capacity: 1000+
Annual Performances: 100+
Policies: Rent and Present

San Francisco War Memorial and Performing Arts Center
Website: www.sfwmpac.org
Email: info@sfwmpac.org
Phone: 415 621 6600
Address: 401 Van Ness Avenue, Room 110, US
Country: United States
Contact: Managing Director Elizabeth Murray
Contact: Director of operations James Baldocchi
Contact: assistant Managing Director Jennifer Norris

San Jose Chamber Music Society
Website: www.sjchambermusic.org
Email: sjcms@sjchambermusic.org
Phone: 408 286 5111
Address: PO Box 108, US
Information: concert series from Oct through April Sunday evenings; venue address: 72 N. Fifth Street, San Jose
Country: United States
Contact: event Director Ted Cady

San Juan Community Theatre & Arts Center
Website: www.sanjuancommunitytheatre.org
Email: sjarts@rockisland.com
Phone: 360 378 3211
Address: PO Box 1063, US
Information: visiting address: 100 2nd Street, Friday Harbour, WA 98250
Country: United States
Contact: Executive Director Merritt Olsen

Sandusky Concert Association
Email: ernst@buckeye-exPress.com
Phone: 419 625 8312
Address: 1402 Columbus Avenue, US
Country: United States
Contact: talent coordinator Diane Ernst

Sandusky State Theatre

Website: www.sanduskystate.com
Phone: 419 626 1950
Address: 107 Columbus Ave, US
Information: Artistic, educational and socially merited programming; also produce
Country: United States
Contact: development Director Wendy Brightman
Contact: Director of education and Marketing Matthew Joslyn
Contact: Executive Director Terri Bergman
Contact: operations Manager and technical Director Tim Kostel

Sangamon Auditorium
Website: www.sangamonauditorium.org
Phone: 217 206 6150 adm
Address: University of Illinois at Springfield, US
Information: present and support varied cultural and educational professional arts activities; home to the Illinois Symphony Orchestra and the Springfield Ballet Company
Country: United States
Contact: education outreach Carly Shank
Contact: advertising media coordinator Bryan Leonard
Contact: auditorium Director John Dale Kennedy
Contact: admin secretary Kelly Phillips
Contact: Director of development Terri Noel
Contact: Associate Director of stage services Todd Meyers
Contact: Director of development Angela Griffin
Contact: interim Director David L. Taylor

Sangre de Cristo Arts & Conference Center
Website: www.sdc-arts.org
Email:
mail@sdc-arts.org
Phone:
719 295 7200
Address: 210 North Santa Fe Avenue, US
Information: rent also; all galleries and children's museum have a small admission fee
Country: United States
Contact: Executive Director Dr. Dan Lere
Contact: Marketing Manager Nicki Hart

Santa Clara University – SCU Presents
Website: www.scupresents.org
Email: scupresentstix@scu.edu
Phone: 408 554 4015
Address: SCU Presents – Santa Clara University, 500 El Camino Real, US
Information: SCU Presents enhances arts education where artists are central to our creative culture, as an interdisciplinary and collaborative Performing Arts Center at Santa Clara University. We advance Arts for Social Justice programming creating a catalyst for change in our society and develop creative partnerships, present diverse programming and outreach opportunities, to connect to our community.Country: United States
Contact: Director, SCU Presents Butch Coyne
Email: bcoyne@scu.edu
Phone: 408 554 4073 Business Manager Tina Sciolla
Email: tsciolla@scu.edu
Phone: 408 554 4565 Marketing Associate Alexandra Lopiano
Email: alopiano@scu.edu
Phone: 408 554 5503
Social Media: https://www.facebook.com/SCUPRESENTS https://twitter.com/thescweekly https://www.instagram.com/SCWeekly/
Capacity: 501-1000
Annual Performances: 51-100
Annual Productions: 51-100
Policies: All

Santa Fe Concert Association
Website: www.musicone.org
Email: musicone@swcp.com
Phone: 505 984 8759
Address: PO Box 4626, New Mexico, US
Country: United States
Contact: Managing Director William Mullen

Santa Monica College
Website: events.smc.edu
Email: events@smc.edu
Phone: 310 434 3002
Address: Events Department, 1900 Pico Boulevard, US
Country: United States
Contact: General Manager/Director Charlie Yen

Sarasota Concert Association Inc
Email: jwa003@verizon.com
Phone: 194 195 50040
Address: PO Box 1714, US
Information: alternative e-mail: jwa003@gte.net
Country: United States
Contact: President Melton Miller
Contact: Artistic selection Chairperson Martha Leiter
Contact: membership coordinator John W Ames

Sarasota Opera Association
Website: www.sarasotaopera.org
Email: info@sarasotaopera.org

Phone:
941 366 8450
Address: 61 N Pineapple Ave, US
Information: In addition to being "one of the finest operatic venues in the United States, " the Sarasota Opera House is a resource for many of Sarasota's finest arts and cultural organizations. The Sarasota Orchestra, La Musica Chamber Music Festival, and the Sarasota Ballet all make use of its facilities outside of the opera season. In addition, it is a community resource that has been used for benefits and private events.
Country: United States
 Marketing & public relations Director
 Richard Russell
Contact: Executive Director Susan T Danis
Contact: Artistic Director Victor DeRenzi

Saratoga Performing Arts Center (SPAC)
Website: www.spac.org
Email: media@spac.org
Phone:
518 584 9330
Address: 108 Avenue of The Pines, US
Information: The Saratoga Performing Arts Center is home to an acoustically ideal amphitheater, the Spa Little Theatre, the Charles R. Wood Gazebo Stage and The Jazz Bar — all nestled in an idyllic park setting surrounded by hiking trails, geysers and natural mineral springs. Our main stage has a 25, 000 person capacity with sheltered seats for 5, 200 people and a sloping lawn for an additional 20, 000 people. The stage is home to New York City Ballet and Philadelphia Orchestra. An intimate, 500-seat theatre showcasing our Chamber Music Society of Lincoln Center and Opera Saratoga
Country: United States
 President & CEO
 Elizabeth Sobol
Contact: Chief Finance Officer Jay Lafond
Email: jlafond@spac.org
Contact: Director of Communications Kristy Godette
Email: kgodette@spac.org
Contact: Chief Marketing Officer Michele Desrosiers
Email: mdesrosiers@spac.org
Policies: Multi-purpose

Savannah State University – Fine Arts Department
Website: www.savstate.edu
Email: mettsr@savstate.edu
Phone: 912 356 2248
Address: Savannah State University, US
Country: United States
Contact: Chair Rose Smith
Contact: head Peggy Blood

Schermerhorn Symphony Center
Website: www.nashvillesymphony.org
Email: tdedee@nashvillesymphony.org
Phone: 615 467 6503
Address: 127 Third Avenue South, Suite 200, US
Information: opened in Sept 2006; see also Orchestras (Nashville Symphony Orchestra)
Country: United States
Contact: Director of event services Ellen Hollis
Contact: Executive Director Ted DeDee, CFE

Schneider Concerts at New School
Website: www.schneiderconcerts.org
Email: info@schneiderconcerts.org
Phone: 212 243 9937
Address: 515 Greenwich Street, Suite 403, US
Information: visiting address: 515 Greenwich Street No. 403, NY 10013
Country: United States
Contact: Administration Frank Salomon
Contact: Administration Rohana Elias-Reyes

School of Music, University of Akron
Phone: 330 972 7590
Address: Univ of Akron, 157 University Ave, US
Information: summer workshops on music education, performance, scholarships and graduate assistantships available
Country: United States
Contact: Director William Guegold

Schubert Club, The
Website: www.schubert.org
Email: schubert@schubert.org
Phone: 651 292 3267
Address: 302 Landmark Center, 75 W 5th Street, US
Information: presents several different concert series, operates a museum of musical instruments, runs an annual scholarship competition, commissions work and produces recordings
Country: United States
Contact: Artistic and Executive Director Barry Kempton
Email: bkempton@schubert.org
Contact: museum and education Manager Kate Cooper
Email: kcooper@schubert.org
Contact: program Associate Max Carlson
Email: mcarlson@schubert.org
Social Media: @schubertclub
Policies: Present and produce, Concert hall

Scottsdale Center for the Performing Arts
Website: www.scottsdaleperformingarts.org
Email: info@sccarts.org
Phone: 480 994 2787
Address: 7380 East Second St, Scottsdale, US
Information: Scottsdale Center for the Performing Arts provides audiences with affordable access to unparalleled artists, diverse and inclusive programs, relevant and cutting-edge experiences, and performances from around the globe
Country: United States
Contact: Facility Rentals Manager Anne Parker
Email: annep@scottsdalearts.org
Phone: 480 874 4604 Managing Director Meribeth Reeves
Contact: Public Relations Specialist Virginia McInnis
Email: VirginiaM@ScottsdaleArts.org
Phone: 480 874 4663
Social Media: https://twitter.com/scottsdalearts www.facebook.com/ScottsdalePerformingArts https:// www.instagram.com/scottsdalearts/
Capacity: 1000+
Annual Performances: 100+
Policies: Rent and Present

Scottsdale Community College
Website: www.sc.maricopa.edu
Email: communications@domail.maricopa.edu
Phone:
480 623 6000
Address: 9000 East Chaparral Road, Scottsdale, US
Information: Scottsdale Community College is student centered, with a focus on active, engaged and intellectually rigorous learning. The college is known for high quality, accessible educational opportunities and innovative teaching, learning and support services. SCC serves approximately 10, 000 students a year, offering more than 100 degrees and 60 certificates of completion in diverse occupational areas.Country: United States
Contact: fine arts division Chair Ted Uran
Contact: Marketing Manager Eric Sells
Email: eric.sells@scottsdalecc.edu
Phone:
480 425 6637
Social Media: https://twitter.com/ScottsdaleCC www.facebook.com/ScottsdaleCC.AZ https:// www.instagram.com/scottsdalecc/
Disabled Access: Yes
Capacity: 1000+
Annual Performances: 100+
Policies: All

Scranton Cultural Center
Website: www.scrantonculturalcenter.org
Phone: 570 346 7369
Address: 420 N Washington Avenue, US
Information: other: all different types of drama, dance and music; promote and co-promote; also rent
Country: United States
Contact: Executive Director Joanne Fremiotti

Seaford Community Concert Association
Website: www.seafordconcerts.org
Email: lanman100@comcast.net
Phone: 302 536 1384
Address: PO Box 337, US
Information: nonprofit organization whose mission is to bring top quality performers to this area at a very affordable cost to its members
Country: United States
Contact: President Allan Kittila

Seaside Summer Concert Series
Website: www.brooklynconcerts.com
Email: brooklyncommunityevents@yahoo.com
Phone: 718 469 1912
Address: Martin Luther King Jr. Concert Series, 31 Prospect Park West, US
Information: July and August
Country: United States
Contact: Executive Director Debra Garcia

Seattle Center
Website: www.seattlecenter.com
Phone: 206 684 7200
Address: 305 Harrison Street, US
Information: home of the three major performing arts organizations in Seattle – Seattle Opera, Pacific Northwest Ballet and the Seattle Repertory Theatre; 75, 000 square feet of exhibition space and 22 meeting and performance venues
Country: United States

Seattle Theatre Group
Website: www.theparamount.com
Email: info@theparamount.com
Phone: 206 682 1414
Address: 911 Pine Street, US
Country: United States
Contact: Executive Director Josh LaBelle
Contact: program Director Cyndi Sorrell

Seattle Youth Symphony Orchestras

Website: www.syso.org
Email: info@syso.org
Phone: 206 362 2300
Address: 11065 Fifth Ave NE, Suite A, US
Information: five full orchestras during the academic year and the Marrowstone Summer Music Festivals in the month of August; see also Orchestras & Choirs
Country: United States
Contact: music Director Stephen Radcliffe
Contact: finance Director Aimee Tan
Contact: orchestra coordinator/marrowstone coordinator Janice Gatti
Contact: Executive Director Daniel Petersen

Secrest Auditorium
Email: auditorium@coz.org
Phone: 740 454 6851
Address: 334 Shinnick Street, US
Country: United States
Contact: Manager John Kunkel
Contact: secretary Marketa Morgan

Segerstrom Center for the Arts
Website: www.scfta.org
Email: boxoffice@scfta.org
Phone: 714 556 2787
Address: 600 Town Center Drive, Costa Messa, US
Information: In the late 1960s, a number of Orange County community leaders decided it was time to have world-class performing arts venues and a dedicated arts campus where local and regional performing arts organizations and esteemed guest artists and companies from all over the world could perform for this rapidly growing and culturally diverse region of Southern California.
Country: United States
Contact: Chairman Lawrence C. Perry
Contact: Executive Vice President Brian Finck
Contact: President Judith O'Dea Morr
Marketing & Communications, Vice President Lisa Middleton
Social Media: https:// www.facebook.com/SegerstromArts/ https:// www.instagram.com/segerstromarts/ https://twitter.com/SegerstromArts
Disabled Access: Yes
Capacity: 1000+

Selma Community Concert Association
Phone: 334 872 3527
Address: PO Box 387, US
Country: United States
Contact: President Doris Holland
Contact: stage Manager Don Speed

Severance Hall
Website: www.clevelandorch.com
Email: info@clevelandorchestra.com
Phone: 216 231 7300
Address: 11001 Euclid Avenue, US
Information: Italian style venue; home of Cleveland Orchestra
Country: United States
Social Media: @CleveOrchestra www.facebook.com/clevelandorchestra

Shasta Community Concert Association
Website: www.shastacommunityconcerts.com
Phone: 153 024 77355
Address: PO Box 493979, US
Country: United States
Contact: President Janet Applegarth

Sheldon Arts Foundation
Website: www.sheldonconcerthall.org
Phone: 314 533 9900
Address: 3648 Washington Boulevard, US
Country: United States
Contact: accounting Director July Tucker
Contact: Executive Director Paul Reuter
Contact: Marketing Director Jennifer Kramer

Sheldon Theatre
Website: www.sheldontheatre.org
Phone: 651 385 3667
Address: 443 W 3rd Street, US
Information: also rents out; toll free tel: 1800-899 5759
Country: United States
Contact: Executive Director Sean Dowse

Shepherd College – Performing Arts Series at Shepherd
Website: www.shepherd.edu/passweb
Email: Rmeads@shepherd.edu
Phone: 304 876 5497
Address: Shepherd College, P.O. Box 5000, US
Information: organise and present the Appal-Achian Heritage festival, annually October
Country: United States
Contact: Director of special events Rachael Meads

Shepherd School of Music Concert Series
Website: www.rice.edu/music
Email: musi@rice.edu
Phone: 713 348 4854
Address: 6100 Main Street, US
Information: all in-house performances. Mailing Address

Shepherd School of Music – MS 532 Rice University P.O.Box 1892 Houston, TX 77251-1892
Country: United States
Contact: Associate dean of music Gary Smith
Email: gasmith@rice.edu
Social Media: @ShepherdSchool www.facebook.com/ShepherdSchool?fref=ts

Shippensburg University Multicultural Activities Committee
Website: www.ship.edu
Email: apb@whars.ship.edu
Phone: 717 477 1747
Address: Cumberland Union Building, US
Country: United States
Contact: Director of student activities Linda Boeckman

Shoreline Alliance for Arts
Website: www.shorelinearts.org
Email: info@shorelinearts.org
Phone: 203 453 3890
Address: 725 Boston Post Road, US
Country: United States
Contact: program and Marketing Director Donita Aruny

Shubert Performing Arts Center
Website: www.shubert.com
Email: jfisher@capa.com
Phone: 203 624 1825
Address: 247 College St, US
Country: United States
Contact: Director of public relations Anthony Lupinacci
Email: AnthonyL@capa.com
Contact: Executive Director John Fisher
Email: Jfisher@capa.com
Contact: General Manager Sheri Kaplan
Email: Skaplan@capa.com
Social Media: @ShubertTheater www.facebook.com/shuberttheater/
Policies: All, Arts centre

Shubert Theatre
Website: www.shubert-theater.com
Phone: 212 944 3700
Address: 225 W 44th Street, US
Country: United States
Contact: management company The Shubert Org. Inc
Capacity: 1449

Silvermine Guild Arts Center
Website: www.silvermineart.org
Phone: 203 966 9700
Address: 1037 Silvermine Rd, US
Information: arts exhibitions; competition; new exhibition every month; school of arts for adults and youth
Country: United States
Contact: Executive Director Leslee Asch

Skidmore Music Department Series
Website: www.skidmore.edu
Email: rhihn@skidmore.edu
Phone: 518 580 7400
Address: Skidmore College, 815 North Broadway, US
Country: United States
artist-in-residence & department Chair Richard Hihn
Contact: Associate prof., orch Director, electronic music Anthony Holland
Contact: prof., theory and musicology Charles Joseph
Contact: Associate prof., ethnomusicology Gordon Thompson
Contact: assistant prof., theory and musicology Deborah Rohr
Contact: Associate prof., musicology and theory Thomas Denny

Skirball Center for the Performing Arts – New York University
Website: nyuskirball.org
Email: skirball.center.info@nyu.edu
Phone: 212 992 8484
Address: 60 Washington Square South, Suite 505, US
Information: NYU Skirball, located in the heart of Greenwich Village, is one of New York City's major presenters of international work, and has been the premier venue for cultural and performing arts events in lower Manhattan since 2003. The 860-seat state-of-the art theater, led by Director Jay Wegman, provides a home for internationally renowned artists, innovators and thinkers. NYU Skirball hosts over 300 events annually, from re-inventions of the classics to cutting-edge premieres, in genres ranging from dance, theater and performance art to comedy, music and film. Member of ISPA
Country: United States
Contact: Director, operations Amy Coombs
Email: amy.coombs@nyu.edu
Contact: Manager, operations Ian Tabatchnick
Email: itabatch@nyu.edu
Contact: senior Director Jay Wegman
Email: jay.wegman@nyu.edu
Social Media: @nyuskirball www.facebook.com/nyuskirball
Capacity: 850

Sleep Train Pavilion Season
Website: www.chroniclepavilion.com
Phone: 925 676 8742
Address: 2000 Kerker Path Road, US
Information: host community as well as commercial events
Country: United States
Contact: box office Manager Gina Bishop
Contact: stage Manager David Martin
Contact: General Manager t.b.a.
Contact: Director of promotions Aaron Siuda
Contact: production coordinator Cindy Wilson
Contact: house Manager Michael McNally

Smithsonian Associates
Website: www.smithsonianAssociates.org/ticketing
Email: customerservice@residentAssociates.org
Phone: 202 633 3030
Address: PO Box 23293, US
Information: a non profit, self sustaining, educational and public programming unit of the Smithsonian Institution that presents programs that highlight the exhibits, research and themes of the Smithsonian. Throughout the year, The Associates presents a variety of related performing arts programs to a DC metro audience**Country:** United States
Policies: Present, produce, co-produce

Snug Harbor Cultural Center Inc
Website: www.snug-harbor.org
Email: info@snug-harbour.org
Phone: 718 448 2500
Address: 1000 Richmond Terrace, US
Country: United States
Contact: President and CEO Frances Huber
Contact: Director of presentation Christopher Catt
Contact: Director of Marketing and pr Carol Ann Curtis

Society for New Music
Website: www.societyfornewmusic.org
Email: snm@societyfornewmusic.org
Phone:
315 446 5733
Address: 438 Brookford Road, US
Information: artists collective featuring new works by regional composers alongside guest composers; composers-in-residence in the public schools; recordings available with works by commissioned composers; weekly "Fresh Ink" program of recent music on WCNY-FM & its affiliates; Cazenovia Counterpoint festival; newsletter; all in an effort to bring new music to as broad an audience as possible, and on the web (societyfornewmusic.org & WCNY.org).
Country: United States
Contact: programme advisor Neva Pilgrim
Email: snm@societyfornewmusic.org
Social Media: @cnynewmusic www.facebook.com/SocietyForNewMusic/
Annual Performances: 30
Annual Productions: 20
Policies: Produce and co-produce

Society for the Performing Arts (SPA Houston)
Website: www.spahouston.org
Email: june@spahouston.org
Phone: 713 632 8108
Address: Jesse H. Jones Hall, , Suite 100, 615 Louisiana St, US
Country: United States
Contact: Director of operations June Christensen
Email: june@spahouston.org

Society of the Cincinnati Concerts at Anderson House, The
Website: www.societyofcincinnati.org
Email: eshulz@societyofcincinnati.org
Phone: 202 785 2040
Address: 2118 Massachusetts Ave, NW, US
Country: United States
Contact: collections Manager Emily Shulz

Society of the Four Arts
Website: www.fourarts.org
Email: contactus@fourarts.org
Phone: 561 655 7227
Address: 2 Four Arts Plaza, US
Information: nonprofit cultural organization
Country: United States
Contact: President Ervin S. Duggan
Social Media: @FourArts www.facebook.com/fourarts
Policies: Other

Sonoma State University Center for Performing Arts
Website: www.gmc.sonoma.edu/education/school-performing-arts
Email: greenmusiccenter@sonoma.edu
Phone: 707 664 2474
Address: 1801 E Cotati Avenue, Center for Performing Arts, US
Information: year-round programming of premiere classical, contemporary, jazz, chamber, and world music artists in concert. The GMC campus includes the 1, 400-

seat Weill Hall, the intimate 240-seat Schroeder Hall, as well as the highly unique summertime concert-going experience of Weill Hall + Lawn.
Country: United States
Contact: Director of Marketing Jana Jackson
Social Media: @greenmusicctr www.facebook.com/greenmusiccenter

Sorenson Center for the Arts
Website: www.babson.edu/student-life/arts/Pages/home.aspx
Email: sorenson@babson.edu
Phone: 781 239 5622
Address: 231 Forest St, , US
Information: presents a diverse array of programming in theater, dance, music, film, video, literary art, and visual arts for on-campus audiences and the General public. Visiting artists act as resources in improving the quality of life and intellectual and creative activity within the Babson community and in the surrounding area
Country: United States
Social Media: @BabsonArts www.facebook.com/BabsonArts

South Berkshire Concerts at Simon's Rock
Website: www.southberkshireconcerts.org
Email: larry@simons-rock.edu
Phone: 413 528 7212
Address: Simon's Rock of Bard College, US
Country: United States
Contact: public relations Briana Della Rocca
Contact: events coordinator Christopher Sink
Contact: Manager Larry Wallach

South Broadway Cultural Center Monthly Events
Website: www.cabq.gov
Phone: 505 848 1320
Address: 1025 Broadway SE, US
Country: United States
Contact: Director Linda G. Ulibarri

South Dakota State University, Student Activities
Phone: 605 688 6129
Address: PO Box 2815, US
Country: United States
South Florida State College
Website: www.sfscarts.org
Email: culturalperformances@southflorida.edu
Phone: 863 784 7178
Address: 600 W College Drive, US
Information: Member of Florida Professional Presenters Consortium; over 30 performances per season, artist series, matinee series, jazz series and kaleidoscope series
Country: United States
Contact: Director, cultural programs Cindy Garren
Email: garrenc@southflorida.edu
Contact: Marketing Manager Chase Smith
Email: smithc@southflorida.edu
Social Media: @sfscarts www.facebook.com/sfs-carts?v=wall
Annual Performances: 30
Policies: Rent and present, Theatre

South Mountain Concerts
Phone: 141 344 22106
Address: PO Box 23, US
Information: August to October season
Country: United States
Contact: Director Lou Steigler

South Puget Sound Community College Presents
Website: www.spscc.ctc.edu
Email: eventmanagement@spscc.ctc.edu
Phone: 360 596 5333
Address: South Puget Sound CC/College Center Performing Art, 2011 Mottman Road SW, US
Information: also do Artist and Lectures Series
Country: United States
Social Media: @SPSCC www.facebook.com/southpugetsoundcc

Southern Illinois University
Website: www.siu.edu/~shryock
Phone: 618 453 3379
Address: Shryock Auditorium, US
Country: United States
Contact: shryock auditorium Director Robert Cerchio

Southern Illinois University at Edwardsville Arts and Issues Series
Website: artsandissues.com
Email: gandree@siue.edu
Phone: 618 650 2626
Address: SIUE Box 1608, Packhall, Room 3422, US
Information: student-centered educational community dedicated to communicating, expanding and integrating knowledge; brings Artistic excellence to the SIUE campus through an eclectic blend of speakers and performers
Country: United States

Southern Kentucky Performing Arts Center (SKyPAC)
Website: www.theskypac.com
Email: info@theskypac.com

Phone: 270 904 5000
Address: 601 College Street, P.O.Box 748, US
Country: United States
Contact: Executive Director Tom Tomlinson
Email: ttomlinson@theskypac.com
Contact: Executive assistant Betty McGuire
Email: Bmcguire@theskypac.com
 Marketing & p.r. Director
 Greg Keightley
Email: gkeightley@theskypac.com
Social Media: @TheSKyPAC www.facebook.com/TheSKyPAC
Policies: Rent only, Arts centre

Southern University & A&M College
Website: www.subr.edu
Email: rdowns@subr.edu
Phone: 225 771 2130
Address: Division for Student Affairs, Southern University, J.S.Clark Hall Annex, PO Box 13405, US
Country: United States
Contact: co-ordinator Terral C Jackson
Contact: vice chancellor Raymond Downs

Southwest Arts and Entertainment
Website: www.southwestae.com
Email: swae@southwestae.com
Phone: 602 482 6410
Address: PO Box 55566, US
Information: accompaniment varies: orchestra and tape
Country: United States
Contact: President Charles F Fischl

Southwestern College Cultural Arts Series
Website: www.sckans.edu
Email: tshook@sckans.edu
Phone: 620 221 3300
Address: Southwestern College, 100 College St, US
Country: United States
Contact: Chair Timothy Shook

Special Audiences, New Jersey
Email: specialaudiences@earthlink.net
Phone: 973 465 3999
Address: 20 Ferry St, US
Spencer Theater for the Performing Arts
Website: www.spencertheater.com
Phone: 505 336 4800
Address: PO Box 140, US
Information: non-profit institution; featuring hospitality spaces and state-of-the-art electronic, acoustic and theatrical equipment
Country: United States
Contact: Executive Director Charles Centilli
Contact: Director of Marketing Brad Cooper

Spencertown Academy Music Series
Website: www.spencertown.org
Email: spencertown@taconic.net
Phone: 518 392 3693
Address: Box 80, US
Information: non profit organisation
Country: United States
Contact: series co-ordinator Michael Collier
Contact: assistant Director Susan Davies
Contact: Director Judy Staber

Spivey Hall, Clayton College & State University
Website: www.spiveyhall.org
Email: spiveyhall@mail.clayton.edu
Phone: 678 466 4200
Address: Clayton State University, US
Information: located just south of Atlanta, GA, is an acoustically acclaimed concert hall offering an annual celebrated series of classical, jazz and world music
Country: United States
Contact: patron services Manager Tammy Moore
Email: tammymoore@clayton.edu
Contact: Executive Director Samuel C Dixon
Email: sam.dixon@clayton.edu
Contact: education Manager Melanie Darby
Email: melaniedarby@clayton.edu
Contact: production Manager Chris Tollack
Email: christollack@clayton.edu
Social Media: @spiveyhall www.facebook.com/groups/22727252271/
Policies: Concert hall

Springer Opera House
Website: www.springeroperahouse.org
Email: s_macmillan@springeroperahouse.org
Phone: 706 324 5714
Address: 103 Tenth Street, US
Information: official state theatre of Georgia, national historic landmark; a non-profit organisation
Country: United States
Contact: Director Marketing and Sales Scooter MacMillan
Contact: Artistic Director Paul R. Pierce
Contact: Associate Artistic Director Ron Anderson

Springfield Ballet Inc
Website: www.springfieldballet.org
Email: spballet@mindspring.com
Phone: 417 862 1343

Address: 411 North Sherman Parkway, US
Information: non-profit organization celebrating 30 years of highest-caliber dance training and performance
Country: United States
Contact: school and Artistic Director Marsha Warnke
Contact: Executive Director Scott Miller
Social Media: @SpfldBallet www.facebook.com/Spring-fieldBallet

St Cloud State University Performing Arts Series
Website: www.stcloudstate.edu
Email: upbperformingarts@stcloudstate.edu
Phone: 320 308 1669
Address: Atwood Memorial Center, St Cloud State University, 720 4th Avenue South, Room 118, US
Country: United States
Contact: performing arts coordinator Lola Bello
Contact: performing arts adviser Luke Hartog
Annual Performances: 6
Policies: Other

St John's College Concert Series
Website: www.sjca.edu
Phone: 410 263 2371
Address: PO Box 2800, US
Country: United States
Contact: events coordinator Eric Stoltzfus

St John's Triune Concert Series
Website: www.stjohnsemh.org
Email: stjohnsucc@juno.com
Phone: 614 224 8634
Address: 59 E Mound St, St John's Evangelical Church, US
Country: United States
Contact: minister of music May Schwarz

St Norbert College Guest Artist Series
Website: www.snc.edu
Phone: 920 403 3950
Address: 100 Grant Street, St Norbert College, US
Country: United States
 Director of communication & media relations
 Ruth Hunter
Contact: guest artist series coordinator Tammera Klumpyan
St Olaf College Artist Series
Website: www.stolaf.edu
Email: musicman@stolaf.edu
Phone: 507 786 – 3179
Address: Music Department, St Olaf College, US
Information: see also Orchestras & Choirs
Country: United States
Contact: music organisations Manager B. J. Johnson

St Paul's Chamber Music Series
Email: stpauls@mississippi.net
Phone: 601 693 2502/595
Address: 1116 23rd Avenue, US
Information: artists drawn from MS and AL
Country: United States
Contact: Director Ronnie Miller

St Paul's School Keiser Series
Email: dseaton@sps.edu
Phone: 603 229 4600 sch
Address: 325 Pleasant St, US
Country: United States
Contact: head music department David Seaton

St Peter's College
Website: www.spc.edu
Phone: 201 915 9238
Address: 2641 Kennedy Blvd, US
Country: United States
Contact: Director campus activities and programmes Eileen Poiani
Contact: President James Loughran

St. Ann's Warehouse
Website: www.stannswarehouse.org
Email: info@stannswarehouse.org
Phone: 718 834 8794
Address: 45 Water Street, US
Information: For 36 years, St. Ann's Warehouse has commissioned, produced, and presented a unique and eclectic body of innovative theater and concert presentations that meet at the intersection of theater and rock and roll. Since 2000, the organisation has helped vitalize the Brooklyn Waterfront in DUMBO, where St. Ann's Warehouse has become one of New York City's most important and compelling live performance destinations
Country: United States
Contact: production Manager Elizabeth Moreau
Email: emoreau@stannswarehouse.org
Contact: Artistic Director Susan Feldman
Email: info@stannswarehouse.org
Social Media: @stannswarehouse www.facebook.com/stannswarehouse
Policies: Present, produce, co-produce, Arts centre

Stage One: Professional Theatre for Young Audiences
Website: www.stageone.org
Email: stageone@stageone.org

Phone: 502 589 5946
Address: 501 W Main Street, US
Country: United States
Contact: Artistic Director J Daniel Herring
Contact: stage one Marketing coordinator Erin Cooper

Staller Center for the Arts
Website: www.stallercenter.com
Email: webmaster@stallercenter.com
Phone: 631 632 7235
Address: 2032 Staller Center, Long Island, US
Information: host film festival every summer; Emerson String Quartet ((q.v.)) is quartet-in-residence
Country: United States
Contact: Director of Marketing Julie Rulon Greene
Contact: Director Alan Inkles

Stanford Live
Website: live.stanford.edu/contact
Email: whausam@stanford.edu
Phone: 650 724 2464
Address: Bing Concert Hall Box Office, 327 Lasuen Street, Stanford University, US
Information: member of ISPA
Country: United States
Social Media: @stanfordlive www.facebook.com/StanfordLive

Stanly County Agri-Civic Center
Website: www.stanlyciviccenter.com
Email: information@stanlyciviccenter.com
Phone: 704 986 3666
Address: 26032-B Newt Rd, US
Information: a modern performing arts centre with 1500 sq ft stage
Country: United States
Contact: secretary Lee Thompson
Contact: Director Edmund Roush

Star Plaza Theater
Website: www.starplazatheater.com
Phone: 219 769 6311
Address: 8001 Delaware Place, US
Information: also rent
Country: United States
Star-Spangled Series
Email: louhart@yahoo.com
Phone: 336 883 3401
Address: PO Box 230, US
Country: United States
Contact: theatre Director Louisa Hart

Starlight Theatre
Website: www.kcstarlight.com
Phone: 816 363 7827
Address: 6601 Swope Parkway, US
Country: United States
Contact: public affairs Warren K. Erdman
Contact: Marketing Gregory A. Reid
Contact: Chair Peggy J. Dunn
Contact: President and Producer Robert Rohlf

State Theatre
Website: www.statetheatrenj.org
Email: info@statetheatrenj.org
Phone: 732 247 7200
Address: 15 Livingston Avenue, US
Information: Crossroads Theatre address: 7 Livingston Avenue
Country: United States
Contact: President Wesley Brustad
Contact: General Manager Dave Hartkern
Contact: Director of Marketing Daniel B. Grossman
Contact: Director of pr Josephine V. Anderson
Contact: Director of education Lian Farrer
Contact: Director of development Melinda Gorny McAleer

State Theatre Center for the Arts
Website: www.statetheatre.info
Email: info@statetheatre.info
Phone: 724 439 1360
Address: 27 E Main St, US
Information: also rent
Country: United States
Contact: stage Manager Erica Miller
Contact: Executive Director Marty Schiff

State Theatre Inc
Website: www.statetheatre.org
Email: mcook@statetheatre.org
Phone: 610 258 7766
Address: 453 Northampton St, US
Country: United States
Contact: facility Manager Mike Cook
Contact: Managing Director John Trembler
Contact: Executive Director Shelley Brown
Contact: Marketing Director Jamie Balliet
Contact: Director of development Sandra Gaspar

State University College at Oneonta
Website: www.oneonta.edu
Email: harclewg@oneonta.edu
Phone: 607 436 2550

Address: Hunt College Union, US
Country: United States
Contact: Director of campus activities Bill Harcleroet

State University College at Oswego Fine Arts Committee-Program Policy Board
Website: www.oswego.edu
Email: cl-info@oswego.edu
Phone: 315 312 2301
Address: 125 Hewitt Union, US
Country: United States
Contact: committee member Sherri-Ann Feinman

State University College at Potsdam
Website: www.potsdam.edu
Email: cps@potsdam.edu
Phone: 315 267 2277
Address: Crane School of Music, 44 Pierrepont Ave, US
Information: New Music Competition held annually in April; alternative email: stoltijm@potsdam.edu
Country: United States
Contact: facilities Manager Lorelei Murdie
Contact: Director and dean of music Alan Sollman
Contact: Executive Director of community performance series Kathy Olsen
Contact: outreach and Marketing coordinator Kay Caldwell

State University College Potsdam Union Board
Website: www.potsdam.edu
Email: sga@potsdam.edu
Phone: 315 267 2583
Address: Student Entertainment Service, SUNY, US
Country: United States
Contact: President Alden Bashalv

State University of New York at Cortland Campus Artist and Lecture Series
Email: cals@sny.cortland.edu
Phone: 607 753 2321
Address: SUNY Cortland, PO Box 2000, Corey Union, US
Information: member of Upstate New York Presenters
Country: United States
State University of New York College at Brockport, School of Arts and Performance
Website: www.brockport.edu
Phone: 158 539 52797
Address: US
Country: United States
dean of the school of arts & performance
Sharon Vasquez
Contact: events Manager Susan Bixler

State University of New York College of Technology at Canton
Website: www.canton.edu
Email: connorb@canton.edu
Phone: 315 386 7315
Address: 34 Cornell Drive, US
Country: United States
Contact: Director Michael Perry
Contact: contact Brian Connor

State University of West Georgia-Townsend Center for the Performing Arts
Website: www.townsendcenter.org
Email: wballew@westga.edu
Phone: 678 839 4722
Address: 1600 Maple Street, US
Country: United States
Contact: General Manager Ren
Contact: technical Director David Manuel
Contact: Director Robert Jennings
Contact: auditorium Manager Wende Ballew

Steamboat Springs Council of the Arts & Humanities
Website: www.steamboatspringarts.com
Email: arts@steamboatspringarts.com
Phone: 970 879 9008
Address: PO Box 774284, US
Information: also present the Arts in the Park Festival July, annual
Country: United States
Contact: Executive Director Nancy B. Kramer

Stelig Theater Productions
Website: www.sullivan.suny.edu
Email: goldfrb@sullivan.suny.edu
Phone: 914 434 5750 ext
Address: 112 College Road, Sullivan County Community Coll, US
Country: United States
Contact: Director of campus activities James Goldfarb
Contact: vice President for admin Elizabeth Kubenik

Stephen F Austin State University – University Series
Website: www.sfasu.edu
Email: boxoffice@sfasu.edu
Phone: 936 468 2801
Address: 2222 Alumni Drive, US

Country: United States
Contact: dean A.C. Himes
Social Media: @SFASU www.facebook.com/sfasu/

Stockbridge Chamber Concerts
Website: www.stockbridgechamberconcerts.org
Email: eahscc@hotmail.com
Phone: 888 528 7728
Address: Searles Castle, 398 Main Street, US
Information: the Stockbridge Chamber of Commerce is a nonprofit, membership organization that is dedicated to promoting and improving the economic welfare of the Town of Stockbridge since 1986. also holiday concerts for children.
Country: United States
Contact: founder/Artistic Director/President Elizabeth Hagenah
Contact: President Mike Duffy
Email: mduffy@nrm.org

Stocker Arts Center
Website: www.stockerartscenter.com
Email: jbarlow@lorainccc.edu
Phone: 440 366 4140
Address: Lorain County Community College, 1005 North Abbe Road, US
Information: can seat a maximum of 984 in fixed seats + 6 wheelChairs. The seating is variable depending on whether the orchestra pit is needed. We do approx 50-60 events during the season; 200+ rentals per year
Country: United States
Contact: Director Janet Herman Barlow
Email: jbarlow@lorainccc.edu
Annual Performances: 300
Annual Productions: 60
Policies: Present, produce, co-produce, Rent and present, Arts centre

Stockton Performing Arts Center
Website: www.stockton.edu/pac
Email: coolm@stockton.edu
Phone: 609 652 4607
Address: Richard Stockton College of New Jersey, Jimmie Leeds Road, PO Box 195, NJ, US
Information: Summer Music Series on the Atlantic City Boardwalk
Country: United States
Contact: Executive Director Michael Cool

Strand Theatre of Shreveport
Website: www.thestrandtheatre.com
Email: strand@thestrandtheatre.com
Phone: 318 226 1481
Address: PO Box 1547, 619 Louisiana, US
Country: United States
Contact: Director Danny Fogger
Contact: assistant Director Charlene Snider

Strand Ventures Inc/Strand Theater
Website: www.strandlakewood.com
Email: marylou@strandlakewood.com
Phone: 732 367 7789
Address: 400 Clifton Avenue, US
Information: available for rent check website for more details
Country: United States
Contact: events coordinator/house Manager Marylou Waddell Gesslein
Contact: Executive Director Theresa Beaugard

Strand-Capitol Performing Arts Center Inc
Website: www.strandcapitol.org
Email: info@strandcapital.org
Phone: 717 846 1155
Address: 50 North George Street, US
Information: member of International Society of Performing Arts, Arts Presenters, League of Historic American Theatres, Consortium of Eastern Regional Theatres and Pennsylvania Presenters
Country: United States
Contact: General Manager Anne Sturm
Email: asturm@strandcapitol.org
Contact: development office Gary Bowman
Email: gbowman@strandcapitol.org
Contact: business Manager Trisha Melikian
Email: tmelikian@strandcapitol.org
Social Media: @strandcapitol www.facebook.com/strandcapitol

Strathmore
Website: www.strathmore.org
Email: Marketing@strathmore.org
Phone: 301 581 5100
Address: 5301 Tuckerman Lane, US
Country: United States
President & CEO
Eliot Pfanstiehl
Contact: Press and Marketing assistant Georgina Javor
Contact: Director of Marketing and Press Jennifer A Buzzell

Strings in the Mountains Festival of Music
Website: www.stringsinthemountains.com

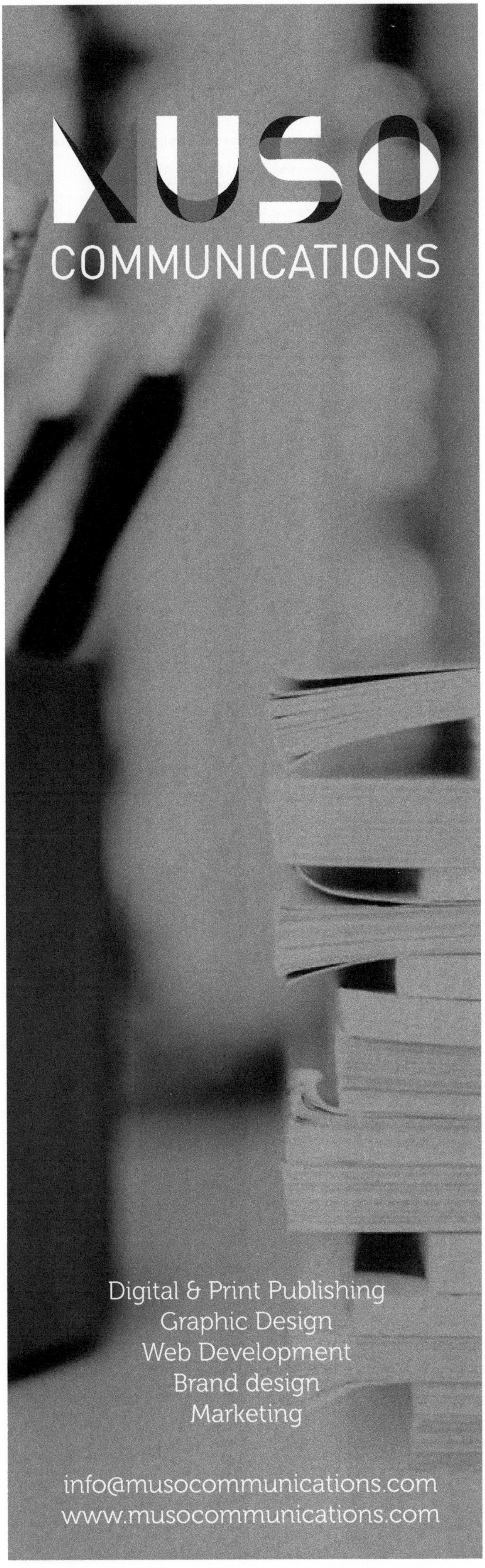

2022 MAY 9-11
DANISH+

DANISH PERFORMING ARTS SHOWCASE FOR CHILDREN & YOUTH

AARHUS, DENMARK

READ MORE: DANISHPLUS.DK

Email: kay@stringsmusicfestival.com
Phone: 970 879 5056
Address: PO Box 774627, US
Country: United States
Contact: operations and non-classical programming Director Betse Grassby
Contact: President Kay Clagett

Sturgis Council of the Arts
Website: www.sturgisarts.com
Phone: 269 659 8508
Address: 310 North Franks Avenue, US
Information: strives to fulfill its mission of making the arts and humanities available to the Sturgis area and to foster participation in and encourage greater awareness of the arts
Country: United States
Contact: Director William C. Boersma

Suffok Theater
Website: www.suffolktheater.com
Email: bobspiotto@optonline.net
Phone: 631 727 4343
Address: 118 East Main St, US
Information: The Suffolk Theater is a 1933 art deco movie house that offers a wide variety of edu-tainment and serves the East End/Hamptons areas, as well as all of Long Island.**Country:** United States
Policies: All, Multi-purpose

Summer Music Associates
Website: www.summermusicAssociates.org
Phone: 160 376 32870
Address: PO Box 603, US
Country: United States
Contact: programme Chairman Barbara Chase
Contact: treasurer Andrew R Supplee

Summermusic
Website: www.newyorkpops.org
Email: info@nypops.org
Phone: 1 (+1) 212-765 7
Address: The New York Pops, , 333 West 52nd Street, US
Information: annual free outdoor series of popular classics
Country: United States
 Director of development & Marketing
 Daniel Bindermann
Contact: Executive Director James Johnson

SUN Entertainment
Website: www.nau.edu/SUN-Entertainment/
Email: sun.ent@nau.edu
Phone: 928 523 5638
Address: 1050 S. Knoles, Dr. Flagstaff, US
Information: SUN Entertainment is Northern Arizona University's entertainment promotion and production company, offering events and activities for students on campus. With programs ranging from movies and concerts to speakers and casino nights
Country: United States
Social Media: https://twitter.com/SUNEventsNAU
https:// www.facebook.com/nausunentertainment
https:// www.instagram.com/sunentertainment/
Disabled Access: Yes
Capacity: 1000+
Annual Performances: 100+
Policies: Rent and Present

Sun Valley Center for the Arts
Website: www.sunvalleycenter.org
Email: information@sunvalleycenter.org
Phone: 208 726 9491
Address: PO Box 656, US
Information: Twilight series June-August; also offer art classes for adults, families, and kids as well as lectures, discussion groups, and conferences on various topics
Country: United States
Contact: Director of visual arts Courtney Gilbert
 Marketing Director & Director of performing arts
 Kristine Bretall
Contact: Artistic Director Kristin Poole

Sunday Afternoons of Music & Sunday Afternoons of Music for Children
Website: www.sundaymusicals.org
Email: info@sundaymusicals.org
Phone: 305 271 7150
Address: PO Box 6688, US
Information: ABC party for children
Country: United States
Contact: Artistic Director Doreen Marx

Sunday Concert Series
Website: www.nga.gov
Email: music@nga.gov
Phone: 202 842 6075
Address: c/o National Gallery of Art, Sixth St & Constitution Ave NW, US
Information: free concerts, Sundays at 6:30pm October – June
Country: United States
Contact: head of the music department Stephen Ackert

Sundays Live
Website: www.sundayslive.org
Email: tcatn0c@sundayslive.org
Phone: 323 857 6234
Address: 433 S. Spring Street, 10th Fl., c/o Cultural Affairs Dept., US
Information: broadcast live on KMZT
Country: United States
Contact: Artistic Director William Vestal

Sunset Cultural Center Performance Carmel
Website: www.sunsetcenter.org
Email: info@sunsetcenter.org
Phone: 831 620 2040
Address: Sunset Cultural Center, PO Box 1950, US
Information: As the premier performing arts facility of the Monterey Peninsula, Sunset Center (a nonprofit organization) presents live music and concerts, dance, theatre, comedy, and family events. With two performance venues, meeting space, an art gallery, and more, Sunset Cultural Center, Inc. serves the communities of the Monterey Peninsula through Artistic and educational programming.
Country: United States
Contact: Executive Director Christine Sandin
Email: execdir@sunsetcenter.org
Social Media: @sunsetcenter www.facebook.com/SunsetCenter

Susquehanna University Artist Series
Website: www.susqu.edu
Email: artistseries@susqu.edu
Phone: 157 037 24294
Address: 514 University Avenue, US
Country: United States
Contact: Director Valerie Martin

Sylvia & Danny Kaye Playhouse at Hunter College
Website: kayeplayhouse.hunter.cuny.edu/
Email:
kayeinfo@hunter.cuny.edu
Phone: 212 772 4448
Address: 695 Park Avenue, US
Country: United States

Symphony Center Presents
Website: www.cso.org
Email: carlinos@chicagosymphony.org
Phone: 312 294 3000
Address: Orchestra Hall, 220 S Michigan Avenue, US
Country: United States
Contact: Director of programming Mati
Contact: Artistic administrator Martha Gilmer
Contact: pr Synneve Carlino

Symphony Space Inc
Website: www.symphonyspace.org
Email: ssadmin@symphonyspace.org
Phone: 212 864 1414
Address: 2537 Broadway, US
Country: United States
Contact: booking Director Patricia Sinnott
Contact: Artistic Director Isaiah Sheffer
Contact: Managing Director Peggy Wreen

Syracuse Friends of Chamber Music Inc.
Website: syracusefriendsofchambermusic.org
Phone: 315 446 0994
Address: 35 Drumlins Terrace, US
Information: non-profit organisation; venue address: 1130 Salt Spring Road, Syracuse, NY 13224
Country: United States
Contact: music Director Henry Palocz

Tacoma Philharmonic Inc
Website: www.tacomaphilharmonic.org
Email: info@tacomaphilharmonic.org
Phone: 253 272 0809
Address: 901 Broadway, Suite 400, US
Country: United States
Contact: Executive assistant Sherry Hall
Contact: Executive Director Andy Wood

Tahoe Arts Project
Website: www.tahoeartsproject.org
Email: tahoearts@aol.com
Phone: 530 542 3632
Address: PO Box 14281, US
Information: school residencies
Country: United States
Contact: Executive Director Peggy Thompson

Tallahassee-Leon County Civic Center
Website: www.tlccc.org
Phone: 850 487 1691
Address: PO Box 10604, US
Country: United States
Contact: Marketing Director Charlotte Brown
Contact: Director Ron Spencer
Contact: deputy Director Roger Englert

Taos Center for the Art
Website: www.taoscenterforthearts.org
Email: carol@taoscenterforthearts.org

Phone: 505 758 2052
Address: 133 Paseo del Pueblo Norte, US
Information: also rent auditorium
Country: United States
Contact: performing arts coordinator Carol Kalom

Tarpon Springs Performing Arts & Cultural Center
Website: www.ci.tarpon-springs.fl.us
Email: info@tarponarts.org
Phone: 727 942 5605
Address: 324 E Pine St, US
Information: the Cultural center is based at 101 Pinellas Avenue, Tarpon Springs Florida
Country: United States
Contact: Director Kathleen Monahan

Taylor University Performing Artist Series
Website: www.taylor.edu
Email: jdkirkwood@tayloru.edu
Phone: 765 998 5289
Address: Taylor University, 236 W. Reade Ave, US
Information: christian campus
Country: United States
Contact: publicity coordinator Judy Kirkwood
Contact: committee Chair Patricia Robertson

Tecumseh Civic Auditorium
Phone: 517 423 6617
Address: 400 N Maumee, US
Country: United States
Contact: Executive Director Rob Steele
Contact: technical Director Karen S Bunch

Tempe Center for the Arts
Website: www.tempe.gov/tca
Email: info@tempe.gov
Phone: 480 350 2829 (ad
Address: 700 W. Rio Salado Parkway, US
Country: United States
Contact: deputy community services Director, cultural services Jody Ulich
Contact: cultural facilities administrator Don Fassinger
Contact: gallery coordinator Michelle Dock
 patron & services coordinator
 Sally Garrison

Temple Square Concert Series
Website: www.lds.org
Phone: 801 240 3323
Address: 3rd Floor, West Wing, 50 East North Temple Street, US
Information: all concerts are free
Country: United States
Contact: Director Ian McKay
Contact: Executive secretary Marilyn Lorensen

Temple University Boyer College of Music and Dance
Website: www.temple.edu/boyer
Email: jason.horst@temple.edu
Phone: 215 204 8391
Address: Presser Hall, 2001 North 13th Street, US
Information: Boyer is part of the Center for Performing and Cinematic Arts at Temple University**Country:** United States
Contact: asst. Director, Marketing and communications Jennifer Hoffmaster
Email: jhoffmaster@temple.edu
Social Media: @BoyerCollege www.facebook.com/BoyerCollege

Tennessee Performing Arts Center
Website: www.tpac.org
Email: Marketing@tpac.org
Phone: 615 782 4040
Address: PO Box 190660, 505 Deaderick Street, US
Information: The Tennessee Performing Arts Center (TPAC) is a private, non-profit organization dedicated to providing and supporting the presentation of the performing arts. visiting address: 505 Deaderick St, Nashville TN 37219-5576
Country: United States
Social Media: @tpac www.facebook.com/TennesseePAC
Capacity: 2474

Texarkana Regional Arts and Humanities Council, Inc (TRAHC) Perot Theatre Series
Website: www.trahc.org
Email: artsinfo@trahc.org
Phone: 903 792 8681
Address: PO Box 1171, 221 Main St, US
Country: United States
Contact: administrative Director Mary Starrett
Contact: operations Manager Randal Conry
Contact: Executive Director Ruth Ellen Whitt

Texas Tech University – Center for Campus Life
Website: www.campuslife.ttu.edu
Email: Jana.Vise@ttu.edu
Phone: 806 742 5433
Address: 201 Student Union, Box 45014, US
Country: United States
Contact: coordinator Jana Vise

Thalian Hall Centre for the Performing Arts
Website: www.thalianhall.org
Email: scoley@thalianhall.org
Phone: 910 632 2241
Address: 310 Chestnut Street, US
Information: Thalian Hall is a 150-year-old theatre in historic downtown Wilmington, NC. Having undergone a 3.5 million dollar renovation completed in May, 2010, Thalian Hall boasts three performing spaces: the historic Main Stage, the intimate Studio Theatre, and the Grand Ballroom. Thalian Hall is mostly a rental facility for the various production companies in town. Thalian Hall hosts an annual Main Attractions series of concerts and other touring acts, as well as the Cinematique film series co-sponsored by WHQR Public Radio
Country: United States
Contact: programme Director Stephen Barefoot
Email: stephen@goingbarefoot.com
Contact: Executive Director Tony Rivenbark
Email: trivenbark@thalianhall.org
Social Media: @thalianhall https:// www.facebook.com/ thcpa/
Annual Performances: 420
Policies: All, Theatre

The Apollo Theater
Website: www.apollotheater.org
Phone: 212 531 5300
Address: 253 West 125th Street, US
Information: member of ISPA
Country: United States
Contact: Chairman Richard D. Parsons
Contact: Executive Producer Mikki Shepard
Contact: vice Chairman Alfred C. Liggins, III
Social Media: @ApolloTheater www.facebook.com/ ApolloTheater
Policies: Present, produce, co-produce, Theatre

The Arts Association of East Alabama
Website: www.opelikaarts.com
Email: info@eastalabamaarts.org
Phone: 334 749 8105
Address: 1032 South Railroad Ave, US
Information: formerly known as Opelika Arts Association Inc
Country: United States

The Capitol Theatre – Yakima
Website: www.capitoltheatre.org
Email: arts@capitoltheatre.org
Phone: 509 853 2787
Address: 19 S 3rd St Yakima, US
Information: The Capitol Theatre stands as a testament to the community's commitment to its heritage and its long standing commitment to the arts. Their stage is home to Yakima Symphony Orchestra, Town Hall, and many local dance studios. They also proudly present top-quality touring Broadway musicals along with Capitol Kids, which is an education and outreach program for school-age children.
Country: United States
Social Media: www.facebook.com/The-Capitol-Theatre-134196885575twitter.com/CapitolBuzz

The Ford Theatres
Website: www.fordtheatres.org
Email: admin@ford.lacounty.gov
Phone: 323 856 5793
Address: 2580 Cahuenga Blvd East, US
Information: The John Anson Ford Theatres are owned by the County of Los Angeles and operated in partnership with the Department of Parks and Recreation and the Ford Theatre Foundation. Located in a 32-acre County regional park, this intimate 1,200-seat amphitheatre is one of the oldest performing arts venues in Los Angeles still in use. Each year, the Ford presents an eclectic and diverse summer season of music, dance and theatre by some of the most exciting LA-based artists, as well as some of the most compelling artists from around the world. Member of ISPA
Country: United States
Contact: operations Manager Alyssa Bellew
Email: abellew@ford.lacounty.gov
Contact: ticket services Manager Ann Jensen
Email: ajensen@ford.lacounty.gov
Contact: production Manager Arthur Trowbridge
Email: atrowbridge@ford.lacounty.gov
Social Media: @FordTheatres www.facebook.com/ FordTheatres
Policies: Theatre

The Kanbar Centre for the Performing Arts @ the Osher Marin JCC
Website: www.marinjcc.org
Email: info@marinjcc.org
Phone: 415 444 8000
Address: 200 N. San Pedro Road, US
Country: United States
Contact: Executive Director Judy Wolff-Bolton

The Kentucky Center
Website: www.kentuckycenter.org
Email: info@kentuckycenter.org
Phone: 800 775 7777
Address: 501 West Main Street, US
Country: United States
Social Media: @KyCtrArts www.facebook.com/kentucky-center

The Mahaiwe Performing Arts Center
Website: http:// www.mahaiwe.org
Email: info@mahaiwe.org
Phone: +1 413-528-0100
Address: 14 Castle Street, Administrative Offices: 413-644-9040. 244 Main Street Suite 3, P.O. Bo, US
Information: Through programs of the highest quality in dance, music, theatre and opera, we ensure a diversity of talent on the stage of our newly restored historic theater, at ticket prices affordable to our community. Our goal is to present available programs that a
Country: United States
Contact: Executive Director Beryl Jolly
Email: info@mahaiwe.org
Contact: General Manager Karin Watkins
Email: karin@mahaiwe.org
Contact: production Manager/lighting supervisor Matthew Adelson
Email: MEAdelson@aol.com
Contact: Manager Marketing and communications Kelly Collins
Email: Marketing@mahaiwe.org
Contact: box office Manager Michael Beuth
Email: michael@mahaiwe.org

The Metropolitan Museum of Art
Website: www.metmuseum.org/
Email: communications@metmuseum.org
Phone: 212 535 7710
Address: 1000 Fifth Avenue, US
Country: United States
Social Media: @metmuseum www.facebook.com/ metmuseum

The Morrison Center for the Performing Arts at Boise State University
Website: mc.boisestate.edu
Email: scottbodmer@boisestate.edu
Phone: 208 426 1629
Address: 1910 University Drive, US
Country: United States
Contact: Executive Director James Patrick

The Music Center at Strathmore
Website: www.strathmore.org
Email: csr@strathmore.org
Phone: 301 581 5200
Address: 5301 Tuckerman Lane, US
Information: independent, 501c3 organization, the arts center presents a lively and diverse program of art exhibitions, concerts and performing arts programs, and literary lectures and events; manison address: The Mansion at Strathmore, 10701 Rockville Pike, North Bet
Country: United States
Contact: vp, Artistic Director Shelley Brown

The Palace Theatre
Website: www.palacestamford.org/online
Email: mmoran@palacestamford.org
Phone: 203 358 2305
Address: 61 Atlantic Street, US
Information: the regional arts centre for exciting entertainment that enhances and enriches the cultural, educational, economic, and social life of the community. The Palace strives to achieve this vision by demonstrating integrity in all work and relationships, providing service and quality in all activities, fostering and promoting diversity of thought, ideas and culture, providing stewardship for the Stamford Arts community, emphasising outreach in the community, and offering creativity in all endeavors. Major funding is provided by the Department of Economic & Community Development and the Office of the Arts. Programmes made possible in part by the Fairfield County Community Foundation
Country: United States
Contact: Executive Director Michael E. Moran, Jr.
Email: mmoran@palacestamford.org
Contact: Director of production Randy Thomas
Email: rthomas@palacestamford.org
Social Media: PalaceStamford www.facebook.com/ ThePalaceTheatreStamford
Annual Performances: 90
Policies: Rent and present, Concert hall

The Pasadena Playhouse
Website: www.pasadenaplayhouse.org
Email: Press@pasadenaplayhouse.org
Phone: 626 792 8672
Address: 600 Playhouse Alley, Suite 300, US
Information: Visiting address: 39 South El Molino Avenue, Pasadena, CA 91101
Country: United States
Director of Marketing & communications Patty Onagan
Social Media: @PasPlayhouse www.facebook.com/ pasadenaplayhouse
Policies: All, Theatre

The Schoenfeld Theatre
Website: www.telecharge.com
Email: tickets@telecharge.com

Phone: 212 944 3700
Address: 236 West 45th Street, US
Country: United States
Contact: vice President of theatre operations Peter Entin
Contact: management company The Shubert Org. Inc

The Source
Website: www.sourcedc.org
Email: info@sourcedc.org
Phone: 202 315 1305
Address: 1835 14th St, NW, US
Information: to re-open 2008 as arts centre after extensive renovation
Country: United States
Contact: Executive Director, cultural development corp. Anne Corbett

The Yard, Inc
Website: www.dancetheyard.org
Email: admin@dancetheyard.org
Phone: 508 645 9662
Address: Middle Road, PO Box 405, US
Information: artists' colony – residencies: on an island off the coast of Massachusetts
Country: United States
Contact: Artistic Director Lois Welk
Contact: Executive Director DiAnn Ray

Theater at Lime Kiln
Website: www.theateratlimekiln.com
Email: info@theateratlimekiln.com
Phone:
154 046 37088
Address: P.O. Box 1244, US
Information: We produce professional and community theatre and present an eclectic music series from April to October., Mailing address: PO Box 1244, Lexington, VA 24450; Map address: 601 Borden Rd. Lexington, VA 24450. We produce professional and community theatre and present an eclectic music series from April to October.
Country: United States
Contact: Executive Director Tony Russell
Contact: box office Manager Alice Williams

Theatre at Raritan Valley Community College
Website: www.rvccarts.org
Email: theatre@rvccarts.org
Phone: 908 218 8867
Address: PO Box 3300, US
Country: United States
Contact: communication assistant Cristina Lankay
Contact: production Manager John Wiedemann
Contact: theatre Manager Cindy Alexander
Contact: theatre Director Alan Liddell

Third Street Music School Settlement Summer Series
Website: www.thirdstreetmusicschool.org
Phone: 212 777 3240
Address: 235 East Eleventh Street, US
Country: United States
Contact: concerts/community activities Director Beth Flusser
Contact: communications Manager Karen Haight

Thomasville Entertainment Foundation
Website: www.TEFconcerts.com
Email: tef@rose.net
Phone: 229 226 7404
Address: P.O. Box 1976, US
Information: Founded in 1937, Thomasville Entertainment Foundation is a volunteer-powered, non-profit organization. In addition to presenting concerts by acclaimed artists, TEF offers a dedicated family series of performances geared toward families and younger children, provides educational outreach programs for students and awards performing arts scholarships and grants to promising young artists.
Country: United States
Social Media: Thomasville Entertainment Foun
Capacity: 500

Thousand Oaks Civic Arts Plaza
Website: www.civicartsplaza.com
Email: theatres@toaks.org
Phone: 805 449 2700
Address: c/o City of Thousand Oaks, 2100 Thousand Oaks Blvd, US
Information: largest performing arts center between LA and San Francisco; funded through a unique public/ private partnership between the City of Thousand Oaks and the Alliance for the Arts
Country: United States
Contact: technical production Manager Michael Tachco
Email: mtachco@toaks.org
Contact: theatres Director Barry McComb
Email: bmccomb@toaks.org
Contact: box office Manager Kristyn Schiavo
Email: KSchiavo@toaks.org
Contact: Director of Marketing Colleen Debler
Email: cdebler@toaks.org
Social Media: @tocap www.facebook.com/civicartsplaza

Policies: Rent and present

Thunder Bay Arts Council, Inc
Website: www.alpenatbarts.org
Email: tbarts@freeway.net
Phone: 198 935 66678
Address: 313 1/2 N 2nd Ave, US
Information: also do Art on the Bay, an annual arts & craft fair which takes place in July
Country: United States
Contact: President Duane Beyer

Tigertail Productions
Website: www.tigertail.org
Email: email@tigertail.org
Phone: 305 324 4337
Address: 842 NW 9th Court, US
Country: United States
Contact: project coordinator Anya Talbot
Contact: Executive Director Mary Luft

Tilles Center for the Performing Arts
Website: www.tillescenter.org
Email: susanna.stickley@liu.edu
Phone: 516 299 3100
Address: LIU Post, 720 Northern Blvd., US
Country: United States
Contact: Director Elliott Sroka
Contact: General Manager George N. Lindsay Jr
Contact: business Manager Marc Courtade
Contact: development Director Marcie Rosenberg
Contact: Marketing Director Susanna Stickley

Tisch Center for the Arts
Website: www.92y.org
Email: webmaster@92y.org
Phone: 212 415 5740
Address: 92nd Street Y, 1395 Lexington Ave, US
Information: see also Harkness Dance Center, 92nd Street Y
Country: United States
Contact: Marketing and customer relations Shelly Felder
Contact: Executive Director Sol Adler
Contact: President Michael Goldstein
Contact: public and media relations Alix Friedman

TITAS, Extraordinary Dance and Music
Website: www.titas.org
Email: csantos@titas.org
Phone: 214 880 0202
Address: 2100 ROSS AVE. SUITE 650, US
Information: TITAS presents a subscription series of five dance and five music attractions each year, in addition to an annual ballet gala and 2-3 special presentations
Country: United States
Contact: box office Manager Sharron Morgan
Contact: Executive Director Charles Santos
Social Media: @TITASPresents www.facebook.com/TITASpresents/

Tivoli Theatre
Website: www.chattanoogaonstage.com
Email: onstage@mail.chattanooga.gov
Phone: 423 757 5156
Address: Mail: 399 McCallie Ave., US
Information: Owned and operated by The City of Chattanooga Civic Facilities Division, Dept. of Education, Arts & Culture (EAC)
Country: United States
Contact: admin George Parker
Contact: Marketing Director Donna Landry
Contact: business Manager Sandy Coulter

Toledo Museum of Art Peristyle Series
Website: www.toledomuseum.org
Email: khensley@toledomuseum.org
Phone: 419 255 8000
Address: PO Box 1013, US
Information: Toledo Symphony organises the concerts in the Peristyle
Country: United States
Contact: visiting services assistant Karen Hensley

Toledo Symphony – Presenting Series
Website: www.toledosymphony.com
Email: music@toledosymphony.com
Phone: 800 348 1253
Address: 1838 Parkwood Avenue, Suite 310, US
Information: see also Orchestras & Choirs
Country: United States
Contact: President and CEO Kathleen Carroll
Email: kcarroll@toledosymphony.com
Contact: Director of Marketing and public relations Ashley Mirakian
Email: amirakian@toledosymphony.com
Contact: President emeritus/chief Artistic officer Robert Bell
Email: rbell@toledosymphony.com
Contact: Artistic Administration Merwin Siu
Email: msiu@toledosymphony.com
Contact: senior development officer Michelle Devine
Email: mdevine@toledosymphony.com
Contact: vice President of finance Randi Dier
Email: rdier@toledosymphony.com

Contact: stage Manager Tim Lake
Email: tlake@toledosymphony.com
Social Media: @toledosymphony www.facebook.com/toledosymphonyorchestra?ref=ts
Policies: Concert hall

Topeka Performing Arts Center
Website: www.tpactix.org
Email: rseitz@tpactix.org
Phone: 785 234 2787
Address: 214 SE Eighth St, US
Information: rent, present, produce jazz festival
Country: United States
Contact: Executive Director Robert Seitz
Contact: Marketing Manager Melanie Kitchner
Contact: assistant Director Mark Radziejeski

Torrance Cultural Arts Center
Website: www.tcac.torrnet.com
Email: jbotiller@torrnet.com
Phone: 310 781 7150
Address: 3330 Civic Center Drive, US
Information: rental facility with limited programming by city; center is currently being reorganised; classes, workshops, lectures, outdoor festivals also held at center
Country: United States
Contact: General services Director t.b.a.
Contact: business Manager Jasun Botiller
Contact: Marketing coordinator Daniel Watt
Contact: theatre technical Director John Sejes
Contact: booking Manager Lisa Gomes
Contact: theater booking Manager Anita Moisen

Tower Theater for the Performing Arts
Website: www.towertheatrefresno.com
Email: info@towertheatrefresno.com
Phone: 559 485 9050
Address: 815 E Olive, US
Country: United States
Contact: Artistic Director Leslie Davis

Town Hall Arts Center
Website: www.townhallartscenter.com
Email: nstalf@townhallartscenter.com
Phone: 303 794 2787
Address: 2450 W Main St, US
Country: United States
Contact: Executive Director Nancy Stalf
Contact: Director of operations Janet Murray

Town Hall Foundation Inc
Website: www.the-townhall-nyc.org
Phone: 212 997 1003
Address: The Town Hall, 123 West 43rd Street, US
Information: a non-profit organisation
Country: United States
Contact: Director of publicity Kerrie L. Smith
Contact: Director of Marketing E.A. Kafkalas
Contact: Director of development Marissa Lewis
Contact: Executive Director Lawrence C. Zucker

Town of Herndon
Email: holly.popple@herndon-va.gov
Phone: 703 435 6868
Address: PO Box 427, US
Country: United States
performing arts & special events
Holly Popple

Township Auditorium
Website: www.thetownship.org
Email: exdirmp@aol.com
Phone: 803 252 2032
Address: 1703 Taylor Street, US
Country: United States
Contact: Executive Director Marshall Perry
Contact: Associate Director Ray Logan
Contact: assistant Director Andre Holloman

Tri-C Cultural Arts Program
Website: www.tri-c.edu/arts-and-entertainment
Email: artsandculture@tri-c.cc.oh.us
Phone: 216 987 3509
Address: Cuyahoga Community College, 4250 Richmond Road, Building E3, Room 1115, US
Information: coordinates Tri C Cleveland Jazz Fest
Country: United States
Contact: Director Karah Vance
Social Media: @TriCedu www.facebook.com/TriC.edu

Tribeca Performing Arts Center
Website: www.tribecapac.org
Email: info@tribecapac.org
Phone: 212 220 1459
Address: 199 Chambers St, US
Information: BMCC Tribeca Performing Arts Center, the longest operating performance venue in lower Manhattan, is dedicated to identifying, supporting and presenting established and emerging artists in a variety of disciplines, including music, dance and children's theatre to the diverse Metropolitan audience.
Country: United States
Contact: publicity Associate Allyson Morgan
Email: amorgan@tribecapac.org

Contact: Executive Director Linda Herring
Email: lherring@tribecapac.org
Contact: office Manager Nancy La Lanne
Email: nlalanne@tribecapac.org
Social Media: @tribecapac www.facebook.com/tribecapac

Triple EsPresso, LLC
Website: www.tripleesPresso.com
Email: dennis@tripleesPresso.com
Phone: 612 874 1100
Address: 12800 Industrial Park Blvd, Ste 252, US
Country: United States
Contact: Associate Producer Rosalie Miller
Email: rosalie@tripleesPresso.com
Contact: President/Executive Producer Dennis Babcock
Email: dennis@tripleesPresso.com

Triton College
Website: www.triton.edu/tcpac
Email: mcorrea@triton.edu
Phone: 708 456 0300 ext
Address: 2000 Fifth Ave, US
Information: The center is also available for rental.
Country: United States
Manager & technical Director
Maria Correa

Troy Chromatic Concerts
Website: www.troychromaticconcerts.org
Phone: 151 827 30038
Address: PO Box 1574, US
Country: United States
Contact: board President Ronald Geuther

Troy Savings Bank Music Hall Jazz at the Hall Series, Music at the Hall Series
Website: www.troymusihall.org
Email: info@troymusihall.org
Phone: 518 273 0038
Address: 30 Second Street, US
Information: alternative e-mail: lkratt@troymusihall.org
Country: United States
Contact: Executive Director Laura Kratt

Truman State University
Website: www.truman.edu
Email: heidi@truman.edu
Phone: 660 785 4016
Address: Lyceum Committee, 202 McClain Hall, US
Country: United States
Contact: public relations Director Heidi Templeton
Contact: Chairman lyceum committee Winston Vanderhoof
Email: ad96@truman.edu
Social Media: @TrumanState www.facebook.com/trumanstateuniversity
Capacity: 1390

Tucson Jazz Society
Website: tucsonjazz.org
Email: info@tucsonjazz.org
Phone: 520 903 1265
Address: P.O. Box 41071 Tucson, AZ , US
Information: The Tucson Jazz Society (TJS) is a non-profit arts organization dedicated to promoting and preserving America's original music – jazz. The Society's mission is to ensure continuity of the jazz art form through its commitment to nurture and champion local talent, bring outstanding national and international artists to southern Arizona, and provide for the young generation via its arts in education program.
Country: United States
Social Media: www.facebook.com/tucsonjazz
Annual Performances: 100+
Policies: Present

Tuesday Evening Concert Series
Website: www.tecs.org
Email: kpellon@tecs.org
Phone: 434 244 9505
Address: 108 5th Street, SE, Suite 208, US
Information: presenting soloists, small ensembles, small chamber orchestras
Country: United States
Contact: Executive Director Karen Pellón
Annual Performances: 7
Policies: Rent and present, Concert hall

Tuesday Musical Concert Series
Website: www.tuesdaymusicalomaha.org
Email: barbarataxman@aol.com
Phone: 402 391 4661
Address: 8543 Hickory, US
Information: non-profit concert series of international artists open to all
Country: United States
Contact: programme Director Barbara Taxman

Tulsa Performing Arts Center Trust
Website: www.tulsapac.com
Email: info@tulsapac.com
Phone: 918 596 7122

Address: 110 E 2nd St, US
Information: operated by The City of Tulsa and supported by the Tulsa Performing Arts Center Trust; Summerstage Festival; hold a Young People's Piano Competition; also rent
Country: United States
Contact: General Manager John E Scott
Contact: programme Director Shirley Elliott
Contact: Marketing coordinator Chad Oliverson

Tuskegee University – Art and Lecture Series
Website: www.tuskegee.edu
Email: clae@mytu.tuskegee.edu
Phone: 334 727 8784
Address: 1200 W. Montgomery Rd., US
Country: United States
Contact: lyceum coordinator Velma Blackwell

Tweeter Center for the Performing Arts
Website: www.tweetercenter.com
Phone: 508 339 2331
Address: PO Box 810, US
Country: United States
Contact: General Manager Bruce Montgomery

Tyler Community Concert Association
Phone: 190 359 26266
Address: PO Box 131673, US
Country: United States
Contact: President Gini Rainey

UApresents
Website: www.uapresents.org
Email: uapresents@arizona.edu
Phone: 520 621 3364
Address: University of Arizona, 888 N Euclid Avenue, Rm 203, PO Box 210158, US
Country: United States
Contact: Director Natalie Bohnet
Contact: Director of development Jennifer Camano

UCLA Performing Arts
Website: www.performingarts.ucla.edu
Email: phil.rosenthalarts.ucla.edu
Phone: 310 825 4401
Address: B100 Royce Hall, PO Box 951529, US
Country: United States
Contact: Executive and Artistic Director Kristy Edmunds
Contact: Director of Marketing and communications Phil Rosenthal

UIC Fine Arts Committee
Website: www.uic.edu
Email: jillr@uic.edu
Phone: 312 413 5180/077
Address: 828 S Wolcott, Room 50, M/C579, US
Country: United States
Contact: coordinator Jill Rothamer

Ulster Performing Arts Center
Website: www.upac.org
Email: slamarca@bardavon.org
Phone: 845 331 1613
Address: 601 Broadway, US
Information: 'Star Packages', Family Theatre, rentals; nonprofit organisation
Country: United States
Contact: Executive Director Ron Marquette
Contact: Executive Director Chris Silva
Contact: booking Stephen LaMarca

Unexpected Productions
Website: www.unexpectedproductions.org
Email: info@unexpectedproductions.org
Phone: 206 587 2414
Address: 1428 Post Alley, US
Country: United States
Contact: Managing Director Jay Hitt
Contact: Artistic Director Randy Dixon

UNH Celebrity Series
Website: cola.unh.edu/celebrity-series
Email: celebrity.series@unh.edu
Phone: 603 862 7222
Address: 330 Huddleston Hall, 73 Main Street, US
Information: alternative contact: Phone (603) 862-2062
Country: United States
Contact: dean Heidi Bostic
Email: heidi.bostic@unh.edu
Social Media: www.facebook.com/unhcelebrity/
Annual Performances: 6
Policies: Other

Union College Concert Series
Website: unioncollegeconcerts.org
Email: mail@unioncollegeconcerts.org
Phone: 518 388 6080
Address: Union College Concert Series, Central Scheduling Office, US
Information: member of Upstate New York Presenters and Chamber Music America
Country: United States
Social Media: www.facebook.com/unioncollegeconcerts

Union Colony Civic Center
Website: www.ucstars.com
Email: mark.breimhorst@greeleygov.com
Phone: 970 356 5000
Address: 701 10th Avenue, US
Country: United States
Contact: events coordinator Jill Droegemueller
Contact: cultural affairs Director Mark Breimhorst
Contact: cultural affairs administrative assistant Susan Hawkey

University Concert & Lecture Series at the University of North Carolina at Greensboro
Website: ucls.uncg.edu
Email: performingarts@uncg.edu
Phone: 336 334 5789
Address: School of Music, Theatre and Dance The University of North Carolina, PO Box 26170, US
Information: also do lectures
Country: United States
Social Media: @UNCGSMTD www.facebook.com/musictheatredance

University Concert Series
Website: www.concertseries.org
Phone: 573 882 3875
Address: 409 Jesse Hall, MU, US
Country: United States
Contact: assistant Manager Kimberley Mouser
Contact: Marketing Director Susan Cameron
Contact: Director Michael Dunn

University Musical Society of the University of Michigan
Website: www.ums.org
Email: umstix@umich.edu
Phone: 734 764 2538
Address: Burton Memorial Tower, 881 N University Avenue, US
Information: Through an uncompromising commitment to Presentation, Education, and the Creation of new work, the University Musical Society (UMS) serves Michigan audiences by bringing to our community an ongoing series of world-class artists, who represent the diverse spectrum of today's vigorous and exciting live performing arts world.

University of Akron E J Thomas Performing Arts Hall
Website: www.ejthomashall.com
Phone: 330 972 7595
Address: E J Thomas Hall, 198 Hill Street, US
Information: also rent
Country: United States
Contact: Executive Director Dan Dahl
Contact: assistant Director Cynthia Hollis

University of Alabama Horizons Series
Website: www.up.ua.edu
Email: up@ua.edu
Phone: 205 348 7525
Address: PO Box 870292, US
Country: United States
Contact: horizons Director Lesley Hines

University of Alabama School of Music
Website: www.music.ua.edu
Phone: 205 348 7110
Address: Box 870366, US
Country: United States
Contact: Director of the community music school Jane Weigel
Contact: coordinator of music Administration Pam Penick
Contact: Director of orchestral studies Carlton McCreery
Social Media: @uaschoolofmusic www.facebook.com/UAschoolofmusic/

University of Alaska-Anchorage Student Activities
Website: www.uaa.alaska.edu/events
Email: uaa_programming@uaa.alaska.edu
Phone: 907 786 1800
Address: University of Alaska Anchorage 3211 Providence Drive Anchorage, US
Information: The University of Alaska Anchorage traces its origins back to 1954, when Anchorage Community College (ACC) was founded. That year, ACC began offering evening classes to 414 students at Elmendorf Air Force Base—the first time that college-level courses were offered in the Anchorage area. In 1962, ACC, along with other community colleges around the state, was incorporated into the University of Alaska statewide system. Five years later, ACC began offering both day and evening classes**Country:** United States
Social Media: www.facebook.com/uaastudentactivities/
Capacity: 1000+
Annual Performances: 100+
Policies: All

University of Arkansas at Little Rock – Artspree
Website: www.ualr.edu/artspree/
Email: music@ualr.edu
Phone: 501 569 3294
Address: UALR Music Department, University of Arkansas at Little Rock, 2801 S University Avenue, US
Country: United States
Contact: Director Naoki Hakutani

University of Arkansas Fort Smith Season of Entertainment
Website: www.uafortsmith.edu
Email: sjones@uafortsmith.edu
Phone: 479 788 7302
Address: 5210 Grand Avenue, PO Box 3649, US
Country: United States
Contact: Associate vice chancellor community events Stacey Jones

University of California at Riverside Cultural Events
Website: www.culturalevents.ucr.edu
Email: UCRiversidePresents@ucr.edu
Phone: 909 787 4629
Address: University of California, University Theatre (Humanities 400), US
Country: United States

University of California at Santa Cruz Arts & Lectures
Website: www.artslectures.ucsc.edu
Email: artslecs@ucsc.edu
Phone: 831 459 4238
Address: UCSC Arts & Lectures, Porter D-106, 1156 High Street, US
Information: The largest performing arts presenting organisation in the Monterey Bay area, UC Santa Cruz Arts & Lectures is committed to presenting artists of national and international reputation to Santa Cruz County and beyond
Country: United States
Contact: Manager Dave Morrison
Contact: production supervisor Michael Palumbo

University of California San Diego
Website: www.ueo.ucsd.edu/
Email: ldileo@ucsd.edu
Phone: 858 534 4090
Address: UCSD Department of Theatre and Dance, 9500 Gilman Drive, Dept. 0078, US
Country: United States
Contact: assistant Chair theatre dept Linda Dileo

University of California Santa Barbara Arts & Lectures
Website: www.artsandlectures.ucsb.edu
Email: info@artsandlectures.ucsb.edu
Phone: 805 893 2080
Address: University of California, Building 402, Santa Barbara, US
Information: Founded in 1959, UCSB Arts & Lectures is the largest and most influential arts and lectures organization between Los Angeles and San Francisco. Arts & Lectures annually presents more than a hundred events, from critically acclaimed concerts and dance performances by world-renowned artists to talks by groundbreaking authors and film series at UCSB and Santa Barbara-area venues.**Country:** United States
Contact: Marketing and communications Director Meghan Bush
Contact: Executive Director Celesta Billeci
Contact: Marketing Manager Mari Levasheff
Social Media: https://twitter.com/ArtsandLectures www.facebook.com/artsandlectures https:// www.instagram.com/artsandlectures/
Disabled Access: Yes
Capacity: 1000+
Annual Performances: 51-100
Annual Productions: 0-5
Policies: All

University of Central Arkansas Public Appearances Committee
Website: www.uca.edu/publicappearances
Email: leighv@uca.edu
Phone: 501 450 3682
Address: University of Central Arkansas, 201 Donaghey Avenue, US
Information: presents a variety of performing arts
Country: United States
Contact: Director Jerry Biebesheimer

University of Chicago Presents
Website: chicagopresents.uchicago.edu
Email: concert-office@uchicago.edu
Phone: 773 702 8068
Address: 5720 South Woodlawn Avenue, Room 102, US
Country: United States
Contact: Associate Director Nicole Proulx
Contact: Director Marna Seltzer

University of Colorado at Boulder Artist Series
Website: www.cupresents.org/events/series/artist-series
Email: musictix@colorado.edu
Phone: 303 492 8008
Address: CU Presents, 302 UCB, US
Country: United States
Contact: Marketing and public relations Manager Laima Haley

Email: laima.haley@colorado.edu
Contact: Executive Director Joan McLean Braun
Contact: box office Manager Andrew Metzroth
Contact: scheduling and programs Manager Myra Jackson
Social Media: www.facebook.com/cuboulder?fref=ts
Policies: Multi-purpose

University of Connecticut – Jorgensen Centre for the Performing Arts
Website: www.jorgensen.uconn.edu
Email: rodney.rock@uconn.edu
Phone: 860 486 4226
Address: 2132 Hillside Rd., Unit 3104, University of Connecticut, US
Country: United States
Contact: Director and programme Director Rodney Rock
Contact: operations Director Gary Yakstis
Contact: technical Director Bryan Wosczyna
Contact: publicity/Marketing Director Catherine Kalonia
Contact: box office Manager Jennifer Darius

University of Connecticut School of Fine Arts
Website: www.sfa.uconn.edu
Email: SFAOffice@uconn.edu
Phone: 860 486 3016
Address: Fine Arts Building, Storrs Campus, 830 Bolton Rd, Unit 1128, US
Information: majority of presentations are in-house productions; occasionally each department employs a guest artist in a regularly scheduled production or presents a strictly guest artist performance
Country: United States
Social Media: @UConnArts
www.facebook.com/UConnSFA

University of Dayton Arts Series
Website: www.udayton.edu/~artseries.htm
Email: arts-series@notes.udayton.edu
Phone: 937 229 2787
Address: 300 College Park, US
Country: United States
Contact: Managing Director Joanie Swedlund

University of Delaware Performing Arts Series
Website: www.udel.edu/performingarts
Email: performingarts@udel.edu
Phone: 302 831 8741
Address: Alumni Hall, 24 East Main Street, US
Country: United States
Contact: assistant Director for university relations Robert Snyder

University of Denver Lamont School of Music
Website: www.du.edu/lamont
Email: vbrandys@du.edu
Phone: 303 871 6400
Address: The Newman Centre, 2344 E. Iliff Avenue, US
Country: United States
Contact: assistant to Director Ruth Fanslow
Contact: Director of music school Joseph Docksey
Contact: admission coordinator Claire Ami
Contact: pr Director Victoria Brandys

University of Georgia – Department of Dance
Website: www.franklin.uga.edu/dance
Email: ugadance@uga.edu
Phone: 706 542 4415
Address: Dance Building, US
Country: United States
Contact: secretary of department Betty Prickett
Contact: Associate professor Joan Buttram
Contact: assistant professor Rebecca Enghauser
Contact: head of department Lisa Fusillo
Contact: instructor Janet Robertson
Contact: Associate professor Bala Sarasvati

University of Hawaii at Hilo Performing Arts Cente
Website: www.artscenter.uhh.hawaii.edu
Email: artsctr@hawaii.edu
Phone: 808 932 7490
Address: 200 W. Kāwili St., US
Information: The University of Hawaii at Hilo Performing Arts Center is the major performing arts educational and cultural center on the Big Island, serving as a joint special use facility for the University and Big Island Communities.Country: United States
Social Media: @UHHilo www.facebook.com/uhhilo
Policies: Rent only, Concert hall

University of Hawaii at Manoa
Website: www.outreach.hawaii.edu/community
Email: tslaught@hawaii.edu
Phone: 808 956 8246
Address: Outreach College Community Services Division, 2440 Campus Road, Box 447, US
Country: United States
Contact: community services division Director Tim Slaughter
Contact: secretary Charlene Lee

University of Illinois Assembly Hall
Website: www.uofiassemblyhall.com
Email: ullestad@uiuc.edu
Phone: 217 333 2923
Address: 1800 S First Street, US
Country: United States
Contact: Director, booking agent Kevin Ullestad

University of Kansas Concert Series
Address: US
Information: see Lied Centre for the Performing Arts, Lawrence, KS
Country: United States

University of Kentucky Student Activities
Website: www.uksab.org
Email: Contact@uksab.org
Phone: 859 257 8867
Address: 365 Blazer Hall, University of Kentucky, US
Country: United States
Contact: student activities Director Rhonda Strouse

University of Kentucky University Artist Series
Website: www.finearts.uky.edu/singletary-center
Email: scfatix@uky.edu
Phone: 859 257 1706
Address: Singletary Center for the Arts, US
Information: the Singletary Center for the Arts is available for rent throughout the year
Country: United States
Contact: Director Michael Grice
Contact: production Director Tanya Harper
Email: tanya.harper@uky.edu

University of Louisiana at Monroe Performing Arts Series
Website: www.ulm.edu
Email: haedicke@ulm.edu
Phone: 318 342 1494
Address: University of Louisiana at Monroe, Dept of English, 700 University avenue, US
Country: United States
Contact: professor Janet Haedicke
Contact: coordinator of media relations Veronika Brown

University of Louisville – School of Music
Website: www.louisville.edu/music
Phone: 502 852 6907 ven
Address: US
Information: Concertline 502-852 0524
Country: United States
Contact: dean of school of music Cristopher Doane

University of Massachusetts at Boston
Website: www.umb.edu
Email: bob.cole@umb.edu
Phone: 617 287 7950
Address: 100 Morrissy Blvd., US
Information: also do the Asian Festival held every April, and the Latino Festival which takes place in October
Country: United States
Contact: Director Joyce Morgan
Contact: Associate Director Donna Neal
Contact: assistant Director for student life programming Robert Cole

University of Massachusetts Fine Arts Center
Website: www.fineartscenter.com
Phone: 413 545 0190
Address: 15 Curry Hicks, 100 Hicks Way, University of Massachusetts, US
Country: United States
Contact: Director of programming t.b.a.

University of Massachusetts Lowell Center for the Art
Website: www.umass.edu
Phone: 978 934 4449
Address: 35 Wilder Street, Suite 1, US
Information: Boarding House Park Performance Series presents ethnic music and dance
Country: United States
Contact: Associate Director community programmes Barbara Nolon
Contact: Director community programmes Christine Brown

University of Michigan
Website: www.umich.edu/~mevents
Phone: 734 936 9358 off
Address: Major Events Office, 530 S State Street, US
Country: United States
Contact: program advisor major events Julie Moran

University of Minnesota Northrop Auditorium
Website: www.northrop.umn.edu
Email: schat001@auxs.umn.edu
Phone: 612 625 9878
Address: 84 Church St SE, US
Country: United States
Contact: Director Dale Schatzlein

University of Minnesota, Morris, Performing Arts Series
Website: www.mrs.umn.edu
Email: haugensj@mrs.umn.edu
Phone: 320 589 6080
Address: Office of Student Activities, US
Country: United States
Contact: programme advisor Sara J Haugen

University of Mississippi – Artist Series
Phone: 662 915 7429
Address: University of Mississippi, US
Country: United States
Contact: Chairman t.b.a.

University of Missouri-Rolla
Website: web.umr.edu/~cpas/
Email: bpalmer@umr.edu
Phone: 573 341 4131
Address: College of Arts Sciences, 121 Fulton Hall, Missouri, US
Country: United States
Contact: dean Paula M Lutz
Contact: administrative assistant Barbara Palmer
Contact: production Manager Shelley Dotson

University of Montana Productions
Website: www.unproductions.org
Email: Director@unproductions.org
Phone: 406 243 6661
Address: University Center 104, The University of Montana, US
Country: United States
Contact: programming Director Elizabeth Wilhelm

University of Montevallo Concert and Lecture Series
Website: www.montevallo.edu/ca
Email: taylorm@montevallo.edu
Phone: 205 665 6000
Address: Station 6210, US
Information: rotate attractions each year
Country: United States
Contact: Chairman Miles Taylor

University of Nevada Las Vegas, Charles Vanda Master Series
Website: pac.nevada.edu
Email: henley@ccmail.nevada.edu
Phone: 702 895 3535
Address: 4505 Maryland Parkway, US
Country: United States
Contact: Director of Artistic program and production Lawrence Henley

University of Nevada Reno Performing Arts Series
Website: www.unr.edu/pas
Email: pas@unr.edu
Phone: 775 784 4046
Address: University of Nevada, Reno, Extended Studies, MS 048, US
Country: United States
Contact: Executive Director and coordinator C.J. Walters

University of New Orleans in Concert – Musical Excursions
Website: www.uno.edu/~music
Email: unomusic@uno.edu
Phone: 504 280 6381
Address: Univ of New Orleans, Performing art Room 331, US
Information: both international and faculty artists
Country: United States
Contact: Chair Jeff Cox

University of North Carolina at Asheville Cultural & Special Events
Website: www.cesap.unca.edu
Email: cultural@unca.edu
Phone: 828 251 6674
Address: Highsmith Center CPO 2150, 1 University Heights, US
Information: alternative e-mail: culturalarts@unca.edu
Country: United States
Contact: Director Holly Beveridge
Email: hbeverid@unca.edu
Contact: program coordinator Cori Anderson
Email: ceander2@unca.edu
Social Media: @UNCACultural www.facebook.com/UNCACulturalandSpecialEvents

University of North Carolina at Charlotte
Website: www.uncc.edu
Phone: 704 687 8622
Address: Department of Dance and Theatre, 9201 University City Blvd, Cab, US
Country: United States
Social Media: @uncccharlotte www.facebook.com/UNCCharlotte

University of North Carolina at Pembroke

Website: www.uncp.edu/gpac
Email: gpac@uncp.edu
Phone: 910 521 6361
Address: Givens Performing Arts Center, UNCP PO Box 1510, US
Country: United States
Social Media: @GivensPAC www.facebook.com/givenspac

University of North Texas Fine Arts Series
Website: union.unt.edu
Email: union@unt.edu
Phone: 940 565 3805
Address: PO Box 310710, US
Information: physical address: 1155 Union Cir Denton TX, 76201
Country: United States
Contact: Director Zane Reif
Social Media: @unt_union www.facebook.com/UNTUnion

University of Northern Colorado
Website: www.unco.edu
Email: Jennifer.Knock@unco.edu
Phone:
970 351 2993
Address: School of Music, Frasier Hall 108, US
Information: the School of Music at UNC is an award winning internationally recognised school of music, preparing fully engaged leaders in the modern musical landscape. With 500 music majors ranging from freshmen to doctoral level, 60 faculty, and 8 staff, the School of Music is actively engaged in creating and learning about music of all styles and genres. Indeed, music faculty and students present hundreds of outstanding recitals, concerts, and special events each year. The School is an exciting musical environment where students have the opportunity to experience tremendous growth. UNC-educated musicians have gone on to success in every musical discipline and field imaginable including orchestral and band performance, opera, composition, jazz performance and arranging, film scoring, conducting, solo instrumental and vocal performance, music publishing, and more. Our graduates are successful as educators in classrooms from Greeley to Los Angeles, New York, and Bangkok, at all levels of instruction
Country: United States
Contact: Associate Director of music Charles Hansen
Email: charles.hansen@unco.edu
Contact: Director school of music Michael Alexander
Email: Michael.Alexander@unco.edu
Social Media: @UNCo_edu www.facebook.com/universitynortherncolorado
Policies: Concert hall

University of Oregon Chamber Music Series
Website: music.uoregon.edu
Email: jjs@uoregon.edu
Phone: 541 346 5678
Address: 1225 University of Oregon, School of Music, US
Information: also organise and present Music Today, a biennial festival
Country: United States
Contact: Manager Janet Stewart

University of Puget Sound
Website: www.ups.edu/
Email: ssolidarios@ups.edu
Phone: 253 879 3366
Address: 1500 North Warner, CMB 1069, US
Country: United States
Contact: Director of student programs Serni Solidarios

University of Rhode Island – Great Performances
Website: www.uri.edu/greatperformances
Email: roxana@uri.edu
Phone: 401 874 2627
Address: 105 Upper College Rd, US
Country: United States
Contact: Director Roxana Tourigny

University of South Dakota Performing Arts Series
Website: www.usd.edu/student-life/orgs/pc/
Email: sharden@usd.edu
Phone: 605 677 5334
Address: 414 E. Clark St, Student Activities Center/Coyote Student Center, US
Country: United States
Contact: advisor Katlyn Adamson

University of South Florida Fine Arts Events
Website: www.arts.usf.edu
Email: info@arts.usf.edu
Phone: 813 974 2301
Address: 4202 E. Fowler Avenue, FAH 110, US
Country: United States
Contact: box office Manager Joyce Baione

University of Southern California Program Board Performing Arts
Website: www.usc.edu/programboard
Email: pbpr@usc.edu
Phone: 213 740 5656

Address: 3107 Trousdale Parkway, Ronald Tutor Campus Center (TCC) 224, US
Country: United States
Contact: head of performing arts Catherine Wirtz

University of Southern Mississippi
Website: www.usm.edu/arts
Email: charles.elliott@usm.edu
Phone: 601 266 5543
Address: Box 5081, US
Country: United States
Contact: dean college of the arts Mary Anne Stringer

University of Tampa Minaret Concert Series
Website: www.ut.edu
Email: music@ut.edu
Phone: 813 253 6212
Address: 401 W. Kennedy Boulevard, Box F 92, US
Country: United States
Contact: Director of bands Jeffrey Traster

University of Tennessee at Chattanooga Dorothy Patten Fine Arts Series
Website: www.utc.edu/finearts
Email: kim-rendz@utc.edu
Phone: 423 425 4269
Address: Dept 1351 UTC Fine Arts Center, 615 McCallie Ave, US
Country: United States
Contact: office/box office Manager Sue Carroll
Contact: Manager Mark Stone

University of Tennessee at Knoxville Cultural Attractions
Website:
www.utk.edu
Email:
cac@utk.edu
Phone: 865 974 1000
Address: 305 Univ Center, Room 305, 1502 W. Cumberland Avenue, US
Country: United States
Contact: Director of student activities Anton Reece
Contact: asst. dir. of student activities Ashleigh Moyer
Policies: Concert hall

University of Texas at Austin Performing Arts Center
Website: texasperformingarts.org
Email: info@texasperformingarts.org
Phone: 512 232 6213
Address: Texas Performing Arts, The University of Texas at Austin PO Box 7818, US
Information: Texas Performing Arts at The University of Texas at Austin is made up of five state-of-the-art theatres, shops, rehearsal spaces, offices and meeting rooms located not only in the PAC building, but also throughout the College of Fine Arts and the University of Texas campus. These five venues range in size from 200 seats to 2, 900 seats, each designed to accommodate a wide range of Artistic disciplines and production demands. Member of ISPA
Country: United States
Contact: Director and Associate dean Kathy Panoff
Email: kpanoff@texasperformingarts.org
Contact: assistant to the Director Judy Lister-Patrick
Email: jpatrick@texasperformingarts.org
Contact: Associate Director April Busby
Email: abusby@texasperformingarts.org
Contact: Associate Director Rachel Durkin-Drga
Email: rdurkindrga@texasperformingarts.org
Social Media: @TXPerfArts www.facebook.com/texas-performingarts
Policies: Theatre

University of Texas, El Paso
Website: www.utepspecialevents.com
Email: vazquezj@utep.edu
Phone: 915 747 5481
Address: Office of Special Events, 151 Glory Road, US
Information: provides entertainment for UTEP and the El Paso/Juarez/Las Cruces communities. Handle a range of events, from stadium blowouts to arena shows to intimate theatre productions
Country: United States
Social Media: www.facebook.com/pages/UTEP-Office-of-Special-Events

University of the Arts
Website: www.uarts.edu
Email: dicciani@netaxs.com
Phone: 215 717 6342
Address: School of Music, 4th floor, 250 South Broad Street, US
Information: alternative e-mail: m.dicciani@uarts.edu
Country: United States
Contact: Director Marc Dicciani

University of Vermont, George Bishop Lane Series
Website: www.uvm.edu/laneseries
Email: jane.ambrose@uvm.edu
Phone: 802 656 4455

Address: 460 South Prospect St, US
Information: other email: nneuert@zoo.uvm.edu
Country: United States
Contact: Manager Natalie Neuert
Contact: Director Jane Ambrose

University of Washington Meany Hall for the Performing Arts
Website: meanycenter.org
Email: ticket@uw.edu
Phone: 206 543 4882
Address: University of Washington, Box 351150, US
Country: United States
Contact: Executive and Artistic Director Michelle Witt
Email: mwitt@uw.edu
Contact: Managing Director Rita Calabro
Email: rcalabro@uw.edu
Social Media: @MeanyCenter www.facebook.com/meanycenter

University of West Florida, Department of Music, Music Hall Artists Series
Website: www.uwf.edu
Email: music@uwf.edu
Phone: 850 474 2147
Address: Building 82, 11000 University Parkway, US
Country: United States
Contact: programme Director. department of music Dr. Joseph Spaniola

University of Wisconsin – Fox Valley
Website: www.uwfox.uwc.edu
Email: foxweb@uwc.edu
Phone: 920 832 2620
Address: 1478 Midway Rd, US
Country: United States
Social Media: @uwfox www.facebook.com/UWFox

University of Wisconsin – Parkside Accent on the Arts
Website: www.uwp.edu
Email: yantis@uwp.edu
Phone: 262 595 2277
Address: 900 Wood Road, PO Box 2000, US
Country: United States
Contact: Director of special events Joann Evans
Social Media: @uwparkside

University of Wisconsin at Stevens Point Performing Arts Series
Website: www.uwsp.edu/centers/campusactivities/Pages/PAS/performing_arts.aspx
Email: caro@uwsp.edu
Phone: 715 346 3265
Address: USWP Performing Arts, 2100 Main Street Stevens Point, US
Country: United States
Director & performing arts co-ordinator
Chris Seefeldt

University of Wisconsin-Green Bay – Weidner Center for the Performing Arts
Website: www.weidnercenter.com
Email: weidner@uwgb.edu
Phone: 920 465 2726
Address: 2420 Nicolet Drive, US
Information: aims to present a wide variety of cultural, entertainment, and educational performing arts to the Northeastern Wisconsin community while also serving as a home for local and University performing arts ensembles. The Weidner Center has presented an array of performances from Broadway to chamber orchestras to pop acts and numerous family events
Country: United States
Contact: Kate Green
Email: weidner@uwgb.edu
Contact: program Manager Stephanie Maufort
Email: mauforts@uwgb.edu
Contact: Director of Marketing Diane Nagy
Email: nagyd@uwgb.edu
Contact: General Manager Brock Neverman
Email: nevermab@uwgb.edu
Contact: event co-ordinator Brittney Roffers
Email: roffersb@uwgb.edu
Contact: technical Director Kellie DeJardin
Email: dejardik@uwgb.edu
Contact: house Manager Elizabeth Anderson
Email: andersoe@uwgb.edu
Social Media: @WeidnerCenter www.facebook.com/pages/Weidner-Center-for-the-Performing-Arts/15015305278
Policies: Rent and present, Arts centre

University of Wisconsin, Eau Claire – University Artists Series
Website: www.uwec.edu
Email: CampusInfo@uwec.edu
Phone: 715 836 2787
Address: 133 Davies Center, US
Information: series includes lectures/forums
Country: United States
Contact: performing arts co-ordinator Beverly Soll
Social Media: @UWEauClaire www.facebook.com/uweauclaire

University of Wisconsin, Irvin L Young Auditorium
Website: www.uww.edu/youngauditorium
Email: youngaud@uww.edu
Phone: 262 472 5630
Address: University of Wisconsin – Whitewater, 930 West Main Street, US
Country: United States
Contact: program Director Ken Kohgerber
Social Media: @YoungAuditorium www.facebook.com/Young.Aud/

University of Wisconsin, Milwaukee, Peck School of the Arts
Website: www4.uwm.edu/psoa
Email: deansofcinfo@uwm.edu
Phone: 414 229 4762
Address: 2400 E. Kenwood Blvd, US
Information: Spanning both UWM's main campus and Milwaukee's East Side, Peck School of the Arts maintains a multitude of performance halls, lecture and conference rooms, digital labs, and other facilities available for rent–each with its own distinct personality, from grand to uniquely innovative. For more info email psoa-hm@uwm.edu
Country: United States
Contact: Director of Administration Ellen Ash
Email: ash@uwm.edu
Social Media: @uwmpsoa www.facebook.com/uwmpsoa

University of Wyoming Cultural Programs
Website: www.uwyo.edu/culturalprograms
Email:
reverand@uwyo.edu
Phone:
307 766 3159
Address: Department 3353, University of Wyoming, 1000 E University Ave, US
Information: A&A Auditorium, capacity 1965, venue for theater and dance
Country: United States
Contact: Director of cultural programs Cedric D Reverand II
Email: reverand@uwyo.edu
Social Media: @UWyonews www.facebook.com/uwpride
Annual Performances: 11
Policies: Present and produce, Concert hall

University Program Board of Slippery Rock University
Website: srupb.com
Email: upb@sru.edu
Phone: 724 738 2729
Address: 1 Morrow Way, US
Information: a student-run organization that brings a variety of entertainment and educational programmes to the Slippery Rock University community
Country: United States
Social Media: @srupbfacebook.com/srupb

University Theatre, California State University Fresno
Website: www.fresnostate.edu/artshum/theatrearts/
Email: universitytheatre@csufresno.edu
Phone: 559 278 3987
Address: California State University, Fresno 5201 N Maple Ave, 5201 N. Maple Ave., US
Information: The Theatre Arts faculty includes performers, designers, and playwrights with top academic credentials as well as professional experience. The department is an accredited institutional member of the National Association of Schools of Theatre.
Country: United States
Contact: Manager Pamela Dyer
Social Media: @FSTheatreArts www.facebook.com/FresnoStateTheatre
Annual Performances: 40

University Wisconsin
Website: www.uwplatt.edu
Email: hassigj@uwplatt.edu
Phone: 608 342 1267
Address: 1 University Plaza, US
Information: alternative e-mail: cfa@uwplatt.edu
Country: United States
Contact: advisor performing arts series John Hassig

UNM Public Events, Popejoy Hall
Website: www.popejoyhall.com
Email: inquires@popejoyhall.com
Phone: 505 277 3824
Address: US
Information: alternative website: www.ovationseries.com
Country: United States
Contact: accounting Bill Eyler
Contact: production coordinator Linda Spaulding
Contact: Director Tom Tkach
Contact: patron services Director Laura Maness

Upper Darby Performing Arts Center
Website: www.udpac.org
Email: hdietzler@rcu.com
Phone: 610 622 1189

Address: 601 N Lansdowne Ave., US
Information: especially interested in youth programs
Country: United States
Contact: Director cultural programming Harry Dietzler

Usdan Center for the Creative & Performing Arts
Website: www.usdan.com
Email: dlewis@usdan.com
Phone: 212 772 6060
Address: 420 East 79th Street, US
Information: Lemburg Drama Center is part of the Usdan Center; summer address: 185 Colonial Springs Rd, Wheatley Heights, NY 11798, Tel: 631-643 7900, Fax: 631-643 6309; see also Festivals
Country: United States
Contact: Executive Director Dale Lewis

Utah Festival Opera Company
Website: www.ufoc.org
Email: opera@ufoc.org
Phone: 435 750 0300
Address: 59 South 100 West, US
Information: see also Festivals
Country: United States
Contact: General Director Michael Ballam
Contact: Managing Director Gary Griffin
Contact: Director of development Lila Geddes
Contact: Director of Marketing Judith Anderson

Utah State University Performing Arts Series
Website: ususa.usu.edu
Email: involvement@aggiemail.usu.edu
Phone: 435 797 2912
Address: Chase Fine Arts Centre 2194, Taggart Student Center 326, US
Country: United States
Contact: Director of student involvement and leadership Linda Zimmerman
Social Media: @UtahStateSA www.facebook.com/UtahStateSA

Valley Artists Series
Website: www.rio.edu
Email: gmiller@rio.edu
Phone: 740 245 7364
Address: University of Rio Grande, Fine & Performing Arts Center, US
Country: United States

Valley Cultural Center 'Concerts in the Park'
Website: www.valleycultural.org
Email: info@valleycultural.org
Phone:
818 704 1358
Address: 21550 Oxnard Street, Suite 470, US
Information: concerts address: Warner Center Park, 5800 Topanga Canyon Blvd., Woodland Hills, CA 91367; also do Awards and Scholarships, and Special Events
Country: United States
Contact: President/CEO James W. Kinsey III

Van Wezel Performing Arts Hall
Website: www.vanwezel.org
Email: vanwezel@verizon.net
Phone: 941 955 7676
Address: 777 N Tamiami Trail, US
Information: member of Florida Professional Presenters consortium
Country: United States
Contact: Executive Director John Wilkes
Contact: box office Manager Loreda Williams
Contact: Marketing Manager Margaret Fuefy

Vanderbilt University Great Performances at Vanderbilt
Website: www.anchorlink.vanderbilt.edu/organization/greatperformancesatvanderbilt
Email: bridgette.k.kohnhorst@vanderbilt.edu
Phone: 615 322 0849
Address: 207 Sarratt Center, US
Information: Great Performances is the longest running, and only consistent, mainstream provider of interantional music, innovative dance, and experimental theatre in the Nashville area. Throughout the years, they have presented artists such as David Sedaris, the Academy of St. Martin the in Fields, Laurie Anderson, and Grupo Fantasma
Country: United States
Contact: assistant Director for perf. arts Bridgette Kohnhorst
Social Media: @gr8performances www.facebook.com/vandygreatperformances

Vanguard Concerts Series
Email: vanguard@woh.rr.com
Phone: 937 434 6902
Address: 5335 Far Hills Ave, Suite 304, US
Country: United States
Contact: Director Elana Bolling

Velma V. Morrison Center for the Performing Arts
Website: mc.boisestate.edu
Email: jamespatrick@boisestate.edu
Phone: 208 426 1609
Address: Morrison Center, 1910 University Drive, US

Information: Idaho's most prestigious performance complex
Country: United States
Contact: Executive Director James Patrick

Verde Valley Concert Association
Website: www.verdevalleyconcerts.org
Email: info@verdevalleyconcerts.org
Phone: 192 863 90636
Address: PO Box 26, US
Information: educational programs for children and adults residency programs for all schools in the area; scholarship competitions vocal, piano, instrumental
Country: United States
Contact: President Arleen Wright

Vero Beach Concert Association
Phone: 561 231 6990 box
Address: 1995 Windward Way, US
Information: member of Florida Professional Theater Association; rent to other organisations
Country: United States
Contact: technical Director Thomas Ahern
Contact: Artistic Director Allen Cornell
Contact: Executive Director Lynn Potter
Contact: Director of education t.b.a.

Victoria Theatre Association
Website: www.victoriatheatre.com
Email: info@victoriatheatre.com
Phone: 937 228 7591
Address: 138 North Main Street, US
Information: works with the Fifth Third Bank Broadway Series; offers the Bank One Young at Heart Family Series, the Michelob Ultra Cool Films series and Discovery; offers curriculum based shows for schools and also rents
Country: United States
Contact: chief financial officer John Douglas
Contact: General/Artistic Director Thomas Bankston
Contact: development Director Michael Roediger
Contact: President Dione Kennedy
Contact: pr Manager Eric Brockman

View
Website: www.artscenteroldforge.org
Email: info@artscenteroldforge.org
Phone: 315 369 6411
Address: 3273 State Route 28, PO Box 1144, US
Information: major performance sequence is July & August
Country: United States
Social Media: @ViewArts www.facebook.com/viewarts
Policies: Arts centre

Village of Park Forest, Freedom Hall Series
Website: www.freedomhall.org
Email: freedomhall@core.com
Phone: 708 747 0580
Address: 410 Lakewood Blvd, US
Information: also rented
Country: United States
Contact: cultural arts coordinator Denise Adducci

Villar Center Arts Foundation
Website: www.vilarcenter.org
Email: infovpac@vvf.org
Phone: 970 845 8497
Address: PO Box 3822, US
Country: United States
Contact: Director of Marketing and pr Shelley Woodworth
Contact: box office Manager Larry Matthews

Virginia Tech Union Lively Arts Season
Website: www.vtu.org
Email: vtupres@vt.edu
Phone: 540 231 7117
Address: UUSA PASE Office, Virginia Tech, 327 Squires Student Center, US
Country: United States
Contact: Director of lively arts Megan Jordan
Contact: President Kelley McKew
Contact: vice President Elizabeth Engel

Virginia Theatre
Phone: 212 840 8181
Address: 245 W 52nd Street, US
Country: United States
Contact: management company Jujamcyn Theaters
Capacity: 1236

Visalia Convention Centre & Theatres
Website: www.visalia.org
Email: vcc@ci.visalia.ca.us
Phone: 559 713 4000
Address: 303 E Acequia, US
Country: United States
Contact: General Manager Wally Roeben

Viterbo University – Fine Arts Center
Website: www.viterbo.edu
Email: finearts@viterbo.edu
Phone: 608 796 3737/100
Address: 900 Viterbo Drive 9th Street, US

Country: United States
Contact: production coordinator Chris Scheuermann
Contact: Director of programs and operations Michael Ranscht
Contact: technical Director Andrew Watkins

Vocal Arts Society
Website: www.vocalartssociety.org
Email: npetrisko@rcn.com
Phone: 202 265 8177
Address: 1818 24th Street NW, US
Information: outreach programme, outreach programme in association with the Marilyn Horn Foundation
Country: United States
Contact: Artistic Director W. O. Wears
Contact: Chair Martha Ellison
Contact: President and Artistic Director Gerald Perman

Von Braun Civic Centre
Website: www.vonbrauncenter.com
Email: vbcinfo@vonbrauncenter.com
Phone: 256 533 1953
Address: 700 Monroe Street admin. office, US
Information: rent only; varies arts types
Country: United States
Contact: Executive Director Steve Maples
Contact: Marketing and Sales Director Marie Arighi
Contact: assistant Director Mike Vojticek
Contact: Director of operations Johnny Hunkapiller
Contact: Assistant Director/Public Relations Brandi Quick

VSA arts
Website: www.vsarts.org
Email: info@vsarts.org
Phone: 202 628 2800
Address: 1300 Connecticut Avenue NW, Suite 700, US
Information: international organisation that creates learning opportunities through the arts for people with disabilities
Country: United States
Contact: contact Tanya Travis

VSA Arts of Georgia
Website: www.vsaartsga.org
Email: info@vsaartsga.org
Phone: 404 221 1270
Address: 57 Forsyth NW Street, Suite R1, US
Information: provides arts education and cultural arts opportunities for and with Georgians who are disabled, disadvantaged or institutionalized as audience members, participants and professional artists in order to enrich their lives and the lives of us all
Country: United States
Contact: Executive Director Jay Triby

VSA Arts of Ohio
Website: www.vsao.org
Email: info@vsao.org
Phone: 614 241 5325
Address: Riffe Center, 2nd Floor, 77 S. High Street, US
Country: United States
Contact: programs assistance Julie Bagley
Contact: President Steve Pleasnick

Wabash Valley Music Association
Website: www.honeywellcenter.org
Email: tinas@honeywellcenter.org
Phone: 260 563 1102
Address: 275 West Market St, US
Country: United States
Contact: secretary Tina Snyder
Contact: theater Manager Bruce Hively
Contact: President Suzie Jones
Contact: vice President James McCann

Waco Performing Arts Alliance
Website: www.wacohippodrome.com
Email: boxoffice@wacohippodrome.com
Phone: 254 752 9797
Address: 724 Austin Avenue, US
Information: rentals
Country: United States
Contact: President Nancy Moore
Contact: box office Manager Cristina Calaf

Wake Forest University Secrest Artists Series
Website: www.wfu.edu/secrestartists
Email: sheltolb@wfu.edu
Phone: 336 758 5757
Address: Box 7411 Reynolda Station, US
Country: United States
Contact: Director Lillian Britt Shelton

Walker Art Center
Website: www.walkerart.org
Email: leigha.horton@walkerart.org
Phone: 612 375 7624
Address: Performing Arts Department, 1750 Hennepin Avenue, US
Information: commission artists & choreographers; The Walker supports established, innovative masters, mid-career artists and a range of more emerging voices
Country: United States

Contact: performing arts assistant Leigha Horton
Contact: senior curator, performing arts Philip Bither

Walker Events, Inc
Website: www.walkercenteronline.org
Email: kathy.gray@wilkes.cc.edu
Phone: 336 838 6133
Address: PO Box 120, US
Information: non-profit organisation
Country: United States
Contact: dean of development B Townes
Contact: special projects coordinator Kathy T Gray

Walnut Street Theatre
Website: www.walnutstreettheatre.org
Email: pr@wstonline.org
Phone: 215 574 3550
Address: 825 Walnut Street, US
Information: oldest theatre in continuing use in the English speaking world since 1809; most subscribed to theatre in English speaking world with over 54, 000 subscribers; see also Drama
Country: United States
Contact: assistant to producing Artistic Director Kate Galvin
Contact: Managing Director Mark Sylvester
Contact: communications Manager Tom Miller
Contact: education Director Susan N. Quinn
Contact: assistant to Managing Director Jessica Doheny
Contact: production Manager Roy Backes
Contact: producing Artistic Director Bernard Havard
Contact: Director of institutional advancement Rebekah Sassi

Walt Disney Concert Hall
Website: www.musiccenter.org
Email: General@musiccenter.org
Phone: 212 972 7211
Address: 111 South Grand Avenue, US
Information: Home of the Los Angeles Philharmonic
Country: United States

Walt Disney World
Website: www.disneycareers.com
Phone: 407 566 6700/397
Address: PO Box 10000, US
Country: United States
Contact: audition Manager Darla Hancock

Walt Whitman Cultural Arts Center
Website: www.waltwhitmancenter.org
Email: wwhitma@waltwhitmancenter.org
Phone: 856 964 8300
Address: 2nd & Cooper Sts, US
Information: also do education and outreach projects in schools
Country: United States
Contact: folklife center Director t.b.a.
Contact: Artistic Director Ozzie Jones
Contact: Executive Director Pamela Bridgeforth
Contact: public relations officer Mareen Mullin
Contact: General programme Manager Patrick Rinehart
Contact: finance and admin Tony Lewis
Contact: t.b.a.

Walter Kerr Theatre
Phone: 212 840 8181
Address: 219 West 48th Street, US
Country: United States
Contact: management company Jujamcyn Theaters

Walton Arts & Ideas Series
Website: www.ozarks.edu
Email: gsain@ozarks.edu
Phone: 479 979 1349
Address: University of the Ozarks, US
Country: United States
Contact: Director Ginny Sain

Walton Arts Center
Website: www.waltonartscenter.org
Email: info@waltonartscenter.org
Phone: 479 443 9216info
Address: PO Box 3547, US
Information: also educational activities
Country: United States
Contact: vice presient, finance Tim Vogt
Contact: senior vice President, programmes Jenni Taylor Swain
Contact: President/CEO Peter B. Lane
Contact: vice President, communications Jodi Beznoska

Warfield Concerts
Website: www.warfieldconcerts.com
Phone: 870 572 1123
Address: PO Box 81, US
Information: also master classes and student presentations run from sept-may culminating in the Warfield Music Festival
Country: United States
Contact: Chairman Tom Faust
Contact: secretary Cassie Brothers
Contact: contact Betty Hendrix

Warner Theatre

Website: www.warnertheatre.org
Email: giving@warnertheatre.org
Phone: 860 489 7180
Address: 68 Main Street, US
Country: United States
Contact: Executive Director Lynn Gelormino
Email: LGelormino@warnertheatre.org
Contact: Director of operations Kyle Passaro
Email: kpassaro@warnertheatre.org
Social Media: @warnerct www.facebook.com/warnertheatrect
Policies: Rent and present, Theatre

Warren Civic Music Association
Email: jobob91956@aol.com
Phone: 133 065 21118
Address: 1025 Near Street, US
Country: United States
Contact: President K Robert Matheny

Warren Performing Arts Center
Website: www.wchs.warren.k12.in.us/performingarts/
Email: pmitchel@warren.k12.in.us
Phone: 317 532 6280
Address: 9500 E 16th Street, US
Country: United States
Contact: Director Penny Mitchel

Warren Wilson College/Swannanoa Chamber Music Festival
Website: www.warren-wilson.edu/~chamber/
Phone: 828 298 3325/771
Address: 701 Warren Wilson Road, Box 9000, US
Country: United States
Contact: coordinator Leland Bartholomew
Contact: music Director Frank Ell

Wartburg College Artists Series
Website: www.wartburg.edu
Email: artistseries@wartburg.edu
Phone: 319 352 8409
Address: 100 Wartburg Blvd., PO Box 1003, US
Country: United States
Contact: artist series Director Myrna Culbertson
Annual Performances: 4
Policies: Rent and present, Other

Washington & Jefferson College Fine Arts Series
Website: www.washjeff.edu
Email: dshaw@washjeff.edu
Phone: 724 223 6546
Address: Olin Fine Arts Center, US
Country: United States
Contact: Managing Director of fine arts center Dan Shaw

Washington and Lee University – Concert Guild Series; Lenfest Series; Sonoklect Series
Website: www.wlu.edu
Email: gaylardt@wlu.edu
Phone: 540 458 8000
Address: Lenfest Center for the Performing Arts, US
Information: alternative e-mails: bkolman@wlu.edu, vosbeint@wlu.edu
Country: United States
Contact: lenfest series Michael Gorman
Contact: concert guild series Barry Kolman
Contact: sonoklect series Terry Vosbein
Social Media: www.facebook.com/washingtonandlee

Washington Center for the Performing Arts
Website: www.washingtoncenter.org
Email: info@washingtoncenter.org
Phone: 360 753 8585
Address: 512 Washington Street, SE, US
Country: United States

Washington Performing Arts Society
Website: www.wpas.org
Email: ticketservices@wpas.org
Phone: 202 785 9727
Address: 2000 L Street, NW, Suite 510, US
Information: performances by local professional artists in 300+ schools around Washington DC area and 'Enriching Experiences for Seniors', 'Embassy Adoption Program' and others
Country: United States
President & CEO
Jenny Bilfield
Email: President@washingtonperformingarts.org
Contact: chief administrative officer Allen Lassinger
Email: alassinger@washingtonperformingarts.org
Social Media: @WashPerformArts www.facebook.com/WashingtonPerformingArtsSociety

Washington Square Contemporary Music Series
Website: www.nyu.edu/gsas/dept/music
Phone: 212 998 8300
Address: NYU Music Dept FAS, 24 Waverly Place, Room268, US
Country: United States
Contact: co-Director Louis Karchin

Waterville Opera House

Website: www.operahouse.com
Email: operainfo@operahouse.com
Phone: 207 873 5381
Address: 93 Main Street, 3rd Floor, US
Information: also available for hire
Country: United States
Contact: Director Diane Bryan

Wave Hill
Website: www.wavehill.org
Email: programs@wavehill.org
Phone: 718 549 3200
Address: 675 West 252nd St, US
Information: strong emphasis on Chamber Music
Country: United States
Contact: public relations Manager Mary Weitzman
Contact: concert coordinator Jenifer McGregor
Contact: assistant Director of public programs Paula Morvay

Wayne Center for the Arts
Website: www.wayneartscenter.org
Email: waynectr@sssnet.com
Phone: 330 264 2787
Address: 237 S Walnut Street, PO Box 382, US
Country: United States
Contact: business Manager Dick Swartz
Contact: education and exhibition coordinator Stephanie Pevec
Contact: Executive Director Bill Buckingham
outreach & special events coordinator
Andrea Clements

Wayne State College Special Programs Black & Gold Series
Website: www.wsc.edu
Email: jacolli1@wsc.edu
Phone: 402 375 7131
Address: 1111 Maine Street, US
Information: Wayne State College is a leading comprehensive college in Northeast Nebraska distinguished by providing educational excellence in a small, personalized setting
Country: United States
Contact: Director James O'Donnell
Social Media: @waynestcollege www.facebook.com/waynestate

Web Concert Hall
Website: www.webconcerthall.com/
Email: webconcerthall@usa.com
Address: US
Country: United States
Policies: Concert hall

Weber State University Department of Performing Arts
Website: www.weber.edu/performingarts
Email: tpriest@weber.edu
Phone: 801 626 6437
Address: Val A. Browning Center, Room 331, 1905 University Circle, US
Information: also hosts WSU Cultural Affairs events, the Utah Symphony, Ballet West, Utah Opera and other cultural events, independent of department productions
Country: United States
Contact: Marketing Director Christine Denniston
Email: cdenniston@weber.edu
Social Media: @WeberStateArts www.facebook.com/weberstateperformingarts

Webster University
Website: www.webster.edu
Email: sargenpe@webster.edu
Phone: 314 968 7006/692
Address: 470 E Lockwood Ave, US
Information: sponsors Webster University, the Opera Studio and the Webster University Conservatory of Theatre Arts
Country: United States
Contact: Chair of the theatre and dance dept Doroty Marshall Englis
Contact: dean of college of fine arts Peter Sargent
Contact: Chair of the music dept Michael Parkinson

Weidner Center for the Performing Arts
Website: www.weidnercenter.com
Email: weidner@uwgb.edu
Phone: 920 465 2726
Address: 2420 Nicolet Drive, University of Wisconsin, US
Information: The mission of the Weidner Center for the Performing Arts, University of Wisconsin-Green Bay, is to present a wide variety of cultural, entertainment, and educational performing arts to the Northeastern Wisconsin community while also serving as a home for local and University performing arts ensembles
Country: United States
Social Media: @weidnercenter www.facebook.com/pages/Weidner-Center-for-the-Performing-Arts/15015305278

Weis Center for the Performing Arts – Weis Center Performance Series
Website: www.bucknell.edu/WeisCenter

Email: boswell@bucknell.edu
Phone: 570 577 3700
Address: Bucknell University, US
Information: A concert hall convertible for some theatre and dance, a university facility NOT available for rental
Country: United States
Contact: Executive Director William Boswell

Wellington Memorial Auditorium
Phone: 620 326 3303
Address: 208 North Washington, US
Country: United States
Contact: Manager Ellen McCue

Wells College Arts and Lecture Series
Website: www.wells.edu
Email: jgoddard@wells.edu
Phone: 315 364 3330
Address: 170 main Street, US
Country: United States
Contact: theatre Director Sioux Sie Easter
Contact: technical Director Jo De Forest
Contact: public relations Tina Post
Contact: co-Chairs Jeannie Goddard

Wells Fargo Center for the Arts
Website: www.wellsfargocenterarts.org
Email: info@wellsfargocenterarts.org
Phone: 707 527 7006
Address: 50 Mark West Springs Road, US
Information: present folk festival, international series, children's series
Country: United States
Contact: development Director Robin Seltzer
Contact: operations Director Marc Hagenlocher
Contact: programme Director Anita Wiglesworth
Contact: Executive Director Richard Nowlin

Wesleyan University Center for the Arts
Website: www.wesleyan.edu/cfa/
Email: ptatge@wesleyan.edu
Phone: 860 685 2695
Address: 283 Washington Terrace, US
Information: strong dept. of ethnomusicology with faculties in South Indian, Javanese, Japanese, Carribean and West African music and dance, dance series, experimental & solo performance theater series
Country: United States

West Shore Community College Cultural Arts Series
Website: www.westshore.edu
Email: rjplummer@westshore.edu
Phone: 231 845 6211 ext
Address: 3000 North Stiles Road, PO Box 277, US
Country: United States
Contact: Managing Director cultural arts Rick Plummer

West Side Cultural Center
Website: www.ecofest.com
Email: ecofest@yahoo.com
Phone: 212 496 2030
Address: 136 W 70 St, Suite 1, US
Information: organisers of annual Ecofest environmental festival in NYC
Country: United States
Contact: Managing Director Nanci Callahan

West Virginia University Arts Series
Website: www.events.wvu.edu
Email: booking@events.wvu.edu
Phone: 304 293 4406
Address: PO Box 6017, US
Country: United States
Social Media: @wvuevents www.facebook.com/wvuevents?ref=ts
Policies: Present and produce, Arts centre

West Virginia University at Parkersburg Distinguished Performance Series
Website: www.wvup.edu
Email: business.office@wvup.edu
Phone: 304 424 8000
Address: West Virginia University at Parkersburg, 300 Campus Drive, US
Country: United States
Contact: senior vice President Hank Dunn
Email: hank.dunn@wvup.edu
Social Media: @wvuparkersburg www.facebook.com/wvuparkersburg

Western Illinois University/Bureau of Cultural Affairs Series
Website: www.wiu.edu/bca
Email: cl-steelman@wiu.edu
Phone: 309 298 3571
Address: College of Fine Arts and Communication, 1 University Circle, US
Country: United States
Contact: cultural events coordinator Christina Steelman

Western Plain Arts Association
Website: www.colbycc.edu
Email: patz@colby.ixks.com
Phone: 785 462 3984 ext

Address: 1255 South Range, US
Country: United States
Contact: Executive Director Pat Ziegelmeier

Western Stage of Hartnell College
Website: www.westernstage.com
Email: hlanda@hartnell.edu
Phone: 831 755 6987
Address: 411 Central Ave, US
Country: United States
Contact: assoc Artistic Director Melissa J Chin Parker
Contact: Artistic Director John Selover

Western Washington University College of Fine and Performing Arts
Website: www.cfpa.wwu.edu
Email: cfpa.publicity@wwu.edu
Phone: 360 650 3000
Address: College of Fine & Performing Arts, 516 High Street, US
Information: disabled access; facilities for hearing disabled; signed performances upon request
Country: United States
Social Media: @wwu_music www.facebook.com/wwucfpa

Westminster College Celebrity Series
Website: www.westminster.edu/celebrity
Email: mcginncl@westminster.edu
Phone:
724 946 7371
Address: Westminster College, US
Country: United States
Contact: Director Connie L. McGinnis
Email: mcginncl@westminster.edu
Contact: box office Manager Georgene Gib
Email: gibg@westminster.edu
Social Media: @westminsterpa www.facebook.com/westminstercelebrityseries

Wexner Center for the Arts
Website: www.wexarts.org
Email: info@wexarts.org
Phone:
614 292 3535
Address: The Ohio State University, 1871 North High Street, US

Information: Ohio State University's multidisciplinary, international laboratory for the exploration and the advancement of contemporary art; through exhibitions, screenings, performances, artist residencies and educational programs, the Wexner Center acts as a forum where established and emerging artists can test ideas and where diverse audiences can participate in cultural experiences that enhance understanding of the art of our time.
Country: United States
Contact: Director of media and public relations Erik Pepple
Email: epepple@wexarts.org
Contact: Marketing and media assistant Jennifer Wray
Email: jwray@wexarts.org
Social Media: @wexarts www.facebook.com/WexArts
Policies: Present, produce, co-produce, Arts centre

Wharton Center for Performing Arts
Website: www.whartoncenter.com
Email: wharton@msu.edu
Phone: 517 353 1982
Address: Michigan State University, 750 E Shaw LN, US
Information: also rent; Michigan State University's Wharton Center for Performing Arts has a long history of presenting quality programs; since opening its doors in 1982, the Center has generated state and national prominence for its success with touring megahits and sold-out sensations, making Producers, performers and patrons turn their attention toward mid-Michigan
Country: United States
Contact: Executive Director Mike Brand
Email: mike.brand@whartoncenter.com
Contact: programming and engagement Manager Bryan Jao
Email: bryan.jao@whartoncenter.com
Contact: receptionist Roslyn Riddle
Email: roslyn.riddle@whartoncenter.com
Social Media: @WhartonCenter www.facebook.com/wharton.center
Capacity: 1000

Wheaton College The Artist Series at Wheaton College
Website: www.wheaton.edu/artistseries
Email: thearts@wheaton.edu
Phone: 630 752 5099
Address: Wheaton Conservatory of Music, 501 College Ave., US
Country: United States
Contact: Director/General Manager Tony Payne
Contact: promotion Manager Rhonda Sisson

Wheeler Opera House
Website: www.wheeleroperahouse.com
Email: info@wheeleroperahouse.com

Phone: 970 920 5770
Address: 320 East Hyman Avenue, US
Country: United States
Contact: Executive Director Gram Slaton

White Bird
Website: www.whitebird.org
Email: info@whitebird.org
Phone: 503 245 1600
Address: PO BOX 99, US
Country: United States
Contact: co-founder Walter Jaffe
Contact: Director of Marketing Jonathan Krebs
Contact: co-founder Paul King

Wichita State University Connoisseur Series
Website: www.finearts.wichita.edu
Email: wendy.hanes@wichita.edu
Phone: 316 978 3581
Address: 1845 N Fairmount, Campus Box 151, US
Country: United States
Contact: assistant to dean Wendy Hanes
Contact: dean Rodney Miller

Wildwood Park
Website: www.wildwoodpark.org
Email: info@wildwoodpark.org
Phone: 501 821 7275
Address: 20919 Denny Road, US
Information: To request rental information for a special event email rentals@wildwoodpark.org.
Country: United States
Contact: Executive Director Leslie Golden
Email: leslie@wildwoodpark.org
Social Media: @WildwoodPark www.facebook.com/wildwoodparkforthearts

Wildwood Park for the Arts
Website: www.wildwoodpark.org
Email: info@wildwoodpark.org
Phone: 501 821 7275
Address: To promote events such as main stage performances, festivals, community days, concerts and more, as well as to stay abreast of news relating to tourism in AR.
Information: Wildwood Park for the Arts enriches the lives of Arkansans of all ages by creating community through nature and the arts

Country: United States
Contact: Executive Director Bevan Keating
Email: bevan@wildwoodpark.org
Phone: 501 821 7275Rentals Coordinator Sharyn Davies
Email: rentals@wildwoodpark.org
Phone: 501 821 7275, ext. 225Arts Administrator Elizabeth Riddick
Email: elizabeth@wildwoodpark.org
Phone: 501 821 7275
Social Media: https:// www.facebook.com/wildwoodparkforthearts https:// www.instagram.com/wildwoodparkforthearts/ https://twitter.com/WildwoodPark
Disabled Access: Yes
Capacity: 501-1000
Annual Performances: 11-25
Annual Productions: 0-5
Policies: All

Willett Hall
Website: www.willetthall.com
Phone: 757 393 5144
Address: 3701 Willet Drive, US
Country: United States
Contact: facility Manager Valora Baskerville
Contact: Director Sheila Martin

William Paterson University of New Jersey Midday Artist Series
Website: www.wpunj.edu
Email: kirkpatrickg@wpunj.edu
Phone: 197 372 02217 m
Address: Shea Center for the Performing Arts, William Paterson, 300 Pompton Road, US
Information: Midday Artist Series; guest artists and WPC faculty; modest admission fee for outsiders; students and faculty free
Country: United States
 dean, college of arts & communications
 Stephen Marcone
Contact: coordinator Gary Kirkpatrick

Williams Center for the Performing Arts
Website: www.williamscenter.org
Phone: 201 939 6969
Address: 1 Williams Plaza, US
Country: United States
Contact: Executive Director William McLucky

Williams College – Department of Music
Website: www.williams.edu/music/
Email: eclark@williams.edu
Phone: 413 597 2127 adm
Address: 54 Chapin Hall Drive, US
Country: United States
Contact: concert Manager Ernest Clark

Williamstown Chamber Concerts
Phone: 141 345 88273
Address: PO Box 287, US
Country: United States
Contact: co-Artistic Director Stephen Walt

Wiltern
Website: www.wiltern.com
Phone: 213 388 1400
Address: 3790 Wilshire Blvd, US
Country: United States
Contact: General Manager Rena Wasserman

Wingate University Lyceum Series
Website: www.wingate.edu
Email: lcoleman@wingate.edu
Phone: 704 233 8302
Address: Campus Box 3031, US
Information: also Noel Musical Artist Series, two events annually – chamber music, solo recitals, master classes and residencies – artist fee budget 6k
Country: United States
Contact: Director of performance facilities Larry Coleman
Contact: assistant Manager Martha Asti

Winona State University – Lyceum Series
Website: www.winona.edu
Email: mkaofidowfki@winona.edu
Phone: 507 457 5022
Address: PO Box 5838 Somsen, US
Country: United States
Contact: Director of grants Nancy Kay Peterson
Contact: Chair t.b.a

Winspear Opera House
Website:
www.attpac.org/
Email: info@attpac.org
Phone: 214 954 9925
Address: 2403 Flora Street, US
Information: The Grand Opening of the AT&T Performing Arts Center in October 2009 marked the long-anticipated completion of the Dallas Arts District, an idea first conceived more than 30 years ago. The Center's mission is to provide a public gathering place that strengthens community and fosters creativity through the presentation of performing arts.
Country: United States

Winston-Salem Symphony Association
Website: www.wssymphony.org
Email: info@wssymphony.org
Phone: 336 725 1035
Address: 201 N. Broad Street, US
Information: also do an annual Youth Talent Search for instrumentalists aged 6-9 years, held in spring
Country: United States
Contact: music Director Robert Moody
Contact: Executive Director Merritt Vale

Winston-Salem/Forsyth County Schools Cultural Arts Series
Phone: 336 727 2629
Address: 1605 Miller Street, US
Country: United States
Contact: superintendent Donald Martin
Contact: programme Manager of cultural arts Angelo Pittman

Winter Garden Theatre
Website: www.telecharge.com
Email: tickets@telecharge.com
Phone: 212 944 3700
Address: 1634 Broadway, US
Country: United States
Contact: vice President of theatre operations Peter Entin
Contact: management company The Shubert Org. Inc

Wisconsin Union Theatre
Email: rfriusso@wisc.edu
Phone: 608 262 2202
Address: 800 Langdon Street, US
Country: United States
Contact: operating Manager Bruce Ehlinger
Contact: Director Ralph Russo
Contact: publicity coordinator Esty Dinur

WITF, Inc.
Website: www.witf.org
Email: info@witf.org
Phone: 717 704 3000
Address: 4801 Lindle Road, US
Information: some performances are free of charge
Country: United States

Wittenberg Series
Website: www.wittenberg.edu
Email: gscheffel@wittenberg.edu
Phone: 937 327 7341
Address: PO Box 720, US
Information: also lectures
Country: United States
Contact: wittenberg series coordinator Gwendolyn W Scheffel

WJCT Inc
Website: www.wjct.org
Email: audienceservices@wjct.org
Phone: 904 353 7770
Address: 100 Festival Park Avenue, US
Information: public tv and radio station
Country: United States
Contact: President and CEO Michael Boylan
Contact: contact radio Scott Kim

Wolf Trap Foundation for the Performing Arts
Website: www.wolftrap.org
Email: wolftrap@wolftrap.org
Phone: 703 255 1900
Address: 1645 Trap Road, US
Information: also scholarships and internship programs
Country: United States
Contact: Chairman John C. Backus, Jr
Contact: President, CEO Terrence D. Jones
Contact: vice Chairman, secretary Lester L. Lyles

Woodland Concert Series
Website: www.woodlandconcertseries.org
Email: info@woodlandconcertseries.org
Phone: 860 527 8121
Address: 10 Woodland Street, US
Country: United States
Contact: Artistic Director Donald Funk

Woodruff Arts Center
Website: www.woodruffcenter.org
Email: info@woodruffcenter.org
Phone: 404 733 4200
Address: 1280 Peachtree Street NE Atlanta, US
Information: Today, the Woodruff Arts Center is home to three world-class Artistic institutions: The Alliance Theatre, Atlanta Symphony Orchestra, and High Museum of Art. The Arts Center enriches the lives of more than 800, 000 patrons annually, including more than 170, 000 students and teachers, making the Woodruff Arts Center the largest arts educator in the state of Georgia.
Country: United States
Contact: President and CEO Hala Moddelmog
Contact: Artistic Director Susan V. Booth
Social Media: https://twitter.com/thewoodruff/ https://www.instagram.com/woodruffartscenter/ https://www.facebook.com/WoodruffArtsCenter/
Capacity: 1000+

Woodstock Opera House
Website: www.woodstockoperahouse.com
Email: ophsedir@woodstock-il.com
Phone: 815 338 4212
Address: 121 Van Buren Street, US
Information: Restored 1890's Opera House owned and operated by the City of Woodstock
Country: United States
Contact: Managing Director John Scharres

Worcester State College Visual and Performing Arts
Website: www.worcester.edu
Email: cnigro@worcester.edu
Phone: 508 929 8000
Address: 486 Chandler St, US
Country: United States
Contact: visual arts and exhibitions Michael Hachey
Contact: theatre Director A M Shea
 Chair & music, choral Director
 Christie Nigro

World Arts West
Website: www.worldartswest.org
Email: info@worldartswest.org
Phone: 415 474 3914
Address: Fort Mason, Building D, 2nd Floor South, US
Country: United States
Contact: Artistic Director CK Ladzekpo
Contact: Executive Director Julie Mushet
Contact: Artistic Director Carlos Carvajal

World Music
Website: www.worldmusic.org
Email: info@worldmusic.org
Phone: 617 876 4275
Address: 720 Massachusetts Avenue, US
Information: co-presenter of globalFest: www.globalfest-ny.com
Country: United States
Contact: Executive Director Maure Aronson

World Music Institute
Website: www.worldmusicinstitute.org
Email: isabel@worldmusicinstitute.org / orders@worldmusicinstitute.org – genreal inquiries
Phone: 212 545 7536
Address: 49 West 27th Street, Suite 930, US
Information: co-presenter of globalFest:
Country: United States
Contact: Director of programming Isabel Soffer
Contact: Director of promotion Helene Browning
 Artistic & Executive Director
 Robert H Browning
Contact: Director of finance and Administration Aaron Dalton

Worthington Arts Council Inc. – Worthington Performance Series
Website: www.worthingtonarts.org
Email: info@worthingtonarts.org
Phone: 614 431 0329
Address: 777 High Street, US
Country: United States

Wright State University Artist Series
Website: www.wright.edu
Phone: 937 775 2346
Address: c/o Music Dept M153 CAC, 3640, Col Glenn Highway, Wright State University, US
Country: United States
Contact: Chair of music dept Herbert Dregalla

WYO Theater, Inc
Website: www.wyotheater.com
Email: execdir@wyotheater.com
Phone: 307 672 9084
Address: 42 North Main St, PO Box 528, US
Country: United States
Contact: Executive Director Nick Johnson
Contact: technical Director Pam Thompson
Contact: box office Manager Pam Overton

Xavier University Music Series
Website: www.xavier.edu/musicseries/
Email: bespalkop@xavier.edu
Phone: 513 745 3162
Address: 3800 Victory Parkway, US
Information: classical piano, classical guitar, swing
Country: United States
Contact: music series co-ordinator Polina Bespalko
Email: bespalkop@xavier.edu
Contact: box office Manager Rick Endres
Social Media: @XavierMusicSeri www.facebook.com/xavieruniversity/

Y Music Society of the Jewish Community Center
Website: www.jccpgh.org
Email: m.roth@jccpgh.org
Phone: 141 239 24900
Address: 5738 Forbes Ave, US
Country: United States
Contact: President Brian Schreiber

Yakima Community Concert Association
Phone: 509 575 6267

Address: PO Box 102, US
Country: United States
Contact: President Talara McCollough

Yavapai College Performance Hall
Website: www.yc.edu
Email: debbie_mccasland@yc.edu
Phone: 928 776 2034
Address: 1100 E Sheldon St, Box 6001, US
Country: United States
Contact: community events Manager Deb K McCasland
Capacity: 1100

Yerba Buena Center for the Arts
Website: www.ybca.org
Email: hello@ybca.org
Phone: 415 978 2700
Address: 701 Mission Street (at 3rd Street), US
Information: also have educational programmes; work with local arts institutions and with minority groups in the Bay area
Country: United States
Contact: President Johann Zimmern
Social Media: @ybca www.facebook.com/YBCA

YM-YWHA of North Jersey
Phone: 973 595 0100
Address: One Pike Drive, US
Country: United States
Contact: cultural arts Director Steven Kantrowitv
Contact: Executive Director Joshua Samborn

Young Audiences of New Jersey
Website: www.yanj.org
Email: info@yanj.org
Phone: 609 683 7966
Address: 12 Rosdel Road, Suite B102, US
Country: United States
Contact: Executive Director Kristin Golden

Young People's Theatre Series
Email: kfmith5770@aol.com
Phone: 231 946 0695
Address: 14 Peninsula Hills Drive, US
Country: United States
co-founder & co-Director
Karen Smith

Youngstown State University Dana Concert Series

Website: www.fpa.ysu.edu/music
Email: mrcrist@ysu.edu
Phone: 330 941 3636
Address: Dana School of Music Youngstown State University, 1 University Plaza, US
Information: see also Festivals: Dana New Music Festival; alternative web page: fpa.ysu.edu/index.htm
Country: United States
Contact: coordinator of dana concert series Michael Gelfand

Yreka Community Theatre
Website: www.ci.yreka.ca.us/community/entertainment/theater
Email: yctheatre@hotmail.com
Phone: 530 842 2332
Address: 810 N Oregon St, US
Country: United States
Contact: city Manager Steven Baker
Contact: complex Manager Jeff Shinn

Yuba Sutter Arts
Website: www.yubasutterarts.org
Email: email@yubasutterarts.org
Phone:
530 742 2787
Address: 624 and 630 E Street, US
Information: Our mission is to expand Artistic awareness of and engagement in the arts, to encourage local communities to reach their full potential by developing arts programs that serve their needs, and to provide access to the arts in rural and under-served areas throughout Yuba and Sutter counties. Yuba Sutter Arts plays an essential role in the communities to ensure the highest quality and widest variety of arts and cultural activities and presentations are available for the community
Country: United States
Contact: Executive Director Eliza Tudor
Social Media: @YubaSutterArts www.facebook.com/ysrac
Policies: Present and produce

Z-Space Artaud Theater
Website:
www.zspace.org
Email: zspace@zspace.org
Phone: 415 626 4370
Address: 450 Florida Street, US
Information: visiting address: 450 Florida Street, SF, CA

94110
Country: United States
Contact: programming Director David Szlasa

Zanesville Concert Association
Website: www.zanesvilleconcertassociation.com
Email: zca@y-city.net
Phone: 740 588 0871
Address: 2620 Douglas Drive, US
Country: United States
Contact: President Janet C. Stults
Contact: secretary Anna Marie Katt

Zeiterion Theatre
Website: www.zeiterion.com
Email: zeiterion@usa.net
Phone: 508 997 5664
Address: PO Box 4084, 684 Purchase St, US
Country: United States
Contact: Executive Director Katherine Knowles
Contact: Marketing Director Beatriz Oliveira

Zoellner Arts Center – Lehigh University
Website: www.lehigh.edu/Zoellner
Email: els7@lehigh.edu
Phone: 610 758 5323
Address: 420 East Packer Avenue, US
Country: United States
Contact: Managing Director Elizabeth Scofield
Contact: programming Director Deborah Sacarakis
Contact: rental Manager Mount V. Allen

VIRGIN ISLANDS, U.S.

Reichhold Center for the Arts
Website: www.reichholdcenter.com
Phone: 340 693 1550
Address: University of Virgin Islands, 2 John Brewer's Bay, VI
Information: also rent
Country: Virgin Islands, U.S
Contact: co-Director/technical and facilities Denise R Humphrey
Contact: operations Manager/volunteer coordinator Cindy Rollins-Williams
Contact: co-Director/business and finance Pamela Sanes

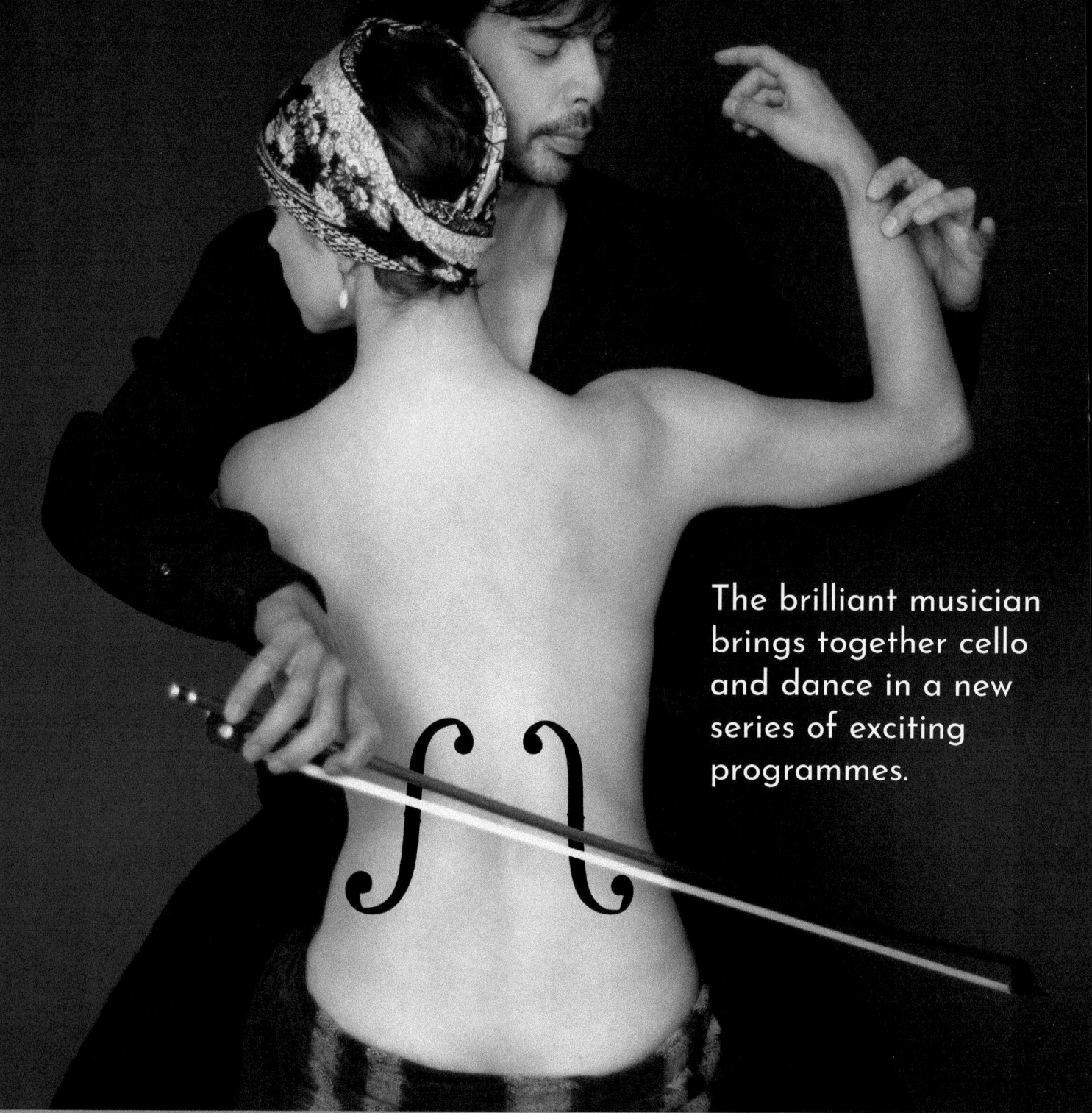

The brilliant musician brings together cello and dance in a new series of exciting programmes.

香港中樂團
HONG KONG CHINESE ORCHESTRA
藝術總監：閻惠昌
ARTISTIC DIRECTOR：YAN HUICHANG

Hong Kong Chinese Orchestra
Anytime! Anywhere!

HKCO
NET CONCERT HALL

www.hkconetconcerthall.com

Elisabeth Möst
Flautist

The internationally acclaimed flautist has three shows on tour right now, including the critic's favourite *TAU: A Sign of Change*

EVER SO SLIGHTLY

Ten dancers and two live musicians – for a large stage

Photo: Marie-Noële Pilon

Faster, easier, with Giveo. It's all in the app.

Give. Buy. Help. Waste Less. Save Planet.

Cashless donation fundraising and marketplace app

GIVEO is the new app that is revolutionising fundraising.

Download it for free right now for Apple and Android and start raising money right away.

9:41

Want to be a fundraiser? Great!

But first, let us verify your profile.

Verify as individual

Verify as non-profit

"It's a very simple way to raise $100 or $100,000. It's just point and click and that's it."

Fundraising expert and arts leader Douglas Evans

LE VENT DU NORD

New Album
20 Printemps
Now available

www.leventdunord.com

Click for more on
BYOM.academy

Make your music a business!

BYOM Academy - Be Your Own Manager
A Career Program for Classical Musicians